FEATURES AND BENEFITS
Mathematics: Applications and Connections, Course 2

		See page(s):
Integration	... of mathematical topics helps students to see mathematics as a whole.	
	Algebra lessons prepare students for first-year algebra.	12
	Other integrated topics: • geometry	215
	• measurement	74
	• statistics	464
	• probability	438
	• proportional reasoning	332
Applications	... show students how mathematics relates to the real world around them.	
	• Lessons open with an application or connection relevant to teenagers	88
	• *"When am I ever going to use this?"* answers the age-old question.	249
	• *School to Career* demonstrates careers in which mathematics is used.	187
	• *Math in the Media* helps students interpret mathematics in print.	324
Connections	... to other subject areas help students appreciate the role of mathematics in the other courses they are taking, such as science, social studies, and literature.	
	• *Chapter Projects*	183
	• Connection examples and exercises	247, 351
	• *Interdisciplinary Investigations*	128-129
Problem Solving	... activities and applications are integrated into every chapter.	
	• problem-solving strategies through *Thinking Labs*	330-331
	• 4-step problem-solving plan used throughout each chapter	4
	• Study Hints	326
Labs and Investigations	... provide students with an opportunity to explore, create mathematical models, and work cooperatively with a partner or group.	
	• Optional Hands-On Labs and Technology Labs provide a preview of the next lesson or can extend the concepts in the preceding lesson.	201, 329
	• Mini-labs introduce or reinforce concepts within a lesson.	333
	• Activities from ***Interactive Mathematics: Activities and Investigations*** provide additional options for extension activities in real-world settings.	2d
Ample Practice and Review	... reinforces new skills and concepts.	
	• Extra Practice for each lesson in the back of the text.	562-606
	• Mixed Review exercises in each exercise set	345
	• *Let the Games Begin* helps students maintain skills in previous lessons	328
Test Preparation and Assessment	... provides practice for local, state, and national tests.	
	• Test Practice questions in each exercise set	91
	• Standardized Test Practice at the end of each chapter includes multiple-choice and free-response questions.	356-357
	• Alternative Assessment options in the Study Guide and Assessment	355
	• A free-response test for each chapter in the back of the text.	607-619
Technology	... strand prepares students to function in a technological society through a variety of instruction and activities, including Technology Labs.	
	• scientific calculators	134
	• graphing calculators	195
	• spreadsheets	137
	• Internet Connections	190
Teacher Support	... in the ***Teacher's Wraparound Edition*** makes it easy for you to organize, present, and enhance the content. The extensive set of resource materials denoted in the Teacher's Edition helps you increase each student's chance for success.	

Teacher's Wraparound Edition

Glencoe

Mathematics

Applications and Connections

Course 2

New York, New York Columbus, Ohio Woodland Hills, California Peoria, Illinois

Mathematics: Applications and Connections Course 2

Student Edition
Teacher's Wraparound Edition
Spanish Student Edition

Applications

Classroom Games
Diversity Masters
Family Letters and Activities
Investigations and Projects Masters
School to Career Masters
Science and Mathematics Lab Manual

Meeting Individual Needs

Enrichment Masters
Investigations for the Special Education Student
Parent and Student Study Guide Workbook
Practice Masters
Spanish Parent and Student Study Guide Workbook
Spanish Study Guide and Assessment
Study Guide and Practice Workbook
Study Guide Masters
Transition Booklet

Technology/Multimedia

CD-ROM Program

Interactive Mathematics Tools Software

Technology Masters

MathPASS CD-ROM

Assessment/Evaluation

Assessment and Evaluation Masters

MindJogger Videoquizzes

Test and Review Software

Manipulatives/Modeling

Hands-On Lab Masters
Glencoe Mathematics Classroom Manipulative Kit
Overhead Manipulative Resources
Glencoe Mathematics Student Manipulative Kit

Teaching Aids

Answer Key Masters

Answer Key Transparencies

Block Scheduling Booklet

5-Minute Check Transparencies
Teaching Transparencies

Lesson Planning Guide
Solutions Manual

Interactive Lesson Planner

Glencoe/McGraw-Hill

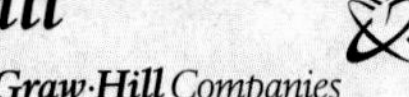

A Division of The ***McGraw-Hill*** *Companies*

Send all inquiries to:
Glencoe/McGraw-Hill
8787 Orion Place
Columbus, OH 43240-4027

ISBN: 0-07-822859-X (Student Edition)
0-07-822861-1 (Teacher's Wraparound Edition)

6 7 8 9 10 027/043 08 07 06 05

LETTER FROM THE AUTHORS

Dear Students, Teachers, and Parents,

Mathematics students are very special to us! That's why we wrote **Mathematics: Applications and Connections,** a math program designed specifically for you. The exciting, relevant content and up-to-date design will hold your interest and answer the question "When am I ever going to use this?"

As you page through your text, you'll notice the variety of ways math is presented for you. You'll see real-world applications as well as connections to other subjects like science, history, language arts, and music. You'll have opportunities to use technology tools such as the Internet, CD-ROM, graphing calculators, and computer applications like spreadsheets.

You'll appreciate the easy-to-follow lesson format. Each new concept is introduced with an interesting application or connection followed by clear explanations and examples. As you complete the exercises and solve interesting problems, you'll learn a great deal of useful math. You'll also have the opportunity to complete relevant Chapter Projects, Hands-On Labs, and Interdisciplinary Investigations. Test Practice, Test-Taking Tips, and Reading Math Study Hints will help you improve your test-taking skills.

Each day, as you use **Mathematics: Applications and Connections,** you'll see the practical value of math. You'll quickly grow to appreciate how often math is used in ways that relate directly to your life. If you don't already realize the importance of math in your life, you soon will!

Sincerely, The Authors

Kay McClain
Patricia S. Wilson
Patricia Frey
Linda Dritsas
Barbara Smith
Jack M. Ott
Ron Pelfrey
David Molina
Beatrice Moore-Harris

Meet Our Authors

William Collins
Director of The Sisyphus Mathematics Learning Center
W.C. Overfelt High School
San Jose, CA

William Collins provides mathematics support services to the students of Overfelt and the East Side community. He also has many years of experience as a mathematics instructor and mathematics department chairperson. Mr. Collins received his B.A. in Mathematics and his B.A. in Philosophy from Herbert H. Lehman College, CUNY, and his M.S. in Mathematics Education from California State University, Hayward. He is active in several professional mathematics organizations.

Linda Dritsas
District Coordinator
Fresno Unified School District
Fresno, CA

Linda Dritsas is highly involved with the Fresno Urban Systemic Initiative. She received her B.A. and M.A. from California State University, Fresno, where she also taught. Ms. Dritsas has published numerous articles, workbooks, and other supplementary materials. She received the Edward Begle Award from the California Mathematics Council. Ms. Dritsas has is an active member of NCTM and the Association for Supervision and Curriculum Development.

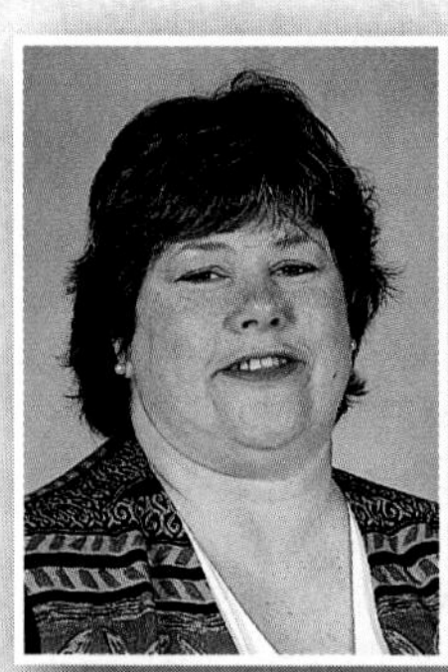

Patricia Frey
Mathematics Department Chairperson
Buffalo Academy for Visual and Performing Arts
Buffalo, NY

Patricia Frey received her B.A. from D'Youville College in Buffalo, and her M.Ed. from the State University of New York at Buffalo. Her publications include articles in mathematics education journals as well as mathematics, computer, and calculator curriculum journals. Ms. Frey is a Woodrow Wilson fellow and a New York State Math Mentor. She is an active member of NCTM and other professional mathematics organizations.

Arthur C. Howard
Program Director for Secondary Mathematics
Aldine Independent School District
Houston, TX

Arthur Howard is also an adjunct mathematics teacher at North Harris College and a member of the Executive Board of the Rice University School Mathematics Project. He received his B.S. in Mathematics and M.Ed. in Mathematics Education from the University of Houston. Mr. Howard is active in NCTM and has made presentations at local, state, regional, and national mathematics conferences.

Kay McClain
Lecturer
George Peabody College
Vanderbilt University
Nashville, TN

Kay McClain is currently working on a Ph.D. at Vanderbilt University. While a teacher at Mountain Brook Middle School in Birmingham, Alabama. She received the Presidential Award for Excellence in the Teaching of Mathematics and was a Woodrow Wilson Fellow. Ms. McClain received her B.A. for Auburn University and her Educational specialist degree from the University of Montevallo. She is an active member of NCTM.

David Molina
Adjunct Professor of Mathematics Education
The University of Texas at Austin
Austin, TX

Dr. David Molina is the Associate Director of the Charles A. Dana Center. He earned his B.S. in Mathematics from the University of Notre Dame and his M.A. and Ph.D. in Mathematics Education from The University of Texas at Austin. Dr. Molina is active in every area of mathematics education. He has published numerous articles about professional development and educational technology.

Beatrice Moore-Harris
Staff Development Specialist
Bureau of Education and Research
Houston, TX

Beatrice Moore-Harris is a former middle school mathematics teacher and Mathematics Supervisor for the Houston and Fort Worth Independent School Districts. She received her B.A. from Prairie View A&M University. Ms. Moore-Harris is also a consultant and one of four official spokespersons for NCTM. She is also an active member of several professional mathematics organizations.

Jack M. Ott
Distinguished Professor of Mathematics Education
University of South Carolina
Columbia, SC

Jack Ott has taught grades 5-12 and college. He recently received the South Carolina Council of Teachers of Mathematics Award for Outstanding Contributions in Mathematics Education. Dr. Ott received his A.B. from Indiana Wesleyan University, his M.A. from Ball State University, and Ph.D. from The Ohio State University. He has written articles for The Mathematics Teacher and The Arithmetic Teacher and has been a speaker at national and state mathematics conferences.

Ronald Pelfrey
Mathematics Consultant
Lexington, KY

Ronald S. Pelfry is a former middle school and high school mathematics teacher and district-level mathematics supervisor. He received his B.S., M.A., and Ed.D. from the University of Kentucky. Dr. Pelfrey has been active with NCTM and its local and state affiliates in Kentucky. He has been an author of several articles on curriculum and assessment, a speaker, and both a regional and state conference chair.

Jack Price
Professor, Mathematics Education
California State Polytechnic University
Pomona, CA

Past-president of the National Council of Teacher of Mathematics, Dr. Price teaches mathematics and mathematics methods classes to prospective teachers. He received his B.A. from Eastern Michigan University and his M.Ed. and Ed. D. from Wayne State University in Detroit. Dr. Price also serves on the Expert Panel on Mathematics and Science Education of the U.S. Department of Education and the standing mathematics committee for NAEP.

Barbara Smith
Mathematics Consultant
Unionville-Chadds Ford School District
Kennett Square, PA

Barbara Smith is a former mathematics teacher with 13 years experience at the middle school level and 3 years at the high school level. She received her B.S. from Grove City College and her M.Ed. from the University of Pittsburgh. Ms. Smith is an active member of NCTM and has held offices in several state and local mathematics organizations.

Patricia S. Wilson
Associate Professor of Mathematics Education
University of Georgia
Athens, GA

Patricia Wilson, a former middle school mathematics teacher, is currently working with preservice and inservice teachers. She received the Excellence in Teaching Award from the College of Education at the University of Georgia. Dr. Wilson received her B.S. from Ohio University and her M.A. and Ph.D. from The Ohio State University. She is an active member of NCTM and other professional mathematics organizations.

Academic Consultants and Teacher Reviewers

Each of the Academic Consultants read all 39 chapters in Courses 1, 2, and 3, while each Teacher Reviewer read two chapters. The Consultants and Reviewers gave suggestions for improving the Student Editions and the Teacher's Wraparound Editions.

ACADEMIC CONSULTANTS

Richie Berman, Ph.D.
Mathematics Lecturer and Supervisor
University of California, Santa Barbara
Santa Barbara, California

Robbie Bonneville
Mathematics Coordinator
La Joya Unified School District
Alamo, Texas

Cindy J. Boyd
Mathematics Teacher
Abilene High School
Abilene, Texas

Gail Burrill
Mathematics Teacher
Whitnall High School
Hales Corners, Wisconsin

Georgia Cobbs
Assistant Professor
The University of Montana
Missoula, Montana

Gilbert Cuevas
Professor of Mathematics Education
University of Miami
Coral Gables, Florida

David Foster
Mathematics Director
Robert Noyce Foundation
Palo Alto, California

Eva Gates
Independent Mathematics Consultant
Pearland, Texas

Berchie Gordon-Holliday
Mathematics/Science Coordinator
Northwest Local School District
Cincinnati, Ohio

Deborah Grabosky
Mathematics Teacher
Hillview Middle School
Whittier, California

Deborah Ann Haver
Principal
Great Bridge Middle School
Virginia Beach, Virginia

Carol E. Malloy
Assistant Professor, Math Education
The University of North Carolina, Chapel Hill
Chapel Hill, North Carolina

Daniel Marks, Ed.D.
Associate Professor of Mathematics
Auburn University at Montgomery
Montgomery, Alabama

Melissa McClure
Mathematics Consultant
Teaching for Tomorrow
Fort Worth, Texas

TEACHER REVIEWERS

Course 1

Carleen Alford
Math Department Head
Onslow W. Minnis, Sr. Middle School
Richmond, Virginia

Margaret L. Bangerter
Mathematics Coordinator K-6
St. Joseph School District
St. Joseph, Missouri

Diana F. Brock
Sixth and Seventh Grade Math Teacher
Memorial Parkway Junior High
Katy, Texas

Mary Burkholder
Mathematics Department Chair
Chambersburg Area Senior High
Chambersburg, Pennsylvania

Eileen M. Egan
Sixth Grade Teacher
Howard M. Phifer Middle School
Pennsauken, New Jersey

Melisa R. Grove
Sixth Grade Math Teacher
King Philip Middle School
West Hartford, Connecticut

David J. Hall
Teacher
Ben Franklin Middle School
Baltimore, Maryland

Ms. Karen T. Jamieson, B.A., M.Ed.
Teacher
Thurman White Middle School
Henderson, Nevada

David Lancaster
Teacher/Mathematics Coordinator
North Cumberland Middle School
Cumberland, Rhode Island

Jane A. Mahan
Sixth Grade Math Teacher
Helfrich Park Middle School
Evansville, Indiana

Margaret E. Martin
Mathematics Teacher
Powell Middle School
Powell, Tennessee

Diane Duggento Sawyer
Mathematics Department Chair
Exeter Area Junior High
Exeter, New Hampshire

Susan Uhrig
Teacher
Monroe Middle School
Columbus, Ohio

Cindy Webb
Title 1 Math Demonstration Teacher
Federal Programs LISD
Lubbock, Texas

Katherine A. Yule
Teacher
Los Alisos Intermediate School
Mission Viejo, California

Course 2

Sybil Y. Brown
Math Teacher Support Team-USI
Columbus Public Schools
Columbus, Ohio

Ruth Ann Bruny
Mathematics Teacher
Preston Junior High School
Fort Collins, Colorado

BonnieLee Gin
Junior High Teacher
St. Mary of the Woods
Chicago, Illinois

Larry J. Gonzales
Math Department Chair
Desert Ridge Middle School
Albuquerque, New Mexico

Susan Hertz
Mathematics Teacher
Revere Middle School
Houston, Texas

Rosalin McMullan
Mathematics Teacher
Honea Path Middle School
Honea Path, South Carolina

Mrs. Susan W. Palmer
Teacher
Fort Mill Middle School
Fort Mill, South Carolina

Donna J. Parish
Teacher
Zia Middle School
Las Cruces, New Mexico

Ronald J. Pischke
Mathematics Coordinator
St. Mary of the Woods
Chicago, Illinois

Sister Edward William Quinn I.H.M.
Chairperson Elementary Mathematics Curriculum
Archdiocese of Philadelphia
Philadelphia, Pennsylvania

Marlyn G. Slater
Title 1 Math Specialist
Paradise Valley USD
Paradise Valley, Arizona

Sister Margaret Smith O.S.F.
Seventh and Eighth Grade Math Teacher
St. Mary's Elementary School
Lancaster, New York

Pamela Ann Summers
Coordinator, Secondary Math/Science
Lubbock ISD
Lubbock, Texas

Dora Swart
Teacher/Math Department Chair
W. F. West High School
Chehalis, Washington

Rosemary O'Brien Wisniewski
Middle School Math Chairperson
Arthur Slade Regional School
Glen Burnie, Maryland

Laura J. Young, Ed.D.
Eighth Grade Mathematics Teacher
Edwards Middle School
Conyers, Georgia

Susan Luckie Youngblood
Teacher/Math Department Chair
Weaver Middle School
Macon, Georgia

Course 3

Beth Murphy Anderson
Mathematics Department Chair
Brownell Talbot School
Omaha, Nebraska

David S. Bradley
Mathematics Teacher
Thomas Jefferson Junior High School
Salt Lake City, Utah

Sandy Brownell
Math Teacher/Team Leader
Los Alamos Middle School
Los Alamos, New Mexico

Eduardo Cancino
Mathematics Specialist
Education Service Center, Region One
Edinburg, Texas

Sharon Cichocki
Secondary Math Coordinator
Hamburg High School
Hamburg, New York

Nancy W. Crowther
Teacher, retired
Sandy Springs Middle School
Atlanta, Georgia

Charlene Mitchell DeRidder, Ph.D.
Mathematics Supervisor K-12
Knox County Schools
Knoxville, Tennessee

Ruth S. Garrard
Mathematics Teacher
Davidson Fine Arts School
Augusta, Georgia

Lolita Gerardo
Secondary Math Teacher
Pharr San Juan Alamo High School
San Juan, Texas

Donna Jorgensen
Teacher of Mathematics/Science
Toms River Intermediate East
Toms River, New Jersey

Statha Kline-Cherry, Ed.D.
Director of Elementary Education
University of Houston – Downtown
Houston, Texas

Charlotte Laverne Sykes Marvel
Mathematics Instructor
Bryant Junior High School
Bryant, Arkansas

Albert H. Mauthe, Ed.D.
Supervisor of Mathematics
Norristown Area School District
Norristown, Pennsylvania

Barbara Gluskin McCune
Teacher
East Middle School
Farmington, Michigan

Laurie D. Newton
Teacher
Crossler Middle School
Salem, Oregon

Indercio Abel Reyes
Mathematics Teacher
PSJA Memorial High School
Alamo, Texas

Fernando Rosa
Mathematics Department Chair
Edinburg High School
Edinburg, Texas

Mary Ambriz Soto
Mathematics Coordinator
PSJA I.S.D.
Pharr, Texas

Judy L. Thompson
Eighth Grade Mathematics Teacher
Adams Middle School
North Platte, Nebraska

Karen A. Universal
Eighth Grade Mathematics Teacher
Cassadaga Valley Central School
Sinclairville, New York

Tommie L. Walsh
Teacher
S. Wilson Junior High School
Lubbock, Texas

Marcia K. Ziegler
Mathematics Teacher
Pharr-San Juan- Alamo North High School
Pharr, Texas

Student Advisory Board

The Student Advisory Board gave the editorial staff and design team feedback on the design, content, and covers of the Student Editions. We thank these students from Crestview Middle School in Columbus, Ohio, and McCord Middle School in Worthington, Ohio, for their hard work and creative suggestions in making ***Mathematics: Applications and Connections*** more student friendly.

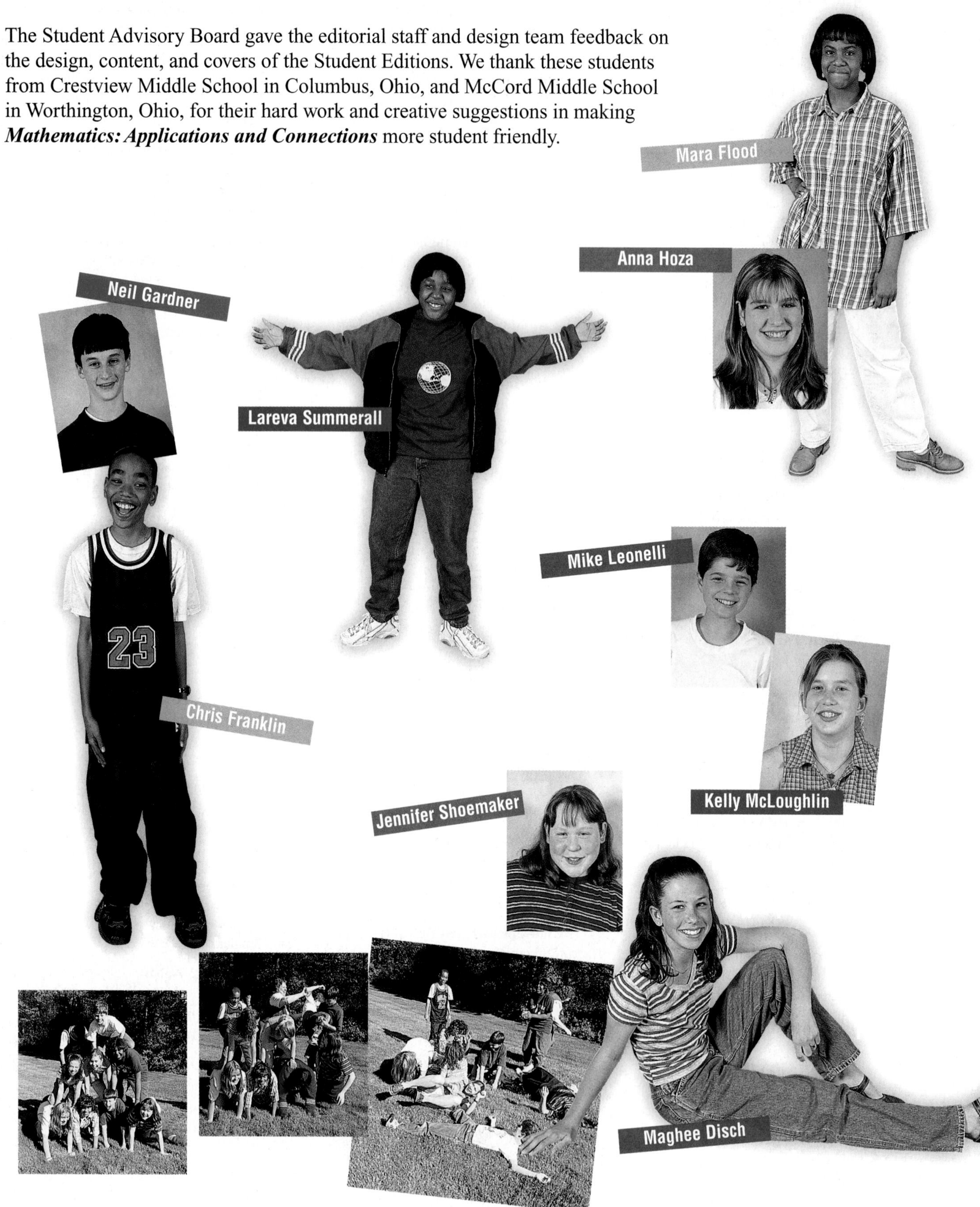

CHAPTER 1 Problem Solving, Algebra, and Geometry

CHAPTER Project **Theme: Fitness**
Fun Ways to be Fit 3

1-1 A Plan for Problem Solving 4
1-2 Order of Operations 8
1-3A **Hands-On Lab:** Cooperative Learning
Variables and Expressions 11
1-3 **Integration:** Algebra
Variables and Expressions 12
Mid-Chapter Self Test 15
1-3B **Technology Lab:** Graphing Calculators
Evaluating Expressions 16
1-4 **Integration:** Algebra
Powers and Exponents 17
1-5 **Integration:** Algebra
Solving Equations 21
1-6 **Integration:** Geometry
Fractals and Other Patterns 24
1-7A **Hands-On Lab:** Cooperative Learning
Area 28
1-7 **Integration:** Geometry
Area 30
1-7B **Thinking Lab:** Problem Solving
Choose the Method of Computation ... 34
Study Guide and Assessment 36
Standardized Test Practice 40

Applications, Connections, and Integration Index, pages xxii–1.

Let the Games Begin

- Alge-bridge, **20**

interNET CONNECTION

- Chapter Project, **3**
- Let the Games Begin, **20**
- Data Update, **23**
- Chapter Review, **36**
- Test Practice, **41**

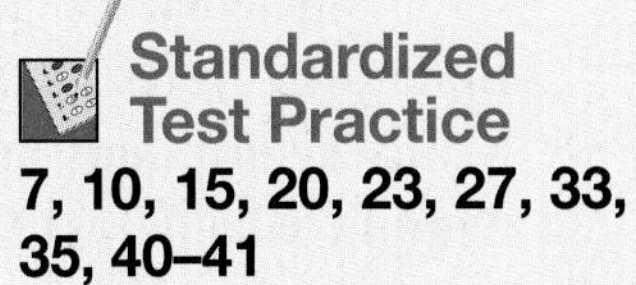

Standardized Test Practice

7, 10, 15, 20, 23, 27, 33, 35, 40–41

MATH IN THE MEDIA

- The Far Side, **27**

CHAPTER 2

Applying Decimals

CHAPTER Project **Theme: Solar System**
How Big is Our Solar System?....... **43**

2-1 Comparing and Ordering Decimals................ **44**
2-2 Rounding Decimals **47**
2-3 Estimating with Decimals............................... **50**
2-3B **Thinking Lab:** Problem Solving
Reasonable Answers **54**
2-4 Multiplying Decimals **56**
Mid-Chapter Self Test **59**
2-5 Powers of Ten... **61**
2-6A **Hands-On Lab:** Cooperative Learning
Division with Decimal Models............ **64**
2-6 Dividing Decimals **66**
2-7 Decimals and Fractions.................................. **70**
2-8 **Integration:** Measurement
The Metric System............................. **74**
2-9 Scientific Notation.. **77**
Study Guide and Assessment **80**
Standardized Test Practice........................... **84**

- Match-Up, **73**

SCHOOL to CAREER

- Aerospace, **60**

interNET CONNECTION

- Chapter Project, **43**
- School to Career, **60**
- Data Update, **73**
- Let the Games Begin, **73**
- Chapter Review, **80**
- Test Practice, **85**

Standardized Test Practice

46, 49, 53, 55, 59, 63, 69, 73, 76, 79, 84–85

CHAPTER 3

Statistics: Analyzing Data

CHAPTER Project Theme: Movies
Lights! Camera! Action! 87

3-1 Frequency Tables 88
3-2A **Thinking Lab:** Problem Solving
Use a Graph 92
3-2 Making Predictions 94
3-3 Line Plots 98
3-4 Mean, Median, and Mode 102
Mid-Chapter Self Test 105
3-4B **Hands-On Lab:** Cooperative Learning
Are You Average? 106
3-5 Stem-and-Leaf Plots 108
3-6A **Hands-On Lab:** Cooperative Learning
Quartiles 112
3-6 Box-and-Whisker Plots 114
3-6B **Hands-On Lab:** Cooperative Learning
How Much is a Handful? 118
3-7 Misleading Statistics 119
Study Guide and Assessment 122
Standardized Test Practice 126

If the Shoe Fits..., **128**

Let the Games Begin

- Can You Guess?, **107**

- Chapter Project, **87**
- Let the Games Begin, **107**
- Data Update, **117**
- Interdisciplinary Investigation, **129**
- Chapter Review, **122**
- Test Practice, **127**
- Data Collection, **129**

Standardized Test Practice

91, 93, 97, 101, 105, 111, 117, 121, 126–127

Applications, Connections, and Integration Index, pages xxii–1.

CHAPTER 4

Using Number Patterns, Fractions, and Percents

CHAPTER Project **Theme: Cars**
What Color Was That Car? 131

4-1A **Hands-On Lab:** Cooperative Learning
Exploring Factors 132
4-1 Divisibility Patterns 133
4-1B **Technology Lab:** Spreadsheets
Divisibility 137
4-2 Prime Factorization 138
4-3 **Integration:** Patterns and Functions
Sequences 142
4-3B **Hands-On Lab:** Cooperative Learning
Exploring Sequences 146
4-4A **Thinking Lab:** Problem Solving
Make a List 148
4-4 Greatest Common Factor 150
Mid-Chapter Self Test 153
4-5 Simplifying Fractions and Ratios 154
4-6 Ratios and Percents 158
4-7 Fractions, Decimals, and Percents 161
4-8 **Integration:** Probability
Simple Events 165
4-9 Least Common Multiple 169
4-10 Comparing and Ordering Fractions 172
Study Guide and Assessment 176
Standardized Test Practice 180

Let the Games Begin

- The Factor Fair, **136**
- Fractions and Ladders, **175**

interNET CONNECTION

- Chapter Project, **131**
- Let the Games Begin, **136, 175**
- Data Update, **174**
- Chapter Review, **176**
- Test Practice, **181**

Standardized Test Practice

136, 141, 145, 149, 153, 157, 160, 164, 168, 171, 175, 180–181

CHAPTER 5 Algebra: Using Integers

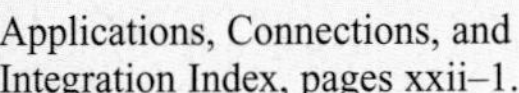

CHAPTER Project **Theme: Meteorology**
Latitude vs. Temperature **183**

5-1 Integers **184**
5-2 Comparing and Ordering Integers **188**
5-3 **Integration:** Geometry
The Coordinate System **191**
5-3B **Technology Lab:** Graphing Calculators
Graphing Points **195**
5-4A **Hands-On Lab:** Cooperative Learning
Adding Integers **196**
5-4 Adding Integers **197**
5-5A **Hands-On Lab:** Cooperative Learning
Subtracting Integers **201**
5-5 Subtracting Integers **202**
Mid-Chapter Self Test **205**
5-6A **Hands-On Lab:** Cooperative Learning
Multiplying Integers **206**
5-6 Multiplying Integers **207**
5-7A **Thinking Lab:** Problem Solving
Look for a Pattern **210**
5-7 Dividing Integers **212**
5-8 **Integration:** Geometry
Graphing Transformations **215**
Study Guide and Assessment **218**
Standardized Test Practice **222**

- Tic-Tac-Toe, **192**
- War of Integers, **198**

- Meteorology, **187**

interNET CONNECTION

- Chapter Project, **183**
- School to Career, **187**
- Data Update, **190**
- Let the Games Begin, **192, 198**
- Chapter Review, **218**
- Test Practice, **223**

Standardized Test Practice

186, 190, 194, 200, 205, 209, 211, 214, 217, 222–223

Applications, Connections, and Integration Index, pages xxii–1.

CHAPTER 6 Algebra: Exploring Equations and Functions

CHAPTER Project Theme: Roller Coasters
America's Scream Machines 225

6-1A	**Hands-On Lab:** Cooperative Learning Solving Equations Using Models	226
6-1	Solving Addition and Subtraction Equations	228
6-1B	**Thinking Lab:** Problem Solving Work Backward	232
6-2	Solving Multiplication Equations	234
6-3A	**Hands-On Lab:** Cooperative Learning Solving Two-Step Equations	238
6-3	Solving Two-Step Equations	239
6-4	Writing Expressions and Equations	242
	Mid-Chapter Self Test	245
6-5	Inequalities	246
6-6	Functions and Graphs	249
6-7A	**Hands-On Lab:** Cooperative Learning A Function of Time	253
6-7	Functions and Equations	254
	Study Guide and Assessment	258
	Standardized Test Practice	262

"A" is for Apple, **264-265**

Let the Games Begin

- Math-O, **237**

- Chapter Project, **225**
- Let the Games Begin, **237**
- Data Update, **257**
- Interdisciplinary Investigation, **265**
- Chapter Review, **258**
- Test Practice, **263**
- Data Collection, **265**

Standardized Test Practice

231, 233, 237, 241, 245, 248, 252, 257, 262–263

CHAPTER 7 Applying Fractions

CHAPTER Project **Theme: Stock Market**
Ups and Downs 267

7-1	Estimating with Fractions	268
7-2	Adding and Subtracting Fractions	272
7-3	Adding and Subtracting Mixed Numbers	276
7-3B	**Thinking Lab:** Problem Solving Eliminate Possibilities	280
7-4A	**Hands-On Lab:** Cooperative Learning Multiplying Fractions and Mixed Numbers	282
7-4	Multiplying Fractions and Mixed Numbers	284
	Mid-Chapter Self Test	287
7-4B	**Hands-On Lab:** Cooperative Learning Fractal Patterns	288
7-5	**Integration:** Measurement Changing Customary Units	289
7-6	**Integration:** Geometry Perimeter	292
7-7	**Integration:** Measurement Circles and Circumference	297
7-8	Properties	301
7-9	Dividing Fractions and Mixed Numbers	305
	Study Guide and Assessment	308
	Standardized Test Practice	312

Applications, Connections, and Integration Index, pages xxii–1.

- Totally Mental, **285**

- Finance, **296**

interNET CONNECTION

- Chapter Project, **267**
- Let the Games Begin, **285**
- Data Update, **291**
- School to Career, **296**
- Chapter Review, **308**
- Test Practice, **313**

Standardized Test Practice

271, 275, 279, 281, 287, 291, 295, 300, 304, 307, 312–313

Table of Contents

CHAPTER 8

Using Proportional Reasoning

CHAPTER Project Theme: Recycling
Waste Not, Want Not 315

8-1A **Hands-On Lab:** Cooperative Learning
Equal Ratios 316
8-1 Ratios 317
8-2 Rates 321
8-3 Solving Proportions 325
8-3B **Hands-On Lab:** Cooperative Learning
Wildlife Sampling 329
8-4A **Thinking Lab:** Problem Solving
Draw a Diagram 330
8-4 Scale Drawings 332
Mid-Chapter Self Test 335
8-5 Percents and Fractions 336
8-6 Percents and Decimals 339
8-7 Percents Greater Than 100% and
Percents Less Than 1% 342
8-8 Percent of a Number 346
8-9 The Percent Proportion 349
Study Guide and Assessment 352
Standardized Test Practice 356

Let the Games Begin
- Left from the Start, **328**

interNET CONNECTION
- Chapter Project, **315**
- Let the Games Begin, **328**
- Data Update, **351**
- Chapter Review, **352**
- Test Practice, **357**

Standardized Test Practice
320, 324, 328, 331, 335, 338, 341, 345, 348, 351, 356–357

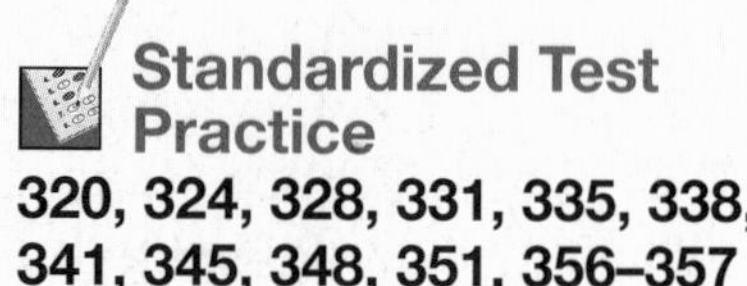

- B.C., **324**

CHAPTER 9 Geometry: Investigating Patterns

CHAPTER Project **Theme: Art**
Geometric Art 359

9-1A	**Hands-On Lab:** Cooperative Learning Measuring Angles	360
9-1	Angles	362
9-1B	**Hands-On Lab:** Cooperative Learning Perpendicular and Parallel Lines	366
9-2A	**Hands-On Lab:** Cooperative Learning Angles of a Polygon	369
9-2	Polygons	370
9-2B	**Hands-On Lab:** Cooperative Learning Inscribed Polygons	374
9-3	**Integration:** Algebra Similar Polygons	376
	Mid-Chapter Self Test	379
9-3B	**Hands-On Lab:** Cooperative Learning Dilations	380
9-4A	**Hands-On Lab:** Cooperative Learning Investigating Triangles and Quadrilaterals	381
9-4	Triangles and Quadrilaterals	382
9-4B	**Thinking Lab:** Problem Solving Use Logical Reasoning	386
9-5	Tessellations	388
9-6	Translations	392
9-7	Reflections	395
	Study Guide and Assessment	398
	Standardized Test Practice	402

Applications, Connections, and Integration Index, pages xxii–1.

Pi for Polygons, **404**

- Tic-Tac Squares, **391**

- Fashion, **368**

interNET CONNECTION

- Chapter Project, **359**
- School to Career, **368**
- Let the Games Begin, **391**
- Data Update, **392**
- Interdisciplinary Investigation, **405**
- Chapter Review, **398**
- Test Practice, **403**

Standardized Test Practice
365, 373, 379, 385, 387, 391, 394, 397, 402–403

CHAPTER 10

Geometry: Exploring Area

CHAPTER Project Theme: Geography
It's a Small World 407

10-1A **Thinking Lab:** Problem Solving
Guess and Check 408
10-1 Squares and Square Roots 410
10-2 Estimating Square Roots 415
10-3A **Hands-On Lab:** Cooperative Learning
The Pythagorean Theorem 418
10-3 The Pythagorean Theorem 419
10-4 Area of Irregular Figures 423
Mid-Chapter Self Test 426
10-5A **Hands-On Lab:** Cooperative Learning
Finding the Area of a Triangle 427
10-5 Area of Triangles and Trapezoids 428
10-6 Area of Circles 432
10-7A **Hands-On Lab:** Cooperative Learning
Probability and Area Models 436
10-7 **Integration:** Probability
Area Models 438
Study Guide and Assessment 442
Standardized Test Practice 446

Let the Games Begin
- Tic Tac Root, **414**

interNET CONNECTION
- Chapter Project, **407**
- Let the Games Begin, **414**
- Data Update, **434**
- Chapter Review, **442**
- Test Practice, **447**

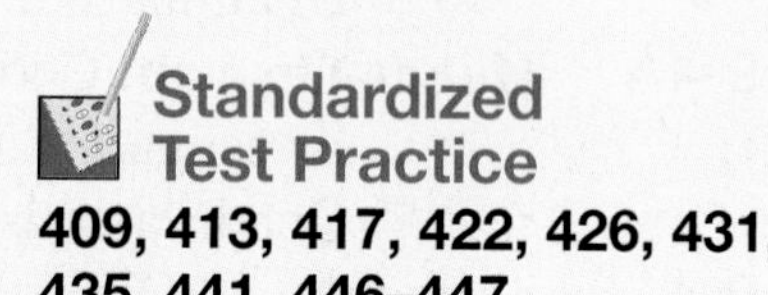

409, 413, 417, 422, 426, 431, 435, 441, 446–447

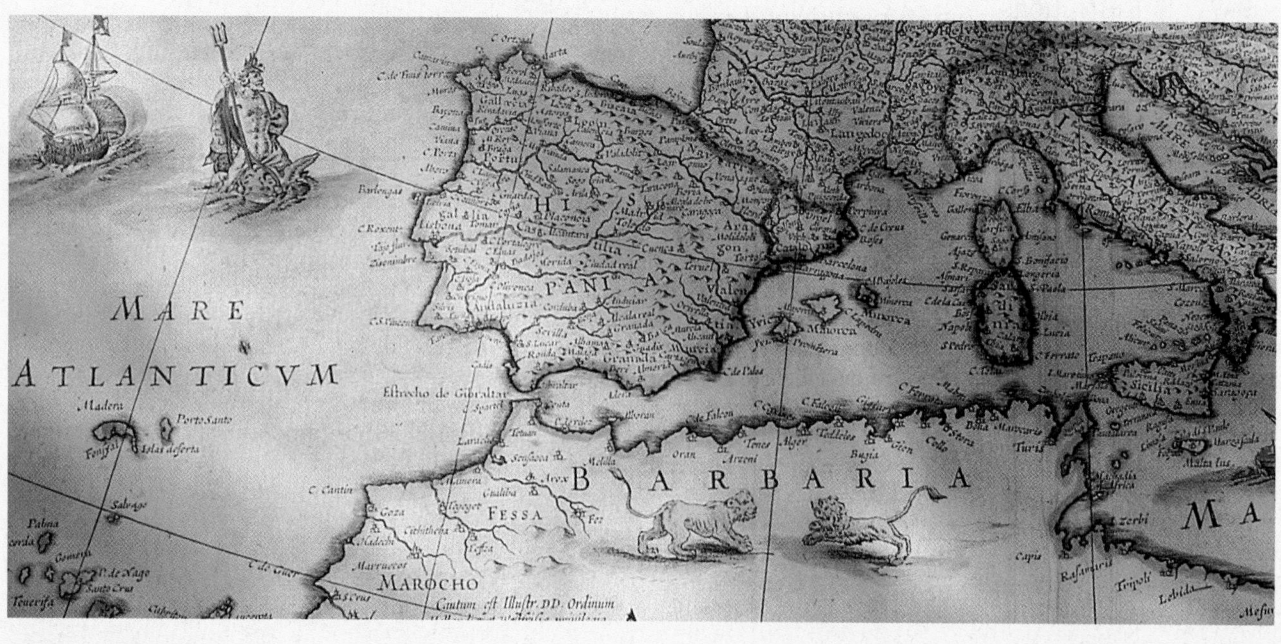

Table of Contents

CHAPTER 11

Applying Percents

CHAPTER Project **Theme: Radio**
Don't Turn That Dial! **449**

11-1 Percent and Estimation **450**
11-1B **Thinking Lab:** Problem Solving
Solve a Simpler Problem **454**
11-2 **Integration:** Algebra
The Percent Equation **456**
11-3A **Hands-On Lab:** Cooperative Learning
Jelly Bean Statistics **459**
11-3 **Integration:** Statistics
Making Circle Graphs **460**
11-4 **Integration:** Statistics
Using Statistics to Predict **464**
Mid-Chapter Self Test **467**
11-5A **Hands-On Lab:** Cooperative Learning
Percent of Change **468**
11-5 Percent of Change **469**
11-6 Discount and Sales Tax **474**
11-7 Simple Interest **478**
11-7B **Technology Lab:** Spreadsheets
Simple Interest **481**
Study Guide and Assessment **482**
Standardized Test Practice **486**

Applications, Connections, and Integration Index, pages xxii–1.

Let the Games Begin

- Time to Shop, **477**

interNET CONNECTION

- Chapter Project, **449**
- Data Update, **465**
- School to Career, **473**
- Let the Games Begin, **477**
- Chapter Review, **482**
- Test Practice, **487**

Standardized Test Practice

453, 455, 458, 463, 467, 472, 477, 480, 486–487

MATH IN THE MEDIA

- Smart Shopping, **472**

- Media, **473**

Table of Contents

CHAPTER 12 Geometry: Finding Volume and Surface Area

CHAPTER Project **Theme: Plants**
Turn Over a New Leaf **489**

12-1A **Hands-On Lab:** Cooperative Learning
Building Three-Dimensional Figures **490**
12-1 Drawing Three-Dimensional Figures **492**
12-1B **Thinking Lab:** Problem Solving:
Make a Model **496**
12-2 Volume of Rectangular Prisms **498**
12-2B **Hands-On Lab:** Cooperative Learning
Volume of Pyramids **502**
12-3 Volume of Cylinders **503**
Mid-Chapter Self Test **506**
12-4A **Hands-On Lab:** Cooperative Learning
Nets and Surface Area **508**
12-4 Surface Area of Rectangular Prisms **510**
12-5 Surface Area of Cylinders **514**
Study Guide and Assessment **518**
Standardized Test Practice **522**

The Perfect Package, **524**

- Shape-Tac-Toe, **513**

- Biochemistry, **507**

interNET CONNECTION

- Chapter Project, **489**
- School to Career, **507**
- Let the Games Begin, **513**
- Data Update, **517**
- Interdisciplinary Investigation, **525**
- Chapter Review, **518**
- Test Practice, **523**

Standardized Test Practice

495, 497, 501, 506, 513, 517, 522–523

MATH IN THE MEDIA

- SHOE, **495**

CHAPTER 13

Exploring Discrete Math and Probability

CHAPTER Project **Theme: Games**
Advance to *GO* and Collect $200 **527**

13-1A **Thinking Lab: Problem Solving**
Act It Out **528**
13-1 Theoretical and Experimental Probability **530**
13-2 Tree Diagrams **534**
13-3 The Counting Principle **538**
13-4 Independent and Dependent Events **542**
Mid-Chapter Self Test **545**
13-5A **Hands-On Lab:** Cooperative Learning
Exploring Permutations **546**
13-5 Permutations **547**
13-6A **Hands-On Lab:** Cooperative Learning
Exploring Combinations **550**
13-6 Combinations **551**
Study Guide and Assessment **554**
Standardized Test Practice **558**

Student Handbook **561**
Extra Practice **562–606**
Chapter Tests **607–619**
Getting Acquainted with the Graphing
Calculator **620–621**
Getting Acquainted with Spreadsheets **622–623**
Selected Answers **624–653**
Photo Credits **654–655**
Glossary **656–663**
Spanish Glossary **664–672**
Index **673–682**
Symbols, Formulas, and Measurement
Conversions .... **inside back cover**

- Take a Chance, **530**
- Cherokee Butterbean Game, **541**

- Design, **537**

interNET CONNECTION

- Chapter Project, **527**
- Let the Games Begin, **530, 541**
- Data Update, **536**
- School to Career, **537**
- Chapter Review, **554**
- Test Practice, **559**

Standardized Test Practice

529, 533, 536, 541, 545, 549, 553, 558–559

Applications, Connections, and Integration Index, pages xxii–1.

Applications, Connections, and Integration Index

APPLICATIONS

Activities, 179

Advertising, 477

Age, 257

Agriculture, 105, 516

Animals
Fish, 290
Pets, 295, 458, 521

Architecture, 115, 295, 321, 333, 383, 384, 413, 434, 441, 495

Aviation, 231, 245, 458

Ballooning, 411

Braille, 539

Buildings, 83

Business, 97, 348, 500
Construction, 271, 430
Economics, 337, 345
Employment, 291, 476
Inventory, 534
Jobs, 125
Manufacturing, 323, 511, 517, 521

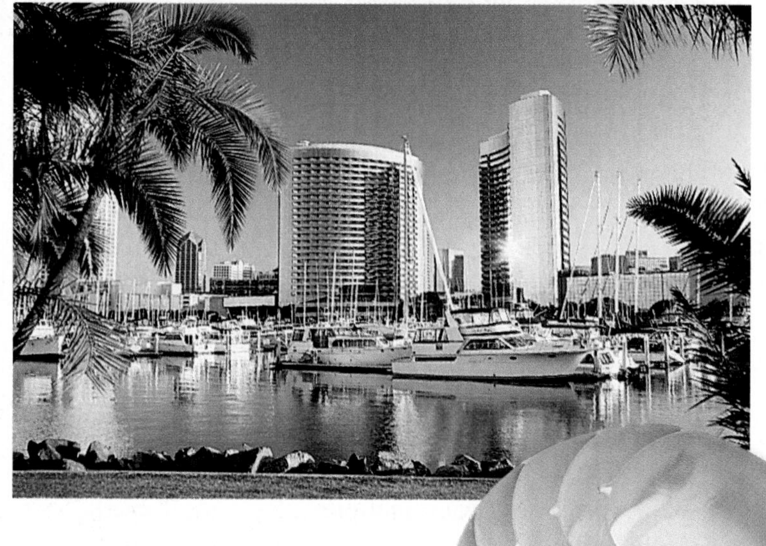

Marketing, 111, 121
Real Estate, 91
Retail Sales, 538
Salaries, 119
Sales, 95, 214
Stockbroker, 204
Stock Market, 279

Calendars, 153

Cameras, 88

Careers, 338, 465
Astronaut, 60
Banker, 296
Civil Engineering, 335
Engineering, 304
Inventors, 537
Mathematician, 187
Meteorologist, 187
See also Index on pages 673–682

Carpentry, 422

City Planning, 334

Clothes, 373, 557
Fashion, 433

Coins, 338

Coin Minting, 435

Communication, 7, 55, 445

Computers, 48, 96
See also Index on pages 673–682

Conservation, 76

Consumerism, 306

Crayons, 168

Current Events, 252

Decorating, 15

Design, 390, 517
Native American Designs, 26

Games, 20, 46, 73, 136, 192, 198, 233, 328, 391, 414, 439, 445, 477, 530, 531, 541, 544, 557
Chess, 217
Contests, 140, 144
Darts, 441
Lottery, 553
Mancala, 184
Number Puzzles, 135, 141
Parcheesi, 533
Puzzles, 331, 387
Raffle, 557
Shows, 543, 545

Diamonds, 168

Drawings, 166

Education, 331, 344, 453

Elections, 101

Entertainment, 10, 466
Animation, 394
Movies, 164, 251, 275, 471, 517
Movie Tickets, 6
Radio, 467
Television, 119, 320, 327, 465
Theme Parks, 53, 91, 97
Ticket Sales, 409
Tourist Attractions, 230
Video Games, 175

Environment, 204, 300

Exploration, 157

Flags, 217
Flag Day, 294

Food, 45, 49, 63, 93, 99, 101, 109, 115, 163, 233, 248, 290, 291, 307, 340, 373, 464, 551, 552
Baking, 269, 281, 424
Catering, 261
Cooking, 311, 327
Fast Food, 7, 96, 279, 401
Snacks, 244

Forestry, 422

Gardening, 311, 417, 445, 466, 499

Gifts, 214

Government, 171, 286

Greeting Cards, 245

Health, 15, 101, 211, 247, 251, 252

Blood Pressure, 13
Health Clubs, 273
Nutrition, 153, 214, 351, 470

Heating and Air Conditioning, 425

Hiking, 209

Hobbies
Collectibles, 319
Crafts, 401
Sailing, 553
Sewing, 277

Home Improvement, 479

Horticulture, 270

Housing, 33, 307

Interior Design, 431

Internet, 3, 20, 23, 43, 60, 73, 87, 107, 117, 129, 131, 136, 174, 175, 183, 187, 190, 192, 198, 225, 237, 252, 265, 267, 285, 291, 296, 315, 328, 351, 359, 368, 391, 392, 405, 407, 414, 434, 449, 465, 473, 477, 507, 513, 517, 525, 527, 530, 536, 537, 541

Inventions, 189

Jewels, 278

Kites, 235

Landscaping, 295, 413, 501

Law Enforcement, 249

Leisure Time, 46

Libraries, 45

Life, 466
Advertising, 533
Marketing, 464

Medicine, 466

Models, 326, 327

Money Matters, 55, 110, 134, 233, 241, 245, 281, 474–475, 476
Baby-sitting, 15
Better Buy, 435
Buying Food, 69
Credit Cards, 480
Earning Money, 248, 256, 261
Eating Out, 455
Finance, 479, 480
Fund-raising, 221
Interest, 485
Investing, 478
Loans, 495
Making Purchases, 39, 97, 331
Personal Finance, 200
Sales, 62, 480
Sales Tax, 347, 485
Shopping Networks, 243
Tipping, 161
Tips, 348
Unit Cost, 194, 323

Mountain Bikes, 53

Packaging, 141, 151, 497, 512

Painting, 31

Parades, 549

Photography, 9, 379

Pottery, 521

Quilts, 25

Reading, 168

Recreation, 135, 186, 257, 300, 328, 343, 472

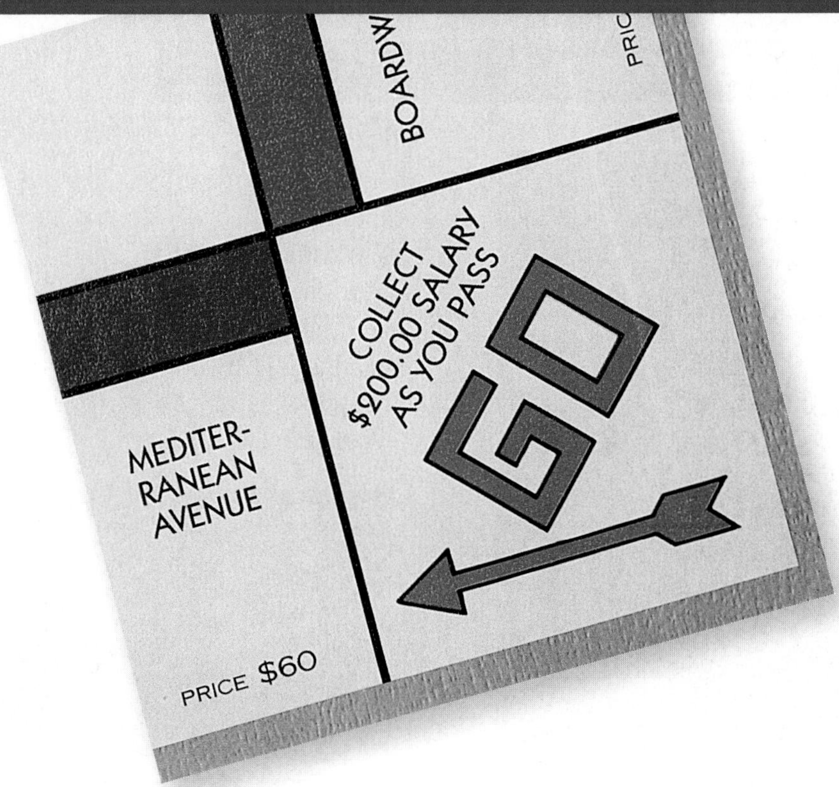

Recycling, 79, 120, 171

Safety, 93, 173, 291, 419–420

Scheduling, 171

School, 160, 168, 174, 350, 485, 497, 541, 553
- Public Schools, 453
- Test Scores, 103, 120, 179

Scuba Diving, 257, 275

Sewing, 385

Shopping, 192, 348, 451, 475
- Catalog, 557
- Sales Tax, 48
- Unit Cost, 67, 69

Space, 105

Sports, 7, 10, 73, 93, 341, 422
- Baseball, 15, 91, 319, 457, 545
- Basketball, 32, 251, 300, 462
- Bowling, 532
- Boxing, 413
- Cycling, 156, 199, 299
- Fitness, 14
- Football, 185, 200, 221, 409, 426
- Golf, 230, 440
- Gymnastics, 51
- In-Line Skating, 89
- NBA, 117
- Olympics, 71, 96, 194
- Physical Fitness, 300
- Racing, 141
- Shoes, 104
- Skateboarding, 423
- Skydiving, 412, 438
- Snowboarding, 96
- Soccer, 159
- Softball, 331, 549
- Swimming, 350, 501
- Table Tennis, 68
- Tennis, 401
- Track, 69
- Triathalon, 164
- World Series, 39

Submarines, 209

Technology, 159, 167, 271, 281, 335, 341, 421, 441, 457
- Industrial Technology, 494
- Photocopying, 455
- *See also* Computers, Internet, and Index on pages 673–682

Telecommunications, 93

Toys, 495

Transportation, 55, 149, 157, 163, 274, 477
- Accident Investigations, 416, 417
- Driving, 311, 409
- Traffic Planning, 545
- Traffic Safety, 372

Travel, 7, 58, 328, 332, 535
- Airplane, 539
- Airports, 52
- Car, 22
- Highway, 540

Volunteering, 160, 175, 497

Weather
- Barometer, 83
- Dallas, Texas, 72
- Windchill Factor, 221

CONNECTIONS

Archaeology, 209

Art, 27, 216, 390, 393, 394, 396, 397, 493, 495, 525

Civics, 117, 248, 324, 331, 348, 351

Geography, 425, 533
- Alaska, 93
- Angel Falls, 186
- Arizona, 251
- Caribbean islands, 121
- Chicago, 79
- Delaware, 431
- Earth, 365
- Kenya, 172
- Landmarks, 320
- Mali, 548
- Mount Everest, 149
- Nevada, 431
- New Zealand, 463
- Nicaragua, 428
- Population, 23, 51, 63, 174, 355, 471, 536
- Rivers, 55
- U.S. census, 99
- Virginia, 536
- Water, 101

Geology, 193, 452

Health, 13

History, 116, 164
- Ancient Civilizations, 204
- England, 90
- Eratosthenes, 149
- Florida, 286
- George Washington, 135
- Math, 72, 135
- Mayflower, 323
- Voyager, 287

Language Arts, 19, 129, 405, 525

Literature, 105

Meteorology, 103

Music, 57, 63, 156, 214, 287, 298, 455, 465

Oceanography, 461

Science, 129, 405, 525
- Earth Science, 14, 69, 76, 78, 79, 83, 91, 93, 125, 145, 155, 157, 170, 189, 190, 194, 199, 202, 205, 211, 221, 261, 275, 287, 303, 345, 365, 373, 391, 455
- Life Science, 39, 52, 55, 58, 59, 72, 75, 94, 95, 110, 111, 116, 145, 157, 163, 179, 194, 211, 236, 250, 271, 279, 285, 290, 291, 300, 303, 305, 318, 323, 338, 340, 342, 345, 355, 391, 453, 455, 458
- Physical Science, 22, 23, 149, 156, 190, 211, 387, 513
- Physics, 331

Social Studies, 129, 405

INTEGRATION

371, 373, 385, 389, 413, 453, 458, 533
Solving Inequalities, 287
Writing Equations, 231, 243-245, 453, 501, 512
Writing Expressions, 53, 242-245, 248, 271, 341, 369
See also Index on pages 673-682

Data Analysis, Statistics, and Probability

Data Analysis, 205, 534-536
Population, 5
Probability, 200, 295, 530-533, 549
Sample, 5
Statistics, 59, 97, 117, 121, 136, 145, 164, 175, 186, 188, 200, 231, 237, 244, 291, 304, 322, 324, 341, 345, 347, 355, 413, 459-467, 472
Surveys, 136

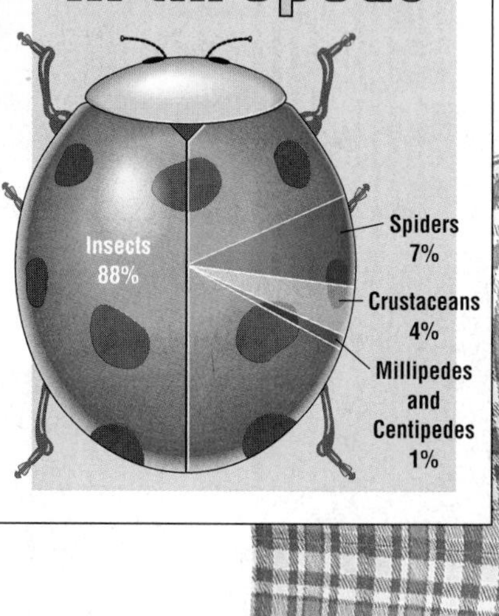

Algebra

Evaluating Expressions, 12–15, 16, 18–20, 23, 49, 58, 63, 69, 73, 139, 140, 145, 203, 204, 208, 213, 245, 252, 278, 286, 307, 549
GCF, 151, 152, 153
Graphing, 412, 435
Modeling, 226-230, 236, 239-240
Proportions, 326, 327, 376-379, 413
Solving Equations, 21-23, 27, 49, 53, 63, 226, 231, 234-240, 243-245, 248, 271, 275, 279, 295, 302, 304, 320, 326, 351, 364, 365,

Geometry and Spatial Sense

Angles, 362-365
Area, 28-33, 58, 69, 141, 160, 213, 245, 255, 406-441, 470
Circles, 553
Circumference, 304
Fractals, 24-27
Graphing, 300, 335, 345
Lines, 366-367
Measurement Precision, 49
Parallelogram, 31, 213
Perimeter, 9, 10, 23, 257, 307
Perspective Drawings, 501
Polygons, 369-379
Rectangle, 30, 46
Reflections, 395-397
Sequences, 145
Squares, 410-413, 415-416, 426
Surface Area, 508-517
Three-Dimensional Figures, 19, 490–521, 536
Transformations, 215, 216, 217
Translations, 392-394
Triangles, 231, 472
Two-Dimensional Figures, 7, 143, 387
Volume, 498-506
See also Index on pages 673-682

Measurement

Customary, 279, 293, 295, 338, 348, 377, 501
Metric, 79, 141, 257, 431
Temperature, 240, 241

Numbers and Operations

Sense, 153, 171, 174
Systems, 19
Theory, 149, 387, 409

Patterns and Functions

Functions, 253-257
Geometric Patterns, 33
Number Patterns, 73, 345
Patterns, 7, 13, 25-27, 32, 38, 153, 233
Sequences, 142-145

Problem Solving, 552

Act it Out, 528–529
Choose a Method of Computation, 34–35
Draw a Diagram, 330–331
Eliminate Possibilities, 280–281
Guess and Check, 408–409
Look for a Pattern, 210–211
Make a List, 148–149
Make a Model, 496–497
Reasonable Answers, 54–55
Solve a Simpler Problem, 454–455
Use a Graph, 92–93
Use Logical Reasoning, 386–387
Work Backward, 232–233

Proportionality

Area, 28-29
Percent, 346-351
Perimeter, 376-377
Probability, 438-441
Surface Area, 508-517
Volume, 498-506

Visit the Glencoe Mathematics Internet Site for
Mathematics: Applications and Connections at

www.glencoe.com/sec/math/mac/mathnet

You'll find:

Chapter Review

Test Practice

Data Collection

Games

interNET CONNECTION links to websites relevant to Chapter Projects, Interdisciplinary Investigations, exercises

and much more!

About the Timepieces Hologram

The optimum viewing angle for the timepieces hologram on the cover of this textbook is a 45° angle. For best results, view the hologram at this angle under a direct light source, such as sunlight or incandescent lighting.

Table of Contents

Mathematics: Applications and Connections, Course 2

Pages T2-T31 provide a brief overview of the latest trends and research in mathematics education as well as to illustrate ways in which Glencoe has responded to these.

Pathways to Success T2
Bridging the Gap T4
Mathematics: Applications and Connections Exemplifies the NCTM Standards . T6
Motivating Middle School Students T8
Developing Problem Solving T10
Using Technology T12
Assessment T14
Using Projects T16
Using Games in the Math Classroom T19
Multiple Learning Styles T20
Involving Parents and Family T21
Classroom Management T22
Classroom Vignettes T23
Mathematics: Applications and Connections Research Activities T24
Scope and Sequence T25
Planning Your Course of Study T30

Chapter Overviews

Chapter 1 .... 2a-2f
Chapter 2 .... 42a-42f
Chapter 3 .... 86a-86f
Chapter 4 .... 130a-130f
Chapter 5 .... 182a-182f
Chapter 6 .... 224a-224f
Chapter 7 .... 266a-266f
Chapter 8 .... 314a-314f
Chapter 9 .... 358a-358f
Chapter 10 .... 406a-406f
Chapter 11 .... 448a-448f
Chapter 12 .... 488a-488f
Chapter 13 .... 526a-526f

Student Handbook

Extra Practice 562-606
(Basic Skills, Lesson by Lesson, Mixed Problem Solving)
Chapter Tests 607-619
Getting Acquainted with the Graphing Calculator 620-621
Getting Acquainted with Spreadsheets 622-623
Selected Answers 624-653
Photo Credits 654-655
Glossary 656-663
Spanish Glossary 664-672

Teacher's Wraparound Edition Index 673-684
Additional Answers AA1-AA25
Symbols, Formulas, and Measurement Conversions ...... inside back cover

PATHWAYS TO SUCCESS

For the last several years, it's been difficult to find a newspaper or magazine that does not have an article about how poorly U.S. students score on international math exams compared to students from other countries such as Japan or Germany. For example, in the **Third International Mathematics and Science Study (TIMSS),** U.S. eighth grade students scored *below* the average for industrialized countries.

This result should not be surprising given the well-known study by James Flanders. He found that only 30-40% of the content in grades 6-8 of the most widely used K-8 mathematics series was new while algebra textbooks contained about 88% new content. (*Arithmetic Teacher*, "How Much of the Content in Mathematics Textbooks is New?", September 1987). This lack of new content in middle school combined with almost all new content in algebra 1 often leads to student frustration and failure in algebra 1. Flanders' research and the TIMSS data were both obtained before the first edition of ***Mathematics: Applications and Connections*** was published.

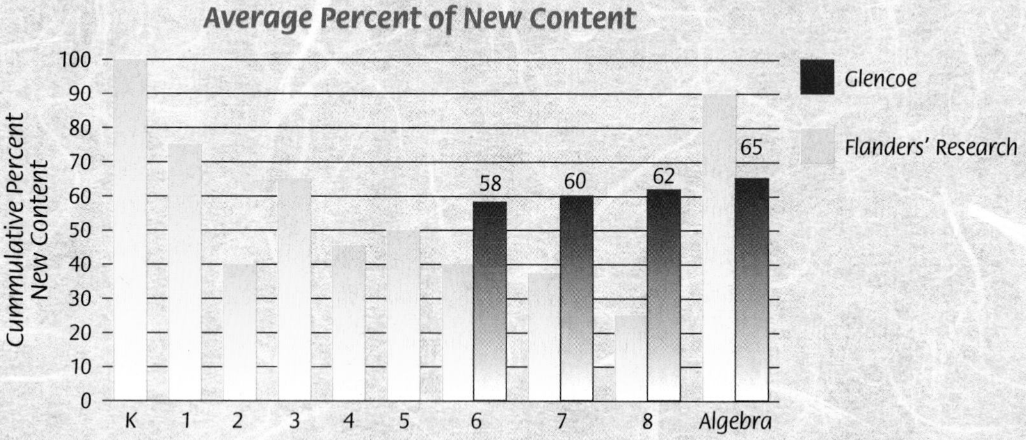

*Note that the TIMSS data was collected when the programs described in the Flanders study were **very** widely used.*

Glencoe changed this pattern with the publication of ***Mathematics: Applications and Connections.***

Glencoe understands that the middle school experience is critical in preparing students for success in algebra 1 and geometry. ***Mathematics: Applications and Connections*** is designed to smooth the path to algebra and geometry by creating a program that has about the same amount of new material in Grade 6, Grade 7, and Grade 8 as well as in Glencoe's *Algebra 1.*

Here are some of the key findings from TIMSS and Glencoe's response.

TIMSS Finding	Glencoe's Response
Achievement U.S. eighth-grade students test at about the international average in algebra, fractions, statistics, and probability. U.S. students do not do as well in geometry, measurement, and proportionality.	All mathematics topics are integrated throughout Course 1-3 of ***Mathematics: Applications and Connections.***
Curriculum The content taught in U.S. eighth-grade classrooms is at a seventh-grade level in comparison to other countries.	***Mathematics: Applications and Connections*** meets or exceeds international standards in grades 6-8. It emphasizes geometry, measurement, and proportionality, as well as algebra, fractions, and statistics.
Curriculum Topic coverage in U.S. eighth-grade mathematics classes is not as focused as in Germany and Japan. (The U.S. curriculum is "a mile wide and an inch deep.)	***Mathematics: Applications and Connections*** follows a structured scope and sequence that introduces, reinforces, and extends topics needed for success in algebra 1 and geometry.

In addition to Glencoe's progressive response to the Flanders' research and the TIMSS, here are some other key features and benefits that middle school mathematics educators asked us to include in ***Mathematics: Applications and Connections.***

Feature	Benefit
Integrated Content There is an emphasis on integrating algebra, geometry, measurement, proportional reasoning, statistics, probability, technology, and problem solving.	Students will be prepared for success in algebra 1 and geometry, the gateway courses for success in college and careers.
Applications and Connections Relevant, real-life applications and interdisciplinary connections are a part of every lesson. Every application and connection is written in an engaging style and often accompanied by colorful, high-interest photos, graphs, tables, and charts.	Students are motivated to learn mathematics when it is interesting and related to their lives. Every page is designed to help you answer the question, "When am I ever going to use this?".
Test Preparation Every lesson has at least one multiple-choice *Test Practice* question. Every chapter has two pages of *Standardized Test Practice,* which includes multiple-choice test items, open-ended test items, and a *Test-Taking Tip.*	Test scores will increase because students will be prepared for success on state, national, and international standardized tests as well as classroom tests and end-of-course examinations.

As you examine ***Mathematics: Applications and Connections,*** you will see that this program will help you prepare your students for success in school and in their lives. As students use the program, they will repeatedly receive this message: "Math is for everyone...You can do it...You'll use it every day."

Mathematics: Applications and Connections— something good just got better!

BRIDGING THE GAP

From Elementary Mathematics to High School Mathematics

Students' experiences in middle school mathematics are crucial in preparing them for success in algebra and geometry.

Glencoe's ***Mathematics: Applications and Connections*** prepares all students for success in algebra and geometry. How? By introducing a variety of new concepts at the right time in the right way and by integrating them appropriately into all three courses. For example, integers are introduced in Chapter 11 of Course 1, in Chapter 5 of Course 2, and in Chapter 2 of Course 3. Because algebra and geometry are introduced in Chapter 1 in all three courses – and because both are reinforced throughout – students are much better prepared to take these courses in high school.

Manipulatives help students bridge the gap from the concrete to the abstract.

How does *Mathematics: Applications and Connections* help students bridge from the concrete, number-oriented mathematics in elementary school to abstract, symbol-centered algebra and geometry in high school? Many middle school students' learning styles lend themselves to concrete operations. They may not be able to grasp abstract concepts easily, but they can understand abstract concepts on a concrete level.

"Hands-on experiential learning in which students take an active role and assume responsibility for their own learning is an integral part of the instructional practices of this program."

Beatrice Moore-Harris, Author

Hands-On Labs and Mini-Labs help students discover concepts on their own.

Glencoe's ***Mathematics: Applications and Connections*** encourages students to **do** mathematics. **Hands-On Labs** give students hands-on experiences, with a partner or group, in discovering mathematical concepts for themselves. The **Hands-On Lab Masters** provide students with a way to record what they observe and discover in the Hands-On Labs. Students may also participate in shorter **Hands-On Mini-Labs** in which they investigate mathematical concepts within a lesson. **Hands-On Math** exercises provide even more opportunities for concrete learning.

The **Overhead Manipulative Resources** include a wealth of transparent manipulatives for use with overhead projectors such as a compass, spinner, counters, geoboard, and coordinate planes. A complete Teacher's Guide, correlated to the Hands-On Labs and Hands-On Mini-Labs, provides suggestions for demonstrations by the teacher or students.

The Glencoe **Mathematics Manipulative Kit** offers the tools students need to work through the Hands-On Labs and Hands-On Mini-Labs. A Teacher's Guide provides a correlation to all three courses.

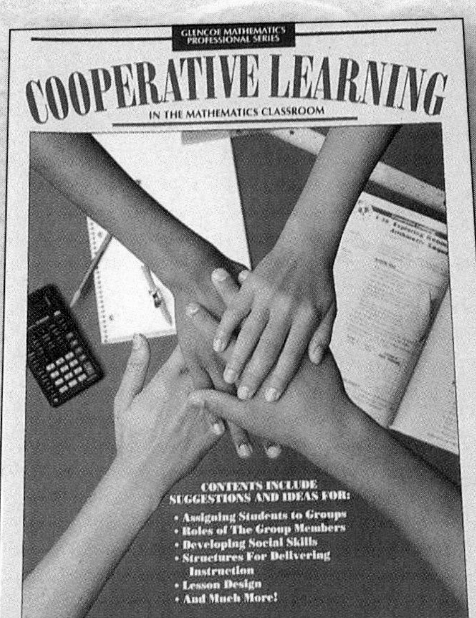

Cooperative Learning in the Mathematics Classroom, part of the Glencoe Mathematics Professional Series, provides suggestions for implementing cooperative learning techniques in your classroom.

Cooperative learning helps students with academic achievement and interpersonal skills.

In cooperative learning, small groups of students work as teams to share ideas, solve problems, and justify conclusions. At the same time, they develop vital skills in cooperating with others toward a common goal. The increased communication that takes place in cooperative learning experiences clarifies and strengthens individual students' understanding.

Glencoe's ***Mathematics: Applications and Connections*** offers an abundance of ways for students to learn cooperatively. **Chapter Projects** provide open-ended activities that often include collecting and organizing data. Students work together to explore, analyze, and report their results. **Interdisciplinary Investigations** relate mathematics to other content areas students are studying. These long-term projects are ideal for cooperative learning groups. The **Investigations and Projects Masters** provide students with ways to organize their explorations in the Chapter Projects and Interdisciplinary Investigations.

Hands-On Labs, Technology Labs, Thinking Labs, and **Mini-Labs** throughout all three courses of Mathematics: Applications and Connections also provide excellent opportunities for cooperative learning experiences. **Let the Games Begin** features interesting and fun games to help students reinforce and extend concepts.

Mathematics: Applications and Connections
Exemplifies NCTM Standards 2000

Mathematics: Applications and Connections thoroughly integrates all ten curriculum standards for grades 6-8 as outlined in the NCTM Standards 2000. For more information on the Standards, refer to pages 28–71 and 210–285 of *Principles and Standards for School Mathematics* ©2000 by the National Council of Teachers of Mathematics.

Glencoe has assigned numbers to the ten standards for ease of reference later in this text. The assigned reference numbers are listed in blue beside each standard.

Number and Operations Standard (1)

Course 1 (Chapters 1-13)
4-37, 46-85, 94-121, 132-148, 150-169, 178-180, 182-219, 228-241, 245-357, 268-301, 310-343, 352-366, 370-373, 375-383, 396-414, 416-425, 434-461, 464-467, 476-503, 514-534, 536-539

Course 2 (Chapters 1-13)
4-20, 28-35, 44-79, 88-121, 132-175, 184-217, 226-257, 268-307, 316-351, 362-373, 376-379, 382-385, 408-441, 450-481, 496-506, 510-517, 528-533, 538-553

Course 3 (Chapters 1-13)
4-47, 56-95, 104-129, 140-155, 158-177, 188-192, 194-199, 201-204, 206-212, 214-218, 232-267, 278-321, 330-373, 382-417, 428-444, 446-467, 476-481, 486-493, 495-507, 518-543, 546-548

Algebra Standard (2)

Course 1 (Chapters 1, 2, 4-13)
8-11, 16-31, 34-37, 46-57, 64-85, 133-139, 141-143, 149-155, 161-163, 167-169, 178-184, 197-201, 214-219, 243-245, 250-253, 273-283, 285-294, 296-301, 317-327, 330-343, 356-357, 370-373, 384-385, 398-409, 416-420, 425, 434-467, 476-503, 514-534, 536-539

Course 2 (Chapters 1-9, 11-13)
8-10, 12-33, 56-63, 66-69, 94-97, 133-136, 138-149, 197-200, 202-205, 207-217, 226-231, 234-245, 249-257, 284-288, 297-304, 317-320, 325-328, 332-335, 346-348, 360-365, 369-373, 376-379, 382-385, 388-397, 456-467, 469-481, 498-502, 510-513, 538-541

Course 3 (Chapters 1-13)
11-29, 32-47, 62-89, 92-95, 111-119, 140-147, 153-162, 167-177, 188-192, 194-212, 215-223, 232-234, 239-252, 257-260, 278-321, 330-373, 385-409, 414-417, 428-467, 476-479, 490-493, 528-533, 560-591

Geometry Standard (3)

Course 1 (Chapters 1, 3-13)
34-37, 102-111, 141-143, 149-155, 161-163, 178-181, 188-190, 198-201, 228-234, 238-241, 246-249, 268-272, 277-283, 296-301, 310-315, 317-327, 334-336, 340-353, 352-385, 396-425, 434-436, 445-448, 456-467, 484-487, 500-503, 522-534, 536-539

Course 2 (Chapters 1, 2, 4-10, 12)
17-20, 28-33, 56-59, 66-69, 146-147, 191-195, 215-217, 254-257, 292-300, 317-320, 362-365, 369-385, 388-397, 410-441, 490-517

Course 3 (Chapters 1-11, 13)
8-10, 17-25, 38-42, 81-83, 107-110, 118-123, 126-129, 148-151, 186-223, 239, 245-248, 253-256, 296-299, 301-314, 342-343, 357-373, 382-384, 386-389, 396-401, 404-417, 433-435, 442-444, 446-449, 452-467, 476-503, 560

Measurement Standard (4)

Course 1 (Chapters 1, 3-13)
4-7, 12-15, 28-31, 34-37, 95-104, 109-111, 118-121, 133-136, 145-155, 161-166, 188-190, 197-213, 228-234, 238-241, 246-249, 254-257, 268-283, 292-301, 312-315, 317-327, 334-336, 340-343, 352-355, 358-366, 370-373, 379-383, 396-414, 416-425, 434-436, 449-452, 459-461, 464-467, 484-487, 522-534, 536-539

Course 2 (Chapters 1-4, 7-9, 11, 12)
4-7, 54-55, 66-69, 74-76, 118, 148-149, 272-279, 284-287, 289-300, 305-307, 325-328, 360-385, 388-391, 469-472, 502-506

Course 3 (Chapters 1-9, 11)
38-47, 56-58, 62-72, 92-95, 118-119, 126-129, 148-151, 186-193, 196-199, 201-205, 213-214, 249-252, 265-267, 278-280, 301-311, 361-373, 396-401, 404-417, 482-485, 499-507

Data Analysis & Probability Standard (5)

Course 1 (Chapters 1-11, 13)
12-15, 34-37, 46-85, 105-108, 132-139, 141-143, 150-151, 157-159, 182-184, 206-209, 242, 250-253, 289-291, 316, 330-343, 358-361, 410-411, 434-439, 456-461, 514-539

Course 2 (Chapters 2-6, 8, 10, 11, 13)
44-63, 66-73, 88-121, 165-168, 172-175, 212-214, 253, 317-320, 342-345, 436-441, 459-467, 467-472, 528-553

Course 3 (Chapters 2-6, 10-12)
56-61, 73-76, 107-110, 120-123, 126-129, 140-177, 194-195, 200, 253-256, 260-264, 441, 450-451, 476-479, 516-531, 534-548

Problem Solving Standard (6)

Course 1 (Chapters 1-13)
4-37, 46-85, 94-121, 132-155, 157-169, 178-219, 229-257, 268-283, 285-301, 310-343, 352-385, 396-425, 434-467, 476-503, 514-539

Course 2 (Chapters 1-13)
4-35, 44-79, 88-121, 132-175, 184-217, 226-257, 268-287, 289-307, 316-351, 360-387, 408-441, 450-458, 460-481, 490-517, 528-553

Course 3 (Chapters 1-13)
4-47, 56-76, 78-95, 104-129, 140-177, 186-223, 232-267, 278-321, 330-373, 382-417, 428-431, 433-467, 476-507, 516-548, 560-591

Reasoning & Proof Standard (7)

Course 1 (Chapters 1-13)
4-37, 46-85, 94-121, 132-169, 178-219, 228-257, 268-283, 285-301, 310-343, 352-385, 396-425, 434-467, 476-503, 514-539

Course 2 (Chapters 1-13)
4-10, 12-23, 28-35, 44-79, 88-121, 132-175, 184-217, 226-257, 268-307, 316-351, 376-379, 382-387, 408-441, 450-458, 464-467, 490-517, 528-553

Course 3 (Chapters 1-13)
4-15, 17-47, 56-76, 78-95, 104-129, 140-177, 186-223, 232-267, 278-321, 330-373, 382-417, 428-431, 433-467, 476-507, 516-548, 560-591

Communication Standard (8)

Course 1 (Chapters 1-13)
4-37, 46-85, 94-121, 132-169, 178-219, 228-257, 268-301, 310-343, 352-385, 396-425, 434-467, 476-503, 514-539

Course 2 (Chapters 1-13)
4-10, 12-35, 44-79, 88-121, 132-175, 184-217, 226-257, 268-307, 316-351, 360-397, 408-441, 450-481, 490-517, 528-553

Course 3 (Chapters 1-13)
4-47, 56-76, 78-95, 104-129, 140-177, 186-223, 232-267, 278-321, 330-373, 382-417, 428-431, 433-467, 476-507, 516-548, 560-591

Connections Standard (9)

Course 1 (Chapters 1-13))
4-37, 46-85, 94-121, 133-139, 141-169, 178-180, 182-190, 193-219, 228-241, 243-257, 268-270, 273-283, 285-301, 312-343, 352-361, 364-366, 370-373, 375-383, 396-414, 416-425, 434-439, 441-461, 464-467, 476-487, 492-493, 496-503, 514-539

Course 2 (Chapters 1-13)
4-35, 44-79, 88-121, 132-136, 138-175, 184-194, 196-217, 226-257, 268-287, 289-307, 316-351, 360-361, 370-373, 382-385, 388-397, 408-441, 450-472, 478-481, 490-517, 528-553

Course 3 (Chapters 1-13)
4-15, 17-47, 56-76, 78-95, 104-129, 140-177, 186-192, 194-223, 232-267, 278-321, 330-373, 382-417, 428-431, 433-467, 476-507, 516-548, 560-591

Representation Standard (10)

Course 1 (Chapters 1-13)
4-25, 28-33, 46-85, 94-121, 132-136, 140-143, 145-148, 150-159, 167-169, 178-196, 198-205, 210-219, 228-231, 238-241, 243-257, 268-276, 280-288, 292-294, 296-300, 310-343, 352-385, 396-424, 434-452, 456-467, 476-491, 494-503, 514-521, 526-529, 531-534, 536-539

Course 2 (Chapters 1-13)
4-15, 17-20, 24-33, 44-59, 64-65, 70-76, 88-105, 108-117, 119-121, 138-145, 150-171, 184-191, 196-217, 226-231, 234-252, 254-257, 268-279, 282-307, 316-320, 325-328, 332-351, 360-385, 388-397, 410-437, 450-463, 468-472, 490-495, 498-517, 534-546, 551-553

Course 3 (Chapters 1-12)
17-29, 32-36, 38-47, 56-65, 69-76, 78-80, 84-85, 90-95, 104-123, 126-129, 140-146, 148-161, 167-170, 174-177, 186-199, 201-204, 210-213, 215-218, 235-239, 242-256, 261-264, 278-292, 300-304, 307-314, 335-341, 344-351, 357-373, 382-403, 408-417, 433-435, 442-444, 446-467, 476-502, 518-537

"When are we ever going to use it?"

Motivating Middle School Students

"Why do I have to learn this?"

Although these may be just complaints from our middle school students, they are legitimate questions that deserve answers. We at Glencoe realize that effective mathematics programs that really motivate middle school students must have more than strong content. They must demonstrate the usefulness of mathematics in a way that relates to student interests.

Mathematics: Applications and Connections makes math a part of students' daily school lives.

- **Applications** begin lessons with a real-life situation that points out how mathematics is used in students' everyday lives as well as in the world about them.
- **When am I ever going to use this?** gives an example of when the math concepts of the lesson will be useful in students' lives.
- **Connection** examples and exercises show how mathematics is used in other courses they may be taking such as Language Arts, Life Science, Geography, Music, Health, Physical Education, and Art.
- **Integration** examples and exercises illustrate how the math they are learning relates to mathematics courses they may take later such as Algebra, Geometry, and Probability and Statistics.

> "The curriculum must go beyond the basics—to be relevant, it must be of interest to students and emphasize the usefulness of mathematics."
>
> Ron Pelfrey, Author

Mathematics: Applications and Connections invites students to look beyond their textbook to see mathematics in the world.

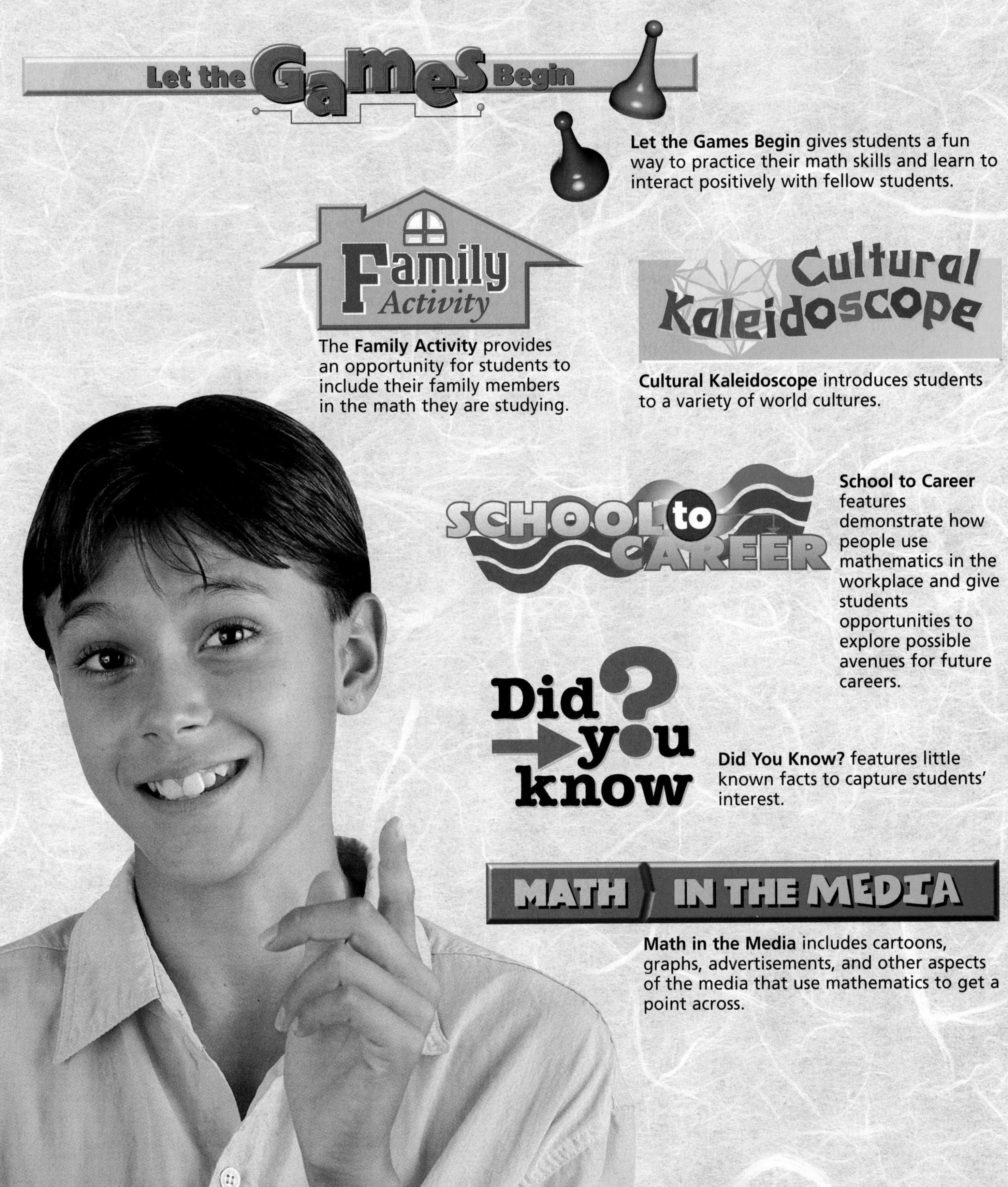

Let the Games Begin gives students a fun way to practice their math skills and learn to interact positively with fellow students.

The **Family Activity** provides an opportunity for students to include their family members in the math they are studying.

Cultural Kaleidoscope introduces students to a variety of world cultures.

School to Career features demonstrate how people use mathematics in the workplace and give students opportunities to explore possible avenues for future careers.

Did You Know? features little known facts to capture students' interest.

Math in the Media includes cartoons, graphs, advertisements, and other aspects of the media that use mathematics to get a point across.

Developing Problem Solving

According to the NCTM Standards, "Problem solving is the process by which students experience the power and usefulness of mathematics in the world around them. It is also a method of inquiry and application ... to provide a consistent context for learning and applying mathematics. Problem situations can establish a 'need to know' and foster the motivation for the development of concepts."

Problem solving is an integral part of every lesson in every course of Glencoe's ***Mathematics: Applications and Connections.*** How is this accomplished?

The **first chapter** of each course focuses on problem solving.

- Course 1: **Problem Solving, Numbers, and Algebra**
- Course 2: **Problem Solving, Algebra, and Geometry**
- Course 3: **Problem Solving and Algebra**

Thinking Labs in every chapter focus on problem-solving strategies, such as solving a simpler problem and working backward, and present opportunities to solve nonroutine problems.

Frequent **Problem-Solving Study Hints** suggest using various problem-solving strategies to investigate and understand mathematical content and apply strategies to new problem situations.

Reading Math Study Hints provide tips on how to read and interpret the language or symbolism of mathematics.

Study Hint

Reading Math The symbols < and > always point to the lesser of the two numbers.

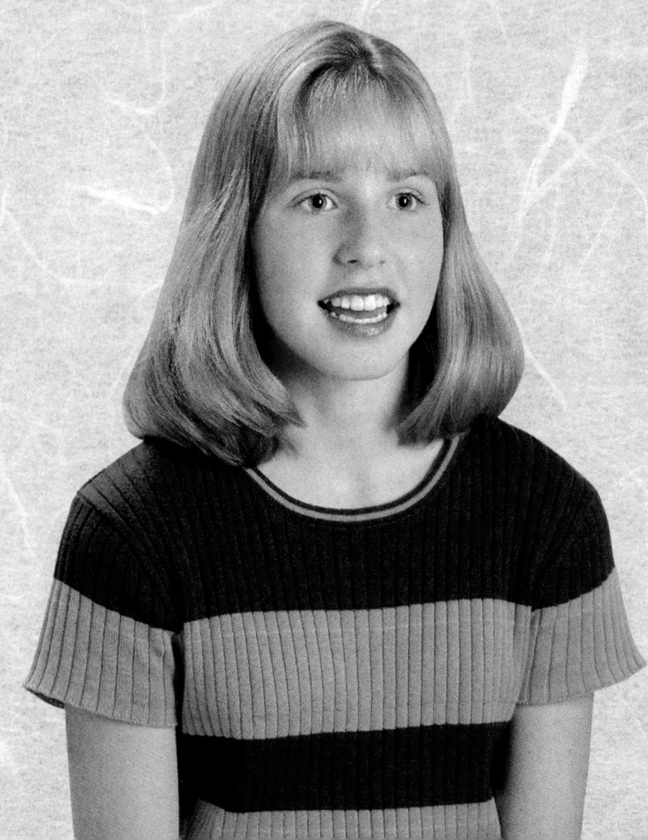

Critical Thinking exercises in every lesson give students practice in developing and applying higher-order thinking skills.

Glencoe's ***Mathematics: Applications and Connections*** links practical problem solving to students' real-life interests. Mathematics becomes a vital force in the lives of middle school students as their eyes are opened to the relationship between mathematics and sports, shopping, and other teen interests. They "take ownership" of their skills by writing their own problems and presenting class projects connected to real life.

> "Problem solving is an integral component of this program. It requires students to think critically, examine new concepts, and then extend or generalize what they already know."
>
> **Linda Dritsas, Author**

Most lessons begin with either a real-world **Application,** an interdisciplinary **Connection,** or content **Integration** that provides students with a reason to learn mathematics. Application, connection, and integration examples also occur throughout the texts to give students the opportunity to study completely worked-out problems.

Applications and Problem Solving exercises in every lesson directly link mathematics to real-world topics like entertainment, and to art, history, science, and other subjects.

The **Chapter Projects** and **Interdisciplinary Investigations** enable students to become more deeply engaged in a problem situation.

USING TECHNOLOGY

Is there a day that goes by when you don't encounter a computer-operated machine? The future world of our students will be even more involved in high technology. Clearly, technology is changing the workplace and the home at an increasingly rapid pace. Without technical mathematical skills, today's students will have little or no chance of finding good jobs.

Mathematics: Applications and Connections provides many opportunities for you to introduce your students to the world of technology as they learn mathematics.

Internet Connections throughout the Student Edition refer students to the Glencoe ***Mathematics: Applications and Connections*** site **www.glencoe.com/sec/math/mac/mathnet** that provides links to other websites on the Internet. These sites provide more information on the topics that students are studying.

Technology Labs and **Mini-Labs** give students hands-on opportunities to use a computer or a graphing calculator to solve problems. Students learn how to use a spreadsheet to organize data and make predictions. Graphing calculator programs provide an introduction to logic and a way to perform calculations in a timely manner.

Technology Study Hints provide helpful suggestions on how students can use scientific calculators, graphing calculators, or software in studying the topics of the lesson.

In the **Chapter Projects** and **Interdisciplinary Investigations,** students are encouraged to use the Internet and application software like word processing, publishing software, and spreadsheets.

Additional materials in the Teacher's Classroom Resources provide other ways for you to incorporate technology in your lesson planning.

The **CD-ROM Program** for ***Mathematics: Applications and Connections*** contains a variety of activities correlated to each chapter. These include a Chapter Introduction and a Resource Lesson for each lesson in the Student Edition. The activities also include Interactive Lessons and Extended Activities for some of the lessons in the chapter. Every chapter includes an Assessment Game that is a cumulative review of skills they have learned.

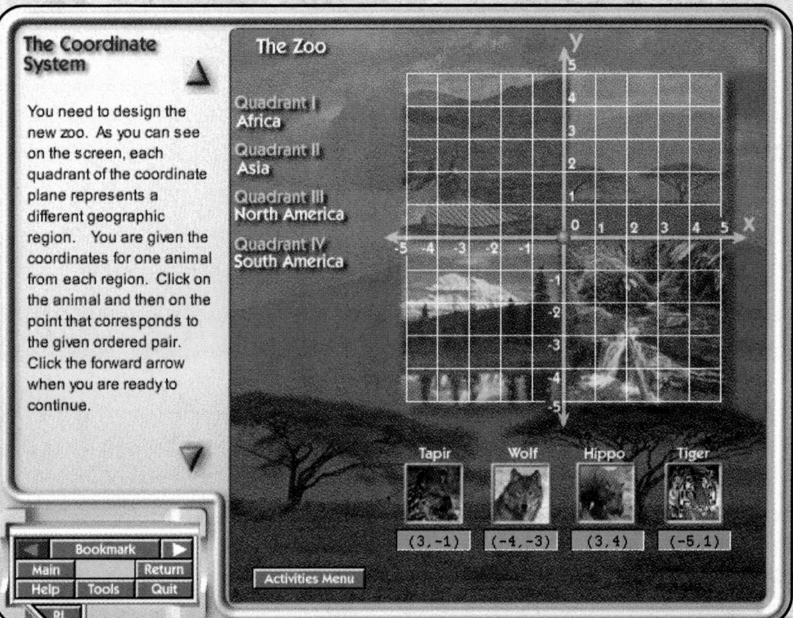

CD-ROM Program, Course 2, Chapter 7

MindJogger Videoquizzes feature a game show format that provides an alternative assessment and an entertaining way for your students to review chapter concepts and problem-solving skills.

Interactive Mathematics Tools Software helps students gain mathematical power through interactive activities that combine video, sound, animation, graphics, and text.

All of the blackline masters for ***Mathematics: Applications and Connections*** are available on the **Electronic Teacher's Classroom Resources** CD-ROM. There's no need to carry a large array of booklets from room to room—just print out the masters you wish to use from a single CD-ROM that works on both Macintosh and Windows formats.

Ass(E)ssment

The assessment tools built into ***Mathematics: Applications and Connections*** are designed to assess traditional basic skills as well as those skills that will be required for success in the 21st century. In addition to basic skills, ***Mathematics: Applications and Connections*** also helps you assess students' ability to organize information, apply previously-learned information, and make conjectures based on gathered data. The curriculum alignment in ***Mathematics: Applications and Connections*** also enables students to perform well on standardized testing at both state and national levels.

The following features and components help you accurately assess each student's achievement.

In the Student Editions...

- Every lesson has a **Mixed Review** that includes a **Test Practice** item.
- Every chapter has **Math Journals**, a **Chapter Project**, a **Mid-Chapter Self Test**, **Standardized Test Practice**, and a **Chapter Test**.
- Every chapter has a **Study Guide and Assessment** that includes Vocabulary, Understanding and Using Vocabulary, Examples and Review Exercises for each Objective, Applications and Problem Solving, a **Performance Task**, and a **Portfolio** suggestion.
- Since practically every mathematics test is also a reading test, several **Reading Math** study hints are included in every chapter.

In the Teacher's Wraparound Editions...

- Every lesson is correlated to the major national standardized tests: CAT, CTBS, ITBS, MAT, SAT, and Terra Nova.
- Every lesson includes a **5-Minute Check** that covers the previous lesson or chapter.
- Every lesson has a **Closing Activity** that involves writing, speaking, or modeling.

In the supplementary materials...

Assessment and Evaluation Masters include:

1. For each chapter: three Multiple Choice tests (Basic, Average, Honors), three Free-Response Tests (Basic, Average, Honors), Performance Assessment (includes a Scoring Guide), Standardized Test Practice, a Cumulative Review, four quizzes, and a Mid-Chapter Test.
2. Also Included: a Placement Test, two Semester Tests and a Final Test

MindJogger Videoquizzes (VHS) review each chapter by using a game show format. As students compete on teams, they hear and see each review problem as it is presented and then completely solved.

Test and Review Software (Windows & Macintosh) combines a test generator and test bank. You can easily create your own free-response, multiple choice, and open-ended tests for honors, average, and basic students.

5-Minute Check Transparencies provide a quick review of the previous lesson or chapter. There is one full-color transparency for every lesson. The 5-Minute Check is also printed in the Teacher's Wraparound Edition to make your lesson plans easier to prepare.

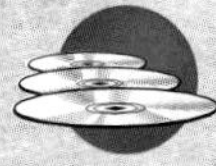

The CD-ROM Program includes guided practice and an Assessment Game that is similar to Trivial Pursuit.

Alternative Assessment in the Mathematics Classroom, part of the Glencoe Mathematics Professional Series, gives an overview of the latest trends in assessment.

Using Projects

Doing mathematics is so much more effective than memorizing mathematics!

Mathematics: Applications and Connections gives you and your students several opportunities to engage in projects of varying lengths that put mathematics into motion.

The **Chapter Project** is introduced at the beginning of the chapter and sets in motion several activities that culminate with **Completing the Chapter Project** in the Chapter Study Guide and Assessment. Students apply the mathematics they learn in the chapter to various real-life situations. They are often asked to represent their results as a working model or in statistical graph form. Throughout the chapter, **Working on the Chapter Project** exercises remind students of the next steps in their project. These activities not only implement the mathematics student are learning, but give students the opportunity to work together as a team.

Interdisciplinary Investigation

The **Interdisciplinary Investigations** found at the ends of Chapters 3, 6, 9, and 12 show how the mathematics students have learned can be applied to other courses they may be taking. Each investigation uses the skills from the previous three chapters. In addition to the problem they are assigned to investigate, they are given writing assignments that explore other areas such as Language Arts, Foreign Language, Science, Health, Physical Education, and Social Studies.

Interactive Mathematics: Activities and Investigations

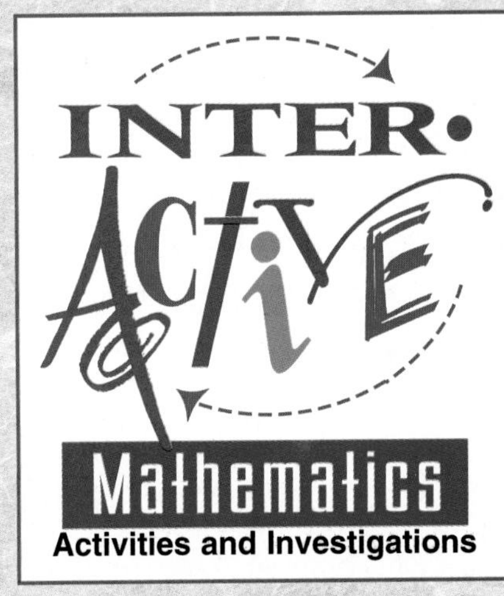

is based on a NSF-funded program that offers an innovative approach to teaching and learning middle school mathematics. Each of the 18 units that make up this comprehensive, activity-based program may be used to enhance chapters in ***Mathematics: Applications and Connections.***

The interleaf pages of each chapter in the Teacher's Wraparound Edition highlight two activities from ***Interactive Mathematics: Activities and Investigations*** that are appropriate for that lesson. However, there are many other activities that may be useful.

The chart below summarizes the mathematical focus of each unit of ***Interactive Mathematics: Activities and Investigations.***

	Unit	Title	Mathematical Focus
Course 1	1	From the Beginning	Building Math Power
	2	A Million to One	Number Sense
	3	Just the Right Size	Scale Drawings and Proportional Reasoning
	4	Through the Looking Glass	Spatial Visualization
	5	Get a Clue	Logical Reasoning
	6	The Road Not Taken	Graph Theory and Networks
Course 2	7	Take It From the Top	Building Math Power
	8	Data Sense	Statistics and Data Analysis
	9	Don't Fence Me In	Area and Perimeter
	10	Against the Odds	Probability
	11	Cycles	Algebra Patterns
	12	Treasure Island	Geometry and Measurement
Course 3	13	Start Your Engines	Building Math Power
	14	Run for Cover	Surface Area and Volume
	15	On the Move	Graphing and Functions
	16	Growing Pains	Linear and Exponential Growth
	17	Infinite Windows	Fractals and Chaos Theory
	18	Quality Control	Applied Data Analysis

Glencoe has correlated ***Mathematics: Applications and Connections (MAC)*** with the ***Interactive Mathematics: Activities and Investigations (IMAI)*** units to provide a unique opportunity for you to tailor a program to your middle school students. Integrating the two programs allows you to emphasize areas and mathematical ideas that interest and fit the unique needs of the students in your class.

MAC Course 1 Chapter	IMAI Units 1-6	Other IMAI Units
1	1, 5	
2	6	8
3	2	
4	2	7, 9
5	2, 3	
6	3	11
7	3	10
8	3	10
9	4	12
10	4	14
11		11
12		11
13	6	10

MAC Course 2 Chapter	IMAI Units 7-12	Other IMAI Units
1	7	
2	7	2
3	8	
4	11	18
5	11	16
6	11	15
7	9, 10	
8	10	3
9	12	
10	9	
11	10	
12	9	4, 14
13	10	6

MAC Course 3 Chapter	IMAI Units 13-18	Other IMAI Units
1	15	8
2	15	
3	16	3
4	18	8
5	14	4
6	16, 17	
7	16, 17	
8	16, 17	3, 12
9	17, 18	10
10	15, 16	
11	14	
12	17	6, 10
13	16	5

Interactive Mathematics: Activities and Investigations is available as individual units or as a three book series that groups Units 1-6, 7-12, and 13-18. Each unit also has a Classroom Instructional Resources binder that includes teaching instructions, blackline masters, transparencies, and guidance on using projects in the classroom.

For more information on ***Interactive Mathematics: Activities and Investigations,*** contact your nearest Glencoe Regional Office or call 1-800-334-7344.

Using Games in the Math Classroom

During the past few years, the use of games in the mathematics classroom has increased dramatically. These activities tend to be very motivational, and they often help improve students' attitudes toward mathematics in general. Because games are enjoyable, they allow students to learn and review mathematical skills and concepts while they unknowingly increase their problem-solving, logic, and computational skills.

Why Use Games? While mathematical games are not the only method you can use to provide individualized instruction or enrichment, they may be a very effective strategy. According to NCTM, most mathematical games serve one or more of the following functions.

- To develop concepts.
- To provide drill and reinforcement.
- To develop perceptual abilities.
- To provide opportunities for logical thinking and/or problem solving.

Therefore, mathematical games can be used in a number of different ways. You may want to use a game to introduce a new topic, thus encouraging students to employ discovery learning. You may want to use a game within the framework of your lesson instruction, for example, in the last few moments of a class period. Finally, you may want to use a game to review a concept previously taught.

The games presented in **Let the Games Begin** are designed to be useful and enjoyable to all students. Feel free to develop new and fun variations that will make each game your own.

Let the Games Begin

More information on games is available from Glencoe on the Internet at **www.glencoe.com/sec/math/mac/mathnet.**

In addition to the games presented in the Student Edition, more games are available in the **Classrooms Games** booklet.

Multiple Learning Styles

People learn in many different ways. There are several different learning styles that help us approach and solve problems. Everyone possesses varying degrees of each of these learning styles, but the ways in which they combine and blend are as varied as the personalities of the individuals. Glencoe's ***Mathematics: Applications and Connections*** provides you with ways to accommodate students with these diverse learning styles.

Learning Style	Characteristics of Students	Activities in Student Edition
verbal/ linguistic	read regularly, write clearly, and easily understand the written word	**Communicating Mathematics** exercises ask students to tell, write, and explain mathematical concepts. Students also express what they have learned in their **Math Journals.**
logical	use numbers, logic, and critical thinking skills	Clearly-written **Examples** present important concepts, and **Critical Thinking** exercises extend those concepts. **Thinking Labs** encourage students to practice their logical thinking skills by using various strategies.
visual/ spatial	think in terms of pictures and images	**Integration** and **Hands-On Lab** exercises ask students to draw or show mathematical concepts through modeling, coordinate grids, charts, and graphs.
auditory/ musical	have "good ears" and can produce rhythms and melodies	Multimedia software, such as the **CD-ROM Program, MindJogger Videoquizzes,** and **Interactive Mathematics Tools Software,** can be easily incorporated into lessons.
kinesthetic	learn from touch, movement, and manipulating objects	**Hands-On Labs** and **Mini-Labs** provide for physical involvement in learning.
interpersonal	understand and work well with other people	**Chapter Projects, Interdisciplinary Investigations,** as well as **Hands-On Labs, Technology Labs,** and **Mini-Labs,** allow students to collaborate with others.
intrapersonal	have a realistic understanding of their strengths and weaknesses	**Math Journals, Portfolios,** and **Family Activities** help students personalize mathematics.
naturalist	can distinguish among, classify, and use features of the environment	**Application** and **Connection** examples and exercises show students how mathematics relates to the world around them.

As mathematics teacher, you may want to assign activities to students that accommodate their strongest learning styles, but frequently ask them to use their weakest learning styles. Additional activities are provided in the bottom margins of the lesson notes in the Teacher's Wraparound Edition.

The resources available in ***Mathematics: Applications and Connections*** guarantee that your classroom will be a multisensory environment, providing multiple paths for student learning.

Involving Parents and the Community

When children enter 6th grade, for a variety of reasons, it may become difficult for parents or guardians to remain on top of what's going on at school. The curricula grow more specialized, the typical middle school student becomes more independent of his or her parents, and multiple teachers replace the primary teacher of the elementary school years.

When parents do have the opportunity to meet with teachers, they often ask what they can do to motivate their children. Here are some ideas to share with parents. Developed by Reginald Clark of the Academy for Educational Development in Washington, D.C., they are designed to foster positive attitudes and boost learning.

- Share the fact that there is an inverse correlation between excessive TV viewing and high achievement in school.
- Stress the importance of seeing that their children complete homework assignments.
- Urge them to provide time, space, and materials needed for homework and reading.
- Remind them how important it is to listen to their children read and/or to read to their children.

Each chapter in Glencoe's ***Mathematics: Applications and Connections*** contains a suggested **Family Activity** for your students to complete with a family member. The **Family Letters and Activities** provide a letter and activity for each chapter to encourage students' families to become active participants in their students' learning.

Fostering Community Involvement

There are many ways to involve the community in your mathematics classroom and to share your learning with them.

- Send photos and press releases to your local newspaper to inform the community about the exciting things your students are learning.
- Have a "math career day" and invite local people to describe to students how they use math in their jobs.
- Set up a "shadow day" in which students spend a half-day "shadowing" people in the workplace who use math in their careers.
- Find out about – or implement your own – math fairs and competitions that give your students a chance to shine in the "outside world."

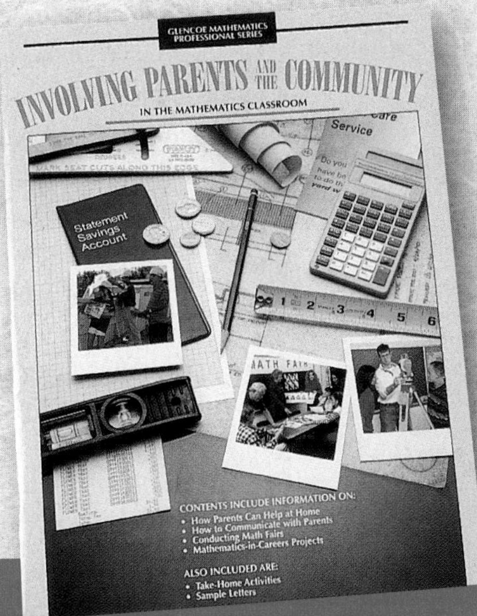

Involving Parents and the Community in the Mathematics Classroom, one of the booklets in Glencoe's Mathematics Professional Series, presents additional suggestions on how parents and the community can be active participants in supporting mathematics instruction.

Classroom Management

Meet Susan Uhrig. Mrs. Uhrig has taught in the Columbus Public Schools in Columbus, Ohio, for more than 25 years. She currently uses ***Mathematics: Applications and Connections*** in her classroom at Monroe Middle School.

Just one look at her classroom tells you that Mrs. Uhrig enjoys teaching middle school students. Their work is displayed throughout her bright classroom. Positive sayings on the bulletin boards encourage students to do their best. Manipulatives are kept out so they are easy to use—evidence that Mrs. Uhrig encourages her students to do mathematics.

Mrs. Uhrig says that she enjoys the diverse personalities of her students. You never know what challenges lie ahead each day! She organizes her classroom in ways that really get her students involved and keep their parents informed. Here are some of her ideas.

- Write the **assignment** and **objective** for the day on the chalkboard for students to copy when they come into class.
- Keep a **master notebook** where assignments are written so students can refer to the notebook if they miss a class.
- Have students keep assignment **logs** throughout the year. This helps students get and stay organized.
- Keep **manipulatives** on a table so they are easy to find and use. Mrs. Uhrig assigns several students to help distribute and collect manipulatives and calculators.
- Use "homework coupons" as a **reward** for special behavior.
- Have students write in their **journals** every day. Mrs. Uhrig has her students do the Check for Understanding exercises and 5-Minute Checks in their journals and allows them to refer to their journals during tests.
- Communicate with **parents and guardians** early and often. At the beginning of the year, Mrs. Uhrig sends each parent a letter that indicates her classroom policies. Throughout the year, she communicates with parents through student logs, interim reports, and grade cards.

There are many teachers like Mrs. Uhrig who, through years of experience, have acquired classroom management techniques that help their classrooms run smoothly. They also possess a wealth of knowledge about how to teach mathematics. Glencoe allows you to network with these teachers through the **Classroom Vignettes** in the Teacher's Wraparound Edition. Teachers from across the country share their ideas with you so that you may add to your own list of classroom management techniques.

Classroom Vignettes

Glencoe's unique **Classroom Vignettes** are classroom-tested teaching suggestions made by experienced mathematics educators. Each vignette was written by a teacher who uses Glencoe's ***Mathematics: Applications and Connections*** or by a Glencoe reviewer, consultant, or author. Glencoe thanks these outstanding mathematics educators for their unique contributions.

Travis A. Aslesen (p. 197)
Elk Point Jefferson
Elk Point, SD

Cindy J. Boyd (p. 432)
Abilene High School
Abilene, TX

Cheryl Chang (p. 212)
Samuel Enoka Kalama Intermediate
Makawao, HI

Alice C. Coates (p. 30)
Stafford Middle School
King George, VA

Joan Cooper (p. 110)
Ocean Township Intermediate School
Ocean, NJ

Judy Dexter (p. 298)
Lathrop Middle School
Lathrop, MO

Margaret F. Friedman (p. 133)
Roxboro Middle School
Cleveland Heights, OH

Travis H. Garrett (p. 138)
Swainsboro Middle School
Swainsboro, GA

Suetta Gladfelter (p. 370)
Caroline Middle School
Milford, VA

Kathy Granquist (p. 150)
Indian Mills Memorial School
Shamong, NJ

Alvin Hampton (p. 474)
Stafford Middle School
Stafford, VA

Deborah Haver (p. 531)
Great Bridge Middle School
Virginia Beach, VA

Virginia Healy (p. 346)
Thomas Harrison Middle School
Harrisonburg, VA

JoEllyn Heinkel (p. 228)
Sabish Junior High
Fond du Lac, WI

Leslee Hoey (p. 204)
Welsh Valley School
Narberth, PA

Tim A. Klein (p. 239)
Wamego Middle School
Wamego, KS

Kathy Kunkel (p. 423)
Hastings Middle School
Hastings, MN

Gary Lilla (p. 193)
East Troy Middle School
East Troy, WI

Joy Metzger (p. 294)
Buckeye Valley Middle School
Radnor, OH

Greg Rusnak (p. 332)
Madison Middle School
Madison, OH

Theresa Szczublewski (p. 74)
Jones Junior High
Toledo, OH

Carol Thornton (p. 382)
Purks Middle School
Cedartown, GA

Kym Timpano (p. 114)
Pierre Van Cortland Middle School
Croton-on-Hudson, NY

Steve Werges (p. 67)
LaSalle Springs Middle School
Glencoe, MD

Amy Wohler (p. 119)
Kirksville Junior High
Kirksville, MO

Laura J. Young, Ed.D. (p. 512)
Edwards Middle School
Conyers, CA

Research Activities

Glencoe's **Mathematics: Applications and Connections,** as well as the entire Glencoe Mathematics Series, is the product of ongoing, classroom-oriented research that involves students, teachers, curriculum supervisors, administrators, parents, and college-level mathematics educators.

The programs that make up the Glencoe Mathematics Series are currently being used by millions of students and tens of thousands of teachers. The key reason that Glencoe Mathematics programs are so successful in the classroom is the fact that each Glencoe author team is a mix of practicing classroom teachers, curriculum supervisors, and college-level mathematics educators. Glencoe's balanced author teams help ensure that Glencoe Mathematics programs are both practical and progressive.

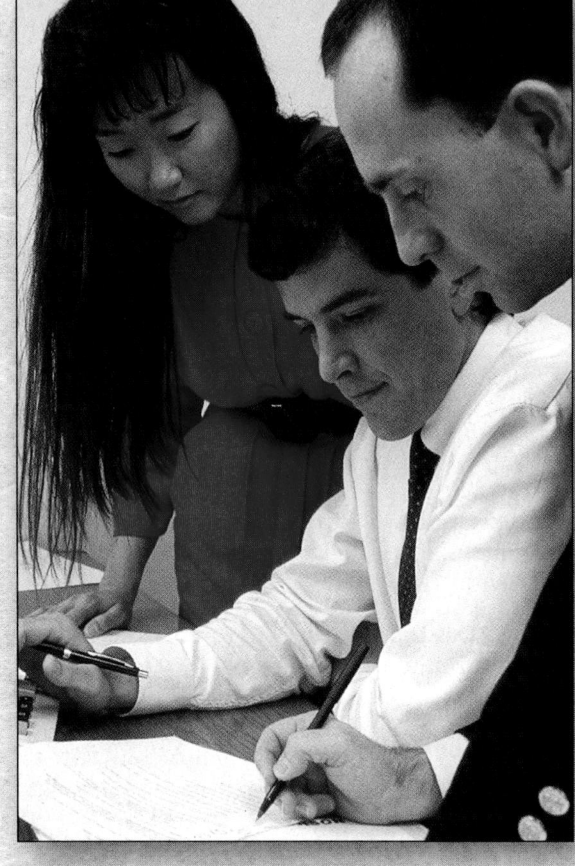

Prior to publication of a Glencoe program, typical research activities include:

- a review of educational research and recommendations made by groups such as NCTM
- mail surveys of mathematics educators
- discussion groups involving mathematics teachers, department heads, and supervisors
- focus groups involving mathematics educators
- face-to-face interviews with mathematics educators
- telephone surveys of mathematics educators
- in-depth analyses of manuscript by a wide range of reviewers and consultants
- field tests in which students and teachers use pre-publication manuscript in the classroom

Feedback from teachers, curriculum supervisors, and even students who currently use Glencoe Mathematics programs is also incorporated as Glencoe plans and publishes new and revised programs. For example, Classroom Vignettes, which are printed in the *Teacher's Wraparound Editions*, are one result of this feedback.

All of this research and information is used by Glencoe's authors and editors to publish the best instructional resources possible.

Scope and Sequence

Mathematics: Applications and Connections is a comprehensive, well-balanced, three-course program that prepares middle school students for success in algebra and geometry. Through a carefully planned scope and sequence of mathematical topics, students encounter, practice, and extend their knowledge of mathematics to promote confidence and mastery.

The chart below shows the chapter titles for the three courses in ***Mathematics: Applications and Connections.*** The following pages present a detailed chart describing the depth to which each topic is covered.

Chapter	Course 1	Course 2	Course 3
1	Problem Solving, Numbers, and Algebra	Problem Solving, Algebra, and Geometry	Problem Solving and Algebra
2	**Statistics:** Graphing Data	Applying Decimals	**Algebra:** Using Integers
3	Adding and Subtracting Decimals	**Statistics:** Analyzing Data	Using Proportion and Percent
4	Multiplying and Dividing Decimals	Using Number Patterns, Fractions, and Percents	**Statistics:** Analyzing Data
5	Using Number Patterns, Fractions, and Ratios	**Algebra:** Using Integers	**Geometry:** Investigating Patterns
6	Adding and Subtracting Fractions	**Algebra:** Exploring Equations and Functions	Exploring Number Patterns
7	Multiplying and Dividing Fractions	Applying Fractions	**Algebra:** Using Rational Numbers
8	Exploring Ratio, Proportion, and Percent	Using Proportional Reasoning	Applying Proportional Reasoning
9	**Geometry:** Investigating Patterns	**Geometry:** Investigating Patterns	**Algebra:** Exploring Real Numbers
10	**Geometry:** Understanding Area and Volume	**Geometry:** Exploring Area	**Algebra:** Graphing Functions
11	**Algebra:** Investigating Integers	Applying Percents	**Geometry:** Using Area and Volume
12	**Algebra:** Exploring Equations	**Geometry:** Finding Volume and Surface Area	Investigating Discrete Math and Probability
13	Using Probability	Exploring Discrete Math and Probability	**Algebra:** Exploring Polynomials

Mathematics: Applications and Connections

Scope and Sequence

Legend
- Introduce
- Develop
- Reinforce

Course	1	2	3
PROBLEM SOLVING			
Develop a plan	●	●	●
Strategies			
Look for a pattern	●	●	●
Solve a simpler problem	●	●	●
Act it out		●	●
Guess and check	●	●	●
Draw a diagram	●	●	●
Make a table	●	●	●
Work backward	●	●	●
Choose the method of computation	●	●	●
Make a list	●	●	●
Eliminate the possibilities	●	●	●
Determine reasonable answers	●	●	●
Make a model	●	●	●
Use a graph	●	●	●
Use an equation	●	●	●
Use logical reasoning	●	●	●
Use the Pythagorean Theorem	●	●	●
Use a Venn diagram	●	●	●
Use a frequency table	●	●	●
Use a spreadsheet	●	●	●
Use proportional reasoning			●
NUMBER AND OPERATIONS			
Number Relationships			
Decimals			
Decimal concepts	●	●	●
Reading and writing	●	●	●
Decimal place value	●	●	●
Comparing and ordering	●	●	●
Rounding	●	●	●
Relating decimals and fractions	●	●	●
Relating decimals, ratios, and percents	●	●	●
Terminating and repeating decimals	●	●	●
Scientific notation		●	●
Powers of ten		●	●
Fractions			
Fraction concepts	●	●	●
Writing mixed numbers as fractions	●	●	●
Mixed numbers and improper fractions	●	●	●
Equivalent fractions	●	●	●
Comparing and ordering fractions	●	●	●
Simplifying fractions	●	●	●
Least common denominator (LCD)	●	●	●
Rounding and estimating fractions	●	●	●
Relating fractions and decimals	●	●	●
Relating fractions and percents		●	●
Proportional Reasoning			
Ratio			
Concept of ratio	●	●	●
Reading and writing ratios	●	●	●
Simplifying ratios	●	●	●
Relating ratios and fractions	●	●	●
Relating ratios and rates	●	●	●
Ratio and probability	●	●	●
The Golden Ratio			●
Proportion			
Concept of proportion	●	●	●
Solving proportions	●	●	●
Property of proportion (cross product)	●	●	●
Scale drawings	●	●	●
Similar figures	●	●	●
Dilations		●	●
Indirect measurement		●	●
Percent			
Concept of percent	●	●	●
Writing fractions and decimals as percent	●	●	●
Percents greater than 100% or less than 1%	●	●	●
Find percent of a number	●	●	●
Percent one number is of another		●	●
Finding number when percent is known		●	●
Percent proportion		●	●
Relating percent and ratio		●	●
Percent equation		●	●
Capture/recapture		●	
Non-proportional relationships			●
Computations and Estimation			
Order of operations	●	●	●
Decimals			
Adding and subtracting	●	●	●
Multiplying by a whole number	●	●	●

Course	1	2	3
Multiplying two decimals	●	●	●
Dividing by a whole number	●	●	●
Dividing by decimals	●	●	●
Dividing with zeros in the quotient	●		
Fractions			
Adding and subtracting	●	●	●
Subtracting with renaming	●	●	●
Multiplying and dividing	●	●	●
Add and subtract mixed numbers	●	●	●
Multiply and divide mixed numbers	●	●	●
Percents			
Discount	●	●	●
Sales tax		●	
Simple interest		●	●
Percent of change		●	●
Integers			
Adding and subtracting		●	●
Multiplying and dividing		●	●
Estimation			
Whole numbers			
Rounding	●	●	●
Sums and differences	●	●	●
Products and quotients	●	●	●
Decimals			
Rounding	●	●	●
Sums and differences	●	●	●
Products and quotients	●	●	●
Fractions			
Sums and differences	●	●	●
Products and quotients	●	●	●
Percents	●	●	●
Use equivalent fractions, decimals, and percents			●
Strategies for estimating			
Rounding	●	●	●
Compatible numbers	●		
Capture-recapture		●	
Clustering	●	●	
Square roots		●	●
Area or volume	●	●	●
Mental math			
Divisibility patterns	●	●	●
Compatible numbers	●		
Solving equations mentally		●	
Finding percents			●
Powers of ten		●	
Using formulas	●	●	●
Number Systems and Number Theory			
Reading and writing whole numbers	●	●	●

Course	1	2	3
Place value of whole numbers	●	●	●
Place value of decimals	●	●	●
Comparing and ordering			
Whole numbers	●	●	●
Decimals	●	●	●
Fractions	●	●	●
Integers	●	●	●
Rationals			●
Positive exponents	●	●	●
Negative exponents			●
Divisibility patterns	●	●	●
Prime and composite numbers	●	●	●
Relative primes			●
Prime factorization	●	●	●
Greatest common factor (GCF)	●	●	●
Least common multiple (LCM)	●	●	●
Scientific notation		●	●
Square roots		●	●
Factorials		●	●
Properties			
Properties of numbers		●	●
Distributive property	●	●	●
Property of proportions (cross products)	●	●	●
Properties of equality		●	●
Density property			●

PATTERNS AND FUNCTIONS

Course	1	2	3
Numeric patterns			
Sequences	●	●	●
Fibonacci sequence			●
Pascal's triangle		●	●
Divisibility patterns	●	●	●
Geometric patterns			
Recognizing geometry patterns	●	●	●
Tessellations	●	●	●
Fractals		●	
Represent relationships			
Tables	●	●	●
Graphs		●	●
Function rules		●	●
Analyze functional relationships			●
Use patterns and functions to solve problems	●	●	●

ALGEBRA

Course	1	2	3
Integers			
Reading and writing integers	●	●	●
Graphing integers on a number line	●	●	●
Comparing and ordering integers	●	●	●
Adding and subtracting integers	●	●	●

Course	1	2	3
Multiplying and dividing integers	●	●	●
Absolute value		●	●
Rational numbers			
Identify and simplify rational numbers			●
Properties of rational numbers			●
Density property			●
Rational numbers and decimals			●
Scientific notation			●
Comparing and ordering			●
Solving equations with rational number solutions			●
Real numbers			
Identify and classify real numbers			●
Square roots		●	●
Irrational numbers			●
Density property			●
Functions			
Function machine	●		●
Function tables	●	●	●
Linear functions			●
Analyze tables and graphs	●	●	●
Equations and expressions			
Concepts of variable, expression, equation	●	●	●
Order of operations		●	●
Evaluate algebraic expressions	●	●	●
Write algebraic expressions and equations		●	●
Solve addition and subtraction equations	●	●	●
Solve multiplication and division equations	●	●	●
Solve two-step equations	●	●	●
Solve equations with two variables		●	●
Solve inequalities		●	●
Solve equations with concrete methods	●	●	●
Solve equations with informal methods	●	●	●
Solve equations with formal methods		●	●
Graphing			
Integers on a number line	●	●	●
Irrational numbers on a number line			●
Inequalities on a number line		●	●
Points on a coordinate plane	●	●	●
Transformations on a coordinate plane	●	●	●
Functions	●	●	●
Linear functions			●
Quadratic functions			●
Equations		●	●
Systems of equations			●
Using graphing calculators		●	●
Polynomials			
Model with algebra tiles			●
Represent and simplify polynomials			●
Add, subtract, and multiply polynomials			●
Factor polynomials			●
Multiply binomials			●
Apply algebra to real-world and math problems	●	●	●
Use spreadsheets and formulas	●	●	●

STATISTICS

Course	1	2	3
Taking a survey	●	●	●
Analyzing survey data	●	●	●
Organizing data			
Using a table to organize data	●	●	●
Frequency tables	●	●	●
Using tables to solve problems	●	●	●
Using matrices to organize data			●
Constructing and interpreting graphs			
Bar graphs	●	●	●
Circle graphs	●	●	●
Line graphs	●	●	
Stem-and-leaf plots	●	●	
Box-and-whisker plots	●	●	●
Line plots		●	●
Histograms			●
Scatter plots		●	●
Maps that show statistics			●
Choosing an appropriate display			●
Interpreting data			
Clusters		●	●
Mean, median, and mode	●	●	●
Range and quartiles	●	●	●
Misleading graphs and statistics	●	●	●
Making predictions from statistics	●	●	●
Making predictions from graphs	●	●	●
Making predictions from a sample	●	●	●

PROBABILITY

Course	1	2	3
Outcomes	●	●	●
Simple event	●	●	●
Independent events	●	●	●
Dependent events		●	●
Complementary events	●		
Experimental probability	●	●	●
Theoretical probability		●	●
Tree diagrams	●	●	●
Counting principle		●	●
Permutations and combinations	●	●	●
Probability and ratio	●	●	●
Fair and unfair games	●	●	●
Simulations or experiments	●	●	●
Area models	●	●	●
Capture-recapture		●	

Course	1	2	3
Punnett squares			●

GEOMETRY

Course	1	2	3
Constructions			
Congruent segments	●		●
Perpendicular lines		●	●
Parallel lines		●	●
Segment bisectors	●		
Congruent angles	●		●
Angle bisectors	●		
Polygons, inscribed	●	●	●
Congruent triangles			●
Angles			
Classify and measure angles	●	●	●
Sum of angle measures		●	●
Parallel lines and transversal		●	●
Polygons			
Identify polygons	●	●	●
Classify triangles and quadrilaterals	●	●	●
Identify congruent figures	●	●	●
Using polygons as networks			●
Triangles			
Determine congruent triangles			●
Right triangle relationships (trigonometry)			●
Pythagorean Theorem		●	●
Special right triangles			●
Similarity			
Corresponding parts of similar figures	●	●	●
Identify similar figures	●	●	●
Scale drawings	●	●	●
Dilations	●	●	
Circles			
Circumference (radius, diameter)	●	●	●
Area	●	●	●
Perimeter	●	●	●
Area			
Rectangles	●	●	●
Parallelograms (base, height)	●	●	●
Trapezoids		●	●
Triangles	●	●	●
Circles	●	●	●
Square roots and area of squares		●	●
Pick's Theorem			●
Area and probability	●	●	
Transformations			
Translations, reflections, and rotations	●	●	●
Dilations		●	●
On the coordinate plane	●	●	●
Tessellations	●	●	●

Course	1	2	3
Symmetry	●	●	●
Solids			
Identify, draw three-dimensional figures	●	●	●
Nets	●	●	●
Surface area		●	●
Volume	●	●	●
Coordinate Geometry			
Graphing ordered pairs	●	●	●
Distance in the coordinate plane			●
Transformations on the coordinate plane	●	●	●
Patterns			
Recognizing geometric patterns	●	●	●
Symmetry	●	●	●
Tessellations	●	●	●
Fractals		●	
Trigonometry			●
Inductive and deductive thinking			●

MEASUREMENT

Course	1	2	3
Metric System			
Units of length, capacity, and mass	●	●	●
Changing units within the metric system	●	●	●
Customary system			
Units of length, capacity, and weight	●	●	●
Change units within the customary system	●	●	●
Time	●		
Non-standard units	●		
Perimeter and circumference	●	●	●
Area			
Irregular figures	●	●	●
Rectangles	●	●	●
Parallelograms	●	●	●
Triangles	●	●	●
Circles	●	●	●
Trapezoids		●	●
Surface area			
Rectangular prisms		●	●
Triangular prisms			●
Cylinders		●	●
Volume			
Rectangular prisms	●	●	●
Cylinders		●	●
Pyramids and circular cones		●	●
Relating area and perimeter	●		
Relating surface area and volume			●
Precision and significant digits			●
Indirect measurement		●	●

Legend ● Introduce ● Develop ● Reinforce

Planning Your

The charts on these two pages contain course planning guides for three types of classes. A Pacing Chart included in the interleaf of each chapter shows in greater detail the number of days suggested for all three types of pacing and which lessons are appropriate. This same pacing is repeated in the margin notes for each lesson for your convenience.

40- TO 50-MINUTE CLASS PERIODS

The chart below gives suggested pacing guides for two options, Standard and Honors, for four 9-week grading periods. The Standard option covers Chapters 1-12 while the Honors option covers Chapter 1-13.

The total number of days suggested for each option is 165 days. This allows for teacher flexibility in planning due to school cancellation or shortened class periods.

Grading Period	Standard		Honors	
	Chapter	**Days**	**Chapter**	**Days**
1	1 2 3 4-1 and 4-2	13 14 12 4	1 2 3 4-1 to 4-3	13 13 11 5
2	4-3 to end 5 6	11 15 14	4-4A to end 5 6 7-1 to 7-4A	10 13 13 6
3	7 8 9	15 14 15	7-4A to end 8 9 10-1 to 10-3	8 14 14 6
4	10 11 12	14 13 11	10-4 to end 11 12 13	7 12 10 10

Course of Study

BLOCK SCHEDULE, 90-MINUTE CLASS PERIODS

The chart below gives a suggested pacing guide for teaching Course 2 using block scheduling in one semester (classes meet every day) or during the entire year (classes meet every other day). A total of 85 class periods is suggested to cover Chapters 1-12.

Chapter	Class Periods
1	7
2	7
3	6
4	8
5	8
6	7
7	8
8	7
9	8
10	7
11	7
12	5

For more detailed descriptions for lesson planning and pacing, please refer to the **Lesson Planning Guide** and the **Block Scheduling Booklet** for **Course 2** of ***Mathematics: Applications and Connections.***

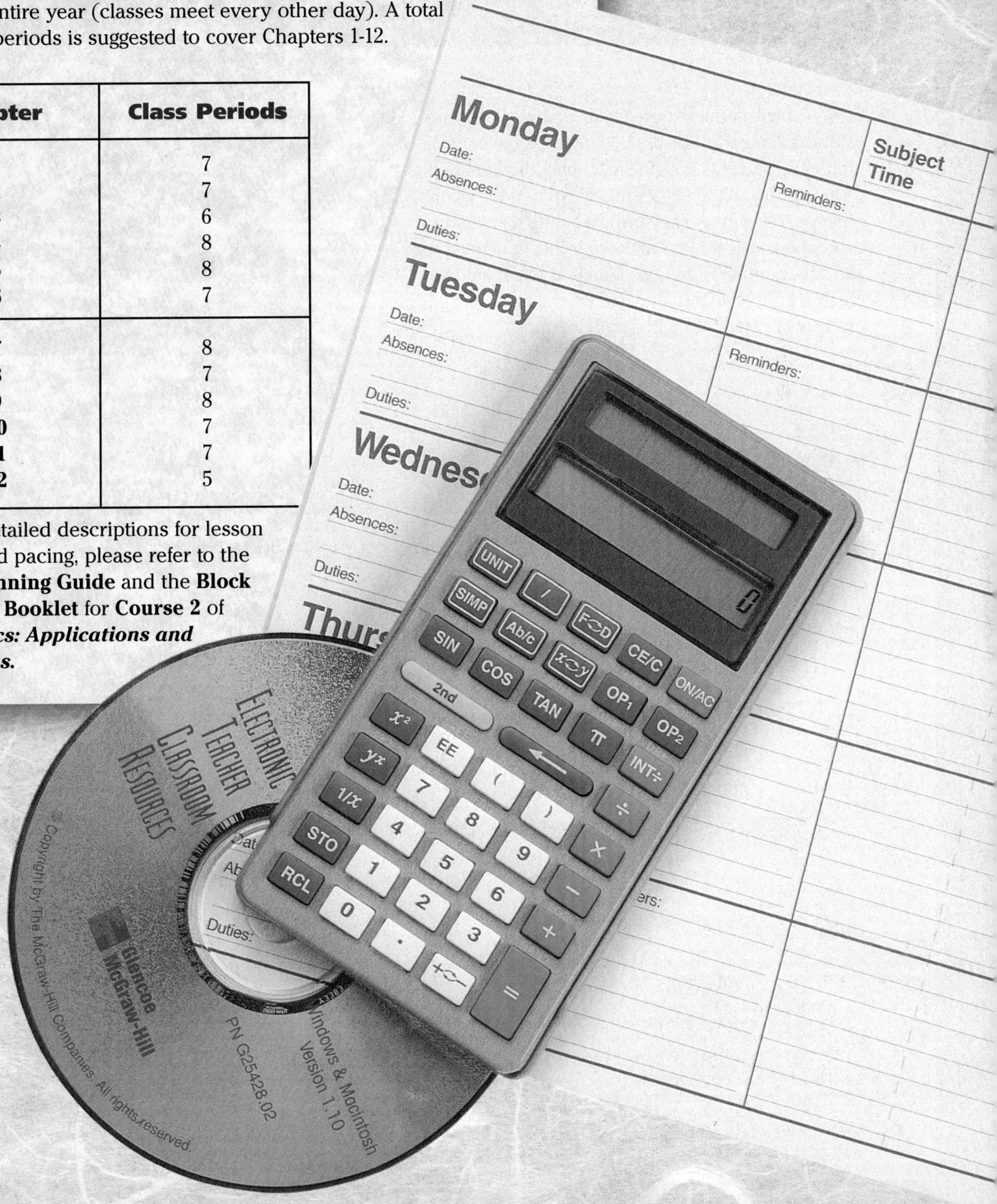

CHAPTER 1 Problem Solving, Algebra, and Geometry

Previewing the Chapter

Overview

This chapter outlines strategies for problem solving and explores the use of algebra and geometry to solve problems. Students practice and apply the four-step plan for problem solving and evaluate expressions using the order of operations. They evaluate simple algebraic expressions, use powers and exponents in expressions, and solve simple equations. Geometry is related to algebra when students find and extend patterns and find the area of rectangles and parallelograms.

Lesson (pages)	Lesson Objectives	NCTM Standards 2000	Standardized Tests	State/Local Objectives
1-1 (4–7)	Solve problems using the four-step plan.	1, 4, 6–10		
1-2 (8–10)	Evaluate expressions using the order of operations.	1, 2, 6–10	CAT, MAT, SAT	
1-3A (11)	Use cups and counters to model algebraic expressions.	1, 6, 9, 10	MAT	
1-3 (12–15)	Evaluate simple algebraic expressions.	1, 2, 6–10	CAT, MAT, SAT	
1-3B (16)	Evaluate algebraic expressions by using a graphing calculator.	1, 2, 6–9		
1-4 (17–20)	Use powers and exponents in expressions.	1–3, 6–10	CTBS, TN	
1-5 (21–23)	Solve equations using mental math.	1, 2, 6–9		
1-6 (24–27)	Find and extend patterns.	2, 6, 8–10	CTBS, MAT, SAT, TN	
1-7A (28–29)	Use models to find the areas of rectangles and parallelograms.	1–3, 6–10		
1-7 (30–33)	Find the areas of rectangles and parallelograms.	1–3, 6–10	CAT, ITBS, MAT, SAT	
1-7B (34–35)	Choose the best method of computation for solving a problem.	1, 6–9		

CAT = California Achievement Tests, CTBS = Comprehensive Tests of Basic Skills, ITBS = Iowa Tests of Basic Skills, MAT = Metropolitan Achievement Tests, SAT = Stanford Achievement Tests, TN = Terra Nova
For the key to numbering of NCTM Standards 2000, see page T6.

Organizing the Chapter

The **Interactive Lesson Planner** contains all of the blackline masters and transparencies. This CD-ROM also includes an easy-to-use lesson planning calendar.

LESSON PLANNING GUIDE

Lesson	Extra Practice (Student Edition)	Blackline Masters (page numbers)										
		Study Guide	Practice	Enrichment	Assessment & Evaluation	Classroom Games	Diversity	Hands-On Lab	School to Career	Science and Math Lab Manual	Technology	Transparencies A and B
1-1	p. 568	1	1	1								1-1
1-2	p. 568	2	2	2	15		14				28	1-2
1-3A								38				
1-3	p. 568	3	3	3								1-3
1-3B												
1-4	p. 569	4	4	4	14, 15	1–4		72			27	1-4
1-5	p. 569	5	5	5								1-5
1-6	p. 569	6	6	6	16							1-6
1-7A								39				
1-7	p. 570	7	7	7	16				14			1-7
1-7B	p. 570											
Study Guide/ Assessment					1–13, 17–19							

Other Chapter Resources

Student Edition

Chapter Project, pp. 3, 7, 10, 23, 39
Math in the Media, p. 27
Let the Games Begin, p. 20

Technology

MathPASS CD-ROM
Interactive Mathematics Tools Software

Teacher's Classroom Resources

Applications

Family Letters and Activities, pp. 27–28
Investigations and Project Masters, pp.17–20

Meeting Individual Needs

Transition Booklet, pp. 7–12
Investigations for the Special Education Student, pp. 1–2

Teaching Aids

Answer Key Masters
Block Scheduling Booklet
Lesson Planning Guide
Solutions Manual

Professional Publications

Glencoe Mathematics Professional Series

Planning the Chapter

MindJogger Videoquizzes provide a unique format for reviewing concepts presented in the chapter.

Assessment Resources

Student Edition

Mixed Review, pp. 10, 15, 20, 23, 27, 33
Mid-Chapter Self Test, p. 15
Math Journal, pp. 6, 18
Study Guide and Assessment, pp. 36–39
Performance Task, p. 39
Portfolio Suggestion, p. 39
Standardized Test Practice, pp. 40–41
Chapter Test, p. 607

Assessment and Evaluation Masters

Multiple-Choice Tests (Forms 1A, 1B, 1C), pp. 1–6
Free-Response Tests (Forms 2A, 2B, 2C), pp. 7–12
Performance Assessment, p. 13
Mid-Chapter Test, p. 14
Quizzes A–D, pp. 15–16
Standardized Test Practice, pp. 17–18
Cumulative Review, p. 19

Teacher's Wraparound Edition

5-Minute Check, pp. 4, 8, 12, 17, 21, 24, 30
Building Portfolios, p. 2
Math Journal, pp. 11, 16, 29
Closing Activity, pp. 7, 10, 15, 20, 23, 27, 33, 35

Technology

Test and Review Software
MindJogger Videoquizzes
CD-ROM Program

Materials and Manipulatives

Lesson 1-3A
cups and counters*†
mat*†

Lesson 1-3
isometric dot paper†

Lesson 1-3B
graphing calculator

Lesson 1-4
calculator
scissors*
number cube*
index cards

Lesson 1-6
isometric dot paper†

Lesson 1-7A
grid paper†
scissors*

Lesson 1-7
calculator
grid paper†

*Glencoe Manipulative Kit

†Glencoe Overhead Manipulative Resources

Pacing Chart

See pages T25–T27 for the Course Planning Calendar.

COURSE	DAY 1	DAY 2	DAY 3	DAY 4	DAY 5	DAY 6	DAY 7
Standard	Chapter Project	Lesson 1-1	Lesson 1-2	Lessons 1-3A & 1-3		Lesson 1-4	Lesson 1-5
Honors	Chapter Project	Lesson 1-1	Lesson 1-2	Lessons 1-3 & 1-3B		Lesson 1-4	Lesson 1-5
Block	Chapter Project & Lesson 1-1	Lesson 1-2	Lessons 1-3A & 1-3	Lessons 1-4 & 1-5	Lessons 1-6 & 1-7A	Lessons 1-7 & 1-7B	Study Guide and Assessment, Chapter Test

The ***Transition Booklet*** (Skills 2–4) can be used to practice basic operations with whole numbers.

Interactive Mathematics: Activities and Investigations

is an activity-based program that may be used as an enhancement for chapters in ***Mathematics: Applications and Connections.***

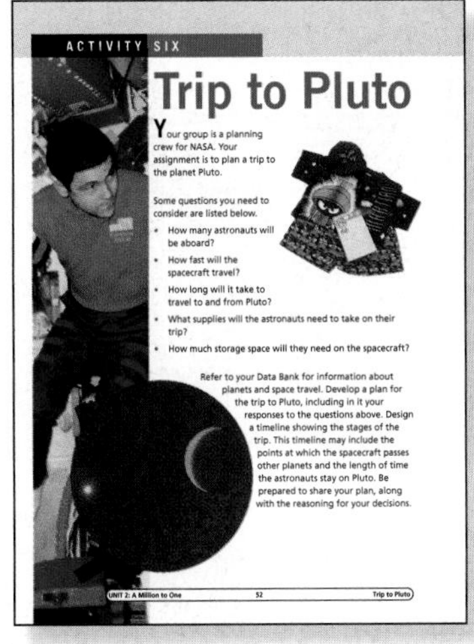

ACTIVITY SIX

Trip to Pluto

Your group is a planning crew for NASA. Your assignment is to plan a trip to the planet Pluto.

Some questions you need to consider are listed below.

- How many astronauts will be aboard?
- How fast will the spacecraft travel?
- How long will it take to travel to and from Pluto?
- What supplies will the astronauts need to take on their trip?
- How much storage space will they need on the spacecraft?

Refer to your Data Bank for information about planets and space travel. Develop a plan for the trip to Pluto, including in it your responses to the questions above. Design a timeline showing the stages of the trip. This timeline may include the points at which the spacecraft passes other planets and the length of time the astronauts stay on Pluto. Be prepared to share your plan, along with the reasoning for your decisions.

UNIT 2: A Million to One 52 Trip to Pluto

Unit 2, Activity Six
Use with Lesson 1-1.

Summary Students work in groups to plan a trip to Pluto. They will consider how far it is, how long it will take, what supplies will be needed, and other relevant issues. Each group presents their plan, explaining the process and rationale for their decisions.

Math Connections Students use the distance formula $d = rt$, where d is the distance, r is the rate, and t is the time. Distances in scientific study are usually expressed as metric measurements and are often expressed in scientific notation.

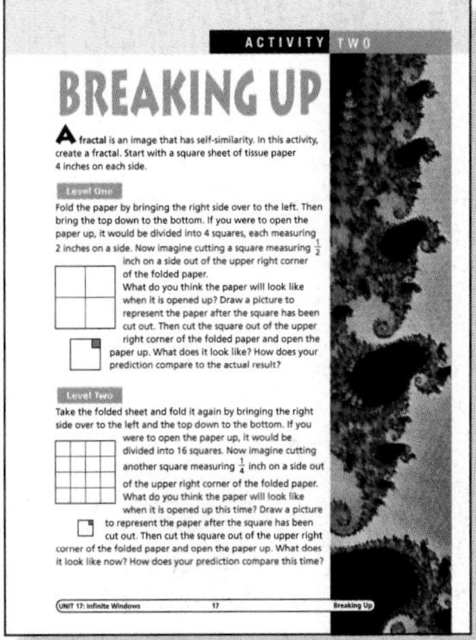

ACTIVITY TWO

BREAKING UP

A fractal is an image that has self-similarity. In this activity, create a fractal. Start with a square sheet of tissue paper 4 inches on each side.

Level One

Fold the paper by bringing the right side over to the left. Then bring the top down to the bottom. If you were to open the paper up, it would be divided into 4 squares, each measuring 2 inches on a side. Now imagine cutting a square measuring $\frac{1}{2}$ inch on a side out of the upper right corner of the folded paper.

What do you think the paper will look like when it is opened up? Draw a picture to represent the paper after the square has been cut out. Then cut the square out of the upper right corner of the folded paper and open the paper up. What does it look like? How does your prediction compare to the actual result?

Level Two

Take the folded sheet and fold it again by bringing the right side over to the left and the top down to the bottom. If you were to open the paper up, it would be divided into 16 squares. Now imagine cutting another square measuring $\frac{1}{4}$ inch on a side out of the upper right corner of the folded paper. What do you think the paper will look like when it is opened up this time? Draw a picture to represent the paper after the square has been cut out. Then cut the square out of the upper right corner of the folded paper and open the paper up. What does it look like now? How does your prediction compare this time?

UNIT 17: Infinite Windows 17 Breaking Up

Unit 17, Activity Two
Use with Lesson 1-6.

Summary Students create a fractal by examining the stages or levels in a recursive procedure. They fold and cut paper to create a model of a fractal and draw a model of Sierpinski's Triangle. The students explore the relationship between the self-similar shapes in the fractals and the depth or level of the emerging fractal.

Math Connection Students will be introduced to fractals—images that have self-similarity. Self-similarity occurs when each subpart of a fractal is similar to the original fractal.

DAY 8	DAY 9	DAY 10	DAY 11	DAY 12	DAY 13	DAY 14	DAY 15
Lesson 1-6	Lessons 1-7A & 1-7		Lesson 1-7B	Study Guide and Assessment	Chapter Test		
Lesson 1-6	Lessons 1-7A & 1-7		Lesson 1-7B	Study Guide and Assessment	Chapter Test		

Enhancing the Chapter

APPLICATIONS

Classroom Games, pp. 1–4

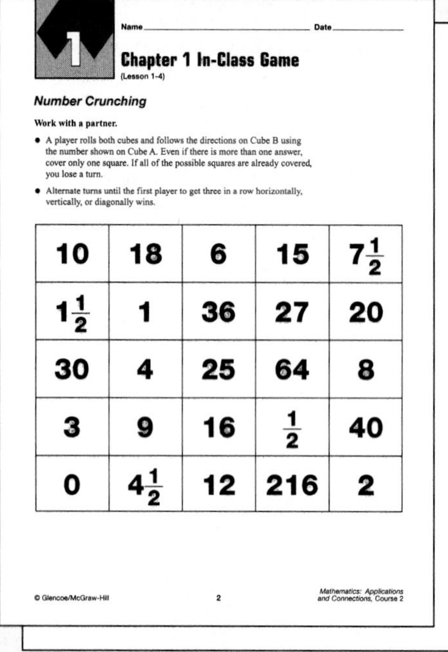

Name ______ Date ______

Chapter 1 In-Class Game
(Lesson 1-4)

Number Crunching

Work with a partner.

- A player rolls both cubes and follows the directions on Cube B using the number shown on Cube A. Even if there is more than one answer, cover only one square. If all of the possible squares are already covered, you lose a turn.
- Alternate turns until the first player to get three in a row horizontally, vertically, or diagonally wins.

10	18	6	15	$7\frac{1}{2}$
$1\frac{1}{2}$	1	36	27	20
30	4	25	64	8
3	9	16	$\frac{1}{2}$	40
0	$4\frac{1}{2}$	12	216	2

© Glencoe/McGraw-Hill 2 *Mathematics: Applications and Connections, Course 2*

Diversity Masters, p. 14

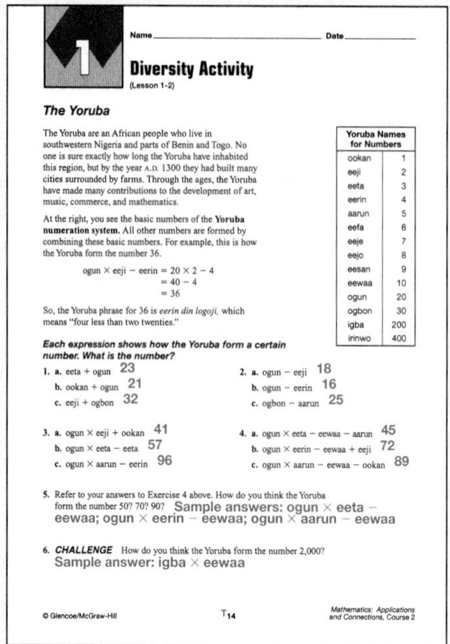

Name ______ Date ______

Diversity Activity
(Lesson 1-2)

The Yoruba

The Yoruba are an African people who live in southwestern Nigeria and parts of Benin and Togo. No one is sure exactly how long the Yoruba have inhabited this region, but by the year A.D. 1300 they had built many cities surrounded by farms. Through the ages, the Yoruba have made many contributions to the development of art, music, commerce, and mathematics.

At the right, you see the basic numbers of the **Yoruba numeration system.** All other numbers are formed by combining these basic numbers. For example, this is how the Yoruba form the number 36.

$$\text{ogun} \times \text{eeji} - \text{eerin} = 20 \times 2 - 4 = 40 - 4 = 36$$

So, the Yoruba phrase for 36 is *eerin din logoji,* which means "four less than two twenties."

Yoruba Names for Numbers	
ookan	1
eeji	2
eeta	3
eerin	4
aarun	5
eefa	6
eeje	7
eejo	8
eesan	9
eewaa	10
ogun	20
ogbon	30
igba	200
irinwo	400

Each expression shows how the Yoruba form a certain number. What is the number?

1. a. eeta + ogun 23
   b. ookan + ogun 21
   c. eeji + ogbon 32
2. a. ogun − eeji 18
   b. ogun − eerin 16
   c. ogbon − aarun 25
3. a. ogun × eeji + ookan 41
   b. ogun × eeta − eeta 57
   c. ogun × aarun − eerin 96
4. a. ogun × eeta − eewaa − aarun 45
   b. ogun × eerin − eewaa + eeji 72
   c. ogun × aarun − eewaa − ookan 89
5. Refer to your answers to Exercise 4 above. How do you think the Yoruba form the number 50? 70? 90? Sample answers: ogun × eeta − eewaa; ogun × eerin − eewaa; ogun × aarun − eewaa
6. ***CHALLENGE*** How do you think the Yoruba form the number 2,000? Sample answer: igba × eewaa

© Glencoe/McGraw-Hill T14 *Mathematics: Applications and Connections, Course 2*

School to Career Masters, p. 14

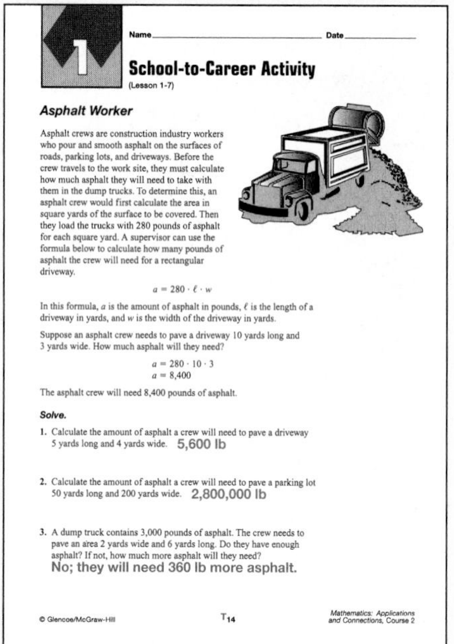

Name ______ Date ______

School-to-Career Activity
(Lesson 1-7)

Asphalt Worker

Asphalt crews are construction industry workers who pour and smooth asphalt on the surfaces of roads, parking lots, and driveways. Before the crew travels to the work site, they must calculate how much asphalt they will need to take with them in the dump trucks. To determine this, an asphalt crew would first calculate the area in square yards of the surface to be covered. Then they load the trucks with 280 pounds of asphalt for each square yard. A supervisor can use the formula below to calculate how many pounds of asphalt the crew will need for a rectangular driveway.

$$a = 280 \cdot \ell \cdot w$$

In this formula, a is the amount of asphalt in pounds, ℓ is the length of a driveway in yards, and w is the width of the driveway in yards.

Suppose an asphalt crew needs to pave a driveway 10 yards long and 3 yards wide. How much asphalt will they need?

$$a = 280 \cdot 10 \cdot 3$$
$$a = 8{,}400$$

The asphalt crew will need 8,400 pounds of asphalt.

Solve.

1. Calculate the amount of asphalt a crew will need to pave a driveway 5 yards long and 4 yards wide. 5,600 lb
2. Calculate the amount of asphalt a crew will need to pave a parking lot 50 yards long and 200 yards wide. 2,800,000 lb
3. A dump truck contains 3,000 pounds of asphalt. The crew needs to pave an area 2 yards wide and 6 yards long. Do they have enough asphalt? If not, how much more asphalt will they need? No; they will need 360 lb more asphalt.

© Glencoe/McGraw-Hill T14 *Mathematics: Applications and Connections, Course 2*

Family Letters and Activities, pp. 27–28

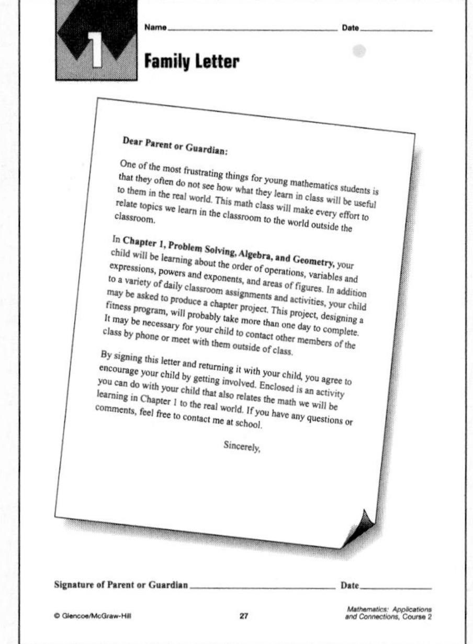

Name ______ Date ______

Family Letter

Dear Parent or Guardian:

One of the most frustrating things for young mathematics students is that they often do not see how what they learn in class will be useful to them in the real world. This math class will make every effort to relate topics we learn in the classroom to the world outside the classroom.

In **Chapter 1, Problem Solving, Algebra, and Geometry,** your child will be learning about the order of operations, variables and expressions, powers and exponents, and areas of figures. In addition to a variety of daily classroom assignments and activities, your child may be asked to produce a chapter project. This project, designing a fitness program, will probably take more than one day to complete. It may be necessary for your child to contact other members of the class by phone or meet with them outside of class.

By signing this letter and returning it with your child, you agree to encourage your child by getting involved. Enclosed is an activity you can do with your child that also relates the math we will be learning in Chapter 1 to the real world. If you have any questions or comments, feel free to contact me at school.

Sincerely,

Signature of Parent or Guardian ______ Date ______

© Glencoe/McGraw-Hill 27 *Mathematics: Applications and Connections, Course 2*

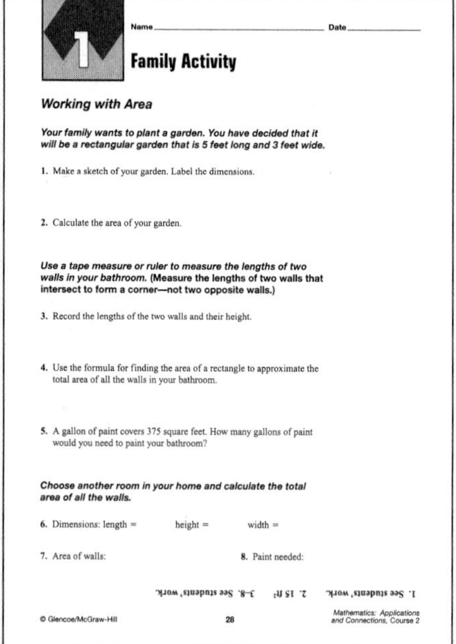

Name ______ Date ______

Family Activity

Working with Area

Your family wants to plant a garden. You have decided that it will be a rectangular garden that is 5 feet long and 3 feet wide.

1. Make a sketch of your garden. Label the dimensions.
2. Calculate the area of your garden.

***Use a tape measure or ruler to measure the lengths of two walls in your bathroom.* (Measure the lengths of two walls that intersect to form a corner—not two opposite walls.)**

3. Record the lengths of the two walls and their height.
4. Use the formula for finding the area of a rectangle to approximate the total area of all the walls in your bathroom.
5. A gallon of paint covers 375 square feet. How many gallons of paint would you need to paint your bathroom?

Choose another room in your home and calculate the total area of all the walls.

6. Dimensions: length = height = width =
7. Area of walls:
8. Paint needed:

1. See students' work. 2. 15 ft² 3–8. See students' work.

© Glencoe/McGraw-Hill 28 *Mathematics: Applications and Connections, Course 2*

MANIPULATIVES/MODELING

Hands-On Lab Masters, p. 72

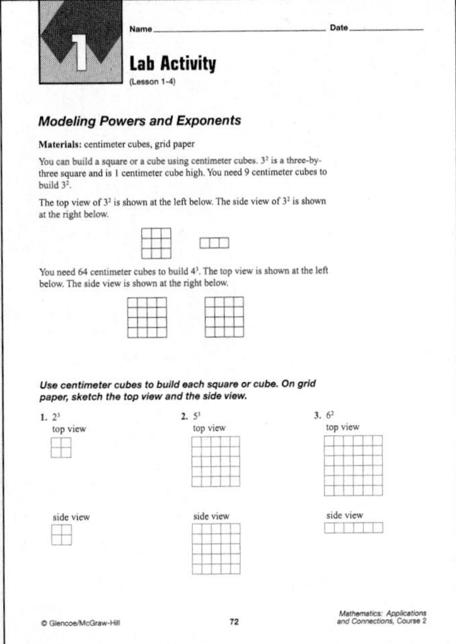

Name ________ Date ________

Lab Activity
(Lesson 1-4)

Modeling Powers and Exponents

Materials: centimeter cubes, grid paper

You can build a square or a cube using centimeter cubes. 3^2 is a three-by-three square and is 1 centimeter cube high. You need 9 centimeter cubes to build 3^2.

The top view of 3^2 is shown at the left below. The side view of 3^2 is shown at the right below.

You need 64 centimeter cubes to build 4^3. The top view is shown at the left below. The side view is shown at the right below.

Use centimeter cubes to build each square or cube. On grid paper, sketch the top view and the side view.

1. 2^3 top view / side view
2. 5^3 top view / side view
3. 6^2 top view / side view

© Glencoe/McGraw-Hill 72 *Mathematics: Applications and Connections, Course 2*

ASSESSMENT/EVALUATION

Assessment and Evaluation Masters, pp. 14–16

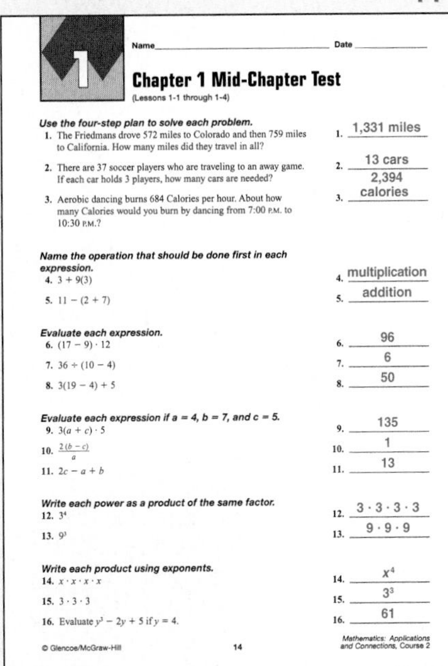

Name ________ Date ________

Chapter 1 Mid-Chapter Test
(Lessons 1-1 through 1-4)

Use the four-step plan to solve each problem.

1. The Friedmans drove 572 miles to Colorado and then 759 miles to California. How many miles did they travel in all? — 1. 1,331 miles
2. There are 37 soccer players who are traveling to an away game. If each car holds 3 players, how many cars are needed? — 2. 13 cars
3. Aerobic dancing burns 684 Calories per hour. About how many Calories would you burn by dancing from 7:00 P.M. to 10:30 P.M.? — 3. 2,394 calories

Name the operation that should be done first in each expression.

4. $3 + 9(3)$ — 4. multiplication
5. $11 - (2 + 7)$ — 5. addition

Evaluate each expression.

6. $(17 - 9) \cdot 12$ — 6. 96
7. $36 \div (10 - 4)$ — 7. 6
8. $3(19 - 4) + 5$ — 8. 50

Evaluate each expression if a = 4, b = 7, and c = 5.

9. $3(a + c) \cdot 5$ — 9. 135
10. $\frac{2(b - c)}{a}$ — 10. 1
11. $2c - a + b$ — 11. 13

Write each power as a product of the same factor.

12. 3^4 — 12. $3 \cdot 3 \cdot 3 \cdot 3$
13. 9^3 — 13. $9 \cdot 9 \cdot 9$

Write each product using exponents.

14. $x \cdot x \cdot x \cdot x$ — 14. x^4
15. $3 \cdot 3 \cdot 3$ — 15. 3^3
16. Evaluate $y^2 - 2y + 5$ if $y = 4$. — 16. 61

© Glencoe/McGraw-Hill 14 *Mathematics: Applications and Connections, Course 2*

Name ________ Date ________

Chapter 1 Quiz A
(Lessons 1-1 and 1-2)

Use the four-step plan to solve the problem.

1. The Changs traveled 475 miles to visit relatives in Toronto. They returned a different way in order to see Niagara Falls. The Changs traveled 817 miles on the return trip. How many miles did they travel in all? — 1. 1,292 miles

Name the operation that should be done first in each expression.

2. $14 - 6 \div 2 + 8$ — 2. division
3. $(38 - 8) - 5 \times 6$ — 3. subtraction

Evaluate each expression.

4. $6 \cdot (7 + 5) \div 3$ — 4. 24
5. $7(3 + 1) - 6$ — 5. 22

Name ________ Date ________

Chapter 1 Quiz B
(Lessons 1-3 and 1-4)

Evaluate each expression if a = 5, b = 3, and c = 4.

1. $2a - 3b$ — 1. 1
2. $a(c + b) - c$ — 2. 31
3. $7(\frac{a + c}{b})$ — 3. 21
4. $\frac{3c}{2}$ — 4. 6
5. Write 8^5 as a product of the same factor. — 5. $8 \cdot 8 \cdot 8 \cdot 8 \cdot 8$
6. Write $25 \cdot 25$ using exponents. — 6. 25^2

Evaluate each expression.

7. 9^3 — 7. 729
8. $(15 \div 3)^4 - 10$ — 8. 615
9. Evaluate $x^2 + 4x + 7$ if $x = 2$. — 9. 23
10. Evaluate $y + 6 + y^2$ if $y = 12$. — 10. 146

© Glencoe/McGraw-Hill 15 *Mathematics: Applications and Connections, Course 2*

TECHNOLOGY/MULTIMEDIA

Technology Masters, pp. 27–28

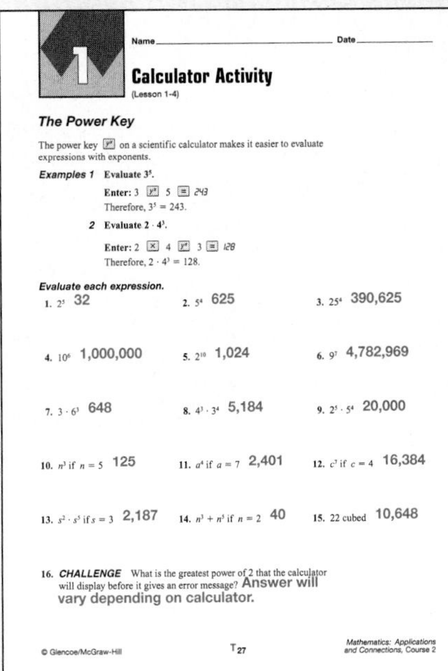

Name ________ Date ________

Calculator Activity
(Lesson 1-4)

The Power Key

The power key y^x on a scientific calculator makes it easier to evaluate expressions with exponents.

Examples **1** Evaluate 3^5.

Enter: 3 y^x 5 = *243*
Therefore, $3^5 = 243$.

2 Evaluate $2 \cdot 4^3$.

Enter: 2 × 4 y^x 3 = *128*
Therefore, $2 \cdot 4^3 = 128$.

Evaluate each expression.

1. 2^5 32
2. 5^4 625
3. 25^4 390,625
4. 10^6 1,000,000
5. 2^{10} 1,024
6. 9^7 4,782,969
7. $3 \cdot 6^3$ 648
8. $4^3 \cdot 3^4$ 5,184
9. $2^5 \cdot 5^4$ 20,000
10. n^3 if $n = 5$ 125
11. a^4 if $a = 7$ 2,401
12. c^7 if $c = 4$ 16,384
13. $x^2 \cdot x^3$ if $x = 3$ 2,187
14. $n^3 + n^2$ if $n = 2$ 40
15. 22 cubed 10,648
16. *CHALLENGE* What is the greatest power of 2 that the calculator will display before it gives an error message? Answer will vary depending on calculator.

© Glencoe/McGraw-Hill T27 *Mathematics: Applications and Connections, Course 2*

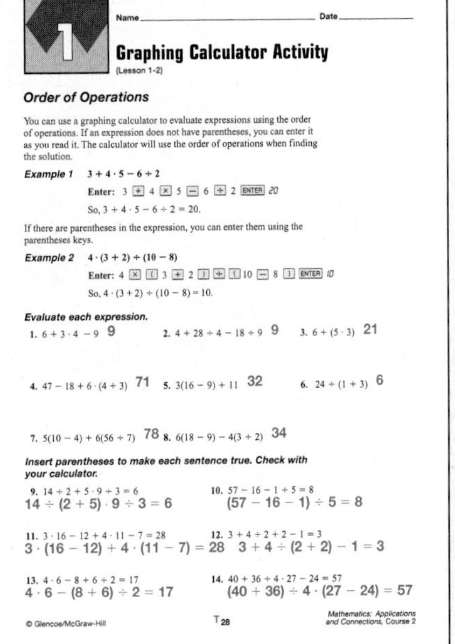

Name ________ Date ________

Graphing Calculator Activity
(Lesson 1-2)

Order of Operations

You can use a graphing calculator to evaluate expressions using the order of operations. If an expression does not have parentheses, you can enter it as you read it. The calculator will use the order of operations when finding the solution.

Example 1 $3 + 4 \cdot 5 - 6 \div 2$

Enter: 3 + 4 × 5 − 6 ÷ 2 ENTER *20*
So, $3 + 4 \cdot 5 - 6 \div 2 = 20$.

If there are parentheses in the expression, you can enter them using the parentheses keys.

Example 2 $4 \cdot (3 + 2) \div (10 - 8)$

Enter: 4 × (3 + 2) ÷ (10 − 8) ENTER *10*
So, $4 \cdot (3 + 2) \div (10 - 8) = 10$.

Evaluate each expression.

1. $6 + 3 \cdot 4 - 9$ 9
2. $4 + 28 \div 4 - 18 \div 9$ 9
3. $6 + (5 \cdot 3)$ 21
4. $47 - 18 + 6 \cdot (4 + 3)$ 71
5. $3(16 - 9) + 11$ 32
6. $24 \div (1 + 3)$ 6
7. $5(10 - 4) + 6(56 \div 7)$ 78
8. $6(18 - 9) - 4(3 + 2)$ 34

Insert parentheses to make each sentence true. Check with your calculator.

9. $14 \div 2 + 5 \cdot 9 \div 3 = 6$ — $14 \div (2 + 5) \cdot 9 \div 3 = 6$
10. $57 - 16 - 1 \div 5 = 8$ — $(57 - 16 - 1) \div 5 = 8$
11. $3 \cdot 16 - 12 + 4 \cdot 11 - 7 = 28$ — $3 \cdot (16 - 12) + 4 \cdot (11 - 7) = 28$
12. $3 + 4 \div 2 + 2 - 1 = 3$ — $3 + 4 \div (2 + 2) - 1 = 3$
13. $4 \cdot 6 - 8 + 6 \div 2 = 17$ — $4 \cdot 6 - (8 + 6) \div 2 = 17$
14. $40 + 36 \div 4 \cdot 27 - 24 = 57$ — $(40 + 36) \div 4 \cdot (27 - 24) = 57$

© Glencoe/McGraw-Hill T28 *Mathematics: Applications and Connections, Course 2*

MEETING INDIVIDUAL NEEDS

Investigations for the Special Education Student, pp. 1–2

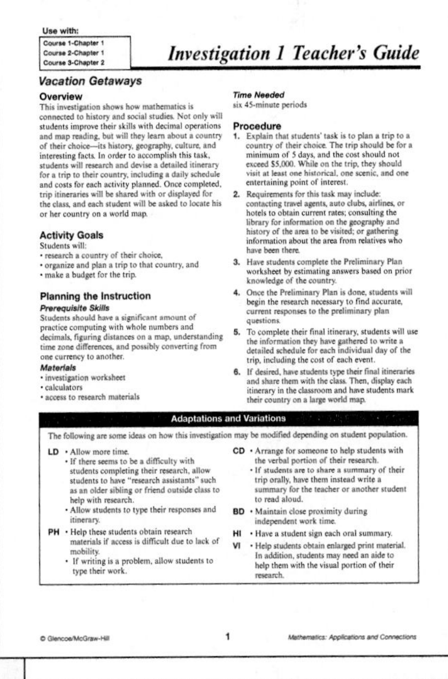

Use with:
Course 1-Chapter 1
Course 2-Chapter 1
Course 3-Chapter 2

Investigation 1 Teacher's Guide

Vacation Getaways

Overview

This investigation shows how mathematics is connected to history and social studies. Not only will students improve their skills with decimal operations and map reading, but will they learn about a country of their choice—its history, geography, culture, and interesting facts. In order to accomplish this task, students will research and devise a detailed itinerary for a trip to their country, including a daily schedule and costs for each activity planned. Once completed, trip itineraries will be shared with or displayed for the class, and each student will be asked to locate his or her country on a world map.

Activity Goals

Students will:
- research a country of their choice,
- organize and plan a trip to that country, and
- make a budget for the trip.

Planning the Instruction

Prerequisite Skills

Students should have a significant amount of practice computing with whole numbers and decimals, figuring distances on a map, understanding time zone differences, and possibly converting from one currency to another.

Materials
- investigation worksheet
- calculators
- access to research materials

Time Needed

six 45-minute periods

Procedure

1. Explain that students' task is to plan a trip to a country of their choice. The trip should be for a minimum of 5 days, and the cost should not exceed $5,000. While on the trip, they should visit at least one historical, one scenic, and one entertaining point of interest.
2. Requirements for this task may include: contacting travel agents, auto clubs, airlines, or hotels to obtain current rates; consulting the library for information on the geography and history of the area to be visited; or gathering information about the area from relatives who have been there.
3. Have students complete the Preliminary Plan worksheet by estimating answers based on prior knowledge of the country.
4. Once the Preliminary Plan is done, students will begin the research necessary to find accurate, current responses to the preliminary plan questions.
5. To complete their final itinerary, students will use the information they have gathered to write a detailed schedule for each individual day of the trip, including the cost of each event.
6. If desired, have students type their final itineraries and share them with the class. Then, display each itinerary in the classroom and have students mark their country on a large world map.

Adaptations and Variations

The following are some ideas on how this investigation may be modified depending on student population.

LD
- Allow more time.
- If there seems to be a difficulty with students completing their research, allow students to have "research assistants" such as an older sibling or friend outside class to help with research.
- Allow students to type their responses and itinerary.

PH
- Help these students obtain research materials if access is difficult due to lack of mobility.
- If writing is a problem, allow students to type their work.

CD
- Arrange for someone to help students with the verbal portion of their research.
- If students are to share a summary of their trip orally, have them instead write a summary for the teacher or another student to read aloud.

BD
- Maintain close proximity during independent work time.

HI
- Have a student sign each oral summary.

VI
- Help students obtain enlarged print material. In addition, students may need an aide to help them with the visual portion of their research.

© Glencoe/McGraw-Hill 1 *Mathematics: Applications and Connections*

CHAPTER 1 NOTES

Theme: Fitness

Between 1997 and 2002, the United States will help build and launch the International Space Station. Nutritionists at the NASA Johnson Space Center are developing diets for the people who will live on the station. One difference between diets on Earth and those in space is the amount of iron needed. People in space require less iron than on Earth because their bodies produce fewer red blood cells.

Question of the Day In space, a person needs 10 milligrams of iron a day. How many milligrams of iron will a person in space need a week? 70

Assess Prerequisite Skills

Ask students to read through the list of objectives presented in "What you'll learn in Chapter 1." You may wish to ask them what each of the objectives means or if they have experienced or used any of these math concepts before.

Building Portfolios

A portfolio is each student's collection of work that expresses how the student has grown as a mathematics student. It is not necessarily a collection of the best work done by the student, but rather the portfolio should demonstrate how the student has improved. You may want to have students attach an explanation to each paper in their portfolio to state why they chose to add it to the collection. Students should update their portfolios with the completion of each chapter.

Math and the Family

In the *Family Letters and Activities* booklet (pp. 27–28), you will find a letter to the parents explaining what students will study in Chapter 1. An activity appropriate for the whole family is also available.

CHAPTER 1 Problem Solving, Algebra, and Geometry

What you'll learn in Chapter 1

- to solve problems using the four-step plan,
- to evaluate algebraic expressions using the order of operations,
- to evaluate expressions with exponents,
- to find the areas of rectangles and parallelograms, and
- to choose the best method of computation to solve real-world problems.

CD-ROM Program

Activities for Chapter 1

- Chapter 1 Introduction
- Interactive Lessons 1-3, 1-7
- Assessment Game
- Resource Lessons 1-1 through 1-7

CHAPTER Project

FUN WAYS TO BE FIT

In this project, you will use the four-step plan to design a week-long fitness program. You will assume that you eat about 2,400 to 2,800 Calories per day, which is the amount recommended for young adults ages 11 to 14.

Getting Started

- Which activity from the table burns the least Calories per hour? Which activity burns the most Calories per hour? About how many Calories would you burn in one hour of in-line skating?
- To maintain the same weight over a period of time, you must eat and burn about an equal number of Calories. Suppose you weigh 150 pounds and you eat two pieces of pizza having 287 Calories in all. Name an activity that you can do to burn off those Calories.

Technology Tips

- Use a **spreadsheet** to find the number of Calories burned for your activity plan.
- Use a **word processor**.

Data Update For up-to-date information on fitness, visit:

www.glencoe.com/sec/math/mac/mathnet

Working on the Project

You can use what you'll learn in Chapter 1 to help you design your fitness program.

Page	Exercise
7	11
10	37
23	40
39	Alternative Assessment

Calories Burned During Selected Activities		
Activity	Calories/Hour (100-lb person)	Calories/Hour (150-lb person)
sleeping, watching TV	60	90
aerobic dance	456	684
basketball	376	564
bicycling (15 mph)	472	708
cross-country skiing	389	583
downhill skiing	280	420
in-line skating	400	600
running (8-minute mile)	595	893
walking (15-minute mile)	195	292
swimming (35 yd/min)	331	497

CHAPTER Project NOTES

Objectives Students should
- gain an understanding of the relationship between weight and exercise.
- be able to determine the kinds of activities that burn a high number of Calories.

Project Pointer You may suggest that students keep their work in a *Project Folder* as they complete each stage of the Chapter Project. The completed project may also be added to their portfolios.

Students may want to implement their exercise programs, modified to accommodate their real weight. Remind students that being physically fit is a goal that should be reached gradually. Drastic dieting and/or exercise can be harmful to their health and usually produces only short-term results.

Using the Table As students read the information in the table, have them keep in mind that 3,500 Calories is equivalent to 1 pound of body weight.

***Investigations and Projects Masters,* p. 20**

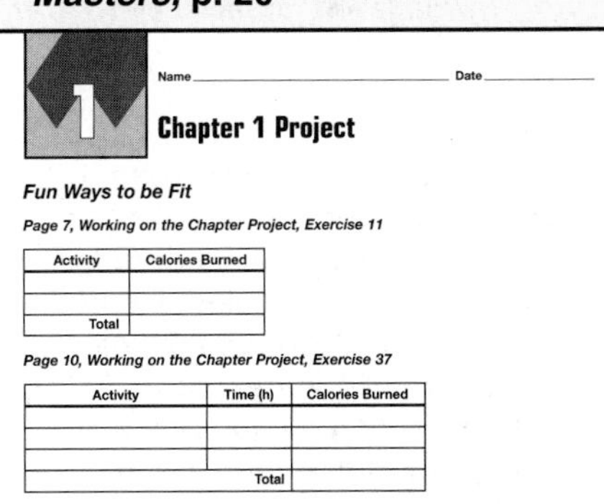

Name ______________________ Date ____________

1 **Chapter 1 Project**

Fun Ways to be Fit

Page 7, Working on the Chapter Project, Exercise 11

Activity	Calories Burned
Total	

Page 10, Working on the Chapter Project, Exercise 37

Activity	Time (h)	Calories Burned
	Total	

Expression ______________________ = ______ Total Calories Burned

© Glencoe/McGraw-Hill 20 *Mathematics: Applications and Connections, Course 2*

interNET CONNECTION

Glencoe has made every effort to ensure that the website links for *Mathematics: Applications and Connections* at **www.glencoe.com/sec/math/mac/mathnet** are current and contain appropriate content. However, these website links are not under Glencoe's control.

Instructional Resources ▶▶▶
A recording sheet to help students organize their data for the Chapter Project is shown at the right and is available in the *Investigations and Projects Masters,* p. 20.

1-1 Lesson Notes

Instructional Resources

- *Study Guide Masters,* p. 1
- *Practice Masters,* p. 1
- *Enrichment Masters,* p. 1
- Transparencies 1-1, A and B

CD-ROM Program
- Resource Lesson 1-1

Recommended Pacing	
Standard	Day 2 of 13
Honors	Day 2 of 13
Block	Day 1 of 7

1 FOCUS

5-Minute Check
(Lesson 1-1)

1. Suppose you have 10 stacks of pennies. Each stack contains 6 pennies. How many pennies do you have? **60 pennies**
2. You have a bag of 6 apples. Each apple weighs 6 ounces. How much does the bag of apples weigh? **36 ounces, or 2 pounds, 4 ounces**
3. $272 \div 8 = 34$
4. $32 \times 104 = 3{,}328$
5. $18{,}000 \div 48 = 375$

The 5-Minute Check is also available on **Transparency 1-1A** for this lesson.

Motivating the Lesson

Hands-On Activity Show the class a scale and a clear plastic bag of marbles. Ask a student to weigh the bag of marbles. Remove a marble from the bag and weigh the marble. Ask students to estimate how many marbles are in the bag. Count the marbles and discuss the difference between estimates and exact measurements.

1-1 A Plan for Problem Solving

What you'll learn

You'll learn to solve problems using the four-step plan.

When am I ever going to use this?

Knowing how to solve problems can help you play games such as Clue.

Word Wise

population
sample

When Martin Handford was a boy, he was fascinated by picture books with colorful crowd scenes. As an adult, he is famous as the author of the *Where's Waldo* books in which Waldo is hidden somewhere in detailed crowd scenes.

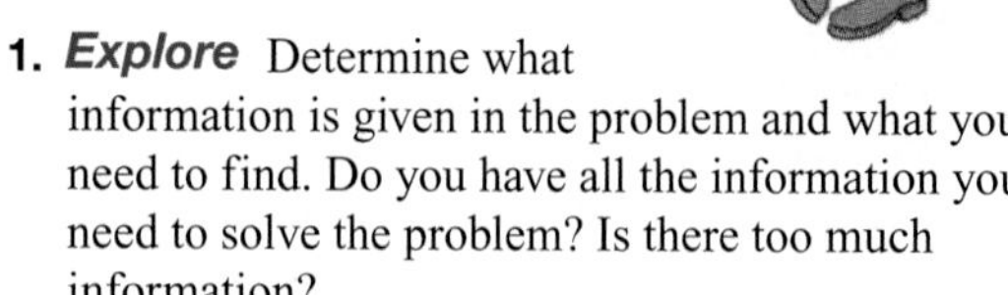

About how many characters are there in this *Where's Waldo* scene?

Where would you begin to solve this problem? In mathematics, we have a four-step plan to solve problems.

1. ***Explore*** Determine what information is given in the problem and what you need to find. Do you have all the information you need to solve the problem? Is there too much information?
2. ***Plan*** After you understand the problem, select a strategy for solving it. There may be several ideas or strategies that you can use. It is usually helpful to make an estimate of what you think the answer should be.
3. ***Solve*** Solve the problem by carrying out your plan. If your plan doesn't work, try another, and maybe even another.
4. ***Examine*** Finally, examine your answer carefully. See if it fits the facts given in the problem. Compare it to your estimate. You may also want to solve the problem again in a different way. If the answer is not correct, make a new plan and start again.

Example 1 Let's try our plan on the opening problem.

Explore *What do you know?*

There are many characters in the picture. They seem to be evenly scattered throughout the picture.

What are you trying to find?

You need to find an *estimate* of the total number of characters in the picture. You do *not* need an exact answer.

Multiple Learning Styles

Logical Have groups of students use their problem-solving skills to give a best guess for each of the following:

- the number of nickels it would take to reach the ceiling of your classroom
- the number of days a million seconds equals
- the number of cans of soft drink it would take to fill up their bathtub to the brim
- the number of pictures in today's newspaper

Have the groups use their skills to get an actual or logical value for each situation. Compare the estimates to the actual.

Plan The total number of characters is called the **population**. Counting all the characters would take a lot of time. Besides, you only need an estimate, not an exact count.

You could count the number of characters in a small section of the picture. This small section is called a **sample**. Then multiply the number in the sample by the number of sections to get an estimate of the population.

One way to divide the picture into sections is by placing a rectangular grid over the picture.

Sample

Population

Study Hint

Estimation One way to estimate the number of characters in the sample is to count the number of faces you see.

Solve There are 18 characters in the sample shown above and 16 sections in the picture. Multiply 16 by 18 to find the population.

$16 \times 18 = 288$

There are about 288 characters in the picture.

Examine Is your answer reasonable? You can check by using another small section as your sample. If your two samples are very different, try using a third sample as a check and revise your estimate.

Throughout this textbook, you will be solving many kinds of problems. Some can be solved easily by adding, subtracting, multiplying, or dividing. Others can be solved by using a strategy like finding a pattern, solving a simpler problem, making a model, drawing a graph, and so on. No matter which strategy you use, you can always use the four-step plan to solve a problem.

2 TEACH

Transparency 1-1B contains a teaching aid for this lesson.

Reading Mathematics The first example in this lesson includes the term *population*. Discuss with students the meaning of the term. *Population* refers to *all* of the people in a city, state, or country. Likewise, in science it can refer to *all* of a group of organisms. Here it refers to *all* of the characters in the picture.

In-Class Examples

For Example 1
The picture on the jigsaw puzzle you just put together is filled with buttons. Suppose you divide the picture into 16 sections. You count 8 buttons in one section. About how many buttons are in the picture? 128

For Example 2
The chart below shows the price of stamps since 1974. Suppose the price of stamps goes up in 2003. Estimate the new price. **$0.35 or $0.36**

Price of a First-Class Postage Stamp

Year	Price ($)
1974	0.10
1975	0.13
1978	0.15
1981	0.20
1985	0.22
1988	0.25
1991	0.29
1995	0.32
1999	0.33

MathPASS CD-ROM

This CD-ROM offers a complete, self-paced mathematics curriculum. Each lesson includes a pretest, tutorial, guided practice, and posttest. MathPASS Lesson 1 is correlated to this Student Edition lesson.
For Windows & Macintosh

3 PRACTICE/APPLY

Check for Understanding

If students need additional practice or instruction after completing Exercises 1–5, you may find one of the following options helpful.

- Extra Practice, see p. 568
- Reteaching Activity
- *Study Guide Masters,* p. 1
- *Practice Masters,* p. 1

Additional Answers

1. You need to determine how all the facts are related and what strategy to use to solve the problem.
2. Make a new plan and solve again.

Example 2 — Real World APPLICATION

Entertainment In 1996, there were 1.3 billion movie tickets sold for a record $5.9 billion. The table shows movie admissions since 1946. If the recent trend continues, estimate how many movie tickets will be sold in 2001.

Movie Tickets (billions)	
Year	**Number**
1946	4.1
1951	2.8
1956	1.9
1961	1.2
1966	1.0
1971	0.8
1976	1.0
1981	1.1
1986	1.0
1991	1.2
1996	1.3

Source: Motion Picture Association

Explore You know the number of admissions for each year. You need to find any trend in the data and predict how many tickets will be sold in 2001.

Plan One good way to find a trend in the data is to show the data on a graph. Usually a line graph is used to show trends in data. Then look for a pattern in the graph.

Solve

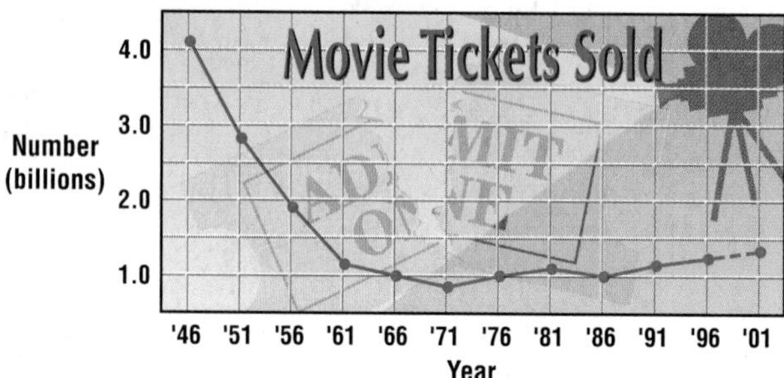

The data shows a steep drop for the years between 1946 and 1961. Then the graph levels off and shows a slight increase until 1996. To predict the number of tickets in 2001, extend the line to 2001 with a dashed line. About 1.4 billion tickets will be sold in 2001.

Examine Look for another pattern in the data for the last ten years. The number 1.4 billion seems reasonable.

Year	Number (billions)
1986	1.0
1991	1.2
1996	1.3
2001	1.4

+ + +

CHECK FOR UNDERSTANDING

Communicating Mathematics

Read and study the lesson to answer each question. 1–2. See margin.

Math Journal

1. ***Tell*** why it is important to plan before solving a problem.
2. ***Explain*** what to do if your plan to solve a problem doesn't work.
3. ***Write*** two or three sentences in your journal that describe what you expect to learn in this course. See students' work.

Reteaching the Lesson

Activity Make 8 stacks of checkers, varying the number of checkers per stack between 7, 8, and 9. Have students determine how to figure out about how many checkers there are without counting each one. Point out that this is useful as an estimate, not an exact count.

Error Analysis

Watch for students who correctly count the number of items in a sample, but then multiply incorrectly.

Prevent by having students check their answers for reasonableness, then check with a calculator.

***Study Guide Masters,* p. 1**

Name________ Date________

1-1 Study Guide

A Plan for Problem Solving

In 1966 the average salary for a major league baseball player was $22,500. By 1990 it was over $1,000,000. How many times the 1966 salary is the 1990 salary?

Explore What is given? 1966 average salary = $22,500; 1990 average salary = over $1,000,000

What is asked? How many times the 1966 salary is the 1990 salary?

Plan To find the number of times one number is of another, you need to divide.

Solve

1990 average	divided by	1966 average	is about	times as great
1,000,000	÷	22,500	≈	44.44

The 1990 average salary is about 44 times the 1966 average salary.

Examine You can use multiplication to check division.

$44.44 \times 22{,}500$ is about 1,000,000.

So 44.44 is correct.

Use the four-step plan to solve each problem.

1. Kings Canyon National Park is 462 thousand acres. Yellowstone National Park is 2,220 thousand acres. About how many times as large as Kings Canyon is Yellowstone? **about 5 times**
2. The flight of Apollo 7 in 1968 was 260 hours and 8 minutes long. The flight of Apollo 17 in 1972 was 301 hours and 52 minutes long. How much longer was the Apollo 17 flight? **41 hours and 44 minutes**
3. The Snake River, which runs from Wyoming to Washington, is 1,038 miles long. The Yukon River, which runs from the Yukon territory in Canada to Alaska, is 1,979 miles long. How much longer than the Snake River is the Yukon River? **941 miles**
4. It is 536 miles from Buffalo, New York, to Chicago, Illinois. It is 695 miles from Chicago to Washington, D.C. It is 386 miles from Washington, D.C. to Buffalo. How many miles is it from Buffalo to Chicago to Washington and back to Buffalo? **1,617 miles**

 T1 *Mathematics: Applications and Connections, Course 2*

Guided Practice **Use the four-step plan to solve each problem.**

4. ***Travel*** The Masons traveled 753 miles to the Great Smoky Mountains for their vacation. They took a different route home and traveled 856 miles. How many miles did they travel in all? **1,609 miles**

5. ***Sports*** There will be 460 people at the sports award banquet. If each table seats 8 people, how many tables are needed? **58 tables**

EXERCISES

Practice **Use the four-step plan to solve each problem.** **7. See margin.**

6. ***Communication*** According to a business magazine, the average American makes 184,702 phone calls in a life-time. Of these, 176 are international, 17,827 are long distance, and the others are local calls. How many local calls are made? **166,699 calls**
Source: *U.S. News and World Report*

7. ***Geometry*** Write one sentence describing how the shapes at the right are the same and one sentence describing how they are different.

8. **Standardized Test Practice** In a wheat field near Duns, Scotland, a reproduction of the painting *Sunflowers* was created with 250,000 plants and flowers. The "painting" covered a 46,000-square foot area. What is a reasonable number of flowers and plants per square foot? **A**

A 5 **B** 50 **C** 100 **D** 500 **E** 1,000

9. ***Patterns*** Predict how long it would take you to count out loud from one to one million. Explain your reasoning. **See margin.**

10. ***Fast Food*** The graph shows the amount of fast food that was served daily in the United States in 1990 and 1995.

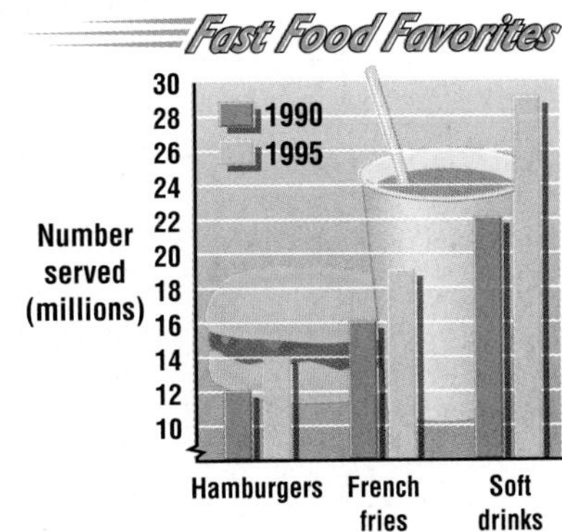

a. How many more hamburgers were served in 1995 than in 1990? **2 million hamburgers**

b. If the amount served grows at the same rate, predict how many hamburgers, French fries, and soft drinks will be served in the year 2000.

10b. hamburgers: about 16 million, French fries: about 22 million, soft drinks: about 36 million

11. ***Working on the*** CHAPTER Project Refer to the table on page 3. Suppose you weigh 150 pounds and want to burn about 1,300 Calories in two hours. Find two different activities you could do for one hour each to burn about 1,300 Calories altogether. **See margin.**

12. ***Critical Thinking*** Use the digits 1, 2, 3, 4, and 5 to form a two-digit and a three-digit number so that their product is the least product possible. Use each digit only once. **Sample answer: 245 × 13**

For **Extra Practice,** see page 568.

Assignment Guide

Core: 6–10, 12
Enriched: 6–10, 12

Exercise 11 asks students to advance to the next stage of work on the Chapter Project. You may want to have them look for all possible combinations of activities to burn the 1,300 Calories.

4 ASSESS

Closing Activity

Speaking Have students work with a partner. Have one student formulate a multi-step problem *without* numbers. The other student describes how he or she would solve the problem using the four-step plan.

Additional Answers

7. **Sample answer: They both have 4 congruent sides; one has right angles and the other does not.**
9. **Sample answer: If it takes 1 second to say a number, it would take about 11.5 days.**

Practice Masters, p. 1

Name______________ Date________

1-1 Practice

A Plan for Problem Solving

Use the four-step plan to solve each problem.

1. **Sports** "Go Dogs, Go Dogs, Go, Go, Go!" is a cheer for the Bulldogs' basketball team. If 15 cheerleaders yell the cheer 5 times, how many times is "Go" said?

Explore: 15 cheerleaders yell the cheer 5 times. How many times do they say "Go?"

Plan: 5 "Go's" in one cheer 5 × 5 is number of "Go's" for one cheerleader. 5 × 5 × 15 is total number of "Go's."

Solve: 5 × 5 = 25 "Go's" per cheerleader. 25 × 15 = 375 "Go's" altogether.

Examine: Seems like a lot of "Go's." Use 5 × 5 × 10 to estimate 5 × 5 × 15. The product 250 is close to 375.

2. **Cooking** A can of orange juice concentrate holds 12 ounces. If you mix it with 3 cans of water, how big a pitcher do you need to hold it all?

Explore: One can holds 12 ounces. Mix it with 3 cans of water (12 ounces each). Pitcher has to be as big as water plus concentrate.

Plan: 4 cans, 12 ounces each. 4 × 12 gives total amount of orange juice after mixing.

Solve: 4 × 12 = 48 ounces of juice. I need a pitcher that holds at least 48 ounces of liquid.

Examine: 12 oz + 12 oz + 12 oz + 12 oz = 48 oz

 T1 *Mathematics: Applications and Connections, Course 2*

Extending the Lesson

Enrichment Masters, p. 1

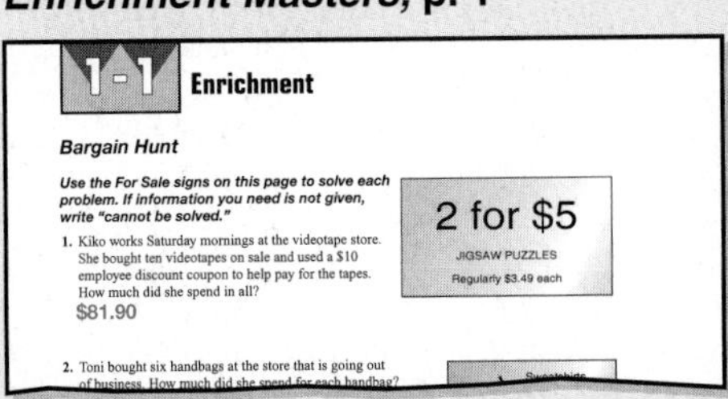
1-1 Enrichment

Bargain Hunt

Use the For Sale signs on this page to solve each problem. If information you need is not given, write "cannot be solved."

1. Kiko works Saturday mornings at the videotape store. She bought ten videotapes on sale and used a $10 employee discount coupon to help pay for the tapes. How much did she spend in all?
$81.90

2. Toni bought six handbags at the store that is going out of business. How much did she spend for each handbag?

2 for $5
JIGSAW PUZZLES
Regularly $3.49 each

Activity The distance from Albuquerque, NM, to Charlotte, NC, is 1,625 miles. Truck driver Jim Cronin makes the trip in 4 days. How many miles a day is this? **about 406 miles**

If Mr. Cronin traveled at 60 miles per hour, how many hours a day did he travel? **about 7 hours**

1-2 Lesson Notes

Instructional Resources

- *Study Guide Masters,* p. 2
- *Practice Masters,* p. 2
- *Enrichment Masters,* p. 2
- Transparencies 1-2, A and B
- *Assessment and Evaluation Masters,* p. 15
- *Diversity Masters,* p. 14
- *Technology Masters,* p. 28

CD-ROM Program
- Resource Lesson 1-2

Recommended Pacing	
Standard	Day 3 of 13
Honors	Day 3 of 13
Block	Day 2 of 7

1 FOCUS

5-Minute Check (Lesson 1-1)

Use the four-step plan to solve each problem.

1. Phyllis needs an 80-foot piece of string. She has pieces 22 feet, 17 feet, and 31 feet long. Tied together, will these work? Explain. **no; 22 + 17 + 31 = 70, 70 < 80**
2. If a bus carries 40 passengers, how many buses will be needed to take 288 students to a play? **8 buses**
3. Pat and Mei began work at the same time. It took Mei 110 minutes to mow the lawn, while Pat took 1 hour 45 minutes to paint the fence. Who finished first? **Pat**

The 5-Minute Check is also available on **Transparency 1-2A** for this lesson.

Motivating the Lesson

Problem Solving Present the following problem: *Use five 2s to make the number 1. You may use the symbols +, −, ×, and ÷ as well as parentheses.* **Sample answer: (2 × 2) − (2 ÷ 2) − 2 = 1**

1-2 Order of Operations

***What* you'll learn**
You'll learn to evaluate expressions using the order of operations.

***When* am I ever going to use this?**
Knowing the order of operations will help you find the total cost of adults' and children's admissions to the zoo.

Word Wise
order of operations

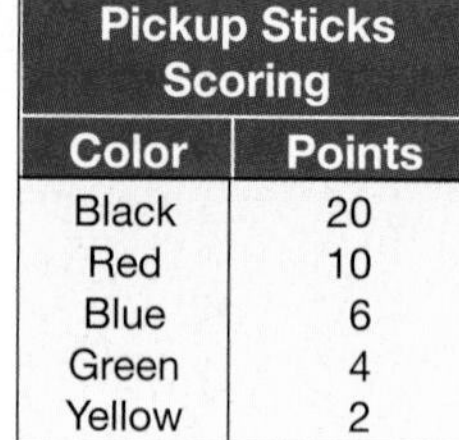

Pickup sticks is a game that originated in China many thousands of years ago. If you've played the game before, you know that when the sticks land parallel to each other, they are easy to pick up. If they intersect, it is difficult to pick one up without moving the others.

After all of the sticks have been picked up, you tally your score. Different-colored sticks receive different point values. These values are shown at the right.

Pickup Sticks Scoring	
Color	**Points**
Black	20
Red	10
Blue	6
Green	4
Yellow	2

Suppose you picked up 2 red sticks, 1 blue stick, and 4 yellow sticks. Here's how you can find your score.

$$\underbrace{2 \times 10}_{red} + \underbrace{1 \times 6}_{blue} + \underbrace{4 \times 2}_{yellow} = 20 + 6 + 8 \text{ or } 34$$

In the expression above, you multiplied before adding. You were using the **order of operations** that mathematicians have agreed on. The order of operations ensures that expressions have only one value. Grouping symbols, like parentheses, are used to change the order of operations.

Order of Operations	
	1. Do all operations within grouping symbols first. 2. Multiply and divide in order from left to right. 3. Add and subtract in order from left to right.

Examples

1 **Evaluate (8 − 2) ÷ 3.**

$(8 - 2) \div 3 = 6 \div 3$ *Subtract first since 8 − 2 is in parentheses.*
$= 2$ *Divide by 3.*

2 **Evaluate 13 + 6 − 4 + 12.**

$13 + 6 - 4 + 12 = 19 - 4 + 12$ *13 + 6 = 19*
$= 15 + 12$ *19 − 4 = 15*
$= 27$ *15 + 12 = 27*

Study Hint
Technology To change the order of operations, use the parentheses keys.

In addition to the symbol ×, there are other ways to indicate multiplication. One way is to use a raised dot. Another way is to use parentheses.

$3 \cdot 5$ means 3×5

$2(4 + 5)$ means $2 \times (4 + 5)$

Examples

3 Evaluate $3(24 - 7) - 2 \cdot 13$.

$3(24 - 7) - 2 \cdot 13 = 3(17) - 2 \cdot 13$ *Subtract 7 from 24.*
$= 51 - 2 \cdot 13$ *Multiply 3 and 17.*
$= 51 - 26$ *Multiply 2 and 13.*
$= 25$ *Subtract 26 from 51.*

INTEGRATION

4 **Geometry** The distance around a geometric figure is called its *perimeter.* In a rectangle, the opposite sides have the same measure.

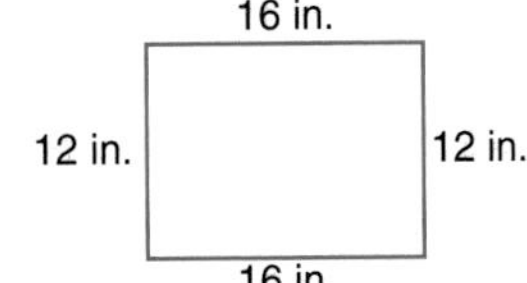

a. Write an expression to find the perimeter of the rectangle.

$2 \cdot 12 + 2 \cdot 16$ *The expression represents two widths plus two lengths.*

b. Evaluate the expression.

$2 \cdot 12 + 2 \cdot 16 = 24 + 32$ *Multiply 2 by 12 and 2 by 16.*
$= 56$ *Add 24 and 32.*

The perimeter is 56 inches.

CHECK FOR UNDERSTANDING

Communicating Mathematics

Read and study the lesson to answer each question.

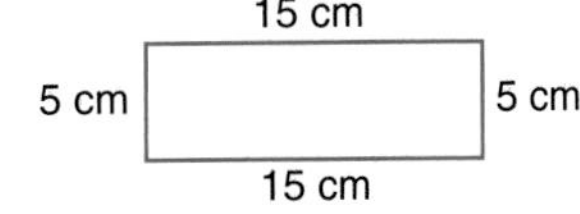

1. ***Tell*** which operation you should do first in the expression $(3 + 5) \times 6$. **addition**
2. ***Write*** an expression to find the perimeter of the rectangle at the right. **$2 \cdot 5 + 2 \cdot 15$**
3. ***You Decide*** Tia thinks that $16 - 8 \div 8$ is 15. Antoine thinks $16 - 8 \div 8$ is 1. Who is correct? Explain your reasoning. **Tia; you should divide first.**

Guided Practice

Name the operation that should be done first in each expression.

4. $12 - 3 \cdot 4$ **multiplication**
5. $7 + 3(5 - 2)$ **subtraction**

Evaluate each expression.

6. $12 - 3(4)$ **0**
7. $12 \div 3(4)$ **16**
8. $3 \cdot 4(5 - 3)$ **24**
9. $3(4 + 7) - 5 \cdot 4$ **13**
10. ***Photography*** Juanita has 2 rolls of film with 36 exposures and 3 rolls of film with 24 exposures. How many photos can she take with this film? **144**

EXERCISES

Practice

11–16. See margin.

Name the operation that should be done first in each expression.

11. $3 + 5 \cdot 6$
12. $10 - (3 + 4)$
13. $4 + 2(8 - 6)$
14. $5 + 7(8)$
15. $(8 - 4) \div 2$
16. $7 \times 9 - (4 + 3)$

2 TEACH

Transparency 1-2B contains a teaching aid for this lesson.

In-Class Examples

For Example 1
Evaluate $(6 + 2) \div 4$. **2**

For Example 2
Evaluate $25 + 10 - 8 + 15$. **42**

For Example 3
Evaluate $4(3 + 5) - 2 \cdot 7$. **18**

For Example 4
Ryan's garden is a rectangle 50 feet wide by 25 feet long.

a. Write an expression to find the perimeter of the garden. **$2 \cdot 50 + 2 \cdot 25$**

b. Evaluate the expression. $2 \cdot 50 + 2 \cdot 25$ **150 feet**

3 PRACTICE/APPLY

Check for Understanding

If students need additional practice or instruction after completing Exercises 1–10, you may find one of the following options helpful.

- Extra Practice, see p. 568
- Reteaching Activity
- *Study Guide Masters,* p. 2
- *Practice Masters,* p. 2
-  Interactive Mathematics Tools Software

***Study Guide Masters,* p. 2**

1-2 Name ________ Date ________

Study Guide

Order of Operations

Algebraic expressions are evaluated using these rules.

Order of Operations
1. Do all operations within grouping symbols first.
2. Multiply and divide in order from left to right.
3. Add and subtract in order from left to right.

Example **Evaluate $56 \div (17 - 9) + 7 \times 3$.**

$56 \div (17 - 9) + 7 \times 3 = 56 \div 8 + 7 \times 3$ *Subtract 9 from 17.*
$= 7 + 7 \times 3$ *Divide 56 by 8.*
$= 7 + 21$ *Multiply 7 and 3.*
$= 28$ *Add 7 and 21.*

Name the operation that should be done first in each expression.

1. $(9 + 3) \times 7$ addition
2. $98 - 5 \times 7$ multiplication
3. $5 \times (9 - 1)$ subtraction
4. $(15 \div 3) + (4 + 5)$ division
5. $5 \times 4 \div 2$ multiplication
6. $5(5 - 3) \times 2$ subtraction

Evaluate each expression.

7. $2 \times 9 + 5 \times 3$ 33
8. $(9 - 4) \div 5$ 1
9. $10 - 4 + 1$ 7
10. $15 - 18 \div 9 + 3$ 16
11. $30 \div (12 - 6) + 4$ 9
12. $(72 - 12) \div 2$ 30
13. $2(16 - 9) - (5 + 1)$ 8
14. $(43 - 23) - 2 \times 5$ 10
15. $90 - 45 - 24 \div 2$ 33
16. $81 \div (13 - 4)$ 9
17. $7 \times 8 - 2 \times 8$ 40
18. $71 + (34 - 34)$ 71

 T2 *Mathematics: Applications and Connections, Course 2*

■ Reteaching the Lesson ■

Activity Have groups of students use different colored counters to model how the expressions in Examples 1 and 2 are evaluated. They should write an explanation for each step in the process.

Additional Answers

11. multiplication
12. addition
13. subtraction
14. multiplication
15. subtraction
16. addition

Thinking Algebraically Have students compare the following:

$4 + (2 + 12)$ $4 \times (2 + 12)$
$4 + (2 \times 12)$ $(4 \times 2) \times 12$

In which expression(s) will the value change if the parentheses are dropped? $4 \times (2 + 12)$

Assignment Guide

Core: 11–35 odd, 38–40
Enriched: 12–34 even, 35, 36, 38–40

CHAPTER Project

Exercise 37 asks students to advance to the next stage of work on the Chapter Project. You may wish to have students work in groups to answer the questions.

4 ASSESS

Closing Activity

Modeling Have students work in a group to create expressions for others in the group to evaluate. Have students use manipulatives to model the expressions.

Chapter 1, Quiz A (Lessons 1-1 and 1-2) is available in the *Assessment and Evaluation Masters,* p. 15.

***Practice Masters,* p. 2**

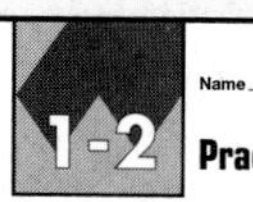

Name________________________ Date__________

Practice

Order of Operations

Name the operation that should be done first in each expression.

1. $5 + 4 \cdot 7$ multiplication
2. $13(6 + 3)$ addition
3. $(4 - 2) + 6$ subtraction
4. $6 \times 8 \div 4$ multiplication
5. $32 \div 4 \times 2$ division
6. $9(4 + 2) \div 3$ addition

Evaluate each expression.

7. $8 \cdot 7 + 8 \cdot 3$ 80
8. $(9 - 3) \div 3$ 2
9. $8 - 6 + 3$ 5
10. $18 \div 3 \cdot 6$ 36
11. $9 - 4 \div 2 + 6$ 13
12. $24 \div (6 - 2)$ 6
13. $18 - (7 - 7)$ 18
14. $32 \div (8 - 4)$ 8
15. $90 - 16 \div 4$ 86
16. $3(18 - 12) - (5 - 3)$ 16
17. $(24 - 10) - 3 \times 3$ 5
18. $4(22 - 18) - 3 \cdot 5$ 1
19. $12(5 - 5) + 3 \cdot 5$ 15
20. $18(4 - 3) \div 3 + 3$ 9
21. $(34 + 46) \div 20 + 20$ 24
22. $92 - 66 - 12 \div 4$ 23
23. $9 \cdot 3 + 8 \div 4$ 29
24. $9 + (18 \div 3)$ 15

Insert parentheses to make each sentence true.

25. $(32 + 8) \times 3 \div 4 = 30$
26. $(15 - 3) \div (1 \cdot 6) = 2$
27. $\left(\frac{88}{22} + 8\right) \div 3 = 4$
28. $18 \div (3 + 3) - 2 = 1$
28. $(16 - 8) \div 4 + 10 = 12$
30. $5 \cdot (5 + 5) - 5 = 45$
31. $(6 + 6 \div 6) \cdot 6 = 42$
32. $200 - (90 + 80 + 20) = 10$

 T2 *Mathematics: Applications and Connections, Course 2*

Evaluate each expression.

17. $3 + 5 \cdot 4$ 23
18. $(12 - 4) \div 2$ 4
19. $5 \cdot 8 - 3 \cdot 4$ 28
20. $5 - 3 + 1$ 3
21. $16 \div 4 \cdot 2$ 8
22. $12 - 8 \div 4 + 6$ 16
23. $(8 + 3) - 5$ 6
24. $(17 + 3) \div (4 + 1)$ 4
25. $4(6 + 4) \div 2$ 20
26. $24 \div (7 - 3)$ 6
27. $14 - (19 - 19)$ 14
28. $25 \div (9 - 4)$ 5
29. What is the value of $84 - 28 \div (4 \cdot 7)$? 83
30. Evaluate $82 - 43 - 6 \div 6$. 38

Copy each sentence below. Insert parentheses to make each sentence true. 31. $2(14 - 9) - (17 - 14) = 7$ 32. $(16 + 5) \times 4 \div 2 = 42$

31. $2 \cdot 14 - 9 - 17 - 14 = 7$
32. $16 + 5 \times 4 \div 2 = 42$
33. $64 \div 8 + 24 - 1 = 1$ $64 \div (8 + 24) - 1 = 1$
34. $36 \div 3 - 9 \div 3 = 1$ $(36 \div 3 - 9) \div 3 = 1$

Applications and Problem Solving

Real World

35. ***Entertainment*** An adult ticket to the zoo costs \$5, a student ticket costs \$3, and a senior ticket costs \$4.
    a. Write an expression to find the total cost of 2 adult, 1 senior, and 3 student tickets. $2 \cdot 5 + 1 \cdot 4 + 3 \cdot 3$
    b. Evaluate the expression. \$23

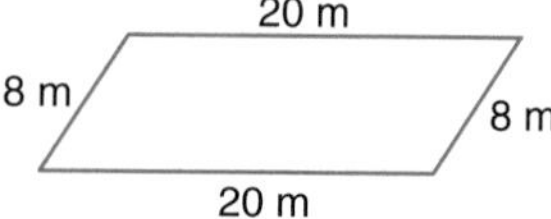

36. ***Geometry*** Find the perimeter of the parallelogram at the right. 56 meters
37. ***Working on the CHAPTER Project*** Refer to the table on page 3. Choose a weight of 100 or 150 pounds. Use a combination of at least 3 activities, each for a certain number of hours, that would burn approximately 2,400 Calories. Write an expression that shows the total number of Calories burned. See Answer Appendix.
38. ***Critical Thinking*** Some calculators are programmed to follow the order of operations. Explain how you could tell whether your calculator follows the order of operations. See Answer Appendix.

Mixed Review

39. **Standardized Test Practice** There are 72 tables set up at the music luncheon. If each table seats 6 people and all of the tables will be filled, how many people are expected to attend the music luncheon? *(Lesson 1-1)* A

    A 432 **B** 78 **C** 66 **D** 12 **E** Not Here

40. ***Sports*** The graph shows the yearly average spent for sports apparel in the United States by each age group. On average, how much more was spent by the 13-to-17 age group than the 25-to-34 age group? *(Lesson 1-1)* \$124

Who Buys Sports Apparel?

Yearly spending by age group

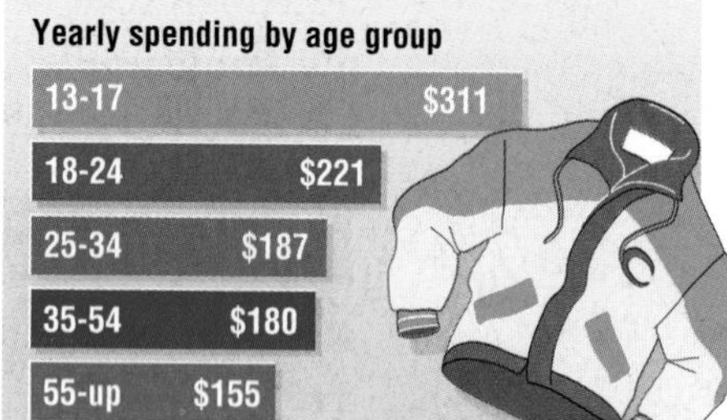

Source: Sporting Goods Manufacturers Assoc.

For **Extra Practice,** see page 568.

Extending the Lesson

***Enrichment Masters,* p. 2**

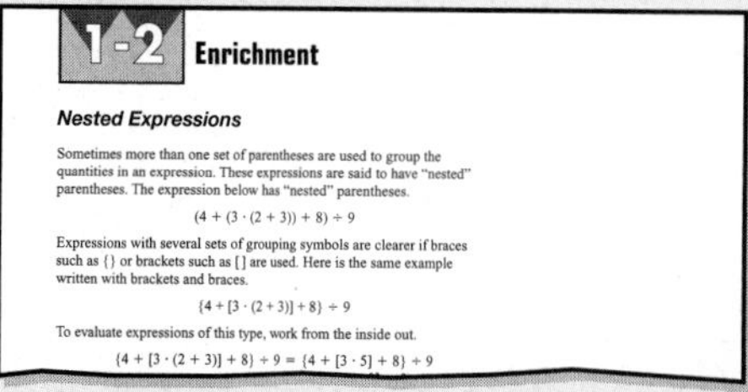

1-2 **Enrichment**

Nested Expressions

Sometimes more than one set of parentheses are used to group the quantities in an expression. These expressions are said to have "nested" parentheses. The expression below has "nested" parentheses.

$$(4 + (3 \cdot (2 + 3)) + 8) \div 9$$

Expressions with several sets of grouping symbols are clearer if braces such as { } or brackets such as [ ] are used. Here is the same example written with brackets and braces.

$$\{4 + [3 \cdot (2 + 3)] + 8\} \div 9$$

To evaluate expressions of this type, work from the inside out.

$$\{4 + [3 \cdot (2 + 3)] + 8\} \div 9 = \{4 + [3 \cdot 5] + 8\} \div 9$$

Activity Taxis usually charge a certain price for the first part of a trip, perhaps $\frac{1}{5}$ of a mile, and then a price per fraction of a mile for the rest of the trip. Have students use the rates of a local taxi company to estimate the cost of a trip from the school to the nearest airport or bus station.

COOPERATIVE LEARNING

1-3A Variables and Expressions

A Preview of Lesson 1-3

cups and counters

integer mat

The backpack on the table has some books inside of it. There are 2 more books on the table. The total number of books is *the sum of 2 and the number of books in the backpack.* This phrase contains a constant that you know, 2, and an unknown value.

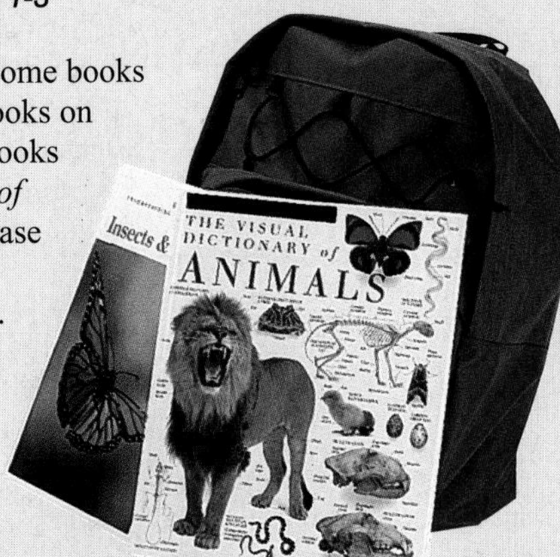

In mathematics, you will work with unknown numbers and constants. You can represent unknown numbers with cups and constants with counters.

TRY THIS

Work with a partner.

1. Model *the sum of some number and 2.*
   - Use a cup to represent the unknown value and 2 counters to represent the constant.
   - Any number of counters may be in the cup. Suppose you put 3 counters in the cup. Instead of an unknown value, you now know the cup has a value 3. When you empty the cup and count all the counters, the expression has a value of 5.

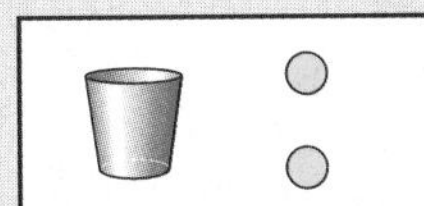

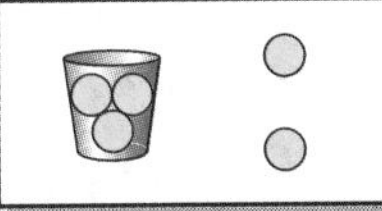

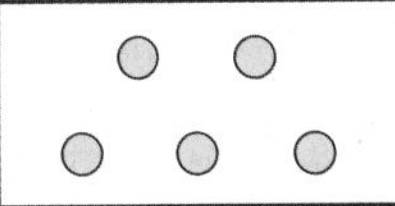

2. Model the phrase *twice some number.* You don't know the value of the number, so let a cup represent this value. You will need to use 2 cups to represent *twice* some number.

The same number of counters should be in each cup.

5. Sample answer: The cup represents the variable or unknown quantity.

ON YOUR OWN

Model each phrase with cups and counters. Then put four counters in each cup. How many counters are there in all? Record your answers by drawing pictures of your models.

1. the sum of 3 and a number **7**
2. 3 times a number **12**
3. 5 more than a number **9**
4. twice a number plus 1 **9**
5. Write a sentence to describe what the cup represents.

Math Journal Have students write a paragraph describing a real or imaginary shopping trip involving the purchase of multiple items (the variable) at a fixed price (the constant).

1-3A HANDS-ON LAB Notes

GET READY

Objective Students use cups and counters to model algebraic expressions.

Optional Resources

Hands-On Lab Masters
- counters, p. 5
- pattern for cup, p. 7
- integer mat, p. 8
- worksheet, p. 38

Overhead Manipulative Resources
- counters
- cups
- integer mat

Manipulative Kit
- counters
- cups
- integer mat

MANAGEMENT TIPS

Recommended Time
20 minutes

Getting Started Provide groups of students with cups and counters or other small objects that are uniform in size. Discuss with students how using algebraic expressions to represent unknown quantities can be an effective problem-solving strategy.

Activities 1 and 2 ask students to model phrases with unknown values. To help students understand the concept of an unknown value, have them identify the constants (known numbers) and the unknown values in the algebraic phrases in each of the two activities.

ASSESS

Have students make up situations containing unknown values. Then have other students interpret the situations as algebraic expressions and model the expressions using the counters and cups.

1-3 Lesson Notes

Instructional Resources

- *Study Guide Masters*, p. 3
- *Practice Masters*, p. 3
- *Enrichment Masters*, p. 3
- Transparencies 1-3, A and B

- CD-ROM Program
  - Resource Lesson 1-3
  - Interactive Lesson 1-3

Recommended Pacing	
Standard	Days 4 & 5 of 13
Honors	Day 4 of 13
Block	Day 3 of 7

1 FOCUS

5-Minute Check
(Lesson 1-2)

Evaluate each expression.

1. $15 - 3 \cdot 2$ 9
2. $25 \div (10 - 5)$ 5
3. $12 \div 3 + 1$ 5
4. $3(5 + 4) - 4 \times 2$ 19
5. $(24 + 36) \div 12 + 7$ 12

The 5-Minute Check is also available on **Transparency 1-3A** for this lesson.

Motivating the Lesson

Hands-On Activity Separate the class into groups. Give each group of students 10 counters, each worth $50.00. Distribute catalog pages or sales flyers to each group and have them determine which items they could purchase with their counters.

1-3

Integration: Algebra
Variables and Expressions

What you'll learn
You'll learn to evaluate simple algebraic expressions.

When am I ever going to use this?
Knowing how to evaluate algebraic expressions can help you determine the amount of your paycheck.

Word Wise
variable
algebra
algebraic expression
evaluate

Study Hint
Reading Math The letter *x* is often used as a variable. It is also common to use the first letter of the value you are representing.

Can you twirl a hula hoop? Hula hoops have been around since the 1950s, when they were created by a company in California. At that time, they cost about $2 each and were so popular that 25 *million* were sold in just two months.

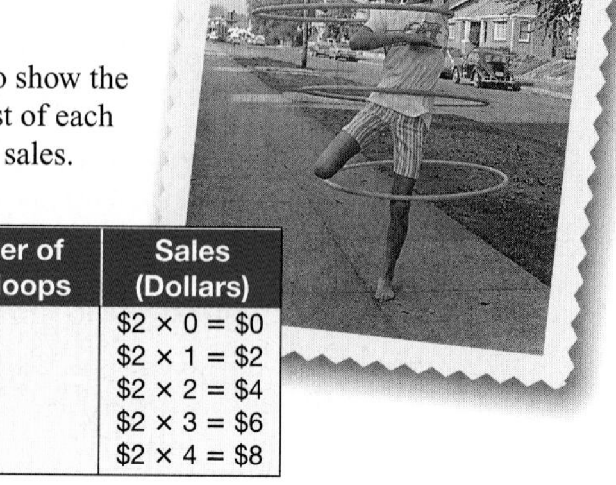

You can make a table to show the pattern between the cost of each hula hoop and the total sales.

Number of Hula Hoops	Sales (Dollars)
0	$2 × 0 = $0
1	$2 × 1 = $2
2	$2 × 2 = $4
3	$2 × 3 = $6
4	$2 × 4 = $8

Notice that the cost of each hula hoop is a constant, $2, but the number of hula hoops varies. You can use a placeholder, or **variable**, to represent the number of hula hoops. The expression for the amount earned is $2 × ❑ or $2 × *n*.

cost per hula hoop → $2 \times n$ ← *number of hula hoops*
$2 \times n$ → *total sales*

The branch of mathematics that involves expressions with variables is called **algebra**. The expression $2 \times n$ is called an **algebraic expression** because it contains variables, numbers, and at least one operation.

You can **evaluate** an algebraic expression by replacing the variable with a number and then finding the value of the numerical expression.

Example 1 Evaluate $n + 2$ if $n = 7$.

$n + 2 = 7 + 2$ *Replace n with 7.*
$= 9$

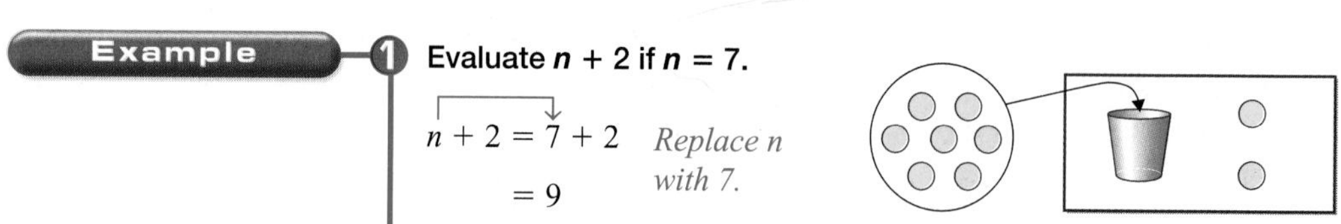

Multiple Learning Styles

Interpersonal Have students work with a partner. Taking turns, one writes an algebraic expression for the other to read orally. Students then work together to evaluate the expression for a given value.

In mathematics, the following symbols are used for multiplication and division with variables.

$3a$	means	$3 \times a$ or $3 \cdot a$	$4cd$	means	$4 \times c \times d$
rs	means	$r \times s$	$\frac{m}{2}$	means	$m \div 2$

Examples

Study Hint

Reading Math In Example 2, 4a means 4 times a, but 48 does not mean 4 times 8. So, there are parentheses around the 8 in 4(8).

2 **Evaluate $4a + 5b$ if $a = 8$ and $b = 3$.**

$4a + 5b = 4(8) + 5(3)$ *Replace a with 8 and b with 3.*

$= 32 + 15$ *Multiply first.*

$= 47$ *Add 32 and 15.*

3 **Evaluate $\frac{xy}{3}$ if $x = 7$ and $y = 9$.**

$\frac{xy}{3} = \frac{(7)(9)}{3}$ *Replace x with 7 and y with 9.*

$= \frac{63}{3}$ or 21

4 **Health CONNECTION** **The expression $110 + \frac{A}{2}$, where A stands for a person's age, is used to estimate a person's normal systolic blood pressure. Estimate the normal blood pressure for an 18-year-old person.**

$110 + \frac{A}{2} = 110 + \frac{18}{2}$ *Replace A with 18.*

$= 110 + 9$ or 119 *Divide 18 by 2. Then add.*

The normal blood pressure for an 18-year-old person is about 119.

MINI-LAB

Work with a partner.

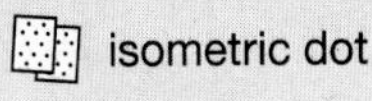 isometric dot paper

The pattern below is made up of equilateral triangles.

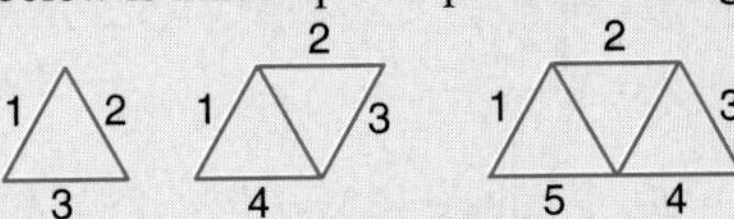

Try This

1. Draw the next three figures in the pattern. **1–2. See margin.**
2. Find the perimeter of each figure and record your data in a table. The first three are completed for you.

Number of Triangles	1	2	3	4	5	6
Perimeter	3	4	5	?	?	?

Talk About It

3. Without drawing the figure, determine the perimeter of a figure made up of 10 triangles. Check by making a drawing. 12

2 TEACH

Transparency 1-3B contains a teaching aid for this lesson.

Using the Mini-Lab Help students realize that once a pattern is identified, the pattern can be summed up in an expression or general rule. People can use the expression or rule to solve problems.

In-Class Examples

For Example 1

Evaluate $n + 8$ if $n = 9$. 17

For Example 2

Evaluate $6a + 7b$ if $a = 5$ and $b = 4$. 58

For Example 3

Evaluate $\frac{xy}{4}$ if $x = 4$ and $y = 6$. 6

For Example 4

The expression $15 + \frac{B}{3}$, where B stands for leftover boxes of markers, is used to estimate the number of boxes of markers a class gets. Estimate the number of boxes a class gets if the number of leftover boxes is 39. 28

Teaching Tip Before students evaluate the expressions in Examples 2–4, have them translate each phrase verbally, for example, in Example 2, *the sum of 4 times one number and 5 times a different number.*

Additional Answers for the Mini-Lab

1.

2.

Number of Triangles	1	2	3	4	5	6
Perimeter	3	4	5	6	7	8

3 PRACTICE/APPLY

Check for Understanding

If students need additional practice or instruction after completing Exercises 1–10, you may find one of the following options helpful.

- Extra Practice, see p. 568
- Reteaching Activity
- *Transition Booklet,* pp. 7–12
- *Study Guide Masters,* p. 3
- *Practice Masters,* p. 3
- Interactive Mathematics Tools Software

Assignment Guide

Core: 11–31 odd, 32–36
Enriched: 12–28 even, 30–36
All: Self Test 1–5

Additional Answers

1. **Sample answer: Numbers have a constant value, while variables represent many different values.**
2. **Sample answer: The cup can hold any amount, like the variable can represent any number.**

3a. **Sample answer: The perimeter is two more than the number of triangles.**

CHECK FOR UNDERSTANDING

Communicating Mathematics

Read and study the lesson to answer each question. **1–2. See margin.**

1. ***Tell,*** in your own words, the difference between numbers and variables.
2. ***Explain*** how evaluating an expression is similar to using the cups and counters model in Lesson 1-3A.

HANDS-ON MATH

3. Refer to the Mini-Lab on page 13.
   a. If you know the number of triangles in the pattern, explain how you can find the perimeter of the figure. **See margin.**
   b. If n represents the number of triangles, write an expression that represents the perimeter of the figure. $n + 2$

Guided Practice

Evaluate each expression if $x = 6$, $y = 4$, $z = 0$, $a = 3$, $b = 2$, and $c = 7$.

4. $9 - c$ **2**
5. $x + y$ **10**
6. $4ab$ **24**
7. $xy - 4$ **20**
8. $10x - 2z$ **60**
9. $\frac{2x}{a}$ **4**

10. ***Fitness*** You can estimate how fast you walk in miles per hour by evaluating the expression $\frac{s}{30}$, where s is the number of steps you take in one minute. Estimate your speed if you take 93 steps in one minute. **3.1 miles per hour**

EXERCISES

Practice

Evaluate each expression if $a = 6$, $b = 3$, and $c = 2$.

11. $a + b$ **9**
12. ac **12**
13. $\frac{8b}{2}$ **12**
14. $a - b + 5$ **8**
15. $ab - 1$ **17**
16. $a + c - 2b$ **2**
17. $a + b + c$ **11**
18. $3a + b$ **21**
19. $ab - c$ **16**
20. $\frac{a}{c} + 4$ **7**
21. $2ab$ **36**
22. $\frac{a}{b} + c$ **4**
23. $\frac{2a}{3} - c$ **2**
24. $2(a + b) - c$ **16**
25. $2a - 3b$ **3**
26. $5 - \frac{2b}{c}$ **2**
27. $\frac{6(a + c)}{b}$ **16**
28. $c(b + a) - a$ **12**
29. Evaluate $125x + 75x$ if $x = 5$. **1,000**

Applications and Problem Solving

30. ***Earth Science*** One way to estimate how many miles a thunderstorm is from you is to count the number of seconds between the lightning and the thunder. Then divide the number of seconds by five.
    a. Write an expression to estimate the distance. $\frac{s}{5}$ **or** $s \div 5$
    b. Estimate the distance if you count 6 seconds. **about 1 mile**

Study Guide Masters, p. 3

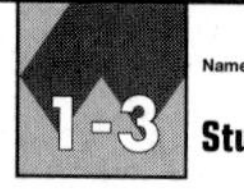

Name________________ Date________

1-3 Study Guide

Integration: Algebra
Variables and Expressions

The area of a triangle can be found by multiplying the base of the triangle by the height of the triangle and then dividing by 2.

If we use b to represent the base of the triangle and h to represent the height of the triangle, the area of the triangle can be found by evaluating the **algebraic expression** below.

height h / base b

$$\frac{bh}{2}$$

The values of b and h change for different triangles. They are called **variables**.

Examples **Find the area of each triangle.**

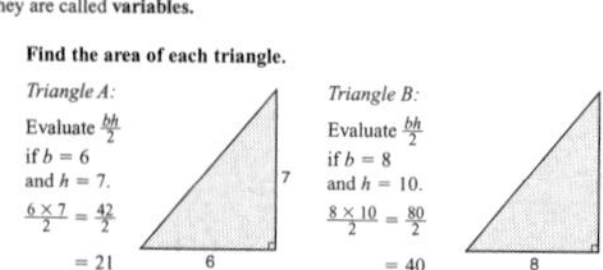

Triangle A: Evaluate $\frac{bh}{2}$ if $b = 6$ and $h = 7$. $\frac{6 \times 7}{2} = \frac{42}{2} = 21$ The area is 21 square units.

Triangle B: Evaluate $\frac{bh}{2}$ if $b = 8$ and $h = 10$. $\frac{8 \times 10}{2} = \frac{80}{2} = 40$ The area is 40 square units.

Evaluate each expression if a = 2, b = 3, c = 4, and d = 12.

1. $c + 2a$ **8**
2. $19 - d$ **7**
3. $3(b + 5)$ **24**
4. $bc \div 12$ **1**
5. $d - c + 6$ **14**
6. $a(d - b)$ **18**
7. $15 - ab$ **9**
8. $6ca$ **48**
9. $6 + \frac{d}{c}$ **9**
10. $\frac{d}{a} - b$ **3**
11. $20 - \frac{2b}{a}$ **17**
12. $6c - 4b$ **12**
13. $7ab$ **42**
14. $a(6 + c) + 1$ **21**
15. $2c + 2b - d$ **2**
16. $d + ac$ **20**

 T3 *Mathematics: Applications and Connections, Course 2*

Reteaching the Lesson

Activity Have students use counters or centimeter cubes with circles drawn on paper to model expressions in the beginning of the lesson, showing the pattern between cost of Hula-Hoops and amount earned.

Error Analysis

Watch for students who incorrectly evaluate expressions by performing operations out of order.

Prevent by reviewing the order of operations with those students and having them read the expressions aloud to clearly identify each operation in the order in which it occurs.

31. ***Money Matters*** Tammy charges \$3 per hour for baby-sitting. **c. \$24**
   a. Make a chart that shows how much money Tammy earns for baby-sitting 1, 2, 3, 4, and 5 hours. **See margin.**
   b. Write an expression to find how much money Tammy will earn for any number of hours. Let n be the number of hours she baby-sits. **$3n$**
   c. Suppose Tammy baby-sits for 8 hours. How much money will she earn?

32. ***Critical Thinking*** Find values of x and y so that the value of $7x + 2$ is greater than the value of $3y + 23$. **Sample answer: $x = 5$, $y = 2$**

Mixed Review

33. ***Decorating*** Wallpaper for a bedroom costs \$16 per roll for the walls and \$9 per roll for the border. If the room requires 12 rolls of paper for the walls and 6 rolls for the border, compute the total cost for the wallpaper and border. *(Lesson 1-2)* **\$246**

34. Evaluate the expression $36 + 9 \div 3$. *(Lesson 1-2)* **39**

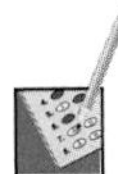

35. **Standardized Test Practice** Suppose there are 15 tables set up for the football banquet at Walnut Springs Middle School. Each table seats 8 people. You notice there are 5 empty seats. Which expression could you use to find the number of people seated at the banquet? *(Lesson 1-2)* **C**

   A $15 + 8 - 5$　　B $15 \times 8 + 5$　　C $15 \times 8 - 5$
   D $15 + 8 + 5$　　E $15 \times (8 - 5)$

36. ***Sports*** A baseball stadium holds 20,000 people. If 3,650 people can be seated in the bleachers, how many seats are available in the rest of the stadium? *(Lesson 1-1)* **16,350 seats**

For **Extra Practice,** see page 568.

Mid-Chapter Self Test

1. ***Transportation*** Nine school buses serve Maplewood Middle School. The buses travel a total of 4,485 miles in one week. On average, about how many miles does each bus travel weekly? *(Lesson 1-1)* **about 498 miles**
2. Evaluate the expression $12 - 6 \div 3 + 8$. *(Lesson 1-2)* **18**

Evaluate each expression if $x = 5$, $y = 4$, and $z = 10$. *(Lesson 1-3)*

3. $5(x + y) - z$ **35**
4. $xy + 2z$ **40**
5. ***Health*** Do you know how much blood is in your body? You can find the approximate number of quarts by evaluating the expression $\frac{w}{30}$, where w is your weight in pounds. Estimate how much blood a 120-pound person has. *(Lesson 1-3)* **about 4 quarts**

4 ASSESS

Closing Activity

Writing Have students work in pairs to create algebraic expressions and choose values for the variables. Have students evaluate each other's expressions.

Mid-Chapter Self Test

The Mid-Chapter Self Test reviews the concepts in Lessons 1-1 through 1-3. Lesson references are given so students can review concepts not yet mastered.

Additional Answer

31a.

Number of Hours	1	2	3	4	5
Amount Earned	3	6	9	12	15

Extending the Lesson

Enrichment Masters, p. 3

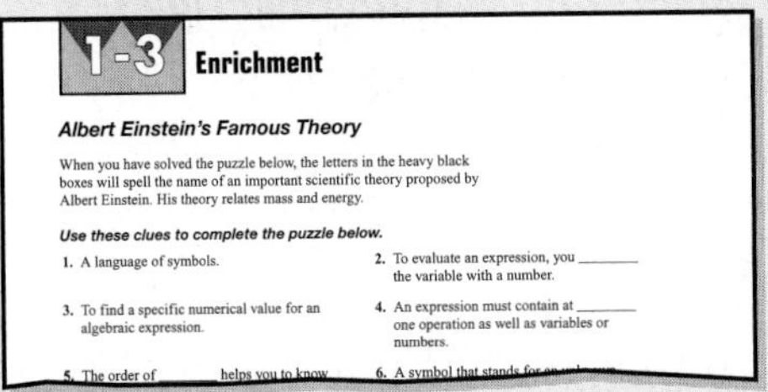

1-3 Enrichment

Albert Einstein's Famous Theory

When you have solved the puzzle below, the letters in the heavy black boxes will spell the name of an important scientific theory proposed by Albert Einstein. His theory relates mass and energy.

Use these clues to complete the puzzle below.

1. A language of symbols.
2. To evaluate an expression, you ______ the variable with a number.
3. To find a specific numerical value for an algebraic expression.
4. An expression must contain at ______ one operation as well as variables or numbers.
5. The order of ______ helps you to know
6. A symbol that stands for an unknown

Activity Have students write and evaluate an algebraic expression for the phrase "the cost of five roses at \$6 each and three tulips at \$2 each."
$(5 \times 6) + (3 \times 2) = 36$

Practice Masters, p. 3

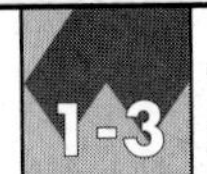

Name ______________ Date ________

1-3 Practice

Integration: Algebra
Variables and Expressions

Evaluate each expression if x = 5, y = 4, and z = 3.

1. $x + 3$ 8	2. $z - 3$ 0	3. $10 - z$ 7
4. $13 + y$ 17	5. $x + z$ 8	6. $y + z$ 7
7. $y + 3 - z$ 4	8. $x - 2 + z$ 6	9. $x - x + 4$ 4
10. $x - y + 8$ 9	11. $xy - 2$ 18	12. $xz - 4$ 11
13. $yz + 10$ 22	14. $yz - 10$ 2	15. $xz + 4$ 19

Evaluate each expression if a = 8, b = 4, and c = 2.

16. $a + b + c$ 14	17. $4b + a$ 24	18. $cb - a$ 0
19. $\frac{a}{b} + 5$ 7	20. $3bc$ 24	21. $\frac{a}{b} + c$ 4
22. $\frac{2a}{4} - b$ 0	23. $3(b + a) - c$ 34	24. $2b - 3c$ 2
25. $\frac{2b}{c}$ 4	26. $\frac{6(a + c)}{b}$ 15	27. $b(b + a) - b$ 44

Evaluate each expression if a = 12, b = 3, c = 4, m = 9, and n = 3.

28. $\frac{m}{n} + 6$ 9	28. $1mn$ 27	30. $\frac{a}{c} - b$ 0
31. $\frac{3n}{m} + 4$ 5	32. $3(n + n) - m$ 9	33. $4c - 3b$ 7
34. $10 - \frac{2m}{n}$ 4	35. $\frac{3(b + c)}{(b + c)}$ 3	36. $b(c - b) + c$ 7

 T3 *Mathematics: Applications and Connections, Course 2*

GET READY

Objective Students evaluate algebraic expressions by using a graphing calculator.

Technology Resources
- TI-80, TI-81, TI-82, or TI-83 graphing calculator

MANAGEMENT TIPS

Recommended Time
40 minutes

Getting Started Have students practice using the alpha keys by entering their names. Also have them enter a few expressions to evaluate so they get used to how the different symbols look on the calculator.

Using a Graphing Calculator Discuss with students some of the advantages of using a graphing calculator for non-graphing calculations. Some advantages: larger screen, shows everything that is typed in and the answer, and the ability to store up to 26 numbers. Students can also re-evaluate the expression without re-keying every part of the expression by pressing [2nd] [ENTER] and using the arrow keys to find the appropriate numbers to replace.

ASSESS

After students answer Exercises 1–6, ask them to develop a problem that would be difficult to do mentally. Then have them work the problem on the graphing calculator.

Use Exercise 7 to determine whether students understand evaluating expressions on a calculator.

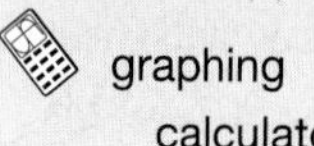

1-3B Evaluating Expressions

A Follow-Up of Lesson 1-3

graphing calculator

You can use a graphing calculator to evaluate algebraic expressions. You can store a value in memory using a variable and then recall that value when evaluating an expression.

TRY THIS

Work with a partner.

Use a graphing calculator to evaluate $4x - 6$ and $5y + 8$ if $x = 3$ and $y = 2$.

Step 1 Store each value in its respective variable. To store the value 3 in the variable x, enter

3 [STO▸] [ALPHA] [X] [ENTER].

To store the value 2 in the variable y, enter

2 [STO▸] [ALPHA] [Y] [ENTER].

Step 2 Evaluate each expression. To evaluate $4x - 6$, enter

4 [ALPHA] [X] [−] 6 [ENTER]. The result is 6.

To evaluate $5y + 8$, enter

5 [ALPHA] [Y] [+] 8 [ENTER]. The result is 18.

ON YOUR OWN

Use a graphing calculator to evaluate each expression if $m = 6$ and $n = 2$.

1. $8m$ **48**
2. $2m + 12$ **24**
3. $24 \div 2m$ **72**
4. mn **12**
5. $2m - 3n$ **6**
6. $3m + 5n - 8$ **20**
7. How could you use a graphing calculator to evaluate the expression ab if $a = 4 + 8 \times 2$ and $b = 15 - 4 + 2$? **Sample answer: Store the value of $4 + 8 \times 2$ in a and the value of $15 - 4 + 2$ in b. Then find ab.**

Have students write a paragraph that compares evaluating expressions by using a calculator and by using a pencil and paper.

1-4

Integration: Algebra

Powers and Exponents

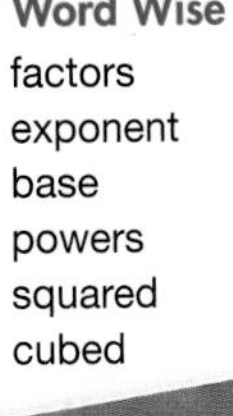

***What** you'll learn*

You'll learn to use powers and exponents in expressions.

***When** am I ever going to use this?*

Powers and exponents are used to express very large numbers more simply.

Word Wise

factors
exponent
base
powers
squared
cubed

The Rajah's Rice, A Mathematical Folktale from India is the story of a young girl named Chandra. She loved elephants and helped take care of the Rajah's elephants. In fact, she helped cure the elephants when they were sick. The Rajah was so pleased that he decided to give her a reward.

Chandra also loved mathematics. So she asked for this reward.

"If Your Majesty pleases, place two grains of rice on the first square of this chessboard. Place four grains on the second square, eight on the next, and so on, doubling each pile of rice till the last square."

Do you think this was a good reward?

The chart lists the grains of rice placed on the first eight squares of the chessboard.

Square	1	2	3	4	5	6	7	8
Grains of Rice	2	4	8	16	32	64	128	256

Notice the pattern 2, 4, 8, 16, ... When two or more numbers are multiplied, these numbers are called **factors** of the product. The number of grains of rice can be written using only factors of 2. For example, 16 can be written as $2 \cdot 2 \cdot 2 \cdot 2$. When the same factor is used, you may use an **exponent** to simplify the notation.

$$16 = \underbrace{2 \cdot 2 \cdot 2 \cdot 2}_{\text{four factors}} = 2^4 \leftarrow \text{exponent}$$

base (the 2 in 2^4)   *2^4 is a power of 2.*

The common factor is called the **base**. Numbers expressed using exponents are called **powers**.

The powers 4^2, 2^3, and 5^4 are read as follows.

Symbols	Words
4^2	four to the second power or four **squared**
2^3	two to the third power or two **cubed**
5^4	five to the fourth power

Cross-Curriculum Cue

Inform other teachers that your classes are studying exponents. Suggestions for curriculum are:
Earth Science: space exploration
Civics: population statistics, values of products and services

1-4 Lesson Notes

Instructional Resources

- *Study Guide Masters,* p. 4
- *Practice Masters,* p. 4
- *Enrichment Masters,* p. 4
- Transparencies 1-4, A and B
- *Assessment and Evaluation Masters,* pp. 14, 15
- *Classroom Games,* pp. 1–4
- *Hands-On Lab Masters,* p. 72
- *Technology Masters,* p. 27

CD-ROM Program
- Resource Lesson 1-4

Recommended Pacing	
Standard	Day 6 of 13
Honors	Day 6 of 13
Block	Day 4 of 7

1 FOCUS

5-Minute Check
(Lesson 1-3)

1. Evaluate $n + m + 5$ if $m = 2$ and $n = 8$. 15
2. Evaluate $4x + 3y$ if $x = 4$ and $y = 6$. 34
3. Evaluate $\frac{cd}{4}$ if $c = 3$ and $d = 8$. 6
4. Evaluate $\frac{a}{b} + 30$ if $a = 18$ and $b = 9$. 32
5. Given that $s \div 5 = n$ miles, estimate how many miles a thunderstorm is away from you if you count 11 seconds between the lightning and the thunder. about 2 miles

The 5-Minute Check is also available on **Transparency 1-4A** for this lesson.

Motivating the Lesson

Problem Solving Read the opening story to the class. Ask students to predict what will happen. Then, display a chessboard for the class. Point out that the board has 8 squares across and 8 squares down. Discuss with students how to determine the total number of squares on the board. $8^2 = 64$

2 TEACH

Transparency 1-4B contains a teaching aid for this lesson.

Reading Mathematics Have students use a table to help them visualize patterns with exponents. Have them label the columns n^1, n^2, n^3, n^4, n^5, and n^6. Then have them place the numbers 1 through 10 in the first column. Students should use their calculators to complete the table. Ask students what they notice about the products as the value of the exponent increases.

In-Class Examples

For Example 1
Write 2^3 as a product. $2 \cdot 2 \cdot 2$

For Example 2
Write $7 \cdot 7 \cdot 7 \cdot 7 \cdot 7 \cdot 7$ using exponents. 7^6

For Example 3
Evaluate 6^4. 1,296

For Example 4
Evaluate $3^3 + 5 \cdot 3$. 42

For Example 5
Write a^5 as a product.
$a \cdot a \cdot a \cdot a \cdot a$

For Example 6
Write $y \cdot y \cdot y \cdot y \cdot y \cdot y$ using exponents. y^6

For Example 7
Evaluate x^3 if $x = 4$. 64

Teaching Tip Inform students that the term *power* can also refer to the exponent only.

Examples

1 **Write 3^5 as a product.**

The base is 3. The exponent 5 means 3 is used as a factor 5 times.

$3^5 = 3 \cdot 3 \cdot 3 \cdot 3 \cdot 3$

2 **Write $10 \cdot 10 \cdot 10$ using exponents.**

10 is the base. It is used as a factor 3 times. So, the exponent is 3.

$10 \cdot 10 \cdot 10 = 10^3$

When you evaluate expressions with powers, you should evaluate powers before other operations.

Order of Operations	
	1. Do all operations within grouping symbols first. 2. Do all powers before other operations. 3. Multiply and divide in order from left to right. 4. Add and subtract in order from left to right.

Examples

Study Hint
Technology Many calculators have a y^x key that allows you to compute exponents. To find 5^4, press 5 y^x 4 =. The display shows 625.

3 **Evaluate 5^4.**

$5^4 = 5 \cdot 5 \cdot 5 \cdot 5$ *Definition of power*

$= 625$

4 **Evaluate $2 \cdot 6 + 4^2$.**

$2 \cdot 6 + 4^2 = 2 \cdot 6 + 16$ *Evaluate the power first, $4^2 = 4 \cdot 4$ or 16.*

$= 12 + 16$ *Multiply.*

$= 28$ *Add.*

5 **Write m^3 as a product.**

$m^3 = m \cdot m \cdot m$

6 **Write $x \cdot x \cdot x \cdot x$ using exponents.**

$x \cdot x \cdot x \cdot x = x^4$

INTEGRATION

7 **Algebra** **Evaluate $y^4 + 10$ if $y = 3$.**

$y^4 + 10 = 3^4 + 10$ *Replace y with 3.*

$= 81 + 10$ *$3^4 = 81$*

$= 91$

CHECK FOR UNDERSTANDING

Communicating Mathematics

Math Journal

Read and study the lesson to answer each question. 2–3. See margin.

1. ***Explain*** how to find the value of the expression *6 squared*. $6 \cdot 6 = 36$
2. ***Define*** *power*. Use the terms *factor*, *base*, and *exponent* in your definition.
3. ***Write*** a short paragraph explaining why expressions like 10^6 are written with exponents.

Guided Practice

Write each power as a product of the same factor.

4. 7^5 $7 \cdot 7 \cdot 7 \cdot 7 \cdot 7$
5. z^3 $z \cdot z \cdot z$

Additional Answers

2. Sample answer: A power is a product of equal factors. It has a base (the common factor) and an exponent (the number of times the factor occurs).
3. Sample answer: Using exponents is more convenient and saves space.

Write each product using exponents.

6. $5 \cdot 5 \cdot 5$ 5^3
7. $x \cdot x \cdot x \cdot x \cdot x \cdot x$ x^6

Evaluate each expression.

8. 8^3 512
9. $6 \div 3 \cdot 2^3$ 16

Evaluate each expression if $n = 4$, $x = 5$, and $t = 2$.

10. $n^3 - t$ 62
11. $2x + x^2$ 35
12. ***Number System*** The base-ten number system uses powers of ten to express numbers. Write 1,000,000,000 as a power of ten. 10^9

EXERCISES

Practice

14. $9 \cdot 9 \cdot 9 \cdot 9 \cdot 9 \cdot 9 \cdot 9$

Write each power as a product of the same factor.

13. 2^4 $2 \cdot 2 \cdot 2 \cdot 2$
14. 9^7
15. 4^5 $4 \cdot 4 \cdot 4 \cdot 4 \cdot 4$
16. a^3 $a \cdot a \cdot a$
17. m^4 $m \cdot m \cdot m \cdot m$
18. y^2 $y \cdot y$

Write each product using exponents.

19. $12 \cdot 12$ 12^2
20. $8 \cdot 8 \cdot 8 \cdot 8 \cdot 8$ 8^5
21. $15 \cdot 15 \cdot 15 \cdot 15$ 15^4
22. $b \cdot b \cdot b$ b^3
23. $n \cdot n$ n^2
24. $r \cdot r \cdot r \cdot r \cdot r$ r^5

Evaluate each expression.

25. 7^2 49
26. 1^{10} 1
27. $5 + 4^2$ 21
28. $(5 + 4)^2$ 81
29. $5 \cdot 3 + 2^3$ 23
30. $(16 \div 4)^3 - 6$ 58

Evaluate each expression if $a = 3$, $b = 9$, and $c = 2$.

31. $a^4 + b$ 90
32. $c^2 + ab$ 31
33. $2a^3$ 54
34. $bc - a^2$ 9
35. $a^2 + b^2$ 90
36. $a^2(a + b)$ 108
37. ***Algebra*** Find the value of $x^2 + 2x + 1$ if $x = 3$. 16

Use a calculator to determine whether each sentence is *true* or *false*.

38. $3^7 > 7^3$ true
39. $14^4 = 182$ false
40. $6^3 < 4^4$ true

Applications and Problem Solving

41. ***Geometry*** Refer to the figures.

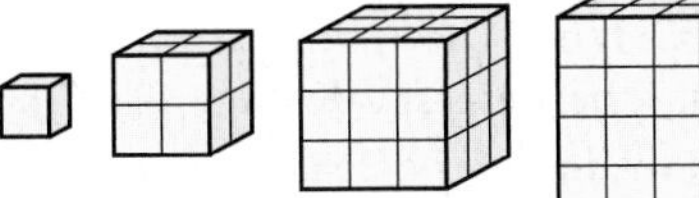
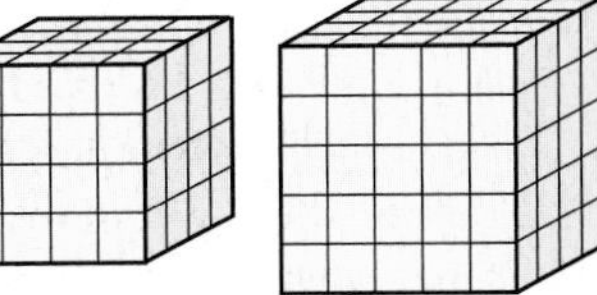

   a. Find the number of unit cubes that make up each large cube. Write your answers using exponents. 1^3, 2^3, 3^3, 4^3, 5^3 41b. See margin.
   b. Why do you suppose the expression 2^3 is sometimes read as 2 *cubed*?
42. ***Language Arts*** Refer to the beginning of the lesson. Write an expression using exponents to determine how many grains of rice would be on the 64th square of Rajah's chessboard. 2^{64}

3 PRACTICE/APPLY

Check for Understanding

If students need additional practice or instruction after completing Exercises 1–12, you may find one of the following options helpful.

- Extra Practice, see p. 569
- Reteaching Activity
- *Transition Booklet,* pp. 9–10
- *Study Guide Masters,* p. 4
- *Practice Masters,* p. 4

Assignment Guide

Core: 13–41 odd, 43–47
Enriched: 14–40 even, 41–47

Additional Answer

41b. Sample answer: A number, *n*, taken to the third power is the same as the volume of a cube whose edge is *n* units long.

Study Guide Masters, p. 4

Name______________ Date______________

Study Guide

Integration: Algebra
Powers and Exponents

A **power** can be used to show repeated multiplication of a number.

4×4 can be written 4^2. This is read *4 squared* or *4 to the second power.*

The exponent, 2, tells you how many times the base, 4, is used as a factor. base → 4^2 ← exponent

Examples

1 **Write $6 \times 6 \times 6 \times 6$ using exponents.**
The base, 6, is used as a factor 4 times. So, $6 \times 6 \times 6 \times 6 = 6^4$.

2 **Write 12^3 as a product.**
The exponent 3 means that 12 is used as a factor 3 times.
$12^3 = 12 \times 12 \times 12$

3 **Evaluate 6^4.**
$6 \times 6 \times 6 \times 6 = 1{,}296$

Write each power as a product of the same factor.

1. 7^4 $7 \times 7 \times 7 \times 7$
2. 5^5 $5 \times 5 \times 5 \times 5 \times 5$
3. 4^6 $4 \times 4 \times 4 \times 4 \times 4 \times 4$
4. 8^2 8×8
5. 9^3 $9 \times 9 \times 9$
6. 6^1 6
7. 2^5 $2 \times 2 \times 2 \times 2 \times 2$
8. m^4 $m \times m \times m \times m$

Write each product using exponents.

9. $5 \times 5 \times 5$ 5^3
10. 10×10 10^2
11. $6 \times 6 \times 6 \times 6 \times 6$ 6^5
12. $3 \times 3 \times 3 \times 3$ 3^4

Evaluate each expression.

13. 8^2 64
14. 1^6 1
15. 3^4 81
16. 12^1 12
17. 2^5 32
18. 5^3 125
19. 4^4 256
20. 6^2 36

 T4 *Mathematics: Applications and Connections, Course 2*

■ Reteaching the Lesson ■

Activity Have students visualize squared numbers by using tiles to model them. Students should use exponents to express the area of each square they create.

MathPASS CD-ROM

This CD-ROM offers a complete, self-paced mathematics curriculum. Each lesson includes a pretest, tutorial, guided practice, and posttest. MathPASS Lesson 2 is correlated to this Student Edition lesson.
For Windows & Macintosh

4 ASSESS

Closing Activity

Writing Write an exponential expression on the chalkboard of the form b^c. Have students first write the expression using expanded products and then evaluate it.

Chapter 1, Quiz B (Lessons 1-3 and 1-4) is available in the *Assessment and Evaluation Masters,* p.15.

Mid-Chapter Test (Lessons 1-1 through 1-4) is available in the *Assessment and Evaluation Masters,* p.14.

Additional Answer

43. Sample answer: $3^3 = 27$, $3^2 = 9$, $3^1 = 3$, $3^0 = 1$; Each power is three times greater than the next.

43. ***Critical Thinking*** Based on the pattern shown at the right, write a convincing argument that any number, except 0, raised to the 0 power equals 1. **See margin.**

$2^4 = 16$
$2^3 = 8$
$2^2 = 4$
$2^1 = 2$
$2^0 = ?$

Mixed Review

44. **Standardized Test Practice** Cameron is planning how much money he will need to wash his clothes at a laundromat. Each load costs $1.50 to wash and $0.75 to dry. The total cost is represented by the expression $1.50n + 0.75n$, where n is the number of loads. How much would it cost to wash and dry 7 loads? *(Lesson 1-3)* **D**

   A $5.25 **B** $10.50 **C** $12.75 **D** $15.75

For **Extra Practice,** see page 569.

45. ***Algebra*** Evaluate $3a - 2b + 6(a - b)$ if $a = 14$ and $b = 2$. *(Lesson 1-3)* **110**
46. Evaluate $3(6 - 2) + 2 + 4$. *(Lesson 1-2)* **18**
47. *True* or *false*? In the four-step plan, the *Solve* step comes last. *(Lesson 1-1)* **false**

Alge-bridge

Math Skill
Evaluating Expressions

Get Ready This game is for two, three, or four players.

 18 index cards scissors  one number cube

Get Set Cut the index cards in half so you have 36 smaller cards. On each card, write a different expression containing only one variable.

Go

- Deal all the cards to the players. The dealer then rolls the number cube. The number on the number cube is the value of the variable for the first round.
- The player to the left of the dealer puts a card faceup on the table and announces its value. Play continues until all players have placed one card on the table. This is the end of the first round. The person whose card has the greatest value wins all of the cards for that round.
- The player to the left of the dealer rolls the number cube. This is the value of the variable for the next round. Play continues until all cards are played.
- The person who has the most cards at the end of the game is the winner.

Visit www.glencoe.com/sec/math/mac/mathnet for more games.

Practice Masters, p. 4

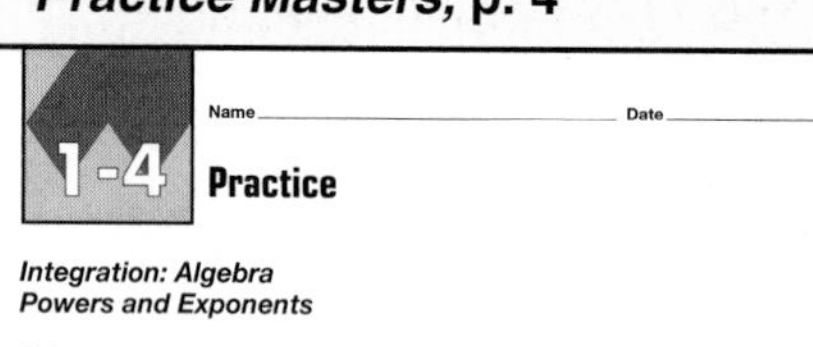
Name ______ Date ______

1-4 Practice

Integration: Algebra
Powers and Exponents

Write each power as a product of the same factor.

1. 5^4 $5 \cdot 5 \cdot 5 \cdot 5$
2. 3^5 $3 \cdot 3 \cdot 3 \cdot 3 \cdot 3$
3. 8^4 $8 \cdot 8 \cdot 8 \cdot 8$
4. 15^4 $15 \cdot 15 \cdot 15 \cdot 15$
5. 6^7 $6 \cdot 6 \cdot 6 \cdot 6 \cdot 6 \cdot 6 \cdot 6$
6. n^4 $n \cdot n \cdot n \cdot n$

Write each product using exponents.

7. $8 \cdot 8 \cdot 8$ 8^3
8. $12 \cdot 12 \cdot 12 \cdot 12 \cdot 12 \cdot 12$ 12^6
9. $m \cdot m \cdot m \cdot m$ m^4
10. $3 \cdot 3 \cdot 3$ 3^3
11. $1 \cdot 1 \cdot 1 \cdot 1 \cdot 1$ 1^5
12. $r \cdot r \cdot r \cdot r \cdot r \cdot r$ r^6

Evaluate each expression.

13. 3^2 9
14. 3^3 27
15. 2^5 32
16. 0^6 0
17. 12 squared 144
18. 3 to the fourth power 81
19. In 1980, the federal government spent about 2×10^9 dollars on school lunches. In 1995, the amount was up to about 4×10^9 dollars. How much did the government spend on school lunches in 1995? $4,000,000,000

Use a calculator to determine whether each sentence is true or false.

20. $4^5 > 5^4$ true
21. $6^5 = 5^8$ false
22. $5^4 = 10^2$ false

Evaluate each expression.

23. y^2 if $y = 9$ 81
24. m^6 if $m = 3$ 729
25. x^5 if $x = 10$ 100,000
26. z^4 if $z = 6$ 1,296
27. x^3 if $x = 6$ 216
28. y^5 if $y = 7$ 16,807

 T4 *Mathematics: Applications and Connections, Course 2*

Extending the Lesson

Enrichment Masters, p. 4

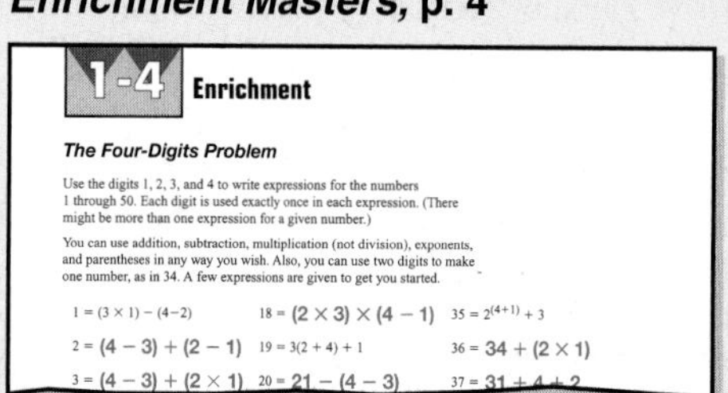
1-4 Enrichment

The Four-Digits Problem

Use the digits 1, 2, 3, and 4 to write expressions for the numbers 1 through 50. Each digit is used exactly once in each expression. (There might be more than one expression for a given number.)

You can use addition, subtraction, multiplication (not division), exponents, and parentheses in any way you wish. Also, you can use two digits to make one number, as in 34. A few expressions are given to get you started.

$1 = (3 \times 1) - (4 - 2)$ $18 = (2 \times 3) \times (4 - 1)$ $35 = 2^{(4+1)} + 3$

$2 = (4 - 3) + (2 - 1)$ $19 = 3(2 + 4) + 1$ $36 = 34 + (2 \times 1)$

$3 = (4 - 3) + (2 \times 1)$ $20 = 21 - (4 - 3)$ $37 = 31 + 4 + 2$

Make sure that students are following the order of operations in calculating the correct values of their expressions. You may wish to examine the expressions written on the cards to make sure none of them would yield a negative number for any roll of the number cube.

1-5 Integration: Algebra
Solving Equations

What you'll learn
You'll learn to solve equations using mental math.

When am I ever going to use this?
Knowing how to solve equations mentally can help you solve problems in science.

Word Wise
equation
solve
solution
modeling

Suppose you had this question on a geography test.

The __?__ is the body of water on the east coast of Texas.

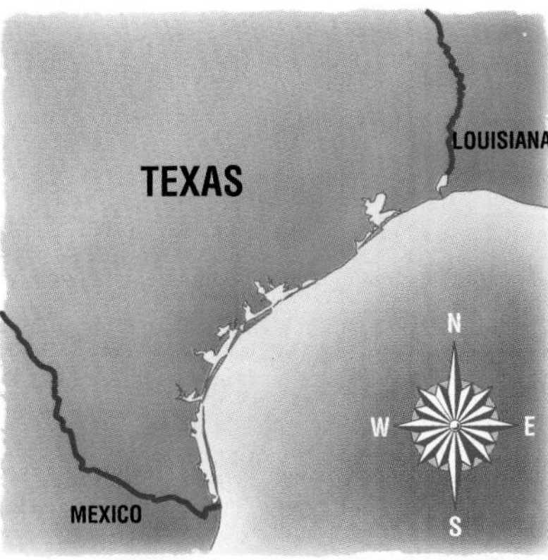

If you fill in the blank with *Gulf of Mexico,* the sentence is true. But if you choose *Pacific Ocean,* the sentence is false. Solving equations in mathematics is like answering fill-in-the-blank questions.

An **equation** is a sentence in mathematics that contains an equals sign.

$48 + 12 = 60$ $\quad$ $5 \times 4 = 20$ $\quad$ $9 = 81 \div 9$

Some equations also contain variables. The equation $x + 9 = 17$ is neither true nor false until x is replaced with a number. You **solve** the equation when you replace the variable with a number that makes the equation true. Any number that makes the equation true is called a **solution**. The solution of $x + 9 = 17$ is 8 because $8 + 9 = 17$.

Example 1 Which of the numbers 10, 11, or 12 is a solution of $9x = 99$?

Replace x with 10.	Replace x with 11.	Replace x with 12.
$9x = 99$	$9x = 99$	$9x = 99$
$9(10) \stackrel{?}{=} 99$	$9(11) \stackrel{?}{=} 99$	$9(12) \stackrel{?}{=} 99$
$90 = 99$ *false*	$99 = 99$ ✓*true*	$108 = 99$ *false*

The solution is 11.

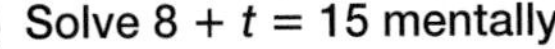

Some equations can be solved mentally by using basic facts or arithmetic skills you know.

Example 2 Solve $8 + t = 15$ mentally.

$8 + t = 15$

$8 + 7 \stackrel{?}{=} 15$ *You know that $8 + 7 = 15$.*

$15 = 15$ ✓

The solution is 7.

1-5 Lesson Notes

Instructional Resources

- *Study Guide Masters,* p. 5
- *Practice Masters,* p. 5
- *Enrichment Masters,* p. 5
- Transparencies 1-5, A and B

CD-ROM Program
- Resource Lesson 1-5

Recommended Pacing	
Standard	Day 7 of 13
Honors	Day 7 of 13
Block	Day 4 of 7

1 FOCUS

5-Minute Check
(Lesson 1-4)

1. Write 4^5 as a product of the same factor. $4 \cdot 4 \cdot 4 \cdot 4 \cdot 4$
2. Write $3 \cdot 3 \cdot 3 \cdot 3 \cdot 3 \cdot 3$ using exponents. 3^6

Evaluate each expression.

3. 6^3 216
4. 12^5 248,832
5. n^4 if $n = 3$ 81

The 5-Minute Check is also available on **Transparency 1-5A** for this lesson.

Motivating the Lesson

Problem Solving Tell students that you are thinking of a number and they can guess it using the following clue. *The number plus 15 adds up to 26. What is the number?* Then ask them how they can check the solution.

2 TEACH

Transparency 1-5B contains a teaching aid for this lesson.

Using Discussion Students should realize that even with variables in the equation, an equation must be balanced on both sides of the equal sign. Discuss how variables actually represent numbers.

Multiple Learning Styles

Verbal/Linguistic Have students tell in their own words how an equation differs from an expression. Have them write an example of each.

MathPASS CD-ROM

This CD-ROM offers a complete, self-paced mathematics curriculum. Each lesson includes a pretest, tutorial, guided practice, and posttest. MathPASS Lesson 3 is correlated to this Student Edition lesson.
For Windows & Macintosh

In-Class Examples

For Example 1
Which of the numbers 7, 8, or 9 is the solution of $6 + r = 14$? 8

For Example 2
Solve $10 + y = 21$ mentally. 11

For Example 3
Solve $t = \frac{84}{7}$ mentally. 12

For Example 4
Columbus landed in the West Indies in 1492. Sixty-five years later the equals sign appeared in the first algebra book published in English. In what year was that book published? 1557

3 PRACTICE/APPLY

Check for Understanding

If students need additional practice or instruction after completing Exercises 1–12, you may find one of the following options helpful.

- Extra Practice, see p. 569
- Reteaching Activity
- *Study Guide Masters,* p. 5
- *Practice Masters,* p. 5

Study Guide Masters, p. 5

Name ______________________ Date __________

Study Guide

Integration: Algebra
Solving Equations

An equation is a mathematical sentence that contains an equals sign.

Example **Phil can address 50 envelopes in an hour. How long will it take him to address 300 envelopes?**

Let h represent the number of hours. The problem can be represented by $50 \times h = 300$.

$50 \times h = 300$
$50 \times 6 \stackrel{?}{=} 300$
You know that $50 \times 6 = 300$.
The solution is 6.

It will take Phil 6 hours to address 300 envelopes.

Name the number that is a solution of the given equation.

1. $r - 12 = 20$; 8, 24, 32 32
2. $10m = 80$; 8, 10, 70 8
3. $k + 25 = 50$; 15, 25, 75 25
4. $y \div 9 = 8$; 64, 72, 80 72
5. $6p = 72$; 8, 10, 12 12
6. $48 - n = 12$; 32, 36, 60 36

Solve each equation.

7. $x + 22 = 66$ 44
8. $t - 17 = 23$ 40
9. $12f = 144$ 12
10. $\frac{\ell}{7} = 10$ 70
11. $25w = 225$ 9
12. $176 - 45 = b$ 131
13. $19 \times s = 171$ 9
14. $210 \div v = 14$ 15

 T5 *Mathematics: Applications and Connections, Course 2*

Example 3 Solve $y = \frac{30}{6}$ mentally.

You will learn other methods of solving equations in Chapter 6.

$y = \frac{30}{6}$
$5 \stackrel{?}{=} \frac{30}{6}$ *You know that $\frac{30}{6}$ is 5.*
$5 = 5$ ✓ The solution is 5.

When you write an equation that represents a real-world problem, you are **modeling** the problem.

Example 4 CONNECTION

Physical Science Atoms are the "building blocks" of matter. The nucleus of an atom is composed of protons and neutrons. The mass number of an atom is equal to the sum of the number of protons and neutrons.

a. Write an equation to model this situation.

b. A scientist can tell the mass number of an atom by how much it weighs and the number of protons by the atom's electrical properties. A certain isotope of carbon has 6 protons and a mass number of 14. How many neutrons does it have?

a. An equation is $p + n = m$, where p is the number of protons, n is the number of neutrons, and m is the mass number.

b. $p + n = m$
$6 + n = 14$ *Replace p with 6 and m with 14.*
$6 + 8 \stackrel{?}{=} 14$
$14 = 14$ ✓

The solution is 8. Therefore, this isotope of carbon has 8 neutrons.

CHECK FOR UNDERSTANDING

Communicating Mathematics

Read and study the lesson to answer each question.

1. ***Explain*** what it means to solve an equation. See margin.
2. ***Tell*** the solution of $5x = 45$. 9
3. ***You Decide*** Jermaine thinks the solution of $t \div 7 = 49$ is 7; Latisha thinks the solution is 343. Who is correct? Explain your reasoning. Latisha; $343 \div 7 = 49$

Guided Practice

Name the number that is the solution of the given equation.

4. $s + 8 = 21$; 12, 13, 14 13
5. $d - 14 = 27$; 39, 40, 41 41

Solve each equation.

6. $25 + 19 = r$ 44
7. $w \div 4 = 20$ 80
8. $3y = 33$ 11
9. $g + 12 = 30$ 18
10. $12m = 120$ 10
11. $56 \div 7 = a$ 8
12. ***Travel*** If it takes you 5 hours to travel 250 miles in a car, what is your average speed? Use the equation $250 = 5r$, where r is the average speed. 50 miles per hour

▪ Reteaching the Lesson ▪

Activity Using an overhead projector, write an equation that involves coins, such as $n + \$0.10 = \$0.25$. Have students use actual coins to model the equation. Ask students to choose the coins that will make the equation true. Emphasize that n represents the value of the coins needed.

Additional Answer

1. Sample answer: Find the value of the variable that makes a true sentence.

EXERCISES

Practice

Name the number that is the solution of the given equation.

13. $a + 15 = 19$; 4, 5, 6 **4**
14. $b - 13 = 29$; 40, 41, 42 **42**
15. $11a = 77$; 6, 7, 8 **7**
16. $v \div 10 = 4$; 20, 30, 40 **40**
17. $33 + t = 51$; 18, 19, 20 **18**
18. $13 \cdot 9 = g$; 107, 117, 127 **117**

Solve each equation.

19. $x + 35 = 91$ **56**
20. $m + 18 = 24$ **6**
21. $x - 15 = 71$ **86**
22. $15s = 105$ **7**
23. $\frac{n}{8} = 9$ **72**
24. $\frac{f}{3} = 61$ **183**
25. $j + 4 = 14$ **10**
26. $10k = 200$ **20**
27. $42 \div 7 = t$ **6**
28. $p - 18 = 20$ **38**
29. $24 + 39 = x$ **63**
30. $9a = 108$ **12**
31. $d + 25 = 80$ **55**
32. $z \div 14 = 8$ **112**
33. $13(11) = k$ **143**
34. $r - 29 = 117$ **146**
35. $a - 75 = 98$ **173**
36. $43 + z = 65$ **22**

Applications and Problem Solving

37. Sheila was paid \$9 per hour and earned \$67.50. How many hours did Sheila work? Use the equation $67.50 = 9h$, where h is hours worked. **$7\frac{1}{2}$h**

38. ***Physical Science*** Refer to Example 4. An isotope of uranium has 92 protons and a mass number of 235. How many neutrons does it have? **143**

39. ***Geometry*** The perimeter of a square is four times the length of one of its sides. Use the equation $p = 4s$ to find the perimeter of a square whose side has a length of 21 centimeters. **84 centimeters**

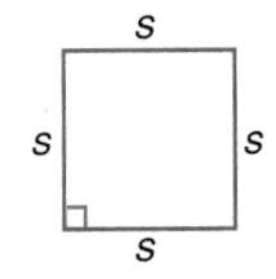

40. ***Working on the*** CHAPTER Project Refer to the table on page 3. Write and solve an equation to find how many hours you would have to in-line skate to burn 2,400 Calories. **$600h = 2{,}400$; $h = 4$**

41. ***Critical Thinking*** Consider the equation $0 + b = c$. What can you say about b and c? **They are equal.**

Mixed Review

42. **Standardized Test Practice** Which is equivalent to 4^3? *(Lesson 1-4)* **B**

A 4(3) **B** $4 \times 4 \times 4$ **C** $4 + 4 + 4$ **D** $3 \times 3 \times 3 \times 3$

43. ***Algebra*** Evaluate b^5 if $b = 2$. *(Lesson 1-4)* **32**

44. ***Algebra*** Evaluate the expression $2x + 3(x + y) - xy$ if $x = 10$ and $y = 2$. *(Lesson 1-3)* **36**

45. Evaluate $5(6 + 3) \div (3 + 2)$. *(Lesson 1-2)* **9**

For the latest statistics about languages, visit: www.glencoe.com/sec/math/mac/mathnet

For **Extra Practice,** see page 569.

46. ***Population*** According to the 1990 census, nearly 32 million people in the United States speak a language other than English in their homes. The chart shows the five most common languages. How many more people speak French than Chinese? *(Lesson 1-1)* **452,963 people**

Most Common Foreign Languages Spoken in U.S.

Rank	Language	Number
1	Spanish	17,339,172
2	French	1,702,176
3	German	1,547,099
4	Italian	1,308,648
5	Chinese	1,249,213

Source: U.S. Census

Assignment Guide

Core: 13–39 odd, 41–46
Enriched: 14–38 even, 39, 41–46

Exercise 40 asks students to advance to the next stage of work on the Chapter Project. You may wish to give students the option of using a calculator to solve the equation.

4 ASSESS

Closing Activity

Writing Have students make up a word problem that can be solved by writing and solving an equation. Then have them give their problem to a classmate to solve.

Practice Masters, p. 5

Name__________ Date__________

Practice

Integration: Algebra
Solving Equations

Name the number that is a solution of the given equation.

1. $y + 12 = 16$ 4, 5, 6 **4**
2. $m - 15 = 23$ 8, 38, 18 **38**
3. $12x = 72$ 6, 7, 8 **6**
4. $n \div 10 = 11$ 9, 100, 110 **110**
5. $44 + s = 92$ 48, 58, 52 **48**
6. $15 \div 8 = r$ 40, 80, 120 **120**
7. $z \div 11 = 9$ 20, 90, 99 **99**
8. $32 - 16 = t$ 6, 16, 24 **16**

Solve each equation.

9. $x + 42 = 83$ **41**
10. $w - 13 = 77$ **90**
11. $x + 5 = 22$ **17**
12. $q - 12 = 44$ **56**
13. $5m = 35$ **7**
14. $u \div 10 = 100$ **1,000**
15. $25v = 650$ **26**
16. $14x = 154$ **11**
17. $\frac{84}{m} = 7$ **12**
18. $\frac{y}{10} = 67$ **670**
19. $q - 92 = 138$ **230**
20. $p \div 12 = 9$ **108**

21. A number plus 7 is 12. What is the number? Use the equation $x + 7 = 12$. **5**

22. The quotient of a number and 19 is 6. Find the number. Use the equation $\frac{y}{19} = 6$. **114**

23. Consider the equation $1 \cdot x = y$. What can you say about x and y? **They are equal.**

T5 *Mathematics: Applications and Connections, Course 2*

Extending the Lesson

Enrichment Masters, p. 5

1-5 Enrichment

Equations as Models

When you write an equation that represents the information in a problem, the equation serves as a *model* for the problem. One equation can be a model for several different problems.

Each of Exercises 1-8 can be modeled by one of these equations.

$n + 2 = 10$ $n - 2 = 10$ $2n = 10$ $\frac{n}{2} = 10$

Choose the correct equation. Then solve the problem.

1. Chum earned \$10 for working two hours. How much did he earn per hour? **$2n = 10$; \$5**

2. Ana needs \$2 more to buy a \$10 scarf. How much money does she already have? **$n + 2 = 10$; \$8**

Activity Have students solve the following problem. *A tape player and a car radio cost \$340 together. The tape player costs 3 times as much as the radio. What does the radio cost?* **\$85**

1-6 Lesson Notes

Instructional Resources

- *Study Guide Masters,* p. 6
- *Practice Masters,* p. 6
- *Enrichment Masters,* p. 6
- Transparencies 1-6, A and B
- *Assessment and Evaluation Masters,* p. 16

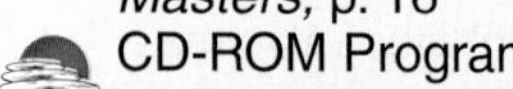

CD-ROM Program
- Resource Lesson 1-6

Recommended Pacing	
Standard	Day 8 of 13
Honors	Day 8 of 13
Block	Day 5 of 7

1 FOCUS

5-Minute Check
(Lesson 1-5)

1. Which of the numbers 4, 5, or 6 is the solution of $11 + n = 17$? 6
2. Tess was born in 1987. She will graduate from high school at age 18. What year will she graduate? 2005

Solve each equation.

3. $y = \frac{105}{5}$ 21
4. $9m = 72$ 8
5. $w \div 4 = 15$ 60

The 5-Minute Check is also available on **Transparency 1-6A** for this lesson.

Motivating the Lesson

Communication Many books on fractals and fractal geometry contain pictures of fractals. Bring a book to class to show more examples to students. Have the students point out what makes the pictures fractals.

1-6 Integration: Geometry
Fractals and Other Patterns

***What** you'll learn*

You'll learn to find and extend patterns.

***When** am I ever going to use this?*

Knowing how to find patterns can help you solve problems in art and architecture.

Word Wise

fractal

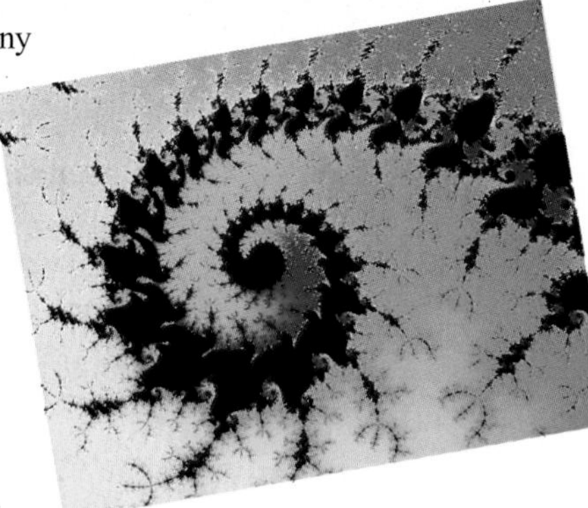

Look around and you can see many patterns that are made of geometric shapes. But there are many things in nature like nautilus shells, clouds, trees, and coastlines that cannot be described by points, lines, and polygons. Look closer, and you can also see patterns in them.

In this century, a new branch of mathematics, called **fractal** geometry, is providing models of nature's designs. One of the most obvious fractal patterns occurs in a tree. In the following Mini-Lab, you will make a fractal tree.

Cultural Kaleidoscope

Fractal geometry began in 1980, when Benoit Mandelbrot discovered a complex geometric structure. Today, it is called the *Mandelbrot Set* in his honor.

HANDS-ON MINI-LAB

Work with a partner.

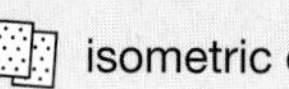

isometric dot paper

Try This

- The tree shown below starts with a vertical line segment 4 units long to represent the trunk of the tree. From the endpoint, two branches, each half as long as the trunk, are drawn.
- Continue drawing branches until they become too small to draw. Each branch is half as long as the previous branch.

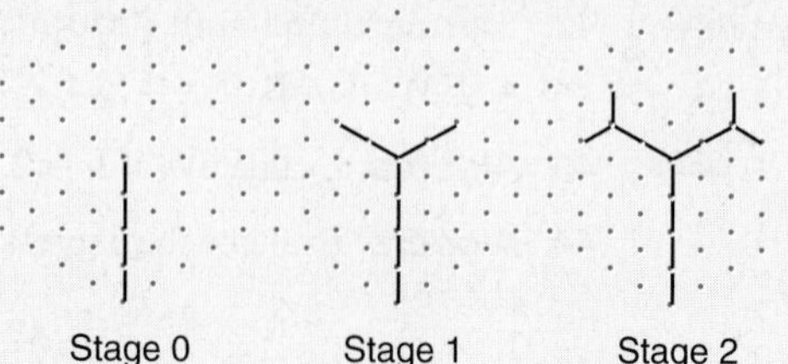

- On isometric dot paper, draw a fractal tree. The trunk of your tree should be 16 units long.

Talk About It 1–2. Yes; see students' work.

1. Are there parts of your completed tree that look like the entire tree? If so, draw a circle around one such part.
2. Are there other parts of a different size that look like the entire tree? If so, draw a circle around one part.

Investigations for the Special Education Student

This blackline master booklet helps you plan for the needs of your special education students by providing long-term projects along with teacher notes. Investigation 1, *Vacation Getaways,* may be used with this chapter.

One of the characteristics of fractals is that they are made up of smaller replicas of the entire shape repeated over and over again in different sizes. Another characteristic is that they are made by a "rule" that describes a pattern. At each stage, you apply the rule to smaller and smaller parts of the figure.

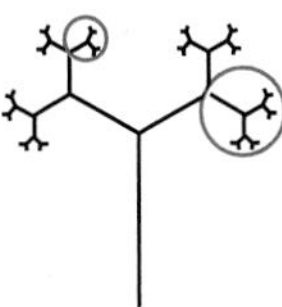

In the following example, you will construct a famous fractal.

Example INTEGRATION

1 **Geometry** **Construct a variation of Sierpinski's triangle using the following rules.**

1. **Draw a triangle with sides equal in length.**
2. **Connect the center of the sides with line segments.**
3. **Shade the middle triangle.**
4. **Apply Steps 1–3 to each of the remaining unshaded triangles. Continue this process until the triangles become too small to draw.**

The first four stages of Sierpinski's triangle are shown below.

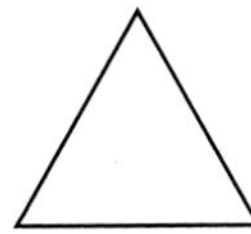
Stage 0

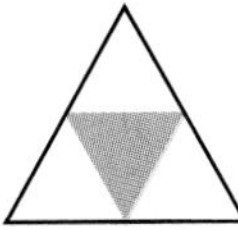
Stage 1

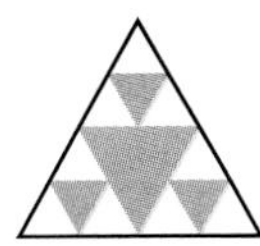
Stage 2

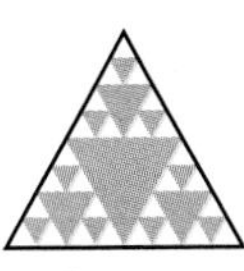
Stage 3

Many patterns in real-life are not fractals. One of them involves quilting techniques. A quilt often features a geometric design made by sewing together pieces of fabric.

2 **Quilts** **The first five squares in one row of a *Steeple Chase* quilt are shown below. Draw the next two squares in the row.**

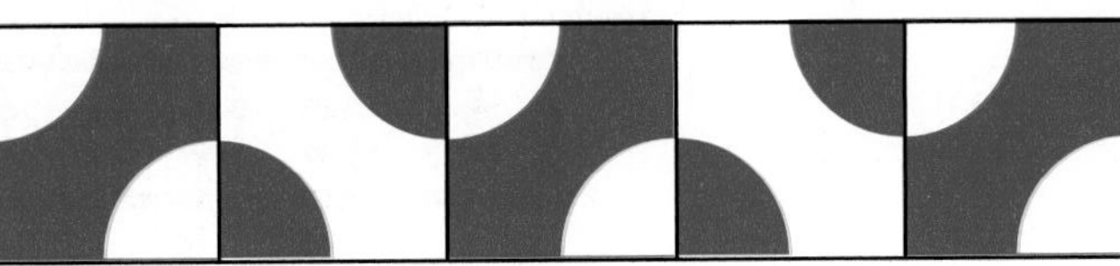

The pattern is made of alternating squares. The inside of each square is dark (D) or light (L). So the pattern is DLDLD. The next two squares should be LD.

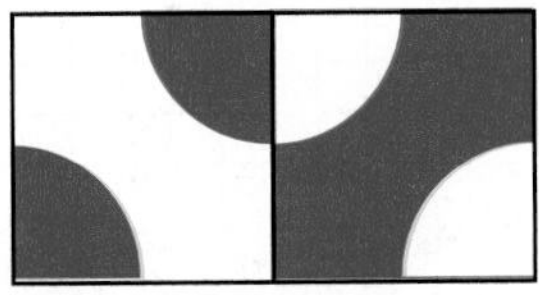

2 TEACH

Transparency 1-6B contains a teaching aid for this lesson.

Using the Mini-Lab Explain to students that one of the characteristics of a fractal is that any of its parts contain the same pattern as the whole.

In-Class Examples

For Example 1

Draw the next step in the fractal pattern.

For Example 2

Draw the next step in the pattern.

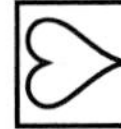

Teaching Tip Point out to students that the fractal structures generated in mathematics are idealized structures. Objects in the natural world may not be as symmetrical.

3 PRACTICE/APPLY

Check for Understanding

If students need additional practice or instruction after completing Exercises 1–5, you may find one of the following options helpful.

- Extra Practice, see p. 569
- Reteaching Activity
- *Study Guide Masters,* p. 6
- *Practice Masters,* p. 6

Assignment Guide
Core: 7–11 odd, 12–14
Enriched: 6–8 even, 10–14

Additional Answers

3.

6.

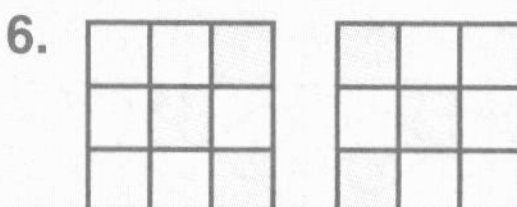

7.

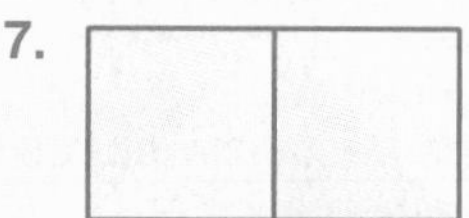

8.

9.

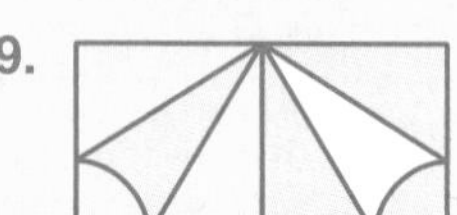

Study Guide Masters, p. 6

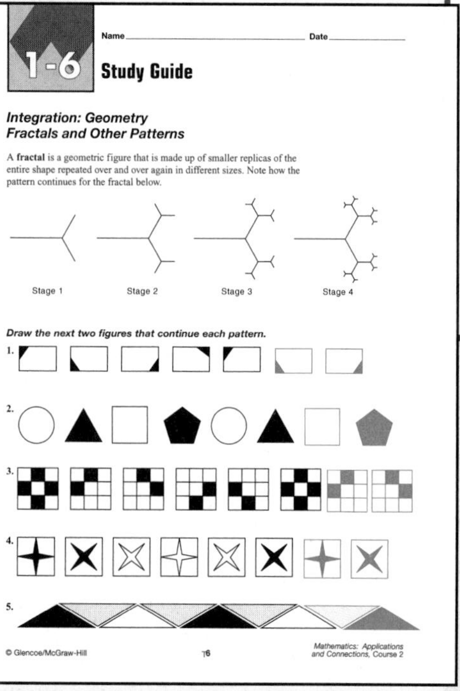

Name ______________________ Date ____________

1-6 **Study Guide**

Integration: Geometry
Fractals and Other Patterns

A **fractal** is a geometric figure that is made up of smaller replicas of the entire shape repeated over and over again in different sizes. Note how the pattern continues for the fractal below.

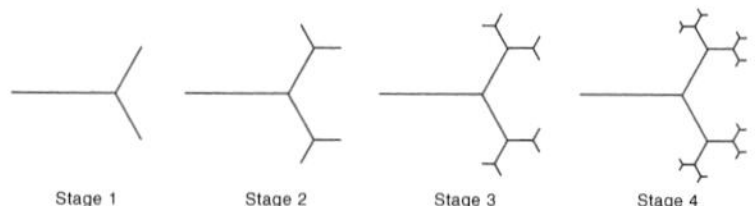

Stage 1 Stage 2 Stage 3 Stage 4

Draw the next two figures that continue each pattern.

1.

2.

3.

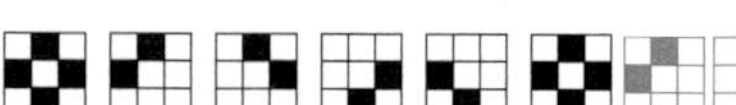

4.

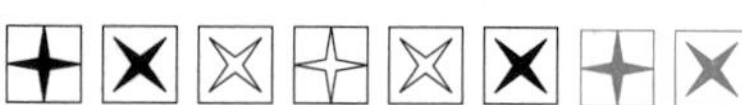

5.

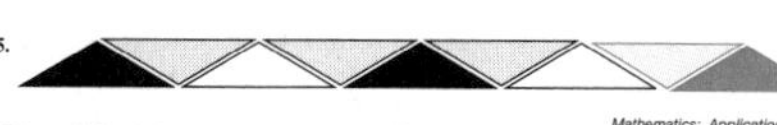

 T6 *Mathematics: Applications and Connections, Course 2*

CHECK FOR UNDERSTANDING

Communicating Mathematics

Read and study the lesson to answer each question.

1. ***Explain*** why a fern is an example of a fractal. **1. Small parts of the fern look like the entire fern.**
2. ***Choose*** the figure that continues the pattern. **c**

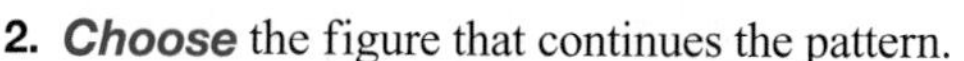

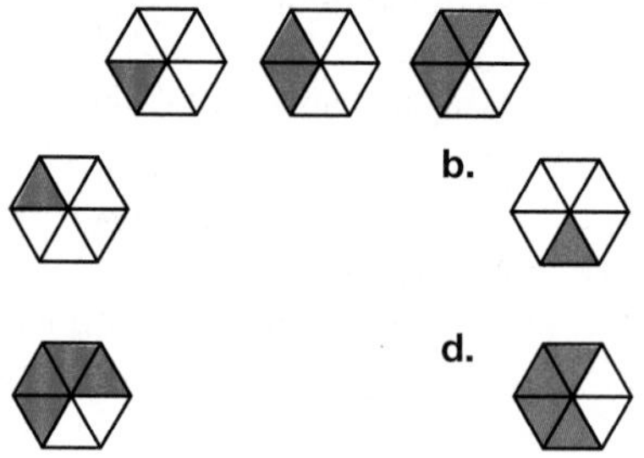

a. b.

c. d.

HANDS-ON MATH

3. Another famous fractal is a Koch curve. It starts with a line segment. Divide the segment into thirds. Then, construct a triangle with sides equal in length on the middle third of each segment. Then remove the base of the triangle. The first two stages are shown at the right. Draw the next stage of the fractal. **See margin.**

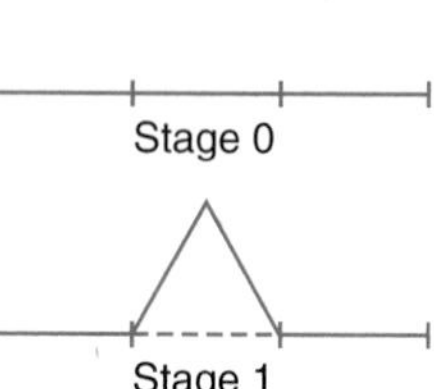

Guided Practice

4. Draw the next two figures that continue the pattern.

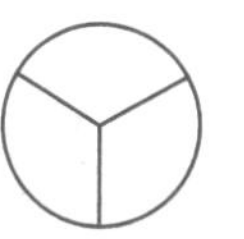
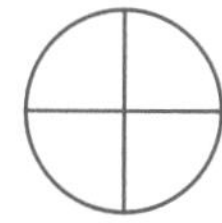

5. ***Native-American Designs*** The Yup'ik live in southwestern Alaska. The borders of their parkas are often decorated with repeated patterns. A traditional Yup'ik pattern is shown. Create your own repeated design. **See students' work.**

EXERCISES

Practice

Draw the next two figures that continue each pattern. **6–9. See margin.**

6.

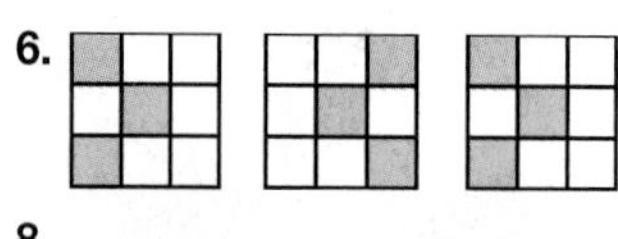
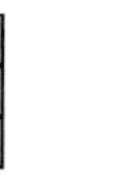

7.

8.

9.

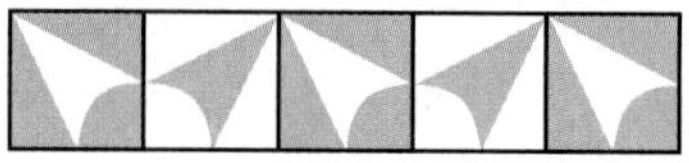

■ Reteaching the Lesson ■

Activity Have each student draw a square. Explore several ways of dividing the square. Point out that each way leads to a different fractal.

Applications and Problem Solving

10. ***Square Carpet*** A fractal can be formed by dividing a square into 9 smaller squares and shading the middle square.
    a. Draw the next stage. **See margin.**
    b. Suppose the rule was changed to shade only the four corner squares. Draw the first three stages of the fractal. **See margin.**

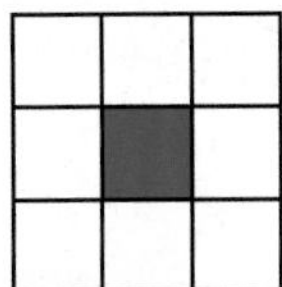

Stage 0 Stage 1

11. See students' work.

11. ***Art*** The photograph at the right shows how Sierpinski's triangle was used in the design on a twelfth-century pulpit of the Ravello cathedral. Create your own design using Sierpinski's triangle.

12. There are no smaller replicas of the pattern.

12. ***Critical Thinking*** Explain why the quilt design in Example 2 is *not* a fractal.

Mixed Review

13. 75

13. ***Algebra*** Solve $\frac{t}{5} = 15$ mentally. *(Lesson 1-5)*

14. **Standardized Test Practice** Paint for the bedroom costs $12 per gallon, and paint for the bathroom costs $8 per gallon. If it requires 5 gallons of paint for the bedroom and 2 for the bathroom, what is the total cost of paint for the two rooms? *(Lesson 1-2)* **C**

    A $20 **B** $64 **C** $76 **D** $496 **E** Not Here

For **Extra Practice,** see page 569.

MATH IN THE MEDIA

1. What pattern in nature is shown in the comic?
2. Explain why the "map" is of no help to Fred.
3. Is this pattern a fractal? Explain your reasoning.

1. a beehive

2. Since all the shapes are the same, it is impossible to tell one part of the beehive from another.

3. No; each hexagon is the same size, and in a fractal, small parts of the figures are repeated in different sizes.

THE FAR SIDE By GARY LARSON

"Face it Fred—you're lost!"

Extending the Lesson

***Enrichment Masters,* p. 6**

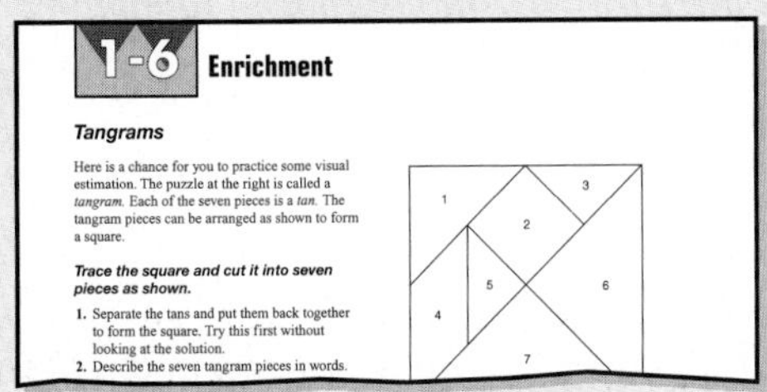

1-6 Enrichment

Tangrams

Here is a chance for you to practice some visual estimation. The puzzle at the right is called a *tangram.* Each of the seven pieces is a *tan.* The tangram pieces can be arranged as shown to form a square.

Trace the square and cut it into seven pieces as shown.

1. Separate the tans and put them back together to form the square. Try this first without looking at the solution.
2. Describe the seven tangram pieces in words.

MATH IN THE MEDIA

Have students research how and why bees create their hives using the honeycomb pattern. They may also research repeating patterns made by other insects.

4 ASSESS

Closing Activity

Speaking Have students describe how to tell when a pattern is a fractal.

Chapter 1, Quiz C (Lessons 1-5 and 1-6) is available in the *Assessment and Evaluation Masters,* p. 16.

Additional Answers

10a.

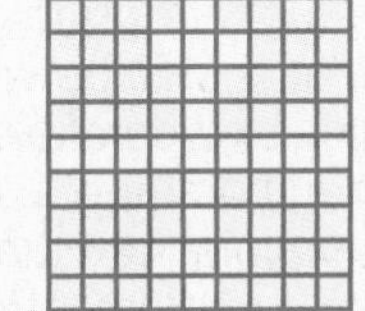

10b.

***Practice Masters,* p. 6**

Name________ Date________

1-6 Practice

Integration: Geometry
Fractals and Other Patterns

Draw the next two figures that continue each pattern. Answers may vary.

1. 

2. 

3. 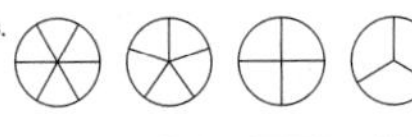 

4. 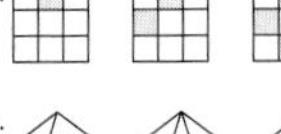  

5. 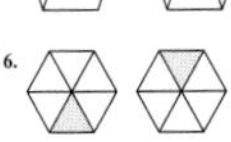 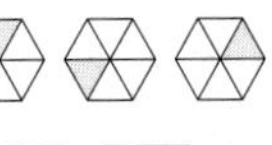 

6. 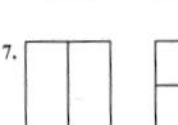 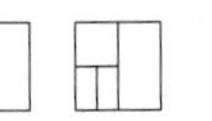 

7. 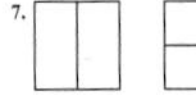 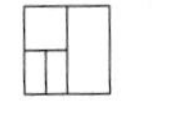 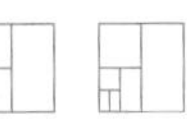

 16 *Mathematics: Applications and Connections, Course 2*

1-7A HANDS-ON LAB Notes

GET READY

Objective Students use models to find the areas of rectangles and parallelograms.

Optional Resources
Hands-On Lab Masters
- grid paper, p. 10
- worksheet, p. 39

Overhead Manipulative Resources
- centimeter grid

Manipulative Kit
- scissors

MANAGEMENT TIPS

Recommended Time
45 minutes

Getting Started Before presenting the lesson, ask questions to assess students' prior knowledge of the relationship between rectangles and parallelograms. On grid paper, compare a rectangle and a parallelogram that have the same base and height. Ask students to count squares to compare the areas of the two figures.

Activity 1 shows how to find the areas of a rectangle by counting squares. Have students compare their counts with the product of the dimensions.

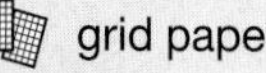

HANDS-ON LAB

COOPERATIVE LEARNING

1-7A Area

A Preview of Lesson 1-7

grid paper

scissors

In this lab, you will investigate the areas of rectangles and parallelograms by using models. The *area* of a geometric figure is the number of square units needed to cover the surface of the figure.

TRY THIS

Work with a partner.

1 On grid paper, draw a rectangle with a length of 6 units and a width of 4 units.
Count the number of squares within the rectangle. Each square represents an area of 1 square unit. So, the area is 24 square units.

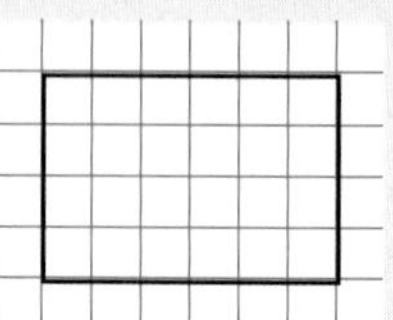

ON YOUR OWN

Find the area of each rectangle.

1. 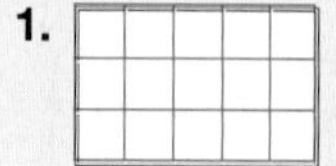
15 square units

2. 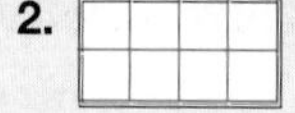
8 square units

3. 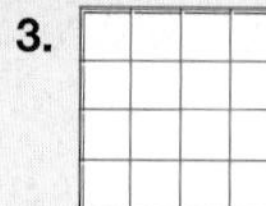
16 square units

Find the area of each rectangle. Draw rectangles if necessary.

4. length, 8; width, 3 **24 square units**
5. length, 5; width, 2 **10 square units**
6. length, 10; width, 8 **80 square units**
7. length, 9; width, 4 **36 square units**
8. length, 20; width, 10 **200 square units**
9. length, 15; width, 9 **135 square units**

10. ***Look Ahead*** Let ℓ represent the length, w represent the width, and A represent the area of a rectangle. Write an equation that shows how to find the area if you know the length and width. $A = \ell w$

w A
ℓ

Now, let's find the area of a parallelogram. A *parallelogram* is a four-sided figure whose opposite sides are parallel. One of its sides is the *base*. The distance from the base to the opposite side is called the *height.*

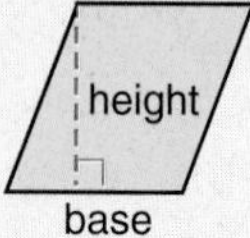

TRY THIS

2 On grid paper, draw a parallelogram with a base of 6 units and a height of 4 units.

- Draw a line for the height.
- Cut out the parallelogram.

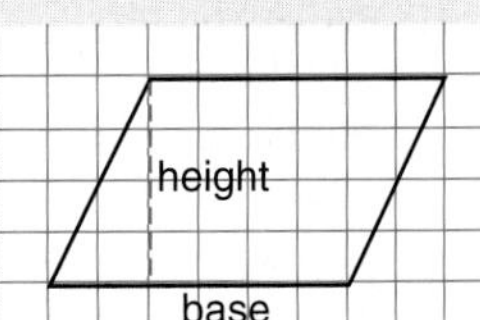

- Then cut the parallelogram along the line for the height as shown.
- Move the triangle to the opposite end of the parallelogram to form a rectangle.

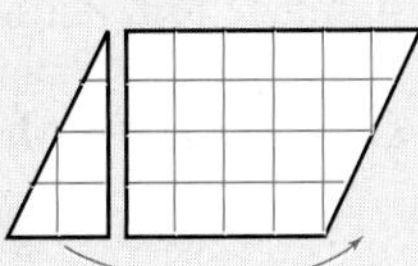

- Count the number of squares within the newly formed rectangle. The area is 24 square units. So, the area of the parallelogram is 24 square units.

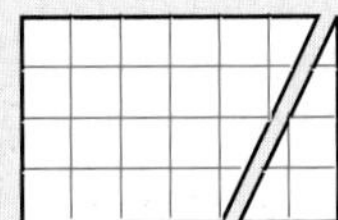

ON YOUR OWN

11. The rectangle in Example 1 has a length of 6 units and a height of 4 units. The parallelogram in Example 2 has a base of 6 units and a height of 4 units. Compare the area of these two figures. **They have the same area.**

Find the area of each parallelogram by drawing the figure on grid paper, cutting it out, and counting the squares in the newly formed rectangle.

12. 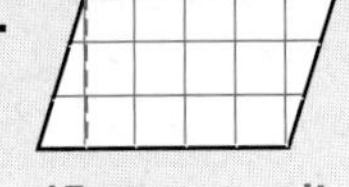
15 square units

13. **8 square units**

14. 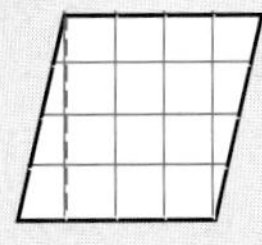
16 square units

15. In Exercises 12–14, how are the base and height of the original parallelogram related to the length and width of the newly formed rectangle? **See margin.**

Find the area of each parallelogram. Use models if necessary.

16. base, 6; height, 3 **18 square units**

17. base, 8; height, 4 **32 square units**

18. base, 5; height, 5 **25 square units**

19. base, 10; height, 6 **60 square units**

20. ***Look Ahead*** Let b represent the base, h represent the height, and A represent the area of a parallelogram. Write an equation that shows how to find the area if you know the base and height. $A = bh$

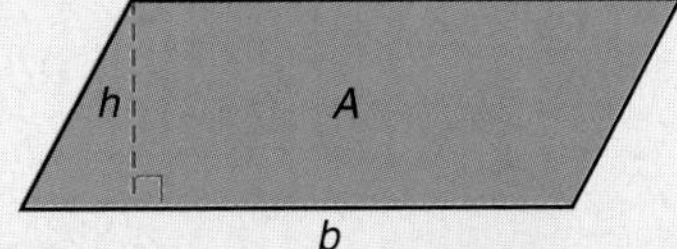

Have students write a paragraph explaining how the formula for finding the area of a rectangle is related to the formula for finding the area of a parallelogram.

Activity 2 shows how to find areas of rectangles and parallelograms. Activity 2 shows how the area of a parallelogram is related to the area of a rectangle. Have students work with a partner and compare answers.

ASSESS

Have students complete Exercises 1–20. Make sure that students understand how the height of a parallelogram is measured and that it is not the length of the side (unless the parallelogram is a rectangle).

Additional Answer

15. **The base and height of the parallelogram are the same as the length and width of the rectangle.**

***Hands-On Lab Masters*, p. 39**

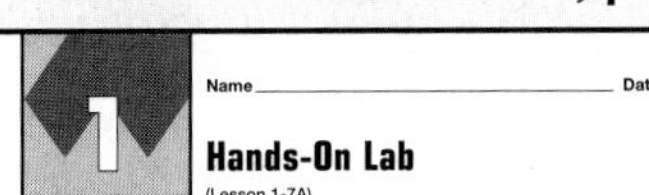

Name ______ Date ______

Hands-On Lab
(Lesson 1-7A)

Area

On Your Own

1. 15 square units 2. 8 square units 3. 16 square units
4. 24 square units 5. 10 square units 6. 80 square units
7. 36 square units 8. 200 square units 10. 135 square units

10. **Look Ahead** Write an equation that shows how to find the area of a rectangle. Area = length times width; $A = \ell w$

11. Compare the areas of the rectangle and the parallelogram. They have the same area.

12. 15 square units 13. 8 square units 14. 16 square units

15. How are the base and height of the parallelogram related to the length and width of the rectangle? The base and height of the parallelogram are the same as the length and width of the rectangle.

16. 18 square units 17. 32 square units

18. 25 square units 19. 60 square units

20. **Look Ahead** Write an equation that shows how to find the area of a parallelogram. Area = base times height; $A = bh$

 39 *Mathematics: Applications and Connections, Course 2*

1-7 Lesson Notes

Instructional Resources

- *Study Guide Masters,* p. 7
- *Practice Masters,* p. 7
- *Enrichment Masters,* p. 7
- Transparencies 1-7, A and B
- *Assessment and Evaluation Masters,* p. 16
- *School to Career Masters,* p. 14

- CD-ROM Program
  - Resource Lesson 1-7
  - Interactive Lesson 1-7

Recommended Pacing	
Standard	Days 9 & 10 of 13
Honors	Days 9 & 10 of 13
Block	Day 6 of 7

1 FOCUS

5-Minute Check (Lesson 1-6)

1. Draw the missing square in the following pattern.

  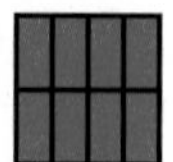 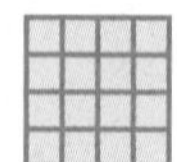

2. Which of the following shows the beginning stages of a fractal pattern? b

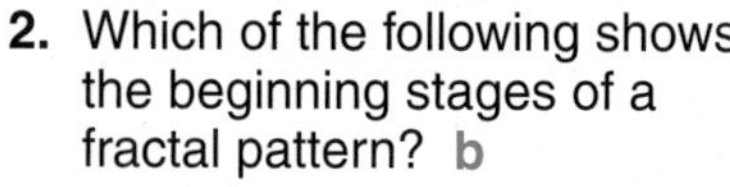

a. 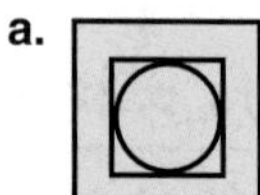 b. 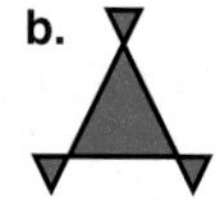 c. 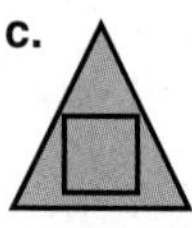

The 5-Minute Check is also available on **Transparency 1-7A** for this lesson.

Motivating the Lesson

Communication Read the lesson opener with students. Then have students estimate the area of their classroom floor. Compare their estimate to the area of the Mall of America. Discuss how many of your classrooms might fit into the mall.

1-7 Integration: Geometry
Area

What you'll learn

You'll learn to find the areas of rectangles and parallelograms.

When am I ever going to use this?

Knowing how to find area can help you find the amount of wallpaper needed to decorate a room.

Word Wise

area
rectangle
parallelogram
base
height

If you like to shop at malls, you might want to schedule a visit to Minnesota's Mall of America. Not only does the mega-mall cover more than 4 *million* square feet, it also has a roller coaster and a 74-foot Ferris wheel!

The **area** of a figure is the number of square units needed to cover its surface. For the Mall of America, its area is measured in square feet. The area of a **rectangle** can be found as follows.

Area of Rectangles

Words: The area (A) of a rectangle equals the product of its length (ℓ) and width (w).

Symbols: $A = \ell w$

Model: (rectangle with width w, length ℓ, area A)

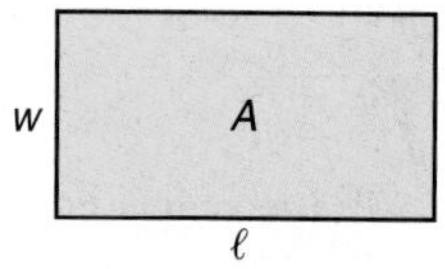

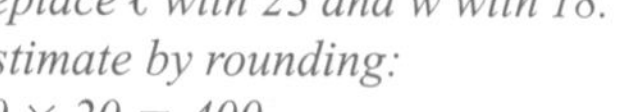

1 Find the area of the rectangle at the right.

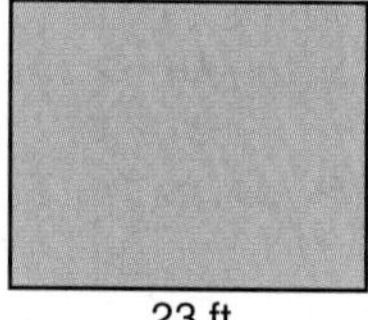

$A = \ell w$ *Write the formula for area.*

$A = 23 \cdot 18$ *Replace ℓ with 23 and w with 18.*

Estimate by rounding: $20 \times 20 = 400$

$23 \times 18 = 414$

$A = 414$ The area is 414 square feet.

2 Find the width of a rectangle with an area of 30 square inches and a length of 6 inches.

$A = \ell w$ *Write the formula for area.*

$30 = 6w$ *Replace A with 30 and ℓ with 6.*

$30 \stackrel{?}{=} 6 \cdot 5$ *Solve the equation mentally.*

$30 = 30$ ✓

$w = 5$ The width is 5 inches.

Classroom Vignette

"We use area tiles to compare the perimeters and areas of different figures composed of 1 tile, 2 tiles, 3 tiles, and 4 tiles. Then students use dot paper to draw all of the pentomino patterns. They discover all of the pentominoes have an area of 5 square units and a perimeter of 12 units except one."

Alice C. Coates, Educator
Stafford Middle School
King George, VA

A **parallelogram** is a four-sided figure whose opposite sides are parallel. One of its sides is called its **base**. The distance from the base to the opposite side is called the **height**. The area of a parallelogram is closely related to the area of a rectangle.

Area of Parallelograms	**Words:** The area of a parallelogram (A) equals the product of its base (b) and height (h). **Symbols:** $A = bh$ **Model:**

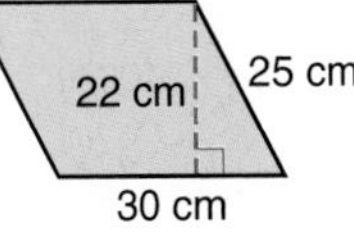

Examples

3 **Find the area of the parallelogram.**

$A = bh$ *Write the formula for area.*

$A = 30 \cdot 22$ *Replace b with 30 and h with 22.*
Estimate by rounding:
$30 \times 20 = 600$

$30 \times 22 = 660$

$A = 660$

The area is 660 square centimeters.

APPLICATION Real World

4 **Painting** **Cecilia wants to paint two walls of her bedroom bright blue. She knows that 1 gallon of paint will cover about 350 square feet of surface. One bedroom wall is 14 feet long and 8 feet high. The other is 12 feet long and 8 feet high. If she wants to put two coats of paint on the walls, will 1 gallon of paint be enough?**

area of first wall

$14 \times 8 = 112$

area of second wall

$12 \times 8 = 96$

total area

$\underbrace{112 + 96 =}_{\text{area of both walls}} \quad \underbrace{\times 2}_{\text{2 coats of paint}} = 416$

Cecilia needs to have enough paint to cover 416 square feet of surface. One gallon of paint will cover 350 square feet of surface. Therefore, one gallon of paint will not be enough.

Study Hint
Reading Math
Area is expressed in square units. So, the abbreviations for area often use the exponent 2.
square inch → in^2

2 TEACH

Transparency 1-7B contains a teaching aid for this lesson.

In-Class Examples

For Example 1
Find the area of the rectangle. **1,711 ft²**

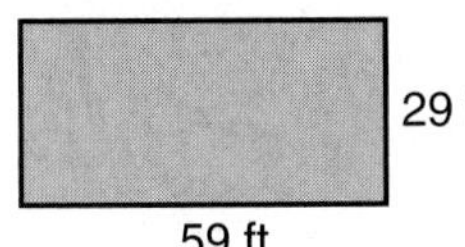

For Example 2
Find the length of a rectangle with an area of 252 square feet and a width of 12 feet. **21 ft**

For Example 3
Find the area of the parallelogram. **12 in²**

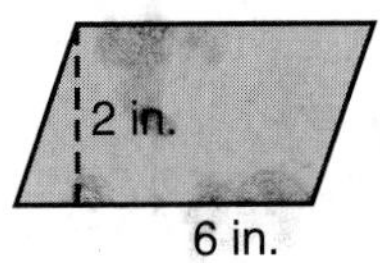

For Example 4
Jacob needs to fertilize his lawn. The back yard is 100 feet wide by 40 feet long. The front yard is 75 feet wide by 22 feet long. Each bag of fertilizer covers 1,000 square feet. How many bags of fertilizer will Jacob need to buy? **6 bags**

Using the Mini-Lab Refer to page 32. Remind students of the meaning of *perimeter.* Encourage students to look for the pattern before writing an expression for a square with sides one unit long. Point out the relationship between algebra and geometry.

Additional Answer for the Mini-Lab

1.

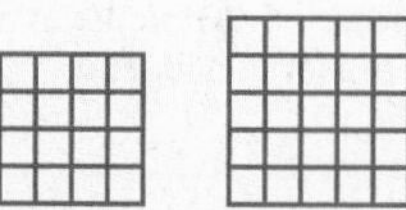

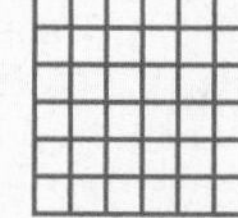

3 PRACTICE/APPLY

Check for Understanding

If students need additional practice or instruction after completing Exercises 1–8, you may find one of the following options helpful.

- Extra Practice, see p. 570
- Reteaching Activity
- *Study Guide Masters*, p. 7
- *Practice Masters*, p. 7

Assignment Guide
Core: 9–23 odd, 25–28
Enriched: 10–22 even, 23–28

Additional Answers

1.

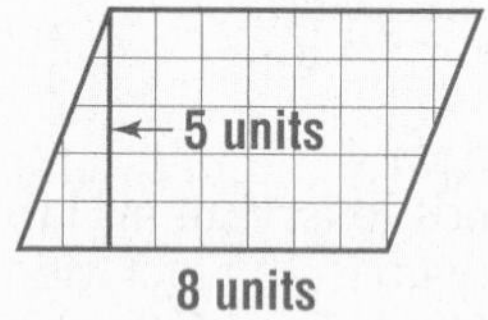

3. Since the length and width are each doubled, the area increases by 2 × 2 or 4 times.

***Study Guide Masters*, p. 7**

Name ____________ Date ________

1-7 Study Guide

Integration: Geometry
Area

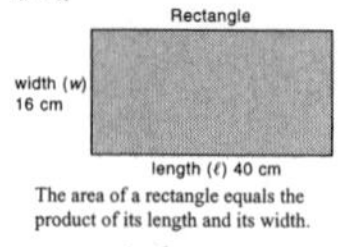

The area of a rectangle equals the product of its length and its width.

$A = \ell w$
$A = 40 \cdot 16$
$A = 640 \text{ cm}^2$

Parallelogram
height (h) 12 in.
base (b) 30 in.

The area of a parallelogram equals the product of its base and its height.

$A = bh$
$A = 30 \cdot 12$
$A = 360 \text{ in}^2$

Find the area of each rectangle or parallelogram.

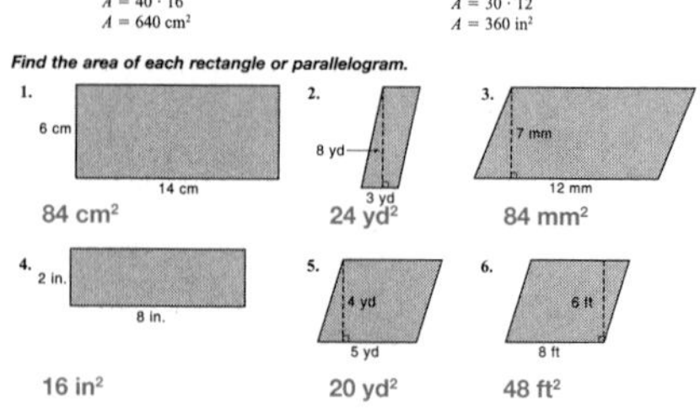

1. 84 cm²
2. 24 yd²
3. 84 mm²
4. 16 in²
5. 20 yd²
6. 48 ft²
7. parallelogram: $b = 15$ ft, $h = 21$ ft 315 ft²
8. rectangle: $\ell = 8$ cm, $w = 12$ cm 96 cm²
9. parallelogram: $b = 5$ m, $h = 2$ m 10 m²
10. rectangle: $\ell = 100$ yd, $w = 50$ yd 5,000 yd²

 T7 *Mathematics: Applications and Connections, Course 2*

HANDS-ON MINI-LAB

Work with a partner.

 grid paper

The pattern at the right is made up of unit squares.

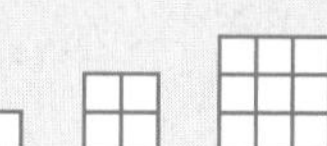

Try This

1. Draw the next three figures in the pattern. **See margin.**
2. Find the perimeter and area of each figure. **Perimeter: 4, 8, 12, 16, 20, 24 Area: 1, 4, 9, 16, 25, 36**

Talk About It

3. Without drawing the figure, determine the perimeter and area of a square with a length of 10 units. **Perimeter: 40; Area: 100**
4. Suppose you have a square with a length of n units. Write expressions for the perimeter and area of the square. **$4n$, n^2**

Study Hint
Problem Solving List your data in a table.

CHECK FOR UNDERSTANDING

Communicating Mathematics

Read and study the lesson to answer each question. **1. See margin.**

1. ***Model*** a parallelogram with a base of 8 units and a height of 5 units using grid paper.
2. ***Tell*** how to find the length of the rectangle. **2. Divide 50 by 5.**

5 m	Area = 50 m²

3. If you double the length and width of a rectangle, how does its area change? Explain your reasoning in words or by drawing diagrams. **See margin.**

Guided Practice

Find the area of each rectangle or parallelogram.

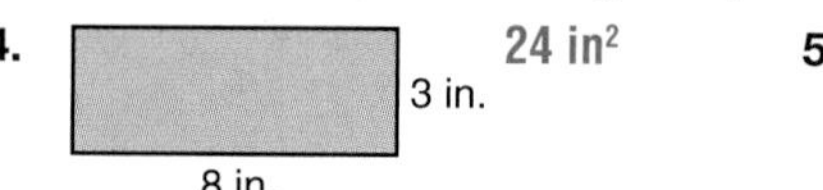

4. **24 in²**
5. **40 cm²**
6. rectangle: ℓ, 1 in.; w, 6 in. **6 in²**
7. parallelogram: b, 6 ft; h, 5 ft **30 ft²**
8. ***Basketball*** The length of a regulation court for professional and college basketball is 94 feet, and the width is 50 feet. What is the area of the court? **4,700 ft²**

EXERCISES

Practice

Find the area of each rectangle or parallelogram. **10. 153 mm²**

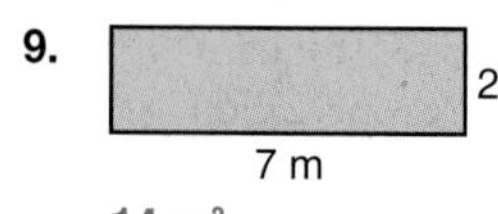

9. **14 m²**

10. 9 mm, 17 mm

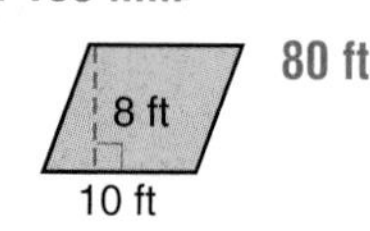

11. **80 ft²**

Reteaching the Lesson

Activity Guide students to see that the formula for the area of parallelograms is derived from the formula for the area of rectangles. Use a geoboard and rubber bands to construct a rectangle. Stretch the rubber band to form a parallelogram of the same base and height as the rectangle.

Error Analysis
Watch for students who try to calculate the area of a parallelogram by multiplying its base by the length of one of its sides. **Prevent by** stressing that the length of the side of a parallelogram is its height only when the figure is a rectangle.

12. 5 yd, 3 yd **15 yd²**

13. 7 ft, 6 ft, 12 ft **72 ft²**

14. 9 in., 8 in., 3 in. **24 in²**

15. rectangle: ℓ, 18 cm; w, 12 cm **216 cm²**

16. rectangle: ℓ, 48 in.; w, 20 in.

17. parallelogram: b, 25 ft; h, 15 ft **375 ft²**

18. parallelogram: b, 5 cm; h, 15 cm

19. parallelogram: b, 12 yd; h, 11 yd **132 yd²**

20. rectangle: ℓ, 16 mi; w, 16 mi **256 mi²**

16. 960 in²
18. 75 cm²

21. ***Algebra*** What is the length of a rectangle with an area of 35 square yards and a width of 5 yards? **7 yd**

22. ***Algebra*** What is the base of a parallelogram with an area of 100 square feet and a height of 10 feet? **10 ft**

Applications and Problem Solving

23. ***Housing*** The graph shows the breakdown of new homes in America based on the number of square feet. One such house is a two-story rectangular house that is 35 feet long and 28 feet wide. Into which category would it be placed? **1,960 ft²; from 1,200 to 1,999 ft²**

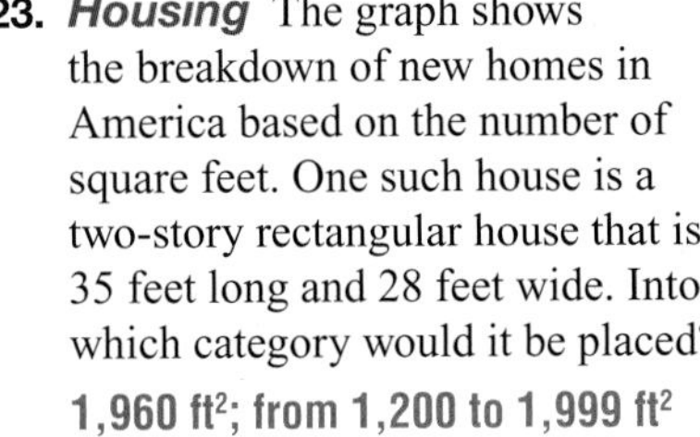

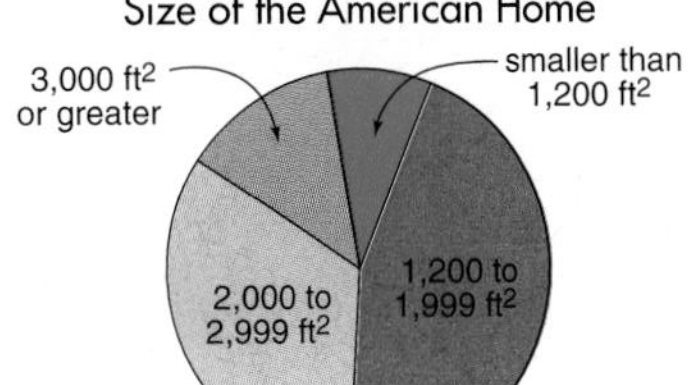

Source: *American Homestyle*

Family Activity

Measure the floor of a rectangular room in your home and record the measures on a drawing. How many square feet of tile would you need to cover the floor?

24. ***Geography*** The shape of the state of Tennessee resembles a parallelogram. Estimate its area in square miles. **about 50,830 square miles**

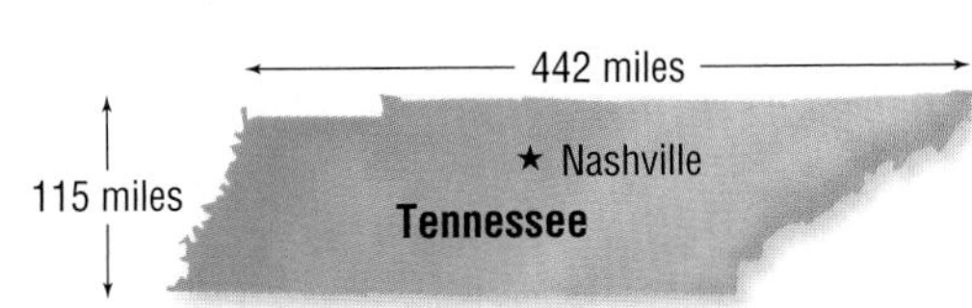

25. ***Critical Thinking*** Draw three different parallelograms, each with an area of 16 square units. **See margin.**

Mixed Review

26. ***Geometry*** Draw the next two figures that continue the pattern. *(Lesson 1-6)*

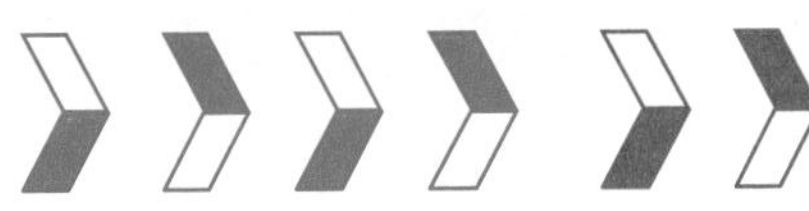

27. **Standardized Test Practice** Ali runs a pizza parlor. Her daily cost of operating the parlor consists of a constant cost of \$75 for rent, employee wages, and utilities plus \$2 for every pizza she makes. If n represents the number of pizzas Ali makes during the day, which expression represents Ali's total daily cost? *(Lesson 1-3)* **A**

A $\$75 + 2n$ **B** \$77 **C** $\$2 + 75n$ **D** $\$75n + 2n$

For **Extra Practice,** see page 570.

28. Evaluate $12(5) - 16 \div 8 + 5$. *(Lesson 1-2)* **63**

Discuss with students which room in their home they chose to measure and why. Ask students, if tile costs \$8.00 per square foot, how much it would cost to cover their floor.

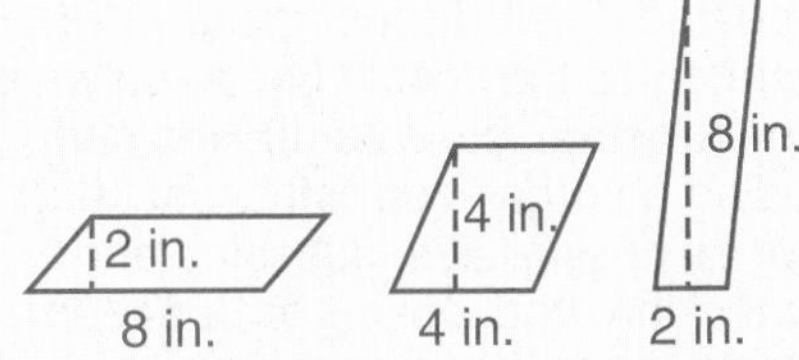

Closing Activity

Speaking Have students explain how the formulas for areas of rectangles and parallelograms are related.

Chapter 1, Quiz D (Lesson 1-7) is available in the *Assessment and Evaluation Masters,* p. 16.

Additional Answer

25. Sample answer:

2 in., 8 in.; 4 in., 4 in.; 8 in., 2 in.

Practice Masters, p. 7

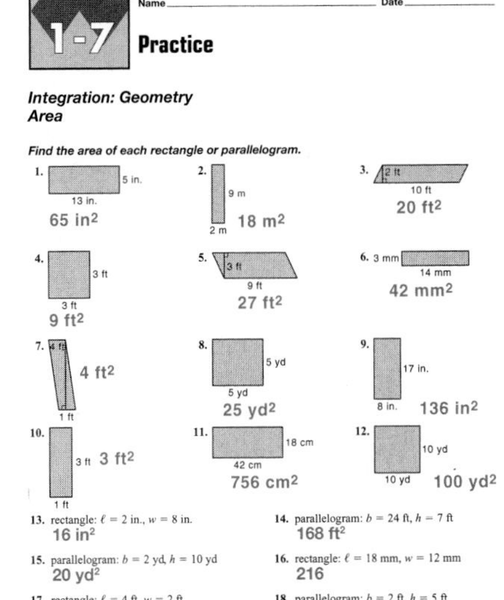

1-7 Practice

Name ____ Date ____

Integration: Geometry Area

Find the area of each rectangle or parallelogram.

1. 5 in., 13 in. 65 in²
2. 9 m, 2 m 18 m²
3. 2 ft, 10 ft 20 ft²
4. 3 ft, 3 ft 9 ft²
5. 3 ft, 9 ft 27 ft²
6. 3 mm, 14 mm 42 mm²
7. 4 ft, 1 ft 4 ft²
8. 5 yd, 5 yd 25 yd²
9. 17 in., 8 in. 136 in²
10. 3 ft, 1 ft 3 ft²
11. 18 cm, 42 cm 756 cm²
12. 10 yd, 10 yd 100 yd²
13. rectangle: ℓ = 2 in., w = 8 in. 16 in²
14. parallelogram: b = 24 ft, h = 7 ft 168 ft²
15. parallelogram: b = 2 yd, h = 10 yd 20 yd²
16. rectangle: ℓ = 18 mm, w = 12 mm 216
17. rectangle: ℓ = 4 ft, w = 2 ft 8 ft²
18. parallelogram: b = 2 ft, h = 5 ft 10 ft²
19. What is the length of a rectangle whose area is 84 in² and whose width is 7 inches? 12 in.
20. Find the height of a parallelogram with a base of 12 yards and an area of 38 yd². $3\frac{1}{6}$ yd²

 T7 *Mathematics: Applications and Connections, Course 2*

Extending the Lesson

Enrichment Masters, p. 7

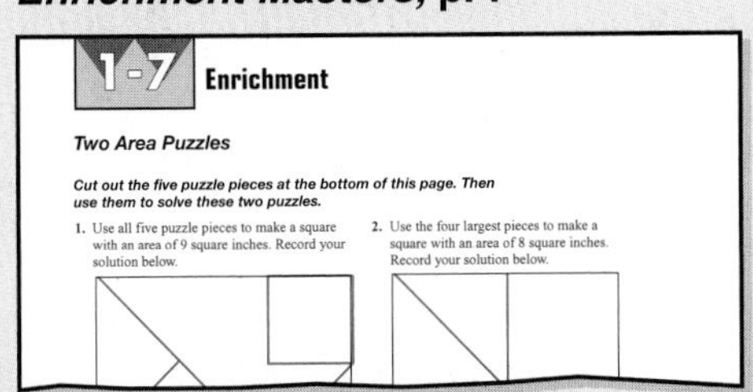

1-7 Enrichment

Two Area Puzzles

Cut out the five puzzle pieces at the bottom of this page. Then use them to solve these two puzzles.

1. Use all five puzzle pieces to make a square with an area of 9 square inches. Record your solution below.
2. Use the four largest pieces to make a square with an area of 8 square inches. Record your solution below.

Activity Suppose you have 28 feet of fencing. Ask students to find the whole-number dimensions of a rectangular garden with the greatest area that could be formed with that fencing. **7 ft by 7 ft**

1-7B THINKING LAB Notes

Objective Students choose the best method of computation for solving a problem.

Recommended Pacing	
Standard	Day 11 of 13
Honors	Day 11 of 13
Block	Day 6 of 7

1 FOCUS

Getting Started Ask volunteers to act out the opening problem. Ask students to work through Exercises 1–4 and discuss their results.

2 TEACH

Teaching Tip Begin by discussing with students why Antonio and Winona chose each computational method. Then discuss other strategies they could use to solve the problem, such as making and using an organized list, accounting for all possibilities, guessing and checking, and looking for a pattern using simpler numbers.

In-Class Example

Each wolf at the research center needs a space 70 feet wide by 125 feet long in order to run. What is the area required by each wolf? **8,750 square feet**

Additional Answers

1. **Sample answer: You can use the exact answer as a basis when you estimate other quantities.**
3. **Sample answer: If no advantage is obtained by having an exact answer then estimation is an acceptable method.**
4. **Sample answer: One box will feed 250 square feet, so they'll need two boxes to cover 384 square feet; mental**

PROBLEM SOLVING

1-7B Choose the Method of Computation

A Follow-Up of Lesson 1-7

The student council at Fort Couch Middle School has decided to plant a garden and donate the produce to the local food bank. Let's listen in as two students discuss how to plan the garden.

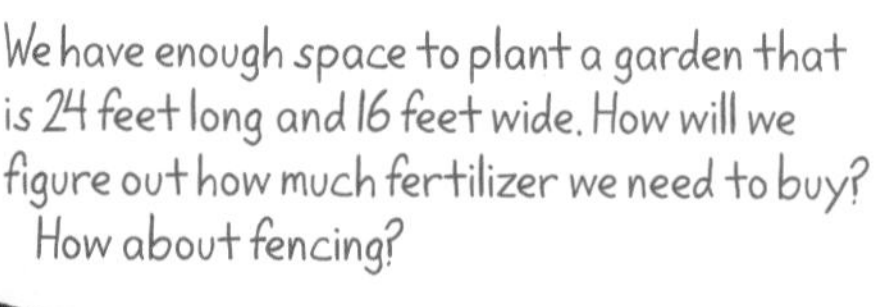

We have enough space to plant a garden that is 24 feet long and 16 feet wide. How will we figure out how much fertilizer we need to buy? How about fencing?

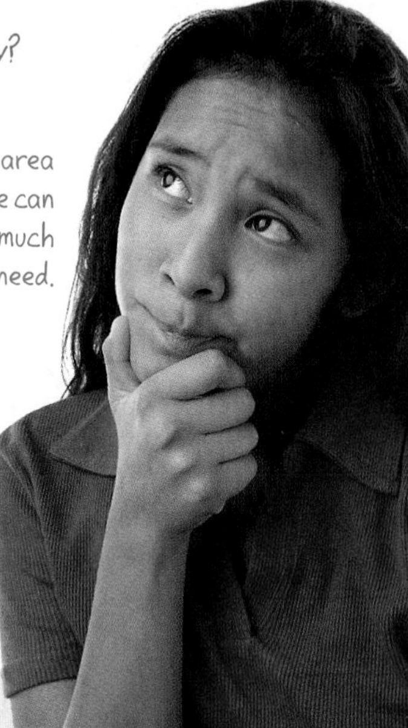

I think we should find the exact area and perimeter first. Then we can estimate to figure out how much fertilizer and fencing we'll need.

I can use my calculator to multiply 24 and 16. The area is 384 square feet.

I added 24 and 16 in my head and doubled my answer. The perimeter is 80 feet.

THINK ABOUT IT

Work with a partner.

1. ***Explain*** why it is a good idea to find the exact area and perimeter instead of estimating. **See margin.**
2. ***Tell*** another tool you might use to find an exact answer. **paper and pencil**
3. ***Write*** a sentence explaining how you know when estimation is an acceptable method for solving a problem. **See margin.**
4. ***Apply*** what you have learned from Antonio and Winona's situation to solve this problem. *One box of fertilizer will feed 250 square feet of garden. How many boxes should the student council buy? Explain your reasoning. Did you use mental math, estimation, a calculator, or paper and pencil to get your answer?* **See margin.**

Reteaching the Lesson

Activity Have students work in cooperative groups to choose strategies for solving the problems and to discuss methods. Encourage students to try different methods and then to compare their results.

For **Extra Practice,** see page 570.

ON YOUR OWN

5. When you use the four-step plan for problem solving, you make an estimate of the solution even though you may be asked for an exact solution. ***Explain*** how estimating is useful when solving problems. **See margin.**

6. Use information from a newspaper or magazine advertisement and write two problems — one that needs an exact answer and one that needs an estimate.

7. ***Explain*** why an estimate might not be a good way to solve Exercise 23 on page 33.

6. See students' work. 7. See margin.

MIXED PROBLEM SOLVING

STRATEGIES
Look for a pattern.
Solve a simpler problem.
Act it out.
Guess and check.
Draw a diagram.
Make a chart.
Work backward.

Solve. Use any strategy.

8. ***Money Matters*** Max needs to buy four markers to make posters for a social studies project. He has \$4. Does he have enough money if the cost of each marker, including tax, is 89¢? **yes**

9. ***Construction*** Reynaldo wants to build a deck with an area of at least 120 square feet. He has space for a length of up to 14 feet, but no more than 9 feet for the width.

a. Will he be able to build a deck as large as he wants? **yes**

b. If so, what will be the area of the largest deck possible? **126 ft²**

10. ***Geography*** The Mediterranean Sea is an almost completely closed sea of about 900,000 cubic miles of water. It takes water entering at the Strait of Gibraltar about 150 years to circulate through the sea and leave through the Strait of Gibraltar. About how many cubic miles of water enter the sea in one day? **about 16 cubic miles**

11. ***Money Matters*** Hakeem saw an advertisement for piano lessons at \$15.95 per lesson. Estimate how much 12 lessons will cost. **about \$16 × 12 or \$192**

12. ***Food*** Kelly's Family Restaurant offers a Healthy Start Breakfast Special. The menu items and the number of Calories are shown in the chart below. About how many Calories are there in the meal? **about 550 Calories**

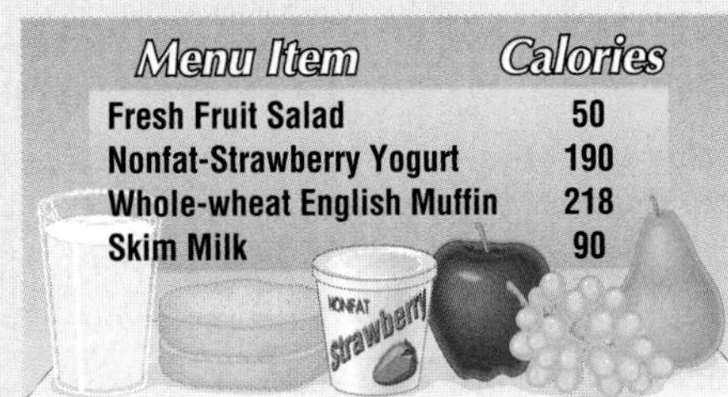

Menu Item	Calories
Fresh Fruit Salad	50
Nonfat-Strawberry Yogurt	190
Whole-wheat English Muffin	218
Skim Milk	90

13. yes; 3,000 + 3,000 + 4,000 + 3,000 = 13,000

13. ***Community Service*** There were four drop-off centers for the community food drive. One center collected 2,629 cans of food, the second collected 2,892 cans, the third collected 4,429 cans, and the fourth collected 3,298 cans. The newsletter editor reported that over 13,000 cans of food were collected. Is this answer reasonable? Explain.

14. ***Standardized Test Practice*** An elephant in a zoo eats 57 cabbages in a week. About how many cabbages does an elephant eat in one year? **D**

A 7 **B** 700 **C** 1,500
D 3,000 **E** 21,000

3 PRACTICE/APPLY

Check for Understanding

Use the results from Exercise 4 to show that the exact answer is not a feasible one in real life. Many times you must buy more than you need because of how items are packaged.

Extra Practice If students need additional practice in problem solving, extra practice is available on the following pages.

- Look for a Pattern, see p. 570
- Mixed Problem Solving, see pp. 605–606

Teaching Tip For Exercise 14, students will need to know that there are 52 weeks in a year in order to arrive at the correct answer.

Assignment Guide

All: 5–14

4 ASSESS

Closing Activity

Writing Have students list the methods of problem solving and describe how each could be useful. Have them give examples.

Additional Answers

5. Sample answer: You can compare your answer against your estimate to determine whether your answer is reasonable.

7. Sample answer: An estimate is close to 1,999 square feet, which is the dividing point for two categories.

Extending the Lesson

Activity Have students formulate a problem for others to solve for which it is reasonable to use more than one method of problem solving. Ask each problem writer to compare the methods he or she had in mind with those used by the problem solver.

Sample problem: *During a charity fund-raiser, each of 320 persons donated \$50. How much money was donated?* **\$16,000**

Study Guide and Assessment

Vocabulary

This section provides a listing of the new terms, properties, and phrases that were introduced in this chapter. Have students define each term and provide an example or two of it, if appropriate.

Understanding and Using the Vocabulary

These exercises check students' understanding of the terms by using a variety of verbal formats including matching, completion, and true/false.

Glossaries A complete glossary of terms appears on pages 656–663. The glossary also appears in Spanish on pages 664–672.

Additional Answer

12. Sample answer: When numbers are multiplied, they are called factors. When a factor is used more than once, an exponent can be used to simplify the notation. Numbers expressed using exponents are called powers.

CHAPTER 1

Study Guide and Assessment

interNET CONNECTION Chapter Review For additional review, visit: www.glencoe.com/sec/math/mac/mathnet

Vocabulary

After completing this chapter, you should be able to define each term, concept, or phrase and give an example or two of each.

Number and Operations
base (p. 17)
cubed (p. 17)
exponent (p. 17)
factors (p. 17)
order of operations (p. 8)
powers (p. 17)
squared (p. 17)

Problem Solving
choose the method of computation (p. 34)

Geometry
area (p. 30)
base (p. 31)
fractal (p. 24)
height (p. 31)
parallelogram (p. 31)
rectangle (p. 30)

Probability and Statistics
population (p. 5)
sample (p. 5)

Algebra
algebra (p. 12)
algebraic expression (p. 12)
equation (p. 21)
evaluate (p. 12)
modeling (p. 22)
solution (p. 21)
solve (p. 21)
variable (p. 12)

Understanding and Using the Vocabulary

State whether each sentence is *true* or *false*. If *false*, replace the underlined word or number to make a true statement. 10. false, parallel

1. The base of 4^7 is <u>4</u>. true
2. When the same factor is used, you may use an <u>exponent</u> to simplify the notation. true
3. Seven <u>cubed</u> is written as 7^2. false, squared
4. Numbers expressed using exponents are called <u>variables</u>. false, powers
5. The branch of mathematics that involves expressions with variables is called <u>algebra</u>. true
6. An <u>algebraic expression</u> is a sentence in mathematics that contains an equals sign. false, equation
7. The solution of $x + 5 = 18$ is <u>13</u>. true
8. When you write an equation that represents a real-world problem, you are <u>modeling</u> the problem. true
9. The area of a rectangle with a base of 5 inches and a height of 3 inches is <u>8 inches</u>. false, 15 square inches
10. A parallelogram is a four-sided figure whose opposite sides are <u>equal</u>.
11. The area of a parallelogram equals the product of its base and <u>height</u>. true

In Your Own Words

12. ***Explain*** the relationship among factors, exponents, and powers. See margin.

MindJogger Videoquizzes

MindJogger Videoquizzes provide an alternative review of concepts presented in this chapter. Students work in teams to answer questions, gaining points for correct answers. The questions are presented in three rounds.
Round 1 Concepts–5 questions
Round 2 Skills–4 questions
Round 3 Problem Solving–4 questions

Objectives & Examples

Upon completing this chapter, you should be able to:

- solve problems using the four-step plan *(Lesson 1-1)*

Bill practiced the trumpet 3 hours each day for 7 days. How many hours did he practice?

Explore He practiced 3 hours each day for 7 days.

Plan Multiply 3 by 7.

Solve $3 \cdot 7 = 21$
He practiced 21 hours.

Examine Add 3 seven times to find that the answer is correct.

Review Exercises

Use these exercises to review and prepare for the chapter test.

Use the four-step plan to solve.

13. ***Travel*** A car traveling at 60 mph will travel how far in 7 hours? **420 miles**

14. ***Money Matters*** Ann starts the day with \$100. If she spends \$35 at the mall, how much is left for groceries? **\$65**

15. ***Books*** A school library has 13,274 books; 327 are reference books, 7,015 are nonfiction, and the rest are fiction. How many fiction books are there? **5,932 books**

- evaluate expressions using the order of operations *(Lesson 1-2)*

Evaluate $3(9 + 7) - 4 \div 2 + 3$.

$3(9 + 7) - 4 \div 2 + 3$
$= 3(16) - 4 \div 2 + 3$
$= 48 - 2 + 3$ or 49

Evaluate each expression.

16. $3 + 7 \cdot 4 - 6$ **25**

17. $8(16 - 5) - 6$ **82**

18. $12 - 18 \div 9$ **10**

19. $83 + 3(4 - 2)$ **89**

20. $75 \div 3 + 6(5 - 1)$ **49**

21. $10(12 - 2) \div 10$ **10**

- evaluate simple algebraic expressions *(Lesson 1-3)*

Evaluate $6x - xy + y$ if $x = 10$ and $y = 3$.

$6x - xy + y = 6(10) - (10)(3) + 3$
$= 60 - 30 + 3$ or 33

Evaluate each expression if $p = 12$, $q = 3$, and $r = 5$.

22. $p + q - r$ **10**

23. $\frac{p + q}{r}$ **3**

24. $4q - p$ **0**

25. $3(p + q) - r$ **40**

26. $25 - 2(p - 2q)$ **13**

27. $6qr - p$ **78**

- use powers and exponents in expressions *(Lesson 1-4)*

Evaluate 2^5.

$2^5 = 2 \cdot 2 \cdot 2 \cdot 2 \cdot 2$
$= 32$

Evaluate each expression.

28. 10^3 **1,000**

29. 3^6 **729**

30. $3 + 2^4$ **19**

31. 15 squared **225**

32. $6 \cdot 2 + 4^2$ **28**

33. y^3, if $y = 4$ **64**

Assessment and Evaluation

Six forms of Chapter 1 Test are available in the *Assessment and Evaluation Masters* as shown in the chart.

1A	Multiple Choice	Honors
1B	Multiple Choice	Average
1C	Multiple Choice	Basic
2A	Free Response	Honors
2B	Free Response	Average
2C	Free Response	Basic

Chapter 1 Test, Form 1B, is shown at the right. Chapter 1 Test, Form 2B, is shown on the next page.

Objectives & Examples

This section reviews the skills and concepts of the chapter and shows completely worked examples.

Review Exercises

These exercises provide practice for the corresponding objectives.

***Assessment and Evaluation Masters*, pp. 3–4**

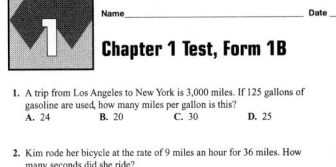

Name__________ Date__________

Chapter 1 Test, Form 1B

1. A trip from Los Angeles to New York is 3,000 miles. If 125 gallons of gasoline are used, how many miles per gallon is this?
A. 24 **B.** 20 **C.** 30 **D.** 25 — **1.** A

2. Kim rode her bicycle at the rate of 9 miles an hour for 36 miles. How many seconds did she ride?
A. 250 **B.** 14,400 **C.** 324 **D.** 19,440 — **2.** B

3. Evaluate $(25 + 35) \div 2 + 3$.
A. 55 **B.** 65 **C.** 12 **D.** 33 — **3.** D

4. Evaluate $12 + (40 + 10) \div 2$.
A. 37 **B.** 31 **C.** 300 **D.** 60 — **4.** A

5. Evaluate $82 - 43 - 6 \div 6$.
A. 5.5 **B.** 7.5 **C.** 38 **D.** 27 — **5.** C

6. Evaluate $pq + 8$ if $p = 2$ and $q = 1$.
A. 16 **B.** 24 **C.** 11 **D.** 10 — **6.** D

7. Evaluate $\frac{ab}{3}$ if $a = 7$ and $b = 9$.
A. 66 **B.** 60 **C.** 21 **D.** 189 — **7.** C

8. Evaluate $2(ab) \times 4 + 8$ if $a = 3$ and $b = 5$.
A. 72 **B.** 48 **C.** 128 **D.** 360 — **8.** C

9. Write 7^3 as a product of the same factor.
A. $3 \cdot 3 \cdot 3$ **B.** $7 \cdot 7$ **C.** $3 \cdot 3 \cdot 3 \cdot 3$ **D.** $7 \cdot 7 \cdot 7$ — **9.** D

10. Write $3 \cdot 3 \cdot 3 \cdot 3 \cdot 3$ using exponents.
A. 5^2 **B.** 3^5 **C.** 5^3 **D.** 3^4 — **10.** B

11. Evaluate 7^4.
A. 2,401 **B.** 13 **C.** 42 **D.** 16,807 — **11.** A

 3 *Mathematics: Applications and Connections*, Course 2

Chapter 1 Test, Form 1B (continued)

Solve each equation.

12. $5k = 125$
A. 625 **B.** 25 **C.** 120 **D.** 130 — **12.** B

13. $5 + x + 6 = 12$
A. 8 **B.** 3 **C.** 1 **D.** 6 — **13.** C

14. $x \div 5 = 6$
A. 30 **B.** 11 **C.** 150 **D.** 1 — **14.** A

15. $19 = \ell - 16$
A. 304 **B.** 53 **C.** 35 **D.** 3 — **15.** C

16. Which figure continues the pattern?
A. **B.** **C.** **D.** — **16.** A

17. Which is a fractal pattern?
A. **B.** **C.** **D.** — **17.** B

18. Find the area of the figure.
8 m
7 m
5 m
A. 40 m^2 **B.** 35 m^2 **C.** 56 m^2 **D.** 13 m^2 — **18.** A

19. What is the base of a parallelogram with an area of 30 square miles and a height of 5 miles?
A. 35 mi **B.** 25 mi **C.** 152 mi **D.** 6 mi — **19.** D

20. A student council convention had 4,293 students registered. The convention manager had to assign 537 students per hotel. To how many different hotels did the manager have to assign students?
A. 9 **B.** 7 **C.** 8 **D.** 5 — **20.** C

 4 *Mathematics: Applications and Connections*, Course 2

Study Guide and Assessment

Additional Answers

41.

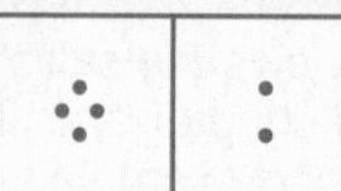

42.

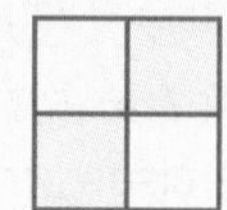

Assessment and Evaluation Masters, pp. 9–10

Name______________________ Date__________

Chapter 1 Test, Form 2B

Solve each problem.

1. Manuel decided to eat lunch in the cafeteria of the art museum. He bought a sandwich for \$4 and an orange juice for \$1. He only had a \$10 bill. How much change did he get? — 1. \$5
2. Laura buys her audiocassettes in bulk to save money. There are 10 audiocassettes in a package for \$16. How much will 40 cassettes cost? — 2. \$64

Evaluate each expression.

3. $(25 - 9) - 5 \times 3$ — 3. 1
4. $(19 - 4) \div 3 + 2$ — 4. 7
5. $2(5 + 3) - 4$ — 5. 12
6. $12 + 6(30 \div 5)$ — 6. 48
7. $(7 \times 8) - (6 \times 7)$ — 7. 14

Evaluate each expression if a = 3, b = 5, and c = 7.

8. $3b - a$ — 8. 12
9. $2(b + c) - a$ — 9. 21
10. $\frac{a + b}{4}$ — 10. 2
11. $\frac{a(b + c)}{9}$ — 11. 4
12. Write 6^5 as a product of the same factor. — 12. $6 \cdot 6 \cdot 6 \cdot 6 \cdot 6$
13. Write $11 \cdot 11 \cdot 11 \cdot 11$ using exponents. — 13. 11^4
14. Evaluate 12^3. — 14. 1,728
15. Write $7 \cdot 7 \cdot 7 \cdot 7 \cdot 7$ using exponents. — 15. 7^5

Solve each equation.

16. $\frac{m}{3} = 35$ — 16. 105
17. $4(8 + x) = 40$ — 17. 2

© Glencoe/McGraw-Hill 9 *Mathematics: Applications and Connections, Course 2*

Chapter 1 Test, Form 2B (continued)

Solve each equation.

18. $9 + a + 7 = 25$ — 18. 9
19. $64 = \ell - 36$ — 19. 100
20. $\frac{r + 5}{11} = 6$ — 20. 61
21. Draw the next two figures that continue the pattern. — 21.

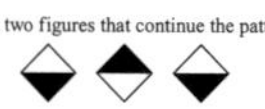

22. Draw the next figure in the fractal pattern. — 22. 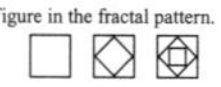
23. Find the area of the figure. — 23. 32 square feet

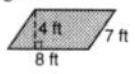

4 ft
7 ft
8 ft

Solve each problem.

24. Pierre is selecting a frame for a painting with a length of 7 inches and a width of 3 inches. What is the area of the painting? — 24. 21 square feet
25. The Sears Tower in Chicago is 1,454 feet tall. The Chrysler Building in New York City is 1,046 feet tall. What is the difference between the two heights? — 25. 408 feet

© Glencoe/McGraw-Hill 10 *Mathematics: Applications and Connections, Course 2*

Chapter 1 Study Guide and Assessment

Objectives & Examples

solve equations using mental math *(Lesson 1-5)*

Solve $3s = 36$.

$3s = 36$

$3 \cdot 12 = 36$ *You know that $3 \cdot 12 = 36$.*

$36 = 36$ ✓

The solution is 12.

Review Exercises

Name the number that is a solution of the given equation.

34. $t + 11 = 23$; 11, 12, 13 **12**
35. $63 \div 7 = m$; 7, 9, 11 **9**
36. $16 - a = 9$; 5, 6, 7 **7**

Solve each equation.

37. $t - 12 = 35$ **47**
38. $8x = 88$ **11**
39. $\frac{m}{4} = 16$ **64**
40. $28 + r = 128$ **100**

find and extend patterns *(Lesson 1-6)*

Draw the next two figures that continue the pattern.

The next two figures are

.

Draw the next two figures that continue each pattern.

41.

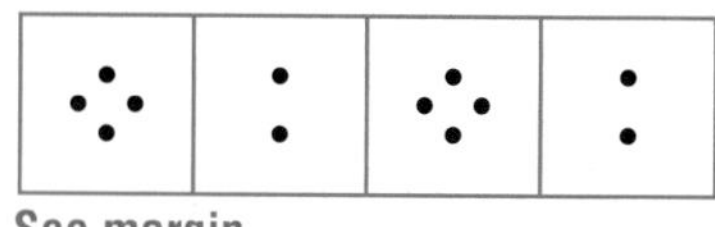

See margin.

42.

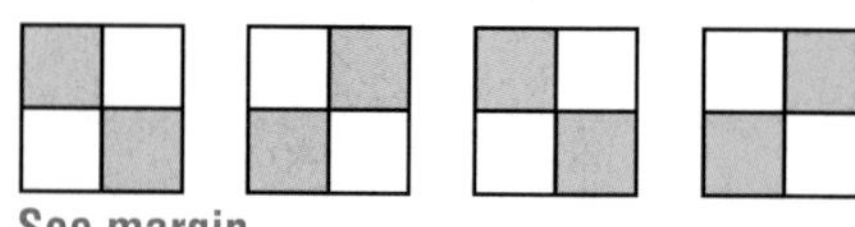

See margin.

find the areas of rectangles and parallelograms *(Lesson 1-7)*

Find the area of a parallelogram with a base of 6 inches and a height of 3 inches.

$A = bh$

$A = 6 \cdot 3$ *Replace b with 6 and h with 3.*

$A = 18$

The area is 18 square inches.

Find the area of each rectangle or parallelogram.

43. 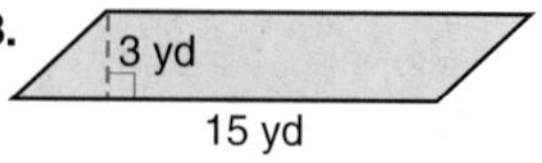 3 yd, 15 yd **45 yd²**

44. 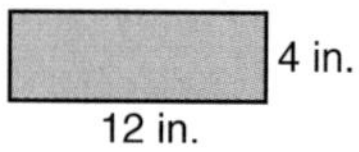 4 in., 12 in. **48 in²**

45. rectangle: ℓ, 14 m; w, 12 m **168 m²**
46. parallelogram: b, 2 cm; h, 1 cm **2 cm²**
47. rectangle: ℓ, 6 ft; w, 2 ft **12 ft²**
48. parallelogram: b, 7 mm; h, 3 mm **21 mm²**

Test and Review Software

You may use this software, a combination of an item generator and item bank, to create your own tests or worksheets. Types of items include free response, multiple choice, short answer, and open ended.

CD-ROM Program

The CD-ROM Program contains an Assessment Game whose questions review the concepts in this chapter.

Applications & Problem Solving

49. ***Choose the Method of Computation*** Carlos wants to buy two speakers for his sound system. Each speaker costs \$59.99. If Carlos has \$112 in his savings account, can he afford to buy the speakers now? *(Lesson 1-7B)* **no**

50. ***Money Matters*** At a local coffee shop, Mexican coffee is \$5 per pound, and Spanish coffee is \$9 per pound. How much would you pay for 3 pounds of Mexican coffee and 2 pounds of Spanish coffee? *(Lesson 1-2)* **\$33**

51. ***Life Science*** You can estimate the temperature in degrees Fahrenheit by using the expression $\frac{c}{4} + 37$, where c is the number of times a cricket chirps per minute. Find the temperature if a cricket chirps 104 times in one minute. *(Lesson 1-3)* **63°F**

52. ***Sports*** The graph shows the number of World Series Championships for selected teams from 1903-1996. How many total championships have been won by these teams? *(Lesson 1-1)* **47 championships**

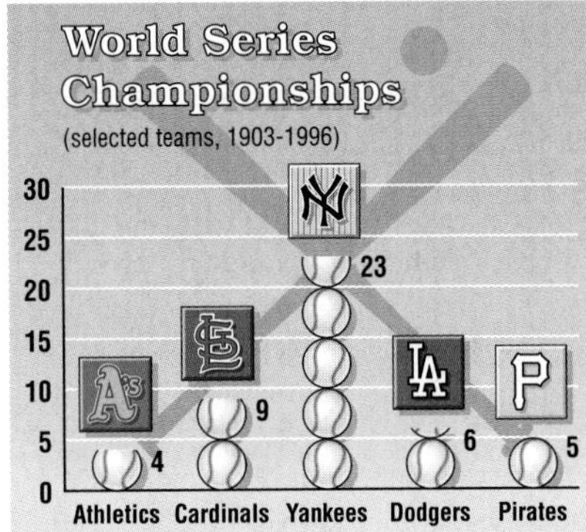

Source: *World Almanac*, 1996

Alternative Assessment

Open Ended

Suppose you are in charge of purchasing the decorations for a school dance. You have decided to buy 4 packages of balloons at \$1.39 each, 10 rolls of streamers at 89¢ each, and one dozen table decorations at \$2.49 each. You also want to purchase a few bags of confetti that cost \$2.25 each. Write an expression that represents the cost of the party items.
4(1.39) + 10(0.89) + 12(2.49) + *x*(2.25)

If you have \$50 to spend, how many packages of confetti can you buy? **2 bags of confetti**

A practice test for Chapter 1 is provided on page 607.

Completing the 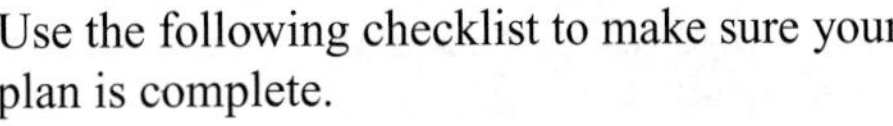

Use the following checklist to make sure your plan is complete.

- ☑ You have included at least six different activities for the week, the amount of time you do each activity, and how many Calories are burned.
- ☑ The amount of Calories eaten each day is between 2,400 and 2,800.
- ☑ Your plan is reasonable.

Select one of the assignments from this chapter and place it in your portfolio. Attach a note to it explaining why you selected it.

Performance Assessment

Additional performance assessment tasks for this chapter are included in the *Assessment and Evaluation Masters* on page 13. A scoring guide is also provided on page 25.

Applications & Problem Solving

This section provides additional practice in solving real-world problems that involve the skills of this chapter.

Alternative Assessment

The ***Open Ended*** section provides students with a performance assessment opportunity to evaluate their work and understanding.

Students should complete the final stages of their project and prepare a class demonstration of their results. A scoring guide for the project is available in the *Investigations and Projects Masters,* p. 19

Students should add to their portfolios at this time.

Assessment and Evaluation Masters, p. 13

Name________________ Date________

Chapter 1 Performance Assessment

Instructions: Demonstrate your knowledge by giving a clear, concise solution to each problem. Be sure to include all relevant drawings and justify your answers. You may show your solutions in more than one way or investigate beyond the requirements of the problems.

1. a. Give the four-step plan for problem solving. In your own words, describe each step.
   b. Write a word problem where you must choose an operation to solve the problem.
   c. Show how to use the four-step plan to solve the problem in part b.
2. a. Tell how to use the order of operations to evaluate $a^2 + 3(b - 2)$ if $a = 5$ and $b = 8$.
   b. Explain what the expression n^3 means. Evaluate the expression if $n = 4$.
   c. Solve the equation $x - 3 = 5$. Explain each step.
3. Shahine and Faisal Rahman plan to cover their patio floor with bricks this weekend. The patio is 10 feet wide and 15 feet long. The Rahmans plan on using square bricks, rectangular bricks, or a pattern using both. The square bricks measure 4 inches by 4 inches. The rectangular bricks measure 8 inches by 4 inches. Choose a brick size or design a pattern. How many bricks and of what sort will they need to purchase to cover the patio? Explain each step.
4. Elijah has been given permission to decorate his bedroom walls. He decided to paint a repeating pattern with a stencil around the top of the walls. Design a pattern for your room. Show what each stencil you need will look like.

 13 *Mathematics: Applications and Connections, Course 2*

Standardized Test Practice

The Standardized Test Practice may be used to help students prepare for standardized tests. The test items are written in the same style as those in state proficiency tests and standardized tests like CAT, CTBS, ITBS, MAT, SAT, and Terra Nova. The test items cover skills and concepts covered up to this point in the text.

The pages can be used as an overnight assessment. After students have completed the pages, discuss how each problem can be solved, or provide copies of the solutions from the *Solutions Manual.*

***Assessment and Evaluation Masters*, p. 19**

Name__________ Date__________

Cumulative Review, Chapter 1

Evaluate each expression. (Lesson 1-2)

1. $48 \div (12 - 8)$ — **12**
2. $(33 + 66) \div 9 - 9$ — **2**

Evaluate each expression if a = 6, b = 4, and c = 2. (Lesson 1-3)

3. $3a - c$ — **16**
4. $2(b + c) - a$ — **6**
5. Write 8^3 as a product of the same factor. (Lesson 1-4) — **$8 \cdot 8 \cdot 8$**
6. Write $3 \cdot 3 \cdot 3 \cdot 3 \cdot 3$ using exponents. (Lesson 1-4) — **3^5**

Evaluate each expression. (Lesson 1-4)

7. 7^4 — **2,401**
8. 5 squared — **25**

Solve each equation mentally. (Lesson 1-5)

9. $17a = 136$ — **8**
10. $b - 42 = 59$ — **101**
11. $39 + c = 121$ — **82**
12. $\frac{d}{6} = 34$ — **204**
13. Name the number that is a solution of the equation $6b - 4 = 2$; 1, 2, 3. (Lesson 1-5) — **1**

Draw the next two figures that continue each pattern. (Lesson 1-6)

14.

15.

16. Find the area of a parallelogram with $b = 7$ feet and $h = 3.5$ feet. (Lesson 1-7) — **24.5 ft²**

Find the area of each rectangle or parallelogram. (Lesson 1-7)

17. 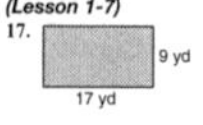

— **153 yd²**

18. 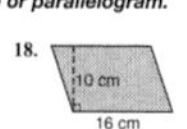

— **160 cm²**

Solve each problem. Use any method. (Lessons 1-1 and 1-7B)

19. Will $50.00 buy a dozen golf balls at $21.95 and a sweater at $28.50? — **no**
20. Use each of the digits 1, 2, 3, and 4 exactly once to make 2 two-digit numbers that when multiplied have the greatest product possible. What is the product? — **$41 \times 32 = 1,312$**

 19 *Mathematics: Applications and Connections, Course 2*

CHAPTER 1

Standardized Test Practice

Assessing Knowledge & Skills

Section One: Multiple Choice

There are nine multiple choice questions in this section. Choose the best answer. If a correct answer is *not here* choose the letter for Not Here.

1. What is the value of $x + y + 5$ if $x = 6$ and $y = 15$? **C**
   - **A** 21
   - **B** 25
   - **C** 26
   - **D** 28

2. How many square inches of tile are needed to cover a rectangular art project that measures 18 inches by 10 inches? **H**
   - **F** 28 in²
   - **G** 8 in²
   - **H** 180 in²
   - **J** 90 in²

3. Using this chart, Wesley will write a report on the major rivers of the world.

River	Length (miles)
Amazon	4,000
Chang	3,964
Huang	3,395
Nile	4,160
Ob-Irtysh	3,362

If he wants to list the three rivers in order from greatest to least, which list should he choose? **C**
   - **A** Ob-Irtysh, Huang, Chang
   - **B** Nile, Chang, Huang
   - **C** Nile, Amazon, Chang
   - **D** Amazon, Chang, Huang

Please note that Questions 4-9 have five answer choices.

4. One page of a textbook is 14 inches long and 11 inches wide. If the only graphic on the page measures 3 inches by 4 inches, which sentence could be used to find x, the amount of space left for text and borders? **J**

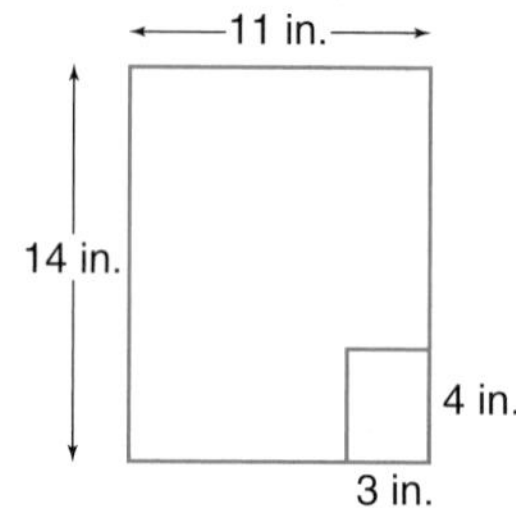

   - **F** $x = (14 + 11) - (4 + 3)$
   - **G** $x = 2(14 + 11) - 2(4 + 3)$
   - **H** $x = 14 \times 11 \times 4 \times 3$
   - **J** $x = (14 \times 11) - (3 \times 4)$
   - **K** $x = \frac{14 \times 11}{4 \times 3}$

5. The student council sells pizzas for a fundraising activity. They charge $6 for each pizza. Which is the best estimate of their earnings if they sell 175 pizzas? **C**
   - **A** $6,000
   - **B** $1,200
   - **C** $1,050
   - **D** $900
   - **E** $750

◀◀◀ Instructional Resources

Another cumulative review is shown at the left and is available in the *Assessment and Evaluation Masters,* p. 19.

6. 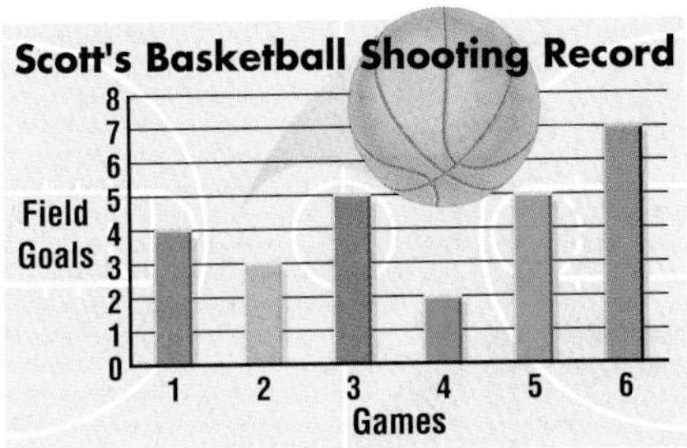

How many field goals did Scott make in the first five games? J

F 4

G 5

H 10

J 19

K 26

7. One can of soup contains 12 ounces. How many ounces are there in 48 cans? D

A 4

B 36

C 60

D 576

E Not Here

8. Each tent is put up with 12 poles. How many tents can be put up with 200 poles? F

F 16

G 16 R8

H 17

J 20

K Not Here

9. Sonia spent $68 for a tent, $27 for a sleeping bag, and $25 for a backpack. How much more did she spend for the tent than the backpack? B

A $93

B $43

C $52

D $120

E Not Here

Test-Taking Tip — THE PRINCETON REVIEW

When taking standardized tests, be careful not to make stray marks on your answer sheet. These marks may be misread by the scoring machine. Any question that appears to have more than one answer will be marked as incorrect.

Section Two: Free Response

This section contains six questions for which you will provide short answers. Write your answers on your paper.

10. What is the value of $3[2(23 - 11) - (3 + 9)]$? **36**

11. Tai is reading a 258-page novel. If he reads 8 pages an hour, about how long will it take him to read the entire book? **See margin.**

12. Lucy is knitting scarves for her 3 sisters. She needs to buy 9 skeins of yarn. Each skein costs $2.59, including tax. Which information in the problem is *not* needed to find the total cost of the yarn? **Lucy has 3 sisters.**

13. Find the number of seconds in one week. **604,800 seconds**

14. At the end of a 478-mile trip, the odometer reading in the car was 15,015 miles. What was the reading at the start of the trip? **14,537 miles**

15. The members of a cycling club are planning a 1,800-mile trip. They believe they can average 15 miles per hour for 6 hours each day. How many days will it take for them to complete the trip? **20 days**

interNET CONNECTION Test Practice For additional test practice questions, visit:

www.glencoe.com/sec/math/mac/mathnet

Additional Answer

11. Sample answer: 240 ÷ 8 = 30; about 30 hours

Instructional Resources ▶▶▶

Additional standardized test practice is shown at the right and is available in the *Assessment and Evaluation Masters,* pp. 17–18.

Test-Taking Tip

Emphasize to students that when they mark more than one answer, such as to narrow down their choices to the best solution, they must completely erase any marks other than the answer chosen.

Assessment and Evaluation Masters, pp. 17–18

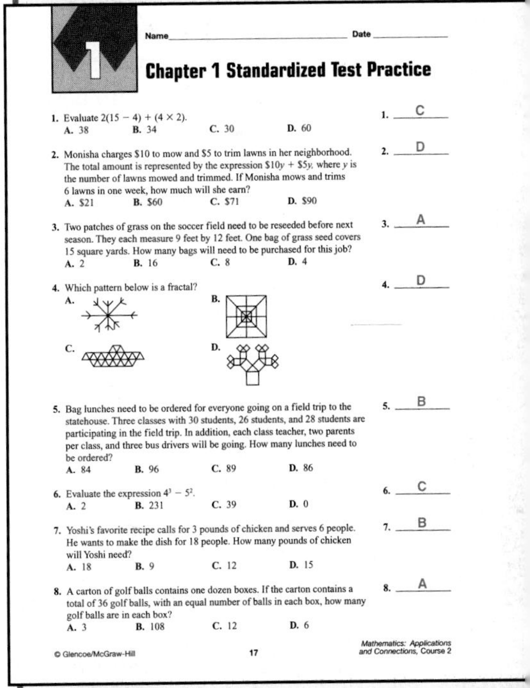

Name__________ Date________

Chapter 1 Standardized Test Practice

1. Evaluate $2(15 - 4) + (4 \times 2)$. 1. C
A. 38 B. 34 C. 30 D. 60

2. Monisha charges $10 to mow and $5 to trim lawns in her neighborhood. The total amount is represented by the expression $10*y* + $5*y*, where *y* is the number of lawns mowed and trimmed. If Monisha mows and trims 6 lawns in one week, how much will she earn? 2. D
A. $21 B. $60 C. $71 D. $90

3. Two patches of grass on the soccer field need to be reseeded before next season. They each measure 9 feet by 12 feet. One bag of grass seed covers 15 square yards. How many bags will need to be purchased for this job? 3. A
A. 2 B. 16 C. 8 D. 4

4. Which pattern below is a fractal? 4. D
A. B. C. D.

5. Bag lunches need to be ordered for everyone going on a field trip to the statehouse. Three classes with 30 students, 26 students, and 28 students are participating in the field trip. In addition, each class teacher, two parents per class, and three bus drivers will be going. How many lunches need to be ordered? 5. B
A. 84 B. 96 C. 89 D. 86

6. Evaluate the expression $4^3 - 5^2$. 6. C
A. 2 B. 231 C. 39 D. 0

7. Yoshi's favorite recipe calls for 3 pounds of chicken and serves 6 people. He wants to make the dish for 18 people. How many pounds of chicken will Yoshi need? 7. B
A. 18 B. 9 C. 12 D. 15

8. A carton of golf balls contains one dozen boxes. If the carton contains a total of 36 golf balls, with an equal number of balls in each box, how many golf balls are in each box? 8. A
A. 3 B. 108 C. 12 D. 6

© Glencoe/McGraw-Hill 17 *Mathematics: Applications and Connections,* Course 2

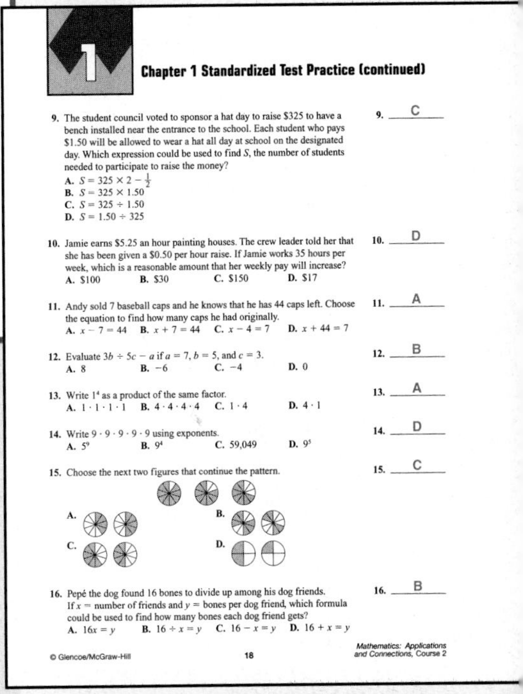

Chapter 1 Standardized Test Practice (continued)

9. The student council voted to sponsor a hat day to raise $325 to have a bench installed near the entrance to the school. Each student who pays $1.50 will be allowed to wear a hat all day at school on the designated day. Which expression could be used to find *S*, the number of students needed to participate to raise the money? 9. C
A. $S = 325 \times 2 - \frac{1}{2}$
B. $S = 325 \times 1.50$
C. $S = 325 \div 1.50$
D. $S = 1.50 \div 325$

10. Jamie earns $5.25 an hour painting houses. The crew leader told her that she has been given a $0.50 per hour raise. If Jamie works 35 hours per week, which is a reasonable amount that her weekly pay will increase? 10. D
A. $100 B. $30 C. $150 D. $17

11. Andy sold 7 baseball caps and he knows that he has 44 caps left. Choose the equation to find how many caps he had originally. 11. A
A. $x - 7 = 44$ B. $x + 7 = 44$ C. $x - 4 = 7$ D. $x + 44 = 7$

12. Evaluate $3b \div 5c - a$ if $a = 7$, $b = 5$, and $c = 3$. 12. B
A. 8 B. −6 C. −4 D. 0

13. Write 1^4 as a product of the same factor. 13. A
A. $1 \cdot 1 \cdot 1 \cdot 1$ B. $4 \cdot 4 \cdot 4 \cdot 4$ C. $1 \cdot 4$ D. $4 \cdot 1$

14. Write $9 \cdot 9 \cdot 9 \cdot 9 \cdot 9$ using exponents. 14. D
A. 5^9 B. 9^4 C. 59,049 D. 9^5

15. Choose the next two figures that continue the pattern. 15. C
A. B. C. D.

16. Pepé the dog found 16 bones to divide up among his dog friends. If x = number of friends and y = bones per dog friend, which formula could be used to find how many bones each dog friend gets? 16. B
A. $16x = y$ B. $16 \div x = y$ C. $16 - x = y$ D. $16 + x = y$

© Glencoe/McGraw-Hill 18 *Mathematics: Applications and Connections,* Course 2

CHAPTER 2

Applying Decimals

Previewing the Chapter

Overview

This chapter investigates operations with decimals and some of their many applications. Students compare, order, and round decimals, and estimate sums, differences, products, and quotients of decimals. They explore the relationship between fractions and decimals. They use powers of ten and express numbers in scientific notation. Students also use estimation to determine whether their answers are reasonable.

Lesson (pages)	Lesson Objectives	NCTM Standards 2000	Standardized Tests	State/Local Objectives
2-1 (44–46)	Compare and order decimals.	1, 5–10	CAT, CTBS, ITBS, MAT, SAT, TN	
2-2 (47–49)	Round decimals.	1, 5–10	CAT, CTBS, ITBS, SAT, TN	
2-3 (50–53)	Estimate with decimals.	1, 5–10	CAT, CTBS, ITBS, SAT, TN	
2-3B (54–55)	Solve problems by determining reasonable answers.	1, 4–10	CAT, CTBS, ITBS, MAT, TN	
2-4 (56–59)	Multiply decimals.	1–3, 5–10	CAT, CTBS, ITBS, MAT, SAT, TN	
2-5 (61–63)	Multiply decimals mentally by powers of ten.	1, 2, 5–10	CAT, CTBS, ITBS, MAT, SAT, IN	
2-6A (64–65)	Divide decimals using models.	1, 6–10		
2-6 (66–69)	Divide decimals.	1–9	CAT, CTBS, ITBS, MAT, SAT, TN	
2-7 (70–73)	Express fractions as terminating or repeating decimals.	1, 5–10	CAT, CTBS, ITBS, MAT, SAT, TN	
2-8 (74–76)	Change metric units of length, capacity, and mass.	1, 4, 6–10	CAT, CTBS, MAT, SAT, TN	
2-9 (77–79)	Express numbers greater than 100 in scientific notation.	1, 6–9	CAT, CTBS, ITBS, MAT, SAT, TN	

CAT = California Achievement Tests, CTBS = Comprehensive Tests of Basic Skills, ITBS = Iowa Tests of Basic Skills, MAT = Metropolitan Achievement Tests, SAT = Stanford Achievement Tests, TN = Terra Nova
For the key to numbering of NCTM Standards 2000, see page T6.

Organizing the Chapter

The **Interactive Lesson Planner** contains all of the blackline masters and transparencies. This CD-ROM also includes an easy-to-use lesson planning calendar.

LESSON PLANNING GUIDE

Lesson	Extra Practice (Student Edition)	Blackline Masters (page numbers)										Transparencies A and B
		Study Guide	Practice	Enrichment	Assessment & Evaluation	Classroom Games	Diversity	Hands-On Lab	School to Career	Science and Math Lab Manual	Technology	
2-1	p. 570	8	8	9								2-1
2-2	p. 571	9	9	9				73				2-2
2-3	p. 571	10	10	10	43							2-3
2-3B	p. 571											
2-4	p. 572	11	11	11								2-4
2-5	p. 572	12	12	12	42, 43							2-5
2-6A								40				
2-6	p. 572	13	13	13			15				29	2-6
2-7	p. 573	14	14	14	44							2-7
2-8	p. 573	15	15	15		5–8				25–28		2-8
2-9	p. 573	16	16	16	44				15		30	2-9
Study Guide/ Assessment					29–41, 45–47							

Other Chapter Resources

Student Edition

Chapter Project, pp. 43, 46, 59, 76, 83
School to Career, p. 60
Let the Games Begin, p. 73

Technology

MathPASS CD-ROM
Interactive Mathematics Tools Software

Teacher's Classroom Resources

Applications

Family Letters and Activities, pp. 29–30
Investigations and Projects Masters, pp. 21–24

Meeting Individual Needs

Transition Booklet, pp. 13–22
Investigations for the Special Education Student, p. 7

Teaching Aids

Answer Key Masters
Block Scheduling Booklet
Lesson Planning Guide
Solutions Manual

Professional Publications

Glencoe Mathematics Professional Series

Planning the Chapter

MindJogger Videoquizzes provide a unique format for reviewing concepts presented in the chapter.

Assessment Resources

Student Edition

Mixed Review, pp. 46, 49, 53, 59, 63, 69, 73, 76, 79
Mid-Chapter Self Test, p. 59
Math Journal, pp. 45, 51, 62
Study Guide and Assessment, pp. 80–83
Performance Task, p. 83
Portfolio Suggestion, p. 83
Standardized Test Practice, pp. 84–85
Chapter Test, p. 608

Assessment and Evaluation Masters

Multiple-Choice Tests (Forms 1A, 1B, 1C), pp. 29–34
Free-Response Tests (Forms 2A, 2B, 2C), pp. 35–40
Performance Assessment, p. 41
Mid-Chapter Test, p. 42
Quizzes A–D, pp. 43–44
Standardized Test Practice, pp. 45–46
Cumulative Review, p. 47

Teacher's Wraparound Edition

5-Minute Check, pp. 44, 47, 50, 56, 61, 66, 70, 74, 77
Building Portfolios, p. 42
Math Journal, p. 65
Closing Activity, pp. 46, 49, 53, 55, 59, 63, 69, 73, 76, 79

Technology

Test and Review Software
MindJogger Videoquizzes
CD-ROM Program

Materials and Manipulatives

Lesson 2-4
grid paper†
markers

Lesson 2-6A
grid paper†
markers

Lesson 2-6
calculator

Lesson 2-7
calculator

Lesson 2-8
meterstick

Lesson 2-9
calculator

*Glencoe Manipulative Kit

†Glencoe Overhead Manipulative Resources

Pacing Chart

See pages T25–T27 for the Course Planning Calendar.

COURSE	DAY 1	DAY 2	DAY 3	DAY 4	DAY 5	DAY 6	DAY 7
Standard	Chapter Project	Lesson 2-1	Lesson 2-2	Lesson 2-3	Lesson 2-3B	Lesson 2-4	Lesson 2-5
Honors	Chapter Project	Lesson 2-1	Lesson 2-2	Lesson 2-3	Lesson 2-3B	Lesson 2-4	Lesson 2-5
Block	Chapter Project & Lesson 2-1	Lessons 2-2 & 2-3	Lessons 2-3B & 2-4	Lessons 2-5 & 2-6A	Lessons 2-6 & 2-7	Lessons 2-8 & 2-9	Study Guide and Assessment, Chapter Test

The *Transition Booklet* (Skills 5–9, 16) can be used to practice basic operations with whole numbers.

Interactive Mathematics:
Activities and Investigations

is an activity-based program that may be used as an enhancement for chapters in ***Mathematics: Applications and Connections.***

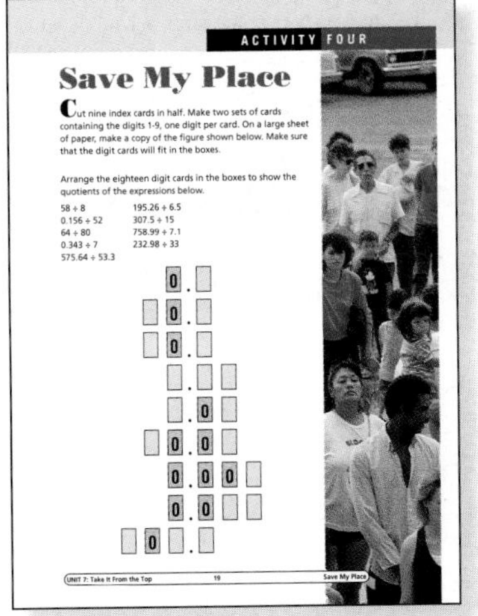

ACTIVITY FOUR

Save My Place

Cut nine index cards in half. Make two sets of cards containing the digits 1-9, one digit per card. On a large sheet of paper, make a copy of the figure shown below. Make sure that the digit cards will fit in the boxes.

Arrange the eighteen digit cards in the boxes to show the quotients of the expressions below.

58 ÷ 8	195.26 ÷ 6.5
0.156 ÷ 52	307.5 ÷ 15
64 ÷ 80	758.99 ÷ 7.1
0.343 ÷ 7	232.98 ÷ 33
575.64 ÷ 53.3	

UNIT 7: Take It From the Top 19 Save My Place

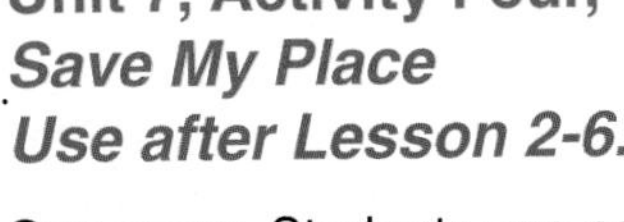

Unit 7, Activity Four,
Save My Place
Use after Lesson 2-6.

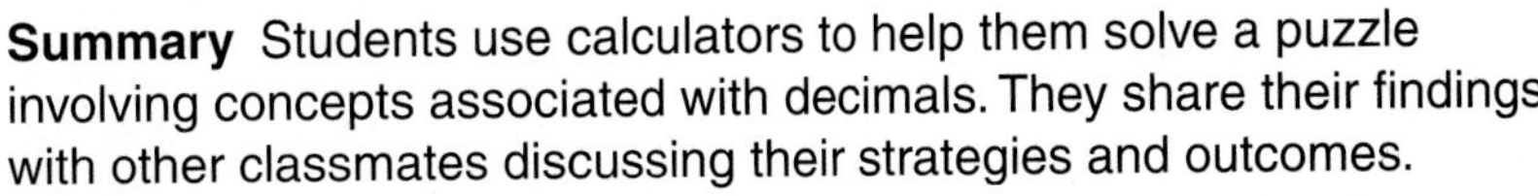

Summary Students use calculators to help them solve a puzzle involving concepts associated with decimals. They share their findings with other classmates discussing their strategies and outcomes.

Math Connection Students use calculators and the operation of division to solve a puzzle involving decimals. Encourage students to use their calculators to verify that their quotients are correct.

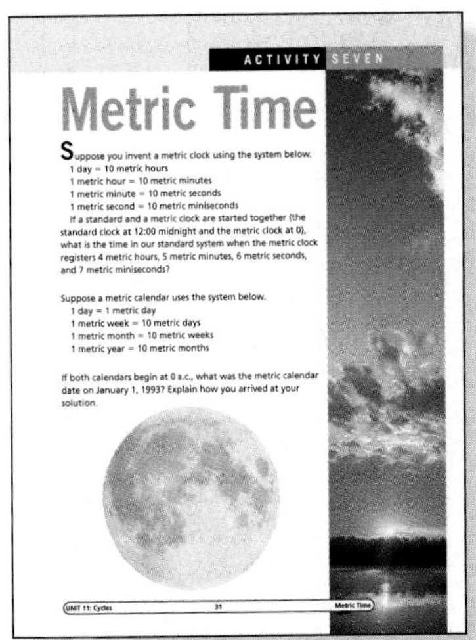

ACTIVITY SEVEN

Metric Time

Suppose you invent a metric clock using the system below.
1 day = 10 metric hours
1 metric hour = 10 metric minutes
1 metric minute = 10 metric seconds
1 metric second = 10 metric miniseconds

If a standard and a metric clock are started together (the standard clock at 12:00 midnight and the metric clock at 0), what is the time in our standard system when the metric clock registers 4 metric hours, 5 metric minutes, 6 metric seconds, and 7 metric miniseconds?

Suppose a metric calendar uses the system below.
1 day = 1 metric day
1 metric week = 10 metric days
1 metric month = 10 metric weeks
1 metric year = 10 metric months

If both calendars begin at 0 B.C., what was the metric calendar date on January 1, 1993? Explain how you arrived at your solution.

UNIT 11: Cycles 31 Metric Time

Unit 11, Activity Seven
Use with Lesson 2-8.

Summary Students work in groups to convert time measurements between standard time units and a metric (base-ten) system. Each group makes a presentation of the methods used to arrive at their answers.

Math Connection Students convert a metric time to a standard time, and a standard date into a metric date. A standard day is equivalent to a metric day. There are 10 metric hours in a metric day, 10 metric minutes in a metric hour, 10 metric seconds in a metric minute, and so on.

DAY 8	DAY 9	DAY 10	DAY 11	DAY 12	DAY 13	DAY 14	DAY 15
Lessons 2-6A & 2-6		Lessons 2-7A & 2-7	Lesson 2-8	Lesson 2-9	Study Guide and Assessment	Chapter Test	
Lesson 2-6	Lesson 2-7	Lesson 2-8	Lesson 2-9	Study Guide and Assessment	Chapter Test		

Enhancing the Chapter

APPLICATIONS

Classroom Games, pp. 5–8

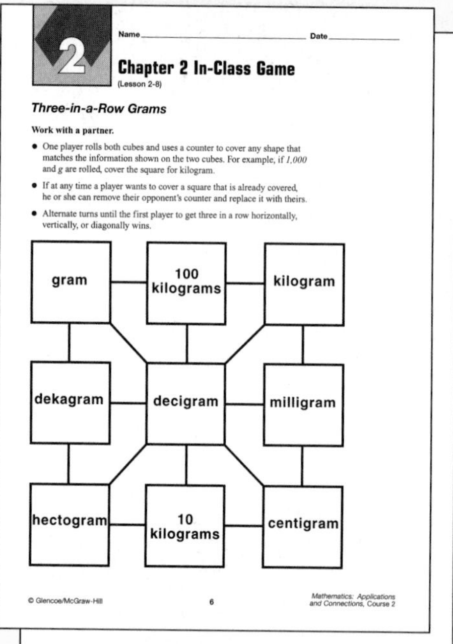

2

Name ________ Date ________

Chapter 2 In-Class Game
(Lesson 2-8)

Three-in-a-Row Grams

Work with a partner.

- One player rolls both cubes and uses a counter to cover any shape that matches the information shown on the two cubes. For example, if *1,000* and *g* are rolled, cover the square for kilogram.
- If at any time a player wants to cover a square that is already covered, he or she can remove their opponent's counter and replace it with theirs.
- Alternate turns until the first player to get three in a row horizontally, vertically, or diagonally wins.

© Glencoe/McGraw-Hill 6 *Mathematics: Applications and Connections, Course 2*

Diversity Masters, p. 15

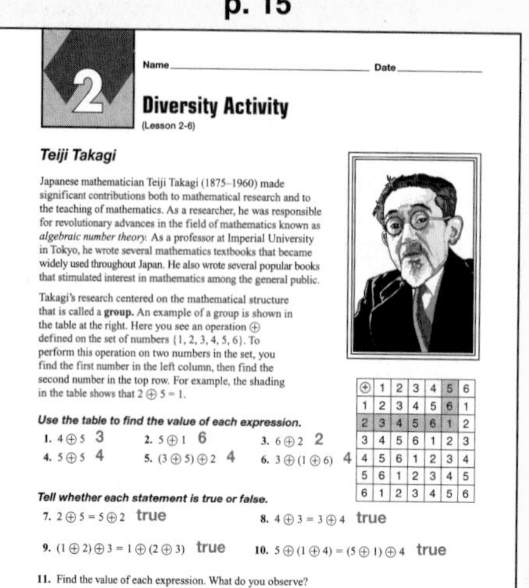

2

Name ________ Date ________

Diversity Activity
(Lesson 2-6)

Teiji Takagi

Japanese mathematician Teiji Takagi (1875–1960) made significant contributions both to mathematical research and to the teaching of mathematics. As a researcher, he was responsible for revolutionary advances in the field of mathematics known as *algebraic number theory.* As a professor at Imperial University in Tokyo, he wrote several mathematics textbooks that became widely used throughout Japan. He also wrote several popular books that stimulated interest in mathematics among the general public.

Takagi's research centered on the mathematical structure that is called a **group.** An example of a group is shown in the table at the right. Here you see an operation $\oplus$ defined on the set of numbers {1, 2, 3, 4, 5, 6}. To perform this operation on two numbers in the set, you find the first number in the left column, then find the second number in the top row. For example, the shading in the table shows that $2 \oplus 5 = 1$.

$\oplus$	1	2	3	4	5	6
1	2	3	4	5	6	1
2	3	4	5	6	1	2
3	4	5	6	1	2	3
4	5	6	1	2	3	4
5	6	1	2	3	4	5
6	1	2	3	4	5	6

Use the table to find the value of each expression.

1. $4 \oplus 5$ 3
2. $5 \oplus 1$ 6
3. $6 \oplus 2$ 2
4. $5 \oplus 5$ 4
5. $(3 \oplus 5) \oplus 2$ 4
6. $3 \oplus (1 \oplus 6)$ 4

Tell whether each statement is true or false.

7. $2 \oplus 5 = 5 \oplus 2$ true
8. $4 \oplus 3 = 3 \oplus 4$ true
9. $(1 \oplus 2) \oplus 3 = 1 \oplus (2 \oplus 3)$ true
10. $5 \oplus (1 \oplus 4) = (5 \oplus 1) \oplus 4$ true
11. Find the value of each expression. What do you observe?
    a. $1 \oplus 6$ 1 b. $2 \oplus 6$ 2 c. $3 \oplus 6$ 3 d. $4 \oplus 6$ 4 e. $5 \oplus 6$ 5 f. $6 \oplus 6$ 6
    When you perform the operation $n \oplus 6$, the result is n.
12. In the group shown on this page, the operation $\oplus$ is sometimes referred to as *clock arithmetic.* Can you explain why? The results are the same as if you were adding hours on a "six-hour clock," like the one shown at the right.

© Glencoe/McGraw-Hill T15 *Mathematics: Applications and Connections, Course 2*

School to Career Masters, p. 15

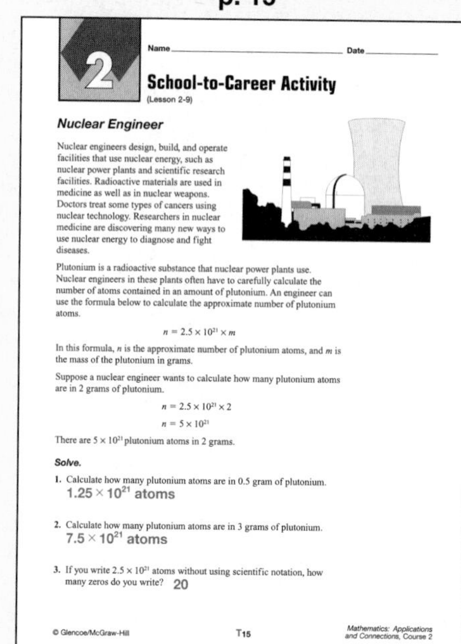

2

Name ________ Date ________

School-to-Career Activity
(Lesson 2-9)

Nuclear Engineer

Nuclear engineers design, build, and operate facilities that use nuclear energy, such as nuclear power plants and scientific research facilities. Radioactive materials are used in medicine as well as in nuclear weapons. Doctors treat some types of cancers using nuclear technology. Researchers in nuclear medicine are discovering many new ways to use nuclear energy to diagnose and fight diseases.

Plutonium is a radioactive substance that nuclear power plants use. Nuclear engineers in these plants often have to carefully calculate the number of atoms contained in an amount of plutonium. An engineer can use the formula below to calculate the approximate number of plutonium atoms.

$$n = 2.5 \times 10^{21} \times m$$

In this formula, n is the approximate number of plutonium atoms, and m is the mass of the plutonium in grams.

Suppose a nuclear engineer wants to calculate how many plutonium atoms are in 2 grams of plutonium.

$$n = 2.5 \times 10^{21} \times 2$$
$$n = 5 \times 10^{21}$$

There are 5×10^{21} plutonium atoms in 2 grams.

Solve.

1. Calculate how many plutonium atoms are in 0.5 gram of plutonium. 1.25×10^{21} atoms
2. Calculate how many plutonium atoms are in 3 grams of plutonium. 7.5×10^{21} atoms
3. If you write 2.5×10^{21} atoms without using scientific notation, how many zeros do you write? 20

© Glencoe/McGraw-Hill T15 *Mathematics: Applications and Connections, Course 2*

Family Letters and Activities, pp. 29–30

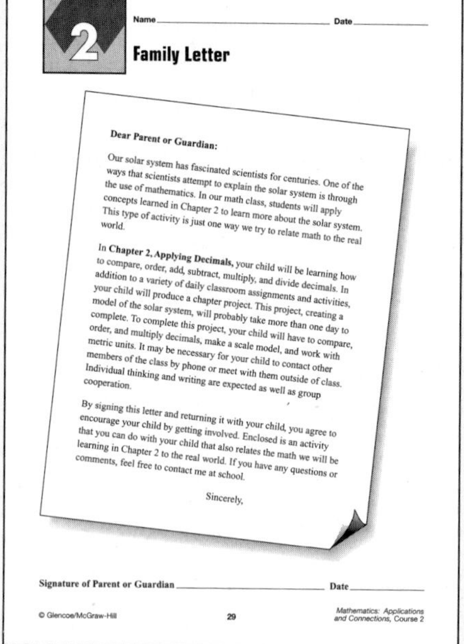

2

Name ________ Date ________

Family Letter

Dear Parent or Guardian:

Our solar system has fascinated scientists for centuries. One of the ways that scientists attempt to explain the solar system is through the use of mathematics. In our math class, students will apply concepts learned in Chapter 2 to learn more about the solar system. This type of activity is just one way we try to relate math to the real world.

In **Chapter 2, Applying Decimals,** your child will be learning how to compare, order, add, subtract, multiply, and divide decimals. In addition to a variety of daily classroom assignments and activities, your child will produce a chapter project. This project, creating a model of the solar system, will probably take more than one day to complete. To complete this project, your child will have to compare, order, and multiply decimals, make a scale model, and work with metric units. It may be necessary for your child to contact other members of the class by phone or meet with them outside of class. Individual thinking and writing are expected as well as group cooperation.

By signing this letter and returning it with your child, you agree to encourage your child by getting involved. Enclosed is an activity that you can do with your child that also relates the math we will be learning in Chapter 2 to the real world. If you have any questions or comments, feel free to contact me at school.

Sincerely,

Signature of Parent or Guardian ________ **Date** ________

© Glencoe/McGraw-Hill 29 *Mathematics: Applications and Connections, Course 2*

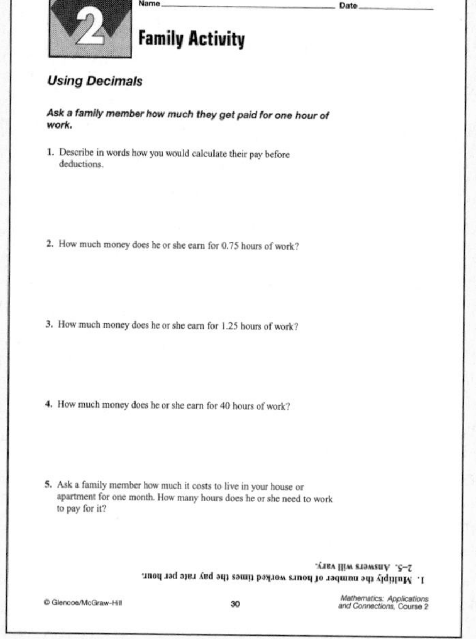

2

Name ________ Date ________

Family Activity

Using Decimals

Ask a family member how much they get paid for one hour of work.

1. Describe in words how you would calculate their pay before deductions.
2. How much money does he or she earn for 0.75 hours of work?
3. How much money does he or she earn for 1.25 hours of work?
4. How much money does he or she earn for 40 hours of work?
5. Ask a family member how much it costs to live in your house or apartment for one month. How many hours does he or she need to work to pay for it?

1. Multiply the number of hours worked times the pay rate per hour.
2–5. Answers will vary.

© Glencoe/McGraw-Hill 30 *Mathematics: Applications and Connections, Course 2*

Science and Math Lab Manual, pp. 25–28

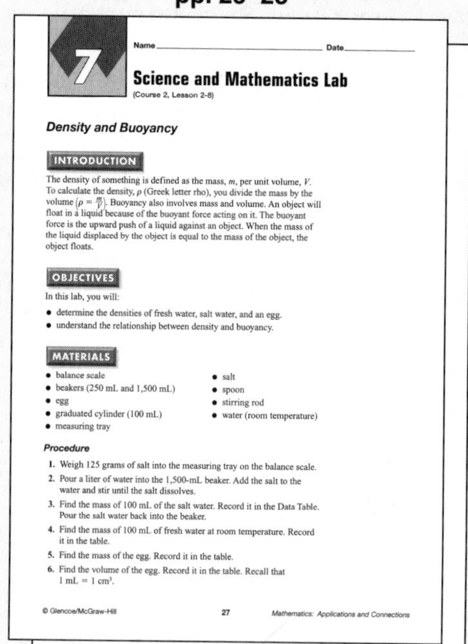

7

Name ________ Date ________

Science and Mathematics Lab
(Course 2, Lesson 2-8)

Density and Buoyancy

INTRODUCTION

The density of something is defined as the mass, m, per unit volume, V. To calculate the density, ρ (Greek letter rho), you divide the mass by the volume $\left(\rho = \frac{m}{V}\right)$. Buoyancy also involves mass and volume. An object will float in a liquid because of the buoyant force acting on it. The buoyant force is the upward push of a liquid against an object. When the mass of the liquid displaced by the object is equal to the mass of the object, the object floats.

OBJECTIVES

In this lab, you will:

- determine the densities of fresh water, salt water, and an egg.
- understand the relationship between density and buoyancy.

MATERIALS

- balance scale
- beakers (250 mL and 1,500 mL)
- egg
- graduated cylinder (100 mL)
- measuring tray
- salt
- spoon
- stirring rod
- water (room temperature)

Procedure

1. Weigh 125 grams of salt into the measuring tray on the balance scale.
2. Pour a liter of water into the 1,500-mL beaker. Add the salt to the water and stir until the salt dissolves.
3. Find the mass of 100 mL of the salt water. Record it in the Data Table. Pour the salt water back into the beaker.
4. Find the mass of 100 mL of fresh water at room temperature. Record it in the table.
5. Find the mass of the egg. Record it in the table.
6. Find the volume of the egg. Record it in the table. Recall that $1 \text{ mL} = 1 \text{ cm}^3$.

© Glencoe/McGraw-Hill 27 *Mathematics: Applications and Connections*

MANIPULATIVES/MODELING

Hands-On Lab Masters, p. 73

Name ______ Date ______

2 Lab Activity
(Lesson 2-2)

Rounding Decimals

materials: centimeter ruler

Measure each line segment to the nearest whole centimeter.

1. 8 cm
2. 8 cm
3. 7 cm
4. 7 cm
5. 9 cm
6. 9 cm
7. Draw a line segment 6.0 cm long.
8. Draw a line segment 10.0 cm long.
9. Draw a line segment that is shorter than 10 cm, but rounds to 10 cm when rounded to the nearest centimeter.
This sample is 9.8 cm long.
10. Draw a line segment that is longer than 10 cm, but rounds to 10 cm when rounded to the nearest centimeter.
This sample is 10.2 cm long.

© Glencoe/McGraw-Hill 73 *Mathematics: Applications and Connections, Course 2*

ASSESSMENT/EVALUATION

Assessment and Evaluation Masters, pp. 42–44

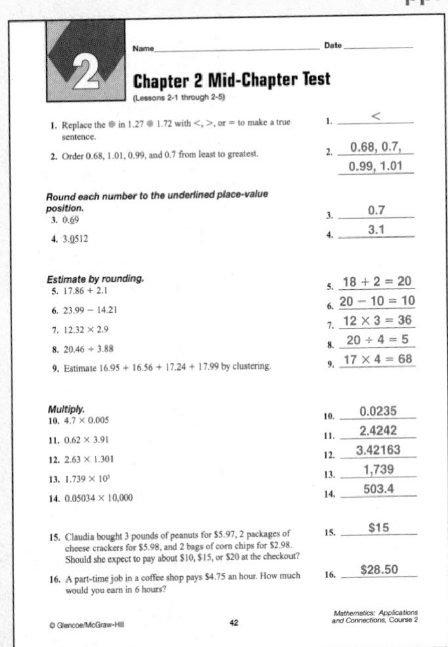

Name ______ Date ______

2 Chapter 2 Mid-Chapter Test
(Lessons 2-1 through 2-5)

1. Replace the ● in 1.27 ● 1.72 with $<$, $>$, or $=$ to make a true sentence. — 1. $<$
2. Order 0.68, 1.01, 0.99, and 0.7 from least to greatest. — 2. 0.68, 0.7, 0.99, 1.01

Round each number to the underlined place-value position.

3. 0.69 — 3. 0.7
4. 3.0512 — 4. 3.1

Estimate by rounding.

5. 17.86 + 2.1 — 5. 18 + 2 = 20
6. 23.99 − 14.21 — 6. 20 − 10 = 10
7. 12.32 × 2.9 — 7. 12 × 3 = 36
8. 20.46 ÷ 3.88 — 8. 20 ÷ 4 = 5
9. Estimate 16.95 + 16.56 + 17.24 + 17.99 by clustering. — 9. 17 × 4 = 68

Multiply.

10. 4.7 × 0.005 — 10. 0.0235
11. 0.62 × 3.91 — 11. 2.4242
12. 2.63 × 1.301 — 12. 3.42163
13. 1.739×10^3 — 13. 1,739
14. 0.05034 × 10,000 — 14. 503.4
15. Claudia bought 3 pounds of peanuts for \$5.97, 2 packages of cheese crackers for \$5.98, and 2 bags of corn chips for \$2.98. Should she expect to pay about \$10, \$15, or \$20 at the checkout? — 15. \$15
16. A part-time job in a coffee shop pays \$4.75 an hour. How much would you earn in 6 hours? — 16. \$28.50

© Glencoe/McGraw-Hill 42 *Mathematics: Applications and Connections, Course 2*

Name ______ Date ______

Chapter 2 Quiz A (Lessons 2-1 through 2-3)

Replace each ● with $<$, $>$, or $=$ to make a true sentence.

1. 0.0026 ● 0.026 — 1. $<$
2. 8.08 ● 8 — 2. $>$

Order each set of numbers from least to greatest.

3. 2.305, 3.205, 4.102, 1.420, 1.425 — 3. 1.420, 1.425, 2.305, 3.205, 4.102
4. 19.1, 17.6, 11.9, 16.7 — 4. 11.9, 16.7, 17.6, 19.1

Round each number to the underlined place-value position.

5. 0.95 — 5. 1.0
6. 16.712 — 6. 17

Estimate by rounding.

7. 46.12 + 19.6 — 7. 50 + 20 = 70
8. 76.96 − 34.25 — 8. 80 − 30 = 50
9. 7.52 × 8 — 9. 8 × 8 = 64
10. $0.9\overline{)7.83}$ — 10. 8 ÷ 1 = 8

Name ______ Date ______

Chapter 2 Quiz B (Lessons 2-4 and 2-5)

Multiply.

1. 0.52 × 18 — 1. 9.36
2. 0.0032 × 0.49 — 2. 0.001568
3. 17.21 × 3.9 — 3. 67.119
4. 28.12 × 0.04 — 4. 1.1248
5. Pears cost \$1.29 a pound. How much will 7 pounds cost? — 5. \$9.03

Multiply mentally.

6. 13.470 × 1,000 — 6. 13,470
7. 0.0391 × 100 — 7. 3.91
8. 1.753×10^3 — 8. 1,753
9. $1{,}937 \times 10^2$ — 9. 193,700
10. 3.7141×10^5 — 10. 371,410

© Glencoe/McGraw-Hill 43 *Mathematics: Applications and Connections, Course 2*

TECHNOLOGY/MULTIMEDIA

Technology Masters, pp. 29–30

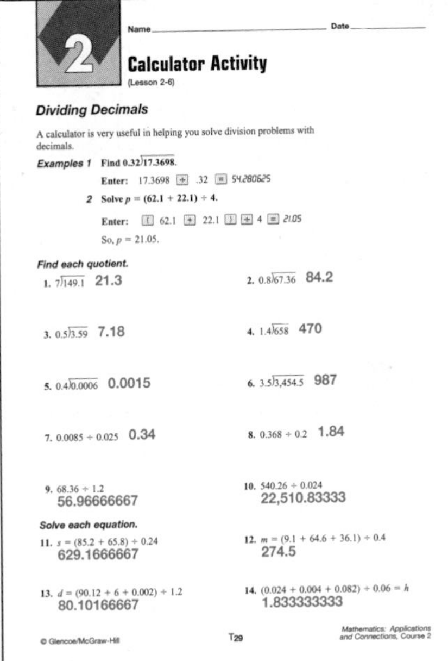

Name ______ Date ______

2 Calculator Activity
(Lesson 2-6)

Dividing Decimals

A calculator is very useful in helping you solve division problems with decimals.

Examples 1 **Find $0.32\overline{)17.3698}$.**

Enter: 17.3698 [÷] .32 [=] 54.280625

2 **Solve $p = (62.1 + 22.1) \div 4$.**

Enter: [(] 62.1 [+] 22.1 [)] [÷] 4 [=] 21.05

So, $p = 21.05$.

Find each quotient.

1. $7\overline{)149.1}$ 21.3
2. $0.8\overline{)67.36}$ 84.2
3. $0.5\overline{)3.59}$ 7.18
4. $1.4\overline{)658}$ 470
5. $0.4\overline{)0.0006}$ 0.0015
6. $3.5\overline{)3{,}454.5}$ 987
7. 0.0085 ÷ 0.025 0.34
8. 0.368 ÷ 0.2 1.84
9. 68.36 ÷ 1.2 56.96666667
10. 540.26 ÷ 0.024 22,510.83333

Solve each equation.

11. $s = (85.2 + 65.8) \div 0.24$ 629.1666667
12. $m = (9.1 + 64.6 + 36.1) \div 0.4$ 274.5
13. $d = (90.12 + 6 + 0.002) \div 1.2$ 80.10166667
14. $(0.024 + 0.004 + 0.082) \div 0.06 = h$ 1.833333333

© Glencoe/McGraw-Hill T29 *Mathematics: Applications and Connections, Course 2*

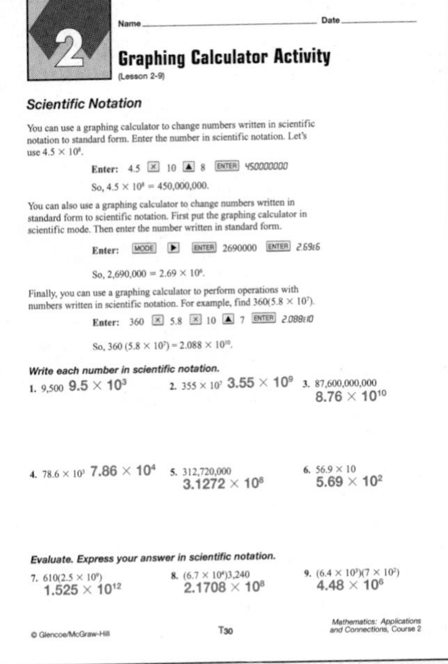

Name ______ Date ______

2 Graphing Calculator Activity
(Lesson 2-9)

Scientific Notation

You can use a graphing calculator to change numbers written in scientific notation to standard form. Enter the number in scientific notation. Let's use 4.5×10^8.

Enter: 4.5 [×] 10 [▲] 8 [ENTER] 450000000

So, $4.5 \times 10^8 = 450{,}000{,}000$.

You can also use a graphing calculator to change numbers written in standard form to scientific notation. First put the graphing calculator in scientific mode. Then enter the number written in standard form.

Enter: [MODE] [▶] [ENTER] 2690000 [ENTER] 2.69E6

So, $2{,}690{,}000 = 2.69 \times 10^6$.

Finally, you can use a graphing calculator to perform operations with numbers written in scientific notation. For example, find $360(5.8 \times 10^7)$.

Enter: 360 [×] 5.8 [×] 10 [▲] 7 [ENTER] 2.088E10

So, $360\,(5.8 \times 10^7) = 2.088 \times 10^{10}$.

Write each number in scientific notation.

1. 9,500 9.5×10^3
2. 355×10^7 3.55×10^9
3. 87,600,000,000 8.76×10^{10}
4. 78.6×10^3 7.86×10^4
5. 312,720,000 3.1272×10^8
6. 56.9×10 5.69×10^2

Evaluate. Express your answer in scientific notation.

7. $610(2.5 \times 10^9)$ 1.525×10^{12}
8. $(6.7 \times 10^4)3{,}240$ 2.1708×10^8
9. $(6.4 \times 10^3)(7 \times 10^2)$ 4.48×10^6

© Glencoe/McGraw-Hill T30 *Mathematics: Applications and Connections, Course 2*

MEETING INDIVIDUAL NEEDS

Investigations for the Special Education Student, p. 7

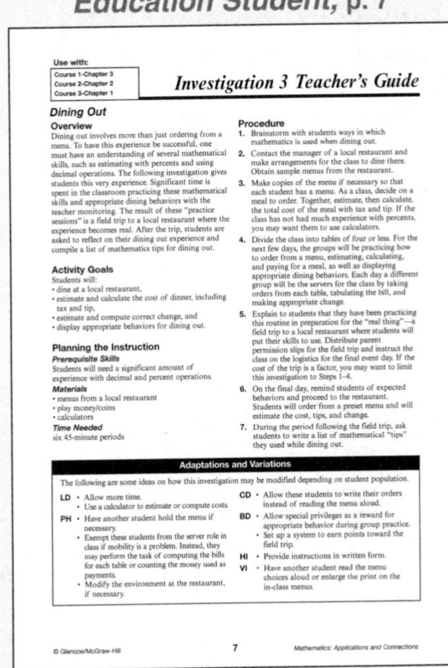

Use with:
Course 1-Chapter 3
Course 2-Chapter 2
Course 3-Chapter 1

Investigation 3 Teacher's Guide

Dining Out

Overview

Dining out involves more than just ordering from a menu. To have this experience be successful, one must have an understanding of several mathematical skills, such as estimating with percents and using decimal operations. The following investigation gives students this very experience. Significant time is spent in the classroom practicing these mathematical skills and appropriate dining behaviors with the teacher monitoring. The result of these "practice sessions" is a field trip to a local restaurant where the experience becomes real. After the trip, students are asked to reflect on their dining out experience and compile a list of mathematics tips for dining out.

Activity Goals

Students will:
- dine at a local restaurant,
- estimate and calculate the cost of dinner, including tax and tip,
- estimate and compute correct change, and
- display appropriate behaviors for dining out.

Planning the Instruction

Prerequisite Skills

Students will need a significant amount of experience with decimal and percent operations.

Materials
- menus from a local restaurant
- play money/coins
- calculators

Time Needed

six 45-minute periods

Procedure

1. Brainstorm with students ways in which mathematics is used when dining out.
2. Contact the manager of a local restaurant and make arrangements for the class to dine there. Obtain sample menus from the restaurant.
3. Make copies of the menu if necessary so that each student has a menu. As a class, decide on a meal to order. Together, estimate, then calculate, the total cost of the meal with tax and tip. If the class has not had much experience with percents, you may want them to use calculators.
4. Divide the class into tables of four or less. For the next few days, the groups will be practicing how to order from a menu, estimating, calculating, and paying for a meal, as well as displaying appropriate dining behaviors. Each day a different group will be the servers for the class by taking orders from each table, tabulating the bill, and making appropriate change.
5. Explain to students that they have been practicing this routine in preparation for the "real thing"—a field trip to a local restaurant where students will put their skills to use. Distribute parent permission slips for the field trip and instruct the class on the logistics for the final event day. If the cost of the trip is a factor, you may want to limit this investigation to Steps 1–4.
6. On the final day, remind students of expected behaviors and proceed to the restaurant. Students will order from a preset menu and will estimate the cost, tips, and change.
7. During the period following the field trip, ask students to write a list of mathematical "tips" they used while dining out.

Adaptations and Variations

The following are some ideas on how this investigation may be modified depending on student population.

LD • Allow more time.
• Use a calculator to estimate or compute costs.

PH • Have another student hold the menu if necessary.
• Exempt these students from the server role in class if mobility is a problem. Instead, they may perform the task of computing the bills for each table or counting the money used as payments.
• Modify the environment at the restaurant, if necessary.

CD • Allow these students to write their orders instead of reading the menu aloud.

BD • Allow special privileges as a reward for appropriate behavior during group practice.
• Set up a system to earn points toward the field trip.

HI • Provide instructions in written form.

VI • Have another student read the menu choices aloud or enlarge the print on the in-class menus.

© Glencoe/McGraw-Hill 7 *Mathematics: Applications and Connections*

CHAPTER 2 NOTES

Theme: Solar System

Some students may not realize that new planets and stars are always being discovered.

Astronomers William Cochran of the University of Texas and Geoffrey Marcy of San Francisco State have discovered a strange, huge planet—about 1.6 times the size of Jupiter. The unnamed planet circles one of the twin stars in the constellation Cygus, 600 trillion miles from Earth. Investigations of its odd-shaped orbit are expected to lead to many other discoveries.

Question of the Day If Jupiter is 11.2 times the size of Earth, how large is this new planet compared to Earth? **17.92 times the size of Earth**

Assess Prerequisite Skills

Ask students to read through the list of objectives presented in "What you'll learn in Chapter 2." You may wish to ask them what each of the objectives means or if they have experienced or used any of these math concepts before.

Building Portfolios

Encourage students to revise their portfolios as they study this chapter. They may find some lessons more challenging than others and wish to include work that shows how they have improved their mathematical skills.

Math and the Family

In the *Family Letters and Activities* booklet (pp. 29–30), you will find a letter to the parents explaining what students will study in Chapter 2. An activity appropriate for the whole family is also available.

CHAPTER 2 Applying Decimals

What you'll learn in Chapter 2

- to compute, estimate, and solve problems using decimals,
- to express decimals in scientific notation and fractions as decimals,
- to find patterns in repeating decimals,
- to use metric units of length, mass, and capacity, and
- to determine reasonable answers in real-world problems.

42 Chapter 2 Applying Decimals

CD-ROM Program

Activities for Chapter 2

- Chapter 2 Introduction
- Interactive Lessons 2-1, 2-4, 2-6, 2-8
- Assessment Game
- Resource Lessons 2-1 through 2-9

CHAPTER Project

HOW BIG IS OUR SOLAR SYSTEM?

In this project, you will use decimals to make a model of our solar system. You can use any type of material for your model such as Styrofoam, modeling clay, balls, marbles, or balloons.

Getting Started

- Look at the solar system table. About how many times bigger is Jupiter's diameter than Earth's diameter?
- Use the table to determine which planet's average distance from the Sun is about 30 times Earth's distance from the sun.

Planet	Diameter (Earth = 1)	Average Distance to Sun (AU) (Earth = 1)
Mercury	0.38	0.387
Venus	0.95	0.723
Earth	1.00	1.000
Mars	0.53	1.524
Jupiter	11.19	5.203
Saturn	9.46	9.529
Uranus	4.01	19.191
Neptune	3.88	30.061
Pluto	0.18	39.529

Technology Tips

- Use a **spreadsheet** to convert from miles or kilometers to astronomical units (AU).
- Use an **electronic encyclopedia** to do your research.
- Use a **word processor.**

Data Update For up-to-date information on the solar system, visit: www.glencoe.com/sec/math/mac/mathnet

Working on the Project

You can use what you'll learn in Chapter 2 to help you make your solar system model.

Page	Exercise
46	28
59	32
76	27
83	Alternative Assessment

interNET CONNECTION

Glencoe has made every effort to ensure that the website links for *Mathematics: Applications and Connections* at www.glencoe.com/sec/math/mac/mathnet are current and contain appropriate content. However, these website links are not under Glencoe's control.

Instructional Resources ▶▶▶

A recording sheet to help students organize their data for the Chapter Project is shown at the right and is available in the *Investigations and Projects Masters*, p. 24.

CHAPTER Project NOTES

Objectives Students should

- gain an understanding of what an astronomical unit is and how it is used in astronomy.
- be able to differentiate the size of each planet in comparison to Earth and estimate how far each planet is from the Sun.

Project Pointer You may suggest that students begin a *Project Folder* to keep their work as they complete each stage of the Chapter Project. The completed project may also be added to their portfolios.

Using the Table Students may not be able to understand how to interpret the measures given in the Diameter column. They are probably not familiar with the concept of using one measurement as the base and all measures represented in terms of that base. Students should explore how these numbers were derived as they work on the Chapter Project.

***Investigations and Projects Masters,* p. 24**

Name ________ Date ________

Chapter 2 Project

How Big Is Our Solar System?

Page 46, Working on the Chapter Project, Exercise 28

Page 59, Working on the Chapter Project, Exercise 32

Page 76, Working on the Chapter Project, Exercise 27

a.

Planet	Diameter	Actual Diameter (km)	Diameter (cm)

b.

Planet	Distance from Sun	Actual Average Distance (million km)	Distance (cm)

 24 *Mathematics: Applications and Connections, Course 2*

2-1 Lesson Notes

Instructional Resources

- *Study Guide Masters,* p. 8
- *Practice Masters,* p. 8
- *Enrichment Masters,* p. 8
- Transparencies 2-1, A and B

- CD-ROM Program
  - Resource Lesson 2-1
  - Interactive Lesson 2-1

Recommended Pacing	
Standard	Day 2 of 14
Honors	Day 2 of 13
Block	Day 1 of 7

1 FOCUS

5-Minute Check (Chapter 1)

1. Evaluate the expression $18 - (7 \times 2) + 5$. **9**
2. Evaluate $\frac{ab}{4}$ if $a = 6$ and $b = 12$. **18**
3. Write $3 \cdot 3 \cdot 3 \cdot x \cdot x \cdot x \cdot x$ using exponents. 3^3x^4
4. Solve $9 + y = 17$ mentally. **8**
5. Find the length of a rectangle with an area of 45 square meters and a width of 5 meters. **9 meters**

The 5-Minute Check is also available on **Transparency 2-1A** for this lesson.

Motivating the Lesson

Communication Ask students why they think there are decimal values in the chart. Have students calculate the frequency of letters in the names of all the students in their class.

2 TEACH

Transparency 2-1B contains a teaching aid for this lesson.

Using Calculators Students can use calculators to compare two decimals. If they subtract the two numbers and get a value with a negative sign, the first number is less than the second. If they get a zero, the numbers are equal. Otherwise, the first number is greater.

2-1 Comparing and Orderi ecimals

***What** you'll learn*

You'll learn to compare and order decimals.

***When** am I ever going to use this?*

Knowing how to order decimals can help you find books in the library.

Have you ever noticed that contestants on a television word game show often choose the letter R and almost *never* choose Q? They know that the letter R is used more often than the letter Q. The chart shows that an R is used, on average, 6.8 times out of 100 letters, but Q is used only 0.1 time.

Number of Times, per 100, That Each Letter is Used

Letter	Times	Letter	Times	Letter	Times
A	8.2	J	0.1	S	6.0
B	1.4	K	0.4	T	10.5
C	2.8	L	3.4	U	2.5
D	3.8	M	2.5	V	0.9
E	13.0	N	7.0	W	1.5
F	3.0	O	8.0	X	0.2
G	2.0	P	2.0	Y	2.0
H	5.3	Q	0.1	Z	0.07
I	6.5	R	6.8		

When you use words like *more, less,* or *equal to,* you are comparing numbers. You can compare decimals like 6.8 and 0.1 using a number line.

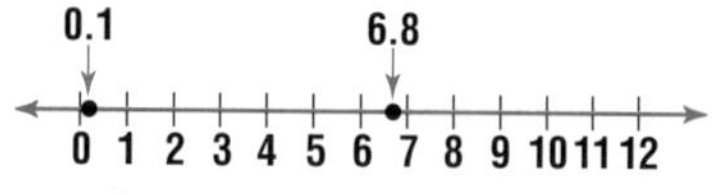

On a number line, numbers to the right are greater than numbers to the left.

6.8 is greater than 0.1. $6.8 > 0.1$

0.1 is less than 6.8. $0.1 < 6.8$

Study Hint

Reading Math The symbols < and > always point to the lesser of the two numbers.

You can also compare decimals by comparing the digits in each place-value position. For example, to compare 3.47 and 3.82, align the numbers by their decimal points.

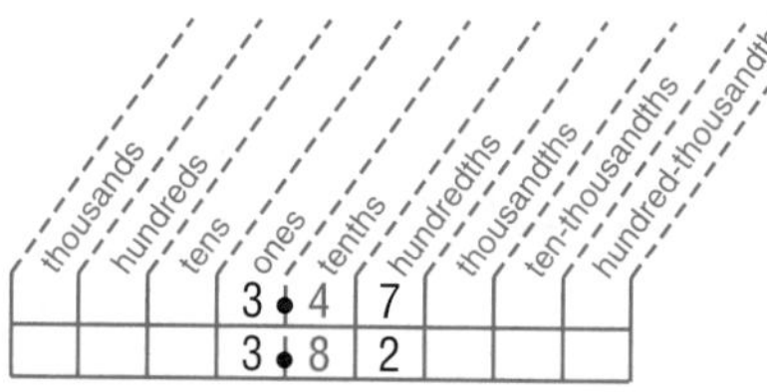

Start at the left and compare the digits in each place-value position. In the ones place, the digits are the same. In the tenths place, $4 < 8$. So, $3.47 < 3.82$.

Example 1 **Compare 0.3 and 0.30.**

0.3 *In the ones and tenths places,*
0.30 *the digits are the same.*

Annexing zeros to the right of a decimal produces *equivalent* decimals.

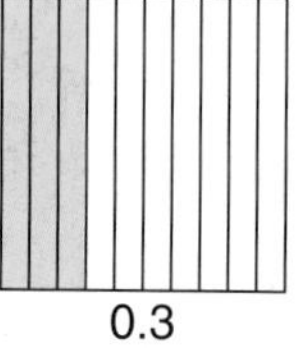

0.3

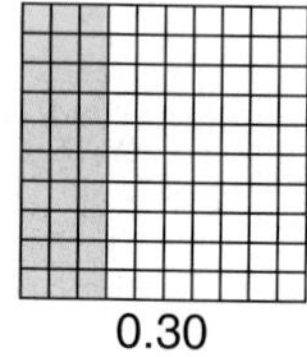

0.30

So, $0.3 = 0.30$. *The models also show that 0.3 and 0.30 are equivalent.*

Cross-Curriculum Cue

Inform the other teachers on your team that your students are studying decimals. Suggestions for curriculum integration are:

Physical Education: measuring speed and distance

Earth Science: astronomical measurements; formulas; weather

2 Libraries When Katie was doing research on whales for a science project, she found the titles of four books. She knows that the books are placed on the shelf by numbers ordered from least to greatest. In what order will she find the books?

Books About Whales

Title	Number
Where the Whales Are	599.5097
The World of the Arctic Whales	599.5091
Gentle Giant: The Humpback Whale	599.51
Giants of the Sea	599.5

The numbers of the books are 599.5097, 599.5091, 599.51, and 599.5. Locate the numbers on a number line.

599.5 599.5091 599.5097 599.51

599.500 599.505 599.510

The least number is 599.5.
The greatest number is 599.51.

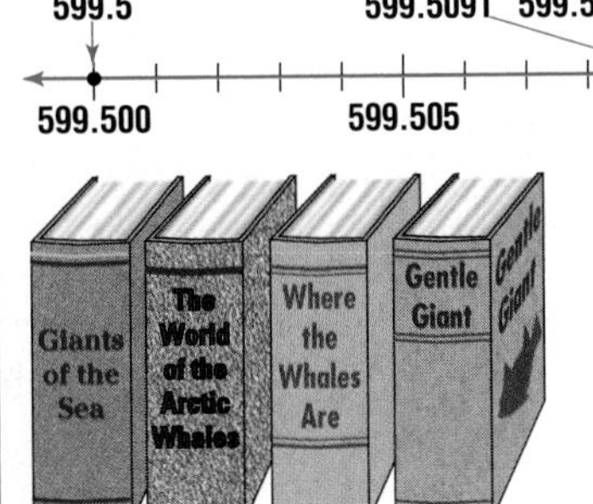

From least to greatest, the numbers are 599.5, 599.5091, 599.5097, 599.51. So, Katie will find the books in this order from left to right.

CHECK FOR UNDERSTANDING

Communicating Mathematics

Read and study the lesson to answer each question.

1. ***Write*** a number sentence comparing two of the numbers shown on the number line.

   0.30 0.50 0.70

2. ***Draw*** models of 0.2 and 0.18. Then write a number sentence that compares them. **See Answer Appendix.**

3. ***Write*** a few sentences explaining why 0.4 is the same as 0.40. **See margin.**

1. Sample answer: 0.30 < 0.50

Guided Practice

Replace each ● with <, >, or = to make a true sentence.

4. 1.22 ● 1.02 **>**
5. 0.97 ● 1.06 **<**
6. 7.90 ● 7.9 **=**
7. 1.3 ● 1.31 **<**
8. Order 5.13, 5.07, and 5.009 from least to greatest. **5.009, 5.07, 5.13**
9. ***Food*** One serving of chocolate jimmies on your frozen yogurt adds 144 Calories and 5.9 grams of fat. One serving of peanut butter cup crumbles adds 92 Calories and 5.3 grams of fat. Which topping has more grams of fat? **chocolate jimmies**

In-Class Examples

For Example 1
Compare 34.7 and 32.9.
34.7 > 32.9

For Example 2
The readouts from four scales for the same object were 34.5, 34.505, 34.05, and 34.005. List these weights in order from greatest to least. **34.505, 34.5, 34.05, 34.005**

3 PRACTICE/APPLY

Check for Understanding

If students need additional practice or instruction after completing Exercises 1–9, one of these options may be helpful.

- Extra Practice, see p. 570
- Reteaching Activity
- *Transition Booklet,* pp. 13–14
- *Study Guide Masters,* p. 8
- *Practice Masters,* p. 8
- Interactive Mathematics Tools Software

Additional Answer

3. Sample answer: You can add a zero to the right of a decimal without changing the value. So, 0.4 = 0.40.

***Study Guide Masters,* p. 8**

Name________________ Date________

Study Guide

Comparing and Ordering Decimals

Which is greater, 36.74 or 36.704?

You can compare decimals like 36.74 and 36.704 on a number line. Numbers to the right are greater than numbers to the left.

36.704 36.74

36.70 36.71 36.72 36.73 36.74

You can also compare decimals by comparing the digits in each place-value position.

Find the first place in which the digits are different.	Compare the digits.	The decimal with the greater digit is greater.
36.704 36.74	0 is less than 4. 0 < 4	36.704 < 36.74

Draw a number line to show which decimal is greater.

1. 0.39, 0.35
2. 1.95, 2.02
3. 6.55, 6.50

1. 0.35 0.39 — 0.34 0.35 0.36 0.37 0.38 0.39 0.40

2. 1.95 2.02 — 1.92 1.94 1.96 1.98 2.00 2.02 2.04

3. 6.50 6.55

Replace each ○ with <, >, or = to make a true sentence.

4. 8.05 ○ 8.5 **<**
5. 0.76 ○ 0.67 **>**
6. 18.20 ○ 18.2 **=**
7. 7.004 ○ 7.044 **<**
8. 6.79 ○ 6.8 **<**
9. 29.922 ○ 29.299 **>**

Order each set of numbers from least to greatest.

10. 0.067, 0.6, 0.76, 0.07 **0.067, 0.07, 0.6, 0.76**
11. 56.2, 55.6, 52.2, 56.02 **52.2, 55.6, 56.02, 56.2**
12. 600.09, 609.06, 600.9, 609.9 **600.09, 600.9, 609.06, 609.9**
13. 0.88, 0.9, 0.08, 0.89 **0.08, 0.88, 0.89, 0.9**

 T8 *Mathematics: Applications and Connections, Course 2*

Reteaching the Lesson

Activity Use a newspaper to find common baseball statistics such as batting averages. Students can easily understand that a batting average of ".324" is greater than one of ".299." Point out that these are actually decimals, so 0.324 > 0.299.

Error Analysis
Watch for students who incorrectly use the > and < symbols.
Prevent by reinforcing the fact that the > and < symbols always point to the lesser number and their open sides always face the greater number.

Assignment Guide

Core: 11–27 odd, 29–33
Enriched: 10–26 even, 27, 29–33

Exercise 28 asks students to advance to the next stage of work on the Chapter Project. You may require students to place their work in their Project Folders.

4 ASSESS

Closing Activity

Modeling Have students use decimal models to demonstrate how two decimals can be compared physically and then in symbolic language.

EXERCISES

Practice

Replace each ● with <, >, or = to make a true sentence.

10. 4.03 ● 4.01 **>** **11.** 0.77 ● 0.69 **>** **12.** 0.8 ● 0.08 **>**
13. 0.68 ● 0.680 **=** **14.** 3.28 ● 3.279 **>** **15.** 0.23 ● 0.32 **<**
16. 0.55 ● 0.65 **<** **17.** 1.29 ● 1.43 **<** **18.** 2.36 ● 2.3600 **=**
19. 0.0034 ● 0.034 **<** **20.** 1.67 ● 0.48 **>** **21.** 9.09 ● 9 **>**

22. Which is the greatest, 0.9, 0.088, 1.02, or 0.98? **1.02**

23. Which is the least, 0.087, 0.901, 2, or 1.001? **0.087**

24. Order 12.3, 12.008, 1.273, 12.54 from least to greatest. **24. 1.273, 12.008, 12.3, 12.54**

25. Order 6.5, 6.05, 6.55, 6.505 from greatest to least. **6.55, 6.505, 6.5, 6.05**

Applications and Problem Solving

26. ***Games*** During the bonus round on a television word game show, the consonants R, S, T, L, N and the vowel E are automatically turned over. The contestant then gets to choose three more consonants and one more vowel. Refer to the chart on page 44. What letters should the contestant choose? **26. H, D, F, A**

27. ***Leisure Time*** The chart shows how teenagers and unmarried adults spend some of their leisure time.

a. On which activities do the teenagers spend less time than the adults? **27a. visiting friends, reading**

b. Order each list from greatest number of hours to least number of hours. **27b. teenagers: 17.7, 4.4, 1.3, 1.2, 1.1, 0.9; unmarried adults: 14.2, 7.8, 1.9, 0.7, 0.7, 0.5**

c. Make a graph to show the information. **See Answer Appendix.**

Leisure Time (hours per week)

Activity	Teenagers age 12–17	Unmarried Adults age 18–29
organizations	1.2	0.5
visiting friends	4.4	7.8
hobbies	1.1	0.7
listening to music	0.9	0.7
television	17.7	14.2
reading	1.3	1.9

Source: Americans' Use of Time Project

28. ***Working on the*** **CHAPTER Project** Refer to the table on page 43.

a. Make a chart listing the planets in order from greatest to least diameter. **28a. See Answer Appendix.**

b. Make another chart listing the planets in order from greatest to least average distance from the Sun. **See Answer Appendix.**

29. ***Critical Thinking*** Place decimal points in 999, 463, 208, and 175 so that the resulting decimals will be in order from least to greatest. **0.999, 4.63, 20.8, 175**

Mixed Review

30. ***Geometry*** Find the width of a rectangle with an area of 35 square inches and a length of 7 inches. *(Lesson 1-7)* **5 in.**

31. **Standardized Test Practice** Carla is six years old and is 12 years younger than Maria. Which equation can be used to find Maria's age? *(Lesson 1–5)* **B**

A $c = m + 12$ **B** $c = m - 12$ **C** $m = 12$ **D** $c + m = 12$

For **Extra Practice**, see page 570.

32. Write 2^5 as a product. *(Lesson 1–4)* **$2 \cdot 2 \cdot 2 \cdot 2 \cdot 2$**

33. Evaluate $3(4 + 8) - 2 \cdot 5$. *(Lesson 1–2)* **26**

Practice Masters, p. 8

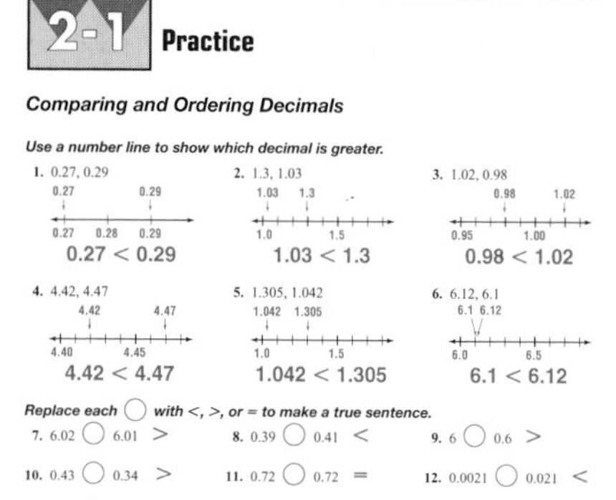

Name ______ Date ______

2-1 Practice

Comparing and Ordering Decimals

Use a number line to show which decimal is greater.

1. 0.27, 0.29 — 0.27 < 0.29
2. 1.3, 1.03 — 1.03 < 1.3
3. 1.02, 0.98 — 0.98 < 1.02
4. 4.42, 4.47 — 4.42 < 4.47
5. 1.305, 1.042 — 1.042 < 1.305
6. 6.12, 6.1 — 6.1 < 6.12

Replace each ◯ with <, >, or = to make a true sentence.

7. 6.02 ◯ 6.01 > 8. 0.39 ◯ 0.41 < 9. 6 ◯ 0.6 >
10. 0.43 ◯ 0.34 > 11. 0.72 ◯ 0.72 = 12. 0.0021 ◯ 0.021 <
13. 0.34 ◯ 0.48 < 14. 5.2 ◯ 5 > 15. 3.7 ◯ 3.7 =
16. 1.47 ◯ 1.47 = 17. 1.75 ◯ 0.77 > 18. 4.52 ◯ 0.98 >

Write a sentence comparing two of the numbers shown on the number line. Sample answers are given.

19. 0.40 0.60 0.80 — 0.40 < 0.80
20. 1.30 1.50 1.70 — 1.70 > 1.50
21. 6.1 6.3 6.5 — 6.3 < 6.5

Order each set of numbers from least to greatest.

22. 4.03, 4.003, 4.3 — 4.003, 4.03, 4.3
23. 0.82, 1.2, 0.92 — 0.82, 0.92, 1.2
24. 1.12, 1.135, 1.02 — 1.02, 1.12, 1.135
25. 13.72, 1.372, 137.2 — 1.372, 13.72, 137.2
26. 6.5, 0.65, 0.065 — 0.065, 0.65, 6.5
27. 7.9, 3.46, 9.87, 2.1 — 2.1, 3.46, 7.9, 9.87

 T8 *Mathematics: Applications and Connections, Course 2*

Extending the Lesson

Enrichment Masters, p. 8

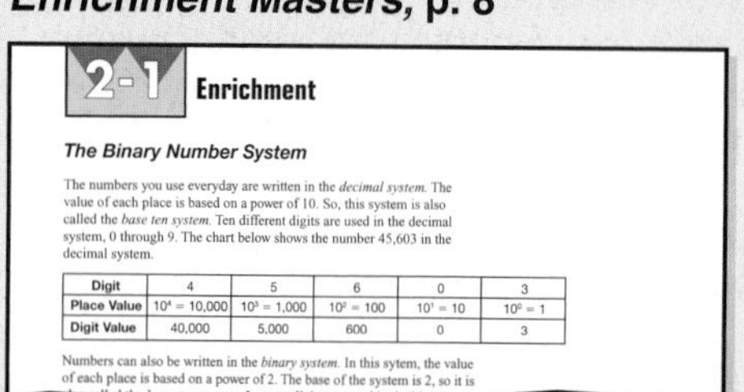

2-1 Enrichment

The Binary Number System

The numbers you use everyday are written in the *decimal system.* The value of each place is based on a power of 10. So, this system is also called the *base ten system.* Ten different digits are used in the decimal system, 0 through 9. The chart below shows the number 45,603 in the decimal system.

Digit	4	5	6	0	3
Place Value	$10^4 = 10{,}000$	$10^3 = 1{,}000$	$10^2 = 100$	$10^1 = 10$	$10^0 = 1$
Digit Value	40,000	5,000	600	0	3

Numbers can also be written in the *binary system.* In this sytem, the value of each place is based on a power of 2. The base of the system is 2, so it is

Activity Refer to Exercise 27. Ask students what inference can be made from this data. Then have them survey their classmates and compare results with their conjecture.

2-2 ounding Decimals

***What** you'll learn*

You'll learn to round decimals.

***When** am I ever going to use this?*

Knowing how to round can help you estimate with money.

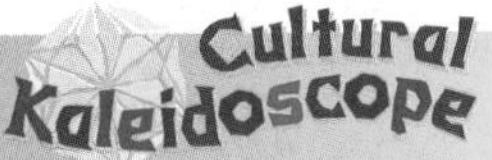

One of the best historical estimates for π was made by the Chinese astronomer Tsu Ch'ung-Chi (A.D. 470). He stated the value of π as 3.1415929, which is correct to six decimal places.

Are you a science fiction fan? In a TV show about a spaceship, an evil computer threatened to take over. To distract the computer, the ship's captain asked it to compute the exact value of pi.

Pi is a decimal that never ends and never has a pattern in its digits. So, the computer couldn't find the exact value, and the spaceship was saved!

Today, pi has been computed to over two billion decimal places. Here are the first fifteen.

The symbol for pi is π.

$$\pi \approx 3.141592653589793...$$

On the number line, the graph of π is closer to 3.14 than to 3.15. To the nearest hundredth, π rounds to 3.14.

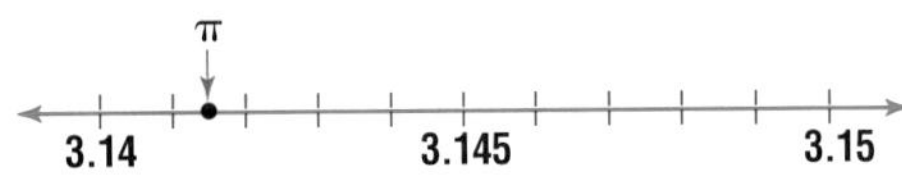

You can round to any place-value position without using a number line.

Rounding Decimals	Look at the digit to the right of the place being rounded. • The digit being rounded remains the same if the digit to the right is 0, 1, 2, 3, or 4. • Round up if the digit to the right is 5, 6, 7, 8, or 9.

Examples

1 Round 3.92 to the nearest tenth.

Look at the digit to the right of the tenths place.

3.92 *Since $2 < 5$, the digit in the tenths place stays the same.*

↑ *tenths place*

3.92 rounded to the nearest tenth is 3.9.

2 Round 46.297 to the nearest hundredth.

Look at the digit to the right of the hundredths place.

46.297 *Round up since $7 > 5$.*

↑ *hundredths place*

46.297 rounded to the nearest hundredth is 46.30.

2-2 Lesson Notes

Instructional Resources

- *Study Guide Masters,* p. 9
- *Practice Masters,* p. 9
- *Enrichment Masters,* p. 9
- Transparencies 2-2, A and B
- CD-ROM Program
  - Resource Lesson 2-2

Recommended Pacing	
Standard	Day 3 of 14
Honors	Day 3 of 13
Block	Day 2 of 7

1 FOCUS

5-Minute Check
(Lesson 2-1)

Replace each ● with $<$, $>$, or $=$ to make a true sentence.

1. 3.06 ● 3.08 $<$
2. 1.34 ● 0.86 $>$
3. 7 ● 0.7 $>$

Order each set of numbers from least to greatest.

4. 0.5, 0.55, 0.05, 0.505
   0.05, 0.5, 0.505, 0.55
5. 0.076, 1, 0.76, 1.007
   0.076, 0.76, 1, 1.007

The 5-Minute Check is also available on **Transparency 2-2A** for this lesson.

Motivating the Lesson

Problem Solving Ask students which measurements are probably a rounded amount.

- 2.72 lb of hamburger
- 1.7 light years away
- 6.75 g of sugar

Multiple Learning Styles

Interpersonal Have each group of students write a different one-digit number on each of four index cards and place a decimal point on a fifth card. Have students manipulate the cards to find and write the least and greatest number possible with these cards. Then have each student in the group describe a different activity to perform with the cards. For example, how many numbers less than 50 but greater than 0.01 can be named using all of the cards?

2 TEACH

Transparency 2-2B contains a teaching aid for this lesson.

Reading Mathematics The introduction to this lesson includes many mathematical concepts printed in verbal form. Make sure students know how to pronounce pi and have some concept of *two billion decimal places.*

In-Class Examples

For Example 1
Round 1.48 to the nearest tenth. **1.5**

For Example 2
Round 23.579 to the nearest hundredth. **23.58**

For Example 3
Mrs. Roberson buys 1.68 pounds of sausage and 3.36 pounds of hamburger for a party-size meatloaf. To the nearest pound, how much meat did she buy? **5 lb**

Teaching Tip When discussing rounding, you may want to point out situations in which the usual rounding rules do not apply, as in many money situations.

***Study Guide Masters,* p. 9**

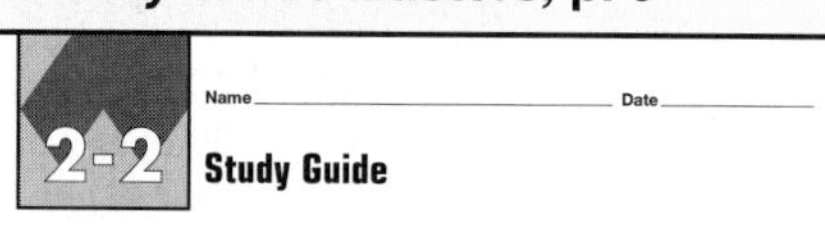

Name________________ Date________

2-2 Study Guide

Rounding Decimals

Round 24.625 to the nearest tenth.

You can use a number line.

24.625
24.6 24.7 24.8

Find the approximate location of 24.625 on the number line.

24.625 is closer to 24.6 than to 24.7.
24.625 rounded to the nearest tenth is 24.6.

You can also round without a number line.

Find the place to which you want to round.	Look at the digit to the right of the place being rounded. The digit remains the same if the digit to the right is 0, 1, 2, 3, or 4. Round up if the digit to the right is 5, 6, 7, 8, or 9.	2 is less than 5. Do not change the digit.
24.625	24.625	24.6

Round each number to the underlined place-value position.

1. 46.124 **46**	**2.** 29.915 **29.9**	**3.** 15.1733 **15.17**	**4.** 0.159 **0.16**
5. 308.862 **308.9**	**6.** 0.0561 **0.056**	**7.** 0.577 **0.6**	**8.** 0.0089 **0.01**
9. 2.62 **3**	**10.** 76.0552 **76.055**	**11.** 12.1903 **12.19**	**12.** 0.855 **0.9**
13. 331.98 **330**	**14.** 0.0549 **0.055**	**15.** 6.03 **6.0**	**16.** 173.99 **200**
17. 84.012 **84**	**18.** 0.846 **0.85**	**19.** 12.7642 **12.764**	**20.** 0.062 **0.1**

 T9 *Mathematics: Applications and Connections, Course 2*

Whole numbers are often expressed using a combination of decimals and words. For example, 2,500,000 is sometimes written as 2.5 million. In this case, the 2 is in the millions place.

3 **Computers** **The number of personal computers grew from 82.4 million in 1997 to 97.3 million in 1998. To the nearest million, about how many more personal computers were expected to be in use in 1998 than in 1997?**

Sources: *International Data; Dataquest*

Since both numbers are expressed in millions, you can subtract as you would with decimals.

$$\begin{array}{r} 97.3 \\ -\ 82.4 \\ \hline 14.9 \end{array}$$ *Align the decimal points.*

To the nearest million, 14.9 million rounds to 15 million. So, there were about 15 million more personal computers in 1998 than in 1997.

CHECK FOR UNDERSTANDING

Communicating Mathematics

Read and study the lesson to answer each question. **1. 14.4**

1. ***Show,*** using a number line, to what tenth you would round 14.37.

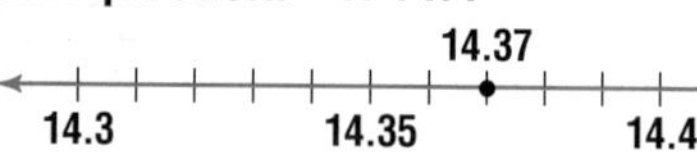

2. ***Explain*** why you can ignore all the digits to the right of 7 when rounding 4.23715 to the nearest hundredth. **See margin.**
3. ***You Decide*** Tomas rounds 11.96 to the nearest tenth and gets 12.0; Cynthia gets 12. Who is correct? Explain your reasoning. **Tomas; 12.0 is expressed in tenths.**

Guided Practice

Round each number to the place indicated.

4. 0.315; tenth **0.3**
5. 0.2456; hundredth **0.25**
6. 17.499; tenth **17.5**

Round each number to the underlined place-value position.

7. 0.789 **0.79**
8. 0.96 **1.0**
9. 1.57246 **1.57**
10. ***Shopping*** Calculations involving money are usually rounded to the nearest cent or hundredth. Diego uses his calculator to find the sales tax on purchases that total $15.99. His calculator display is shown at the right. How much sales tax will Diego pay? **$0.88**

■ Reteaching the Lesson ■

Activity Reinforce the concept of rounding by having students use a number line to round several additional numbers to the nearest whole number and to the nearest tenth.

Additional Answer

2. All numbers between 4.23700 . . . and 4.23799 . . . (inclusive) round to 4.24 to the nearest hundredth. So the digits to the right of 7 can be ignored.

EXERCISES

Practice

Round each number to the place indicated. 14. 7.038 17. 9.128

11. 0.219; hundredth **0.22** **12.** 15.552; tenth **15.6** **13.** 9.6; unit **10**

14. 7.0375; thousandth **15.** 16.399; tenth **16.4** **16.** 6.95; tenth **7.0**

17. 9.1283; thousandth **18.** 0.37; tenth **0.4** **19.** 0.445; hundredth **0.45**

Round each number to the underlined place-value position.

20. 23.48 **23** **21.** 1.704 **1.70** **22.** 0.163 **0.2**

23. 15.451 **15.5** **24.** 4.52988 **4.530** **25.** 0.787 **0.8**

26. 38.56 **40** **27.** 59.61 **60** **28.** 0.555 **0.6**

29. Draw a number line to show how 5.67 rounds to 6. **See margin.**

Applications and Problem Solving

30. ***Measurement Precision*** After adding or subtracting measurements, the sum or difference should always be rounded to the least precise place-value position. In the triangle, 8.2 is the least precise measure because it is expressed in tenths and 9.25 and 10.73 are expressed in hundredths. Find the perimeter of the triangle to the nearest tenth. **28.2 cm**

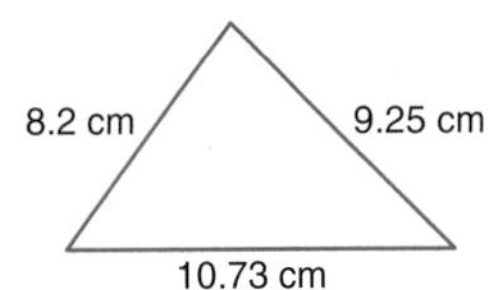

31. ***Food*** The graph shows how many pounds of breakfast cereal are consumed each year by the average person in several countries. **a. 11.9 lb**

a. Which measurement is the least precise?

b. To the nearest tenth, how many more pounds of cereal are consumed by a person in the United States than in Canada? **5.9 lb**

Breakfast Champs
Annual per capita consumption of breakfast cereal in selected countries

U.S. 11.9 lb
Great Britain 7.34 lb
Canada 6.02 lb
France 1.78 lb
South Korea 0.07 lb

Source: *Gale Book of Averages*

32. ***Critical Thinking*** Write three different decimals that round to 4.63. **Sample answer: 4.631, 4.634, 4.625**

Mixed Review

33. Order 8.75, 9.5, 8, and 9.15 from least to greatest. *(Lesson 2-1)*

33. 8, 8.75, 9.15, 9.5

34. ***Algebra*** Solve $\frac{x}{3} = 6$ mentally. *(Lesson 1-5)* **18**

35. ***Algebra*** Evaluate $y^3 + 2$ if $y = 3$. *(Lesson 1-4)* **29**

36. **Standardized Test Practice** Juanita is preparing for her birthday party. She buys 2 boxes of cookies containing 24 cookies each and 3 packages of brownies containing 15 brownies each. Which expression *cannot* be used to find the total number of dessert items she has bought? *(Lesson 1-2)* **B**

A $3 \times 15 + 2 \times 24$ **B** $5 \times (24 + 15)$ **C** $2 \times 24 + 3 \times 15$

D $48 + 45$ **E** $15 + 15 + 15 + 24 + 24$

For **Extra Practice,** see page 571.

3 PRACTICE/APPLY

Check for Understanding

If students need additional practice or instruction after completing Exercises 1–10, one of these options may be helpful.

- Extra Practice, see p. 571
- Reteaching Activity, see. 48
- *Study Guide Masters,* p. 9
- *Practice Masters,* p. 9

Assignment Guide

Core: 11–31 odd, 32–36
Enriched: 12–28 even, 30–36

4 ASSESS

Closing Activity

Speaking Have students explain why 12.803 rounded to the nearest hundredth is not 12.8. Ask them to give the correct answer. **12.8 is not expressed in hundredths; 12.80 is correct.**

Additional Answer

29.

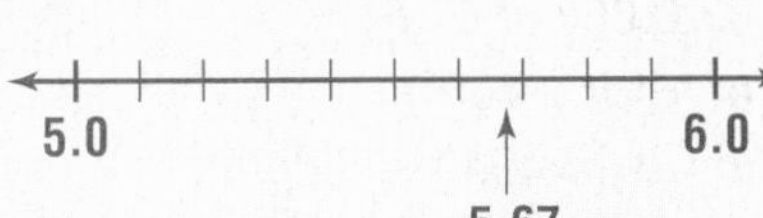

***Practice Masters,* p. 9**

Name________ Date________

2-2 Practice

Rounding Decimals

Round each number to the underlined place-value position.

1. 0.235 **0.2**
2. 3.492 **3.49**
3. 8.0769 **8.077**
4. 9.4 **9**
5. 17.145 **17.15**
6. 0.392 **0.4**
7. 19.3208 **19.32**
8. 0.0063 **0.006**
9. 16.742 **16.7**
10. 6.13982 **6.1398**
11. 0.336 **0.34**
12. 1.873 **1.87**
13. 0.892 **0.9**
14. 0.444 **0.44**
15. 67.903 **67.9**
16. 84.590 **85**
17. 5.129806 **5.130**
18. 99.105 **100**
19. 62.017 **60**
20. 0.129866 **0.1**
21. 37.09 **40**
22. Draw a number line to show that, when rounded to the nearest whole number, 9.8 rounds to 10.

   9.8
   9.0 9.5 10.0

23. The Sears Tower, once the world's tallest building, is 1,454 feet tall. Round this height to the nearest 100 feet.
   1,500 ft
24. In 1990, the population of St. Louis, Missouri, was 396,685. Round this number to the nearest ten thousand and to the nearest hundred thousand. How do the numbers compare?
   400,000; 400,000; They are equal.

T9 *Mathematics: Applications and Connections,* Course 2

Extending the Lesson

***Enrichment Masters,* p. 9**

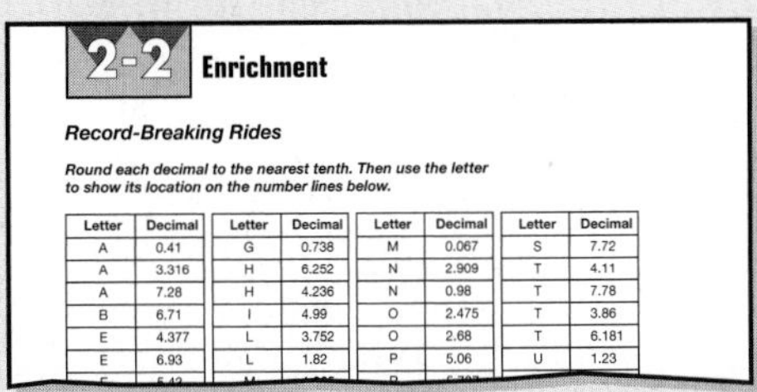

2-2 Enrichment

Record-Breaking Rides

Round each decimal to the nearest tenth. Then use the letter to show its location on the number lines below.

Letter	Decimal	Letter	Decimal	Letter	Decimal	Letter	Decimal
A	0.41	G	0.738	M	0.067	S	7.72
A	3.316	H	6.252	N	2.909	T	4.11
A	7.28	H	4.236	N	0.98	T	7.78
B	6.71	I	4.99	O	2.475	T	3.86
E	4.377	L	3.752	O	2.68	T	6.181
E	6.93	L	1.82	P	5.06	U	1.23

Activity Have students write both the least and the greatest numbers, expressed in thousandths, that round to 5.5 when rounded to the nearest tenth, and round to 5.48 when rounded to the nearest hundredth. Ask students to explain how they solved the problem and to make up others like it. **5.475; 5.484; problems will vary.**

2-3 Lesson Notes

Instructional Resources

- *Study Guide Masters,* p. 10
- *Practice Masters,* p. 10
- *Enrichment Masters,* p. 10
- Transparencies 2-3, A and B
- *Assessment and Evaluation Masters,* p. 43

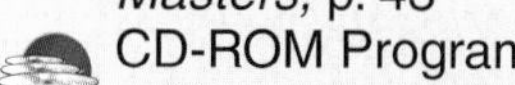

CD-ROM Program
- Resource Lesson 2-3

Recommended Pacing	
Standard	Day 4 of 14
Honors	Day 4 of 13
Block	Day 2 of 7

1 FOCUS

5-Minute Check *(Lesson 2-2)*

Round each number to the underlined place-value position.

1. 4.2672 **4.27**
2. 0.645 **0.6**
3. 0.668 **0.67**
4. 64.77 **60**
5. At 14,494 feet, Mount Whitney is the tallest peak in California. Round this height to the nearest hundred feet. **14,500 feet**

The 5-Minute Check is also available on **Transparency 2-3A** for this lesson.

Motivating the Lesson

Hands-On Activity Have groups of students write the prices of five items they would buy at a grocery store. Ask them to estimate their total purchase without using a calculator. Then have them use play money to model an estimate to the nearest quarter.

2-3 Estimating with Decimals

What you'll learn

You'll learn to estimate with decimals.

When am I ever going to use this?

You'll use estimation to help determine the total cost of items at the grocery store.

Word Wise

clustering

Do you like to swim but get bored swimming lap after lap? Wouldn't it be more exciting to swim the English Channel or the Atlantic Ocean? Believe it or not, you can swim that in a pool! The chart at the right shows the swimming equivalents assuming that a lap in the pool is 60 feet. If you wanted to swim all of the bodies of water, *about* how many laps would you need to swim?

Swimming Equivalents (thousands of laps)	
English Channel	1.848
Lake Michigan	10.384
Mississippi River	206.624
Atlantic Ocean	365.200

Source: *Health Scan*

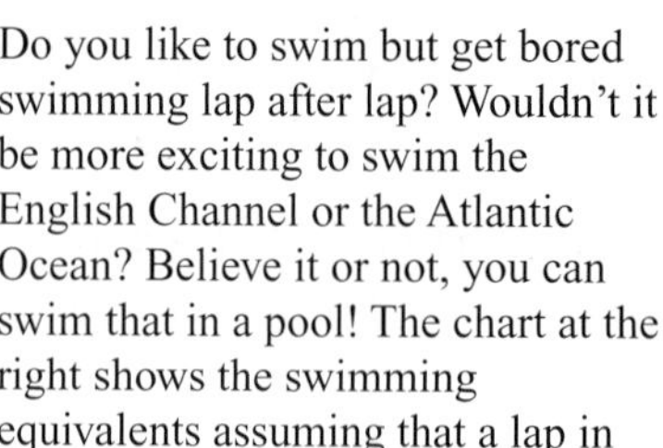

To solve this problem, you can use rounding to estimate the answer. First, round each addend to the same place-value position. In this case, we'll round to tens. Then add.

$$\begin{array}{rcr} 1.8 & \rightarrow & 0 \\ 10.4 & \rightarrow & 10 \\ 206.6 & \rightarrow & 210 \\ 365.2 & \rightarrow & +\ 370 \\ \hline & & 590 \end{array}$$

Change 590 to 590,000 since the answer is in thousands.

You would need to swim about 590,000 laps if you wanted to swim the English Channel, Lake Michigan, the Mississippi River, and the Atlantic Ocean.

Examples

Estimate by rounding.

1 23.485 − 9.757

$$\begin{array}{rcr} 23.485 & \rightarrow & 23 \\ -9.757 & \rightarrow & -10 \\ \hline & & 13 \end{array}$$

The difference is *about* 13.

2 43.9 × 37.5

$$\begin{array}{rcr} 43.9 & \rightarrow & 40 \\ \times 37.5 & \rightarrow & \times 40 \\ \hline & & 1{,}600 \end{array}$$

The product is *about* 1,600.

3 6.43 + 2.17 + 9.1 + 4.87

$$\begin{array}{rcr} 6.43 & \rightarrow & 6 \\ 2.17 & \rightarrow & 2 \\ 9.1 & \rightarrow & 9 \\ +4.87 & \rightarrow & +\ 5 \\ \hline & & 22 \end{array}$$

The sum is *about* 22.

4 432.87 ÷ 8.9

Round the divisor.

$8.9 \rightarrow 9$

Round the dividend to a multiple of 9.

$432.87 \rightarrow 450$

$8.9\overline{)432.87} \rightarrow 9\overline{)450}$ = 50

The quotient is *about* 50.

Investigations for the Special Education Student

This blackline master booklet helps you plan for the needs of your special education students by providing long-term projects along with teacher notes. Investigation 3, *Dining Out,* may be used with this chapter.

You can also use **clustering** to estimate sums. Clustering is used in addition situations if the numbers seem to be clustered around a common quantity.

5 **Gymnastics** Marissa watched her favorite gymnast, Shannon Miller, compete during the Summer Olympics in Atlanta. Marissa used her calculator to determine the total score before it was announced on TV.

Scores Shannon Miller	
Uneven bars	9.775
Balance beam	9.862
Floor exercise	9.475
Vault	9.724

Source: *USA TODAY*

Marissa's total read 30.0594. Use clustering to check her answer.

All of the scores were clustered around 10. There are four numbers. So, the sum is *about* 10 × 4, or 40.

30.0594 is not very close to 40. Marissa must have made an error in entering the numbers. She should add the four numbers again.

CHECK FOR UNDERSTANDING

Communicating Mathematics

Read and study the lesson to answer each question.

1. ***Tell*** why estimation is helpful when using a calculator to solve math problems. **See margin.**
2. ***Write*** a sentence describing when it makes sense to use the clustering method to estimate a sum. **See margin.**

3. ***Write*** about a situation where you have used estimation to solve a problem involving decimals. **See students' work.**

Guided Practice

Estimate by rounding. **5. 30 − 20 = 10**

4. $\begin{array}{r} 8.56 \\ +5.34 \\ \hline \end{array}$ **9 + 5 = 14**
5. $\begin{array}{r} 34.84 \\ -17.69 \\ \hline \end{array}$
6. $\begin{array}{r} 6.8 \\ \times 2.4 \\ \hline \end{array}$ **7 × 2 = 14**
7. $6.8\overline{)40.79}$ **42 ÷ 7 = 6**
8. $38.1\overline{)984.76}$ **1,000 ÷ 40 = 25**

Estimate by clustering.

9. 18.4 + 22.5 + 20.7 **3(20) = 60**
10. 56.9 + 63.2 + 59.3 + 61.1 **4(60) = 240**
11. ***Population*** In 1996, Hispanics replaced non-Hispanic blacks as the second largest ethnic/racial group for ages 19 and under. There were 12.0 million Hispanic teens and 11.4 million non-Hispanic, black teens. About how many more Hispanic teens are there? **about 1 million**

2 TEACH

Transparency 2-3B contains a teaching aid for this lesson.

Using Discussion Some students may be reluctant to make estimates using the methods presented, thinking that only exact answers are acceptable. Discuss situations in which estimates are more useful or descriptive than exact answers.

In-Class Examples

For Example 1
Estimate 14.388 − 9.563 by rounding. **14 − 10 = 4**

For Example 2
Estimate 28.7 × 62.6 by rounding. **30 × 60 = 1,800**

For Example 3
Estimate 6.27 + 3.4 + 7.9 + 8.75 by rounding. **6 + 3 + 8 + 9 = 26**

For Example 4
Estimate 6.4 ÷ 3.7. **6 ÷ 3 = 2**

For Example 5
Toby added 19.45, 21.5, 20.77, 19.05, 21.1, and 20.64 on a calculator and got an answer of 162.61. Check his answer by clustering. **6 × 20 or 120; his answer is probably incorrect.**

Additional Answers

1. **Sample answer: to help you catch errors in entering the numbers**
2. **It make sense to use the clustering method when the numbers seem to be clustered around a common quantity.**

3 PRACTICE/APPLY

Check for Understanding

If students need additional practice or instruction after completing Exercises 1–11, one of these options may be helpful.

- Extra Practice, see p. 571
- Reteaching Activity
- *Transition Booklet,* pp. 15–18
- *Study Guide Masters,* p. 10
- *Practice Masters,* p. 10
-  Interactive Mathematics Tools Software

Assignment Guide

Core: 13–37 odd, 39–44
Enriched: 12–34 even, 35–44

Study Guide Masters, p. 10

Name ______________ Date ______________

2-3 Study Guide

Estimating with Decimals

One way to estimate is by rounding to the greatest place-value position.

Example 1 73.2 × 9.6 ⟶ 70 × 10 = 700

Estimate a division problem by rounding the divisor. Then round the dividend to a multiple of the divisor.

Example 2 72.8 ÷ 8.9 ⟶ 72.8 ÷ 9
72 ÷ 9 = 8

Use clustering to estimate sums if the numbers group around a common quantity.

Example 3 **19.3 + 22.4 + 20.9 + 18.6 + 21.2 + 19.1 + 20.5 + 18.9**

All 8 numbers are clustered around 20. The sum is about 20 × 8 or 160.

Estimate. Use an appropriate strategy.

1. 32.19 + 29.36 + 30.08 + 28.9 + 31.0 — 30 × 5 = 150
2. 5.6 × 2.1 — 6 × 2 = 12
3. 16.7 − 12.2 — 17 − 12 = 5
4. 93.5 + 22.1 + 49.9 + 18.8 — 90 + 20 + 50 + 20 = 180
5. 61.9 ÷ 7.1 — 63 ÷ 7 = 9
6. 8.8 × 2.1 — 9 × 2 = 18
7. 41.2 ÷ 5.9 — 42 ÷ 6 = 7
8. 56.82 − 21.12 — 60 − 20 = 40
9. \$3.92 + 4.18 — \$4 + \$4 = \$8
10. 49.7 × 30.5 — 50 × 30 = 1,500
11. 9.74 × 4.08 — 10 × 4 = 40
12. \$41.15 − 19.09 — \$40 − \$20 = \$20
13. 878 ÷ 8 — 880 ÷ 8 = 110
14. 18.6 × 2.4 — 20 × 2 = 40
15. 97.7 ÷ 9.8 — 100 ÷ 10 = 10
16. \$45.92 − 33.35 — \$50 − \$30 = \$20

 T10 *Mathematics: Applications and Connections, Course 2*

EXERCISES

Practice

12. 20 + 10 = 30
13. 30 − 20 = 10
14. 8 × 8 = 64
16. 26 × 10 = 260
17. 30 − 8 = 22
18. 70 − 20 = 50
20. \$100 + 500 = \$600
23. 30 × 80 = 2,400
24. 120 ÷ 20 = 6
25. 36 ÷ 12 = 3
26. 600 ÷ 400 = 1.5

Estimate by rounding. **12–34. Sample answers given.**

12. 23.84 + 12.13
13. 34.3 − 18.9
14. 7.5 × 8.4
15. $9.3\overline{)65.48}$ **63 ÷ 9 = 7**
16. 26.3 × 9.7
17. 33.21 − 8.23
18. 67.86 − 24.35
19. $18.4\overline{)41.7}$ **40 ÷ 20 = 2**
20. \$121.5 + 487.8
21. $8.1\overline{)73.8}$ **72 ÷ 8 = 9**
22. $2.6\overline{)8.99}$ **9 ÷ 3 = 3**
23. 32.5 × 81.4
24. $23.3\overline{)119}$
25. $11.4\overline{)35.7}$
26. $373.4\overline{)645.49}$
27. Estimate the product of 6.8 and 5.2. **7 × 5 = 35**
28. Estimate 41.79 divided by 7.23. **42 ÷ 7 = 6**

Estimate by clustering.

29. 42.3 + 41.5 + 39.8 + 40.4 **4(40) = 160**
30. 77.8 + 75.6 + 81.2 + 79.9 **4(80) = 320**
31. 239.8 + 242.43 + 236.20 + 240.77 **4(200) = 800**
32. 9.9 + 10.0 + 10.3 + 11.1 + 9.8 + 11.2 **6(10) = 60**
33. 50.4 + 51.1 + 48.9 + 49.5 + 50.8 **5(50) = 250**
34. 100.5 + 97.8 + 101.6 + 100.2 + 99.3 + 99.1 **6(100) = 600**

Applications and Problem Solving

35. ***Travel*** Some of the busiest airports in the United States are listed in the chart at the right. About how many million passengers use these airports in one year? **about 340 million**

Airport	Passengers (millions)
Atlanta	73.5
Chicago (O'Hare)	72.5
Dallas/Ft. Worth	60.5
Denver	36.8
Los Angeles	61.2
San Francisco	40.0

Source: *Airports Council International*

36. ***Life Science*** A blue whale, the largest creature to live on Earth, can weigh up to 153.26 tons. An eighteen-wheel tractor and semitrailer, fully loaded, can weigh up to 48.5 tons. About how many times heavier is the blue whale? **about 3 times heavier**

Reteaching the Lesson

Activity Have students use shopping as a format to make up problems involving addition, subtraction, multiplication, and division of decimals. Have them investigate which estimation strategy or strategies provide the most useful answers to each problem.

Error Analysis

Watch for students who always use rounding to estimate.

Prevent by offering a situation in which rounding is not an appropriate strategy. Deciding whether a \$5-bill will pay for purchases of \$1.39, \$1.40, \$1.41, and \$1.38 is better suited to clustering than rounding.

37. ***Entertainment*** The graph shows the number of people who visited several theme parks. About how many people visited the theme parks? **about 70 million**

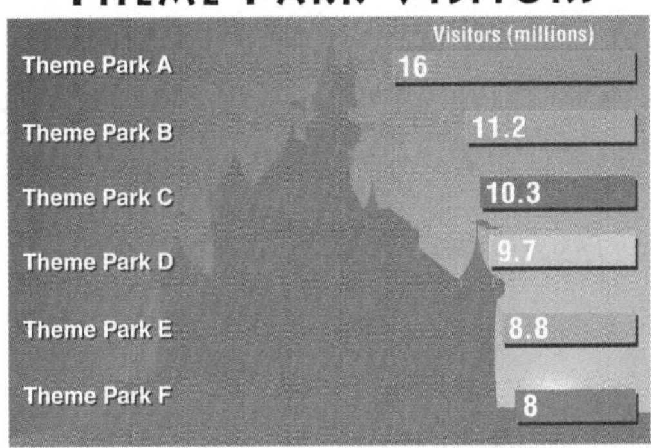

38. ***Mountain Bikes*** The Marion Police Department is planning to start a bicycle patrol in its city. The chart at the right shows prices of several mountain bikes. If the department is planning to buy 7 bikes from this list, about how much money will they spend? **300 × 7 or $2,100**

Bike	Price
Brand A	$325
Brand B	270
Brand C	300
Brand D	270
Brand E	320
Brand F	260
Brand G	270
Brand H	290

39. ***Critical Thinking*** Mr. Stewart's car can travel between 12 and 18 miles on each gallon of gasoline. Gasoline costs between $1.23 and $1.31 per gallon. About how much will Mr. Stewart pay to travel 100 miles?

39. Sample answer: Using 15 miles per gallon, he will use 100 ÷ 15 or about 6 gallons of gasoline. At $1.25 per gallon, he will pay about $7.50.

Mixed Review

40. **Standardized Test Practice** A ski resort advertises a new cross-country ski trail that is 9.673 kilometers long. To the nearest 0.1 kilometer, what is the length of the trail? *(Lesson 2-2)* **D**

A 9.67 km **B** 9.68 km

C 9.6 km **D** 9.7 km

41. Replace the ● in 0.2 ● 0.214 with <, >, or = to make a true sentence. *(Lesson 2-1)* <

42. ***Algebra*** Solve $m + 18 = 33$. *(Lesson 1-5)* **15**

43. ***Algebra*** Write an expression that represents a $500 donation plus $5 for every event. Let n represent the number of events. *(Lesson 1-3)* **500 + 5*n***

44. Evaluate $7 \cdot 4 - 9 \div 3$. *(Lesson 1-2)* **25**

For **Extra Practice,** see page 571.

4 ASSESS

Closing Activity

Speaking Have students discuss problems for which each estimation strategy works well. Ask them to estimate the answers to each problem using the strategy they think is appropriate. Have them justify their choices.

Chapter 2, Quiz A (Lessons 2-1 through 2-3) is available in the *Assessment and Evaluation Masters,* p. 43.

Practice Masters, p. 10

Name______ Date______

2-3 Practice

Estimate with Decimals

Estimate by rounding.

1. 5.98 + 9.82 6 + 10 = 16	2. 8.2 × 9.1 8 × 9 = 72	3. 6.8)49.42 49 ÷ 7 = 7
4. 7.2)84.1 84 ÷ 7 = 12	5. 29.8)986.24 990 ÷ 30 = 33	6. 6.3)89.92 90 ÷ 6 = 15

Estimate by clustering.

7. 71.1 + 69.8 + 70.9 3(70) = 210	8. 6.8 + 7.3 + 7.1 3(7) = 21	9. 15.2 + 14.9 + 14.8 3(15) = 45

Estimate. Use an appropriate strategy.

10. $9.82 + 8.71 + 6.18 $10 + $9 + $6 = $25	11. 2.4 + 8.87 2 + 9 = 11	12. 29.53 − 18.12 30 − 18 = 12
13. 8.9 × 6.1 9 × 6 = 54	14. 27.2 × 9.7 27 × 10 = 270	15. 5.3)39.61 40 ÷ 5 = 8
16. 3.1 + 2.9 + 2.87 + 3.3 4(3) = 12	17. 81.2 + 79.9 + 80.22 3(80) = 240	18. 30.2)119.1 120 ÷ 30 = 4

 T10 *Mathematics: Applications and Connections, Course 2*

Extending the Lesson

Enrichment Masters, p. 10

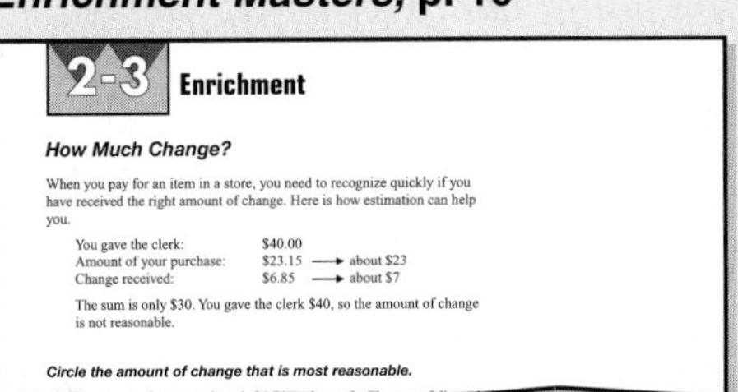

2-3 Enrichment

How Much Change?

When you pay for an item in a store, you need to recognize quickly if you have received the right amount of change. Here is how estimation can help you.

You gave the clerk:	$40.00	
Amount of your purchase:	$23.15	→ about $23
Change received:	$6.85	→ about $7

The sum is only $30. You gave the clerk $40, so the amount of change is not reasonable.

Circle the amount of change that is most reasonable.

Activity Provide copies of a take-out menu from a local restaurant. Have pairs of students pretend that they have a certain amount of money to spend. Have them choose meals they could order without spending more than they have.

Objective Students solve problems by determining reasonable answers.

Recommended Pacing	
Standard	Day 5 of 14
Honors	Day 5 of 13
Block	Day 3 of 7

1 FOCUS

Getting Started Have students act out the situation presented in the beginning of the lesson. Then have them work in pairs to answer Exercises 1–3. Have the class discuss the results. Then have them solve Exercise 4.

2 TEACH

Teaching Tip In addition to solving the opening problem, you may wish to have students formulate a problem based on their recollection of a similar decision they had to make.

In-Class Example

Roberta has $65 to spend on sports equipment. She decides to buy a bat for $29.95, 2 balls for $4.59 each, and a batting glove for $14.89. She thinks she will have enough left over to buy a cap for $15. Does this seem reasonable? **no**

PROBLEM SOLVING

2-3B Reasonable Answers

A Follow-Up of Lesson 2-3

Megan and her friend Molly are standing in the snack line at the movies. Megan is trying to figure out whether she has enough money to buy the snacks she wants. Let's listen in!

ABC THEATERS
Adult Ticket $7.50
Student Ticket 6.50
Popcorn, Large 3.25
Popcorn, Medium 2.75
Popcorn, Small 2.00
Candy 1.75
Nachos 3.75
Soft Drinks, Large 2.25
Soft Drinks, Med. 1.75
Soft Drinks, Small 1.25
Megan

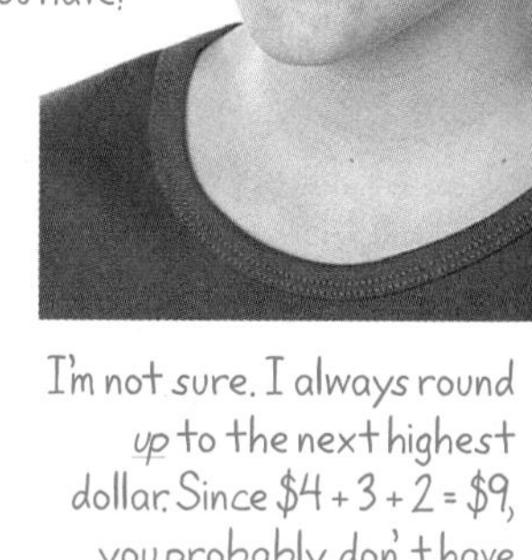

I'm starving! I hope I have enough money to buy a large popcorn, a large drink, and some candy.

Well, how much money do you have?

I have $7.00. A large popcorn costs $3.25, a large drink is $2.25, and the candy is $1.75. I think I have enough because $3 + 2 + 2 = $7.

I'm not sure. I always round up to the next highest dollar. Since $4 + 3 + 2 = $9, you probably don't have enough money.

THINK ABOUT IT

Work with a partner. **1–3. See students' work.**

1. ***Compare and contrast*** Megan's and Molly's thinking. Whose thinking do you like better? Why?
2. ***Think*** of another way to help Megan decide whether she has enough money.
3. ***Choose*** three items that Megan can buy with $7.00. Explain your reasoning.
4. ***Apply*** the strategy of determining **reasonable answers** to solve this problem.

   Chase earns $4.25 per hour at a sub shop. He usually works 12 hours each week. At his six-month review, he is given a $0.35 per hour raise. Chase used a calculator to determine that his weekly pay will increase by $42.00. Is this answer reasonable? **No; it would increase only about $4 per week.**

Reteaching the Lesson

Activity Have students work with partners to choose strategies for solving problems like those in the lesson that use simpler numbers.

For **Extra Practice,** see page 571.

ON YOUR OWN

5. The last step of the 4-step plan for problem solving asks you to *examine* your solution. ***Explain*** how you can use estimation with decimals to help you examine a solution. **Sample answer: Estimate before you calculate.**

6. ***Write a Problem*** with an unreasonable answer and ask a classmate to explain why they think the answer is unreasonable.

7. ***Explain*** how you know that the answer to Exercise 37 on page 53 is reasonable. **6–7. See students' work.**

MIXED PROBLEM SOLVING

STRATEGIES
Look for a pattern.
Solve a simpler problem.
Act it out.
Guess and check.
Draw a diagram.
Make a chart.
Work backward.

Solve. Use any strategy.

8. ***Money Matters*** Vinny's Video Haven is selling 3 blank tapes for \$14.96. Brad says he can get 9 tapes at Vinny's for under \$40. Is this reasonable? **No; $3 \times \$15 > \$40$**

9. ***Transportation*** New car carriers deliver new cars from the loading dock at the auto plant to car dealerships. Each truck can carry about 20,000 pounds. If an economy-size car weighs about 2,330 pounds, what is a reasonable number of cars that could be transported on one truck? **10 cars**

10. ***Money Matters*** At the Book Fair, Ernesto wants to buy 2 science fiction books for \$3.95 each, 3 magazines for \$2.95 each, and 1 bookmark for \$0.39. Does he need to bring \$20 or will \$15 be enough? Explain your reasoning. **\$20; $2 \times \$4 + 3 \times \$3 > \$15$**

11. ***Life Science*** A photograph of a paramecium that is 0.23 millimeter long is enlarged to 60 millimeters for a science book. *About* how many times longer is the paramecium in the photograph than the actual paramecium? **about 300 times**

12. ***Money Matters*** Suppose a relative matches your age with dollars each birthday. You are 13. How much money have you been given over the years by this relative? **\$91**

13. ***Communication*** Peta places a long distance phone call to her grandparents in California and talks for 45 minutes. The phone company bills the call at a rate of \$0.10 per half-minute. How much does the call cost Peta? **\$9**

14. ***Geography*** The graph shows the lengths in miles of the longest rivers in the world. *About* how many total miles long are the three rivers? **about 12,000 mi**

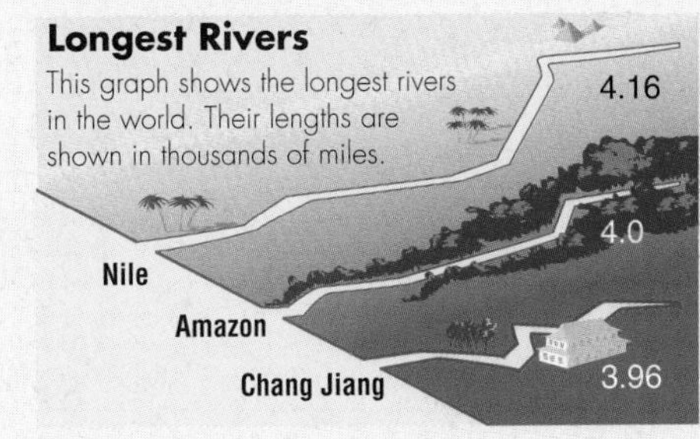
Longest Rivers
This graph shows the longest rivers in the world. Their lengths are shown in thousands of miles.
4.16
4.0
Nile
Amazon
Chang Jiang
3.96

Source: *The World Almanac*

15. **Standardized Test Practice** For lunch yesterday, Micah bought a hot dog for \$1.79, potato chips for \$0.89, and a milkshake for \$1.15. How much did this lunch cost, not including tax? **C**

A \$2.68 **B** \$2.94
C \$3.83 **D** \$9.51
E Not Here

3 PRACTICE/APPLY

Check for Understanding

Use the results from Exercise 4 to determine whether students comprehend how to determine whether an answer is reasonable.

Extra Practice If students need additional practice in problem solving, extra practice is available on the following pages.
- Reasonable Answers, see p. 571
- Mixed Problem Solving, see pp. 605–606

Assignment Guide
All: 5–15

4 ASSESS

Closing Activity

Speaking Have students imagine that during the course of the rest of the school year they are going to get 2 hours of math homework each night, for a total of 1,750 hours. Ask them to explain how they can determine if that number of hours makes sense.

Extending the Lesson

Activity Have students use the numbers 15, 57, 3, 9, 100, 2, and 43 and any dollar signs they need, to write a paragraph describing a purchase of five items in a store. Then ask students to make up problems like the one at the beginning of the lesson for others to solve. Have groups exchange problems and solve. Sample problem: *Sara spent \$57 on 3 books for \$9 each and 2 T-shirts for \$15 each. She paid with a \$100 bill and got \$43 back in change. Is this reasonable?*

2-4 Lesson Notes

Instructional Resources

- *Study Guide Masters,* p. 11
- *Practice Masters,* p. 11
- *Enrichment Masters,* p. 11
- Transparencies 2-4, A and B

- CD-ROM Program
  - Resource Lesson 2-4
  - Interactive Lesson 2-4

Recommended Pacing	
Standard	Day 6 of 14
Honors	Day 6 of 13
Block	Day 3 of 7

1 FOCUS

5-Minute Check
(Lesson 2-3)

Estimate by rounding.

1. \$57.79 + \$32.88 **\$60 + \$30 = \$90**
2. 8.2 + 2.7 + 3.6 + 12.5 **8 + 3 + 4 + 13 = 28**
3. 28.9 × 42.3 **30 × 40 = 1,200**
4. 89.97 ÷ 2.8 **90 ÷ 3 = 30**
5. Estimate \$21.19 + \$20.37 + \$18.99 by clustering. **3 × \$20 = \$60**

The 5-Minute Check is also available on **Transparency 2-4A** for this lesson.

Motivating the Lesson

Hands-On Activity Instead of grid paper, you can give students decimal models (available on p. 2 of the *Hands-On Lab Masters*) and ask them to determine what each square, row, and column represents.

Additional Answer for the Mini-Lab

3. **The sum of the number of decimal places in the factors is the number of decimal places in the product.**

2-4 Multiplying Decimals

What you'll learn
You'll learn to multiply decimals.

When am I ever going to use this?
Knowing how to multiply decimals can help you find the amount of interest earned on a savings account.

You use models in geometry to picture the concepts that you are learning. For example, the model below shows that the area of a rectangle is found by multiplying its length by its width. You can also use grid paper to represent multiplication problems.

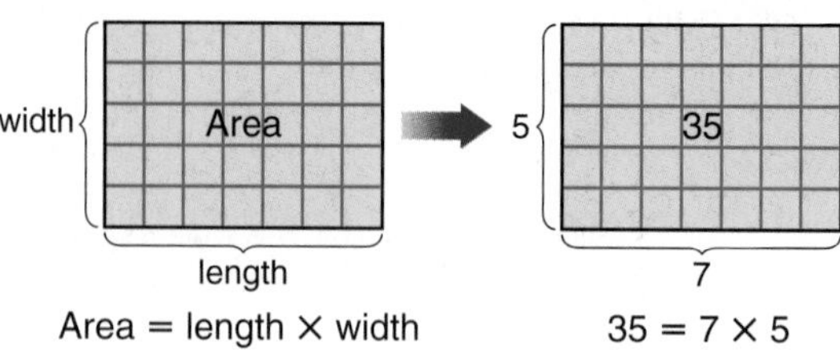

HANDS-ON MINI-LAB

Work with a partner.  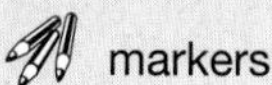

Multiplying decimals is similar to multiplying whole numbers. Here the area of the large square represents 1.00, and the area of each small square represents 1 hundredth or 0.01.

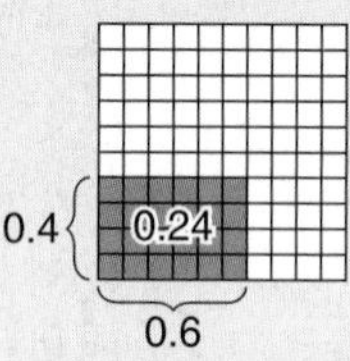

The length of a side of each small square is 1 tenth or 0.1.

Try This **1. See Answer Appendix for models.**

1. Use grid paper to show each product.
   a. 0.2 × 0.9 **0.18** **b.** 0.7 × 0.5 **0.35**
   c. 0.3 × 0.3 **0.09** **d.** 0.6 × 2 **1.2**
2. Tell how many decimal places there are in each factor and in each product in Exercise 1.

2a. 1, 1, 2
2b. 1, 1, 2
2c. 1, 1, 2
2d. 1, 0, 1

Study Hint
Problem Solving
Organize your data for Exercise 2 into a table.

Talk About It

3. How does the number of decimal places in the product relate to the number of decimal places in the factors? **See margin.**

Multiple Learning Styles

Logical Have students study the multiplication problem in the Mini-Lab and the examples. Ask them to look for a pattern about when the product is greater than either factor and when it is less. Then read some of the practice exercises and have students determine mentally whether the product will be greater than or less than either of the factors. If they think that the product will be greater, have them give a thumbs-up sign, and if they think it will be less, a thumbs-down sign.

These and other similar models suggest the following.

Multiplying Decimals	The number of decimal places in the product of two decimals is the sum of the number of decimal places in the factors.

Examples

1 **Multiply 1.3 and 0.9.** *Estimate: $1 \times 1 = 1$*

1.3 ← *one decimal place*
×0.9 ← *one decimal place*
1.17 ← *two decimal places*

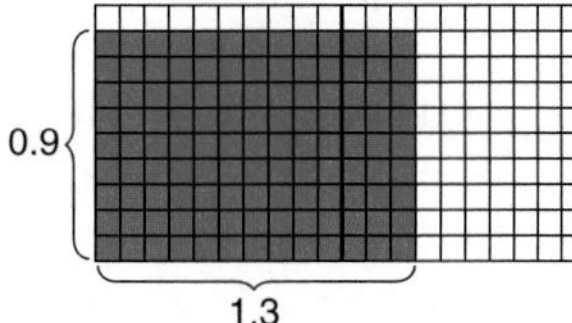

The product is 1.17. Compared to the estimate, the product is reasonable.

2 **Find the product of 0.054 and 1.6.** *Estimate: $0 \times 2 = 0$*

0.054 ← *three decimal places*
× 1.6 ← *one decimal place*
0.0864 ← *To make four decimal places, annex a zero on the left.*

The product is 0.0864. *Is the answer reasonable?*

Many real-world problems can be solved by multiplying decimals. For example, did you know that all sound, including music, is caused by vibrations? The number of vibrations per second determines the pitch of the sound. The more vibrations per second, the higher the pitch. The number of vibrations per second is called the *frequency.*

Example CONNECTION

3 **Music** **The frequency of any note multiplied by 1.06 gives the frequency of the note one-half step higher. The frequency of the A directly above middle C on a piano is 440 vibrations per second. What is the frequency of A#?** *Read A# as "A sharp."*

These are each a half step.
C# D# F# G# A# C#
middle C D E F G A B C
whole step, half step, whole step, half step
whole step, whole step, whole step

To find the frequency of A#, multiply 440 by 1.06.

440
× 1.06 *Estimate: $440 \times 1 = 440$*
466.40

The frequency of A# is 466.4 vibrations per second.

Did you know Of today's musicians, 63% learned to play before they were 12 years old.

2 TEACH

Transparency 2-4B contains a teaching aid for this lesson.

Using the Mini-Lab Have students work through Exercises 1 and 2 with a partner. Then use Exercise 3 to verbalize the rule for multiplying decimals.

In-Class Examples

For Example 1
Multiply 1.1 and 0.8. **0.88**

For Example 2
Find the product of 1.3 and 1.8. **2.34**

For Example 3
The speed of the spine-tailed swift has been measured at 106.25 mph. At that rate, how far can it travel in 1.5 hours? **159.375 mi**

Teaching Tip After reading Example 3, ask students what could be done to find the frequency of a note one whole step higher. **Multiply by 2.12.**

Teaching Tip Since students commonly place the decimal point incorrectly in the product, strongly encourage them to estimate products in the Guided Practice before computing the answers.

MathPASS CD-ROM

This CD-ROM offers a complete, self-paced mathematics curriculum. Each lesson includes a pretest, tutorial, guided practice, and posttest. MathPASS Lesson 4 is correlated to this Student Edition lesson.
For Windows & Macintosh

3 PRACTICE/APPLY

Check for Understanding

If students need additional practice or instruction after completing Exercises 1–9, one of these options may be helpful.

- Extra Practice, see p. 572
- Reteaching Activity
- *Transition Booklet,* pp. 19–20
- *Study Guide Masters,* p. 11
- *Practice Masters,* p. 11
- Interactive Mathematics Tools Software

Assignment Guide

Core: 11–31 odd, 33–37
Enriched: 10–28 even, 29–31, 33–37
All: Self Test, 1–5

Exercise 32 asks students to advance to the next stage of work on the Chapter Project. Encourage students to use a calculator. Then have them place their work in their Project Folders.

CHECK FOR UNDERSTANDING

Communicating Mathematics

Read and study the lesson to answer each question.

1. ***Explain*** how you can use estimation to check whether you have placed the decimal correctly in the product of two decimals. **See students' work.**
2. ***Write*** a multiplication problem using decimals for the model shown at the right. **0.2 × 0.7 = 1.4**
3. ***Make*** a model to show why 0.1 × 0.1 = 0.01. **See Answer Appendix.**

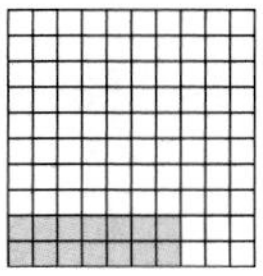

HANDS-ON MATH

Guided Practice

Place the decimal point in each product.

4. 1.32 × 4 = 528 **5.28**
5. 0.07 × 1.1 = 77 **0.077**

Multiply.

6. 3.4 × 7.8 **26.52**
7. 0.15 × 1.23 **0.1845**
8. 11.5 × 0.47 **5.405**

9. ***Life Science*** A giant tortoise can travel at a speed of about 0.2 kilometer per hour. At this rate, how far can it travel in 1.75 hours? **0.35 kilometer**

EXERCISES

Practice

Place the decimal point in each product.

10. 0.4 × 0.7 = 28 **0.28**
11. 1.9 × 0.6 = 114 **1.14**
12. 1.4 × 0.09 = 126 **0.126**
13. 5.48 × 3.6 = 19728 **19.728**
14. 4.5 × 0.34 = 153 **1.53**
15. 0.45 × 0.02 = 9 **0.009**

Multiply.

16. 0.2 × 6 **1.2**
17. 0.3 × 0.9 **0.27**
18. 0.45 × 0.12 **0.0540**
19. 0.0023 × 32 **19. 0.0736**
20. 10.1 × 9 **90.9**
21. 0.0023 × 0.35 **21. 0.000805**
22. 6.78 × 1.3 **8.814**
23. 1.5 × 2.7 **4.05**
24. 5.1 × 4.3 **21.93**
25. 0.08 × 1.9 **0.152**
26. 0.25 × 0.004 **0.001**
27. 1.17 × 0.09 **0.1053**
28. ***Algebra*** Evaluate xy if $x = 0.32$ and $y = 3.1$. **0.992**

Applications and Problem Solving

29. ***Travel*** Karen was helping plan the Spanish Club's trip to Spain. On a recent trip, one United States dollar could be exchanged for 128.46 Spanish pesetas. How many pesetas would she receive for $50 in United States money? **6,423 pesetas**
30. ***Geometry*** To the nearest tenth, find the area of the rectangle. **0.6m²**

0.4 m
1.5 m

Reteaching the Lesson

Activity Some students may need further exploration using 10 × 10 grids to understand that the product of two decimals may be less than either of the two factors, in between the two factors, or greater than either factor.

Error Analysis

Watch for students who incorrectly place the decimal point in a product.

Prevent by reminding them to mentally multiply the place values, such as 10(ths) times 10(ths) equals 100(ths). Hundredths is two decimal places.

***Study Guide Masters,* p. 11**

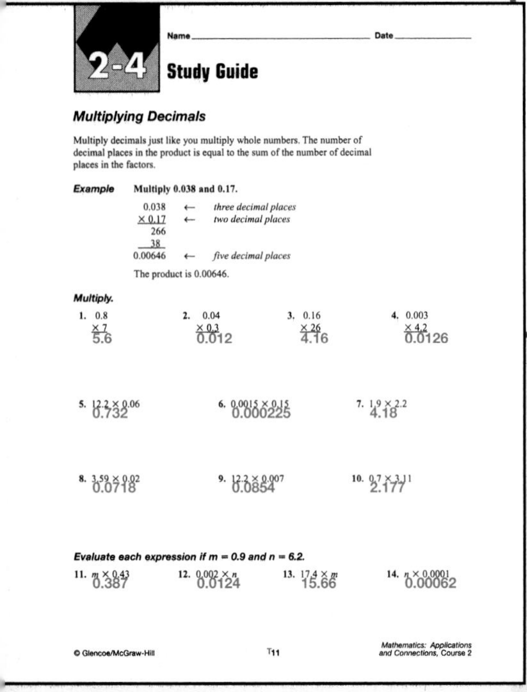

Name__________ Date________

2-4 **Study Guide**

Multiplying Decimals

Multiply decimals just like you multiply whole numbers. The number of decimal places in the product is equal to the sum of the number of decimal places in the factors.

Example **Multiply 0.038 and 0.17.**

```
  0.038   ←  three decimal places
× 0.17    ←  two decimal places
    266
    38
0.00646   ←  five decimal places
```

The product is 0.00646.

Multiply.

1. 0.8 × 7 **5.6**
2. 0.04 × 0.3 **0.012**
3. 0.16 × 26 **4.16**
4. 0.003 × 4.2 **0.0126**
5. 12.2 × 0.06 **0.732**
6. 0.0015 × 0.15 **0.000225**
7. 1.9 × 2.2 **4.18**
8. 3.59 × 0.02 **0.0718**
9. 12.2 × 0.007 **0.0854**
10. 0.7 × 3.11 **2.177**

Evaluate each expression if $m = 0.9$ and $n = 6.2$.

11. $m \times 0.43$ **0.387**
12. $0.002 \times n$ **0.0124**
13. $17.4 \times m$ **15.66**
14. $n \times 0.0001$ **0.00062**

 T11 *Mathematics: Applications and Connections, Course 2*

31a. VCR, 33.6; video game, 27.0; cable, 23.1; computer, 16.1; cellular phone, 12.3; on-line service, 6.0

31. ***Statistics*** The graph shows what part of all teenagers own or use technology.

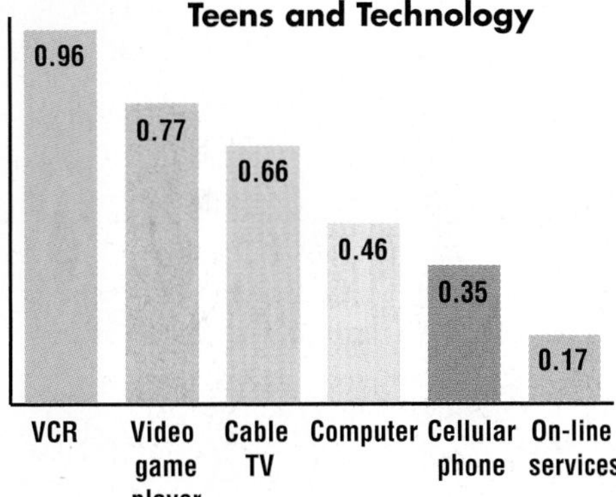

Source: Chilton Research Services

a. Suppose you survey 35 teenagers. Predict about how many of those surveyed use each kind of technology. Round to the nearest tenth.

b. Survey your classmates. How do these results compare with the data in the graph? Explain any differences. **See students' work.**

32a. Mercury - 4,847; Venus - 12,118; Mars - 6,761; Jupiter - 142,740; Saturn - 120,672; Uranus - 51,152; Neptune - 49,493; Pluto - 2,296

32. ***Working on the*** CHAPTER Project Refer to the table on page 43.

a. The diameter of Earth is 12,756 kilometers. Find the diameters of all the other planets to the nearest kilometer. Include this information in your diameter chart.

b. The average distance from the Sun to Earth is 149 million kilometers. Find the actual average distances of all the other planets in millions of kilometers. Include this information in your distance chart. **See margin.**

33. ***Critical Thinking*** Two decimals, both less than 1, are multiplied. Is the product *always* less than 1, *sometimes* less than 1, or *never* less than 1? Explain. **Always; the rectangle will always be a portion of the full model.**

Mixed Review

34. Estimate the sum of 5.82, 2.19, 8.1, and 6.05. *(Lesson 2-3)* **22**

35. Round 0.99 to the nearest tenth. *(Lesson 2-2)* **1.0**

36. See margin.

36. Draw a number line to show which is greater, 3.77 or 3.7. *(Lesson 2-1)*

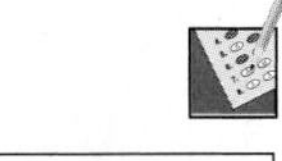

37. **Standardized Test Practice** Which expression could be used to find the cost of buying b baseball bats at \$75 each and g baseball gloves at \$98 each? *(Lesson 1-3)* **C**

A $75 + 98$ **B** $b + g$ **C** $75b + 98g$ **D** $75b \times 98g$

For **Extra Practice,** see page 572.

CHAPTER 2

Mid-Chapter Self Test

1. Which is greater, 0.28 or 0.028? *(Lesson 2-1)* **0.28**
2. Round 0.<u>4</u>9 to the underlined place-value position. *(Lesson 2-2)* **0.5**
3. Estimate the sum of 71.28, 68.4, 70.73, 69.45, and 73.21. *(Lesson 2-3)* **350**
4. Find the product of 0.7 and 0.9. *(Lesson 2-4)* **0.63**
5. ***Life Science*** A snail moves at a speed of about 0.005 kilometer per hour. How far can it travel in 0.5 hour? *(Lesson 2-4)* **0.0025 km**

4 ASSESS

Closing Activity

Speaking Present a word problem requiring multiplication of decimals, such as having to find the cost of filling an empty 11.6-gallon tank with fuel that costs \$1.38 per gallon. Have students explain each step of their solution. **\$16.01**

Mid-Chapter Self Test

The Mid-Chapter Self Test reviews the concepts and skills in Lessons 2-1 through 2-4. Lesson references are given so students can review concepts not yet mastered.

Additional Answers

32b. Mercury–58; Venus–108; Mars–227; Jupiter–775; Saturn–1,420; Uranus–2,859; Neptune–4,479; Pluto–5,890

36.

***Practice Masters*, p. 11**

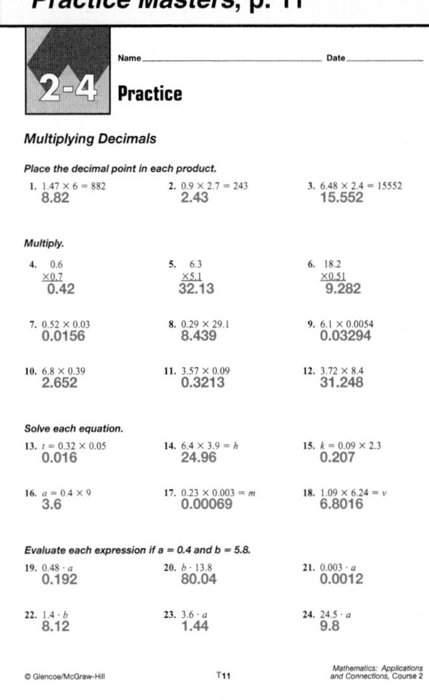

Name ______ Date ______

2-4 **Practice**

Multiplying Decimals

Place the decimal point in each product.

1. 1.47 × 6 = 882 **8.82**
2. 0.9 × 2.7 = 243 **2.43**
3. 6.48 × 2.4 = 15552 **15.552**

Multiply.

4. 0.6 × 0.7 **0.42**
5. 6.3 × 5.1 **32.13**
6. 18.2 × 0.51 **9.282**
7. 0.52 × 0.03 **0.0156**
8. 0.29 × 29.1 **8.439**
9. 6.1 × 0.0054 **0.03294**
10. 6.8 × 0.39 **2.652**
11. 3.57 × 0.09 **0.3213**
12. 3.72 × 8.4 **31.248**

Solve each equation.

13. $t = 0.32 \times 0.05$ **0.016**
14. $6.4 \times 3.9 = h$ **24.96**
15. $k = 0.09 \times 2.3$ **0.207**
16. $a = 0.4 \times 9$ **3.6**
17. $0.23 \times 0.003 = m$ **0.00069**
18. $1.09 \times 6.24 = v$ **6.8016**

Evaluate each expression if a = 0.4 and b = 5.8.

19. $0.48 \cdot a$ **0.192**
20. $b \cdot 13.8$ **80.04**
21. $0.003 \cdot a$ **0.0012**
22. $1.4 \cdot b$ **8.12**
23. $3.6 \cdot a$ **1.44**
24. $24.5 \cdot a$ **9.8**

 T11 *Mathematics: Applications and Connections, Course 2*

Extending the Lesson

***Enrichment Masters*, p. 11**

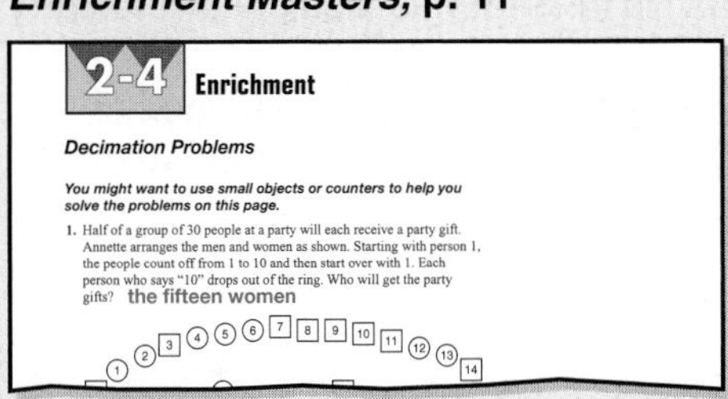

2-4 **Enrichment**

Decimation Problems

You might want to use small objects or counters to help you solve the problems on this page.

1. Half of a group of 30 people at a party will each receive a party gift. Annette arranges the men and women as shown. Starting with person 1, the people count off from 1 to 10 and then start over with 1. Each person who says "10" drops out of the ring. Who will get the party gifts? **the fifteen women**

Activity To correct for the small difference between 365 days and 365.24 days, a leap year of 366 days is interposed every four years except in years that are divisible by 100, but not by 400. Why does this rule work? **The rule adjusts for the fact that 3 × 365 + 366 is slightly greater than 4 × 365.24.**

Motivating Students

As students learned in the Chapter Project on page 43, there are many opportunities for them to explore aerospace. They may be interested in a career in that or a related field. To start the discussion, you may ask students questions about space history.

- Who was the first man to go into space? From what country? On what date? **Yuri A. Gagarin, USSR, April 12, 1961**
- When did the first man walk on the moon? **July 1969**
- At what altitudes are you "in space"? **over 60 miles**
- Who was the first woman in space? **Lt. Col. Valentina V. Tereshkova, June 16, 1963**

Making the Math Connection

On her shuttle flight, Dr. Jemison conducted experiments in both life and material sciences and was co-investigator for the bone cell research project. All scientific data was reported using decimals, and the computers on board the shuttle gave back information in decimal form. Dr. Jemison needed to know how to compute and estimate with decimals in order to interpret the data she received correctly.

Working on *Your Turn*

Students may want to work in groups to develop their brochure that describes the benefits of a career in the aerospace industry. Make sure they understand that being an astronaut is only one of thousands of jobs available in this industry and not all of the jobs are located at Cape Canaveral, Florida.

An additional School to Career activity is available on page 15 of the ***School to Career Masters****.*

Dr. Mae Carol Jemison
ASTRONAUT

Someday, I'd like to fly in the space shuttle like Dr. Jemison.

When Dr. Jemison flew on the space shuttle *Endeavor,* she became the first African-American woman in the space program. She took objects from Africa with her to symbolize that space exploration belongs to all nations.

To be an astronaut, you'll need at least a bachelor's degree in engineering, biological sciences, physical sciences, or mathematics and three years of professional experience related to the degree. However, there are many positions in the aerospace industry that do not require a college degree. A typical space-related company also needs mechanics, electricians, drafters, salespeople, personnel specialists, and assembly workers.

For more information:
Astronaut Selection Office
Mall Code AHX
Johnson Space Center
Houston, Texas 77058

www.glencoe.com/sec/math/mac/mathnet

Your Turn
Write and design a brochure that describes the benefits of a career in the aerospace industry.

More About Dr. Mae Carol Jemison

- Dr. Jemison was on the 50th NASA shuttle mission. It lifted off from Cape Canaveral, Florida, on September 12, 1992. This mission was also the first to carry a married couple.
- Dr. Jemison entered Stanford University at age 16 and graduated with degrees in Chemical Engineering and Afro-American Studies in 1977. She received her M.D. from Cornell University in 1981.

2-5 Powers of Ten

What you'll learn
You'll learn to multiply decimals mentally by powers of ten.

When am I ever going to use this?
Mental math strategies can be used to find the cost of 100 items quickly.

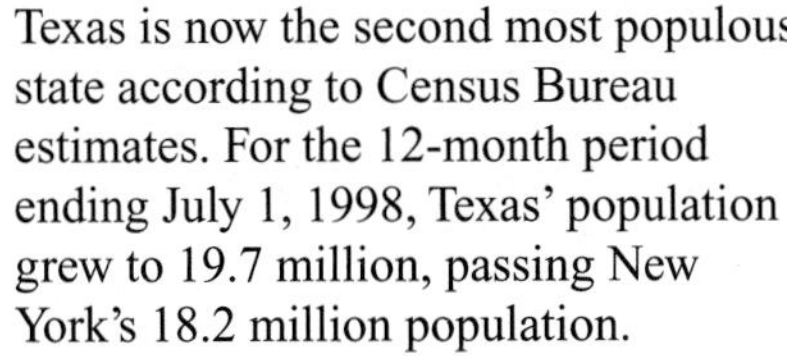

Texas is now the second most populous state according to Census Bureau estimates. For the 12-month period ending July 1, 1998, Texas' population grew to 19.7 million, passing New York's 18.2 million population.

You can write numbers like 19.7 million in standard form by multiplying by a power of ten. In this case, multiply by 1,000,000.

$$19.7 \times 1{,}000{,}000 = 19{,}700{,}000$$

In standard form, 19.7 million is 19,700,000.

How can you find the product of a power of 10 and another number without using a calculator or paper and pencil? Look for a pattern in the following products.

Decimal		Power of Ten		Product
19.7	×	10^0 (or 1)	=	19.7
19.7	×	10^1 (or 10)	=	197
19.7	×	10^2 (or 100)	=	1,970
19.7	×	10^3 (or 1,000)	=	19,700
19.7	×	10^4 (or 10,000)	=	197,000

Study Hint
Mental Math You can also determine the number of places to move the decimal point by counting the number of zeros in the power of ten.

What pattern did you find? Notice that the digits in the original decimal and the product are the same. The difference is the position of the decimal point. The exponent in the power of 10 tells you the number of places to move the decimal point.

Since you are multiplying by a power of ten that is greater than one, the product will be greater than the original decimal. Thus, the decimal point moves to the right. You can use this pattern to multiply mentally.

Examples

1 **Multiply 0.59 and 10^4 mentally.**

$0.59 \times 10^4 = 5{,}900.$

Move the decimal point four places to the right.

$0.59 \times 10^4 = 5{,}900$

2 **Solve $c = 27.2 \times 1{,}000$.**

$c = 27.2 \times 1{,}000$

$c = 27.2 \times 10^3$ *$1{,}000 = 10^3$*

$c = 27{,}200.$

Move the decimal point three places to the right.

The solution is 27,200.

2-5 Lesson Notes

Instructional Resources

- *Study Guide Masters,* p. 12
- *Practice Masters,* p. 12
- *Enrichment Masters,* p. 12
- Transparencies 2-5, A and B
- *Assessment and Evaluation Masters,* pp. 42–43

CD-ROM Program
- Resource Lesson 2-5

Recommended Pacing	
Standard	Day 7 of 14
Honors	Day 7 of 13
Block	Day 4 of 7

1 FOCUS

5-Minute Check
(Lesson 2-4)

Multiply.

1. 0.43×0.6 **0.258**
2. 8.8×0.28 **2.464**
3. 0.0052×0.09 **0.000468**
4. Solve $r = 0.61 \times 0.02$. **0.0122**

Evaluate each expression if *a* = 0.7 *and b* = 2.5.

5. $0.5 \cdot a$ **0.35**
6. $b \cdot 0.003$ **0.0075**

The 5-Minute Check is also available on **Transparency 2-5A** for this lesson.

Motivating the Lesson

Problem Solving Ask students how they would write the length of the Amazon River, which is 3.9×10^3 miles long, in standard notation. **3,900 miles**

Multiple Learning Styles

Intrapersonal One of the best ways to determine whether you know the concept is if you have to teach it to others. After working through the examples in the Student Edition, ask students to write about how they would explain multiplying by a power of 10 to someone who was absent. They can record their writings in their math journals.

2 TEACH

Transparency 2-5B contains a teaching aid for this lesson.

Thinking Algebraically Students should realize that using powers of 10 is an example of multiple representations of the same values. Ask them why this form of notation is used.

In-Class Examples

For Example 1
Multiply 0.53 and 10^5 mentally. **53,000**

For Example 2
Solve $t = 15.4 \times 10{,}000$. **154,000**

For Example 3
Multiply 1.23 and 0.0001 mentally. **0.000123**

For Example 4
Joe's Used Cars is running a special for one day only. If you pay cash, you can take $\frac{5}{100}$ or 0.05 off the sticker price. Suppose a car has a sticker price of $2300.

a. How much would you save if you paid cash for the car? **$115**

b. What is the sale price of the car with the cash discount? **$2,185**

***Study Guide Masters*, p. 12**

Name________________ Date________

2-5 Study Guide

Powers of Ten

You can find the product of a number and a power of 10 without using a calculator or paper and pencil. Suppose you wanted to find the product of 23.7 and powers of 10.

Decimal		Power of Ten		Product
23.7	×	0.001	=	0.0237
23.7	×	0.01	=	0.237
23.7	×	0.1	=	2.37
23.7	×	10^0 or 1	=	23.7
23.7	×	10^1 or 10	=	237
23.7	×	10^2 or 100	=	2,370
23.7	×	10^3 or 1,000	=	23,700
23.7	×	10^4 or 10,000	=	237,000

For powers of 10 that are greater than 1, the exponent in the power of 10 tells you the number of places to move the decimal point to the right. For powers of 10 that are less than 1, the decimal point moves to the left.

Examples **1** $0.08 \times 10^4 = 800$ *Move the decimal point 4 places to the right.*
2 $6.25 \times 0.001 = 0.00625$ *Move the decimal point 3 places to the left.*

Multiply mentally.

1. 0.8×0.1 0.08
2. 6.12×10^2 612
3. $8.4 \times 1{,}000$ 8,400
4. 9.3×0.001 0.0093
5. 4.006×100 400.6
6. 67.8×0.01 0.678

Solve each equation.

7. $x = 89 \times 10{,}000$ 890,000
8. $2.9 \times 10^3 = n$ 2,900
9. $y = 24.78 \times 0.01$ 0.2478
10. $0.0004 \times 10^4 = p$ 4
11. $v = 589 \times 0.001$ 0.589
12. $r = 0.01 \times 10^0$ 0.01

 T12 *Mathematics: Applications and Connections, Course 2*

Study Hint
Mental Math When multiplying by a power of ten less than 1, count the number of places after the decimal point. Then move the decimal point that many places to the left.

You can also use a similar pattern when multiplying by a power of ten that is less than 1. Look for a pattern in the following products.

Decimal		Power of Ten		Product
23.9	×	0.1 $\left(\text{or } \frac{1}{10^1}\right)$	=	2.39
23.9	×	0.01 $\left(\text{or } \frac{1}{10^2}\right)$	=	0.239
23.9	×	0.001 $\left(\text{or } \frac{1}{10^3}\right)$	=	0.0239

Since you are multiplying by a power of ten that is less than 1, the product is less than the original decimal. Therefore, the decimal point moves to the left.

Examples

3 **Multiply 1.05 and 0.01 mentally.**

$1.05 \times 0.01 = 0.0105$ $\quad 0.01 = \frac{1}{100}$

Move the decimal point two places to the left.

$1.05 \times 0.01 = 0.0105$

APPLICATION

4 **Money Matters** **A department store is having a special sale in which the price of every item in the store is $\frac{1}{10}$ or 0.1 off the original price.**

a. If the original price of a sweater is $35, how much does Samuel save by buying it on sale?

b. What is the sale price?

a. To find how much is saved, find $0.1 \times \$35$.

$0.1 \times 35 = 3.5$ *Move the decimal point one place to the left.*

Samuel saves $3.50.

b. To find the sale price, find $\$35 - \$3.50$. *Estimate: $35 - 4 = 31$*

$35 - 3.5 = 31.5$ The sale price is $31.50.

CHECK FOR UNDERSTANDING

Communicating Mathematics

Read and study the lesson to answer each question. **1–2. See Answer Appendix.**

1. ***Tell*** a classmate how you would solve $x = 2.378 \times 100$ mentally.
2. ***Explain*** how you can mentally find the cost of 10 items that are the same price.
3. ***Write*** the steps you would take to multiply 0.01×28.8 using paper and pencil. Compare it to solving the problem mentally. **See students' work.**

Math Journal

Guided Practice

Multiply mentally.

4. 12.53×10 **125.3**
5. 4.6×10^3 **4,600**
6. 78.4×0.01 **0.784**

Reteaching the Lesson

Activity Each player rolls a number cube two times to make the tens and ones place of a number. A third roll determines either (1) the exponent for a power of 10 or (2) the tenths place of the number and then a fourth roll is required for the exponent. Example: (1) 1, 4, 6 = 14×10^6, (2) 1, 4, 6, 5 = 14.6×10^5. The player with the greatest number wins.

Error Analysis

Watch for students who move the decimal point to the *left* when multiplying mentally by a power of 10 greater than one.

Prevent by stressing that when a number is multiplied by this power of 10, it is being increased in size, not decreased as would be the result of moving the decimal left.

Solve each equation. 7. 20,310 9. 0.045

7. $n = 2.031 \times 10^4$ **8.** $a = 0.78 \times 10^2$ 78 **9.** $x = 0.1 \times 0.45$

10. ***Food*** Suppose a can of soup costs $0.73. If you purchase 100 cans to donate to a food bank, what will the cost be? $73.00

EXERCISES

Practice

Multiply mentally.

11. 0.05×100 5 **12.** 4.527×10^0 4.527 **13.** $2.78 \times 1{,}000$ 2,780

14. 13.58×0.01 0.1358 **15.** 5.49×10^3 5,490 **16.** 0.1×0.8 0.08

17. 0.925×10 9.25 **18.** 99.44×10^2 9,944 **19.** 0.01×16 0.16

Solve each equation. 20. 1,320 21. 560 23. 1,123,000

20. $1.32 \times 10^3 = x$ **21.** $c = 0.56 \times 1{,}000$ **22.** $m = 1.4 \times 0.1$ 0.14

24. 0.6894
26. 0.281

23. $h = 11.23 \times 10^5$ **24.** $68.94 \times 0.01 = y$ **25.** $0.8 \times 10^0 = w$ 0.8

26. $28.1 \times 0.01 = z$ **27.** $t = 9.3 \times 100$ 930 **28.** $3.76 \times 10{,}000 = b$ 37,600

29. Find the product of 0.1 and 25.3 mentally. 2.53

Applications and Problem Solving

30a. $175,400,000

30b. $1,275,000,000

30. ***Music*** The chart shows the sales of selected music products for the United States.

a. Write the number of dollars spent for percussion in standard form.

b. How much money was spent for guitars and sound amplifiers? Write in standard form.

The Sounds of Music

Sales in millions of dollars of selected musical products

guitars	$665.8
sound amplifiers	$609.2
acoustic pianos	$605.2
school music products	$489.9
printed music	$400.1
microphones	$259.2
percussion	$175.4

Axis: $0, $100, $200, $300, $400, $500, $600, $700

31. ***Population*** In 1995, the population of Georgia was estimated at 7.2 million. It is expected to increase $\frac{1}{10}$ by the year 2000.

a. By how many people will the population increase? 0.72 million

b. Predict the population of Georgia in the year 2000. 7.92 million

32. Sample answer: Find the product of 0.1 and the number and double it; 8.4.

32. ***Critical Thinking*** Devise a method to find the product of 0.2 and a number mentally. Use your method to find 0.2×42.

Mixed Review

33. ***Algebra*** Evaluate the expression xy if $x = 0.4$ and $y = 3$. *(Lesson 2-4)* 1.2

34. **Standardized Test Practice** On Manuel's trip, he drove 178.5 miles in 3.3 hours. Which is a reasonable average speed for his trip? *(Lesson 2-3)* C

A 6 mph **B** 40 mph **C** 60 mph **D** 90 mph **E** 180 mph

For **Extra Practice,** see page 572.

35. Round 0.006 to the hundredths place. *(Lesson 2-2)* 0.01

36. ***Algebra*** Solve $12m = 120$ mentally. *(Lesson 1-5)* 10

3 PRACTICE/APPLY

Check for Understanding

If students need additional practice or instruction after completing Exercises 1–10, one of these options may be helpful.

- Extra Practice, see p. 572
- Reteaching Activity, see p. 62
- *Study Guide Masters,* p. 12
- *Practice Masters,* p. 12

Assignment Guide

Core: 11–31 odd, 32–36
Enriched: 12–28 even, 30–36

4 ASSESS

Closing Activity

Writing Have students work with partners to make a simple cross-number puzzle with clues that involve multiplying decimals and powers of 10. Answers should be in standard form.

Chapter 2, Quiz B (Lessons 2-4 and 2-5) is available in the *Assessment and Evaluation Masters,* p. 43.

Mid-Chapter Test (Lessons 2-1 through 2-5) is available in the *Assessment and Evaluation Masters,* p. 42.

***Practice Masters,* p. 12**

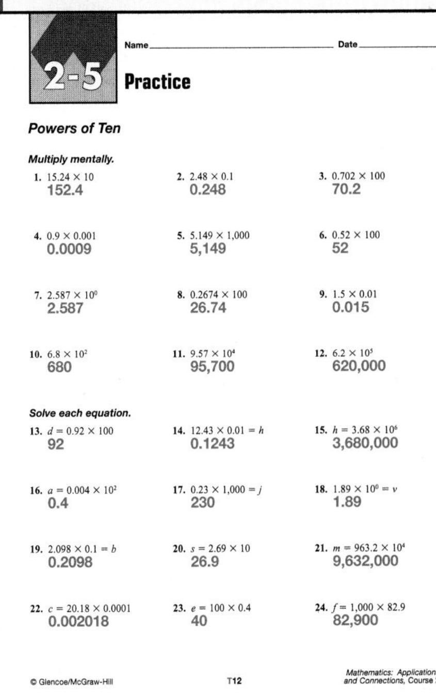

Name______ Date______

2-5 Practice

Powers of Ten

Multiply mentally.

1. 15.24×10 152.4
2. 2.48×0.1 0.248
3. 0.702×100 70.2
4. 0.9×0.001 0.0009
5. $5.149 \times 1{,}000$ 5,149
6. 0.52×100 52
7. 2.587×10^0 2.587
8. 0.2674×100 26.74
9. 1.5×0.01 0.015
10. 6.8×10^2 680
11. 9.57×10^4 95,700
12. 6.2×10^5 620,000

Solve each equation.

13. $d = 0.92 \times 100$ 92
14. $12.43 \times 0.01 = h$ 0.1243
15. $h = 3.68 \times 10^6$ 3,680,000
16. $a = 0.004 \times 10^2$ 0.4
17. $0.23 \times 1{,}000 = j$ 230
18. $1.89 \times 10^0 = v$ 1.89
19. $2.098 \times 0.1 = b$ 0.2098
20. $s = 2.69 \times 10$ 26.9
21. $m = 963.2 \times 10^4$ 9,632,000
22. $c = 20.18 \times 0.0001$ 0.002018
23. $e = 100 \times 0.4$ 40
24. $f = 1{,}000 \times 82.9$ 82,900

 T12 *Mathematics: Applications and Connections, Course 2*

Extending the Lesson

Enrichment Masters, p. 12

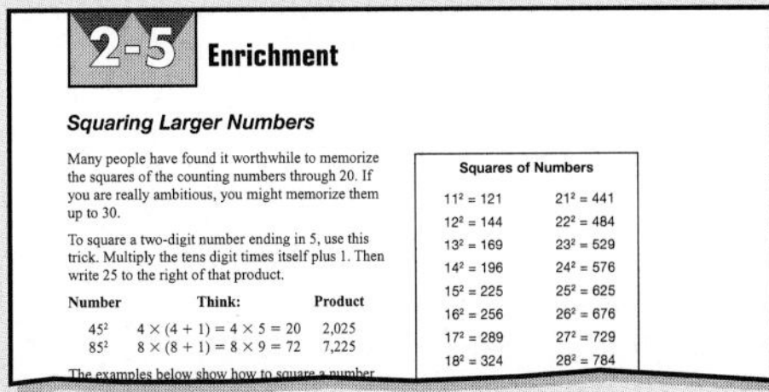

2-5 Enrichment

Squaring Larger Numbers

Many people have found it worthwhile to memorize the squares of the counting numbers through 20. If you are really ambitious, you might memorize them up to 30.

To square a two-digit number ending in 5, use this trick. Multiply the tens digit times itself plus 1. Then write 25 to the right of that product.

Number	Think:	Product
45^2	$4 \times (4 + 1) = 4 \times 5 = 20$	2,025
85^2	$8 \times (8 + 1) = 8 \times 9 = 72$	7,225

The examples below show how to square a number

Squares of Numbers

$11^2 = 121$	$21^2 = 441$
$12^2 = 144$	$22^2 = 484$
$13^2 = 169$	$23^2 = 529$
$14^2 = 196$	$24^2 = 576$
$15^2 = 225$	$25^2 = 625$
$16^2 = 256$	$26^2 = 676$
$17^2 = 289$	$27^2 = 729$
$18^2 = 324$	$28^2 = 784$

Activity Have students experiment with their calculators to see how the product $234{,}567 \times 1{,}000{,}000$ appears on the screen. Have them explain what the numbers on the screen mean. Sample answer: "2.34567 11" means 2.34567×10^{11}.

2-6A HANDS-ON LAB Notes

GET READY

Objective Students divide decimals using models.

Optional Resources
Hands-On Lab Masters
- grid paper, p. 10
- worksheet, p. 40

Overhead Manipulative Resources
- decimal models

MANAGEMENT TIPS

Recommended Time
35 minutes

Getting Started Draw a 10 × 10 grid square on an overhead transparency to show how each block of the model represents 0.01. Have students use grid paper to show 0.24 in various ways. Make sure students recall that 0.2 is equivalent to 0.20.

Activities 1 and 2 demonstrate division of decimals when the dividend is a positive value less than 1. Before students shade their models, ask them what the dimensions of the rectangle are that they should use.

HANDS-ON LAB

COOPERATIVE LEARNING

2-6A Division with Decimal Models

A Preview of Lesson 2-6

grid paper

markers

Since multiplication and division are inverse operations, you can also use grid paper to make decimal models to show division of decimals.

TRY THIS

Work with a partner.

1. To model 0.24 ÷ 0.6, follow these steps.
   - You need to shade a rectangle with an area of 0.24. So, shade 24 small squares in a decimal model.
   - There are many rectangles with an area of 0.24. You need to shade one that has a length of 0.6.
   - The missing factor is 0.4.

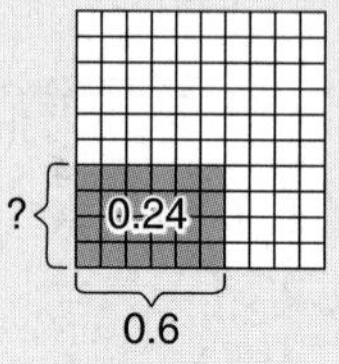

   The area of a 0.4 by 0.6 rectangle is 0.24. Therefore, 0.24 ÷ 0.6 = 0.4.

2. To model 0.2 ÷ 0.4 you need to shade a rectangle with an area of 0.2.
   - Since you are using decimal models, first write 0.2 as 0.20.
   - Shade a rectangle with an area of 0.20 and a length of 0.4.
   - The missing factor is 0.5.

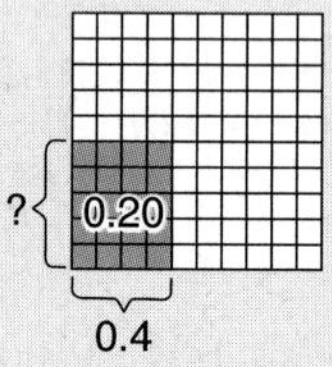

   The area of a 0.4 by 0.5 rectangle is 0.20 or 0.2. Therefore, 0.2 ÷ 0.4 is 0.5.

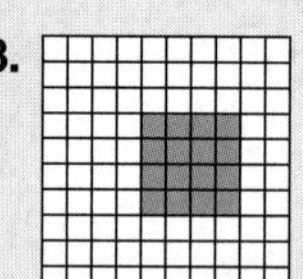

ON YOUR OWN

Write a division problem using decimals for each model shown below.

1. 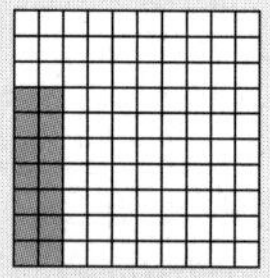 **0.14 ÷ 0.2 = 0.7**
2. 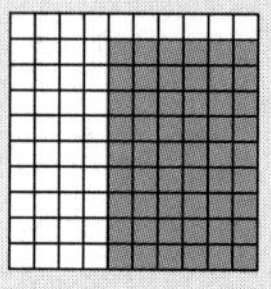 **0.54 ÷ 0.6 = 0.9**
3. **0.16 ÷ 0.4 = 0.4**

Use decimal models to show each quotient. **4–9. See Answer Appendix for models.**

4. 0.35 ÷ 0.5 **0.7**
5. 0.36 ÷ 0.6 **0.6**
6. 0.4 ÷ 0.8 **0.5**
7. 0.9 ÷ 0.9 **1**
8. 0.64 ÷ 0.8 **0.8**
9. 0.48 ÷ 0.8 **0.6**

TRY THIS

Work with a partner.

3 To model 1 ÷ 0.5, follow these steps.

- You need to shade a rectangle with an area of 1. In a decimal model, 1 is represented by 100 small squares.
- The length of the rectangle is 0.5.
- If you shade a rectangle with a length of 0.5, you will only shade 50 squares instead of 100 squares. So, you need to use two decimal models, side by side.
- The missing factor is 2.

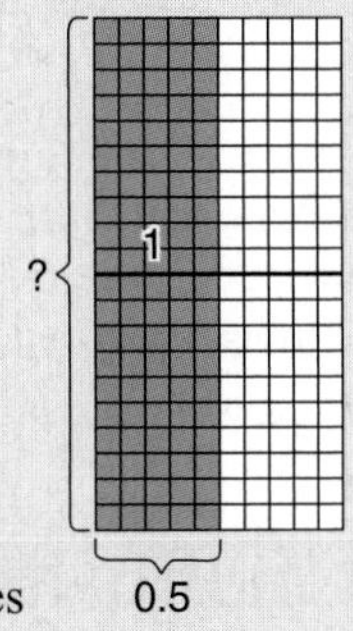

The area of a 0.5 by 2 rectangle is 1.
Therefore, 1 ÷ 0.5 = 2.

4 Model 1.2 ÷ 0.4.

- Shade a rectangle whose area is 120 small squares. The width is 0.4.

The area of a 0.4 by 3 rectangle is 1.2.
Therefore, 1.2 ÷ 0.4 = 3.

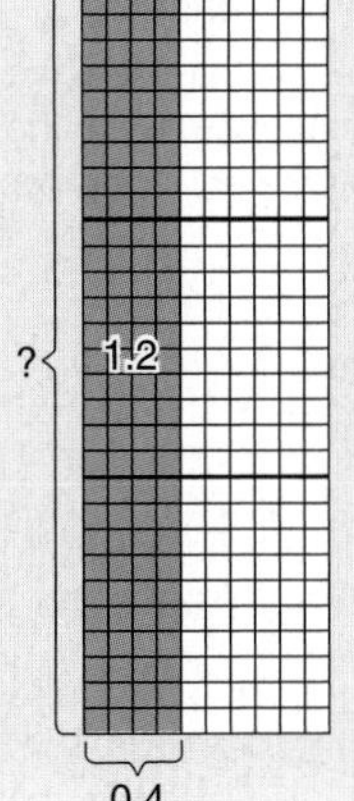

ON YOUR OWN

Write a division problem using decimals for each model shown below.

10.

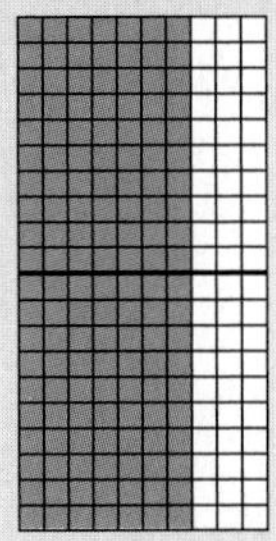

11.

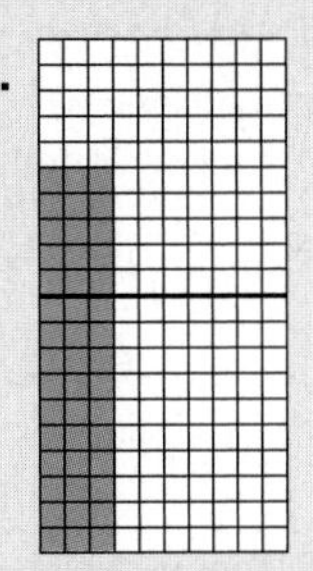

0.45 ÷ 0.3 = 1.5

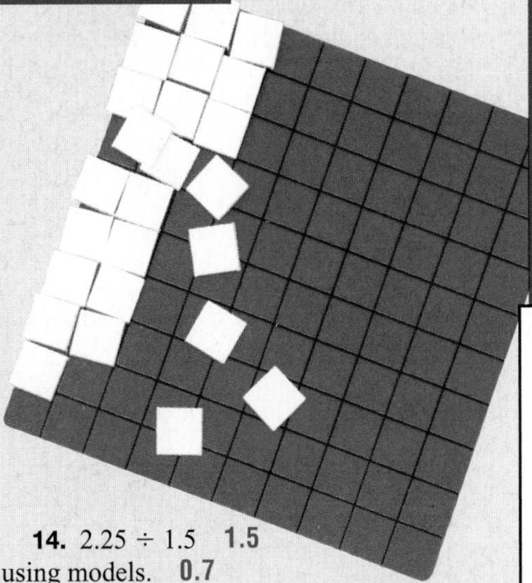

12–14. See Answer Appendix for models.

Use decimal models to show each quotient.

12. 1.2 ÷ 0.6 **2**
13. 1.6 ÷ 0.4 **4**
14. 2.25 ÷ 1.5 **1.5**

15. *Look Ahead* Find the quotient 0.49 ÷ 0.7 without using models. **0.7**

Have students write a paragraph explaining how the models show the division of decimals and how they might use the models if they forget the pattern they discovered in this lab.

Activities 3 and 4 use the same modeling techniques, but the dividend is a value of 1 or greater. Point out that in order to model a value of 1 or greater in a rectangle of width less than 1, they must use more than one set of 100 squares.

ASSESS

Have students complete Exercises 1–14. Watch for students who may have difficulty deciding how to model each dividend. Make sure they realize that the divisor is the width of the rectangle to be used.

Use Exercise 15 to determine whether students have discovered the pattern shown in each model.

***Hands-On Lab Masters,* p. 40**

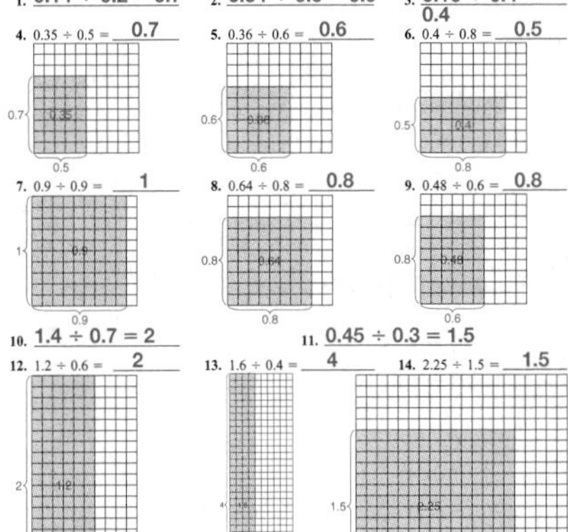

Name ______ Date ______

Hands-On Lab
(Lesson 2-6A)

Division with Decimal Models

On Your Own

1. 0.14 ÷ 0.2 = 0.7
2. 0.54 ÷ 0.6 = 0.9
3. 0.16 ÷ 0.4 = 0.4
4. 0.35 ÷ 0.5 = 0.7
5. 0.36 ÷ 0.6 = 0.6
6. 0.4 ÷ 0.8 = 0.5
7. 0.9 ÷ 0.9 = 1
8. 0.64 ÷ 0.8 = 0.8
9. 0.48 ÷ 0.6 = 0.8
10. 1.4 ÷ 0.7 = 2
11. 0.45 ÷ 0.3 = 1.5
12. 1.2 ÷ 0.6 = 2
13. 1.6 ÷ 0.4 = 4
14. 2.25 ÷ 1.5 = 1.5
15. Look Ahead 0.49 ÷ 0.7 = 0.7

© Glencoe/McGraw-Hill 40 *Mathematics: Applications and Connections, Course 2*

2-6 Lesson Notes

Instructional Resources

- *Study Guide Masters,* p. 13
- *Practice Masters,* p. 13
- *Enrichment Masters,* p. 13
- Transparencies 2-6, A and B
- *Diversity Masters,* p. 15
- *Technology Masters,* p. 29

CD-ROM Program
- Resource Lesson 2-6

Recommended Pacing	
Standard	Days 8 & 9 of 14
Honors	Day 8 of 13
Block	Day 5 of 7

1 FOCUS

5-Minute Check (Lesson 2-5)

Multiply mentally.

1. 0.06 × 100 **6**
2. 3.192×10^3 **3,192**
3. 83.11 × 0.1 **8.311**
4. Solve $n = 42.4 \times 10^5$. **4,240,000**
5. Suppose a can of peaches costs $0.89. What would 1,000 cans cost? **$890**

The 5-Minute Check is also available on **Transparency 2-6A** for this lesson.

Motivating the Lesson

Communication Complete each statement.

100 ÷ 10 = 10, so hundredths ÷ tenths = _?_. **tenths**

1,000 ÷ 100 = 10, so thousandths ÷ hundredths = _?_. **tenths**

2 TEACH

Transparency 2-6B contains a teaching aid for this lesson.

Using the Mini-Lab Encourage students to count decimal places in parts a and b of Exercise 1. You may wish to show the verification of this pattern by using fractions involving powers of 10.

2-6 Dividing Decimals

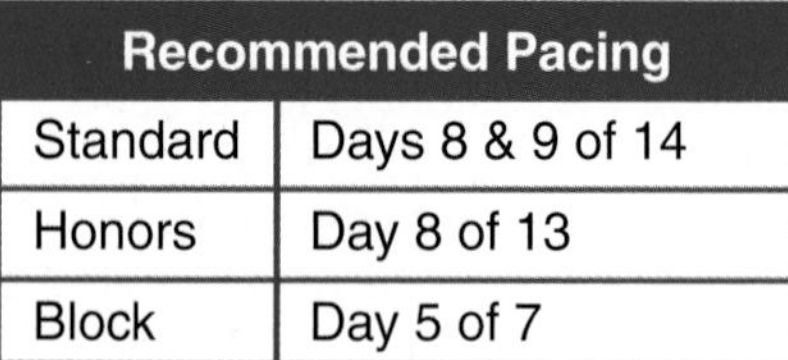

What you'll learn
You'll learn to divide decimals.

When am I ever going to use this?
Decimal division can be used to compare the costs of different-sized items.

Ceres, one of the largest known asteroids, is 690.4 kilometers in diameter. Jupiter, the first planet beyond the asteroid belt, has a diameter of 142,748.8 kilometers. How many times greater is Jupiter's diameter than Ceres' diameter? To find out, divide 142,748.8 by 690.4. *This problem will be solved in Exercise 38.*

As you saw in Lab 2-6A, area models are useful for simple division problems. However, as the numbers increase, you need another method for dividing. In the following Mini-Lab, you will use a calculator to discover a pattern for dividing any two decimals.

MINI-LAB

Work with a partner.  calculator

Try This

1. Use a calculator to find each quotient.
   a. 0.035 ÷ 0.05 **0.7**
   0.35 ÷ 0.5 **0.7**
   3.5 ÷ 5 **0.7**
   35 ÷ 50 **0.7**
   b. 0.00132 ÷ 0.012 **0.11**
   0.0132 ÷ 0.12 **0.11**
   0.132 ÷ 1.2 **0.11**
   1.32 ÷ 12 **0.11**
   13.2 ÷ 120 **0.11**
2. Find the similarities and differences in Exercise 1.

Talk About It

3. Which of the quotients in Exercise 1 would be easier to find *without* a calculator? Explain your reasoning.
4. Rewrite each problem so you can find the quotient without using a calculator. Then find the quotient.
   a. 0.36 ÷ 0.4 b. 1.25 ÷ 0.5 c. 1.68 ÷ 0.2

2. Sample answer: digits in problems are the same; quotients are the same.
3. 3.5 ÷ 5 and 1.32 ÷ 12; you're dividing by small whole numbers.
4a. 3.6 ÷ 4 = 0.9
4b. 12.5 ÷ 5 = 2.5
4c. 16.8 ÷ 2 = 8.4

The pattern in the Mini-Lab suggests the following.

Dividing Decimals	To divide two decimals, change the divisor to a whole number by moving the decimal point to the right. Then move the decimal point in the dividend the same number of places to the right. Then divide as with whole numbers.

Moving the decimal points in the dividend and divisor is a result of multiplying both numbers by a power of ten.

Examples

1 **Find 199.68 ÷ 9.6.** *Estimate: 200 ÷ 10 = 20*

```
       20.8
9.6 )199.68
    -192
       7 68
      -7 68
          0
```

Change 9.6 to 96 and 199.68 to 1,996.8 by moving each decimal point one place to the right.

So, 199.68 ÷ 9.6 = 20.8. *Compared to the estimate, the quotient is reasonable.*

2 **Solve $n = 0.9 \div 0.05$.**

```
         18
0.05 )0.90
      -5
       40
      -40
        0
```

Annex a zero.

The solution is 18.

You can use decimal division to compare the costs of items that are different sizes. It may be necessary to round quotients.

Real World Example APPLICATION

3 **Shopping** **The cost of three different sizes of peanut butter are shown at the right. Which size jar costs the least per ounce?**

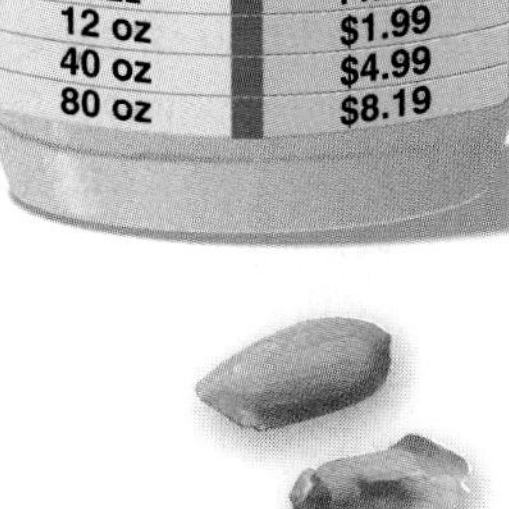

PEANUT BUTTER
SIZE
12 oz
40 oz
80 oz
PRICE
$1.99
$4.99
$8.19

Study Hint

Reading Math The symbol ≈ is read as *is approximately equal to.*

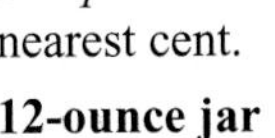

To find the price per ounce, divide the price by the number of ounces of peanut butter in each jar. The quotient tells you the price of one ounce of peanut butter, which is also called the *unit price*. Round the unit price to the nearest cent.

12-ounce jar

1.99 [÷] 12 [=] 0.1658333

≈ 0.17

The unit price is $0.17.

40-ounce jar

4.99 [÷] 40 [=] 0.12475

≈ 0.12

The unit price is $0.12.

80-ounce jar

8.19 [÷] 80 [=] 0.102375

≈ 0.10

The unit price is $0.10.

The 80-ounce jar of peanut butter costs the least per ounce.

In-Class Examples

For Example 1

Find 3.64 ÷ 1.3. **2.8**

For Example 2

Solve $n = 0.6 \div 0.05$. **12**

For Example 3

A dolphin can swim at a speed of about 37 miles per hour. The fastest human swimmer can reach a speed of about 5.2 miles per hour. About how many times faster are dolphins than humans? **about 7.12 times faster**

Classroom Vignette

"I have my students turn their notebook paper sideways so that the lines run vertically and have them write their multiplication and division problems with each digit of the numbers in its own column. It helps them keep the proper numbers lined up."

Steve Werges

Steve Werges, Teacher
LaSalle Springs Middle School
Glencoe, MD

3 PRACTICE/APPLY

Check for Understanding

If students need additional practice or instruction after completing Exercises 1–11, one of these options may be helpful.

- Extra Practice, see p. 572
- Reteaching Activity
- *Transition Booklet,* pp. 21–22
- *Study Guide Masters,* p. 13
- *Practice Masters,* p. 13

Assignment Guide

Core: 13–41 odd, 42–47
Enriched: 12–36 even, 38–47

Have students share with the class the different ways in which decimals are used in sports. You may wish to draw a graph that pictures how many times each way was reported.

Additional Answer

1. Sample answer: Yes; dividing both the dividend and divisor of 35 ÷ 0.5 by 10 results in 3.5 ÷ 0.05.

Study Guide Masters, p. 13

Name____________ Date______

2-6 Study Guide

Dividing Decimals

To divide by a decimal, change the divisor to a whole number.

Example **Find 0.5194 ÷ 0.49.**

$0.49\overline{)0.5194}$ = 1.06; 49; 2 94; 2 94; 0	*Change 0.49 to 49. Move the decimal point two places to the right.* *Move the decimal point in the dividend the same number of places to the right.* *Divide as with whole numbers.*

Without finding or changing each quotient, change each problem so that the divisor is a whole number.

1. 3.4 ÷ 1.1 — 34 ÷ 11
2. 76.44 ÷ 0.006 — 76,440 ÷ 6
3. 0.56 ÷ 0.4 — 5.6 ÷ 4
4. 89.45 ÷ 0.908 — 89,450 ÷ 908
5. 5.675 ÷ 6.8 — 56.75 ÷ 68
6. 0.00864 ÷ 0.012 — 8.64 ÷ 12

Divide.

7. $0.9\overline{)6.3}$ — 7
8. $0.6\overline{)0.540}$ — 0.9
9. $0.3\overline{)129}$ — 430
10. $2.4\overline{)0.192}$ — 0.08
11. $0.44\overline{)5.28}$ — 12
12. $0.025\overline{)0.04}$ — 1.6
13. $1.3\overline{)780}$ — 600
14. $0.08\overline{)0.0012}$ — 0.015
15. $0.7\overline{)5.95}$ — 8.5

Solve each equation.

16. $y = 0.0528 \div 0.06$ — 0.88
17. $16.84 \div 0.4 = m$ — 42.1
18. $k = 2.05 \div 0.5$ — 4.1

 T13 *Mathematics: Applications and Connections, Course 2*

CHECK FOR UNDERSTANDING

Communicating Mathematics

Read and study the lesson to answer each question. **1. See margin.**

1. ***Tell*** whether 35 ÷ 0.5 is the same as 3.5 ÷ 0.05. Explain your reasoning.
2. ***Give an example*** of a division problem in which it is necessary to annex one or more zeros to the dividend. **Sample answer: 3.2 ÷ 0.04**

Guided Practice

Without finding or changing each quotient, change each problem so that the divisor is a whole number.

3. 0.36 ÷ 0.4 **3.6 ÷ 4**
4. 4.4 ÷ 1.1 **44 ÷ 11**
5. 50.4 ÷ 0.56 **5,040 ÷ 56**

Divide.

6. 3 ÷ 0.6 **5**
7. $0.056\overline{)0.084}$ **1.5**
8. 51 ÷ 0.8 **63.75**

Solve each equation.

9. $0.42 \div 3.5 = w$ **0.12**
10. $1.35 \div 0.5 = s$ **2.7**
11. ***Sports*** A table tennis table has an area of 4.165 square meters, while a tennis court has an area of 260.76 square meters. To the nearest hundredth, how many times larger is the tennis court than the table tennis table? **62.61 times**

EXERCISES

Practice

Without finding or changing each quotient, change each problem so that the divisor is a whole number. **13. 2,940 ÷ 84 16. 68,130 ÷ 3**

12. 1.05 ÷ 0.7 **10.5 ÷ 7**
13. 2.94 ÷ 0.084
14. 1.89 ÷ 0.9 **18.9 ÷ 9**
15. 0.82 ÷ 0.4 **8.2 ÷ 4**
16. 68.13 ÷ 0.003
17. 2.6 ÷ 1.3 **26 ÷ 13**
18. 0.00945 ÷ 0.21 **0.945 ÷ 21**
19. 1.488 ÷ 3.1 **14.88 ÷ 31**
20. 14.42 ÷ 0.206 **14,420 ÷ 206**

Divide.

21. 4.2 ÷ 1.2 **3.5**
22. 0.287 ÷ 0.035 **8.2**
23. 0.245 ÷ 0.7 **0.35**
24. $0.6\overline{)4.8}$ **8**
25. $0.7\overline{)0.21}$ **0.3**
26. $0.5\overline{)35}$ **70**
27. $1.6\overline{)0.768}$ **0.48**
28. $9\overline{)8.19}$ **0.91**
29. $0.075\overline{)0.345}$ **4.6**

Solve each equation. **31. 0.088 32. 12 34. 7.8 35. 0.65**

30. $3.68 \div 0.92 = x$ **4**
31. $g = 0.4664 \div 5.3$
32. $a = 7.56 \div 0.63$
33. $74.2 \div 0.53 = y$ **140**
34. $17.94 \div 2.3 = m$
35. $c = 2.665 \div 4.1$
36. Round the quotient of 56.38 and 2.6 to the nearest tenth. **21.7**
37. What is $7.69 divided by 5, rounded to the nearest cent? **$1.54**

▪ Reteaching the Lesson ▪

Activity Have students use centimeter cubes to model division of decimals. For example, an individual cube can represent 0.1 and a stack of 10 cubes can represent 1. Ask students how they would model 7.5 ÷ 1.5.

MathPASS CD-ROM

This CD-ROM offers a complete, self-paced mathematics curriculum. Each lesson includes a pretest, tutorial, guided practice, and posttest. MathPASS Lessons 5 and 6 are correlated to this Student Edition lesson.

For Windows & Macintosh

Applications and Problem Solving

38. 206.8 times

39a. \$0.26, \$0.24

38. ***Earth Science*** Refer to the beginning of the lesson. To the nearest tenth, how many times greater is Jupiter's diameter than Ceres' diameter?

39. ***Shopping*** A snack-sized box of microwave popcorn has five 1.75-ounce bags and costs \$2.29. A large box has six 3.5-ounce bags and costs \$4.99.

Microwave Popcorn			
Kind of Box	Number of Bags	Size of Bags	Cost
Snack Size	5	1.75 oz	\$2.29
Large	6	3.5 oz	\$4.99

   a. Find the unit price of each box.
   b. Which box costs less per ounce? **the large box**
   c. Describe a situation when it would make sense to buy the box that is *not* less per ounce. **Sample answer: You only want small servings.**
   d. A regular box of popcorn has three 3.5-ounce servings and costs \$2.29. Would it make sense to buy one large box or two regular boxes? Explain your reasoning. **Two regular boxes cost \$4.58, which is less than \$4.99.**

Family Activity

Search newspapers or magazines for examples of how decimals are used in sports. Then explain it to a family member.

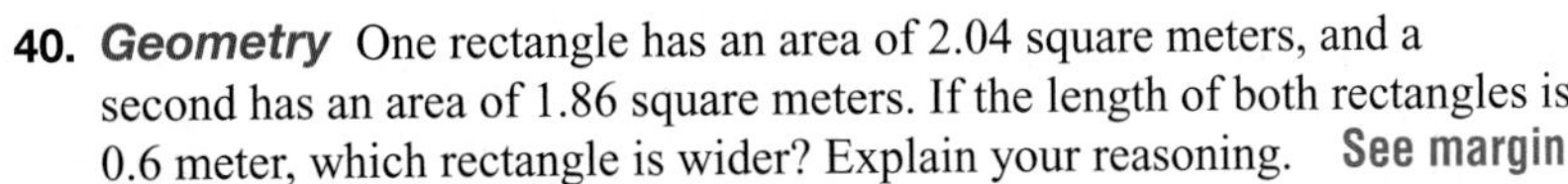

40. ***Geometry*** One rectangle has an area of 2.04 square meters, and a second has an area of 1.86 square meters. If the length of both rectangles is 0.6 meter, which rectangle is wider? Explain your reasoning. **See margin.**

41. ***Track*** At the Atlanta Olympics, U.S. track star Michael Johnson set an Olympic record of 43.49 seconds in the 400-meter event. To the nearest tenth, find his speed in meters per second. **9.2 meters per second**

42. ***Critical Thinking*** Without actually dividing, choose the division problem that has the greatest quotient. **d**
   a. $2.4 \div 6$ **b.** $2.4 \div 0.6$
   c. $2.4 \div 0.06$ **d.** $2.4 \div 0.006$

Mixed Review

43. Solve $x = 2.83 \times 100$ mentally. *(Lesson 2-5)* **283**

44. **Standardized Test Practice** Terrence walks to and from school every day. The round trip is 3.21 kilometers. If he walks every day for 5 days, how far does he walk? *(Lesson 2-4)* **E**
   A 16.25 kilometers
   B 16.07 kilometers
   C 12.64 kilometers
   D 1.605 kilometers
   E Not Here

45. $20 \times 6 = 120$

45. Estimate 21.7×6.3. *(Lesson 2-3)*

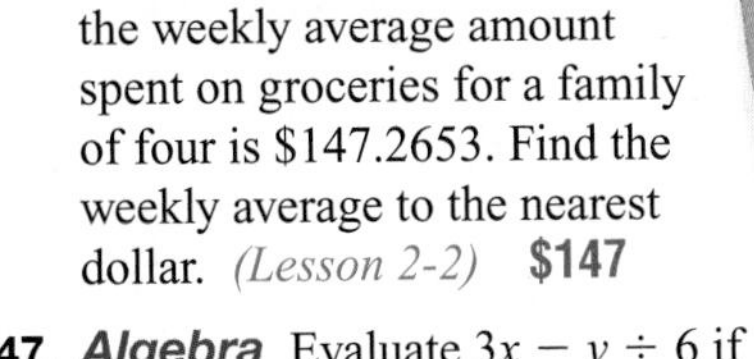

46. ***Money Matters*** A survey of the weekly average amount spent on groceries for a family of four is \$147.2653. Find the weekly average to the nearest dollar. *(Lesson 2-2)* **\$147**

For **Extra Practice,** see page 572.

47. ***Algebra*** Evaluate $3x - y \div 6$ if $x = 4$ and $y = 12$. *(Lesson 1-3)* **10**

4 ASSESS

Closing Activity

Modeling Have students use play money to demonstrate division problems, such as $1.75 \div 0.5$ and $3.6 \div 1.5$.

Additional Answer

40. Sample answer: The first rectangle; you would divide 2.04 by 0.6 and 1.86 by 0.6 to find the widths. The divisors are the same, so $2.04 \div 0.6$ will be greater than $1.86 \div 0.6$.

Practice Masters, p. 13

Name__________ Date________

2-6 Practice

Dividing Decimals

Without finding or changing each quotient, change each problem so that the divisor is a whole number.

1. $0.84 \div 0.2$ — $8.4 \div 2$
2. $1.02 \div 0.3$ — $10.2 \div 3$
3. $3.9 \div 1.3$ — $39 \div 13$
4. $13.6 \div 0.003$ — $13{,}600 \div 3$
5. $1.622 \div 1.4$ — $16.22 \div 14$
6. $0.00025 \div 0.035$ — $0.25 \div 35$

Divide.

7. $0.5\overline{)9.5}$ — 19
8. $0.8\overline{)0.048}$ — 0.06
9. $0.4\overline{)82}$ — 205
10. $3.5\overline{)2.38}$ — 0.68
11. $0.62\overline{)600.16}$ — 968
12. $0.015\overline{)0.06}$ — 4
13. $1.4\overline{)121.8}$ — 87
14. $8\overline{)0.0092}$ — 0.00115
15. $0.38\overline{)760.38}$ — 2,001

Solve each equation.

16. $7.8 \div 2.6 = k$ — 3
17. $3.92 \div 0.08 = m$ — 49
18. $s = 149.73 \div 0.23$ — 651
19. $v = 155 \div 0.1$ — 1,550
20. $c = 1{,}098 \div 6.1$ — 180
21. $3{,}633.4 \div 3.7 = d$ — 982
22. $903.6 \div 25.1 = n$ — 36
23. $363.6 \div 5 = r$ — 72.72
24. $2.004 \div 0.2 = b$ — 10.02
25. $w = 84.7 \div 3.85$ — 22
26. $165.2 \div 8.26 = t$ — 20
27. $29.28 \div 1.22 = s$ — 24

 T13 *Mathematics: Applications and Connections, Course 2*

Extending the Lesson

Enrichment Masters, p. 13

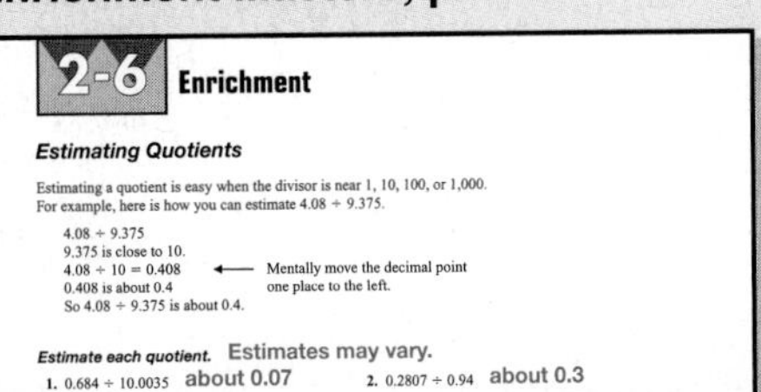

2-6 Enrichment

Estimating Quotients

Estimating a quotient is easy when the divisor is near 1, 10, 100, or 1,000. For example, here is how you can estimate $4.08 \div 9.375$.

$4.08 \div 9.375$
9.375 is close to 10.
$4.08 \div 10 = 0.408$ ← Mentally move the decimal point one place to the left.
0.408 is about 0.4
So $4.08 \div 9.375$ is about 0.4.

Estimate each quotient. Estimates may vary.

1. $0.684 \div 10.0035$ about 0.07
2. $0.2807 \div 0.94$ about 0.3

Activity Have students find the cost of a gallon of gasoline at a gasoline station where a sale of 6.8 gallons costs a customer \$8.77. **about \$1.29** Also have them make up problems using prices at local gas stations.

2-7 Lesson Notes

Instructional Resources

- *Study Guide Masters,* p. 14
- *Practice Masters,* p. 14
- *Enrichment Masters,* p. 14
- Transparencies 2-7, A and B
- *Assessment and Evaluation Masters,* p. 44

CD-ROM Program
- Resource Lesson 2-7

Recommended Pacing	
Standard	Day 10 of 14
Honors	Day 9 of 13
Block	Day 5 of 7

1 FOCUS

5-Minute Check (Lesson 2-6)

Divide.

1. $0.7\overline{)4.2}$ 6
2. 0.625 ÷ 0.25 2.5
3. Find the quotient of 1.856 and 0.2. 9.28

Solve each equation.

4. 26.5 ÷ 0.5 = t 53
5. p = 0.72 ÷ 0.009 80

The 5-Minute Check is also available on **Transparency 2-7A** for this lesson.

Motivating the Lesson

Problem Solving Weights on packages of meat are expressed as decimals. Ask students to give sample weights that would satisfy a recipe that calls for a 4- to $4\frac{3}{4}$-pound roast.

2-7 Decimals and Fractions

What you'll learn

You'll learn to express fractions as terminating or repeating decimals.

When am I ever going to use this?

Knowing how to express a fraction as a decimal can help you calculate a batting average.

Word Wise

terminating decimal
repeating decimal
bar notation

Are you a "lefty?" President Clinton, Oprah Winfrey, and Tom Cruise are all left-handed. Actually, about 3 out of every 25 people or $\frac{3}{25}$ of the population are left-handed. Any fraction can be written as a decimal by dividing.

Method 1

Use paper and pencil.

$\frac{3}{25}$ indicates 3 ÷ 25.

$$\begin{array}{r} 0.12 \\ 25\overline{)3.00} \\ \underline{25} \\ 50 \\ \underline{50} \\ 0 \end{array}$$

Write 3 as 3.00. Place the decimal point in the quotient. Divide as with whole numbers.

Method 2

Use a calculator.

3 [÷] 25 [=] *0.12*

The fraction $\frac{3}{25}$ can be written as the decimal 0.12. A decimal like 0.12 is called a **terminating decimal** because the division ends, or terminates, when the remainder is zero.

Study Hint

Technology Calculators may round or truncate answers. *Truncate* means to cut off at a certain place-value position, ignoring the digits that follow.

However, not all decimals are terminating decimals. Decimals like 0.44444444. . . are called **repeating decimals** because there is a pattern in the digits that repeats forever. You can use the **bar notation** $0.\overline{4}$ to indicate that the 4 repeats forever. Study the pattern below.

$0.131313131313... = 0.\overline{13}$ *The digits 13 repeat.*
$5.8666666666... = 5.8\overline{6}$ *The digit 6 repeats.*
$72.0831831831... = 72.0\overline{831}$ *The digits 831 repeat.*

Example 1 Express $\frac{2}{3}$ as a decimal using division.

Method 1 Use paper and pencil.

$$\begin{array}{r} 0.666... \\ 3\overline{)2.000} \\ \underline{18} \\ 20 \\ \underline{18} \\ 20 \\ \underline{18} \\ 2 \end{array}$$

The digit 6 will repeat since 2 will continue to be the remainder.

Method 2 Use a calculator.

2 [÷] 3 [=] *0.666666667*
This calculator rounds.

2 [÷] 3 [=] *0.666666666*
This calculator truncates.

Use bar notation to indicate that the digit 6 repeats. So, $\frac{2}{3} = 0.\overline{6}$.

Example 2 Express $4\frac{5}{6}$ as a decimal.

Method 1 Paper and pencil

$$\begin{array}{r} 0.833... \\ 6\overline{)5.000} \\ \underline{48} \\ 20 \\ \underline{18} \\ 20 \\ \underline{18} \\ 2 \end{array}$$

Divide 5 by 6. The digit 3 will repeat since 2 will continue to be the remainder.

Method 2 Calculator

5 ÷ 6 + 4 = 4.833333333

Therefore, $4\frac{5}{6} = 4.8333...$ or $4.8\overline{3}$.

Repeating decimals often occur in real-world situations. However, they are usually rounded to a certain place-value position.

Example 3

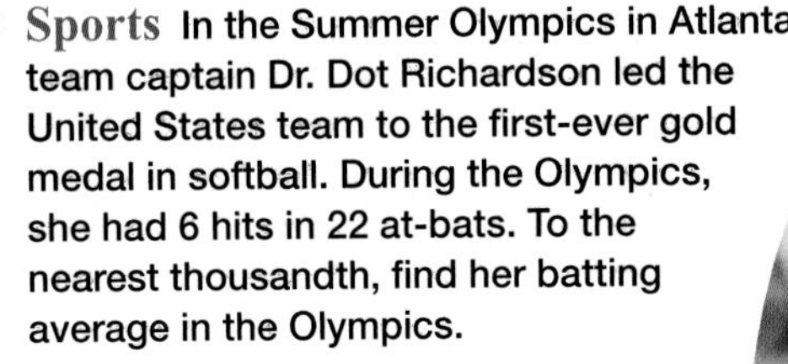

Sports In the Summer Olympics in Atlanta, team captain Dr. Dot Richardson led the United States team to the first-ever gold medal in softball. During the Olympics, she had 6 hits in 22 at-bats. To the nearest thousandth, find her batting average in the Olympics.

To find a batting average, divide the number of hits, 6, by the times at bat, 22.

6 ÷ 22 = 0.272727273

Look at the digit to the right of the thousandths place. Round up since 7 > 5.

Dr. Dot Richardson's batting average in the Olympics was 0.273.

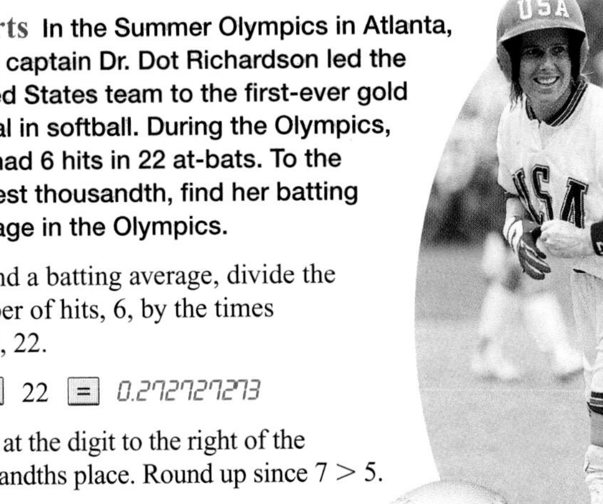

Did you know The United States women's soccer team also won the first gold medal awarded in that event at the Summer Olympics in Atlanta.

CHECK FOR UNDERSTANDING

Communicating Mathematics

Read and study the lesson to answer each question.

1. ***Explain*** how to express a fraction as a decimal. **1. Divide the numerator by the denominator.**
2. ***Describe*** the difference between a terminating and a repeating decimal. Give an example of each. **See margin.**
3. ***You Decide*** Mika thinks that 0.5 and $0.\overline{5}$ are equal. Kim thinks they are not. Who is correct? Explain your reasoning. **Kim; $0.\overline{5}$ = 0.55555555...**

Guided Practice

Write each repeating decimal using bar notation.

4. 0.7555555... **$0.7\overline{5}$**
5. 6.34343434... **$6.\overline{34}$**
6. 10.123123123... **$10.\overline{123}$**

2 TEACH

Transparency 2-7B contains a teaching aid for this lesson.

Reading Mathematics The symbolism used in writing repeating decimals may not be familiar. Have students write all of the ways they can think of to express a value that stands for *4 out of 11.*

In-Class Examples

For Example 1

Express $\frac{1}{6}$ as a decimal using division. $0.1\overline{6}$

For Example 2

Express $7\frac{21}{99}$ as a decimal. $7.\overline{21}$

For Example 3

Rosa made 14 of the 23 free throws she attempted during the basketball season. To the nearest hundredth, what was her shooting average for free throws? 0.61

Teaching Tip Once you are convinced that students understand how to express a fraction as a decimal, you may want to encourage them to work more efficiently by using calculators to find decimal answers.

3 PRACTICE/APPLY

Check for Understanding

If students need additional practice or instruction after completing Exercises 1–10, one of these options may be helpful.

- Extra Practice, see p. 573
- Reteaching Activity
- *Study Guide Masters,* p. 14
- *Practice Masters,* p. 14

Additional Answer

2. A repeating decimal is a decimal whose digits repeat forever; 0.066 . . . . A terminating decimal does not; 0.875.

Reteaching the Lesson

Activity Use hundreds squares and tens strips to show the relationship between fractions and decimals. Each square represents $\frac{1}{100}$ and each strip, $\frac{1}{10}$.

Error Analysis

Watch for students who choose the incorrect power of 10 when writing a decimal as a fraction.

Prevent by having students read the decimal aloud so that they can hear the correct power of 10 to use.

Assignment Guide

Core: 11–39 odd, 40–44
Enriched: 12–34 even, 36–44

Express each fraction or mixed number as a decimal. If the decimal is a repeating decimal, use bar notation.

7. $\frac{4}{5}$ **0.8** **8.** $1\frac{7}{8}$ **1.875** **9.** $\frac{7}{9}$ **$0.\overline{7}$**

10. ***Weather*** Dallas, Texas, averages $32\frac{1}{4}$ inches of precipitation each year. Express the mixed number as a decimal. **32.25**

EXERCISES

Practice

Write each repeating decimal using bar notation.

11. 0.4444444. . . **$0.\overline{4}$** **12.** 0.6666666. . . **$0.\overline{6}$** **13.** 1.12121212. . . **$1.\overline{12}$**

14. 4.67676767. . . **$4.\overline{67}$** **15.** 13.245245245. . . **16.** 0.989989989. . .

17. 0.833333. . . **$0.8\overline{3}$** **18.** 2.03454545. . . **$2.03\overline{45}$** **19.** 3.01523523. . . **$3.01\overline{523}$**

15. $13.\overline{245}$
16. $0.\overline{989}$

Express each fraction or mixed number as a decimal. If the decimal is a repeating decimal, use bar notation.

20. $\frac{8}{25}$ **0.32** **21.** $\frac{11}{20}$ **0.55** **22.** $\frac{1}{11}$ **$0.\overline{09}$** **23.** $\frac{5}{6}$ **$0.8\overline{3}$**

24. $1\frac{5}{8}$ **1.625** **25.** $\frac{8}{250}$ **0.032** **26.** $\frac{15}{9}$ **$1.\overline{6}$** **27.** $3\frac{14}{16}$ **3.875**

Replace each ● with <, >, or = to make a true sentence.

28. $5\frac{1}{5}$ ● 5.18 **>** **29.** 23.25 ● $23\frac{1}{4}$ **=** **30.** 0.8 ● $\frac{8}{9}$ **<**

31. $\frac{1}{12}$ ● $0.08\overline{3}$ **=** **32.** $\frac{1}{2}$ ● $\frac{1}{6}$ **>** **33.** $\frac{4}{5}$ ● $\frac{3}{4}$ **>**

34. Express $\frac{7}{12}$ as a decimal using bar notation. **$0.58\overline{3}$**

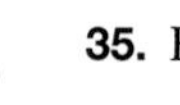

35. Express $\frac{34}{125}$ as a decimal rounded to the nearest hundredth. **0.27**

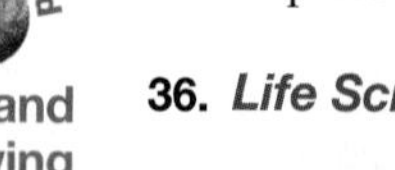

Applications and Problem Solving

36. ***Life Science*** Monarch butterflies migrate up to 2,000 miles from the northern United States to the warmer climates of Mexico, California, and Florida. The fastest monarch butterfly can fly $\frac{1}{3}$ mile per minute. Express $\frac{1}{3}$ as a decimal rounded to the nearest hundredth. **0.33**

37. ***Math History*** The value of pi is 3.1415927. . . . Pi is a non-repeating, nonterminating decimal. Mathematicians have used many methods to find the value of π.

a. Archimedes believed that π was between $3\frac{1}{7}$ and $3\frac{10}{71}$. Express each fraction as a decimal rounded to the nearest thousandth. Was Archimedes correct? **3.141, 3.143; yes**

b. The Rhind Papyrus records that the Egyptians used $\frac{256}{81}$ for π. Express the fraction as a decimal rounded to the nearest thousandth. Which value is closer to the actual value of π, Archimedes' or the Egyptians' value? **3.160, Archimedes'**

Study Guide Masters, p. 14

Name________________ Date________

2-7 Study Guide

Decimals and Fractions

To express a fraction as a decimal, divide the numerator of the fraction by the denominator.

Example *1* **Express $\frac{3}{8}$ as a decimal.**

$8\overline{)3.000}$ = 0.375 $\frac{3}{8} = 0.375$

A decimal like 0.375 is a terminating decimal. The decimal equivalents for some fractions are repeating decimals rather than terminating decimals. Use a bar to indicate the digits that repeat.

Examples *2* **Express $\frac{5}{12}$ as a decimal.**

$12\overline{)5.00000}$ = 0.41666 $= 0.41\overline{6}$

3 **Express $\frac{13}{33}$ as a decimal.**

$33\overline{)13.000000}$ = 0.393939. . . $= 0.\overline{39}$

4 **Express $5\frac{2}{5}$ as a decimal.**

$5\overline{)2.0}$ = 0.4 $= 0.4$ $5\frac{2}{5} = 5.4$

Express each fraction or mixed number as a decimal. If the decimal is a repeating decimal, use bar notation.

1. $\frac{7}{20}$ 0.35 **2.** $\frac{7}{10}$ 0.7 **3.** $\frac{3}{4}$ 0.75 **4.** $\frac{4}{5}$ 0.8

5. $\frac{9}{50}$ 0.18 **6.** $\frac{1}{99}$ $0.\overline{01}$ **7.** $\frac{7}{11}$ $0.\overline{63}$ **8.** $\frac{1}{2}$ 0.5

9. $\frac{11}{12}$ $0.91\overline{6}$ **10.** $\frac{5}{8}$ 0.625 **11.** $\frac{7}{200}$ 0.035 **12.** $\frac{17}{25}$ 0.68

 T14 *Mathematics: Applications and Connections, Course 2*

38. ***Find a Pattern*** If $\frac{1}{8} = 0.125$, find the decimal value of each fraction.

a. $\frac{2}{8}$ **0.25** **b.** $\frac{3}{8}$ **0.375** **c.** $\frac{4}{8}$ **0.5** **d.** $\frac{5}{8}$ **0.625**

39. ***Critical Thinking*** Find one terminating decimal and one repeating decimal between $\frac{2}{3}$ and $\frac{3}{4}$. **Sample answer: $0.7, 0.\overline{71}$**

Mixed Review

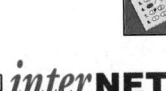

40. Divide 0.108 by 0.2. *(Lesson 2-6)* **0.54**

41. Multiply 0.54 by 0.2. *(Lesson 2-4)* **0.108**

42. **Standardized Test Practice** Using the chart, Jeremy will write a report on the American League Batting Champions. If he wants to list the 4 years with the greatest batting averages in order from greatest to least, which should he choose? *(Lesson 2-1)* **D**

Year	Name	Average
1990	George Brett	0.329
1991	Julio Franco	0.341
1992	Edgar Martinez	0.343
1993	John Olerud	0.363
1994	Paul O'Neill	0.359
1995	Edgar Martinez	0.356
1996	Alex Rodriguez	0.358
1997	Frank Thomas	0.347

A 1990, 1991, 1992, 1997 **B** 1997, 1996, 1995, 1994
C 1993, 1996, 1992, 1990 **D** 1993, 1994, 1996, 1995

interNET CONNECTION For the latest statistics, visit: www.glencoe.com/sec/math/mac/mathnet

43. ***Algebra*** Evaluate a^4, if $a = 3$. *(Lesson 1-4)* **81**

44. ***Sports*** Four hundred sixty people are scheduled to attend a banquet. If each table seats 8 people, how many tables are needed? *(Lesson 1-1)* **58 tables**

For **Extra Practice,** see page 573.

Let the Games Begin

Match-Up

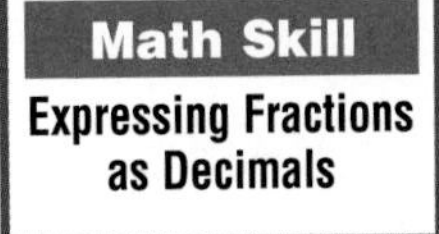

Math Skill
Expressing Fractions as Decimals

Get Ready This game is for two players.

 10 index cards 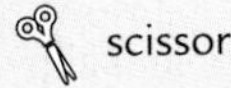 scissors

Get Set Cut an index card in half. On one part, write a fraction. On the other part, write its decimal equivalent. Continue until you have 10 fraction-decimal pairs.

Go
- Mix the cards and arrange them facedown into a rectangle.
- The first player turns over two cards. If they match, the player scores one point and turns over two more cards. If they do not match, the player turns the cards facedown again, no points are scored, and it becomes the next player's turn.
- Players take turns until all cards are matched. The player with the most points wins.

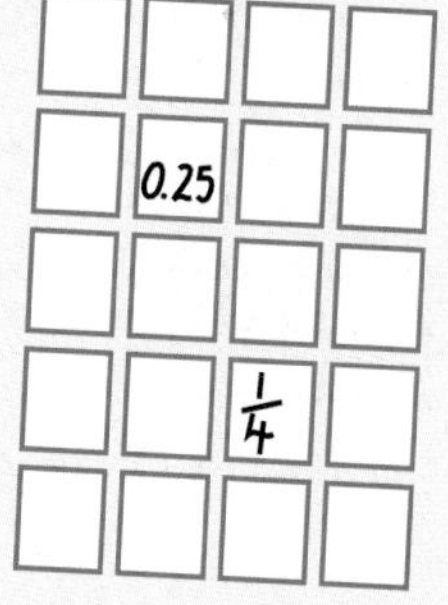

 Visit www.glencoe.com/sec/math/mac/mathnet for more games.

4 ASSESS

Closing Activity

Writing Have students express each of the following fractions as a decimal and order them from least to greatest: $\frac{5}{8}, \frac{2}{3}, \frac{7}{16}, \frac{5}{6}, \frac{7}{10}$, and $\frac{3}{4}$. **0.625, 0.666. . ., 0.4375, 0.8333. . ., 0.7, 0.75; $\frac{7}{16}, \frac{5}{8}, \frac{2}{3}, \frac{7}{10}, \frac{3}{4}, \frac{5}{6}$**

Chapter 2, Quiz C (Lessons 2-6 and 2-7) is available in the *Assessment and Evaluation Masters,* p. 44.

***Practice Masters,* p. 14**

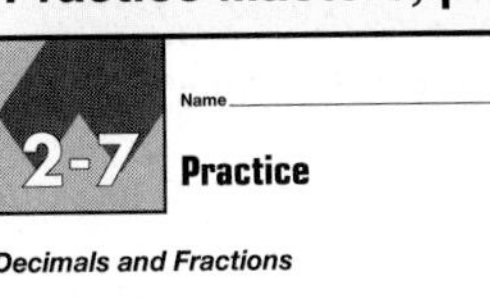

Name______ Date______

2-7 Practice

Decimals and Fractions

Write each repeating decimal using bar notation.

1. 0.4666666. . . $0.4\overline{6}$ 2. 0.5833333. . . $0.58\overline{3}$ 3. 0.1272727. . . $0.1\overline{27}$

Express each fraction or mixed number as a decimal. If the decimal is a repeating decimal, use bar notation.

4. $\frac{3}{5}$ 0.6 5. $\frac{19}{20}$ 0.95 6. $3\frac{4}{5}$ 3.8

7. $\frac{23}{50}$ 0.46 8. $1\frac{5}{8}$ 1.625 9. $\frac{19}{25}$ 0.76

10. $\frac{46}{180}$ $0.2\overline{5}$ 11. $\frac{24}{40}$ 0.6 12. $\frac{7}{8}$ 0.875

13. $14\frac{37}{50}$ 14.74 14. $8\frac{7}{8}$ 8.875 15. $3\frac{8}{9}$ $3.\overline{8}$

Replace each ◯ with $<$, $>$, or $=$ to make a true sentence.

16. $\frac{1}{4}$ ◯ $\frac{9}{40}$ $>$ 17. $11\frac{13}{40}$ ◯ $11\frac{3}{8}$ $<$ 18. $1\frac{3}{8}$ ◯ 1.375 $=$

19. $\frac{2}{25}$ ◯ $\frac{22}{250}$ $<$ 20. 2.78 ◯ $2\frac{39}{50}$ $=$ 21. $\frac{3}{10}$ ◯ $\frac{29}{100}$ $>$

 T14 *Mathematics: Applications and Connections,* Course 2

Extending the Lesson

***Enrichment Masters,* p. 14**

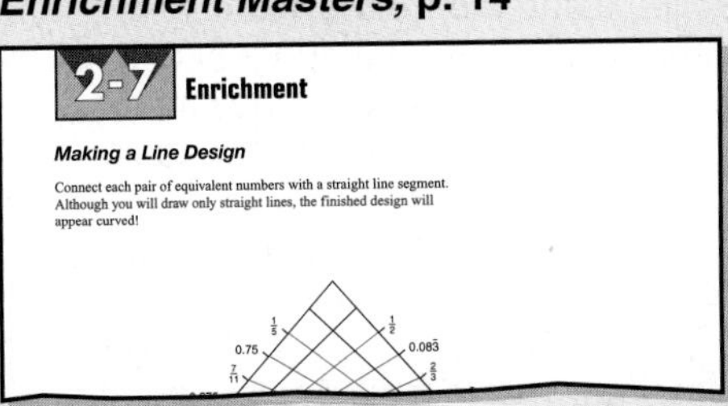

2-7 Enrichment

Making a Line Design

Connect each pair of equivalent numbers with a straight line segment. Although you will draw only straight lines, the finished design will appear curved!

Students can use the game to practice their knowledge of fraction and decimal equivalents. This game also helps students' memories by having them remember where the non-matching cards were when it becomes their turn.

2-8 Lesson Notes

Instructional Resources

- *Study Guide Masters,* p. 15
- *Practice Masters,* p. 15
- *Enrichment Masters,* p. 15
- Transparencies 2-8, A and B
- *Classroom Games,* pp. 5-8
- *Science and Math Lab Manual,* pp. 25–28

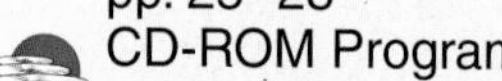

CD-ROM Program
- Resource Lesson 2-8
- Interactive Lesson 2-8

Recommended Pacing	
Standard	Day 11 of 14
Honors	Day 10 of 12
Block	Day 6 of 7

1 FOCUS

5-Minute Check
(Lesson 2-7)

Write each repeating decimal using bar notation.

1. 0.222222. . . $0.\overline{2}$
2. 0.2142857214. . . $0.\overline{2142857}$

Express each fraction as a decimal.

3. $\frac{6}{25}$ 0.24 4. $\frac{3}{8}$ 0.375
5. $\frac{7}{11}$ $0.\overline{63}$

The 5-Minute Check is also available on **Transparency 2-8A** for this lesson.

Motivating the Lesson

Hands-On Activity Have students use a meterstick to find something in the classroom 5 meters long. Use a scale to find something that weighs 5 kilograms, and draw a picture of a container with a capacity of about 1 liter.

2 TEACH

Transparency 2-8B contains a teaching aid for this lesson.

2-8 Integration: Measurement
The Metric System

What you'll learn
You'll learn to change metric units of length, capacity, and mass.

When am I ever going to use this?
You will use the metric system when working on an automobile engine.

Word Wise
meter
metric system
gram
liter

Most eagles have a wingspan of about 180 centimeters. The harpy eagle has a wingspan of 2.4 meters. Which is greater, 180 centimeters or 2.4 meters? Both measurements above are based on the **meter (m)**, which is the basic unit of length in the **metric system**. A meter is about the distance from the floor to a doorknob. All units of length in the metric system are defined in terms of the meter. A prefix is added to indicate the decimal place-value position of the measurement. The metric prefixes are shown in the chart below.

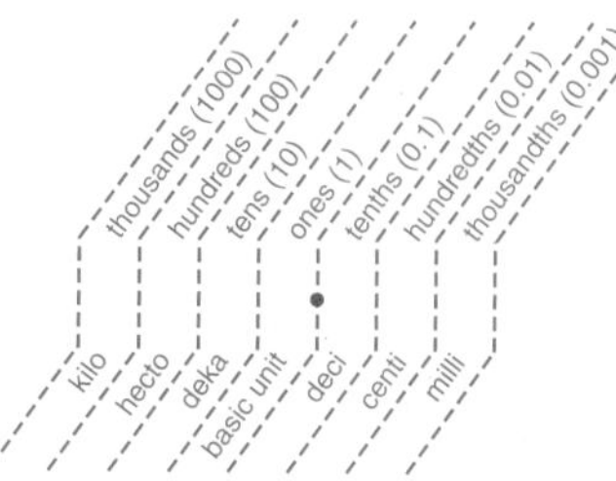

Notice that each place value is 10 times the place value to its right.

Notice that the value of each metric prefix is 10 times the value of the prefix to its right.

One way to solve the problem above is to change 2.4 meters to centimeters. Since 1 meter = 100 centimeters, multiply by 100.

$$2.4 \times 100 = 240$$

Study Hint
Mental Math To multiply or divide by a power of ten, you can move the decimal point.

The harpy eagle's wingspan is 240 centimeters. Since 240 > 180, the harpy eagle's wingspan is greater than most other eagles.

This diagram can help you change metric units.

MULTIPLY to change from larger units to smaller units.

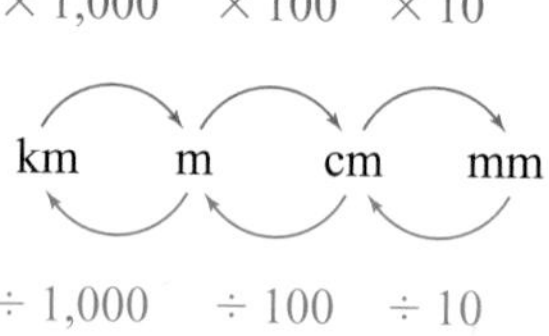

DIVIDE to change from smaller units to larger units.

Classroom Vignette

"Students need a lot of practice using the metric system. To review the relationships in the metric system, I suggest that students go home, open the cupboard, and guess how much is contained in each box, can, or bottle and then check their guess by reading the product label."

Theresa Szczublewski, Teacher
Jones Junior High
Toledo, OH

Examples

1 0.7 cm = __?__ mm

To change from centimeters to millimeters, multiply by 10 since 1 cm = 10 mm.

0.7 × 10 = 7
0.7 cm = 7 mm

2 3,850 m = __?__ km

To change from meters to kilometers, divide by 1,000 since 1 km = 1,000 m.

3,850 ÷ 1,000 = 3.85
3,850 m = 3.85 km

The **kilogram (kg)** is the basic unit of mass in the metric system. *Mass* is the amount of matter that an object contains. Your math textbook has a mass of about one kilogram. Kilogram, gram, and milligram are related in a manner similar to kilometer, meter, and millimeter.

Examples

3 8,249 g = __?__ kg

To change from grams to kilograms, divide by 1,000 since 1 kg = 1,000 g.

8,249 ÷ 1,000 = 8.249
8,249 g = 8.249 kg

4 2 g = __?__ mg

To change from grams to milligrams, multiply by 1,000 since 1 g = 1,000 mg.

2 × 1,000 = 2,000
2 g = 2,000 mg

The **liter (L)** is the basic unit of capacity in the metric system. *Capacity* is the amount of dry or liquid material an object can hold. Soft drinks often come in a 2-liter plastic container. Kiloliter, liter, and milliliter are also related in a manner similar to kilometer, meter, and millimeter.

Examples

5 1.5 L = __?__ mL

Multiply by 1,000 since 1 L = 1,000 mL.

1.5 × 1,000 = 1,500
1.5 L = 1,500 mL

6 483 L = __?__ kL

Divide by 1,000 since 1 kL = 1,000 L.

483 ÷ 1,000 = 0.483
483 L = 0.483 kL

Scientists around the world use the metric system. Using the same system gives them a common language and makes it easy to understand each other's research.

Example CONNECTION

7 **Life Science** **The bacterium *E. coli* has a diameter of 0.001 millimeter. The head of a pin has a diameter of 1 millimeter. How many *E. coli* bacteria could fit across the head of a pin?**

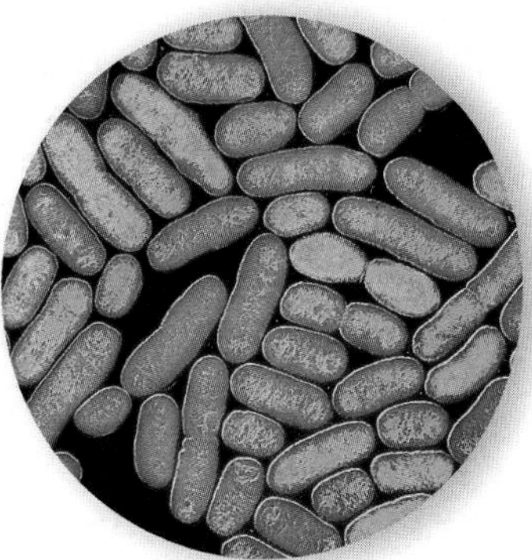

Both measures are expressed in millimeters. So you divide 1 by 0.001.

1 ÷ 0.001 = 1,000

Therefore, 1,000 *E. coli* bacteria could fit across the head of a pin.

In-Class Examples

For Example 1
0.8 cm = __?__ mm **8**

For Example 2
3,700 m = __?__ km **3.7**

For Example 3
3,429 g = __?__ kg **3.429**

For Example 4
8 g = __?__ mg **8,000**

For Example 5
0.4 L = __?__ mL **400**

For Example 6
628 mL = __?__ L **0.628**

For Example 7
How many 0.02-gram tablets can be made from 1 gram of ingredients? **50 tablets**

3 PRACTICE/APPLY

Check for Understanding

If students need additional practice or instruction after completing Exercises 1–9, one of these options may be helpful.

- Extra Practice, see p. 573
- Reteaching Activity
- *Transition Booklet,* pp. 35–36
- *Study Guide Masters,* p. 15
- *Practice Masters,* p. 15

Study Guide Masters, p. 15

Name______________ Date__________

Study Guide

Integration: Measurement
The Metric System

The metric system is a base-10 system. The meter is the basic unit of length. The liter is the basic unit of capacity. The gram is the basic unit of mass.

Prefix	Meaning	Length	Capacity	Mass
kilo–	1,000	kilometer (km)	kiloliter (kL)	kilogram (kg)
	1	meter (m)	liter (L)	gram (g)
centi–	0.01	centimeter (cm)	centiliter (cL)	centigram (cg)
milli–	0.001	millimeter (mm)	milliliter (mL)	milligram (mg)

You can change units by multiplying or dividing by multiples of 10.

Examples *1* **1.543 L = _____ mL**

To change from liters to milliliters, multiply by 1,000 since 1 L = 1,000 mL.

1.543 L × 1,000 = 1,543 mL

2 **6,724 g = _____ kg**

To change from grams to kilograms, divide by 1,000 since 1 kg = 1,000 g.

6,724 g × 1,000 = 6.724 kg

Complete.

1. 0.6 L = _____ mL **600**
2. 89 L = _____ kL **0.089**
3. 62.4 kg = _______ g **62,400**
4. 673 mm = _______ cm **67.3**
5. 9.2 m = _______ cm **920**
6. 55.2 g = _______ kg **0.0552**
7. 20 km = _______ m **20,000**
8. 0.6 cm = _______ mm **6**
9. 2.2 kL = _______ L **2,200**
10. 4.5 g = _______ mg **4,500**
11. 5,900 mL = _______ L **5.9**
12. 2.5 m = _______ mm **2,500**

 T15 *Mathematics: Applications and Connections, Course 2*

■ Reteaching the Lesson ■

Activity To provide a different perspective, you may wish to have students convert among metric units by always multiplying rather than by choosing between multiplying and dividing. When converting to larger units, students can multiply by 0.1, 0.01, 0.001, and so on.

MathPASS CD-ROM

This CD-ROM offers a complete, self-paced mathematics curriculum. Each lesson includes a pretest, tutorial, guided practice, and posttest. MathPASS Lesson 7 is correlated to this Student Edition lesson.
For Windows & Macintosh

Assignment Guide

Core: 11–25 odd, 26, 28–32
Enriched: 10–26 even, 28–32

Exercise 27 asks students to advance to the next stage of work on the Chapter Project. Have them practice with metric rulers before completing the exercise.

4 ASSESS

Closing Activity

Writing Have a group of students create a matching puzzle that consists of a list of units of measurement in the left column and equivalent units of measurement listed in random order in the right column of the page. The remaining students must match the pairs of equivalent measures.

Additional Answer

1. You should divide because you are changing from a smaller unit to a larger unit.

***Practice Masters,* p. 15**

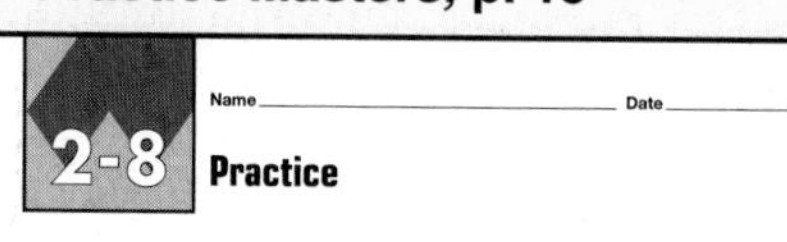

Name__________ Date__________

2-8 Practice

Integration: Measurement
The Metric System

Complete.

1. 470 mm = __47__ cm
2. 63.5 km = __63,500__ m
3. 612 g = __0.612__ kg
4. 12.8 g = __12,800__ mg
5. 8 L = __8,000__ mL
6. 68.2 kg = __68,200__ g
7. 0.8 L = __800__ mL
8. 65 km = __65,000__ m
9. 30 g = __0.03__ kg
10. 368 mL = __0.368__ L
11. 84 cm = __840__ mm
12. 15.4 cm = __0.154__ m
13. 43 m = __4,300__ cm
14. 92 kg = __92,000__ g
15. 3 L = __3,000__ mL
16. 24 cm = __0.24__ m
17. 9 m = __900__ cm
18. 53 km = __53,000__ m
19. 9.5 kg = __9,500__ g
20. 1.5 L = __1,500__ mL
21. 9,876 g = __9.876__ kg
22. 1.1 m = __110__ cm
23. 2.3 mm = __0.23__ cm
24. 6,200 cm = __62__ m
25. How many milliliters are in 0.09 liters? 90
26. How many centimeters are in 9.02 kilometers? 902,000
27. How many millimeters are in 4.2 kilometers? 4,200,000
28. How many milligrams are in 0.012 kilograms? 12,000

 T15 *Mathematics: Applications and Connections, Course 2*

CHECK FOR UNDERSTANDING

Communicating Mathematics

Read and study the lesson to answer each question. 1. See margin.

1. ***Tell*** why you should divide when changing from grams to kilograms.
2. ***Explain*** how the metric system and decimals are similar. Sample answer: both are based on 10

Guided Practice

3. 75,000
4. 5.28
5. 0.923
6. 16,500
7. 8.2
8. 76,000

Complete.

3. 750 m = ? cm
4. 52.8 mm = ? cm
5. 923 g = ? kg
6. 16.5 g = ? mg
7. 8,200 mL = ? L
8. 76 L = ? mL
9. ***Earth Science*** The mass of a sample of rocks is 1.24 kilograms. How many grams are in 1.24 kilograms? 1,240 g

EXERCISES

Practice

15. 0.132
17. 46,000
18. 6.7
19. 0.567
20. 80,000
21. 8,100
22. 0.329
23. 0.047
24. 520

Complete. 10. 89,000 11. 67,100 12. 600 13. 23.4 14. 580

10. 89 km = ? m
11. 67.1 kg = ? g
12. 0.6 L = ? mL
13. 234 mm = ? cm
14. 5.8 m = ? cm
15. 13.2 cm = ? m
16. 0.9 cm = ? mm
17. 46 km = ? m
18. 6,700 m = ? km
19. 567 mg = ? g
20. 80 g = ? mg
21. 8.1 L = ? mL
22. 329 mL = ? L
23. 47 L = ? kL
24. 0.52 km = ? m
25. How many milliliters are in 0.09 liter? 90 mL

Applications and Problem Solving

26. ***Conservation*** The average shower uses 19 liters of water per minute. If you take a five-minute shower each day, how many kiloliters of water do you use in one year by showering? 34.675 kL
27. ***Working on the* CHAPTER Project** Refer to the table on page 43.
    a. Let one centimeter represent the diameter of Earth. Use this scale to find the diameter of each planet. See Answer Appendix.
    b. Let one centimeter represent the average distance from Earth to the Sun. Determine the distances for all the other planets. See Answer Appendix.
    c. Decide whether you want to make a model of the planets showing their diameters or their distances from the Sun. Make your model.

27c. See students' work.

28. ***Critical Thinking*** Find the meaning of the prefixes *giga-* and *nano-*. How many nanometers are in 0.005 meter? How many meters are in 8.3 gigameters? 5,000,000 nanometers; 8,300,000,000 meters

Mixed Review

29. Write 0.59595959. . . using bar notation. *(Lesson 2-7)* $0.\overline{59}$
30. **Standardized Test Practice** A 30-second advertisement on a local television station during prime time costs the advertiser $1,280. To the nearest cent, how much does the ad cost per second? *(Lesson 2-6)* B
    A $4.27 **B** $42.67 **C** $43 **D** $426.67 **E** Not Here
31. Solve $n = 11.45 \times 0.01$. *(Lesson 2-5)* 0.1145
32. Evaluate 5^4. *(Lesson 1-4)* 625

For **Extra Practice,** see page 573.

Extending the Lesson

***Enrichment Masters,* p. 15**

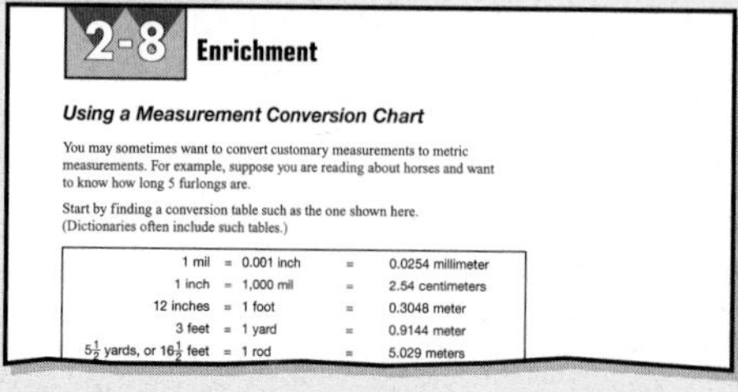

2-8 Enrichment

Using a Measurement Conversion Chart

You may sometimes want to convert customary measurements to metric measurements. For example, suppose you are reading about horses and want to know how long 5 furlongs are.

Start by finding a conversion table such as the one shown here. (Dictionaries often include such tables.)

1 mil	=	0.001 inch	=	0.0254 millimeter
1 inch	=	1,000 mil	=	2.54 centimeters
12 inches	=	1 foot	=	0.3048 meter
3 feet	=	1 yard	=	0.9144 meter
$5\frac{1}{2}$ yards, or $16\frac{1}{2}$ feet	=	1 rod	=	5.029 meters

Activity Have students make up a multiple-choice quiz for classmates to test their understanding of *length, mass,* and *capacity* in the metric system. Questions should be phrased similar to the following: A bowling ball might have a mass of ? . 6 kg
a. 6 mg **b.** 6 g **c.** 6 kg

2-9 Scientific Notation

What you'll learn
You'll learn to express numbers greater than 100 in scientific notation.

When am I ever going to use this?
You can use scientific notation to express the distances between planets.

Word Wise
scientific notation

Long ago, people thought that they were the center of the universe and that everything revolved around them. Today, you know that isn't true. Earth revolves around the sun, and the sun is part of the Milky Way Galaxy. But did you know that there are other galaxies beside the Milky Way in the universe? One such galaxy, the Andromeda galaxy, is 2.2 million light-years away from Earth. *A light-year is the distance light travels in one year.*

You can write numbers like 2.2 million in **scientific notation** by using a power of ten.

2.2 million = $2.2 \times 1{,}000{,}000$
= 2.2×10^6 *$10^6 = 1{,}000{,}000$*

In scientific notation, 2.2 million is 2.2×10^6.

Scientific Notation	Numbers expressed in scientific notation are written as the product of a number that is at least one but less than 10 and a power of ten. The power of ten is written with an exponent.

To write a number in scientific notation, move the decimal point to the right of the first nonzero digit, and multiply this number by a power of ten. To find the power of ten, count the number of places you moved the decimal point.

Example 1 **Write 352,000 in scientific notation.**

3.52000 *Move the decimal point 5 places to get a number between 1 and 10.*

3.52×10^5

In scientific notation, 352,000 is 3.52×10^5.

The decimal part of a number written in scientific notation is often rounded to the hundredths place.

Multiple Learning Styles

Kinesthetic Separate students into two teams. The first student on each team is given a height such as 5 decimeters and they are to make a pile that tall using items such as books or blocks. Have a member from the opposing team measure the pile to see how close it is to the given height. The student who completes the task first and is closer to the given height gets a point for his or her team. Continue with the next pair of students until all team members have played. Then have the students estimate how high a pile 5×10^4 decimeters tall would be.

2-9 Lesson Notes

Instructional Resources

- *Study Guide Masters,* p. 16
- *Practice Masters,* p. 16
- *Enrichment Masters,* p. 16
- Transparencies 2-9, A and B
- *Assessment and Evaluation Masters,* p. 44
- *Technology Masters,* p. 30
- *School to Career Masters,* p. 15

CD-ROM Program
- Resource Lesson 2-9

Recommended Pacing	
Standard	Day 12 of 14
Honors	Day 11 of 13
Block	Day 6 of 7

1 FOCUS

5-Minute Check *(Lesson 2-8)*

Complete.
1. 440 mm = _?_ cm **44**
2. 54 km = _?_ m **54,000**
3. 22.6 g = _?_ mg **22,600**
4. 6.1 L = _?_ mL **6,100**
5. How many centimeters are in 4.036 kilometers? **403,600 cm**

The 5-Minute Check is also available on **Transparency 2-9A** for this lesson.

Motivating the Lesson

Hands-On Activity Write "6,000,000,000,000,000,000 = 6 quintillion" on the chalkboard. Have students work in groups to count out specified grains of rice so that when compiled it equals 1,000 grains of rice. Ask them to estimate how big a room they would need to hold 6 quintillion grains of rice. Ask them how they could write this number in a more compact form.

2 TEACH

Transparency 2-9B contains a teaching aid for this lesson.

Using Calculators Have students explore multiplication of very great numbers using their calculators. How does each type of calculator present the result? Is it exact or has it been truncated?

In-Class Examples

For Example 1
Write 42,000,000 in scientific notation. **4.2×10^7**

For Example 2
Write 887,000,000 in scientific notation. **8.87×10^8 miles**

For Example 3
The diameter of Neptune is about 4.95×10^4 kilometers. The diameter of Venus is about 1.21×10^4 kilometers. About how much greater is Neptune's diameter? **about 37,400 km**

***Study Guide Masters,* p. 16**

Name ________ Date ________

2-9 Study Guide

Scientific Notation

A number in scientific notation is written as the product of a number that is at least one but less than 10 and a power of ten.

Example **Write 254,000,000 in scientific notation.**

2.54000000 *Move the decimal point to get a number between 1 and 10.*

2.54×10^8 *The decimal point was moved 8 places. The exponent is 8.*

Write each number in scientific notation.

1. 760 7.6×10^2	**2.** 8,400 8.4×10^3	**3.** 17,400 1.74×10^4	**4.** 900,000 9×10^5
5. 12,000,000 1.2×10^7	**6.** 64 6.4×10^1	**7.** 5,130,000 5.13×10^6	**8.** 189,000,000,000 1.89×10^{11}
9. 91,000 $9.1\ 10^4$	**10.** 800 8×10^2	**11.** 114,500 1.145×10^5	**12.** 3,060 3.06×10^3
13. 26,600,000 2.66×10^7	**14.** 7,500,000 7.5×10^6	**15.** 303 3.03×10^2	**16.** 810,000,000 8.1×10^8

 T16 *Mathematics: Applications and Connections, Course 2*

Example 2 **Write 141,710,000 in scientific notation.**

1.41710000 *Move the decimal point 8 places to get a number between 1 and 10.*

1.4171×10^8

1.42×10^8 *Round 1.4171 to the nearest hundredth.*

In scientific notation, 141,710,000 is 1.42×10^8.

When you use a calculator to compute with large numbers, the numbers are often displayed in scientific notation.

Example 3 CONNECTION

Earth Science **The average distance from Earth to the Sun is 93,000,000 miles. Neptune is about 30 times as far away from the Sun. Find the average distance from Neptune to the Sun.**

Multiply 93,000,000 by 30.

93000000 [×] 30 [=] 2.79 09

Some calculators display the factor 2.79 and the exponent 9. This represents the number 2.79×10^9.

Neptune is about 2.79×10^9 or 2.79 billion miles from the Sun.

Study Hint
Technology Use the [EE] key to enter numbers in scientific notation. Enter the factor, press [EE], then enter the exponent.

CHECK FOR UNDERSTANDING

Communicating Mathematics

1. It is more convenient.
3. Alma; 24.59 is not less than 10.

Read and study the lesson to answer each question.

1. ***Tell*** why scientific notation is used with large numbers.
2. ***Show*** a classmate how to write 5,280, the number of feet in a mile, in scientific notation. **5.28×10^3**
3. ***You Decide*** Hiroshi thinks that 24.59×10^3 is written in scientific notation. Alma thinks it is not. Who is correct? Explain your reasoning.

Guided Practice

Write each number in scientific notation. **9. 1.264×10^8**

4. 890 **8.9×10^2**
5. 8,300 **8.3×10^3**
6. 6,235 **6.235×10^3**
7. 52,000 **5.2×10^4**
8. 820,000 **8.2×10^5**
9. 126,400,000

10. ***Finance*** The Social Security Administration estimates that there will be 54 million people receiving benefits in 2010. Write 54 million in scientific notation. **5.4×10^7**

Reteaching the Lesson

Activity Have students work with partners to use an almanac or other source to find the populations of five near-by states. Have them list the states in order from least populous to most populous. Next, have them round each number to its greatest place-value position and write it in scientific notation.

Error Analysis
Watch for students who use a whole number greater than 10 when writing scientific notation.
Prevent by reminding them that the number to the left of the decimal can only be between 1 and 9 (inclusive).

EXERCISES

Practice

Write each number in scientific notation.

11. 7,500 **7.5×10^3**
12. 8,450 **8.45×10^3**
13. 40,700 **4.07×10^4**
14. 630,000 **6.3×10^5**
15. 600 **6.0×10^2**
16. 17,500 **1.75×10^4**
17. 23,000 **2.3×10^4**
18. 400,000 **4.0×10^5**
19. 32,000,000
20. 495,000,000
21. 570,000 **5.7×10^5**
22. 9,500,000
23. 8,080 **8.08×10^3**
24. 602,400,000
25. 27,100,000
26. 7,900,000 **7.9×10^6**
27. 558,000 **5.58×10^5**
28. 160,000,000

19. 3.2×10^7
20. 4.95×10^8
22. 9.5×10^6
24. 6.024×10^8
25. 2.71×10^7
28. 1.6×10^8

Replace each ● with <, >, or = to make a true sentence.

29. 3,000 ● 3.0×10^3 **=**
30. 200 ● 2.0×10^1 **>**
31. 72,500 ● 7.25×10^5 **<**
32. 5 million ● 5.0×10^6 **=**
33. 9.3 billion ● 9.3×10^8 **>**
34. 5.56×10^9 ● 5.56 billion **=**
35. A calculator displays 3.4 06. Write the number in scientific notation and in standard form. **3.4×10^6, 3,400,000**
36. Order 9.05×10^3, 5.29×10^3, and 5.29×10^4 from least to greatest.

36. 5.29×10^3, 9.05×10^3, 5.29×10^4

Applications and Problem Solving

Real World

37. ***Geography*** Which number describes the population of Chicago, 3.0×10^6 or 3.0×10^3? Explain your reasoning.
38. ***Earth Science*** Scientists divide Earth's history into small units based on the types of life-forms living then. In the Jurassic Period, which occurred about 208,000,000 years ago, dinosaurs ruled. Express 208,000,000 in scientific notation. **2.08×10^8**

37. 3.0×10^6; Chicago is one of the largest cities in the U.S., and a population of 3,000,000 is reasonable.

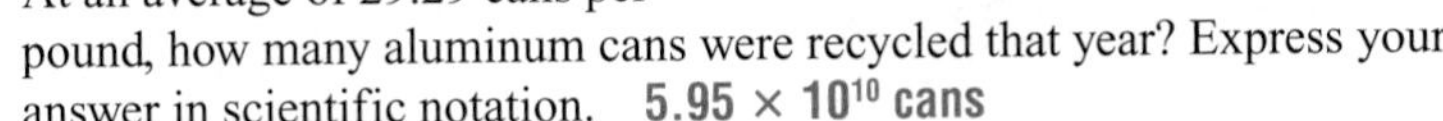

39. ***Recycling*** According to the Aluminum Association, 2,031,000,000 pounds of aluminum cans were recycled in a recent year. At an average of 29.29 cans per pound, how many aluminum cans were recycled that year? Express your answer in scientific notation. **5.95×10^{10} cans**
40. ***Critical Thinking*** One *light-year* is the distance light travels in one year. If the speed of light is 3×10^5 kilometers per second, about how many kilometers does light travel in one year? **about 9.5×10^{12} km**

Mixed Review

41. ***Measurement*** How many grams are in 1.01 kilograms? *(Lesson 2-8)* **1,010 g**
42. Solve $16.2 \div 2.5 = n$. *(Lesson 2-6)* **6.48**

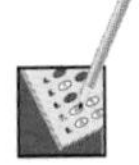

43. **Standardized Test Practice** Enrique earns $4.75 per hour for babysitting. Which is the best estimate of his earnings if he babysits 12 hours during spring break? *(Lesson 2-3)* **C**
    A $20 **B** $48 **C** $60 **D** $80 **E** $100
44. ***Algebra*** Solve $x \div 8 = 14$. *(Lesson 1-5)* **112**
45. Evaluate $100 \div 10 + 2 \cdot 6 \div 4$. *(Lesson 1-2)* **13**

For **Extra Practice**, see page 573.

3 PRACTICE/APPLY

Check for Understanding

If students need additional practice or instruction after completing Exercises 1–10, one of these options may be helpful.

- Extra Practice, see p. 573
- Reteaching Activity, see p. 78
- *Study Guide Masters,* p. 16
- *Practice Masters,* p. 16

4 ASSESS

Closing Activity

Writing Tell students that the speed of sound at sea level is about 7.61×10^2 miles per hour. Ask them to write the speed in standard form. **761 mph** Tell them the speed of light is about 186,000 miles per second. Ask them to write that speed in scientific notation. **1.86×10^5 mi/s**

Chapter 2, Quiz D (Lessons 2-8 and 2-9) is available in the *Assessment and Evaluation Masters,* p. 44.

Assignment Guide

Core: 11–39 odd, 40–45
Enriched: 12–36 even, 37–45

***Practice Masters,* p. 16**

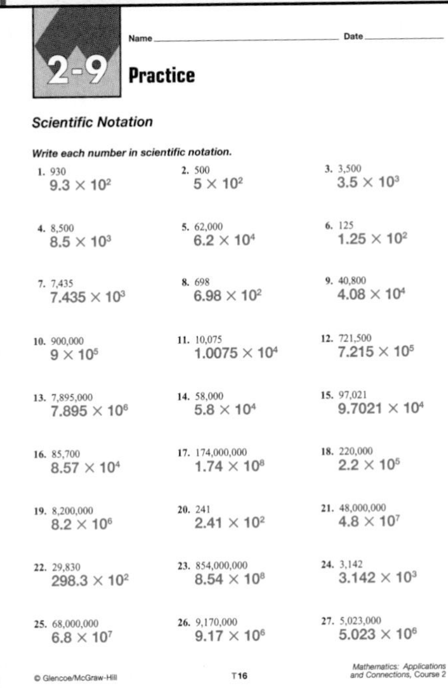

2-9 Practice

Name ______________ Date ______

Scientific Notation

Write each number in scientific notation.

1. 930 9.3×10^2	2. 500 5×10^2	3. 3,500 3.5×10^3
4. 8,500 8.5×10^3	5. 62,000 6.2×10^4	6. 125 1.25×10^2
7. 7,435 7.435×10^3	8. 698 6.98×10^2	9. 40,800 4.08×10^4
10. 900,000 9×10^5	11. 10,075 1.0075×10^4	12. 721,500 7.215×10^5
13. 7,895,000 7.895×10^6	14. 58,000 5.8×10^4	15. 97,021 9.7021×10^4
16. 85,700 8.57×10^4	17. 174,000,000 1.74×10^8	18. 220,000 2.2×10^5
19. 8,200,000 8.2×10^6	20. 241 2.41×10^2	21. 48,000,000 4.8×10^7
22. 29,830 298.3×10^2	23. 854,000,000 8.54×10^8	24. 3,142 3.142×10^3
25. 68,000,000 6.8×10^7	26. 9,170,000 9.17×10^6	27. 5,023,000 5.023×10^6

 T16 *Mathematics: Applications and Connections, Course 2*

Extending the Lesson

***Enrichment Masters,* p. 16**

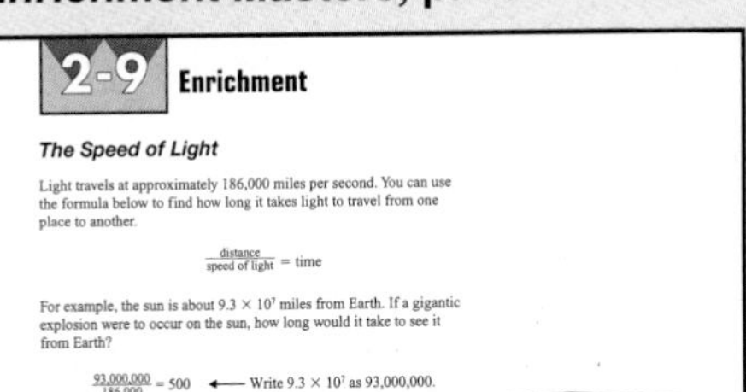

2-9 Enrichment

The Speed of Light

Light travels at approximately 186,000 miles per second. You can use the formula below to find how long it takes light to travel from one place to another.

$$\frac{\text{distance}}{\text{speed of light}} = \text{time}$$

For example, the sun is about 9.3×10^7 miles from Earth. If a gigantic explosion were to occur on the sun, how long would it take to see it from Earth?

$\frac{93{,}000{,}000}{186{,}000} = 500$ ← Write 9.3×10^7 as 93,000,000.

Activity Have students explore with their calculators to find what happens with negative exponents in scientific notation. Are these values greater than 1 or less than 1? Then have students explore the results of multiplying and dividing numbers written in scientific notation.

Study Guide and Assessment

Vocabulary

This section provides a listing of the new terms, properties, and phrases that were introduced in this chapter. Have students define each term and provide an example or two of it, if appropriate.

Understanding and Using the Vocabulary

These exercises check students' understanding of the terms by using a variety of verbal formats including matching, completion, and true/false.

Glossaries A complete glossary of terms appears on pages 656–663. The glossary also appears in Spanish on pages 664–672.

CHAPTER 2 Study Guide and Assessment

interNET CONNECTION Chapter Review **For additional lesson-by-lesson review, visit: www.glencoe.com/sec/math/mac/mathnet**

Vocabulary

After completing this chapter, you should be able to define each term, concept, or phrase and give an example or two of each.

Number and Operations
bar notation (p. 70)
clustering (p. 51)
repeating decimal (p. 70)
scientific notation (p. 77)
terminating decimal (p. 70)

Measurement
kilogram (p. 75)
liter (p. 75)
meter (p. 74)
metric system (p. 74)

Problem Solving
reasonable answers (p. 54)

Understanding and Using the Vocabulary

Choose the correct term or number to complete each sentence.

1. The number 0.04 is (less, greater) than 0.041.
2. When rounding decimals, the digit in the place being rounded should be rounded up if the digit to the right is a (4, 7).
3. The number of decimal places in the product when multiplying decimals is the (sum, product) of the number of places in the factors.
4. In scientific notation, a number is written as a (sum, product) of a decimal number and a power of ten.
5. The basic unit of mass in the metric system is the (kilogram, meter).
6. A model that can be used to represent multiplication problems is called a(n) (area, perimeter) model.
7. The model at the right represents ($0.5 \times 0.3 = 0.15$, $0.05 \times 0.03 = 0.15$).
8. The fraction $\frac{3}{4}$ can be expressed as a (terminating, repeating) decimal.
9. Using bar notation, 0.23333 . . . is expressed as ($0.2\overline{3}$, $0.\overline{23}$).
10. Using scientific notation, 2.4 million is written as (2.4×10^6, 2,400,000).

In Your Own Words 11. Sample answer: One centimeter is one-hundredth of a meter.

11. ***Explain*** the relationship between a meter and a centimeter.

MindJogger Videoquizzes

MindJogger Videoquizzes provide an alternative review of concepts presented in this chapter. Students work in teams to answer questions, gaining points for correct answers. The questions are presented in three rounds.
Round 1 Concepts–5 questions
Round 2 Skills–4 questions
Round 3 Problem Solving–4 questions

Objectives & Examples

Upon completing this chapter, you should be able to:

Review Exercises

Use these exercises to review and prepare for the chapter test.

- compare and order decimals *(Lesson 2-1)*

Order the following decimals from least to greatest: 3.2, 0.4, 0.43, 3.5, 4.

0.4, 0.43, 3.2, 3.5, 4

Order each set of decimals from least to greatest. **15. 15.0, 15.99, 16, 16.03, 16.3**

12. 4.2, 3.9, 3.15, 3.04, 3.7
13. 15.91, 1.59, 0.159, 0.06, 1.4
14. 0.15, 0.149, 0.105, 0.015, 0.501
15. 16.3, 16.03, 16, 15.99, 15.0

12. 3.04, 3.15, 3.7, 3.9, 4.2
13. 0.06, 0.159, 1.4, 1.59, 15.91
14. 0.015, 0.105, 0.149, 0.15, 0.501

- round decimals *(Lesson 2-2)*

Round 247.359 to the nearest tenth.

The digit to the right of the 3 in the tenths place is 5, so round up.

247.359 → 247.4

Round each number to the underlined place-value position.

16. $\underline{5}.75$ **6**　　**17.** $13.2\underline{7}4$ **13.27**
18. $12\underline{9},342$ **129,000**　　**19.** $0.\underline{0}76$ **0.1**
20. $81.\underline{3}49$ **81.3**　　**21.** $57.1\underline{9}6$ **57.20**

- estimate with decimals *(Lesson 2-3)*

Estimate 4.7 + 5.2 + 5.1 + 4.9.

All of the numbers are clustered around 5. There are four numbers. So, the sum is about 5 × 4 or 20.

You can also estimate using rounding.

5 + 5 + 5 + 5 = 20

Estimate.

22. 13.72 + 12.07 **14 + 12 = 26**
23. 36.8 + 39.2 + 41.3 **40 × 3 = 120**
24. 25.73 − 2.19 **26 − 2 = 24**
25. 11.75 × 3.13 **12 × 3 = 36**
26. 72.4 ÷ 9.3 **72 ÷ 9 = 8**
27. 150.96 ÷ 4.76 **150 ÷ 5 = 30**

- multiply decimals *(Lesson 2-4)*

3.2	←	*1 decimal place*
×0.6	←	*1 decimal place*
1.92	←	*Count 2 decimal places from the right.*

Multiply.

28. 2.6 × 3.7 **9.62**
29. 0.13 × 2 **0.26**
30. 12.5 × 0.0017 **0.02125**
31. 7.5 ×3.03 **22.725**
32. 1.001 × 0.4 **0.4004**

Assessment and Evaluation

Six forms of Chapter 2 Test are available in the *Assessment and Evaluation Masters* as shown in the chart.

1A	Multiple Choice	Honors
1B	Multiple Choice	Average
1C	Multiple Choice	Basic
2A	Free Response	Honors
2B	Free Response	Average
2C	Free Response	Basic

Chapter 2 Test, Form 1B, is shown at the right. Chapter 2 Test, Form 2B, is shown on the next page.

Objectives & Examples

This section reviews the skills and concepts of the chapter and shows completely worked examples.

Review Exercises

These exercises provide practice for the corresponding objectives.

***Assessment and Evaluation Masters,* pp. 31–32**

Name________________ Date ________

Chapter 2 Test, Form 1B

1. Which symbol makes 13.54 ● 13.45 a true sentence?　　1. B
A. <　B. >
C. =　D. None of the above

2. Order 6.24, 6.08, 6.009, and 0.6 from least to greatest.　　2. A
A. 0.6, 6.009, 6.08, 6.24　B. 6.24, 6.009, 6.08, 0.6
C. 6.24, 6.08, 6.009, 0.6　D. 0.6, 6.08, 6.009, 6.24

Round each number to the underlined place-value position.

3. $3.0\underline{5}91$　　3. C
A. 3.05　B. 3.059　C. 3.06　D. 3.1

4. $1.2\underline{4}31$　　4. A
A. 1.24　B. 1.241　C. 1.243　D. 1.250

Estimate by rounding.

5. 18.75 + 6.16　　5. C
A. 23　B. 24　C. 25　D. 27

6. 42.8 × 7.7　　6. B
A. 301　B. 344　C. 51　D. 294

7. $6.1\overline{)71.77}$　　7. C
A. 10　B. 11　C. 12　D. 13

8. Estimate 97.5 + 98.2 + 97.9 + 98.1 by clustering.　　8. B
A. 388　B. 392　C. 396　D. 500

Multiply or divide.

9. 25 × 0.096　　9. A
A. 2.4　B. 2.5　C. 24　D. 25

10. 0.61 × 2.9　　10. A
A. 1.769　B. 2.03　C. 2.30　D. 2.5

11. 2.0503×10^4　　11. C
A. 205　B. 2,050.3　C. 20,503　D. 205,030

12. 0.001 × 0.567　　12. A
A. 0.000567　B. 0.5　C. 0.567　D. 567

 31 *Mathematics: Applications and Connections, Course 2*

Chapter 2 Test, Form 1B (continued)

Multiply or divide.

13. 0.256 ÷ 0.16　　13. B
A. 0.16　B. 1.6　C. 1.7　D. 1.8

14. $3.6\overline{)18.036}$　　14. C
A. 4.05　B. 4.5　C. 5.01　D. 5.1

15. $1.423\overline{)8.538}$　　15. D
A. 12.1　B. 5　C. 6.1　D. 6

16. 0.645 ÷ 0.031　　16. A
A. 20.81　B. 22　C. 0.02　D. 2.08

17. Express $\frac{9}{11}$ as a decimal.　　17. C
A. $0.\overline{818}$　B. $8.\overline{181}$　C. $0.\overline{81}$　D. 0.8

18. Write 1.2666... using bar notation.　　18. A
A. $1.2\overline{6}$　B. 1.26　C. $126.\overline{6}$　D. $12\overline{6.6}$

19. Express $\frac{7}{4}$ as a decimal.　　19. B
A. 0.175　B. 1.75　C. 1.75　D. 17.5

20. Complete: 3.64 kg = __?__ g.　　20. D
A. 0.364　B. 36.4　C. 364　D. 3,640

21. Complete: 2,725 m = __?__ km.　　21. B
A. 0.2725　B. 2.725　C. 27.25　D. 272.5

22. Write 73,450 in scientific notation.　　22. A
A. 7.345×10^4　B. 73.450×10^3
C. 73.450×10^4　D. 734.50×10^2

23. Write 973 in scientific notation.　　23. B
A. 0.973×10^3　B. 9.73×10^2
C. 9.73×10^3　D. 97.3×10^1

24. Ken walked 3.5 miles more than Jorge. If Ken walked 11.25 miles, how many miles did Jorge walk?　　24. B
A. 7 mi　B. 7.75 mi　C. 14.75 mi　D. 15 mi

25. Lee buys 100 postcards for his business. If each postcard costs 19¢, how much did he spend?　　25. C
A. $1.90　B. $19.90　C. $19　D. $190

 32 *Mathematics: Applications and Connections, Course 2*

Study Guide and Assessment

Additional Answers

49. 0.027
50. 0.0039
51. 0.0033
52. 6,850
53. 160
54. 40
55. 0.043
56. 3,900,000

Assessment and Evaluation Masters, pp. 37–38

Name____________ Date________

Chapter 2 Test, Form 2B

Replace each ● with <, >, or = to make a true sentence.

1. 0.19 ● 0.019 — 1. >
2. 3.42 ● 3.4 — 2. >
3. Order 10.44, 10.172, 10.4, and 10.006 from least to greatest. — 3. 10.172, 10.006, 10.4, 10.44
4. Order 6.515, 6.009, 6.5, and 6.99 from least to greatest. — 4. 6.009, 6.5, 6.515, 6.99

Round each number to the underlined place-value position.

5. 0.124 — 5. 0.12
6. 6.1501 — 6. 6.2
7. 2.572 — 7. 2.57
8. 56.89 — 8. 57

Estimate by rounding.

9. 8.76 + 6.4 — 9. 9 + 6 = 15
10. 2.8 × 49.3 — 10. 3 × 50 = 150
11. $4.2\overline{)0.78}$ — 11. $4\overline{)0.8}$ = 0.2
12. Estimate 11.87 + 12.35 + 13.002 + 12.45 by clustering. — 12. 12 × 4 = 48

Multiply or divide.

13. 4.7 × 0.005 — 13. 0.0235
14. 51.3 × 2.4 — 14. 123.12
15. 10,000 × 3.9 — 15. 39,000
16. 0.00029×10^7 — 16. 2,900
17. 0.0892 ÷ 0.08 — 17. 1.115
18. Divide 0.085 by 0.04. Round to the nearest hundredth. — 18. 2.13
19. What is $72.93 divided by 5, rounded to the nearest cent? — 19. $14.59
20. How many dimes are there in $45.00? — 20. 450
21. Write 2.9111... using bar notation. — 21. $2.9\overline{1}$

© Glencoe/McGraw-Hill 37 *Mathematics: Applications and Connections, Course 2*

Chapter 2 Test, Form 2B (continued)

Express each fraction or mixed number as a decimal. Use bar notation when necessary.

22. $\frac{8}{3}$ — 22. $2.\overline{6}$
23. $1\frac{5}{9}$ — 23. $1.\overline{5}$
24. $7\frac{1}{33}$ — 24. $7.\overline{03}$
25. Complete: 0.75 L = _?_ mL. — 25. 750
26. Complete: _?_ kg = 13, 412 g. — 26. 13.412

Write each number in scientific notation.

27. 4392.7 — 27. 4.3927×10^3
28. 890,000 — 28. 8.9×10^5
29. 74.321 — 29. 7.4321×10^4
30. 94,000,000 — 30. 9.4×10^7
31. Mrs. Tsao needs a 45.5-centimeter piece of molding. How many centimeters remain after she cut the 45.5 centimeters off the end of a 1-meter piece of molding? — 31. 54.5 cm
32. Vicki vacationed for 7 days and 6 nights. She spent $98 a night for the hotel and $40 a day for food. How much did she spend on food and lodging? — 32. $868
33. During a twelve-week period, Ramon saved $10.25 per week. Estimate the amount he saved in twelve weeks. — 33. $120

© Glencoe/McGraw-Hill 38 *Mathematics: Applications and Connections, Course 2*

Chapter 2 Study Guide and Assessment

Objectives & Examples	Review Exercises
● multiply decimals mentally by powers of ten *(Lesson 2-5)* 100 × 2.3 = 230 0.1 × 25.16 = 2.516 $8.37 \times 10^2 = 837$	**Multiply.** **33.** 13.7×10^3 **13,700** **34.** 0.0065 × 10,000 **65** **35.** 6.37 × 0.01 **0.0637** **36.** 128.63×10^4 **1,286,300**
● divide decimals *(Lesson 2-6)* $$\begin{array}{r} 12.6 \\ 3.6\overline{)45.36} \\ -36 \\ 9\,3 \\ -7\,2 \\ 2\,16 \\ -2\,16 \\ 0 \end{array}$$	**Divide.** **37.** 12 ÷ 1.2 **10** **38.** 8.4 ÷ 0.2 **42** **39.** 0.0036 ÷ 0.9 **0.004** **40.** 5 ÷ 0.005 **1,000** **Divide. Round to the indicated place-value position.** **41.** 3.5 ÷ 1.3; tenth **2.7** **42.** 14.78 ÷ 2.6; whole number **6**
● express fractions as terminating or repeating decimals *(Lesson 2-7)* $$\frac{1}{6} \rightarrow \begin{array}{r} 0.166... \\ 6\overline{)1.000} \\ -6 \\ 40 \\ -36 \\ 40 \end{array} \rightarrow 0.1\overline{6}$$	**Express each fraction or mixed number as a decimal. If the decimal is a repeating decimal, use bar notation.** **43.** $\frac{10}{25}$ **0.4** **44.** $1\frac{2}{3}$ **$1.\overline{6}$** **45.** $\frac{3}{8}$ **0.375** **46.** $10\frac{1}{4}$ **10.25** **47.** $\frac{5}{9}$ **$0.\overline{5}$** **48.** $\frac{5}{12}$ **$0.41\overline{6}$**
● change metric units of length, capacity, and mass *(Lesson 2-8)* 1.39 kg = _?_ g Multiply by 1,000 since 1 kg = 1,000 g. 1.39 kg = 1,390 g	**Complete. 49–56. See margin.** **49.** 27 mm = _?_ m **50.** 3.9 mg = _?_ g **51.** 3.3 mL = _?_ L **52.** 6.85 km = _?_ m **53.** 16 cm = _?_ mm **54.** 0.04 kL = _?_ L **55.** 43 g = _?_ kg **56.** 3.9 kL = _?_ mL
● express numbers greater than 100 in scientific notation *(Lesson 2-9)* $256{,}000 = 2.56 \times 10^5$	**Write each number in scientific notation.** **57.** 6,000 **6×10^3** **58.** 459,000,000 **4.59×10^8**

Test and Review Software

You may use this software, a combination of an item generator and item bank, to create your own tests or worksheets. Types of items include free response, multiple choice, short answer, and open ended.

CD-ROM Program

The CD-ROM Program contains an Assessment Game whose questions review the concepts in this chapter.

Applications & Problem Solving

59. ***Weather*** A barometer is an instrument that measures atmospheric pressure in terms of millimeters of mercury. The higher the mercury rises in the tube, the higher the atmospheric pressure. Order the following barometer readings from least to greatest: 29.97 mm, 30.22 mm, 29.13 mm, 30.53 mm, 31.01 mm. *(Lesson 2-1)* **29.13, 29.97, 30.22, 30.53, 31.01**

60. ***Reasonable Answers*** Adam bought a pair of sunglasses for $15.79, two rolls of film at $2.29 per roll, and a bottle of sunscreen for $3.69. The cashier asked for $24.06. Is that total reasonable? *(Lesson 2-3B)* **yes**

61. ***Earth Science*** In 1872, Yellowstone National Park became the first national park in the United States. The park has about 2,000 hot springs. If 0.1 of these are geysers, how many geysers are there in the park? *(Lesson 2-5)* **200 geysers**

62. ***Buildings*** Each story in an office building is about 3.66 meters tall. Use the graph below to find the number of stories for each structure. Round to the nearest whole number. *(Lesson 2-6)*

a. Great Pyramid of Cheops **40 stories**

b. Gateway Arch **52 stories**

c. Statue of Liberty **25 stories**

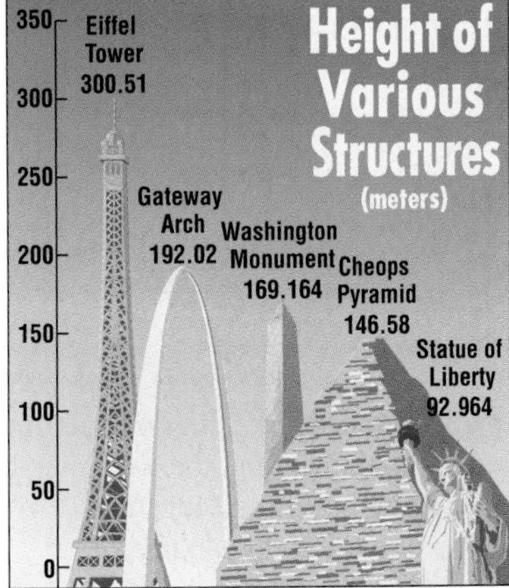

Source: *World Book Encyclopedia*

Alternative Assessment

Open Ended

Suppose you are in charge of supplying a certain brand of soft drink for a picnic. At the store, you find two possible ways to buy the soft drink: 2-L bottles costing $1.30 each, and six-packs of 355-mL cans costing $2.50 per pack. Assuming cups are already provided, how will you decide which type of package is the more economical way to purchase the soft drink? **See Answer Appendix.**

Suppose you have $40 to purchase this brand of soft drink. What is the maximum number of liters of soda you can purchase? **See Answer Appendix.**

A practice test for Chapter 2 is provided on page 608.

Completing the CHAPTER Project

Use the following checklist to make sure your solar system model is complete.

- ☑ The planets are the correct size.
- ☑ The planets are the correct distance from the Sun.
- ☑ The charts of the planets' actual diameters and average distances from the Sun are included.

PORTFOLIO Select one of the assignments from this chapter and place it in your portfolio. Attach a note to it explaining why you selected it.

Applications & Problem Solving

This section provides additional practice in solving real-world problems that involve the skills of this chapter.

Alternative Assessment

The ***Open Ended*** section provides students with a performance assessment opportunity to evaluate their work and understanding.

Students should complete the final stages of their project and prepare a class demonstration of their results. A scoring guide for the project is available in the *Investigations and Projects Masters,* p. 23.

Students should add to their portfolios at this time.

Performance Assessment

Additional performance assessment tasks for this chapter are included in the *Assessment and Evaluation Masters* on page 41. A scoring guide is also provided on page 53.

***Assessment and Evaluation Masters,* p. 41**

2 Name________________ Date________

Chapter 2 Performance Assessment

Instructions: Demonstrate your knowledge by giving a clear, concise solution to each problem. Be sure to include all relevant drawings and justify your answers. You may show your solutions in more than one way or investigate beyond the requirements of the problems.

1. A surveyor is surveying an industrial park.

a. Kentucky Industrial's rectangular lot is to be 0.9 mile by 0.5 mile. Use the 10-by-10 grid to model 0.9×0.5 and to find the area occupied by Kentucky Industrial.

b. Delta Chemical's rectangular lot is 2.3 miles by 0.8 mile. Use the 10-by-10 grids to find the area of Delta Chemical's lot.

c. Another industrial park is 5.25 miles by 4.8 miles. Estimate the area of the park. Explain each step.

d. Explain how to multiply decimals. Use the dimensions in part c to find the area of the industrial park.

e. Kentucky Industrial may increase the area of its lot to 0.72 square mile. The length would remain 0.9 mile. Use the 10-by-10 grid to find the new width.

f. Explain how to divide decimals. Then divide to find the length of a rectangular lot that is 1.6 miles wide and has an area of 2.8 square miles.

2. The masses of four boxes of cereal are 486,000 milligrams, 0.510 kilogram, 167,000 milligrams, and 35 grams.

a. Explain how to change larger units to smaller units and how to change smaller units to larger units.

b. Change the mass of each cereal box to grams.

c. Arrange the masses of the cereal boxes in order from least to greatest. Explain how you know in which order to list the masses.

 41 *Mathematics: Applications and Connections,* Course 2

Standardized Test Practice

The Standardized Test Practice may be used to help students prepare for standardized tests. The test items are written in the same style as those in state proficiency tests and standardized tests like CAT, CTBS, ITBS, MAT, SAT, and Terra Nova. The test items cover skills and concepts covered up to this point in the text.

The pages can be used as an overnight assessment. After students have completed the pages, discuss how each problem can be solved, or provide copies of the solutions from the *Solutions Manual.*

***Assessment and Evaluation Masters,* p. 47**

Name________________ Date________

Cumulative Review, Chapters 1 and 2

1. Evaluate $16(5 - 2) \div 24 + 5$. (Lesson 1-2) — 1. 7
2. Evaluate $2(x - z) + y$ if $x = 8$, $y = 5$, and $z = 4$. (Lesson 1-3) — 2. 13
3. Write 11^2 as a product of the same factor. (Lesson 1-4) — 3. $11 \cdot 11$
4. Write $5 \cdot 5 \cdot 5 \cdot 5 \cdot 5 \cdot 5$ using exponents. (Lesson 1-4) — 4. 5^6

Solve each equation mentally. (Lesson 1-5)

5. $p + 21 = 38$ — 5. 17
6. $18r = 162$ — 6. 9
7. Find the area of a parallelogram with $b = 7$ feet and $h = 3.5$ feet. (Lesson 1-7) — 7. 24.5 square ft
8. Order 0.58, 0.91, 0.89, and 0.6 from least to greatest. (Lesson 2-1) — 8. 0.58, 0.6, 0.89, 0.91

Round to the underlined place-value position. (Lesson 2-2)

9. $19.\underline{7}89$ — 9. 19.8
10. $0.00\underline{5}478$ — 10. 0.005

Estimate by rounding. (Lesson 2-3)

11. 33.9×68.2 — 11. $30 \times 70 = 2{,}100$
12. $3.7\overline{)0.81}$ — 12. $0.8 \div 4 = 0.2$

Multiply. (Lessons 2-4 and 2-5)

13. 8.5×0.004 — 13. 0.034
14. 8.16×10^4 — 14. 81,600
15. Find $0.05\overline{)0.0951}$ to the nearest hundredth. (Lesson 2-6) — 15. 1.90

Multiply mentally. (Lesson 2-5)

16. 6.125×10^4 — 16. 61,250
17. $j = 0.015 \times 100$ — 17. 1.5

Express each fraction or mixed number as a decimal. If the decimal is a repeating decimal, use bar notation. (Lesson 2-7)

18. $\frac{9}{16}$ — 18. 0.5625
19. $6\frac{1}{6}$ — 19. $6.1\overline{6}$

Complete. (Lesson 2-8)

20. 1.58 L = _?_ mL — 20. 1,580
21. 679 g = _?_ kg — 21. 0.679

Write each number in scientific notation. (Lesson 2-9)

22. 69,000,000 — 22. 6.9×10^7
23. 753,820 — 23. 7.5382×10^5

Solve. (Lessons 1-1 and 2-3B)

24. Rosie walked 5 miles more than Toshio. If Rosie walked 12.5 miles, how many miles did Toshio walk? — 24. 7.5 mi
25. The ingredients for a standard U.S. breakfast cost $9.79 in the United States, compared with $23.12 in Tokyo. About how many times as expensive is breakfast in Tokyo than in the U.S.? — 25. about 3 times

 47 *Mathematics: Applications and Connections, Course 2*

CHAPTERS **1–2**

Standardized Test Practice

Assessing Knowledge & Skills

Section One: Multiple Choice

There are twelve multiple-choice questions in this section. Choose the best answer. If a correct answer is *not here,* choose the letter for Not Here.

1. Which is equivalent to 3^6? **D**
   - **A** 36
   - **B** 18
   - **C** $6 \cdot 6 \cdot 6$
   - **D** $3 \cdot 3 \cdot 3 \cdot 3 \cdot 3 \cdot 3$

2. What is the value of $x + y + 5$ if $x = 6$ and $y = 15$? **H**
   - **F** 21
   - **G** 25
   - **H** 26
   - **J** 28

3. Suppose you need 0.65 liter of water for a science experiment, but the container is measured in milliliters. How many milliliters of water do you need? **D**
   - **A** 0.00065 milliliter
   - **B** 0.65 milliliter
   - **C** 6.5 milliliters
   - **D** 650 milliliters

4. Which is correct for rounding to the nearest tenth? **G**
   - **F** 0.56 rounds to 0.5
   - **G** 0.95 rounds to 1.0
   - **H** 1.205 rounds to 1.3
   - **J** 0.4173 rounds to 0.42

5. What is the solution of the equation $x + 4 = 15$? **B**
   - **A** 10
   - **B** 11
   - **C** 12
   - **D** 13

Please note that Questions 6–12 have five answer choices.

6. At age 16, about how much taller is the average boy than the average girl? **G**

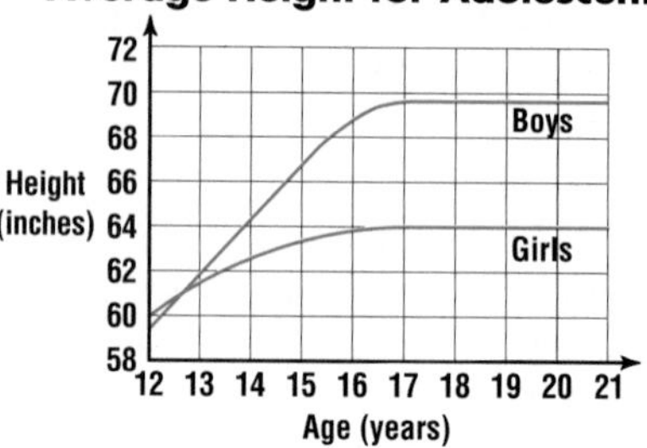

   - **F** 2 in.
   - **G** 5 in.
   - **H** 6 in.
   - **J** 63.5 in.
   - **K** 67.5 in.

7. Brookside Middle School's 72 choir students and 10 adult chaperones are planning a trip to see a musical. Each school bus will carry at most 48 people. All tickets to the musical cost $12.95, but schools get a $3.00 discount per ticket. Which piece of information is *not* needed for the school principal to determine the amount of money required for the musical tickets? **C**
   - **A** There are 72 students in the choir.
   - **B** There are 10 adult chaperones.
   - **C** Each school bus will carry at most 48 people.
   - **D** The price of each ticket is $12.95.
   - **E** The discount per ticket is $3.00.

◄◄◄ Instructional Resources

Another cumulative review is shown at the left and is available in the *Assessment and Evaluation Masters,* p. 47.

8. Earth is about 93,000,000 miles from the Sun. How is this written in scientific notation? **G**
   - **F** 93×10^6
   - **G** 9.3×10^7
   - **H** 9.3×10^8
   - **J** 0.93×10^8
   - **K** 93 million

9. Alexis charges $5.25 per hour to mow lawns. Which is the best estimate of her earnings if she mows lawns 15 hours during the week? **D**
   - **A** $3 **B** $45
   - **C** $55 **D** $75
   - **E** $95

10. Tomato juice is priced at three cans for $2.39. To the nearest cent, what is the cost of one can? **G**
    - **F** $0.79 **G** $0.80
    - **H** $0.89 **J** $7.17
    - **K** Not Here

11. Three tablecloths are sewn together end-to-end to make one long tablecloth. The tablecloths are about 48 inches, 64 inches, and 54 inches long. What is the combined length? **D**
    - **A** 102 in. **B** 112 in.
    - **C** 118 in. **D** 166 in.
    - **E** 226 in.

12. Marcus had $65.72 in his pocket. He spent $32 at a clothing store. How much money did he have left? **K**
    - **F** $31.72 **G** $34.72
    - **H** $65.65 **J** $72.72
    - **K** Not Here

Test-Taking Tip THE PRINCETON REVIEW

Most standardized tests have a time limit, so you must budget your time carefully. If you cannot answer a question within a few minutes, go on to the next one. If there is still time left when you get to the end of the test, go back to the questions that you skipped.

Section Two: Free Response

This section contains five questions for which you will provide short answers. Write your answers on your paper.

13. Felicia's vacation lasted 8 days and 7 nights. She spent $95 per night for the hotel and $30 per day for food. How much did she spend on food and lodging? **$905**

14. Evaluate $2a + 5b$ if $a = 15$ and $b = 4$. **50**

15. To the nearest tenth of a centimeter, what is the length of the ribbon shown below? **9.2 cm**

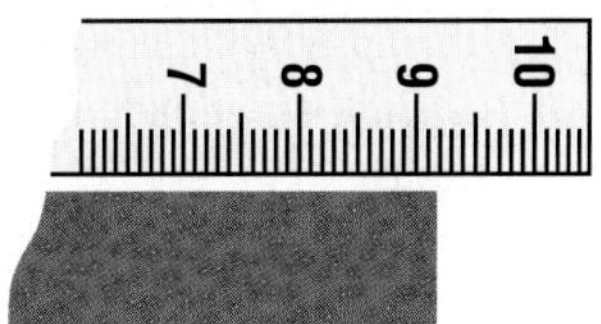

16. Write the product $4 \cdot 4 \cdot 4 \cdot 4 \cdot 4$ using exponents. **4^5**

17. One of the fastest roller coasters in the world is The Beast at King's Island in Ohio. Its top speed is 64.77 miles per hour. What is its top speed rounded to the nearest whole number? **65 miles per hr**

Test Practice For additional test practice questions, visit:

www.glencoe.com/sec/math/mac/mathnet

Test-Taking Tip

One of the important skills in test-taking is time management. This tip is to give students guidelines on how to judge how long they should spend on each part of the test.

Instructional Resources ▶▶▶

Additional standardized test practice is shown at the right and is available in the *Assessment and Evaluation Masters,* pp. 45–46.

Assessment and Evaluation Masters, pp. 45–46

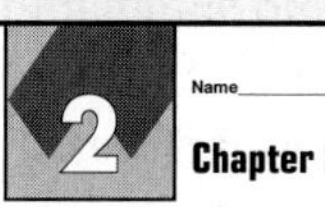

Name________________ Date________

Chapter 2 Standardized Test Practice

Choose the best answer. Write A, B, C, or D.

Indianapolis 500 Statistics	
Year	Average Speed
1992	134.477
1993	157.207
1994	160.872
1995	153.616
1996	147.956

1. If you wanted to list the three years with the greatest average speeds in order from greatest to least, which should you choose? 1. **D**
   - **A.** 1995, 1992, 1993 **B.** 1995, 1993, 1996
   - **C.** 1993, 1992, 1996 **D.** 1994, 1993, 1995

2. Maria pays $246.75 each month on her car loan. What is this amount rounded to the nearest ten dollars? 2. **D**
   - **A.** $246.80 **B.** $247
   - **C.** $240 **D.** $250

3. Khalid bought a shirt for $26.95, a pair of shoes for $49.50, and a belt for $14.29. Which is the best estimate of the total cost of the three items? 3. **B**
   - **A.** $89 **B.** $90
   - **C.** $91 **D.** $92

4. The Save the Planet Club placed a jar in the office to collect money for a project. At the end of the week, the jar contained 28 quarters, 35 nickels, and 123 dimes. Which expression could be used to find the total amount of money in the jar? 4. **A**
   - **A.** $(28 \times 0.25) + (35 \times 0.05) + (123 \times 0.10)$
   - **B.** $(28 + 0.25) \times (35 \times 0.05) + (123 + 0.10)$
   - **C.** $(28 \div 0.25) \times (35 \div 0.05) \times (123 \div 0.10)$
   - **D.** $(28 \div 0.25) + (35 \div 0.05) + (123 \div 0.10)$

5. If Sarah wants to purchase 10^4 magnets for her store at $0.05 each, how much will she pay? 5. **D**
   - **A.** $5,000.00 **B.** $50.00
   - **C.** $5.00 **D.** $500.00

 45 *Mathematics: Applications and Connections,* Course 2

Chapter 2 Standardized Test Practice (continued)

6. The Learning Express store in Dallas averaged sales of 1,000 Beanie Babies per weekend. If the toys are priced at $5.50 each, on average, how much did Learning Express make on Beanie Babies each weekend? 6. **C**
   - **A.** $55.00 **B.** $550.00
   - **C.** $5,500.00 **D.** $5,550.00

7. Akira has a piece of wire that is 78 inches long. What is the greatest number of 12-inch pieces that he can cut from this wire? 7. **B**
   - **A.** 5 **B.** 6
   - **C.** 7 **D.** 8

8. Americans spend about $1.7 billion per year on writing utensils. About $\frac{4}{25}$ of these sales are markers and highlighters, and about $\frac{1}{9}$ are mechanical pencils. Rounded to the nearest hundredth, how would you write $\frac{1}{9}$ and $\frac{4}{25}$ as decimals? 8. **A**
   - **A.** 0.11, 0.16 **B.** 1.11, 1.60
   - **C.** 11, 16 **D.** 110, 160

9. The length of this paper clip is about— 9. **B**
   - **A.** 4.5 millimeters. **B.** 4.5 centimeters.
   - **C.** 4.5 meters. **D.** 4.5 kilometers.

10. An estimated 100 million frogs legs are consumed each year in the United States. What is this number in scientific notation? 10. **C**
    - **A.** 1×10^6 **B.** 1×10^7
    - **C.** 1×10^8 **D.** 1×10^9

 46 *Mathematics: Applications and Connections,* Course 2

CHAPTER 3

Statistics: Analyzing Data

Previewing the Chapter

Overview

This chapter focuses on statistics—the collecting, organizing, and summarizing of data. Students use frequency tables; find scales and intervals; interpret line and bar graphs and scatter plots; and analyze graphs to make predictions. They also make line plots, stem-and-leaf plots, and box-and-whisker plots. They work with three statistical measures of central tendency—the mean, median, and mode. Students also examine ways in which statistics and graphs are misleading.

Lesson (pages)	Lesson Objectives	NCTM Standards 2000	Standardized Tests	State/Local Objectives
3-1 (88–91)	Choose appropriate scales and intervals for data, and organize data in a frequency table.	1, 5–10	CTBS, ITBS, MAT, TN	
3-2A (92–93)	Solve problems by using graphs.	1, 5–10	CTBS, MAT, SAT, TN	
3-2 (94–97)	Make predictions from graphs.	1, 2, 5–10	CTBS, ITBS, MAT, SAT, TN	
3-3 (98–101)	Construct line plots.	1, 5–10		
3-4 (102–105)	Find the mean, median, and mode of a set of data.	1, 5–10	CAT, CTBS, ITBS, MAT, TN	
3-4B (106)	Use mean, median, and mode to describe a set of data.	1, 5–9	CAT, CTBS, TN	
3-5 (108–111)	Construct and interpret stem-and-leaf plots.	1, 5–10	CTBS, TN	
3-6A (112–113)	Graph quartiles and determine the interquartile range.	1, 5–10		
3-6 (114–117)	Construct and interpret box-and-whisker plots.	1, 5–10	CTBS, TN	
3-6B (118)	Use data to make predictions.	1, 4–9	CAT, CTBS, ITBS, MAT, SAT, TN	
3-7 (119–121)	Recognize when statistics and graphs are misleading.	1, 5–10		

CAT = California Achievement Tests, CTBS = Comprehensive Tests of Basic Skills, ITBS = Iowa Tests of Basic Skills, MAT = Metropolitan Achievement Tests, SAT = Stanford Achievement Tests, TN = Terra Nova
For the key to numbering of NCTM Standards 2000, see page T6.

Organizing the Chapter

The **Interactive Lesson Planner** contains all of the blackline masters and transparencies. This CD-ROM also includes an easy-to-use lesson planning calendar.

LESSON PLANNING GUIDE

		BLACKLINE MASTERS (PAGE NUMBERS)										
Lesson	**Extra Practice (Student Edition)**	**Study Guide**	**Practice**	**Enrichment**	**Assessment & Evaluation**	**Classroom Games**	**Diversity**	**Hands-On Lab**	**School to Career**	**Science and Math Lab Manual**	**Technology**	**Transparencies A and B**
3-1	p. 574	17	17	17			16		16			3-1
3-2A	p. 574											
3-2	p. 574	18	18	18	71			74		29-32, 77–80		3-2
3-3	p. 575	19	19	19								3-3
3-4	p. 575	20	20	20	70, 71	9–10				73–76	31	3-4
3-4B								41				
3-5	p. 575	21	21	21								3-5
3-6A								42				
3-6	p. 576	22	22	22	72							3-6
3-6B								43				
3-7	p. 576	23	23	23	72						32	3-7
Study Guide/ Assessment					57–69, 73–75							

OTHER CHAPTER RESOURCES

Student Edition

Chapter Project, pp. 87, 91, 105, 121, 125

Let the Games Begin, p. 107

Technology

 MathPASS CD-ROM

 Interactive Mathematics Tools Software

Teacher's Classroom Resources

Applications

Family Letters and Activities, pp. 31–32

Investigations and Projects Masters, pp. 25–28

Meeting Individual Needs

Transition Booklet, pp. 5–6

Investigations for the Special Education Student, pp. 3–5

Teaching Aids

Answer Key Masters

Block Scheduling Booklet

Lesson Planning Guide

Solutions Manual

Professional Publications

Glencoe Mathematics Professional Series

Planning the Chapter

MindJogger Videoquizzes provide a unique format for reviewing concepts presented in the chapter.

Assessment Resources

Student Edition

Mixed Review, pp. 91, 97, 101, 105, 111, 117, 121
Mid-Chapter Self Test, p. 105
Math Journal, pp. 109, 116, 120
Study Guide and Assessment, pp. 122–125
Performance Task, p. 125
Portfolio Suggestion, p. 125
Standardized Test Practice, pp. 126–127
Chapter Test, p. 609

Assessment and Evaluation Masters

Multiple-Choice Tests (Forms 1A, 1B, 1C), pp. 57–62
Free-Response Tests (Forms 2A, 2B, 2C), pp. 63–68
Performance Assessment, p. 69
Mid-Chapter Test, p. 70
Quizzes A–D, pp. 71–72
Standardized Test Practice, pp. 73–74
Cumulative Review, p. 75

Teacher's Wraparound Edition

5-Minute Check, pp. 88, 94, 98, 102, 108, 114, 119
Building Portfolios, p. 86
Math Journal, pp. 106, 113, 118
Closing Activity, pp. 91, 93, 97, 101, 105, 111, 117, 121

Technology

Test and Review Software
MindJogger Videoquizzes
CD-ROM Program

Materials and Manipulatives

Lesson 3-2
ruler*†
marbles*
drinking glass

Lesson 3-4
scientific calculator

Lesson 3-4B
markers
ruler*†
self-adhesive notes
coins
cup*
water droppers

Lesson 3-6
graphing calculator

Lesson 3-6B
popped popcorn

*Glencoe Manipulative Kit

†Glencoe Overhead Manipulative Resources

Pacing Chart

See pages T25–T27 for the Course Planning Calendar.

COURSE	DAY 1	DAY 2	DAY 3	DAY 4	DAY 5	DAY 6	DAY 7
Standard	Chapter Project	Lesson 3-1	Lesson 3-2A	Lesson 3-2	Lesson 3-3	Lesson 3-4	Lesson 3-5
Honors	Chapter Project	Lesson 3-1	Lesson 3-2A	Lesson 3-2	Lesson 3-3	Lessons 3-4 & 3-4B	Lesson 3-5
Block	Chapter Project & Lesson 3-1	Lessons 3-2A & 3-2	Lessons 3-3 & 3-4	Lessons 3-5 & 3-6A	Lessons 3-6 & 3-7	Study Guide and Assessment, Chapter Test	

The *Transition Booklet* (Skill 1) can be used to practice basic operations with whole numbers.

Interactive Mathematics: Activities and Investigations

is an activity-based program that may be used as an enhancement for chapters in ***Mathematics: Applications and Connections.***

ACTIVITY SIX

Every Picture Tells a Story

Design a travel brochure describing the temperature a tourist can expect in San Diego during the summer. Be sure to make your brochure attractive to the clients who frequently use your travel agency. Use a histogram and other information to persuade clients to travel to San Diego.

The high temperatures recorded each day in San Diego during the months of July and August, measured in degrees Fahrenheit, are given below.

UNIT 8: Data Sense 29 Every Picture Tells a Story

Unit 8, Activity Six
Use with Lesson 3-7.

Summary Students work in groups to create a travel brochure. Each group is given a different potential client profile and identical lists of San Diego temperatures. The brochure should be designed to encourage the potential client to take a vacation in San Diego.

Math Connection Students apply their knowledge of statistics and graphs to simulate a real-world situation. They will construct graphs that support a particular point of view.

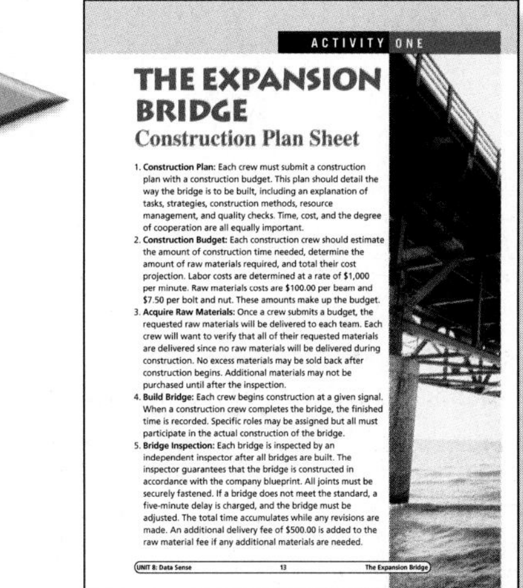

ACTIVITY ONE

THE EXPANSION BRIDGE
Construction Plan Sheet

1. **Construction Plan:** Each crew must submit a construction plan with a construction budget. This plan should detail the way the bridge is to be built, including an explanation of tasks, strategies, construction methods, resource management, and quality checks. Time, cost, and the degree of cooperation are all equally important.
2. **Construction Budget:** Each construction crew should estimate the amount of construction time needed, determine the amount of raw materials required, and total their cost projection. Labor costs are determined at a rate of $1,000 per minute. Raw materials costs are $100.00 per beam and $7.50 per bolt and nut. These amounts make up the budget.
3. **Acquire Raw Materials:** Once a crew submits a budget, the requested raw materials will be delivered to each team. Each crew will want to verify that all of their requested materials are delivered since no raw materials will be delivered during construction. No excess materials may be sold back after construction begins. Additional materials may not be purchased until after the inspection.
4. **Build Bridge:** Each crew begins construction at a given signal. When a construction crew completes the bridge, the finished time is recorded. Specific roles may be assigned but all must participate in the actual construction of the bridge.
5. **Bridge Inspection:** Each bridge is inspected by an independent inspector after all bridges are built. The inspector guarantees that the bridge is constructed in accordance with the company blueprint. All joints must be securely fastened. If a bridge does not meet the standard, a five-minute delay is charged, and the bridge must be adjusted. The total time accumulates while any revisions are made. An additional delivery fee of $500.00 is added to the raw material fee if any additional materials are needed.

UNIT 8: Data Sense 13 The Expansion Bridge

Unit 8, Activity One
Use with Chapter 3.

Summary Students work in groups as construction crews to build a bridge. Each group receives blueprints for the bridge, creates a bid proposal based on estimations of materials needed and amount of time needed to construct the bridge, and then builds it. Students will write individual narratives of their construction process.

Math Connection Students use estimation, measurement, geometry, spatial visualization, and accuracy to submit a bid proposal to build a bridge. They compare their estimate to the actual materials used.

<table>
<tr><th>DAY 8</th><th>DAY 9</th><th>DAY 10</th><th>DAY 11</th><th>DAY 12</th><th>DAY 13</th><th>DAY 14</th><th>DAY 15</th></tr>
<tr><td colspan="2">Lessons 3-6A & 3-6</td><td>Lesson 3-7</td><td>Study Guide and Assessment</td><td>Chapter Test</td><td></td><td></td><td></td></tr>
<tr><td>Lessons 3-6 & 3-6B</td><td>Lesson 3-7</td><td>Study Guide and Assessment</td><td>Chapter Test</td><td></td><td></td><td></td><td></td></tr>
<tr><td></td><td></td><td></td><td></td><td></td><td></td><td></td><td></td></tr>
</table>

Enhancing the Chapter

APPLICATIONS

Classroom Games, pp. 9–10

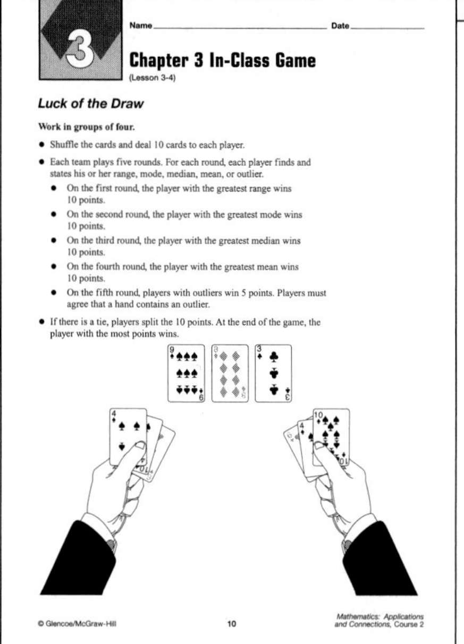

3

Name ____________ Date ________

Chapter 3 In-Class Game
(Lesson 3-4)

Luck of the Draw

Work in groups of four.

- Shuffle the cards and deal 10 cards to each player.
- Each team plays five rounds. For each round, each player finds and states his or her range, mode, median, mean, or outlier.
  - On the first round, the player with the greatest range wins 10 points.
  - On the second round, the player with the greatest mode wins 10 points.
  - On the third round, the player with the greatest median wins 10 points.
  - On the fourth round, the player with the greatest mean wins 10 points.
  - On the fifth round, players with outliers win 5 points. Players must agree that a hand contains an outlier.
- If there is a tie, players split the 10 points. At the end of the game, the player with the most points wins.

© Glencoe/McGraw-Hill 10 *Mathematics: Applications and Connections, Course 2*

Diversity Masters, p. 16

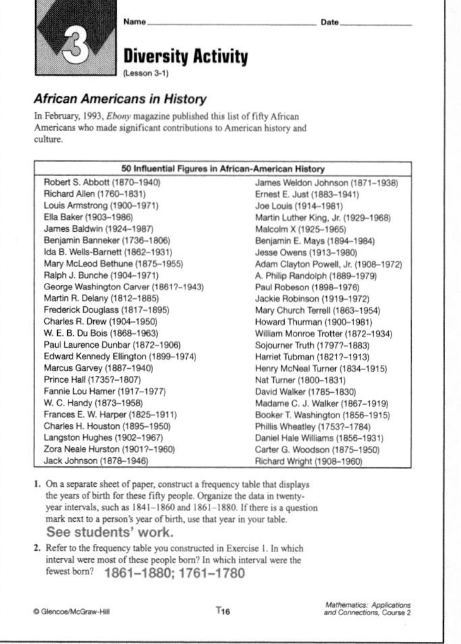

3

Name ____________ Date ________

Diversity Activity
(Lesson 3-1)

African Americans in History

In February, 1993, *Ebony* magazine published this list of fifty African Americans who made significant contributions to American history and culture.

50 Influential Figures in African-American History	
Robert S. Abbott (1870–1940)	James Weldon Johnson (1871–1938)
Richard Allen (1760–1831)	Ernest E. Just (1883–1941)
Louis Armstrong (1900–1971)	Joe Louis (1914–1981)
Ella Baker (1903–1986)	Martin Luther King, Jr. (1929–1968)
James Baldwin (1924–1987)	Malcolm X (1925–1965)
Benjamin Banneker (1736–1806)	Benjamin E. Mays (1894–1984)
Ida B. Wells-Barnett (1862–1931)	Jesse Owens (1913–1980)
Mary McLeod Bethune (1875–1955)	Adam Clayton Powell, Jr. (1908–1972)
Ralph J. Bunche (1904–1971)	A. Philip Randolph (1889–1979)
George Washington Carver (1861?–1943)	Paul Robeson (1898–1976)
Martin R. Delany (1812–1885)	Jackie Robinson (1919–1972)
Frederick Douglass (1817–1895)	Mary Church Terrell (1863–1954)
Charles R. Drew (1904–1950)	Howard Thurman (1900–1981)
W. E. B. Du Bois (1868–1963)	William Monroe Trotter (1872–1934)
Paul Laurence Dunbar (1872–1906)	Sojourner Truth (1797?–1883)
Edward Kennedy Ellington (1899–1974)	Harriet Tubman (1821?–1913)
Marcus Garvey (1887–1940)	Henry McNeal Turner (1834–1915)
Prince Hall (1735?–1807)	Nat Turner (1800–1831)
Fannie Lou Hamer (1917–1977)	David Walker (1785–1830)
W. C. Handy (1873–1958)	Madame C. J. Walker (1867–1919)
Frances E. W. Harper (1825–1911)	Booker T. Washington (1856–1915)
Charles H. Houston (1895–1950)	Phillis Wheatley (1753?–1784)
Langston Hughes (1902–1967)	Daniel Hale Williams (1856–1931)
Zora Neale Hurston (1901?–1960)	Carter G. Woodson (1875–1950)
Jack Johnson (1878–1946)	Richard Wright (1908–1960)

1. On a separate sheet of paper, construct a frequency table that displays the years of birth for these fifty people. Organize the data in twenty-year intervals, such as 1841–1860 and 1861–1880. If there is a question mark next to a person's year of birth, use that year in your table. **See students' work.**
2. Refer to the frequency table you constructed in Exercise 1. In which interval were most of these people born? In which interval were the fewest born? **1861–1880; 1761–1780**

© Glencoe/McGraw-Hill T16 *Mathematics: Applications and Connections, Course 2*

School to Career Masters, p. 16

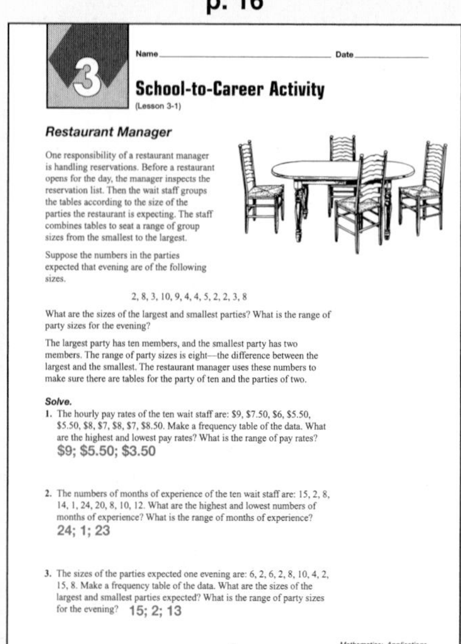

3

Name ____________ Date ________

School-to-Career Activity
(Lesson 3-1)

Restaurant Manager

One responsibility of a restaurant manager is handling reservations. Before a restaurant opens for the day, the manager inspects the reservation list. Then the wait staff groups the tables according to the size of the parties the restaurant is expecting. The staff combines tables to seat a range of group sizes from the smallest to the largest.

Suppose the numbers in the parties expected that evening are of the following sizes.

2, 8, 3, 10, 9, 4, 4, 5, 2, 2, 3, 8

What are the sizes of the largest and smallest parties? What is the range of party sizes for the evening?

The largest party has ten members, and the smallest party has two members. The range of party sizes is eight—the difference between the largest and the smallest. The restaurant manager uses these numbers to make sure there are tables for the party of ten and the parties of two.

Solve.

1. The hourly pay rates of the ten wait staff are: \$9, \$7.50, \$6, \$5.50, \$5.50, \$8, \$7, \$8, \$7, \$8.50. Make a frequency table of the data. What are the highest and lowest pay rates? What is the range of pay rates? **\$9; \$5.50; \$3.50**
2. The numbers of months of experience of the ten wait staff are: 15, 2, 8, 14, 1, 24, 20, 8, 10, 12. What are the highest and lowest numbers of months of experience? What is the range of months of experience? **24; 1; 23**
3. The sizes of the parties expected one evening are: 6, 2, 6, 2, 8, 10, 4, 2, 15, 8. Make a frequency table of the data. What are the sizes of the largest and smallest parties expected? What is the range of party sizes for the evening? **15; 2; 13**

© Glencoe/McGraw-Hill T16 *Mathematics: Applications and Connections, Course 2*

Family Letters and Activities, pp. 31–32

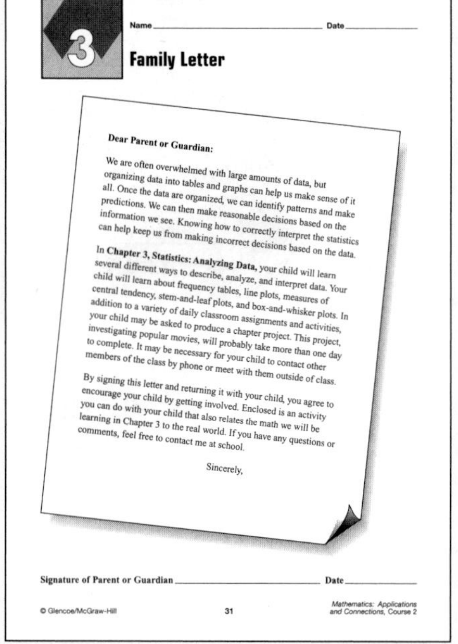

3

Name ____________ Date ________

Family Letter

Dear Parent or Guardian:

We are often overwhelmed with large amounts of data, but organizing data into tables and graphs can help us make sense of it all. Once the data are organized, we can identify patterns and make predictions. We can then make reasonable decisions based on the information we see. Knowing how to correctly interpret the statistics can help keep us from making incorrect decisions based on the data.

In **Chapter 3, Statistics: Analyzing Data,** your child will learn several different ways to describe, analyze, and interpret data. Your child will learn about frequency tables, line plots, measures of central tendency, stem-and-leaf plots, and box-and-whisker plots. In addition to a variety of daily classroom assignments and activities, your child may be asked to produce a chapter project. This project, investigating popular movies, will probably take more than one day to complete. It may be necessary for your child to contact other members of the class by phone or meet with them outside of class.

By signing this letter and returning it with your child, you agree to encourage your child by getting involved. Enclosed is an activity you can do with your child that also relates the math we will be learning in Chapter 3 to the real world. If you have any questions or comments, feel free to contact me at school.

Sincerely,

Signature of Parent or Guardian ____________ **Date** ________

© Glencoe/McGraw-Hill 31 *Mathematics: Applications and Connections, Course 2*

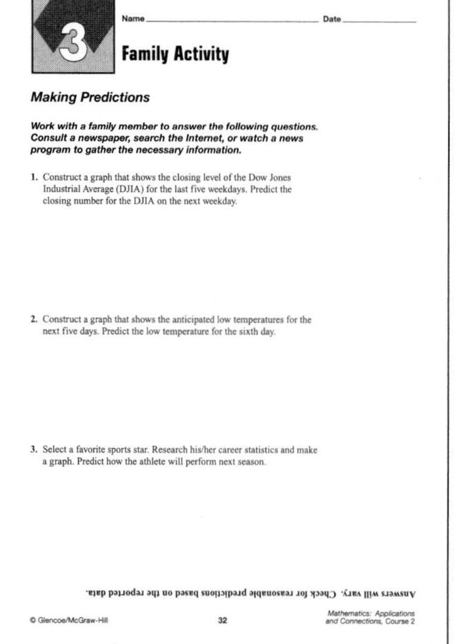

3

Name ____________ Date ________

Family Activity

Making Predictions

Work with a family member to answer the following questions. Consult a newspaper, search the Internet, or watch a news program to gather the necessary information.

1. Construct a graph that shows the closing level of the Dow Jones Industrial Average (DJIA) for the last five weekdays. Predict the closing number for the DJIA on the next weekday.
2. Construct a graph that shows the anticipated low temperatures for the next five days. Predict the low temperature for the sixth day.
3. Select a favorite sports star. Research his/her career statistics and make a graph. Predict how the athlete will perform next season.

Answers will vary. Check for reasonable predictions based on the reported data.

© Glencoe/McGraw-Hill 32 *Mathematics: Applications and Connections, Course 2*

Science and Math Lab Manual, pp. 29–32, 73–80

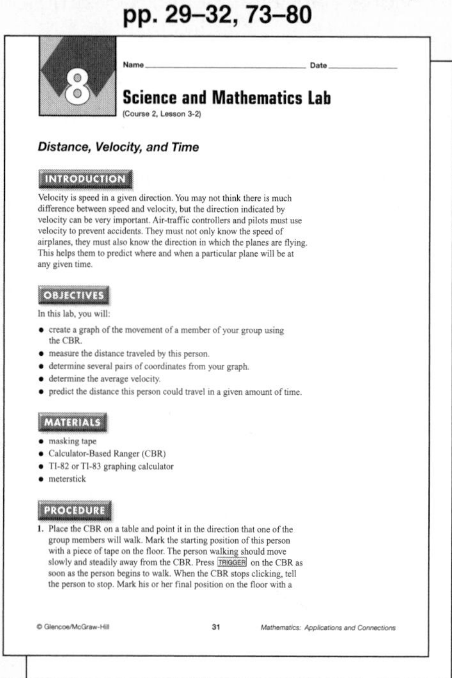

8

Name ____________ Date ________

Science and Mathematics Lab
(Course 2, Lesson 3-2)

Distance, Velocity, and Time

INTRODUCTION

Velocity is speed in a given direction. You may not think there is much difference between speed and velocity, but the direction indicated by velocity can be very important. Air-traffic controllers and pilots must use velocity to prevent accidents. They must not only know the speed of airplanes, they must also know the direction in which the planes are flying. This helps them to predict where and when a particular plane will be at any given time.

OBJECTIVES

In this lab, you will:

- create a graph of the movement of a member of your group using the CBR.
- measure the distance traveled by this person.
- determine several pairs of coordinates from your graph.
- determine the average velocity.
- predict the distance this person could travel in a given amount of time.

MATERIALS

- masking tape
- Calculator-Based Ranger (CBR)
- TI-82 or TI-83 graphing calculator
- meterstick

PROCEDURE

1. Place the CBR on a table and point it in the direction that one of the group members will walk. Mark the starting position of this person with a piece of tape on the floor. The person walking should move slowly and steadily away from the CBR. Press TRIGGER on the CBR as soon as the person begins to walk. When the CBR stops clicking, tell the person to stop. Mark his or her final position on the floor with a

© Glencoe/McGraw-Hill 31 *Mathematics: Applications and Connections*

MANIPULATIVES/MODELING

Hands-On Lab Masters, p. 74

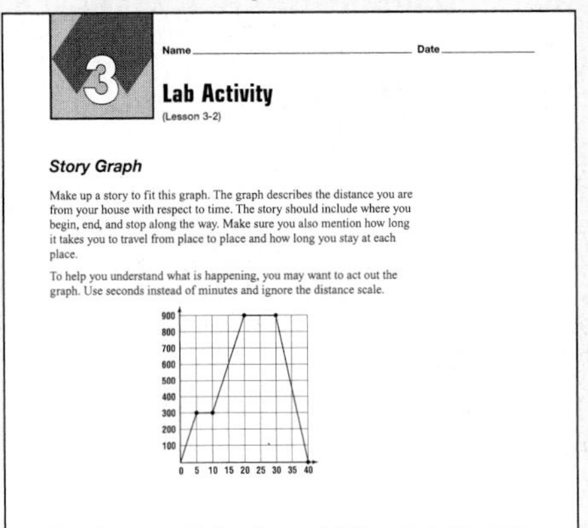

Name ______________________ Date __________

3

Lab Activity

(Lesson 3-2)

Story Graph

Make up a story to fit this graph. The graph describes the distance you are from your house with respect to time. The story should include where you begin, end, and stop along the way. Make sure you also mention how long it takes you to travel from place to place and how long you stay at each place.

To help you understand what is happening, you may want to act out the graph. Use seconds instead of minutes and ignore the distance scale.

Sample answer: I left my house at 4:15 P.M. to go the store for Mom. She asked me to buy some milk and tortillas for dinner. I walked 5 minutes before meeting my friend, Lina. We talked for 5 minutes. Then I continued walking to the store at the same pace I had been walking. I arrived at the store 10 minutes later. It took me 10 minutes to buy milk and tortillas. On the way home, I walked a little faster because Mom wanted the groceries by 5 P.M. I made it home in 10 minutes. I was early.

© Glencoe/McGraw-Hill 74 *Mathematics: Applications and Connections, Course 2*

ASSESSMENT/EVALUATION

Assessment and Evaluation Masters, pp. 70–72

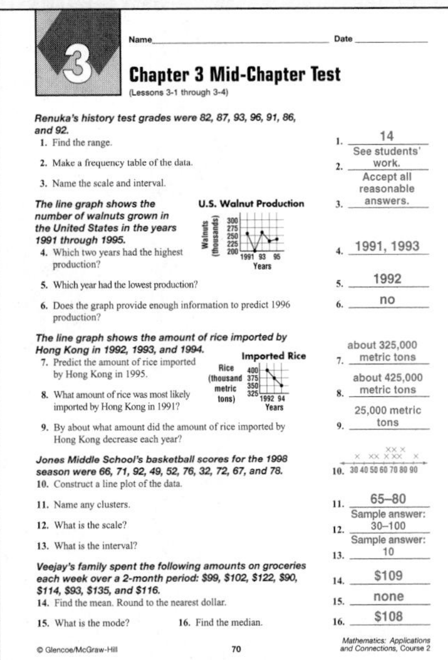

Name ______________________ Date __________

3

Chapter 3 Mid-Chapter Test

(Lessons 3-1 through 3-4)

Renuka's history test grades were 82, 87, 93, 96, 91, 86, and 92.

1. Find the range. — 1. 14
2. Make a frequency table of the data. — 2. See students' work.
3. Name the scale and interval. — 3. Accept all reasonable answers.

The line graph shows the number of walnuts grown in the United States in the years 1991 through 1995.

4. Which two years had the highest production? — 4. 1991, 1993
5. Which year had the lowest production? — 5. 1992
6. Does the graph provide enough information to predict 1996 production? — 6. no

The line graph shows the amount of rice imported by Hong Kong in 1992, 1993, and 1994.

7. Predict the amount of rice imported by Hong Kong in 1995. — 7. about 325,000 metric tons
8. What amount of rice was most likely imported by Hong Kong in 1991? — 8. about 425,000 metric tons
9. By about what amount did the amount of rice imported by Hong Kong decrease each year? — 9. 25,000 metric tons

Jones Middle School's basketball scores for the 1998 season were 66, 71, 92, 49, 52, 76, 32, 72, 67, and 78.

10. Construct a line plot of the data. — 10. (line plot) 30 40 50 60 70 80 90
11. Name any clusters. — 11. 65–80
12. What is the scale? — 12. Sample answer: 30–100
13. What is the interval? — 13. Sample answer: 10

Veejay's family spent the following amounts on groceries each week over a 2-month period: $99, $102, $122, $90, $114, $93, $135, and $116.

14. Find the mean. Round to the nearest dollar. — 14. $109
15. What is the mode? — 15. none
16. Find the median. — 16. $108

© Glencoe/McGraw-Hill 70 *Mathematics: Applications and Connections, Course 2*

Name ______________________ Date __________

Chapter 3 Quiz A

(Lessons 3-1 and 3-2)

Make a frequency table.

Sea City Temperatures (°F)				
40	40	20	30	10
40	20	20	30	30
30	20	10	30	40

1. Choose an appropriate scale for the data. — 1. Accept reasonable answers.
2. Choose an appropriate interval for the data. — 2. Accept reasonable answers.
3. Find the range for 28, 78, 53, 37, and 59. — 3. 50

Sixty-five students were asked who they would choose for class secretary. The graph shows the results.

Election for Secretary

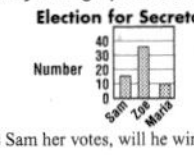

Number: 0, 10, 20, 30, 40 — Sam, Zoe, Maria

4. If Maria gives Sam her votes, will he win? — 4. no
5. Who is least likely to win? — 5. Maria

Name ______________________ Date __________

Chapter 3 Quiz B

(Lessons 3-3 and 3-4)

Make a line plot for each set of data.

1. 5, 7, 6, 7, 4, 6, 5, 7, 6 — 1. (line plot) 4 6 8
2. 25, 15, 20, 20, 10, 15, 25 — 2. (line plot) 10 20

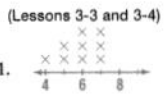

Find the mode(s), median, and mean for each set of data.

3. 4, 5, 8, 7, 6, 8, 9 — 3. 8; 7; 6.7
4. 88, 89, 92, 90, 88, 92, 93 — 4. 88, 92; 90; 90.3
5. 755, 780, 755, 805, 805 — 5. 755, 805; 780; 780

© Glencoe/McGraw-Hill 71 *Mathematics: Applications and Connections, Course 2*

TECHNOLOGY/MULTIMEDIA

Technology Masters, pp. 31–32

Name ______________________ Date __________

Calculator Activity

(Lesson 3-4)

Finding the Mean

Use a calculator to help you find the mean (average) temperature for each city listed below. Round each answer to the nearest tenth.

Mean of Monthly Temperature (°F)					
City	Chicago, Illinois	Seattle, Washington	Denver, Colorado	El Paso, Texas	Burlington, Vermont
Jan.	21.4	39.1	29.5	44.2	16.6
Feb.	26.0	42.8	33.5	48.4	18.1
Mar.	36.0	44.2	38.0	55.0	29.3
Apr.	48.8	48.7	47.4	63.6	42.7
May	59.0	55.0	57.2	71.8	55.2
June	68.6	60.2	67.0	80.8	65.0
July	73.0	64.8	73.3	82.5	69.6
Aug.	71.9	64.1	71.4	80.3	67.1
Sept.	64.7	60.0	62.6	74.1	58.8
Oct.	53.5	52.4	51.9	63.6	47.9
Nov.	39.8	44.8	38.8	51.4	36.6
Dec.	27.6	41.0	32.5	44.4	22.6
Mean Temp.	49.2	51.4	50.3	63.3	44.1

1. The warmest month in a city with a *continental climate* has a mean temperature of more than 50°F, while its coldest month has a mean temperature of 27°F or below. Do any of the cities in the table above have a continental climate? If so, which ones?
   yes; Chicago, Burlington
2. The mean temperature of the coldest month in a city with a *subtropical climate* is between 27°F and 64°F. Do any of the cities in the table above have a subtropical climate? If so, which ones?
   yes; Seattle, Denver, El Paso
3. In a *polar climate,* the mean temperature of the warmest month is less than 50°F. Do any of the cities in the table above have a polar climate?
   no

© Glencoe/McGraw-Hill T31 *Mathematics: Applications and Connections, Course 2*

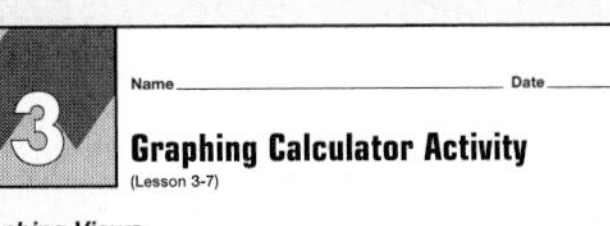

Name ______________________ Date __________

Graphing Calculator Activity

(Lesson 3-7)

Graphing Views

The window and zoom functions on a graphing calculator can be used to change the view of a graph. These functions are most often used to help you better see a graph or a portion of a graph. Using these functions can also change the appearance of a graph.

The table at the right shows the mean number of pets for students surveyed.

Student's Age	Mean No. of Pets
5	1
6	2
7	2
8	1
9	1
10	2
11	2
12	3
13	2
14	3

Clear all lists by pressing [2nd] [MEM] 4 [ENTER]. Enter the data. Then follow the instructions to see how the window and zoom features can change the way your graph looks.

Enter: [2nd] [STAT PLOT] [ENTER] [ENTER] [▼] [▶]

[ENTER] [STAT] [ENTER]

Enter the data from the table under L1 and L2.

[ZOOM] 9

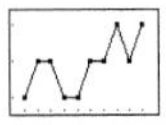

The display should show a graph similar to the one at the right. This is the optimal view. It shows all of the graph on the screen as large as possible.

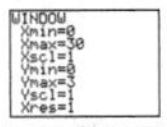

When you press [WINDOW], you will see several options. Xmin is the least value shown on the graph for X, or the age of the students. Xmax is the greatest value shown. Likewise, Ymin and Ymax are the least and greatest values of Y, or the mean number of pets. Set the values in the window as shown.

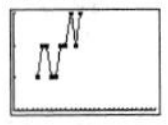

WINDOW
Xmin=0
Xmax=30
Xscl=1
Ymin=0
Ymax=3
Yscl=1
Xres=1

Press [GRAPH]. Notice how the graph has changed. The data did not change at all, only the way they appear on the screen.

Continue to change the values using the window function. Describe how your changes affect the way the graph appears on the screen.

Students should notice that the greater the values entered for Xmax and Ymax, the smaller the graph will appear on the screen. If they enter values for Xmin greater than 5, Xmax less than 14, Ymin greater than 1, or Ymax less than 3, the calculator will only show a portion of the graph or none of the graph. Students should see that this happens because they have cut off some or all of the data by making those changes.

© Glencoe/McGraw-Hill T32 *Mathematics: Applications and Connections, Course 2*

MEETING INDIVIDUAL NEEDS

Investigations for the Special Education Student, pp. 3–5

Use with:
Course 1-Chapter 2
Course 2-Chapter 3
Course 3-Chapter 4

Investigation 2 Teacher's Guide

Commercial Success

Overview

This investigation gives students the opportunity to learn how important mathematics is in the business world. Students may work alone, with a partner, or in a small group to propose a brand-new product that is in demand. Then, students design, model, and test-market the product to determine its effectiveness. Success during the test-marketing process allows students to progress to the final stage—creating a business plan. This business plan, which is videotaped and presented to the class, includes a plan to market and sell the product.

Activity Goals

Students will:
- create a new product based on demand,
- graph data about the product, and
- develop a plan to market and sell the product.

Planning the Instruction

Prerequisite Skills

Students should have a significant amount of practice computing with whole numbers and collecting and graphing sets of data.

Materials
- investigation worksheets
- calculators
- graph paper
- supplies for making the product
- video camera or cassette recorder and tapes

Time Needed
- ten 45-minute periods

Procedure

1. Brainstorm product ideas with the class. Students should then agree on their own product idea.
2. Have students validate the demand for their product idea by surveying 20–50 people. If there is not sufficient demand, the students should rethink their product idea.
3. Using the Product Development worksheet, students will:
   a. design the product,
   b. list the steps needed to make the product,
   c. list the materials needed to make the product,
   d. estimate the cost to make the product.
4. Gather materials and have students create a model of the product.
5. Students should then test market their product by showing the model to the people surveyed originally, recording their opinions and comments, and summarizing the new data with a graph.
6. If test marketing was a success, have students devise a business plan using the Business Plan worksheet. Otherwise, revise the product according to the feedback from the survey.
7. Finally, have students write and videotape an advertisement for their product to present to the class.

Adaptations and Variations

The following are some ideas on how this investigation may be modified depending on student population.

LD
- Allow more time.
- If graphing is difficult, use computer graphics.

PH
- Decrease the number of people in the survey if access is a problem due to lack of mobility.
- If drawing is difficult, have students use computer graphics or provide a partner or aide to help them.

CD
- Encourage students to work with a partner who is able to perform the verbal tasks in the investigation, such as asking survey questions or speaking on videotape.

BD
- To prevent inappropriate behavior, monitor students closely and set aside a semiprivate place for them to work to avoid any distractions.
- Isolate from other students if a problem occurs.

HI
- Have another student sign the advertisements.
- Allow students to sit close to the tape player.

VI
- Decrease the number of people in the survey if mobility is a problem.
- Provide alternative ways for graphing data, such as using larger sheets of paper and thick markers, or use a computer with a large-screen monitor.

© Glencoe/McGraw-Hill 3 *Mathematics: Applications and Connections*

Theme: Movies

The new releases of movies incorporate advances in computer graphics that have revolutionized the special effects industry. Computer-generated people and animals have been inserted into the films, and battle scenes and cityscapes have become livelier and more realistic.

Question of the Day Movie A had ticket sales totaling $46.5 million its first week, Movie B, $27 million its first week; and Movie C, $20 million its first week. What is the difference in ticket sales between Movie A and Movie C? Between Movie B and Movie C? **$26.5 million; $7 million**

Assess Prerequisite Skills

Ask students to read through the list of objectives presented in "What you'll learn in Chapter 3." You may wish to ask them what each of the objectives means or if they have experienced or used any of these math concepts before.

Building Portfolios

Encourage students to revise their portfolios as they study this chapter. Suggest that it may prove helpful later if they include examples of the different kinds of graphs they find.

Math and the Family

In the *Family Letters and Activities* booklet (pp. 31–32), you will find a letter to the parents explaining what students will study in Chapter 3. An activity appropriate for the whole family is also available.

CHAPTER 3 Statistics: Analyzing Data

What you'll learn in Chapter 3

- to organize data in a frequency table,
- to solve problems and make predictions by using a graph,
- to find the mean, median, and mode of a set of data,
- to construct line plots, stem-and-leaf plots, and box-and-whisker plots, and
- to recognize when statistics and graphs are misleading.

CD-ROM Program

Activities for Chapter 3
- Chapter 3 Introduction
- Interactive Lessons 3-1, 3-2A, 3-3
- Extended Activity 3-2
- Assessment Game
- Resource Lessons 3-1 through 3-7

CHAPTER Project

LIGHTS! CAMERA! ACTION!

In this project, you will use statistics to investigate the most popular movies, according to ticket sales. You will also conduct your own survey about favorite movies and display your data using graphs.

Getting Started

Survey 15 to 20 people. Ask each person to pick a movie from the list below. Record the results.

Movie	Ticket Sales (millions $)
A	460.9
B	399.8
C	356.8
D	329.5
E	312.8
F	309.0
G	305.4
H	290.2
I	285.8
J	260.0

Technology Tips

- Use a **spreadsheet** to record the results of your survey.
- Use **computer software** to make graphs.
- Use a **word processor** to summarize your survey results.

Data Update **For up-to-date information on movie statistics, visit:**

www.glencoe.com/sec/math/mac/mathnet

Working on the Project

You can use what you'll learn in Chapter 3 to help you conduct your survey.

Page	Exercise
91	22
105	19
121	10
125	Alternative Assessment

Glencoe has made every effort to ensure that the website links for *Mathematics: Applications and Connections* at **www.glencoe.com/sec/math/mac/mathnet** are current and contain appropriate content. However, these website links are not under Glencoe's control.

Instructional Resources ▶▶▶

A recording sheet to help students organize their data for the Chapter Project is shown at the right and is available in the *Investigations and Projects Masters,* p. 28.

Objectives Students should

- learn to use statistics to compare and classify information.
- gain an understanding of the usefulness of surveys.

Project Pointer You may suggest that students begin a *Project Folder* to keep their work as they complete each stage of the Chapter Project. The completed project may also be added to their portfolios.

Remind students that it is important to record their survey responses in an organized way. You may want to discuss with students different ways to arrange a table for recording responses.

Using the Tables Make sure that students understand that the ticket sales are in millions of dollars. Students should pay close attention to the column heads and footnotes when reading a table. You may want to discuss with students the importance of citing sources for statistics.

***Investigations and Projects Masters,* p. 28**

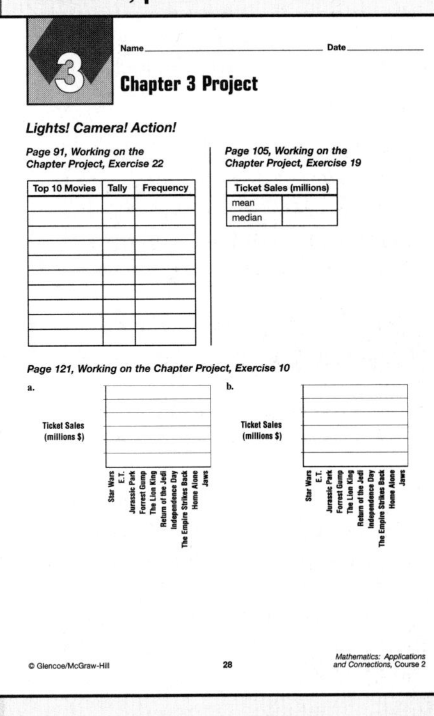

3

Name__________ Date__________

Chapter 3 Project

Lights! Camera! Action!

Page 91, Working on the Chapter Project, Exercise 22

Top 10 Movies	Tally	Frequency

Page 105, Working on the Chapter Project, Exercise 19

Ticket Sales (millions)	
mean	
median	

Page 121, Working on the Chapter Project, Exercise 10

a.

b.

 28 *Mathematics: Applications and Connections,* Course 2

3-1 Lesson Notes

Instructional Resources

- *Study Guide Masters,* p. 17
- *Practice Masters,* p. 17
- *Enrichment Masters,* p. 17
- Transparencies 3-1, A and B
- *Diversity Masters,* p. 16
- *School to Career Masters,* p. 16

CD-ROM Program
- Resource Lesson 3-1
- Interactive Lesson 3-1

Recommended Pacing	
Standard	Day 2 of 12
Honors	Day 2 of 11
Block	Day 2 of 6

1 FOCUS

5-Minute Check *(Chapter 2)*

1. Order the following set of numbers from least to greatest. 3.4, 11.8, 4, 1.28, 0.98. **0.98, 1.28, 3.4, 4, 11.8**
2. Round 12.375 to the underlined place-value position. **12.4**

Multiply or divide.

3. 0.6 × 7.003 **4.2018**
4. 0.072 ÷ 0.012 **6**
5. Write 31,000 using scientific notation. **3.1×10^4**

The 5-Minute Check is also available on **Transparency 3-1A** for this lesson.

Motivating the Lesson

Problem Solving Have students name their favorite color. Ask them how they would design a table to record this information.

2 TEACH

Transparency 3-1B contains a teaching aid for this lesson.

Reading Mathematics The introduction to this lesson includes the terms *range, scale,* and *interval.* Make sure students understand the relationship among the range of data, the scale, and the appropriate intervals.

3-1 Frequency Tables

What **you'll learn**

You'll learn to choose appropriate scales and intervals for data, and organize data in a frequency table.

When **am I ever going to use this?**

Frequency tables are useful when you take surveys.

Word Wise

range
frequency table
scale
interval

Single-use cameras are convenient to use, and they come in panoramic, waterproof, and 3-D models. The chart shows the prices of 21 single-use cameras. What could you conclude about the prices? *This problem will be solved in Example 1.*

Prices of Cameras ($)		
10	6	10
5	10	9
7	8	15
10	16	10
11	14	8
15	10	9
18	6	7

One way to summarize data is to use the **range**. The range is the difference between the greatest number and the least number in a set of data.

The range for the data above is 18 − 5 or 13.
greatest number (18) *least number* (5)

So, the difference between the least expensive and most expensive camera is $13.

A useful way to organize large amounts of data is in a **frequency table**. This kind of table shows the number of times each item of data appears.

There is only one range for a set of data. However, there is more than one way to choose the scale and the interval for a set of data.

First, choose a **scale** for the data. The scale must include all of the numbers from 5 to 18. One scale that will allow you to record all of the numbers is 1 to 20.

You must also decide on the **interval**. The interval separates the scale into equal parts. One possible interval is 5.

About four to six categories is a good number, though more could be used.

1 Cameras **Refer to the application above. Make a frequency table of the data. What could you conclude about the prices of single-use cameras?**

The scale is 1 to 20, and the interval is 5. Therefore, the categories are 1-5, 6-10, 11-15, and 16-20.

In the "Tally" column, record the number of cameras in each category.

Cost ($)	Tally	Frequency
1-5	I	1
6-10	~~IIII~~ ~~IIII~~ IIII	14
11-15	IIII	4
16-20	II	2

Write the number of tallies or frequency in the "Frequency" column. There should be at least one number in the data set in the highest category, and one in the lowest category. If there are not, choose the scale and interval again.

The frequency table shows that most of these single-use cameras cost from $6 to $10.

Multiple Learning Styles

Interpersonal Have students work with a partner to design a frequency table to record the number of times each student observes their partner blink in one minute. Have them first guess the number of blinks. Then have them do the experiment and fill in the table.

Not all frequency tables have categories with scales or intervals.

2 **In-Line Skating** Recently, 26 types of in-line skates were tested. The chart shows the kind of brakes that the skates had: toe-stop (*T*), heel-stop (*H*), cuff-activated (*C*), rear-wheel (*R*) or heel-stop/rear-wheel (*H/R*).

H	H	R	H	H
C	C	H/R	H	C
H	H	H	C	R
H	H	H	H/R	H
H	H	H	H	T
H				

Source: *Zillions*

a. Make a frequency table of the data.

b. What advantage is there to using a frequency table instead of a chart?

a. Draw a table with three columns.

In the first column, list the types of brakes. In the second column, tally the data. In the third column, add the number of tallies.

Brakes	Tally	Frequency
toe-stop	|	1
heel-stop	~~||||~~ ~~||||~~ ~~||||~~ ||	17
cuff-activated	||||	4
rear-wheel	||	2
heel-stop/ rear-wheel	||	2

b. The frequency table makes it easier to see quickly the number of skates with each type of brakes.

CHECK FOR UNDERSTANDING

Communicating Mathematics

Read and study the lesson to answer each question.

1–2. See Answer Appendix.

1. ***Explain*** how to find the range, scale, and interval for a set of data.
2. ***Make*** a frequency table for the data in Example 1 using a different scale and interval. Summarize the data in the new table.
3. ***You Decide*** Tatanka says that a frequency table includes the least number and the greatest number in a set of data. Stephen argues that only the numbers appearing most frequently are included in a frequency table. Who is correct? Explain. **See margin.**

Guided Practice

4a. Copy and complete the frequency table.

b. Name the scale and the interval. **61-100, 10**

Fitness Test Scores		
Score	**Tally**	**Frequency**
61-70	|	1
71-80	||	2
81-90	~~||||~~	5
91-100	~~||||~~ |	6

5–6. See Answer Appendix for tables.
5. 19; Sample answer: 0-19, 5
6. 5.5; Sample answer: 2.0-7.9, 2

Find the range for each set of data. Choose an appropriate scale and interval. Then make a frequency table.

5. 9, 0, 18, 19, 2, 9, 8, 13, 4
6. 4.5, 2.3, 4.5, 7.8, 5.5, 5.1, 3.9

In-Class Examples

For Example 1

The number of absences from class each day during January are shown below.

0	1	2	0	0	4	0
0	0	0	3	1	0	0
1	1	3	1	2	2	0

Make a frequency table. What is the most common number of absences? **0**

Number	Tally	Frequency
0	~~||||~~ ~~||||~~	10
1	~~||||~~	5
2	|||	3
3	||	2
4	|	1

For Example 2

Ask students to survey the class to find out each person's favorite food.

a. Have students make a frequency table to record the results.

b. What is the main advantage in using a frequency table? **It organizes data to provide a quick summary.**

Teaching Tip In Example 1, remind students that tally marks generally are written in sets of 5, with the fifth mark written diagonally across the other four.

3 PRACTICE/APPLY

Check for Understanding

If students need additional practice or instruction after completing Exercises 1–7, one of these options may be helpful.

- Extra Practice, see p. 574
- Reteaching Activity
- *Study Guide Masters,* p. 17
- *Practice Masters,* p. 17
- Interactive Mathematics Tools Software

Reteaching the Lesson

Activity Talk about the purpose of each column in the frequency table, paying particular attention to the reason for having a tally column and frequency column. Guide students to see that using tally marks is an organized way to record information as it is being received.

Additional Answer

3. Tatanka is correct. A frequency table includes all the numbers in a set of data.

Assignment Guide

Core: 9–21 odd, 23–26
Enriched: 8–20 even, 21, 23–26

Additional Answers

7b. Sample answer: 1–70, 10

Reign	Tally	Frequency
1–10	||||	4
11–20	||	2
21–30	|	1
31–40	|	1
41–50	|	1
51–60	|	1
61–70	|	1

14–17. Sample answers are given.

14.

Length	Tally	Frequency
10–19	𝍸	5
20–29	𝍸 |	6
30–39	𝍸 |	6
40–49	|	1
50–59		0
60–69	|||	3

15.

Number of Books	Tally	Frequency
0	|||	3
1	𝍸 |	6
2	𝍸 |||	8
3	|||	3
4	|	1
5	||	2
6	|	1

Study Guide Masters, p. 17

Name ______________________ Date ____________

Study Guide

Frequency Tables

Members of a seventh-grade class were surveyed to determine when to hold the winter dance. The results are shown at the right. On what date should the dance be held?

Dates Reported			
Dec. 9	Dec. 2	Dec. 9	Dec. 8
Dec. 2	Dec. 9	Dec. 8	Dec. 9
Dec. 9	Dec. 2	Dec. 9	Dec. 1
Dec. 2	Dec. 9	Dec. 9	Dec. 9
Dec. 8	Dec. 2	Dec. 9	Dec. 1
Dec. 2	Dec. 9	Dec. 2	Dec. 2
Dec. 8	Dec. 9		

Explore What do you know?
You know how each person responded.

What are you trying to find?
You are deciding on what date to hold the dance.

Plan Make a frequency table.

Solve The frequency table shows that the greatest number of people want to hold the dance on December 9.

Date	Tally	Frequency
Dec. 1	||	2
Dec. 2	𝍸 |||	8
Dec. 8	||||	4
Dec. 9	𝍸 𝍸 ||	12

Examine Since December 9 received the greatest number of votes, the winter dance should be held on December 9.

Solve.

1. Julia asked 12 people she bicycles with how many miles they rode their bicycles last week. She recorded the data in the table at the right.

Miles Bicycled			
Dave	47.8	Gloria	56.9
Mary	19.9	Izumi	82.1
Lung	66.7	Monty	36.8
Iris	71.2	Kara	61.0
Cruz	56.0	Toshi	76.4
Leon	45.3	Burt	17.5

   a. What was the greatest distance ridden? 82.1
   b. What was the least distance? 17.5
   c. What was the range of the distances? 64.6
   d. Choose an appropriate scale and interval. 10-90; 10

2. Twenty-one people were asked to name the state in which they were born. The data are shown below.

NY TX PA NY NY TX CA
NY CA CA CA NY PA PA
NY NY PA NY NY CA TX

State	Tally	Frequency
CA	𝍸	5
NY	𝍸 ||||	9
PA	||||	4
TX	|||	3

   a. Make a frequency table for the data.
   b. In which state were the fewest people surveyed born? TX
   c. How many of the people surveyed were born in California? 5

 T17 *Mathematics: Applications and Connections,* Course 2

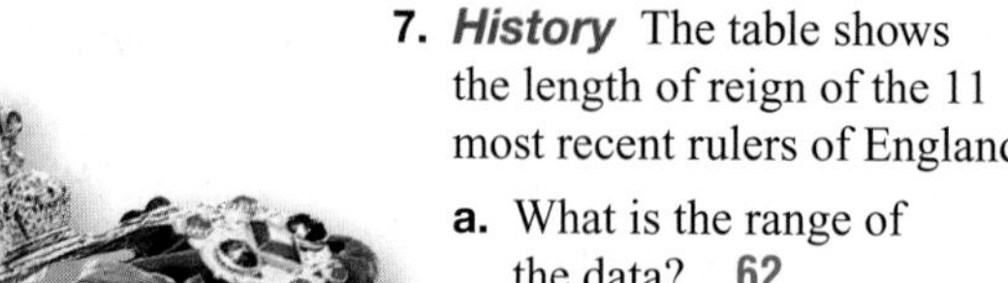

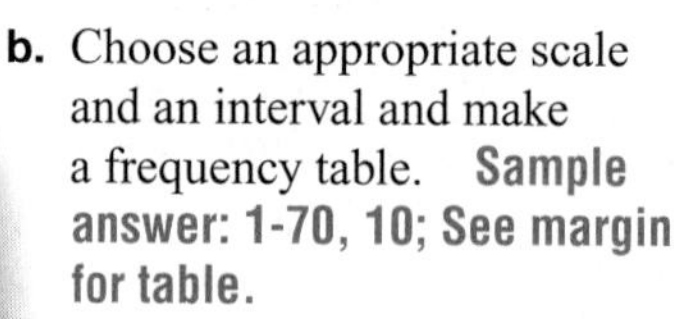

7. ***History*** The table shows the length of reign of the 11 most recent rulers of England.
   a. What is the range of the data? **62**
   b. Choose an appropriate scale and an interval and make a frequency table. **Sample answer: 1-70, 10; See margin for table.**

Ruler	Reign (years)
George I	13
George II	33
George III	59
George IV	10
William IV	7
Victoria	63
Edward VII	9
George V	25
Edward VIII	1
George VI	15
Elizabeth II	45*

*as of 1997
Source: *Academic American Encyclopedia*

EXERCISES

Practice

Find the range for each set of data. Choose an appropriate scale and interval for a frequency table. **8–13. Sample scales and intervals are given.**

9. 100; 20-120, 20
10. 444; 400-900, 100
11. 19; 0-20, 2

8. 6, 2, 8, 9, 12, 4 **10; 2-12, 2**
9. 30, 20, 60, 80, 90, 120, 40
10. 456, 900, 785, 832, 678
11. 14, 19, 4, 0, 13, 8, 2
12. 13, 15, 17, 21, 28, 25, 26, 29, 31, 32, 26, 23, 34, 29 **21; 10-35, 5**
13. 18.2, 14.5, 21.6, 18.8, 17.3, 14.1, 14.6, 15.0 **7.5; 14-22, 1**

Choose an appropriate scale and interval for each set of data. Then make a frequency table.

14–17. Sample scales and intervals are given. See margin for tables.

14.

Lengths of TV Commercial (s)						
25	30	10	20	60	10	10
30	60	15	20	20	30	45
20	10	60	20	35	30	30

10-69, 10

15.

Number of Books Read During the Summer							
0	2	6	2	5	1	3	0
1	2	5	1	3	1	3	1
2	0	2	2	4	1	2	2

0-6, 1

16.

Favorite Fast Food Restaurant						
M	M	T	B	T	M	T
B	T	B	M	M	T	M
B	M	T	M	T	B	B

B=Burger Barn M=Murray's T=Terry's Tacos

no scales or intervals

17.

Average Rainfall in Little Rock, Arkansas (in.)			
Jan.	10	July	8
Feb.	9	Aug.	7
Mar.	10	Sept.	7
Apr.	10	Oct.	7
May	10	Nov.	8
June	8	Dec.	9

Source: *Statistical Abstract of the United States,* 1996

7-10, 1

18. 2-10, 2

18. Name the scale and the interval of the number line. 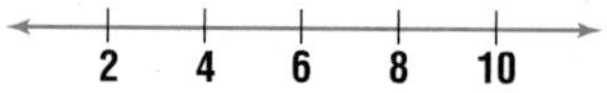
    (number line: 2, 4, 6, 8, 10)
19. Draw a number line that shows a scale of 0 to 50 and an interval of 5. **See margin.**

Additional Answers

16.

Fast Food	Tally	Frequency
Burger Barn	𝍸 |	6
Murray's	𝍸 |||	8
Terry's Tacos	𝍸 ||	7

17.

Rainfall (in.)	Tally	Frequency
7	|||	3
8	|||	3
9	||	2
10	||||	4

19. (number line: 0 5 10 15 20 25 30 35 40 45 50)

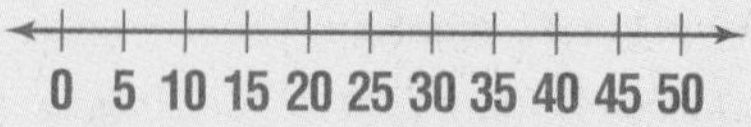

Applications and Problem Solving

20. ***Baseball*** The chart shows recent prices of field box seats for baseball teams.

Team	Price	Team	Price
A's	$17.50	Mets	$17
Angels	14.50	Orioles	20
Astros	21	Padres	16
Braves	30	Phillies	16
Brewers	20	Pirates	15
Blue Jays	25	Rangers	20
Cardinals	19	Red Sox	23
Cubs	21	Reds	14
Dodgers	19	Rockies	22
Expos	20	Royals	13
Giants	21	Tigers	15
Indians	23	Twins	18
Mariners	22	White Sox	20
Marlins	40	Yankees	23

Source: *USA TODAY*

a. Find the range of the prices. **$27**

b. Choose an appropriate scale and an interval and make a frequency table of the data.

c. In which interval do the greatest number of prices fall? **$16-$20** **b. Sample answer: 11–40, 5; See margin for table.**

21. ***Earth Science*** The chart shows years in the twentieth century in which major hurricanes occurred in the United States.

Years of Major Hurricanes				
1900	1909	1957	1965	1915
1938	1935	1989	1980	1926
1961	1969	1979	1972	1992
1955	1947	1954	1992	1928
1944	1960			

Source: *The World Almanac*

a. Make a frequency table of the data. Use the intervals 1900-1919, 1920-1939, 1940-1959, 1960-1979, and 1980-1999. **See margin.**

b. In which time interval did the greatest number of major hurricanes occur? **1960-1979**

22. ***Working on the CHAPTER Project*** Make a frequency table of the data from your survey. **See students' work.**

23. ***Critical Thinking*** Refer to Exercise 2. Tell the advantages and disadvantages of the two different scales and intervals used for the data in Example 1. **See students' work.**

Mixed Review

24. ***Entertainment*** The pool for Shamu the whale contains 6 million gallons of water. Write 6 million in scientific notation. *(Lesson 2-9)* **6.0×10^6**

25. **Standardized Test Practice** Kalinda bought a skirt for $21.95, a shirt for $19.30, and a pair of shoes for $39.60. All of the prices included tax. Which is the best estimate of the total cost of the three items? *(Lesson 2-3)* **C**

A less than $65
B between $65 and $75
C between $75 and $85
D between $85 and $95
E more than $95

26. ***Real Estate*** A house advertised in the real estate section of the newspaper claims to have a rectangular lot with a length of 250 feet and a width of 120 feet. What is the area of the lot? *(Lesson 1-7)* **30,000 sq ft**

For **Extra Practice,** see page 574.

CHAPTER Project

Exercise 22 asks students to advance to the next stage of work on the Chapter Project. You may wish to have students share their findings.

4 ASSESS

Closing Activity

Writing Have students gather a set of data related to a daily experience, such as the number of hours spent reading. Ask them to write the range and to determine a reasonable interval.

Additional Answers

20b.

Prices	Tally	Frequency
11–15	𝍸	5
16–20	𝍸𝍸 II	12
21–25	𝍸 IIII	9
26–30	I	1
31–35		0
36–40	I	1

21a.

Year	Tally	Frequency
1900–1919	III	3
1920–1939	IIII	4
1940–1959	𝍸	5
1960–1979	𝍸 I	6
1980–1999	IIII	4

Practice Masters, p. 17

Name__________ Date__________

Practice

Frequency Tables

Find the range for each set of data. Choose an appropriate scale and an interval for a frequency table. Sample answers are given.

1. 8, 2, 6, 10, 3, 4
range: 8; scale: 0 to 10; interval: 1

2. 10, 15, 0, 13, 13, 17, 5
range: 17; scale: 0 to 20; interval: 2

3. 18, 70, 33, 61, 20, 20, 54
range: 52; scale: 15 to 70; interval: 5

4. 664, 320, 500, 500, 425
range: 344; scale: 300 to 700; interval: 100

5. 1, 5, 9, 12, 12, 4, 7
range: 11; scale: 0 to 12; interval: 1

6. 27, 22, 19, 21, 12, 15, 11
range: 16; scale: 10 to 30; interval: 5

7. 55, 59, 53, 95, 98, 76
range: 45; scale: 50 to 100; interval: 10

8. 400, 1,200, 800, 900, 1,100
range: 800; scale: 400 to 1,200; interval: 100

Choose an appropriate scale and an interval for each set of data. Then make a frequency table.

9.

Hours of TV Watched on Saturdays by Mrs. Mulrooney's Students				
8	7	3	7	6
8	2	4	4	6
6	12	7	6	8
5	4	6	5	2

scale: 0 to 12; interval: 3

Number of Hours	Tally	Frequency
0–3	III	3
4–6	𝍸𝍸	10
7–9	𝍸 I	6
10–12	I	1

10.

Weights of Members of Fox Valley Wrestling Team (pounds)			
100	97	84	98
112	98	96	84
96	100	85	98

scale: 80 to 120; interval: 10

Weight	Tally	Frequency
80–90	III	3
91–100	𝍸 I	6
101–110	II	2
111–120	I	1

Name the scale and interval of each number line.

11. Number line: 3, 6, 9, 12, 15, 18, 21
scale: 3 to 21; interval: 3

12. Number line: 100, 110, 120, 130
scale: 100 to 130; interval: 10

 T17 *Mathematics: Applications and Connections, Course 2*

Extending the Lesson

Enrichment Masters, p. 17

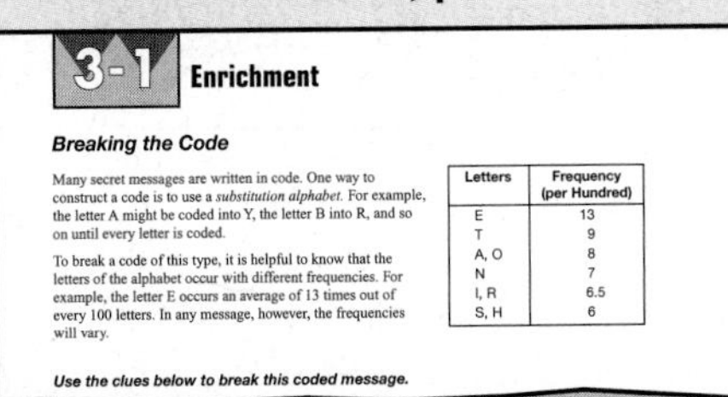

3-1 Enrichment

Breaking the Code

Many secret messages are written in code. One way to construct a code is to use a *substitution alphabet.* For example, the letter A might be coded into Y, the letter B into R, and so on until every letter is coded.

To break a code of this type, it is helpful to know that the letters of the alphabet occur with different frequencies. For example, the letter E occurs an average of 13 times out of every 100 letters. In any message, however, the frequencies will vary.

Letters	Frequency (per Hundred)
E	13
T	9
A, O	8
N	7
I, R	6.5
S, H	6

Use the clues below to break this coded message.

Activity Have students suggest kinds of graphs they could make to display a set of data that would require them to figure out the range, scale, and interval of the data being recorded. **Sample answers: bar graph, line graph**

Objective Students solve problems by using graphs.

Recommended Pacing	
Standard	Day 3 of 12
Honors	Day 3 of 11
Block	Day 2 of 6

1 FOCUS

Getting Started Have students act out the situation presented at the beginning of the lesson. Then ask them to work in pairs to answer Exercises 1 and 2. Have the class discuss the results. Then have them solve Exercise 3.

2 TEACH

Teaching Tip You may wish to have students compare the different kinds of graphs presented in the lesson. Ask students which of the graphs is most effective for showing changes over time. Which is best for comparing quantities? Which is best for showing the relationship between two items?

Additional Answers

1. **Sample answer: The table gives information about each kind of bike. The graph shows the relationship between rating and price.**
2. **Sample answer: You could recommend Brand G because it has the highest rating, but it is not the most expensive.**

PROBLEM SOLVING

3-2A Use a Graph

A Preview of Lesson 3-2

Marian received information on 8 mountain bikes. She's talking to her friend Robert about which one to buy. Let's listen in!

Marian: Okay, I have $350 to spend on a new bike. And I want the best bike for my money.

Robert: Well, I graphed the data, and the graph shows that the most expensive bike isn't the best.

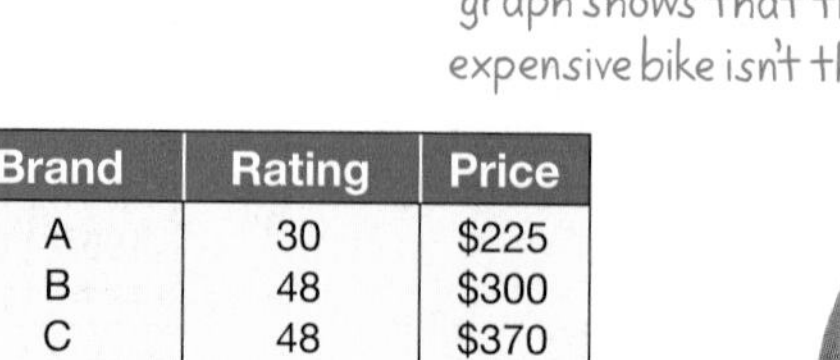

Brand	Rating	Price
A	30	$225
B	48	$300
C	48	$370
D	46	$290
E	45	$320
F	37	$240
G	54	$325
H	43	$250

Higher ratings represent better bikes.

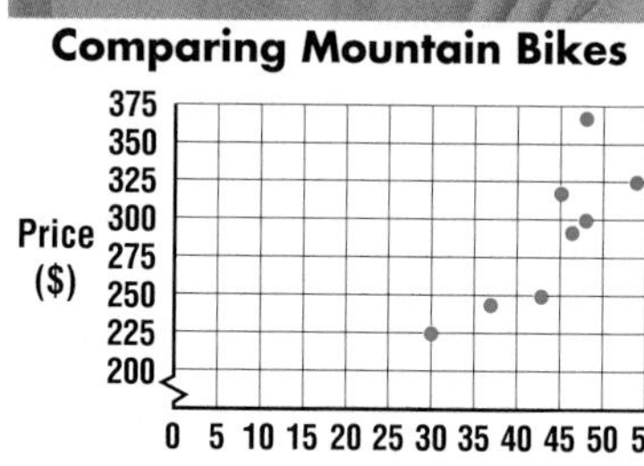

The *scatter plot* shows the relationship between rating and price.

THINK ABOUT IT

Work with a partner. **1–2. See margin.**

1. ***List*** different advantages in using the table and the graph to get information about mountain bikes.
2. ***Analyze*** the data in the graph to see which bike you would recommend for Marian to purchase and why.
3. ***Apply*** the **use-a-graph** strategy to solve the following problem.

   Kids ages 11-13 tested 18 computer games and rated them based on graphics, sound, action, challenge, and fun. Ratings of 41-60 were Good, 61-80 were Very Good, and 81-100 were Excellent. Use the graph at the right to find how many games were rated Excellent. **2 games**

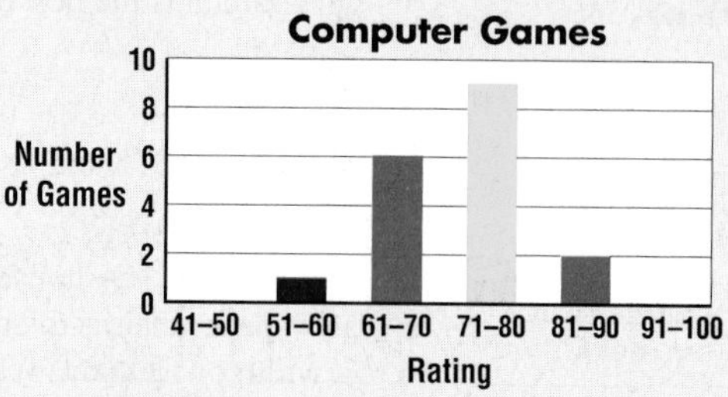

Reteaching the Lesson

Activity The dashed line represents the projected population of Phoenix, and the solid line represents the projected population of Detroit. Ask students in what year the population of Phoenix is predicted to pass that of Detroit. **2010**

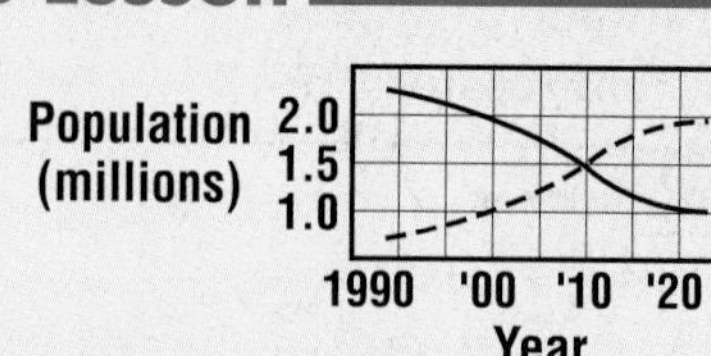

For **Extra Practice,** see page 574.

ON YOUR OWN

4. ***Explain*** why the use-a-graph strategy can make solving problems easier. **A graph is a quick and easy way to get a summary of data.**

5. The last step of the 4-step plan for problem solving asks you to *examine* the solution. ***Explain*** how you can use a graph to help you examine a solution. **Using a graph can help you analyze whether a solution is correct.**

MIXED PROBLEM SOLVING

STRATEGIES

- Look for a pattern.
- Solve a simpler problem.
- Act it out.
- Guess and check.
- Draw a diagram.
- Make a chart.
- Work backward.

Solve. Use any strategy.

6. ***Safety*** An elevator sign reads *Do not exceed 2,500 pounds.* How many people, each weighing about 150 pounds, can be in the elevator at the same time? **16 people**

7. ***Telecommunications*** Fiber optic cables are made up of bundled strands of glass. If each fiber is 0.0005 inch thick, how thick is a bundle that is 3,000 fibers wide? **1.5 in.**

8. ***Sports*** The graph shows the percent of kids ages 9-13 who say they know "a lot" about the rules for playing sports.

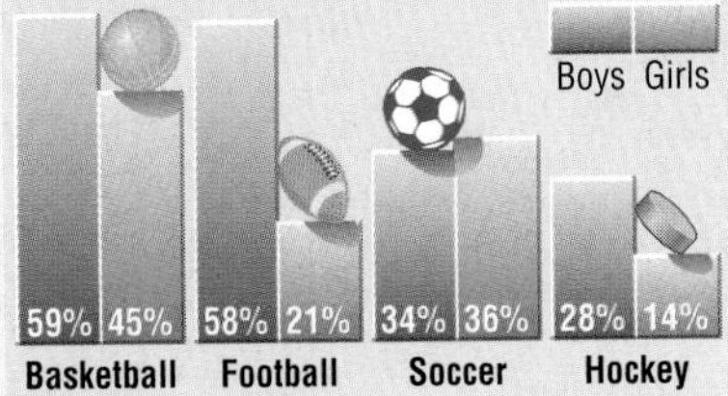

Source: *Sports Illustrated for Kids Omnibus*

According to the survey, do a greater percent of girls understand the rules of basketball or soccer? **basketball**

9. ***Food*** A soup can display has 66 cans. There is one less can in each row than in the row below, with a single can in the top row. How many cans are in the bottom row? **11**

10. ***Geography*** Alaska, the largest U.S. state, has an area of 1,478,458 square kilometers. Rhode Island, the smallest state, has an area of 2,732 square kilometers. How many times larger is Alaska? **about 541.2 times**

11. ***Earth Science*** In 1997, for the first time on record, Los Angeles had no rain during March or April.

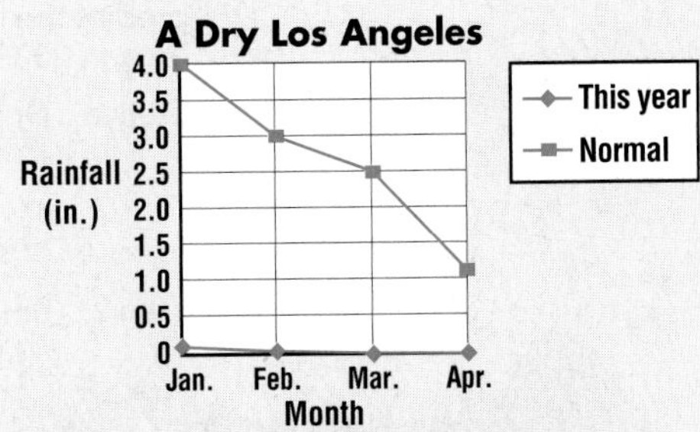

Source: National Weather Service

a. About how many inches below normal was the rainfall in February? **about 3 in.**

b. Use the graph to predict what month this year's rainfall will equal the normal rainfall. **Sample answer: May**

12. **Standardized Test Practice** Francisca bought 6 tickets to the circus. She gave the cashier \$170 and received \$8 in change. How much did one ticket cost? **C**

A \$20.33 **B** \$48.00
C \$27.00 **D** \$28.33
E \$15.25

In-Class Example

The scatter plot shows the price of a piece of pizza and its tastiness rating. What is the price of the piece that has the highest rating? Does the piece with the highest rating cost the most? **about \$0.90; no**

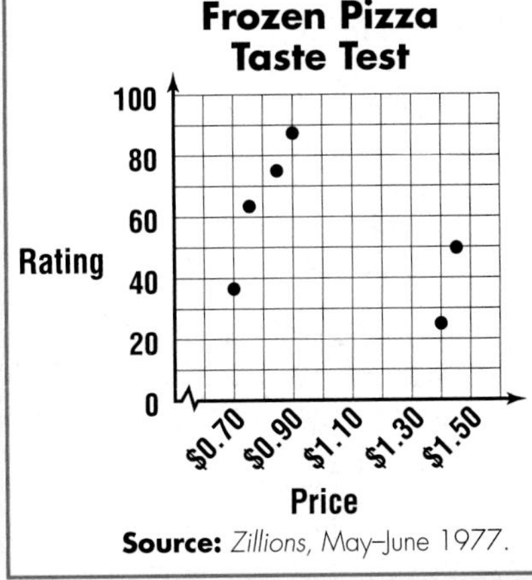

Source: *Zillions,* May–June 1977.

3 PRACTICE/APPLY

Check for Understanding

Use the results from Exercise 3 to determine whether students understand how to use graphs to solve problems.

Extra Practice If students need additional practice in problem solving, extra practice is available on the following pages.

- Use a Graph, see p. 574
- Mixed Problem Solving, see pp. 605–606

Assignment Guide
All: 4–12

4 ASSESS

Closing Activity

Speaking Have students imagine that they own an ice cream store. Ask them to describe how they might use a graph in their business.

Extending the Lesson

Activity Have students look through a newspaper or magazine to find examples of graphs. Ask them to summarize the information the graph shows. Ask students to share their findings with the class.

3-2 Lesson Notes

Instructional Resources

- *Study Guide Masters,* p. 18
- *Practice Masters,* p. 18
- *Enrichment Masters,* p. 18
- Transparencies 3-2, A and B
- *Assessment and Evaluation Masters,* p. 71
- *Hands-On Lab Masters,* p. 74
- *Science and Math Lab Manual,* pp. 29–32 & 77–80

CD-ROM Program
- Resource Lesson 3-2
- Extended Activity 3-2

Recommended Pacing	
Standard	Day 4 of 12
Honors	Day 4 of 11
Block	Day 3 of 6

1 FOCUS

5-Minute Check
(Lesson 3-1)

The graph shows daily high and low temperatures in one city for one week.

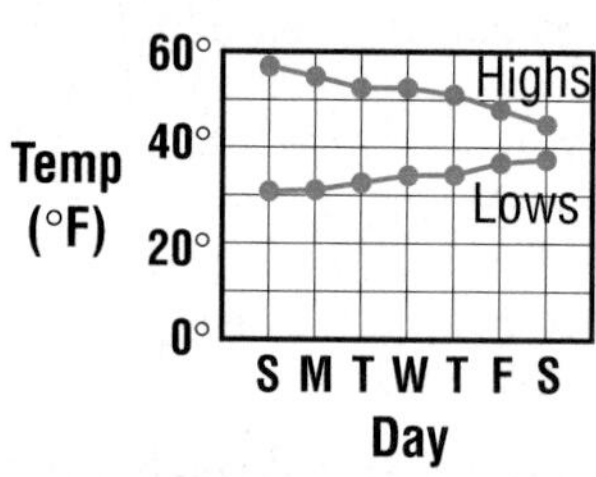

1. Which day had the lowest high temperature? **Saturday**
2. Summarize the information shown in the graph. **Sample answer: The difference between the high and low temperatures decreased through the week.**

The 5-Minute Check is also available on **Transparency 3-2A** for this lesson.

Motivating the Lesson

Hands-On Activity Have students take turns shooting 10 free throws each and recording how many out of 10 go in. After 3 sets of trials by each student, have them graph their data and predict how many of their next 10 shots will go in.

3-2 Making Predictions

What you'll learn

You'll learn to make predictions from graphs.

When am I ever going to use this?

You'll be able to make predictions from graphs in newspapers and in magazines.

Word Wise

line graph
bar graph
scatter plot

More students are graduating from high school than did in the past. The graph shows the percent of adults that have a high school diploma from 1960 to 1995. Can you predict what percent of the population will have a high school diploma in 2000?

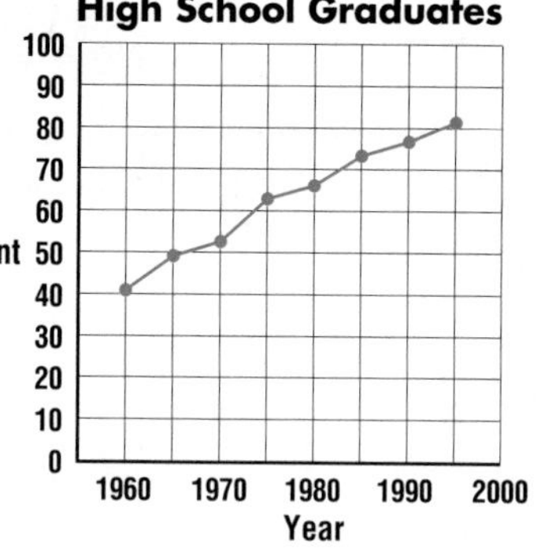

Line graphs such as the one at the right are useful in predicting future events since they show trends over time. You can use the graph to predict that in the year 2000, about 90% of adults will have high school diplomas.

Example CONNECTION

1 Life Science **In 1995, biologists began releasing gray wolves into different areas of the wild in an effort to increase the species. The table shows the projected population of wolves in one area. Make a line graph of the data and predict the number of wolves in that area in 2002.**

Year	Number of Wolves
1995	8
1996	14
1997	27
1998	45
1999	56
2000	68
2001	83

Source: *USA Today*

Step 1 Draw a horizontal and a vertical axis. Label the axes and include a title of the graph.

Step 2 Since the data values go from 8 to 83, an appropriate scale for the vertical axis is 0-100 with an interval of 10.

Step 3 Graph the data.

Step 4 Connect the points.

Step 5 Draw a continuation of the graph, dotted, in the same direction it has been going in, to take it one more year into the future.

Projected Population

Number of Wolves: 0, 10, 20, 30, 40, 50, 60, 70, 80, 90, 100
Year: 1995, 1996, 1997, 1998, 1999, 2000, 2001, 2002

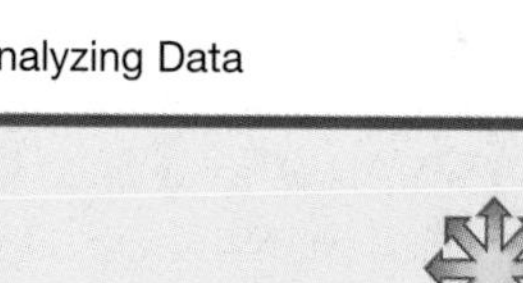

In 2002, the projected wolf population in that area would be about 95.

A **bar graph** can also be used to make predictions. A bar graph uses bars to make comparisons.

Cross-Curriculum Cue

Inform other teachers on your team that your students are learning to make predictions from graphs. Suggestions for curriculum integration are:
Life Science: predicting species extinction
Economics: predicting standards of living, economic changes

2 **Sales** The manager of Sweatshirts Unlimited kept a record of how many sweatshirts of each color she sold last month. Use the graph to predict which color will sell the most in the next three months.

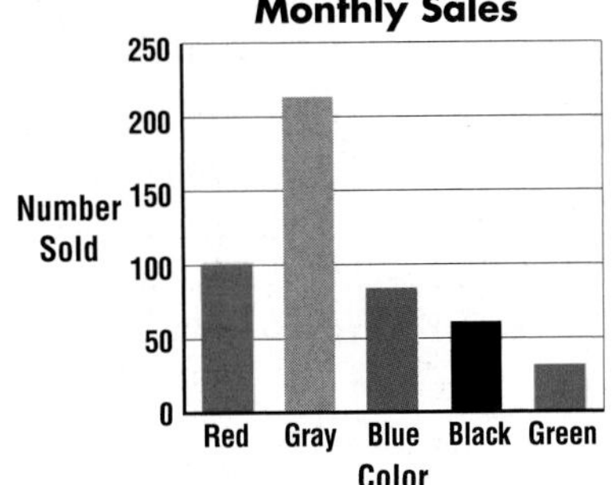

The graph shows that gray sweatshirts sold the most. You could predict that gray would continue to be the greatest number sold during the next three months.

A **scatter plot** shows two sets of related data on the same graph.

Example
CONNECTION

3 **Life Science** The graph shows the average heights and weights of different species of buffalo. Could you conclude that the tallest buffalo are the heaviest?

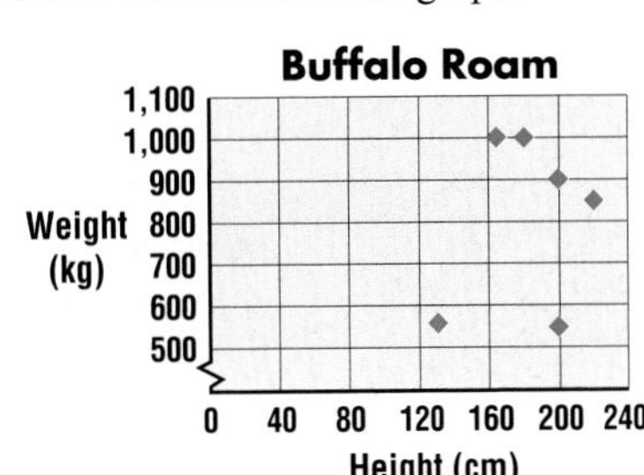

The tallest species of buffalo measure 220 centimeters, but weigh only 850 kilograms. Therefore, the tallest buffalo are not the heaviest.

HANDS-ON MINI-LAB

Work with a partner. ruler marbles drinking glass

Try This

- Make a table. Label the first column "Number of Marbles" and the second column "Height."
- Put one cup of water in a glass. Measure the height of the water.
- Place two marbles in the glass and measure the height of the water. Record the data in your table. Repeat this procedure with 4, 6, and 8 marbles.

Talk About It **1–2. See students' work.**

1. Draw a graph of the data.
2. Predict the height of the water if a total of ten marbles were in the glass.

Using the Mini-Lab Students should understand that science experiments are often used to make predictions. For example, the growth pattern of a bean plant for 10 days could be used to make a prediction about what the growth would be on the fourteenth day.

2 TEACH

Transparency 3-2B contains a teaching aid for this lesson.

In-Class Examples

For Example 1

Make a line graph of the data and predict how much butter each person will consume in 2000.

U.S. Yearly Butter Consumption	
Year	**Butter Per Person (lb)**
1960	7.5
1970	5.3
1980	4.5
1990	4.4

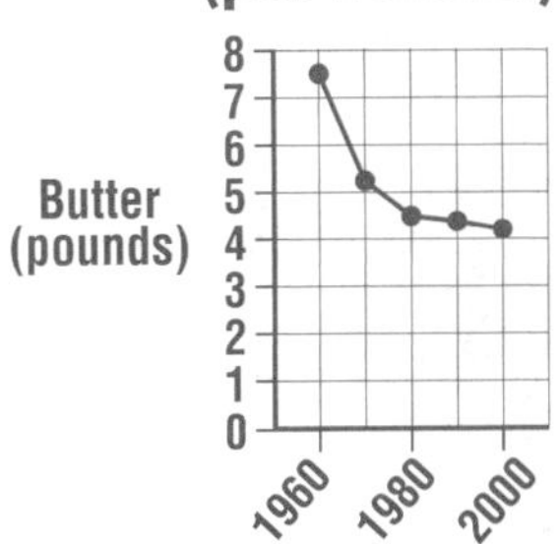

For Example 2

Use the graph from a pet store to predict which animal will be sold the most in the next three months. fish

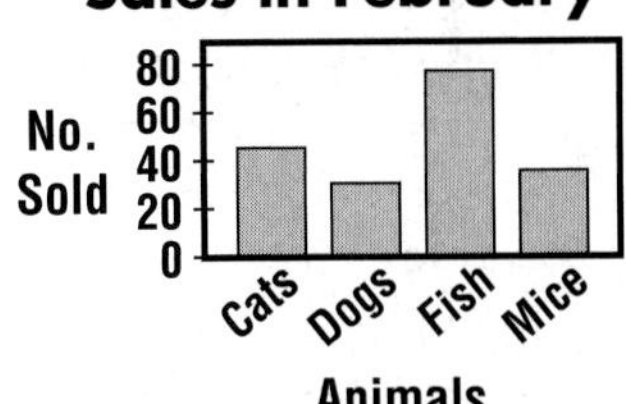

For Example 3

Refer to the graph. Could you conclude that the animals that weigh the least run the fastest? no

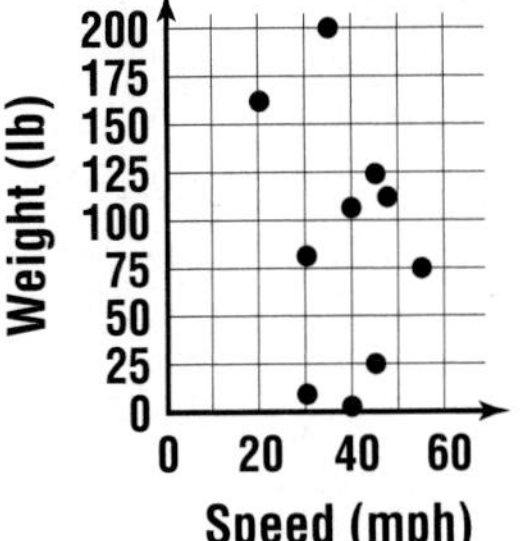

3 PRACTICE/APPLY

Check for Understanding

If students need additional practice or instruction after completing Exercises 1–5, one of these options may be helpful.

- Extra Practice, see p. 574
- Reteaching Activity
- *Study Guide Masters,* p. 18
- *Practice Masters,* p. 18
- Interactive Mathematics Tools Software

Assignment Guide

Core: 6–13
Enriched: 6–13

Additional Answers

1. Graphs often show trends over time.

7b. Students in grades 7–8 and 9–12 spend the most time using computers, so the new computer software should be designed for students in these grades.

***Study Guide Masters,* p. 18**

Name________________ Date________

3-2 Study Guide

Making Predictions

Graphs can be used to make predictions.

Example **If the trend in the graph continues, predict about how many records the Sound Store will sell their fifth year in business.**

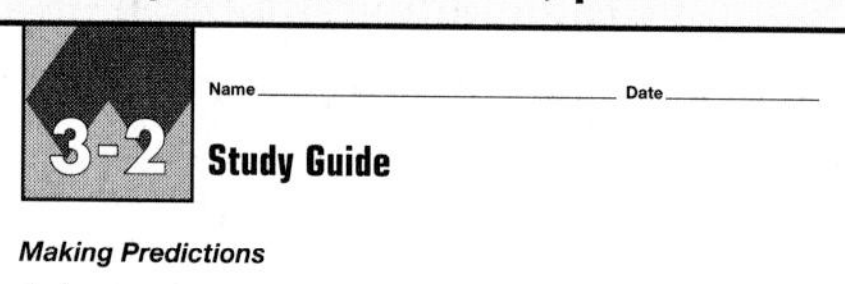

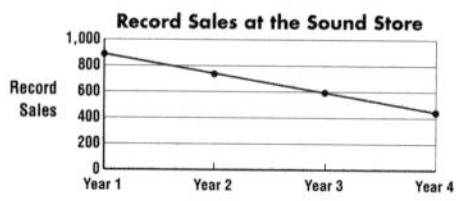

Each year about 150 fewer records have been sold. If the trend continues, the Sound Store will sell about 300 records in the fifth year.

Solve.

1. A store owner is deciding how much of each brand of shampoo to order. She made a graph to show sales for the previous month. Based on the graph, of which brand should she order the most? Brand X

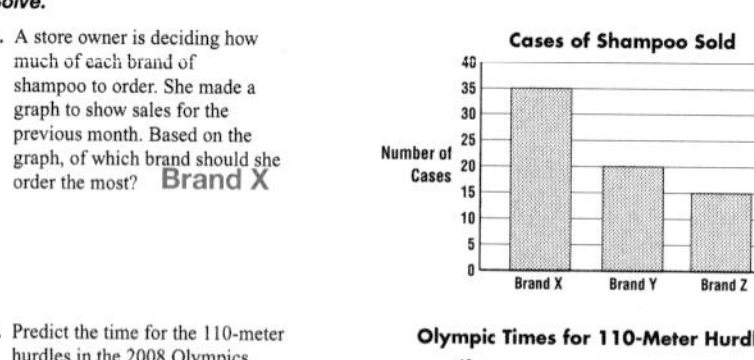

2. Predict the time for the 110-meter hurdles in the 2008 Olympics. Sample: between 12 and 13 seconds

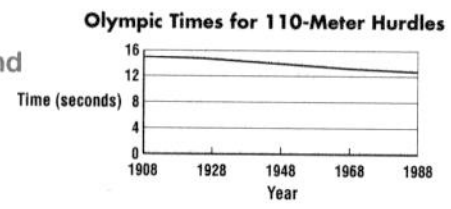

Olympic Times for 110-Meter Hurdles

Time (seconds)

1908 1928 1948 1968 1988

Year

 T18 *Mathematics: Applications and Connections, Course 2*

CHECK FOR UNDERSTANDING

Communicating Mathematics

Read and study the lesson to answer each question.

1. ***Tell*** how a graph can be used to make predictions. **See margin.**
2. Refer to the beginning of the lesson. ***Predict*** what percent of the population will have high school diplomas when you graduate from high school. **2. See students' work.**
3. HANDS-ON MATH Take a balloon and blow it up slightly. Record the number of breaths you took and use a ruler to measure the width of the balloon. Repeat, taking measurements every couple of breaths. Make a table of your data and use the data to draw a graph. Summarize your results. **See students' work.**

Guided Practice

4. ***Food*** Extra help is needed at Ralphy's Burgers whenever the number of orders in one hour exceeds 60. During which hours would extra help be needed? **between 11:00 A.M. and 2:00 P.M. and between 5:00 P.M. and 9:00 P.M.**

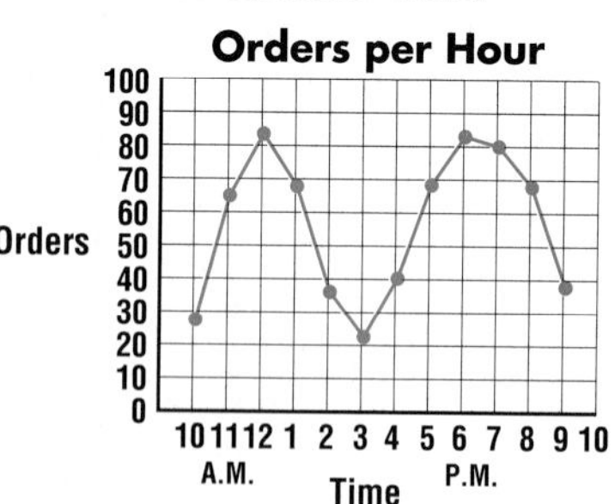

5. ***Snowboarding*** The graph shows the millions of people who have snowboarded more than once. Predict how many people will snowboard more than once in the year 2001. **Sample answer: 3.5 million people**

Source: National Sporting Goods Association

EXERCISES

Practice

The 1940 and 1944 Olympics were cancelled due to World War II.

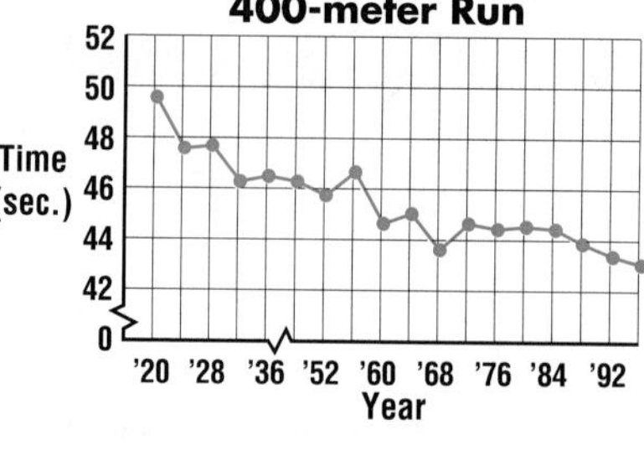

6. ***Sports*** The line graph shows the winning times in seconds for the 400-meter run in the Olympic Games from 1920 to 1996. Predict the winning time for the 400-meter run in the 2000 Olympics. **Sample answer: 42.5 s**

7. ***Computers*** A survey showed the number of hours each week that students use a computer.
   a. Draw a bar graph of the data. **7a. See Answer Appendix.**
   b. Determine what grades computer companies should design new software for, according to this data. Explain. **See margin.**

Grade	Hours Per Week
Pre K–K	3.9
1st–3rd	4.9
4th–6th	4.2
7th–8th	6.9
9th–12th	6.7

Source: Find/SVP American Learning Household Survey

Reteaching the Lesson

Activity Have students record the time of sunrise for five consecutive days. Construct a line graph to show the data. Next, ask them to discuss any pattern visible in the graph. Ask how students could use the graph to predict what time the sun will rise tomorrow and on a day next week.

Error Analysis

Watch for students who have a hard time correctly reading points that fall between scale marks.

Prevent by having them place a ruler or the edge of a paper across the graph, just below the point they want to read. Then they can estimate what the point represents.

Applications and Problem Solving

8. ***Business*** Montez started his own lawn care company. The graph shows how much money he made over 15 weeks last summer.

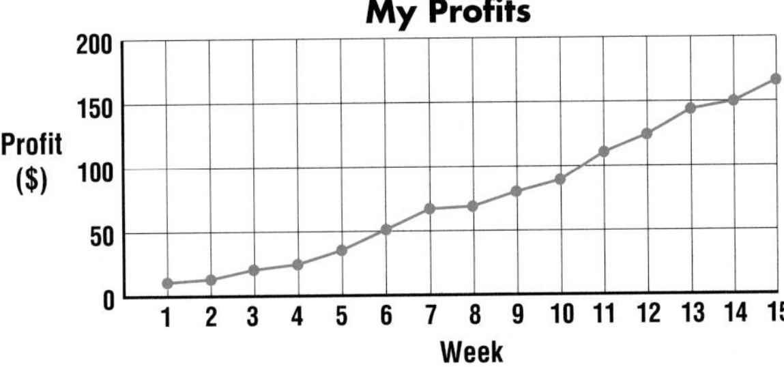

His friends are thinking about starting a similar company. Based on the graph of Montez's profits, what would you recommend to his friends?

8. See margin.

9. ***Entertainment*** Although attendance at Wally World is growing, it still attracts fewer people than Valley World. Use the graph to make predictions about attendance at the two parks. Do you think that Wally World will catch up to Valley World in attendance? Explain. **See margin.**

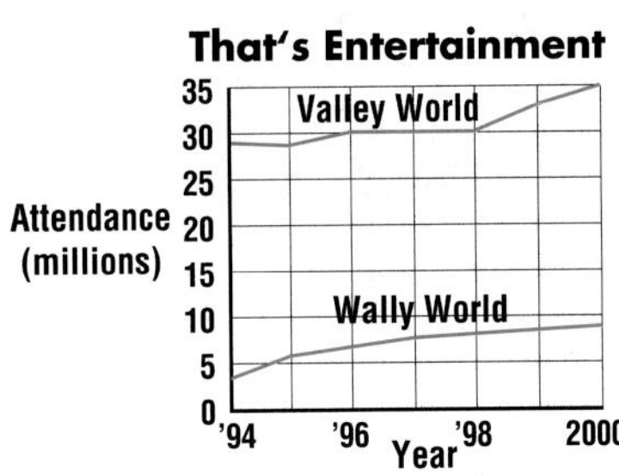

10. ***Critical Thinking*** Refer to the beginning of the lesson.
    a. Draw a bar graph of the data. Which graph seems easier to understand, the bar graph or the line graph? Explain. **See Answer Appendix.**
    b. Which types of graphs are more useful to use in making predictions, line graphs, bar graphs, or scatter plots? Explain.

10b. Sample answer: since line graphs show change over time, they are usually the most useful when making predictions.

Mixed Review

11. ***Statistics*** Find the range for the following set of data. Choose an appropriate scale and an interval: 35, 42, 18, 25, 32, 47, 34. *(Lesson 3-1)*

11. 29; Sample answer: 18–48, 2

12. ***Money Matters*** Suzanne bought 3.5 yards of fabric for $7.52. Find the price per yard rounded to the nearest cent. *(Lesson 2-6)* **$2.15**

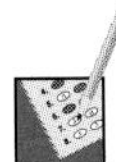

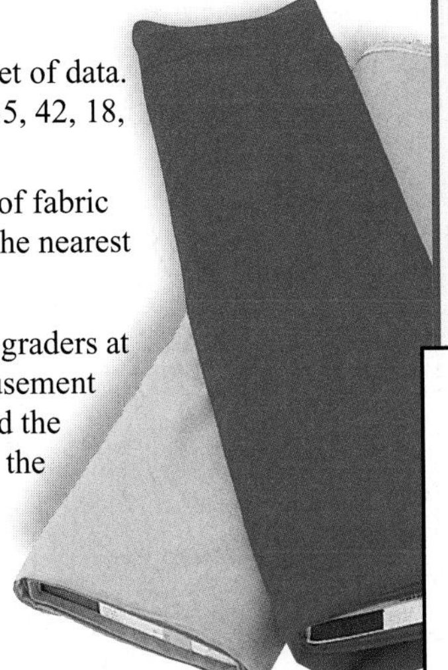

13. **Standardized Test Practice** The seventh graders at McKinley Middle School are going to an amusement park for a class trip. There are 90 students, and the admission price is $10.75 per person. What is the total cost for all of the students to enter the amusement park? *(Lesson 2-4)* **C**
    A $1,350 **B** $1,100
    C $967.50 **D** $875.50
    E Not Here

For **Extra Practice,** see page 574.

4 ASSESS

Closing Activity

Modeling Ask students how they would decide how many school lunches would be needed in one week. Have them research how many students pack a lunch and how many buy their lunch each day for a week, graph the data, and predict how many lunches will be needed for the following week.

Chapter 3, Quiz A (Lessons 3-1 and 3-2) is available in the *Assessment and Evaluation Masters,* p. 71.

Additional Answers

8. Sample answer: His friends should be sure they have customers before they start their business, since the graph shows that it was several weeks before Montez made any money.

9. Sample answer: Wally World probably will not catch up to Valley World in attendance, since Valley World's attendance appears to be increasing faster than Wally World's.

***Practice Masters,* p. 18**

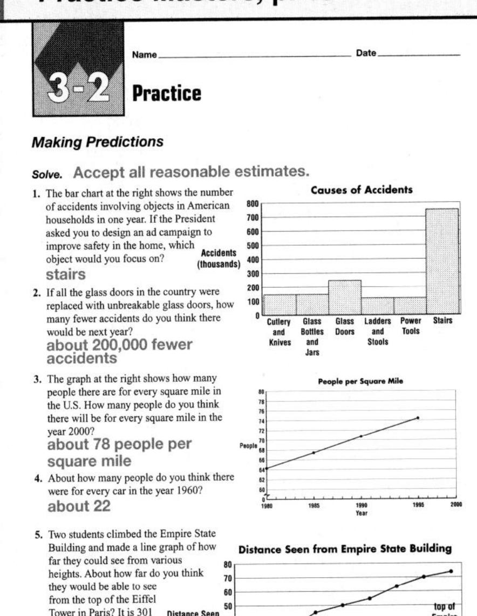
Name______ Date______

3-2 Practice

Making Predictions

Solve. Accept all reasonable estimates.

1. The bar chart at the right shows the number of accidents involving objects in American households in one year. If the President asked you to design an ad campaign to improve safety in the home, which object would you focus on? **stairs**
2. If all the glass doors in the country were replaced with unbreakable glass doors, how many fewer accidents do you think there would be next year? **about 200,000 fewer accidents**
3. The graph at the right shows how many people there are for every square mile in the U.S. How many people do you think there will be for every square mile in the year 2000? **about 78 people per square mile**
4. About how many people do you think there were for every car in the year 1960? **about 22**
5. Two students climbed the Empire State Building and made a line graph of how far they could see from various heights. About how far do you think they would be able to see from the top of the Eiffel Tower in Paris? It is 301 meters tall. **about 65 km**
6. About how far would they see from the top of the KTHI-TV tower in Fargo, North Dakota? The tower is 629 meters tall. **90 km**

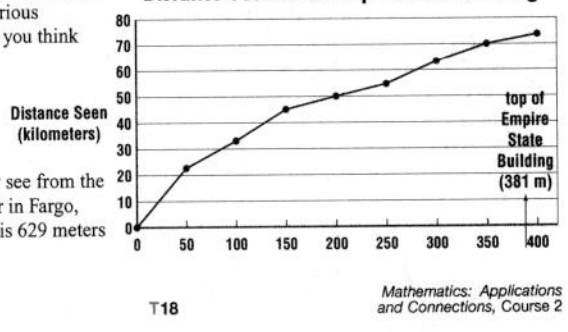

© Glencoe/McGraw-Hill T18 *Mathematics: Applications and Connections, Course 2*

Extending the Lesson

***Enrichment Masters,* p. 18**

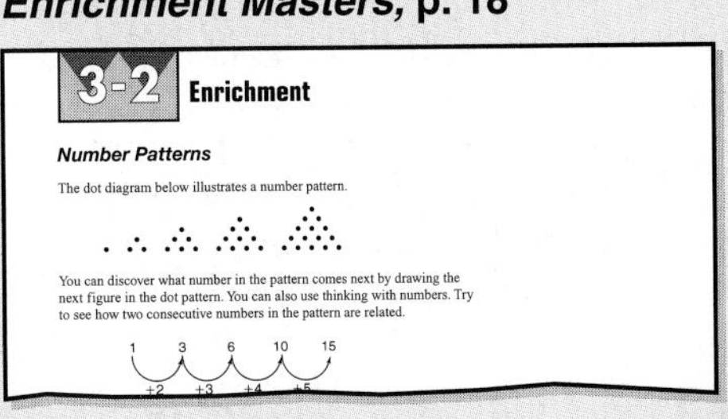
3-2 Enrichment

Number Patterns

The dot diagram below illustrates a number pattern.

You can discover what number in the pattern comes next by drawing the next figure in the dot pattern. You can also use thinking with numbers. Try to see how two consecutive numbers in the pattern are related.

Activity Have students work with partners to choose a local store and draw a bar graph or line graph to show its customer traffic either by the hour or within time periods. They should formulate problems that can be solved by making predictions.

3-3 Lesson Notes

Instructional Resources

- *Study Guide Masters,* p. 19
- *Practice Masters,* p. 19
- *Enrichment Masters,* p. 19
- Transparencies 3-3, A and B

CD-ROM Program
- Resource Lesson 3-3
- Interactive Lesson 3-3

Recommended Pacing	
Standard	Day 5 of 12
Honors	Day 5 of 11
Block	Day 3 of 6

1 FOCUS

5-Minute Check
(Lesson 3-2)

1. The graph shows how many shirts of each size were sold at a store last week. Based on the graph, of which size should the store order the least? **size S**

Shirts Sold in Week 8

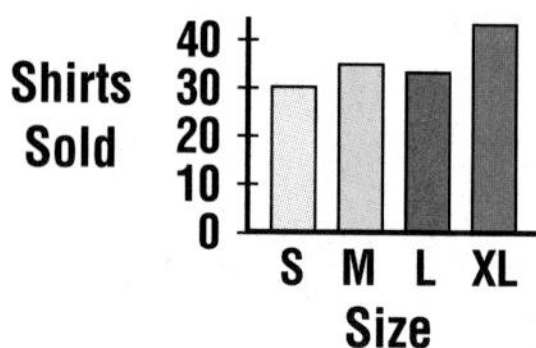

2. This graph shows how many sit-ups Lucinda has been doing each day. How many sit-ups do you predict she will do on day 10? **about 40**

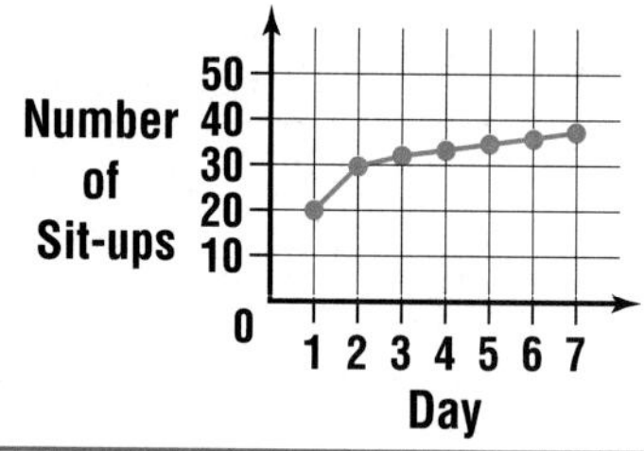

The 5-Minute Check is also available on **Transparency 3-3A** for this lesson.

3-3 Line Plots

What you'll learn

You'll learn to construct line plots.

When am I ever going to use this?

In line plots, you can see useful characteristics of data that can't be seen in tables.

Word Wise

line plot
cluster

Cultural Kaleidoscope

Phiops II became pharaoh of Egypt in 2281 B.C., when he was six years old. It is believed that he ruled until the age of 100.

At 42 years old, Theodore Roosevelt became the youngest President of the United States.

The chart lists the Presidents from Grover Cleveland to William Clinton and their age when they first took office.

One way to organize this data is to use a **line plot**. A line plot is a picture of information on a number line. To make a line plot, you must first determine the scale and the interval.

Grover Cleveland	47	Harry Truman	60
Benjamin Harrison	55	Dwight Eisenhower	62
William McKinley	54	John Kennedy	43
Theodore Roosevelt	42	Lyndon Johnson	55
William Taft	51	Richard Nixon	56
Woodrow Wilson	56	Gerald Ford	61
Warren Harding	55	James Carter	52
Calvin Coolidge	51	Ronald Reagan	69
Herbert Hoover	54	George Bush	64
Franklin Roosevelt	51	William Clinton	46

Step 1 Draw a number line. Since the least age is 42 and the greatest is 69, you can use a scale of 40 to 70 and an interval of 2.

Other scales and intervals could also be used.

40 42 44 46 48 50 52 54 56 58 60 62 64 66 68 70

A line plot does not need to start at 0.

Step 2 Put an "×" above the number that represents the age of each President. If the number is odd, place the "×" halfway between the appropriate notches.

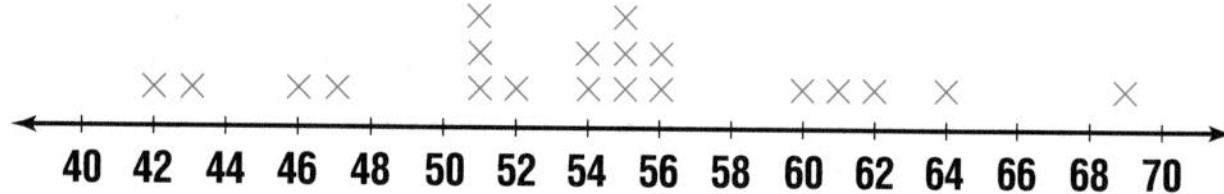

You can make some observations about the data from the line plot.

- The age that occurred most often is 55.
- There seems to be a **cluster** of data between 50 and 55. Data that are grouped closely together are called a cluster.

Motivating the Lesson

Communication Ask students to read the lesson's opening paragraphs and to review the table. Ask students to describe both the advantages and disadvantages of displaying data in a table.

Investigations for the Special Education Student

This blackline master booklet helps you plan for the needs of your special education students by providing long-term projects along with teacher notes. Investigation 2, *Commercial Success,* may be used with this chapter.

1 **Food** Restaurants often serve meals that are much larger than the "official" serving sizes shown on labels of similar store-bought items. The chart shows the fat content of typical portions of selected restaurant foods.

a. Draw a line plot of these data.

b. Are there any clusters?

Food	Fat (grams)
Pancakes	16
Blueberry muffin	18
Spaghetti with meatballs	39
French fries	26
Ranch salad dressing	21
Tuna salad sandwich	43
Ham sandwich	27
Hamburger with bun	36
Pepperoni pizza	28
Small movie popcorn	27
Chocolate chip cookie	13
Sirloin steak	20
Chicken pot pie	42

Source: *Nutrition Action Newsletter*

a. The least number of fat grams is 13, and the greatest is 43. An appropriate scale for this graph is 12 to 44 with an interval of 2.

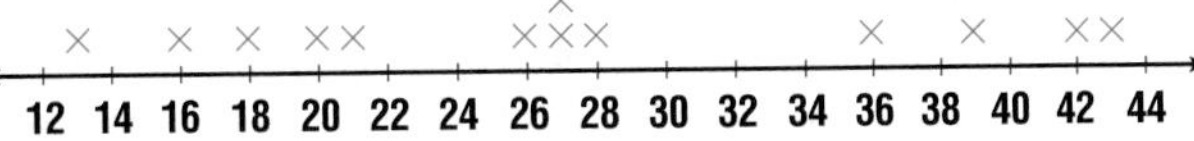

b. There is a small cluster of data from 26–28.

CONNECTION

There are 18 other ancestry groups not shown in the table. People could choose more than one ancestry.

2 **Geography** Every 10 years, the Census Bureau conducts a census of the United States population. The top 15 ancestry groups reported in the 1990 census are shown in the table.

a. Draw a line plot of the data.

b. Is there a cluster? What does this represent?

Ancestry	% of Population
Afro-American	10
American	5
American Indian	4
Dutch	3
English	13
French	4
German	23
Irish	16
Italian	6
Mexican	5
Norwegian	2
Polish	4
Scotch-Irish	2
Scottish	2
Swedish	2

Source: Bureau of the Census

a. The least number is 2, and the greatest is 23. An appropriate scale for this graph is 2 to 24 with an interval of 2.

2 4 6 8 10 12 14 16 18 20 22 24

b. There is a cluster from 2 to 6, so most of the ancestries make up between 2% and 6% of the population.

Multiple Learning Styles

Visual/Spatial Have groups of students repeat one of the following activities 10–20 times, record each distance, then create a graph, line plot, or table for the data.

- Bounce a pencil by dropping it eraser down and then measure how far it moved from where it landed.
- Toss a coin across a smooth surface and measure the distance.
- Spin a top and measure how far it moves from where it started.

2 TEACH

Transparency 3-3B contains a teaching aid for this lesson.

Thinking Algebraically To help students understand how a line plot is interpreted, have them work with partners to write questions about the line plot constructed from the ages of the Presidents. For example, can any conclusions be drawn concerning the age of the Presidents when they took office?

In-Class Examples

For Example 1

The table shows the voter turnout for the presidential elections from 1960 to 1996. Draw a line plot of these data, rounding to the nearest whole percent.

Year	Voter Turnout (%)
1960	62.8
1964	61.9
1968	60.9
1972	55.2
1976	53.5
1980	52.6
1984	53.1
1988	50.2
1992	55.9
1996	48.4

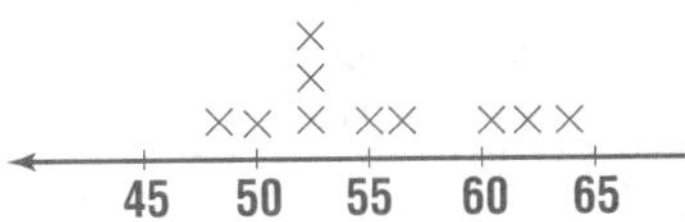

For Example 2

The table shows the number of immigrants to the United States by country of origin. Draw a line plot of the data.

Country	Number (thousands)
Russia	63
China	53
Philippines	53
Vietnam	41
India	34
Ireland	17
Canada	16

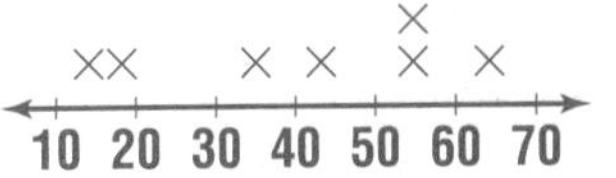

3 PRACTICE/APPLY

Check for Understanding

If students need additional practice or instruction after completing Exercises 1–5, you may find one of the following options helpful.

- Extra Practice, see p. 574
- Reteaching Activity
- *Study Guide Masters,* p. 19
- *Practice Masters,* p. 19

Assignment Guide

Core: 7–15 odd, 17–20
Enriched: 6–12 even, 14–20

Additional Answers

3.

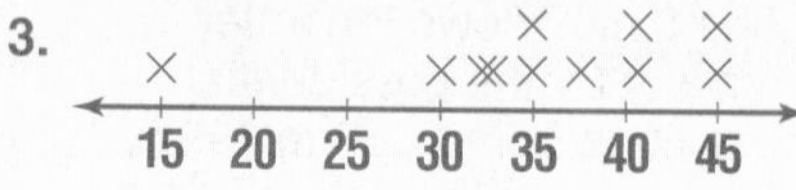

4.

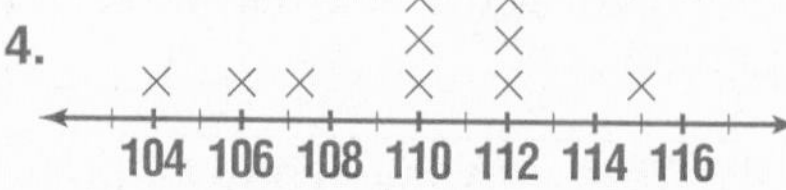

5a.

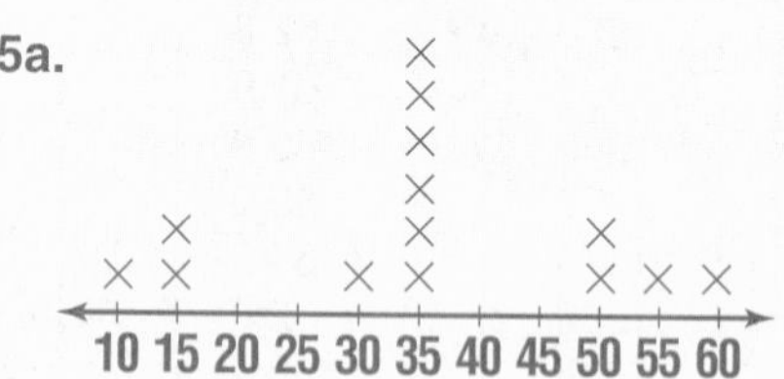

***Study Guide Masters,* p. 19**

Name ______ Date ______

Study Guide

Line Plots

Darrell surveyed some kennels to find the cost of grooming his dog. The prices given were: $25.00, $27.00, $32.00, $22.00, $43.00, $28.00, $18.00, $24.00, $25.00, $27.00, $30.00, $24.00, $22.00, $30.00, $12.00, $25.00, and $20.00.

Darrell made a line plot to organize the data on a number line. First he found the range of the data: $43.00 − $12.00 = $31.00. He chose a scale of $10.00 to $45.00 to include all of the data and an interval of $5.00 to separate the data into 7 sections. He drew an × to represent each price. For prices between marked intervals he estimated to position the ×.

The data are grouped or **clustered** between $20 and $30.

Make a line plot for each set of data.

1. 560, 790, 800, 850, 350, 760, 810, 650, 850, 790, 690, 600

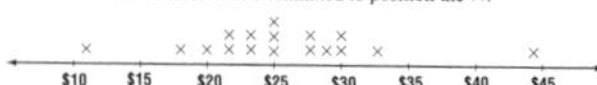

2. 1,750, 2,000, 2,450, 1,900, 1,950, 1,900, 1,900, 1,900, 1,800, 2,100, 2,000, 1,800

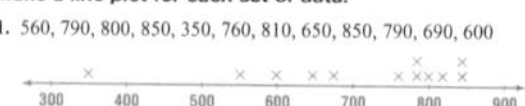

3. 7.1, 7.7, 7.8, 8.2, 8.4, 7.5, 7.8, 8.0, 8.3, 8.2, 8.4, 7.6, 8.0

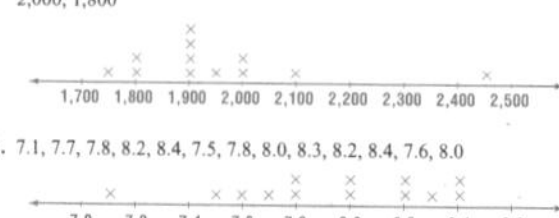

 T19 *Mathematics: Applications and Connections, Course 2*

CHECK FOR UNDERSTANDING

Communicating Mathematics

Read and study the lesson to answer each question.

1. ***Tell*** the advantage of using a line plot rather than a table to display data. **1. Sample answer: It's easier to see trends over time.**
2. ***Draw*** a line plot that displays ten pieces of data. Use a range of at least 15. Arrange the data so that there is a cluster. Then describe what the data represent. **See students' work.**

Guided Practice

Make a line plot for each set of data. **3–4. See margin.**

3. 32, 41, 45, 35, 45, 35, 15, 41, 38, 30, 33
4. 110, 112, 106, 104, 110, 112, 112, 110, 115, 107
5. ***Food*** The table shows various beverages and their caffeine content.

Beverage	Caffeine (mg)	Beverage	Caffeine (mg)
Caffè Americano (8 oz)	35	Coffee, decaf (16 oz)	15
Caffè Latte (8 oz)	35	Coffee, decaf (8 oz)	10
Caffè Mocha (8 oz)	35	Espresso (1 oz)	35
Cappuccino (8 oz)	35	Lemon Lime (12 oz)	55
Cola (12 oz)	35	Tea, bottled (12 oz)	15
Cola (16 oz)	50	Tea, instant (8 oz)	30
Cola (20 oz)	60	Tea, bag (8 oz)	50

Source: *Nutrition Action Healthletter, 1996*

a. Make a line plot of the data. **See margin.**
b. Name the cluster and describe what it tells you about the caffeine content of the items in the table. **35; Many of the items contain 35 mg of caffeine.**

EXERCISES

Practice

Make a line plot for each set of data. **6–13. See Answer Appendix.**

6. 45, 35, 50, 40, 40, 55, 30, 35, 45, 35
7. 500, 640, 600, 340, 730, 600, 520, 560, 490, 670
8. 17, 12, 30, 22, 36, 18, 18, 4, 20, 12
9. 1990, 1993, 1995, 1995, 1994, 1995, 1990, 1999, 1988, 1992, 1999
10. 3.8, 4.0, 3.2, 3.6, 3.7, 3.3, 3.2, 3.0, 4.0, 3.6, 3.2
11. 101, 110, 103, 111, 111, 102, 110, 101, 105, 107, 110, 108
12. Make a line plot of the test scores: 84, 100, 89, 88, 83, 90, 97, 100, 89, 90, 90, 80, 91, 95. Name any clusters.
13. Make a line plot of shampoo prices: $2.40, $2.80, $2.50, $2.35, $3.25, $2.75, $2.50, $3.00, $3.25.

Reteaching the Lesson

Activity Ask students how to determine how many magazine articles most of their classmates read every month. Then take a survey to find how many articles each student read in the last month. Have students make a line plot of the data and note any clusters.

Error Analysis

Watch for students who don't align the x's in vertical columns.

Prevent by having students make their line plots using graph paper or lined paper oriented so that the lines are vertical.

Applications and Problem Solving

14a. 6,550; Sample answer: 0–7,000; 500

14c. The data appear to cluster from 0 to 1,000.

15b. A majority of the players lose between 7.5 and 9 pounds during the game.

16a–b. See margin.

14. ***Geography*** The table shows the approximate square miles of water in fifteen states.

State	Water (sq mi)	State	Water (sq mi)
Colorado	350	New Hampshire	400
Georgia	1,500	South Dakota	1,200
Illinois	2,300	Tennessee	900
Iowa	400	Texas	6,700
Kansas	450	Utah	2,700
Maryland	2,600	Virginia	3,200
Montana	150	Wyoming	700
Nevada	750		

Source: *Statistical Abstract*

a. Find the range and determine the scale and an interval.

b. Make a line plot of the data. **See Answer Appendix.**

c. Do the data cluster in one area?

15. ***Health*** Professional basketball players can lose as much as 12 pounds of water each game. The list shows the number of pounds lost by twelve players during one game.

3, 4, 2, 11, 10.5, 8, 8.5, 7.5, 9, 10, 8.5, 9

a. Make a line plot of the data. **See margin.**

b. What conclusions can you draw from your graph?

16. ***Food*** Refer to Example 1. The chart shows the fat content of the "official" serving size of each store-bought food item.

a. Draw a line plot of the data.

b. Compare this line plot to the line plot in Example 1. What conclusions could you make, based on these line plots?

Food	Fat (grams)
Pancakes	6
Blueberry muffin	8
Spaghetti with meatballs	5
French fries	10
Ranch salad dressing	11
Tuna salad sandwich	17
Ham sandwich	8
Hamburger with bun	19
Pepperoni pizza	11
Small movie popcorn	11
Chocolate chip cookie	8
Sirloin steak	8
Chicken pot pie	16

17. ***Critical Thinking*** Compare a line plot to a bar graph.

a. How is a line plot similar to a bar graph? **a–b. See margin.**

b. How is it different?

c. Which do you think is easier to construct? Explain.

Mixed Review

17c. See students' work.

18. ***Elections*** On the day before the class elections, 100 students were asked who they would choose for class president. The graph shows the results. Who do you think will win? *(Lesson 3-2)* **Ana**

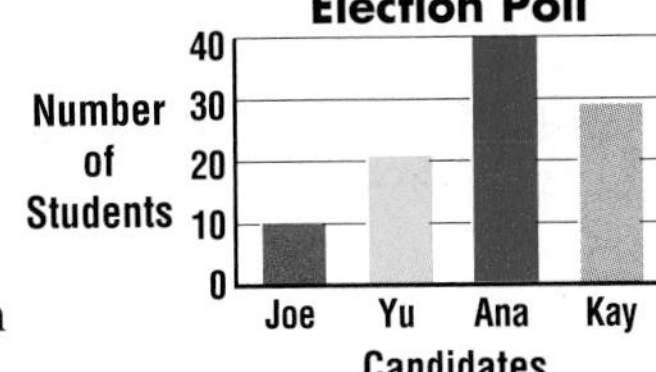

19. **Standardized Test Practice** The length of a pencil is about — *(Lesson 2-8)* **B**

A 6 millimeters.

B 6 centimeters.

C 6 meters.

D 6 kilometers.

For **Extra Practice,** see page 575.

20. Write 4.23232323… using bar notation. *(Lesson 2-7)* **$4.\overline{23}$**

4 ASSESS

Closing Activity

Speaking Ask students to explain what statistical facts about a set of data can be seen easily in a line plot that are not clearly shown by tables such as those presented in this lesson.

Additional Answers

15a.

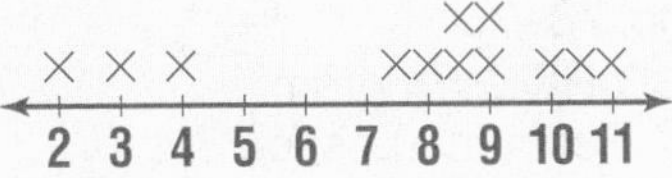

16a.

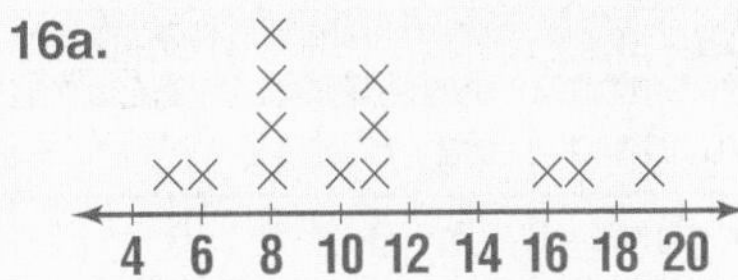

16b. In this line plot, the data are clustered at 8 and between 10–11. The fat content of an official serving size is much smaller than a restaurant portion of food.

17a. They both can show the number of times data occur.

17b. A line plot shows points of data. A bar graph can show intervals of data.

Practice Masters, p. 19

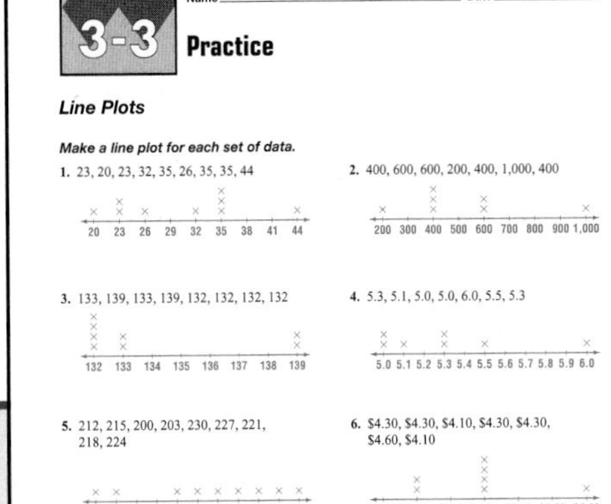

Name______ Date______

3-3 Practice

Line Plots

Make a line plot for each set of data.

1. 23, 20, 23, 32, 35, 26, 35, 35, 44

2. 400, 600, 600, 200, 400, 1,000, 400

3. 133, 139, 133, 139, 132, 132, 132, 132

4. 5.3, 5.1, 5.0, 5.0, 6.0, 5.5, 5.3

5. 212, 215, 200, 203, 230, 227, 221, 218, 224

6. \$4.30, \$4.30, \$4.10, \$4.30, \$4.30, \$4.60, \$4.10

7. Tom was born in 1958. His brothers and sisters were born in 1950, 1970, 1952, 1955, 1953 and 1956.

a. Make a line plot for the birth years.

b. Describe the plot in terms of range and scale.

c. What have you learned about Tom's family?

The range of the data is 20 years. The scale is 1950 to 1971. Tom has five siblings just a few years older than he is and one much younger.

 T19 *Mathematics: Applications and Connections, Course 2*

Extending the Lesson

Enrichment Masters, p. 19

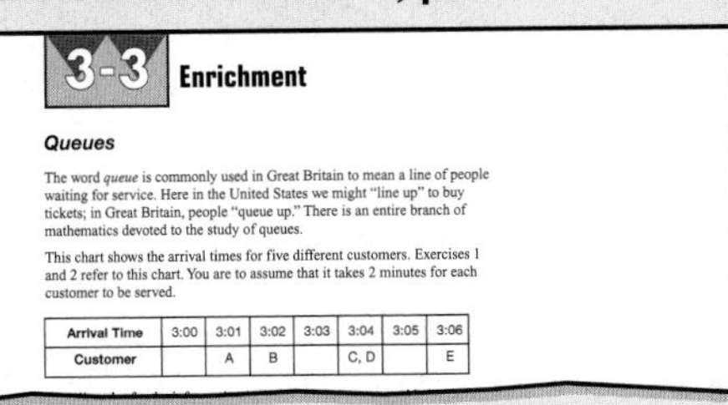

3-3 Enrichment

Queues

The word *queue* is commonly used in Great Britain to mean a line of people waiting for service. Here in the United States we might "line up" to buy tickets; in Great Britain, people "queue up." There is an entire branch of mathematics devoted to the study of queues.

This chart shows the arrival times for five different customers. Exercises 1 and 2 refer to this chart. You are to assume that it takes 2 minutes for each customer to be served.

Arrival Time	3:00	3:01	3:02	3:03	3:04	3:05	3:06
Customer		A	B		C, D		E

Activity Have students work with partners to construct bar graphs using data provided in the lesson. Ask the students to compare their bar graphs with their line plots of the same data. Ask them to tell which way of visualizing the data is more useful and to explain why they think so.

3-4 Lesson Notes

Instructional Resources

- *Study Guide Masters,* p. 20
- *Practice Masters,* p. 20
- *Enrichment Masters,* p. 20
- Transparencies 3-4, A and B
- *Assessment and Evaluation Masters,* pp. 70, 71
- *Classroom Games,* pp. 9–11
- *Technology Masters,* p. 31
- *Science and Math Lab Manual,* pp. 73–76

CD-ROM Program

- Resource Lesson 3-4

Recommended Pacing	
Standard	Day 6 of 12
Honors	Day 6 of 11
Block	Day 3 of 6

1 FOCUS

5-Minute Check (Lesson 3-3)

Make a line plot for each set of data.

1. 4, 6, 4, 5, 6, 6, 3, 11, 6, 7

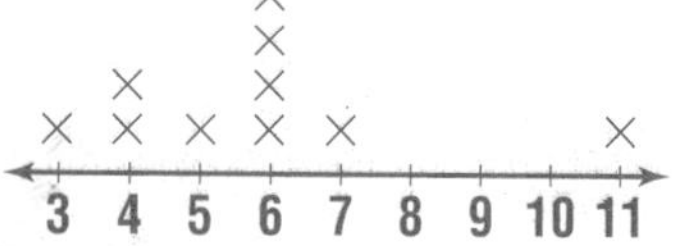

2. 20, 25, 15, 30, 35, 20, 25, 15, 25, 30

3. 85, 75, 80, 55, 70, 70, 70

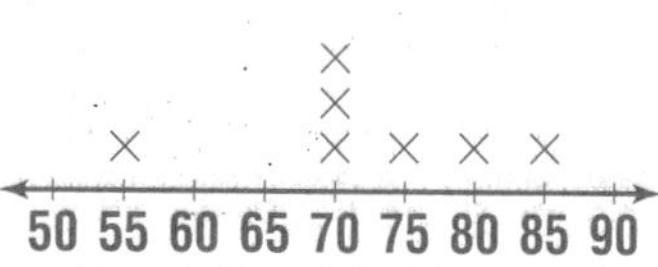

The 5-Minute Check is also available on **Transparency 3-4A** for this lesson.

3-4 Mean, Median, and Mode

What you'll learn

You'll learn to find the mean, median, and mode of a set of data.

When am I ever going to use this?

You can use mean to find the average of your test scores.

Word Wise

mean
arithmetic average
mode
median

Priscilla's allowance is \$6 per week, and she wants to ask her parents to increase it. She surveyed other students in her class to see how much they get for an allowance. The results are shown below.

\$15, \$0, \$5, \$10, \$3, \$4, \$10, \$6, \$5, \$10, \$0, \$6, \$8, \$8, \$15

In mathematics, there are three common ways to summarize the data with a single number: the mean, the mode, and the median. These are all types of averages.

Mean	The mean of a set of data is the arithmetic average.

The **mean**, or **arithmetic average**, is found by adding the numbers in the data set and dividing by the number of items in the set.

$$\text{mean} = \frac{15 + 0 + 5 + 10 + 3 + 4 + 10 + 6 + 5 + 10 + 0 + 6 + 8 + 8 + 15}{15}$$

$$= \frac{105}{15} \text{ or } 7$$ The mean allowance is \$7 per week.

Mode	The mode of a set of data is the number(s) or item(s) that appear most often.

A line plot of the survey results can quickly give you the mode.

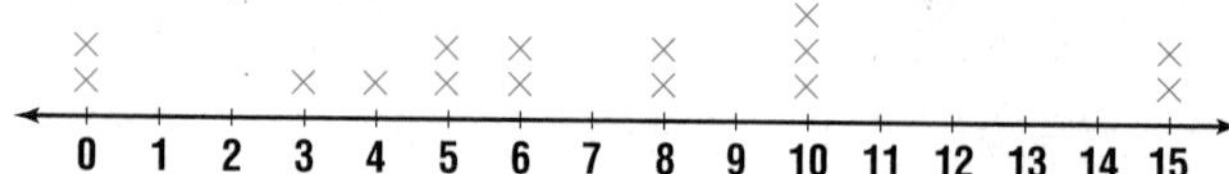

The **mode** is \$10 because \$10 occurs most often.

Study Hint

Technology You can use a graphing calculator to find the mean and median. Press STAT 1 and enter the data into list L1. Then press STAT ▶ 1 ENTER. $\bar{x}$ is the mean, and Med is the median.

Median	The median is the middle number in a set of data when the data are arranged in numerical order.

The **median** can also be found by using the line plot. Since there are 15 numbers, the eighth number is the median. If you count from either end of the plot, you will find that the eighth data point is 6.

Note that the mean, the median, and the mode for this set of data are all different. Priscilla could use the mode to argue that more kids get \$10 for an allowance than any other amount. She could also say that the average student's allowance is \$7.

Motivating the Lesson

Problem Solving A store owner is studying her sales records before placing an order for more CDs. She must decide which CD to order the most of from 20 available groups. Ask students whether she should use the mode, the median, or the mean to help her decide.

1 **Meteorology** **The high temperatures (°F) in Nashville, Tennessee, for the first week in April were 68°, 65°, 60°, 62°, 67°, 72°, and 71°. Find the mean, mode, and median.**

mean Calculate the arithmetic average.

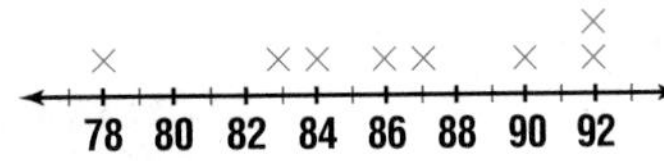

÷ 7) 66.42857143 The mean is about 66.

mode None, since each temperature occurs only once.

median 60, 62, 65, 67, 68, 71, 72 *Arrange the numbers in order.*

Since there are 7 numbers, the median is the fourth number, or 67.

APPLICATION

2 **School** **Darrell's test scores for the first grading period are graphed on the line plot. How might he use the mean, mode, or median of the data to describe his scores to his parents? Is this statistic an accurate description?**

78 80 82 84 86 88 90 92

Explore Which statistic would make the test scores appear better? This would be the greatest number.

Plan Find the mean, mode, and median of the test scores and find which is the greatest.

Solve mean $= \frac{78 + 83 + 84 + 86 + 87 + 90 + 92 + 92}{8}$ or $\frac{692}{8}$ or 86.5

mode = 92, since it occurred most often

Since there is an even number of data points, the median is the mean of the two middle numbers, 86 and 87.

78, 83, 84, 86, 87, 90, 92, 92

The mean of 86 and 87 is 86.5. Therefore, the median is 86.5. Since the mode is the greatest, Darrell might use this statistic to describe his test scores.

Examine The mode, 92, is not an accurate description of Darrell's test scores since all his other scores were less than 92.

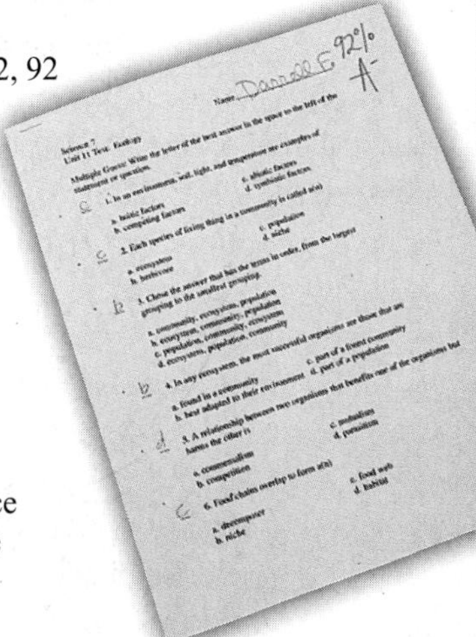

For this particular data set, the mean and the median are the same. Thus, 86.5 might be a better indicator of his score.

2 TEACH

Transparency 3-4B contains a teaching aid for this lesson.

Reading Mathematics Before students have read the lesson, discuss with them the meaning of the word *average* as it is used in daily situations. Have them give examples of how statements using the word *average* can be interpreted in different ways. You may wish to start the discussion by writing the phrase "average amount of homework" on the chalkboard. Ask students what *average* might mean in that phrase. Then discuss the meaning of *arithmetic average.*

Teaching Tip You can also use a graphing calculator to enter data and automatically compute the mean and median of the data. You can sort the data to find the mode(s).

In-Class Examples

For Example 1
The daily rainfall (in.) in Barnesville from Sunday to Saturday was 0.0, 0.8, 1.4, 0.2, 0.0, 0.6, and 1.1. Find the mean, mode, and median. **0.6, 0.0, 0.6**

For Example 2
Alonzo's science test scores for the second half of the year are 70, 85, 76, 81, 97, 85, and 88. Find the mode, median, and mean. **mode: 85; median: 85; mean: about 83**

Teaching Tip For Example 2, point out how the mode can be misleading, since the highest score was the only one to occur twice.

3 PRACTICE/APPLY

Check for Understanding

If students need additional practice or instruction after completing Exercises 1–7, one of these options may be helpful.

- Extra Practice, see p. 575
- Reteaching Activity
- *Study Guide Masters,* p. 20
- *Practice Masters,* p. 20

Assignment Guide	
Core:	9–17 odd, 20–23
Enriched:	8–16 even, 17, 18, 20–23
All:	Self Test, 1–5

Exercise 19 asks students to advance to the next stage of work on the Chapter Project. Ask students to write a paragraph explaining why a movie producer might be interested in this data before starting production of a new film.

Additional Answers

1a. List the data in ascending order. Choose the middle number.

1b. List the data in ascending order. Find the mean of the two middle numbers.

***Study Guide Masters,* p. 20**

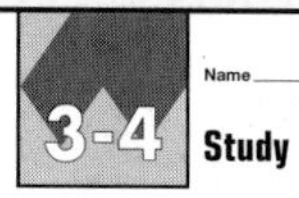

Name________________ Date________

Study Guide

Mean, Median, and Mode

To find the **mean,** or arithmetic average, of a set of numbers, find the sum of the numbers and divide by the number of items in the set.

To find the **median** of a set of numbers, arrange the numbers in order from least to greatest and find the middle number.

To find the **mode** of a set of numbers, find the number or item that appears most often.

Length of Nine Ladybugs (in inches)		
0.30	0.28	0.34
0.32	0.30	0.31
0.34	0.34	0.30

Example **Find the mean, median, and mode of the ladybug lengths.**

mean $\frac{0.30 + 0.28 + 0.34 + 0.32 + 0.30 + 0.31 + 0.34 + 0.34 + 0.30}{9} \approx 0.31$

mode There are two modes for the data, 0.30 and 0.34.

median 0.28, 0.30, 0.30, 0.30, 0.31, 0.32, 0.34, 0.34, 0.34,
↑ median

Find the mean, mode(s), and median for each set of data.

1. 6, 3, 7, 1, 8, 4, 8, 9, 4, 5.6; 4 and 8; 6
2. 5.6, 3.2, 7.1, 7.7, 9.0, 6.0, 5.3, 3.2, 4.2 5.7; 3.2; 5.6
3. 70, 55, 42, 31, 78, 93, 54, 75, 35, 41, 64 58; no mode; 55
4. 2,300, 2,350, 2,240, 2,500, 2,300 2,338; 2,300; 2,300
5. 21, 56, 34, 27, 42, 21, 77, 41, 77 44; 21 and 77; 41
6. 450, 370, 190, 220, 540, 560, 270, 110, 230 326.7; no mode; 270

 T20 *Mathematics: Applications and Connections, Course 2*

CHECK FOR UNDERSTANDING

Communicating Mathematics

1a–b. See margin.

2a–c. Sample answers given.

2b. 1, 1, 2, 2, 4

Read and study the lesson to answer each question.

1. ***Tell*** how you would find each of the following from a set of data.
   a. the median, if there is an odd number of items
   b. the median, if there is an even number of items
2. ***Write a Problem*** in which a set of data meets each condition.
   a. one mode **2, 2, 3** b. two modes c. no modes **1, 2, 3, 4**
3. ***You Decide*** Cynthia says that if the mean, median, and mode of a set of data are equal, then all the numbers in the set must be the same. Erica says that this is not always true. Who is correct? Explain. **See margin.**

Guided Practice

5. 8.95, none, 9.05

Find the mean, mode(s), and median for each set of data.

4. 2, 6, 7, 4, 3, 5, 7, 8 **5.25, 7, 5.5**
5. 8.0, 9.1, 8.9, 9.0, 9.3, 9.4
6. **28, 20, 20**

Length of Stoplights (s)	Tally	Number of Stoplights
10	|||	3
20	卌	5
30	||	2
40	|||	3
50	|	1
60	|	1

7. ***Shoes*** The manager of a shoe store keeps a record of the sizes of each athletic shoe sold. When she is ready to place an order, she uses the information to decide what sizes she needs. Which number is probably most useful to her, the mean, mode, or median? Explain. **The mode, because it appears most often.**

EXERCISES

Practice

8. 16, 17, 17
9. 93, 90 and 94, 93
10. $4\frac{2}{5}$, 3 and 5, $4\frac{1}{2}$
11. $65\frac{1}{2}$, 65, 65
15. 90.95, 95, 95

Find the mean, mode(s), and median for each set of data.

8. 17, 13, 18, 20, 17, 15, 12
9. 90, 92, 94, 91, 90, 94, 95, 98
10. 2, 7, 1, 5, 8, 3, 5, 4, 6, 3
11. 56, 65, 57, 75, 76, 66, 65, 64
12. 14, 80, 78, 25, 30, 59, 69, 55, 25, 59, 50, 59 **$50\frac{1}{4}$, 59, 57**
13. 1,780; 1,755; 1,755; 1,805; 1,805 **1,780; 1,755 and 1,805; 1,780**
14. number of minutes spent on homework **51, 35, 50**

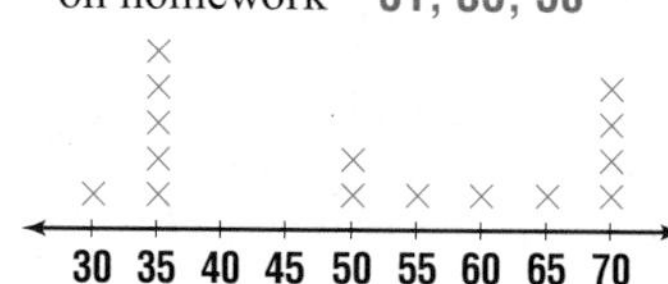

15.

Quiz Score	Tally	Number
100	||||	4
95	卌 ||	7
90	|||	3
85	||||	4
80	||	2
75	|	1

16. Find the mean, mode, and median for 16, 4, 14, 5, 15, 9, 7, 7, 14, 2. **9.3, 7 and 14, 8**

Reteaching the Lesson

Activity Ask 10 students how long it took to get to school. Have students arrange the data from least to greatest. Discuss what is meant by *mode.* Then introduce *median* as the middle-most number in the list. Have students use calculators to find the mean.

Additional Answer

3. Erica; the data do not all have to be the same for the mean, median, and mode to be equal. For example, in the set 7, 8, 8, 9, the mean, median, and mode all equal 8.

Applications and Problem Solving

17. ***Literature*** In *The Phantom Tollbooth,* a boy visits a place called Digitopolis, where each family has 2.58 children. National statistics often report American family size using a "fractional size" family. Do you think they are using the mode, median, or mean? Is this the most informative way to report family size? Explain why or why not. **See Answer Appendix.**

18. ***Space*** Find the mean, mode, and median for the length of the space shuttle flights (in days) from February, 1994 to March, 1996. **10.82, 8, 10**

    8, 14, 11, 14, 10, 11, 10, 8, 16, 9, 8, 10, 15, 8, 8, 15, 9

19. mean: \$331.0 million; median: \$310.9 million

19. ***Working on the CHAPTER Project*** Refer to the table on page 87. Find the mean and median of the ticket sales.

20. ***Critical Thinking*** A data set contains 50, 100, 75, 60, 75, 1,000, 90, 100, 125, and 75. Without calculating, would the mean, median, or mode be most affected by eliminating 1,000 from the list? Which would be the least affected? Explain. **See margin.**

Mixed Review

21. ***Nutrition*** The grams of fiber in 15 different cereals are 5, 5, 4, 3, 3, 3, 1, 1, 1, 2, 1, 1, 1, 1 and 0. Make a line plot of the data. *(Lesson 3-3)* **See Answer Appendix.**

22. Solve $a = 0.8 \div 0.04$. *(Lesson 2-6)* **20**

23. **Standardized Test Practice** Which expression is equivalent to 6×2^3? *(Lesson 1-4)* **C**

    A 6×4 **B** $12 \times 12 \times 12$

    C $6 \times 2 \times 2 \times 2$ **D** $6 \times 6 \times 6 \times 2 \times 2 \times 2$

For **Extra Practice,** see page 575.

CHAPTER 3 Mid-Chapter Self Test

1. Find the range for the following set of data. Choose an appropriate scale and interval. 12, 15, 23, 20, 18, 19, 10, 15, 20, 11 *(Lesson 3-1)* **13; Sample answer: 10-24, 2**

2. ***Use a Graph*** How much more money is spent on photography than design? *(Lesson 3-2A)* **\$279.55**

Publishing Budget for School Newspaper

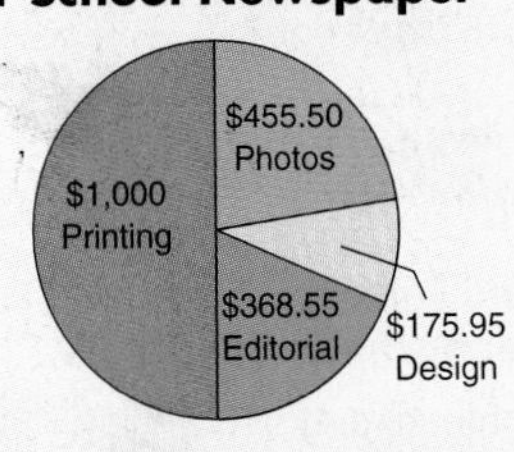

3. ***Agriculture*** The production of cotton in the United States is shown in the graph. Predict the number of bales that will be produced in the year 2000. *(Lesson 3-2)*

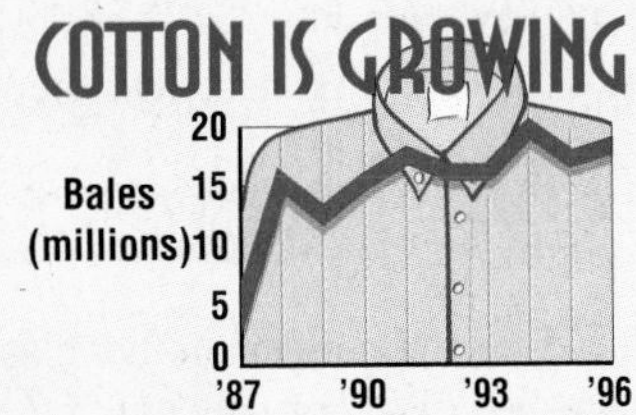

Source: Agriculture Department

Sample answer: 25 million bales

4. See Answer Appendix.

4. Make a line plot of the data: 48, 50, 44, 52, 46, 45, 45, 48, 45, 46. *(Lesson 3-3)*

5. Find the mean, mode(s), and median for the data set in Exercise 4. *(Lesson 3-4)* **46.9, 45, 46**

4 ASSESS

Closing Activity

Writing Have students create a set of data using information from their daily lives. Have them find the mode(s), median, and mean of the data.

Chapter 3, Quiz B (Lessons 3-3 and 3-4) is available in the *Assessment and Evaluation Masters,* p. 71.

Mid-Chapter Test (Lessons 3-1 through 3-4) is available in the *Assessment and Evaluation Masters,* p. 70.

Mid-Chapter Self Test

The Mid-Chapter Self Test reviews the concepts in Lessons 3-1 through 3-4. Lesson references are given so students can review concepts not yet mastered.

Additional Answer

20. The mean would be most affected; the mode would be the least affected, since it would not change.

Practice Masters, p. 20

Name______ Date______

3-4 Practice

Mean, Median, and Mode

Find the mean, mode(s), and median for each set of data.

1. 31, 18, 19, 18, 18, 17, 12
   mean: 19; mode: 18; median: 18
2. 5, 0, 9, 9, 3, 0, 5, 5, 4
   mean: 4.4; mode: 5; median: 5
3. 81, 81, 83, 84, 83, 85, 86
   mean: 83.3; modes: 81, 83; median: 83
4. 77, 70, 65, 62, 65, 80, 85
   mean: 72; mode: 65; median: 70
5. 5, 6, 3, 9, 0, 4, 1, 2, 7
   mean: 4.1; mode: none; median: 4
6. 9, 9, 3, 2, 8, 7, 1, 1, 8
   mean: 5.3; modes: 1, 8, and 9; median: 7
7. 24, 33, 43, 44, 23, 41, 40
   mean: 35.4; mode: none; median: 40
8. 77, 76, 55, 76, 66, 58, 55
   mean: 66.1; modes: 76, 55; median: 66
9. 3.8, 4.2, 4.0, 4.2, 4.2
   mean: 4.1; mode: 4.2; median: 4.2
10. 8.1, 9.0, 9.1, 8.4, 8.4, 8.4, 8.4
    mean: 8.5; mode: 8.4; median: 8.4
11. 1,220, 1,440, 1,220, 1,660, 1,660
    mean: 1,440; modes: 1,220, 1,660; median: 1,440
12. 3,200, 3,100, 3,100, 3,000, 3,300
    mean: 3,140; mode: 3,100; median: 3,100

Use the table at the right to answer the following.

Money spent on Research and Development in Selected Countries (billions of dollars)		
Country	Military	Civilian
United States	37.3	79.4
United Kingdom	3.5	8.5
France	3.5	14.6
West Germany	1.4	26.1
Japan	0.3	44.0

13. Find the mean, mode(s), and median of the five countries military research and development spending.
    mean: \$9.2 billion; mode: \$3.5 billion; median: \$3.5 billion
14. Find the mean, mode, and median of the countries' civilian research and development spending.
    mean: \$34.52 billion; mode: none; median: \$26.1 billion

 T20 *Mathematics: Applications and Connections, Course 2*

Extending the Lesson

Enrichment Masters, p. 20

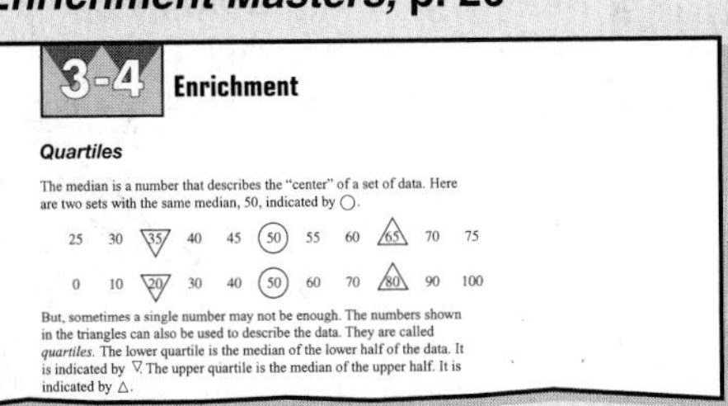

3-4 Enrichment

Quartiles

The median is a number that describes the "center" of a set of data. Here are two sets with the same median, 50, indicated by ○.

25 30 ▽35 40 45 ○50 55 60 △65 70 75

0 10 ▽20 30 40 ○50 60 70 △80 90 100

But, sometimes a single number may not be enough. The numbers shown in the triangles can also be used to describe the data. They are called *quartiles.* The lower quartile is the median of the lower half of the data. It is indicated by ▽. The upper quartile is the median of the upper half. It is indicated by △.

Activity Have students write three problems involving averages of sets of data, one for which the mode is the most descriptive measure, one for which the median is most descriptive, and one for which the mean is the most descriptive measure. Have students solve each other's problems.

3-4B HANDS-ON LAB Notes

GET READY

Objective Students use mean, median, and mode to describe a set of data.

Optional Resources
Hands-On Lab Masters
- worksheet, p. 41

Manipulative Kit
- rulers

MANAGEMENT TIPS

Recommended Time
30 minutes

Getting Started Work with students to list 10 characteristics that might describe the average student. Ask whether the five questions listed are all important in determining "average" characteristics.

The **Activity** demonstrates that determining "average" depends upon what questions are asked. Note that not all questions will have numerical values for answers. In this case, the mode will best describe the data.

ASSESS

Have students complete Exercises 1–3. After answering the questions, ask students to suggest uses for the information they have compiled. Why might certain businesses, political groups, or others be interested in the data?

Additional Answer

1. Sample answer: You would probably not get exactly the same results, but the average student would probably be similar.

HANDS-ON LAB

COOPERATIVE LEARNING

3-4B Are You Average?

A Follow-Up of Lesson 3-4

 markers

 ruler

How would you describe an "average" student in your school? The average student in your school may vary quite a bit from the average student in another school. In this lab, you will find out what the average student in your math class is like.

TRY THIS

Work together as a class.

Step 1 List at least ten questions you would like to ask to help you describe what the "average" student is like. For example:

What is your height in inches?
What is your age in months?
How many children are in your family?
What is your favorite TV program?
What is your favorite extracurricular activity?

Step 2 Prepare a survey with your ten questions. Each student in the class should complete the survey.

Work in groups of three.

Step 3 Each group should take at least two of the questions and compile the data in a frequency table or on a line plot.

Step 4 Find the mean, mode, median, and range of the data for each question. Decide which one best describes each set of data and justify your choices.

Step 5 Compile the results of all the groups. Choose an appropriate graph to display your data.

Step 6 Make a poster that describes the "average" student in the classroom.

ON YOUR OWN

1. If you surveyed students in another class in your school, would you expect the same results? Why or why not? **1–2. See margin for sample answers.**
2. If you designed another survey, which questions would you change and why?
3. ***Reflect Back*** **a–b. Sample answers are given.**
   a. Which did you use to represent your data, the mean, mode, median, or range? Explain why. **The median; it averages the data.**
   b. Which graph did you use to display your data? Explain why you chose that graph. **Line plots; they show the distribution graphically.**

Additional Answer

2. Answer should include the questions student would change and their reasons. Sample answer: I would not ask the opinion questions "What is your favorite TV program" and "What is your favorite extracurricular activity" because I want to know what a biologically average student is like.

Have students write a paragraph discussing different meanings of the word *average,* expressing their view of which sense of *average* is most meaningful.

Let the Games Begin

Can You Guess?

Math Skill
Finding the Mean

Get Ready This game is for the entire class divided into 3-person teams.

- self adhesive notes
- coins
- cup
- water droppers

Get Set Fill the cup with water. Draw a number line on the chalkboard with a scale from 0 to 15.

Go

- Each team tries to see how many drops of water they can get to stay on the head of a dime. Write the results on a self-adhesive note. Post it on the chalkboard above the appropriate place on a number line.
- Use the information on the chalkboard to predict how many drops of water will fit on the head of a penny. Record your prediction.
- Find how many drops of water you can get to stay on the head of a penny. Post the results and find the mean. If your prediction is within five drops of the mean, your team gets to stay in the game.
- Repeat using a nickel. Continue predicting and testing using different coins. The teams left at the end of the game win.

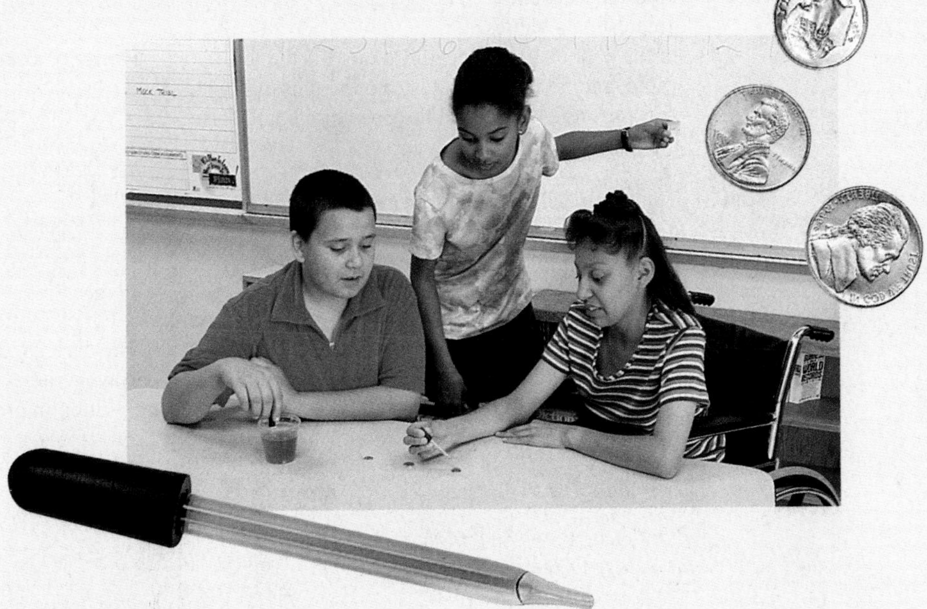

interNET CONNECTION Visit www.glencoe.com/sec/math/mac/mathnet for more games.

Let the Games Begin

Ask students whether the mean, median, or mode is most useful in predicting how many drops will fit on a coin. Have them explain their answers.

3-5 Lesson Notes

Instructional Resources

- *Study Guide Masters,* p. 21
- *Practice Masters,* p. 21
- *Enrichment Masters,* p. 21
- Transparencies 3-5, A and B

- CD-ROM Program
  - Resource Lesson 3-5

Recommended Pacing	
Standard	Day 7 of 12
Honors	Day 7 of 11
Block	Day 4 of 6

1 FOCUS

5-Minute Check
(Lesson 3-4)

Find the mean, mode(s), and median for each set of data.

1. 2, 6, 5, 6, 7, 8, 3, 2, 6 **5; 6; 6**
2. 54, 73, 63, 55, 74, 64, 62, 63 **63.5; 63; 63**
3. 1,255; 1,280; 1,305; 1,305; 1,255 **1,280; 1,255 and 1,305; 1,280**

The 5-Minute Check is also available on **Transparency 3-5A** for this lesson.

Motivating the Lesson

Communication Ask students to state the number of tens and the number of ones in each of the following measurements.

- 84 cm **8 tens, 4 ones**
- 6 ft **0 tens, 6 ones**
- 37 mm **3 tens, 7 ones**

2 TEACH

Transparency 3-5B contains a teaching aid for this lesson.

Using Discussion Have students work in groups of six to measure one another's height. Then have them make a stem-and-leaf plot of the heights. Discuss advantages of stem-and-leaf plots with students, focusing on how the plots make it easy to find outliers and data that form a cluster. The mode(s) and median are also easily found.

3-5 Stem-and-Leaf Plots

What you'll learn

You'll learn to construct and interpret stem-and-leaf plots.

When am I ever going to use this?

You can use a stem-and-leaf plot to record data in science experiments.

Word Wise

stem-and-leaf plot
stem
leaf
back-to-back stem-and-leaf plot

Which countries do you think consume the most pasta each year? Many people would guess that Italy tops the list, but would you have guessed that Venezuela is second? The data can be displayed in a **stem-and-leaf-plot**.

In a stem-and-leaf plot, the last digit can be used for the **leaves**, and the digits in front of it can be used as the **stems**.

Follow these steps to make a stem-and-leaf plot of the data.

Country (EU = European Union)	Pasta per Person Each Year (lb)
Argentina	15
Australia	5
Canada	14
Egypt	15
France (EU)	15
Germany (EU)	10
Greece (EU)	19
Italy (EU)	59
Japan	3
Mexico	8
Netherlands (EU)	9
Portugal (EU)	15
Russia	15
Spain (EU)	9
Sweden (EU)	8
Switzerland (EU)	20
Turkey	11
United Kingdom (EU)	4
United States	20
Venezuela	28

Source: National Pasta & National Restaurant Associations

Step 1 Find the least and greatest data values. In the data on pasta consumption, 3 is the least value, and 59 is the greatest. So the tens digits will form the stems, and the ones digits will form the leaves.

Step 2 The stems will be the digits in front of the final digit: that is, the digit in the tens place. List the digits 0 to 5 in order from least to greatest.

Stem	Leaf
0	
1	
2	
3	
4	
5	

Step 3 The leaves are the digits in the ones place for each stem. For example, there are three numbers that have a 2 in the tens place. They are 28, 20, and 20. The 8, 0, and 0 are the leaves for the stem 2. Always write every leaf, even if it is a repeat of another leaf. The leaves are written in order from least to greatest.

Step 4 Include a key to the data.

On the stem-and-leaf plot, it is easy to see that 59 pounds is by far the greatest amount.

Stem	Leaf
0	3 4 5 8 8 9 9
1	0 1 4 5 5 5 5 5 9
2	0 0 8
3	
4	
5	9

5 | 9 = 59 pounds

Multiple Learning Styles

Verbal/Linguistic Have students research to find the heights in feet and in number of stories of well-known buildings as well as buildings in your area. Make a table of this information. Then make a stem-and-leaf plot to display the data. Finally, write a summary of the data.

You can use a **back-to-back stem-and-leaf plot** to compare two sets of data. In this type of plot, the leaves for one set of data are on one side of the stems, and the leaves for the other set of data are on the other side of the stems. Two keys to the data are needed.

Food **Refer to the beginning of the lesson. Make a back-to-back stem-and-leaf plot to compare pasta consumption in European Union (EU) countries and nonmember countries.**

European Union	Stem	Nonmembers
9 9 8 4	0	3 5 8
9 5 5 0	1	1 4 5 5 5
0	2	0 8
	3	
	4	
9	5	
9 | 5 = 59 pounds		*2 | 0 = 20 pounds*

Notice that the greatest data for each stem are always the outermost leaves.

The back-to-back stem-and-leaf plot shows that pasta consumption in most European Union and nonmember countries is between 0 and 20 pounds per person each year. The greatest number of countries fall in the interval 10-19 under nonmembers.

CHECK FOR UNDERSTANDING

Communicating Mathematics

Read and study the lesson to answer each question. **1–2. See margin.**

1. ***Compare and contrast*** a stem-and-leaf plot and a bar graph.
2. ***Give two examples*** of data that could be organized in a back-to-back stem-and-leaf plot. Why would you choose a back-to-back stem-and-leaf plot?

3. ***Find*** some data that you find interesting in a magazine, newspaper, or on the Internet. Make a stem-and-leaf plot of the data. Write a few sentences in your journal about the results. **See students' work.**

Guided Practice

4. Refer to the stem-and-leaf plot in the Example.
   a. What is the smallest average amount of pasta consumed by each person in the European Union? **4 lb**
   b. Would you say that, in general, European Union countries consume more or less pasta than nonmember countries? Explain. **See margin.**

Write the stems that would be used in a stem-and-leaf plot for each set of data. Then make the stem-and-leaf plot. **5–6. See Answer Appendix.**

5. 28, 32, 38, 30, 31, 13, 36, 35, 38, 32, 38, 15, 13, 24
6. 80, 80, 69, 93, 66, 55, 95, 63, 90, 93, 60, 91, 67, 60, 56, 70, 96, 62

Reteaching the Lesson

Activity Write a stem-and-leaf plot on the chalkboard, leaving spaces between the leaves. Point to the various leaves and have students state the two-digit numbers they represent. Then name several two-digit numbers and have students add the leaves in the correct spaces in the plot.

Error Analysis
Watch for students who omit data when making a stem-and-leaf plot.
Prevent by having students count to see that the number of leaves and the number of data items are the same.

In-Class Example

For the Example
Make a back-to-back stem-and-leaf plot to compare the birth dates of Mrs. Jensen's students.
Boys—22, 18, 9, 3, 5, 28, 11
Girls—9, 3, 8, 27, 15, 6, 31

Boys	Stem	Girls
9 5 3	0	3 6 8 9
8 1	1	5
8 2	2	7
8 | 2 = 28	3	1 *3 | 1 = 31*

3 PRACTICE/APPLY

Check for Understanding

If students need additional practice or instruction after completing Exercises 1–7, you may find one of the following options helpful.

- Extra Practice, see p. 575
- Reteaching Activity
- *Transition Booklet,* pp. 5–6
- *Study Guide Masters,* p. 21
- *Practice Masters,* p. 21

Additional Answers

1. Both a stem-and-leaf plot and a bar graph show the frequency of data occurring. However, a stem-and-leaf plot shows individual data values and a bar graph shows only a bar for each interval with the length representing the number of data in the interval.
2. Sample answers: Scores of tests 1 and 2, heights of boys and girls in a class; a back-to-back stem-and-leaf plot is used to compare two sets of data.

4b. Sample answer: The stems 0 and 1 have the most leaves on both sides of the back-to-back stem-and-leaf plot. However, most of the leaves on the side representing the European Union countries are greater than the leaves on the side representing the nonmember countries. So, it seems that the European Union countries consume more pasta than nonmember countries.

Assignment Guide

Core: 9–13 odd, 15–18
Enriched: 8–12 even, 13–18

Additional Answer

7b.

Stem	Leaf
0	1 3 4 5 6 7 7
1	0 0 0 2 2 2 2 5 5 8
2	0 0 0 0 5
3	
4	0
5	
6	
7	
8	
9	
10	0

1|2 = 12 years

Study Guide Masters, p. 21

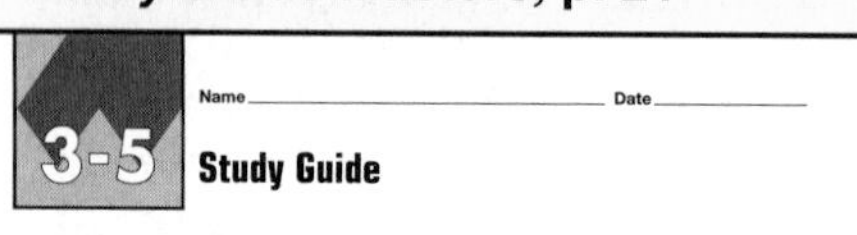

Name__________ Date__________

3-5 **Study Guide**

Stem-and-Leaf Plots

The table below shows the number of home runs Hank Aaron hit by year.

Home Runs Hit by Hank Aaron												
Year	1954	1955	1956	1957	1958	1959	1960	1961	1962	1963	1964	1965
Home Runs	13	27	26	44	30	39	40	35	45	44	24	32
Year	1966	1967	1968	1969	1970	1971	1972	1973	1974	1975	1976	
Home Runs	44	39	29	44	38	47	34	40	20	12	10	

A **stem-and-leaf plot** of the data is shown below.

The tens digits are the *stems*.
The ones digits are the *leaves*.
They are arranged in each row from least to greatest.
4|0 means 40.

Stem	Leaf
1	0 2 3
2	0 4 6 7 9
3	0 2 4 5 8 9 9
4	0 0 4 4 4 4 5 7

Make a stem-and-leaf plot for each set of data.

1. 89, 54, 67, 78, 65, 89, 57, 87, 75, 59, 65, 72, 59, 60, 73, 65

Stem	Leaf
8	7 9 9
7	2 3 5 8
6	0 5 5 5 7
5	4 7 9 9

2. 85, 124, 90, 113, 107, 94, 88, 114, 106, 109, 110, 117, 100, 101, 119

Stem	Leaf
12	4
11	0 3 4 7 9
10	0 1 6 7 9
9	0 4
8	5 8

Refer to the stem-and-leaf plot for Hank Aaron's home runs.

3. What was the greatest number of home runs in a year? What was the fewest home runs in a year? 47, 10
4. In how many years did Hank Aaron hit 30 or more home runs? 15
5. What is the mode for the data? 44
6. What is the median for the data? 35

 T21 *Mathematics: Applications and Connections, Course 2*

7. ***Life Science*** Do you consider 14 to be old? If you were a rhesus monkey, you would! Most rhesus monkeys live only 15 years. The average life span for several animals are shown in the table.

a. What numbers would be used as the stems in a stem-and-leaf plot of these data? **0, 1, 2, 3, 4, 5, 6, 7, 8, 9, 10**

b. Make a stem-and-leaf plot of the life spans. **See margin.**

c. What are the shortest and longest life spans? **1 year, 100 years**

d. What interval is most representative of these life spans? **10–19 years**

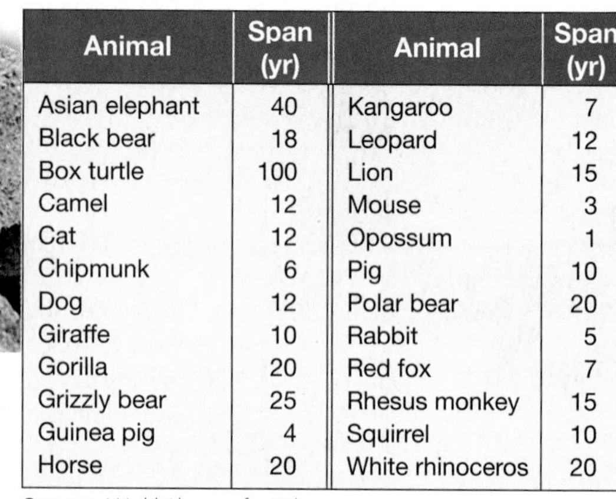

Animal	Span (yr)	Animal	Span (yr)
Asian elephant	40	Kangaroo	7
Black bear	18	Leopard	12
Box turtle	100	Lion	15
Camel	12	Mouse	3
Cat	12	Opossum	1
Chipmunk	6	Pig	10
Dog	12	Polar bear	20
Giraffe	10	Rabbit	5
Gorilla	20	Red fox	7
Grizzly bear	25	Rhesus monkey	15
Guinea pig	4	Squirrel	10
Horse	20	White rhinoceros	20

Source: *World Almanac for Kids*

EXERCISES

Practice

Write the stems that would be used in a stem-and-leaf plot for each set of data. Then make the stem-and-leaf plot. **8–12. See Answer Appendix.**

8. 16, 19, 21, 23, 25, 25, 29, 31, 33, 34, 35, 39, 41, 47, 49

9. 14, 19, 11, 2, 21, 8, 12, 7, 18, 9, 22, 18, 31, 1

10. 498, 472, 459, 443, 491, 481, 469, 403, 439, 444, 411, 492

11. 56, 49, 15, 18, 36, 39, 27, 75, 44, 90, 37, 26, 68, 61, 58

12. 9.3, 8.2, 9.9, 10, 8, 9.2, 8.7, 8, 8.2, 9, 9.9, 8.7, 8.5, 8.1, 8.8, 9.3

Applications and Problem Solving

13. ***Money Matters*** You may have heard it said, "You get what you pay for." Do you think it's true? Study the table of jeans prices and quality ratings below. **a–b. See Answer Appendix.**

a. Make a back-to-back stem-and-leaf plot of the prices of top-ranked and lower-ranked jeans. Do better jeans cost more? Explain.

Type	Top Ranked Price ($)	Lower Ranked Price ($)
Girls'	20, 28, 18	18, 26, 31
Boys'	17, 25, 25	13, 15, 20
Women's	30, 29, 25	38, 17, 30
Men's	30, 29, 30	30, 22, 22

Source: *Zillions*

b. Make a back-to-back stem-and-leaf plot of the prices of jeans for males and females. Do males or females pay more for jeans? Explain.

Classroom Vignette

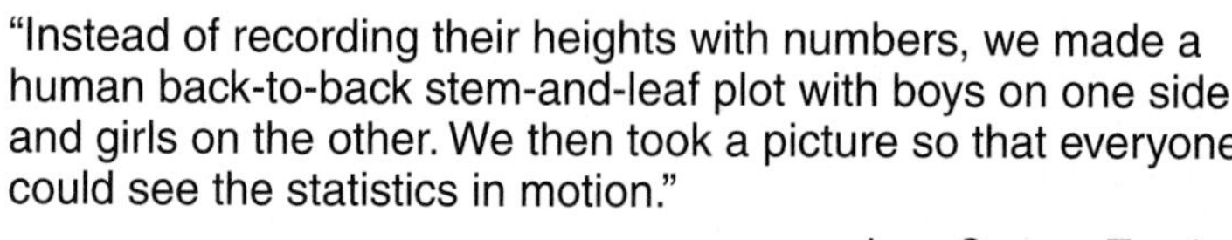

"Instead of recording their heights with numbers, we made a human back-to-back stem-and-leaf plot with boys on one side and girls on the other. We then took a picture so that everyone could see the statistics in motion."

Joan Cooper, Teacher
Ocean Township Intermediate School
Ocean, NJ

14. ***Marketing*** Advertisers decide when to advertise their products on television based on when the people who are likely to buy will be watching. The table shows the percents of boys and girls ages 6 to 14 who watch television at different times of day. (Values are rounded to the nearest percent.)

Time	Boys	Girls
Monday-Friday, 6 A.M.-9 A.M.	11	9
Monday-Friday, 3 P.M.-5 P.M.	21	22
Monday-Friday, 5 P.M.-8 P.M.	30	29
Monday-Saturday, 8 P.M.-10 P.M., and Sunday, 7 P.M.-10 P.M.	29	27
Saturday, 6 A.M.-8 A.M.	7	4
Saturday, 8 A.M.-1 P.M.	26	23
Saturday, 1 P.M.-5 P.M.	12	8
Saturday, 5 P.M.-8 P.M.	18	12
Sunday, 6 A.M.-8 A.M.	3	3
Sunday, 8 A.M.-1 P.M.	10	9
Sunday, 1 P.M.-5 P.M.	12	7
Sunday, 5 P.M.-7 P.M.	15	9

Source: CMR KIDTRENDS REPORT

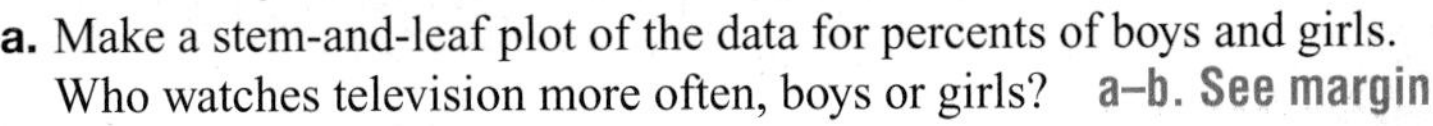

Family Activity

Survey at least 20 relatives and friends about their birthdays. Make a stem-and-leaf plot of the day of the month for each birthday. Write about any patterns you see in the plot.

a. Make a stem-and-leaf plot of the data for percents of boys and girls. Who watches television more often, boys or girls? **a–b. See margin.**

b. If you were scheduling advertising for a product aimed at pre-teen girls, when would you advertise? Explain your reasoning.

15a–c. See Answer Appendix.

15. ***Critical Thinking*** Refer to the stem-and-leaf plot on page 109.

a. Make a stem-and-leaf plot of the data, replacing each leaf with either E for a European Union (EU) country or N for a nonmember country.

b. What kind of information is gained and what type of information is lost in this type of plot?

c. How does this plot compare to a line plot with two symbols for different sets of data?

Mixed Review

16. **Standardized Test Practice** The Cardinals baseball team played 8 games. They scored a total of 96 runs. What was the mean number of runs scored per game? *(Lesson 3-4)* **A**

A 12

B 13

C 88

D 104

17. Solve $n = 0.8 \div 0.05$. *(Lesson 2-6)* **16**

18. ***Life Science*** Refer to the data in Exercise 7. Suppose the life span of a white rhinoceros is r years. Find which animal has an average life span of $r - 16$ years. *(Lesson 1-5)* **guinea pig**

For **Extra Practice,** see page 575.

4 ASSESS

Closing Activity

Modeling Write several two-digit numbers on the chalkboard. Have students model the numbers using place-value models, stating the number of tens and the number of ones in each number.

Ask students if any pattern emerged in their birthday stem-and-leaf plots. Did any clusters appear?

Additional Answers

14a.

Boys	Stem	Girls
7 3	0	3 4 7 8 9 9 9
8 5 2 2 1 0	1	2
9 6 1	2	2 3 7 9
0	3	

8|1 = 18   1|2 = 12

It appears that boys watch television more often than girls do.

14b. Sample answer: Monday–Friday, 5 P.M.–8 P.M. because that is when the highest percentage of girls that age are watching television.

Practice Masters, p. 21

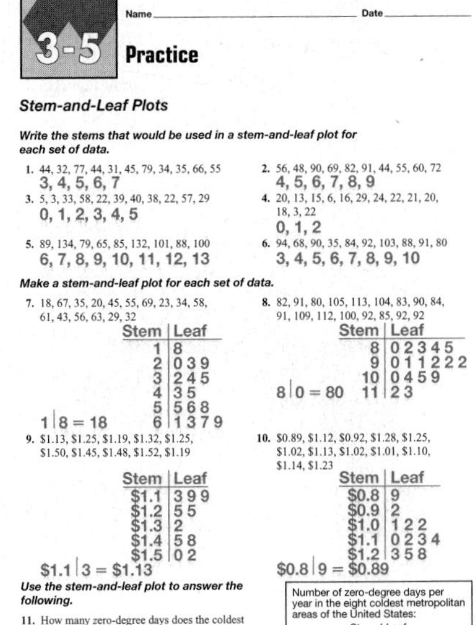

3-5 Practice

Name ______ Date ______

Stem-and-Leaf Plots

Write the stems that would be used in a stem-and-leaf plot for each set of data.

1. 44, 32, 77, 44, 31, 45, 79, 34, 35, 66, 55
   3, 4, 5, 6, 7
2. 56, 48, 90, 69, 82, 91, 44, 55, 60, 72
   4, 5, 6, 7, 8, 9
3. 5, 3, 33, 58, 22, 39, 40, 38, 22, 57, 29
   0, 1, 2, 3, 4, 5
4. 20, 13, 15, 6, 16, 29, 24, 22, 21, 20, 18, 3, 22
   0, 1, 2
5. 89, 134, 79, 65, 85, 132, 101, 88, 100
   6, 7, 8, 9, 10, 11, 12, 13
6. 94, 68, 90, 35, 84, 92, 103, 88, 91, 80
   3, 4, 5, 6, 7, 8, 9, 10

Make a stem-and-leaf plot for each set of data.

7. 18, 67, 35, 20, 45, 55, 69, 23, 34, 58, 61, 43, 56, 63, 29, 32

Stem	Leaf
1	8
2	0 3 9
3	2 4 5
4	3 5
5	5 6 8
6	1 3 7 9

1|8 = 18

8. 82, 91, 80, 105, 113, 104, 83, 90, 84, 91, 109, 112, 100, 92, 85, 92, 92

Stem	Leaf
8	0 2 3 4 5
9	0 1 1 2 2 2
10	0 4 5 9
11	2 3

8|0 = 80

9. \$1.13, \$1.25, \$1.19, \$1.32, \$1.25, \$1.50, \$1.45, \$1.48, \$1.52, \$1.19

Stem	Leaf
\$1.1	3 9 9
\$1.2	5 5
\$1.3	2
\$1.4	5 8
\$1.5	0 2

\$1.1|3 = \$1.13

10. \$0.89, \$1.12, \$0.92, \$1.28, \$1.25, \$1.02, \$1.13, \$1.02, \$1.01, \$1.10, \$1.14, \$1.23

Stem	Leaf
\$0.8	9
\$0.9	2
\$1.0	1 2 2
\$1.1	0 2 3 4
\$1.2	3 5 8

\$0.8|9 = \$0.89

Use the stem-and-leaf plot to answer the following.

Number of zero-degree days per year in the eight coldest metropolitan areas of the United States:

Stem	Leaf
3	1 3 4 5
4	1
5	1 1 4

3|1 = 31 zero-degree days per year

11. How many zero-degree days does the coldest metropolitan area in the United States have in a year? **54 zero-degree days**
12. What is the range of the zero-degree day data? **23 days**

 T21 *Mathematics: Applications and Connections, Course 2*

Extending the Lesson

Enrichment Masters, p. 21

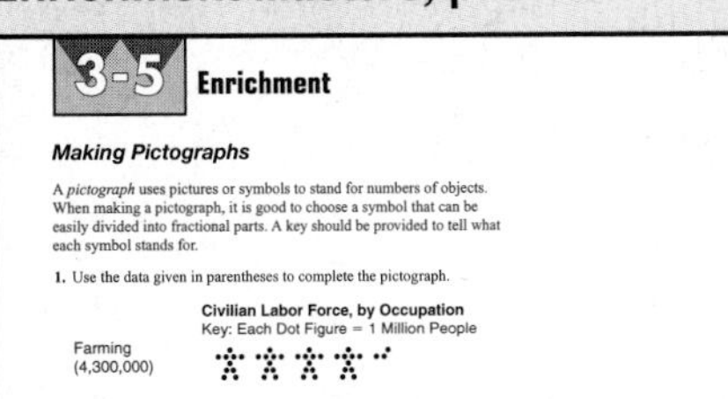

3-5 Enrichment

Making Pictographs

A *pictograph* uses pictures or symbols to stand for numbers of objects. When making a pictograph, it is good to choose a symbol that can be easily divided into fractional parts. A key should be provided to tell what each symbol stands for.

1. Use the data given in parentheses to complete the pictograph.

Civilian Labor Force, by Occupation
Key: Each Dot Figure = 1 Million People

Farming (4,300,000)

Activity Have students use a newspaper to find the high and low temperatures for 15 cities in the U.S. Ask students to make a back-to-back stem-and-leaf plot for this data. Have students determine what categories to use to compare data, such as northern states compared to southern states.

3-6A HANDS-ON LAB Notes

GET READY

Objective Students graph quartiles and determine the interquartile range.

Optional Resources
Hands-On Lab Masters
- number lines, p. 15
- worksheet, p. 42

Overhead Manipulative Resources
- number line transparency

MANAGEMENT TIPS

Recommended Time
45 minutes

Getting Started Tell students that *quarter* and *quartile* have the same Latin root—meaning "fourth." Just as a dollar can be separated into 4 parts, data can be separated into 4 quartiles. Explain that when people must deal with a large set of data, it is frequently easier to summarize pieces of the data to make the information easier to handle. Separating data into quartiles accomplishes this. *Quartiles* may refer to the division points or to the parts of data.

The **Activity** shows how to separate data into quartiles. Ask students to read over the steps briefly before beginning. Make sure students correctly remember what *median* means. Stress to students the importance of following the steps in order.

Teaching Tip
You can enter data in a list on a graphing calculator. Then press STAT, ▶ (to select the CALC menu), 1 (to select 1 variable statistics), and ENTER. Scroll down to the end of the results to find the quartiles of the data.

COOPERATIVE LEARNING

3-6A Quartiles

A Preview of Lesson 3-6

In a large set of data, it is helpful to separate the data into four equal parts called *quartiles*. In this lab, you will find and graph the quartiles. The *interquartile range* is the range of the middle half of the data.

TRY THIS

Work with a partner.

The table shows various waterfalls in the United States and their heights.

Name, Location	Height (ft)	Name, Location	Height (ft)
Akaka, Hawaii	442	Niagara, New York	182
Big Manitou, Wisconsin	165	Passaic, New Jersey	70
Cumberland, Kentucky	68	Seven, Colorado	300
Fall Creek, Tennessee	256	Shoshone, Idaho	212
Feather, California	640	Sluiskin, Washington	300
Great, Maryland	71	Snoqualmie, Washington	268
Illilouette, California	370	Taughannock, New York	215
Minnehaha, Minnesota	53	Yellowstone, Wyoming	308
Multnomah, Oregon	620		

Source: *The World Almanac, 1996*

Step 1 List the data in order from least to greatest.

53 68 70 71 165 182 212 215 256 268 300 300 308 370 442 620 640

Step 2 Find the median.

53 68 70 71 165 182 212 215 (256) 268 300 300 308 370 442 620 640

(8 values below the median; 8 values above the median)

The median separates the data into two equal groups.

Step 3 Find the median of the lower group and the median of the upper group.

When the data set has an odd number of members, don't include the original median in either group.

53 68 70 71 ↓ 165 182 212 215 (256) 268 300 300 308 ↓ 370 442 620 640

$\frac{71 + 165}{2} = 118$ *Lower quartile* $\frac{308 + 370}{2} = 339$ *Upper quartile*

Half of the data numbers (the middle half) lie between the lower and upper quartiles, 118 and 339.

ON YOUR OWN

1. What is the interquartile range? **221**

2. Copy the number line below.

The median of the waterfall data is graphed above the number line. Graph the least value, the greatest value, the upper quartile, and the lower quartile above the number line. **See margin.**

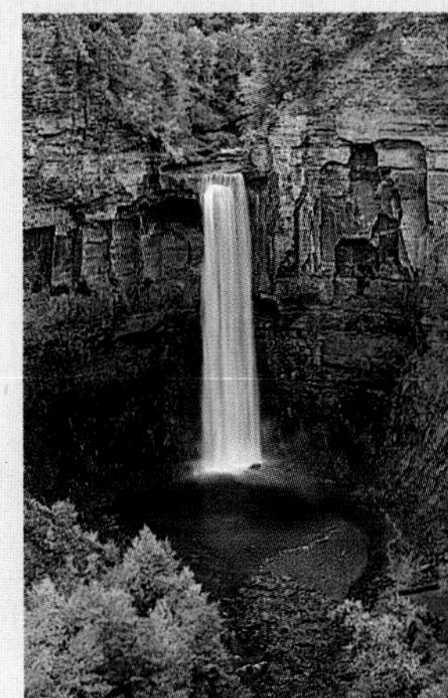

3. The five numbers that are graphed on the number line divide the data into four groups. How many of the numbers in the data set fall in each group? **3 or 4**

4. ***Look Ahead*** The table shows various waterfalls in Europe and their heights.

Name, Location	Height (ft)	Name, Location	Height (ft)
Frua, Italy	470	Reichenbach, Switzerland	656
Gastein, Austria	492	Rhaiadr, Wales	240
Gavarnie, France	1,385	Simmen, Switzerland	459
Giessbach, Switzerland	984	Skjeggedal, Norway	1,378
Glomach, Scotland	370	Skykje, Norway	984
Handol, Sweden	427	Staubbach, Switzerland	984
Krimml, Austria	1,312	Trummelbach, Switzerland	1,312
Mardalsfossen (N), Norway	1,535	Vetti, Norway	900
Mardalsfossen (S), Norway	2,149		

Source: *The World Almanac, 1996*

a. What is the median? **984**
b. What is the upper quartile? **1,345**
c. What is the lower quartile? **464.5**
d. What is the least value? **240**
e. What is the greatest value? **2,149**
f. Draw a number line and graph the median, upper and lower quartiles, and least and greatest values. **See margin.**
g. Compare this number line with the number line in the activity above. What can you conclude about the heights of the waterfalls in the United States compared to the heights of the waterfalls in Europe? **See margin.**

Have students write a paragraph explaining how number lines such as the one they just plotted are useful in making comparisons.

ASSESS

Have students complete Exercises 1–3. Watch for students who confuse the least value with the lower quartile and the greatest value with the upper quartile. Make sure they realize that they must refer to the original data to find the least and greatest value.

Use Exercise 4 to determine whether students understand how to find quartiles.

Additional Answers

2.

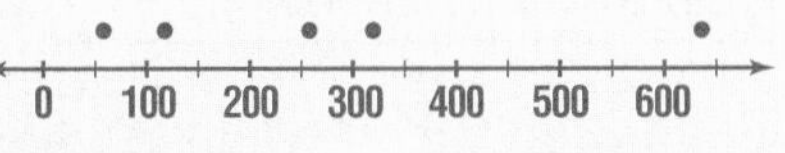

4f.

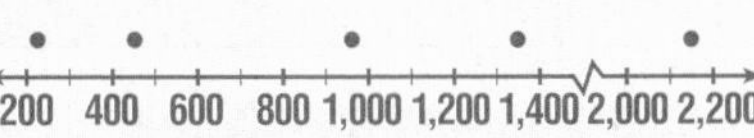

4g. **The data in this number line are more spread out. The waterfalls in Europe are generally higher than those in the United States.**

3-6 Lesson Notes

Instructional Resources

- *Study Guide Masters,* p. 22
- *Practice Masters,* p. 22
- *Enrichment Masters,* p. 22
- Transparencies 3-6, A and B
- *Assessment and Evaluation Masters,* p. 72

CD-ROM Program
- Resource Lesson 3-6

Recommended Pacing	
Standard	Days 8 & 9 of 12
Honors	Day 5 of 11
Block	Day 5 of

1 FOCUS

5-Minute Check
(Lesson 3-5)

1. Make a stem-and-leaf plot for these data: 46, 37, 32, 51, 48, 44, 33, 54, 39, 40, 56, 59.

Stem	Leaf
3	2 3 7 9
4	0 4 6 8
5	1 4 6 9

5|1 = 51

The stem-and-leaf plot below shows the heights, in stories, of the 15 tallest buildings in a city.

Stem	Leaf
2	7 8
3	2 2 3 7 9
4	0 1 1 3 5 8
5	2 4

5|2 = 52

2. How tall is the tallest building? **54 stories**
3. In which 10-story interval do most of the buildings lie? **40–49 stories**

The 5-Minute Check is also available on **Transparency 3-6A** for this lesson.

3-6 Box-and-Whisker Plots

What you'll learn

You'll learn to construct and interpret box-and-whisker plots.

When am I ever going to use this?

Business executives use box-and-whisker plots to analyze their employees' salaries.

Word Wise

box-and-whisker plot
upper quartile
lower quartile
upper extreme
lower extreme
interquartile range
outlier

Study Hint

Technology You can use a graphing calculator to find the quartiles and extreme values. Refer to the Study Hint on page 102. minX = lower extreme, Q1 = LQ, Q3 = UQ, and maxX = upper extreme.

Scientists estimate that there are more than 40,000 earthquakes each year. The table gives information on recent major earthquakes.

Date	Location	Magnitude	Date	Location	Magnitude
3/13/92	Turkey	6.2	6/6/94	Colombia	6.8
3/15/92	Turkey	6.0	8/19/94	Algeria	6.0
6/28/92	California	7.5	1/17/95	Japan	7.2
12/12/92	Indonesia	7.5	5/27/95	Russia	7.6
7/12/93	Japan	7.7	10/1/95	Turkey	6.0
9/29/93	India	6.4	10/9/95	Mexico	7.6
1/17/94	California	6.8	2/3/96	China	7.0
2/15/94	Indonesia	7.0	2/17/96	Indonesia	7.5

Source: Global Volcanism Network, Smithsonian Institution, U.S.

You can use a **box-and-whisker plot** to display and summarize data. A box-and-whisker plot summarizes data using the median, the **upper quartile (UQ)**, the **lower quartile (LQ)**, the **upper extreme** and the **lower extreme**.

Step 1 First, find the median, the quartiles, and the extreme values. Write the data in order from least to greatest.

6.0 6.0 6.0 6.2 6.4 6.8 6.8 7.0
7.0 7.2 7.5 7.5 7.5 7.6 7.6 7.7

$$\text{median} = \frac{7.0 + 7.0}{2} \text{ or } 7.0$$

The lower quartile is the median of the lower half of the data. The upper quartile is the median of the upper half of the data.

$$LQ = \frac{6.2 + 6.4}{2} \text{ or } 6.3 \qquad UQ = \frac{7.5 + 7.5}{2} \text{ or } 7.5$$

The lower extreme is the least value, 6.0. The upper extreme is the greatest value, 7.7.

Step 2 Graph each value above a number line.

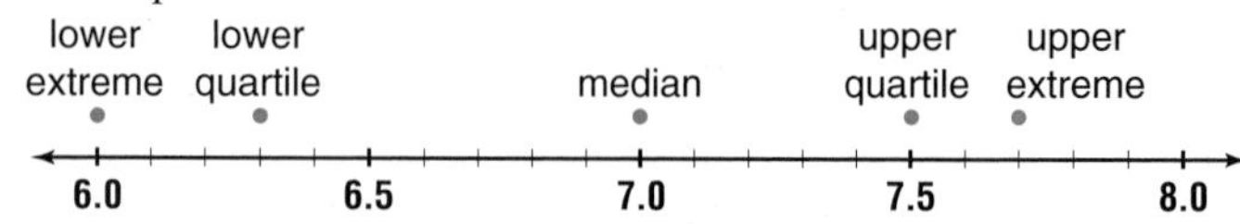

Step 3 Draw a box around the upper quartile and lower quartile and draw a vertical line through the median value.

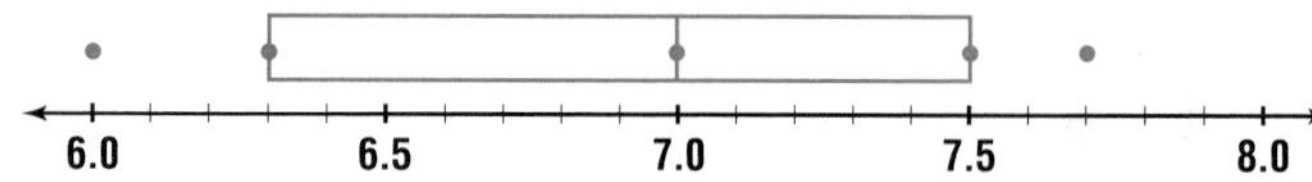

Step 4 Extend *whiskers* from each quartile to the extreme points.

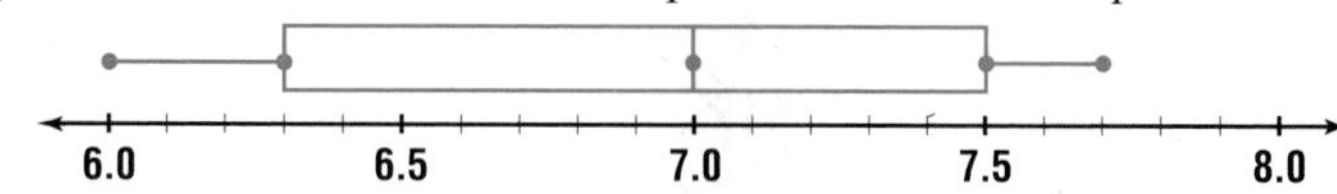

Classroom Vignette

"I provide students with a list of all the seventh graders. They do a survey asking every other seventh grader. Results are posted using frequency tables, stem-and-leaf plots, and various graphs."

Kym Timpano, Teacher
Pierre Van Cortland Middle School
Croton-on-Hudson, NY

A box-and-whisker plot divides the data into four parts using the lower extreme, LQ, median, UQ, and upper extreme. One-fourth of the data fall between each of these adjacent numbers.

1 Architecture **Make a box-and-whisker plot of the data on the heights of the tallest buildings in St. Louis, Missouri.**

St. Louis Metropolitan Square Tower

Find the median, the quartiles, and the extremes. Then construct the plot.

median $= \frac{434 + 420}{2} = 427$

LQ = 394 UQ = 564

upper extreme = 593

lower extreme = 375

Building	Height (ft)
Metropolitan Square Tower	593
One Bell Center	588
Mercantile Center Tower	540
Laclede Gas Building	434
Boatmen's Plaza	420
SW Bell Telephone Building	398
Civil Courts Building	390
One City Center	375

Source: *World Almanac*

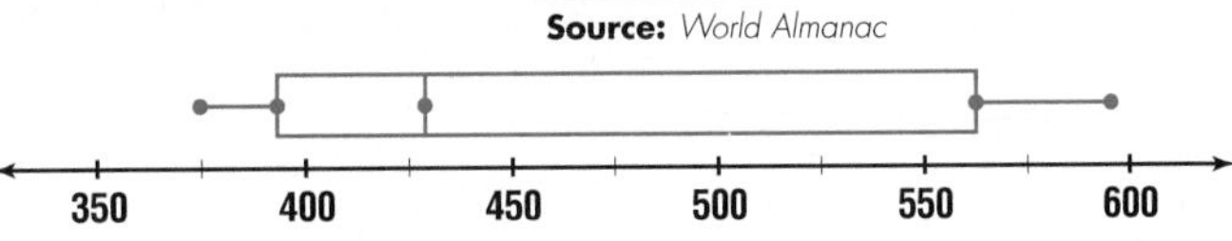

The graph shows how the data are spread. Half of the tallest buildings are between 394 and 564 feet high. The largest range of the four quartiles is from 427 to 564 feet. One-fourth of the tallest buildings are within these heights.

You can locate the quartiles by the left and right sides of the box and then subtract to find the **interquartile range**. *The interquartile range is 170.*

Some values in a set of data may be much greater or much less than the other data. Data that are more than 1.5 times the interquartile range from the quartiles are called **outliers**.

2 Food **Snacks sold at movie theaters often have as many Calories as fast-food meals. Make a box-and-whisker plot of the data.**

Snack (oz)	Calories	Snack (oz)	Calories
Peanut butter cups, 3.2	380	Popcorn, medium unbuttered	901
Fruit-flavored candy, 2.6	286	Raisins, 2.3	270
Chocolate wafer candy bar, 4	588	Candy bar, 4	492
Colored peanut candy, 2.6	363	Mints, 3	360
Colored chocolate candy, 2.6	350	Licorice, 5	500
Popcorn, medium buttered	1,221		

Study Hint

Technology You can use a graphing calculator to draw a box-and-whisker plot.

270 286 350 360 363 380 492 500 588 901 1,221

350 ↑ LQ 380 ↑ Median 588 ↑ UQ

(continued on next page)

Motivating the Lesson

Hands-On Activity Have students take their pulse rates and record each number of beats per minute. Ask students to find which pulse rates comprise the middle half of the data when arranged on a number line.

2 TEACH

Transparency 3-6B contains a teaching aid for this lesson.

Reading Mathematics Ask students what quarter or quarters of the data the upper and lower *quartiles* define. Have them explain in their own words what it means that the upper quartile is the "median of the upper half" of the data.

In-Class Examples

For Example 1

Make a box-and-whisker plot for these automobile gas mileages.

31 27 12 23 45 24 39 19
48 24 20 22 29 17 34

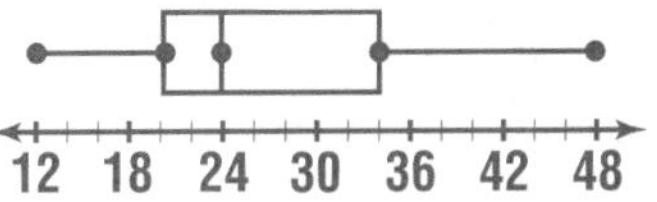

For Example 2

Make a box-and-whisker plot for the bicycle club member ages displayed in the stem-and-leaf plot.

Stem	Leaf
1	0 6 7 9
2	2 2 3 5 7 8
3	1 1 2 3 4 7
4	6 6
5	5

$5|5 = 55$

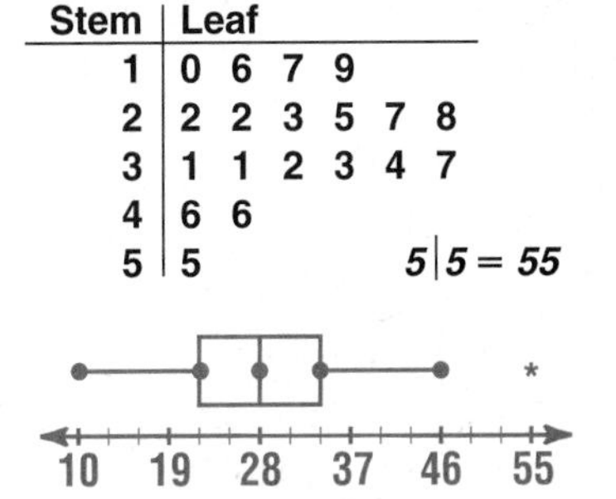

Reteaching the Lesson

Activity Discuss the five key parts of a box-and-whisker plot. Tell students that a set of data has the extremes 4 and 19, upper and lower quartiles 8 and 12, and median 11. Have students draw a number line, find these five points, and draw a box-and-whisker plot.

Error Analysis

Watch for students who find quartiles by dividing the range into four equal sections.

Prevent by stressing the quartile refers to one-fourth of the *number of items*, not one-fourth of the range.

3 PRACTICE/APPLY

Check for Understanding

If students need additional practice or instruction after completing Exercises 1–5, you may find one of the following options helpful.

- Extra Practice, see p. 576
- Reteaching Activity, see p. 115
- *Study Guide Masters,* p. 22
- *Practice Masters,* p. 22

Additional Answers

1. **Sample answer: You can see the range of each quartile, and you know that one-fourth of the data fall in each quartile.**
2. **If a number is more than 1.5 times the interquartile range from the quartile, then it is an outlier.**
3. **Sample answer: All of the data do not need to be displayed; it doesn't show all the frequency.**

Draw a box to show the median and the quartiles.

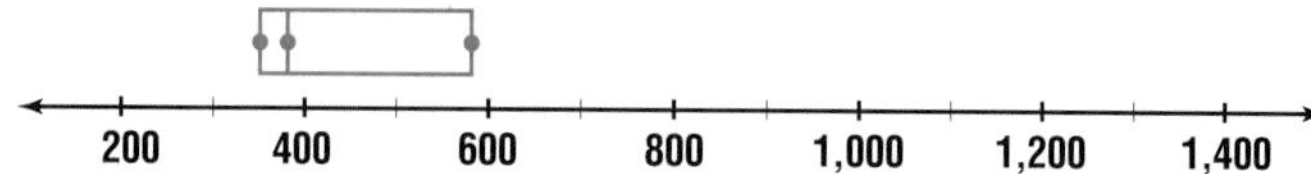

The interquartile range is 588 – 350 or 238. So, data more than 1.5 · 238, or 357, from the quartiles are outliers.

Subtract 357 from the lower quartile. $350 - 357 = -7$
Add 357 to the upper quartile. $588 + 357 = 945$

So, −7 and 945 are the limits for the outliers. There is one outlier in the data, 1,221. Plot the outlier with an asterisk. Then draw the lower whisker to the lower extreme, 270, and the upper whisker to the last value that is not an outlier, 901.

Outliers may be noted with asterisks in a box-and-whisker plot.

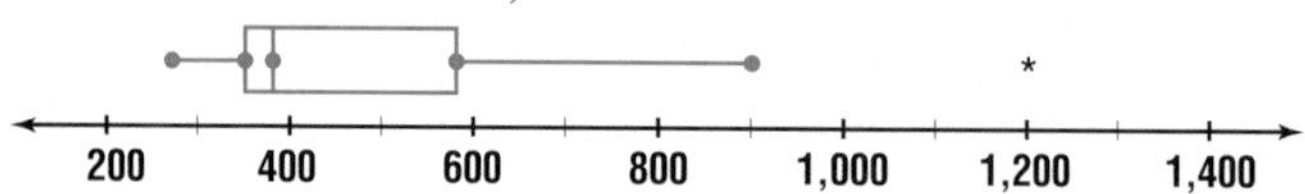

CHECK FOR UNDERSTANDING

Communicating Mathematics

Read and study the lesson to answer each question. **1–3. See margin.**

1. ***Describe*** what information you can get about a data set by looking at a box-and-whisker plot.
2. ***Explain*** how to determine whether a number is an outlier.
3. ***Write*** a few sentences to tell why a box-and-whisker plot might be used to display a large number of data. What drawbacks does a box-and-whisker plot have, if any?

Math Journal

Guided Practice

4. ***Life Science*** The box-and-whisker plot represents data on the average life spans of different animals found in Exercise 7 on page 110.

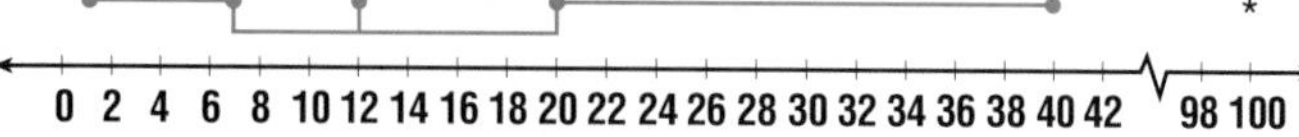

   a. Find the median. **12** b. Find the interquartile range. **13**

5. ***History*** Refer to the chart of Presidents' ages on page 98.
   a. What is the median? **54.5** b. What is the upper quartile? **58**
   c. What is the lower quartile? **51** d. What is the upper extreme? **69**
   e. What is the lower extreme? **42** f. What is the interquartile range? **7**
   g. What are the limits on outliers? **40.5, 68.5**
   h. Draw a box-and-whisker plot of the ages. **See margin.**
   i. Compare the box-and-whisker plot you drew in part h to the line plot on page 98. What similarities and differences do you see? **See students' work.**

***Study Guide Masters,* p. 22**

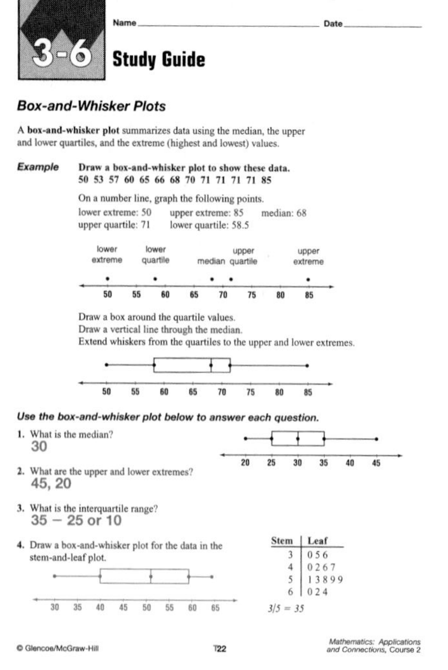

Name__________ Date________

3-6 Study Guide

Box-and-Whisker Plots

A **box-and-whisker plot** summarizes data using the median, the upper and lower quartiles, and the extreme (highest and lowest) values.

Example **Draw a box-and-whisker plot to show these data.**
50 53 57 60 65 66 68 70 71 71 71 71 85

On a number line, graph the following points.
lower extreme: 50 upper extreme: 85 median: 68
upper quartile: 71 lower quartile: 58.5

lower extreme, lower quartile, median, upper quartile, upper extreme
50 55 60 65 70 75 80 85

Draw a box around the quartile values.
Draw a vertical line through the median.
Extend whiskers from the quartiles to the upper and lower extremes.

50 55 60 65 70 75 80 85

Use the box-and-whisker plot below to answer each question.

20 25 30 35 40 45

1. What is the median?
   30
2. What are the upper and lower extremes?
   45, 20
3. What is the interquartile range?
   35 − 25 or 10
4. Draw a box-and-whisker plot for the data in the stem-and-leaf plot.

30 35 40 45 50 55 60 65

Stem	Leaf
3	0 5 6
4	0 2 6 7
5	1 3 8 9 9
6	0 2 4

3|5 = 35

© Glencoe/McGraw-Hill T22 *Mathematics: Applications and Connections,* Course 2

Additional Answer

5h.

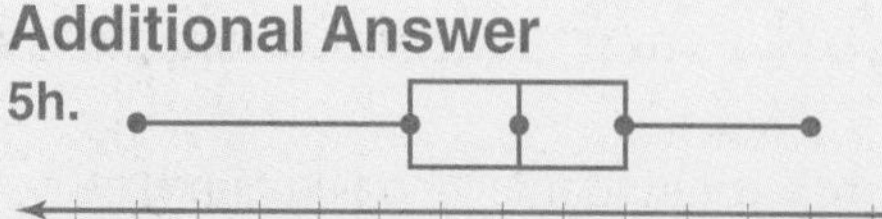

MathPASS CD-ROM

This CD-ROM offers a complete, self-paced mathematics curriculum. Each lesson includes a pretest, tutorial, guided practice, and posttest. MathPASS Lesson 8 is correlated to this Student Edition lesson.
For Windows & Macintosh

EXERCISES

Practice

6. Use the box-and-whisker plot of high temperatures (°F) below.

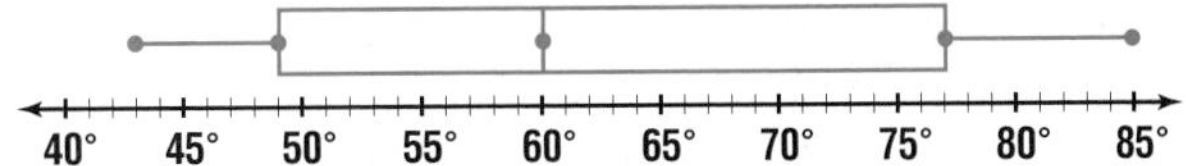

a. What is the median? **60** b. What is the upper quartile? **77**

c. What is the lower quartile? **49** d. What is the upper extreme? **85**

e. What is the lower extreme? **43** f. What is the interquartile range? **28**

g. What are the limits on outliers? Are there any outliers? **7, 119; no**

h. What fraction of the temperatures are less than 49°? $\frac{1}{4}$

7. Make a box-and-whisker plot of the data shown in the stem-and-leaf plot. **See Answer Appendix.**

Stem	Leaf
1	2 7 7
2	0 4 5 5 6 7 9 9
3	1 3 5 8 *1|7 = 17*

8. Compare the box-and-whisker plots.

a. What is similar about the data in the two plots? **a–c. See margin.**

b. What is different about the data in the two plots?

c. Which set of data is more concentrated around the median? Explain.

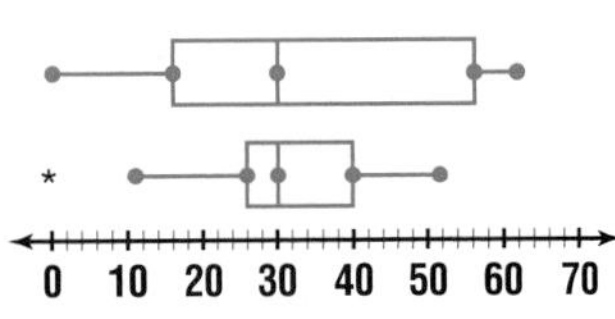

Applications and Problem Solving

9. ***Sports*** The table shows the games won by each men's professional basketball team in the 1995–1996 season. Make a box-and-whisker plot of the data. **See Answer Appendix.**

Team	Wins	Team	Wins	Team	Wins
Atlanta	46	Indiana	52	Phoenix	41
Boston	33	L.A Clippers	29	Portland	44
Charlotte	41	L.A. Lakers	53	Sacramento	39
Chicago	72	Miami	42	San Antonio	59
Cleveland	47	Milwaukee	25	Seattle	64
Dallas	26	Minnesota	26	Toronto	21
Denver	35	New Jersey	30	Utah	55
Detroit	46	New York	47	Vancouver	15
Golden State	36	Orlando	60	Washington	39
Houston	48	Philadelphia	18		

For the latest statistics, visit: www.glencoe.com/sec/math/mac/mathnet

For **Extra Practice,** see page 576.

10. ***Critical Thinking*** Describe a set of data in which there is only one whisker in its box-and-whisker plot. **See margin.**

Mixed Review

11. ***Statistics*** Make a stem-and-leaf plot for 20, 21, 35, 34, 18, 56, 11, 10, 12, 22, and 38. *(Lesson 3-5)* **See Answer Appendix.**

12. **Standardized Test Practice** Choose the solution to the equation $\frac{48}{c} = 4 + 2$. *(Lesson 1-5)* **D**

A 2 **B** 4 **C** 6 **D** 8

Assignment Guide

Core: 6, 7, 9–12
Enriched: 6, 8, 9–12

4 ASSESS

Closing Activity

Speaking Draw a box-and-whisker plot on the chalkboard. Have students identify the lower and upper extremes, the lower and upper quartiles, and the median.

Chapter 3, Quiz C (Lessons 3-5 and 3-6) is available in the *Assessment and Evaluation Masters,* p. 72.

Additional Answers

8a. They have the same median and the same least value.

8b. The top set of data is more widely dispersed than the lower set.

8c. the bottom plot; the box is shorter

10. A set in which an extreme value and a quartile are the same has no whisker on that side of the box-and-whisker plot.

***Practice Masters,* p. 22**

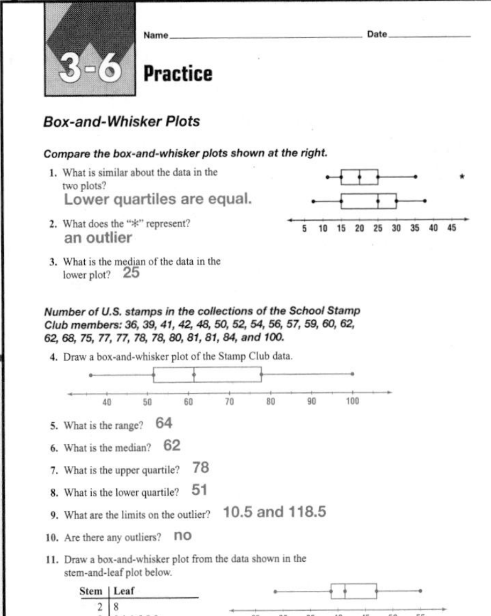

Name________ Date________

3-6 Practice

Box-and-Whisker Plots

Compare the box-and-whisker plots shown at the right.

1. What is similar about the data in the two plots? **Lower quartiles are equal.**
2. What does the "*" represent? **an outlier**
3. What is the median of the data in the lower plot? **25**

Number of U.S. stamps in the collections of the School Stamp Club members: 36, 39, 41, 42, 48, 50, 52, 54, 56, 57, 59, 60, 62, 62, 68, 75, 77, 77, 78, 78, 80, 81, 81, 84, and 100.

4. Draw a box-and-whisker plot of the Stamp Club data.
5. What is the range? **64**
6. What is the median? **62**
7. What is the upper quartile? **78**
8. What is the lower quartile? **51**
9. What are the limits on the outlier? **10.5 and 118.5**
10. Are there any outliers? **no**
11. Draw a box-and-whisker plot from the data shown in the stem-and-leaf plot below.

Stem	Leaf
2	8
3	0 1 1 5 8 9
4	0 0 1 1 1 3 3 4 5 7 8
5	0 2 4 5

5|2 = 52

© Glencoe/McGraw-Hill T22 *Mathematics: Applications and Connections, Course 2*

Extending the Lesson

***Enrichment Masters,* p. 22**

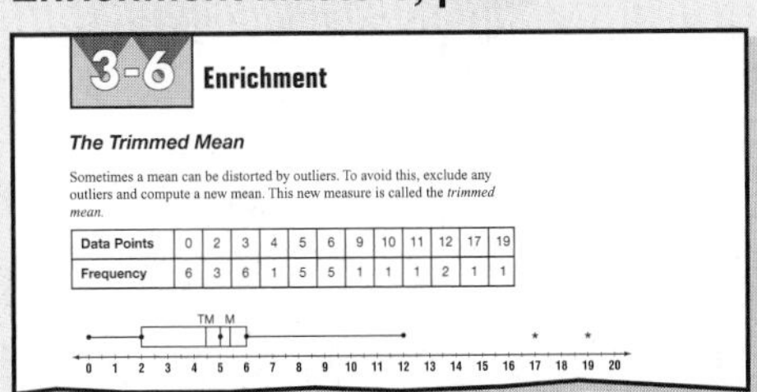

3-6 Enrichment

The Trimmed Mean

Sometimes a mean can be distorted by outliers. To avoid this, exclude any outliers and compute a new mean. This new measure is called the *trimmed mean.*

Data Points	0	2	3	4	5	6	9	10	11	12	17	19
Frequency	6	3	6	1	5	5	1	1	1	2	1	1

Activity Have small groups analyze the data represented by this box-and-whisker plot.

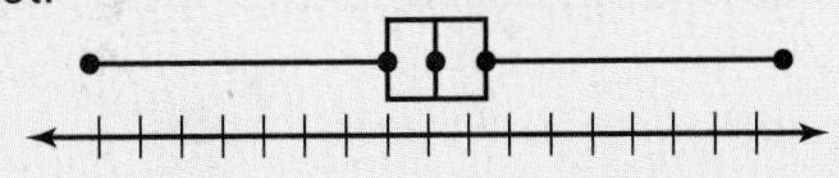

Sample answer: The middle half of the data is tightly clustered; the lower and upper fourths of the data are widely dispersed.

GET READY

Objective Students use data to make predictions.

Optional Resources
Hands-On Lab Masters
- worksheet, p. 43

MANAGEMENT TIPS

Recommended Time
30 minutes

Getting Started Before students grab handfuls of popcorn, challenge each to guess how many kernels he or she can hold. Once students have their handfuls, ask them to estimate how many kernels they have. Students can compare their initial guesses with actual results.

The **Activity** gives the students a choice of methods to use. Have students discuss the advantages and disadvantages of each method of data presentation before choosing one to use. Ask students to explain why one presentation seems more effective than the others.

ASSESS

Have students complete Exercises 1 through 3. To determine whether students understand the usefulness of the different ways of presenting data, have students suggest an *ineffective* way to present the data about popcorn. Ask them to explain why it would not work well in this case.

COOPERATIVE LEARNING

3-6B How Much is a Handful?

A Follow-Up of Lesson 3-6

popped popcorn

Leon and his older brother ask their mother if they can have some popcorn. She replies, "Only one handful each." How much is a handful? Will Leon and his older brother get the same amount of popcorn? You can use data to make predictions.

TRY THIS

Work together as a class.

Step 1 Each student should grab a handful of popped popcorn.

Step 2 Count the number of popped kernels in each handful and record the information on the chalkboard.

Work in groups of three.

Step 3 Choose one of the following ways to represent the data: frequency table, bar graph, line plot, stem-and-leaf plot, or box-and-whisker plot.

Step 4 Find the mode, median, and mean of the data.

Step 5 Display your graphical representation and explain it to the rest of the class.

ON YOUR OWN

1. Which value, the mode, median, or mean, best describes the set of data? Why? **1–3. See Answer Appendix for sample answers.**
2. Which graphical representation is the best representation of the data? Why?
3. ***Reflect Back*** Examine the data you collected.
   a. Predict how many popped kernels other students your age might get in one handful.
   b. Randomly choose 10 students who are not in your math class and have them grab a handful of popcorn. Compare the number of popped kernels in their handfuls with your prediction.
   c. Ask your teacher to grab a handful of popcorn. How does the number of kernels that he or she grabbed compare with your data? Could you use this information to predict about how many kernels other adults in your school might get in one handful? Why or why not?

Have students write a paragraph summarizing the activity and describing how they could tell which graphical representation best displayed the data.

3-7 Misleading Statistics

What you'll learn

You'll learn to recognize when statistics and graphs are misleading.

When am I ever going to use this?

Being able to recognize misleading statistics is useful when you're reading advertisements.

6 days, 7 nights for only $299

Orlando

Have you ever seen a vacation advertisement that appeared too good to be true? Was the ad misleading, or did it not give all the information? As a selling strategy, advertisements sometimes distort the facts by taking images and words out of context or by leaving out important information. Similarly, when you are given insufficient background information or an incomplete picture of the data, you may be looking at misleading statistics.

Whenever there are outliers in the data, the mean is not a good way to describe the data.

Examples

Real World APPLICATION

1 Salaries **Amara is interviewing for a technology company. She is told that the average salary of the 37 employees is more than $40,000. Using the information at the right, should Amara expect a salary of more than $40,000 if she gets the job? Explain.**

Employee	Salary
President	$375,000
Vice President	$325,000
Sales Staff (15)	$35,000
Secretaries (10)	$16,000
Phone Order Staff (10)	$12,000

The company has 37 employees, but only two have a salary over $40,000. The two very high salaries result in a misleading mean. Amara should not expect a salary of more than $40,000.

APPLICATION

2 Television **Both bar graphs show the percent of viewers that watch network television. Which graph could be misleading?**

Graph A

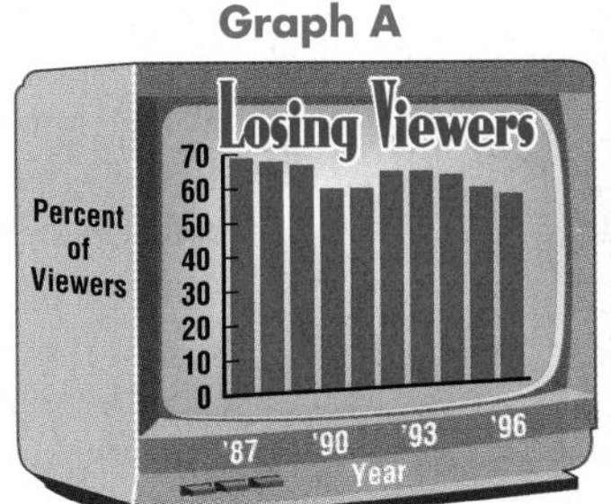

Graph B

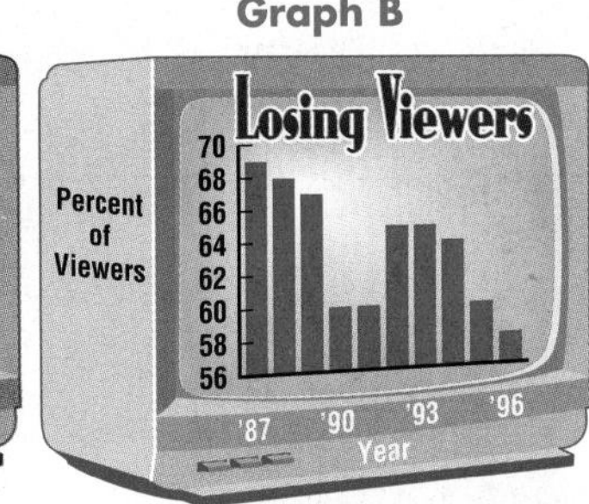

Although both graphs show a decrease in network viewers, a change in the vertical scale makes Graph B look misleading. The loss of viewer looks more drastic than in Graph A.

3-7 Lesson Notes

Instructional Resources

- *Study Guide Masters,* p. 23
- *Practice Masters,* p. 23
- *Enrichment Masters,* p. 23
- Transparencies 3-7, A and B
- *Assessment and Evaluation Masters,* p. 72
- *Technology Masters,* p. 32

CD-ROM Program
- Resource Lesson 3-7

Recommended Pacing	
Standard	Day 10 of 12
Honors	Day 9 of 11
Block	Day 5 of 6

1 FOCUS

5-Minute Check
(Lesson 3-6)

Make a box-and-whisker plot for this list of average class sizes in 15 schools.

22 25 33 31 28 22 26 22
30 27 31 28 33 23 29

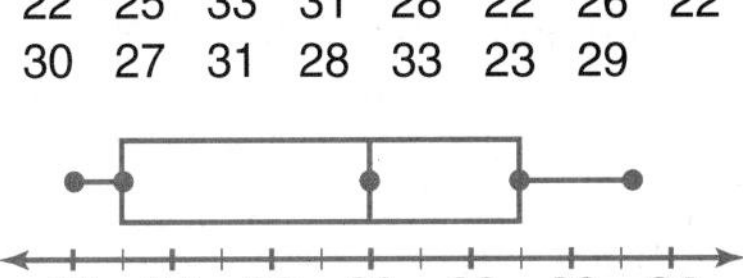

The 5-Minute Check is also available on **Transparency 3-7A** for this lesson.

2 TEACH

Transparency 3-7B contains a teaching aid for this lesson.

Using Critical Thinking Bring in and display an ad on a self-help program, for example, on weight loss. Have students suggest ways in which the ad may be misleading. Guide students to see whether enough information is given and whether any facts are hidden.

Classroom Vignette

"I have students use their last 10 assignment scores to make two graphs: one misleading and one that accurately reflects the data. Then they write a paragraph explaining how they organized and created their graphs. I also ask them to tell which graph they would show their parents as a reflection of their scores and why."

Amy Wohler, Department Chair
Kirksville Jr. High
Kirksville, MO

In-Class Examples

For Example 1

Crooks Construction Co. advertises that houses they build cost an average of $224,000. Using the following information, tell why this figure is misleading.

10 houses @ $300,000
10 houses @ $250,000
5 houses @ $20,000

The mean is misleading because only a few very inexpensive houses are less than the mean, and most are greater than the mean.

For Example 2

Two hundred students at King School have raised money for the library.

Money Raised	Number of Students
$50	12
$40	
$30	
$20	
$10	
$5	

Which statistic in this set of data is misleading, the mode, median, or mean? Why? **mean; The data are skewed by the outliers. Most students raised $5.**

***Study Guide Masters,* p. 23**

Name______ Date______

3-7 Study Guide

Misleading Statistics

Don't be misled by statistics. Choose the best measure of central tendency to describe the data.

Measure of Central Tendency	When to Use
mean	when no numbers are much greater or much less than the rest
mode	when the most frequently occurring number is needed
median	when there are numbers that are much greater or much less than the rest

Example **A car dealer advertised that the average savings on a new car purchased from her was $1,500.**

Number of Sales	Amount of Savings
2	$5,000
1	$3,500
9	$500

The mean of the data in the table is $1,500. The median and the mode are both $500. $500 is more representative of the savings you might expect if you buy a car from this dealer.

The members of a health club compiled the table below. It shows how many laps various swimmers completed.

Number of Laps	People
10	9
15	7
20	5
25	10

1. Find the mean, mode, and median of the data. 17.6, 25, 15
2. Which measure is least descriptive? the mode, which is 25
3. Which number most accurately describes the data? the mean, which is about 17.6

 T23 *Mathematics: Applications and Connections, Course 2*

CHECK FOR UNDERSTANDING

Communicating Mathematics

Read and study the lesson to answer each question. **1–2. See Answer Appendix.**

1. ***Tell*** three ways data can be misleading.
2. ***Tell*** which graph in Example 2 could be better used to convince advertisers not to air their commercials on network television.
3. **Math Journal** ***Write*** about at least two newspaper or magazine advertisements that you find that are misleading. **See students' work.**

Guided Practice

4. The line graphs both show monthly CD sales for one year at the Music Barn. Which graph could be misleading? Explain.

4. Both graphs show the same data, but Graph B could be misleading because the vertical scale on the graph does not begin with 0.

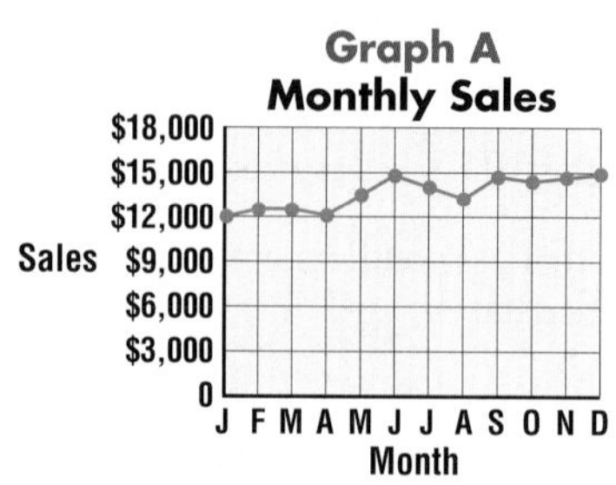

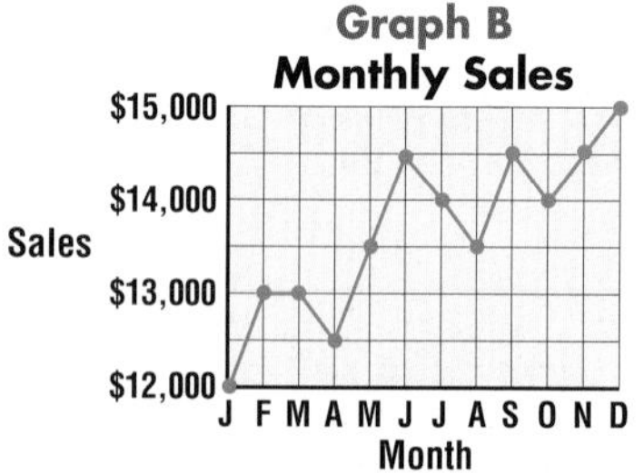

5. ***Recycling*** Both graphs show the number of pounds of aluminum cans that students at Walker Middle School recycled in eight weeks.

5b. Graph B could be misleading because of the change in the vertical scale.

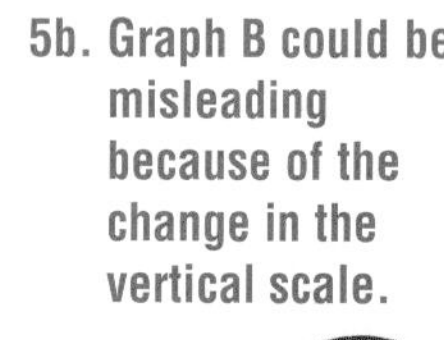

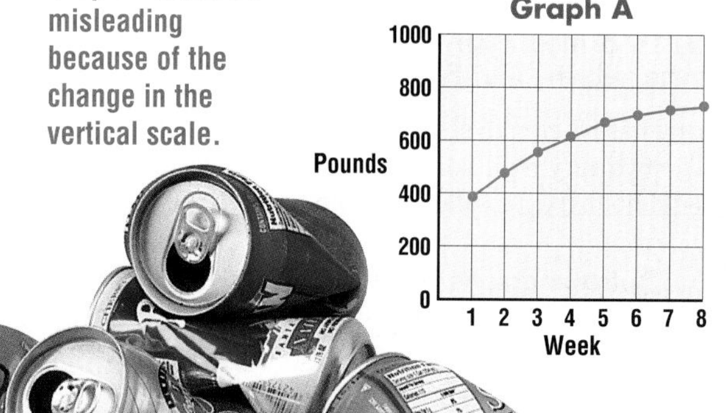

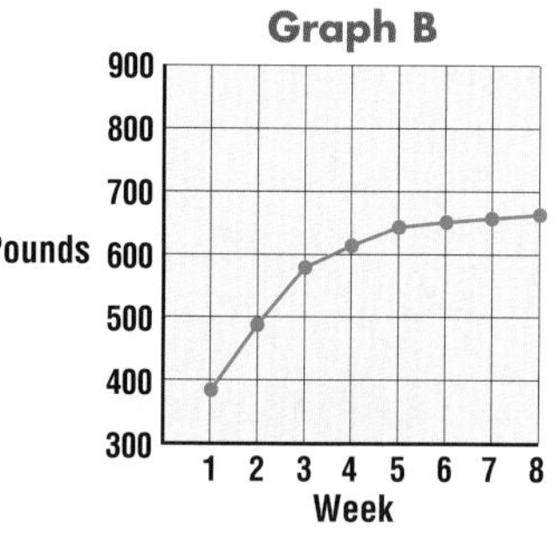

a. Which graph might be used to show that recycling efforts are greatly improving? **Graph B**

b. Which graph could be considered misleading? Explain.

6. ***School*** Belinda's math scores for the quarter are 72, 89, 92, 96, 82, 96, 90, 87, and 91. What misleading statistic could Belinda use to describe how well she's done in class? Explain. **See Answer Appendix.**

3 PRACTICE/APPLY

Check for Understanding

If students need additional practice or instruction after completing Exercises 1–6, one of these options may be helpful.

- Extra Practice, see p. 576
- Reteaching Activity
- *Study Guide Masters,* p. 23
- *Practice Masters,* p. 23

Reteaching the Lesson

Activity Help students make a checklist of all things that might indicate whether a graph or table is misleading. Include checking the vertical scale, checking that the most descriptive measures are used, checking whether all data are shown, and checking how all parts are labeled.

EXERCISES

Practice

7. Either; accept answers students can justify.

7. Both line graphs show ship sales at Marvin's Marina in thousands of dollars. Which graph could be misleading? Explain.

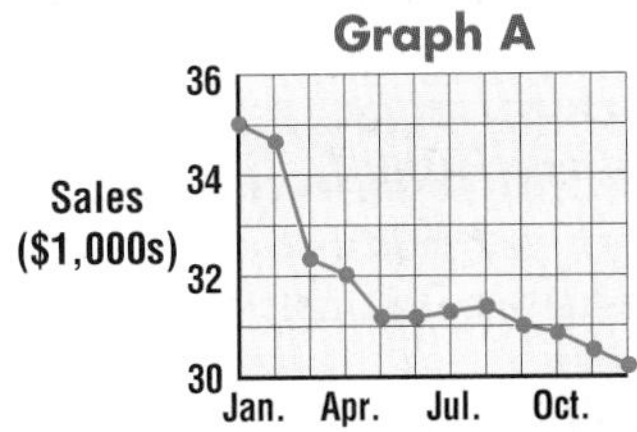

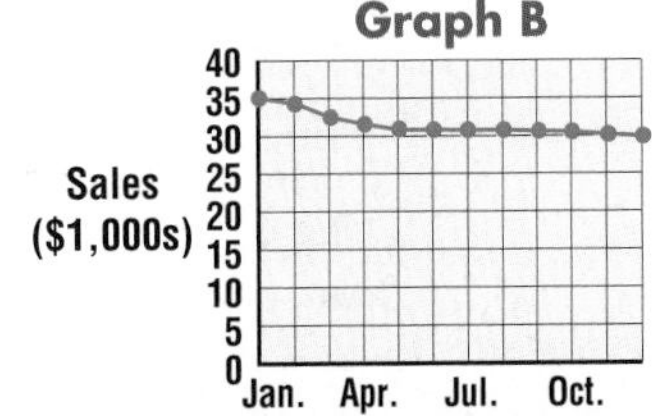

8. ***Geography*** The table shows the areas of 10 Caribbean islands.
   a. Find the mean, mode, and median.
   b. Which average is misleading?
   c. Which average would most accurately describe the data? **median**

   8a. 488.3, none, 150 8b. See margin.

Island	Area (sq mi)	Island	Area (sq mi)
Antiqua	108	Martinique	425
Aruba	75	Puerto Rico	3,339
Barbados	166	Tobago	116
Curacao	171	Virgin Islands, UK	59
Dominica	290	Virgin Islands, U.S.	134

Source: Bureau of the Census

Applications and Problem Solving

Real World

9. ***Marketing*** *Best Bikes* is running an ad claiming that their prices are comparable with *Deals on Wheels,* but their bikes are a much better quality.

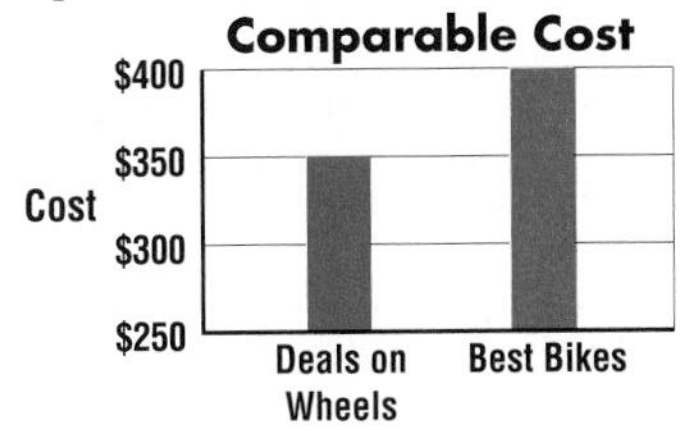

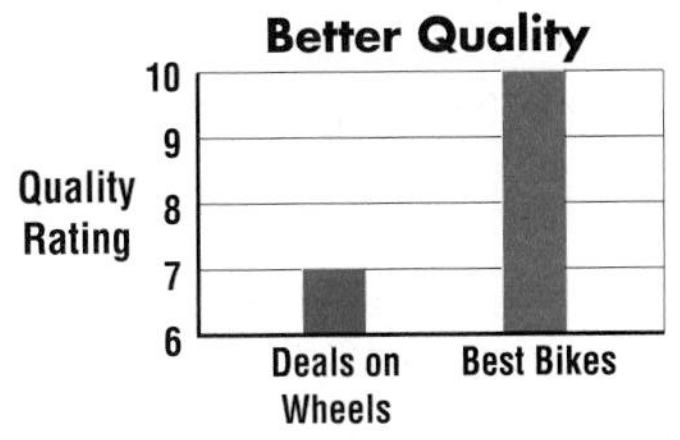

Draw graphs of the same data so that Deals on Wheels' lower prices are better shown. **See Answer Appendix.**

11. No, for example, the median of the set 9, 10, 11, 12, 100 is the same as the median of the set 9, 10, 11, 12, 13.

10. ***Working on the CHAPTER Project*** Refer to the table on page 87.
    a. Draw a bar graph of the data that could be misleading. Explain how the graph is misleading. **a–b. See students' work.**
    b. Draw a bar graph that better represents the data.

For **Extra Practice,** see page 576.

11. ***Critical Thinking*** Do great or small values affect the median of a set of data? Give several examples to support your answer.

Mixed Review

12. ***Statistics*** Refer to the data on countries consuming pasta on page 108. Find the interquartile range. *(Lesson 3-6)* **8.5**

13. **Standardized Test Practice** The rental charge for a car is $78 per day. The 7% sales tax is $5.46. What is the total cost of renting a car for one day? *(Lesson 2-3)* **E**

    A $73.30 **B** $73.46 **C** $83.54 **D** $90.46 **E** Not Here

Assignment Guide

Core: 7–11 odd, 12–13
Enriched: 8, 9, 11–13

Exercise 10 asks students to advance to the next stage of work on the Chapter Project. Encourage students to work together to determine the range and interval of their graphs.

4 ASSESS

Closing Activity

Writing Have students draw a misleading graph or write a misleading advertisement. Have them exchange ads and graphs, examine the one they receive, and explain why it is misleading.

Chapter 3, Quiz D (Lesson 3-7) is available in the *Assessment and Evaluation Masters,* p. 72.

Additional Answer

8b. The mean could be misleading, since all but one of the islands have areas less than that number.

Practice Masters, p. 23

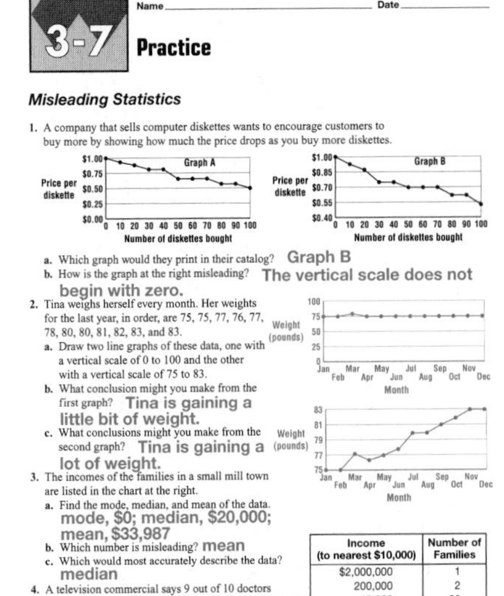

Name ______ Date ______

3-7 **Practice**

Misleading Statistics

1. A company that sells computer diskettes wants to encourage customers to buy more by showing how much the price drops as you buy more diskettes.

   a. Which graph would they print in their catalog? **Graph B**
   b. How is the graph at the right misleading? **The vertical scale does not begin with zero.**

2. Tina weighs herself every month. Her weights for the last year, in order, are 75, 75, 77, 76, 77, 78, 80, 80, 81, 82, 83, and 83.
   a. Draw two line graphs of these data, one with a vertical scale of 0 to 100 and the other with a vertical scale of 75 to 83.
   b. What conclusion might you make from the first graph? **Tina is gaining a little bit of weight.**
   c. What conclusions might you make from the second graph? **Tina is gaining a lot of weight.**

3. The incomes of the families in a small mill town are listed in the chart at the right.
   a. Find the mode, median, and mean of the data. **mode, $0; median, $20,000; mean, $33,987**
   b. Which number is misleading? **mean**
   c. Which would most accurately describe the data? **median**

Income (to nearest $10,000)	Number of Families
$2,000,000	1
200,000	2
40,000	30
30,000	30
20,000	20
10,000	30
0	40

4. A television commercial says 9 out of 10 doctors recommend Blyer's Aspirin. Do you think this survey is reliable? Why or why not? **The survey is not reliable because it says nothing about which doctors were surveyed or exactly what questions were asked.**

© Glencoe/McGraw-Hill T23 *Mathematics: Applications and Connections, Course 2*

Extending the Lesson

Enrichment Masters, p. 23

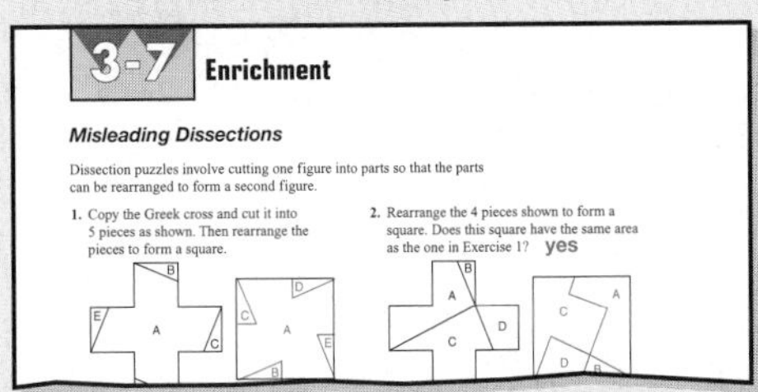

3-7 **Enrichment**

Misleading Dissections

Dissection puzzles involve cutting one figure into parts so that the parts can be rearranged to form a second figure.

1. Copy the Greek cross and cut it into 5 pieces as shown. Then rearrange the pieces to form a square.
2. Rearrange the 4 pieces shown to form a square. Does this square have the same area as the one in Exercise 1? **yes**

Activity Have students investigate the current population of the world compared to Earth's land area. How many people could live on each square mile of land? Have students contrast this number with the population density of your state. Given the results, ask why they often hear about a "problem of overpopulation." Is this term misleading?

Vocabulary

This section provides a listing of the new terms, properties, and phrases that were introduced in this chapter. Have students define each term and provide an example or two of it, if appropriate.

Understanding and Using the Vocabulary

These exercises check students' understanding of the terms by using a variety of verbal formats including matching, completion, and true/false.

Glossaries A complete glossary of terms appears on pages 656–663. The glossary also appears in Spanish on pages 664–672.

Additional Answers

11. Find the least and greatest numbers. Draw a vertical line and determine the stems. Write these numbers from least to greatest to the left of the line. Write the leaves, which are the last digits, from least to greatest to the right of the line, next to the corresponding stems. Include an explanation.

12. 42; Sample answer: 0–45; 5

13. 475; Sample answer: 50–600; 50

14. 10.6; Sample answer: 0–12; 2

15. Sample answer: 2–6; 1

Number of People	Tally	Frequency
2	||	2
3	𝍸	5
4	𝍸 𝍸	10
5	𝍸	5
6	||	2

16. Sample answer: between $35,000 and $40,000

Study Guide and Assessment

interNET CONNECTION Chapter Review **For additional lesson-by-lesson review, visit: www.glencoe.com/sec/math/mac/mathnet**

Vocabulary

After completing this chapter, you should be able to define each term, concept, or phrase and give an example or two of each.

Statistics and Probability
arithmetic average (p. 102)
back-to-back stem-and-leaf plot (p. 109)
bar graph (p. 94)
box-and-whisker plot (p. 114)
cluster (p. 98)
frequency table (p. 88)
interquartile range (pp. 112, 115)
interval (p. 88)
leaf (p. 108)
line graph (p. 94)
line plot (p. 98)
lower extreme (p. 114)
lower quartile (p. 114)
mean (p. 102)
median (p. 102)
mode (p. 102)
outlier (p. 115)
quartile (p. 112)
range (p. 88)
scale (p. 88)
scatter plot (p. 92, 95)
stem (p. 108)
stem-and-leaf plot (p. 108)
upper extreme (p. 114)
upper quartile (p. 114)

Problem Solving
use a graph (p. 92)

Understanding and Using the Vocabulary

Choose the letter of the term that best matches each phrase.

1. the difference between the greatest number and the least number in a set of data **e**
2. separates the scale into equal parts **a**
3. graphs that are useful in predicting future events since they show trends over time **g**
4. graphs that use bars to make comparisons **f**
5. plots showing two sets of related data on the same graph **b**
6. data that are grouped closely together **j**
7. the arithmetic average of a set of data **k**
8. the number or item that appears most often in a set of data **h**
9. the middle number in a set of data when the data are arranged in numerical order **d**
10. a plot used to display a large data set to make it easier to read **i**

a. interval
b. scatter plot
c. outlier
d. median
e. range
f. bar graph
g. line graph
h. mode
i. stem-and-leaf plot
j. cluster
k. mean

In Your Own Words

11. ***Explain*** how to make a stem-and-leaf plot. **See margin.**

MindJogger Videoquizzes

MindJogger Videoquizzes provide an alternative review of concepts presented in this chapter. Students work in teams to answer questions, gaining points for correct answers. The questions are presented in three rounds.
Round 1 Concepts–5 questions
Round 2 Skills–4 questions
Round 3 Problem Solving–4 questions

Objectives & Examples

Upon completing this chapter, you should be able to:

- choose appropriate scales and intervals for data and organize data in a table *(Lesson 3-1)*

Find the range and an appropriate scale and interval for 11, 2, 22, 13, 15, 14, 18, 7, 20, 10, 19.

range = 22 − 2 = 20
scale: 0 to 24
interval of 6

Make a frequency table of the data.

Interval	Tally	Frequency
0-6	I	1
7-12	III	3
13-18	IIII	4
19-24	III	3

Review Exercises

Use these exercises to review and prepare for the chapter test.

Find the range for each set of data. Choose an appropriate scale and interval. **12–15. See margin.**

12. 3, 12, 1, 43, 25, 16

13. 75, 150, 100, 400, 550

14. 2.3, 11.9, 7.6, 1.3, 4.8

15. Choose the appropriate scale and an interval for the data. Then make a frequency table.

People in Your Family					
3	2	4	4	3	5
6	4	5	6	4	4
5	3	4	5	4	5
3	4	2	4	3	4

- make predictions from graphs *(Lesson 3-2)*

What is the most common response to the question "How many children are in your family?"

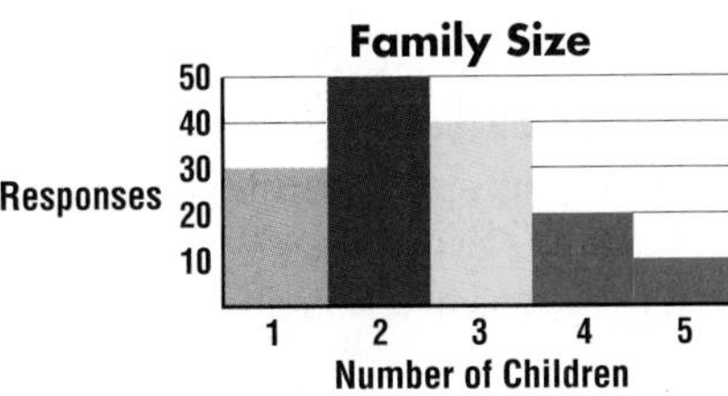

The most common response is 2.

16. ***Finance*** Isabel displayed her salary for the last five years in the line graph. Predict her salary after three more years. **See margin.**

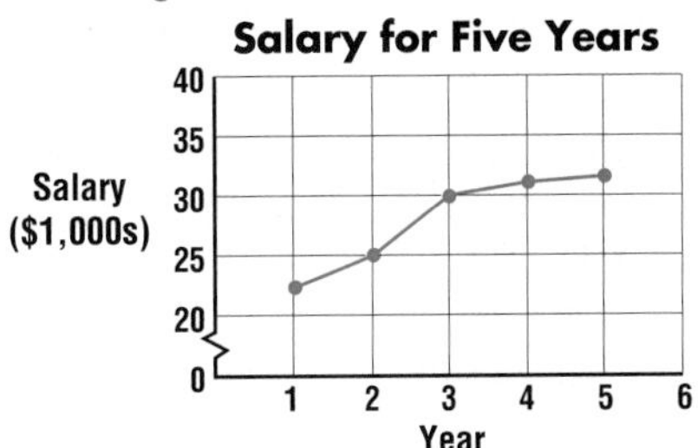

- construct line plots *(Lesson 3-3)*

Make a line plot for 5, 7, 3, 8, 3, 2, 8, 4, 15, 12.

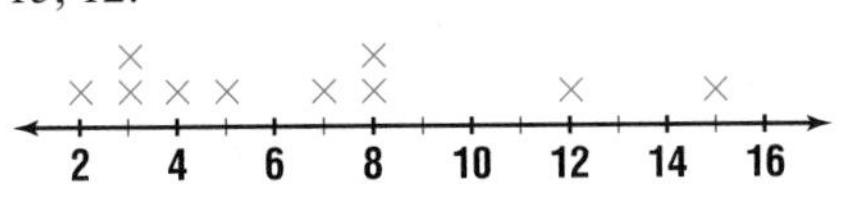

17–20. See Answer Appendix.
Make a line plot for each set of data.

17. 10, 12, 10, 8, 13, 10, 8, 12

18. 7.9, 8.3, 8.1, 8.3, 8.5, 8.9, 8.3, 8.5

19. 550, 554, 545, 553, 550, 554, 548, 553, 554

20. 43, 41, 42, 45, 43, 42, 43, 46, 44, 44

Assessment and Evaluation

Six forms of Chapter 3 Test are available in the *Assessment and Evaluation Masters* as shown in the chart.

1A	Multiple Choice	Honors
1B	Multiple Choice	Average
1C	Multiple Choice	Basic
2A	Free Response	Honors
2B	Free Response	Average
2C	Free Response	Basic

Chapter 3 Test, Form 1B, is shown at the right. Chapter 3 Test, Form 2B, is shown on the next page.

Objectives & Examples

This section reviews the skills and concepts of the chapter and shows completely worked examples.

Review Exercises

These exercises provide practice for the corresponding objectives.

***Assessment and Evaluation Masters*, pp. 59–60**

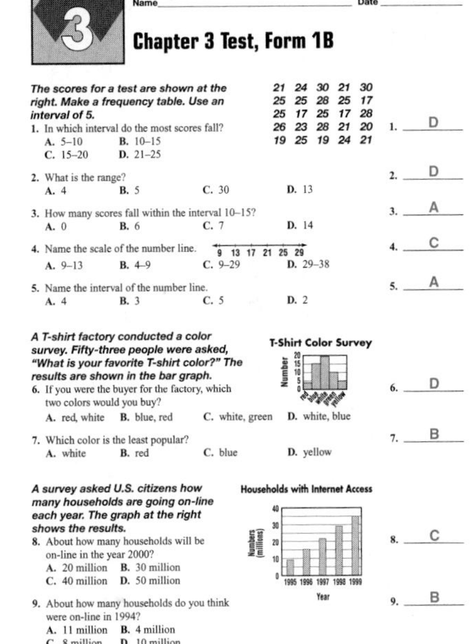

Name______________ Date__________

Chapter 3 Test, Form 1B

The scores for a test are shown at the right. Make a frequency table. Use an interval of 5.

21	24	30	21	30
25	25	28	25	17
25	17	25	17	28
26	23	28	21	20
19	25	19	24	21

1. In which interval do the most scores fall? A. 5–10 B. 10–15 C. 15–20 D. 21–25 — 1. D
2. What is the range? A. 4 B. 5 C. 30 D. 13 — 2. D
3. How many scores fall within the interval 10–15? A. 0 B. 6 C. 7 D. 14 — 3. A
4. Name the scale of the number line. (9 13 17 21 25 29) A. 9–13 B. 4–9 C. 9–29 D. 29–38 — 4. C
5. Name the interval of the number line. A. 4 B. 3 C. 5 D. 2 — 5. A

A T-shirt factory conducted a color survey. Fifty-three people were asked, "What is your favorite T-shirt color?" The results are shown in the bar graph.

T-Shirt Color Survey (Number: 0, 5, 10, 15, 20; red, blue, white, green, yellow)

6. If you were the buyer for the factory, which two colors would you buy? A. red, white B. blue, red C. white, green D. white, blue — 6. D
7. Which color is the least popular? A. white B. red C. blue D. yellow — 7. B

A survey asked U.S. citizens how many households are going on-line each year. The graph at the right shows the results.

Households with Internet Access (Numbers (millions): 0, 10, 20, 30, 40; Year: 1995, 1996, 1997, 1998, 1999)

8. About how many households will be on-line in the year 2000? A. 20 million B. 30 million C. 40 million D. 50 million — 8. C
9. About how many households do you think were on-line in 1994? A. 11 million B. 4 million C. 8 million D. 10 million — 9. B

© Glencoe/McGraw-Hill 59 *Mathematics: Applications and Connections, Course 2*

Chapter 3 Test, Form 1B (continued)

10. Name the cluster in the line plot. A. 0 – 12 B. 0 – 6 C. 3 – 6 D. 6 – 12 — 10. B 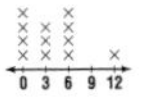
11. Find the mode(s) of 22, 25, 27, 28, 30, 27, and 23. A. 30 B. 25 C. 23 D. 27 — 11. D
12. Find the median of 15, 19, 20, 21, 22, 24, and 24. A. 21 B. 20 C. 15 D. 24 — 12. A
13. Find the mean of 31, 25, 20, 18, 22, and 28. A. 22 B. 24 C. 144 D. 25 — 13. B
14. Which digit in the numbers 59, 69, 67, 66, 74, 78, 79, 83, and 88 would *not* appear as a *stem* when drawing a stem-and-leaf plot? A. 5 B. 8 C. 7 D. 9 — 14. D

The stem-and-leaf plot shows the scores on a mathematics test.

Stem	Leaf
6	3 5 8
7	5 6 6 7
8	3 5 5 5
9	6 9

6|5 = 65

15. Name the highest score on the test. A. 100 B. 98 C. 99 D. 58 — 15. C
16. Name the score that appears the most often. A. 85 B. 76 C. 67 D. 58 — 16. A

Use the box-and-whisker plot for Questions 17 and 18. (40 50 60 70 80 90 100)

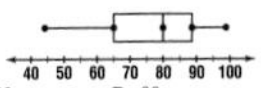

17. Find the median. A. 65 B. 89 C. 80 D. 99 — 17. C
18. Find the lower and upper quartiles. A. 44, 99 B. 65, 89 C. 65, 80 D. 89, 99 — 18. B
19. The salaries at the Economy Company are $76,000, $18,000, $12,000, $24,000, $28,000, $58,000, $12,000, $18,000, $24,000, $24,000, $18,000, $24,000, and $18,000. What number would make the company look the most attractive to new employees? A. mean B. mode C. median or mode D. median — 19. A
20. Jed wants to prove that his English grades have improved. He graphs them as shown at the right. What makes his graph misleading? A. the origin B. the scale C. Some information is missing. D. the origin and the scale — 20. D

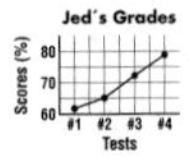

Jed's Grades (Scores (%): 60, 70, 80; Tests: #1 #2 #3 #4)

© Glencoe/McGraw-Hill 60 *Mathematics: Applications and Connections, Course 2*

Additional Answer

29b. The mean; six of the scores were well above 81.6.

Assessment and Evaluation Masters, pp. 65–66

Name____________________ Date__________

3 Chapter 3 Test, Form 2B

Use the frequency table for Questions 1–3.

Grade 7 Students

Weight (kg)	Tally	Number of Students
40–44	III	3
45–49	𝍸I	6
50–54	𝍸𝍸	10
55–59	IIII	4
60–64	III	3
65–69	I	1

1. How many students weigh 50 kilograms or more? 1. 18
2. What is the scale? 2. 40–69
3. What is the interval? 3. 5
4. Sonja's golf scores for five rounds were 88, 83, 87, 80, and 90. Find an appropriate scale and interval. Draw a line plot to show them. 4.

The graph shows men's shirt sales for the month of March.

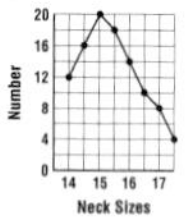

5. Which were the two most popular neck sizes? 5. 15, $15\frac{1}{2}$
6. About how many men might be a size 18 shirt? 6. 2

Make a line plot for each set of data.

7. 0, 2, 1, 0, 2, 3, 2, 1, 3, 4, 3, 4, 7 7.

8. 15, 20, 20, 17, 17, 19, 18, 19, 18, 19, 18, 17 8.

Find the mode(s), median, and mean for each set of data.

9. 6, 11, 40, 11, 5, 2, 9, 12, 12 9. 11, 12; 11; 12
10. 60, 68, 64, 60, 63, 60, 67, 73, 58, 60, 49 10. 60; 60; 62

John Stockton scored 27, 33, 18, 32, 35, 22, 31, 39, 28, and 26 points in ten games.

11. Make a stem-and-leaf plot of these data. 11.

Stem	Leaf
1	8
2	2 6 7 8
3	1 2 3 5 9

2|2 = 22

12. About how many points might you expect John Stockton to score in a game? 12. Sample answer: 25 to 35

3 Chapter 3 Test, Form 2B (continued)

Use the box-and-whisker plot for Questions 13–16.

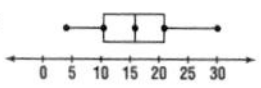

13. What is the lower quartile? 13. 10.5
14. What is the upper extreme? 14. 30
15. What is the interquartile range? 15. 10.5
16. Are there any outliers? 16. no
17. Draw a box-and-whisker plot of the data shown in the stem-and-leaf plot. 17.

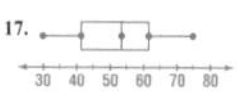

Stem	Leaf
3	0 1 1 2
4	1 2 2 3
5	4 5 5 5
6	0 1 1 2
7	0 5

3|0 = 30

Both graphs show the number of congressional bills vetoed by U.S. presidents from 1974–1996.

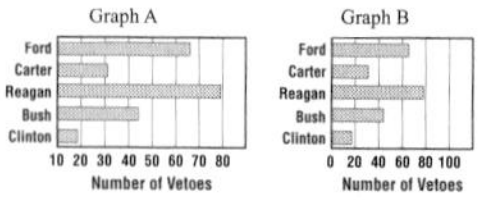

18. Which graph could be misleading? 18. Graph A
19. What could be changed to make the graph less misleading? 19. Sample answers: set the origin to 0; reduce the scale.
20. Keisha is helping her parents plan a family reunion. She tallies the number of people who have come to the last six reunions. Keisha needs to find out about how many guests to expect. Why will the mean not help her? 20. The data contain an outlier.

Year	Number of Guests
1992	13
1993	65
1994	72
1995	72
1996	105
1997	86

Objectives & Examples

Review Exercises

find the mean, median, and mode of a set of data *(Lesson 3-4)*

Find the mean, mode(s), and median for 23, 21, 18, 19, 20, 19, 20, and 19.

mean: $\frac{23 + 21 + 18 + 19 + 20 + 19 + 20 + 19}{8} = 19.875$

mode: 19 median: 19.5

Find the mean, mode(s), and median for each set of data. 22. 24.4, 18 and 31, 24

21. 2, 3, 4, 3, 4, 3, 8, 7, 2 **4, 3, 3**
22. 31, 24, 26, 18, 23, 31, 18
23. 89, 76, 93, 100, 72, 86, 74 **84.3, none, 86**
24. 54,000, 49,000, 112,000, 89,000, 76,000, 65,000 **74,166.7; none; 70,500**

construct and interpret stem-and-leaf plots *(Lesson 3-5)*

Construct a stem-and-leaf plot for 12, 15, 17, 20, 22, 22, 23, 25, 27, 35, 52.

Stem	Leaf
1	2 5 7
2	0 2 2 3 5 7
3	5
4	
5	2 *5|2 = 52*

25–27. See Answer Appendix.

Write the stems that would be used in a stem-and-leaf plot for each set of data. Then make the stem-and-leaf plot.

25. 75, 61, 83, 99, 78, 85, 87, 92, 77, 78, 60, 53, 87, 89, 91, 90
26. 29¢, 54¢, 31¢, 26¢, 38¢, 46¢, 23¢, 21¢, 32¢, 37¢
27. Make a back-to-back stem-and-leaf plot for the following temperatures (°F).

    Seattle: 52, 60, 61, 46, 80, 62, 70, 77, 53, 85, 54, 62, 72, 68, 78, 69

    Olympia: 60, 53, 68, 72, 66, 80, 73, 51, 62, 48, 56, 84, 77, 45, 79, 65

construct and interpret box-and-whisker plots *(Lesson 3-6)*

Construct a box-and-whisker plot of the English quiz scores: 12, 12, 13, 14, 14, 15, 15, 15, 16, 16, 17, 18, 20.

median: 15 UQ: 16.5 LQ: 13.5
upper extreme: 20 lower extreme: 12

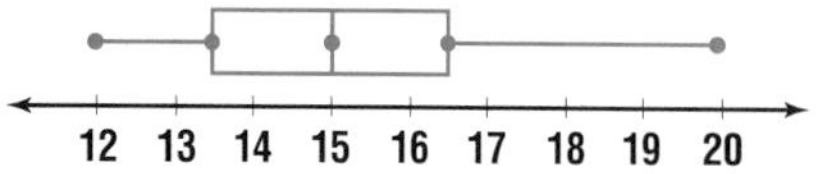

28. The points scored in a game by each player on the girls basketball team are 6, 4, 15, 3, 11, 8, 2, 9, 4, and 2.
    a. What is the median? **5**
    b. What is the upper quartile and lower quartile? **9, 3**
    c. What is the upper extreme and the lower extreme? **15, 2**
    d. Draw a box-and-whisker plot of the points scored. **See Answer Appendix.**

recognize when statistics and graphs are misleading *(Lesson 3-7)*

When you are given insufficient background information or an incomplete picture of the data, the data may be misleading.

29. Gina's test scores are 89, 92, 87, 86, 95, 93, and 29.
    a. Find the mean, mode, and median of the scores. **81.6, none, 89**
    b. Which number is misleading? Explain. **See margin.**

Test and Review Software

You may use this software, a combination of an item generator and item bank, to create your own tests or worksheets. Types of items include free response, multiple choice, short answer, and open ended.

CD-ROM Program

The CD-ROM Program contains an Assessment Game whose questions review the concepts in this chapter.

Applications & Problem Solving

30. ***Use a Graph*** Francine is keeping track of her savings account balance each month. How much money do you think she will have in her savings account in the 7th month? *(Lesson 3-2A)*

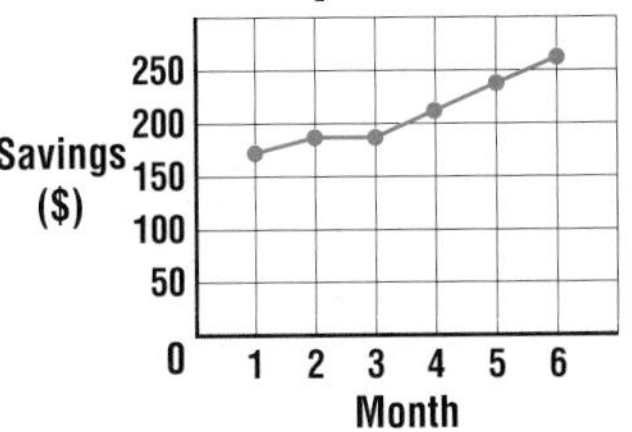

Sample answer: $275

31. ***Jobs*** The hourly wage of eight students at their after-school jobs is $4.65, $5.15, $4.90, $5.25, $4.90, $5.00, $5.50, $4.80. Find the mean, mode, and median. *(Lesson 3-4)* **$5.02, $4.90, $4.95**

32. ***Earth Science*** The table shows the average water speeds of various ocean currents, rivers, and bores (tidal waves). Make a stem-and-leaf plot of the data. *(Lesson 3-5)* **See margin.**

Water	Speed (mph)
Amazon River	2
Antarctic Circumpolar Current	1
Ganges Bore	17
Gulf Stream	5
Lava Falls, Colorado R.	30
Mississippi River	2
Pentland Firth	12
Severn Bore	13
Saltstraumen Current	18

Source: *Encyclopedia Britannica*

Alternative Assessment

Open Ended

Suppose you took a survey, asking your classmates how much they spent for lunch yesterday. The responses are $1.50, $2.30, $0.99, $1.50, $2.00, $1.50, $1.75, $2.30, $1.75, $2.00, $3.15, $1.75, $2.00, $3.15, $1.75, $2.00, $1.75, $2.30, $1.75, and $1.50. How can you organize the data to determine the most common response? **See Answer Appendix.**

Select your favorite application problem from this chapter and place it in your portfolio. Attach a note explaining why it is your favorite.

Completing the CHAPTER Project

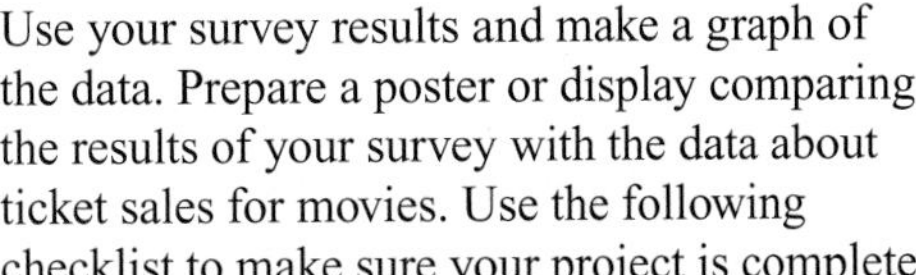

Use your survey results and make a graph of the data. Prepare a poster or display comparing the results of your survey with the data about ticket sales for movies. Use the following checklist to make sure your project is complete.

- ☑ The frequency table of your survey results is included.
- ☑ A graph of your survey results is clear and easy to read.
- ☑ A paragraph comparing your survey results to the rating in the table on page 87 includes which method you think is best for determining the most popular movies—using ticket sales or surveying people.

A practice test for Chapter 3 is provided on page 609.

Additional Answer

32.

Stem	Leaf
0	1 2 2 5
1	2 3 7 8
2	
3	0

1|2 = 12 mph

Performance Assessment

Additional performance assessment tasks for this chapter are included in the *Assessment and Evaluation Masters* on page 69. A scoring guide is also provided on page 81.

Applications & Problem Solving

This section provides additional practice in solving real-world problems that involve the skills of this chapter.

Alternative Assessment

The ***Open Ended*** section provides students with a performance assessment opportunity to evaluate their work and understanding.

Students should complete the final stages of their project and prepare a class demonstration of their results. A scoring guide for the project is available in the *Investigations and Projects Masters,* p. 27.

Students should add to their portfolios at this time.

Assessment and Evaluation Masters, p. 69

Name____________ Date______

Chapter 3 Performance Assessment

Instructions: Demonstrate your knowledge by giving a clear, concise solution to each problem. Be sure to include all relevant drawings and justify your answers. You may show your solutions in more than one way or investigate beyond the requirements of the problems.

1. The graph below gives the mean of the total scores of two teams for all of their football games in each year from 1990 through 1999.

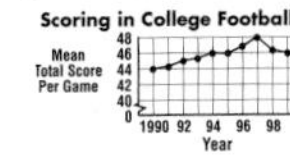

   a. What was the mean total score per college football game in 1994?

   b. What would you expect the mean total score to be in 2000? Explain your answer.

   c. Give two or three changes, real or imagined, that could account for the decline in total scores after 1997. Example: The time of play may have been shortened.

   d. Explain why the graph might be considered misleading.

2. The number of home runs hit by Babe Ruth each year from 1918 through 1931 were 11, 29, 54, 59, 35, 41, 46, 33, 47, 60, 54, 46, 49, and 46.

   a. Make a line plot for the set of data. Explain what is meant by a *cluster.* Circle any clusters on the line plot.

   b. Explain in your own words what is meant by the *mean, median,* and *mode* of a set of data. Find the mean, median, and mode of the set of data. Show your work.

   c. Make a stem-and-leaf plot of the number of home runs Babe Ruth hit each year. Explain each step.

   d. Draw a box-and-whisker plot of the data. Explain each step.

 69 *Mathematics: Applications and Connections, Course 2*

The Standardized Test Practice may be used to help students prepare for standardized tests. The test items are written in the same style as those in state proficiency tests and standardized tests like CAT, CTBS, ITBS, MAT, SAT, and Terra Nova. The test items cover skills and concepts covered up to this point in the text.

The pages can be used as an overnight assessment. After students have completed the pages, discuss how each problem can be solved, or provide copies of the solutions from the *Solutions Manual.*

***Assessment and Evaluation Masters*, p. 75**

3

Name__________ Date__________

Cumulative Review, Chapters 1–3

Evaluate each expression if a = 4, b = 5, and c = 2. (Lesson 1-3)

1. $b + \frac{a}{c}$ 2. $a(b + c)$

3. Write $5 \cdot 5 \cdot 5 \cdot 5 \cdot 5 \cdot 5 \cdot 5$ using exponents. (Lesson 1-4)

4. Write 6^4 as a product of the same factor. (Lesson 1-4)

5. Solve $10 + x = 16$. (Lesson 1-5)

6. Find the length of a rectangular lawn with an area of 160 square feet and a width of 8 feet. (Lesson 1-7)

Estimate by rounding. (Lesson 2-3)

7. $42.8 - 17.3$ 8. 50.3×5.1

Multiply or divide. (Lessons 2-4 and 2-6)

9. $19.20\overline{)54.72}$ 10. 3.25×9.79

Write each number in scientific notation. (Lesson 2-9)

11. 6,700,000 12. 31,400

13. Make a line plot for the data 32, 29, 35, 30, 32, 29, 34, 33, and 29. (Lesson 3-3)

Find the following for the data in Question 13. (Lessons 3-1 and 3-4)

14. range 15. mode(s)

16. median 17. mean

18. Make a stem-and-leaf plot for the data 11, 19, 35, 44, 25, 17, 23, 19, 40, 33, 14, and 19. (Lesson 3-5)

19. Make a box-and-whisker plot for the data 0, 4, 6, 11, 9, 8, 9, 1, 5, 9, and 7. (Lesson 3-6)

20. What are the upper quartile and the lower extreme for Question 19? (Lesson 3-6)

Answers:

1. 7
2. 28
3. 5^7
4. $6 \cdot 6 \cdot 6 \cdot 6$
5. 6
6. 20 feet
7. $43 - 17 = 26$
8. $50 \times 5 = 250$
9. 2.85
10. 31.8175
11. 6.7×10^6
12. 3.14×10^4
13. 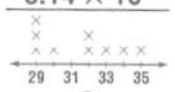

14. 6
15. 29
16. 32
17. $31.\overline{4}$
18.

stem	leaf
1	1 4 7 9 9 9
2	3 5
3	3 5
4	0 4

4|0 = 40

19. 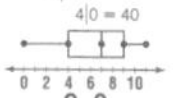

20. 9, 0

 75 *Mathematics: Applications and Connections, Course 2*

CHAPTERS 1–3

Standardized Test Practice

Assessing Knowledge & Skills

Section One: Multiple Choice

There are eight multiple choice questions in this section. Choose the best answer. If a correct answer is *not here,* choose the letter for Not Here.

1. Armando has 3 fewer hats than Denise. Tien has twice as many hats as Armando. If Denise has x hats, which number sentence represents the number of hats that Tien has? **C**

A $x - 3$
B $3x$
C $2(x - 3)$
D $3(x - 3)$

2. Which expression is the same as v^6? **J**

F $v + v + v + v + v + v$
G $6v$
H $v^3 + v^3$
J $v \times v \times v \times v \times v \times v$

3. The line plot shows how far in kilometers some students live from the school. How many students are represented in the plot? **C**

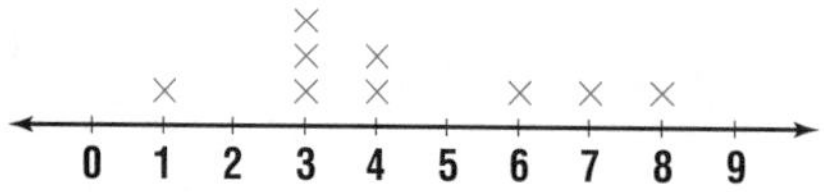

A 5
B 7
C 9
D 8

Please note that Questions 4–8 have five answer choices.

4. Students at Karlon High School have collected money this year for a charity.

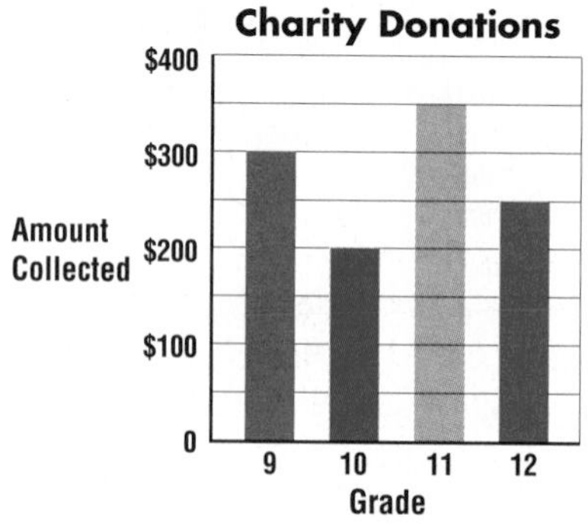

According to the graph, how much did all four classes collect this year? **G**

F $950
G $1,100
H $1,050
J $1,000
K $1,150

5. There are 22 tables in the cafeteria at Evan Middle School. If there are 10 chairs at each table and 15 chairs in the cafeteria are empty, which number sentence can be used to find the number of students seated, N? **A**

A $N = (22 \times 10) - 15$
B $N = (22 + 10) + 15$
C $N = (22 - 10) + 15$
D $N = (22 \times 10) + 15$
E $N = (22 - 10) \times 15$

◀◀◀Instructional Resources

Another cumulative review is shown at the left and is available in the *Assessment and Evaluation Masters,* p. 75.

6. The table shows the cost of three items that Ricci bought, all including tax.

Item	Cost
purse	$12.45
pair of earrings	$3.95
wallet	$5.85

Which is the best estimate of the total cost of the three items? **H**

F less than $10
G between $10 and $20
H between $20 and $30
J between $30 and $40
K more than $40

7. Franklin earned $13.75 in one week by baby-sitting 5.5 hours. How much was Franklin paid per hour? **B**

A $2.10
B $2.50
C $3.05
D $3.50
E Not Here

8. A soybean harvesting company collects soybeans to be used in the production of baby formula. If the company sold 158.6 tons, 200 tons, and 82.04 tons of soybeans in the last three months, what were the company's total soybean sales for that period? **F**

F 440.64 tons
G 438.84 tons
H 441.0 tons
J 438.0 tons
K Not Here

Test-Taking Tip THE PRINCETON REVIEW

Sometimes it is better to study in groups for a standardized test. If other students will motivate you to succeed, then working together is a great advantage. Explaining concepts to others will reinforce those concepts in your own mind. Teaching others is a great way to find out how much you know.

Section Two: Free Response

This section contains four questions for which you will provide short answers. Write your answers on your paper.

9. What is the value of $3[2(20-18)-4]$? **0**

10. Use the data in Exercise 3. What is the median distance? If necessary, round to the nearest tenth. **4 km**

11. A business had weekly profits of $5,000, $3,000, $2,000, $2,500, and $5,000. Which average might be misleading: the mode, the median, or the mean? **mode**

12. To the nearest tenth, find the area of the rectangle shown below. **3.5 m²**

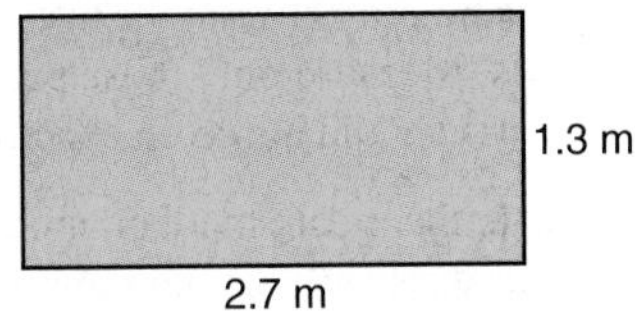

Test Practice For additional test practice questions, visit:

www.glencoe.com/sec/math/mac/mathnet

Instructional Resources ►►►

Additional standardized test practice is shown at the right and is available in the *Assessment and Evaluation Masters,* pp. 73–74.

Test-Taking Tip

Remind students that studying with other students can be mutually beneficial. By discussing what is clear and what is not clear to them, students can help each other fill in the gaps in their understanding.

Assessment and Evaluation Masters, pp. 73–74

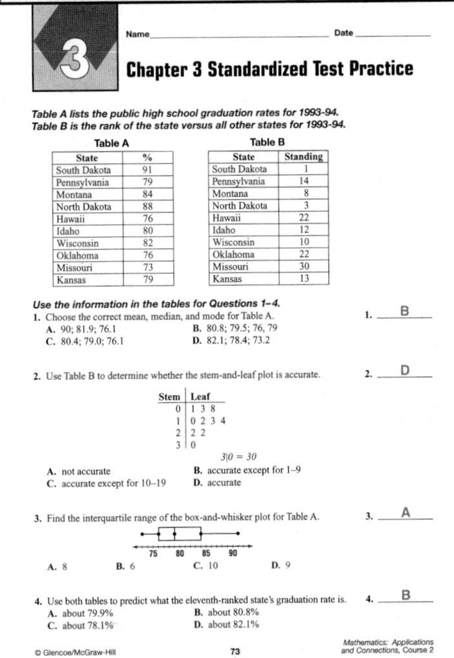

Name ____________ Date ____________

3 Chapter 3 Standardized Test Practice

Table A lists the public high school graduation rates for 1993-94.
Table B is the rank of the state versus all other states for 1993-94.

Table A

State	%
South Dakota	91
Pennsylvania	79
Montana	84
North Dakota	88
Hawaii	76
Idaho	80
Wisconsin	82
Oklahoma	76
Missouri	73
Kansas	79

Table B

State	Standing
South Dakota	1
Pennsylvania	14
Montana	8
North Dakota	3
Hawaii	22
Idaho	12
Wisconsin	10
Oklahoma	22
Missouri	30
Kansas	13

Use the information in the tables for Questions 1–4.

1. Choose the correct mean, median, and mode for Table A. — 1. B
   A. 90; 81.9; 76.1 B. 80.8; 79.5; 76, 79
   C. 80.4; 79.0; 76.1 D. 82.1; 78.4; 73.2

2. Use Table B to determine whether the stem-and-leaf plot is accurate. — 2. D

Stem	Leaf
0	1 3 8
1	0 2 3 4
2	2 2
3	0

3|0 = 30

   A. not accurate B. accurate except for 1–9
   C. accurate except for 10–19 D. accurate

3. Find the interquartile range of the box-and-whisker plot for Table A. — 3. A

75 80 85 90

   A. 8 B. 6 C. 10 D. 9

4. Use both tables to predict what the eleventh-ranked state's graduation rate is. — 4. B
   A. about 79.9% B. about 80.8%
   C. about 78.1% D. about 82.1%

 73 *Mathematics: Applications and Connections, Course 2*

3 Chapter 3 Standardized Test Practice (continued)

Table D

Baseball Stadiums' Home Run Distance to Center Field			
Home Team (NL)	**Distance (ft)**	**Home Team (AL)**	**Distance (ft)**
Braves	400	Yankees	410
Cubs	400	Tigers	440
Astros	400	Angels	404
Phillies	408	Mariners	405
Mets	410	A's	400
Marlins	410	White Sox	400
Giants	400	Twins	408
Brewers	402	Royals	400
Cardinals	402	Orioles	400
Rockies	415	Red Sox	420
Padres	405	Indians	405
Dodgers	395	Rangers	400
Reds	404	Blue Jays	400
Expos	404	Devil Rays	407
Pirates	400		
Diamondbacks	402		

Distance (ft)	Tally	Frequency
395–399	I	1
400–404	卌 卌 卌 II	17
405–409	卌 I	6
410–414	III	3
415–500	III	3

5. The frequency table for Table D is: — 5. C
   A. accurate.
   B. inaccurate, because the numbers don't match up.
   C. accurate, though the interval of the scale is inaccurate.
   D. inaccurate, because the frequency is wrong.

6. How many square feet of carpet are needed to cover a floor that measures 8.5 feet by 12 feet? — 6. D
   A. 41 ft² B. 53.6 ft² C. 204 ft² D. 102 ft²

7. Evaluate $b - \frac{c}{a}$ if $a = 3$, $b = 7$, and $c = 12$. — 7. B
   A. −2 B. 3 C. 4 D. 10

8. Write 4,600,510 in scientific notation. — 8. A
   A. 4.60051×10^6 B. 46.00510×10^5
   C. 4.600510×10^5 D. 4.600510×10^4

9. Estimate the product of 7.3 and 5.8. — 9. D
   A. 1.5 B. 50 C. 21 D. 42

10. Complete 240,100 mg = __?__ kg. — 10. B
   A. 2.401 B. 0.2401 C. 240.1 D. 24.01

 74 *Mathematics: Applications and Connections, Course 2*

Interdisciplinary Investigation

GET READY

This optional investigation is designed to be completed by a group of 4 or 5 students over several days or several weeks.

Mathematical Overview

This investigation utilizes the concepts from Chapters 1–3.

- measuring length
- finding the mean, median, mode, and range of a set of data
- drawing statistical graphs

Time Management	
Gathering Data	30 minutes
Calculations	30 minutes
Creating Graphs	40 minutes
Summarizing Data	20 minutes
Presentation	10 minutes

Instructional Resources

- *Investigations and Projects Masters,* pp. 1–4
- *Manipulative Kit*
  - tape measure

***Investigations and Projects Masters,* p. 4**

Name ____________ Date ____________

Interdisciplinary Investigation
(Student Edition, Pages 128–129)

If the Shoe Fits...

Use this table to record your data.

Person	Length (Boys)	Length (Girls)	Length (Boys & Girls)
Mean			
Median			
Mode			
Range			

Display your results in a graph.

Write a concluding statement that describes the data.

 4 *Mathematics: Applications and Connections, Course 2*

Interdisciplinary Investigation

IF THE SHOE FITS . . .

What do you look like? The answer to this question would probably include how tall you are, what color eyes you have, what color hair you have, and whether you are light-skinned or dark-skinned. These traits are passed from parents to their children by the action of *genes.*

Another trait you have is the length of your foot. There may be other students in your class who have the same foot length as you do. However, most probably have a different foot length. There are many different foot lengths because this trait is influenced by genetic and other factors.

What You'll Do

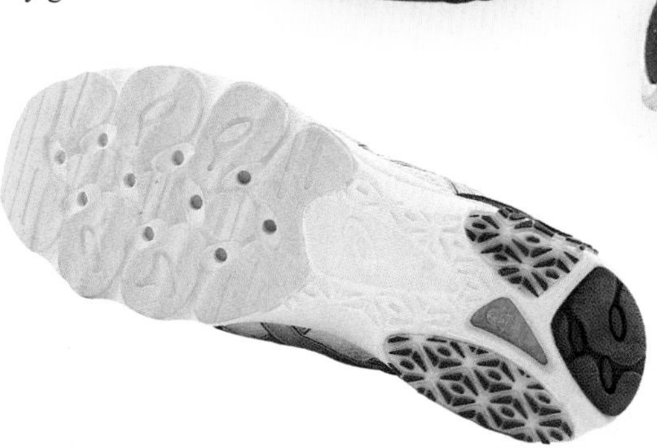

In this investigation, you will collect data about the human foot, analyze it, and design a method to display the results.

Materials  tape measure

 calculator

Procedure

1. Work in a group. Each group should measure the feet of at least ten people who are between the ages of 10 and 18. Include both boys and girls. Measure only those people who are willing to let you. Your class should agree on exactly how to measure the length.
2. Calculate the mean, median, mode, and range of foot length for boys, for girls, and for boys and girls together.
3. Display your results graphically.
4. Write a concluding statement that describes the data.

Technology Tips

- Use a **spreadsheet** or **database** to determine the mean.
- Use **graphing software** to display the data.
- Use **publishing software** to develop ads and brochures.

◀◀◀ Instructional Resources

A recording sheet to help students organize their data for this investigationis shown at the left and is available in the *Investigations and Projects Masters,* p. 4.

Cooperative Learning

This investigation offers an excellent opportunity for using cooperative learning groups. For more information on cooperative learning strategies and group management, see Cooperative Learning in the Mathematics Classroom.

Making the Connection

Use the data collected about foot lengths as needed to help in these investigations.

Language Arts

Suppose you are the manager of a shoe store and are planning to sell some hot new shoes for the teenage market. Predict how many shoes of each size you expect to sell. Plan a newspaper advertisement to market the shoes.

Social Studies

Research the contribution Jan Earnst Matzeliger made to the shoe industry. Include some statistics that tell the economic effect of his invention.

Science

Show how a Punnett Square can be used to make predictions about the traits of a population.

Go Further

- Collect data from different age groups about foot length. Make a graph for each age group.
- Ask a local podiatrist for charts that list the average foot size for various age groups. See how close your results come to these published averages.

Research For current information on shoes, visit the following website.

Data Collection and Comparison To share and compare your data with other students in the U.S., visit:

www.glencoe.com/sec/math/mac/mathnet

You may want to place your work on this investigation in your portfolio.

Instructional Resources ▶▶▶

Sample solutions for this investigation are provided in the *Investigations and Projects Masters* on p. 2. The scoring guide for assessing student performance shown at the right is also available on p. 3.

MANAGEMENT TIPS

Working in Teams Dividing the tasks involved will make the investigation move ahead more quickly. For example, each student can measure 3 people's feet.

Making the Connection

You may wish to alert other teachers on your team that your students may need their assistance in this investigation.
Language Arts Using fewer words may impact more potential customers.
Social Studies Students may research manufacturing industries in New England during the 19th century.
Science Dominant traits in genetics are useful in determining the probability of inheriting certain features from parents.

ASSESS

Encourage students to consider carefully what information they express graphically, orally, and in written form. Ask students whether age, sex, or family relationships has a greater effect on foot length.

Investigations and Projects Masters, **p. 3**

SCORING GUIDE

Interdisciplinary Investigation
(Student Edition, Pages 128–129)

If the Shoe Fits...

Level	Specific Criteria
3 Superior	• Shows a thorough understanding of the concepts of *mean, median, mode,* and *range.* • Uses appropriate strategies to solve problems. • Computations are correct. • Written explanations are exemplary. • Charts, model, and any statements included are appropriate and sensible. • Goes beyond the requirements of some or all problems.
2 Satisfactory, with minor flaws	• Shows understanding of the concepts of *mean, median, mode,* and *range.* • Uses appropriate strategies to solve problems. • Computations are mostly correct. • Written explanations are effective. • Charts, model, and any statements included are appropriate and sensible. • Satisfies the requirements of problems.
1 Nearly Satisfactory, with obvious flaws	• Shows understanding of most of the concepts of *mean, median, mode,* and *range.* • May not use appropriate strategies to solve problems. • Computations are mostly correct. • Written explanations are satisfactory. • Charts, model, and any statements included are appropriate and sensible. • Satisfies the requirements of problems.
0 Unsatisfactory	• Shows little or no understanding of the concepts of *mean, median, mode,* and *range.* • Does not use appropriate strategies to solve problems. • Computations are incorrect. • Written explanations are not satisfactory. • Charts, model, and any statements included are not appropriate or sensible. • Does not satisfy the requirements of the problems.

 3 *Mathematics: Applications and Connections,* Course 2

CHAPTER 4

Using Number Patterns, Fractions, and Percents

Previewing the Chapter

Overview

This chapter explores several aspects of number theory including divisibility, prime and composite numbers, and factorization. Students study geometric and arithmetic sequences, factors and multiples, fractions, percents, decimals, ratios, and probability of simple events. They also explore problem solving by making an organized list and studying the Fibonacci sequence of numbers.

Lesson (pages)	Lesson Objectives	NCTM Standards 2000	Standardized Tests	State/Local Objectives
4-1A (132)	Discover factors of whole numbers by using number cards.	1, 6–9	CAT, CTBS, ITBS, MAT, SAT, TN	
4-1 (133–136)	Use divisibility rules.	1, 2, 6–9	CAT, CTBS, ITBS, MAT, SAT, TN	
4-1B (137)	Use spreadsheets to test for divisibility.	1, 6–8		
4-2 (138–141)	Find the prime factorization of a composite number.	1, 2, 6–10	CAT, CTBS, MAT, TN	
4-3 (142–145)	Recognize and extend a pattern for sequences.	1, 2, 6–10	CTBS, ITBS, MAT, SAT, TN	
4-3B (146–147)	Explore patterns in sequences.	1–3, 6–9	CTBS, ITBS, TN	
4-4A (148–149)	Solve problems by making an organized list.	1, 2, 4, 6–9		
4-4 (150–153)	Find the greatest common factor of two or more numbers.	1, 6–10	CAT, CTBS, MAT, SAT, TN	
4-5 (154–157)	Express fractions and ratios in simplest form.	1, 6–10	MAT, SAT	
4-6 (158–160)	Illustrate the meaning of percent using models or symbols.	1, 6–10	CTBS, MAT, TN	
4-7 (161–164)	Express fractions as percents, and percents and decimals as fractions.	1, 6–10	CTBS, MAT, SAT, TN	
4-8 (165–168)	Find the probability of a simple event.	1, 5–10	CAT, CTBS, ITBS, MAT, SAT, TN	
4-9 (169–171)	Find the least common multiple of two or more numbers.	1, 6–10	CAT, CTBS, MAT, SAT, TN	
4-10 (172–175)	Compare and order fractions.	1, 5–9	CAT, CTBS, ITBS, MAT, SAT, TN	

CAT = California Achievement Tests, CTBS = Comprehensive Tests of Basic Skills, ITBS = Iowa Tests of Basic Skills, MAT = Metropolitan Achievement Tests, SAT = Stanford Achievement Tests, TN = Terra Nova
For the key to numbering of NCTM Standards 2000, see page T6.

Organizing the Chapter

The **Interactive Lesson Planner** contains all of the blackline masters and transparencies. This CD-ROM also includes an easy-to-use lesson planning calendar.

LESSON PLANNING GUIDE

Lesson	Extra Practice (Student Edition)	Blackline Masters (Page Numbers)										Transparencies A and B
		Study Guide	Practice	Enrichment	Assessment & Evaluation	Classroom Games	Diversity	Hands-On Lab	School to Career	Science and Math Lab Manual	Technology	
4-1A								44				
4-1	p. 576	24	24	24				75				4-1
4-1B												
4-2	p. 577	25	25	25		11–12						4-2
4-3	p. 577	26	26	26	99		17					4-3
4-3B								45				
4-4A	p. 577											
4-4	p. 578	27	27	27								4-4
4-5	p. 578	28	28	28	98, 99							4-5
4-6	p. 578	29	29	29								4-6
4-7	p. 579	30	30	30							33–34	4-7
4-8	p. 579	31	31	31	100				17			4-8
4-9	p. 579	32	32	32								4-9
4-10	p. 580	33	33	33	100							4-10
Study Guide/ Assessment					85–97, 101–103							

Other Chapter Resources

Student Edition

Chapter Project, pp. 131, 157, 164, 168, 179

Let the Games Begin, pp. 136, 175

Technology

 MathPASS CD-ROM

 Interactive Mathematics Tools Software

Teacher's Classroom Resources

Applications

Family Letters and Activities, pp. 33–34

Investigations and Projects Masters, pp. 29–32

Meeting Individual Needs

Transition Booklet, pp. 23–28

Investigations for the Special Education Student, pp. 13–14

Teaching Aids

Answer Key Masters

Block Scheduling Booklet

Lesson Planning Guide

Solutions Manual

Professional Publications

Glencoe Mathematics Professional Series

Planning the Chapter

MindJogger Videoquizzes provide a unique format for reviewing concepts presented in the chapter.

Assessment Resources

Student Edition

Mixed Review, pp. 136, 141, 145, 153, 157, 160, 164, 168, 171, 175
Mid-Chapter Self Test, p. 153
Math Journal, pp. 140, 170
Study Guide and Assessment, pp. 176–179
Performance Task, p. 179
Portfolio Suggestion, p.179
Standardized Test Practice, pp. 180–181
Chapter Test, p. 610

Assessment and Evaluation Masters

Multiple-Choice Tests (Forms 1A, 1B, 1C), pp. 85–90
Free-Response Tests (Forms 2A, 2B, 2C), pp. 91–96
Performance Assessment, p. 97
Mid-Chapter Test, p. 98
Quizzes A–D, pp. 99–100
Standardized Test Practice, pp. 101–102
Cumulative Review, p. 103

Teacher's Wraparound Edition

5-Minute Check, pp. 133, 138, 142, 150, 154, 158, 161, 165, 169, 172
Building Portfolios, pp. 130, 179
Math Journal, pp. 132, 137, 147
Closing Activity, pp. 136, 141, 145, 149, 153, 157, 160, 164, 168, 171, 175

Technology

Test and Review Software
MindJogger Videoquizzes
CD-ROM Program

Materials and Manipulatives

Lesson 4-1A
index cards

Lesson 4-1
base-ten blocks*†
index cards
tape

Lesson 4-1B
computer
spreadsheet software

Lesson 4-3B
calculator
paper

Lesson 4-6
grid paper†
colored pencils

Lesson 4-8
paper
ruler*†

Lesson 4-10
calculator
poster board

*Glencoe Manipulative Kit

†Glencoe Overhead Manipulative Resources

Pacing Chart

See pages T25–T27 for the Course Planning Calendar.

COURSE	DAY 1	DAY 2	DAY 3	DAY 4	DAY 5	DAY 6	DAY 7
Standard	Chapter Project	Lessons 4-1A & 4-1		Lesson 4-2	Lesson 4-3	Lesson 4-4A	Lesson 4-4
Honors	Chapter Project	Lessons 4-1 & 4-1B	Lesson 4-2	Lessons 4-3 & 4-3B		Lesson 4-4A	Lesson 4-4
Block	Chapter Project, Lessons 4-1A & 4-1	Lessons 4-2 & 4-3	Lessons 4-4A & 4-4	Lesson 4-5	Lessons 4-6 & 4-7	Lesson 4-8	Lessons 4-9 & 4-10

The *Transition Booklet* (Skills 10–12) can be used to practice basic operations with whole numbers.

Interactive Mathematics: Activities and Investigations

is an activity-based program that may be used as an enhancement for chapters in ***Mathematics: Applications and Connections.***

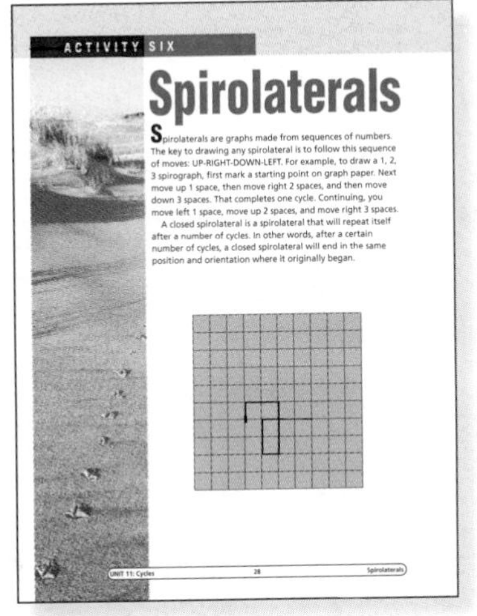

ACTIVITY SIX

Spirolaterals

Spirolaterals are graphs made from sequences of numbers. The key to drawing any spirolateral is to follow this sequence of moves: UP-RIGHT-DOWN-LEFT. For example, to draw a 1, 2, 3 spirograph, first mark a starting point on graph paper. Next move up 1 space, then move right 2 spaces, and then move down 3 spaces. That completes one cycle. Continuing, you move left 1 space, move up 2 spaces, and move right 3 spaces.

A closed spirolateral is a spirolateral that will repeat itself after a number of cycles. In other words, after a certain number of cycles, a closed spirolateral will end in the same position and orientation where it originally began.

UNIT 11: Cycles 28 Spirolaterals

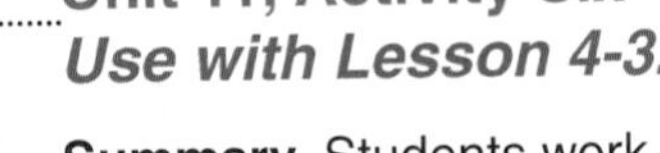

Unit 11, Activity Six
Use with Lesson 4-3.

Summary Students work in pairs to explore spirolaterals with the aid of computers. They summarize the characteristics of spirolaterals after drawing them on graph paper. The computer program used will allow students to generate further spirolaterals so that each pair may collect data. Each pair then produces a report discussing their findings.

Math Connection Students use computers and a program written in LOGO to investigate spirolaterals and their properties. A spirolateral is a geometric representation of a sequence of numbers.

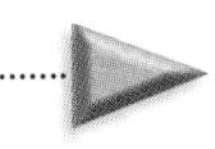

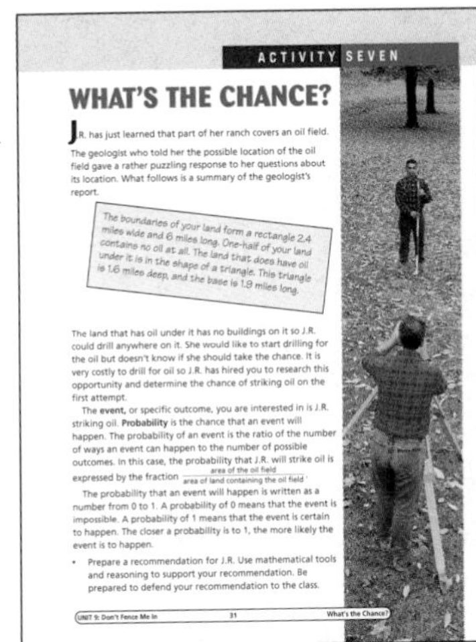

ACTIVITY SEVEN

WHAT'S THE CHANCE?

J.R. has just learned that part of her ranch covers an oil field. The geologist who told her the possible location of the oil field gave a rather puzzling response to her questions about its location. What follows is a summary of the geologist's report.

The boundaries of your land form a rectangle 2.4 miles wide and 6 miles long. One-half of your land contains no oil at all. The land that does have oil under it is in the shape of a triangle. This triangle is 1.6 miles deep, and the base is 1.9 miles long.

The land that has oil under it has no buildings on it so J.R. could drill anywhere on it. She would like to start drilling for the oil but doesn't know if she should take the chance. It is very costly to drill for oil so J.R. has hired you to research this opportunity and determine the chance of striking oil on the first attempt.

The **event,** or specific outcome, you are interested in is J.R. striking oil. **Probability** is the chance that an event will happen. The probability of an event is the ratio of the number of ways an event can happen to the number of possible outcomes. In this case, the probability that J.R. will strike oil is expressed by the fraction $\frac{\text{area of the oil field}}{\text{area of land containing the oil field}}$.

The probability that an event will happen is written as a number from 0 to 1. A probability of 0 means that the event is impossible. A probability of 1 means that the event is certain to happen. The closer a probability is to 1, the more likely the event is to happen.

- Prepare a recommendation for J.R. Use mathematical tools and reasoning to support your recommendation. Be prepared to defend your recommendation to the class.

UNIT 9: Don't Fence Me In 31 What's the Chance?

Unit 9, Activity Seven
Use with Lesson 4-8.

Summary Students work in groups to analyze a geologist's report and draw a model of the ranch based on the report. Then students make individual recommendations to the owner on whether to drill for oil.

Math Connection Students create area models to assist them in determining the chance that an event will happen. In this activity the specific outcome is striking oil. The probability of an event is the ratio of the number of ways that an event can occur to the total number of possible outcomes.

DAY 8	DAY 9	DAY 10	DAY 11	DAY 12	DAY 13	DAY 14	DAY 15
Lesson 4-5	Lesson 4-6	Lesson 4-7	Lesson 4-8	Lesson 4-9	Lesson 4-10	Study Guide and Assessment	Chapter Test
Lesson 4-5	Lesson 4-6	Lesson 4-7	Lesson 4-8	Lesson 4-9	Lesson 4-10	Study Guide and Assessment	Chapter Test
Study Guide and Assessment, Chapter Test							

Enhancing the Chapter

APPLICATIONS

Classroom Games, pp. 11–12

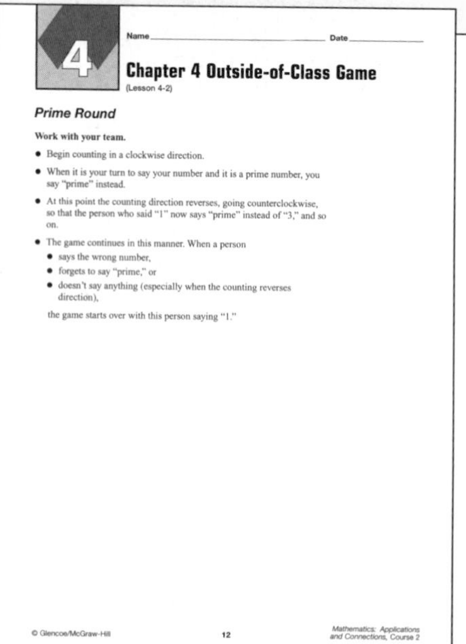

Name ______________________ Date ____________

Chapter 4 Outside-of-Class Game
(Lesson 4-2)

Prime Round

Work with your team.

- Begin counting in a clockwise direction.
- When it is your turn to say your number and it is a prime number, you say "prime" instead.
- At this point the counting direction reverses, going counterclockwise, so that the person who said "1" now says "prime" instead of "3," and so on.
- The game continues in this manner. When a person
  - says the wrong number,
  - forgets to say "prime," or
  - doesn't say anything (especially when the counting reverses direction),

  the game starts over with this person saying "1."

© Glencoe/McGraw-Hill 12 *Mathematics: Applications and Connections, Course 2*

Diversity Masters, p. 17

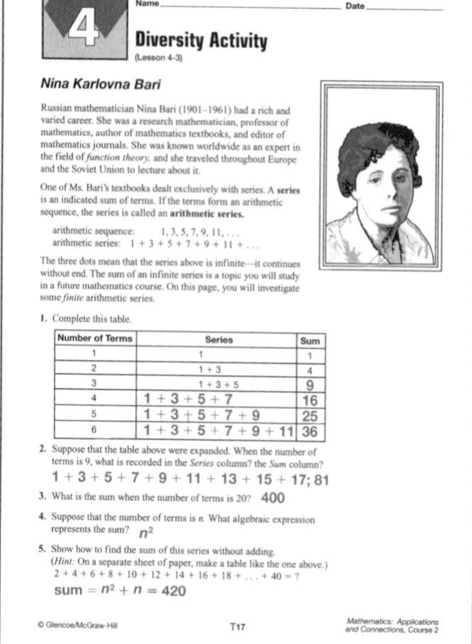

Name ______________________ Date ____________

Diversity Activity
(Lesson 4-3)

Nina Karlovna Bari

Russian mathematician Nina Bari (1901–1961) had a rich and varied career. She was a research mathematician, professor of mathematics, author of mathematics textbooks, and editor of mathematics journals. She was known worldwide as an expert in the field of *function theory,* and she traveled throughout Europe and the Soviet Union to lecture about it.

One of Ms. Bari's textbooks dealt exclusively with series. A **series** is an indicated sum of terms. If the terms form an arithmetic sequence, the series is called an **arithmetic series.**

arithmetic sequence: 1, 3, 5, 7, 9, 11, . . .
arithmetic series: 1 + 3 + 5 + 7 + 9 + 11 + . . .

The three dots mean that the series above is infinite—it continues without end. The sum of an infinite series is a topic you will study in a future mathematics course. On this page, you will investigate some *finite* arithmetic series.

1. Complete this table.

Number of Terms	Series	Sum
1	1	1
2	1 + 3	4
3	1 + 3 + 5	9
4	1 + 3 + 5 + 7	16
5	1 + 3 + 5 + 7 + 9	25
6	1 + 3 + 5 + 7 + 9 + 11	36

2. Suppose that the table above were expanded. When the number of terms is 9, what is recorded in the *Series* column? the *Sum* column?
   1 + 3 + 5 + 7 + 9 + 11 + 13 + 15 + 17; 81
3. What is the sum when the number of terms is 20? 400
4. Suppose that the number of terms is n. What algebraic expression represents the sum? n^2
5. Show how to find the sum of this series without adding.
   (*Hint:* On a separate sheet of paper, make a table like the one above.)
   2 + 4 + 6 + 8 + 10 + 12 + 14 + 16 + 18 + . . . + 40 = ?
   sum = $n^2 + n = 420$

© Glencoe/McGraw-Hill T17 *Mathematics: Applications and Connections, Course 2*

School to Career Masters, p. 17

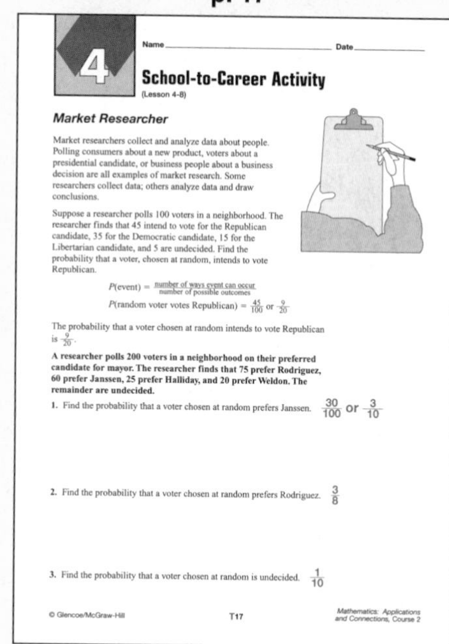

Name ______________________ Date ____________

School-to-Career Activity
(Lesson 4-8)

Market Researcher

Market researchers collect and analyze data about people. Polling consumers about a new product, voters about a presidential candidate, or business people about a business decision are all examples of market research. Some researchers collect data; others analyze data and draw conclusions.

Suppose a researcher polls 100 voters in a neighborhood. The researcher finds that 45 intend to vote for the Republican candidate, 35 for the Democratic candidate, 15 for the Libertarian candidate, and 5 are undecided. Find the probability that a voter, chosen at random, intends to vote Republican.

$$P(\text{event}) = \frac{\text{number of ways event can occur}}{\text{number of possible outcomes}}$$

$$P(\text{random voter votes Republican}) = \frac{45}{100} \text{ or } \frac{9}{20}$$

The probability that a voter chosen at random intends to vote Republican is $\frac{9}{20}$.

A researcher polls 200 voters in a neighborhood on their preferred candidate for mayor. The researcher finds that 75 prefer Rodriguez, 60 prefer Janssen, 25 prefer Halliday, and 20 prefer Weldon. The remainder are undecided.

1. Find the probability that a voter chosen at random prefers Janssen. $\frac{30}{100}$ or $\frac{3}{10}$
2. Find the probability that a voter chosen at random prefers Rodriguez. $\frac{3}{8}$
3. Find the probability that a voter chosen at random is undecided. $\frac{1}{10}$

© Glencoe/McGraw-Hill T17 *Mathematics: Applications and Connections, Course 2*

Family Letters and Activities, pp. 33–34

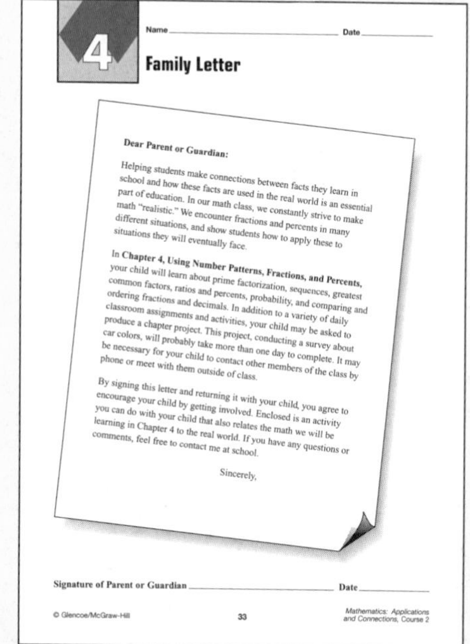

Name ______________________ Date ____________

Family Letter

Dear Parent or Guardian:

Helping students make connections between facts they learn in school and how these facts are used in the real world is an essential part of education. In our math class, we constantly strive to make math "realistic." We encounter fractions and percents in many different situations, and show students how to apply these to situations they will eventually face.

In **Chapter 4, Using Number Patterns, Fractions, and Percents,** your child will learn about prime factorization, sequences, greatest common factors, ratios and percents, probability, and comparing and ordering fractions and decimals. In addition to a variety of daily classroom assignments and activities, your child may be asked to produce a chapter project. This project, conducting a survey about car colors, will probably take more than one day to complete. It may be necessary for your child to contact other members of the class by phone or meet with them outside of class.

By signing this letter and returning it with your child, you agree to encourage your child by getting involved. Enclosed is an activity you can do with your child that also relates the math we will be learning in Chapter 4 to the real world. If you have any questions or comments, feel free to contact me at school.

Sincerely,

Signature of Parent or Guardian ______________________ **Date** ____________

© Glencoe/McGraw-Hill 33 *Mathematics: Applications and Connections, Course 2*

Name ______________________ Date ____________

Family Activity

Color by Numbers

Work with a family member to answer the questions below. Purchase a small bag of M & Ms or a small box of colored paper clips. Separate by color.

Count the total number of pieces in the bag or box. Count the number of each color. In the table below, write the name of each color and its number. Find the fraction of the total amount for each color. Simplify the fractions and write them in the table. Then write the decimal number for each color.

There are a total of _______ colored pieces.

Color	Number	Fraction	Decimal

Graph the fraction for each color on the number line.

0 1

Write the fractions in order from least to greatest.

Which color had the largest fractional part? the smallest?

© Glencoe/McGraw-Hill 34 *Mathematics: Applications and Connections, Course 2*

MANIPULATIVES/MODELING

Hands-On Lab Masters, p. 75

4 Name ______ Date ______

Lab Activity
(Lesson 4-1)

Divisibility Patterns

1. List the factors of 18. 1, 2, 3, 6, 9, 18
2. Take 18 beans. Find all of the rectangular arrangements you can make using the beans. Sketch each arrangement. Sample answer:
3. How many rectangular arrangements did you make? 6
   Write the area of each arrangement as a product of its length and width.
   $18 = 1 \times 18$; $18 = 2 \times 9$; $18 = 3 \times 6$; $18 = 6 \times 3$; $18 = 9 \times 2$; $18 = 1 \times 18$
4. Put your 18 beans into a jar with everyone else's beans. Grab a handful of beans from the jar without counting. How many beans do you have? Sample answer: 15
5. List the factors of the number you found in Exercise 4. Sample answer: 1, 3, 5, 15
6. Find all of the rectangular arrangements you can make using the beans. Sketch each arrangement. Sample answer:
7. How many rectangular arrangements did you make? Sample answer: 4
   Write the area of each arrangement as a product of its length and width. Sample answer: $15 = 1 \times 15$; $15 = 3 \times 5$; $15 = 5 \times 3$; $15 = 15 \times 1$

© Glencoe/McGraw-Hill 75 *Mathematics: Applications and Connections, Course 2*

ASSESSMENT/EVALUATION

Assessment and Evaluation Masters, pp. 98–100

4 Name ______ Date ______

Chapter 4 Mid-Chapter Test
(Lessons 4-1 through 4-5)

Determine whether the first number is divisible by 2, 3, 4, 5, 6, 9, or 10.

1. 372 — 2, 3, 4, and 6
2. 515 — 5
3. 1,664 — 2 and 4

Find the prime factorization of each number.

4. 336 — $2^4 \cdot 3 \cdot 7$
5. 280 — $2^3 \cdot 5 \cdot 7$
6. 450 — $2 \cdot 3^2 \cdot 5^2$

Identify each sequence as arithmetic, geometric, or neither. Then find the next three terms.

7. 75, 100, 125, 150, ... — arithmetic; 175, 200, 225
8. $1, 2\frac{1}{2}, 3\frac{1}{3}, 4\frac{1}{4}, \ldots$ — neither; $5\frac{1}{5}, 6\frac{1}{6}, 7\frac{1}{7}$
9. 1, 4, 16, 64, ... — geometric; 256, 1024, 4096

Find the GCF of each set of numbers.

10. 28, 49 — 7
11. 27, 81 — 27
12. 20, 48, 64 — 4

Express each fraction or ratio in simplest form.

13. $\frac{27}{36}$ — $\frac{3}{4}$
14. $\frac{32}{48}$ — $\frac{2}{3}$
15. 12:72 — 1:6
16. 27:99 — 3:11

© Glencoe/McGraw-Hill 98 *Mathematics: Applications and Connections, Course 2*

Name ______ Date ______

Chapter 4 Quiz A (Lessons 4-1 through 4-3)

Determine whether each number is divisible by 2, 3, 4, 5, 6, 9, or 10.

1. 720 — all
2. 5,400 — all
3. 333 — 3 and 9
4. 4,925 — 5

Write the prime factorization of each number.

5. 28 — $2^2 \cdot 7$
6. 64 — 2^6
7. 315 — $3^2 \cdot 5 \cdot 7$
8. 1,944 — $2^3 \cdot 3^5$

Identify the sequence as arithmetic, geometric, or neither. Then find the next three terms in the sequence.

9. 2, 4, 8, 14, ... — neither; 22, 32, 44
10. 40, 51, 62, 73, ... — arithmetic; 84, 95, 106

Name ______ Date ______

Chapter 4 Quiz B (Lessons 4-4 and 4-5)

Find the GCF of each set of numbers.

1. 28, 42 — 14
2. 16, 36, 44 — 4

Express each fraction or ratio in simplest form.

3. $\frac{12}{64}$ — $\frac{3}{16}$
4. $\frac{30}{36}$ — $\frac{5}{6}$
5. 54:9 — 6:1

© Glencoe/McGraw-Hill 99 *Mathematics: Applications and Connections, Course 2*

TECHNOLOGY/MULTIMEDIA

Technology Masters, pp. 33–34

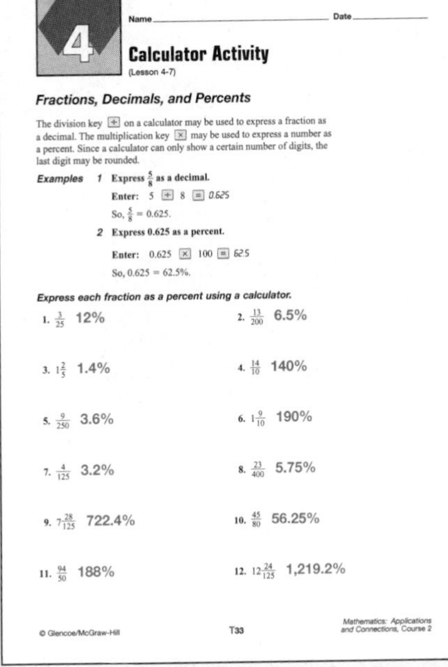

4 Name ______ Date ______

Calculator Activity
(Lesson 4-7)

Fractions, Decimals, and Percents

The division key [÷] on a calculator may be used to express a fraction as a decimal. The multiplication key [×] may be used to express a number as a percent. Since a calculator can only show a certain number of digits, the last digit may be rounded.

Examples *1* **Express $\frac{5}{8}$ as a decimal.**
Enter: 5 [÷] 8 [=] *0.625*
So, $\frac{5}{8} = 0.625$.

2 **Express 0.625 as a percent.**
Enter: 0.625 [×] 100 [=] *62.5*
So, 0.625 = 62.5%.

Express each fraction as a percent using a calculator.

1. $\frac{3}{25}$ 12%
2. $\frac{13}{200}$ 6.5%
3. $1\frac{2}{5}$ 1.4%
4. $\frac{14}{10}$ 140%
5. $\frac{9}{250}$ 3.6%
6. $1\frac{9}{10}$ 190%
7. $\frac{4}{125}$ 3.2%
8. $\frac{23}{400}$ 5.75%
9. $7\frac{28}{125}$ 722.4%
10. $\frac{45}{80}$ 56.25%
11. $\frac{94}{50}$ 188%
12. $12\frac{24}{125}$ 1,219.2%

© Glencoe/McGraw-Hill T33 *Mathematics: Applications and Connections, Course 2*

4 Name ______ Date ______

Spreadsheet Activity
(Lesson 4-7)

Fractions, Decimals, and Percents

You can use a spreadsheet to help you find equivalent fractions, decimals, and percents.

Create a spreadsheet with four columns. Label column A numerator, column B denominator, column C decimal, and column D percent.

To express a fraction as a decimal, divide the numerator by the denominator. So the formula for column C is A ÷ B.

To express a decimal as a percent, multiply by 100. So the formula for column D is C × 100.

A	B	C	D
numerator	denominator	decimal	percent
1	2	0.5	50
1	5		

Use a spreadsheet to express each fraction as a percent.

1. $\frac{1}{5}$ 20%
2. $\frac{1}{8}$ 12.5%
3. $\frac{3}{4}$ 75%
4. $\frac{5}{8}$ 62.5%
5. $\frac{9}{10}$ 90%
6. $\frac{4}{25}$ 16%
7. $\frac{14}{100}$ 14%
8. $\frac{27}{50}$ 54%
9. $\frac{9}{20}$ 45%
10. Express 0.15 as a fraction in simplest form. $\frac{3}{20}$
11. Express 34% as a fraction in simplest form. $\frac{17}{50}$
12. Suppose you want to make a spreadsheet with two columns to calculate the decimal form of a percent. Column A is a percent. You want column B to be the decimal. What formula would you use for column B? A/100
13. Suppose you want to make a spreadsheet that shows only the numerator and denominator of a fraction and the fraction expressed as a percent. Column A is the numerator of the fraction, column B is the denominator, and column C is the percent. What formula would you use for column C? A/B × 100

© Glencoe/McGraw-Hill T34 *Mathematics: Applications and Connections, Course 2*

MEETING INDIVIDUAL NEEDS

Investigations for the Special Education Student, pp. 13–14

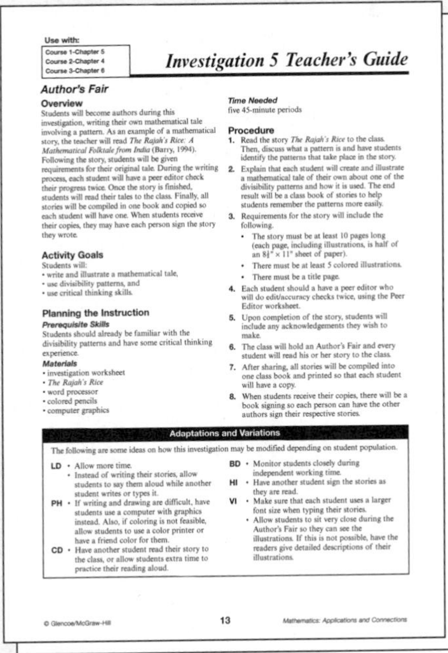

Use with:
Course 1-Chapter 5
Course 2-Chapter 4
Course 3-Chapter 6

Investigation 5 Teacher's Guide

Author's Fair

Overview
Students will become authors during this investigation, writing their own mathematical tale involving a pattern. As an example of a mathematical story, the teacher will read *The Rajah's Rice: A Mathematical Folktale from India* (Barry, 1994). Following the story, students will be given requirements for their original tale. During the writing process, each student will have a peer editor check their progress twice. Once the story is finished, students will read their tales to the class. Finally, all stories will be compiled in one book and copied so each student will have one. When students receive their copies, they may have each person sign the story they wrote.

Activity Goals
Students will:
- write and illustrate a mathematical tale,
- use divisibility patterns, and
- use critical thinking skills.

Planning the Instruction
Prerequisite Skills
Students should already be familiar with the divisibility patterns and have some critical thinking experience.
Materials
- investigation worksheet
- *The Rajah's Rice*
- word processor
- colored pencils
- computer graphics

Time Needed
five 45-minute periods

Procedure
1. Read the story *The Rajah's Rice* to the class. Then, discuss what a pattern is and have students identify the patterns that take place in the story.
2. Explain that each student will create and illustrate a mathematical tale of their own about one of the divisibility patterns and how it is used. The end result will be a class book of stories to help students remember the patterns more easily.
3. Requirements for the story will include the following.
   - The story must be at least 10 pages long (each page, including illustrations, is half of an $8\frac{1}{2}" \times 11"$ sheet of paper).
   - There must be at least 5 colored illustrations.
   - There must be a title page.
4. Each student should a have a peer editor who will do edit/accuracy checks twice, using the Peer Editor worksheet.
5. Upon completion of the story, students will include any acknowledgements they wish to make.
6. The class will hold an Author's Fair and every student will read his or her story to the class.
7. After sharing, all stories will be compiled into one class book and printed so that each student will have a copy.
8. When students receive their copies, there will be a book signing so each person can have the other authors sign their respective stories.

Adaptations and Variations

The following are some ideas on how this investigation may be modified depending on student population.

LD • Allow more time.
• Instead of writing their stories, allow students to say them aloud while another student writes or types it.

PH • If writing and drawing are difficult, have students use a computer with graphics instead. Also, if coloring is not feasible, allow students to use a color printer or have a friend color for them.

CD • Have another student read their story to the class, or allow students extra time to practice their reading aloud.

BD • Monitor students closely during independent working time.

HI • Have another student sign the stories as they are read.

VI • Make sure that each student uses a larger font size when typing their stories.
• Allow students to sit very close during the Author's Fair so they can see the illustrations. If this is not possible, have the readers give detailed descriptions of their illustrations.

© Glencoe/McGraw-Hill 13 *Mathematics: Applications and Connections*

CHAPTER 4 NOTES

Theme: Cars

Southern California has announced a plan for stricter controls of air pollution caused by automobiles. This plan would phase out cars fueled by gasoline by the year 2010. Electric cars and new mass transportation systems would take their place.

Question of the Day If one bus takes the place of 60 cars, by what percent could traffic be decreased by a bus on a road that usually has 1,000 cars every morning? 6%

Assess Prerequisite Skills

Ask students to read through the list of objectives presented in "What you'll learn in Chapter 4." You may wish to ask them what each of the objectives means or if they have experienced any of these math concepts before.

Building Portfolios

Encourage students to revise their portfolios as they study this chapter. They should include material that demonstrates their understanding of each of the objectives in this chapter.

Math and the Family

In the *Family Letters and Activities* booklet (pp. 33–34), you will find a letter to the parents explaining what students will study in Chapter 4. An activity appropriate for the whole family is also available.

CHAPTER 4 Using Number Patterns, Fractions, and Percents

What you'll learn in Chapter 4

- to find the prime factorization of a composite number,
- to recognize and extend a pattern for sequences,
- to solve problems by making a list,
- to illustrate the meaning of percent using models or symbols,
- to find the greatest common factor and least common multiple of two or more numbers, and
- to find the probability of a simple event.

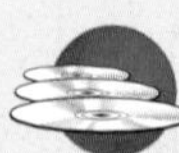

CD-ROM Program

Activities for Chapter 4

- Chapter 4 Introduction
- Interactive Lessons 4-4, 4-9
- Extended Activity 4-8
- Assessment Game
- Resource Lessons 4-1 through 4-10

CHAPTER Project

WHAT COLOR WAS THAT CAR?

In this project, you will design and conduct a survey about favorite car colors. You will use fractions, decimals, and percents to display the results of your survey, and you will find probabilities based on your survey. You will also investigate data about the production of cars in the United States.

Getting Started

- Look at the car production table. What company produced the greatest number of cars? How many total cars were produced?
- Select six common car colors and include a category labeled, "other colors." Survey 20 people and record their favorite car color. Try to survey both students and adults.

U.S. Car Production	
Company	**Number of Cars**
A	149,562
B	576,846
C	1,395,710
D	2,515,136
E	552,995
F	218,161
G	333,234
H	80,660
I	516,557
J	11,872
Total Production	**6,350,733**

Technology Tips

- Use a **spreadsheet** to convert fractions to decimals and percents.
- Use **computer software** to make graphs.
- Use a **word processor** to summarize your survey results.

Data Update For up-to-date information on car production, visit:

www.glencoe.com/sec/math/mac/mathnet

Working on the Project

You can use what you'll learn in Chapter 4 to help you conduct your survey.

Page	Exercise
157	34
164	43
168	26
179	Alternative Assessment

interNET CONNECTION

Glencoe has made every effort to ensure that the website links for *Mathematics: Applications and Connections* at **www.glencoe.com/sec/math/mac/mathnet** are current and contain appropriate content. However, these website links are not under Glencoe's control.

Instructional Resources ▶▶▶

A recording sheet to help students organize their data for the Chapter Project is shown at the right and is available in the *Investigations and Projects Masters,* p. 32.

CHAPTER Project NOTES

Objectives Students should

- use fractions, decimals, and percents to display the results of their surveys.
- investigate data about the production of cars in the United States by using a table.

Project Pointer You may suggest that students begin a *Project Folder* to keep their work as they complete each stage of the Chapter Project. The completed project may also be added to their portfolios.

Encourage students to survey both students and adults. Be sure that participants select fairly generic colors such as "blue," and not "dark metallic blue."

Using the Table Point out to students that this table is arranged in alphabetical order. Another arrangement could be from greatest number of cars produced to the least number produced. Also, point out that the "other" category includes an unknown number of companies.

***Investigations and Projects Masters,* p. 32**

Name ______________________ Date __________

Chapter 4 Project

What Color Was That Car?

Page 131, Getting Started

Name	Color						Name	Color					
						Other							Other

Page 157, Working on Chapter Project, Exercise 34

Page 164, Working on Chapter Project, Exercise 43

U.S. Car Production, 1995

Company	Number of Cars	Number to Nearest Hundred Thousand	Fraction	Decimal	Percent
Auto Alliance	149,562				
Chrysler Corp.	576,846				
Ford Motor Company	1,395,710				
General Motors Corp.	2,515,136				
Honda	552,995				
Mitsubishi	218,161				
Nissan	333,234				
Subaru Legacy	80,660				
Toyota	516,557				
Other	11,872				

Page 168, Working on Chapter Project, Exercise 26

The probability of a new student selecting a white car is:

 32 *Mathematics: Applications and Connections, Course 2*

4-1A  Notes

GET READY

Objective Students discover factors of whole numbers by using number cards.

Optional Resources
Hands-On Lab Masters
- worksheet, p. 44

MANAGEMENT TIPS

Recommended Time
45 minutes

Getting Started Ask students to suppose that a group of 30 students was going to be divided into a number of teams of equal size to compete in a science fair. Ask them how the organizers can decide upon how many students would be on each team.

The **Activity** demonstrates factors that make up the number 30. Before students begin, ask them to look for patterns as they carry out the activity.

Teaching Tip You may wish to point out to students that there will be one person between "every second student," two people between "every third student," three between every fourth, and so on.

You may also have students "count off" to find factors. For example, to find every fifth student, count 1, 2, 3, 4, 5. Then begin again with 1.

ASSESS

Have students complete Exercises 1–6. Ask students to explain the connection between the numbers 2 through 35 and the cards with the fewest and most numbers written on them.

Use Exercise 7 to determine whether students understand how factors are related to whole numbers.

HANDS-ON LAB **COOPERATIVE LEARNING**

4-1A Exploring Factors

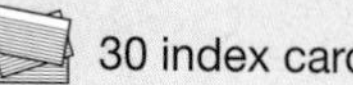

30 index cards

A Preview of Lesson 4-1

You can use number cards to discover the factors of whole numbers.

TRY THIS

Step 1 Number the index cards 1 through 30.

Step 2 In order around the classroom, give thirty students one of the index cards. Have each of them stand up and write the number 1 on the back of his or her card. (The front of each index card will have a number from 1 to 30.)

Step 3 Start with the student holding the "2" card. Have every second student sit down and write the number 2 on the back of his or her card.

Step 4 Start with the student holding the "3" card. Have every third student stand up or sit down (depending on whether the student is already sitting or standing) and write the number 3 on the back of his or her card.

Step 5 Continue this process for each of the remaining numbers until the thirtieth student has stood up or sat down and has written the number 30 on the back of his or her card.

2. 31: 1, 31; 32: 1, 2, 4, 8, 16, 32; 33: 1, 3, 11, 33; 34: 1, 2, 17, 34; 35: 1, 5, 7, 35
7. 1, 4, 9, 16, 25, 36, 49; perfect square numbers because there is an odd number of factors.

ON YOUR OWN

1. Make a conjecture about the numbers written on the back of each number card. **Numbers on back are factors of the numbers on the front.**
2. Use your conjecture to predict the numbers that would be written on the back of number cards from 31 to 35.
3. Which number cards have exactly two numbers on the back? **2, 3, 5, 7, 11, 13, 17, 19, 23, 29**
4. Which number cards have the fewest numbers on the back? **1**
5. Which number cards have the most numbers on the back? **24 and 30**
6. Which number cards are held by those students standing at the end of the activity? **1, 4, 9, 16, 25**
7. ***Look Ahead*** Suppose there were 50 students holding index cards. Which numbers do you predict would be held by students standing at the end of the activity? Why?

Have students write a paragraph discussing their experience during the exercise of representing factors by standing and sitting.

4-1 Divisibility Patterns

What you'll learn

You'll learn to use divisibility rules.

When am I ever going to use this?

Divisibility rules can be used to find factors of numbers.

Word Wise

factor
divisible

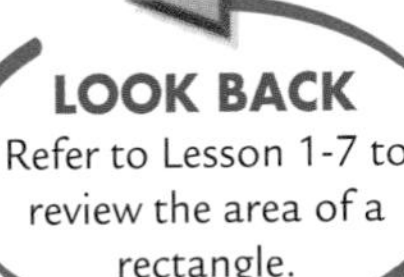

LOOK BACK

Refer to Lesson 1-7 to review the area of a rectangle.

How many different ways can you form a rectangle using 24 squares?

HANDS-ON MINI-LAB

Work with a partner.  24 square base-ten blocks

One possible rectangle with side lengths of 1 and 24 is shown below.

Try This 1–3. See margin.

1. One partner should build a different rectangle that has 24 square units with the base-ten blocks.
2. The other partner should build a third rectangle with the 24 blocks.
3. Continue to take turns building rectangles until both partners agree that no more rectangles can be built.

Talk About It

4. What patterns do you see? How do the length and width of the rectangles you built relate to the number 24?
5. What is the area of each rectangle that you built? **24 square units**
6. Did you build a rectangle with a width of 5 units? Explain.

4. The length and width of the rectangles are factors of 24.
6. No; 5 is not a factor of 24.

The length and width of the rectangles are the **factors** of 24.

In $24 \div 6 = 4$, the quotient, 4, is a whole number. So, we say 24 is **divisible** by 6, or 6 is a factor of 24. Study the division sentences below. What other numbers are factors of 24?

$24 \div 1 = 24$	$24 \div 6 = 4$
$24 \div 2 = 12$	$24 \div 8 = 3$
$24 \div 3 = 8$	$24 \div 12 = 2$
$24 \div 4 = 6$	$24 \div 24 = 1$

You can use the following rules to check the divisibility of numbers.

A number is divisible by:

- 2 if the digit in the ones place is even.
- 3 if the sum of the digits is divisible by 3.
- 4 if the number formed by the last two digits is divisible by 4.
- 5 if the digit in the ones place is 5 or 0.
- 6 if the number is divisible by both 2 and 3.
- 9 if the sum of the digits is divisible by 9.
- 10 if the digit in the ones place is 0.

Classroom Vignette

"After reviewing divisibility rules, I use the overhead spinner to randomly generate 2-, 3-, and 4-digit numbers. Then I have students work in groups to check whether each number is divisible by 2, 3, 4, 5, 6, 9, or 10. I also have them attempt to discover a rule for divisibility by 8."

Margaret F. Friedman, Teacher
Roxboro Middle School
Cleveland Heights, OH

4-1 Lesson Notes

Instructional Resources

- *Study Guide Masters,* p. 24
- *Practice Masters,* p. 24
- *Enrichment Masters,* p. 24
- Transparencies 4-1, A and B
- Hands-On Lab Masters, p. 75
- CD-ROM Program
  - Resource Lesson 4-1

Recommended Pacing	
Standard	Days 2 & 3 of 15
Honors	Day 2 of 15
Block	Day 1 of 8

1 FOCUS

5-Minute Check *(Chapter 3)*

Refer to the following set of data: 62, 66, 65, 62, 70, 45.

1. Find the range. **25**
2. Find the mode(s). **62**
3. Find the median. **$63\frac{1}{2}$**
4. Find the mean. **$61\frac{2}{3}$**
5. Make a stem-and-leaf plot for the following set of data: 113, 103, 105, 96, 97, 129, 116.

Stem	Leaf
9	6 7
10	3 5
11	3 6
12	9

11|3 = 113

The 5-Minute Check is also available on **Transparency 4-1A** for this lesson.

Motivating the Lesson

Communication Ask students: *can a box of 24 pencils be divided evenly among three children? among four? among five? What other numbers divide into 24 evenly?* **6, 8, 12, 24**

Answers for the Mini-Lab

1–3. Rectangles should be built with dimensions 2 × 12, 3 × 8, 4 × 6.

2 TEACH

Transparency 4-1B contains a teaching aid for this lesson.

Using the Mini-Lab Suggest that students record the dimensions of each rectangle in order to keep track of what they have done. Explain that when they are finished, they can use their notes to help determine patterns. Students can also use grid paper to draw rectangles if tiles are not available.

Teaching Tip In Example 1, point out to students another way to tell whether a number is divisible by 9—if the sum of its digits adds to 9 or to a multiple of 9.

In-Class Examples

For Example 1
Determine whether 104 is divisible by 2, 3, 4, 5, 6, 9, or 10. **2, 4**

For Example 2
Use your calculator to determine whether 397 is divisible by 7. **No; the quotient is not a whole number.**

For Example 3
Find a number that is divisible by 2, 6, 9, and 10. **Sample answers: 90, 180, 270**

Additional Answers

1. **Sample answer: 15 is not divisible by 4, because a rectangle cannot be formed with 4 as the length of one side.**
3. **Rectangles should have dimensions 1×18, 2×9, 3×6; 7 is not a factor of 18.**

Examples

1 **Determine whether 156 is divisible by 2, 3, 4, 5, 6, 9, or 10.**

2: Yes; the ones digit, 6, is even.
3: Yes; the sum of the digits, 12, is divisible by 3.
4: Yes; the number formed by the last two digits, 56, is divisible by 4.
5: No; the ones digit is not 5 or 0.
6: Yes; the number is divisible by 2 and 3.
9: No; the sum of the digits, 12, is not divisible by 9.
10: No; the ones digit, 6, is not 0.

APPLICATION

2 **Money Matters** **Alonso has $249 in spending money to use during his 7-day vacation. Can he spend the same amount of money each day? Use your calculator to determine whether 249 is divisible by 7.**

249 [÷] 7 [=] 35.57142857

Since the quotient is not a whole number, 249 is not divisible by 7. Alonso cannot spend exactly the same amount of money each day. He will be able to spend *about* $35.57 each day.

3 **Find a number that is divisible by 2, 4, 5, and 10.**

The ones digit must be 0 in order for the number to be divisible by 10, which means the number will also be divisible by 2 and by 5. The number formed by the last two digits must be divisible by 4.

The numbers 120, 680, and 1,340 are just a few of the numbers that meet these requirements.

CHECK FOR UNDERSTANDING

Communicating Mathematics

Read and study the lesson to answer each question. **1, 3. See margin.**

1. ***Tell*** what the figure at the right suggests about the number 15 and whether it is divisible by 4. 
2. ***Draw diagrams*** showing how 36 dots can be equally divided into 4 rows or 6 rows or 12 rows. **See Answer Appendix.**

HANDS-ON MATH

3. ***Make a model*** to show the factors of 18. Use square base-ten blocks or draw rectangles on grid paper. Use rectangular arrangements to determine whether 7 is a factor of 18.

Guided Practice

Determine whether the first number is divisible by the second number.

4. 447; 3 **yes** **5.** 9,015; 6 **no** **6.** 1,287; 9 **yes**

Investigations for the Special Education Student

This blackline master booklet helps you plan for the needs of your special education students by providing long-term projects along with teacher notes. Investigation 5, *Author's Fair,* may be used with this chapter.

Determine whether each number is divisible by 2, 3, 4, 5, 6, 9, or 10.

7. 712 **2, 4** **8.** 1,035 **3, 5, 9** **9.** 8,928

10. ***Recreation*** A magazine had kids test several kinds of sleds. The table shows the weights of some of the sleds. If a shipment of sleds weighs 351 pounds and contains only one kind of sled, which sleds could it contain? (*Hint:* Determine whether 351 is divisible by 2, 3, 6, or 9.) **Paris Glad-A-Boggan or Laserluge**

Sled	Weight (lb)
Mega Saucer	2
Paris Glad-A-Boggan	3
Arctic Circle Steel Saucer	6
Laserluge	9

9. 2, 3, 4, 6, 9

EXERCISES

Practice

Determine whether the first number is divisible by the second number.

11. 419; 3 **no** **12.** 7,110; 5 **yes** **13.** 4,408; 4 **yes**
14. 831; 3 **yes** **15.** 6,670; 4 **no** **16.** 2,984; 9 **no**
17. 7,026; 6 **yes** **18.** 1,260; 10 **yes** **19.** 8,903; 6 **no**

Determine whether each number is divisible by 2, 3, 4, 5, 6, 9, or 10.

21. 2, 3, 5, 6, 9, 10
24. 2, 3, 4, 5, 6, 10

20. 462 **2, 3, 6** **21.** 270 **22.** 1,005 **3, 5**
23. 32,221 **none** **24.** 8,340 **25.** 920 **2, 4, 5, 10**
26. 50,319 **3, 9** **27.** 64,042 **2** **28.** 75,396 **2, 3, 4, 6**

29. Use your calculator to determine whether 17,136 is divisible by 8. **yes**

30. Sample answer: 90, 180

30. Find two numbers that are divisible by 2, 9, and 10.

Applications and Problem Solving

31. ***Math History*** Ancient Babylonians (who lived in what is now Iraq) used the number 60 as a base for computation and commerce, just as we use 10 as a base. There were 60 bushels in a mana and 60 mana in a talent. Some mathematicians think that the Babylonians used 60 instead of 10 because 60 is divisible by many numbers. Find all factors of 60 that are not factors of 10. **3, 4, 6, 12, 15, 20, 30, 60**

32a. 1800, 1820, 1840, 1860, 1880, 1900, 1920, 1940, 1960, 1980, 2000
32b. The election years are every 20 years.

32. ***History*** George Washington was elected president in 1789 and re-elected in 1792. Since that time, elections are held every four years.

a. Which presidential election years since George Washington were divisible by 10?

b. Describe the pattern in the election years in part a.

c. Name the next two times in which the presidential election years will be divisible by 10. **2020, 2040**

33. ***Number Puzzle*** Find the mystery number from the following clues. **252**

- This whole number is divisible by 4, 7, and 9.
- Two of its digits are the same.
- The tens digit is greater than the sum of the other two digits.
- It is less than 300, divisible by 12, and has only one odd digit.

3 PRACTICE/APPLY

Check for Understanding

If students need additional practice or instruction after completing Exercises 1–10, you may find one of the following options helpful.

- Extra Practice, see p. 576
- Reteaching Activity
- *Study Guide Masters,* p. 24
- *Practice Masters,* p. 24

Assignment Guide

Core: 11–33 odd, 34–38
Enriched: 12–30 even, 31–38

Teaching Tip In Exercise 29, point out that there is a rule for divisibility by 8: A number is divisible by 8 if the number formed by its last three digits is divisible by 8.

▪ Reteaching the Lesson ▪

Activity Have students make a chart in which they list the divisibility rules with several examples of each. Focus on the relationship between some of the rules, such as for 2, 3, and 6 and for 5 and 10.

***Study Guide Masters,* p. 24**

Name________________ Date________

Study Guide

Divisibility Patterns

The following rules will help you determine if a number is divisible by 2, 3, 4, 5, 6, 9, or 10.

A number is divisible by:

- 2 if the digit in the ones place is even.
- 3 if the sum of the digits is divisible by 3.
- 4 if the number formed by the last two digits is divisible by 4.
- 5 if the digit in the ones place is 0 or 5.
- 6 if the number is divisible by 2 and 3.
- 9 if the sum of the digits is divisible by 9.
- 10 if the digit in the ones place is 0.

Example **Determine whether 2,346 is divisible by 2, 3, 4, 5, 6, 9, or 10.**

2: Yes; the ones digit, 6, is even.
3: Yes; the sum of the digits, 2 + 3 + 4 + 6 = 15, is divisible by 3.
4: No; the number formed by the last two digits, 46, is not divisible by 4.
5: No; the ones digit is not 0 or 5.
6: Yes; the number is divisible by 2 and 3.
9: No; the sum of the digits, 15, is not divisible by 9.
10: No; the ones digit, 6, is not 0.

2,346 is divisible by 2, 3, and 6.

Determine whether the first number is divisible by the second number.

1. 65; 5 yes **2.** 2,641; 3 no **3.** 6,780; 10 yes **4.** 4,185; 9 yes
5. 4,889; 2 no **6.** 8,826; 4 no **7.** 60,003; 6 no **8.** 642; 4 no

Determine whether each number is divisible by 2, 3, 4, 5, 6, 9, or 10.

9. 660 2, 3, 4, 5, 6, 10 **10.** 5,025 3, 5 **11.** 5,091 3 **12.** 356 2, 4

 T24 *Mathematics: Applications and Connections,* Course 2

4 ASSESS

Closing Activity

Writing Have students write a problem for a classmate to solve by applying divisibility rules for 3 and 4.

Practice Masters, p. 24

Name ____________ Date ______

4-1 Practice

Divisibility Patterns

Determine whether the first number is divisible by the second number.

1. 112; 4 yes	2. 3,465,870; 5 yes	3. 34,456,433; 9 no
4. 5,653,121; 3 no	5. 6,432; 10 no	6. 3,469; 6 no
7. 42,981; 2 no	8. 73,125; 3 yes	9. 3,522; 6 yes

Determine whether each number is divisible by 2, 3, 4, 5, 6, 9, or 10.

10. 240 2, 3, 4, 5, 6, 10	11. 657 3, 9	12. 8,760 2, 3, 4, 5, 6, 10
13. 3,408 2, 3, 4, 6	14. 4,605 3, 5	15. 7,800 2, 3, 4, 5, 6, 10
16. 8,640 2, 3, 4, 5, 6, 9, 10	17. 432 2, 3, 4, 6, 9	18. 8,000 2, 4, 5, 10

Find two numbers that are divisible by both of the given numbers. Sample answers are given.

19. 3, 5 15, 30	20. 5, 9 45, 90	21. 6, 10 30, 60
22. 4, 10 20, 40	23. 9, 6 36, 54	24. 2, 9 18, 36

 T24 Mathematics: Applications and Connections, Course 2

34. *Critical Thinking* 3,075 is not divisible by 6. Rearrange the digits to form as many different numbers as possible that are divisible by 6. Use all the digits of 3,075 exactly once as you form each number.
3,570, 3,750, 5,370, 5,730, 7,350, 7,530

Mixed Review

35. *Statistics* The average income for five people in an accounting department is $29,080. The individual salaries are $26,700, $23,500, $24,800, $28,300, and $42,100. Why could the average income be considered misleading to a person applying for a job? *(Lesson 3-7)*

35. **$42,100 is considerably higher than all the other salaries.**

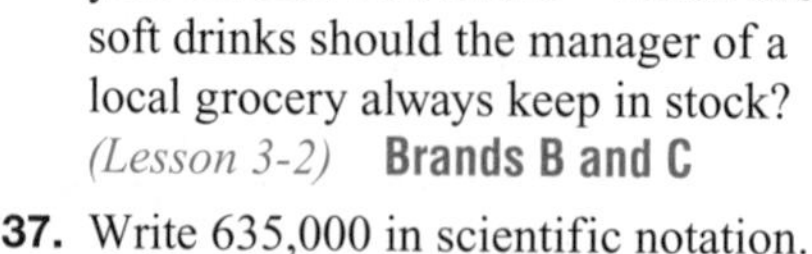

36. *Surveys* The bar graph shows the responses to the question, "What is your favorite soft drink?" Which two soft drinks should the manager of a local grocery always keep in stock? *(Lesson 3-2)* **Brands B and C**

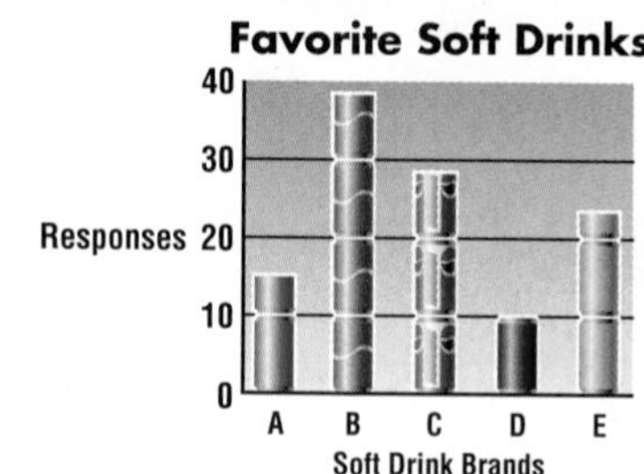

37. Write 635,000 in scientific notation. *(Lesson 2-9)* **6.35×10^5**

38. Standardized Test Practice Which of the following expressions is equivalent to $7 \cdot 2^4$? *(Lesson 1-4)* **C**

A $7 \cdot 8$ **B** $14 \cdot 14 \cdot 14$
C $7 \cdot 2 \cdot 2 \cdot 2 \cdot 2$ **D** $7 \cdot 7 \cdot 7 \cdot 7 \cdot 2 \cdot 2 \cdot 2 \cdot 2$

For **Extra Practice**, see page 576.

Let the Games Begin

The Factor Fair

Math Skill
Factors

Get Ready This game is for two teams.

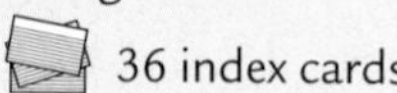

36 index cards

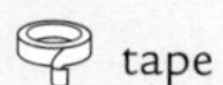

tape

Get Set Number the index cards 1 through 36. Tape the index cards in order on the chalkboard. Divide the class into two teams, Team A and Team B.

Go

- Team A chooses one of the index cards, such as the 8 card, and takes it off the chalkboard. Team A receives 8 points. Team B gets all the cards that are factors of 8 that have not yet been taken. The factors are the points they receive. In this case, Team B would receive 1 + 2 + 4 or 7 points.

Team A	Team B
8	1 2 4 7

- Team B then chooses a card and gets that many points.
- A team loses a turn if it selects an illegal number. A number is considered illegal if the opposing team does not have at least one factor available.
- Teams continue to take turns until there are no legal plays remaining. The team with the most points wins.

Visit www.glencoe.com/sec/math/mac/mathnet for more games.

Extending the Lesson

Enrichment Masters, p. 24

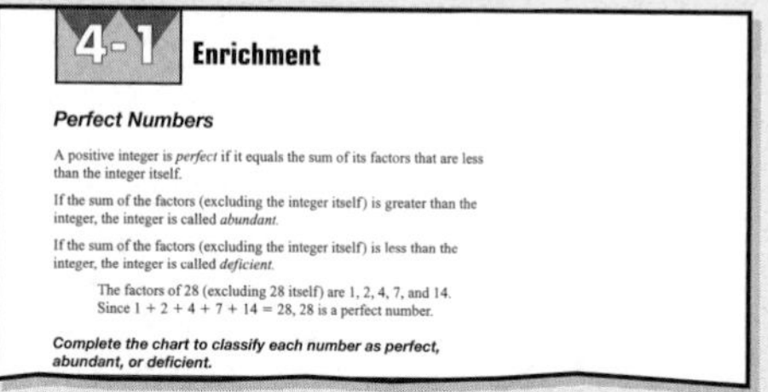

4-1 Enrichment

Perfect Numbers

A positive integer is *perfect* if it equals the sum of its factors that are less than the integer itself.

If the sum of the factors (excluding the integer itself) is greater than the integer, the integer is called *abundant.*

If the sum of the factors (excluding the integer itself) is less than the integer, the integer is called *deficient.*

The factors of 28 (excluding 28 itself) are 1, 2, 4, 7, and 14. Since 1 + 2 + 4 + 7 + 14 = 28, 28 is a perfect number.

Complete the chart to classify each number as perfect, abundant, or deficient.

Students can use the game to practice their knowledge of factors. The game can also be played by two students, instead of two teams. Remind students that choosing a number card is a team decision.

SPREADSHEETS

4-1B Divisibility

A Follow-Up of Lesson 4-1

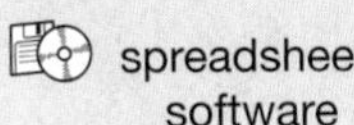
computer

spreadsheet software

You can test for divisibility by using a *spreadsheet*. A spreadsheet is made up of *cells*. A cell can contain data, labels, or formulas. In the cells in column A, enter the numbers to be tested. Then divide each number in column A by the numbers at the top of columns B, C, and D. Divisibility is indicated by whole number quotients.

TRY THIS

Work with a partner.

Use the spreadsheet to determine whether 96, 57, 108, 36, and 154 are divisible by 12, 14, or 19 by making the following substitutions.

A2 = 96, A3 = 57, A4 = 108,

A5 = 36, A6 = 154, B1 = 12,

C1 = 14, D1 = 19

	A	B	C	D
1		B1	C1	D1
2	A2	=A2/B1	=A2/C1	=A2/D1
3	A3	=A3/B1	=A3/C1	=A3/D1
4	A4	=A4/B1	=A4/C1	=A4/D1
5	A5	=A5/B1	=A5/C1	=A5/D1
6	A6	=A6/B1	=A6/C1	=A6/D1

The screen at the right shows the results of making the substitutions and running the spreadsheet. Since cell B2 contains a whole number, the number in cell A2, 96, is divisible by the number in cell B1, 12.

	A	B	C	D
1		12	14	19
2	96	8	6.857143	5.052632
3	57	4.75	4.071429	3
4	108	9	7.714286	5.684211
5	36	3	2.571429	1.894737
6	154	12.83333	11	8.105263

ON YOUR OWN

1. Which numbers are divisible by 12? **96, 108, 36**
2. Which number is not divisible by 12 or 19? **154**
3. How could you use the spreadsheet to determine whether a number is divisible by 228? **3–5. See margin.**
4. Change row 1 of the spreadsheet to test divisibility by 15, 18, and 23. Then change column A to test numbers 90, 253, and 574. Which numbers are divisible by 15, 18, or 23?
5. Create a spreadsheet that determines whether the numbers 1 through 100 are divisible by 2, 3, 4, 5, 6, 7, 8, 9, or 10.

Have students write a paragraph giving at least two advantages of using a spreadsheet to determine divisibility.

GET READY

Objective Students use spreadsheets to test for divisibility.

Technology Resources
Suggested spreadsheet software:
- *Microsoft Excel*
- *ClarisWorks*
- *Lotus 1·2·3*

MANAGEMENT TIPS

Recommended Time
30 minutes

Getting Started Review with students how each cell of a spreadsheet is named. Also review how formulas are written in a spreadsheet.

Using a Calculator If spreadsheet software is not available, you can have groups of students create a table similar to a spreadsheet. Have one member of the team act as the recorder and let other members of the team be responsible for computing each column of division. After the recorder puts the proper values in the table, proceed as if the table is the printed spreadsheet.

Exercise 4 will require a new table and more calculations.

ASSESS

After students answer Exercises 1–5, ask them to explain how the spreadsheet helped them determine divisibility.

Additional Answers

3. **In column A, beginning with A2, enter the numbers to be tested. In E1, enter the number 228. In E2, enter A2/E1; in E3, enter A3/E1, and so on.**
4. **90 is divisible by 15 and 18; 253 is divisible by 23.**
5. **Place the numbers 2, 3, 4, 5, 6, 7, 8, 9, and 10 in row 1. Place the numbers 1 through 100 in column A.**

4-2 Lesson Notes

Instructional Resources

- *Study Guide Masters*, p. 25
- *Practice Masters*, p. 25
- *Enrichment Masters*, p. 25
- Transparencies 4-2, A and B
- *Classroom Games*, pp. 11–12

 CD-ROM Program
- Resource Lesson 4-2

Recommended Pacing	
Standard	Day 14 of 15
Honors	Day 13 of 15
Block	Day 2 of 8

1 FOCUS

5-Minute Check
(Lesson 4-1)

Determine whether the first number is divisible by the second number.

1. 724; 3 **no**
2. 4,118; 4 **no**

Determine whether each number is divisible by 2, 3, 4, 5, 6, 9, or 10.

3. 620 **2, 4, 5, 10**
4. 4,254 **2, 3, 6**
5. Find two numbers that are divisible by both 6 and 9. **Sample answer: 18, 36**

 The 5-Minute Check is also available on **Transparency 4-2A** for this lesson.

Motivating the Lesson

Communication Ask students to explain how to determine whether a number is prime. Ask them to figure out whether 201 is a prime number and to explain their strategy for doing so. **Sample answer: No; 201 is divisible by 3 = 2 + 0 + 1.**

4-2 Prime Factorization

What you'll learn
You'll learn to find the prime factorization of a composite number.

When am I ever going to use this?
You'll use prime factorization to determine whether numbers are composite or prime and to help simplify fractions.

Word Wise
prime number
composite number
prime factorization
factor tree

The world's most popular card game has 108, or 9 dozen, numbered cards. The numbers 9 and 12 (one dozen) are factors of 108 because $9 \times 12 = 108$.

For some numbers, such as 2, 3, 7, and 13, the only product that can be written is 1 times the number itself. These numbers are called **prime numbers**.

Prime Number	A prime number is a whole number greater than 1 that has exactly two factors, 1 and itself.

Numbers that have more than two factors, such as 9 and 12, are called **composite numbers**.

Composite Number	A composite number is a whole number greater than 1 that has more than two factors.

Notice that 0 and 1 are neither prime nor composite numbers.

Every composite number can be written as the product of prime numbers in exactly one way if you ignore the order of the factors. This product is called the **prime factorization** of the number.

Example 1 Write the prime factorization of 108.

The figure formed by the steps of the factorization of 108 is called a factor tree.

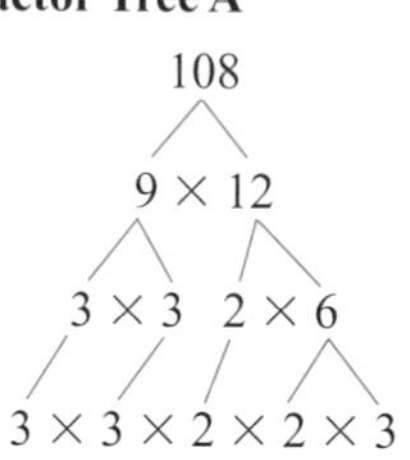

Factor Tree A

108
9×12
$3 \times 3 \quad 2 \times 6$
$3 \times 3 \times 2 \times 2 \times 3$

Factor Tree B

108
4×27
$2 \times 2 \quad 3 \times 9$
$2 \times 2 \times 3 \times 3 \times 3$

Notice that both trees give the same prime factors, except in different orders. Since 2 and 3 are prime numbers, $2 \times 2 \times 3 \times 3 \times 3$ is the prime factorization of 108. Using exponents, $2 \times 2 \times 3 \times 3 \times 3 = 2^2 \times 3^3$.

Classroom Vignette

"We make a Sieve of Eratosthenes to recognize prime numbers and keep it handy when doing prime factorization. When we do factor trees we use "power trees" in which each prime number is considered in order to make the factor tree. This also helps to compare numbers when finding the LCM and GCF."

Travis H. Garrett
Travis H. Garrett, Teacher
Swainsboro Middle School
Swainsboro, GA

Examples

2 Find the prime factors of 420. Then write the prime factorization.

Method 1 Use a factor tree.

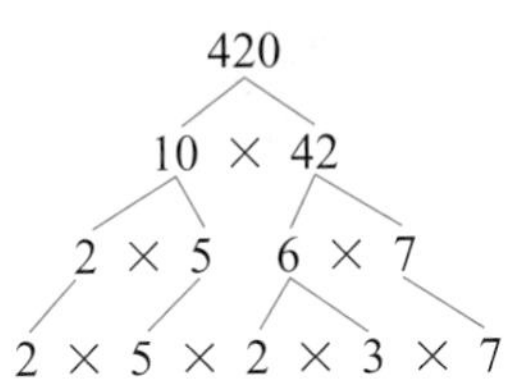

Method 2 Use division.

$420 \div 2 = 210$
$\div 2 = 105$
$\div 3 = 35$
$\div 5 = 7$
$\div 7 = 1$

The divisors are 2, 2, 3, 5, and 7.

The prime factors of 420 are 2, 3, 5, and 7. The prime factorization is $2 \times 2 \times 3 \times 5 \times 7$ or, using exponents, $2^2 \times 3 \times 5 \times 7$.

INTEGRATION **3** **Algebra** The algebraic expression $n^2 + n + 11$ may result in a prime number when n is replaced with a whole number.

a. Evaluate the expression $n^2 + n + 11$ for $n = 0, 1, 2,$ and 3. Are the resulting numbers prime or composite?

$n = 0$	$n = 1$	$n = 2$	$n = 3$
$0^2 + 0 + 11$ $= 0 + 0 + 11$ $= 11$	$1^2 + 1 + 11$ $= 1 + 1 + 11$ $= 13$	$2^2 + 2 + 11$ $= 4 + 2 + 11$ $= 17$	$3^2 + 3 + 11$ $= 9 + 3 + 11$ $= 23$

The numbers 11, 13, 17, and 23 are all prime.

b. Find the least whole number n for which the expression $n^2 + n + 11$ is not prime.

Since the expression is prime for $n = 0, 1, 2,$ and 3, we can start evaluating for $n = 4$.

- $n = 4$
  $4^2 + 4 + 11 = 31$ (prime)
- $n = 5$
  $5^2 + 5 + 11 = 41$ (prime)
- $n = 6$
  $6^2 + 6 + 11 = 53$ (prime)
- $n = 7$
  $7^2 + 7 + 11 = 67$ (prime)
- $n = 8$
  $8^2 + 8 + 11 = 83$ (prime)
- $n = 9$
  $9^2 + 9 + 11 = 101$ (prime)
- $n = 10$
  $10^2 + 10 + 11 = 121$ (composite)

So, 10 is the least whole number for which the expression is not prime.

2 TEACH

Transparency 4-2B contains a teaching aid for this lesson.

Mastering Basic Skills Suggest that students use the divisibility rules for prime numbers 2, 3, and 5 when they begin the prime factorization of a number.

Teaching Tip Work through Example 1 with students step by step. Then encourage them to suggest other ways to arrive at the same set of prime factors. Have students put their solution steps on the chalkboard, and ask them to explain their methods. Repeat the process with another composite number.

In-Class Examples

For Example 1
Write the prime factorization of 460. **$2^2 \times 5 \times 23$**

For Example 2
Find the prime factors of 144. Then write the prime factorization. **2, 3; $2^4 \cdot 3^2$**

For Example 3
a. Evaluate $n^2 + n + 41$ for $n = 0, 1, 2,$ and 3. Are the resulting numbers prime or composite? **41, 43, 47, 53; prime**
b. Find the least whole number n for which the expression $n^2 + n + 21$ is not prime. **2**

3 PRACTICE/APPLY

Check for Understanding

If students need additional practice or instruction after completing Exercises 1–13, you may find one of the following options helpful.

- Extra Practice, see p. 577
- Reteaching Activity
- *Study Guide Masters,* p. 25
- *Practice Masters,* p. 25
- Interactive Mathematics Tools Software

Assignment Guide

Core: 15–41 odd, 43–48
Enriched: 14–38 even, 40–48

Additional Answers

1. The sum of the digits is divisible by 3, so 3 is a factor of 387.
2. 10 is not prime.
3. Sample answer: You can use divisibility rules to find factors of a number. If the number has a factor other than 1 and itself, then it is not prime.

***Study Guide Masters,* p. 25**

Name______________ Date______

4-2 Study Guide

Prime Factorization

A **prime number** is a whole number greater than 1 that has exactly two factors, 1 and itself.

Examples 7 factors: 1, 7
23 factors: 1, 23

A **composite number** is a whole number greater than 1 that has more than two factors. Every composite number can be written as the product of prime numbers. This is called the **prime factorization** of the number.

Example Write the prime factorization of 420.

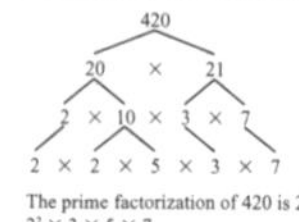

420
20 × 21
2 × 10 × 3 × 7
2 × 2 × 5 × 3 × 7
Write 420 as the product of two factors.
Keep factoring until all of the factors are prime numbers.

The prime factorization of 420 is 2 × 2 × 3 × 5 × 7, or $2^2 \times 3 \times 5 \times 7$.

Determine whether each number is composite or prime.

1. 34 composite
2. 77 composite
3. 37 prime
4. 89 prime
5. 69 composite
6. 67 prime
7. 123 composite
8. 71 prime

Write the prime factorization of each number.

9. 490 $2 \times 5 \times 7^2$
10. 225 $3^2 \times 5^2$
11. 1,155 $3 \times 5 \times 7 \times 11$
12. 1,105 $5 \times 13 \times 17$

© Glencoe/McGraw-Hill T25 *Mathematics: Applications and Connections, Course 2*

CHECK FOR UNDERSTANDING

Communicating Mathematics

Read and study the lesson to answer each question. 1–3. See margin.

1. ***Explain*** how you know that the number 387 is not a prime number.
2. ***Demonstrate*** why $2^5 \times 10$ is not the prime factorization of 320.
3. ***Write*** a paragraph explaining how you can use divisibility rules to help find prime factors.

Guided Practice

Determine whether each number is *composite* or *prime*.

4. 24 composite
5. 19 prime
6. 447 composite

Use a factor tree to find the prime factorization of each number.

7. 132 $2^2 \times 3 \times 11$
8. 45 $3^2 \times 5$
9. 288 $2^5 \times 3^2$

Use your calculator to find the prime factors of each number. Then write the prime factorization of each number.

10. 66 $2 \times 3 \times 11$
11. 375 3×5^3
12. 400 $2^4 \times 5^2$

13. ***Algebra*** Is the value of $6a + 3b$ prime or composite if $a = 5$ and $b = 1$? composite

EXERCISES

Practice

22. $2 \times 3 \times 13$
24. $2^4 \times 5 \times 7$
27. $2 \times 3^2 \times 5 \times 11$
36. $2^2 \times 3 \times 5 \times 29$
40b. Sample answer: 81 sq ft: 3' × 27' or 9' × 9'; 225 sq ft: 9' × 25' or 15' × 15'; 441 sq ft: 9' × 49' or 21' × 21'

Determine whether each number is *composite* or *prime*.

14. 85 composite
15. 423 composite
16. 17 prime
17. 333 comp.
18. 642 composite
19. 139 prime
20. 739 prime
21. 1,492 comp.

Use a factor tree to find the prime factorization of each number.

22. 78
23. 96 $2^5 \times 3$
24. 560
25. 144 $2^4 \times 3^2$
26. 300 $2^2 \times 3 \times 5^2$
27. 990
28. 222 $2 \times 3 \times 37$
29. 1,700 $2^2 \times 5^2 \times 17$

Use your calculator to find the prime factors of each number. Then write the prime factorization of each number. 35. $2^4 \times 5 \times 11$

30. 166 2×83
31. 64 2^6
32. 221 13×17
33. 270 $2 \times 3^3 \times 5$
34. 146 2×73
35. 880
36. 1,740
37. 1,475 $5^2 \times 59$

38. Find numbers that are factors of both 8 and 12. 1, 2, 4
39. Find the missing factor: $2 \times \underline{\ ?\ } \times 5^2 = 450$. 3^2

Applications and Problem Solving

40. ***Contests*** Sandcastle Day has been an annual event in Cannon Beach, Oregon, since 1964. Entrants from each age division are given plots measuring 81 square feet, 225 square feet, or 441 square feet, on which to build their sandcastles.
    a. Find the prime factorization of 81, 225, and 441. 3^4, $3^2 \times 5^2$, $3^2 \times 7^2$
    b. Use the prime factors to determine two possible dimensions for each plot.

Reteaching the Lesson

Activity Begin by finding the prime factors of a relatively small number, such as 18. Then review divisibility rules that students have learned. Then find the factors of 44 and 120. Suggest that students first see whether a number is divisible by 10 or by 2 to begin the factor tree.

Error Analysis
Watch for students who stop factoring before all of the factors are prime numbers.
Prevent by having students make and refer to a list of prime numbers as a guide.

41a. Sample answer: $2 \times 2 \times 6$, $1 \times 3 \times 8$, $1 \times 4 \times 6$, or $1 \times 1 \times 24$

41b. Sample answer: $2 \times 3 \times 6$, $2 \times 2 \times 9$, $3 \times 3 \times 4$, $1 \times 6 \times 6$, $1 \times 2 \times 18$, or $1 \times 4 \times 9$

41e. Sample answer: 32; $2 \times 4 \times 4$; it takes the least amount of space.

41. ***Packaging*** Kien is ordering cartons to ship games to retail stores. The height, width, and length of the cartons must be measured in whole game packages. For example, a carton could be 2 packages high, 3 packages wide, and 4 packages long. Such a carton would contain $2 \times 3 \times 4$ or 24 packages of games.
   a. List two other ways to arrange 24 packages.
   b. List three ways to arrange 36 packages in a carton.
   c. How many different ways could you arrange 30 packages? **5 ways**
   d. How would you arrange 17 game packages? **$1 \times 1 \times 17$**
   e. After researching costs, Kien finds that shipping from 30-35 packages is cost effective. What number and arrangement of game packages would you recommend be shipped in each carton? Why?

42. ***Number Puzzle*** Find the mystery number from the following clues. **36**
   - This whole number is between 30 and 40.
   - It has only two prime factors.
   - The sum of its prime factors is 5.

43. ***Critical Thinking*** Numbers that can be represented by a triangular arrangement of dots are called *triangular numbers.*

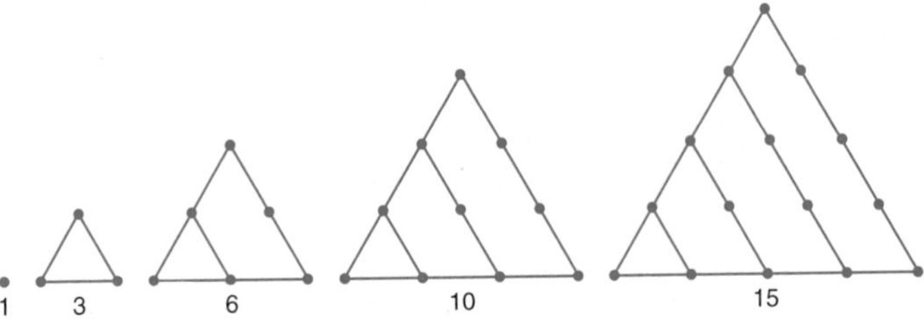

   a. Find the sum of any two consecutive triangular numbers. **4, 9, 16, 25, . . .**
   b. What kind of number is the sum? **a square number**
   c. Determine the next two triangular numbers after 15. Verify your result in part b for these two numbers. **21, 28; $15 + 21 = 36$ or 6^2, $21 + 28 = 49$ or 7^2**

Mixed Review

44. Sample answer: 24, 48

44. Name two numbers that are divisible by both 3 and 8. *(Lesson 4-1)*

45. **Standardized Test Practice** Which number is an outlier in the data shown on the line plot? *(Lesson 3-6)* **A**
   A 6
   B 9
   C 10
   D 12

6	7	8	9	10	11	12
×			××××××	×××	×××	×

46. ***Measurement*** Express 36 milliliters as liters. *(Lesson 2-8)* **0.036 liter**

47. ***Racing*** A trainer recorded a racehorse running at 47.54 miles per hour. What is this speed rounded to the nearest mile per hour? *(Lesson 2-2)* **48 mph**

48. ***Geometry*** Find the area of a rectangle having a length of 8.5 inches and a width of 4 inches. *(Lesson 1-7)* **34 in^2**

For **Extra Practice,** see page 577.

4 ASSESS

Closing Activity

Speaking Tell students that 2 and 3 are consecutive prime numbers. Ask them to explain why there isn't another pair of consecutive prime numbers. **Two is the only even prime number.**

Practice Masters, p. 25

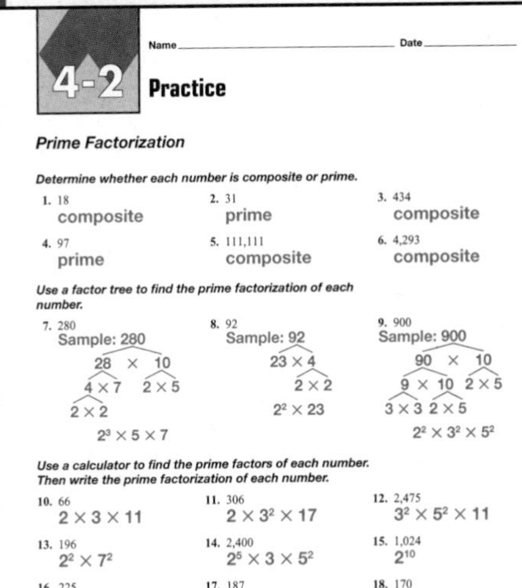
Name ____ Date ____

4-2 Practice

Prime Factorization

Determine whether each number is composite or prime.

1. 18 composite
2. 31 prime
3. 434 composite
4. 97 prime
5. 111,111 composite
6. 4,293 composite

Use a factor tree to find the prime factorization of each number.

7. 280 Sample: 280 → 28 × 10 → 4 × 7, 2 × 5 → 2 × 2; $2^3 \times 5 \times 7$
8. 92 Sample: 92 → 23 × 4 → 2 × 2; $2^2 \times 23$
9. 900 Sample: 900 → 90 × 10 → 9 × 10, 2 × 5 → 3 × 3, 2 × 5; $2^2 \times 3^2 \times 5^2$

Use a calculator to find the prime factors of each number. Then write the prime factorization of each number.

10. 66 $2 \times 3 \times 11$
11. 306 $2 \times 3^2 \times 17$
12. 2,475 $3^2 \times 5^2 \times 11$
13. 196 $2^2 \times 7^2$
14. 2,400 $2^5 \times 3 \times 5^2$
15. 1,024 2^{10}
16. 225 $3^2 \times 5^2$
17. 187 11×17
18. 170 $2 \times 5 \times 17$

Find the missing factor.

19. $3^2 \times 5 \times$ ____ $= 315$ 7
20. $2^4 \times$ ____ $\times 7 = 1{,}008$ 3^2
21. $3^3 \times$ ____ $= 135$ 5
22. $2^2 \times 3^2 \times$ ____ $= 252$ 7
23. $5^2 \times$ ____ $= 275$ 11
24. $3^2 \times 5^2 \times$ ____ $= 2{,}475$ 11

© Glencoe/McGraw-Hill T25 *Mathematics: Applications and Connections, Course 2*

Extending the Lesson

Enrichment Masters, p. 25

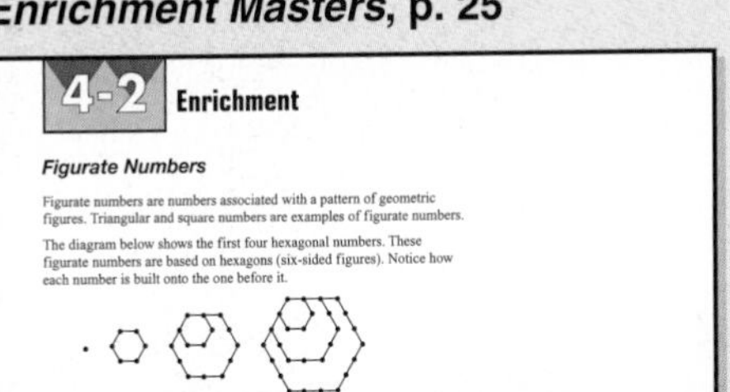
4-2 Enrichment

Figurate Numbers

Figurate numbers are numbers associated with a pattern of geometric figures. Triangular and square numbers are examples of figurate numbers.

The diagram below shows the first four hexagonal numbers. These figurate numbers are based on hexagons (six-sided figures). Notice how each number is built onto the one before it.

Activity Tell students that two numbers that have no common factors other than 1 are *relatively prime.* Ask them to determine whether numbers have to be prime in order to be relatively prime. **No. Examples: 15 and 16**

4-3 Lesson Notes

Instructional Resources

- *Study Guide Masters,* p. 26
- *Practice Masters,* p. 26
- *Enrichment Masters,* p. 26
- Transparencies 4-3, A and B
- *Assessment and Evaluation Masters,* p. 99
- *Diversity Masters,* p. 17

CD-ROM Program
- Resource Lesson 4-3

Recommended Pacing	
Standard	Day 5 of 15
Honors	Days 4 & 5 of 15
Block	Day 3 of 8

1 FOCUS

5-Minute Check
(Lesson 4-2)

Determine whether each number is *composite* or *prime*.

1. 65 composite
2. 161 composite

Write the prime factorization of each number.

3. 54 2×3^3
4. 1,400 $2^3 \times 5^2 \times 7$
5. Use your calculator to find the prime factors of 198. Then write its prime factorization. 2, 3, 11; $2 \times 3^2 \times 11$

The 5-Minute Check is also available on **Transparency 4-3A** for this lesson.

Motivating the Lesson

Hands-On Activity Ask student volunteers to perform an exercise routine that repeats several times. Ask students if it is a sequence. Then ask them to think of other sequences from everyday life. List students' ideas on the chalkboard.

4-3

Integration: Patterns and Functions
Sequences

What you'll learn
You'll learn to recognize and extend a pattern for sequences.

When am I ever going to use this?
Sequences can help you use a simple problem to solve a more complicated one.

Word Wise
sequence
terms
arithmetic sequence
geometric sequence

Did you know Another type of cicada comes up every 13 years. How they know when to surface is still a mystery to biologists.

From North Carolina to New Hampshire, billions of cicadas (suh KAY duhz) emerged from hibernation in 1996. The last time these insects surfaced was in 1979, and biologists say they will surface again in 2013. If this pattern continues, find the next three years in which they will reappear.

Making a table or organized list can help you discover a pattern. Write the years in chronological order.

1979, 1996, 2013, . . . (+17, +17)   *1996 − 1979 = 17*; *2013 − 1996 = 17*

The cicadas surface every 17 years, so add 17 to each year.

2013 + 17 = 2030   2030 + 17 = 2047   2047 + 17 = 2064

The cicadas will surface in 2030, 2047, and 2064.

A **sequence** of numbers is a list in a specific order. The numbers in the sequence are called **terms**. If you can always find the next term in the sequence by adding the same number to the previous term, the sequence is called an **arithmetic sequence**. So the years in which the cicadas surface are an arithmetic sequence.

Example 1 Identify the pattern in the sequence 4, 12, 20, 28, 36, . . . and describe how the terms are created. Then find the next three terms.

4, 12, 20, 28, 36, . . . (+8, +8, +8, +8)   *12 − 4 = 8*; *20 − 12 = 8*; *28 − 20 = 8*; *36 − 28 = 8*

This is an arithmetic sequence in which each term after the first is created by adding 8 to the previous term.

36 + 8 = 44   44 + 8 = 52   52 + 8 = 60

The next three terms are 44, 52, and 60.

If you can always find the next term in the sequence by multiplying the previous term by the same number, the sequence is called a **geometric sequence**.

$$3, \quad 12, \quad 48, \quad 192$$
$$\times 4 \quad \times 4 \quad \times 4$$

$12 \div 3 = 4$
$48 \div 12 = 4$
$192 \div 48 = 4$

Example 2 **Identify the pattern in the sequence 128, 64, 32, 16, . . . and describe how the terms are created. Then find the next three terms.**

$$128, \quad 64, \quad 32, \quad 16, \ldots$$
$$\times 0.5 \quad \times 0.5 \quad \times 0.5$$

$64 \div 128 = 0.5$
$32 \div 64 = 0.5$
$16 \div 32 = 0.5$

This is a geometric sequence in which each term after the first is created by multiplying the previous term by 0.5.

$16 \times 0.5 = 8$ $\quad 8 \times 0.5 = 4$ $\quad 4 \times 0.5 = 2$

The next three terms are 8, 4, and 2.

There are many sequences that are neither arithmetic nor geometric.

Example 3 INTEGRATION

Geometry **A *diagonal* connects two nonconsecutive vertices in a figure. The number of diagonals in each figure is shown below.**

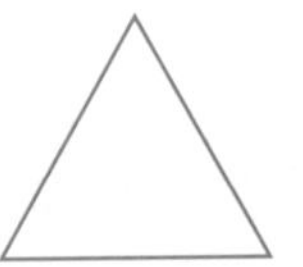

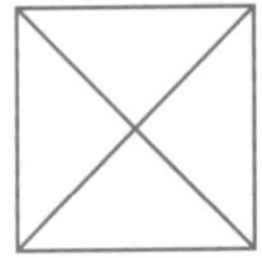
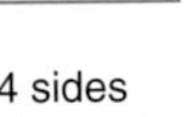

3 sides 0 diagonals	4 sides 2 diagonals	5 sides 5 diagonals	6 sides 9 diagonals

a. **Identify the pattern in the sequence 0, 2, 5, 9, ...**

b. **Find how many diagonals the next three figures would have.**

a. $$0, \quad 2, \quad 5, \quad 9, \ldots$$
$$+2 \quad +3 \quad +4$$

$2 - 0 = 2$
$5 - 2 = 3$
$9 - 5 = 4$

This sequence is neither arithmetic nor geometric. Each term after the first is created by adding 1 more than was added to the previous term.

b. $9 + 5 = 14$ $\quad 14 + 6 = 20$ $\quad 20 + 7 = 27$

The next three figures would have 14, 20, and 27 diagonals.

2 TEACH

Transparency 4-3B contains a teaching aid for this lesson.

Teaching Tip Be sure students understand that an arithmetic sequence is generated by adding the *same* number to each successive term and a geometric sequence is generated by multiplying successive terms by the *same* number.

In-Class Examples

For Example 1
Identify the pattern in the sequence 4, 11, 18, 25, 32, . . . and describe how the terms are created. Then find the next three terms. **Add 7; 39, 46, 53.**

For Example 2
Identify the pattern in the sequence 729, 243, 81, 27, . . . and describe how the terms are created. Then find the next three terms.
Multiply by $\frac{1}{3}$; 9, 3, 1.

For Example 3
Identify the pattern in the sequence 1, 4, 8, 13, 19, ... Then find the next three terms.
Add 3, add 4, add 5, and so on; 26, 34, 43.

MathPASS CD-ROM

This CD-ROM offers a complete, self-paced mathematics curriculum. Each lesson includes a pretest, tutorial, guided practice, and posttest. MathPASS Lesson 9 is correlated to this Student Edition lesson.
For Windows & Macintosh

3 PRACTICE/APPLY

Check for Understanding

If students need additional practice or instruction after completing Exercises 1–9, you may find one of the following options helpful.

- Extra Practice, p. 577
- Reteaching Activity
- *Study Guide Masters,* p. 26
- *Practice Masters,* p. 26
- Interactive Mathematics Tools Software

Assignment Guide

Core: 11–31 odd, 33–37
Enriched: 10–28 even, 30–37

Additional Answers

14. Add 1.1; arithmetic; 6.4, 7.5, 8.6.
15. Multiply by 3; geometric; 405, 1,215, 3,645.
16. Multiply by 0.2; geometric; 0.04, 0.008, 0.0016.
17. Each term has one more digit, and the digits are 1 greater than in the previous term; neither; 55,555, 666,666, 7,777,777.
18. Add 11; arithmetic; 110, 121, 132.
19. The terms are 1^3, 2^3, 3^3, 4^3, . . .; neither; 125, 216, 343.

Study Guide Masters, p. 26

Name________________ Date________

Study Guide

Integration: Patterns and Functions
Sequences

A **sequence** of numbers is a list in a specific order. The numbers in the sequence are called **terms.**

A sequence is an **arithmetic sequence** if you can always find the next term by adding the same number to the previous term.

Examples **1** 7, 11, 15, 19, 23, . . . (+4, +4, +4, +4) *The next term can be found by adding 4 to the previous term.*

The next three terms are 27, 31, and 35.

2 76, 73, 70, 67, 64, . . . (−3, −3, −3, −3) *The next term can be found by subtracting 3 from the previous term.*

The next three terms are 61, 58, and 55.

A sequence is a **geometric sequence** if you can find the next term by multiplying the previous term by the same number.

Example 3 576, 288, 144, 72, . . . (× 0.5, × 0.5, × 0.5) *The next term can be found by multiplying the previous term by 0.5.*

The next three terms are 36, 18, and 9.

A sequence may be neither arithmetic nor geometric.

Example 4 3, 4, 6, 9, 13, . . . (+1, +2, +3, +4) *The next term can be found by adding one more than the number added to the previous term.*

The next three terms are 18, 24, and 31.

Identify each sequence as arithmetic, geometric, or neither. Then find the next three terms.

1. 89, 86, 83, 80, . . . arithmetic; 77, 74, 71
2. 5, 25, 125, 625, . . . geometric; 3,125, 15,625, 78,125
3. 7, 12, 17, 22, . . . arithmetic; 27, 32, 37
4. 78, 75, 77, 74, 76, . . . neither; 73, 75, 72
5. 64, 32, 16, 8, . . . geometric; 4, 2, 1
6. 90, 85, 79, 72, . . . neither; 64, 55, 45

 T26 *Mathematics: Applications and Connections, Course 2*

CHECK FOR UNDERSTANDING

Communicating Mathematics

Read and study the lesson to answer each question.

1. ***Explain*** what pattern you would use to find the next term in the sequence 1, 3, 7, 13, 21, ... **1–2. See Answer Appendix.**
2. ***Write*** a rule to create your own sequence. Trade your sequence with a classmate. See if you can find the rule and the next three numbers in his or her sequence.

Guided Practice

Describe the pattern in each sequence. Identify the sequence as *arithmetic, geometric,* or *neither.* Then find the next three terms.

3. 8, 13, 18, 23, . . .
4. 1, 2, 4, 7, 11, . . .
5. 4, 2, 1, 0.5, . . .

3. Add 5; arithmetic; 28, 33, 38.
4. Add 1 more than was added to the previous term; neither; 16, 22, 29.
5. Multiply by 0.5; geometric; 0.25, 0.125, 0.0625.
6. 12, 16, 20, 24; arithmetic
7. 35, 105, 315, 945; geometric
8. 17.1, 17.3, 17.6, 18.0; neither

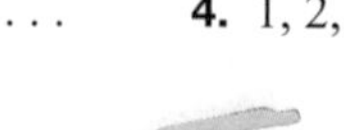

Create a sequence using each rule. Provide four terms for the sequence beginning with the given number. State whether the sequence is *arithmetic, geometric,* or *neither.*

6. Add 4 to each term; 12.
7. Multiply each term by 3; 35.
8. Add 0.2 to the first term, add 0.3 to the 2nd term, add 0.4 to the 3rd term, and so on; 17.1.
9. ***Contests*** Each year, a company sponsors a flying disc contest. First prize is a $1,000 U.S. savings bond. Second prize is a $500 bond, and third prize is a $250 bond. If this pattern continues, what would fourth, fifth, and sixth prizes be?
$125, $62.50, $31.25

EXERCISES

Practice

Describe the pattern in each sequence. Identify the sequence as *arithmetic, geometric,* or *neither.* Then find the next three terms.

10. 0, 13, 26, 39, . . .
11. 4, 12, 36, 108, . . .
12. 0.1, 0.4, 0.7, 1.0, . . .
13. 200, 202, 206, 212, . . .
14. 2.0, 3.1, 4.2, 5.3, . . .
15. 5, 15, 45, 135, . . .
16. 125, 25, 5, 1, 0.2, . . .
17. 1, 22, 333, 4,444, . . .
18. 55, 66, 77, 88, 99, . . .
19. 1, 8, 27, 64, . . .

10. Add 13; arithmetic; 52, 65, 78.
11. Multiply by 3; geometric; 324, 972, 2,916.
12. Add 0.3; arithmetic; 1.3, 1.6, 1.9.
13. Add 2 more than was added to the previous term; neither; 220, 230, 242.
14–19. See margin.

Create a sequence using each rule. Provide four terms for the sequence beginning with the given number. State whether the sequence is *arithmetic, geometric,* or *neither.* **20–25. See margin.**

20. Add 6 to each term; 23.
21. Multiply each term by 5; 7.
22. Multiply each term by 4; 36.
23. Add 0.4 to each term; 5.
24. Add 14 to each term; 58.
25. Multiply each term by 0.1; 70.

Reteaching the Lesson

Activity Have students use number lines drawn on graph paper to plot the opening arithmetic sequence and others. Have them connect the terms to show the distance between them. In this way, students can visualize the distinction between sequences that are arithmetic and those that are not.

Error Analysis

Watch for students who confuse *arithmetic* with *geometric.*

Prevent by having them keep in mind that the *a* in *arithmetic* is the clue that tells them to **add**.

26. Add 2 to the 1st term, add 3 to the 2nd term, add 4 to the 3rd term, and so on; 6. **6, 8, 11, 15; neither**

27. Multiply the 1st term by 1, multiply the 2nd term by 2, multiply the 3rd term by 3, and so on; 3. **3, 3, 6, 18; neither**

28. Find the missing terms in the sequence 12, 19, 26, ?, 40, 47, ?, …. **33, 54**

29. Find the missing terms in the sequence 6, 18, ?, 162, ?, 1,458, …. **54, 486**

Applications and Problem Solving

30. ***Earth Science*** During an earthquake, about 32 times more energy is released for every increase of 1.0 on the Richter scale. (Not 10 times more energy, as was previously thought.) So, a magnitude-6.3 earthquake releases about 32 times more energy than a magnitude-5.3 earthquake. Does the energy increase represent a geometric, arithmetic, or neither type of sequence? **geometric**

31. ***Geometry*** Refer to Exercise 43 on page 141. Write a sequence formed by the first eight triangular numbers. Then write a rule for generating the sequence.

31. 1, 3, 6, 10, 15, 21, 28, 36; add 2 to the first term, add 3 to the second term, add 4 to the third term, and so on.

32. ***Life Science*** The bamboo plant is the fastest growing plant in the world. One bamboo plant grew 36 inches in 24 hours. If the plant grew at a constant rate during the 24 hours and it was 16 inches tall at 8:00 A.M., how tall was the bamboo plant at 4:00 P.M.? (*Hint:* Find how many inches the plant grew per hour.)

32. 28 inches

33. ***Critical Thinking*** You can use an algebraic expression to describe the relationship between the terms in a sequence and their position in the sequence.
    a. You can find any term in an arithmetic sequence by using the expression $a + (n - 1)d$. In the expression, a is the first term, d is the common difference, and n is the position in the sequence. Find the tenth term of the sequence 3, 7, 11, 15, …. **39**
    b. You can find any term in a geometric sequence by using the expression $a \cdot r^{n-1}$. In the expression, a is the first term, r is the common ratio, and n is the position in the sequence. Find the eighth term in the sequence 4, 12, 36, 108, …. **8,748**

Mixed Review

34. Find the prime factorization of 255. *(Lesson 4-2)* **3 × 5 × 17**

35. ***Statistics*** Find the range and appropriate scale and interval for the following data: 3, 17, 21, 19, 36, 15, 12, 9. Draw a number line to show the scale and interval. *(Lesson 3-1)*

35. Sample answer: scale = 0-40; interval = 5; range = 33; See margin for number line.

36. **Standardized Test Practice** Boxes of golf balls containing 3 balls each are on sale for $3.97 per box. What is the cost of 4 boxes of golf balls before tax is added? *(Lesson 2-4)* **C**

    A $7.97 **B** $11.91 **C** $15.88 **D** $18.88 **E** Not Here

For **Extra Practice,** see page 577.

37. ***Algebra*** Evaluate $3x - y \div 6$ if $x = 4$ and $y = 12$. *(Lesson 1-3)* **10**

4 ASSESS

Closing Activity

Modeling Have students use pattern blocks to show how they find the pattern in an arithmetic sequence and in a geometric sequence. Determine the difference between consecutive terms; determine the factor by which neighboring terms are related.

Chapter 4, Quiz A (Lessons 4-1 through 4-3) is available in the *Assessment and Evaluation Masters,* p. 99.

Additional Answer

20. 23, 29, 35, 41; arithmetic
21. 7, 35, 175, 875; geometric
22. 36, 144, 576, 2,304; geometric
23. 5, 5.4, 5.8, 6.2; arithmetic
24. 58, 72, 86, 100; arithmetic
25. 70, 7, 0.7, 0.07; geometric
35. (number line) 0 5 10 15 20 25 30 35 40

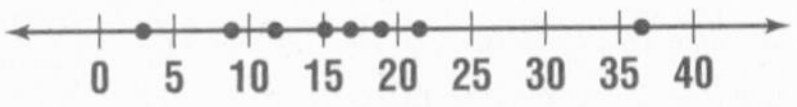

Practice Masters, p. 26

Name ____________ Date ____________

4-3 Practice

Integration: Patterns and Functions
Sequences

Describe the pattern in each sequence. Identify the sequence as arithmetic, geometric, or neither. Then find the next three terms.

1. 6, 12, 18, 24, … Add 6; arithmetic; 30, 36, 42.
2. 1, 4, 16, 64, … Multiply by 4; geometric; 256; 1,024; 4,096.
3. 72, 36, 18, 9, … Multiply by 0.5; geometric; 4.5; 2.25; 1.125.
4. 2, 9, 11, 18, 20, 27, … Add 7, add 2; neither; 29, 36, 38.
5. 9, 18, 27, 36, 45, … Add 9; arithmetic; 54, 63, 72.
6. 0.2, 0.4, 0.8, 1.6, … Multiply by 2; geometric; 3.2, 6.4, 12.8.
7. 1, 3, 9, 27, … Multiply by 3; geometric; 81, 243, 729.
8. 1, 4, 9, 16, 25, … Square each successive integer; neither; 36, 49, 64.
9. 0, 16, 32, 48, 64, … Add 16, arithmetic; 80, 96, 112.
10. 1.2, 2.3, 3.4, 4.5, … Add 1.1; arithmetic; 5.6, 6.7, 7.8.
11. 1, 5, 25, 125, … Multiply by 5; geometric; 625; 3,125; 15,625.
12. 210, 211, 213, 216, … Add 1 more than was added to previous term; neither; 220, 225, 231.

Create a sequence using each rule. Provide four terms for the sequence beginning with the given number. State whether the sequence is arithmetic, geometric, or neither.

13. Add 0.4 to each term; 8. 8, 8.4, 8.8, 9.2; arithmetic
14. Multiply each term by 3; 5. 5, 15, 45, 135; geometric
15. Multiply each term by 0.5; 42. 42, 21, 10.5, 5.25; geometric
16. Add 0.3 to the first term, 0.5 to the next term, 0.7 to the next term, and so on; 10. 10, 10.3, 10.8, 11.5; neither

 T26 *Mathematics: Applications and Connections, Course 2*

Extending the Lesson

Enrichment Masters, p. 26

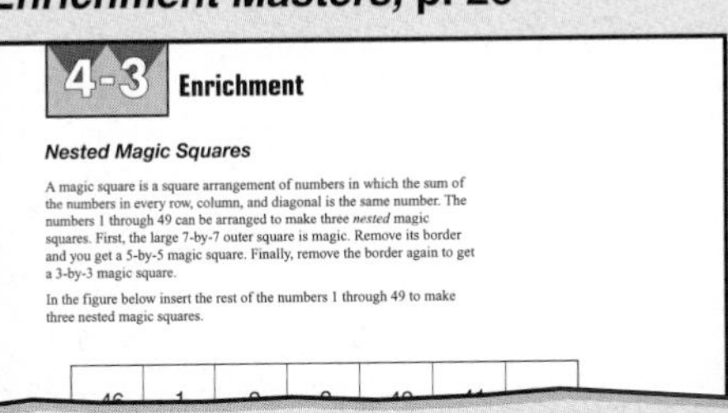

4-3 Enrichment

Nested Magic Squares

A magic square is a square arrangement of numbers in which the sum of the numbers in every row, column, and diagonal is the same number. The numbers 1 through 49 can be arranged to make three *nested* magic squares. First, the large 7-by-7 outer square is magic. Remove its border and you get a 5-by-5 magic square. Finally, remove the border again to get a 3-by-3 magic square.

In the figure below insert the rest of the numbers 1 through 49 to make three nested magic squares.

Activity Give students this problem: A giant kelp seaweed grows 3 feet the first two days. If it continues to grow at the same rate, what would be the length of the seaweed at the end of 80 days? Ask students to find the pattern in the problem. Have them set up the expression 3 + 78 × 1.5 to find the solution. **120 feet**

4-3B HANDS-ON LAB Notes

GET READY

Objective Students explore patterns in sequences.

Optional Resources
Hands-On Lab Masters
• worksheet, p. 45

MANAGEMENT TIPS

Recommended Time
25 minutes

Getting Started To spark student interest in geometric sequences, ask them to suppose they are offered a job caring for someone's dog for 30 days. The pay is to be either $5 a day or 1¢ the first day, 2¢ the second, 4¢ the third, 8¢ the fourth, and so on. Ask them which way they would prefer to be paid. Have them confirm their decisions by direct calculation. **$5 a day produces $150 in a 30-day month. By doubling the number of cents each day, you receive over $5 million on the last day alone. Total: $1,073,741,823**

Activity 1 requires students to identify the factor in each geometric sequence. Before students begin, suggest they look for a pattern as they fill in the table.

HANDS-ON LAB

COOPERATIVE LEARNING

4-3B Exploring Sequences

A Follow-Up of Lesson 4-3

calculator

paper

You can use paper folding to explore patterns in sequences.

TRY THIS

Work with a partner.

1. Fold a piece of paper in half and record the number of layers of paper. (Refer to the table.)
   - Shade one side of the folded paper.
   - Open the piece of paper and record the fractional part of the paper that is *not* shaded. Refold the piece of paper.
   - Fold your paper in half again so the unshaded side is on the outside and record the number of layers of paper.
   - Shade one side of the folded paper.
   - Open the piece of paper and record the fractional part of the paper that is not shaded. Completely refold the paper.
   - Continue folding, shading, and recording until you can no longer fold your paper (at least five folds).

Number of Folds	Layers of Paper	Fraction of Paper Not Shaded
1	2	$\frac{1}{2}$
2	4	$\frac{1}{4}$
3	8	
4		
⋮		

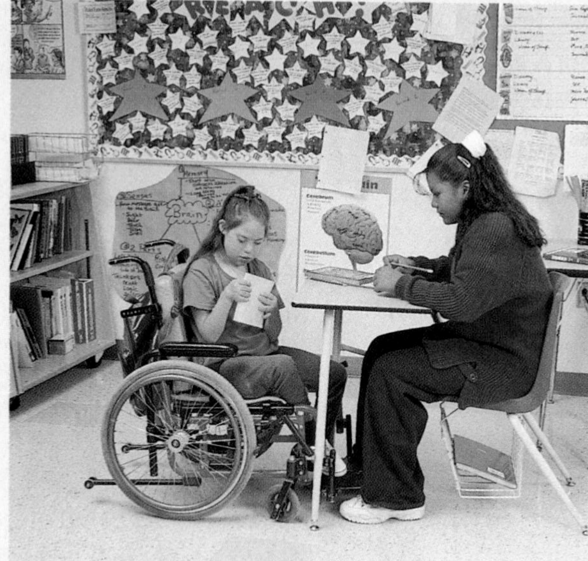

ON YOUR OWN

1. Examine the sequence of numbers in the "Layers" column of your table. Is this sequence arithmetic or geometric? **geometric**
2. Study the sequence in the "Fraction" column. Is this sequence arithmetic or geometric? **geometric**

TRY THIS

Work with a partner.

2 Imagine continuing the paper-folding process from Activity 1 forever. Assuming that your unfolded sheet of paper is 0.002 inch thick, make a table similar to the one below for the first five folds.

Number of Folds	Thickness of the Folded Paper	
	In Layers	In Inches
1	2	0.004
2	4	0.008
3	8	
⋮		

ON YOUR OWN

3. How many folds would it take until the paper is as tall as you?
4. One mile is 5,280 feet. How many folds would it take until the folded paper is one mile tall? **25 folds**
5. How would your data change if you were folding the paper into thirds instead of halves? **The terms in the sequences would increase faster.**

6a. ***Reflect Back*** Write the first ten terms of the geometric sequence 3, 9, 27, … . **6a, d. See margin.**

b. Write the sequence of numbers formed by ones digits of successive terms in the sequence. **3, 9, 7, 1, 3, 9, 7, 1, 3, 9**

c. What pattern do you see? **The terms 3, 9, 7, 1 repeat.**

d. Find the sum of the digits for each term in the sequence created in part a.

e. Which sums are divisible by 3? **all of them**

f. Which sums are divisible by 9? Describe the pattern.

3. 14 folds is 32.768 in., 15 folds is 65.536 in., and 16 folds is 131.072 in.

6f. All but the first term; the pattern is made up of 9's, 18's, and 27's.

Have students write a paragraph about a sequence they create. Have them identify it as an arithmetic or geometric sequence and explain why.

Activity 2 requires students to identify the geometric sequence of the increase in thickness of the folds. Discuss with students why it will be impossible for the paper to fold into the heights described in Exercises 3 and 4 despite the geometric sequence that defines the increasing thickness of the folded paper.

ASSESS

Have students complete Exercises 1–6. To determine whether students understand patterns in arithmetic and geometric sequences, have students describe the difference between an arithmetic sequence and a geometric sequence. Ask them to give an example of each.

Additional Answers

6a. 3; 9; 27; 81; 243; 729; 2,187; 6,561; 19,683; 59,049

6d. 3, 9, 9, 9, 9, 18, 18, 27, 27

***Hands-On Lab Masters*, p. 45**

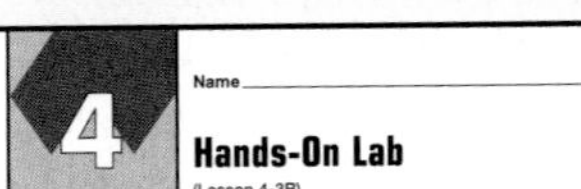

Name________ Date________

Hands-On Lab
(Lesson 4-3B)

Exploring Sequences

Try This 1

Number of Folds	Layers of Paper	Fraction of Paper Not Shaded
1	2	$\frac{1}{2}$
2	4	$\frac{1}{4}$
3	8	$\frac{1}{8}$
4	16	$\frac{1}{16}$
5	32	$\frac{1}{32}$

On Your Own

1. geometric
2. geometric

Try This 2

Number of Folds	Thickness of the Folded Paper	
	In Layers	In Inches
1	2	0.004
2	4	0.008
3	8	0.016
4	16	0.032
5	32	0.064

On Your Own

3. 14 folds is 32.768 in., 15 folds is 65.536 in., and 16 folds is 131.072 in.
4. 25
5. The terms in the sequences would increase faster.
6. **Reflect Back**
   a. 3; 9; 27; 81; 243; 729; 2,187; 6,561; 19,683; 59,049
   b. 3, 9, 7, 1, 3, 9, 7, 1, . X. .
   c. The terms 3, 9, 7, 1 repeat.
   d. 3, 9, 9, 9, 9, 18, 18, 18, 27, 27
   e. all of them
   f. All but the first term. The pattern is made up of 9's, 18's, and 27's.

 45 *Mathematics: Applications and Connections, Course 2*

4-4A THINKING LAB Notes

Objective Students solve problems by making an organized list.

Recommended Pacing	
Standard	Day 6 of 15
Honors	Day 6 of 15
Block	Day 3 of 8

1 FOCUS

Getting Started Discuss the problem-solving strategy of making an organized list. Guide students to see that they can use this strategy to organize information in a way that can help them account for all possibilities while avoiding repetitions.

2 TEACH

Teaching Tip Work through the In-Class Example with students. You may then wish to have students formulate and solve problems of their own. Then have them work through Exercises 1–3.

In-Class Example

Make an organized list to find how many 5-person teams can be selected from a 6-member group. Use the letters A, B, C, D, E, and F to represent the people. **Six different teams are possible.**

Additional Answer

2. **Continue adding the two previous terms to get the next term.**

THINKING LAB **PROBLEM SOLVING**

4-4A Make a List

A Preview of Lesson 4-4

Justin and Monique are on a field trip studying forest conservation. Justin is holding a pinecone, examining its scales. Let's listen in.

Monique

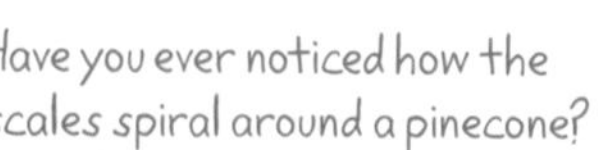

Have you ever noticed how the scales spiral around a pinecone?

No, I didn't think there was any kind of pattern.

Let's check it out. This pinecone has 5 spirals.

The one I have has 13 spirals!

Monique and Justin found more pinecones and counted the spirals. The chart below is an organized list of their data. You can see a pattern in each of the columns.

Pinecone	Number of Spirals	Increase from Previous Number
1	3	-
2	5	2
3	8	3
4	13	5
5	21	8

The numbers 2, 3, 5, and 8 are from the *Fibonacci sequence.* This sequence — 1, 1, 2, 3, 5, 8, 13, 21, . . . — is named after Leonardo Fibonacci, who first presented it in 1201. Notice the pattern in this sequence. Each number is the sum of the two numbers that precede it.

The 6th term in the sequence of spirals would be 13 + 21 or 34, the 7th term would be 21 + 34 or 55, and so on.

THINK ABOUT IT

Work with a partner.

1. ***Write*** the next three numbers in the Fibonacci sequence, 1, 1, 2, 3, 5, 8, 13, 21, 34, 55, ... **89, 144, 233**
2. ***Explain*** in your own words how you could extend the list of Fibonacci numbers through 20 terms. **See margin.**

Reteaching the Lesson

Activity Make a column of 10 squares. Ask a student to write a number in the first square. Ask another student to write a number in the second square. Ask another student to write the sum of the two numbers in the third square. Then have volunteers continue to fill the squares by adding the previous two numbers until all 10 squares are filled. Then have students find the sum of the 10 numbers. Then ask students to find the product of 11 and the seventh number and compare it to the sum. **In any form of the Fibonacci sequence, the seventh term is always $\frac{1}{11}$ of the sum of the first 10 terms.**

For **Extra Practice,** see page 577.

3. ***Apply*** what you have learned to solve the following problem.

   On January 1, there was 1 pair of rabbits that lived in a pen. On February 1, a pair of bunnies was born. Now there are 2 pairs of rabbits: 1 adult pair and 1 baby pair. By March 1, the original parents have had another pair of bunnies and the original bunnies have grown into adult rabbits. Now there are 3 pairs of rabbits: 2 adult pairs and 1 baby pair. The next month the adult pairs each have a pair of babies, while the previous month's babies grow to adulthood. The pattern continues. How many total pairs of rabbits will there be by June 1? Describe the pattern. See margin.

ON YOUR OWN

4. The second step of the 4-step plan for problem solving asks you to *plan* the solution. ***Explain*** how you can **make a list** to help you plan a solution to a problem. See margin.
5. ***Write a Problem*** that you can solve by making a list. Explain your answer. 5. See students' work.
6. ***Find*** the greatest number by which each term of the sequence 2, 2, 4, 6, 10, 16, . . . is divisible. 2

MIXED PROBLEM SOLVING

STRATEGIES

Look for a pattern.
Solve a simpler problem.
Act it out.
Guess and check.
Draw a diagram.
Make a chart.
Work backward.

Solve. Use any strategy.

7. ***History*** During the 3rd century B.C., Greek mathematician Eratosthenes calculated that Earth's circumference was 250,000 *stades.* One mile is approximately 10 stades. If the actual circumference of Earth is about 24,901 miles, was Eratosthenes' calculation reasonable? Explain. See margin.
8. ***Geography*** Mount Everest, the tallest mountain on Earth, is 8,872 meters tall. Olympus Mons, the tallest mountain on Mars, is 23,775 meters tall. How many times taller is Olympus Mons than Mount Everest? about 2.7 times taller
9. ***Physical Science*** Telephone calls travel through optical fibers at the speed of light, which is 186,000 miles per second. A millisecond is 0.001 of a second. How far can your voice travel over an optical line in 1 millisecond? 186 miles
10. ***Number Theory*** Find two numbers that when added, equal 56, and when multiplied, equal 783. 27, 29
11. ***Aircraft*** A Boeing 747 Jumbo Jet, the largest capacity jetliner, is 70.51 meters long. The Stits Skybaby, the smallest fully functional aircraft, is only 2.794 meters long. How many Skybabies, set end-to-end, would it take to equal the length of the 747? 11. about 25 Skybabies
12. **Standardized Test Practice** The table shows the five longest roller coasters at Paramount's Kings Island in Cincinnati, Ohio. Which is the best estimate of the total length of the five coasters? C

Roller Coaster	Length (ft)
The Beast	7,400
Vortex	3,800
Racer	3,415
Adventure Express	2,963
TOP GUN	2,352

A 2,000 ft **B** 12,000 ft
C 20,000 ft **D** 40,000 ft
E 48,000 ft

3 PRACTICE/APPLY

Check for Understanding

Use the results from Exercise 3 to determine whether students understand the process of solving problems by making a list.

Extra Practice If students need additional practice in problem solving, extra practice is available on the following pages.

- Make an Organized List, see p. 577
- Mixed Problem Solving, see pp. 605–606

Assignment Guide

All: 4–12

4 ASSESS

Closing Activity

Writing Write the names of 5 kinds of cheese on the chalkboard. Ask students to list all possible 3-cheese grilled cheese sandwiches that can be formed from these selections.

Additional Answers

3. 13 pairs; the pattern is the Fibonacci sequence.
4. Making a list helps to organize information in order to find a pattern and plan a solution.
7. Yes; 250,000 stades is approximately 25,000 miles. This is close to the actual measure of 24,901 miles.

Extending the Lesson

Activity Have students research to find out more about Leonardo Fibonacci and his sequence. See whether they can discover any applications of the sequence in nature and music.

4-4 Lesson Notes

Instructional Resources

- *Study Guide Masters,* p. 27
- *Practice Masters,* p. 27
- *Enrichment Masters,* p. 27
- Transparencies 4-4, A and B

- CD-ROM Program
  - Resource Lesson 4-4
  - Interactive Lesson 4-4

Recommended Pacing	
Standard	Day 7 of 15
Honors	Day 7 of 15
Block	Day 3 of 8

1 FOCUS

5-Minute Check

Identify each sequence as *arithmetic, geometric,* or *neither.* Then find the next three terms.

1. 0.2, 0.3, 0.5, 0.8, 1.2, . . . **neither; 1.7, 2.3, 3.0**
2. 72, 63, 54, 45, . . . **arithmetic; 36, 27, 18**
3. 5, 10, 20, 40, . . . **geometric; 80, 160, 320**
4. Create a sequence using the following rule. Provide four terms for the sequence beginning with the given number: add 2.5 to each term; 7.5. **7.5, 10, 12.5, 15**

The 5-Minute Check is also available on **Transparency 4-4A** for this lesson.

Motivating the Lesson

Problem Solving Ask students how they would find the greatest common factor of 8 and 12. Ask them to explain whether the same method is practical for finding the GCF of 36 and 212.

Teaching Tip As shown in Example 1, if a common factor occurs more than once, include it the number of times that it is common to the prime factorization of both numbers.

4-4 Greatest Common Factor

***What* you'll learn**

You'll learn to find the greatest common factor of two or more numbers.

***When* am I ever going to use this?**

You'll use greatest common factors to simplify fractions.

Word Wise

greatest common factor (GCF)

In 1903, a company introduced its first box of 8 crayons. In 1958, the 64-box of crayons, with a built-in sharpener, was introduced. Thirty-five years later, the box of 96 crayons came out. Suppose the company is designing boxes so that all sets have the same number of crayons in each row. What would be the greatest number of crayons in each row? *This problem will be solved in Example 4.*

You can determine the **greatest common factor (GCF)** of two or more numbers by making an organized list. The greatest common factor of two or more numbers is the greatest number that is a factor of each number.

One of the following methods can be used to find the GCF.

Method 1 List the factors of each number. Then identify the common factors. The greatest of these common factors is the GCF.

Method 2 Write the prime factorization of each number. Then identify all common prime factors and find their product, the GCF.

Example 1 Find the GCF of 27 and 36.

The GCF of two prime numbers is 1.

Method 1 List the factors.

factors of 27: 1, 3, 9, 27

factors of 36: 1, 2, 3, 4, 6, 9, 12, 18, 36

common factors: 1, 3, 9

Thus, the GCF of 27 and 36 is 9.

Method 2 Write the prime factorization.

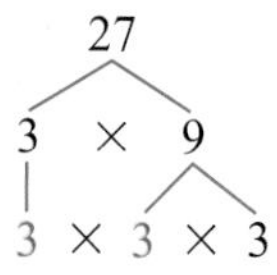

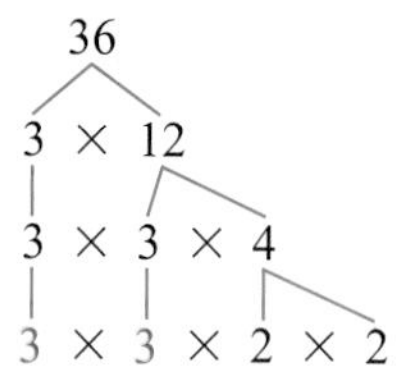

common prime factors: 3, 3

Thus, the GCF of 27 and 36 is 3×3 or 9.

Classroom Vignette

"I feel students should be able to be exposed to different methods to approach the same problems, so I show them how the GCF can be found using Euclid's Ladder. It can also be used to find the LCM."

Kathy Granquist

Kathy Granquist, Teacher
Indian Mills Memorial School
Shamong, NJ

Examples

2 **Find the GCF of 105, 63, and 42.**

Method 1 List the factors.

factors of 105: 1, 3, 5, 7, 15, 21, 35, 105
factors of 63: 1, 3, 7, 9, 21, 63
factors of 42: 1, 2, 3, 6, 7, 14, 21, 42

Since the common factors are 1, 3, 7, and 21, the GCF is 21.

Method 2 Write the prime factorization.

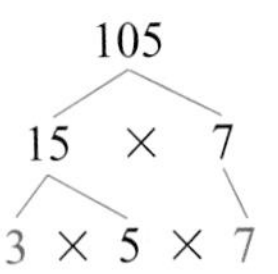

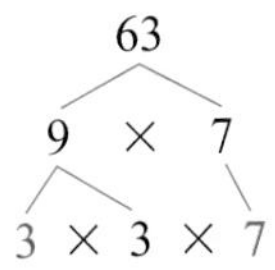

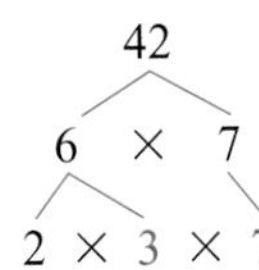

Since the common prime factors of 105, 63, and 42 are 3 and 7, the GCF is 3×7 or 21.

INTEGRATION **3** **Algebra** **Find the GCF of $14xy$ and $7x^2$.**

Write the factors of each expression.

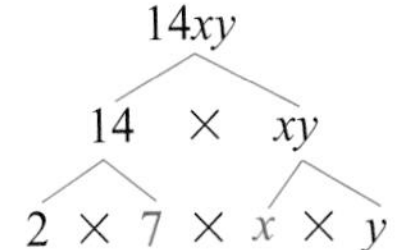

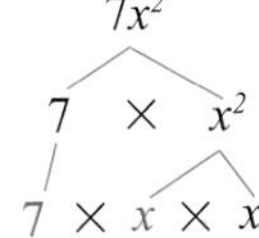

The common prime factors are 7 and x.
Thus, the GCF of $14xy$ and $7x^2$ is $7x$.

APPLICATION **4** **Packaging** **Refer to the beginning of the lesson.**

a. What would be the greatest number of crayons in each row of an 8-, a 64-, and a 96-crayon box if all rows have the same number?

b. How many rows will there be in each box?

a. Find the GCF of 8, 64, and 96.

$8 = 2 \times 2 \times 2$

$64 = 2 \times 2 \times 2 \times 2 \times 2 \times 2$

$96 = 2 \times 2 \times 2 \times 2 \times 2 \times 3$

The GCF is $2 \times 2 \times 2$ or 8. Thus, there would be 8 crayons in each row.

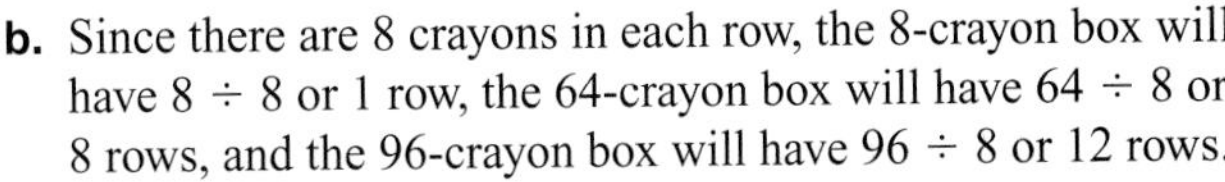

b. Since there are 8 crayons in each row, the 8-crayon box will have $8 \div 8$ or 1 row, the 64-crayon box will have $64 \div 8$ or 8 rows, and the 96-crayon box will have $96 \div 8$ or 12 rows.

2 TEACH

Transparency 4-4B contains a teaching aid for this lesson.

Using Different Methods Students should understand that they can use one method to determine the GCF and the other to check their answer. For example, they can first list factors and then check their answer by writing the prime factorization. Doing this will help them become comfortable using both methods.

In-Class Examples

For Example 1
Find the GCF of 36 and 48 by listing the factors of each number. 12

For Example 2
Find the GCF of 160 and 550 by writing the prime factorization of each number. 10

For Example 3
Find the GCF of $20a^2$ and $14ab$. $2a$

For Example 4
The Whetstone High School marching band has 75 members. If they line up in equal rows, how many rows of how many band members can march together? 3 rows of 25, 5 rows of 15, 15 rows of 5, 25 rows of 3

Teaching Tip Students may find it helpful to use color when finding factors that two numbers have in common. They might shade each set of common factors or use geometric shapes to group them.

Reteaching the Lesson

Activity Help students find prime factors by having them complete partially completed factor trees. In addition, review divisibility rules, and encourage students to use calculators to find factors.

Error Analysis
Watch for students who find the prime factors of two numbers, but use them incorrectly to find the GCF.
Prevent by having students circle all of the *common* prime factors of the two numbers and then multiply them.

3 PRACTICE/APPLY

Check for Understanding

If students need additional practice or instruction after completing Exercises 1–11, you may find one of the following options helpful.

- Extra Practice, see p. 578
- Reteaching Activity, see p. 151
- *Study Guide Masters,* p. 27
- *Practice Masters,* p. 27
- Interactive Mathematics Tools Software

Assignment Guide

Core: 13–39 odd, 40–44
Enriched: 12–34 even, 36–44
All: Self-Test, 1–10

CHECK FOR UNDERSTANDING

Communicating Mathematics

Read and study the lesson to answer each question.

1. ***Explain*** how to find the greatest common factor of 308 and 210 by using the factor trees at the right. Then find the GCF. **1. Identify the common prime factors, 2 and 7, and find their product; 14.**

308
4 × 77
2 × 2 × 7 × 11

210
6 × 35
2 × 3 × 5 × 7

2. ***Draw*** factor trees for 240 and 360, and then circle common factors. What is the GCF of 240 and 360? **120; see margin for factor trees.**

Guided Practice

Find the GCF of each set of numbers by listing factors.

3. 20, 24 **4**
4. 18, 30 **6**
5. 6, 8, 12 **2**

Find the GCF of each pair of numbers by listing common prime factors.

6. $80 = 2^4 \times 5$, $150 = 2 \times 3 \times 5^2$ **10**
7. $45 = 3^2 \times 5$, $60 = 2^2 \times 3 \times 5$ **15**

Find the GCF of each pair of numbers by writing prime factorizations.

8. 30, 48 **6**
9. 125, 40 **5**
10. 12, 90 **6**

11. ***Algebra*** Find the GCF of the terms in the expressions $15a^2$ and $10a$. **5*a***

EXERCISES

Practice

Find the GCF of each set of numbers by listing factors.

12. 33, 121 **11**
13. 28, 84 **28**
14. 96, 56 **8**
15. 6, 10, 12 **2**
16. 18, 42, 60 **6**
17. 36, 50, 130 **2**

Find the GCF of each pair of numbers by listing common prime factors.

18. $18 = 2 \times 3^2$, $54 = 2 \times 3^3$ **18**
19. $60 = 2^2 \times 3 \times 5$, $27 = 3^3$ **3**
20. $36 = 2^2 \times 3^2$, $105 = 3 \times 5 \times 7$ **3**
21. $90 = 2 \times 3^2 \times 5$, $126 = 2 \times 3^2 \times 7$ **18**

Find the GCF of each pair of numbers by writing prime factorizations.

22. 12, 78 **6**
23. 40, 50 **10**
24. 45, 75 **15**
25. 100, 30 **10**
26. 45, 54 **9**
27. 120, 72 **24**

Find the GCF of each pair of numbers. Use any method you prefer.

28. 28, 77 **7**
29. 132, 108 **12**
30. 9, 10 **1**
31. 14, 33 **1**
32. 16, 36 **4**
33. 65, 91 **13**

34. Find the GCF of 82 and 28. **2**
35. Name two different pairs of numbers whose GCF is 26. **35. Sample answer: 26, 52 and 52, 78**

Additional Answer

2. Sample answer:

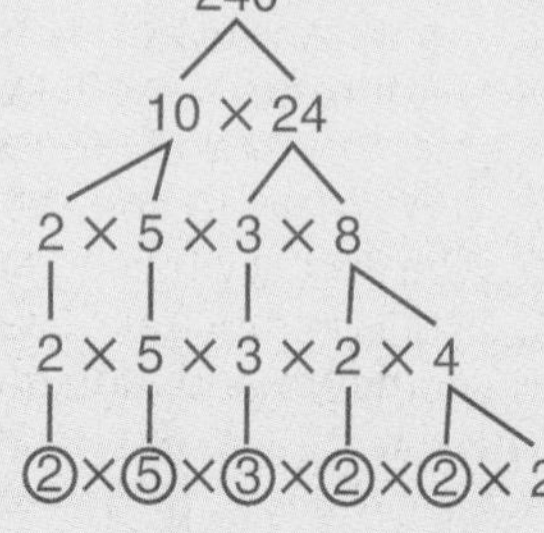

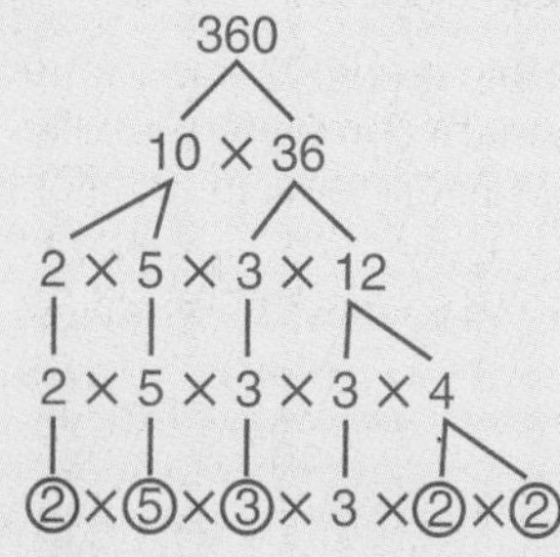

Study Guide Masters, p. 27

Name__________ Date__________

Study Guide

Greatest Common Factor

The **greatest common factor (GCF)** of two or more numbers is the greatest number that is a factor of each number. One way to find the GCF is to list the factors of each number and then choose the greatest of the common factors.

Example **Find the GCF of 72 and 108.**

factors of 72: 1, 2, 3, 4, 6, 8, 9, 12, 18, 24, 36, 72
factors of 108: 1, 2, 3, 4, 6, 9, 12, 18, 27, 36, 54, 108

common factors: 1, 2, 3, 4, 6, 9, 12, 18, 36

The GCF of 72 and 108 is 36.

Another way to find the GCF is to write the prime factorization of each number. Then identify all common prime factors and find their product.

Example **Find the GCF of 210 and 525.**

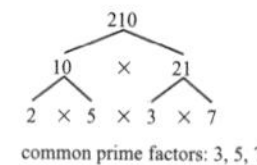

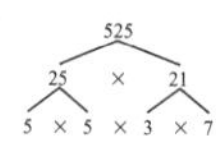

common prime factors: 3, 5, 7

The GCF of 210 and 525 is 3 × 5 × 7 or 105.

Find the GCF of each set of numbers.

1. 18, 30 **6**
2. 60, 45 **15**
3. 24, 72 **24**
4. 32, 48 **16**
5. 100, 30 **10**
6. 54, 36 **18**
7. 120, 200 **40**
8. 81, 153 **9**
9. 77, 121 **11**
10. 60, 24, 72 **12**
11. 32, 48, 80 **16**
12. 90, 120, 180 **30**

 T27 *Mathematics: Applications and Connections, Course 2*

Applications and Problem Solving

36. ***Patterns*** Find the GCF of all the numbers in the sequence 24, 30, 36, 42, 48, 54, … . **6**

37. ***Number Sense*** 14 and 15 are *relatively prime* because their GCF is 1. Find the least composite numbers that are relatively prime. **4, 9**

38. ***Calendars*** Some ancient civilizations used the moon to calculate a lunar month of 30 days. The Maya used the Sun to calculate the solar year of 365 days.
    a. Find the GCF of these two numbers. **5**
    b. Find how many days off the first year would be using lunar months. **5 days**

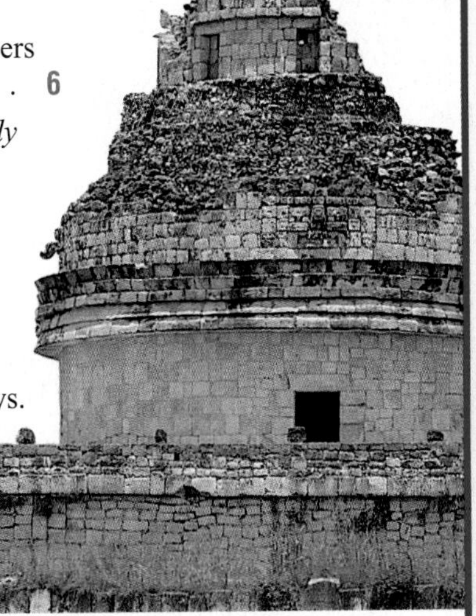

Mayan astronomical observatory

39. See students' work.

39. ***Critical Thinking*** Make a sieve of Eratosthenes up to 100. You can use the Internet to help you research.

Mixed Review

40. ***Patterns*** Identify the pattern in the sequence 13, 26, 52, 104, . . . and find the next three terms. *(Lesson 4-3)* **multiply by 2; 208, 416, 832**

41. **Standardized Test Practice** The tables in the school cafeteria are arranged so there are always the same number of tables in each row. If the tables can be arranged in 4 rows, 5 rows, or 6 rows, what is the fewest number of tables in the cafeteria? *(Lesson 4-1)* **C**

    A 15 **B** 40 **C** 60 **D** 120

42. 17.1 g, 16 g, 16 g

42. ***Nutrition*** The following data are the grams of carbohydrates in 15 different energy bars. Find the mean, mode, and median. *(Lesson 3-4)*

    16, 15, 20, 24, 16, 16, 16, 2, 20, 26, 14, 20, 20, 16, 16

For **Extra Practice**, see page 578.

43. ***Statistics*** Round 17.9 to the nearest whole number. *(Lesson 2-2)* **18**

44. Evaluate the expression $24 - 12 \div 3 \cdot 5 + 6$. *(Lesson 1-2)* **10**

7. Add 5; arithmetic; 29, 34, 39. 9. Multiply by 2; geometric; 384, 768, 1,536.

CHAPTER 4 Mid-Chapter Self Test

Determine whether each number is divisible by 2, 3, 4, 5, 6, 9, or 10. *(Lesson 4-1)*

1. 370 **2, 5, 10**
2. 2,004 **2, 3, 4, 6**
3. 135 **3, 5, 9**

Use a factor tree to find the prime factorization. *(Lesson 4-2)*

4. 106 **2×53**
5. 330 **$2 \times 3 \times 5 \times 11$**
6. 184 **$2^3 \times 23$**

Describe the pattern in each sequence. Identify the sequence as *arithmetic*, *geometric*, or *neither*. Then find the next three terms. *(Lesson 4-3)* **8. See margin.**

7. 9, 14, 19, 24, . . .
8. 0, 1, 3, 6, 10, . . .
9. 12, 24, 48, 96, 192, . . .

10. ***Algebra*** Find the GCF of the terms in the expressions $18w$ and $12w^3$. *(Lesson 4-4)* **$6w$**

4 ASSESS

Closing Activity

Modeling Have students use grid paper to show that the GCF of three numbers can be found by drawing a rectangle to represent each number. All rectangles should have the same width. The greatest width possible for all three is the GCF.

Mid-Chapter Self Test

The Mid-Chapter Self Test reviews the concepts in Lessons 4-1 through 4-4. Lesson references are given so students can review concepts not yet mastered.

Additional Answer for the Self-Test

8. Add 1 more than was added to previous term; neither; 15, 21, 28.

Extending the Lesson

Enrichment Masters, p. 27

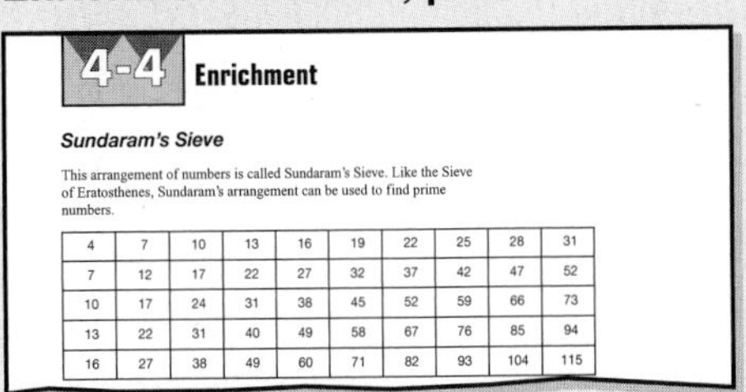

4-4 Enrichment

Sundaram's Sieve

This arrangement of numbers is called Sundaram's Sieve. Like the Sieve of Eratosthenes, Sundaram's arrangement can be used to find prime numbers.

4	7	10	13	16	19	22	25	28	31
7	12	17	22	27	32	37	42	47	52
10	17	24	31	38	45	52	59	66	73
13	22	31	40	49	58	67	76	85	94
16	27	38	49	60	71	82	93	104	115

Activity Another way to find the GCF of two numbers is to divide the greater one by the lesser one, and then divide the divisor by the remainder. Repeat the process until the remainder is 0. The GCF is the last divisor. This is the Euclidean Algorithm. Have students try this method with a few pairs of numbers.

Practice Masters, p. 27

Name__________ Date__________

4-4 Practice

Greatest Common Factor

Find the GCF of each set of numbers by listing the factors of each number.

1. 12, 18 — factors of 12: 1, 2, 3, 4, 6, 12 factors of 18: 1, 2, 3, 6, 9, 18 GCF: 6
2. 16, 30 — factors of 16: 1, 2, 4, 8, 16 factors of 30: 1, 2, 3, 5, 6, 10, 15, 30; GCF: 2
3. 44, 153 — factors of 44: 1, 2, 4, 11, 22, 44; factors of 153: 1, 3, 9, 17, 51, 153; GCF: 1

Find the GCF of each pair of numbers by listing the common prime factors of each number.

4. $80 = 2^4 \times 5$, $110 = 2 \times 5 \times 11$ — common prime factors: 2, 5 GCF: 10
5. $42 = 2 \times 3 \times 7$, $49 = 7 \times 7$ — common prime factor: 7 GCF: 7
6. $16 = 2^4$, $48 = 2^4 \times 3$ — common prime factor: 2^4 GCF: 16

Find the GCF of each pair of numbers by writing the prime factorization of each number.

7. 35, 85 — 35: 5×7; 85: 5×17; common prime factor: 5 GCF: 5
8. 40, 100 — 40: 4×10 → 2×2, 2×5; 100: 10×10 → 2×5, 2×5; common prime factors: 2, 2, 5 GCF: 20
9. 42, 23 — 42: 2×21 → 3×7; 23: 23×1; common prime factor: none GCF: 1

Find the GCF of each set of numbers.

10. 66, 72 — 6
11. 144, 72 — 72
12. 9, 11 — 1
13. 720, 480 — 240
14. 90, 130 — 10
15. 12, 33 — 3
16. 6, 9, 12 — 3
17. 10, 20, 35 — 5
18. 64, 80, 120 — 8

 T27 *Mathematics: Applications and Connections, Course 2*

4-5 Lesson Notes

Instructional Resources

- *Study Guide Masters,* p. 28
- *Practice Masters,* p. 28
- Enrichment Masters, p. 28
- Transparencies 4-5, A and B
- *Assessment and Evaluation Masters,* pp. 98, 99

CD-ROM Program
- Resource Lesson 4-5

Recommended Pacing	
Standard	Day 8 of 15
Honors	Day 8 of 15
Block	Day 4 of 8

1 FOCUS

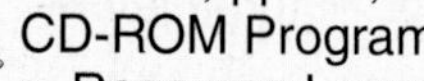

5-Minute Check (Lesson 4-4)

Find the GCF of each set of numbers.

1. 8, 28 4
2. 36, 60 12
3. 124, 280 4
4. 26, 65, 117 13
5. What is the GCF of all the numbers in the sequence 12, 24, 36, 48, . . . ? 12

The 5-Minute Check is also available on **Transparency 4-5A** for this lesson.

Motivating the Lesson

Communication Ask students to read the first paragraph of the first lesson. Ask them why it would be important to determine the portions used to mix the colors. so the color can be reproduced

4-5 Simplifying Fractions and Ratios

What you'll learn

You'll learn to express fractions and ratios in simplest form.

When am I ever going to use this?

Simplest form lets you easily compare fractions and ratios.

Word Wise

ratio
simplest form

Artists have painted Martian landscapes based on actual photographs. Suppose 4 lumps of yellow paint is mixed with 16 lumps of red paint to create a red-orange color for a Martian sunset. Then the yellow-to-red ratio is 4 to 16.

The amounts of colors are compared by using a **ratio**. A ratio is a comparison of two numbers by division. The expressions below represent the ratio used.

4:16 4 to 16

Ratios can also be expressed as fractions. In this case, the fraction is $\frac{4}{16}$.

You can simplify ratios and fractions like $\frac{4}{16}$ by finding the GCF. A fraction is in **simplest form** when the GCF of the numerator and denominator is 1. To express a fraction in simplest form:

- find the GCF of the numerator and the denominator,
- divide the numerator and the denominator by the GCF, and
- write the resulting fraction.

Study Hint
Reading Math The ratio 1:4 is read as 1 to 4.

Let's write the fraction $\frac{4}{16}$ in simplest form.

factors of 4: 1, 2, 4
factors of 16: 1, 2, 4, 8, 16

The GCF of 4 and 16 is 4.

$\frac{4}{16} = \frac{4 \div 4}{16 \div 4} = \frac{1}{4}$ or 1:4

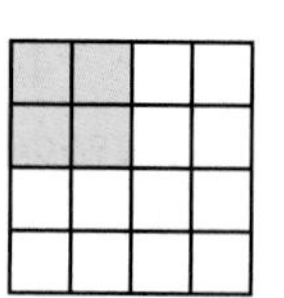
$\frac{4}{16}$

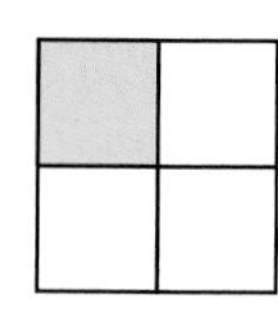
$\frac{1}{4}$

This means that for each lump of yellow, the artist uses 4 lumps of red.

Example 1 Express $\frac{24}{36}$ in simplest form.

If the numerator and denominator do not have any common factors other than 1, then the fraction is in simplest form.

$24 = 2 \times 2 \times 2 \times 3$
$36 = 2 \times 2 \times 3 \times 3$

GCF: $2 \times 2 \times 3$ or 12

Now divide the numerator and denominator by the GCF.

$\frac{24}{36} = \frac{24 \div 12}{36 \div 12} = \frac{2}{3}$

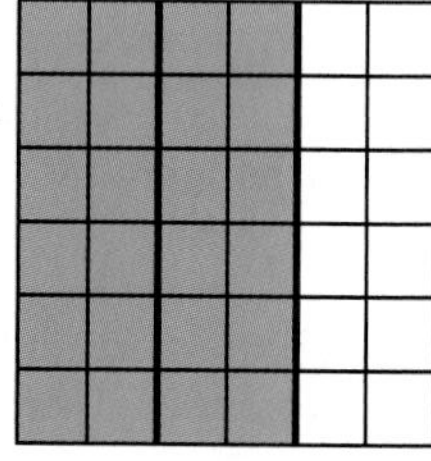
$\frac{24}{36} = \frac{2}{3}$

Cross-Curriculum Cue

Inform other teachers on your team that your students are studying patterns and number sense. Suggestions for curriculum integration are:
Earth Science: patterns in nature
Civics: presidential and congressional election years

Examples

2 Express $\frac{54}{84}$ in simplest form.

factors of 54: 1, 2, 3, 6, 9, 18, 27, 54
factors of 84: 1, 2, 3, 4, 6, 7, 12, 14, 21, 28, 42, 84

The GCF of 54 and 84 is 6.

$$\frac{54}{84} = \frac{54 \div 6}{84 \div 6} = \frac{9}{14}$$

CONNECTION

3 **Earth Science** Australia's Great Barrier Reef is the world's largest structure of living organisms. It is home to about 410 of the 2,290 species of coral in the world. Express the ratio 410:2,290 in simplest form.

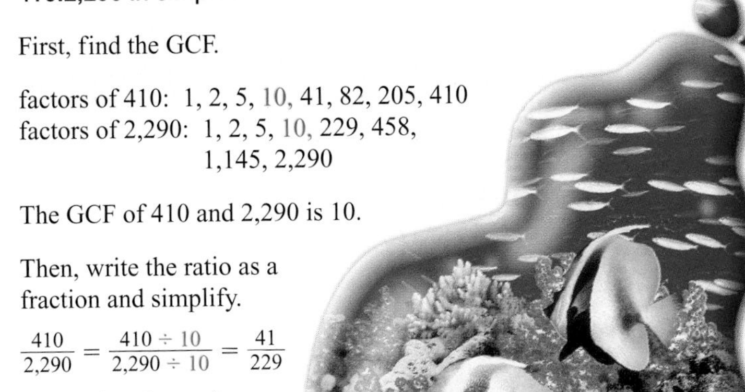

First, find the GCF.

factors of 410: 1, 2, 5, 10, 41, 82, 205, 410
factors of 2,290: 1, 2, 5, 10, 229, 458, 1,145, 2,290

The GCF of 410 and 2,290 is 10.

Then, write the ratio as a fraction and simplify.

$$\frac{410}{2{,}290} = \frac{410 \div 10}{2{,}290 \div 10} = \frac{41}{229}$$

In simplest form, the ratio is 41:229. So there are 41 species of coral in the Great Barrier Reef for every 229 species found in the world.

CHECK FOR UNDERSTANDING

Communicating Mathematics

Read and study the lesson to answer each question.

1. ***Explain*** why the method shown below does not produce an equivalent fraction in simplest form. **See margin.**

$$\frac{16}{36} = \frac{1\not{6}}{3\not{6}} = \frac{1}{3}$$

2. ***Name*** three equivalent fractions that are modeled at the right. $\frac{1}{5}, \frac{2}{10}, \frac{6}{30}$

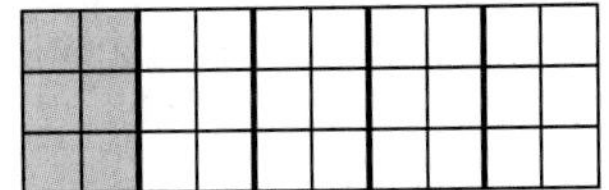

Guided Practice

Express each fraction or ratio in simplest form.

3. $\frac{20}{24}$ $\frac{5}{6}$
4. 18:30 **3:5**
5. $\frac{14}{35}$ $\frac{2}{5}$
6. 81:90 **9:10**

MathPASS CD-ROM

This CD-ROM offers a complete, self-paced mathematics curriculum. Each lesson includes a pretest, tutorial, guided practice, and posttest. MathPASS Lesson 10 is correlated to this Student Edition lesson.
For Windows & Macintosh

Additional Answer

1. You cannot cancel out the units digits in the numerator and the denominator. Divide 16 and 36 by the GCF 4 to get $\frac{4}{9}$, not $\frac{1}{3}$.

2 TEACH

Transparency 4-5B contains a teaching aid for this lesson.

Thinking Algebraically Talk with students about how it is possible to express a quantity in many ways, some simpler than others. Have students write an equation showing how a fraction can be simplified, expressing the numerator and denominator as variables that are multiples of the GCF. **Sample answer:** $\frac{12}{72} = \frac{12x}{12y} = \frac{1}{6}$

In-Class Examples

For Example 1
Express $\frac{28}{49}$ in simplest form. $\frac{4}{7}$

For Example 2
Express $\frac{50}{80}$ in simplest form. $\frac{5}{8}$

For Example 3
Of the 1,276 hazardous wastes sites in the United States, 96 are in California. Express the ratio 96:1,276 in simplest form. **24:319**

Teaching Tip In Example 3, for instance, point out that simplified fractions like $\frac{41}{229}$ are easier to work with than ones such as $\frac{410}{2{,}290}$. However, there are cases when it makes sense or is useful *not* to use the simplest form of a fraction. **Sample answer: When writing a check, for example, one writes "Twenty six and $\frac{25}{100}$ dollars."**

3 PRACTICE/APPLY

Check for Understanding

If students need additional practice or instruction after completing Exercises 1–8, you may find one of the following options helpful.

- Extra Practice, see p. 578
- Reteaching Activity, see p. 156
- *Transition Booklet,* pp. 23–28
- *Study Guide Masters,* p. 27
- *Practice Masters,* p. 27

Assignment Guide
Core: 9–33 odd, 35–39
Enriched: 10–28 even, 30–33, 35–39

7. Sample answer: $\frac{4}{18}, \frac{6}{27}$

7. Write two fractions that can be expressed in simplest form as $\frac{2}{9}$.

8. ***Physical Science*** The table shows the loudness of various sources of sound. Write each ratio of decibels as a fraction in simplest form.

a. Niagara Falls to amplified music

b. car horn to jet aircraft takeoff

c. racing cars to amplified music

8a. $\frac{17}{26}$

8b. $\frac{11}{14}$

8c. $\frac{25}{26}$

Source of Sound	Number of Decibels
Niagara Falls	85
car horn	110
racing cars	125
amplified music	130
jet aircraft takeoff	140

Source: *The Sizesaurus,* Stephen Strauss

EXERCISES

Practice

Express each fraction or ratio in simplest form.

9. $\frac{35}{45}$ $\frac{7}{9}$ **10.** 150:350 3:7 **11.** $\frac{61}{102}$ $\frac{61}{102}$ **12.** 56:96 7:12

13. 16:32 1:2 **14.** $\frac{50}{75}$ $\frac{2}{3}$ **15.** 32:70 16:35 **16.** $\frac{17}{35}$ $\frac{17}{35}$

17. 44:200 11:50 **18.** $\frac{44}{160}$ $\frac{11}{40}$ **19.** 200:500 2:5 **20.** $\frac{80}{96}$ $\frac{5}{6}$

21. $\frac{48}{72}$ $\frac{2}{3}$ **22.** 117:9 13:1 **23.** $\frac{64}{80}$ $\frac{4}{5}$ **24.** 99:66 3:2

Write two different fractions that can be expressed in simplest form as each of the following. 25–27. Sample answers given.

25. $\frac{3}{4}$ $\frac{6}{8}, \frac{9}{12}$ **26.** $\frac{4}{7}$ $\frac{8}{14}, \frac{12}{21}$ **27.** $\frac{5}{9}$ $\frac{10}{18}, \frac{15}{27}$

28. Sample answer: 6:20, 9:30

28. Write two ratios that can be expressed in simplest form as 3:10.

29. Express 16:26 in simplest form. 8:13

Applications and Problem Solving

30. ***Music*** A *sitar* is a South Asian instrument that has two sets of strings. One type of sitar has 6 top strings and 16 bottom strings. Express the number of top strings as a fraction of the total number of strings. Write the fraction in simplest form. $\frac{3}{11}$

31. ***Cycling*** A *gear ratio* of a bike is the comparison of the number of teeth on a chainwheel to the number on a freewheel. If the gear ratio for a 10-speed bike is 52:16, write this as a ratio in simplified form. 13:4

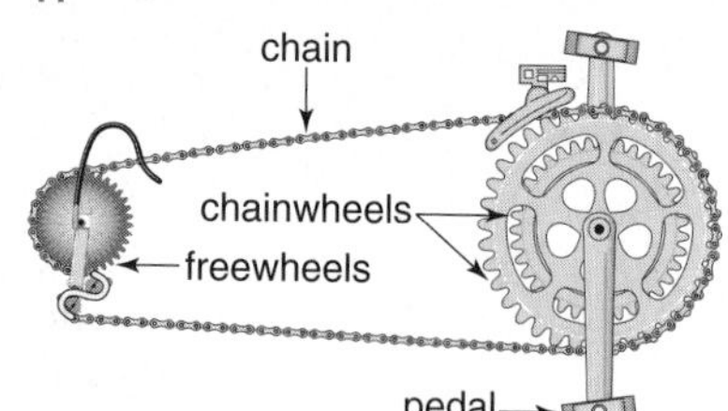

32. ***Life Science*** The human body has 60,000 miles of blood vessels. There are 3,000 miles across the United States from east to west. Express the miles of blood vessels to the miles across the United States as a ratio in simplest form. 20:1

Study Guide Masters, p. 28

Name ______________________ Date ____________

Study Guide

Simplifying Fractions and Ratios

A fraction is in **simplest form** when the greatest common factor (GCF) of the numerator and the denominator is 1.

Example 1 **Express $\frac{36}{54}$ in simplest form.**

factors of 36: 1, 2, 3, 4, 6, 9, 12, 18, 36
factors of 54: 1, 2, 3, 6, 9, 18, 27, 54

The GCF of 36 and 54 is 18.

$\frac{36}{54} = \frac{36 \div 18}{54 \div 18} = \frac{2}{3}$ *Divide the numerator and denominator by the GCF.*

You can also express a ratio in simplest form.

Example 2 **Express 28:63 in simplest form.**

factors of 28: 1, 2, 4, 7, 14, 28
factors of 63: 1, 3, 7, 9, 21, 63

The GCF of 28 and 63 is 7.

$\frac{28}{63} = \frac{28 \div 7}{63 \div 7} = \frac{4}{9}$ *Divide the numerator and denominator by the GCF.*

Express each fraction or ratio in simplest form.

1. $\frac{30}{72}$ $\frac{5}{12}$ 2. 45:60 3:4 3. $\frac{68}{84}$ $\frac{17}{21}$

4. 54:66 9:11 5. 56:64 7:8 6. $\frac{17}{119}$ $\frac{1}{7}$

7. $\frac{60}{75}$ $\frac{4}{5}$ 8. $\frac{75}{375}$ $\frac{1}{5}$ 9. 36:48 3:4

10. 33:132 1:4 11. $\frac{450}{750}$ $\frac{3}{5}$ 12. 25:125 1:5

T28 *Mathematics: Applications and Connections, Course 2*

Reteaching the Lesson

Activity Have students use fraction strips to model different ways of expressing the same quantity, such as $\frac{4}{8}$. Have them express that fraction in simplest form.

Error Analysis

Watch for students who simplify a fraction, but not to its simplest form.

Prevent by reminding students to check their final answer to make sure the numerator and denominator do not have common factors other than 1.

33. ***Exploration*** A team of six explorers took three dogsleds on a 2,000-mile trip across the frozen Arctic Ocean. The table shows the weight of communication equipment needed for such a trip.

Item	Weight (lb)
radio	40
laptop computer	6
computer batteries	5
electrical repair kit	2
satellite equipment	9
satellite batteries	13
battery recharger	10

Write the weight of each item as a fraction of the total in simplest form.

a. radio $\frac{8}{17}$

b. laptop computer $\frac{6}{85}$

c. battery recharger $\frac{2}{17}$

34. ***Working on the CHAPTER Project*** Refer to the table on page 131.

a. Round the number of cars produced by each company to the nearest hundred thousand. Make a table showing this information.

b. The total car production was approximately 6,000,000. Express the rounded numbers in part a as a fraction of 6,000,000. Write the fraction in simplest form. Include this information in your table. **a–b. See Answer Appendix.**

35. ***Critical Thinking*** Explain how you could find a fraction in which the numerator and denominator are greater than 100 and they have a common factor of 13.

35. Multiply the numerator and the denominator of a fraction by 13. (Both numbers must be greater than 7.) Sample answer: $\frac{8 \times 13}{9 \times 13} = \frac{104}{117}$

Mixed Review

36. **Standardized Test Practice** Find the GCF of 126 and 420. *(Lesson 4-4)* **D**

A 52,900 **B** 1,260 **C** 546 **D** 42

37. ***Earth Science*** The table shows the actual thermometer reading in °C and the corresponding wind chill temperatures when the wind is blowing 20 miles per hour. Find the missing temperatures. *(Lesson 4-3)* **−17°, −3°**

Temperature	
Actual	**Wind Chill**
0°	−38°
5°	−31°
10°	−24°
15°	?
20°	−10°
25°	?
30°	4°

38. ***Transportation*** Isabel recorded the number of minutes it took her to drive to work each day for a week. Find the mean and median for the following times: 12, 23, 10, 14, and 11. *(Lesson 3-4)* **14, 12**

39. Multiply 1,000 and 18.7. *(Lesson 2-5)* **18,700**

For **Extra Practice**, see page 578.

Exercise 34 asks students to advance to the next stage of work on the Chapter Project. You may wish to review the rules for rounding before assigning this exercise.

4 ASSESS

Closing Activity

Speaking Have students explain why the fraction $\frac{17}{30}$ is expressed in simplest form and why the fraction $\frac{12}{30}$ is not. **The GCF of 17 and 30 is 1. The GCF of 12 and 30 is 6.**

Chapter 4, Quiz B (Lessons 4-4 and 4-5) is available in the *Assessment and Evaluation Masters,* p. 99.

Mid-Chapter Test (Lessons 4-1 through 4-5) is available in the *Assessment and Evaluation Masters,* p. 98.

***Practice Masters,* p. 28**

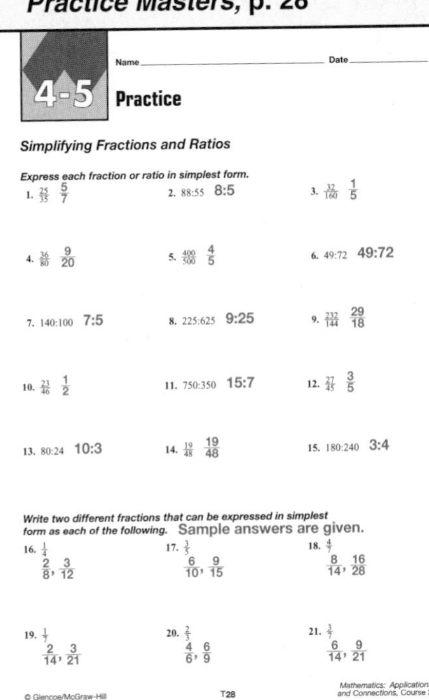

Name ______ Date ______

4-5 Practice

Simplifying Fractions and Ratios

Express each fraction or ratio in simplest form.

1. $\frac{25}{35}$ $\frac{5}{7}$ 2. 88:55 8:5 3. $\frac{32}{160}$ $\frac{1}{5}$

4. $\frac{36}{80}$ $\frac{9}{20}$ 5. $\frac{400}{500}$ $\frac{4}{5}$ 6. 49:72 49:72

7. 140:100 7:5 8. 225:625 9:25 9. $\frac{232}{144}$ $\frac{29}{18}$

10. $\frac{23}{46}$ $\frac{1}{2}$ 11. 750:350 15:7 12. $\frac{27}{45}$ $\frac{3}{5}$

13. 80:24 10:3 14. $\frac{19}{48}$ $\frac{19}{48}$ 15. 180:240 3:4

Write two different fractions that can be expressed in simplest form as each of the following. Sample answers are given.

16. $\frac{1}{4}$ $\frac{2}{8}, \frac{3}{12}$ 17. $\frac{3}{5}$ $\frac{6}{10}, \frac{9}{15}$ 18. $\frac{4}{7}$ $\frac{8}{14}, \frac{16}{28}$

19. $\frac{1}{7}$ $\frac{2}{14}, \frac{3}{21}$ 20. $\frac{2}{3}$ $\frac{4}{6}, \frac{6}{9}$ 21. $\frac{3}{7}$ $\frac{6}{14}, \frac{9}{21}$

 T28 *Mathematics: Applications and Connections, Course 2*

Extending the Lesson

***Enrichment Masters,* p. 28**

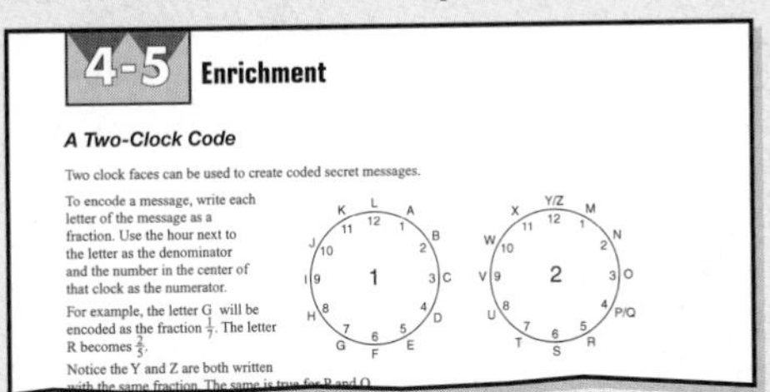

4-5 Enrichment

A Two-Clock Code

Two clock faces can be used to create coded secret messages.

To encode a message, write each letter of the message as a fraction. Use the hour next to the letter as the denominator and the number in the center of that clock as the numerator.

For example, the letter G will be encoded as the fraction $\frac{1}{7}$. The letter R becomes $\frac{2}{5}$.

Notice the Y and Z are both written

Activity Have students work with a partner to make up a five-question True/False quiz that uses fractions with real-world measurements. All answers must be explained. Provide the following as a sample: 4 hours is $\frac{1}{6}$ of a day.

4-6 Lesson Notes

Instructional Resources

- *Study Guide Masters*, p. 29
- *Practice Masters*, p. 29
- *Enrichment Masters*, p. 29
- Transparencies 4-6, A and B

- CD-ROM Program
  - Resource Lesson 4-6

Recommended Pacing	
Standard	Day 9 of 15
Honors	Day 9 of 15
Block	Day 5 of 8

1 FOCUS

5-Minute Check (Lesson 4-5)

Express each fraction or ratio in simplest form.

1. $\frac{14}{28}$ $\frac{1}{2}$
2. 75:125 3:5
3. $\frac{20}{33}$ $\frac{20}{33}$
4. 12:135 4:45
5. Write three different fractions that can be expressed as $\frac{4}{5}$ in simplest form. Sample answer: $\frac{8}{10}$, $\frac{12}{15}$, $\frac{20}{25}$

The 5-Minute Check is also available on **Transparency 4-6A** for this lesson.

Motivating the Lesson

Problem Solving Have students list as many uses of percents as they can. Ask them what is meant by 100% effort. Ask them what is incorrect about claiming to give 110% effort.

2 TEACH

Transparency 4-6B contains a teaching aid for this lesson.

Using the Mini-Lab Ask students how many squares the unshaded region represents. 67 Ask them to represent the number of unshaded squares as a fraction. $\frac{67}{100}$ Ask them to represent one small square as a fraction. $\frac{1}{100}$

4-6 Ratios and Percents

What you'll learn
You'll learn to illustrate the meaning of percent using models or symbols.

When am I ever going to use this?
Percents are often used to illustrate articles in the newspaper.

Word Wise
percent

Think of a state that has the most of its area as water. You may have thought of Florida or Minnesota. But the state with the most water is Michigan! In Michigan, 43 out of every 100 square miles of territory on average is under water. You can write this ratio as a **percent**.

HANDS-ON MINI-LAB

Work with a partner.

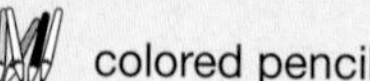

Try This

- Draw a 10 × 10 square on a piece of grid paper.
- Shade the small squares like the model at the right that represents 33 percent.

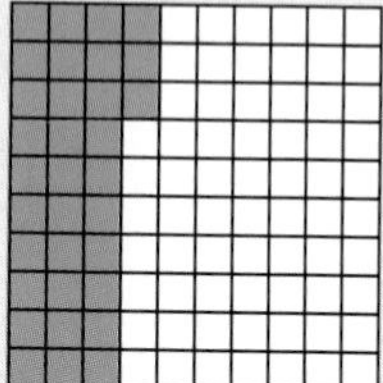

Talk About It

1. How many small squares are in the model? **100**
2. How many small squares are shaded? **33**
3. Write a ratio of shaded squares to squares in the model. $\frac{33}{100}$
4. If the model represents 33 percent, write a conjecture about the meaning of the word *percent*.

4. Sample answer: The percent is the numerator of a ratio with 100 as the denominator.

Percent		
	Words:	A percent is a ratio that compares a number to 100.
	Symbols:	$\frac{n}{100} = n\%$ The symbol % means *percent*.

Examples

Write a percent to represent the shaded area of each model.

1

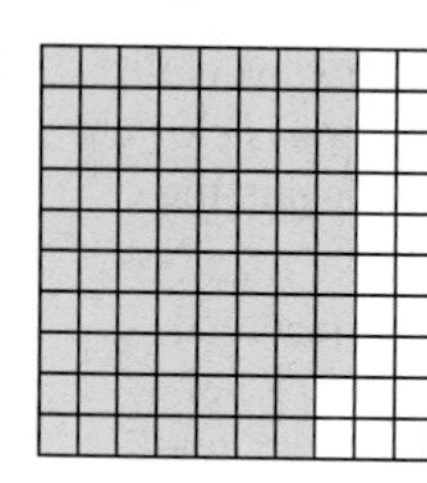

$\frac{78}{100} = 78\%$

2

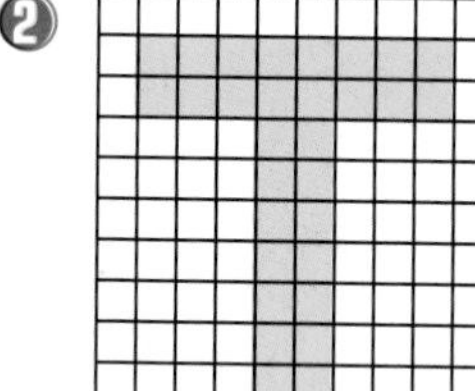

$\frac{30}{100} = 30\%$

Examples

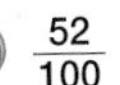

Express each ratio as a percent.

3 $\frac{52}{100}$

$\frac{52}{100} = 52\%$

4 14.4 out of 100

$\frac{14.4}{100} = 14.4\%$

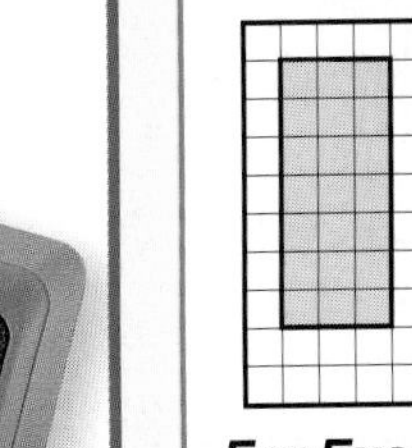

5 $88\frac{1}{4}$ per 100

$\frac{88\frac{1}{4}}{100} = 88\frac{1}{4}\%$

APPLICATION

6 **Technology** In a survey, 99 out of 100 people said that they owned at least one radio. Write the ratio as a percent.

99 out of 100 $= \frac{99}{100}$ or 99%

CHECK FOR UNDERSTANDING

Communicating Mathematics

Read and study the lesson to answer each question.

1. ***Explain*** in your own words the meaning of percent. **See margin.**
2. ***Write*** a percent that means 5 out of 100. **5%**
3. ***Draw*** a model to show 25%. **See margin.**

HANDS-ON MATH

Guided Practice

Write a percent to represent the shaded area.

4. 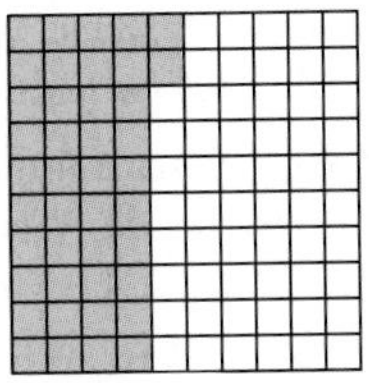 **42%**
5. 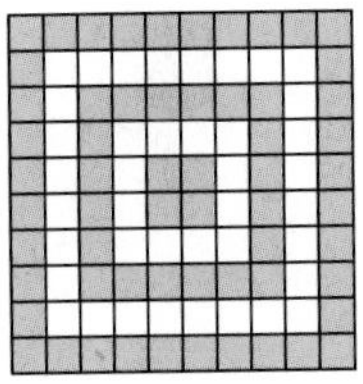 **60%**

Express each ratio as a percent.

6. 18:100 **18%**
7. 34 teams out of 100 **34%**
8. $14.50 per $100 **14.5%**
9. ***Sports*** For every 100 people who play soccer, 77 are under the age of 18. Write this ratio as a percent. **77%**

In-Class Examples

Write a percent to represent the shaded area of each model.

For Example 1

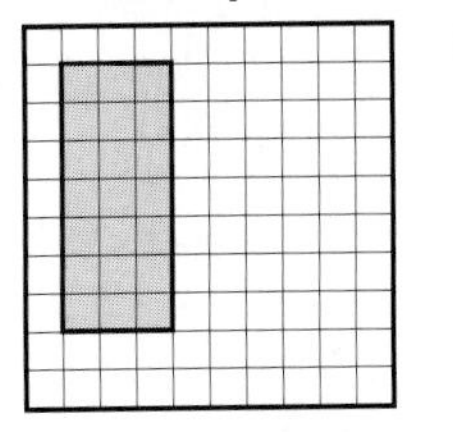

21%

For Example 2

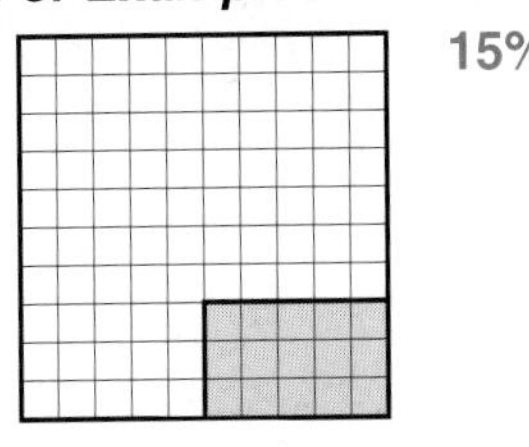

15%

Express each ratio as a percent.

For Example 3

$\frac{37}{100}$ 37%

For Example 4

37.5 out of 100 37.5%

For Example 5

$9\frac{1}{2}$ per 100 $9\frac{1}{2}\%$

For Example 6

Of 100 students surveyed, 44 said chocolate was their favorite ice cream flavor . Write the ratio as a percent. 44%.

Study Guide Masters, p. 29

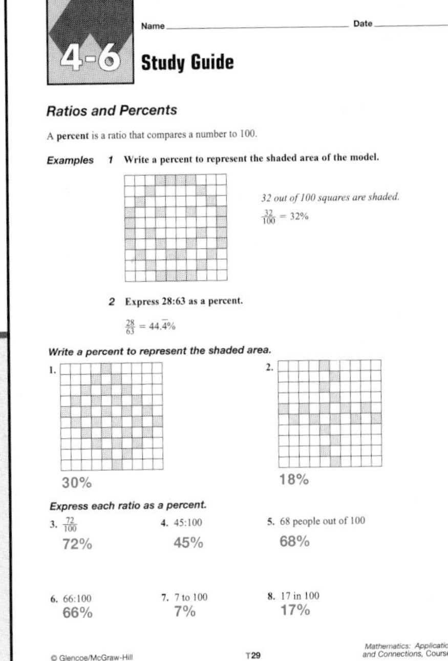

Name ______________ Date ________

4-6 Study Guide

Ratios and Percents

A **percent** is a ratio that compares a number to 100.

Examples 1 **Write a percent to represent the shaded area of the model.**

32 out of 100 squares are shaded.

$\frac{32}{100} = 32\%$

2 **Express 28:63 as a percent.**

$\frac{28}{63} = 44.\overline{4}\%$

Write a percent to represent the shaded area.

1. 30%
2. 18%

Express each ratio as a percent.

3. $\frac{72}{100}$ 72%
4. 45:100 45%
5. 68 people out of 100 68%
6. 66:100 66%
7. 7 to 100 7%
8. 17 in 100 17%

 T29 *Mathematics: Applications and Connections, Course 2*

Reteaching the Lesson

Activity Provide real-life examples of how percent is used, such as in describing tax rates or test scores. Have students use a 10 × 10 grid to make a model of a sales rate of 8% or a test score when 77 out of 100 questions are answered correctly.

Additional Answers

1. Sample answer: a ratio that compares a number to 100.
3. 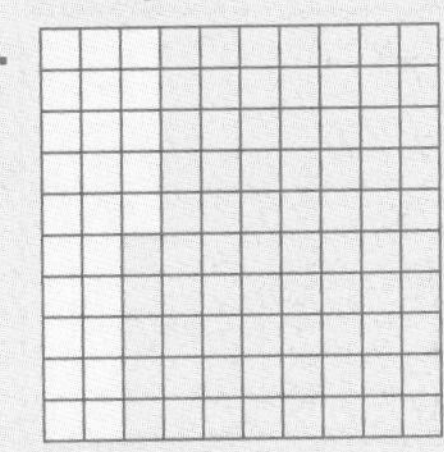

3 PRACTICE/APPLY

Check for Understanding

If students need additional practice or instruction after completing Exercises 1–9, you may find one of the following options helpful.

- Extra Practice, see p. 578
- Reteaching Activity, see p. 159
- *Study Guide Masters,* p. 29
- *Practice Masters,* p. 29

Assignment Guide

Core: 11–29 odd, 30–33
Enriched: 10–26 even, 27–33

4 ASSESS

Closing Activity

Modeling Have students shade a 10 × 10 grid to represent the sales tax in your area.

***Practice Masters,* p. 29**

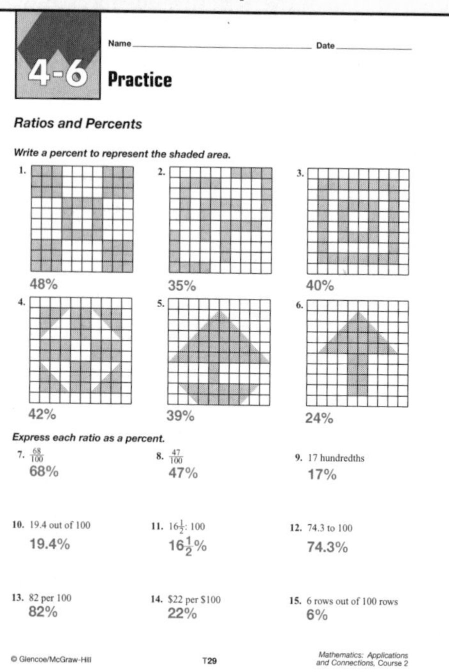

Name ________________ Date ________________

4-6 Practice

Ratios and Percents

Write a percent to represent the shaded area.

1. 48%
2. 35%
3. 40%
4. 42%
5. 39%
6. 24%

Express each ratio as a percent.

7. $\frac{68}{100}$ 68%
8. $\frac{47}{100}$ 47%
9. 17 hundredths 17%
10. 19.4 out of 100 19.4%
11. $16\frac{1}{2}$: 100 $16\frac{1}{2}$%
12. 74.3 to 100 74.3%
13. 82 per 100 82%
14. $22 per $100 22%
15. 6 rows out of 100 rows 6%

 T29 *Mathematics: Applications and Connections, Course 2*

EXERCISES

Practice

Write a percent to represent the shaded area.

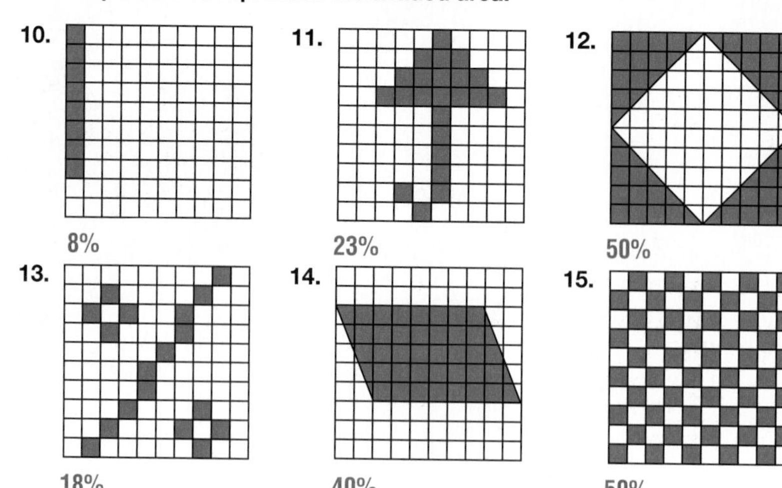

Express each ratio as a percent.

16. $\frac{44}{100}$ **44%**
17. 57 out of 100 **57%**
18. 33:100 **33%**
19. 38.4 to 100 **38.4%**
20. $66\frac{2}{3}$:100 **$66\frac{2}{3}$%**
21. 1 in 100 **1%**
22. $89 per $100 **89%**
23. 15 acres in 100 **15%**
24. 4 species in 100

24. 4%

25. Write 36 track team members in 100 students as a percent. **36%**

26. Express a $7.50 donation from a $100 paycheck as a percent. **7.5%**

Applications and Problem Solving

27. ***Volunteering*** Do you give your time to a favorite charity? Of the 100 teens who answered a women's magazine survey, 61 volunteer more than 3 hours per week. What percent of those who were surveyed volunteer? **Source:** *Ladies Home Journal* **61%**

28. ***Geometry*** Square A measures 10 units on each side. Square B measures 6 units on each side. Write a percent for the ratio of the area of square B to the area of square A. **36%**

29. ***Critical Thinking*** What percent of the model is shaded? **40%**

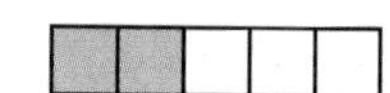

Mixed Review

For **Extra Practice,** see page 578.

30. Express $\frac{10}{24}$ in simplest form. *(Lesson 4-5)* $\frac{5}{12}$

31. ***School*** Mr. Eppick likes to have his math class work in groups of at least two students. If there are 36 students in the class, list all the ways he can arrange the students in equal-sized groups. *(Lesson 4-4)*

31. 2 groups of 18, 3 groups of 12, 4 groups of 9, 6 groups of 6, 9 groups of 4, 12 groups of 3, or 18 groups of 2

32. Solve $b = 12.31 \times 10^4$. *(Lesson 2-5)* **123,100**

33. **Standardized Test Practice** How many square feet of carpet are needed to cover a floor that measures 12 feet by 15 feet? *(Lesson 1-7)* **D**

A 54 ft² **B** 90 ft² **C** 108 ft² **D** 180 ft²

Extending the Lesson

***Enrichment Masters,* p. 29**

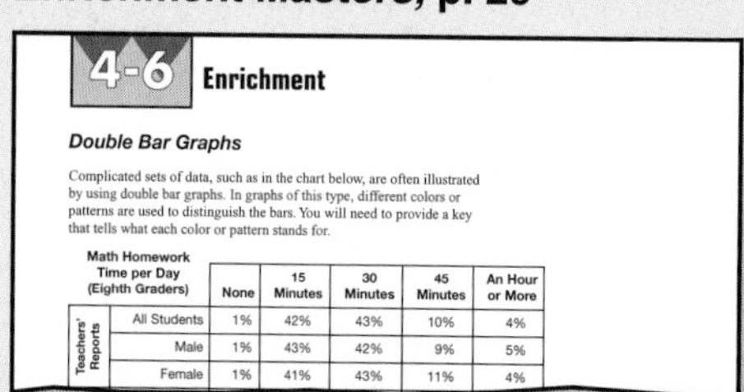

4-6 Enrichment

Double Bar Graphs

Complicated sets of data, such as in the chart below, are often illustrated by using double bar graphs. In graphs of this type, different colors or patterns are used to distinguish the bars. You will need to provide a key that tells what each color or pattern stands for.

Math Homework Time per Day (Eighth Graders)		None	15 Minutes	30 Minutes	45 Minutes	An Hour or More
Teachers' Reports	All Students	1%	42%	43%	10%	4%
	Male	1%	43%	42%	9%	5%
	Female	1%	41%	43%	11%	4%

Activity Have students make the following estimates:

- the percent of students in your school who are seventh graders.
- the percent of the school day you spend in math class.

4-7 Fractions, Decimals, and Percents

***What* you'll learn**

You'll learn to express fractions as percents, and percents and decimals as fractions.

***When* am I ever going to use this?**

Fractions, decimals, and percents are used interchangeably in real-life situations such as the stock market and department store sales.

Have you ever wondered why you can't live without water? It's because your body is mostly water. Brain matter is $\frac{17}{20}$ water. What percent of brain matter is water?

Since a percent is a ratio of a number to 100, you can express $\frac{17}{20}$ as a percent by finding an equivalent fraction with a denominator of 100.

$\frac{17}{20} = \frac{85}{100} = 85\%$ (×5) *Since 100 ÷ 20 = 5, multiply the numerator and denominator by 5.*

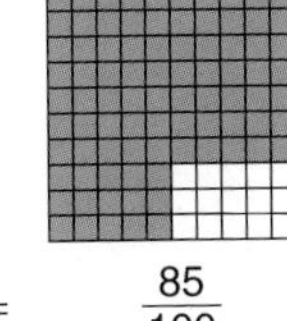

$\frac{17}{20} = \frac{85}{100}$

So, 85% of the brain is water.

Example 1 Express $\frac{3}{5}$ as a percent.

$\frac{3}{5} = \frac{60}{100} = 60\%$ (×20) *Since 100 ÷ 5 = 20, multiply the numerator and denominator by 20.*

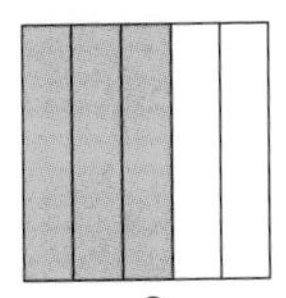

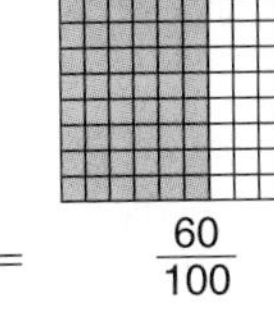

$\frac{3}{5} = \frac{60}{100}$

In Chapter 8, you will express fractions like $\frac{1}{3}$, $\frac{3}{8}$, and $\frac{2}{9}$ as percents.

You can express a percent as a fraction by writing the number over 100 and simplifying.

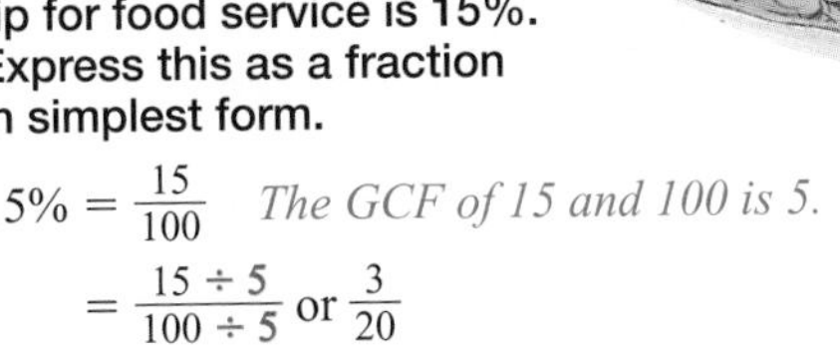

Example 2 Real World APPLICATION

Tipping Author Irene Frankel claims that the word "tip" originated in 18th-century England, where coffeehouse patrons put coins in a box labeled "To Insure Promptness." A standard tip for food service is 15%. Express this as a fraction in simplest form.

$15\% = \frac{15}{100}$ *The GCF of 15 and 100 is 5.*

$= \frac{15 \div 5}{100 \div 5}$ or $\frac{3}{20}$

Multiple Learning Styles

Logical Have students work in pairs to determine the rule for each sequence and the next term.

- 1, 4, 7, 10, 13, 16 **add 3; 19**
- 1, 2, 4, 7, 11, 16 **add 1 more each time; 22**
- 1, 6, 3, 10, 7, 16 **alternately add 5, 7, 9, . . . and subtract 3; 13**

4-7 Lesson Notes

Instructional Resources

- *Study Guide Masters,* p. 30
- *Practice Masters,* p. 30
- *Enrichment Masters,* p. 30
- Transparencies 4-7, A and B
- *Technology Masters,* pp. 33–34

CD-ROM Program
- Resource Lesson 4-7

Recommended Pacing	
Standard	Day 10 of 15
Honors	Day 10 of 15
Block	Day 5 of 8

1 FOCUS

5-Minute Check (Lesson 4-6)

Write a percent to represent the shaded area.

1. 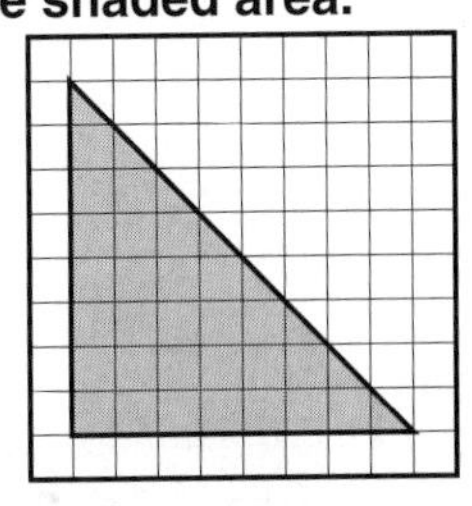 **32%**

2. 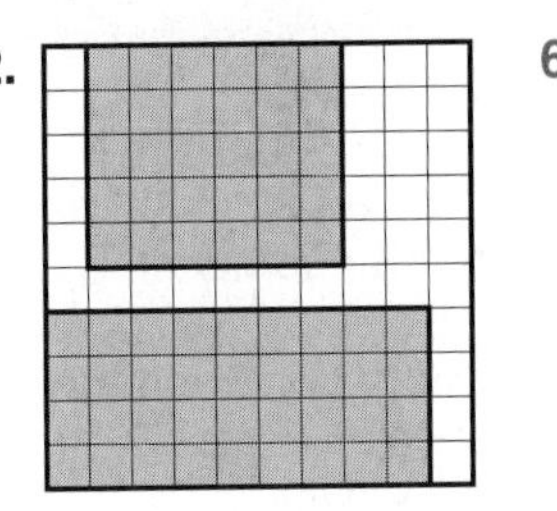 **66%**

Express each ratio as a percent.

3. 46 people out of 100. **46%**
4. 87:100 **87%**

The 5-Minute Check is also available on **Transparency 4-7A** for this lesson.

Motivating the Lesson

Problem Solving Tell students that in one basketball game, Tina made 7 of her 10 free-throw attempts. Ask them to express her free-throw shooting record as a percent.

2 TEACH

Transparency 4-7B contains a teaching aid for this lesson.

Mastering Basic Skills As students learn how to find percents from decimals, they are actually practicing their skills in writing equivalent fractions.

In-Class Examples

For Example 1

Express $\frac{9}{10}$ as a percent. 90%

For Example 2

Some states limit the amount of interest a bank can charge on credit card purchases. In New York and Ohio, for example, the maximum is 25% per year. Express this as a fraction in simplest form. $\frac{1}{4}$

Express each decimal as a fraction.

For Example 3

0.8 $\frac{4}{5}$

For Example 4

0.35 $\frac{7}{20}$

3 PRACTICE/APPLY

Check for Understanding

If students need additional practice or instruction after completing Exercises 1–12, you may find one of the following options helpful.

- Extra Practice, see p. 579
- Reteaching Activity
- *Study Guide Masters,* p. 30
- *Practice Masters,* p. 30

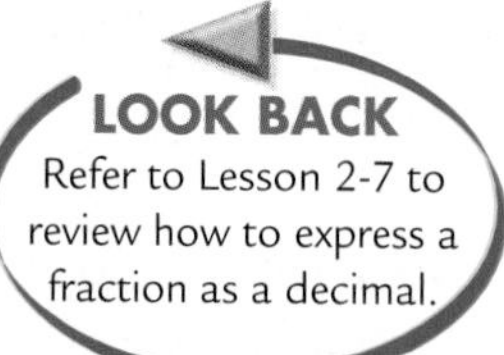

LOOK BACK Refer to Lesson 2-7 to review how to express a fraction as a decimal.

In Chapter 2, you learned how to express a fraction as a decimal. You can also express decimals as fractions. Express the decimal as a fraction with a denominator of a power of 10. This is indicated by the place value of the final digit of the decimal. Then simplify the fraction.

$$0.14 = \frac{14}{100} = \frac{7}{50} \quad \textit{The GCF of 14 and 100 is 2.}$$

Examples Express each decimal as a fraction.

3 0.6

$0.6 = \frac{6}{10}$ or $\frac{3}{5}$

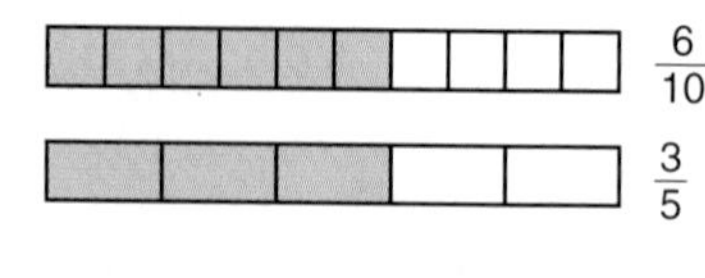

4 0.24

$0.24 = \frac{24}{100}$ or $\frac{6}{25}$

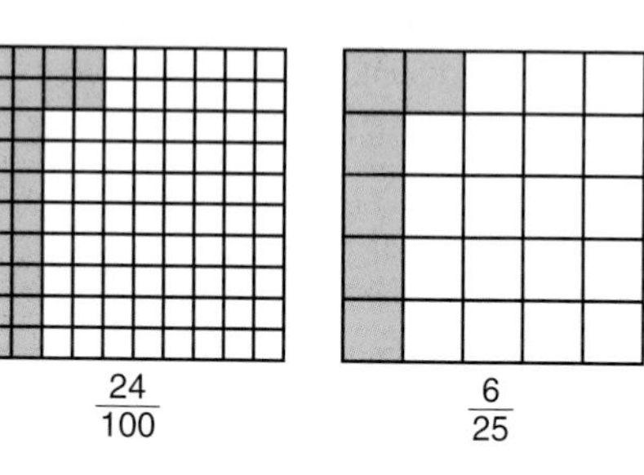

CHECK FOR UNDERSTANDING

Communicating Mathematics

Read and study the lesson to answer each question.

1. ***Express*** the shaded portion of the model at the right as a percent and as a fraction in simplest form. 36%, $\frac{9}{25}$

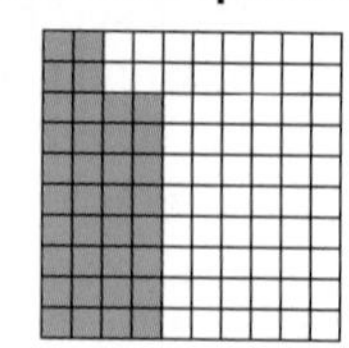

2. ***Describe*** two real-life situations in which you would use percents rather than fractions or decimals. (*Hint:* Recipes use fractions, such as $\frac{1}{2}$ cup, rather than percents or decimals.)
3. ***You Decide*** Ed thinks that 0.250 and 0.025 equal the same fraction. Juliana doesn't think they do. Who is correct? Explain your reasoning.

2. Sample answer: test scores, store sales
3. Juliana; $0.250 = \frac{1}{4}$ and $0.025 = \frac{1}{40}$

Guided Practice

Express each fraction as a percent.

4. $\frac{1}{2}$ 50%
5. $\frac{13}{20}$ 65%
6. $\frac{19}{25}$ 76%
7. $\frac{9}{10}$ 90%

Express each percent or decimal as a fraction in simplest form.

8. 45% $\frac{9}{20}$
9. 0.22 $\frac{11}{50}$
10. 90% $\frac{9}{10}$
11. 0.8 $\frac{4}{5}$

Reteaching the Lesson

Activity Use the concept that coins are percents of a dollar to reinforce the relationship among decimals, fractions, and percents. Have students use combinations of coins to make different money amounts. Help students write these amounts in dollar-and-cents notation, as fractions of a dollar and as percents of a dollar.

12a. $\frac{53}{100}$
12b. $\frac{12}{25}$
12c. $\frac{8}{25}$
12d. $\frac{9}{50}$
12e. $\frac{1}{10}$

12. *Food* The graph shows the percent of family income spent on food for five different countries. Write each percent as a fraction in simplest form.
    a. India b. China
    c. Mexico d. Japan
    e. USA

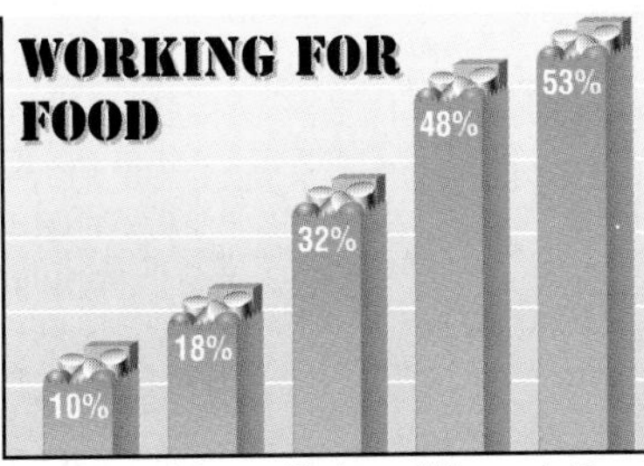

Source: ACA Education Foundation, Inc.

EXERCISES

Practice

Express each fraction as a percent.

13. $\frac{37}{50}$ 74% 14. $\frac{1}{4}$ 25% 15. $\frac{1}{10}$ 10% 16. $\frac{3}{5}$ 60%

17. $\frac{91}{100}$ 91% 18. $\frac{1}{5}$ 20% 19. $\frac{3}{10}$ 30% 20. $\frac{23}{25}$ 92%

21. $\frac{3}{4}$ 75% 22. $\frac{7}{10}$ 70% 23. $\frac{11}{20}$ 55% 24. $\frac{8}{8}$ 100%

Express each percent or decimal as a fraction in simplest form.

25. 25% $\frac{1}{4}$ 26. 0.30 $\frac{3}{10}$ 27. 80% $\frac{4}{5}$ 28. 0.15 $\frac{3}{20}$

29. 0.9 $\frac{9}{10}$ 30. 76% $\frac{19}{25}$ 31. 0.32 $\frac{8}{25}$ 32. 52% $\frac{13}{25}$

33. 10% $\frac{1}{10}$ 34. 0.62 $\frac{31}{50}$ 35. 0.02 $\frac{1}{50}$ 36. 17% $\frac{17}{100}$

37. Express $\frac{5}{25}$ as a percent. 20%

38. Express *thirty-five percent* as a fraction in simplest form. $\frac{7}{20}$

Applications and Problem Solving

39. *Life Science* Cats sleep as much as 18 hours per day. Find the percent of the day that cats spend sleeping. 75%

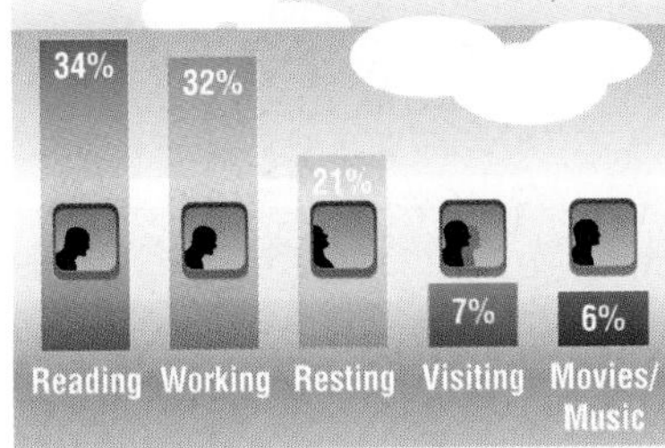

Source: *Frequent Flyer* survey

40. *Transportation* The graph shows how people spend their time in flight. Write each percent of time as a fraction in simplest form.
    a. Reading $\frac{17}{50}$
    b. Working $\frac{8}{25}$
    c. Resting $\frac{21}{100}$
    d. Visiting $\frac{7}{100}$
    e. Movies/Music $\frac{3}{50}$

Assignment Guide

Core: 13–41 odd, 44–49
Enriched: 14–38 even, 39–42, 44–49

Exercise 43 asks students to advance to the next stage of work on the Chapter Project. You may wish to have students use spreadsheets to organize and compute the values in their tables.

***Study Guide Masters*, p. 30**

Name____ Date____

Study Guide

Fractions, Decimals, and Percents

A fraction can be expressed as a percent by finding an equivalent fraction with a denominator of 100.

Example 1 **Express $\frac{19}{20}$ as a percent.**

$\frac{19}{20} = \frac{95}{100} = 95\%$ *Since 100 ÷ 20 = 5, multiply the numerator and denominator by 5.*

When an equivalent fraction cannot easily be found, express the fraction as a decimal first, and then as a percent.

Example 2 **Express $\frac{5}{8}$ as a percent.**

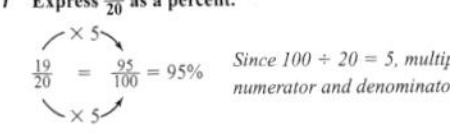
5 ÷ 8 = 0.625 or 62.5%

You can also express decimals and percents as fractions.

Examples **0.4** = $\frac{4}{10}$ or $\frac{2}{5}$

18% = $\frac{18}{100}$
= $\frac{18 \div 2}{100 \div 2}$ or $\frac{9}{50}$

Express each fraction as a percent.

1. $\frac{14}{25}$ 56% 2. $\frac{3}{4}$ 75% 3. $\frac{7}{8}$ 87.5%

4. $\frac{7}{10}$ 70% 5. $\frac{6}{50}$ 12% 6. $\frac{13}{20}$ 65%

Express each percent or decimal as a fraction in simplest form.

7. 20% $\frac{1}{5}$ 8. 0.60 $\frac{3}{5}$ 9. 0.15 $\frac{3}{20}$

10. 72% $\frac{18}{25}$ 11. 54% $\frac{27}{50}$ 12. 0.22 $\frac{11}{50}$

 T30 *Mathematics: Applications and Connections, Course 2*

4 ASSESS

Closing Activity

Writing Have students write a description of how to express a fraction as a percent and a percent as a decimal. Have students include situations in which each form of the number may be used.

Additional Answer

47.

Stem	Leaf
0	2 5 9
1	0 2 3 6 7
2	3 5 5
3	1

$2|3 = 23$

Practice Masters, p. 30

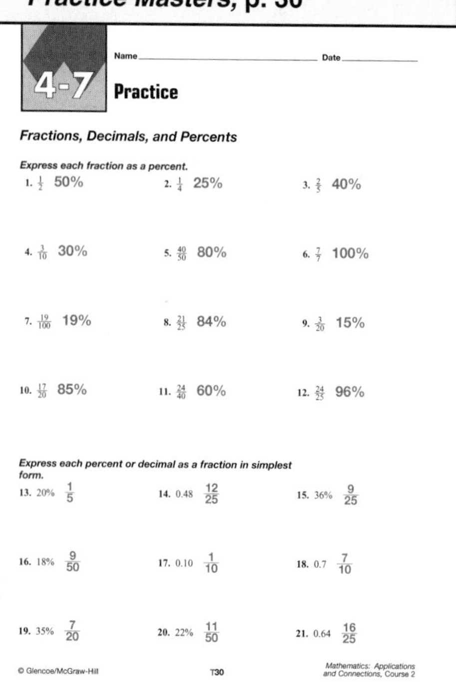

Name______________ Date______________

4-7 **Practice**

Fractions, Decimals, and Percents

Express each fraction as a percent.

1. $\frac{1}{2}$ 50%
2. $\frac{1}{4}$ 25%
3. $\frac{2}{5}$ 40%
4. $\frac{3}{10}$ 30%
5. $\frac{40}{50}$ 80%
6. $\frac{7}{7}$ 100%
7. $\frac{19}{100}$ 19%
8. $\frac{21}{25}$ 84%
9. $\frac{3}{20}$ 15%
10. $\frac{17}{20}$ 85%
11. $\frac{24}{40}$ 60%
12. $\frac{24}{25}$ 96%

Express each percent or decimal as a fraction in simplest form.

13. 20% $\frac{1}{5}$
14. 0.48 $\frac{12}{25}$
15. 36% $\frac{9}{25}$
16. 18% $\frac{9}{50}$
17. 0.10 $\frac{1}{10}$
18. 0.7 $\frac{7}{10}$
19. 35% $\frac{7}{20}$
20. 22% $\frac{11}{50}$
21. 0.64 $\frac{16}{25}$

© Glencoe/McGraw-Hill T30 *Mathematics: Applications and Connections, Course 2*

43. See Answer Appendix.

44. 0.5% is $\frac{1}{2}$ of 1%, not $\frac{1}{2}$ of one whole number; $0.5\% = \frac{1}{200}$.

41. ***History*** In 1896, about 100,000 "stampeders" set out for the Klondike in Bonanza Creek, Canada, in search of gold. Only about 30,000 people made it to the Klondike.
   a. What fraction of the stampeders made it? Express the fraction in simplest form. $\frac{3}{10}$
   b. Express the fraction as a decimal. **0.3**

42. ***History*** Twenty-six states in America have names that come from Native American languages. What percent of the states is this? **52%**

43. ***Working on the* CHAPTER Project** Refer to Exercise 34 on page 157. Express each fraction in your table as a decimal rounded to the nearest hundredth and then as a percent. Add two more columns to your table labeled "Decimal" and "Percent" to display this information.

44. ***Critical Thinking*** Explain why 0.5% is not the same as $\frac{1}{2}$.

Mixed Review

45. Express 47 out of 100 as a percent. *(Lesson 4-6)* **47%**

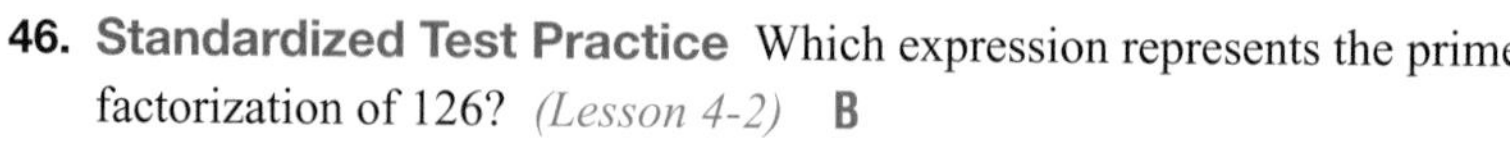

46. **Standardized Test Practice** Which expression represents the prime factorization of 126? *(Lesson 4-2)* **B**

A $2^2 \times 3 \times 7$ **B** $2 \times 3^2 \times 7$ **C** $2 \times 3 \times 7^2$ **D** $2^2 \times 3^2 \times 7^2$

47. ***Statistics*** Construct a stem-and-leaf plot for the following data: 12, 17, 23, 5, 9, 25, 13, 16, 2, 25, 31, 10. *(Lesson 3-5)* **See margin.**

48. ***Entertainment*** The table shows the profits of the five re-released movies in millions of dollars. *(Lesson 2-9)*

Play It Again....	
Movie A	$125.0
Movie B	$70.6
Movie C	$60.8
Movie D	$46.6
Movie E	$44.6

   a. Write how much the re-release of Movie A earned in standard form. **$125,000,000**
   b. How much money did Movie C, Movie D, and Movie E earn altogether by their re-releases? Write in standard form. **$152,000,000**

For **Extra Practice,** see page 579.

49. ***Sports*** A triathalon competition consists of swimming 3 miles, running 10 miles, and bicycling 35 miles. How many miles does an athlete travel during the competition? *(Lesson 1-1)* **48 miles**

Extending the Lesson

Enrichment Masters, p. 30

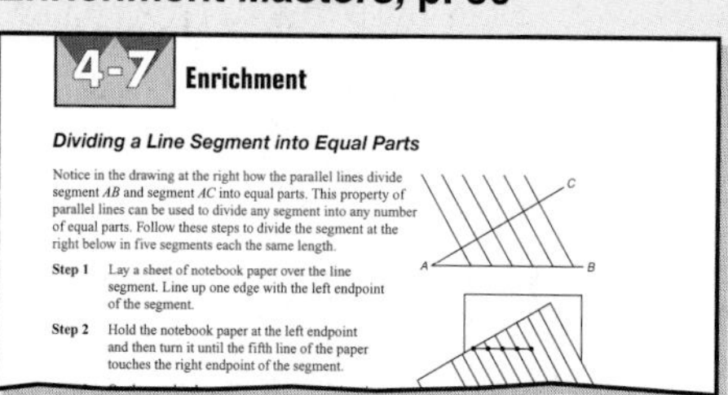

4-7 **Enrichment**

Dividing a Line Segment into Equal Parts

Notice in the drawing at the right how the parallel lines divide segment *AB* and segment *AC* into equal parts. This property of parallel lines can be used to divide any segment into any number of equal parts. Follow these steps to divide the segment at the right below in five segments each the same length.

Step 1 Lay a sheet of notebook paper over the line segment. Line up one edge with the left endpoint of the segment.

Step 2 Hold the notebook paper at the left endpoint and then turn it until the fifth line of the paper touches the right endpoint of the segment.

Activity Provide students with a 10 × 10 array of dots in which you have drawn a triangle and a square that intersect. Ask students to write a percent that expresses the fraction of dots inside both the triangle and the square. Have students make up similar problems for classmates to solve.

4-8 Integration: Probability
Simple Events

What **you'll learn**

You'll learn to find the probability of a simple event.

When **am I ever going to use this?**

You can use probability to find the chances of winning a raffle held by your school.

Word Wise

probability
event
random

The makers of a popular jelly bean recommend combining beans to make gourmet flavors. For example, very cherry and chocolate pudding beans make "chocolate covered cherries." If a bag of 30 jelly beans contains 18 very cherry beans, what is the **probability** that you will get a very cherry bean if you pick one from the bag at random?

The **event**, or specific outcome, we are interested in is a very cherry jelly bean.

Probability		
	Words:	The probability of an event is the ratio of the number of ways an event can occur to the number of possible outcomes.
	Symbols:	$P(\text{event}) = \frac{\text{number of ways event occurs}}{\text{number of possible outcomes}}$

Study Hint

Reading Math $P(A)$ is read as the probability that A occurs.

Outcomes occur at **random** if each outcome is equally likely to occur. Since a jelly bean will be drawn at random,

$$P(\text{very cherry}) = \frac{\text{number of very cherry jelly beans}}{\text{total number of jelly beans}}$$

$$= \frac{18}{30}$$

$$= \frac{3}{5} \quad \textit{Express the fraction in simplest form.}$$

The probability of choosing a very cherry jelly bean is $\frac{3}{5}$ or 60%.

Example 1

Find the probability of drawing a card with a factor of 12 on it from a deck of cards numbered 1 to 24. Express the fraction in simplest form.

$$P(\text{factor of 12}) = \frac{\text{number of ways of drawing a card that is a factor of 12}}{\text{number of ways a card can be drawn}}$$

$$= \frac{6}{24} \begin{array}{l} \leftarrow \textit{There are 6 factors of 12: 1, 2, 3, 4, 6, and 12.} \\ \leftarrow \textit{There are 24 cards.} \end{array}$$

$$= \frac{1}{4} \quad \text{The GCF of 6 and 24 is 6.}$$

The probability of drawing a card with a factor of 12 is $\frac{1}{4}$ or 25%.

Multiple Learning Styles

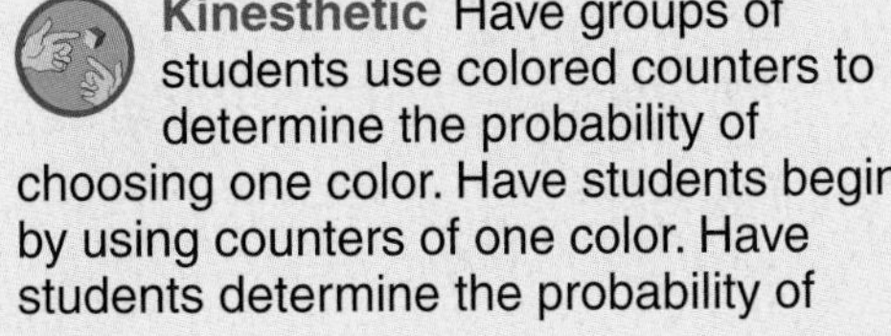

Kinesthetic Have groups of students use colored counters to determine the probability of choosing one color. Have students begin by using counters of one color. Have students determine the probability of choosing one counter of that color. Then have them repeat the process with two counters of one color and two of another, then three of each, and so on, until students explore the range of probabilities from 1 to 0.

4-8 Lesson Notes

Instructional Resources

- *Study Guide Masters,* p. 31
- *Practice Masters,* p. 31
- *Enrichment Masters,* p. 31
- Transparencies 4-8, A and B
- *School to Career Masters,* p. 17
- *Assessment and Evaluation Masters,* p. 100
- *School to Career Masters,* p. 17

CD-ROM Program
- Resource Lesson 4-8
- Extended Activity 4-8

Recommended Pacing	
Standard	Day 11 of 15
Honors	Day 11 of 15
Block	Day 6 of 8

1 FOCUS

5-Minute Check
(Lesson 4-7)

Express each fraction as a percent.

1. $\frac{4}{5}$ **80%**
2. $\frac{9}{20}$ **45%**
3. Express 84% as a fraction in simplest form. $\frac{21}{25}$

Express each percent or decimal as a fraction in simplest form.

4. 11% $\frac{11}{100}$
5. 0.08 $\frac{2}{25}$

The 5-Minute Check is also available on **Transparency 4-8A** for this lesson.

Motivating the Lesson

Hands-On Activity Give one student a deck of cards. Have another student name a card in the deck. Ask the first student to try to select the card, without looking. Have the class discuss the likelihood of selecting the designated card from the deck on the first try.

2 TEACH

Transparency 4-8B contains a teaching aid for this lesson.

In-Class Examples

For Example 1
Find the probability of drawing a red card from a shuffled deck containing 10 red cards, 10 black cards, and 5 yellow cards. $\frac{2}{5}$

For Example 2
Gary's Gas Station is having a contest. Every customer who buys gas gets a ticket with a number on it. Each week, a winning ticket is drawn, and the winner gets a free tank of gas. This week, 220 people bought gas each day. Opal bought gas twice. What is the probability that she will win the free fill-up? $\frac{2}{1{,}540}$

Using the Mini-Lab Begin by asking students to describe each event as either likely or unlikely. Then encourage them to specify how likely or unlikely by assigning them each event a fraction or percent that expresses its probability.

Additional Answers for the Mini-Lab

1–2. Answers will vary for c.

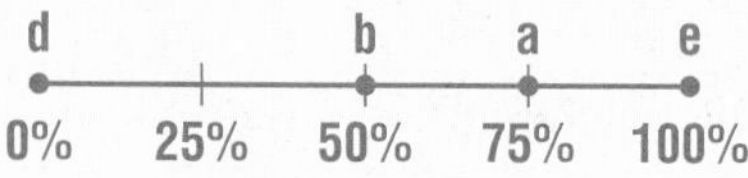

2 **Drawings** **A department store has a weekly drawing in which the winner receives a $50 gift certificate. About 300 customers register each day. If Yvonne registered 3 times this week, what is the probability that she will win this week?**

number of cards: $300 \times 7 = 2{,}100$

number of cards with Yvonne's name on them: 3

$$P(\text{Yvonne}) = \frac{\text{number of cards with Yvonne's name}}{\text{total number of cards}}$$

$$= \frac{3}{2{,}100}$$

$$= \frac{1}{700}$$

The probability of Yvonne's name being drawn is $\frac{1}{700}$.

The probability that an event will happen is somewhere between 0 and 1.

- A probability of 0 means that the event is impossible.
- A probability of 1 means that the event is certain to happen.
- The closer a probability is to 1, the more likely the event is to happen.

You can express the probability of an event as a fraction, decimal, or percent. Since probability is a number, you can picture it on a number line.

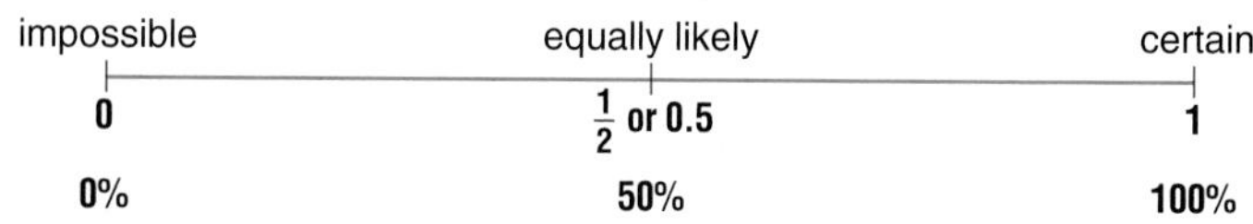

Work with a partner. paper ruler

Try This

1. Draw a number line like the one above. **1–2. See margin.**
2. Locate each of the situations on the number line.
   - **a.** The meteorologist predicts a 75% chance for rain today.
   - **b.** A tossed coin will come up heads.
   - **c.** You will have math homework tonight.
   - **d.** February will have 31 days this year.
   - **e.** The sum of two number cubes will be greater than 1.

Talk About It **3. d, b, a, e; c will vary.** **4. See students' work.**

3. Order the events from least likely to most likely.
4. Write three events of your own. Add them to your number line.

Reteaching the Lesson

Activity Have students describe two simple experiments using a spinner, cards, or a number cube, and write a question for each. One question should have the answer "P(event occurring) = 1," and one should have the answer "P(event occurring) = 0."

CHECK FOR UNDERSTANDING

Communicating Mathematics

Read and study the lesson to answer each question.

1. Refer to the beginning of the lesson. What is the probability that if you choose a jelly bean from the bag of 30 beans, that it is *not* a very cherry jelly bean? $\frac{2}{5}$ or 40%
2. ***Give*** an example of an event that has a probability of 0 and an event that has a probability of 1 when rolling a number cube. See margin.

3. ***Draw*** a spinner with three regions labeled A, B, and C. Make the spinner so that there is a 50% chance that the spinner will stop on A, a 25% chance that the spinner will stop on B, and a 25% chance that the spinner will stop on C. See margin.

Guided Practice

The spinner shown is equally likely to stop on each of its regions numbered 1 to 10. Find the probability that the spinner will stop on each of the following.

4. an even number $\frac{1}{2}$
5. a multiple of 3 $\frac{3}{10}$

A package contains 7 bags of tortilla chips, 3 bags of cheese puffs, and 4 bags of potato chips. If you reach in the package and choose one bag at random, what is the probability that you will select each of the following? Express each ratio as a fraction in simplest form and as a percent.

6. $\frac{1}{2} = 50\%$

7. $\frac{3}{14} \approx 21.4\%$

6. tortilla chips
7. cheese puffs
8. ***Technology*** The graph shows the cost of 22 portable CD players that were tested by a magazine recently. If one of the CD players from the test is chosen at random, what is the probability that it costs between $211-260? $\frac{1}{11}$

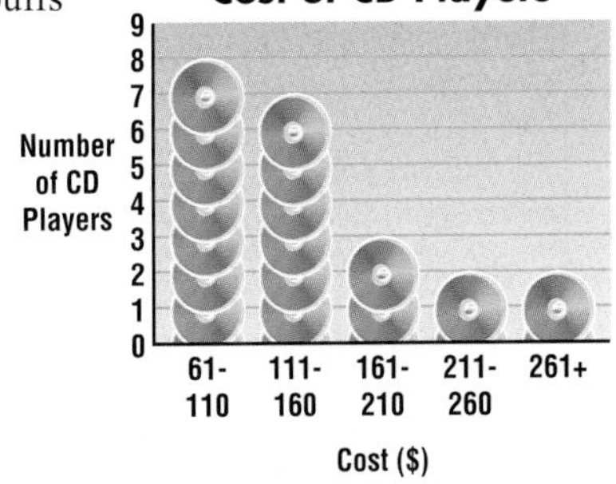

Cost of CD Players

Number of CD Players

0 1 2 3 4 5 6 7 8 9

61-110 111-160 161-210 211-260 261+

Cost ($)

EXERCISES

Practice

A certain spinner is equally likely to stop on each of its regions numbered 1 to 20. Find the probability that the spinner will stop on each of the following.

9. $\frac{1}{20}$
10. $\frac{7}{10}$
11. $\frac{3}{20}$
12. $\frac{1}{2}$
13. $\frac{2}{5}$
14. $\frac{3}{10}$

9. the GCF of 12 and 18
10. a number greater than 6
11. a multiple of 2 and 3
12. an odd number
13. a prime number
14. a factor of 12

A bag of marbles contains 16 blue, 8 green, 9 red, 12 yellow, and 5 black marbles. If you reach in the bag and draw one marble at random, what is the probability that you will draw each of the following? Express each ratio as a fraction in simplest form and as a percent. 15–20. See margin.

15. a green marble
16. a black marble
17. a yellow marble
18. a blue marble
19. either a green or a blue marble
20. a red or a black marble

3 PRACTICE/APPLY

Check for Understanding

If students need additional practice or instruction after completing Exercises 1–8, you may find one of the following options helpful.

- Extra Practice, see p. 579
- Reteaching Activity, see p. 166
- *Study Guide Masters,* p. 31
- *Practice Masters,* p. 31

Assignment Guide

Core: 9–25 odd, 27–30
Enriched: 10–22 even, 23–25, 27–30

Exercise 26 asks students to advance to the next stage of work on the Chapter Project. You may wish to have students also calculate the probability of the favorite color *not* being white.

***Study Guide Masters,* p. 31**

Name ________________ Date ________

Study Guide

Integration: Probability
Simple Events

If you roll a cube with the numbers 1 through 6 on the faces, there are six possible outcomes: 1, 2, 3, 4, 5, and 6. Each of the outcomes is equally likely to occur. A particular outcome, such as rolling a 5, is an event. Probability is the chance that the event will occur.

$$\text{Probability} = \frac{\text{number of ways an event can occur}}{\text{number of possible outcomes}}$$

Rolling a 5 can occur 1 way out of 6 possible outcomes. So, $P(5) = \frac{1}{6}$.

Example **Ping-Pong® balls numbered 1 through 25 are placed in a box and one is drawn at random. Find each probability.**

probability of drawing a 12:

$$P(12) = \frac{\text{number of ways 12 can occur}}{\text{number of possible outcomes}} = \frac{1}{25}$$

probability of drawing an odd number:
The odd numbers are 1, 3, 5, 7, 9, 11, 13, 15, 17, 19, 21, 23, and 25. There are thirteen balls with an odd number.

$$P(\text{odd}) = \frac{\text{number of ways an odd number can occur}}{\text{number of possible outcomes}} = \frac{13}{25}$$

The spinner shown is equally likely to stop on each of the regions. Find the probability that the spinner will stop on each of the following.

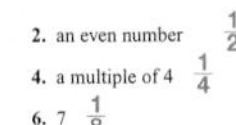

1. a number less than 5 $\frac{1}{2}$
2. an even number $\frac{1}{2}$
3. a prime number $\frac{1}{2}$
4. a multiple of 4 $\frac{1}{4}$
5. a factor of 8 $\frac{1}{2}$
6. 7 $\frac{1}{8}$

A drawer contains 4 blue socks, 8 black socks, and 10 white socks. If one sock is taken out of the drawer without looking, find the probability that each of the following will be drawn. Express each ratio as a fraction in simplest form.

7. a blue sock $\frac{2}{11}$
8. a black sock $\frac{4}{11}$
9. a white sock $\frac{5}{11}$
10. a blue or a black sock $\frac{6}{11}$
11. a black or a white sock $\frac{9}{11}$
12. a blue or a white sock $\frac{7}{11}$

T31 *Mathematics: Applications and Connections, Course 2*

Additional Answers

2. Sample answer: rolling a 7; rolling an odd or even number

3. A B C

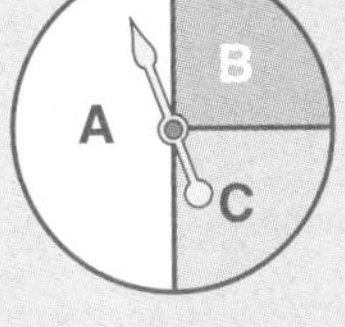

15. $\frac{4}{25} = 16\%$
16. $\frac{1}{10} = 10\%$
17. $\frac{6}{25} = 24\%$
18. $\frac{8}{25} = 32\%$
19. $\frac{12}{25} = 48\%$
20. $\frac{7}{25} = 28\%$

Have students share with the class the roles that chance and skill played in their games. Then have students play "heads or tails" with a coin. How does the part chance and skill play in this game differ from the part they played in the other?

4 ASSESS

Closing Activity

Modeling Have students draw a spinner with 8 sectors of equal size, each with a number on it, designed so that the probability of spinning an even number is $\frac{1}{4}$. **Sample answer: Use two even numbers and six odd numbers.**

Chapter 4, Quiz C (Lessons 4-6 through 4-8) is available in the *Assessment and Evaluation Masters,* p. 100.

***Practice Masters,* p. 31**

Name ________ Date ________

4-8 **Practice**

Integration: Probability Simple Events

The spinner shown is equally likely to stop on each of its regions numbered 1 to 16. Find the probability that the spinner will stop on each of the following.

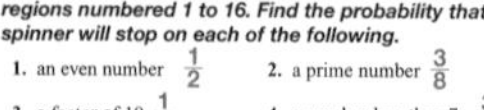

1. an even number $\frac{1}{2}$
2. a prime number $\frac{3}{8}$

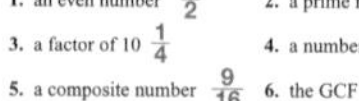

3. a factor of 10 $\frac{1}{4}$
4. a number less than 7 $\frac{3}{8}$
5. a composite number $\frac{9}{16}$
6. the GCF of 10 and 15 $\frac{1}{16}$

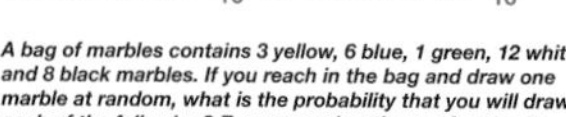

A bag of marbles contains 3 yellow, 6 blue, 1 green, 12 white, and 8 black marbles. If you reach in the bag and draw one marble at random, what is the probability that you will draw each of the following? Express each ratio as a fraction in simplest form and as a percent.

7. a yellow marble $\frac{1}{10}$, 10%
8. a white marble $\frac{2}{5}$, 40%
9. a blue marble $\frac{1}{5}$, 20%
10. either a black or a green marble $\frac{3}{10}$, 30%
11. a white or a blue marble $\frac{3}{5}$, 60%

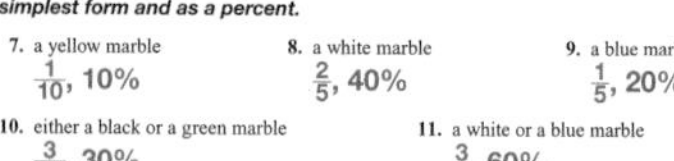

A package of candy contains 14 cherry, 16 orange, 10 lemon, and 10 lime flavored candies. If you reach in the package and draw one piece of candy at random, what is the probability that you will select each of the following? Express each ratio as a fraction in simplest form and as a percent.

12. a lemon candy $\frac{1}{5}$, 20%
13. an orange candy $\frac{8}{25}$, 32%
14. a cherry candy $\frac{7}{25}$, 28%
15. an orange or lemon candy $\frac{13}{25}$, 52%
16. a lime, lemon, or cherry candy $\frac{17}{25}$, 68%
17. any candy 1, 100%
18. a candy that is not lemon, lime or cherry $\frac{8}{25}$, 32%

 T31 *Mathematics: Applications and Connections, Course 2*

21. All of the factors of 48 are written on separate cards. If you randomly choose a card, what is the probability of choosing a prime number? $\frac{1}{5}$
22. There are 52 cards in a deck. Four of these are kings. What is the probability of drawing a king? $\frac{1}{13}$

Applications and Problem Solving

24a. $\frac{1}{50} = 0.02$

24b. $\frac{49}{50} = 0.98$

25. $\frac{1}{6} \approx 16.7\%$

23. ***Reading*** More than half of all books bought by Americans are fiction. A bookshelf contains the following fiction books: 34 general fiction, 15 children's books, 6 romance, 6 science fiction, 5 mystery, and 4 horror. If you randomly choose a book from the shelf, what is the probability that it is a mystery? $\frac{1}{14}$
24. ***School*** Your school is raffling a television set and a total of 750 tickets have been sold. Your family bought 15 tickets.
    a. What is the probability that your family will win the television set?
    b. What is the probability that your family will *not* win the television set?
25. ***Crayons*** Refer to the beginning of Lesson 4-4 on page 150. The box of 96 crayons that was introduced in 1993 contained 16 unnamed crayons. If you randomly pick a crayon from such a box, what is the probability that it doesn't have a name?
26. ***Working on the CHAPTER Project*** Refer to the results of your survey in the Chapter Project on page 131. Based on your data, what is the probability that if a new student joins the class, her or his favorite car color will be white? **See students' work.**
27. ***Critical Thinking*** Marvin and Naomi are playing a game by rolling number cubes. Naomi gets a point each time the sum of the number cubes is 2, 3, 4, 9, 10, 11, or 12. Marvin gets a point when the sum is 5, 6, 7, or 8. Is this a fair game? That is, does each player have an equal chance to win? Explain. **See Answer Appendix.**

Play a card game or board game with a family member. Then discuss whether chance, skill, or both chance and skill determine who wins the game. Explain the role of each in the game.

Mixed Review

28a. $\frac{17}{25}$

28b. $\frac{1}{5}$

28c. $\frac{3}{25}$

28. ***Diamonds*** The graph shows the percent of diamond engagement rings that are different shapes. Express each percent as a fraction in simplest form. *(Lesson 4-7)*
    a. round
    b. marquise
    c. others

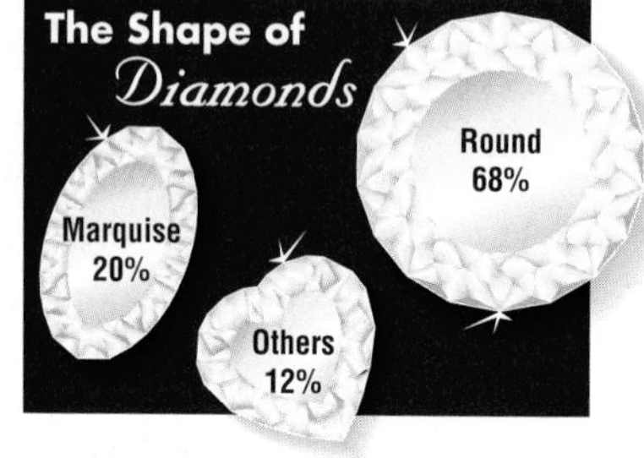

Source: Diamond Information Center

29. **Standardized Test Practice** The Reds baseball team played 12 games. They scored a total of 168 runs. What was the mean number of runs scored per game? *(Lesson 3-4)* **A**

    A 14 **B** 15 **C** 156 **D** 180
30. Estimate 23.69 divided by 4.05. *(Lesson 2-3)* **$24 \div 4 = 6$**

For **Extra Practice,** see page 579.

Extending the Lesson

***Enrichment Masters,* p. 31**

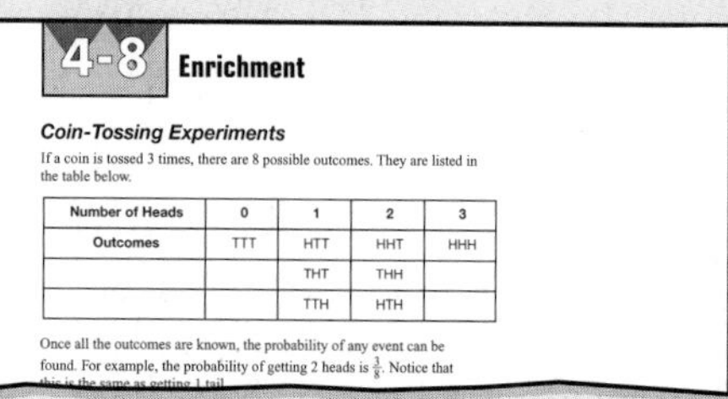

4-8 **Enrichment**

Coin-Tossing Experiments

If a coin is tossed 3 times, there are 8 possible outcomes. They are listed in the table below.

Number of Heads	0	1	2	3
Outcomes	TTT	HTT	HHT	HHH
		THT	THH	
		TTH	HTH	

Once all the outcomes are known, the probability of any event can be found. For example, the probability of getting 2 heads is $\frac{3}{8}$. Notice that

Activity The public library is selling 1,000 raffle tickets for $5 each. If you spend $20 on tickets, what is the probability that you will win? How many tickets would you have to buy so that your probability of winning would be greater than your probability of losing? How much would this cost? **$\frac{1}{250}$; 501; $2,505**

4-9 Least Common Multiple

What you'll learn

You'll learn to find the least common multiple of two or more numbers.

When am I ever going to use this?

You will use least common multiples to write equivalent fractions.

Word Wise

multiple
least common multiple (LCM)

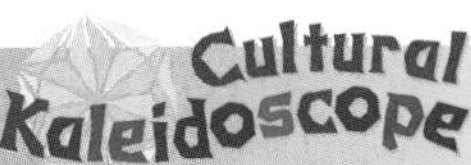

In 1925, Garrett Morgan invented the first three-way traffic signal.

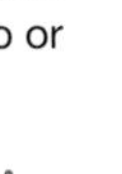

Traffic engineers determine the best traffic-light sequences to ensure orderly traffic flow. Suppose a traffic light on one street turns red every 40 seconds and a second light turns red every 60 seconds. Both lights just turned red. In how many seconds will both lights turn red at the same time again?

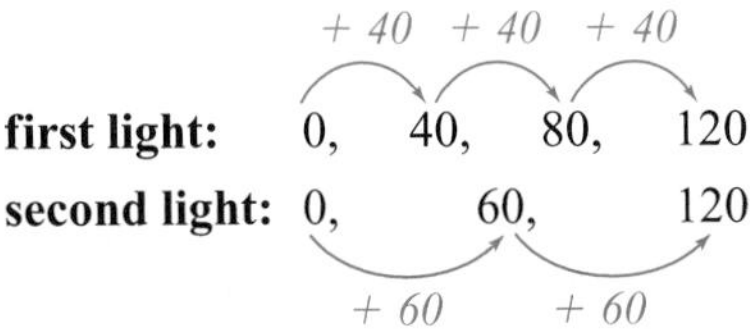

	+40 +40 +40
first light:	0, 40, 80, 120
second light:	0, 60, 120
	+60 +60

Both lights turn red again in 120 seconds.

When you multiply a number by the whole numbers 0, 1, 2, 3, 4, and so on, you get **multiples** of the number. The **least common multiple (LCM)** of two or more numbers is the least of their common multiples, other than 0. The least common multiple of 40 and 60 is 120.

You can use one of two methods to find a least common multiple.

Method 1 Make a list.
List several multiples of each number. Then identify the common multiples. The least of these is the LCM.

Method 2 Use prime factorization.
Write the prime factorization of each number. Identify all common prime factors. For each prime factor, write it down the greatest number of times it appears in any of the numbers. The product is the LCM.

Examples

1 **Use Method 1 to find the LCM of 6 and 9.**

multiples of 6: 6, 12, 18, 24, 30, 36, . . .

multiples of 9: 9, 18, 27, 36, 45, 54, 63, . . .

Zero is a multiple of every number, but cannot be the LCM.

The LCM of 6 and 9 is 18.

2 **Use Method 2 to find the LCM of 9, 12, and 15.**

$9 = 3 \times 3 = 3^2$

$12 = 2 \times 2 \times 3 = 2^2 \times 3$

$15 = 3 \times 5$

The prime factors are 2, 3, and 5. The greatest number of times 2 appears is twice (in 12), so write it down twice. The greatest number of times 3 appears is twice (in 9), so write it down twice. The greatest number of times 5 appears is once (in 15), so write it down once. The LCM of 9, 12, and 15 is $2 \times 2 \times 3 \times 3 \times 5$ or 180.

MathPASS CD-ROM

This CD-ROM offers a complete, self-paced mathematics curriculum. Each lesson includes a pretest, tutorial, guided practice, and posttest. MathPASS Lesson 11 is correlated to this Student Edition lesson.
For Windows & Macintosh

4-9 Lesson Notes

Instructional Resources

- *Study Guide Masters,* p. 32
- *Practice Masters,* p. 32
- *Enrichment Masters,* p. 32
- Transparencies 4-9, A and B

CD-ROM Program
- Resource Lesson 4-9
- Interactive Lesson 4-9

Recommended Pacing	
Standard	Day 12 of 15
Honors	Day 12 of 15
Block	Day 7 of 8

1 FOCUS

5-Minute Check
(Lesson 4-8)

A certain spinner is equally likely to stop on each of its regions numbered 1–20. Find the probability that the spinner will stop on each of the following.

1. an odd number $\frac{1}{2}$
2. a number greater than 15 $\frac{1}{4}$
3. a factor of 20 $\frac{3}{10}$
4. a prime number $\frac{2}{5}$
5. the GCF of 15 and 20 $\frac{1}{20}$

The 5-Minute Check is also available on **Transparency 4-9A** for this lesson.

Motivating the Lesson

Problem Solving Present the following situation: *Starting at the beginning of a block, Art, Bonita, and Connie are each delivering a limited number of different flyers to the houses. Art drops off a flyer to every second house, Bonita gives one to every third house, and Connie delivers one to every fourth house. Which house first gets all three flyers?* **the twelfth house**

2 TEACH

Transparency 4-9B contains a teaching aid for this lesson.

Reading Mathematics Review with students the definition of a *multiple*. Explain that the LCM is the smallest number that is a multiple of each given number.

In-Class Examples

For Example 1
Find the LCM of 12 and 18 by making a list. 36

For Example 2
Find the LCM of 8, 10, and 12 by using prime factorization. 120

For Example 3
Mentally find the LCM of 4, 5, and 8 by listing multiples. 40

For Example 4
Serena plans a fitness program that will include bicycling every 3 days, hiking every 7 days, and swimming every 14 days. How many days will pass before she will do all 3 activities on the same day? 42 days

***Study Guide Masters*, p. 32**

Name____________________ Date__________

4-9 Study Guide

Least Common Multiple

A **multiple** of a number is the product of that number and any whole number. The least nonzero multiple of two or more numbers is the **least common multiple (LCM)** of the numbers.

Example 1 **Find the LCM of 15 and 20.**

multiples of 15: 15, 30, 45, 60, 75, 90, 105, 120, . . .
multiples of 20: 20, 40, 60, 80, 100, 120, 140, . . .

The LCM of 15 and 20 is 60.

Prime factorization can also be used to find the LCM.

Example 2 **Find the LCM of 8, 12, and 18.**

$8 = 2 \times 2 \times 2$ *Find the prime factors of each number.*
$12 = 2 \times 2 \quad \times 3$
$18 = 2 \quad \times 3 \times 3$
2 2 3 *Find the common factors.*
$2 \times 2 \times 2 \times 3 \times 3 = 72$ *Multiply the common factors and any other factors.*

The LCM of 8, 12, and 18 is 72.

Find the LCM of each set of numbers.

1. 12, 16 48	**2.** 15, 24 120	**3.** 7, 9 63	**4.** 8, 10 40
5. 20, 50 100	**6.** 18, 27 54	**7.** 30, 21 210	**8.** 12, 18 36
9. 6, 10, 15 30	**10.** 3, 7, 10 210	**11.** 2, 16, 24 48	**12.** 7, 8, 14 56

Examples

3 Mentally find the LCM of 4, 5, and 8 by listing multiples.

Think: The positive multiples of 8 are 8, 16, 24, 32, 40, 48, ...
Ask: What is the least of these multiples that is divisible by both 4 and 5?
Reason: The number has to be even and end in 0. The first such number in the list is 40. And 40 is divisible by 8.

So, the LCM of 4, 5, and 8 is 40.

CONNECTION

4 Earth Science In 1833, the great Leonid meteor shower was seen all over North America. These showers occur every 33 years. The Schwassmann-Wachmann Comet occurs every 15 years. If both these occurrences coincided one year, use your calculator to find in how many years this would happen again.

Explore You know that the comet occurs every 15 years and the meteor shower occurs every 33 years. Find the least common multiple of 15 and 33.

Plan Write the multiples of the greater number and find the LCM that is divisible by the lesser number.

Solve multiples of 33: 33, 66, 99, 132, 165, 198. . .

Which multiple is divisible by 15? Start with the least multiple, 33.

$33 \div 15 = 2.2$ $\quad$ $132 \div 15 = 8.8$
$66 \div 15 = 4.4$ $\quad$ $165 \div 15 = 11$ ✓
$99 \div 15 = 6.6$

The LCM of 15 and 33 is 165. Thus, these solar occurrences would coincide again in 165 years.

Examine Use prime factorization to find the LCM.

$15 = 3 \cdot 5$
$33 = 3 \cdot 11$
LCM: $3 \cdot 5 \cdot 11 = 165$

The answer is correct.

CHECK FOR UNDERSTANDING

Communicating Mathematics
1–3. See Answer Appendix.

Math Journal

Read and study the lesson to answer each question.

1. ***Tell*** why the LCM of 18, which is 2×3^2, and 24, which is $2^3 \times 3$, must have factors of 2^3 and 3^2. What is the LCM of 18 and 24?
2. ***Explain*** how the LCM of two numbers can be one of the numbers.
3. ***Write*** the steps you would take to find the LCM of 3, 5, and 9 using pencil and paper. Compare it to solving the problem mentally.

Reteaching the Lesson

Activity Use coins to show how the same amounts of money can be made with different coins. For example, \$0.50 is the *smallest* amount of money that can be made using only quarters *or* only dimes, thus 50 is the LCM of 10 and 25.

Error Analysis
Watch for students who confuse the GCF with the LCM.
Prevent by distinguishing between factors and multiples. Stress that multiples are found by *multiplying*, factors by *dividing*.

Guided Practice

Find the LCM of each set of numbers by listing multiples.

4. 35, 14 **70** **5.** 45, 15 **45** **6.** 2, 3, 10 **30**

Find the LCM of each set of numbers by writing prime factorizations.

7. 4, 8, 12 **24** **8.** 18, 8, 36 **72** **9.** 15, 25, 45 **225**

10. ***Government*** Presidential elections are held every four years. Senators are elected every six years. If a senator was elected in the presidential election year 2000, in what year would he or she campaign again during a presidential election year? **2012**

EXERCISES

Practice

Find the LCM of each set of numbers by listing multiples.

11. 12, 60 **60** **12.** 2, 3, 5 **30** **13.** 30, 15 **30**

14. 10, 20, 30 **60** **15.** 18, 300 **900** **16.** 9, 10, 4 **180**

17. 24, 12, 6 **24** **18.** 44, 33, 22 **132** **19.** 10, 12, 15 **60**

Find the LCM of each set of numbers by writing prime factorizations.

20. 16, 176 **176** **21.** 28, 49, 16 **784** **22.** 6, 12, 18 **36**

23. 17, 6, 34 **102** **24.** 33, 44, 55 **660** **25.** 30, 625 **3,750**

26. 12, 15, 28 **420** **27.** 42, 16, 7 **336** **28.** 35, 25, 49 **1,225**

30. $45n$, where $n = 5, 6, 7, \ldots$

29. Mentally compute the LCM of 4, 5, and 10 by listing multiples. **20**

30. List the multiples that 9 and 15 have in common above 180.

Applications and Problem Solving

31. ***Scheduling*** Margo has piano lessons every two weeks. Her brother Roberto has a soccer tournament every three weeks. Her sister Rocio has an orthodontist appointment every four weeks. If they all have activities this Friday, how long will it be before all of their activities fall on the same day again? **12 weeks**

32. when the two numbers are relatively prime; 5 and 6, 15 and 17

32. ***Number Sense*** Explain when the LCM of two numbers is their product. Give two examples to illustrate your rule.

33. ***Critical Thinking*** Write a set of three numbers whose LCM is the product of the numbers. **Sample answer: {2, 3, 5}**

Mixed Review

34. **Standardized Test Practice** In a school raffle, one ticket will be drawn out of a total of 500 tickets. If the Stevenson family has 12 tickets, what is the probability that they will win? *(Lesson 4-8)* **B**

A 1 in 500 **B** 3 in 125 **C** 1 in 12 **D** 1 in 488 **E** 12 in 1,000

35. Find the greatest common factor of 72 and 270. *(Lesson 4-4)* **18**

36. Write 0.4141414141 . . . using bar notation. *(Lesson 2-7)* $0.\overline{41}$

37. ***Recycling*** The math team collected 25 pounds of newspaper during a school newspaper drive. The band collected 19 pounds. If each organization was paid $0.35 per pound of newspaper, how much more money did the math team raise than the band? *(Lesson 2-4)* **$2.10**

For **Extra Practice,** see page 579.

3 PRACTICE/APPLY

Check for Understanding

If students need additional practice or instruction after completing Exercises 1–10, you may find one of the following options helpful.

- Extra Practice, see p. 579
- Reteaching Activity, see p. 170
- *Study Guide Masters,* p. 32
- *Practice Masters,* p. 32

Assignment Guide

Core: 11–31 odd, 33–37
Enriched: 12–30 even, 31–37

4 ASSESS

Closing Activity

Writing Have students use the method they find most reasonable to find the LCM of 4, 8, and 12. Ask them to explain why they chose the method they did.

***Practice Masters,* p. 32**

Name______________ Date__________

Practice

Least Common Multiple

Find the LCM of each set of numbers by listing the multiples of each number.

1. 75, 25
75: 75, 150
25: 25, 50, 75
LCM: 75

2. 40, 50
40: 40, 80, 120 160, 200
50: 50, 100, 150, 200
LCM: 200

3. 2, 4, 5
2: 2, 4, 6, 8, 10, 12, 14, 16, 18, 20; 4: 4, 8, 12, 16, 20; 5: 5, 10, 15, 20; LCM: 20

Find the LCM of each set of numbers by writing the prime factorization of each number.

4. 4, 8, 10
$4 = 2^2$
$8 = 2^3$
$10 = 2 \times 5$
LCM: 40

5. 11, 8, 22
$11 = 11$
$8 = 2^3$
$22 = 2 \times 11$
LCM: 88

6. 39, 9, 117
$39 = 3 \times 13$
$9 = 3^2$
$117 = 3^2 \times 13$
LCM: 117

Find the LCM of each set of numbers.

7. 4, 12 — 12
8. 15, 12 — 60
9. 156, 13 — 156
10. 250, 30 — 750
11. 3, 4, 13 — 156
12. 200, 18 — 1,800
13. 4, 10, 12 — 60
14. 48, 16, 3 — 48
15. 66, 55, 44 — 660
16. 70, 90 — 630
17. 29, 58, 4 — 116
18. 6, 15, 20 — 60
19. 18, 54 — 54
20. 30, 65 — 390
21. 180, 252 — 1,260

 T32 *Mathematics: Applications and Connections, Course 2*

Extending the Lesson

***Enrichment Masters,* p. 32**

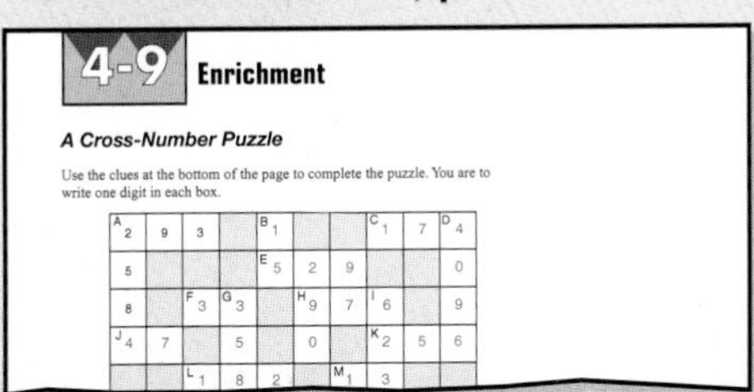

4-9 **Enrichment**

A Cross-Number Puzzle

Use the clues at the bottom of the page to complete the puzzle. You are to write one digit in each box.

A 2	9	3		B 1			C 1	7	D 4
5				E 5	2	9			0
8		F 3	G 3		H 9	7	I 6		9
J 4	7		5		0		K 2	5	6
		L 1	8	2		M 1	3		

Activity Have students find the LCM and GCF for two numbers, the product of the two numbers, and the product of their GCF and LCM. Ask students what they notice. Repeat, using other pairs of numbers. Ask students what conclusions, if any, they can draw. **product of the two numbers = product of GCF and LCM**

4-10 Lesson Notes

Instructional Resources

- *Study Guide Masters,* p. 33
- *Practice Masters,* p. 33
- *Enrichment Masters,* p. 33
- Transparencies 4-10, A and B
- *Assessment and Evaluation Masters,* p. 100

 CD-ROM Program
- Resource Lesson 4-10

Recommended Pacing	
Standard	Day 13 of 15
Honors	Day 13 of 15
Block	Day 7 of 8

1 FOCUS

5-Minute Check *(Lesson 4-9)*

Find the LCM of each set of numbers.

1. 3, 12 12
2. 10, 12 60
3. 6, 9, 15 90
4. 225, 30 450
5. 8, 12, 16 48

 The 5-Minute Check is also available on **Transparency 4-10A** for this lesson.

Motivating the Lesson

Hands-On Activity Give two students 10 pennies each. Ask the two students to take turns tossing their pennies into a plastic cup 3 feet away. Ask students which tosser made a greater fraction of his or her shots.

4-10 Comparing and Ordering Fractions

What you'll learn

You'll learn to compare and order fractions.

When am I ever going to use this?

Knowing how to order fractions will help you compare quantities.

Word Wise

common denominator

least common denominator (LCD)

Kenya is a country in East Africa. Although the official language is Swahili, only 1% of its inhabitants speak this language. In this country, $\frac{1}{5}$ of the people speak *Kikuyu,* and $\frac{7}{50}$ of the people speak *Luo.* Which of these languages is spoken by more Kenyans? *This problem will be solved in Example 2.*

To compare fractions such as $\frac{1}{5}$ and $\frac{7}{50}$, rewrite each fraction using the same denominator. Then you only need to compare the numerators.

A **common denominator** is a common multiple of the denominators of two or more fractions. The **least common denominator (LCD)** is the least common multiple (LCM) of the denominators of two or more fractions.

Examples

1 Compare $\frac{5}{6}$ and $\frac{7}{9}$.

The LCM of the denominators 6 and 9 is 18.

Rewrite each fraction using the LCD, 18.

$\frac{5}{6} = \frac{5 \times 3}{6 \times 3} = \frac{15}{18}$ $\quad \frac{7}{9} = \frac{7 \times 2}{9 \times 2} = \frac{14}{18}$

Since $\frac{15}{18} > \frac{14}{18}$, then $\frac{5}{6} > \frac{7}{9}$.

CONNECTION **2** **Geography** **Refer to the beginning of the lesson. Is Kikuyu or Luo spoken by more Kenyans?**

You need to find which fraction is greater, $\frac{1}{5}$ or $\frac{7}{50}$. First, find the LCD by listing the multiples of each denominator.

multiples of 5: 5, 10, 15, 20, 25, 30, 35, 40, 45, 50, 55, . . .

multiples of 50: 50, 100, 150, 200, 250, . . .

The LCD of $\frac{1}{5}$ and $\frac{7}{50}$ is 50, since 50 is the LCM of 5 and 50. So, rewrite $\frac{1}{5}$ using a denominator of 50.

$$\frac{1}{5} \overset{\times 10}{=} \frac{10}{50}$$

Now, compare $\frac{10}{50}$ and $\frac{7}{50}$. Since $10 > 7$, then $\frac{10}{50} > \frac{7}{50}$. More Kenyans speak Kikuyu than Luo.

You can also compare fractions by seeing how they relate to the nearest one half or by expressing them as decimals.

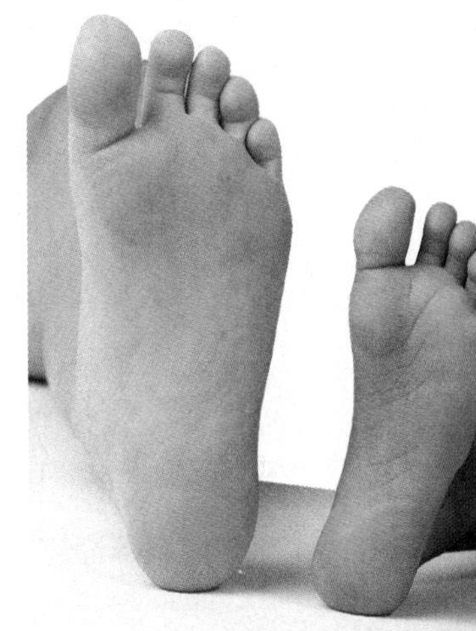

Examples

3 **Faith's foot is $3\frac{3}{16}$" wide. Her friend Raine's foot is $3\frac{7}{8}$" wide. Whose foot is wider?**

Since both widths are at least 3 inches, we will compare only the fractions.

$\frac{3}{16}$ is nearest to 0.

$\frac{7}{8}$ is nearest to 1.

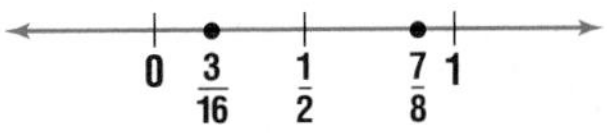

So, $\frac{3}{16} < \frac{7}{8}$ and $3\frac{3}{16} < 3\frac{7}{8}$.

(Number line: 0, $\frac{3}{16}$, $\frac{1}{2}$, $\frac{7}{8}$, 1)

Raine's foot is wider than Faith's.

APPLICATION

4 **Safety** **More than a half-million bike riders go to hospital emergency rooms each year. A recent survey showed that 7 out of 10 bike riders use safety equipment. LaShanda found that 9 of 16 friends that she talked to used safety equipment when they rode their bikes. Are LaShanda's friends safer than most?**

Since $\frac{9}{16}$ and $\frac{7}{10}$ are difficult to compare, express each fraction as a decimal and then compare.

$9 \div 16 = 0.5625$ $\qquad$ $7 \div 10 = 0.7$

Since $0.5625 < 0.7$, then $\frac{9}{16} < \frac{7}{10}$. LaShanda's friends wear safety equipment less than the average bike rider does. So they are not safer than most.

2 TEACH

Transparency 4-10B contains a teaching aid for this lesson.

Using Calculators Students can compare fractions on a calculator by using cross products. For instance, in Example 2, students would multiply 4×50 and 20×7, arriving at 200 and 140, respectively. Since 200 is greater than 140, $\frac{4}{20}$ is greater than $\frac{7}{50}$.

In-Class Examples

For Example 1

Compare $\frac{7}{12}$ and $\frac{5}{8}$ by writing equivalent fractions using the least common denominator. $\frac{5}{8} > \frac{7}{12}$

For Example 2

Compare $\frac{3}{4}$ and $\frac{3}{16}$. $\frac{3}{4} > \frac{3}{16}$

For Example 3

The width of a lawn is $5\frac{1}{4}$ meters. The width of a second lawn is $5\frac{2}{9}$ meters. Which lawn is wider? **the first; $5\frac{1}{4} > 5\frac{2}{9}$**

For Example 4

Jerome's team won 8 of 10 games, and Kevin's team won 15 of 18 games. Whose team won a greater fraction of its games? **Kevin's**

Teaching Tip In Example 2, note that there are several ways to solve this problem. Some students may realize that $\frac{4}{20}$ can be simplified to $\frac{1}{5}$, and then changed to $\frac{10}{50}$. Now both fractions have the same denominator and so can be compared.

3 PRACTICE/APPLY

Check for Understanding

If students need additional practice or instruction after completing Exercises 1–12, you may find one of the following options helpful.

- Extra Practice, see p. 580
- Reteaching Activity
- *Study Guide Masters,* p. 33
- *Practice Masters,* p. 33

Assignment Guide

Core: 13–41 odd, 42–47
Enriched: 14–38 even, 39–47

Additional Answers

3. $\frac{5}{7}$ and $\frac{4}{9}$; you can see from the graph that $\frac{5}{7}$ of the circle is greater than $\frac{4}{9}$ of the circle, so $\frac{5}{7} > \frac{4}{9}$.

40. $\frac{19}{18}$, since it is $\frac{1}{18}$ away from 1. $1\frac{1}{8}$ is $\frac{1}{8}$ away from 1.

***Study Guide Masters,* p. 33**

Name__________ Date__________

4-10 Study Guide

Comparing and Ordering Fractions

To compare fractions, rewrite them so they have the same denominator. The **least common denominator (LCD)** of two fractions is the least common multiple of their denominators.

Example 1 **Which fraction is greater, $\frac{5}{6}$ or $\frac{3}{4}$?**

Find the LCD by listing the multiples of each denominator.

multiples of 6: 6, 12, 18, 24, 30, 36, . . .

multiples of 4: 4, 8, 12, 16, 20, 24, . . .

The LCM of 6 and 4 is 12. So, the LCD of $\frac{5}{6}$ and $\frac{3}{4}$ is 12.

Write $\frac{5}{6}$ and $\frac{3}{4}$ as fractions with a denominator of 12.

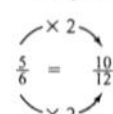

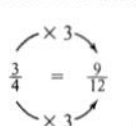

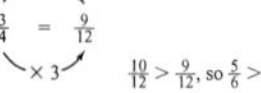

$\frac{10}{12} > \frac{9}{12}$, so $\frac{5}{6} > \frac{3}{4}$.

Another way to compare fractions is to express them as decimals. Then compare the decimals.

Example 2 **Which fraction is greater, $\frac{7}{9}$ or $\frac{3}{4}$?**

Express each fraction as a decimal. Then compare.

$7 \div 9 = 0.\overline{7}$ $3 \div 4 = 0.75$ $0.\overline{7} > 0.75$, so $\frac{7}{9} > \frac{3}{4}$.

Find the LCD for each pair of fractions.

1. $\frac{1}{2}, \frac{1}{3}$ 6
2. $\frac{3}{4}, \frac{1}{8}$ 8
3. $\frac{5}{9}, \frac{1}{2}$ 18
4. $\frac{2}{3}, \frac{3}{7}$ 21
5. $\frac{5}{9}, \frac{5}{6}$ 18
6. $\frac{7}{8}, \frac{5}{12}$ 24
7. $\frac{7}{10}, \frac{4}{5}$ 10
8. $\frac{3}{4}, \frac{1}{2}$ 4

Replace each ◯ with <, >, or = to make a true sentence.

9. $\frac{1}{2}$ ◯ $\frac{5}{9}$ <
10. $\frac{3}{4}$ ◯ $\frac{7}{8}$ <
11. $\frac{5}{12}$ ◯ $\frac{1}{2}$ <
12. $\frac{4}{5}$ ◯ $\frac{7}{10}$ >

 T33 *Mathematics: Applications and Connections, Course 2*

CHECK FOR UNDERSTANDING

Communicating Mathematics

Read and study the lesson to answer each question.

1. ***Tell*** what method you would use to compare $\frac{3}{4}$ and $\frac{5}{6}$ and why you chose that method. **See students' work.**
2. ***You Decide*** Darnell thinks that $\frac{34}{70}$ is less than $\frac{31}{60}$. Jennifer disagrees. Who is correct? Explain your reasoning. **2. Darnell; $\frac{34}{70} \approx 0.49$ and $\frac{31}{60} \approx 0.52$.**
3. ***Write*** the fractions that are modeled at the right. Which fraction is greater? Explain how you know. **See margin.**

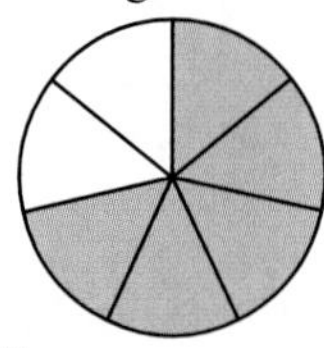
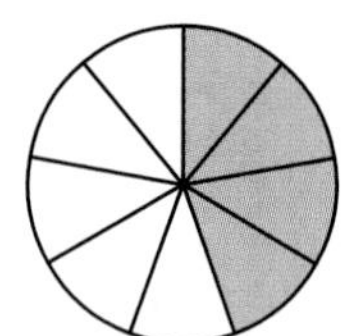

Guided Practice

Find the LCD for each pair of fractions.

4. $\frac{8}{9}, \frac{7}{12}$ **36**
5. $\frac{8}{5}, \frac{15}{13}$ **65**
6. $\frac{7}{18}, \frac{11}{36}$ **36**
7. $\frac{1}{6}, \frac{3}{8}$ **24**

Replace each ● with <, >, or = to make a true sentence.

8. $\frac{1}{6}$ ● $\frac{1}{3}$ **<**
9. $\frac{5}{9}$ ● $\frac{11}{15}$ **<**
10. $\frac{3}{4}$ ● $\frac{5}{8}$ **>**
11. $\frac{4}{7}$ ● $\frac{5}{9}$ **>**

12. ***Population*** The Choctaw tribe makes up $\frac{13}{300}$ of all American Indian tribes. The Pueblo tribe makes up $\frac{7}{250}$ of all tribes. Which of these two tribes makes up a greater fraction of American Indian tribes? **Choctaw**

interNET CONNECTION
For the latest statistics on American Indian tribes, visit: www.glencoe.com/sec/math/mac/mathnet

EXERCISES

Practice

Find the LCD for each pair of fractions.

13. $\frac{4}{5}, \frac{8}{9}$ **45**
14. $\frac{3}{5}, \frac{3}{6}$ **30**
15. $\frac{11}{16}, \frac{3}{4}$ **16**
16. $\frac{1}{3}, \frac{3}{10}$ **30**
17. $\frac{5}{4}, \frac{9}{8}$ **8**
18. $\frac{2}{15}, \frac{1}{6}$ **30**
19. $\frac{7}{12}, \frac{13}{36}$ **36**
20. $\frac{15}{21}, \frac{6}{7}$ **21**
21. $\frac{2}{3}, \frac{17}{24}$ **24**
22. $\frac{3}{10}, \frac{2}{12}$ **60**
23. $\frac{13}{17}, \frac{3}{4}$ **68**
24. $\frac{5}{24}, \frac{3}{8}$ **24**

Replace each ● with <, >, or = to make a true sentence.

25. $\frac{4}{7}$ ● $\frac{5}{8}$ **<**
26. $\frac{1}{3}$ ● $\frac{3}{15}$ **>**
27. $\frac{9}{13}$ ● $\frac{14}{20}$ **<**
28. $\frac{9}{17}$ ● $\frac{9}{13}$ **<**
29. $\frac{5}{9}$ ● $\frac{8}{15}$ **>**
30. $\frac{3}{13}$ ● $\frac{4}{26}$ **>**
31. $\frac{16}{20}$ ● $\frac{40}{50}$ **=**
32. $\frac{4}{5}$ ● $\frac{6}{7}$ **<**
33. $\frac{3}{8}$ ● $\frac{5}{12}$ **<**
34. $\frac{45}{90}$ ● $\frac{15}{30}$ **=**
35. $\frac{7}{5}$ ● $\frac{14}{11}$ **>**
36. $\frac{2}{3}$ ● $\frac{19}{27}$ **<**

37. Find the LCD for $\frac{5}{14}$ and $\frac{11}{18}$. **126**
38. Which is greater, $\frac{12}{32}$ or $\frac{16}{40}$? **$\frac{16}{40}$**

Applications and Problem Solving

39. ***School*** Suppose 17 of the 28 students in math class and 15 of 25 students in music class sign up for the school olympics. Which class has a greater portion of students participating? **students in math**
40. ***Number Sense*** Is $1\frac{1}{8}$, or $\frac{19}{18}$ nearest to 1? Explain your reasoning. **See margin.**

Reteaching the Lesson

Activity Use a ruler to compare and order fractions. Have students compare the numbers by plotting their decimal equivalents on a number line and seeing how the points are ordered.

MathPASS CD-ROM

This CD-ROM offers a complete, self-paced mathematics curriculum. Each lesson includes a pretest, tutorial, guided practice, and posttest. MathPASS Lesson 12 is correlated to this Student Edition lesson.
For Windows & Macintosh

41. 5–6 hours

41. ***Video Games*** Recently, $\frac{2}{25}$ of kids surveyed played video games 5–6 hours per week, and $\frac{3}{50}$ played video games 7–8 hours per week. Did more kids surveyed play video games 5–6 hours or 7–8 hours each week?

42. ***Critical Thinking*** When is the least common denominator of two fractions equal to one of the denominators? Give two examples. **See margin.**

Mixed Review

43. Find the LCM of 14 and 21. *(Lesson 4-9)* **42**

44. $52\% = \frac{13}{25}$; $74\% = \frac{37}{50}$; $93\% = \frac{93}{100}$

44. ***Volunteering*** The graph shows the percent of people in the Peace Corps. Express each percent as a fraction in simplest form. *(Lesson 4-7)*

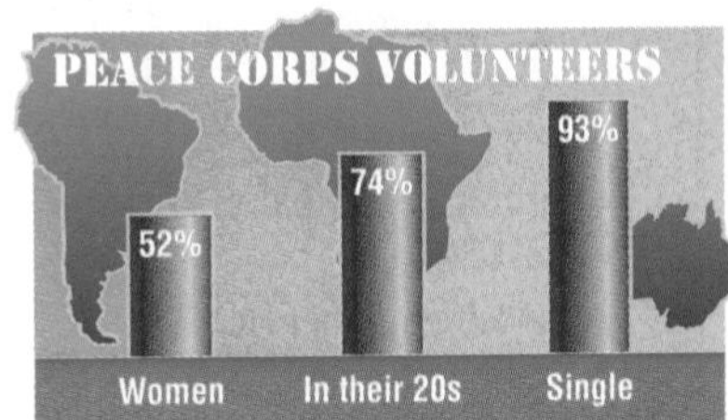

Source: Peace Corps

45. ***Statistics*** Construct a line plot for 75, 65, 82, 93, 75, 72, 81, and 90. *(Lesson 3-3)* **See margin.**

For **Extra Practice,** see page 580.

46. 0.3, 0.33, 3, 3.03, 3.33

46. Order 3, 0.3, 3.33, 0.33, 3.03 from least to greatest. *(Lesson 2-1)*

47. **Standardized Test Practice** Josie was born in 1979. Amanda was born 12 years later. In what year was Amanda born? *(Lesson 1-5)* **B**

A 1996 **B** 1991 **C** 1984 **D** 1967

Let the Games Begin

Fractions and Ladders

Math Skill
Comparing and Ordering Fractions

Get Ready This game is for two players.

calculator ☐ posterboard

Get Set Draw a ladder with 12 rungs on the posterboard. Label the bottom rung 0 and the top rung 1.

Go

- Use your calculator to build a ladder of fractions between 0 and 1 so that each fraction on the ladder is greater than the fraction below it. You may use any numbers in the numerators and denominators of your fractions.
- The first player enters a fraction at the bottom of the ladder. The opponent enters a larger fraction on the next rung of the ladder. He or she must show that this fraction is larger by using one of the strategies described in this lesson.
- Alternate turns. A player wins if the opponent is not able to find a larger fraction and he or she can. A player, in his or her turn, can have only one chance to name a fraction for the next rung before their opponent gets to try. If neither player succeeds, they each try again.

Visit www.glencoe.com/sec/math/mac/mathnet for more games.

4 ASSESS

Closing Activity

Speaking Have students explain a method for writing three fractions in order from least to greatest. Ask them to demonstrate their method.

Chapter 4, Quiz D (Lessons 4-9 and 4-10) is available in the *Assessment and Evaluation Masters,* p. 100.

Additional Answers

42. When one denominator is a factor of the other denominator; sample answers: $\frac{1}{12}, \frac{1}{3}$ or $\frac{4}{15}, \frac{1}{30}$.

45.

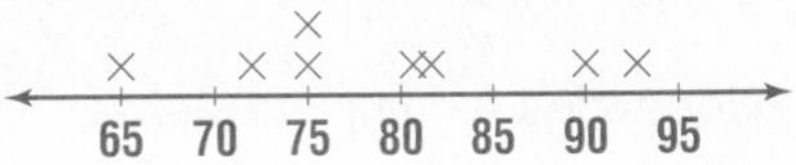

[Line plot from 65 to 95 with X marks: one at 65, one at 72, two at 75, one at 81, one at 82, one at 90, one at 93]

Extending the Lesson

***Enrichment Masters,* p. 33**

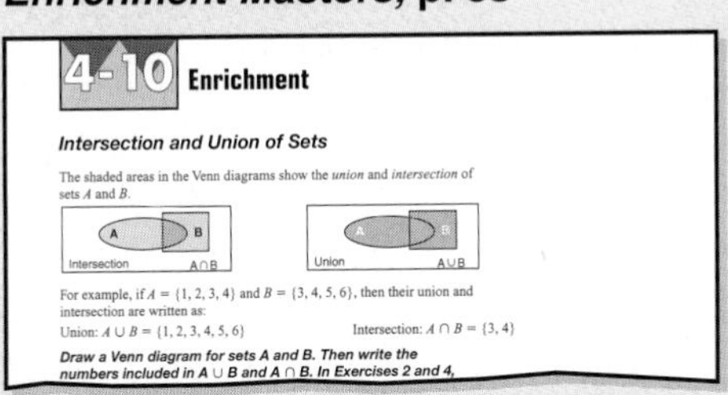

4-10 Enrichment

Intersection and Union of Sets

The shaded areas in the Venn diagrams show the *union* and *intersection* of sets A and B.

Intersection $A \cap B$ — Union $A \cup B$

For example, if $A = \{1, 2, 3, 4\}$ and $B = \{3, 4, 5, 6\}$, then their union and intersection are written as:

Union: $A \cup B = \{1, 2, 3, 4, 5, 6\}$ Intersection: $A \cap B = \{3, 4\}$

Draw a Venn diagram for sets A and B. Then write the numbers included in A ∪ B and A ∩ B. In Exercises 2 and 4,

If students have calculators that express fractions, they can compare fractions by subtracting. A result that is negative means the second number is greater. Encourage students to start with small numbers.

Additional resources for this game can be found on page 41 of the ***Classroom Games.***

***Practice Masters,* p. 33**

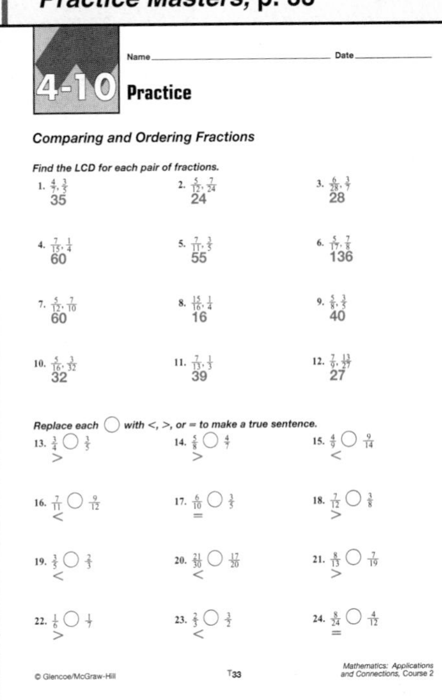

Name ____________ Date ________

4-10 Practice

Comparing and Ordering Fractions

Find the LCD for each pair of fractions.

1. $\frac{4}{7}, \frac{3}{5}$ **35** 2. $\frac{5}{12}, \frac{7}{24}$ **24** 3. $\frac{6}{28}, \frac{3}{7}$ **28**

4. $\frac{7}{15}, \frac{1}{4}$ **60** 5. $\frac{7}{11}, \frac{3}{5}$ **55** 6. $\frac{5}{17}, \frac{7}{8}$ **136**

7. $\frac{5}{12}, \frac{7}{10}$ **60** 8. $\frac{15}{16}, \frac{1}{4}$ **16** 9. $\frac{5}{8}, \frac{3}{5}$ **40**

10. $\frac{5}{16}, \frac{3}{32}$ **32** 11. $\frac{7}{13}, \frac{1}{3}$ **39** 12. $\frac{7}{9}, \frac{13}{27}$ **27**

Replace each ◯ with <, >, or = to make a true sentence.

13. $\frac{3}{4}$ ◯ $\frac{3}{5}$ **>** 14. $\frac{5}{8}$ ◯ $\frac{4}{7}$ **>** 15. $\frac{4}{9}$ ◯ $\frac{9}{14}$ **<**

16. $\frac{7}{11}$ ◯ $\frac{9}{12}$ **<** 17. $\frac{6}{10}$ ◯ $\frac{3}{5}$ **=** 18. $\frac{7}{12}$ ◯ $\frac{3}{8}$ **>**

19. $\frac{3}{5}$ ◯ $\frac{2}{3}$ **<** 20. $\frac{21}{30}$ ◯ $\frac{17}{20}$ **<** 21. $\frac{8}{13}$ ◯ $\frac{7}{19}$ **>**

22. $\frac{1}{6}$ ◯ $\frac{1}{7}$ **>** 23. $\frac{2}{3}$ ◯ $\frac{3}{2}$ **<** 24. $\frac{8}{24}$ ◯ $\frac{4}{12}$ **=**

 T33 *Mathematics: Applications and Connections, Course 2*

Study Guide and Assessment

Vocabulary

This section provides a listing of the new terms, properties, and phrases that were introduced in this chapter. Have students define each term and provide an example or two of it, if appropriate.

Understanding and Using the Vocabulary

These exercises check students' understanding of the terms by using a variety of verbal formats including matching, completion, and true/false.

Glossaries A complete glossary of terms appears on pages 656–663. The glossary also appears in Spanish on pages 664–672.

Additional Answers

6. A prime number can only be written as a product of 1 and itself. A number that has more factors than 1 and itself is a composite number.
21. Add 5; arithmetic; 41, 46, 51.
22. Multiply by 4; geometric; 1,024; 4,096, 16,384.
23. Add 3 more than was added to the previous term; neither; 63, 84, 108.
24. Multiply by 10; geometric; 100,000; 1,000,000; 10,000,000.

CHAPTER 4 Study Guide and Assessment

interNET CONNECTION Chapter Review For additional review, visit: www.glencoe.com/sec/math/mac/mathne

Vocabulary

After completing this chapter, you should be able to define each term, concept, or phrase and give an example or two of each.

Number and Operations
common denominator (p. 172)
composite number (p. 138)
divisible (p. 133)
factor (p. 133)
factor tree (p. 138)
greatest common factor (GCF) (p. 150)
least common denominator (LCD) (p. 172)
least common multiple (LCM) (p. 169)
multiple (p. 169)
percent (p. 158)
prime factorization (p. 138)
prime number (p. 138)
ratio (p. 154)
simplest form (p. 154)

Problem Solving
make a list (p. 148)

Patterns and Functions
arithmetic sequence (p. 142)
geometric sequence (p. 143)
sequence (p. 142)
term (p. 142)

Probability
event (p. 165)
probability (p. 165)
random (p. 165)

Understanding and Using the Vocabulary

State whether each sentence is *true* or *false*. If false, replace the underlined word or number to make a true sentence.

1. The prime factorization of 24 is $\underline{2^3 \times 3^2}$. false, $2^3 \times 3$
2. The numbers in a sequence are called <u>terms</u>. true
3. The greatest common factor of 15 and 18 is <u>3</u>. true
4. A <u>ratio</u> is a comparison of two numbers by division. true
5. The simplest form of $\frac{16}{24}$ is $\underline{\frac{4}{6}}$. false, $\frac{2}{3}$

In Your Own Words

6. ***Explain*** the difference between a prime number and a composite number. See margin.

Objectives & Examples

Upon completing this chapter, you should be able to:

- use divisibility rules *(Lesson 4-1)*

Determine whether 336 is divisible by 2, 4, or 10.

2: Yes. The ones digit, 6, is even.
4: Yes. The number formed by the last two digits, 36, is divisible by 4.
10: No. The ones digit is not 0.

Review Exercises

Use these exercises to review and prepare for the chapter test.

Determine whether the first number is divisible by the second number. 9. no

7. 452; 4 yes **8.** 727; 3 no **9.** 123; 6

Determine whether each number is divisible by 2, 3, 4, 5, 6, 9, or 10.

10. 221 none **11.** 1,225 5 **12.** 630
12. 2, 3, 5, 6, 9, 10

MindJogger Videoquizzes

MindJogger Videoquizzes provide an alternative review of concepts presented in this chapter. Students work in teams to answer questions, gaining points for correct answers. The questions are presented in three rounds.
Round 1 Concepts–5 questions
Round 2 Skills–4 questions
Round 3 Problem Solving–4 questions

Objectives & Examples

Review Exercises

- find the prime factorization of a composite number *(Lesson 4-2)*

Find the prime factorization of 63.

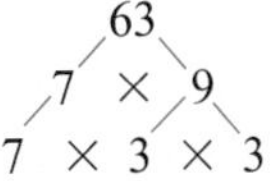

The prime factorization of 63 is 7×3^2.

Find the prime factorization of each number.

13. 1,000 **$2^3 \times 5^3$** **14.** 144 **$2^4 \times 3^2$**
15. 950 **$2 \times 5^2 \times 19$** **16.** 77 **7×11**
17. 96 **$2^5 \times 3$** **18.** 300 **$2^2 \times 3 \times 5^2$**
19. 2,800 **$2^4 \times 5^2 \times 7$** **20.** 1,450 **$2 \times 5^2 \times 29$**

- recognize and extend a pattern for sequences *(Lesson 4-3)*

Find the next three terms in the sequence 32, 16, 8, 4, 2, ...

This is a geometric sequence created by multiplying the previous term by $\frac{1}{2}$. The next three terms are 1, $\frac{1}{2}$, $\frac{1}{4}$.

Describe the pattern in each sequence. Identify the sequence as *arithmetic*, *geometric*, or *neither*. Then find the next three terms. **21–24. See margin.**

21. 16, 21, 26, 31, 36, . . .
22. 1, 4, 16, 64, 256, . . .
23. 0, 3, 9, 18, 30, 45, . . .
24. 10, 100, 1,000, 10,000, . . .

- find the greatest common factor of two or more numbers *(Lesson 4-4)*

Find the GCF of 45 and 75.
$45 = 3 \times 3 \times 5$
$75 = 3 \times 5 \times 5$
GCF: 3×5 or 15

Find the GCF of each set of numbers.

25. 36, 81 **9** **26.** 40, 65 **5**
27. 252, 336 **84** **28.** 57, 240 **3**
29. 56, 280, 400 **8** **30.** 8, 12, 16 **4**

- express fractions and ratios in simplest form *(Lesson 4-5)*

Write $\frac{45}{81}$ in simplest form.

$$\frac{45}{81} = \frac{45 \div 9}{81 \div 9} = \frac{5}{9}$$

Express each fraction or ratio in simplest form.

31. $\frac{56}{70}$ **$\frac{4}{5}$** **32.** 250:750 **1:3**
33. 26:39 **2:3** **34.** $\frac{18}{60}$ **$\frac{3}{10}$**
35. $\frac{77}{121}$ **$\frac{7}{11}$** **36.** 57:95 **3:5**

- illustrate the meaning of percent using models or symbols *(Lesson 4-6)*

Express 18 in 100 as a percent.

18 in 100 = $\frac{18}{100}$ = 18%

Express each ratio as a percent.

37. $\frac{56}{100}$ **56%** **38.** 73 out of 100 **73%**
39. 49 in 100 **49%** **40.** 24:100 **24%**

Assessment and Evaluation

Six forms of Chapter 4 Test are available in the *Assessment and Evaluation Masters* as shown in the chart.

1A	Multiple Choice	Honors
1B	Multiple Choice	Average
1C	Multiple Choice	Basic
2A	Free-Response	Honors
2B	Free-Response	Average
2C	Free-Response	Basic

Chapter 4 Test, Form 1B, is shown at the right. Chapter 4 Test, Form 2B, is shown on the next page.

Objectives & Examples

This section reviews the skills and concepts of the chapter and shows completely worked examples.

Review Exercises

These exercises provide practice for the corresponding objectives.

Assessment and Evaluation Masters, pp. 87–88

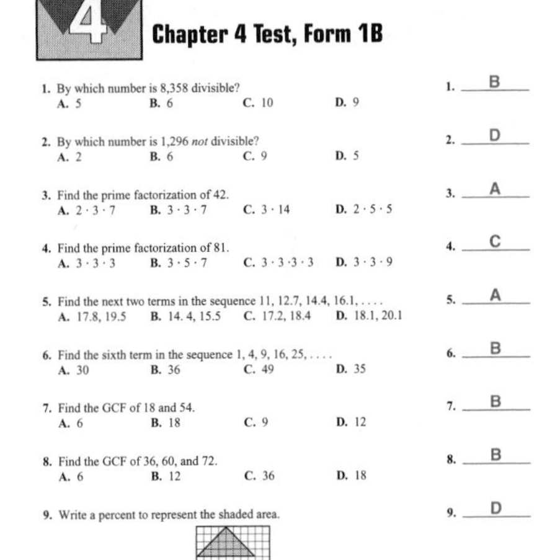

4 Name________ Date________

Chapter 4 Test, Form 1B

1. By which number is 8,358 divisible? A. 5 B. 6 C. 10 D. 9 — 1. B
2. By which number is 1,296 *not* divisible? A. 2 B. 6 C. 9 D. 5 — 2. D
3. Find the prime factorization of 42. A. 2 · 3 · 7 B. 3 · 3 · 7 C. 3 · 14 D. 2 · 5 · 5 — 3. A
4. Find the prime factorization of 81. A. 3 · 3 · 3 B. 3 · 5 · 7 C. 3 · 3 · 3 · 3 D. 3 · 3 · 9 — 4. C
5. Find the next two terms in the sequence 11, 12.7, 14.4, 16.1, ... A. 17.8, 19.5 B. 14. 4, 15.5 C. 17.2, 18.4 D. 18.1, 20.1 — 5. A
6. Find the sixth term in the sequence 1, 4, 9, 16, 25, ... A. 30 B. 36 C. 49 D. 35 — 6. B
7. Find the GCF of 18 and 54. A. 6 B. 18 C. 9 D. 12 — 7. B
8. Find the GCF of 36, 60, and 72. A. 6 B. 12 C. 36 D. 18 — 8. B
9. Write a percent to represent the shaded area. A. 9% B. 16% C. 38% D. 31% — 9. D
10. Express $\frac{72}{81}$ in simplest form. A. $\frac{24}{27}$ B. $\frac{7}{8}$ C. $\frac{3}{4}$ D. $\frac{8}{9}$ — 10. D
11. Express 20 doctors to 25 doctors in simplest form. A. 20:25 B. 10:12 C. 4:5 D. 5:6 — 11. C

© Glencoe/McGraw-Hill 87 *Mathematics: Applications and Connections, Course 2*

4 **Chapter 4 Test, Form 1B (continued)**

12. Express 0.125 as a fraction in simplest form. A. $\frac{1}{8}$ B. $\frac{1}{6}$ C. $\frac{3}{8}$ D. $\frac{1}{5}$ — 12. A
13. Express $\frac{3}{5}$ as a percent. A. 3.5% B. 35% C. 60% D. 6% — 13. C
14. Express 75% as a fraction in simplest form. A. $\frac{1}{4}$ B. $\frac{3}{4}$ C. $\frac{4}{5}$ D. $\frac{1}{5}$ — 14. B
15. Find the LCM of 15, 25, and 125. A. 375 B. 125 C. 5 D. 275 — 15. A
16. Find the LCD for $\frac{11}{12}$ and $\frac{1}{8}$. A. 96 B. 88 C. 12 D. 24 — 16. D

Replace each ● to make a true sentence.

17. $\frac{13}{28}$ ● $\frac{17}{30}$ A. > B. < C. = D. × — 17. B
18. $\frac{5}{9}$ ● $\frac{7}{12}$ A. > B. < C. = D. ÷ — 18. B
19. Eunsook plans to open a holiday savings account with $350 on June 1. How much should she deposit each following month in order to have $800 in her account by December 1? A. $60 B. $65 C. $70 D. $75 — 19. D
20. A bag contains 4 blue, 5 red, 1 green, and 2 white marbles. If you draw a marble at random, what is the probability of drawing a marble that is *not* red? A. $\frac{7}{12}$ B. $\frac{5}{12}$ C. $\frac{1}{4}$ D. $\frac{1}{3}$ — 20. A

© Glencoe/McGraw-Hill 88 *Mathematics: Applications and Connections, Course 2*

Additional Answers

49. $\frac{1}{2} = 50\%$

50. $\frac{1}{4} = 25\%$

51. $\frac{1}{4} = 25\%$

52. $\frac{3}{4} = 75\%$

Assessment and Evaluation Masters, pp. 93–94

Name________________ Date________

Chapter 4 Test, Form 2B

Determine whether each number is divisible by 2, 3, 4, 5, 6, 9, or 10.

1. 480 — 1. 2, 3, 4, 5, 6, 10
2. 1,980 — 2. all

Write the prime factorization of each number.

3. 72 — 3. $2^3 \cdot 3^2$
4. 98 — 4. $2 \cdot 7^2$

Identify each sequence as arithmetic, geometric, or neither. Then find the next three terms in the sequence.

5. $2, 1, \frac{1}{2}, \frac{1}{4}, \ldots$ — 5. geometric; $\frac{1}{8}, \frac{1}{16}, \frac{1}{32}$
6. $3, 4, 7, 11, \ldots$ — 6. neither; 18, 29, 47

Find the GCF of each set of numbers.

7. 48, 56 — 7. 8
8. 20, 36, 48 — 8. 4
9. 32, 42, 92 — 9. 2
10. Write a percent to represent the shaded area. — 10. 36%

Write each fraction or ratio in simplest form.

11. $\frac{28}{48}$ — 11. $\frac{7}{12}$
12. 3:21 — 12. 1:7
13. $\frac{63}{102}$ — 13. $\frac{21}{34}$

 93 *Mathematics: Applications and Connections, Course 2*

Chapter 4 Test, Form 2B (continued)

14. Express 0.58 as a fraction in simplest form. — 14. $\frac{29}{50}$
15. Express $\frac{26}{50}$ as a percent. — 15. 52%
16. Express 35% as a fraction in simplest form. — 16. $\frac{7}{20}$

Find the LCM of each set of numbers.

17. 24, 30, 360 — 17. 360
18. 36, 96, 124 — 18. 8, 928
19. Find the LCD for $\frac{3}{22}$ and $\frac{7}{55}$. — 19. 110
20. Find the LCD for $\frac{9}{10}$ and $\frac{11}{25}$. — 20. 50

Replace each ● with a $<$, $>$, or $=$ to make a true sentence.

21. $\frac{7}{9}$ ● $\frac{15}{17}$ — 21. $<$
22. $\frac{7}{8}$ ● $\frac{8}{10}$ — 22. $>$
23. $\frac{7}{11}$ ● $\frac{35}{55}$ — 23. $=$
24. Adnan plans to add bicep curls to his exercise routine. He will start with 10 pounds the first week and increase by 2 pounds a week. How many weeks will it take him to build up to 30 pounds? — 24. 10 weeks
25. The spinner is equally likely to stop on each of the regions. Find the probability that the spinner will stop on a factor of 15. — 25. $\frac{1}{2}$

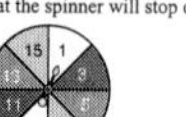

 94 *Mathematics: Applications and Connections, Course 2*

Objectives & Examples

● express fractions as percents, and percents and decimals as fractions *(Lesson 4-7)*

Express $\frac{6}{25}$ as a percent.

$\frac{6}{25} = \frac{24}{100} = 24\%$

Express 25% as a fraction.

$25\% = \frac{25}{100} = \frac{1}{4}$

Review Exercises

Express each fraction as a percent.

41. $\frac{14}{25}$ 56% **42.** $\frac{9}{20}$ 45%

43. $\frac{2}{5}$ 40% **44.** $\frac{7}{7}$ 100%

Express each percent or decimal as a fraction in simplest form.

45. 15% $\frac{3}{20}$ **46.** 0.27 $\frac{27}{100}$

47. 0.58 $\frac{29}{50}$ **48.** 72% $\frac{18}{25}$

● find the probability of a simple event *(Lesson 4-8)*

Find P(odd) when a number cube is rolled.

$P(\text{odd}) = \frac{3}{6}$ ← odd numbers ← total number of outcomes

$= \frac{1}{2}$ or 0.5

A bag contains 6 red, 3 pink, and 3 white bows. If you draw a bow at random, what is the probability of drawing each of the following? Express each ratio as both a fraction and a percent. 49–52. See margin.

49. red **50.** pink

51. white **52.** a red or a white

● find the least common multiple of two or more numbers *(Lesson 4-9)*

Find the LCM of 4 and 18.

$4 = 2^2$

$18 = 2 \times 3^2$

LCM: $2^2 \times 3^2$ or 36

Find the LCM of each set of numbers.

53. 6, 15 30 **54.** 42, 56 168

55. 16, 40 80 **56.** 15, 125, 600 3,000

57. 21, 81, 147 3,969 **58.** 48, 81, 270 6,480

● compare and order fractions *(Lesson 4-10)*

Compare $\frac{5}{9}$ and $\frac{4}{6}$.

$\frac{5}{9} = \frac{10}{18}$ $\frac{4}{6} = \frac{12}{18}$

Since $10 < 12$, then $\frac{5}{9} < \frac{4}{6}$.

Find the LCD for each pair of fractions.

59. $\frac{2}{3}, \frac{3}{4}$ 12 **60.** $\frac{11}{12}, \frac{8}{9}$ 36

Replace each ● with $<$, $>$, or $=$ to make a true sentence.

61. $\frac{3}{8}$ ● $\frac{5}{12}$ $<$ **62.** $\frac{7}{10}$ ● $\frac{13}{25}$ $>$

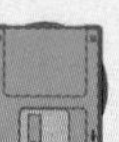

Test and Review Software

You may use this software, a combination of an item generator and item bank, to create your own tests or worksheets. Types of items include free response, multiple choice, short answer, and open ended.

CD-ROM Program

The CD-ROM Program contains an Assessment Game whose questions review the concepts in this chapter.

Applications & Problem Solving

63. ***Make a List*** Find the greatest common factor of the twelfth and fifteenth terms of the Fibonacci sequence, 1, 1, 2, 3, 5, 8, 13, 21, ... *(Lesson 4-4A)* **2**

64. ***School*** Beth scored 21 out of 25 on her spelling test. Ted scored 37 out of 40 on his spelling test. Who scored higher? *(Lesson 4-10)* **Ted**

65. ***Earth Science*** About 97.3 gallons of every 100 gallons of water on Earth are salt water. Write the percent of the water that is salt water. *(Lesson 4-6)* **97.3%**

66. ***Activities*** The graph shows students' favorite activities. Write each percent as a fraction in simplest form. *(Lesson 4-7)*

How Students Spend Free Time

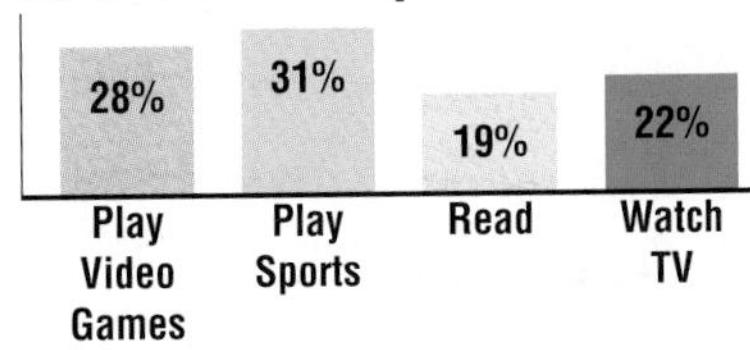

$\frac{7}{25}, \frac{31}{100}, \frac{19}{100}, \frac{11}{50}$

Alternative Assessment

Open Ended

Suppose you are a grocery store manager. You have decided to sell fresh bagels in the store bakery and to charge 45¢ for a bagel. If a customer orders more than one bagel, each additional one costs 40¢. Show how you will find the cost of one dozen bagels.
See margin.

Make a chart listing the price of 1 through 12 bagels. **See Answer Appendix.**

Completing the CHAPTER Project

Use the following checklist to make sure your car survey is complete.

- ☑ table and graph of your car production data
- ☑ table and graph of your car color survey
- ☑ the probability that a new student's favorite car color will be white, based on your survey
- ☑ a paragraph explaining how a car manufacturer would use your survey results

PORTFOLIO Review the items in your portfolio. Make a table of contents of the items, noting why each item was chosen. Replace any items that are no longer appropriate.

A practice test for Chapter 4 is provided on page 610.

Additional Answer for the Open Ended item

This represents an arithmetic sequence. The first bagel costs 45¢, the second would cost 45 + 40 or 85¢, the third would cost 85 + 40 or $1.25, and so on.

Performance Assessment

Additional performance assessment tasks for this chapter are included in the *Assessment and Evaluation Masters* on page 97. A scoring guide is also provided on page 109.

Applications and Problem Solving

The section provides additional practice in solving real-world problems that involve the skills of this chapter.

Alternative Assessment

The ***Open Ended*** section provides students with a performance assessment opportunity to evaluate their work and understanding.

Students should complete the final stages of their project and prepare a class demonstration of their results. A scoring guide for the project is available in the *Investigations and Projects Masters,* p. 31.

Students should add to their portfolios at this time.

Assessment and Evaluation Masters, p. 97

Name__________ Date__________

Chapter 4 Performance Assessment

Instructions: Demonstrate your knowledge by giving a clear, concise solution to each problem. Be sure to include all relevant drawings and justify your answers. You may show your solutions in more than one way or investigate beyond the requirements of the problems.

1. A community is providing a gardening area for its residents. The area will be laid out in individual garden plots as shown below.

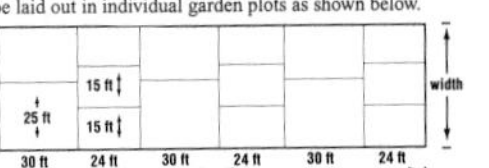

   a. The garden area will be fenced. The fence posts in front are to be equally spaced along the entire length with posts at the corners of each garden plot. Would a spacing of 3 feet between posts work? Explain.
   b. Find the prime factorizations of 30 and 24. Find the common factors of 30 and 24. Explain each step.
   c. What is the longest spacing between posts that can be used? What is this distance called? List the multiples of the widths of each size lot. What is the LCM?
   d. If the fence posts are to be equally spaced along the width of the garden area with posts at the corners of each garden plot, what spacing would you recommend? Why?

2. Choose four or more types of plants for your garden at home. How many seeds of each will you plant? What is the total number of seeds?
   a. Choose one plant from your garden. What percent of the total seeds are seeds for this plant? Explain your answer. Express your answer as a decimal, a simplified ratio, and as a percent. Draw a shaded model on grid paper to show this percent.
   b. If each seed grows into one plant, what is the probability that a plant picked at random will be the plant you chose in 2a? Simplify your answer. How does this last answer compare with the answer to question 2a? Is it greater than, less than, or equal to the answer in question 2a? Explain all of your steps.

3. Create a pattern for a numerical sequence. Provide six terms for the sequence. State the rule for the pattern. Is the sequence *arithmetic*, *geometric*, or *neither*? Why? Explain your steps.

 97 *Mathematics: Applications and Connections, Course 2*

Standardized Test Practice

The Standardized Test Practice may be used to help students prepare for standardized tests. The test items are written in the same style as those in state proficiency tests and standardized tests like CAT, CTBS, ITBS, MAT, SAT, and Terra Nova. The test items cover skills and concepts covered up to this point in the text.

The pages can be used as an overnight assessment. After students have completed the pages, discuss how each problem can be solved, or provide copies of the solutions from the *Solutions Manual.*

***Assessment and Evaluation Masters,* p. 103.**

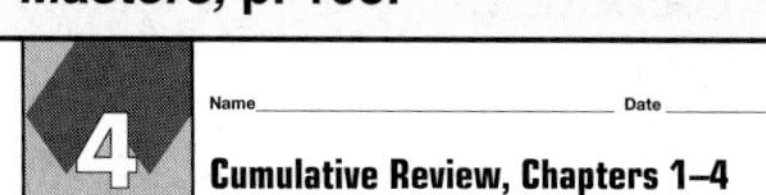

Name__________ Date__________

4 Cumulative Review, Chapters 1–4

Evaluate each expression. (Lesson 1-2)

1. $6 \cdot 4 + 2 \div 2$ — 1. 25
2. $3(13 + 7) \div 15 + 5$ — 2. 9
3. Find 0.000127×10^9. (Lesson 2-5) — 3. 127,000
4. Find $0.002\overline{)0.000139}$. Round to the nearest hundredth. (Lesson 2-6) — 4. 0.07
5. Write 981,000,000,000 in scientific notation. (Lesson 2-9) — 5. 9.81×10^{11}
6. Make a line plot for the data 45, 46, 46, 50, 46, 45. Circle any outliers. (Lesson 3-3) — 6. 45 46 47 48 49 50

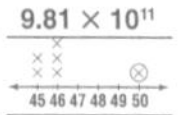

Find the following for the data in Question 6. (Lessons 3-1 and 3-4)

7. range — 7. 5
8. mode(s) — 8. 46
9. median — 9. 46
10. mean — 10. $46.\overline{3}$
11. Determine whether 624 is divisible by 2, 3, 4, 5, 6, 9, or 10. (Lesson 4-1) — 11. 2, 3, 4, and 6
12. Write the prime factorization for 108. (Lesson 4-2) — 12. $2 \cdot 2 \cdot 3 \cdot 3 \cdot 3$
13. Identify the sequence 2, 9, 16, 23, . . . as *arithmetic, geometric,* or *neither*. Then find the next three terms of the sequence. (Lesson 4-3) — 13. arithmetic; 30, 37, 44

Find the GCF of each pair of numbers. Use any method. (Lesson 4-4)

14. 98, 105 — 14. 7
15. 42, 46 — 15. 2
16. Write $\frac{51}{68}$ in simplest form. (Lesson 4-5) — 16. $\frac{3}{4}$

Express each percent or decimal as a fraction in simplest form. (Lesson 4-7)

17. 16% — 17. $\frac{4}{25}$
18. 0.85 — 18. $\frac{17}{20}$
19. The spinner shown at the right is equally likely to stop on each of the regions. Find the probability that the spinner will stop on a prime number. (Lesson 4-8) — 19. $\frac{1}{2}$ 
20. Find the LCM of 21 and 49. (Lesson 4-9) — 20. 147

 103 *Mathematics: Applications and Connections,* Course 2

CHAPTERS 1–4

Standardized Test Practice

Assessing Knowledge & Skills

Section One: Multiple Choice

There are ten multiple-choice questions in this section. Choose the best answer. If a correct answer is *not here,* choose the letter for Not Here.

1. The length of this paper clip is about — B

A 5 millimeters.
B 5 centimeters.
C 5 meters.
D 5 kilometers.

2. Jamal pays $126.82 each month on his student loan. What is this amount rounded to the nearest ten dollars? J

F $120.00
G $126.80
H $126.90
J $130.00

3. Lu-Chan performed a probability experiment by spinning a spinner 100 times. The results of his experiment are in the chart.

Color	Number of Spins
Red	40
Blue	20
Green	40

If the spinner is divided into 5 equal sections, how many sections would you expect to be colored green? A

A 2
B 3
C 4
D 5

Please note that Questions 4–10 have five answer choices.

4. Ms. Rogers buys 6 pounds of strawberries each day for her daycare center. If there are between 15 and 20 strawberries in one pound, what is a reasonable total for the number of strawberries that she buys each day? G

F 75
G 100
H 150
J 175
K 215

5. Rachel earns $5.25 per hour for baby-sitting. Which is the best estimate of her earnings if she baby-sits 13 hours in one week? B

A $60
B $70
C $80
D $90
E $100

6. The girls' chorale placed a bank in the cafeteria to collect money for a trip to sing at the statehouse. At the end of the first week, the bank contained 15 quarters, 10 dimes, and 35 nickels. Which number sentence represents the amount of money M in the bank? F

F $M = (15 \times 0.25) + (10 \times 0.10) + (35 \times 0.05)$
G $M = (15 + 25) \times (10 + 10) \times (35 + 5)$
H $M = (15 + 0.25) \times (10 + 0.10) \times (35 + 0.05)$
J $M = (15 \times 0.25) \times (10 \times 0.10) \times (35 \times 0.05)$
K $M = (15 \div 25) + (10 \div 0.10) + (35 \div 0.05)$

◀◀◀Instructional Resources

Another cumulative review is shown at the left and is available in the *Assessment and Evaluation Masters,* p. 103.

7. Paul's middle school had a drawing for a family pack of movie tickets. A total of 200 tickets was put in a container, and one ticket was drawn. If Paul had 5 tickets, what was the probability that Paul won? **B**

A $\frac{1}{200}$ **B** $\frac{1}{40}$
C $\frac{1}{5}$ **D** $\frac{1}{100}$
E $\frac{1}{195}$

8. Marco rides his bike to and from work every day. If the round trip is 3.23 miles, how far will Marco ride in 7 days? **H**

F 45.22 mi
G 29.07 mi
H 22.61 mi
J 19.38 mi
K Not Here

9. Serina bought 2 packages of hamburger on sale at $1.10 per pound. One package weighed 2.59 pounds, and the other weighed 1.12 pounds. What was the total weight of hamburger that Serina purchased? **E**

A 2.20 lb
B 2.71 lb
C 4.08 lb
D 7.42 lb
E Not Here

10. The student yearbook pages are 8 inches wide and ll inches long. If one page has only one photo that is 3 inches by 5 inches, which sentence can be used to find *s*, the amount of space left for autographs? **J**

F $s = (8 + 11) - (3 + 5)$
G $s = 8 \times 11 \times 3 \times 5$
H $s = 2(8 \times 11) - 2(3 \times 5)$
J $s = (8 \times 11) - (3 \times 5)$
K $s = (8 \times 11) \div (3 \times 5)$

Test-Taking Tip

Most standardized tests are given with test books that can be written in. Use the test book for scratch work and to mark questions that you will return to if you have time. You will not receive credit for answers that you write in the test book. Remember to transfer answers to the answer sheet as you take the test.

Section Two: Free Response

This section contains five questions for which you will provide short answers. Write your answers on your paper.

11. Identify the sequence 14, 26, 38, 50, . . . as *arithmetic, geometric,* or *neither*. Then find the next three terms. **arithmetic; 62, 74, 86**

12. What is the least common multiple of 25 and 45? **225**

13. If $n + 3.9 = 4.2$, what is the value of n? **0.3**

14. Write a percent to represent the shaded area. **36%**

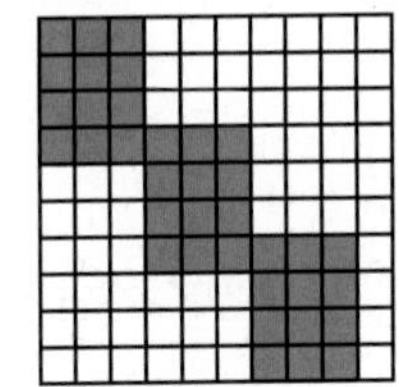

15. At the carnival, 10 prizes were placed inside paper bags. Each bag contained just one prize. If there were 2 one-dollar bills, 3 pencils, 1 ten-dollar bill, and 4 pens, what is the probability that a pen would be chosen? $\frac{2}{5}$

Test Practice For additional test practice questions, visit:

www.glencoe.com/sec/math/mac/mathnet

Instructional Resources ▶▶▶

Additional standardized test practice is shown at the right and is available in the *Assessment and Evaluation Masters,* pp. 101–102.

Test-Taking Tip

Remind students that it is important to establish a sequence in taking tests. Developing the habit of doing certain steps each time will help ensure that no tasks are forgotten.

Assessment and Evaluation Masters, pp. 101–102

Name________________ Date________

Chapter 4 Standardized Test Practice

The line plot represents the points scored per game by the Central High School football team in their last 11 games. Use this information in Questions 1–6.

10 13 16 19 22

1. Name the outlier.
   A. 10 B. 16 C. 13 D. 22 — 1. D
2. Find the range.
   A. 12 B. 16 C. 14.5 D. 22 — 2. A
3. Find the mode(s).
   A. 10 B. 14.5 C. 16 D. 14.2 — 3. C
4. Find the median.
   A. 14.2 B. 14 C. 15 D. 13 — 4. D
5. Find the mean.
   A. 14.5 B. 14.09 C. 12 D. 16 — 5. B
6. Name the cluster.
   A. between 10 and 13 B. between 10 and 16
   C. between 16 and 22 D. between 13 and 22 — 6. B
7. Find the GCF and LCM for 12, 132, and 24.
   A. 12; 48 B. 6; 32 C. 6; 12 D. 12; 264 — 7. D

A bag contains 5 blue, 6 red, 2 green, and 2 white marbles. If you draw a marble at random, what is the probability that you will draw each of the following?

8. a red marble
   A. $\frac{3}{5}$ B. $\frac{1}{5}$ C. $\frac{2}{5}$ D. $\frac{4}{5}$ — 8. C
9. a marble that is *not* blue
   A. $\frac{2}{3}$ B. $\frac{1}{3}$ C. $\frac{13}{15}$ D. $\frac{11}{15}$ — 9. A

Determine whether the answers shown are reasonable.

10. $895 - 598 = 397$
    A. yes B. no — 10. B
11. The sum of 61 and 48 is 109.
    A. yes B. no — 11. A

© Glencoe/McGraw-Hill 101 *Mathematics: Applications and Connections, Course 2*

Chapter 4 Standardized Test Practice (continued)

12. Choose a percent to represent the shaded area.
    A. 49%
    B. 60%
    C. 20%
    D. 50% — 12. A

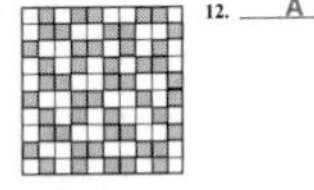

13. Which expression is equivalent to $2 \times 6 \times 18$?
    A. $2 \times 6 \times 9$
    B. $2 \times 2 \times 3 \times 3$
    C. $2 \times 2 \times 2 \times 3 \times 3 \times 3$
    D. $2 \times 2 \times 3 \times 3 \times 3 \times 3$ — 13. C
14. Casey decides to play a carnival game at a fair where a spinner has every month of the year on it. If Casey is born in January and puts a dollar on every month that begins with J, what is the probability that she will win?
    A. $\frac{1}{4}$ B. $\frac{1}{2}$ C. $\frac{1}{3}$ D. $\frac{7}{12}$ — 14. A
15. Cindy has $160 to buy cases of paper for her office. The different-sized cases cost $4, $5, $7, and $10. She wants to spend all of her money on one type of case. If she gets no change back, which types could she buy?
    A. $4, $5, $7, $10
    B. $4, $5, $10
    C. $4, $10
    D. $5, $7, $10 — 15. B
16. Scott paid $24.01 for a car repair. Two weeks later he paid $48.02 for another repair. Three weeks later his car repairs cost him $96.04. If this pattern continues, how much can Scott expect to pay for his next two car repairs?
    A. $144.06, $192.08
    B. $120.05, $144.06
    C. $192.08, $384.16
    D. $384.16, $1,536.64 — 16. C

© Glencoe/McGraw-Hill 102 *Mathematics: Applications and Connections, Course 2*

CHAPTER 5

Algebra: Using Integers

Previewing the Chapter

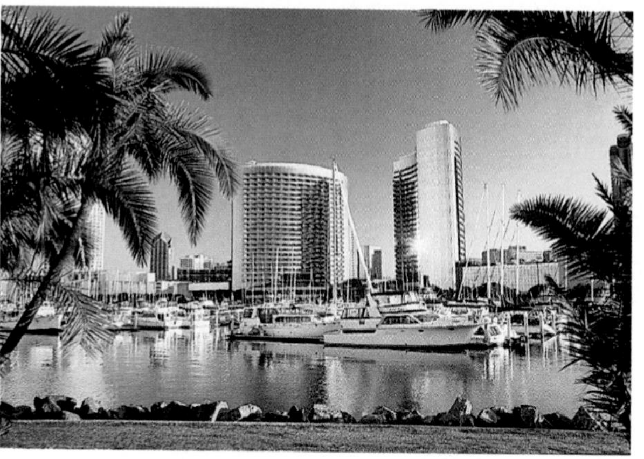

Overview

This chapter explores integers and their many applications. Extensive use is made of models such as counters. Students learn to compare and order integers, graph points on a coordinate plane, and add, subtract, multiply, and divide integers. In addition, students learn to solve problems by finding and extending a pattern and to graph transformations on a coordinate plane.

Lesson (pages)	Lesson Objectives	NCTM Standards 2000	Standardized Tests	State/Local Objectives
5-1 (184–186)	Read and write integers, and find the opposite and absolute value of an integer.	1, 6–10	MAT	
5-2 (188–190)	Compare and order integers.	1, 6–10	CAT, CTBS, MAT, TN	
5-3 (191–194)	Graph points on a coordinate plane.	1, 3, 6–10		
5-3B (195)	Graph points on a graphing calculator.	1, 3, 6–8		
5-4A (196)	Add integers by using models.	1, 6–10		
5-4 (197–200)	Add integers.	1, 2, 6–10	CAT, CTBS, ITBS, MAT, SAT, TN	
5-5A (201)	Subtract integers by using models.	1, 6–10		
5-5 (202–205)	Subtract integers.	1, 2, 6–10	CAT, CTBS, ITBS, MAT, SAT, TN	
5-6A (206)	Multiply integers by using models.	1, 6–10		
5-6 (207–209)	Multiply integers.	1, 2, 6–10	CAT, CTBS, ITBS, MAT, SAT, TN	
5-7A (210–211)	Solve problems by using the look-for-a-pattern strategy.	1, 2, 6–10	MAT	
5-7 (212–214)	Divide integers.	1, 2, 5–10	CAT, CTBS, ITBS, MAT, SAT, TN	
5-8 (215–217)	Graph transformations on a coordinate plane.	1–3, 6–10	CTBS, TN	

CAT = California Achievement Tests, CTBS = Comprehensive Tests of Basic Skills, ITBS = Iowa Tests of Basic Skills, MAT = Metropolitan Achievement Tests, SAT = Stanford Achievement Tests, TN = Terra Nova
For the key to numbering of NCTM Standards 2000, see page T6.

Organizing the Chapter

The **Interactive Lesson Planner** contains all of the blackline masters and transparencies. This CD-ROM also includes an easy-to-use lesson planning calendar.

LESSON PLANNING GUIDE

Lesson	Extra Practice (Student Edition)	Blackline Masters (Page Numbers)										Transparencies A and B
		Study Guide	Practice	Enrichment	Assessment & Evaluation	Classroom Games	Diversity	Hands-On Lab	School to Career	Science and Math Lab Manual	Technology	
5-1	p. 580	34	34	34								5-1
5-2	p. 580	35	35	35	127				18			5-2
5-3	p. 581	36	36	36				76				5-3
5-3B												
5-4A								46				
5-4	p. 581	37	37	37	126, 127						35	5-4
5-5A								47				
5-5	p. 581	38	38	38		13–15						5-5
5-6A								48				
5-6	p. 582	39	39	39	128					89–92		5-6
5-7A	p. 582											
5-7	p. 582	40	40	40			18				36	5-7
5-8	p. 583	41	41	41	128							5-8
Study Guide/ Assessment					113–125, 129–131							

Other Chapter Resources

Student Edition

Chapter Project, pp. 183, 190, 194, 205, 221
School to Career, p. 187
Let the Games Begin, pp. 192, 198

Technology

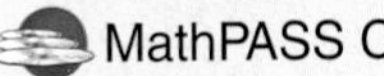
MathPASS CD-ROM
Interactive Mathematics Tools Software

Teacher's Classroom Resources

Applications
Family Letters and Activities, pp. 35–36
Investigations and Projects Masters, pp. 33–36

Meeting Individual Needs
Investigations for the Special Education Student, pp. 9–12

Teaching Aids
Answer Key Masters
Block Scheduling Booklet
Lesson Planning Guide
Solutions Manual

Professional Publications
Glencoe Mathematics Professional Series

Planning the Chapter

MindJogger Videoquizzes provide a unique format for reviewing concepts presented in the chapter.

Assessment Resources

Student Edition

Mixed Review, pp. 186, 190, 194, 200, 205, 209, 214, 217
Mid-Chapter Self Test, p. 205
Math Journal, pp. 193, 216
Study Guide and Assessment, pp. 218–221
Performance Task, p. 221
Portfolio Suggestion, p.221
Standardized Test Practice, pp. 222–223
Chapter Test, p. 611

Assessment and Evaluation Masters

Multiple-Choice Tests (Forms 1A, 1B, 1C), pp. 113–118
Free-Response Tests (Forms 2A, 2B, 2C), pp. 119–124
Performance Assessment, p. 125
Mid-Chapter Test, p. 126
Quizzes A–D, pp. 127–128
Standardized Test Practice, pp. 129–130
Cumulative Review, p. 131

Teacher's Wraparound Edition

5-Minute Check, pp. 184, 188, 191, 197, 202, 207, 212, 215
Building Portfolios, p. 182
Math Journal, pp. 195, 196, 201, 206
Closing Activity, pp. 186, 190, 194, 200, 205, 209, 211, 214, 217

Technology

Test and Review Software
MindJogger Videoquizzes
CD-ROM Program

Materials and Manipulatives

Lesson 5-3
grid paper†

Lesson 5-4A
counters*†
integer mat*†

Lesson 5-4
playing cards

Lesson 5-5A
counters*†
integer mat*†

Lesson 5-6A
counters*†
integer mat*†

Lesson 5-6
counters*†
integer mat*†

*Glencoe Manipulative Kit

†Glencoe Overhead Manipulative Resources

Pacing Chart

See pages T25–T27 for the Course Planning Calendar.

COURSE	DAY 1	DAY 2	DAY 3	DAY 4	DAY 5	DAY 6	DAY 7
Standard	Chapter Project	Lesson 5-1	Lesson 5-2	Lesson 5-3	Lessons 5-4A & 5-4		Lessons 5-5A & 5-5
Honors	Chapter Project	Lesson 5-1	Lesson 5-2	Lessons 5-3 & 5-3B		Lesson 5-4	Lesson 5-5
Block	Chapter Project & Lesson 5-1	Lessons 5-2 & 5-3	Lessons 5-4A & 5-4	Lessons 5-5A & 5-5	Lesson 5-6	Lessons 5-7A & 5-7	Lesson 5-8

Interactive Mathematics:
Activities and Investigations

is an activity-based program that may be used as an enhancement for chapters in ***Mathematics: Applications and Connections.***

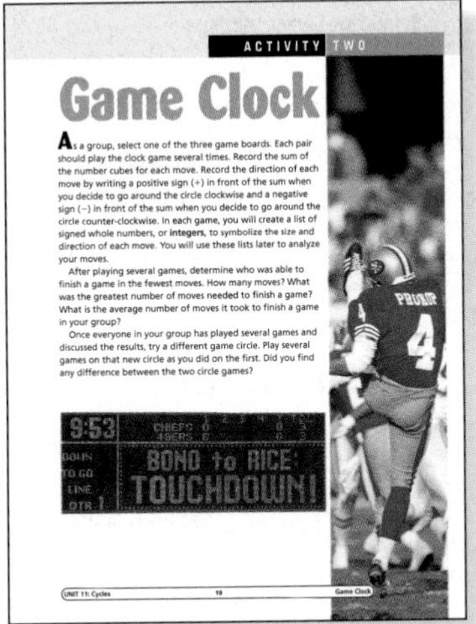
ACTIVITY TWO

Game Clock

As a group, select one of the three game boards. Each pair should play the clock game several times. Record the sum of the number cubes for each move. Record the direction of each move by writing a positive sign (+) in front of the sum when you decide to go around the circle clockwise and a negative sign (−) in front of the sum when you decide to go around the circle counter-clockwise. In each game, you will create a list of signed whole numbers, or **integers,** to symbolize the size and direction of each move. You will use these lists later to analyze your moves.

After playing several games, determine who was able to finish a game in the fewest moves. How many moves? What was the greatest number of moves needed to finish a game? What is the average number of moves it took to finish a game in your group?

Once everyone in your group has played several games and discussed the results, try a different game circle. Play several games on that new circle as you did on the first. Did you find any difference between the two circle games?

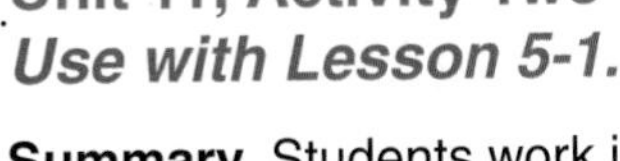

Unit 11, Activity Two
Use with Lesson 5-1.

Summary Students work in pairs to play a series of games involving different-sized clocks. Then they work in groups to make conjectures about how best to play the games, analyzing the possible strategies and performing clock arithmetic operations.

Math Connection Students develop an intuitive sense of clock arithmetic and operations with integers while playing a series of games and finding winning strategies. The major focus of this activity is the students' analysis of the methods used to play the games.

Unit 1, Activity Two, Menu E
Use with Lesson 5-7A.

Summary Students work in groups to make as many rectangles as they can using 48 tiles. They look for patterns and discuss their findings with other groups comparing similarities and differences in making these rectangles.

Math Connection Students explore patterns that exist in building squares and rectangles out of forty-eight 1-inch by 1-inch tiles. Then they discuss their findings concluding a mathematical relationship evidenced in the activity.

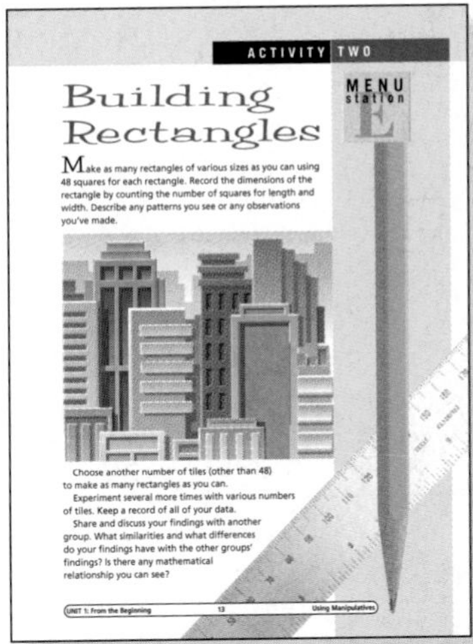
ACTIVITY TWO

MENU station E

Building Rectangles

Make as many rectangles of various sizes as you can using 48 squares for each rectangle. Record the dimensions of the rectangle by counting the number of squares for length and width. Describe any patterns you see or any observations you've made.

Choose another number of tiles (other than 48) to make as many rectangles as you can.

Experiment several more times with various numbers of tiles. Keep a record of all of your data.

Share and discuss your findings with another group. What similarities and what differences do your findings have with the other groups' findings? Is there any mathematical relationship you can see?

UNIT 1: From the Beginning 13 Using Manipulatives

DAY 8	DAY 9	DAY 10	DAY 11	DAY 12	DAY 13	DAY 14	DAY 15
(continue from day 7)	Lessons 5-6A & 5-6		Lesson 5-7A	Lesson 5-7	Lesson 5-8	Study Guide and Assessment	Chapter Test
Lesson 5-6	Lesson 5-7A	Lesson 5-7	Lesson 5-8	Study Guide and Assessment	Chapter Test		
Study Guide and Assessment, Chapter Test							

Enhancing the Chapter

APPLICATIONS

Classroom Games, pp. 13–15

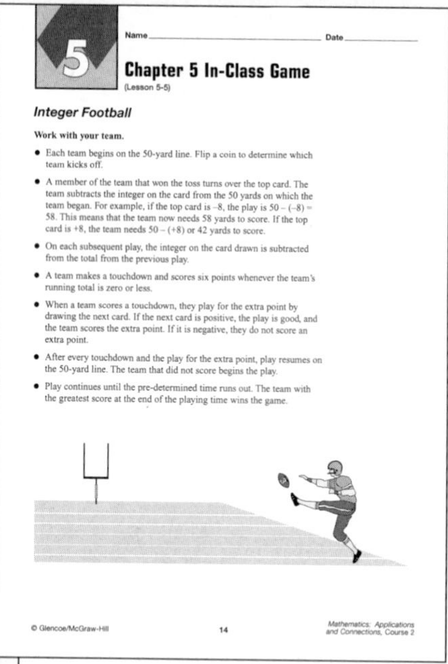

Name ____ Date ____

5 **Chapter 5 In-Class Game** (Lesson 5-5)

Integer Football

Work with your team.

- Each team begins on the 50-yard line. Flip a coin to determine which team kicks off.
- A member of the team that won the toss turns over the top card. The team subtracts the integer on the card from the 50 yards on which the team began. For example, if the top card is –8, the play is 50 – (–8) = 58. This means that the team now needs 58 yards to score. If the top card is +8, the team needs 50 – (+8) or 42 yards to score.
- On each subsequent play, the integer on the card drawn is subtracted from the total from the previous play.
- A team makes a touchdown and scores six points whenever the team's running total is zero or less.
- When a team scores a touchdown, they play for the extra point by drawing the next card. If the next card is positive, the play is good, and the team scores the extra point. If it is negative, they do not score an extra point.
- After every touchdown and the play for the extra point, play resumes on the 50-yard line. The team that did not score begins the play.
- Play continues until the pre-determined time runs out. The team with the greatest score at the end of the playing time wins the game.

© Glencoe/McGraw-Hill 14 Mathematics: Applications and Connections, Course 2

Diversity Masters, p. 18

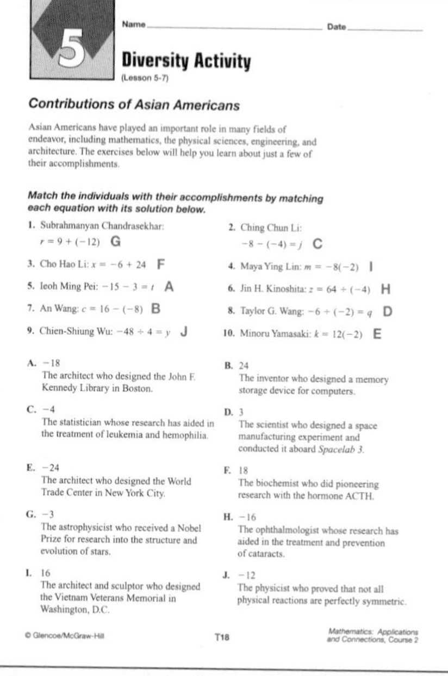

Name ____ Date ____

5 **Diversity Activity** (Lesson 5-7)

Contributions of Asian Americans

Asian Americans have played an important role in many fields of endeavor, including mathematics, the physical sciences, engineering, and architecture. The exercises below will help you learn about just a few of their accomplishments.

Match the individuals with their accomplishments by matching each equation with its solution below.

1. Subrahmanyan Chandrasekhar: $r = 9 + (-12)$ G
2. Ching Chun Li: $-8 - (-4) = j$ C
3. Cho Hao Li: $x = -6 + 24$ F
4. Maya Ying Lin: $m = -8(-2)$ I
5. Ieoh Ming Pei: $-15 - 3 = t$ A
6. Jin H. Kinoshita: $z = 64 \div (-4)$ H
7. An Wang: $c = 16 - (-8)$ B
8. Taylor G. Wang: $-6 \div (-2) = q$ D
9. Chien-Shiung Wu: $-48 \div 4 = y$ J
10. Minoru Yamasaki: $k = 12(-2)$ E

A. –18 The architect who designed the John F. Kennedy Library in Boston.

B. 24 The inventor who designed a memory storage device for computers.

C. –4 The statistician whose research has aided in the treatment of leukemia and hemophilia.

D. 3 The scientist who designed a space manufacturing experiment and conducted it aboard *Spacelab 3*.

E. –24 The architect who designed the World Trade Center in New York City.

F. 18 The biochemist who did pioneering research with the hormone ACTH.

G. –3 The astrophysicist who received a Nobel Prize for research into the structure and evolution of stars.

H. –16 The ophthalmologist whose research has aided in the treatment and prevention of cataracts.

I. 16 The architect and sculptor who designed the Vietnam Veterans Memorial in Washington, D.C.

J. –12 The physicist who proved that not all physical reactions are perfectly symmetric.

© Glencoe/McGraw-Hill T18 Mathematics: Applications and Connections, Course 2

School to Career Masters, p. 18

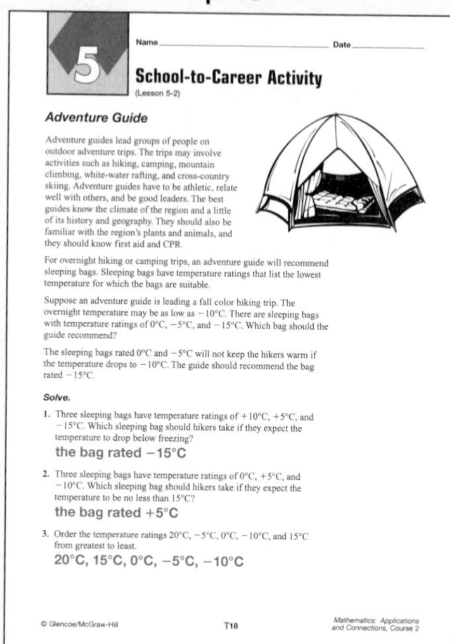

Name ____ Date ____

5 **School-to-Career Activity** (Lesson 5-2)

Adventure Guide

Adventure guides lead groups of people on outdoor adventure trips. The trips may involve activities such as hiking, camping, mountain climbing, white-water rafting, and cross-country skiing. Adventure guides have to be athletic, relate well with others, and be good leaders. The best guides know the climate of the region and a little of its history and geography. They should also be familiar with the region's plants and animals, and they should know first aid and CPR.

For overnight hiking or camping trips, an adventure guide will recommend sleeping bags. Sleeping bags have temperature ratings that list the lowest temperature for which the bags are suitable.

Suppose an adventure guide is leading a fall color hiking trip. The overnight temperature may be as low as –10°C. There are sleeping bags with temperature ratings of 0°C, –5°C, and –15°C. Which bag should the guide recommend?

The sleeping bags rated 0°C and –5°C will not keep the hikers warm if the temperature drops to –10°C. The guide should recommend the bag rated –15°C.

Solve.

1. Three sleeping bags have temperature ratings of +10°C, +5°C, and –15°C. Which sleeping bag should hikers take if they expect the temperature to drop below freezing? **the bag rated –15°C**
2. Three sleeping bags have temperature ratings of 0°C, +5°C, and –10°C. Which sleeping bag should hikers take if they expect the temperature to be no less than 15°C? **the bag rated +5°C**
3. Order the temperature ratings 20°C, –5°C, 0°C, –10°C, and 15°C from greatest to least. **20°C, 15°C, 0°C, –5°C, –10°C**

© Glencoe/McGraw-Hill T18 Mathematics: Applications and Connections, Course 2

Family Letters and Activities, pp. 35–36

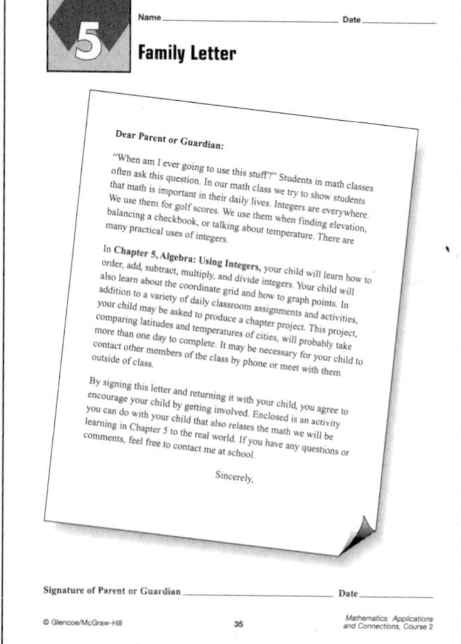

Name ____ Date ____

5 **Family Letter**

Dear Parent or Guardian:

"When am I ever going to use this stuff?" Students in math classes often ask this question. In our math class we try to show students that math is important in their daily lives. Integers are everywhere. We use them for golf scores. We use them when finding elevation, balancing a checkbook, or talking about temperature. There are many practical uses of integers.

In **Chapter 5, Algebra: Using Integers,** your child will learn how to order, add, subtract, multiply, and divide integers. Your child will also learn about the coordinate grid and how to graph points. In addition to a variety of daily classroom assignments and activities, your child may be asked to produce a chapter project. This project, comparing latitudes and temperatures of cities, will probably take more than one day to complete. It may be necessary for your child to contact other members of the class by phone or meet with them outside of class.

By signing this letter and returning it with your child, you agree to encourage your child by getting involved. Enclosed is an activity you can do with your child that also relates the math we will be learning in Chapter 5 to the real world. If you have any questions or comments, feel free to contact me at school.

Sincerely,

Signature of Parent or Guardian ____ Date ____

© Glencoe/McGraw-Hill 35 Mathematics: Applications and Connections, Course 2

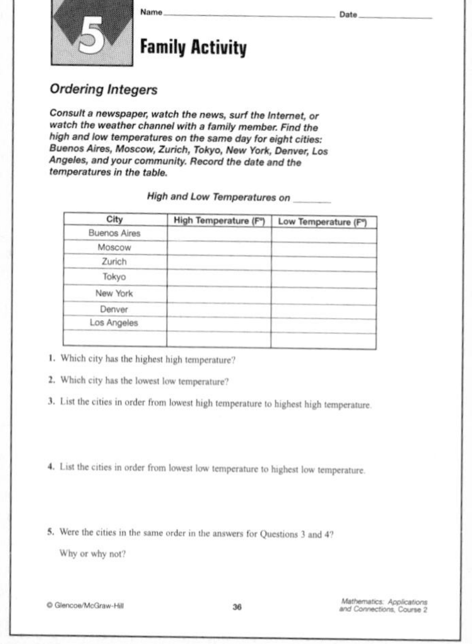

Name ____ Date ____

5 **Family Activity**

Ordering Integers

Consult a newspaper, watch the news, surf the Internet, or watch the weather channel with a family member. Find the high and low temperatures on the same day for eight cities: Buenos Aires, Moscow, Zurich, Tokyo, New York, Denver, Los Angeles, and your community. Record the date and the temperatures in the table.

High and Low Temperatures on ____

City	High Temperature (F°)	Low Temperature (F°)
Buenos Aires		
Moscow		
Zurich		
Tokyo		
New York		
Denver		
Los Angeles		

1. Which city has the highest high temperature?
2. Which city has the lowest low temperature?
3. List the cities in order from lowest high temperature to highest high temperature.
4. List the cities in order from lowest low temperature to highest low temperature.
5. Were the cities in the same order in the answers for Questions 3 and 4? Why or why not?

© Glencoe/McGraw-Hill 36 Mathematics: Applications and Connections, Course 2

Science and Math Lab Manual, pp. 89–92

Name ____ Date ____

23 **Science and Mathematics Lab** (Course 1, Lesson 11-5; Course 2, Lesson 5-6; Course 3, Lesson 2-7)

Pulleys (continued)

PROCEDURE

Part 1 Single Fixed Pulley

1. Attach the utility clamp to the top of the ring stand. Attach one of the pulleys to the utility clamp with the 10-cm long wire tie.
2. Tie a small loop at each end of the 1-m length of string. Then thread the string through the pulley.
3. Tightly wind the 30-cm wire tie to the 0.5-kg mass. Use the tie to attach the 0.5-kg mass to the spring scale. Record its weight in newtons (N) under Resistance Force in the Data Table.
4. Remove the mass from the spring scale and attach it to one loop of the pulley string. Attach the other loop of the string to the spring scale.
5. Pull the spring scale straight down and measure the force needed to lift the mass 15 cm. Record this value as Effort Force in the Data Table.
6. Measure the length of string required to lift the mass 15 cm. Record this value as Effort Distance in the Data Table.

Part 2 Block and Tackle

1. Remove the 0.5-kg mass and spring scale from the string.
2. Attach the string to the second pulley and thread the string through the pulleys as shown in the figure on page 90.
3. Measure the weight of the 0.5-kg mass by attaching the mass to the spring scale. Record this value in the Data Table under Resistance Force.
4. Attach the mass to the second pulley and then attach the spring scale to the loop on the free end of the string. Pull the scale straight up.
5. Measure the force needed to lift the mass 15 cm and record it in the Data Table.
6. Measure the distance the scale moved to lift the mass 15 cm and record it in the Data Table as Effort Distance.

© Glencoe/McGraw-Hill 91 Mathematics: Applications and Connections

MANIPULATIVES/MODELING

Hands-On Lab Masters, p. 76

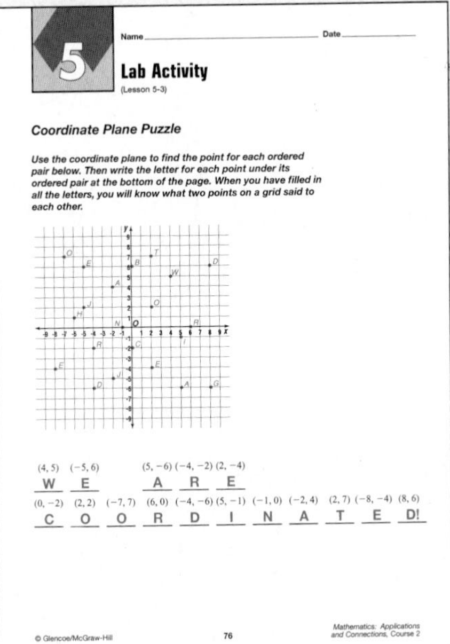

5 Name ________ Date ________

Lab Activity
(Lesson 5-3)

Coordinate Plane Puzzle

Use the coordinate plane to find the point for each ordered pair below. Then write the letter for each point under its ordered pair at the bottom of the page. When you have filled in all the letters, you will know what two points on a grid said to each other.

(4, 5) (−5, 6) (5, −6) (−4, −2) (2, −4)
W E A R E
(0, −2) (2, 2) (−7, 7) (6, 0) (−4, −6) (5, −1) (−1, 0) (−2, 4) (2, 7) (−8, −4) (8, 6)
C O O R D I N A T E D!

© Glencoe/McGraw-Hill 76 Mathematics: Applications and Connections, Course 2

ASSESSMENT/EVALUATION

Assessment and Evaluation Masters, pp. 126–128

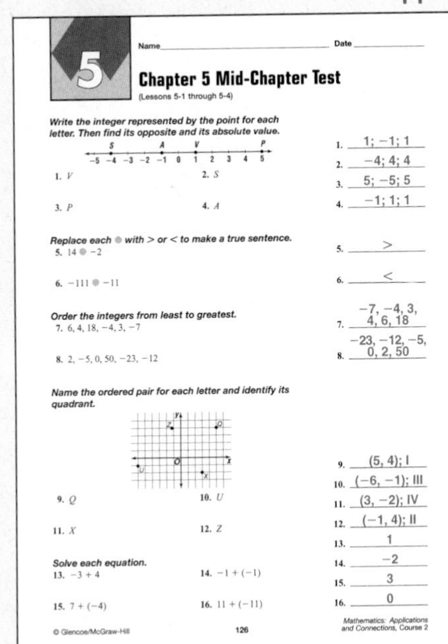

5 Name ________ Date ________

Chapter 5 Mid-Chapter Test
(Lessons 5-1 through 5-4)

Write the integer represented by the point for each letter. Then find its opposite and its absolute value.

1. V 2. S 3. P 4. A

1. 1; −1; 1
2. −4; 4; 4
3. 5; −5; 5
4. −1; 1; 1

Replace each ● with > or < to make a true sentence.

5. 14 ● −2 6. −111 ● −11

5. >
6. <

Order the integers from least to greatest.

7. 6, 4, 18, −4, 3, −7
8. 2, −5, 0, 50, −23, −12

7. −7, −4, 3, 4, 6, 18
8. −23, −12, −5, 0, 2, 50

Name the ordered pair for each letter and identify its quadrant.

9. Q 10. U 11. X 12. Z

9. (5, 4); I
10. (−6, −1); III
11. (3, −2); IV
12. (−1, 4); II

Solve each equation.

13. −3 + 4 14. −1 + (−1) 15. 7 + (−4) 16. 11 + (−11)

13. 1
14. −2
15. 3
16. 0

© Glencoe/McGraw-Hill 126 Mathematics: Applications and Connections, Course 2

Name ________ Date ________

Chapter 5 Quiz A (Lessons 5-1 and 5-2)

Find the opposite and absolute value of each integer.
1. −19 2. 25 3. −7

1. 19, 19
2. −25, 25
3. 7, 7

Order the integers from least to greatest.
4. 3, 0, −2, 4, −4, −1
5. 3, −9, −3, 9, 4, 0
6. 7, −2, 2, 1, −9, 8

4. −4, −2, −1, 0, 3, 4
5. −9, −3, 0, 3, 4, 9
6. −9, −2, 1, 2, 7, 8

Replace each ● with < or > to make a true sentence.
7. −34 ● −134
8. −27 ● −8
9. 12 ● −12
10. −111 ● −888

7. >
8. <
9. >
10. >

Name ________ Date ________

Chapter 5 Quiz B (Lessons 5-3 and 5-4)

On the coordinate plane, graph and label each point.
1. S(1, 0)
2. R(−3, −1)
3. T(3, −2)

Solve each equation.
4. $a = -25 + (-12)$
5. $6 + (-9) = b$

4. −37
5. −3

© Glencoe/McGraw-Hill 127 Mathematics: Applications and Connections, Course 2

TECHNOLOGY/MULTIMEDIA

Technology Masters, pp. 35–36

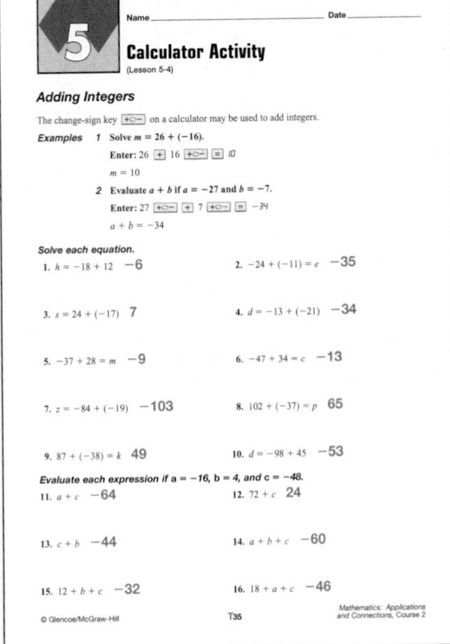

5 Name ________ Date ________

Calculator Activity
(Lesson 5-4)

Adding Integers

The change-sign key [+⁄−] on a calculator may be used to add integers.

Examples 1 Solve $m = 26 + (-16)$.
Enter: 26 [+] 16 [+⁄−] [=] 10
$m = 10$

2 Evaluate $a + b$ if $a = -27$ and $b = -7$.
Enter: 27 [+⁄−] [+] 7 [+⁄−] [=] −34
$a + b = -34$

Solve each equation.

1. $h = -18 + 12$ −6
2. $-24 + (-11) = e$ −35
3. $s = 24 + (-17)$ 7
4. $d = -13 + (-21)$ −34
5. $-37 + 28 = m$ −9
6. $-47 + 34 = c$ −13
7. $z = -84 + (-19)$ −103
8. $102 + (-37) = p$ 65
9. $87 + (-38) = k$ 49
10. $d = -98 + 45$ −53

Evaluate each expression if a = −16, b = 4, and c = −48.

11. $a + c$ −64
12. $72 + c$ 24
13. $c + b$ −44
14. $a + b + c$ −60
15. $12 + b + c$ −32
16. $18 + a + c$ −46

© Glencoe/McGraw-Hill T35 Mathematics: Applications and Connections, Course 2

5 Name ________ Date ________

Graphing Calculator Activity
(Lesson 5-7)

Calculating with Integers

You can solve problems involving integers on a graphing calculator. When a number is positive, you do not need to enter a sign. But when a number is negative, use the [(−)] key before you enter the number.

Examples 1 Solve $v = 6 + (-10)$.
Enter: 6 [+] [(−)] 10 [ENTER] −4
So, $6 + (-10) = (-4)$.

2 Solve $-24 \div (-3) = x$.
Enter: [(−)] 24 [÷] [(−)] 3 [ENTER] 8
So, $-24 \div (-3) = 8$.

3 Evaluate $g - t$ if $g = -4$ and $t = -1$.
Enter: [(−)] 4 [−] [(−)] 1 [ENTER] −3
So, $g - t = -3$ when $g = -4$ and $t = -1$.

Solve each equation.

1. $-8 + 16 = c$ 8
2. $s = 4 + (-11)$ −7
3. $-5 \cdot 17 = h$ −85
4. $b = 6 - 12$ −6
5. $48 \div (-3) = t$ −16
6. $u = -3 - (-9)$ 6
7. $y = -12 \cdot (-11)$ 132
8. $w = -36 + (-11)$ −47
9. $-84 \div (-3) = s$ 28

Evaluate each expression if x = 4, y = −5, and z = −1.

10. $15 - x$ 11
11. $y - (-4)$ −1
12. $-10 \cdot z$ 10
13. $0 \cdot y$ 0
14. $z + (-6)$ −7
15. $14 \div (-z)$ 14
16. $x + y$ −1
17. $-y + z$ −5
18. $x + y \cdot z$ 9
19. $x \div (-z)$ 4
20. $x \cdot y \div (-2)$ 10
21. $x \cdot y \cdot z$ 20

© Glencoe/McGraw-Hill T36 Mathematics: Applications and Connections, Course 2

MEETING INDIVIDUAL NEEDS

Investigations for the Special Education Student, pp. 9–12

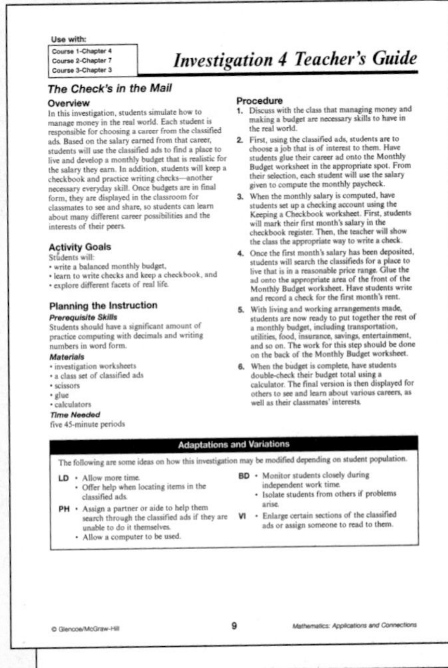

Use with:
Course 1-Chapter 4
Course 2-Chapter 7
Course 3-Chapter 3

Investigation 4 Teacher's Guide

The Check's in the Mail

Overview
In this investigation, students simulate how to manage money in the real world. Each student is responsible for choosing a career from the classified ads. Based on the salary earned from that career, students will use the classified ads to find a place to live and develop a monthly budget that is realistic for the salary they earn. In addition, students will keep a checkbook and practice writing checks—another necessary everyday skill. Once budgets are in final form, they are displayed in the classroom for classmates to see and share, so students can learn about many different career possibilities and the interests of their peers.

Activity Goals
Students will:
• write a balanced monthly budget,
• learn to write checks and keep a checkbook, and
• explore different facets of real life.

Planning the Instruction
Prerequisite Skills
Students should have a significant amount of practice computing with decimals and writing numbers in word form.
Materials
• investigation worksheets
• a class set of classified ads
• scissors
• glue
• calculators
Time Needed
five 45-minute periods

Procedure
1. Discuss with the class that managing money and making a budget are necessary skills to have in the real world.
2. First, using the classified ads, students are to choose a job that is of interest to them. Have students glue their career ad onto the Monthly Budget worksheet in the appropriate spot. From their selection, each student will use the salary given to compute the monthly paycheck.
3. When the monthly salary is computed, have students set up a checking account using the Keeping a Checkbook worksheet. First, students will mark their first month's salary in the checkbook register. Then, the teacher will show the class the appropriate way to write a check.
4. Once the first month's salary has been deposited, students will search the classifieds for a place to live that is in a reasonable price range. Glue the ad onto the appropriate area of the front of the Monthly Budget worksheet. Have students write and record a check for the first month's rent.
5. With living and working arrangements made, students are now ready to put together the rest of a monthly budget, including transportation, utilities, food, insurance, savings, entertainment, and so on. The work for this step should be done on the back of the Monthly Budget worksheet.
6. When the budget is complete, have students double-check their budget total using a calculator. The final version is then displayed for others to see and learn about various careers, as well as their classmates' interests.

Adaptations and Variations

The following are some ideas on how this investigation may be modified depending on student population.

LD • Allow more time.
• Offer help when locating items in the classified ads.
PH • Assign a partner or aide to help them search through the classified ads if they are unable to do it themselves.
• Allow a computer to be used.
BD • Monitor students closely during independent work time.
• Isolate students from others if problems arise.
VI • Enlarge certain sections of the classified ads or assign someone to read to them.

© Glencoe/McGraw-Hill 9 Mathematics: Applications and Connections

CHAPTER 5 NOTES

Theme: Meteorology

A disruption of the atmosphere in the tropical Pacific is called an El Niño. This disruption can cause weather disturbances around the globe, such as flooding in the southern U.S. and Peru, droughts on lands in the west Pacific, and brush fires in Australia. A network of buoys in the ocean measures temperature, ocean currents, and winds, and transmits the data to forecasters.

Question of the Day The temperature at 9:00 P.M. was 8°F. By 11:00 P.M., the temperature dropped by 20°F. What was the temperature at 11:00 P.M.? −12°F

Assess Prerequisite Skills

Ask students to read through the list of objectives presented in "What you'll learn in Chapter 5." You may wish to ask them what each of the objectives means or if they have experienced or used any of these math concepts before.

Building Portfolios

Encourage students to revise their portfolios as they study this chapter. They may wish to include work that shows their mastery of the concepts in Chapter 5.

Math and the Family

In the *Family Letters and Activities* booklet (pp. 35–36), you will find a letter to the parents explaining what students will study in Chapter 5. An activity appropriate for the whole family is also available.

CHAPTER 5 Algebra: Using Integers

What you'll learn in Chapter 5

- to read, write, and compare integers and find the opposite and absolute value of an integer,
- to graph points on a coordinate plane,
- to add, subtract, multiply, and divide integers,
- to solve problems by looking for a pattern, and
- to graph transformations on a coordinate plane.

CD-ROM Program

Activities for Chapter 5

- Interactive Lessons 5-4, 5-5, 5-6, 5-8
- Extended Activity 5-3
- Assessment Game
- Resource Lessons 5-1 through 5-8

LATITUDE VS. TEMPERATURE

In this project, you will make a table comparing latitudes and temperatures of cities. You will graph the data and determine whether there is a relationship between the latitude of cities in the United States and their temperatures. You will then write a paragraph summarizing your findings, describing any relationships or patterns that you noticed.

Getting Started

- Look at the table of cities. Which city had the highest temperature in 1995? Which city had the lowest temperature?
- The higher the latitude number is, the farther the location is from the equator. Use the table to determine which city is closest to the equator. Which city is farthest from the equator?

City	Latitude (nearest degree)	High Temp. (°F, 1995)	Low Temp. (°F, 1995)
New York, NY	41	102	6
Honolulu, HI	21	94	56
Fairbanks, AK	65	88	−48
Seattle, WA	48	96	22
Nashville, TN	36	99	9
San Diego, CA	33	90	43
Bismarck, ND	47	98	−28
Atlanta, GA	34	102	13
Minneapolis, MN	45	101	−11
Denver, CO	40	99	−7

Source: *The World Almanac and Book of Facts*

Technology Tips

- Use a **spreadsheet** to organize your data and to find the difference between the highest and lowest temperatures.
- Use **computer software** to make graphs.
- Use a **word processor** to summarize and analyze your data.

Research For up-to-date information on geography, visit:

www.glencoe.com/sec/math/mac/mathnet

Working on the Project

You can use what you'll learn in Chapter 5 to help you make your graph.

Page	Exercise
190	25
194	33
205	45
221	Alternative Assessment

interNET CONNECTION

Glencoe has made every effort to ensure that the website links for *Mathematics: Applications and Connections* at www.glencoe.com/sec/math/mac/mathnet are current and contain appropriate content. However, these website links are not under Glencoe's control.

Instructional Resources ▶▶▶

A recording sheet to help students organize their data for the Chapter Project is shown at the right and is available in the *Investigations and Projects Masters,* p. 36.

CHAPTER Project NOTES

Objectives Students should

- use integers to compare highest and lowest temperatures.
- determine whether there is a relationship between latitude and temperature.

Project Pointer You may suggest that students begin a *Project Folder* to keep their work as they complete each stage of the Chapter Project. The completed project may also be added to their portfolios.

Using the Table Encourage students to compare the data about the cities in different ways, such as by listing in order of temperature and by graphing the data in different ways, before drawing any conclusions.

Investigations and Projects Masters, **p. 36**

Name ____________ Date ______

5 Chapter 5 Project

Latitude vs. Temperature

Page 190, Working on the Chapter Project, Exercise 25

City	Latitude	Low Temp. (°F)

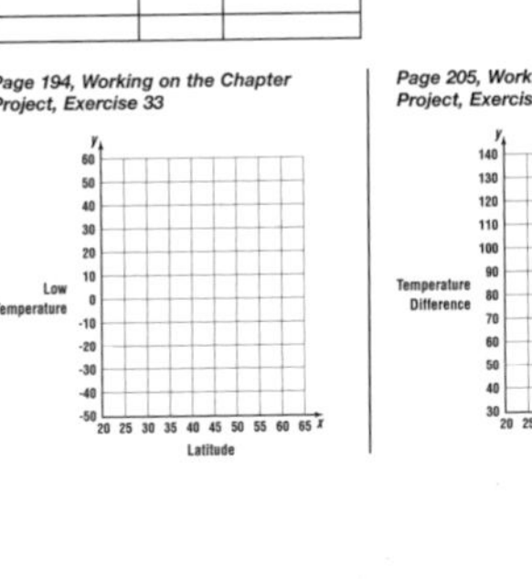

Page 194, Working on the Chapter Project, Exercise 33

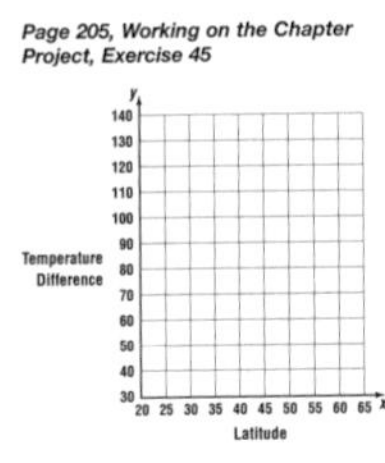

Page 205, Working on the Chapter Project, Exercise 45

 36 *Mathematics: Applications and Connections, Course 2*

5-1 Lesson Notes

Instructional Resources

- *Study Guide Masters,* p. 34
- *Practice Masters,* p. 34
- *Enrichment Masters,* p. 34
- Transparencies 5-1, A and B

CD-ROM Program
- Resource Lesson 5-1

Recommended Pacing	
Standard	Day 2 of 15
Honors	Day 2 of 13
Block	Day 1 of 8

1 FOCUS

5-Minute Check
(Chapter 4)

1. Determine whether 530 is divisible by 2, 3, 4, 5, 6, 9, or 10. **divisible by 2, 5, 10**
2. Identify the sequence as *arithmetic, geometric,* or *neither.* Then find the next three terms. 4, 12, 36, 108, . . . **geometric; 324; 972; 2,916**
3. Express $\frac{33}{60}$ in simplest form. $\frac{11}{20}$
4. Express 0.45 as a fraction in simplest form. $\frac{9}{20}$
5. Find the LCM for 8, 12, and 20. **120**

The 5-Minute Check is also available on **Transparency 5-1A** for this lesson.

Motivating the Lesson

Problem Solving Ask students to name the number with the greater absolute value: a rise in the Dow Jones Industrial Average of 31 points, or a loss of 37 points. **37**

5-1 Integers

What you'll learn

You'll learn to read and write integers and to find the opposite and absolute value of an integer.

When am I ever going to use this?

You can use integers to keep score in sports.

Word Wise

integer
positive integer
negative integer
opposite
absolute value

After the 1990 census, Texas gained 3 seats in the United States House of Representatives. Michigan lost 2 seats. You can use the **integers** $+3$ and -2 to describe these situations, respectively.

Integers	An integer is any number from the set {. . . , −4, −3, −2, −1, 0, +1, +2, +3, +4, . . .}.

Integers greater than 0 are **positive integers**. Integers less than 0 are **negative integers**. Zero is neither positive nor negative. Positive integers usually are written without the + sign, so +5 and 5 are the same. You can represent integers using counters or a number line.

Method 1 Counters

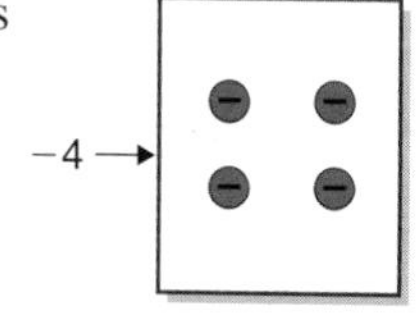

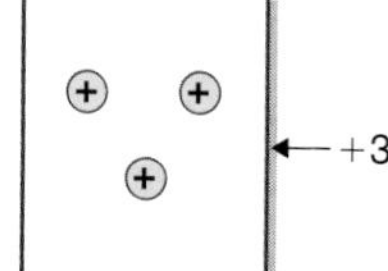

Method 2 Number Line

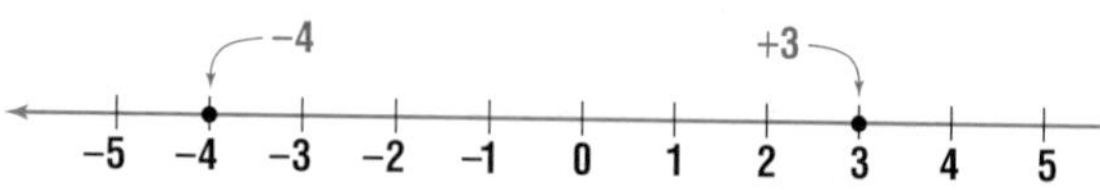

Example APPLICATION Real World

1 **Games** ***Mancala*** **is an African game that is over 3,000 years old. The object is for a player to capture the opponent's stones. Suppose a player removes 12 opponent's stones. Write an integer for this situation.**

Since there is a decrease in stones, the negative integer, -12, represents this situation.

Study Hint

Technology To enter a negative integer on a calculator, use the [+◌−] key. For example, to enter −5, press 5 [+◌−].

Two numbers are **opposites** of one another if they are represented by points that are the same distance from 0, but on opposite sides of 0. The number line below shows that -4 and 4 are opposites.

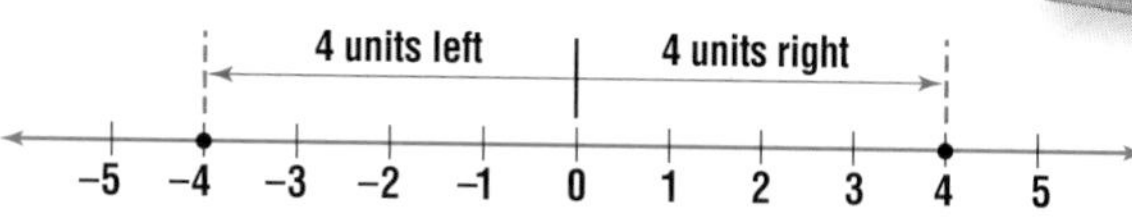

Cross-Curriculum Cue

Inform other teachers that your classes are studying integers. Suggestions for curriculum integration are:
Earth Science: temperature
Social Studies: stock market
Language Arts: antonyms
Health: weight gain and loss

Absolute value is helpful when adding integers.

Remember, distance is never negative.

Absolute Value	The absolute value of an integer is its distance from 0 on a number line.

The absolute value of n is written as $|n|$. So, $|-4| = 4$ and $|4| = 4$.

Example 2

a. Find the opposite of −8.
b. Find the absolute value of −8.

a. On the number line, −8 is at the point 8 units to the left of 0. The opposite of −8 would be at the point 8 units to the right of 0.

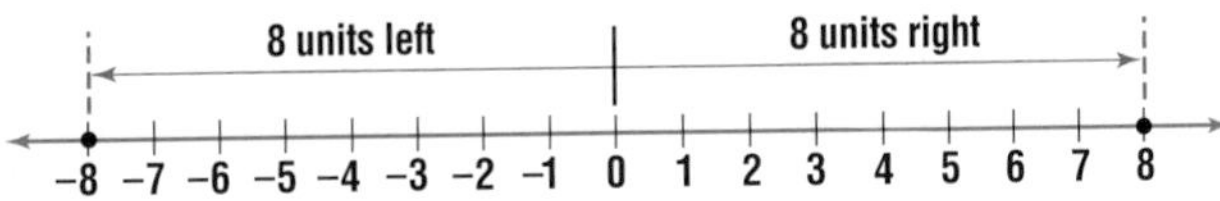

So, the opposite of −8 is 8.

b. The point that represents −8 is 8 units from 0, so the absolute value of −8 is 8. Write $|-8| = 8$.

CHECK FOR UNDERSTANDING

Communicating Mathematics

Read and study the lesson to answer each question.

1. ***Tell*** why −7.5 is not an integer. **It has a decimal part.**
2. ***Write*** each of the following as an integer over a whole number. **See margin.**
   $7, -3, 2\frac{1}{3}, -1\frac{1}{2}, 0, 0.029, -2.5$
3. ***You Decide*** Conner says that the integers represented by A and B are opposites. Keisha thinks they are not. Who is correct? Explain.

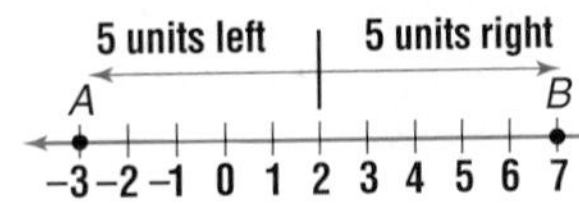

3. Keisha; −3 and 7 are not the same distance from 0.

Guided Practice

Write an integer for each situation.

4. a loss of 6 yards **−6**
5. a profit of \$5 **+5**
6. a deposit of \$10 **+10**
7. 76°F below 0 **−76**

Write the integer represented by the point for each letter. Then find its opposite and its absolute value.

8. C **−4, 4, 4**
9. E **7, −7, 7**
10. ***Football*** On one play, the Baltimore Ravens gained 18 yards. On the next play, they lost 10 yards. Write integers to represent the yards gained and lost. **+18, −10**

2 TEACH

Transparency 5-1B contains a teaching aid for this lesson.

Using Applications Have students come up with as many real-world applications of integers as they can. Ask them to give an example of each.

In-Class Examples

For Example 1

Keenan gained 8 pounds during weight training. Write an integer for this situation. **+8**

For Example 2

a. Find the opposite of −22. **22**

b. Find the absolute value of −22. **22**

3 PRACTICE/APPLY

Check for Understanding

If students need additional practice or instruction after completing Exercises 1–10, one of these options may be helpful.

- Extra Practice, see p. 580
- Reteaching Activity
- *Study Guide Masters,* p. 34
- *Practice Masters,* p. 34
- Interactive Mathematics Tools Software

***Study Guide Masters,* p. 34**

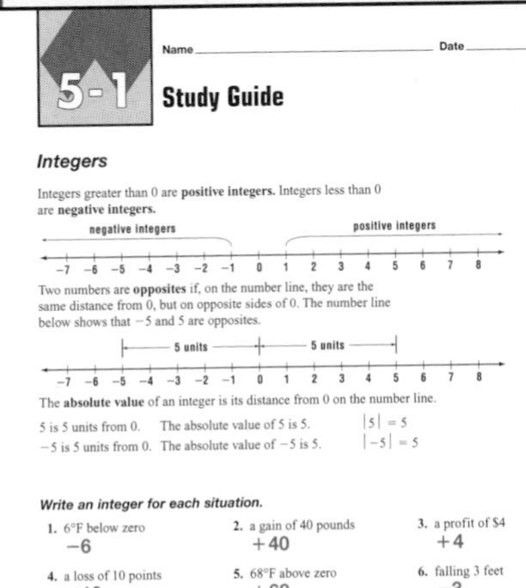

Name ______ Date ______

5-1 Study Guide

Integers

Integers greater than 0 are **positive integers.** Integers less than 0 are **negative integers.**

negative integers — positive integers

−7 −6 −5 −4 −3 −2 −1 0 1 2 3 4 5 6 7 8

Two numbers are **opposites** if, on the number line, they are the same distance from 0, but on opposite sides of 0. The number line below shows that −5 and 5 are opposites.

5 units — 5 units

−7 −6 −5 −4 −3 −2 −1 0 1 2 3 4 5 6 7 8

The **absolute value** of an integer is its distance from 0 on the number line.

5 is 5 units from 0. The absolute value of 5 is 5. $|5| = 5$
−5 is 5 units from 0. The absolute value of −5 is 5. $|-5| = 5$

Write an integer for each situation.

1. 6°F below zero **−6**
2. a gain of 40 pounds **+40**
3. a profit of \$4 **+4**
4. a loss of 10 points **−10**
5. 68°F above zero **+68**
6. falling 3 feet **−3**

Write the integer represented by the point for each letter. Then find its opposite and its absolute value.

Q Z S V Y R W T X
−7 −6 −5 −4 −3 −2 −1 0 1 2 3 4 5 6 7 8

7. Q **−7; 7; 7**
8. R **2; −2; 2**
9. S **−4; 4; 4**
10. T **6; −6; 6**
11. V **−1; 1 1**
12. W **3; −3; 3**
13. X **8; −8; 8**
14. Y **0; 0; 0**
15. Z **−6; 6; 6**

T34
Mathematics: Applications and Connections, Course 2

Reteaching the Lesson

Activity Have students think of absolute value as a distance and relate it to a common activity, such as riding in an elevator or playing football. Guide students to see, for example, that the same distance is traveled whether the elevator goes up 3 floors (+3) or down 3 floors (−3).

Additional Answer

2. $\frac{7}{1}, \frac{-3}{1}, \frac{7}{3}, \frac{-3}{2}, \frac{0}{1}, \frac{29}{1{,}000}, \frac{-5}{2}$

Assignment Guide

Core: 11–33 odd, 34–38
Enriched: 12–30 even, 31–38

4 ASSESS

Closing Activity

Speaking Have students use two integers and the terms *integers*, *opposites*, and *absolute value* in a sentence that explains the relationship of the three terms.

Additional Answer

33c. odd number of times, the result is negative; even number of times, the result is positive

Practice Masters, p. 34

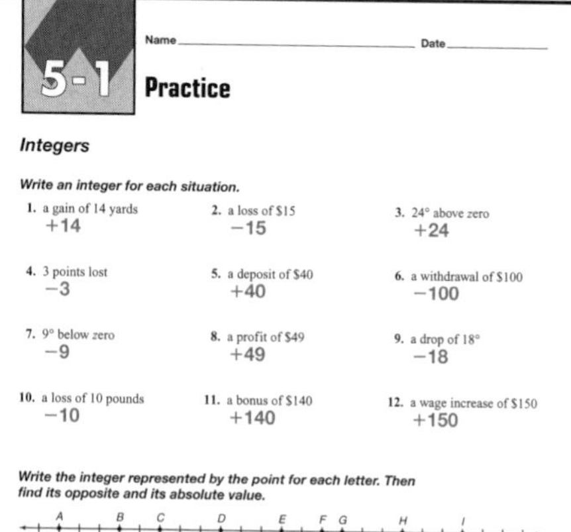
5-1 Practice

Name__________ Date__________

Integers

Write an integer for each situation.

1. a gain of 14 yards +14
2. a loss of \$15 −15
3. 24° above zero +24
4. 3 points lost −3
5. a deposit of \$40 +40
6. a withdrawal of \$100 −100
7. 9° below zero −9
8. a profit of \$49 +49
9. a drop of 18° −18
10. a loss of 10 pounds −10
11. a bonus of \$140 +140
12. a wage increase of \$150 +150

Write the integer represented by the point for each letter. Then find its opposite and its absolute value.

13. A −11; 11; 11
14. B −8; 8; 8
15. C −6; 6; 6
16. D −3; 3; 3
17. E 0; 0; 0
18. F 2; −2; 2
19. G 3; −3; 3
20. H 6; −6; 6
21. I 9; −9; 9
22. What is the least positive integer? 1
23. A submarine is 2,000 meters below sea level. Write this depth as an integer. −2,000

 T34 *Mathematics: Applications and Connections, Course 2*

EXERCISES

Practice

Write an integer for each situation.

11. a gain of 9 points **+9**
12. a withdrawal of \$25 **−25**
13. 120 feet below sea level **−120**
14. 8°C **+8**
15. the year A.D. 1600 **+1600**
16. 3 seconds before liftoff **−3**
17. down 4 strokes **−4**
18. a growth of 2 inches **+2**
19. no gain on 1st down **0**
20. the year 130 B.C. **−130**
21. 15° F above 0 **+15**
22. a gain of 11 pounds **+11**

Write the integer represented by the point for each letter. Then find its opposite and its absolute value.

23. A **−1, 1, 1**
24. B **−9, 9 9**
25. C **0, 0, 0**
26. D **5, −5, 5**
27. E **7, −7, 7**
28. F **−6, 6, 6**
29. What is the absolute value of 0? **0**
30. Find $|x|$ if $x = -10$. **10**

Real World

Applications and Problem Solving

31. 3,212; −8,685

31. ***Geography*** Angel Falls in Venezuela is 3,212 feet above sea level. The Caribbean Sea, which borders Venezuela on the north, has an average depth of 8,685 feet below sea level. Use integers to express these elevations.
32. ***Recreation*** In a travel game, the first person to identify a certain car by color gets 1 point. A certain van is worth 3 points. If you make a mistake, such as getting the color wrong or not seeing the car at all, you lose the points. On a recent trip, Raylene's dad intentionally missed two cars and one van. Use integers to express each of his scores. **−1, −1, −3**
33. ***Calculators*** If you press 7 [+○−], you get −7.
    a. What is the result when you press 7 [+○−] [+○−]? **7**
    b. What is the result when you press 7 [+○−] [+○−] [+○−]? **−7**
    c. What can you conclude about the number of times you press [+○−] and the result? **See margin.**

34. The absolute values would be the same.

34. ***Critical Thinking*** The distance from San Jose north to San Francisco is about the same as the distance from San Jose south to Santa Cruz. Which distance would have a greater absolute value?

Mixed Review

35. Replace ● with <, >, or = to make $\frac{15}{24}$ ● $\frac{17}{32}$ a true sentence. *(Lesson 4-10)* **>**

36. **Standardized Test Practice** Find the LCM of 27 and 30. *(Lesson 4-9)* **C**
    A 3 **B** 810 **C** 270 **D** 300
37. ***Statistics*** Find the mean, median, and mode for the following set of data: 3, 5, 2, 3, 3, 4, 3, 2, 2. *(Lesson 3-4)* **3, 3, 3**
38. ***Write*** 3.075×10^4 in standard form. *(Lesson 2-9)* **30,750**

For **Extra Practice,** see page 580.

Extending the Lesson

Enrichment Masters, p. 34

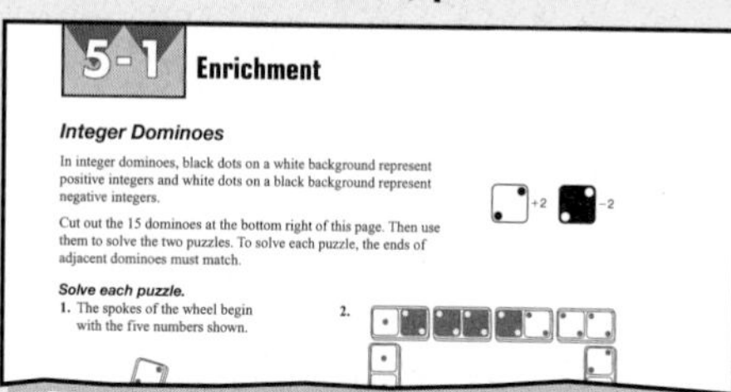
5-1 Enrichment

Integer Dominoes

In integer dominoes, black dots on a white background represent positive integers and white dots on a black background represent negative integers.

+2 −2

Cut out the 15 dominoes at the bottom right of this page. Then use them to solve the two puzzles. To solve each puzzle, the ends of adjacent dominoes must match.

Solve each puzzle.

1. The spokes of the wheel begin with the five numbers shown.
2.

Activity Have students use an almanac to find the height, in feet, of the tallest mountain on Earth and the depth of the deepest undersea trench. Have them compare the absolute values of the two integers. **Mt. Everest (29,028 ft), Marianna Trench (−35,840 ft); |29,028| < |−35,840|**

METEOROLOGY

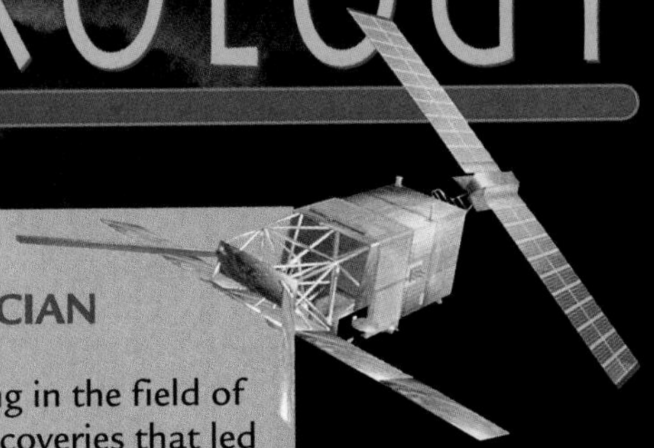

Edward Lorenz
METEOROLOGIST AND MATHEMATICIAN

Edward Lorenz, working in the field of meteorology, made discoveries that led to a new branch of mathematics called Chaos. One of Lorenz's most famous results is the "Butterfly Effect," which states that a butterfly flapping its wings in the Amazon forest might ultimately lead to a tornado in Texas.

A person who is interested in becoming a meteorologist should take high school courses in mathematics, physics, and chemistry. The ability to recognize patterns and make predictions is based on a good understanding of mathematics. Typically, a bachelor's degree in meteorology is required to obtain a job. An advanced degree is required for work in teaching and research.

For more information:
American Meteorological Society
45 Beacon Street
Boston, MA 02108

interNET CONNECTION
www.glencoe.com/sec/math/mac/mathnet

The weather amazes me. I wonder how I could learn to predict the weather.

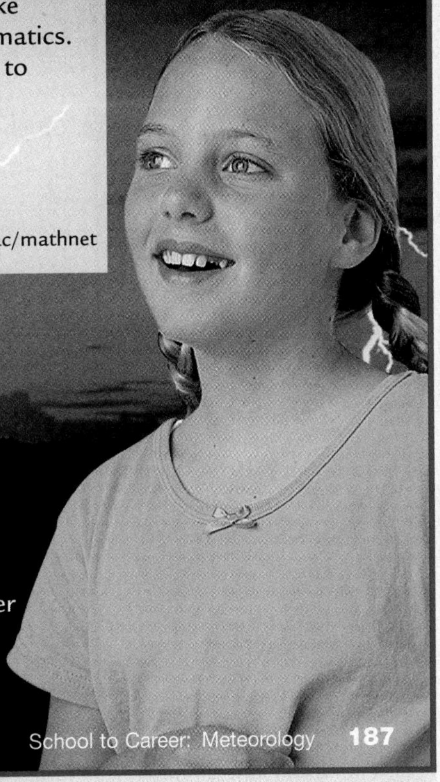

Your Turn
Keep a record, using graphs, tables, and charts, of weather forecasts given on television, radio, or in the newspaper for one week. Then record the actual weather for each day including high and low temperatures and precipitation. Compare the forecasts with the actual conditions. How accurate were the forecasts?

More About Edward Lorenz

- The discovery of the "Butterfly Effect" was the result of Lorenz's experiments in heat convection—the upward movement of air as temperature rises.
- Lorenz was born in Connecticut in 1917 and worked at the Massachusetts Institute of Technology (MIT) beginning in 1946. His research identified unpredictable patterns in weather systems governed by deterministic laws of physics, hence the term "deterministic chaos."
- Other mathematicians used Lorenz's meteorological breakthroughs to discover fractals.

SCHOOL to CAREER

Motivating Students

Meteorologists do much more than predict whether your baseball game will be rained out. To start the discussion about the field of meteorology, ask students the following questions.

- How have meteorologists made air travel safer? **by developing wind-shear detection and warning systems**
- What contributions might meteorologists make to world food production? **studying the causes of droughts and flooding and predicting future trends**
- How might meteorologists save lives? **by predicting the paths of hurricanes and tornadoes and developing better radar systems that provide warnings of severe weather**

Making the Math Connection

Meteorologists work with sophisticated instruments such as radar, satellites, and supercomputers. Mathematical equations exist that represent the physical principles that govern the atmosphere. Meteorologists use these equations and computers to simulate and predict the weather.

Working on *Your Turn*

You may wish to assign a city from every region of the United States to each student or small group of students. Ask students to research the conditions that affected the accuracy of the forecast as compared to the actual weather.

An additional School to Career activity is available on page 18 of the ***School to Career Masters****.*

5-2 Lesson Notes

Instructional Resources

- *Study Guide Masters,* p. 35
- *Practice Masters,* p. 35
- *Enrichment Masters,* p. 35
- Transparencies 5-2, A and B
- *Assessment and Evaluation Masters,* p. 127
- *School to Career Masters,* p. 18

- CD-ROM Program
  - Resource Lesson 5-2

Recommended Pacing	
Standard	Day 3 of 15
Honors	Day 3 of 13
Block	Day 2 of 8

1 FOCUS

5-Minute Check (Lesson 5-1)

Write an integer for each situation.

1. a loss of $12 -12
2. 42°F above 0 $+42$
3. a gain of 8 yards $+8$
4. What is the opposite of -6? 6
5. What is the absolute value of -10? 10

The 5-Minute Check is also available on **Transparency 5-2A** for this lesson.

Motivating the Lesson

Problem Solving Ask students to arrange these numbers in increasing order: 12, -15, 8, and -8. $-15, -8, 8, 12$

2 TEACH

Transparency 5-2B contains a teaching aid for this lesson.

Reading Mathematics Students should be aware that certain words are clues that tell whether to go left or right on a number line. Besides *increase* and *decrease,* which are used in this lesson, key terms include *above* and *below, before* and *after,* and *backward* and *forward.*

5-2 Comparing and Ordering Integers

What you'll learn

You'll learn to compare and order integers.

When am I ever going to use this?

Knowing how to order integers can help you compare historical events.

The table shows the population growth for five cities. A negative number means a decrease in population. If Hartford and Newark started out with the same population at the beginning of that period, which would be greater at the end?

City	Population Growth (%)
Brownsville, TX	14
Chattanooga, TN	0
Durham, NC	5
Hartford, CT	−11
Newark, NJ	−6

Source: *Statistical Abstract of the United States*

You can use a number line.

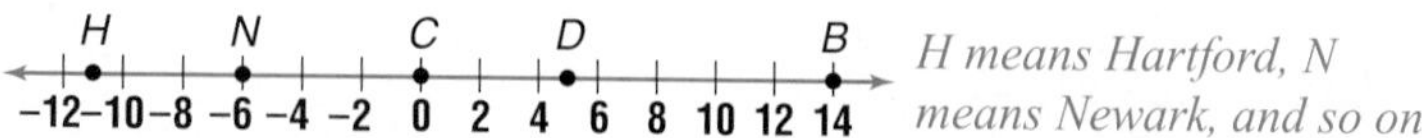

H means Hartford, N means Newark, and so on.

Since Newark is to the right of Hartford on the number line, its population "increase" (-6) represents a greater amount than Hartford's (-11). In symbols, you can write $-6 > -11$ or $-11 < -6$. So, by the end of the period, Newark would have a greater population than Hartford.

Examples

1 **Replace ● with < or > in -7 ● -1 to make a true sentence.**

Draw the graph of each integer on a number line.

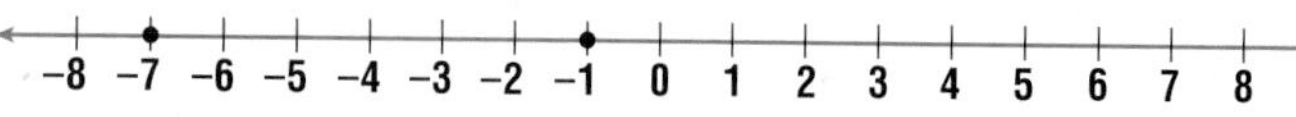

Since -7 is to the left of -1 on the number line, $-7 < -1$.

2 **Order the integers −4, 7, 3, −2, and 1 from least to greatest.**

Draw the graph of each integer on a number line.

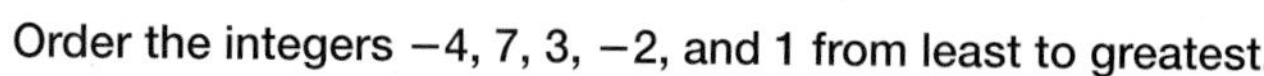
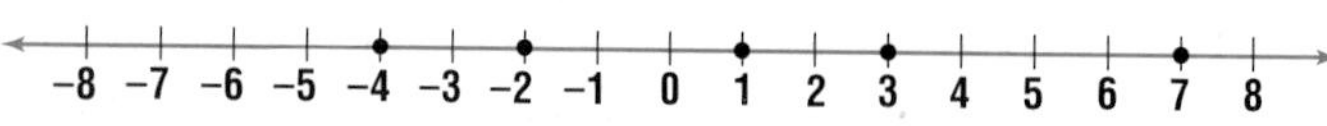

Order the integers by reading from left to right.

$-4, -2, 1, 3, 7$

INTEGRATION

3 **Statistics** **Mars, Venus, and Mercury are the planets most like Earth. Find the median of the temperatures in the chart.**

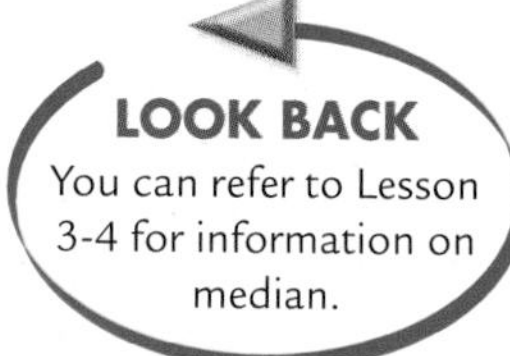

Planet	Average Temperature (°F)
Earth	50
Mars (day)	72
Mars (night)	−94
Mercury (day)	800
Mercury (night)	−300
Venus	900

List the temperatures in order from least to greatest.

$-300, -94, 50, 72, 800, 900$

There are two middle numbers, 50 and 72. So the median is $\frac{50 + 72}{2}$ or 61. The median temperature is 61°F.

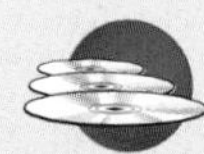

MathPASS CD-ROM

This CD-ROM offers a complete, self-paced mathematics curriculum. Each lesson includes a pretest, tutorial, guided practice, and posttest. MathPASS Lesson 13 is correlated to this Student Edition lesson.

For Windows & Macintosh

Multiple Learning Styles

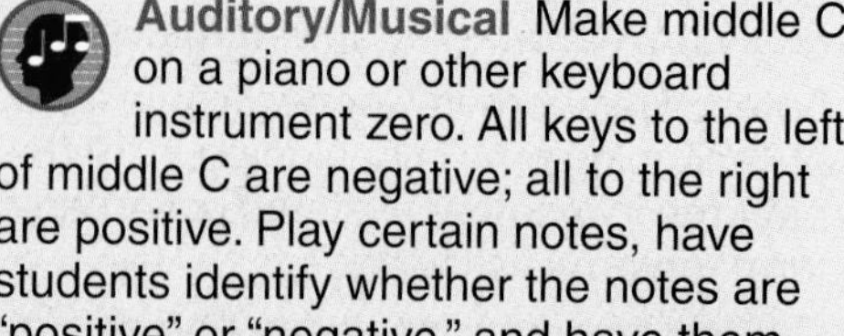

Auditory/Musical Make middle C on a piano or other keyboard instrument zero. All keys to the left of middle C are negative; all to the right are positive. Play certain notes, have students identify whether the notes are "positive" or "negative," and have them guess about how far the notes are from "zero."

CHECK FOR UNDERSTANDING

Communicating Mathematics

Read and study the lesson to answer each question.

1. ***Draw*** a number line showing $-5 < -2$. **1–2. See Answer Appendix.**
2. ***Tell*** how to determine when one integer is greater than another integer.

Guided Practice

Replace each ● with < or > to make a true sentence.

3. -3 ● -12 **>**
4. -17 ● 7 **<**
5. 0 ● -5 **>**
6. Order 43, −4, 29, −12, −17, and −76 from least to greatest. **6. −76, −17, −12, −4, 29, 43**
7. ***Earth Science*** The table below gives the record low temperatures in Boise, Idaho, that occurred through 1994. Find the median of the temperatures. **15**

Month	J	F	M	A	M	J	J	A	S	O	N	D
Temperature (°F)	−17	−15	6	19	22	31	35	34	23	11	−3	−25

EXERCISES

Practice

Replace each ● with < or > to make a true sentence.

8. -121 ● -21 **<**
9. -23 ● -32 **>**
10. -6 ● 0 **<**
11. 3 ● -4 **>**
12. 1 ● -1 **>**
13. 7 ● -89 **>**
14. -38 ● -83 **>**
15. -4 ● -8 **>**
16. -49 ● $|50|$ **<**

Order the integers from least to greatest.

17. 5, −3, 0, −59, −43, 11 **17. −59, −43, −3, 0, 5, 11**
18. −6, 18, −16, 33, 3, −44, 1 **18. −44, −16, −6, 1, 3, 18, 33**
19. Which is greater, −12 or 7? **7**
20. Order 78, −80, 69, −20, 0, and 17 from greatest to least. **20. 78, 69, 17, 0, −20, −80**

Applications and Problem Solving

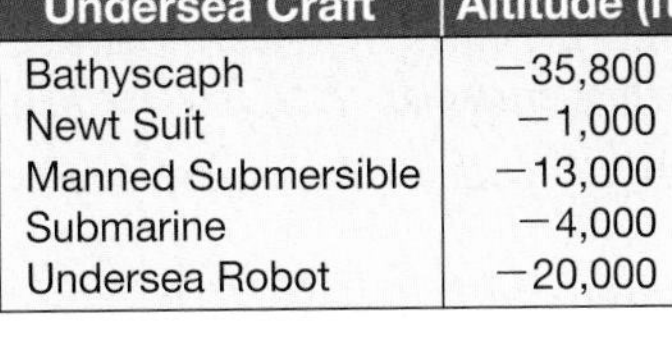

Undersea Craft	Altitude (ft)
Bathyscaph	−35,800
Newt Suit	−1,000
Manned Submersible	−13,000
Submarine	−4,000
Undersea Robot	−20,000

21. ***Earth Science*** The table shows how deep various undersea craft can go. List the depths in order from deepest to most shallow. **−35,800; −20,000; −13,000; −4,000; −1,000**

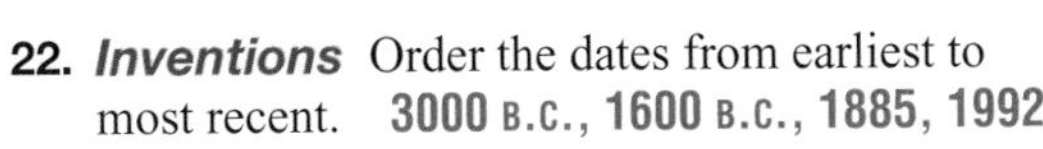

22. ***Inventions*** Order the dates from earliest to most recent. **3000 B.C., 1600 B.C., 1885, 1992**

1600 B.C. Bronze plows are developed in Vietnam.

A.D. 1992 8-year-old Abbey Fleck invents a gadget for cooking bacon in the microwave oven.

A.D. 1885 Gottlieb Daimler invents the gasoline engine.

3000 B.C. SeLing-She invents silk cloth.

Abbey Fleck

In-Class Examples

For Example 1
Replace ● with < or > in -6 ● -2 to make a true sentence. **<**

For Example 2
Order the integers −3, 5, −2, 0 from least to greatest. **−3, −2, 0, 5**

For Example 3
The temperatures for the second week of January for a city in Illinois are −1°, 2°, 8°, 6°, −1°, −7°, and 0°. Find the median. **−7°, −1°, −1°, 0°, 2°, 6°, 8°; median = 0°**

3 PRACTICE/APPLY

Check for Understanding

If students need additional practice or instruction after completing Exercises 1–7, one of these options may be helpful.

- Extra Practice, see p. 580
- Reteaching Activity
- *Study Guide Masters,* p. 35
- *Practice Masters,* p. 35

Study Guide Masters, p. 35

5-2 **Study Guide**

Name__________ Date__________

Comparing and Ordering Integers

To compare or order integers, think of a number line. The number farther to the right on the number line is greater.

−7 −6 −5 −4 −3 −2 −1 0 1 2 3 4 5 6 7 8

Since 2 is to the right of −3 on the number line, $-3 < 2$.

Examples 1 **Replace each ○ with < or > to make a true sentence.**

-3 ○ 3 Since a negative integer is always less than a positive integer, $-3 < 3$.

-2 ○ -5 Since −2 is to the right of the −5 on the number line, $-2 > -5$.

2 **Order the integers 0, 3, −1, −3, and 5 from least to greatest.**

−3 is farthest to the left on the number line, so it is least.

Order the integers from left to right.
−3, −1, 0, 3, 5

Replace each ○ with < or > to make a true sentence.

1. -5 ○ 7 **<**
2. 0 ○ -2 **>**
3. -8 ○ 8 **<**
4. 1 ○ -4 **>**
5. 17 ○ 25 **<**
6. -12 ○ -10 **<**

Order the integers from least to greatest.

7. 12, −4, 31, 0, −50, −12 **−50, −12, −4, 0, 12, 31**
8. 9, −7, 1, −5, 23, −11 **−11, −7, −5, 1, 9, 23**
9. −45, 62, −64, 45, −12, 17 **−64, −45, −12, 17, 45, 62**
10. −2, −14, −8, −19, −24, −1 **−24, −19, −14, −8, −2, −1**
11. −6, 5, 1, −8, 0, −7 **−8, −7, −6, 0, 1, 5**
12. −101, −102, −103, 101, 102, 103 **−103, −102, −101, 101, 102, 103**

T35
Mathematics: Applications and Connections, Course 2

Reteaching the Lesson

Activity Use a thermometer as a vertical number line to help students understand how to compare integers. Guide them to see that a temperature of −8°F is greater (warmer) than a temperature of −9°F. Provide additional examples.

Error Analysis
Watch for students who think −15 has a greater value than −5.
Prevent by telling students to remember that the closer a negative number is to zero on a number line, the greater its value.

Assignment Guide

Core: 9–23 odd, 26–29
Enriched: 8–20 even, 21–24, 26–29

Exercise 25 asks students to advance to the next stage of work on the Chapter Project. You may wish to link math and geography (climate) by having students identify the latitude temperature combinations that did not quite fit the pattern (New York's and Seattle's).

4 ASSESS

Closing Activity

Speaking Points *A, B, C,* and *D* represent different integers on a number line. Have students use these clues to order them from least to greatest. ***D, C, A,* and *B***

- *D* is the least of the integers.
- Points *A* and *D* are the same distance from 0.
- Point *C* is halfway between *A* and *D.*
- Point *B* is the greatest integer.

Chapter 5, Quiz A (Lessons 5-1 and 5-2) is available in the *Assessment and Evaluation Masters,* p. 127.

***Practice Masters,* p. 35**

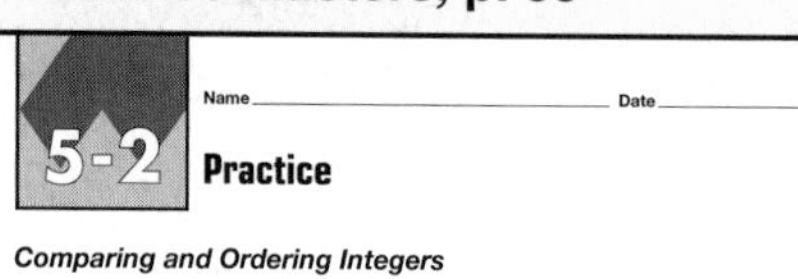

Name______________________ Date__________

5-2 Practice

Comparing and Ordering Integers

Replace each ◯ with < or > to make a true sentence.

1. −6 ◯ −13 >	2. −13 ◯ −6 <	3. 0 ◯ −8 >
4. −18 ◯ −98 >	5. −32 ◯ −23 <	6. −462 ◯ −46 <
7. −1 ◯ 1 <	8. 12 ◯ −12 >	9. −4 ◯ −6 >
10. −9 ◯ 0 <	11. 7 ◯ −3 >	12. 9 ◯ −99 >
13. −2 ◯ −22 >	14. 0 ◯ 8 <	15. −8 ◯ 8 <

Order the integers from least to greatest.

16. 3, −5, 8, −10, −18, 24
−18, −10, −5, 3, 8, 24

17. −9, −4, 19, 32, −34, −18, −2
−34, −18, −9, −4, −2, 19, 32

18. −92, 76, 54, −89, 8, 24, 0
−92, −89, 0, 8, 24, 54, 76

19. −54, −76, 9, −7, −45, 65, 43, 2
−76, −54, −45, −7, 2, 9, 43, 65

20. −12, −34, 8, −1, 5, −6, 54
−34, −12, −6, −1, 5, 8, 54

21. −43, −9, 0, 6, −2, −6, 14, 7
−43, −9, −6, −2, 0, 6, 7, 14

 T35 *Mathematics: Applications and Connections, Course 2*

23. *Earth Science* The highest summit in Arizona is Humphreys Peak at 12,633 feet. The table shows how the highest summits in other states compare to it.

Peak	Height Compared to Humphreys Peak (ft)
Granite Peak, MT	+166
Mt. Hood, OR	−1,394
Mt. Elbert, CO	+1,800
Mt. Rogers, VA	−6,904
Spruce Knob, WV	−7,770
Wheeler Peak, NM	+528

Source: *High Points of the United States, A Guide to the 50 State Summits*

a. Which summit is the highest? **Mt. Elbert**

b. Name the three summits that are closest in height to Humphreys Peak. **Granite Peak, Wheeler Peak, Mt. Hood**

24a. − 29°, −26°, −25°, −22°, −16°, −12°, 7°, 9°, 12°, 53°

24. *Earth Science* The map shows the all-time record low temperatures in ten cities for the month of January.

a. Order the temperatures from lowest to highest.

b. Which city had the coldest temperature? **Cheyenne**

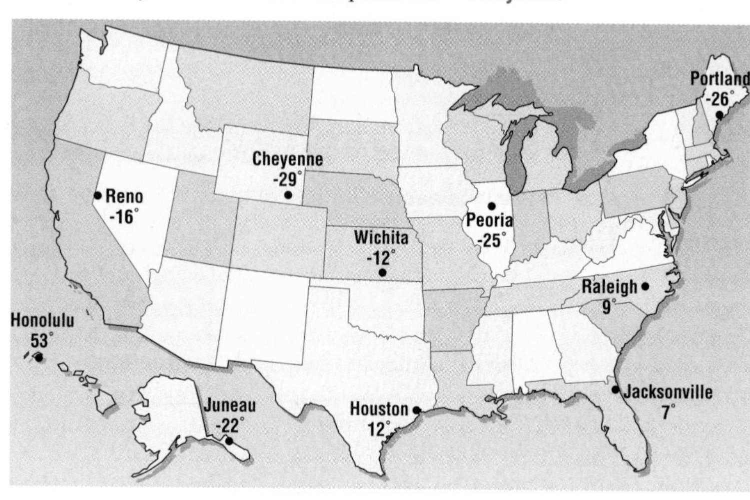

interNET CONNECTION For the latest statistics on record temperatures in the United States, visit: www.glencoe.com/sec/math/mac/mathnet

25b. Generally, as the latitude increases, the low temperature decreases.

25. *Working on the CHAPTER Project* Refer to the table on page 183.

a. Make a table listing the cities from least to greatest latitude. Show latitude and low temperatures. **See Answer Appendix.**

b. What do you notice about the relationship between latitudes and low temperatures?

26. *Critical Thinking* If 0 is the greatest integer in a set of five, what can you conclude about the other four integers? **They are negative.**

Mixed Review

27. Standardized Test Practice Marco dove off a 10-foot diving board into 12 feet of water and touched the bottom. Which integer describes the number of feet below the surface of the water that he dove? *(Lesson 5-1)* **A**

A −12 **B** −10 **C** 10 **D** 12

28. Express $\frac{39}{81}$ in simplest form. *(Lesson 4-5)* $\frac{13}{27}$

29. *Physical Science* An experiment requires 3 milligrams of potassium chloride. How many grams of potassium chloride are needed? *(Lesson 2-8)*

29. 0.003 g

For **Extra Practice,** see page 580.

Extending the Lesson

***Enrichment Masters,* p. 35**

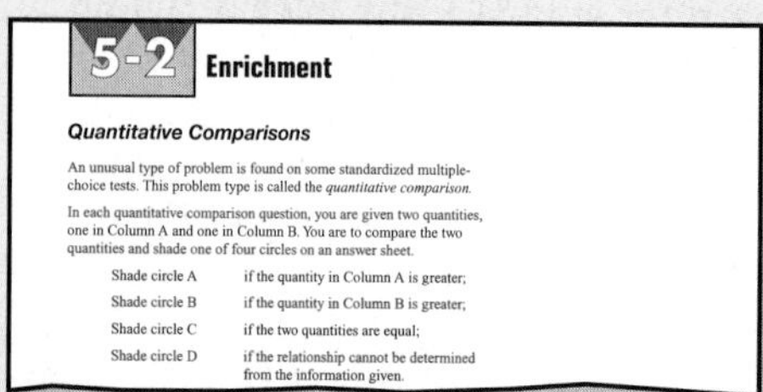

5-2 Enrichment

Quantitative Comparisons

An unusual type of problem is found on some standardized multiple-choice tests. This problem type is called the *quantitative comparison.*

In each quantitative comparison question, you are given two quantities, one in Column A and one in Column B. You are to compare the two quantities and shade one of four circles on an answer sheet.

Shade circle A	if the quantity in Column A is greater;
Shade circle B	if the quantity in Column B is greater;
Shade circle C	if the two quantities are equal;
Shade circle D	if the relationship cannot be determined from the information given.

Activity Challenge students to make up tic-tac-toe game boards with numbers in each section of a 3 × 3 array. Players take turns using counters to cover integers from least to greatest (or from greatest to least.) The boards should include positive and negative integers and zero. The first player to get three in a row wins.

5-3

Integration: Geometry
The Coordinate System

What you'll learn

You'll learn to graph points on a coordinate plane.

When am I ever going to use this?

Knowing how to graph points on a coordinate plane can help you find cities on a map.

Word Wise

coordinate system
origin
x-axis
y-axis
quadrant
ordered pair
x-coordinate
y-coordinate

In-car navigation systems use global positioning satellites (GPS) to pinpoint their positions. Street intersections are often used to locate addresses on a map.

In mathematics, a **coordinate system**, or coordinate plane, is used to graph points in a plane. It is made up of a horizontal number line and a vertical number line that intersect at their zero points. This intersection point is called the **origin**.

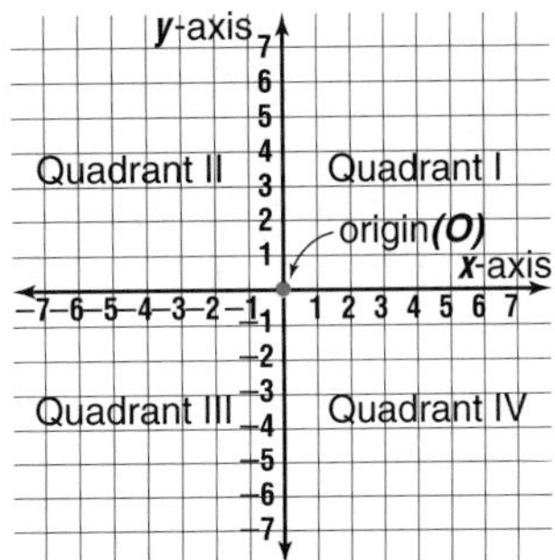

The horizontal line is called the ***x*-axis**, and the vertical line is called the ***y*-axis**. Together, they make up a coordinate system that separates the plane into four **quadrants**.

You can identify any point on a coordinate system using an **ordered pair** of numbers. The first number in an ordered pair is the ***x*-coordinate**, and the second number is the ***y*-coordinate**.

The ordered pairs (2, 4) and (−4, −3) are graphed at the right.

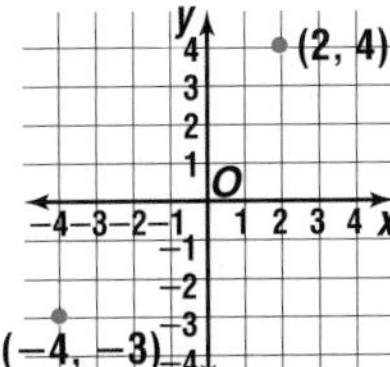

The point at (2, 4) is in quadrant I. The point at (−4, −3) is in quadrant III.

Examples

1 Name the ordered pair for point *A* and identify its quadrant.

- Start at the origin *O*. Locate point *A* by moving left 3 units along the *x*-axis. The *x*-coordinate is −3.
- Now move up 4 units. The *y*-coordinate is +4.
- The ordered pair is (−3, 4). Point *A* is in quadrant II.

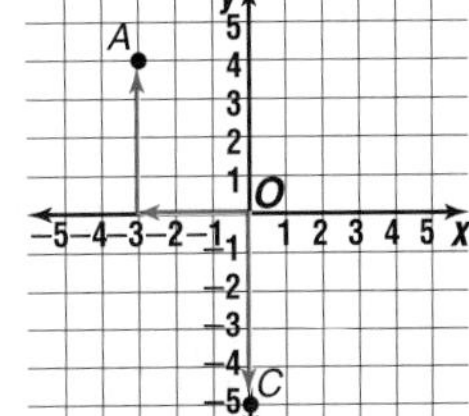

2 Name the ordered pair for point *C* and identify its quadrant.

The ordered pair is (0, −5). Point *C* is not in a quadrant because it is on the *y*-axis.

5-3 Lesson Notes

Instructional Resources

- *Study Guide Masters,* p. 36
- *Practice Masters,* p. 36
- *Enrichment Masters,* p. 36
- Transparencies 5-3, A and B
- *Hands-On Lab Masters,* p. 76
- CD-ROM Program
  - Resource Lesson 5-3
  - Extended Activity 5-3

Recommended Pacing	
Standard	Day 4 of 15
Honors	Days 4 & 5 of 13
Block	Day 2 of 8

1 FOCUS

5-Minute Check
(Lesson 5-2)

Replace each ● with < or > to make a true sentence.

1. 2 ● −6 >
2. −78 ● 3 <
3. −2 ● 2 <

Order the integers from least to greatest.

4. 4, −6, 31, 0, −9
   −9, −6, 0, 4, 31
5. 6, −27, −22, 21, 12, −11,
   −27, −22, −11, 6, 12, 21

The 5-Minute Check is also available on **Transparency 5-3A** for this lesson.

Motivating the Lesson

Communication Focus on the steps students must always follow to graph a point on the coordinate plane: first locate the *x*-coordinate by starting at (0, 0) and moving units to the *right* or *left* along the *x*-axis; then locate the *y*-coordinate by moving *up* or *down* the *y*-axis.

Multiple Learning Styles

Verbal/Linguistic Have each student complete a ten-step "compass-point journey." This is a list of instructions using compass directions. For example, using dot paper and a starting point, draw a line three squares north, continue two squares east, then four squares south, two squares northeast, and so on. Once these are written, separate students into pairs and have one student in each pair verbally instruct the other on his or her "journey" beginning at the origin. Switch roles and repeat.

2 TEACH

Transparency 5-3B contains a teaching aid for this lesson.

Using Applications Use a coordinate system to show locations in your city, neighborhood, school grounds, or classroom. Have students work together to assign coordinates to various locales. Alternatively, have them find a location by graphing its approximate coordinates.

In-Class Examples

Use the coordinate system below for frozen pizza for Examples 1–4.

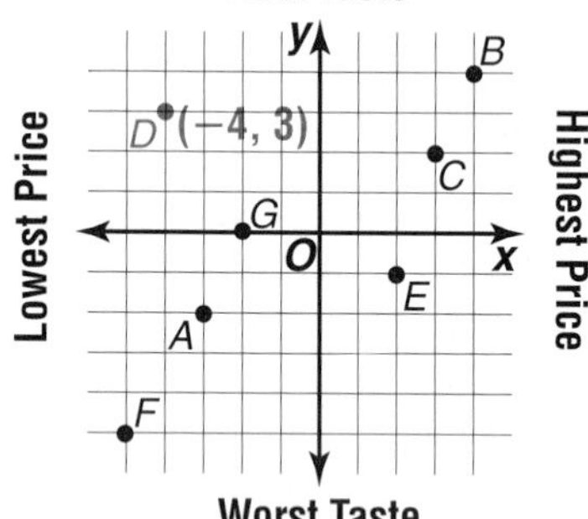

For Example 1
Name the ordered pair for point *C* and identify its quadrant.
(3, 2); I

For Example 2
Name the ordered pair for point *G* and identify its quadrant.
(−2, 0); not in a quadrant

For Example 3
In which quadrant is *A*? What does a score in this quadrant represent? **III; lowest price, worst taste**

For Example 4
Graph the point *D*(−4, 3).

Let the Games Begin

The player who names the coordinate should check to make sure that his or her partner is graphing correctly.
Additional resources for this game can be found on page 42 of the ***Classroom Games.***

Example 3 Real World APPLICATION

In this book when no numbers are given on the x- and y-axis, you can assume that each grid square is one unit.

Shopping The graph shows the ratings of different stores' fashions. In which quadrant is Store C? What does this quadrant represent?

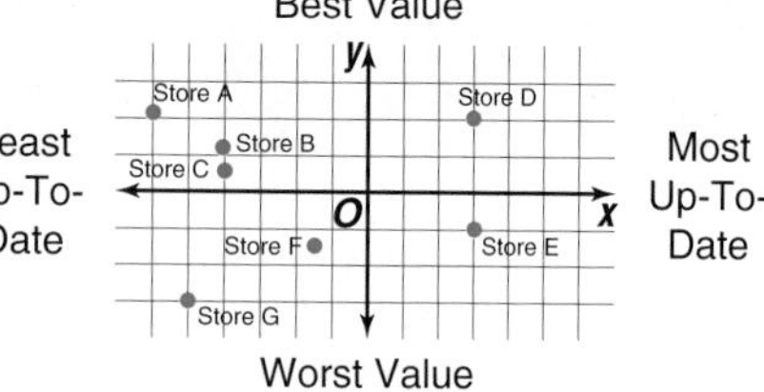

The ordered pair for Store C is (−4, 0.5). This is in quadrant II. Stores in quadrant II have fashions that are less up-to-date, but are a better value.

To graph a point in a coordinate system, draw a dot at the location of its ordered pair.

Example 4 Graph the point *D*(2, 3).

First, draw a coordinate system. Start at the origin *O*. Move 2 units to the right. Then move 3 units up to locate the point. Draw a dot and label it *D*(2, 3).

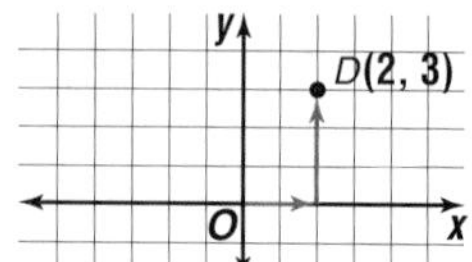

Let the Games Begin

Tic-Tac-Toe

Get Ready This game is for two players.
sheet of paper   grid paper

Get Set Each person should draw a coordinate plane on grid paper.

Go This is like tic-tac-toe, except you must get four Xs or four Os in a row. Players take turns naming two numbers. Each number must be between −10 and 10. The first number is the x-coordinate of an ordered pair, and the second is the y-coordinate. The other player writes these ordered pairs on a sheet of paper and places an X or O in the correct place on the coordinate plane.

- Once you say a number, you may not change it.
- If you say a coordinate that was already used, you lose a turn.

The first player to get four Xs or Os in a row is the winner.

Math Skill
Graphing Points on a Coordinate Plane

Example

	x	y
O	1	3
X	0	0
O	1	−2
X	−1	1

Visit www.glencoe.com/sec/math/mac/mathnet for more games.

Reteaching the Lesson

Activity Show students that ordered pairs can be used to describe the position of each piece during a chess game. Have a pair of students demonstrate the process by beginning a game of chess. After each player has made three moves, have the class record the new coordinates.

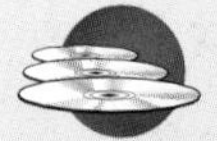

MathPASS CD-ROM

This CD-ROM offers a complete, self-paced mathematics curriculum. Each lesson includes a pretest, tutorial, guided practice, and posttest. MathPASS Lesson 14 is correlated to this Student Edition lesson.
For Windows & Macintosh

CHECK FOR UNDERSTANDING

Communicating Mathematics

Read and study the lesson to answer each question. 2. See margin.

1. ***Name*** the quadrant in which the x-coordinate is negative and the y-coordinate is positive. **quadrant II**
2. ***Explain*** why the point $H(7, -10)$ is different from the point $K(-10, 7)$.
3. Refer to the beginning of the lesson. ***Write*** a few sentences describing how a GPS device uses a coordinate system. **See students' work.**

Guided Practice

4. (−4, −3), III
5. (1, 0), x-axis
6. (3, −2); IV

Name the x-coordinate and the y-coordinate for each point labeled at the right. Then tell in which quadrant each point lies.

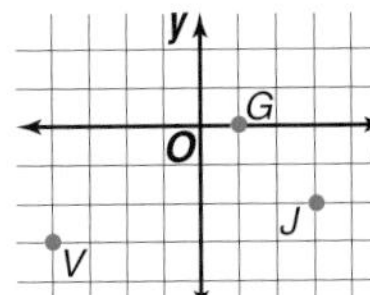

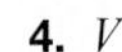

4. V 5. G 6. J

On graph paper, draw a coordinate plane. Then graph and label each point. 7–9. See margin.

7. $P(-3, 5)$ 8. $R(3, -2)$ 9. $S\left(2, \frac{1}{2}\right)$

10. ***Geology*** Geologists use latitude (horizontal) and longitude (vertical) lines to graph volcanoes on a world map. Cotopaxi, for example, is at 10°S latitude and 70°W longitude, or (10°S, 70°W). Write the location of each volcano as an ordered pair (latitude, longitude).

a. Mount Katmai **(60°N, 160°W)** b. Hekla **(70°N, 20°W)**

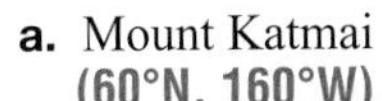

EXERCISES

Practice

11. (2, 2), I
12. (−1, 0), x-axis
13. (5, −2), IV
14. (−4, −4), III
15. (0, −4), y-axis
16. (−3, 1), II
17. (−1, 4), II
18. (3, 0), x-axis
19. (−2, −2), III

Name the x-coordinate and the y-coordinate for each point labeled at the right. Then tell in which quadrant each point lies.

11. A 12. J 13. P
14. F 15. C 16. M
17. T 18. D 19. Y

On graph paper, draw a coordinate plane. Then graph and label each point. 20–28. See Answer Appendix.

20. $T(0, -3)$ 21. $B(-2, 7)$ 22. $R(-2, -3)$
23. $A(7, 4.5)$ 24. $M(5, -1.5)$ 25. $C\left(1\frac{1}{2}, 4\right)$
26. $H(6, -3)$ 27. $E(-5, -5)$ 28. $W(-4, 0)$

Classroom Vignette

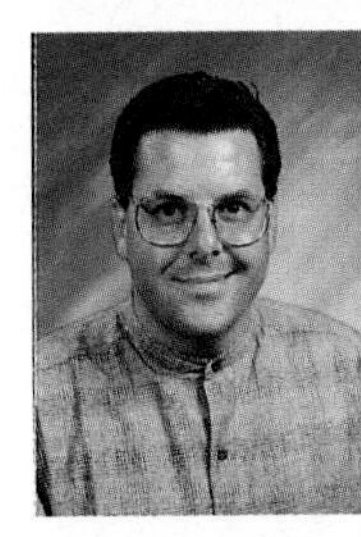

"I let my students play *Coordinate Battleship.* Each player gets two coordinate grids and randomly chooses eight points on one of the grids. Then the two students alternate turns trying to guess where the other's points are located. Each guess must be graphed on the other coordinate grid. Misses are recorded in one color and hits in another."

Gary Lilla

Gary Lilla, Teacher
East Troy Middle School
East Troy, WI

3 PRACTICE/APPLY

Check for Understanding

If students need additional practice or instruction after completing Exercises 1–10, you may find one of the following options helpful.

- Extra Practice, see p. 581
- Reteaching Activity, see p. 192
- *Study Guide Masters,* p. 36
- *Practice Masters,* p. 36

Assignment Guide

Core: 11–31 odd, 34–38
Enriched: 12–30 even, 31, 32, 34–38

Additional Answers

2. Point H is 7 units to the right and 10 units down from the origin. Point K is 10 units to the left and 7 units up from the origin.

7–9.

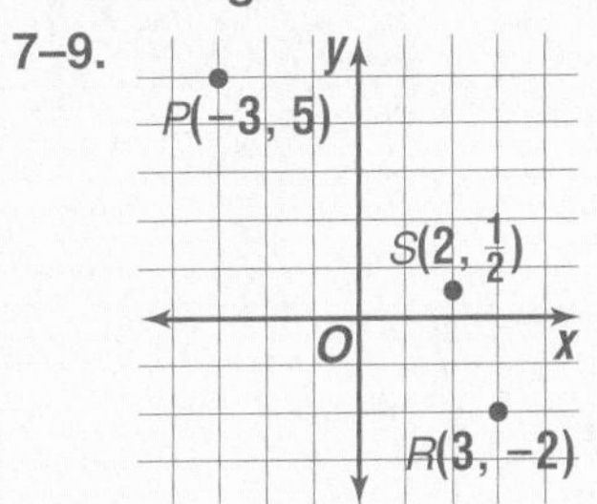

***Study Guide Masters,* p. 36**

Name________________ Date__________

Study Guide

Integration: Geometry
The Coordinate System

The **coordinate system** is used to graph points in a plane. The horizontal line is the **x-axis.** The vertical line is the **y-axis.** Their intersection is the **origin.**

Points are located using **ordered pairs.** The first number in an ordered pair is the **x-coordinate;** the second number is the **y-coordinate.**

Examples 1 **Name the ordered pair for point P.**
Start at the origin.
Move 4 units left along the x-axis.
Move 3 units up on the y-axis.
The ordered pair for point P is $(-4, 3)$.

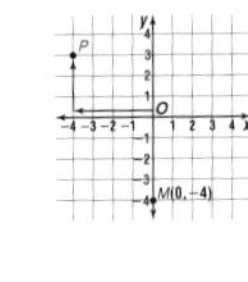

2 **Graph the point $M(0, -4)$.**
Start at the origin.
Move 0 units along the x-axis.
Move 4 units down on the y-axis.
Draw a point and label it M.

Name the x-coordinate and the y-coordinate for each point labeled at the right.

1. B (−4, 2) 2. T (4, −3)
3. W (3, 3) 4. C (−2, −4)
5. F (−4, −2) 6. N (1, −1)
7. A (3, 0) 8. Y (−2, 4)

Graph and label each point on the coordinate plane.

9. $H(-2, 1)$ 10. $Q(0, 4)$
11. $D(4, 2)$ 12. $E(4, -4)$
13. $G(-4, -4)$ 14. $J(0, 0)$
15. $K(-4, 3)$ 16. $M(-3, -2)$

 T36 *Mathematics: Applications and Connections, Course 2*

Exercise 33 asks students to advance to the next stage of work on the Chapter Project.

4 ASSESS

Closing Activity

Modeling Have students explain why the ordered pair (4, −3) is not the same as (−3, 4). Ask them to graph and label each point.

Additional Answer

33b.

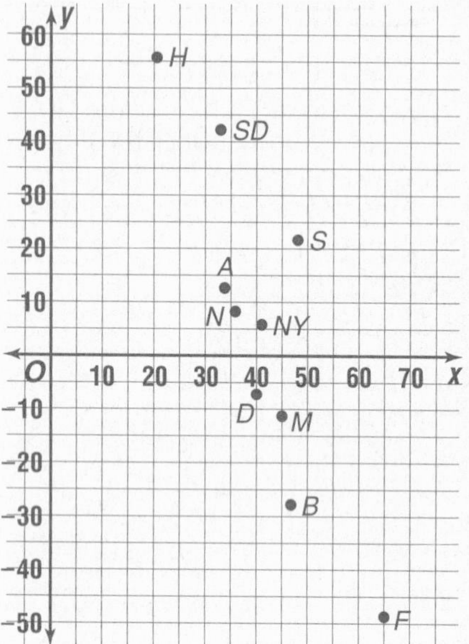

***Practice Masters,* p. 36**

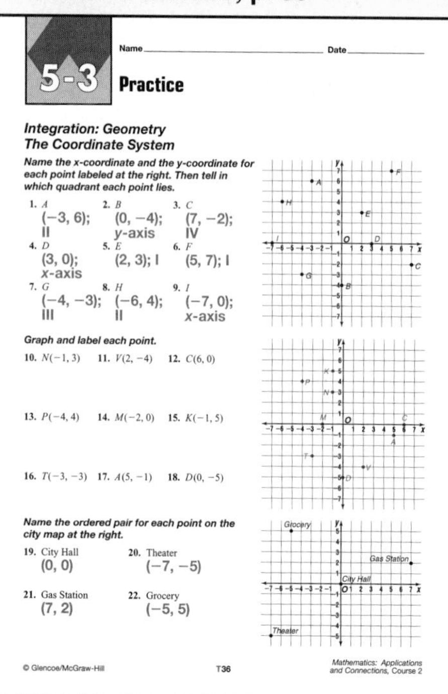

Name ______ Date ______

5-3 Practice

Integration: Geometry
The Coordinate System

Name the x-coordinate and the y-coordinate for each point labeled at the right. Then tell in which quadrant each point lies.

1. A (−3, 6); II
2. B (0, −4); y-axis
3. C (7, −2); IV
4. D (3, 0); x-axis
5. E (2, 3); I
6. F (5, 7); I
7. G (−4, −3); III
8. H (−6, 4); II
9. I (−7, 0); x-axis

Graph and label each point.

10. N(−1, 3)
11. V(2, −4)
12. C(6, 0)
13. P(−4, 4)
14. M(−2, 0)
15. K(−1, 5)
16. T(−3, −3)
17. A(5, −1)
18. D(0, −5)

Name the ordered pair for each point on the city map at the right.

19. City Hall (0, 0)
20. Theater (−7, −5)
21. Gas Station (7, 2)
22. Grocery (−5, 5)

© Glencoe/McGraw-Hill T36 Mathematics: Applications and Connections, Course 2

29. In which quadrant is $T(23, -18)$ located? **quadrant IV**
30. Name the coordinates of the point where the x-axis and the y-axis intersect. What is the name of this point? **(0, 0), origin**

Applications and Problem Solving

31. ***Olympics*** The graph shows a map of the Olympic Village during the 1996 Summer Olympics. Name the ordered pair for each point.
    a. Centennial Park **(3, 3)**
    b. Georgia Dome **(−3, −1)**
    c. Omni **(−2, −2)**
    d. Olympic Center **(−2, 3)**

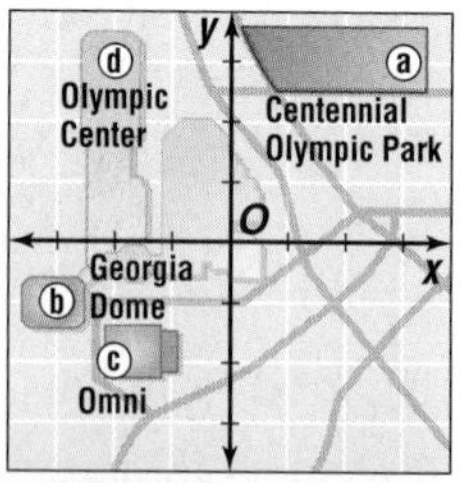

32. ***Earth Science*** Certain patterns of stars, called *constellations,* resemble animals and objects. The constellations at the right are the hunter Orion and his dog Canis Major.
    a. Name the coordinates of Betelgeuse, the star in the right shoulder of Orion. **(3, 7)**
    b. Name the coordinates of Sirius, the brightest star in the winter sky. **(−3, −4)**

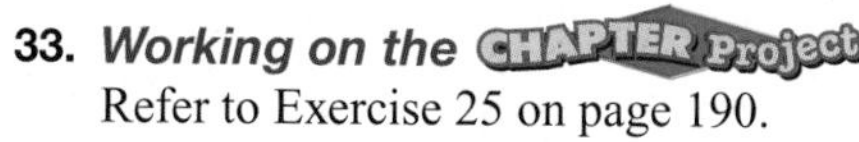

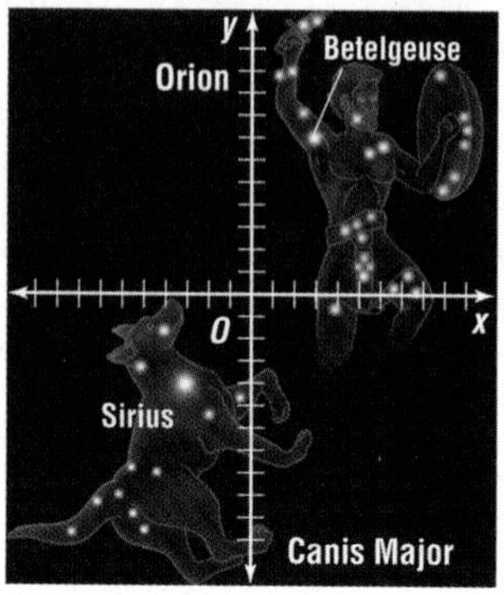

33. ***Working on the* CHAPTER Project** Refer to Exercise 25 on page 190.
    a. Write the latitude and the low temperature of each city as an ordered pair.
    b. Graph the ordered pairs on a coordinate plane. **See margin.**

34. ***Critical Thinking*** Suppose for any ordered pair the x-coordinate and the y-coordinate are always the same integer. Where are the possible locations for these sets of ordered pairs?

33a. Honolulu (21, 56), San Diego (33, 43), Atlanta (34, 13), Nashville (36, 9), Denver (40, −7), New York (41, 6), Minneapolis (45, −11), Bismarck (47, −28), Seattle (48, 22), Fairbanks (65, −48)

34. quadrant I, where both coordinates are the same positive number, quadrant III, where both coordinates are the same negative number, or the origin

35. −5, −1, 3, 5

Mixed Review

35. Order the integers 5, −1, 3, and −5 from least to greatest. *(Lesson 5-2)*
36. **Standardized Test Practice** Koleka has 5 dimes in her pocket. The dates on the dimes are 1995, 1992, 1987, 1983, and 1978. If she chooses 1 dime from her pocket without looking, what is the probability that it will have a date in the 1990s? *(Lesson 4-8)* **D**

    A $\frac{1}{5}$ **B** $\frac{4}{5}$ **C** $\frac{2}{3}$ **D** $\frac{2}{5}$

37. ***Money Matters*** A 39-ounce jar of peanut butter costs $1.95. What is the cost per ounce? *(Lesson 2-6)* **$0.05**
38. ***Life Science*** It is believed that a dog ages 7 human years for every calendar year that it lives. *(Lesson 1-3)* **b. 84 years**
    a. Write an expression for determining a dog's age in human years. Let y represent the number of calendar years the dog has lived. **7y**
    b. Find the human age of a dog that has lived for 12 calendar years.

For **Extra Practice,** see page 581.

Extending the Lesson

***Enrichment Masters,* p. 36**

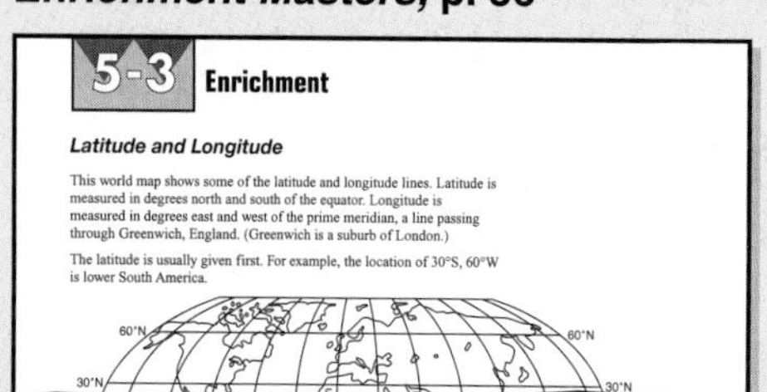

5-3 Enrichment

Latitude and Longitude

This world map shows some of the latitude and longitude lines. Latitude is measured in degrees north and south of the equator. Longitude is measured in degrees east and west of the prime meridian, a line passing through Greenwich, England. (Greenwich is a suburb of London.)

The latitude is usually given first. For example, the location of 30°S, 60°W is lower South America.

60°N 60°N 30°N 30°N

Activity Discuss the concepts of latitude and longitude with students. Have them use a globe, an atlas, or an almanac to locate 10 cities around the world according to their coordinates of latitude and longitude.

TECHNOLOGY LAB

GRAPHING CALCULATORS

5-3B Graphing Points

graphing calculator

A Follow-Up of Lesson 5-3

The graphics screen of a graphing calculator can represent a coordinate plane. You can graph points on a graphing calculator just as you do on a coordinate grid.

TRY THIS

Work with a partner.

Use the TI-83 graphing calculator to graph points $A(1, -2)$, $B(7, 1)$, $C(-3, -4)$, and $D(5, 5)$ in the standard viewing window $[-10, 10]$ by $[-10, 10]$.

First, press [2nd] [DRAW] 1 [ENTER] to clear the drawing screen. Then graph point A.

Enter: [2nd] [DRAW] [▶] [ENTER] 1 [,] [(-)] 2 [)] [ENTER]

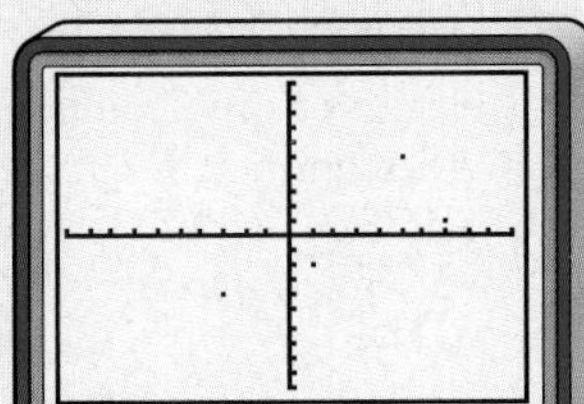

Press [2nd] [QUIT]. Then enter the coordinates of points B, C, and D in the same way. Be sure to press [2nd] [QUIT] after graphing each point.

ON YOUR OWN

Use the program to graph each set of points on a graphing calculator. Then sketch the graph on a separate piece of paper. **1–3. See Answer Appendix.**

1. $H(5, -7)$, $I(9, 1)$, $J(-5, -2)$
2. $W(4, 4)$, $X(-2, 1)$, $Y(8, 1)$, $Z(-6, 5)$
3. $L(3, -5)$, $M(-3, -4)$, $N(-9, 2)$, $O(7, -8)$
4. Explain how to change the viewing window so that you could see the graph of the point $P(-12, 15)$. **Sample answer: Set the viewing window to $[-15, 10]$ by $[-10, 20]$.**

Have students write a paragraph explaining how to graph points using the TI-83.

5-3B TECHNOLOGY LAB Notes

GET READY

Objective Students graph points on a graphing calculator.

Technology Resources
- TI-81, TI-82, or TI-83 graphing calculator

MANAGEMENT TIPS

Recommended Time
45 minutes

Getting Started You may wish to have students work in pairs to begin plotting points on the graphing calculator. Have one student read the instructions aloud while the other enters them into the calculator.

Using a Calculator If students have had little experience with graphing calculators, they can familiarize themselves with the keyboard zones: Graphing keys (top row), Editing keys (next row of 6 keys beside arrow keys), Advanced Function keys (next row of 5 keys), and Scientific Calculator keys (everything else). Students may want to check the Menu Map, beginning on page A-39 of the TI-83 Guidebook.

The TI-82 and TI-83 work similarly. To draw points using a TI-81, press [2nd] [DRAW] 3 *the first coordinate* [ALPHA]  [,] *the second coordinate* [)] [ENTER].

ASSESS

After students answer Exercises 1–4, check their sketches to determine whether they are graphing correctly.

5-4A HANDS-ON LAB Notes

GET READY

Objective Students add integers by using models.

Optional Resources
Hands-On Lab Masters
- integer counters, p. 6
- integer mat, p. 8
- worksheet, p. 46

Overhead Manipulative Resources
- counters
- integer mat

Manipulative Kit
- counters
- integer mat

MANAGEMENT TIPS

Recommended Time
30 minutes

Getting Started Have students work with partners using at least seven yellow counters and at least seven red counters. Each yellow counter represents 1, each red counter represents −1. Have one student in the pair use only positive counters, the other only negative counters. Have students begin by using positive counters to model the number 7.

Activity 1 shows addition of integers with like signs.

Activity 2 differs from Activity 1 in that it shows the addition of integers with different signs. To help students grasp this concept, emphasize the meaning of zero pair. This concept is very important in future modeling of operations with integers.

ASSESS

Have students complete Exercises 1–4. Use Exercise 5 to determine whether students understand when the sum of two integers will be negative.

COOPERATIVE LEARNING

5-4A Adding Integers

A Preview of Lesson 5-4

- counters
- integer mat

You can use counters to model the addition of integers.

TRY THIS

Work with a partner.

1 Model 6 + 2.

Combine a set of 6 positive counters and a set of 2 positive counters on the mat.

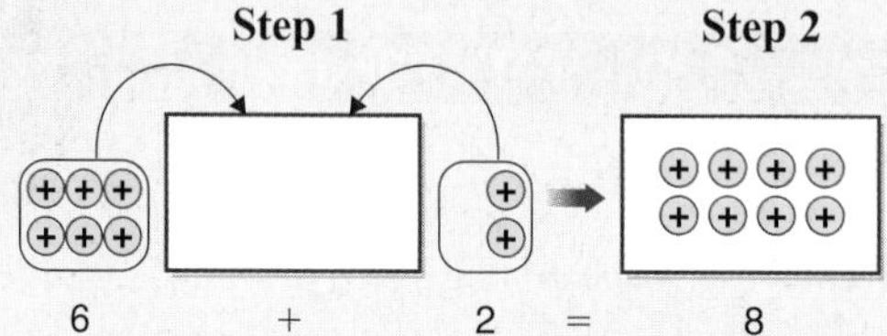

So, 6 + 2 = 8.

2 Model 5 + (−1).

Place 5 positive counters on the mat. Then place 1 negative counter on the mat. When one positive counter is paired with one negative counter, the result is a *zero pair*. Remove all the zero pairs. *You can add or remove zero pairs from a mat because adding or removing zero does not change the value of the counters on the mat.*

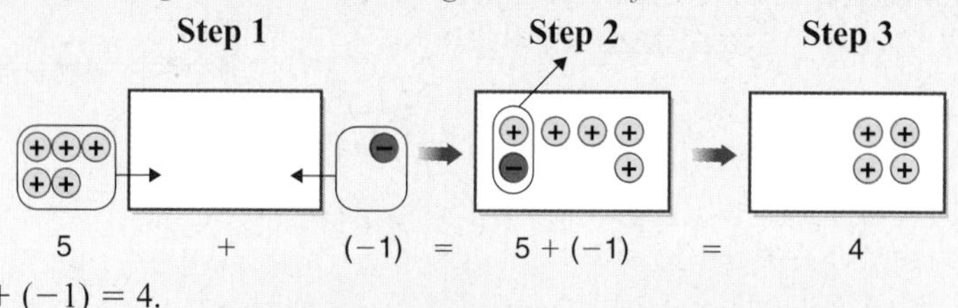

So, 5 + (−1) = 4.

ON YOUR OWN

1. Write the addition problem that is modeled below. **−7 + 2 = −5**

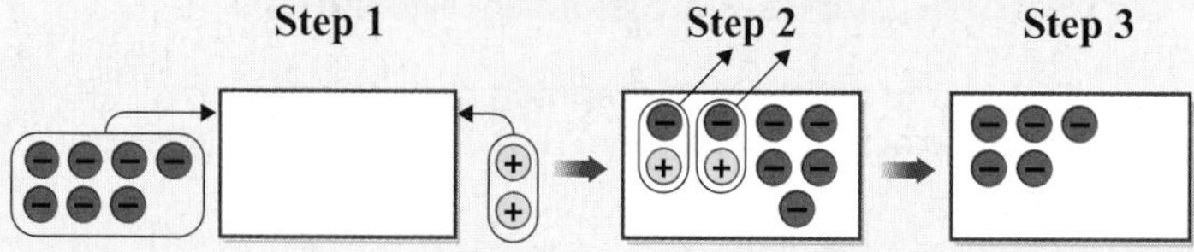

2–4. See Answer Appendix for models.

Use counters to find each sum. Use your result to write an addition sentence.

2. 5 + (−3) **5 + (−3) = 2** **3.** −4 + 1 **−4 + 1 = −3** **4.** −6 + (−5) **−6 + (−5) = −11**

5. ***Look Ahead*** Tell whether 8 + (−12) is *positive, negative,* or *zero.* **negative**

Have students make up a problem to model with counters. Ask them to sketch each stage of this solution.

5-4 Adding Integers

What you'll learn
You'll learn to add integers.

When am I ever going to use this?
Knowing how to add integers can help you check your savings account balance.

Word Wise
additive inverse

In 1996, scientists at the University of California discovered how to preserve a 2,300-year-old papyrus document. An *ionizer* was used to add negatively and positively charged atoms to neutralize the charges and eliminate static. This allowed the sheets of the document to be separated.

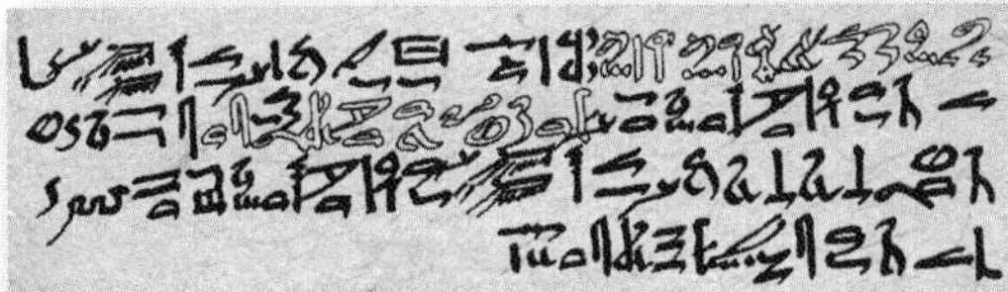

Cultural Kaleidoscope
The papyrus documents were discovered in Egypt in 1899. They had been wrapped around mummified crocodiles.

Like charged ions, integers with opposite signs can be added. What happens when you add integers that are opposites, like 2 and -2? Adding the opposite of an integer "undoes" the integer, and the result is 0. For this reason, two integers that are opposites are called **additive inverses**.

Additive Inverse Property	
Words:	The sum of any number and its additive inverse is 0.
Symbols:	**Arithmetic** $2 + (-2) = 0$ **Algebra** $a + (-a) = 0$

One way to add integers is by using arrows on a number line. Start at 0. Positive integers are represented by arrows pointing *right*. Negative integers are represented by arrows pointing *left*.

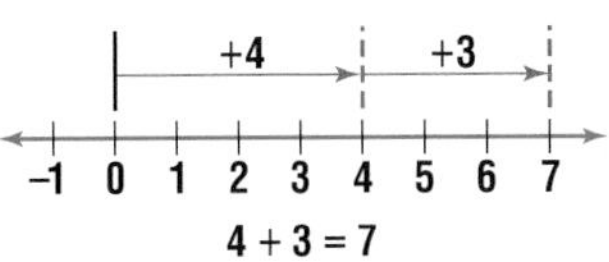

$4 + 3 = 7$

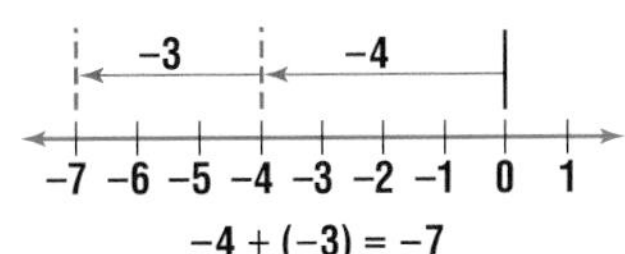

$-4 + (-3) = -7$

Adding Integers with the Same Sign	
	The sum of two positive integers is positive. The sum of two negative integers is negative.

Example 1 Use counters to solve $-6 + (-2) = x$.

Combine a set of 6 negative counters and a set of 2 negative counters.

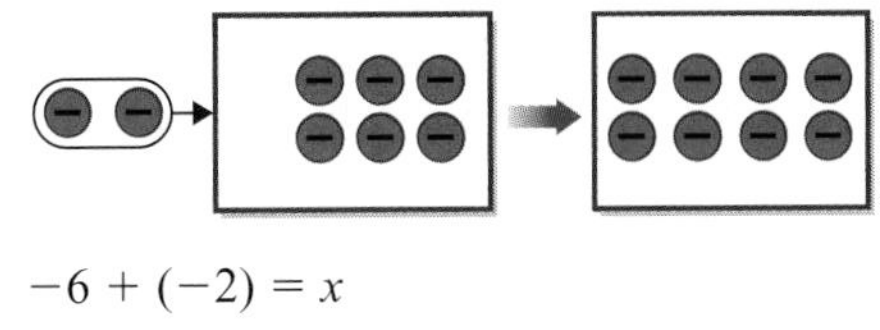

$$-6 + (-2) = x$$
$$-8 = x$$

5-4 Lesson Notes

Instructional Resources

- *Study Guide Masters,* p. 37
- *Practice Masters,* p. 37
- *Enrichment Masters,* p. 37
- Transparencies 5-4, A and B
- *Assessment and Evaluation Masters,* pp. 126, 127
- *Technology Masters,* p. 35

CD-ROM Program
- Resource Lesson 5-4
- Interactive Lesson 5-4

Recommended Pacing	
Standard	Days 5 & 6 of 15
Honors	Days 4 & 5 of 13
Block	Day 3 of 8

1 FOCUS

5-Minute Check
(Lesson 5-3)

On graph paper, draw a coordinate plane. Then graph and label each point.

1. $P(-3, 4)$
2. $F(2, 1)$
3. $R(3, -2)$
4. $J(-6, -2.5)$

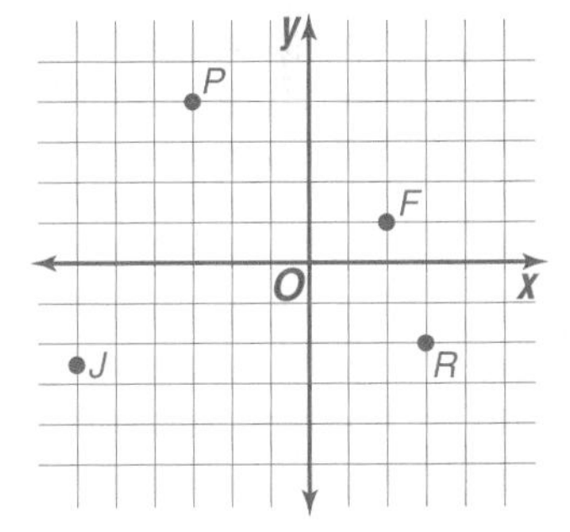

The 5-Minute Check is also available on **Transparency 5-4A** for this lesson.

Motivating the Lesson

Hands-On Activity Ask students to use counters to model the two sums shown on the number lines in the introduction to the lesson. Have students check their answers against the number-line answers and explain their results.

Classroom Vignette

"To practice positive and negative numbers, we play a game of "Stock Market." Groups of students select a name for their company and are given a $50 market value. Then each group draws an integer from a hat to add or subtract to their market value. We draw as many rounds as possible in 40 minutes and reward the team who has the highest market value in the end."

T.A. Aslesen

Travis A. Aslesen, Teacher
Elk Point Jefferson
Elk Point, SD

2 TEACH

Transparency 5-4B contains a teaching aid for this lesson.

Using Discussion Review the meaning of absolute value with students. Since the method for adding integers with different signs may confuse students, try to provide several examples of how the method works, using number lines and models.

In-Class Examples

For Example 1
Use counters to solve $-4 + (-3) = r$. -7

For Example 2
Solve $a = 26 + (-14)$. 12

For Example 3
Evaluate $-33 + k$ if $k = 25$. -8

Students can use the game to practice adding negative numbers. If there is a tie, players turn over their next two cards. The player with the greater total gets all eight cards. You may wish to have students add their own rules to the game. For example, they can make rules about what happens when a player makes a mistake in adding or how the game will be played if there are four players.

Let's look at the sum $4 + (-3)$.

Remove all of the zero pairs.

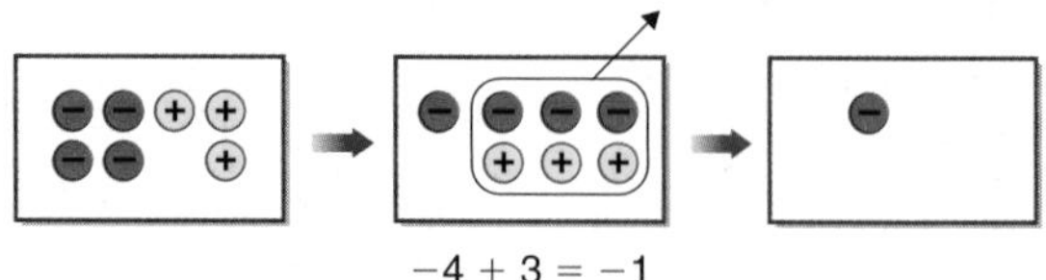

$4 + (-3) = 1$

Now, look at the sum $-4 + 3$.

$-4 + 3 = -1$

Adding Integers with Different Signs	To add integers with different signs, subtract their absolute values. The sum is • positive if the positive integer has the greater absolute value. • negative if the negative integer has the greater absolute value.

Examples

2 Solve $w = -40 + 15$.

$|-40| > |15|$, so the sum is negative.
The difference of 40 and 15 is 25.
So, $w = -25$.

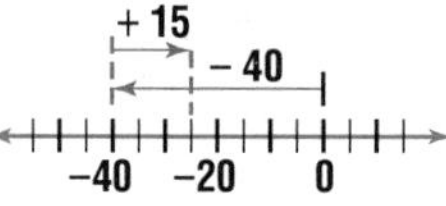

INTEGRATION **3** **Algebra** Evaluate $-13 + a$ if $a = 28$.

$-13 + a = -13 + 28$ *Replace a with 28.*

$|-13| < |28|$, so the sum is positive.
The difference of 13 and 28 is 15. So, $-13 + a = 15$.

Let the Games Begin

War of Integers

Math Skill
Adding Integers

Get Ready This game is for two players.  playing cards 1–10

Get Set In this game, black cards 1 through 10 are positive integers, and red cards 1 through 10 are negative integers. Shuffle and deal all of the cards.

Go Each player turns over his or her top two cards and finds the sum. The player with the greater total gets all of the cards. Play continues until all cards are used. The winner is the one with the most cards.

interNET CONNECTION Visit www.glencoe.com/sec/math/mac/mathnet for more games.

Investigations for the Special Education Student

This blackline master booklet helps you plan for the needs of your special education students by providing long-term projects along with teacher notes. Investigation 4, *The Check's in the Mail,* may be used with this chapter.

Cycling In the Extreme Games, Joe Guel rode his bicycle 17 feet down one side of a ramp and then rode 31 feet up the other side and into the air to do a back flip. How far above his starting position did Joe perform his trick?

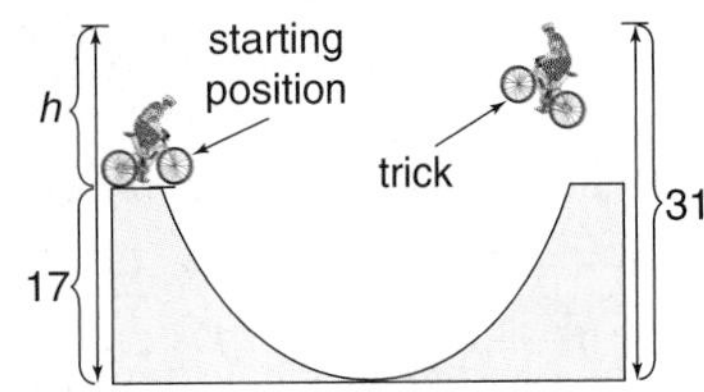

Explore The height of the ramp Joe went down was 17 feet. You can write this drop as -17 feet.

Plan Let h = the height above the ramp. Solve the equation $h = 31 + (-17)$.

Solve $|31| > |-17|$, so the sum is positive. The difference of 31 and 17 is 14. So, $h = 14$. Joe performed his trick 14 feet above his starting position.

Examine To check your solution, use a calculator.
31 [+] 17 [+○−] [=] 14 ✔

CHECK FOR UNDERSTANDING

Communicating Mathematics

Read and study the lesson to answer each question.

1. ***Explain*** whether or not three integers are all negative if their sum is negative. **See margin.**
2. ***Write*** the addition sentence shown by each model.

a. 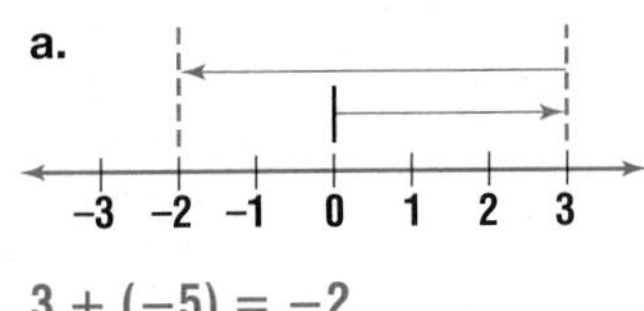

$3 + (-5) = -2$

b. 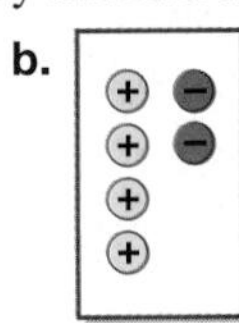

$4 + (-2) = 2$

HANDS-ON MATH

3. ***Model*** the sum of -5 and -2 using counters. **See margin.**

Guided Practice

Tell whether the sum is *positive*, *negative*, or *zero*.

4. $9 + (-11)$ **negative**
5. $-8 + 8$ **zero**
6. $-5 + 12$ **positive**

Solve each equation.

7. $y = 4 + (-13)$ **−9**
8. $-8 + (-2) = g$ **−10**
9. $h = -7 + 14$ **7**

Evaluate each expression if $a = 6$, $b = -2$, and $c = 5$.

10. $a + (-4)$ **2**
11. $-9 + c$ **−4**
12. $0 + b$ **−2**

13. ***Earth Science*** The greatest temperature change recorded in a 24-hour period was a drop of 100°F in 1916 at Browning, Montana. If the highest temperature was 44°F, what was the lowest temperature? **−56°F**

Reteaching the Lesson

Activity As needed, spend more time using either counters or a number line to show the addition of integers. Then use several problems with simple numbers to demonstrate adding by finding the difference between absolute values. Have students work with partners.

Error Analysis

Watch for students who misapply the rule for adding integers by obtaining 8 instead of -8 as the solution to $-33 + 25 = k$.

Prevent by using arrows on a number line to show why the sum has the same sign as the addend with the greater absolute value.

In-Class Example

For Example 4

From sea level, a rock climber ascends 523 feet and then scales down 88 feet to rest. How high above sea level is the resting place? **435 feet**

3 PRACTICE/APPLY

Check for Understanding

If students need additional practice or instruction after completing Exercises 1–13, one of these may be helpful.

- Extra Practice, see p. 581
- Reteaching Activity
- *Study Guide Masters,* p. 37
- *Practice Masters,* p. 37
- Interactive Mathematics Tools Software

Additional Answers

1. Not always; there may be 1 or 2 positive integers, but they have a smaller absolute value than the negative integer(s).

3. 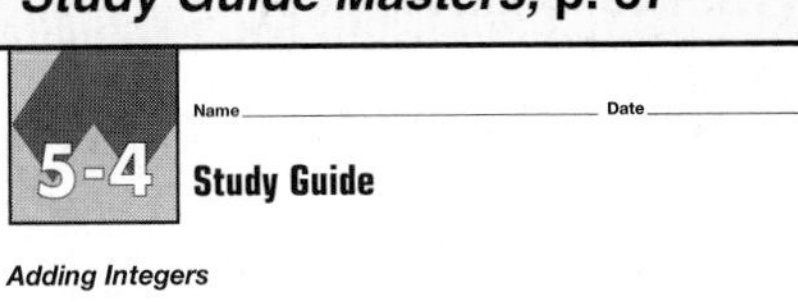

-7

***Study Guide Masters,* p. 37**

Name ________ Date ________

5-4 **Study Guide**

Adding Integers

To add integers, think of a number line. Locate the first addend on the number line. Move right if the second addend is positive. Move left if the second addend is negative.

Example 1 **Solve $t = 4 + (-10)$.**

Start at 0. Since 4 is positive, go 4 units to the right.
Since -10 is negative, go 10 units to the left.

−10 +4
−7 −6 −5 −4 −3 −2 −1 0 1 2 3 4 5 6 7 8

So, $t = -6$.

When you add integers, remember the following.
The sum of two positive integers is positive.
The sum of two negative integers is negative.
The sum of a positive integer and a negative integer is:
- positive if the positive integer has the greater absolute value.
- negative if the negative integer has the greater absolute value.

Examples 2 **Solve $n = 14 + (-11)$.**
$|14| > |-11|$,
so the sum is positive.
$14 - 11 = 3$
So, $n = 3$.

3 **Solve $-24 + 16 = k$.**
$|-24| > |16|$,
so the sum is negative.
$24 - 16 = 8$
So, $k = -8$.

Solve each equation.

1. $p = 16 + (-11)$ **5**
2. $-22 + (-7) = g$ **−29**
3. $y = -6 + 36$ **30**
4. $-50 + 50 = v$ **0**
5. $c = -10 + (-10)$ **−20**
6. $k = 12 + 9$ **21**
7. $100 + (-25) = w$ **75**
8. $n = 38 + (-6)$ **32**
9. $-50 + (-20) = v$ **−70**
10. $r = -89 + 29$ **−60**
11. $85 + (-10) = t$ **75**
12. $4 + (-10) = z$ **−6**

Evaluate each expression if a = 8, b = −8, and c = 4.

13. $a + 16$ **24**
14. $b + (-9)$ **−17**
15. $b + c$ **−4**
16. $-10 + c$ **−6**
17. $a + (-21)$ **−13**
18. $12 + b$ **4**

 T37 *Mathematics: Applications and Connections, Course 2*

Assignment Guide

Core: 15–43 odd, 45–50
Enriched: 14–42 even, 43–50

4 ASSESS

Closing Activity

Modeling Have students use counters to model two problems: one in which they add integers having the same sign and another in which they add integers having different signs.

Chapter 5, Quiz B (Lessons 5-3 and 5-4) is available in the *Assessment and Evaluation Masters,* p. 127.

Mid-Chapter Test (Lessons 5-1 through 5-4) is available in the *Assessment and Evaluation Masters,* p. 126.

Additional Answer

49.

Stem	Leaf
0	3 7 9 9
1	0 3 4 5
2	4
3	1

2|4 = 24

***Practice Masters,* p. 37**

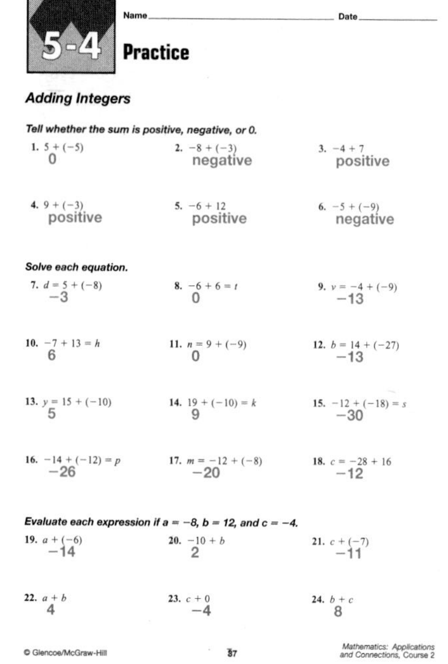
Name________________ Date__________

5-4 Practice

Adding Integers

Tell whether the sum is positive, negative, or 0.

1. $5 + (-5)$ 0	2. $-8 + (-3)$ negative	3. $-4 + 7$ positive
4. $9 + (-3)$ positive	5. $-6 + 12$ positive	6. $-5 + (-9)$ negative

Solve each equation.

7. $d = 5 + (-8)$ −3	8. $-6 + 6 = t$ 0	9. $v = -4 + (-9)$ −13
10. $-7 + 13 = h$ 6	11. $n = 9 + (-9)$ 0	12. $b = 14 + (-27)$ −13
13. $y = 15 + (-10)$ 5	14. $19 + (-10) = k$ 9	15. $-12 + (-18) = s$ −30
16. $-14 + (-12) = p$ −26	17. $m = -12 + (-8)$ −20	18. $c = -28 + 16$ −12

Evaluate each expression if a = −8, b = 12, and c = −4.

19. $a + (-6)$ −14	20. $-10 + b$ 2	21. $c + (-7)$ −11
22. $a + b$ 4	23. $c + 0$ −4	24. $b + c$ 8

 37 Mathematics: Applications and Connections, Course 2

EXERCISES

Practice

Tell whether the sum is *positive*, *negative*, or *zero*. 15. negative

14. $13 + (-8)$ positive **15.** $-4 + (-4)$ **16.** $-5 + 5$ zero
17. $5 + (-2)$ positive **18.** $-7 + 15$ positive **19.** $-11 + (-3)$ negative
20. $-10 + (-8)$ negative **21.** $9 + (-9)$ zero **22.** $-15 + 12$ negative

Solve each equation.

23. $-7 + 11 = w$ 4 **24.** $s = -6 + 6$ 0 **25.** $r = 19 + (-13)$ 6
26. $n = 5 + (-18)$ −13 **27.** $g = 3 + 10$ 13 **28.** $m = -11 + 13$ 2
29. $9 + (-8) = p$ 1 **30.** $-30 + 20 = v$ −10 **31.** $-47 + 28 = x$ −19

Evaluate each expression if *a* = 10, *b* = −10, and *c* = −5.

32. $a + (-3)$ 7 **33.** $-7 + b$ −17 **34.** $c + (-2)$ −7
35. $-8 + a$ 2 **36.** $a + (-10)$ 0 **37.** $16 + c$ 11
38. $0 + b$ −10 **39.** $a + b$ 0 **40.** $c + a$ 5

41. Evaluate $d + 7$ if $d = -93$. −86

42. What is the value of $m + n$ if $m = -3$ and $n = -17$? −20

Applications and Problem Solving

43. ***Football*** The Panthers lost 7 yards on one play and then completed a pass for 16 yards on the next play. What was the total number of yards gained or lost? 9 yards gained

44. ***Personal Finance*** Sean thought he had \$27 in his checking account and wrote a check for \$12 to buy a new CD. On the way home, Sean remembered that he had withdrawn \$20 the day before. What is the minimum amount Sean must quickly deposit in his account to avoid a bank service charge for insufficient funds? \$5

45. Marsha did not owe Yori any money, because she did not initially borrow any money.

45. ***Critical Thinking*** Marsha's friend Yori asked to borrow \$7 so she could go see a movie. When Marsha said she didn't have it, Yori concluded, "O.K., so you owe me \$7." What's wrong with Yori's reasoning?

Mixed Review

46. Name the *x*-coordinate and the *y*-coordinate for each point labeled at the right. Then tell in which quadrant each point lies. *(Lesson 5-3)*

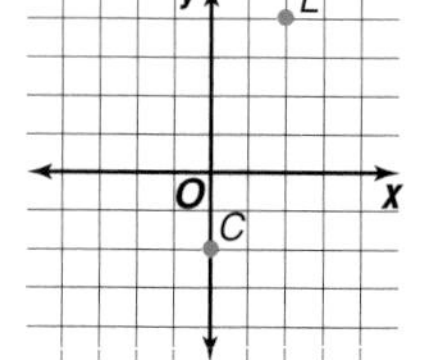

a. *C* **b.** *L* (2, 4), I

46a. (0, −2), *y*-axis

47. Find the opposite and the absolute value of −21. *(Lesson 5-1)* 21, 21

For **Extra Practice,** see page 581.

48. ***Probability*** If a number cube is rolled, find the probability that the result is an even number. Express the probability as a percent. *(Lesson 4-8)* 50%

49. ***Statistics*** The number of absent students during the past two weeks at Lincoln Junior High were 15, 24, 31, 14, 7, 9, 10, 13, 9, and 3. Make a stem-and-leaf plot for the data. *(Lesson 3-5)* See margin.

50. **Standardized Test Practice** How many square feet of wallpaper are needed to cover a wall that measures 9 feet by 16 feet? *(Lesson 1-7)* D

A 48 ft^2 **B** 64 ft^2 **C** 96 ft^2 **D** 144 ft^2

Extending the Lesson

***Enrichment Masters,* p. 37**

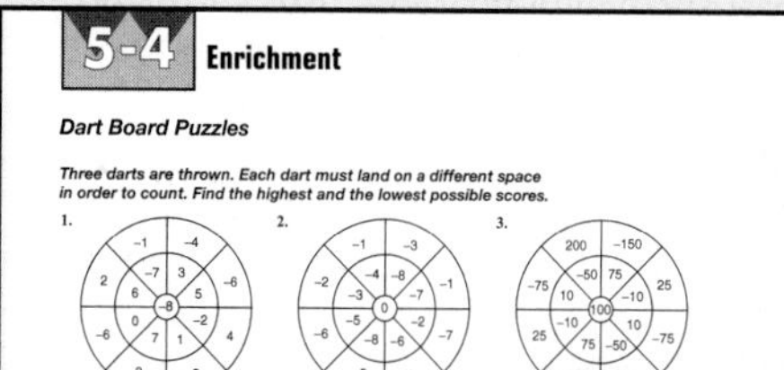
5-4 Enrichment

Dart Board Puzzles

Three darts are thrown. Each dart must land on a different space in order to count. Find the highest and the lowest possible scores.

1. 2. 3.

Activity Tell students that *consecutive integers* are 1 apart. For example, 1 and 2 are consecutive integers, as are also −6, −5, and −4. Ask the students to name two consecutive integers whose sum is −27 and then three consecutive integers whose sum is 0. −13, −14; −1, 0, 1

COOPERATIVE LEARNING

5-5A Subtracting Integers

A Preview of Lesson 5-5

counters

integer mat

You can use counters to model the subtraction of integers.

TRY THIS

Work with a partner.

1 Model 8 − 4.

Place 8 positive counters on the mat and then remove 4.

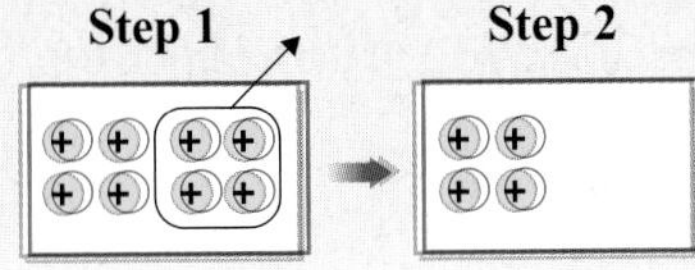

So, 8 − 4 = 4.

2 Model 7 − (−3).

Start with a set of 7 positive counters and try to remove 3 negative counters. Since there are no negative counters, add 3 zero pairs to the set. Now you can remove 3 negative counters.

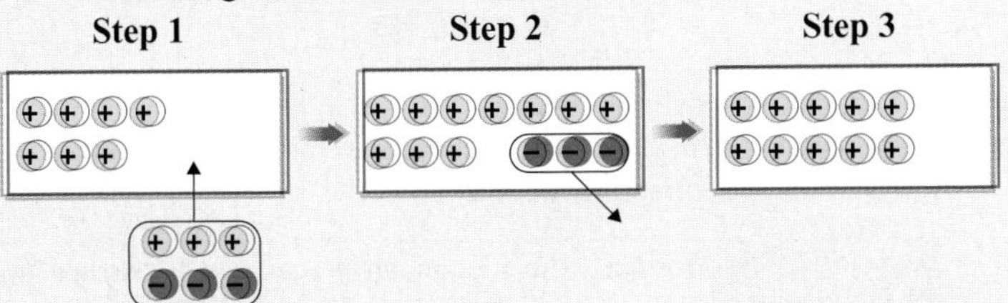

So, 7 − (−3) = 10.

ON YOUR OWN

2–5. See Answer Appendix for models.

1. Write the subtraction problem that is modeled below. **−7 − (−3) = −4**

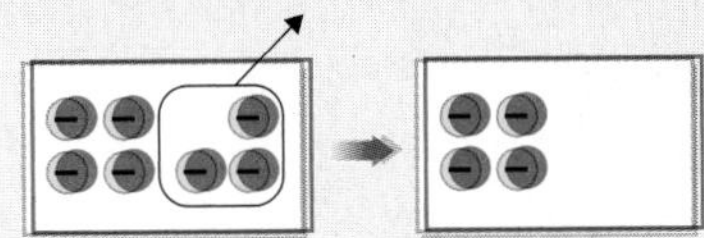

3. −4 − (−1) = −3
4. 5 − (−3) = 8

Use counters to find each difference. Use your result to write a subtraction sentence.

2. 6 − 2 **6 − 2 = 4** 3. −4 − (−1) 4. 5 − (−3) 5. −6 − 1 **−6 − 1 = −7**

6. *Look Ahead* Find $t = -8 - 6$ without using models. **−14**

Math Journal Ask students to make up a subtraction problem where a positive number is subtracted from a negative number. Have students describe how they would model the problem.

5-5A HANDS-ON LAB Notes

GET READY

Objective Students subtract integers by using models.

Optional Resources

Hands-On Lab Masters
- counters, p. 6
- integer mat, p. 8
- worksheet, p. 47

Overhead Manipulative Resources
- counters
- integer mat

Manipulative Kit
- counters
- integer mat

MANAGEMENT TIPS

Recommended Time
25 minutes

Getting Started Remind students of how they used counters to model addition of integers. Have them demonstrate how they think they can use the counters to model subtraction. Recall that subtraction can mean "take away."

Activity 1 shows subtraction of positive integers.

Activity 2 shows subtraction of a negative integer. For Activity 2, remind students of zero pairs.

ASSESS

Have students complete Exercises 1–5.

Use Exercise 6 to determine whether students have discovered the rules for subtracting integers.

5-5 Lesson Notes

Instructional Resources

- *Study Guide Masters,* p. 38
- *Practice Masters,* p. 38
- *Enrichment Masters,* p. 38
- Transparencies 5-5, A and B
- *Classroom Games,* pp. 13–15

- CD-ROM Program
  - Resource Lesson 5-5
  - Interactive Lesson 5-5

Recommended Pacing	
Standard	Days 7 & 8 of 15
Honors	Day 7 of 13
Block	Day 4 of 8

1 FOCUS

5-Minute Check
(Lesson 5-4)

Solve each equation.

1. $4 + (-5) = t$ −1
2. $-6 + 15 = w$ 9
3. $q = 26 + (-16)$ 10

Evaluate each expression if $a = 8$, $b = 12$, and $c = -6$.

4. $-7 + b$ 5
5. $c + a$ 2

The 5-Minute Check is also available on **Transparency 5-5A** for this lesson.

Motivating the Lesson

Communication Have students read the opening paragraph. Ask them to suggest a method for subtracting integers that doesn't involve using counters.

5-5 Subtracting Integers

What **you'll learn**

You'll learn to subtract integers.

When **am I ever going to use this?**

Knowing how to subtract integers can help you find how much temperatures have increased or decreased.

On July 4, 1997, *Sojourner,* the first-ever interplanetary rover, landed on Mars. The temperature on Mars can be −94°F at night and 72°F during the day. What is the range of the temperature *Sojourner* encountered as it explored the surface of Mars? *This problem will be solved in Example 1.*

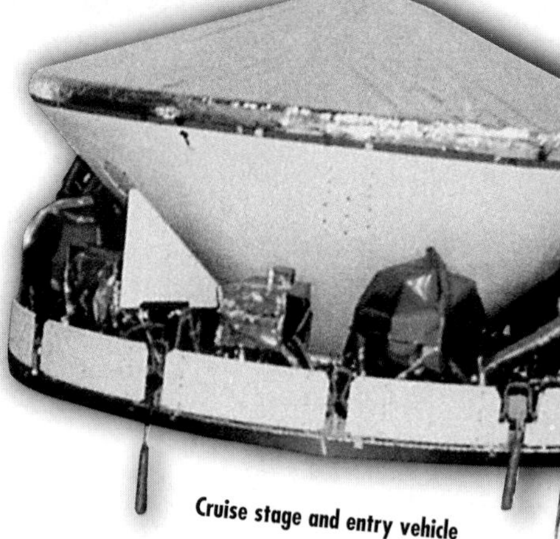

Cruise stage and entry vehicle

To see how addition and subtraction of integers are related, compare the subtraction 6 − 3 to the addition 6 + (−3).

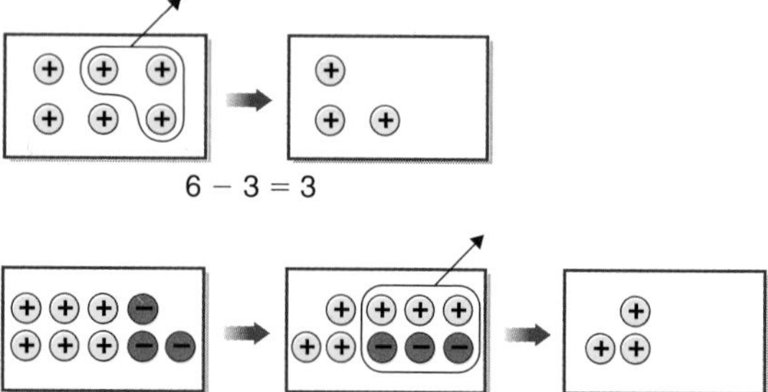

$6 - 3 = 3$

$6 + (-3) = 3$

Did you know The *Sojourner* is named after Sojourner Truth, an African American who promoted freedom for all people during the Civil War.

The diagrams above show that $6 - 3 = 6 + (-3)$. This example suggests that adding the additive inverse of an integer produces the same result as subtracting the integer.

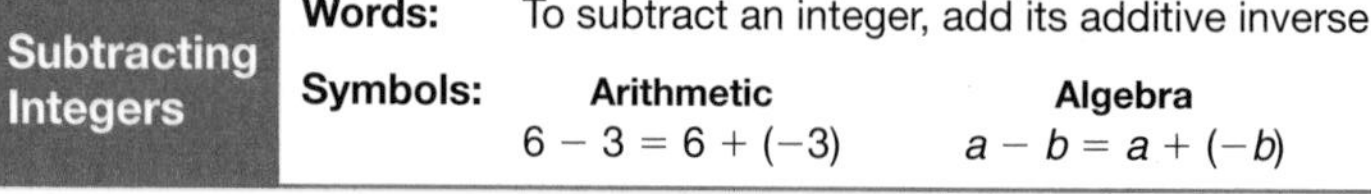

Subtracting Integers			
	Words:	To subtract an integer, add its additive inverse.	
	Symbols:	**Arithmetic** $6 - 3 = 6 + (-3)$	**Algebra** $a - b = a + (-b)$

Example CONNECTION

1 **Earth Science** **Refer to the beginning of the lesson. What is the range of the temperatures *Sojourner* encountered as it explored the surface of Mars?**

Let r = the range of the temperatures.

$r = 72 - (-94)$

$r = 72 + 94$ *To subtract −94, add 94.*

$r = 166$

The range of the temperatures *Sojourner* encountered was 166 degrees.

Multiple Learning Styles

Interpersonal Have teams of students research elevations of various cities and/or landmarks around the world. Have them write problems that can be solved by writing and solving equations with integers.

Examples

2 Solve $x = -9 - 5$.

$x = -9 - 5$

$x = -9 + (-5)$ *To subtract 5, add −5.*

$x = -14$

3 Solve $-15 - (-7) = w$.

$-15 - (-7) = w$

$-15 + 7 = w$ *To subtract −7, add 7.*

$-8 = w$

INTEGRATION 4 **Algebra** Evaluate $a - b$ if $a = 5$ and $b = 13$.

$a - b = 5 - 13$ *Replace a with 5 and b with 13.*

$= 5 + (-13)$ *To subtract 13, add −13.*

$= -8$

Interplanetary rover, Sojourner

CHECK FOR UNDERSTANDING

Communicating Mathematics

Read and study the lesson to answer each question.

1. ***Write*** $a - (-b)$ as an addition expression. **$a + b$**
2. ***Write*** a subtraction sentence shown by the model. **$2 - 4 = -2$**

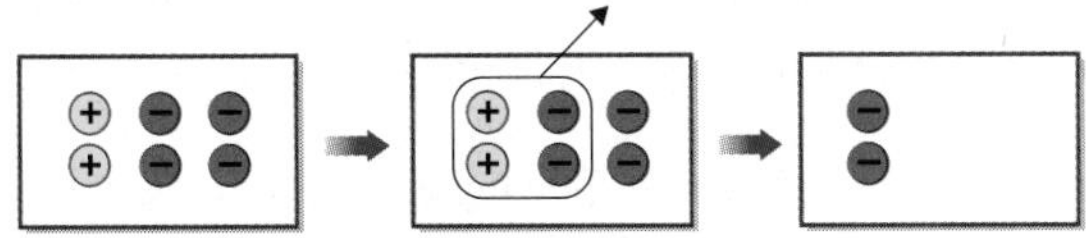

3. ***You Decide*** Antwan says that to solve $15 - 24 = p$, you can rewrite the equation as $24 - (15) = p$. Ellen thinks this is not right. Who is correct? Explain your reasoning. **Ellen; $15 - 24 = -9$, but $24 - (15) = 9$.**

Guided Practice

Solve each equation.

4. $m = 5 - (-10)$ **15**
5. $-7 - 6 = k$ **−13**
6. $s = 9 - (-11)$ **20**
7. $10 - 16 = j$ **−6**
8. $n = -22 - 5$ **−27**
9. $4 - (-19) = p$ **23**

Evaluate each expression if $b = -1$, $q = 6$, and $y = 3$.

10. $8 - q$ **2**
11. $3 - b$ **4**
12. $-y - 10$ **−13**

2 TEACH

Transparency 5-5B contains a teaching aid for this lesson.

Thinking Algebraically Provide students the record high and low temperatures for 5 states, including some for which the low temperature was below 0°F. Ask them first to estimate the difference between each state's high and low temperatures by using distance on a number line, and then to find the difference arithmetically.

In-Class Examples

For Example 1
Mount Whitney, at 14,494 feet above sea level, and Death Valley, at 282 feet below sea level, are the highest and lowest points in the 48 contiguous states and are only 85 miles apart. What is the difference in their elevations? **14,776 feet**

For Example 2
Solve $-12 - 8 = n$. **−20**

For Example 3
Solve $y = 34 - (-7)$. **41**

For Example 4
Evaluate $a - b$ if $a = 4$ and $b = -9$. **13**

Teaching Tip Remind students that they can check their answers using the related addition sentence. That is, if $a - b = c$, then $b + c = a$. For Example 2, $-14 = -9 - 5$ because $-14 + 5 = -9$.

3 PRACTICE/APPLY

Check for Understanding

If students need additional practice or instruction after completing Exercises 1–13, you may find one of the following options helpful.

- Extra Practice, see p. 581
- Reteaching Activity
- *Study Guide Masters,* p. 38
- *Practice Masters,* p. 38
- Interactive Mathematics Tools Software

Reteaching the Lesson

Activity You may wish to use number lines to model the subtraction of integers. Use arrows to the left or right from 0 to indicate the first number and an arrow from that point to show the number being subtracted. This number line shows $2 - 5$.

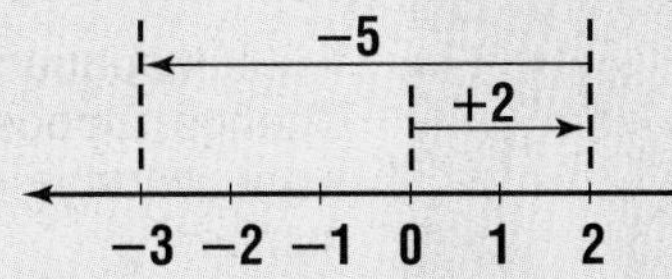

Assignment Guide

Core: 15–43 odd, 46–51
Enriched: 14–42 even, 43–44, 46–51
All: Self Test, 1–10

4 ASSESS

Closing Activity

Writing Have students explain how they would determine how many years ago the tyrant Ch'in Shih Huang-ti united several provinces into the Chinese Empire, in 221 B.C. **Add 221 to the current year.**

Additional Answer

44b. It would not be a good time to call, because it is the middle of the night in Honolulu.

***Study Guide Masters*, p. 38**

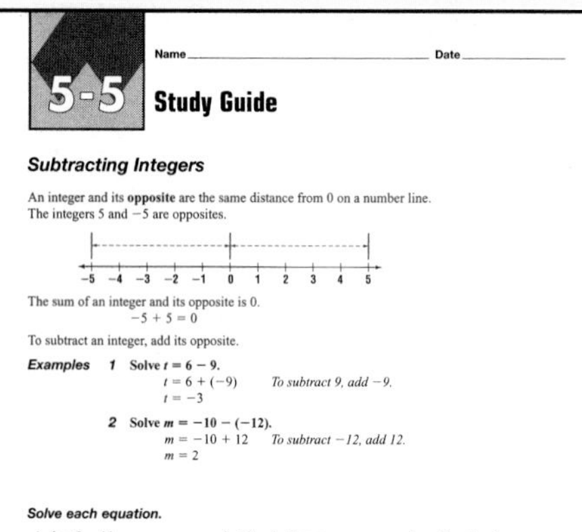

Name__________ Date__________

5-5 Study Guide

Subtracting Integers

An integer and its **opposite** are the same distance from 0 on a number line. The integers 5 and −5 are opposites.

The sum of an integer and its opposite is 0.

$-5 + 5 = 0$

To subtract an integer, add its opposite.

Examples **1** **Solve $t = 6 - 9$.**

$t = 6 + (-9)$ *To subtract 9, add −9.*

$t = -3$

2 **Solve $m = -10 - (-12)$.**

$m = -10 + 12$ *To subtract −12, add 12.*

$m = 2$

Solve each equation.

1. $b = 8 - 11$ −3
2. $18 - (-5) = p$ 23
3. $-10 - 4 = h$ −14
4. $n = -8 - (-6)$ −2
5. $v = -15 - 40$ −55
6. $x = 25 - (-13)$ 38
7. $51 - (-26) = k$ 77
8. $-30 - (-52) = a$ 22
9. $95 - 101 = m$ −6
10. $j = -75 - 50$ −125
11. $r = 5 - 55$ −50
12. $19 - (-10) = y$ 29

Evaluate each expression if $m = -1$, $n = 10$, and $p = 6$.

13. $m - 8$ −9
14. $10 - m$ 11
15. $-n - p$ −16
16. $n - m$ 11
17. $p - (-m)$ 5
18. $-25 - p$ −31

 38 *Mathematics: Applications and Connections, Course 2*

13. ***History*** Refer to the timeline below.

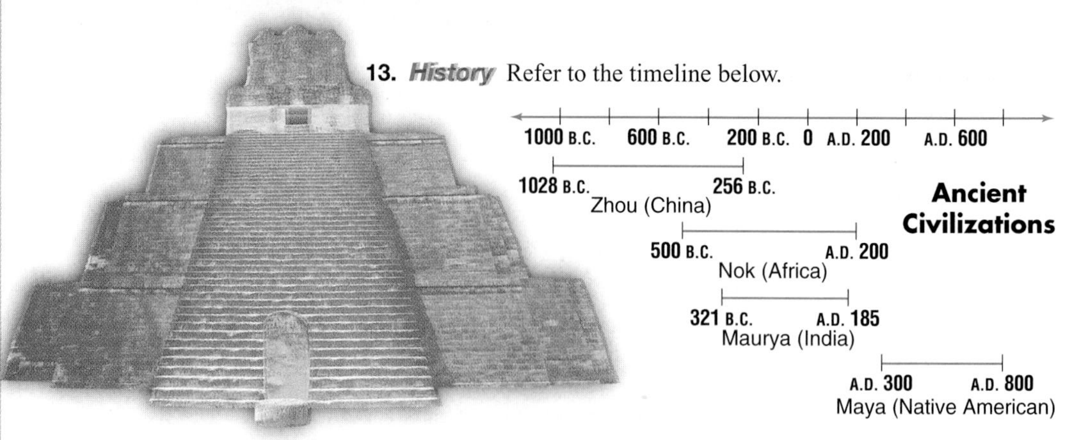

Mayan Temple of the Giant Jaguar

a. For how many years was the Maurya civilization in existence? **13a. 506 years**

b. How many years were there between the beginning of the Nok civilization and the end of the Maya civilization? **1,300 years**

EXERCISES

Practice

Solve each equation.

14. $7 - 13 = t$ **−6** **15.** $27 - (-8) = c$ **35** **16.** $16 - 7 = q$ **9**

17. $m = 2 - (-8)$ **10** **18.** $x = -12 - 9$ **−21** **19.** $14 - 15 = p$ **−1**

20. $-5 - (-5) = b$ **0** **21.** $z = -11 - 42$ **−53** **22.** $-17 - (-9) = r$ **22. −8**

23. $-18 - 14 = s$ **−32** **24.** $h = 13 - (-10)$ **23** **25.** $c = 19 - (-21)$ **25. 40**

26. $18 - 100 = y$ **−82** **27.** $b = 24 - (-14)$ **38** **28.** $-25 - (-10) = d$ **28. −15**

29. $z = 5 - (-27)$ **32** **30.** $17 - (-50) = t$ **67** **31.** $-42 - (-23) = w$ **31. −19**

Evaluate each expression if $m = -3$, $t = 8$, and $a = 4$.

32. $10 - a$ **6** **33.** $m - 5$ **−8** **34.** $-15 - t$ **−23**

35. $a - 7$ **−3** **36.** $6 - m$ **9** **37.** $t - a$ **4**

38. $t - m$ **11** **39.** $m - \text{a}$ **−7** **40.** $-a - m$ **−1**

41. Find the value of $-x - y$ if $x = -3$ and $y = 5$. **−2**

42. Find b if $a - (-b) = 10$ and $a = 8$. **2**

Applications and Problem Solving

43. ***Environment*** The highest temperature recorded in North America is 134°F in Death Valley, California, and the lowest recorded temperature is −87°F in Northice, Greenland. What is the range of temperatures? **221°**

44. ***Business*** Mr. Sanchez is a stockbroker in New York. He uses a table to determine whether it is a good time to contact various brokers' offices around the world.

a. If it is 7 A.M. in his office, what time is it in Honolulu? **2:00 A.M.**

b. Do you think it is a good time for Mr. Sanchez to make a call to Honolulu? Why? **See margin.**

When's a Good Time?

City	Hours
Honolulu	−5
Anchorage	−4
San Francisco	−3
Chicago	−1
New York	0
Paris	6
Tokyo	14

Classroom Vignette

"I teach subtraction of integers by using three words—Leave, Change, Opposite—which means leave the first number alone, change − to +, and take the opposite of the second number."

Leslee Hoey, Teacher
Welsh Valley School
Narberth, PA

Leslee Hoey

45. **Working on the CHAPTER Project** Refer to the table on page 183.

a. Find the difference between the high and low temperatures for each city. Write the latitude and the temperature difference of each city as an ordered pair. **45a. See Margin 45b. See Answer Appendix.**

b. Graph the ordered pairs on a coordinate plane. Let the x-axis represent the latitude and the y-axis represent the temperature difference.

46. True; when a is a positive integer, the sentence is also true.

46. **Critical Thinking** *True* or *false*? When a is a negative integer, $a - a = 0$.

Mixed Review

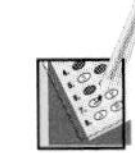

47. **Standardized Test Practice** Leonardo leaves his house and walks east 12 blocks to the store. He then turns around and walks west 17 blocks to his friend's house. Which integer describes Leonardo's final position? *(Lesson 5-4)* **A**

A -5 **B** 5 **C** 15 **D** 29

48. Find the GCF of 36 and 48. *(Lesson 4-4)* **12**

49. 3, 5, 9

49. Determine whether 135 is divisible by 2, 3, 4, 5, 6, 9, or 10. *(Lesson 4-1)*

50. **Data Analysis** The graph shows the number of orders taken each hour one day at a fast food restaurant. What time of the day appears to be the least busy at this restaurant? *(Lesson 3-2)* **3 P.M.**

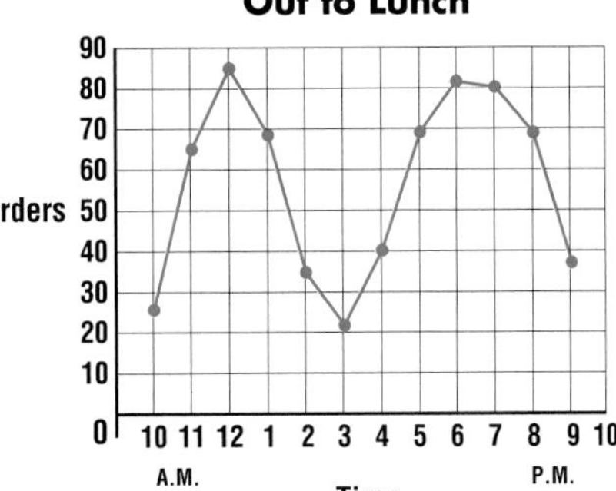

51. Write $\frac{3}{8}$ as a decimal. *(Lesson 2-7)* **0.375**

For **Extra Practice,** see page 581.

CHAPTER 5 Mid-Chapter Self Test

Write an integer for each situation. *(Lesson 5-1)*

1. a gain of 7 pounds **+7**
2. 4 points lost **−4**

Replace each ● with < or > to make a true sentence. *(Lesson 5-2)*

3. -16 ● -18 **>**
4. -12 ● 7 **<**
5. 4 ● -5 **>**

Name the x-coordinate and the y-coordinate for each point graphed. Then tell in which quadrant each point lies. *(Lesson 5-3)*

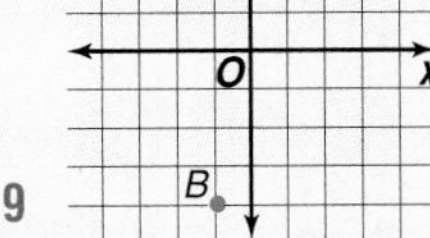

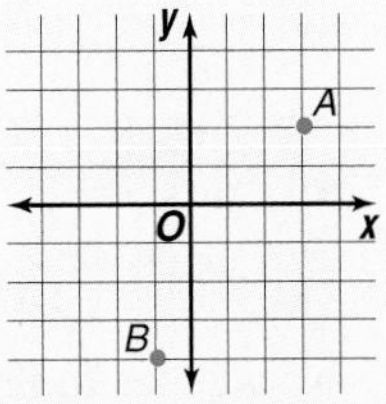

6. A **(3, 2), I**
7. B **(−1, −4), III**

Solve each equation. *(Lesson 5-4)*

8. $-6 + 2 = t$ **−4**
9. $g = 5 + (-14)$ **−9**

10. **Earth Science** Mauna Kea in Hawaii is the tallest mountain on Earth. Its height is 33,000 feet, but it's not all visible because 19,204 feet are below the ocean. How much of Mauna Kea is visible above water? *(Lesson 5-5)* **13,796 feet**

CHAPTER Project

Exercise 45 asks students to advance to the next stage of work on the Chapter Project. You may want students to work individually and then compare their graphs with a partner.

Mid-Chapter Self Test

The Mid-Chapter Self Test reviews the concepts in Lessons 5-1 through 5-5. Lesson references are given so students can review concepts not yet mastered.

Additional Answer

45a. Honolulu (21, 38), San Diego (33, 47), Atlanta (34, 89), Nashville (36, 90), Denver (40, 106), New York (41, 96), Minneapolis (45, 112), Bismark (47, 126), Seattle (48, 74), Fairbanks (65, 136)

Extending the Lesson

Enrichment Masters, p. 38

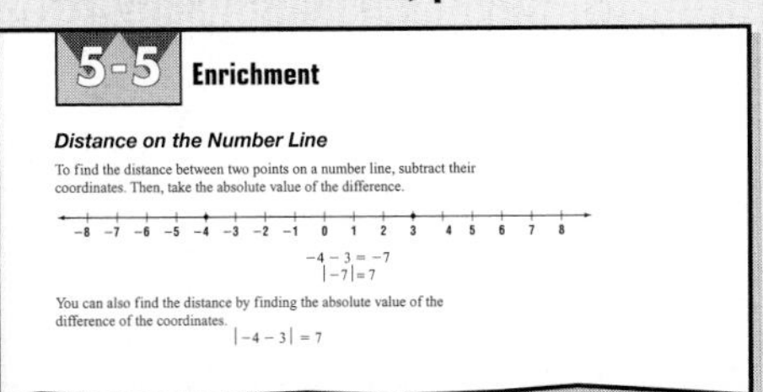

5-5 Enrichment

Distance on the Number Line

To find the distance between two points on a number line, subtract their coordinates. Then, take the absolute value of the difference.

$-4 - 3 = -7$
$|-7| = 7$

You can also find the distance by finding the absolute value of the difference of the coordinates.

$|-4 - 3| = 7$

Activity Have students make up number patterns using addition, subtraction, or both addition and subtraction of integers. Classmates are to find the rule and complete the pattern. Provide this sample: $-6, -2, -4, 0, -2, 2,$ __?__, __?__ **Sample answer: add 4, then add −2, alternately; 0, 4**

Practice Masters, p. 38

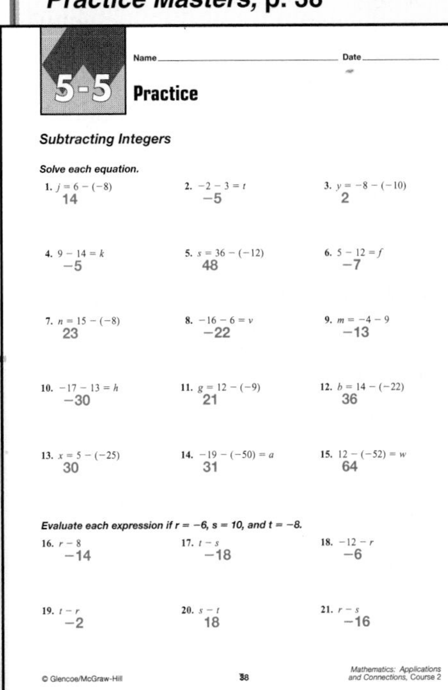

Name______ Date______

5-5 Practice

Subtracting Integers

Solve each equation.

1. $j = 6 - (-8)$ 14
2. $-2 - 3 = t$ −5
3. $y = -8 - (-10)$ 2
4. $9 - 14 = k$ −5
5. $x = 36 - (-12)$ 48
6. $5 - 12 = f$ −7
7. $n = 15 - (-8)$ 23
8. $-16 - 6 = v$ −22
9. $m = -4 - 9$ −13
10. $-17 - 13 = h$ −30
11. $g = 12 - (-9)$ 21
12. $b = 14 - (-22)$ 36
13. $x = 5 - (-25)$ 30
14. $-19 - (-50) = a$ 31
15. $12 - (-52) = w$ 64

Evaluate each expression if $r = -6$, $s = 10$, and $t = -8$.

16. $r - 8$ −14
17. $t - s$ −18
18. $-12 - r$ −6
19. $t - r$ −2
20. $s - t$ 18
21. $r - s$ −16

© Glencoe/McGraw-Hill 38 Mathematics: Applications and Connections, Course 2

GET READY

Objective Students multiply integers by using models.

Optional Resources
Hands-On Lab Masters
- integer counters, p. 6
- integer mat, p. 8
- worksheet, p. 48

Overhead Manipulative Resources
- counters
- integer mat

Manipulative Kit
- counters
- integer mat

MANAGEMENT TIPS

Recommended Time
15 minutes

Getting Started Display two models, one with ten positive counters and the other with nine negative counters. Ask students to identify which model represents two sets of five counters and which represents three sets of three counters.

Activity 1 points out to students that the first factors are positive. This means to *place* counters on the mat.

Activity 2 shows multiplication of two negative numbers. Whenever the first factor is negative, counters must be *removed* from the mat. Whenever counters must be removed, zero pairs must be used to set up the problem.

ASSESS

Have students work with partners to complete Exercises 1–6. Have partners take turns modeling and writing each multiplication problem.

Use Exercise 7 to determine whether students have discovered the rules for multiplying integers.

COOPERATIVE LEARNING

5-6A Multiplying Integers

A Preview of Lesson 5-6

counters

integer mat

You can use counters to model the multiplication of integers.

TRY THIS

Work with a partner.

1 Model $2 \times (-3)$.

Start with an empty mat. Place 2 sets of 3 negative counters on the mat.

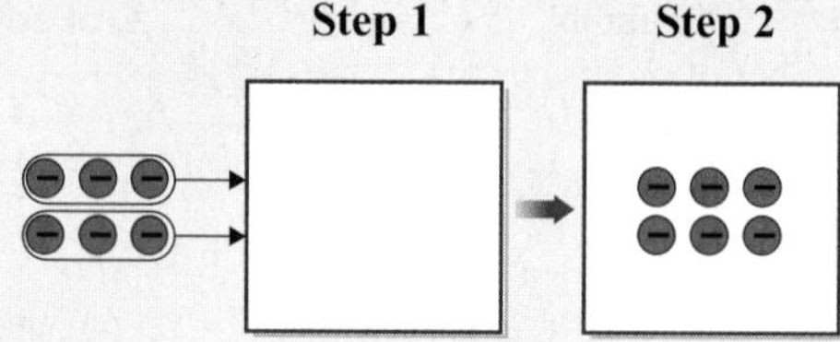

So, $2 \times (-3) = -6$.

2 Model $-2 \times (-4)$.

Start with an empty mat. Since -2 is the opposite of 2, $-2 \times (-4)$ means to *remove* 2 sets of 4 negative counters. Since there are no negative counters, place 8 zero pairs on the mat. Now you can remove 2 sets of 4 negative counters.

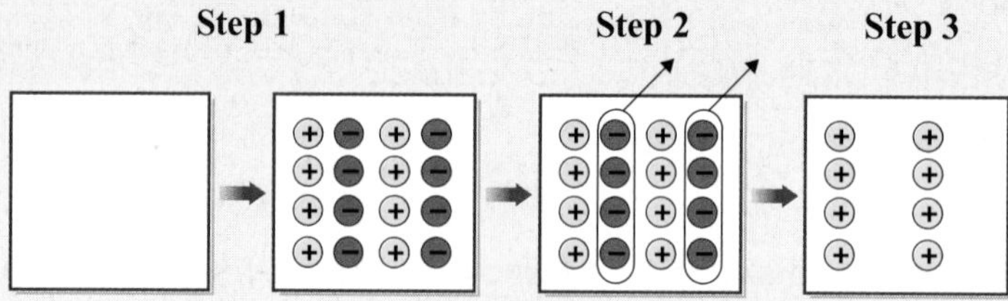

So, $-2 \times (-4) = 8$.

1–6. See Answer Appendix for models.

ON YOUR OWN

Use counters to find each product. Use your result to write a multiplication sentence.

1. 2×3 **$2 \times 3 = 6$**
2. $2 \times (-4)$ **$2 \times (-4) = -8$**
3. $-2 \times (-3)$ **$-2 \times (-3) = 6$**
4. $3 \times (-4)$ **$3 \times (-4) = -12$**
5. 4×0 **$4 \times 0 = 0$**
6. $-1 \times (-5)$ **$-1 \times (-5) = 5$**

7. ***Look Ahead*** Find $9 \times (-3)$ without using models. -27

Have students write a paragraph based on Activities 1–3 and the kind of answer, positive or negative, that results from each problem.

5-6 Multiplying Integers

What you'll learn
You'll learn to multiply integers.

When am I ever going to use this?
Knowing how to multiply integers can help you estimate how far you travel if you know the speed and the time.

In 1964, Jim Marshall of the Minnesota Vikings picked up a fumble and made a 66-yard run for what he thought was a touchdown. Unfortunately, he ran the wrong way and scored for the other team.

In football, the length of a run is important, but so is the direction. In mathematics, when multiplying integers, the size of the integer is important, but so is its direction or sign.

You can find $3(-2)$ by using counters or by looking for a pattern.

Method 1 Use counters.

3 sets of 2 negative counters is 6 negative counters or -6.

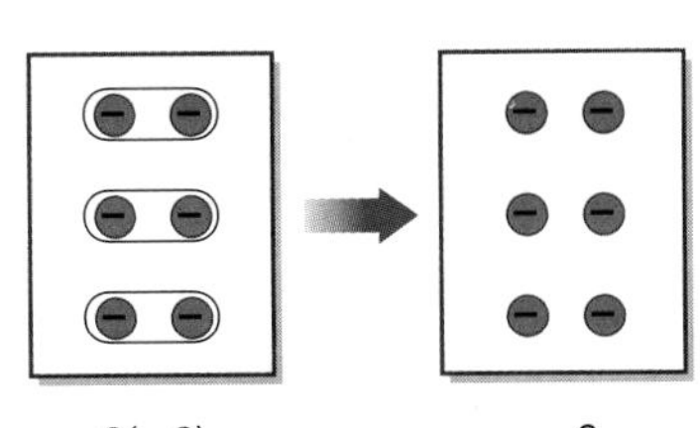

$3(-2) = -6$

Method 2 Look for a pattern.

$3 \cdot 2 = 6$
-3
$3 \cdot 1 = 3$
-3
$3 \cdot 0 = 0$
-3
$3 \cdot (-1) = -3$
-3
$3 \cdot (-2) = -6$

When two integers have different signs, the following rule applies.

Multiplying Integers with Different Signs	The product of two integers with different signs is negative.

Examples

1 **Solve $a = 7(-4)$.**

The two integers have different signs. The product will be negative.

$a = 7(-4)$

$a = -28$

2 **Solve $-9(5) = h$.**

The two integers have different signs. The product will be negative.

$-9(5) = z$

$-45 = z$

How would you find $-3(-2)$? You can use the same methods to multiply two integers with the same sign. When using counters, $-3(-2)$ means that you will remove 3 sets of 2 negative counters.

Motivating the Lesson

Hands-On Activity Fill a checkerboard with checkers. Ask a student to remove two checkers every 5 seconds for 25 seconds. Have the student count the checkers that were removed. Show students that this could be represented by the expression $5x(-2)$.

5-6 Lesson Notes

Instructional Resources

- *Study Guide Masters,* p. 39
- *Practice Masters,* p. 39
- *Enrichment Masters,* p. 39
- Transparencies 5-6, A and B
- *Assessment and Evaluation Masters,* p. 128
- *Science and Math Lab Manual,* pp. 89–92

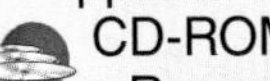
CD-ROM Program
- Resource Lesson 5-6
- Interactive Lesson 5-6

Recommended Pacing	
Standard	Days 9 & 10 of 15
Honors	Day 8 of 13
Block	Day 5 of 8

1 FOCUS

5-Minute Check
(Lesson 5-5)

Solve each equation.
1. $4 - 11 = r$ **−7**
2. $32 - (-15) = t$ **47**
3. $m = -41 - 26$ **−67**
4. $-14 - (-14) = k$ **0**
5. Evaluate the expression $y - x$ if $y = -8$ and $x = -5$. **−3**

The 5-Minute Check is also available on **Transparency 5-6A** for this lesson.

2 TEACH

Transparency 5-6B contains a teaching aid for this lesson.

Mastering Basic Skills Review the commutative property of multiplication as well as the property of multiplication by zero. Then focus on the rules for finding the sign of the product of two numbers: same signs—positive product; different signs—negative product.

In-Class Examples

For Example 1
Solve $r = 4(-6)$. -24

For Example 2
Solve $-5(3) = w$. -15

For Example 3
Solve $a = -6(-2)$. 12

For Example 4
Solve $(-5)^2 = c$. 25

For Example 5
Evaluate xyz if $x = -4$, $y = 2$, and $z = -6$. 48

Teaching Tip In Example 5, remind students that it does not matter in what order the integers are multiplied. The sign of the product will be the same. Have students change the order in the problem in Example 5 to *acb* and evaluate.

3 PRACTICE/APPLY

Check for Understanding

If students need additional practice or instruction after completing Exercises 1–13, one of these options may be helpful.

- Extra Practice, see p. 582
- Reteaching Activity
- *Study Guide Masters,* p. 39
- *Practice Masters,* p. 39

***Study Guide Masters,* p. 39**

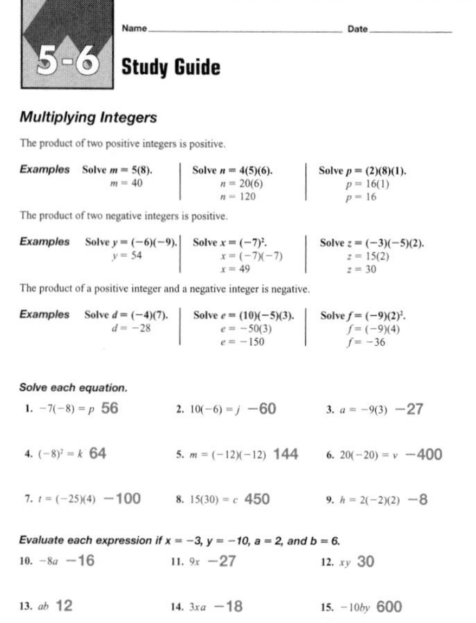

Name ______ Date ______

5-6 Study Guide

Multiplying Integers

The product of two positive integers is positive.

Examples **Solve $m = 5(8)$.** $m = 40$ | **Solve $n = 4(5)(6)$.** $n = 20(6)$, $n = 120$ | **Solve $p = (2)(8)(1)$.** $p = 16(1)$, $p = 16$

The product of two negative integers is positive.

Examples **Solve $y = (-6)(-9)$.** $y = 54$ | **Solve $x = (-7)^2$.** $x = (-7)(-7)$, $x = 49$ | **Solve $z = (-3)(-5)(2)$.** $z = 15(2)$, $z = 30$

The product of a positive integer and a negative integer is negative.

Examples **Solve $d = (-4)(7)$.** $d = -28$ | **Solve $e = (10)(-5)(3)$.** $e = -50(3)$, $e = -150$ | **Solve $f = (-9)(2)^2$.** $f = (-9)(4)$, $f = -36$

Solve each equation.

1. $-7(-8) = p$ 56
2. $10(-6) = j$ -60
3. $a = -9(3)$ -27
4. $(-8)^2 = k$ 64
5. $m = (-12)(-12)$ 144
6. $20(-20) = v$ -400
7. $t = (-25)(4)$ -100
8. $15(30) = c$ 450
9. $h = 2(-2)(2)$ -8

Evaluate each expression if $x = -3$, $y = -10$, $a = 2$, and $b = 6$.

10. $-8a$ -16
11. $9x$ -27
12. xy 30
13. ab 12
14. $3xa$ -18
15. $-10by$ 600
16. $-abx$ 36
17. x^2 9
18. $25y$ -250

 T 39 *Mathematics: Applications and Connections, Course 2*

Method 1 Use counters.

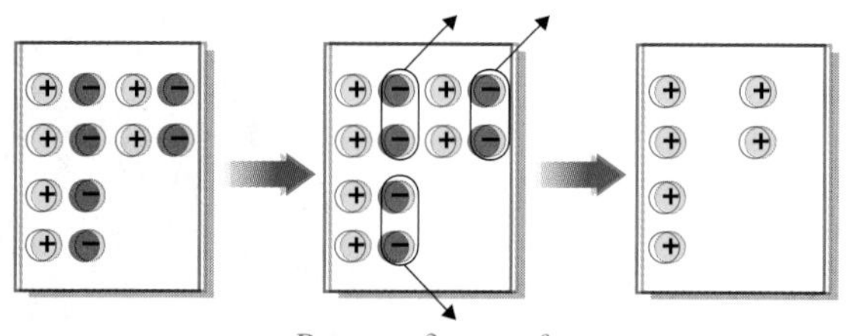

Remove 3 sets of 2 negative counters.

$-3(-2) = 6$

Method 2 Look for a pattern.

$-3 \cdot 2 = -6$
+3
$-3 \cdot 1 = -3$
+3
$-3 \cdot 0 = 0$
+3
$-3 \cdot (-1) = 3$
+3
$-3 \cdot (-2) = 6$

So, $-3(-2)$ is 6. This suggests the following rule.

Multiplying Integers with the Same Sign	The product of two integers with the same sign is positive.

Examples

3 Solve $a = -5(-6)$.

The two integers have the same signs. The product will be positive.

$a = -5(-6)$
$a = 30$

4 Solve $(-7)^2 = z$.

The exponent says there are two factors of -7. The product will be positive.

$(-7)^2 = z$
$(-7)(-7) = z$
$49 = z$

INTEGRATION

5 Algebra Evaluate abc if $a = -3$, $b = 7$, and $c = -2$.

$abc = (-3)(7)(-2)$ *Replace a with −3, b with 7, and c with −2.*
$= [(-3)(7)](-2)$ *First multiply −3 by 7. Then multiply the product by −2.*
$= (-21)(-2)$
$= 42$

CHECK FOR UNDERSTANDING

Communicating Mathematics

Read and study the lesson to answer each question. **1–3. See Answer Appendix.**

1. ***Tell*** what you can say about two integers if their product is negative.
2. ***Show*** a pattern to explain why $7(-3)$ must be -21.
3. ***Model*** $-3 \times (-4)$ using counters and write a multiplication sentence. (HANDS-ON MATH)

Guided Practice

Solve each equation.

4. $b = 10(-4)$ **−40**
5. $(-5)(-7) = x$ **35**
6. $y = 8(-4)$ **−32**
7. $-9(12) = p$ **−108**
8. $a = 15(-3)$ **−45**
9. $(-6)^2 = m$ **36**

Reteaching the Lesson

Activity Some students may benefit from visualizing multiplication of integers as repeated addition shown on a number line. For example, show $4 \times (-2)$ as $-2 + (-2) + (-2) + (-2) = -8$. Try this before illustrating the rules for multiplication by using patterns.

Error Analysis
Watch for students who assign the wrong sign to the products of one or more negative integers.
Prevent by suggesting to them that they should multiply first, disregarding the signs, and then use the rules provided to affix the correct sign.

Evaluate each expression if $x = -8$, $y = -3$, $z = 2$, and $w = 4$.

10. $-4z$ **−8** **11.** xy **24** **12.** x^2 **64**

13. ***Write a Problem*** in which you need to find the product of 6 and −13. Then find the product. **See students' work; −78.**

EXERCISES

Practice

Solve each equation. **16. 169 25. −100**

14. $y = -7(-13)$ **91** **15.** $(-3)^2 = a$ **9** **16.** $(-13)(-13) = c$

17. $-14(4) = j$ **−56** **18.** $b = -16(-5)$ **80** **19.** $10(-2) = s$ **−20**

20. $x = -11(5)$ **−55** **21.** $p = -4(-4)$ **16** **22.** $h = (-9)^2$ **81**

23. $v = 21(-3)$ **−63** **24.** $-4(-17) = t$ **68** **25.** $r = (-10)(10)$

26. $-8(12) = n$ **−96** **27.** $-7(18) = m$ **−126** **28.** $-25(4) = q$ **−100**

Evaluate each expression if $a = -9$, $b = 2$, $c = -5$, and $d = 6$.

29. $-4d$ **−24** **30.** $7a$ **−63** **31.** $-5ac$ **−225** **32.** c^2 **25**

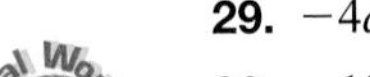

33. $-13d$ **−78** **34.** $-3b^2$ **−12** **35.** $10bc$ **−100** **36.** $-2cd$ **60**

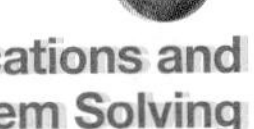

Applications and Problem Solving

37. ***Archaeology*** Archaeologists often use delicate instruments as small as toothbrushes to excavate sites of ancient treasures. Suppose an archaeologist removes 2 cubic meters of sand per day.

a. Write an equation to find how much sand is removed at the end of 14 days. **$-2(14) = x$**

b. Solve this equation. **−28 or 28 cubic meters removed**

38. ***Submarines*** A submarine is diving from the surface at a rate of 76 feet per minute. What is the depth of the submarine after 5 minutes?

39. ***Critical Thinking*** If the product of three integers is negative, what can you conclude about the signs of the integers? Write a rule for determining the sign of the product of three nonzero integers. **See margin.**

Mixed Review

38. −380 or 380 feet below sea level

41. −8, −4, −3, 0, 1, 4, 6

40. ***Hiking*** A Girl Scout troop is hiking on a trail that is 75 feet above sea level. They hike into a canyon that is 12 feet below sea level. Find the difference in altitudes. *(Lesson 5-5)* **87 feet**

41. Order 6, −3, 0, 4, −8, 1, −4 from least to greatest. *(Lesson 5-2)*

42. **Standardized Test Practice** The advertisement shows athletic shoes on sale for 20% off the regular price. What fraction of the regular price is this? *(Lesson 4-7)* **C**

A $\frac{1}{20}$ **B** $\frac{1}{4}$ **C** $\frac{1}{5}$ **D** $\frac{1}{2}$

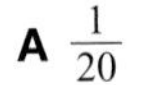

20% OFF our entire stock men's women's children's Athletic Shoes

For **Extra Practice,** see page 582.

43. Find 2.5 × 0.3. *(Lesson 2-4)* **0.75**

44. Evaluate 3 · 0.50 + 4 · 0.75. *(Lesson 1-2)* **4.5**

Assignment Guide

Core: 15–37 odd, 39–44
Enriched: 14–36 even, 37–44

4 ASSESS

Closing Activity

Writing Have students write four integer multiplication exercises, two with positive products and two with negative products.

Chapter 5, Quiz C (Lessons 5-5 and 5-6) is available in the *Assessment and Evaluation Masters,* p. 128.

Additional Answer

39. One of the integers is negative or all three integers are negative. If all three integers are positive, or if two of the integers are negative, the product is positive. If all three integers are negative, or if one of the integers is negative, the product is negative.

***Practice Masters,* p. 39**

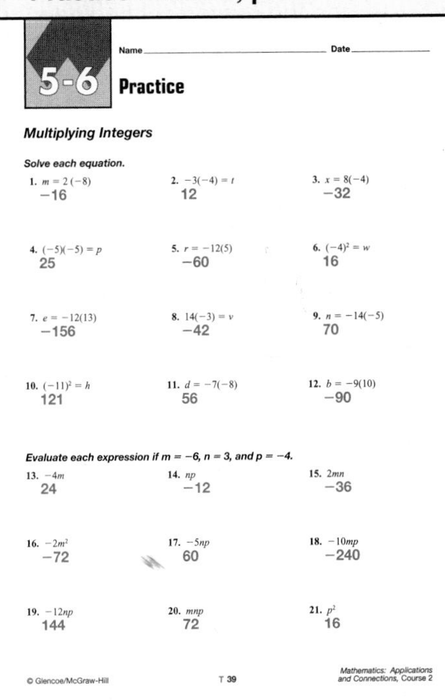

Name______ Date______

5-6 Practice

Multiplying Integers

Solve each equation.

1. $m = 2(-8)$ −16	2. $-3(-4) = t$ 12	3. $x = 8(-4)$ −32
4. $(-5)(-5) = p$ 25	5. $r = -12(5)$ −60	6. $(-4)^2 = w$ 16
7. $e = -12(13)$ −156	8. $14(-3) = v$ −42	9. $n = -14(-5)$ 70
10. $(-11)^2 = h$ 121	11. $d = -7(-8)$ 56	12. $b = -9(10)$ −90

Evaluate each expression if $m = -6$, $n = 3$, and $p = -4$.

13. $-4m$ 24	14. np −12	15. $2mn$ −36
16. $-2m^2$ −72	17. $-5np$ 60	18. $-10mp$ −240
19. $-12np$ 144	20. mnp 72	21. p^2 16

© Glencoe/McGraw-Hill T 39 *Mathematics: Applications and Connections, Course 2*

Extending the Lesson

***Enrichment Masters,* p. 39**

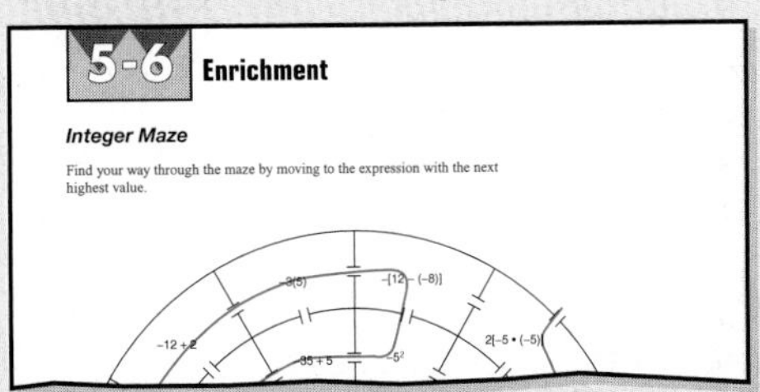

5-6 Enrichment

Integer Maze

Find your way through the maze by moving to the expression with the next highest value.

Activity Have students explore products with more than two negative factors. Ask them to look for a pattern to find a rule for determining the signs. **odd number of negatives: negative product; even number of negatives: positive product**

5-7A THINKING LAB Notes

Objective Students solve problems by using the look-for-a-pattern strategy.

Recommended Pacing	
Standard	Day 11 of 15
Honors	Day 9 of 13
Block	Day 6 of 8

1 FOCUS

Getting Started Have students act out the situation presented at the beginning of the lesson by assigning the role of Ramon to one student. Have Ramon choose two students to e-mail. Have those students each choose two others to e-mail. Repeat the process a third time. Have the class determine the pattern that is being played out.

2 TEACH

Teaching Tip After students complete the opening problem, you may wish to have them discuss the usefulness of examining data to look for patterns. Ask them to suggest jobs, tasks, or situations in which looking for patterns is necessary. Then have them talk about when the strategy of finding and using patterns can be a reasonable one to use.

In-Class Example

Your town has a new soccer team. At the first game, 300 fans showed up. At the next game, each of those fans brought two fans with them. At the third game, each of the previous fans arrived with two more fans. If this pattern continues, how many fans will attend the fifth game? **24,300**

PROBLEM SOLVING

5-7A Look for a Pattern

A Preview of Lesson 5-7

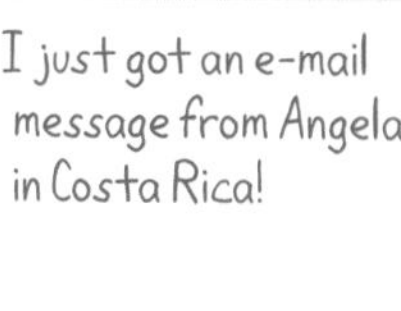

I just got an e-mail message from Angela in Costa Rica!

I wonder if Alysia and Joyce have heard from her? Why don't you forward her message to them?

Good idea! Then they can forward it to other people.

After 10 minutes, Ramon forwarded the e-mail message to 2 of his friends. After 10 more minutes, those 2 friends each forwarded the message to 2 more friends. If the message was forwarded like this every 10 minutes, how many people received Angela's e-mail message after 40 minutes?

You can solve this problem by looking for a pattern.

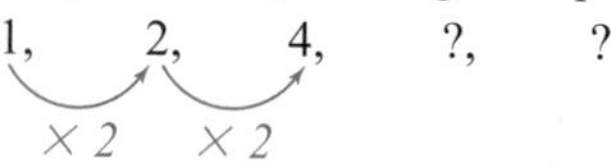

To continue the pattern, multiply 2 by the previous term.

$$4 \times 2 = 8 \qquad 8 \times 2 = 16$$

So, after 40 minutes, $1 + 2 + 4 + 8 + 16$ or 31 people got the message.

Time (min)	People Receiving Message
0	1
10	2
20	4
30	?
40	?

THINK ABOUT IT

Work with a partner. **1. See margin.**

1. ***State*** the pattern and find the next three terms in the sequence 6, 18, 54, 162, ...
2. ***Determine*** how many people would receive Angela's e-mail message at the end of 40 minutes if it is forwarded to 3 people instead of 2 each time. **121 people**
3. ***Apply*** the **look for a pattern** strategy to solve the following problem.
   A display of cereal boxes at Quik Mart is stacked in the shape of a pyramid. There are 4 boxes in the top row, 6 boxes in the next row, 8 boxes in the next row, and so on. The display contains 7 rows of boxes. How many boxes are in the display? **70 boxes**

Reteaching the Lesson

Activity Some students may benefit from additional practice with sequences involving simpler numbers, or from examining patterns containing shapes, colors, or letters.

Additional Answer

1. Multiply by 3; 486; 1,458; 4,374.

For **Extra Practice,** see page 582.

ON YOUR OWN

4. The second step of the 4-step plan for problem solving asks you to *plan* the solution. ***Explain*** how you can use the look for a pattern strategy to help you plan a solution.
5. ***Write a Problem*** in which looking for a pattern would help you solve it. Explain your answer. **See students' work.**

4. See margin.

6. ***Look Ahead*** Study the pattern in the table.

$6 \times (-1) = -6$	→	$-6 \div (-1) = 6$
$6 \times (-2) = -12$	→	$-12 \div (-2) = 6$
$6 \times (-3) = -18$	→	$-18 \div (-3) = 6$
$6 \times (-4) = -24$	→	$-24 \div (-4) = 6$
$6 \times (-5) = -30$	→	$-30 \div (-5) = 6$

Find $-36 \div (-6)$. **6**

MIXED PROBLEM SOLVING

STRATEGIES

Look for a pattern.
Solve a simpler problem.
Act it out.
Guess and check.
Draw a diagram.
Make a chart.
Work backward.

Solve. Use any strategy.

7. ***Health*** Minya has decided to start an exercise program. She plans to begin by working out for 5 minutes and then doubling her exercise time each day for 1 week. Write a sequence showing the length of time she exercises each day. Is her plan reasonable? Why or why not? **See margin.**
8. ***Life Science*** The table shows about how many times a firefly flashes at different temperatures. Estimate how many times a firefly will flash when the temperature is 36°C. **23 times**

Outside Temperature (°C)	Flashes Per Minute
20	9
24	11
28	14
32	18

9. ***Physical Science*** The 176-pound pendulum at the Center of Science and Industry museum in Columbus, Ohio, swings back and forth, knocking down two pegs every 15 minutes. How many pegs are knocked down after 3 hours? **24 pegs**
10. ***Life Science*** The graph shows how this summer's rainfall compares to normal.

Summer Rainfall

a. What does 0 on this graph represent?

b. Write an integer to represent the rainfall for each month shown.

c. Write a sentence that summarizes the message this graph conveys about this summer's rainfall. **a–c. See margin.**

11. ***Earth Science*** The giant kelp seaweed is found in the Pacific Ocean. One plant grows 3 feet the first two days. If it continues to grow at the same rate, what would be the length of the seaweed at the end of 80 days? **120 feet**
12. **Standardized Test Practice** Joan took a bag of cookies to the school musical rehearsal. Half were given to the musicians and five to the director of the play. Joan was left with 15 cookies. How many cookies did she take to rehearsal? **C**

A 30 **B** 35 **C** 40 **D** 45 **E** Not Here

3 PRACTICE/APPLY

Check for Understanding

Use the results from Exercise 3 to determine whether students understand how finding patterns can help them solve a problem.

Extra Practice If students need additional practice in problem solving, extra practice is available on the following pages.

- Look for a Pattern, p. 582
- Mixed Problem Solving, pp. 605–606

Assignment Guide

All: 4–12

4 ASSESS

Closing Activity

Writing Have students write number sequences for others to complete by finding and continuing a pattern. Ask the problem solvers to state the rule being used.

Additional Answers

4. **Once you find a pattern, you can continue the pattern to find the solution.**
7. **5, 10, 20, 40, 80, 160, 320; no, because 320 min. = $5\frac{1}{3}$ hr, so she will be exercising more than 5 hours each day by the 7th day.**

10a. normal rainfall

10b. −3, −2, −4, 2

10c. There was a drought this summer.

Extending the Lesson

Activity The table shows the world's population since 1980, and the estimated world's population for 2000. Approximately what will the world's population be in 2005? **about 6,666 billion**

Year	Population (billions)
1980	4,478
1985	4,889
1990	5,326
1995	5,786
2000 (est.)	6,226

5-7 Lesson Notes

Instructional Resources

- *Study Guide Masters,* p. 40
- *Practice Masters,* p. 40
- *Enrichment Masters,* p. 40
- Transparencies 5-7, A and B
- *Diversity Masters,* p. 18
- *Technology Masters,* p. 36

CD-ROM Program
- Resource Lesson 5-7

Recommended Pacing	
Standard	Day 12 of 15
Honors	Day 10 of 13
Block	Day 6 of 8

1 FOCUS

5-Minute Check
(Lesson 5-6)

Solve each equation.

1. $r = -4(-12)$ 48
2. $f = -8(14)$ −112
3. $p = (-11)^2$ 121
4. $5(-15) = a$ −75
5. Evaluate mn if $m = -9$ and $n = 9$. −81

The 5-Minute Check is also available on **Transparency 5-7A** for this lesson.

Motivating the Lesson

Hands-On Activity Give students index cards with integers and operation symbols. Have them use the cards to make a true multiplication sentence, such as $-8 \times -2 = 16$. Have them use the same numbers and a division sign card to write an associated sentence. $16 \div -2 = -8$

2 TEACH

Transparency 5-7B contains a teaching aid for this lesson.

Mastering Basic Skills

Reemphasize to students that since division is related to multiplication, the same rules apply.

5-7 Dividing Integers

What you'll learn
You'll learn to divide integers.

When am I ever going to use this?
Knowing how to divide integers can help you split the cost of a gift among any number of people.

Did you know The Grand Canyon was carved out as a result of 60 million years of erosion by the Colorado River.

The ocean waves cause some coastlines to recede every year. Suppose a beach receded 8 centimeters in 4 years. If the beach receded at a steady rate, what was the average change in the coastline per year?

Let b represent the average change per year. To find b, divide -8 by 4.

$$-8 \div 4 = b$$

Division of integers is related to multiplication. The division sentence $-8 \div 4 = b$ can be written as the multiplication sentence $4 \times b = -8$.
Think: 4 times what number equals −8?

$$4(2) = 8$$
$$4(-2) = -8 \checkmark$$

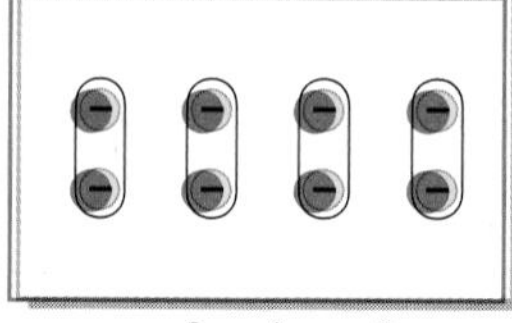
$-8 \div 4 = -2$

So, $b = -2$. The beach receded 2 centimeters per year.

Let's see how some other division sentences are related to multiplication sentences.

$$2 \times 3 = 6 \rightarrow 6 \div 2 = 3$$
$$2(-3) = -6 \rightarrow -6 \div 2 = -3$$
$$-2 \times 3 = -6 \rightarrow -6 \div (-2) = 3$$
$$-2 \times (-3) = 6 \rightarrow 6 \div (-2) = -3$$

The pattern suggests the following rule to determine the sign of a quotient.

Dividing Integers The quotient of two integers with the same sign is positive. The quotient of two integers with different signs is negative.

Examples

Solve each equation.

1. $a = -48 \div (-4)$

$a = -48 \div (-4)$ *The signs are the same.*
$= 12$ *The quotient is positive.*

2. $-20 \div 5 = d$

$-20 \div 5 = d$ *The signs are different.*
$-4 = d$ *The quotient is negative.*

Classroom Vignette

"After students learn to add, subtract, multiply, and divide integers, we play *Integer Concentration* to review and practice. On a grid on an overhead projector, I mix up expressions and their corresponding answers. I cover each grid square with a slip of paper. Students take turns uncovering pairs of squares to find a match."

Cheryl Chang

Cheryl Chang, Teacher
Samuel Enoka Kalama Intermediate
Makawao, HI

You can solve problems in algebra by dividing integers.

Example 3 — INTEGRATION **Algebra** Evaluate $\frac{h}{jk}$ if $h = 36, j = 2$, and $k = -3$.

$$\frac{h}{jk} = \frac{36}{2(-3)} \quad h = 36, j = 2, k = -3$$
$$= \frac{36}{-6} \quad \frac{36}{-6} \text{ means } 36 \div (-6).$$
$$= -6$$

CHECK FOR UNDERSTANDING

Communicating Mathematics

Read and study the lesson to answer each question.

1. **Write** two division sentences related to the multiplication sentence $4 \times (-3) = -12$. **$-12 \div 4 = -3$; $-12 \div (-3) = 4$**
2. **Explain** why $\frac{45}{-9}$ and $\frac{-45}{9}$ are equal. **See margin.**

Guided Practice

Solve each equation.

3. $-20 \div (-5) = k$ **4**
4. $t = -63 \div 7$ **−9**
5. $12 \div (-2) = j$ **−6**
6. $c = -42 \div (-6)$ **7**
7. $n = 51 \div (-17)$ **−3**
8. $-100 \div 20 = b$ **−5**

Evaluate each expression if $x = -18$, $y = 6$, and $q = -3$.

9. $\frac{96}{q}$ **−32**
10. $-108 \div y$ **−18**
11. $\frac{y^2}{x}$ **−2**
12. **Geometry** The formula for the area A of a parallelogram is $A = bh$, where b = base and h = height. Find the height of the parallelogram if the area is 54 cm² and the base is 9 cm. **6 cm**

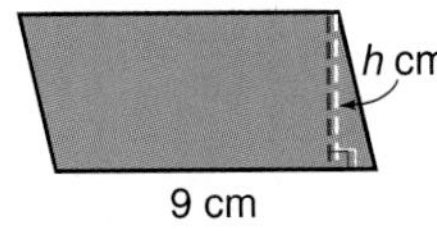

EXERCISES

Practice

Solve each equation. **17. 12 22. 1**

13. $15 \div (-3) = n$ **−5**
14. $p = -44 \div 11$ **−4**
15. $a = -14 \div (-1)$ **14**
16. $c = 72 \div (-2)$ **−36**
17. $-108 \div (-9) = v$
18. $t = -64 \div 4$ **−16**
19. $27 \div (-3) = s$ **−9**
20. $-90 \div 6 = d$ **−15**
21. $-45 \div (-15) = k$ **3**
22. $-100 \div (-100) = y$
23. $q = -56 \div 8$ **−7**
24. $300 \div (-25) = h$ **−12**
25. $r = -220 \div (-1)$ **220**
26. $68 \div (-17) = j$ **−4**
27. $-140 \div 7 = m$ **−20**

In-Class Examples

For Example 1
Solve $a = -28 \div (-7)$. **4**

For Example 2
Solve $-18 \div 3 = y$. **−6**

For Example 3
Evaluate $\frac{ab}{c}$ if $a = 8$, $b = 6$, and $c = -3$. **−16**

Teaching Tip For Example 3, have students show all steps in the evaluation process.

3 PRACTICE/APPLY

Check for Understanding

If students need additional practice or instruction after completing Exercises 1–12, you may find one of the following options helpful.

- Extra Practice, see p. 582
- Reteaching Activity
- *Study Guide Masters,* p. 40
- *Practice Masters,* p. 40

Assignment Guide

Core: 13–37 odd, 39–44
Enriched: 14–36 even, 37–44

***Study Guide Masters,* p. 40**

Name__________ Date__________

5-7 Study Guide

Dividing Integers

If two integers have the same sign, their quotient is positive.

Examples

1 Solve $k = 560 \div 8$. $k = 70$ — *The signs are the same. The quotient is positive.*

2 Solve $h = -120 \div (-6)$. $h = 20$ — *The signs are the same. The quotient is positive.*

If two integers have different signs, their quotient is negative.

Examples

3 Solve $a = -75 \div 5$. $a = -15$ — *The dividend is negative. The divisor is positive. The quotient is negative.*

4 Solve $b = 99 \div (-33)$. $b = -3$ — *The dividend is positive. The divisor is negative. The quotient is negative.*

Solve each equation.

1. $y = 64 \div (-8)$ **−8**
2. $-100 \div 4 = c$ **−25**
3. $f = -250 \div (-5)$ **50**
4. $60 \div (-12) = x$ **−5**
5. $-90 \div (-10) = u$ **9**
6. $-88 \div 4 = k$ **−22**
7. $375 \div (-25) = g$ **−15**
8. $t = -960 \div (-3)$ **320**
9. $r = 700 \div 35$ **20**

Evaluate each expression if $r = -96$, $t = -8$, and $v = 2$.

10. $\frac{r}{t}$ **12**
11. $\frac{t}{v}$ **−4**
12. $\frac{-4r}{t}$ **−48**
13. $\frac{t^2}{v}$ **32**
14. $\frac{728}{t}$ **−91**
15. $\frac{tv}{4}$ **−4**
16. $\frac{r}{-48}$ **2**
17. $\frac{4t}{v}$ **−16**
18. $\frac{r}{tv}$ **6**

 T 40 *Mathematics: Applications and Connections, Course 2*

Reteaching the Lesson

Activity Have students use index cards with an integer on each and cards with 4 and 5 on them to create true division statements involving integers.

Additional Answer

2. Both are equal to −5, because the quotient of two integers with different signs is negative.

4 ASSESS

Closing Activity

Modeling Have students use graph paper to sketch plans for building a stairway to an attic above a 10-foot ceiling. If each step is 8 inches high, how many steps will be needed? 15

***Practice Masters*, p. 40**

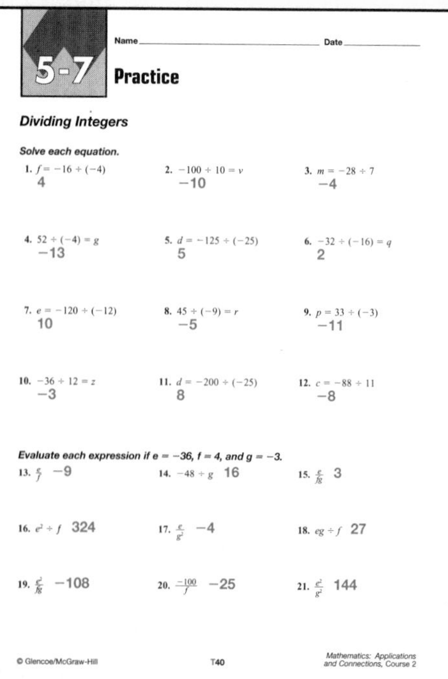

Name__________ Date__________

5-7 Practice

Dividing Integers

Solve each equation.

1. $f = -16 \div (-4)$ 4
2. $-100 \div 10 = v$ −10
3. $m = -28 \div 7$ −4
4. $52 \div (-4) = g$ −13
5. $d = -125 \div (-25)$ 5
6. $-32 \div (-16) = q$ 2
7. $e = -120 \div (-12)$ 10
8. $45 \div (-9) = r$ −5
9. $p = 33 \div (-3)$ −11
10. $-36 \div 12 = z$ −3
11. $d = -200 \div (-25)$ 8
12. $c = -88 \div 11$ −8

Evaluate each expression if e = −36, f = 4, and g = −3.

13. $\frac{e}{f}$ −9
14. $-48 \div g$ 16
15. $\frac{e}{fg}$ 3
16. $e^2 \div f$ 324
17. $\frac{e}{g^2}$ −4
18. $eg \div f$ 27
19. $\frac{e^2}{fg}$ −108
20. $\frac{-100}{f}$ −25
21. $\frac{e^2}{g^2}$ 144

 T40 *Mathematics: Applications and Connections, Course 2*

Evaluate each expression if a = −27, b = 9, and c = −3.

28. $a \div b$ −3
29. $a \div (-3)$ 9
30. $69 \div c$ −23
31. $a^2 \div b$ 81
32. $\frac{126}{b}$ 14
33. $\frac{a}{bc}$ 1
34. $\frac{a}{c}$ 9
35. $\frac{a^2}{bc}$ −27
36. Find the quotient of −36 and −3. 12

Applications and Problem Solving

37. ***Gifts*** The six class officers at Fair Middle School have decided to buy a class gift for their faculty advisor. If the gift costs $24, write an equation that can be used to represent how much each student must contribute towards the purchase of the gift. $y = 24 \div 6$

38. ***Sales*** The graph shows four magazines that had losses between 1989 and 1999. The negative numbers represent how many fewer magazines were sold in 1999 than in 1989. Find the mean of these four numbers. −3,311,100

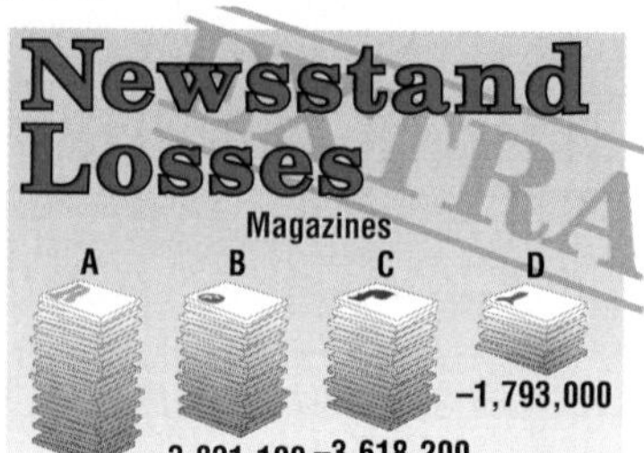

39. ***Critical Thinking*** List all the numbers by which −30 is divisible.

39. −30, −15, −10, −6, −5, −3, −2, −1, 1, 2, 3, 5, 6, 10, 15, 30

Mixed Review

40. **Standardized Test Practice** An oil rig is drilling at a rate of 7 feet per minute. How far has the oil rig dug after 42 minutes? *(Lesson 5-6)* D

    A 35 ft **B** −49 ft **C** −264 ft **D** −294 ft **E** Not Here

41. Replace ● in $\frac{1}{6}$ ● $\frac{2}{15}$ with <, >, or = to make a true sentence. *(Lesson 4-10)* >

42. Describe the pattern in the sequence 4, 12, 36, 108, ... Then find the next three terms. *(Lesson 4-3)* Multiply by 3; 324, 972, 2,916.

43. ***Nutrition*** The table shows the Calorie information for two meals from an Indian restaurant. Find how many of the Calories in each meal come from fat. *(Lesson 2-4)*

    a. Meal A 115.2
    b. Meal B 225.6

Meal	Total Calories	Portion of Calories from Fat
A Nan Shrimp biryani Raita Tamata salat	480	0.24
B Samaso Chicken tandoori Peas and rice Sang paneer	752	0.30

Source: *Vitality*

44. ***Music*** A band is putting together a new CD. It can use up to 60 minutes of music. The band members have selected 6 songs that are each 4 minutes long and 8 songs that are each 5 minutes long. Will all of their selections fit on the CD? Explain. *(Lesson 1-1)* no; $(6 \cdot 4) + (8 \cdot 5) = 64$ minutes

For **Extra Practice,** see page 582.

Extending the Lesson

***Enrichment Masters*, p. 40**

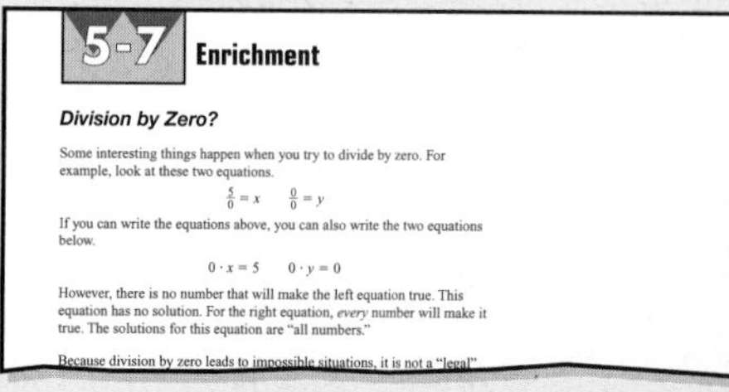

5-7 Enrichment

Division by Zero?

Some interesting things happen when you try to divide by zero. For example, look at these two equations.

$$\frac{5}{0} = x \qquad \frac{0}{0} = y$$

If you can write the equations above, you can also write the two equations below.

$$0 \cdot x = 5 \qquad 0 \cdot y = 0$$

However, there is no number that will make the left equation true. This equation has no solution. For the right equation, *every* number will make it true. The solutions for this equation are "all numbers."

Because division by zero leads to impossible situations, it is not a "legal"

Activity Tell students that the formula $F = \frac{9}{5}C + 32$ converts Celsius degrees to Fahrenheit degrees. Ask them to give the Fahrenheit temperature for −5°C. Then ask what is the Celsius equivalent to 32°F. 23°F, 0°C

Integration: Geometry

Graphing Transformations

What you'll learn

You'll learn to graph transformations on a coordinate plane.

When am I ever going to use this?

You'll be able to see transformations in art and nature.

Word Wise

transformation
reflection
translation

Many flags have a variety of geometric **transformations**. That is, one geometric shape is used in many different positions to form a pattern or design.

Flag of St. Vincent and the Grenadines

There are many ways to move a geometric shape on a coordinate plane. A figure can be flipped, turned, slid, stretched, or shrunk. When a figure is flipped, it is called a **reflection**. When it is slid, it is called a **translation**. Both of these transformations can be described using ordered pairs and their graphs.

Example INTEGRATION

1 Geometry **Triangle *CDE* has vertices *C*(2, 1), *D*(5, 3), and *E*(3, 4). Graph its reflection over the *y*-axis.**

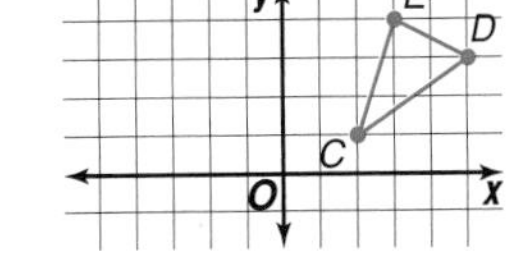

Explore Graph $\triangle CDE$ by graphing each ordered pair and connecting the points to form $\triangle CDE$. Label each vertex.

Plan For a figure reflected over the y-axis, the y-coordinates are exactly the same, and the x-coordinates are the opposite of each other. So, multiply the x-coordinate of each ordered pair by -1. Write the new ordered pair.

Solve

Vertices of $\triangle CDE$	Multiply the x-coordinate by -1.	New Ordered Pairs
$C(2, 1)$	$(2 \times (-1), 1)$	$C'(-2, 1)$
$D(5, 3)$	$(5 \times (-1), 3)$	$D'(-5, 3)$
$E(3, 4)$	$(3 \times (-1), 4)$	$E'(-3, 4)$

Study Hint

Reading Math C' is read as C prime, D' as D prime, and E' as E prime.

Graph the new ordered pairs and label each point. Connect these points to form $\triangle C'D'E'$.

Examine The two triangles have the same shape and size. Triangle $C'D'E'$ is the result of flipping $\triangle CDE$ over the y-axis.

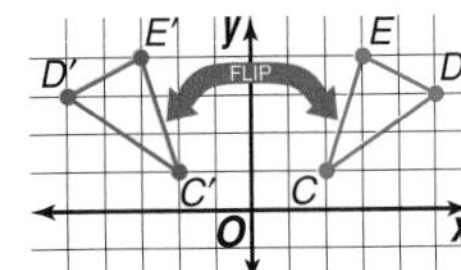

The transformation in Example 1 is a reflection over the y-axis. You can also do a reflection over the x-axis by multiplying the y-coordinates by -1. *You will reflect $\triangle ABC$ over the x-axis in Exercise 1.*

MathPASS CD-ROM

This CD-ROM offers a complete, self-paced mathematics curriculum. Each lesson includes a pretest, tutorial, guided practice, and posttest. MathPASS Lesson 15 is correlated to this Student Edition lesson.
For Windows & Macintosh

5-8 Lesson Notes

Instructional Resources

- *Study Guide Masters,* p. 41
- *Practice Masters,* p. 41
- *Enrichment Masters,* p. 41
- Transparencies 5-8, A and B
- *Assessment and Evaluation Masters,* p. 128

CD-ROM Program
- Resource Lesson 5-8
- Interactive Lesson 5-8

Recommended Pacing	
Standard	Day 13 of 15
Honors	Day 11 of 13
Block	Day 7 of 8

1 FOCUS

5-Minute Check
(Lesson 5-7)

Solve each equation.
1. $d = 54 \div (-6)$ -9
2. $-42 \div (-7) = z$ 6
3. $m = -32 \div 4$ -8

Evaluate each expression if $t = -27$, $u = 9$, and $v = -3$.
4. $\frac{t}{v}$ 9
5. $u^2 \div 9$ 9

The 5-Minute Check is also available on **Transparency 5-8A** for this lesson.

Motivating the Lesson

Communication Have students read the opening paragraph. Ask where else they have seen designs consisting of translations and reflections.

2 TEACH

Transparency 5-8B contains a teaching aid for this lesson.

Reading Mathematics The introduction to this lesson includes the terms *reflection, translation,* and *transformation.* Have students discuss the similarities and differences between the terms as generally used and as generally used to refer to geometric shapes.

In-Class Examples

For Example 1

$\triangle ABC$ has vertices $A(2, 2)$, $B(4, 3)$, and $C(6, 1)$. Graph its reflection over the y-axis.

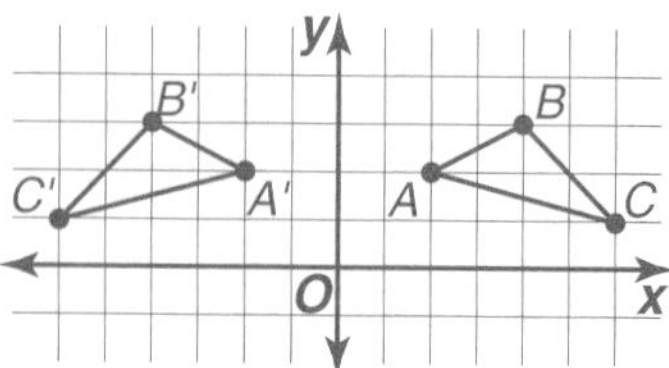

For Example 2

Graph $\triangle XYZ$ with vertices $X(3, -5)$, $Y(6, -4)$, and $Z(4, -2)$. Translate $\triangle XYZ$ 2 units left and 4 units down.

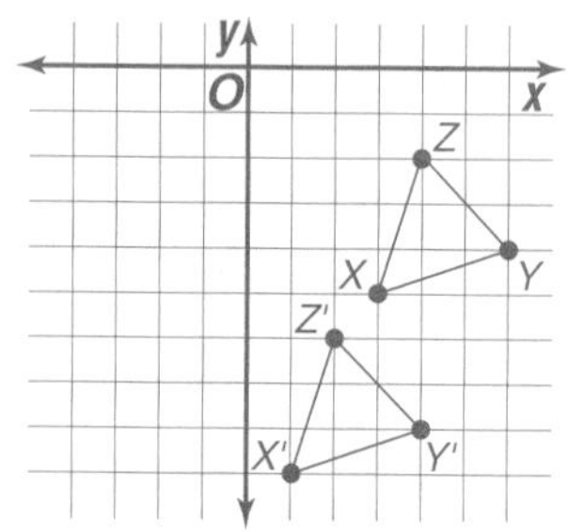

***Study Guide Masters,* p. 41**

Name ____________ Date ________

Study Guide

Integration: Geometry
Graphing Transformations

One kind of transformation is a **reflection.** A reflection is a flip. Multiply the x-coordinate by -1 to reflect over the y-axis. Multiply the y-coordinate by -1 to reflect over the x-axis.

Example 1 **$\triangle ABC$ has vertices $A(1, 2)$, $B(4, 3)$ and $C(3, -1)$. Graph its reflection over the y-axis.**

Multiply each x-coordinate by -1.
$A(1, 2) \to A'(-1, 2)$
$B(4, 3) \to B'(-4, 3)$
$C(3, -1) \to C'(-3, -1)$

Another type of transformation is a **translation.** A translation is a slide.

Example 2 **$\triangle LMN$ has vertices $L(2, -2)$, $M(-1, -3)$ and $N(-1, 1)$. Translate $\triangle LMN$ 2 units up and 3 units right.**

Add 3 to each x-coordinate. Add 2 to each y-coordinate.
$L(2, -2) \to (2 + 3, -2 + 2) \to L'(5, 0)$
$M(-1, -3) \to (-1 + 3, -3 + 2) \to M'(2, -1)$
$N(-1, 1) \to (-1 + 3, 1 + 2) \to N'(2, 3)$

Graph each triangle and its transformation. Write the ordered pairs for the vertices of the new triangle.

1. $\triangle DEF$ with vertices $D(1, 2)$, $E(5, 3)$ and $F(5, 0)$ reflected over the y-axis

2. $\triangle QRS$ with vertices $Q(-6, -2)$, $R(-1, 0)$ and $S(-1, 3)$ translated 1 unit up and 7 units right

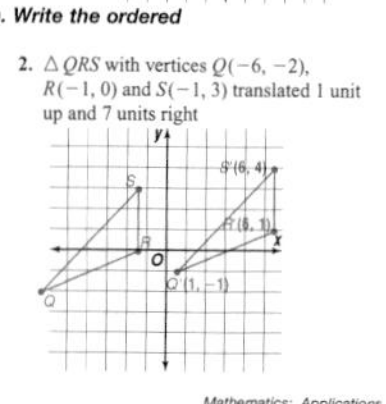

© Glencoe/McGraw-Hill T 41 *Mathematics: Applications and Connections, Course 2*

In a translation, a figure slides from one location to the next without changing its orientation.

Example 2 INTEGRATION

Geometry **Graph $\triangle QRS$ with vertices $Q(6, -2)$, $R(0, 3)$, and $S(-2, -1)$. Translate $\triangle QRS$ 7 units left and 4 units down.**

Graph $\triangle QRS$. Since each x-coordinate is moved 7 units to the left and each y-coordinate is moved 4 units down, the new ordered pairs can be written as $(x, y) + (-7, -4) = (x - 7, y - 4)$.

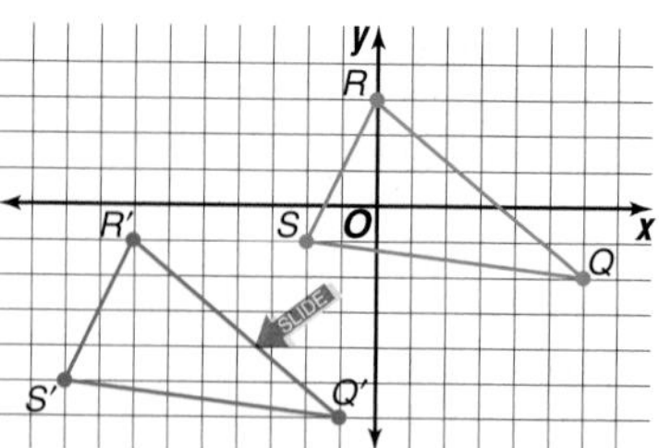

Vertices of $\triangle QRS$	$(x + (-7), y + (-4))$	New Ordered Pairs
$Q(6, -2)$	$(6 + (-7), -2 + (-4))$	$Q'(-1, -6)$
$R(0, 3)$	$(0 + (-7), 3 + (-4))$	$R'(-7, -1)$
$S(-2, -1)$	$(-2 + (-7), -1 + (-4))$	$S'(-9, -5)$

CHECK FOR UNDERSTANDING

Communicating Mathematics

Read and study the lesson to answer each question. **1, 3. See Answer Append**

1. **Draw** the result of reflecting $\triangle CDE$ from Example 1 over the x-axis.
2. **Tell** what type of transformation is shown by the vertices in the table. **reflection over y-axis**

$\triangle LMN$	$\triangle L'M'N'$
$L(4, -2)$	$L'(-4, -2)$
$M(0, 7)$	$M'(0, 7)$
$N(-6, 1)$	$N'(6, 1)$

3. **Write** about the reflections and/or translations found in the St. Vincent flag at the beginning of the lesson.

Guided Practice

4. Classify the graph as a *reflection* or a *translation*. **reflection**

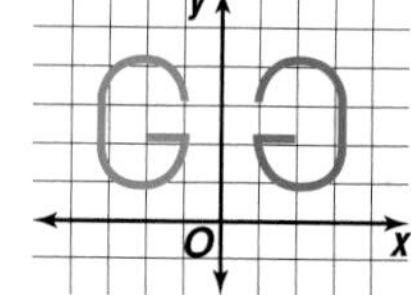

Graph each triangle and its transformation. Write the ordered pairs for the vertices of the new triangle. **5–6. See Answer Appendix for graphs.**

5. $A'(-1, 2)$, $B'(-1, -4)$, $C'(-5, -1)$

5. $\triangle ABC$ with vertices $A(1, 2)$, $B(1, -4)$, and $C(5, -1)$ reflected over the y-axis
6. $\triangle HIJ$ with vertices $H(0, -3)$, $I(2, 4)$, and $J(-4, 3)$ translated 2 units left and 3 units down **$H'(-2, -6)$, $I'(0, 1)$, $J'(-6, 0)$**

7. on the lid: reflections; on the side: translations and reflections

7. **Art** Quillwork was a Native American art in which quills of a porcupine were "embroidered" in patterns on moccasins, belts, and bags. Describe the transformations that were used to create the quilled pattern at the right.

Reteaching the Lesson

Activity Provide students with opportunities to graph transformations that are easier to visualize. Use cutouts of figures to physically move the figures.

Have students share with the class the sketches they made. Have students identify the kinds of transformations their sketches show. You may wish to display students' work on the bulletin board.

EXERCISES

Practice

Classify each graph as a *reflection* or a *translation*.

8. 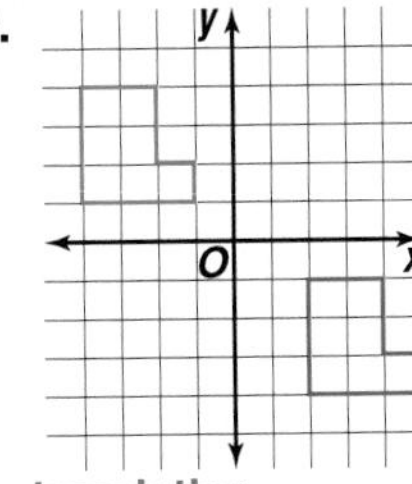
translation

9. translation

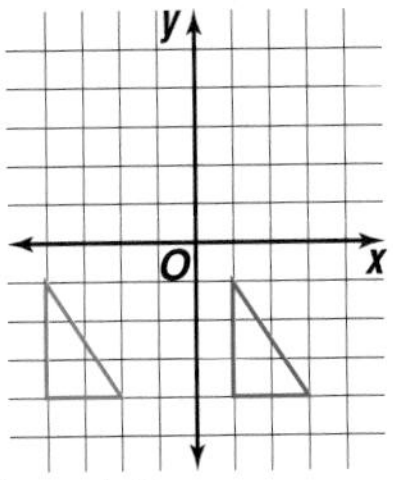

10. 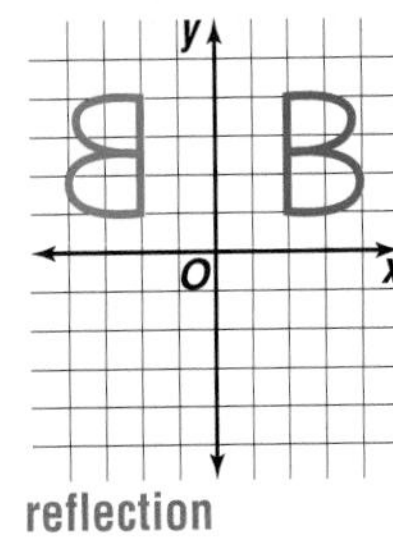
reflection

Family Activity

Transformations can be found in the patterns in fabric, the designs of windows, and other architectural features. Search your home for examples of transformations and sketch at least three of them.

Graph each figure and its transformation. Write the ordered pairs for the vertices of the new figure. 11–16. See Answer Appendix for graphs.

11. $\triangle XYZ$ with vertices $X(1, 3)$, $Y(5, 1)$, and $Z(5, 8)$ reflected over the x-axis $X'(1, -3)$, $Y'(5, -1)$, $Z'(5, -8)$
12. $\triangle KLM$ with vertices $K(-3, -1)$, $L(-5, -6)$, and $M(-1, -6)$ translated 4 units right and 2 units down $K'(1, -3)$, $L'(-1, -8)$, $M'(3, -8)$
13. $\triangle WXY$ with vertices $W(2, 1)$, $X(1, 6)$, and $Y(-2, 4)$ translated 5 units right and 3 units up $W'(7, 4)$, $X'(6, 9)$, $Y'(3, 7)$
14. $\triangle ABC$ with vertices $A(5, 2)$, $B(1, 1)$, and $C(2, 4)$ reflected over the x-axis $A'(5, -2)$, $B'(1, -1)$, $C'(2, -4)$
15. $\triangle JKL$ with vertices $J(-7, 1)$, $K(-2, 5)$, and $L(-5, 7)$ reflected over the y-axis $J'(7, 1)$, $K'(2, 5)$, $L'(5, 7)$
16. rectangle $MNOP$ with vertices $M(-4, 0)$, $N(-4, -3)$, $O(-2, -3)$, and $P(-2, 0)$ translated 5 units right and 2 units down $M'(1, -2)$, $N'(1, -5)$, $O'(3, -5)$, $P'(3, -2)$

17a. translation

Applications and Problem Solving

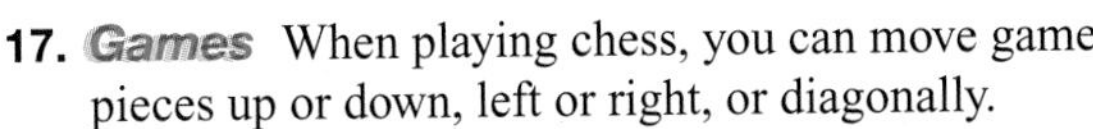
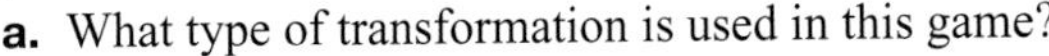
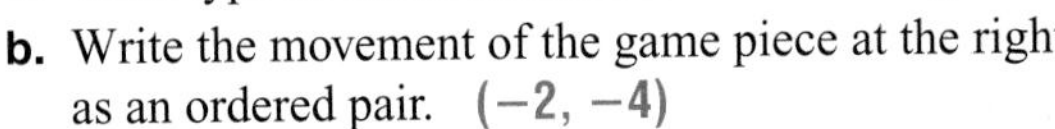

17. **Games** When playing chess, you can move game pieces up or down, left or right, or diagonally.
    a. What type of transformation is used in this game?
    b. Write the movement of the game piece at the right as an ordered pair. $(-2, -4)$

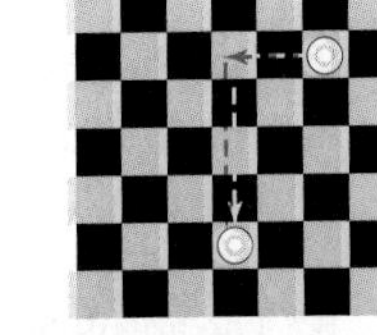

18. The red and blue figures in the flag are reflections of each other.

18. **Flags** Describe the transformation in the Philippines flag at the right. 
19. **Critical Thinking** Graph $\triangle JKL$ with vertices $J(-7, 4)$, $K(-7, 1)$, and $L(-1, 1)$. Then graph $\triangle J'K'L'$ if both the x- and y-coordinates in $\triangle JKL$ are multiplied by -1. Describe this transformation. See Answer Appendix.

For **Extra Practice,** see page 583.

Mixed Review

21. $2 \times 3^2 \times 5 \times 7$

20. Solve $z = 360 \div (-6)$. *(Lesson 5-7)* -60
21. Use a factor tree to find the prime factorization of 630. *(Lesson 4-2)*
22. **Standardized Test Practice** Round 16.2573 to the nearest tenth. *(Lesson 2-2)* D

A 16.2 **B** 20 **C** 16.26 **D** 16.3

3 PRACTICE/APPLY

Check for Understanding

If students need additional practice or instruction after completing Exercises 1–7, one of these options may be helpful.

- Extra Practice, see p. 583
- Reteaching Activity, see p. 216
- *Study Guide Masters,* p. 41
- *Practice Masters,* p. 41

Assignment Guide

Core: 9–17 odd, 19–22
Enriched: 8–16 even, 17–22

4 ASSESS

Closing Activity

Speaking Have students explain how to graph the reflection of a figure over the x-axis. Additionally, ask them to explain the transformation of a figure described by the movement $(5, -4)$.

Chapter 5, Quiz D (Lessons 5-7 and 5-8) is available in the *Assessment and Evaluation Masters,* p. 128.

Extending the Lesson

***Enrichment Masters,* p. 41**

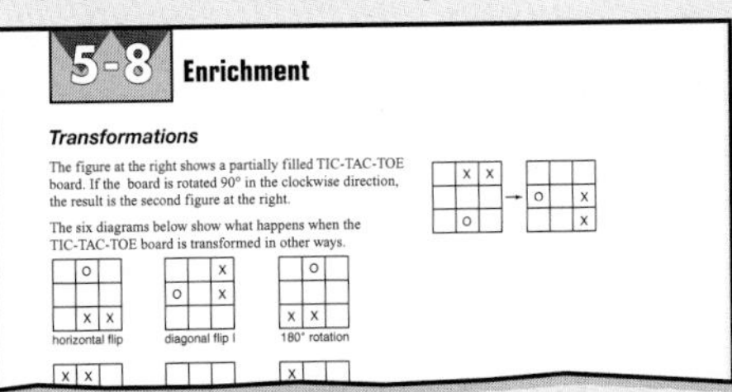

5-8 Enrichment

Transformations

The figure at the right shows a partially filled TIC-TAC-TOE board. If the board is rotated 90° in the clockwise direction, the result is the second figure at the right.

The six diagrams below show what happens when the TIC-TAC-TOE board is transformed in other ways.

horizontal flip diagonal flip I 180° rotation

Activity Quilts made in the United States during the 18th and 19th centuries were often made of colorful geometric forms. Have students use graph paper to design a quilt pattern. They should use reflections and translations to make their patterns.

***Practice Masters,* p. 41**

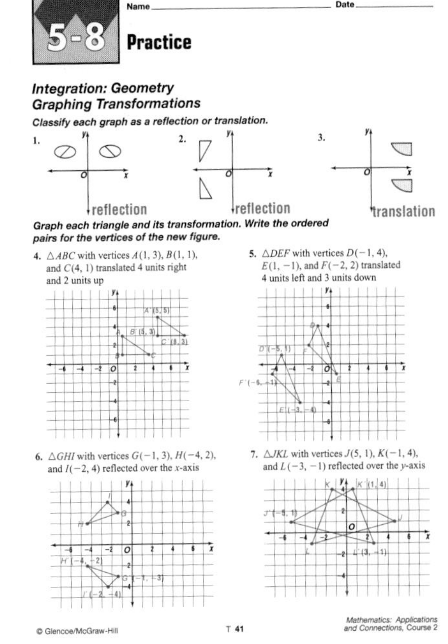

Name Date

5-8 Practice

Integration: Geometry
Graphing Transformations

Classify each graph as a reflection or translation.

1. reflection 2. reflection 3. translation

Graph each triangle and its transformation. Write the ordered pairs for the vertices of the new figure.

4. $\triangle ABC$ with vertices $A(1, 3)$, $B(1, 1)$, and $C(4, 1)$ translated 4 units right and 2 units up
5. $\triangle DEF$ with vertices $D(-1, 4)$, $E(1, -1)$, and $F(-2, 2)$ translated 4 units left and 3 units down
6. $\triangle GHI$ with vertices $G(-1, 3)$, $H(-4, 2)$, and $I(-2, 4)$ reflected over the x-axis
7. $\triangle JKL$ with vertices $J(5, 1)$, $K(-1, 4)$, and $L(-3, -1)$ reflected over the y-axis

© Glencoe/McGraw-Hill T 41 Mathematics: Applications and Connections, Course 2

Study Guide and Assessment

Vocabulary

This section provides a listing of the new terms, properties, and phrases that were introduced in this chapter. Have students define each term and provide an example or two of it, if appropriate.

Understanding and Using the Vocabulary

These exercises check students' understanding of the terms by using a variety of verbal formats including matching, completion, and true/false.

Glossaries A complete glossary of terms appears on pages 656–663. The glossary also appears in Spanish on pages 664–672.

Additional Answers

13. A reflection is a transformation where a figure is flipped. A translation is a transformation where a figure is slid.

28. (−3, 2), II

29. (1, 3), I

30. (4, 0), x-axis

31. (−2, −3), III

32–37.

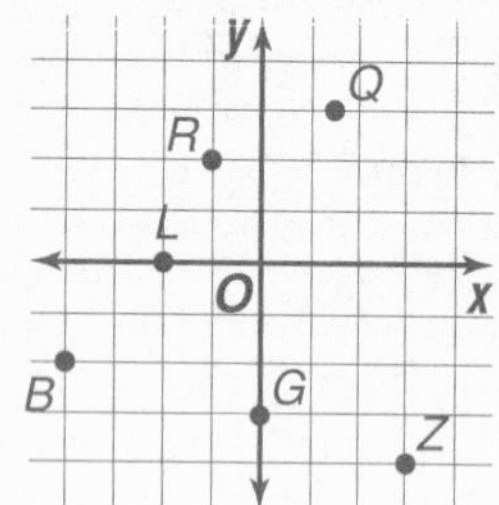

CHAPTER 5

Study Guide and Assessment

interNET CONNECTION Chapter Review For additional lesson-by-lesson review, visit: www.glencoe.com/sec/math/mac/mathnet

Vocabulary

After completing this chapter, you should be able to define each term, concept, or phrase and give an example or two of each.

Number and Operations
absolute value (p. 185)
additive inverse (p. 197)
integer (p. 184)
negative integer (p. 184)
opposite (p. 184)
positive integer (p. 184)
zero pair (p. 196)

Geometry
reflection (p. 215)
transformation (p. 215)
translation (p. 215)

Algebra
coordinate system (p. 191)
ordered pair (p. 191)
origin (p. 191)
quadrant (p. 191)
x-axis (p. 191)
x-coordinate (p. 191)
y-axis (p. 191)
y-coordinate (p. 191)

Problem Solving
look for a pattern (p. 210)

Understanding and Using the Vocabulary

Choose the correct term or number to complete each sentence.

1. Integers less than 0 are (positive, negative) integers.
2. Two numbers represented by points that are the same distance from 0 are (opposites, integers).
3. The absolute value of 7 is (7, −7).
4. The opposite of (12, −12) is −12.
5. The (coordinate system, origin) is the point where the horizontal and vertical number lines intersect.
6. The horizontal number line is called the (x-axis, y-axis).
7. The x-axis and the y-axis separate the plane into four (quadrants, coordinates).
8. The first number in an ordered pair is the (x-coordinate, y-coordinate).
9. The second number in an ordered pair is the (x-coordinate, y-coordinate).
10. The sum of two (positive, negative) integers is negative.
11. The sum of any number and its additive inverse is (zero, positive).
12. A transformation is a design or pattern where a geometric shape is used in (one, many different) position(s).

In Your Own Words

13. ***Explain*** the difference between a reflection and a translation. See margin.

MindJogger Videoquizzes

MindJogger Videoquizzes provide an alternative review of concepts presented in this chapter. Students work in teams to answer questions, gaining points for correct answers. The questions are presented in three rounds.

Round 1 Concepts–5 questions
Round 2 Skills–4 questions
Round 3 Problem Solving–4 questions

Objectives & Examples

Upon completing this chapter, you should be able to:

- read and write integers and find the opposite and absolute value of an integer *(Lesson 5-1)*

Write 4°F below 0 as an integer.

−4°F

Find the opposite and the absolute value of −7.

The opposite of −7 would be at the point 7 units to the right of 0. So, the opposite of −7 is 7. The point that represents −7 is 7 units from 0. So, $|-7| = 7$.

Review Exercises

Use these exercises to review and prepare for the chapter test.

Write an integer for each situation.

14. a withdrawal of \$123 **−123**

15. a gain of 14 yards **+14**

16. a deposit of \$60 **+60**

17. a loss of 5 pounds **−5**

Write the integer represented by the point for each letter. Then find its opposite and its absolute value.

18. *A* **−3, 3, 3** **19.** *B* **−1, 1, 1**

20. *C* **2, −2, 2** **21.** *D* **4, −4, 4**

- compare and order integers *(Lesson 5-2)*

Replace the ● with < or > to make a true sentence.

2 ● −6

Since 2 is to the right of −6 on the number line, 2 > −6.

26. −41, −3, 7, 10, 15, 25

27. −13, −11, 0, 5, 8, 10

Replace each ● with < or > to make a true sentence.

22. −18 ● −19 **>** **23.** 12 ● −12 **>**

24. −100 ● −10 **<** **25.** 0 ● −8 **>**

Order the integers from least to greatest.

26. 7, −3, 10, 25, −41, 15

27. −13, 8, −11, 0, 10, 5

- graph points on a coordinate plane *(Lesson 5-3)*

Name the ordered pair for point *A* and identify its quadrant.

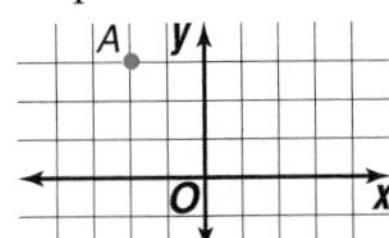

The ordered pair is (−2, 3). Point *A* is in quadrant II.

32–37. See margin.

Name the *x*-coordinate and the *y*-coordinate for each point labeled at the right. Then tell in which quadrant each point lies.

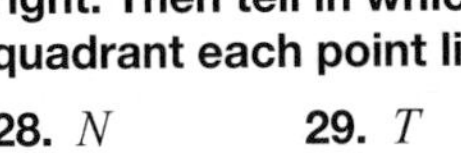

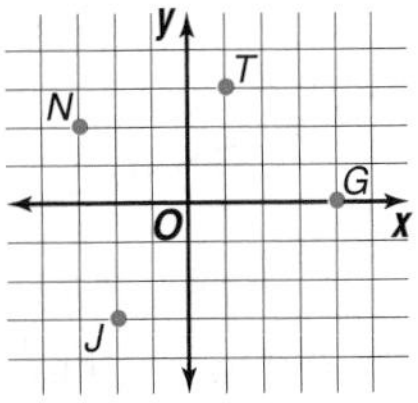

28. *N* **29.** *T*

30. *G* **31.** *J*

28–31. See margin.

On graph paper, draw a coordinate plane. Then graph and label each point.

32. *L*(−2, 0) **33.** *Z*(3, −4)

34. *Q*(1.5, 3) **35.** *B*(−4, −2)

36. *G*(0, −3) **37.** *R*(−1, 2)

Objectives & Examples

This section reviews the skills and concepts of the chapter and shows completely worked examples.

Review Exercises

These exercises provide practice for the corresponding objectives.

Assessment and Evaluation Masters, pp. 115–116

Name________ Date________

Chapter 5 Test, Form 1B

1. Write the integer represented by *G*. Then find its opposite and its absolute value. 1. B

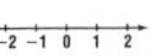

G
−3 −2 −1 0 1 2

A. 3; −3; 3 B. −3; 3; 3 C. −3; −3; 3 D. −3; −3; −3

Replace each ● to make a true sentence.

2. 10 ● −10 2. A
A. > B. < C. = D. +

3. −11 ● 0 3. B
A. > B. < C. = D. +

4. Order 3, −4, 0, 1, and −2 from least to greatest. 4. C
A. 3, 1, 0, −2, −4 B. 3, 1, 0, −4, −2
C. −4, −2, 0, 1, 3 D. −2, −4, 0, 1, 3

Use the graph to name the ordered pair for each point.

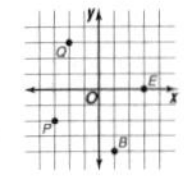

5. *Q* 5. D
A. (0, 3) B. (2, −3)
C. (−2, −3) D. (−2, 3)

6. *E* 6. C
A. (0, 3) B. (2, −3)
C. (3, 0) D. (−3, 0)

7. *P* 7. B
A. (−2, −3) B. (−3, −2)
C. (3, −2) D. (−3, 2)

8. *B* 8. D
A. (−1, −4) B. (−1, 4)
C. (−4, 1) D. (1, −4)

Solve each equation.

9. $w = 11 + (-7)$ 9. A
A. 4 B. −4 C. −18 D. 18

10. $x = -5(-11)$ 10. C
A. 16 B. −16 C. 55 D. −55

© Glencoe/McGraw-Hill 115 *Mathematics: Applications and Connections, Course 2*

Chapter 5 Test, Form 1B (continued)

Solve each equation.

11. $-1 + 1 = n$ 11. B
A. 2 B. 0 C. −2 D. −1

12. $u = 0 - 5$ 12. D
A. 10 B. 0 C. 5 D. −5

13. $v = 7(-3)$ 13. B
A. $-2\frac{1}{3}$ B. −21 C. 4 D. 21

14. $-37 - 8 = c$ 14. C
A. 45 B. −29 C. −45 D. 296

15. $n = -25 \div (-5)$ 15. C
A. 20 B. −20 C. 5 D. −5

16. $b = -48 \div (-24)$ 16. A
A. 2 B. −2 C. −24 D. 0.5

17. Use the graph at the right to describe the movement from $\triangle ABC$ to $\triangle A'B'C'$. 17. D
A. 5 left, 7 down
B. 5 right, 7 up
C. 7 left, 5 down
D. 7 right, 5 up

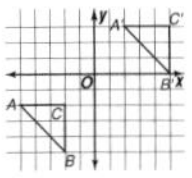

18. Use the graph at the right to tell what type of transformation is shown. 18. B
A. translation
B. reflection over the *y*-axis
C. reflection over the *x*-axis
D. no movement

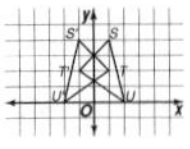

19. Fernando jogged 2 miles on the first day. Then each day after that he jogged 3.5, 5.5, 7, and 9 miles. Including the first day, how many days should it take for him to jog more than 13 miles in one day? 19. D
A. 7 B. 6 C. 5 D. 8

20. Luisa has decided to reduce the 15 hours that she spends playing video games each week. If she plays video games 15 minutes less each week, in how many weeks will she spend only 10 hours per week playing video games? 20. C
A. 10 B. 15 C. 20 D. 25

© Glencoe/McGraw-Hill 116 *Mathematics: Applications and Connections, Course 2*

Assessment and Evaluation

Six forms of Chapter 5 Test are available in the *Assessment and Evaluation Masters* as shown in the chart.

1A	Multiple Choice	Honors
1B	Multiple Choice	Average
1C	Multiple Choice	Basic
2A	Free Response	Honors
2B	Free Response	Average
2C	Free Response	Basic

Chapter 5 Test, Form 1B, is shown at the right. Chapter 5 Test, Form 2B, is shown on the next page.

Study Guide and Assessment

Assessment and Evaluation Masters, pp. 121–122

5 Name______________ Date__________

Chapter 5 Test, Form 2B

Write the integer represented by the point for each letter. Then find its opposite and its absolute value.

P R Q
−6 −5 −4 −3 −2 −1 0 1 2 3 4 5 6

1. Q — 1. 5; −5; 5
2. R — 2. 0; 0; 0
3. P — 3. −3; 3; 3

Replace each ● with < or > to make a true sentence.

4. −7 ● −5 — 4. <
5. 0 ● −35 — 5. >
6. −1 ● 1 — 6. <

7. On the same day, the thermometer registered −10°F in Duluth and −7°F in St. Paul. Which city is warmer? — 7. St. Paul

On graph paper, draw a coordinate plane. Then graph and label each point.

8. Q(2, 3) — 8. See students' work.
9. R(3, −2) — 9. See students' work.
10. P(0, −4) — 10. See students' work.

Solve each equation.

11. $r = 9 + (-5)$ — 11. 4
12. $k = -3 + 8$ — 12. 5
13. $7 + (-2) = j$ — 13. 5

 121 Mathematics: Applications and Connections, Course 2

5 **Chapter 5 Test, Form 2B (continued)**

Solve each equation.

14. $-1 - 3 = u$ — 14. −4
15. $r = 0 - 9$ — 15. −9
16. $k = 11 - 18$ — 16. −7
17. $m = 5(-3)$ — 17. −15
18. $(-3)^2 = t$ — 18. 9
19. $d = (-6)(-2)$ — 19. 12
20. $24 \div (-2) = s$ — 20. −12
21. $x = -48 \div (-3)$ — 21. 16
22. $d = (-72) \div 8$ — 22. −9

Solve each equation.

23. On a separate piece of paper, graph △ABC with vertices A(1, 1), B(3, 1), and C(2, 4) translated 3 units left and 4 units down. Label all vertices. — 23. See students' work.

24. Tricia and Laura are studying the history of International Labor Day, on May 1. Suppose May 1 this year is a Friday. What is the date of the last Friday in May? — 24. May 29

25. Chip and Clint are making a chart of their class schedule. At Franklin School, the bell between classes rings at 8:03, 8:49, 8:55, 9:41, 9:47, and 10:33. When will the bell ring next? — 25. 10:39

 122 Mathematics: Applications and Connections, Course 2

Objectives & Examples | Review Exercises

add integers *(Lesson 5-4)*

Solve $p = 4 + (-3)$.

$|4| > |-3|$, so the sum is positive. The difference of 4 and 3 is 1. So, $p = 1$.

Solve each equation. 41. −13

38. $c = 6 + (-2)$ 4 **39.** $-10 + 4 = r$ −6

40. $-5 + 12 = m$ 7 **41.** $-7 + (-6) = t$

Evaluate each expression if $a = 6$, $b = 12$, and $c = -6$.

42. $b + (-4)$ 8 **43.** $a + c$ 0

subtract integers *(Lesson 5-5)*

Solve $y = -2 - 4$.

$y = -2 - 4$

$y = -2 + (-4)$ *To subtract 4, add −4.*

$y = -6$

Solve each equation. 45. 24

44. $-13 - 4 = q$ −17 **45.** $12 - (-12) = p$

46. $a = -4 - 6$ −10 **47.** $z = 6 - (-2)$ 8

Evaluate each expression if $q = -4$, $r = -2$, and $s = 9$.

48. $-7 - s$ −16 **49.** $r - q$ 2

multiply integers *(Lesson 5-6)*

Solve $h = -2(5)$.

The integers have different signs, so the product will be negative.

$h = -2(5)$

$h = -10$

Solve each equation.

50. $b = -6(-2)$ 12 **51.** $c = (-3)^2$ 9

52. $-8(4) = g$ −32 **53.** $j = -5(5)$ −25

Evaluate each expression if $w = 3$, $x = -6$, and $y = 4$.

54. $-3y$ −12 **55.** $8w$ 24 **56.** $5xy$ −120

divide integers *(Lesson 5-7)*

Solve $-15 \div (-3) = a$.

The signs are the same, so the quotient is positive.

$-15 \div (-3) = a$

$5 = a$

Solve each equation.

57. $v = 45 \div (-9)$ −5 **58.** $s = -10 \div 10$ −1

59. $-12 \div (-2) = b$ 6 **60.** $-52 \div (-4) = g$ 13

Evaluate each expression if $j = -16$, $k = 6$, and $h = 2$.

61. $k \div (-3)$ −2 **62.** $j \div h$ −8

graph transformations on a coordinate plane *(Lesson 5-8)*

Graph △QRS with Q(−3, 4), R(−3, 1), and S(0, 1). Then translate △QRS 2 units left and 3 units down.

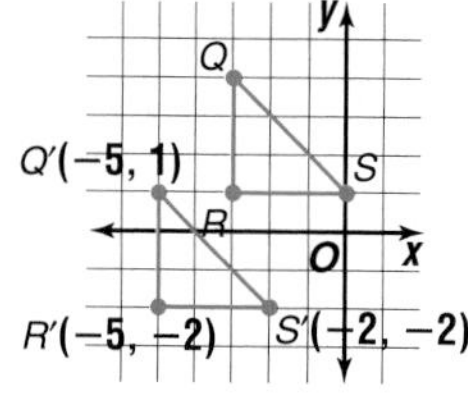

63–64. See Answer Appendix.

Graph each triangle and its transformation. Write the ordered pairs for the vertices of the new triangle.

63. △ABC with vertices A(4, −2), B(−2, −3), and C(−1, 6) translated 3 units right and 4 units up

64. △RST with vertices R(−1, 3), S(2, 6), and T(6, 1) reflected over the x-axis

Test and Review Software

You may use this software, a combination of an item generator and item bank, to create your own tests or worksheets. Types of items include free response, multiple choice, short answer, and open ended.

CD-ROM Program

The CD-ROM Program contains an Assessment Game whose questions review the concepts in this chapter.

Applications & Problem Solving

65. ***Weather*** During a winter storm, a weather announcer stated that the "windchill factor" was 18°F below 0. Write an integer for this situation. *(Lesson 5-1)* **−18**

66. ***Earth Science*** The table gives weekly water-level readings of Turtle Creek Lake over an 8-week period. The readings indicate the number of feet above or below flood level. Find the median of the readings. *(Lesson 5-2)* **−5**

Week	1	2	3	4	5	6	7	8
Water Level	−8	−8	−6	−5	−2	−5	0	3

67. ***Football*** On the first play of the fourth quarter, the Bearcats lost 12 yards. On the second play, they ran for 8 yards. What was the total number of yards gained or lost? *(Lesson 5-4)* **4 yards lost**

68. ***Look for a Pattern*** Find the next three numbers in the sequence 34, 26, 18, 10, … . *(Lesson 5-7A)* **2, −6, −14**

69. ***Fund-raising*** The Debate Team, the Chess Club, and the Pep Club participated in a joint fund-raiser. If \$327 was raised, write an equation that can be used to represent how much each club should receive. *(Lesson 5-7)* **$x = \$327 \div 3$**

Alternative Assessment

Open Ended

Suppose you are the treasurer of a club. The club has a checking account with a balance of \$74. You have written checks in the amounts of \$17, \$14, and \$25 for supplies. You have collected dues of \$6 from 7 members. You are to deposit the collected dues into the account. How can you find the new balance? **See margin.**

If the bank charged a \$10 service fee, find the current balance. **\$50**

Completing the CHAPTER Project

Find the latitude, highest temperature, and lowest temperature for your city and four other cities in the United States. (If your city is one of the selected cities, add another city from your state.) Add this information to your table and the graphs you made in the exercises. Explain whether the new data are consistent with your original conclusions. Use the following checklist to make sure your project is complete.

- ☑ The table of latitudes and highest and lowest temperatures has a total of 15 cities.
- ☑ You have two graphs.
- ☑ You have a paragraph describing any relationships or interesting patterns that you found by studying your graphs and table.

Select one of the assignments from this chapter that you found particularly challenging. Place it in your portfolio.

A practice test for Chapter 5 is provided on page 611.

Applications & Problem Solving

This section provides additional practice in solving real-world problems that involve the skills of this chapter.

Alternative Assessment

The ***Open Ended*** section provides students with a performance assessment opportunity to evaluate their work and understanding.

Students should complete the final stages of their project and prepare a class demonstration of their results. A scoring guide for the project is available in the *Investigations and Projects Masters,* p. 35.

Students should add to their portfolios at this time.

Additional Answer for the Open Ended item

Subtract the amounts of the checks from \$74, then add 7(6) to the total.

Performance Assessment

Additional performance assessment tasks for this chapter are included in the *Assessment and Evaluation Masters* on page 125. A scoring guide is also provided on page 137.

***Assessment and Evaluation Masters,* p. 125**

Name__________ Date__________

Chapter 5 Performance Assessment

Instructions: Demonstrate your knowledge by giving a clear, concise solution to each problem. Be sure to include all relevant drawings and justify your answers. You may show your solutions in more than one way or investigate beyond the requirements of the problems.

1. Horatio, Glen, Carlos, and Meredith played in the company golf tournament. Their scores after the first round are listed below.

Horatio: two over par (+2)
Glen: three under par (−3)
Carlos: four over par (+4)
Meredith: one under par (−1)

- a. Explain how to compare integers.
- b. Order the golf scores from least to greatest.
- c. Explain what is meant by the *absolute value* of a number.
- d. Find the absolute value of Glen's score.
- e. Glen's second round score is +2. Use counters to find Glen's total score after two rounds.
- f. Meredith's second round score is −3. Find her total score after two rounds.
- g. Horatio's second round score is −3. Use counters to find the difference between Horatio's first and second round scores.

2. Tina wants to move a drawing on a page of the school yearbook. Find the coordinates for $\triangle ABC$. Graph its reflection over the x-axis to form $\triangle A'B'C'$. Show all of your steps. Then move it to a position where it lies in all four quadrants. Describe the transformation. Graph the figure and write the ordered pairs for its vertices.

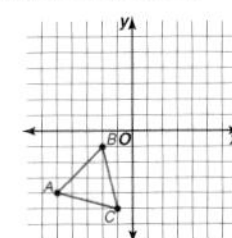

 125 *Mathematics: Applications and Connections, Course 2*

Standardized Test Practice

The Standardized Test Practice may be used to help students prepare for standardized tests. The test items are written in the same style as those in state proficiency tests and standardized tests like CAT, CTBS, ITBS, MAT, SAT, and Terra Nova. The test items cover skills and concepts covered up to this point in the text.

The pages can be used as an overnight assessment. After students have completed the pages, discuss how each problem can be solved, or provide copies of the solutions from the *Solutions Manual.*

***Assessment and Evaluation Masters,* p. 131**

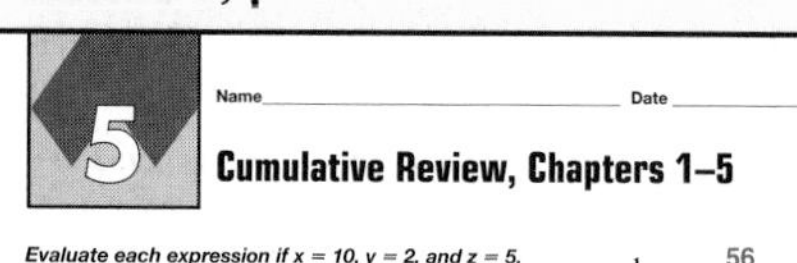

Name________________ Date________

Cumulative Review, Chapters 1–5

Evaluate each expression if x = 10, y = 2, and z = 5. (Lesson 1-3)

1. $3y + 5x$ 2. $8 + 2(x - z)$

Solve each equation. (Lesson 1-5)

3. $18c = 162$ 4. $95 = g + 66$

5. Find $0.00019\overline{)3.42}$. (Lesson 2-6)

6. Express $\frac{5}{6}$ as a decimal. Use bar notation if the decimal is a repeating decimal. (Lesson 2-7)

Use the data 11, 11, 7, 5, 7, 9, and 13 for Questions 7–9. (Lesson 3-4)

7. mode(s) 8. median 9. mean

10. Identify the sequence 79, 73, 67, 61, . . . as *arithmetic, geometric,* or *neither*. Then find the next three terms of the sequence. (Lesson 4-3)

11. Express 0.125 as a fraction in simplest form. (Lesson 4-7)

A bag of marbles contains 3 red, 12 clear, 8 black, 6 blue, and 11 yellow marbles. If you reach into the bag and draw one marble at random, what is the probability that you will draw each of the following? Express each ratio as a fraction in simplest form and as a percent. (Lesson 4-8)

12. a clear marble

13. either a black or blue marble

14. Replace ● with < or > to make −25 ● −26 a true sentence. (Lesson 5-2)

15. Order the integers 9, 0, 15, −4, 3, −3 from least to greatest. (Lesson 5-2)

16. Graph the figure $\triangle XYZ$ with vertices $X(0, -2)$, $Y(-1, 4)$, and $Z(-3, -1)$ and its transformation, a reflection over the y-axis. Write the ordered pairs for the vertices of the new figure. (Lesson 5-3 and 5-8)

Solve each equation. (Lessons 5-4, 5-5, 5-6, and 5-7)

17. $60 \div (-3) = q$ 18. $h = -6 + 14$

19. $-3 - (-9) = j$ 20. $k = -5(13)$

Answers:
1. 56
2. 18
3. 9
4. 29
5. 18,000
6. $0.8\overline{3}$
7. 7 and 11
8. 9
9. 9
10. arithmetic; 55, 49, 43
11. $\frac{1}{8}$
12. $\frac{3}{10}$; 30%
13. $\frac{7}{20}$; 35%
14. >
15. −4, −3, 0, 3, 9, 15
16. 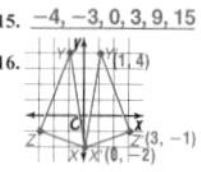 (0, −2), (1, 4), (3, −1)
17. −20
18. 8
19. 6
20. −65

CHAPTERS 1–5

Standardized Test Practice

Assessing Knowledge & Skills

Section One: Multiple Choice

There are ten multiple choice questions in this section. Choose the best answer. If a correct answer is *not here,* choose the letter for Not Here.

1. Which is equivalent to 5^4? **D**
   - **A** 20
   - **B** 125
   - **C** $4 \cdot 4 \cdot 4 \cdot 4 \cdot 4$
   - **D** $5 \cdot 5 \cdot 5 \cdot 5$

2. If 4 computers are needed for every 7 students in a grade, how many computers are needed for 280 students? **H**
   - **F** 40
   - **G** 32
   - **H** 160
   - **J** 280

3. At the school raffle, 20 prizes were placed inside a box. There were 12 dinner gift certificates, 6 movie tickets, and 2 baseball tickets. What is the probability of picking a dinner gift certificate? **C**
   - **A** $\frac{15}{20}$
   - **B** $\frac{1}{4}$
   - **C** $\frac{3}{5}$
   - **D** $\frac{3}{20}$

4. Write the addition sentence shown by the number line. **F**

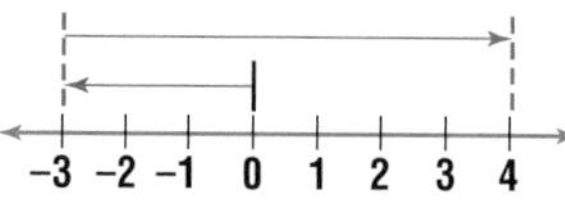

   - **F** $-3 + 7 = 4$
   - **G** $3 + 4 = 7$
   - **H** $-3 + 4 = -1$
   - **J** $-3 + (-7) = -10$

Please note that Questions 5–10 have five answer choices.

Use the chart below to answer Questions 5 and 6.

Several civic groups in Westview collected newspapers to raise money for a spring planting and clean up day. The chart shows the number of pounds collected by each group during a 3-week time period.

Group	Week 1	Week 2	Week 3
Girl Scouts	𝍸 𝍸	𝍸 III	𝍸 III
Boy Scouts	𝍸 II	𝍸 𝍸	𝍸 I
Keep Our City Clean	III	𝍸	𝍸 II
Garden Club	𝍸 𝍸	𝍸 II	𝍸 IIII

5. If the groups were paid \$0.08 per pound for the newspaper, how much more did the Garden Club earn than the Keep Our City Clean group? **C**
   - **A** \$2.08
   - **B** \$1.20
   - **C** \$0.88
   - **D** \$0.48
   - **E** Not Here

6. How many more pounds of newspaper did the Girl Scouts and Boy Scouts collect together than the Keep Our City Clean group and the Garden Club together? **K**
   - **F** 89 lb
   - **G** 49 lb
   - **H** 41 lb
   - **J** 30 lb
   - **K** Not Here

◀◀◀Instructional Resources

Another cumulative review is shown at the left and is available in the *Assessment and Evaluation Masters,* p. 131.

7. Manuel had a bag of marbles. He gave half of them to Olivia and one-third of the remaining marbles to Angela. He had 18 marbles left. How many marbles did Manuel have in the bag to start with? A
   - **A** 54
   - **B** 48
   - **C** 27
   - **D** 36
   - **E** Not Here

8. At the school cafeteria, Jeremy bought a turkey sandwich for $1.99, potato chips for $0.76, and milk for $0.35. How much did his lunch cost assuming there was no tax? G
   - **F** $3.20
   - **G** $3.10
   - **H** $3.00
   - **J** $2.90
   - **K** Not Here

9. Darlene has $18.48 in her purse. If she gets paid $15 from her paper route, how much money will she have? D
   - **A** $12.48
   - **B** $13.48
   - **C** $23.48
   - **D** $33.48
   - **E** $17.48

10. A submarine is diving from the surface at the rate of 79 feet per minute. What is the depth of the submarine after 8 minutes? J
    - **F** −71 ft
    - **G** −87 ft
    - **H** −602 ft
    - **J** −632 ft
    - **K** Not Here

Test-Taking Tip THE PRINCETON REVIEW

Most standardized tests have a time limit, so you must budget your time carefully. Some questions will be easier than others. If you cannot answer a question within a few minutes, go on to the next one. If there is still time left when you get to the end of the test, go back to the questions that you skipped.

Section Two: Free Response

This section contains five questions for which you will provide short answers. Write your answers on your paper.

11. Marcy has a piece of string that is 85 inches long. What is the greatest number of 12-inch pieces that she can cut from the string? 7

12. Joshua had $53.33 in his savings account. He took out $15 to spend at the movies. How much money did he have left? $38.33

13. $|-86| =$ 86

14. Space shuttles encounter temperatures that range from −250°F while in orbit to 3,000°F during reentry of Earth's atmosphere. Find the range of temperatures that space shuttles encounter. 3,250°

15. The human body uses 65% of the oxygen it takes in. Express this as a fraction in simplest form. $\frac{13}{20}$

Test Practice For additional test practice questions, visit:

www.glencoe.com/sec/math/mac/mathnet

Instructional Resources ▶▶▶

Additional standardized test practice is shown at the right and is available in the *Assessment and Evaluation Masters,* pp. 129–130.

Test-Taking Tip

To overcome pre-test jitters or mid-test fatigue, suggest that students take a few deep breaths and stretch without leaving their chairs.

Assessment and Evaluation Masters, pp. 129–130

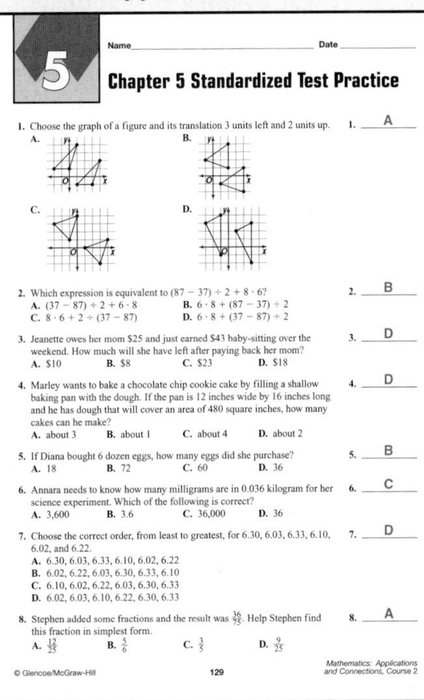

Name__________ Date________

Chapter 5 Standardized Test Practice

1. Choose the graph of a figure and its translation 3 units left and 2 units up. 1. A
   A. B. C. D.
2. Which expression is equivalent to $(87 - 37) \div 2 + 8 \cdot 6$? 2. B
   A. $(37 - 87) \div 2 + 6 \cdot 8$ B. $6 \cdot 8 + (87 - 37) \div 2$
   C. $8 \cdot 6 + 2 \div (37 - 87)$ D. $6 \cdot 8 + (37 - 87) \div 2$
3. Jeanette owes her mom $25 and just earned $43 baby-sitting over the weekend. How much will she have left after paying back her mom? 3. D
   A. $10 B. $8 C. $23 D. $18
4. Marley wants to bake a chocolate chip cookie cake by filling a shallow baking pan with the dough. If the pan is 12 inches wide by 16 inches long and he has dough that will cover an area of 480 square inches, how many cakes can he make? 4. D
   A. about 3 B. about 1 C. about 4 D. about 2
5. If Diana bought 6 dozen eggs, how many eggs did she purchase? 5. B
   A. 18 B. 72 C. 60 D. 36
6. Annara needs to know how many milligrams are in 0.036 kilogram for her science experiment. Which of the following is correct? 6. C
   A. 3,600 B. 3.6 C. 36,000 D. 36
7. Choose the correct order, from least to greatest, for 6.30, 6.03, 6.33, 6.10, 6.02, and 6.22. 7. D
   A. 6.30, 6.03, 6.33, 6.10, 6.02, 6.22
   B. 6.02, 6.22, 6.03, 6.30, 6.33, 6.10
   C. 6.10, 6.02, 6.22, 6.03, 6.30, 6.33
   D. 6.02, 6.03, 6.10, 6.22, 6.30, 6.33
8. Stephen added some fractions and the result was $\frac{36}{75}$. Help Stephen find this fraction in simplest form. 8. A
   A. $\frac{12}{25}$ B. $\frac{5}{6}$ C. $\frac{3}{5}$ D. $\frac{9}{25}$

© Glencoe/McGraw-Hill 129 *Mathematics: Applications and Connections, Course 2*

Chapter 5 Standardized Test Practice (continued)

Eleven out of 15 seventh graders replied to a survey about how many TV shows they watched over the weekend. The line plot shows the results of the survey. Use this information for Questions 9 and 10.

9. What is the correct cluster for the data? 9. B
   A. 8 to 12 B. 8 to 10
   C. 6 to 10 D. 6 to 12

   6 7 8 9 10 11 12

10. Find the mode(s) for the data. 10. D
    A. 10 B. 8 C. 8, 9, 10 D. 8, 10
11. Mrs. Ling has 22 students who will be doing art projects with clay. She has 14 boxes of clay, each weighing 2 pounds 1 ounce. How much clay will each student get? 11. A
    A. 1 lb 5 oz B. 2 lb C. 1 lb 8 oz D. 1 lb 11 oz
12. Find the next two figures that continue the pattern. 12. C
    A. B. C. D.
13. The Dahlinger family purchased 24 tickets in a raffle at a local fire station. The prize was a refrigerator and 392 tickets were sold. What is the probability that the Dahlingers will win the refrigerator? 13. C
    A. $\frac{1}{24}$ B. $\frac{12}{98}$ C. $\frac{3}{49}$ D. $\frac{6}{7}$
14. Dan saw a herd of horses running in a field one night. First 2 horses ran by, then 4, then 8, then 16. How many horses can Dan expect will run by him next? 14. A
    A. 32 B. 24 C. 14 D. 30
15. Alma's test grades in science were 91, 82, 79, 89, and 93. What is her mean (average) test grade? 15. D
    A. 85 B. 90 C. 89 D. 87
16. The Shirt Boutique has 4 different kinds of shirts on sale for $19.95, $12.59, $7.99, and $22.29. If Syreeta wants to buy one of each kind of shirt, estimate how much money she needs. 16. B
    A. $85 B. $65 C. $50 D. $70

© Glencoe/McGraw-Hill 130 *Mathematics: Applications and Connections, Course 2*

Algebra: Exploring Equations and Functions

Previewing the Chapter

Overview

This chapter explores equations, first by emphasizing the use of models, and then by introducing the properties of equality. Students model and solve one- and two-step equations and write algebraic expressions and equations from verbal problems. They also solve inequalities and use ordered pairs to represent functions and solve equations. They also learn to solve problems by working backward.

Lesson (pages)	Lesson Objectives	NCTM Standards 2000	Standardized Tests	State/Local Objectives
6-1A (226–227)	Use models to solve equations.	1, 2, 6–10	CTBS, MAT, TN	
6-1 (228–231)	Solve addition and subtraction equations.	1, 2, 6–10	CAT, ITBS, MAT, SAT	
6-1B (232–233)	Solve problems by working backward.	1, 6–9		
6-2 (234–237)	Solve multiplication equations.	1, 2, 6–10	CAT, ITBS, MAT, SAT	
6-3A (238)	Use models to solve two-step equations.	1, 2, 6–10		
6-3 (239–241)	Solve two-step equations.	1, 2, 6–10	ITBS, MAT	
6-4 (242–245)	Write simple algebraic expressions and equations from verbal phrases and sentences.	1, 2, 6–10	SAT	
6-5 (246–248)	Solve inequalities.	1, 6–10	ITBS	
6-6 (249–252)	Represent functions as ordered pairs.	1, 2, 6–10		
6-7A (253)	Use a function rule to find the output of a function.	1, 2, 5–9	CAT, CTBS, SAT, TN	
6-7 (254–257)	Solve equations with two variables and graph the solution.	1–3, 6–10		

CAT = California Achievement Tests, CTBS = Comprehensive Tests of Basic Skills, ITBS = Iowa Tests of Basic Skills, MAT = Metropolitan Achievement Tests, SAT = Stanford Achievement Tests, TN = Terra Nova
For the key to numbering of NCTM Standards 2000, see page T6.

Organizing the Chapter

The **Interactive Lesson Planner** contains all of the blackline masters and transparencies. This CD-ROM also includes an easy-to-use lesson planning calendar.

LESSON PLANNING GUIDE

Lesson	Extra Practice (Student Edition)	Blackline Masters (page numbers)										Transparencies A and B
		Study Guide	Practice	Enrichment	Assessment & Evaluation	Classroom Games	Diversity	Hands-On Lab	School to Career	Science and Math Lab Manual	Technology	
6-1A								49				
6-1	p. 583	42	42	42							37	6-1
6-1B	p. 583											
6-2	p. 584	43	43	43	155		19	77				6-2
6-3A								50				
6-3	p. 584	44	44	44					19			6-3
6-4	p. 584	45	45	45	154, 155	17–20						6-4
6-5	p. 585	46	46	46								6-5
6-6	p. 585	47	47	47	156					33–36	38	6-6
6-7A								51				
6-7	p. 585	48	48	48	156							6-7
Study Guide/ Assessment					141–153, 157–159							

Other Chapter Resources

Student Edition

Chapter Project, pp. 225, 236, 252, 257, 261
Let the Games Begin, p. 237

Technology

 MathPASS CD-ROM

 Interactive Mathematics Tools Software

Teacher's Classroom Resources

Applications

Family Letters and Activities, pp. 37–38
Investigations and Projects Masters, pp. 37–40

Meeting Individual Needs

Investigations for the Special Education Student, pp. 39–42

Teaching Aids

Answer Key Masters
Block Scheduling Booklet
Lesson Planning Guide
Solutions Manual

Professional Publications

Glencoe Mathematics Professional Series

Planning the Chapter

MindJogger Videoquizzes provide a unique format for reviewing concepts presented in the chapter.

Assessment Resources

Student Edition

Mixed Review, pp. 231, 237, 241, 245, 248, 252, 257
Mid-Chapter Self Test, p. 245
Math Journal, pp. 230, 244
Study Guide and Assessment, pp. 258–261
Performance Task, p. 261
Portfolio Suggestion, p. 261
Standardized Test Practice, pp. 262–263
Chapter Test, p. 612

Assessment and Evaluation Masters

Multiple-Choice Tests (Forms 1A, 1B, 1C), pp. 141–146
Free-Response Tests (Forms 2A, 2B, 2C), pp. 147–152
Performance Assessment, p. 153
Mid-Chapter Test, p. 154
Quizzes A–D, pp. 155–156
Standardized Test Practice, pp. 157–158
Cumulative Review, p. 159

Teacher's Wraparound Edition

5-Minute Check, pp. 228, 234,239, 242, 246, 249, 254
Building Portfolios, p. 224
Math Journal, pp. 227, 238, 253
Closing Activity, pp. 231, 233, 237, 241, 245, 248, 252, 257

Technology

Test and Review Software
MindJogger Videoquizzes
CD-ROM Program

Materials and Manipulatives

Lesson 6-1A
cups and counters*†
equation mat*†

Lesson 6-1
cups and counters*†
equation mat*†
calculator

Lesson 6-2
cups and counters*†
equation mat*†
calculator

Lesson 6-3A
cups and counters*†
equation mat*†

Lesson 6-3
cups and counters*†
equation mat*†
calculator

Lesson 6-5
colored pencils

Lesson 6-6
stopwatch or watch with second hand*
grid paper†
ruler*†
colored pencils

Lesson 6-7A
stopwatch or watch with second hand*
grid paper†

Lesson 6-7
grid paper†
ruler*†

*Glencoe Manipulative Kit

†Glencoe Overhead Manipulative Resources

Pacing Chart

See pages T25–T27 for the Course Planning Calendar.

COURSE	DAY 1	DAY 2	DAY 3	DAY 4	DAY 5	DAY 6	DAY 7
Standard	Chapter Project	Lessons 6-1A & 6-1		Lesson 6-1B	Lesson 6-2	Lessons 6-3A & 6-3	
Honors	Chapter Project	Lesson 6-1	Lesson 6-1B	Lesson 6-2	Lesson 6-3		Lesson 6-4
Block	Chapter Project & Lesson 6-1A	Lessons 6-1 & 6-1B	Lessons 6-2 & 6-3A	Lessons 6-3 & 6-4	Lessons 6-5 & 6-6	Lessons 6-7A & 6-7	Study Guide and Assessment, Chapter Test

Interactive Mathematics: Activities and Investigations

is an activity-based program that may be used as an enhancement for chapters in ***Mathematics: Applications and Connections.***

INTER• ACTIVE Mathematics
Activities and Investigations

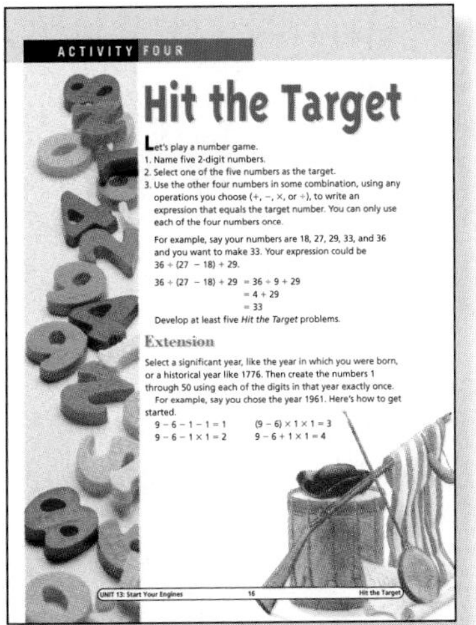

ACTIVITY FOUR

Hit the Target

Let's play a number game.

1. Name five 2-digit numbers.
2. Select one of the five numbers as the target.
3. Use the other four numbers in some combination, using any operations you choose (+, −, ×, or ÷), to write an expression that equals the target number. You can only use each of the four numbers once.

For example, say your numbers are 18, 27, 29, 33, and 36 and you want to make 33. Your expression could be 36 ÷ (27 − 18) + 29.

$$36 \div (27 - 18) + 29 = 36 \div 9 + 29$$
$$= 4 + 29$$
$$= 33$$

Develop at least five *Hit the Target* problems.

Extension

Select a significant year, like the year in which you were born, or a historical year like 1776. Then create the numbers 1 through 50 using each of the digits in that year exactly once.

For example, say you chose the year 1961. Here's how to get started.

$9 - 6 - 1 - 1 = 1$ $\quad (9 - 6) \times 1 \times 1 = 3$
$9 - 6 - 1 \times 1 = 2$ $\quad 9 - 6 + 1 \times 1 = 4$

UNIT 13: Start Your Engines 16 Hit the Target

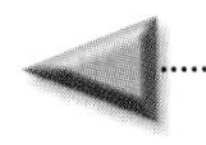

Unit 13, Activity Four
Hit the Target
Use with Lesson 6-4.

Summary Students review basic arithmetic skills as they write expressions. They also use calculators to determine if their expressions are correct.

Math Connection Students review basic arithmetic skills and use the order of operations to write expressions. Encourage them to try to develop some problems that include fractions or decimals and others that use only whole numbers.

Unit 16, Activity One
Pole Beans
Use at the beginning of Chapter 6 and with Lesson 6-7.

Summary Students plant seeds, measure and chart the seeds' growth, and draw conclusions based on their data. Then the groups graph their data and identify the independent and dependent variables.

Math Connection Students use the scientific method by conceiving a problem, collecting data, and formulating and testing a hypothesis. They graph their data using the first quadrant of a coordinate plane. The graph showing the growth of the plants will form an S-curve.

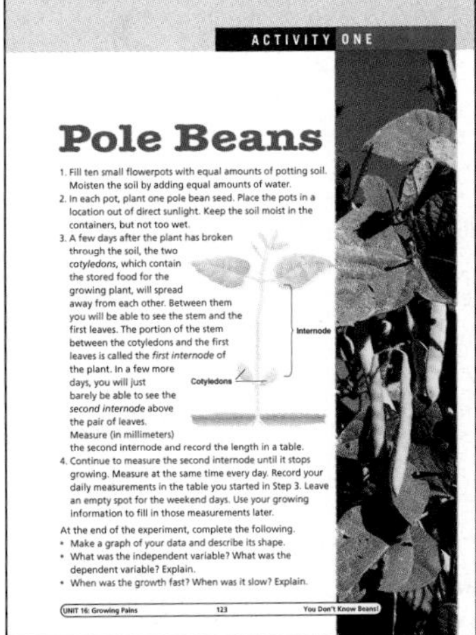

ACTIVITY ONE

Pole Beans

1. Fill ten small flowerpots with equal amounts of potting soil. Moisten the soil by adding equal amounts of water.
2. In each pot, plant one pole bean seed. Place the pots in a location out of direct sunlight. Keep the soil moist in the containers, but not too wet.
3. A few days after the plant has broken through the soil, the two *cotyledons,* which contain the stored food for the growing plant, will spread away from each other. Between them you will be able to see the stem and the first leaves. The portion of the stem between the cotyledons and the first leaves is called the *first internode* of the plant. In a few more days, you will just barely be able to see the *second internode* above the pair of leaves. Measure (in millimeters) the second internode and record the length in a table.
4. Continue to measure the second internode until it stops growing. Measure at the same time every day. Record your daily measurements in the table you started in Step 3. Leave an empty spot for the weekend days. Use your growing information to fill in those measurements later.

At the end of the experiment, complete the following.

- Make a graph of your data and describe its shape.
- What was the independent variable? What was the dependent variable? Explain.
- When was the growth fast? When was it slow? Explain.

UNIT 16: Growing Pains 123 You Don't Know Beans!

DAY 8	DAY 9	DAY 10	DAY 11	DAY 12	DAY 13	DAY 14	DAY 15
Lesson 6-4	Lesson 6-5	Lesson 6-6	Lessons 6-7A & 6-7		Study Guide and Assessment	Chapter Test	
Lesson 6-5	Lesson 6-6		Lesson 6-7	Study Guide and Assessment	Chapter Test		

Enhancing the Chapter

APPLICATIONS

Classroom Games, pp. 17–20

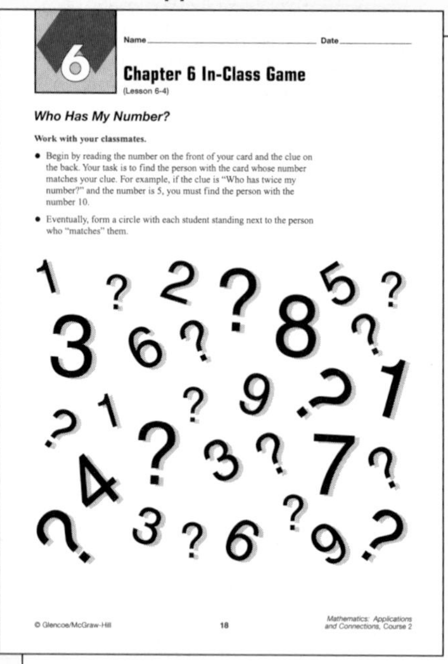
6

Name ______ Date ______

Chapter 6 In-Class Game
(Lesson 6-4)

Who Has My Number?

Work with your classmates.

- Begin by reading the number on the front of your card and the clue on the back. Your task is to find the person with the card whose number matches your clue. For example, if the clue is "Who has twice my number?" and the number is 5, you must find the person with the number 10.
- Eventually, form a circle with each student standing next to the person who "matches" them.

© Glencoe/McGraw-Hill 18 *Mathematics: Applications and Connections, Course 2*

Diversity Masters, p. 19

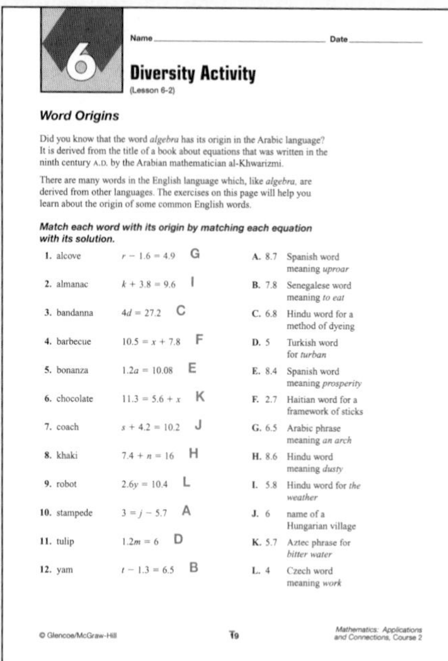
6

Name ______ Date ______

Diversity Activity
(Lesson 6-2)

Word Origins

Did you know that the word *algebra* has its origin in the Arabic language? It is derived from the title of a book about equations that was written in the ninth century A.D. by the Arabian mathematician al-Khwarizmi.

There are many words in the English language which, like *algebra*, are derived from other languages. The exercises on this page will help you learn about the origin of some common English words.

Match each word with its origin by matching each equation with its solution.

Word	Equation	Answer	Solution	Origin
1. alcove	$r - 1.6 = 4.9$	G	A. 8.7	Spanish word meaning *uproar*
2. almanac	$k + 3.8 = 9.6$	I	B. 7.8	Senegalese word meaning *to eat*
3. bandanna	$4d = 27.2$	C	C. 6.8	Hindu word for a method of dyeing
4. barbecue	$10.5 = x + 7.8$	F	D. 5	Turkish word for *turban*
5. bonanza	$1.2a = 10.08$	E	E. 8.4	Spanish word meaning *prosperity*
6. chocolate	$11.3 = 5.6 + x$	K	F. 2.7	Haitian word for a framework of sticks
7. coach	$s + 4.2 = 10.2$	J	G. 6.5	Arabic phrase meaning *an arch*
8. khaki	$7.4 + n = 16$	H	H. 8.6	Hindu word meaning *dusty*
9. robot	$2.6y = 10.4$	L	I. 5.8	Hindu word for *the weather*
10. stampede	$3 = j - 5.7$	A	J. 6	name of a Hungarian village
11. tulip	$1.2m = 6$	D	K. 5.7	Aztec phrase for *bitter water*
12. yam	$t - 1.3 = 6.5$	B	L. 4	Czech word meaning *work*

© Glencoe/McGraw-Hill T9 *Mathematics: Applications and Connections, Course 2*

School to Career Masters, p. 19

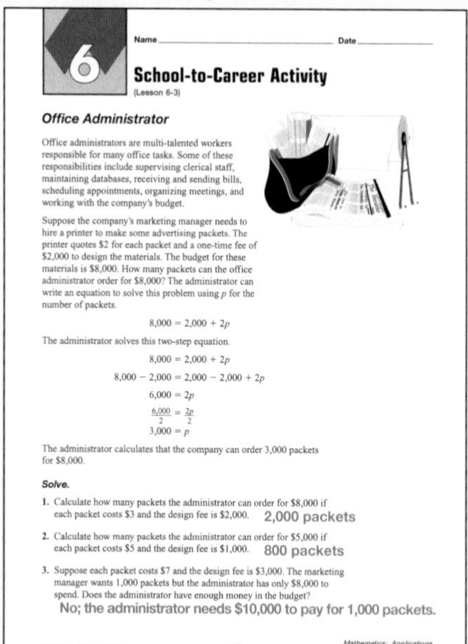
6

Name ______ Date ______

School-to-Career Activity
(Lesson 6-3)

Office Administrator

Office administrators are multi-talented workers responsible for many office tasks. Some of these responsibilities include supervising clerical staff, maintaining databases, receiving and sending bills, scheduling appointments, organizing meetings, and working with the company's budget.

Suppose the company's marketing manager needs to hire a printer to make some advertising packets. The printer quotes $2 for each packet and a one-time fee of $2,000 to design the materials. The budget for these materials is $8,000. How many packets can the office administrator order for $8,000? The administrator can write an equation to solve this problem using p for the number of packets.

$$8{,}000 = 2{,}000 + 2p$$

The administrator solves this two-step equation.

$$8{,}000 = 2{,}000 + 2p$$
$$8{,}000 - 2{,}000 = 2{,}000 - 2{,}000 + 2p$$
$$6{,}000 = 2p$$
$$\frac{6{,}000}{2} = \frac{2p}{2}$$
$$3{,}000 = p$$

The administrator calculates that the company can order 3,000 packets for $8,000.

Solve.

1. Calculate how many packets the administrator can order for $8,000 if each packet costs $3 and the design fee is $2,000. **2,000 packets**
2. Calculate how many packets the administrator can order for $5,000 if each packet costs $5 and the design fee is $1,000. **800 packets**
3. Suppose each packet costs $7 and the design fee is $3,000. The marketing manager wants 1,000 packets but the administrator has only $8,000 to spend. Does the administrator have enough money in the budget? **No; the administrator needs $10,000 to pay for 1,000 packets.**

© Glencoe/McGraw-Hill T9 *Mathematics: Applications and Connections, Course 2*

Family Letters and Activities, pp. 37–38

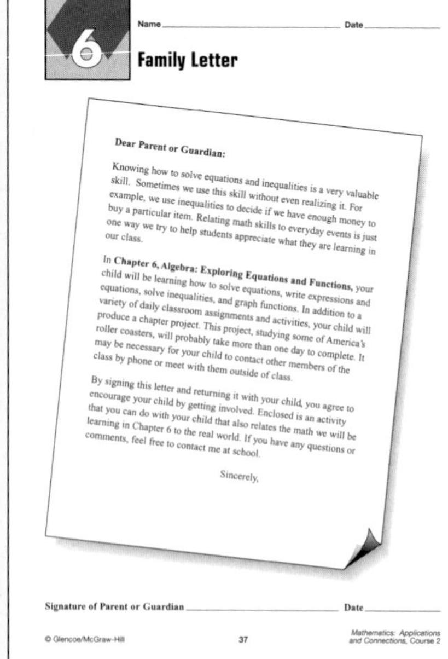
6

Name ______ Date ______

Family Letter

Dear Parent or Guardian:

Knowing how to solve equations and inequalities is a very valuable skill. Sometimes we use this skill without even realizing it. For example, we use inequalities to decide if we have enough money to buy a particular item. Relating math skills to everyday events is just one way we try to help students appreciate what they are learning in our class.

In **Chapter 6, Algebra: Exploring Equations and Functions,** your child will be learning how to solve equations, write expressions and equations, solve inequalities, and graph functions. In addition to a variety of daily classroom assignments and activities, your child will produce a chapter project. This project, studying some of America's roller coasters, will probably take more than one day to complete. It may be necessary for your child to contact other members of the class by phone or meet with them outside of class.

By signing this letter and returning it with your child, you agree to encourage your child by getting involved. Enclosed is an activity that you can do with your child that also relates the math we will be learning in Chapter 6 to the real world. If you have any questions or comments, feel free to contact me at school.

Sincerely,

Signature of Parent or Guardian ______ **Date** ______

© Glencoe/McGraw-Hill 37 *Mathematics: Applications and Connections, Course 2*

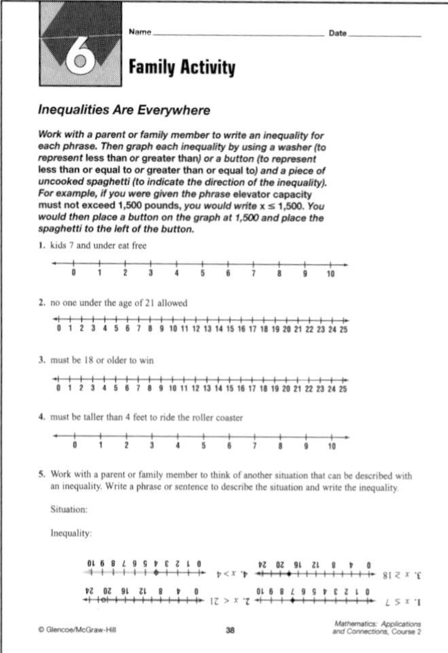
6

Name ______ Date ______

Family Activity

Inequalities Are Everywhere

Work with a parent or family member to write an inequality for each phrase. Then graph each inequality by using a washer (to represent **less than or greater than*****) or a button (to represent*** **less than or equal to** ***or*** **greater than or equal to*****) and a piece of uncooked spaghetti (to indicate the direction of the inequality). For example, if you were given the phrase*** **elevator capacity must not exceed 1,500 pounds,** ***you would write*** **x ≤ 1,500.** ***You would then place a button on the graph at 1,500 and place the spaghetti to the left of the button.***

1. kids 7 and under eat free

   0 1 2 3 4 5 6 7 8 9 10

2. no one under the age of 21 allowed

   0 1 2 3 4 5 6 7 8 9 10 11 12 13 14 15 16 17 18 19 20 21 22 23 24 25

3. must be 18 or older to win

   0 1 2 3 4 5 6 7 8 9 10 11 12 13 14 15 16 17 18 19 20 21 22 23 24 25

4. must be taller than 4 feet to ride the roller coaster

   0 1 2 3 4 5 6 7 8 9 10

5. Work with a parent or family member to think of another situation that can be described with an inequality. Write a phrase or sentence to describe the situation and write the inequality.

   Situation:

   Inequality:

3. $x \geq 18$ 4. $x > 4$ 1. $x \leq 7$ 2. $x < 21$

© Glencoe/McGraw-Hill 38 *Mathematics: Applications and Connections, Course 2*

Science and Math Lab Manual, pp. 33–36

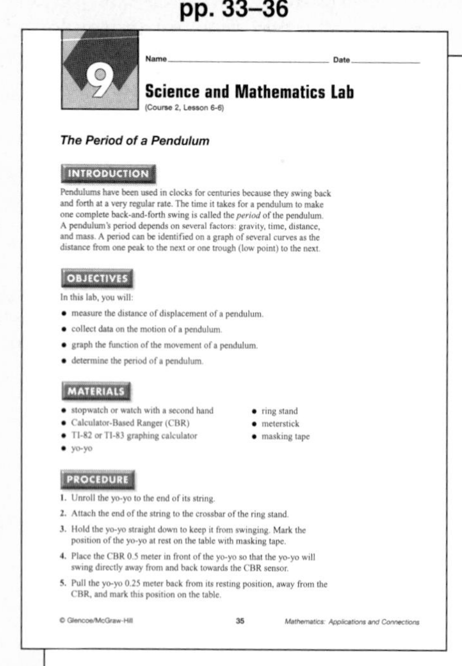
9

Name ______ Date ______

Science and Mathematics Lab
(Course 2, Lesson 6-6)

The Period of a Pendulum

INTRODUCTION

Pendulums have been used in clocks for centuries because they swing back and forth at a very regular rate. The time it takes for a pendulum to make one complete back-and-forth swing is called the *period* of the pendulum. A pendulum's period depends on several factors: gravity, time, distance, and mass. A period can be identified on a graph of several curves as the distance from one peak to the next or one trough (low point) to the next.

OBJECTIVES

In this lab, you will:

- measure the distance of displacement of a pendulum.
- collect data on the motion of a pendulum.
- graph the function of the movement of a pendulum.
- determine the period of a pendulum.

MATERIALS

- stopwatch or watch with a second hand
- Calculator-Based Ranger (CBR)
- TI-82 or TI-83 graphing calculator
- yo-yo
- ring stand
- meterstick
- masking tape

PROCEDURE

1. Unroll the yo-yo to the end of its string.
2. Attach the end of the string to the crossbar of the ring stand.
3. Hold the yo-yo straight down to keep it from swinging. Mark the position of the yo-yo at rest on the table with masking tape.
4. Place the CBR 0.5 meter in front of the yo-yo so that the yo-yo will swing directly away from and back towards the CBR sensor.
5. Pull the yo-yo 0.25 meter back from its resting position, away from the CBR, and mark this position on the table.

© Glencoe/McGraw-Hill 35 *Mathematics: Applications and Connections*

MANIPULATIVES/MODELING

Hands-On Lab Masters, p. 77

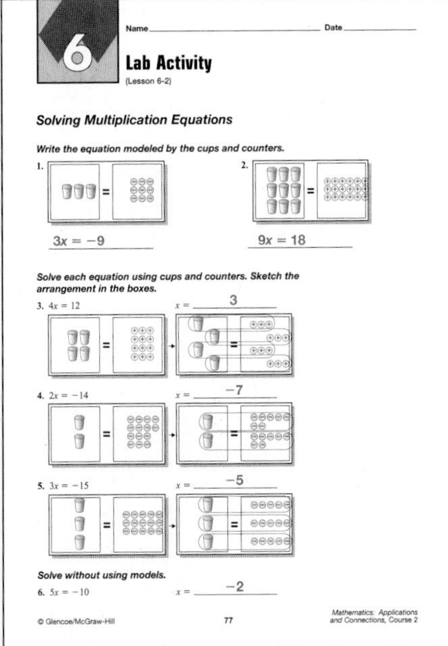

Name ______ Date ______

Lab Activity
(Lesson 6-2)

Solving Multiplication Equations

Write the equation modeled by the cups and counters.

1. $3x = -9$
2. $9x = 18$

Solve each equation using cups and counters. Sketch the arrangement in the boxes.

3. $4x = 12$ $x =$ 3
4. $2x = -14$ $x =$ −7
5. $3x = -15$ $x =$ −5

Solve without using models.

6. $5x = -10$ $x =$ −2

 77 *Mathematics: Applications and Connections, Course 2*

ASSESSMENT/EVALUATION

Assessment and Evaluation Masters, pp. 154–156

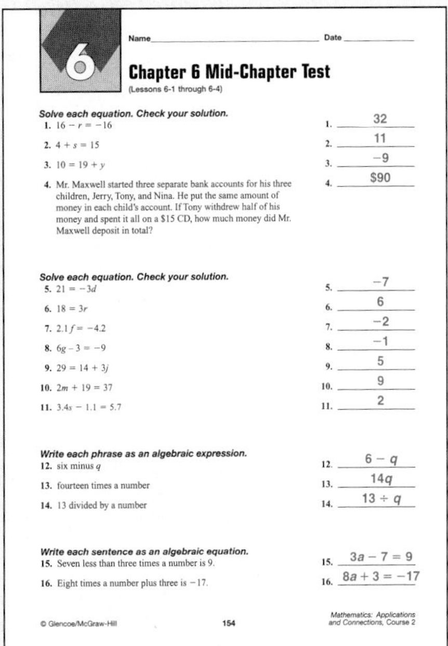

Name ______ Date ______

Chapter 6 Mid-Chapter Test
(Lessons 6-1 through 6-4)

Solve each equation. Check your solution.

1. $16 - r = -16$ — 1. 32
2. $4 + s = 15$ — 2. 11
3. $10 = 19 + y$ — 3. −9
4. Mr. Maxwell started three separate bank accounts for his three children, Jerry, Tony, and Nina. He put the same amount of money in each child's account. If Tony withdrew half of his money and spent it all on a $15 CD, how much money did Mr. Maxwell deposit in total? — 4. $90

Solve each equation. Check your solution.

5. $21 = -3d$ — 5. −7
6. $18 = 3r$ — 6. 6
7. $2.1f = -4.2$ — 7. −2
8. $6g - 3 = -9$ — 8. −1
9. $29 = 14 + 3j$ — 9. 5
10. $2m + 19 = 37$ — 10. 9
11. $3.4s - 1.1 = 5.7$ — 11. 2

Write each phrase as an algebraic expression.

12. six minus q — 12. $6 - q$
13. fourteen times a number — 13. $14q$
14. 13 divided by a number — 14. $13 \div q$

Write each sentence as an algebraic equation.

15. Seven less than three times a number is 9. — 15. $3a - 7 = 9$
16. Eight times a number plus three is −17. — 16. $8a + 3 = -17$

 154 *Mathematics: Applications and Connections, Course 2*

Name ______ Date ______

Chapter 6 Quiz A (Lessons 6-1 and 6-2)

Solve each equation. Check your solution.

1. $t + 7 = 5$ — 1. −2
2. $5 - r = -2$ — 2. 7
3. $3x = -12$ — 3. −4
4. $-18 = -6c$ — 4. 3

Solve. Use any strategy.

5. Lauren brings brownies to class one day. She gives 4 to Gareth, 3 to Tammy, and 8 to Louise. If she brought 20 brownies, how many did she have left for herself? — 5. 5

Name ______ Date ______

Chapter 6 Quiz B (Lessons 6-3 and 6-4)

Solve each equation. Check your solution.

1. $4u - 3 = 5$
2. $-3 = 9 + 4c$
3. $6q + 1 = -11$
4. $22 = 4 + 3w$

1. 2
2. −3
3. −2
4. 6

Write each phrase as an algebraic expression.

5. four times a number — 5. $4m$
6. six less than b — 6. $b - 6$
7. a number divided by 14 — 7. $t \div 14$

Write each sentence as an algebraic expression.

8. Ten more than seven times a number is 35. — 8. $7x + 10 = 35$
9. Seventeen minus a number is 23. — 9. $17 - s = 23$
10. Four divided by three times a number is 11. — 10. $4 \div 3y = 11$

 155 *Mathematics: Applications and Connections, Course 2*

TECHNOLOGY/MULTIMEDIA

Technology Masters, pp. 37–38

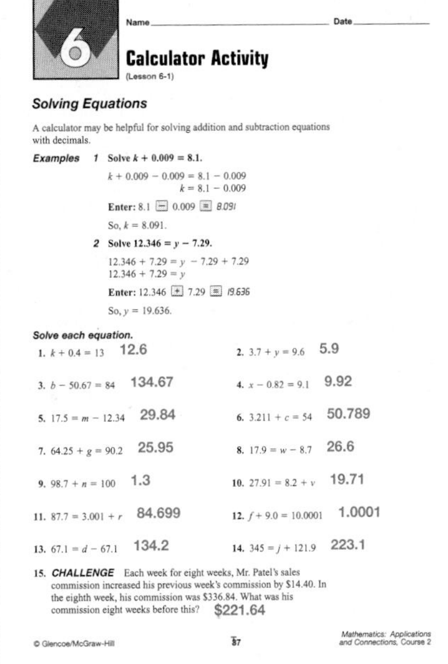

Name ______ Date ______

Calculator Activity
(Lesson 6-1)

Solving Equations

A calculator may be helpful for solving addition and subtraction equations with decimals.

Examples 1 **Solve $k + 0.009 = 8.1$.**

$k + 0.009 - 0.009 = 8.1 - 0.009$
$k = 8.1 - 0.009$

Enter: 8.1 [−] 0.009 [=] 8.091

So, $k = 8.091$.

2 **Solve $12.346 = y - 7.29$.**

$12.346 + 7.29 = y - 7.29 + 7.29$
$12.346 + 7.29 = y$

Enter: 12.346 [+] 7.29 [=] 19.636

So, $y = 19.636$.

Solve each equation.

1. $k + 0.4 = 13$ 12.6
2. $3.7 + y = 9.6$ 5.9
3. $b - 50.67 = 84$ 134.67
4. $x - 0.82 = 9.1$ 9.92
5. $17.5 = m - 12.34$ 29.84
6. $3.211 + c = 54$ 50.789
7. $64.25 + g = 90.2$ 25.95
8. $17.9 = w - 8.7$ 26.6
9. $98.7 + n = 100$ 1.3
10. $27.91 = 8.2 + v$ 19.71
11. $87.7 = 3.001 + r$ 84.699
12. $f + 9.0 = 10.0001$ 1.0001
13. $67.1 = d - 67.1$ 134.2
14. $345 = j + 121.9$ 223.1
15. ***CHALLENGE*** Each week for eight weeks, Mr. Patel's sales commission increased his previous week's commission by $14.40. In the eighth week, his commission was $336.84. What was his commission eight weeks before this? $221.64

 37 *Mathematics: Applications and Connections, Course 2*

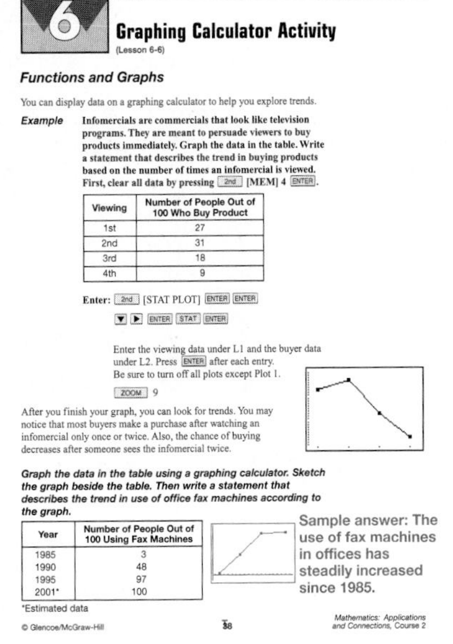

Name ______ Date ______

Graphing Calculator Activity
(Lesson 6-6)

Functions and Graphs

You can display data on a graphing calculator to help you explore trends.

Example **Infomercials are commercials that look like television programs. They are meant to persuade viewers to buy products immediately. Graph the data in the table. Write a statement that describes the trend in buying products based on the number of times an infomercial is viewed. First, clear all data by pressing [2nd] [MEM] 4 [ENTER].**

Viewing	Number of People Out of 100 Who Buy Product
1st	27
2nd	31
3rd	18
4th	9

Enter: [2nd] [STAT PLOT] [ENTER] [ENTER]
[▼] [▶] [ENTER] [STAT] [ENTER]

Enter the viewing data under L1 and the buyer data under L2. Press [ENTER] after each entry. Be sure to turn off all plots except Plot 1.

[ZOOM] 9

After you finish your graph, you can look for trends. You may notice that most buyers make a purchase after watching an infomercial only once or twice. Also, the chance of buying decreases after someone sees the infomercial twice.

Graph the data in the table using a graphing calculator. Sketch the graph beside the table. Then write a statement that describes the trend in use of office fax machines according to the graph.

Year	Number of People Out of 100 Using Fax Machines
1985	3
1990	48
1995	97
2001*	100

*Estimated data

Sample answer: The use of fax machines in offices has steadily increased since 1985.

 38 *Mathematics: Applications and Connections, Course 2*

MEETING INDIVIDUAL NEEDS

Investigations for the Special Education Student, pp. 39–42

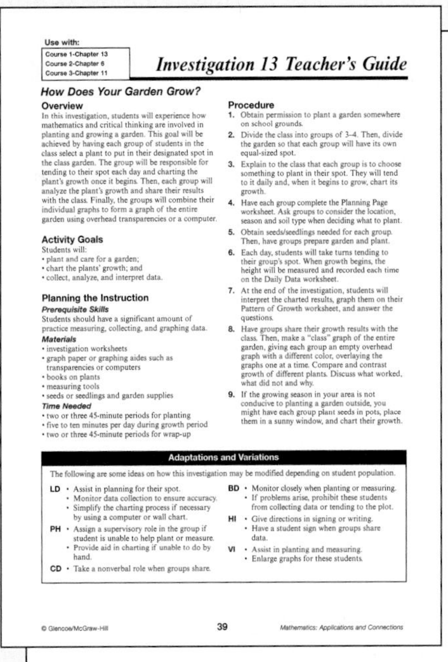

Use with:
Course 1-Chapter 13
Course 2-Chapter 6
Course 3-Chapter 11

Investigation 13 Teacher's Guide

How Does Your Garden Grow?

Overview

In this investigation, students will experience how mathematics and critical thinking are involved in planting and growing a garden. This goal will be achieved by having each group of students in the class select a plant to put in their designated spot in the class garden. The group will be responsible for tending to their spot each day and charting the plant's growth once it begins. Then, each group will analyze the plant's growth and share their results with the class. Finally, the groups will combine their individual graphs to form a graph of the entire garden using overhead transparencies or a computer.

Activity Goals

Students will:
- plant and care for a garden;
- chart the plants' growth; and
- collect, analyze, and interpret data.

Planning the Instruction

Prerequisite Skills
Students should have a significant amount of practice measuring, collecting, and graphing data.

Materials
- investigation worksheets
- graph paper or graphing aides such as transparencies or computers
- books on plants
- measuring tools
- seeds or seedlings and garden supplies

Time Needed
- two or three 45-minute periods for planting
- five to ten minutes per day during growth period
- two or three 45-minute periods for wrap-up

Procedure

1. Obtain permission to plant a garden somewhere on school grounds.
2. Divide the class into groups of 3-4. Then, divide the garden so that each group will have its own equal-sized spot.
3. Explain to the class that each group is to choose something to plant in their spot. They will tend to it daily and, when it begins to grow, chart its growth.
4. Have each group complete the Planning Page worksheet. Ask groups to consider the location, season and soil type when deciding what to plant.
5. Obtain seeds/seedlings needed for each group. Then, have groups prepare garden and plant.
6. Each day, students will take turns tending to their group's spot. When growth begins, the height will be measured and recorded each time on the Daily Data worksheet.
7. At the end of the investigation, students will interpret the charted results, graph them on their Pattern of Growth worksheet, and answer the questions.
8. Have groups share their growth results with the class. Then, make a "class" graph of the entire garden, giving each group an empty overhead graph with a different color, overlaying the graphs one at a time. Compare and contrast growth of different plants. Discuss what worked, what did not and why.
9. If the growing season in your area is not conducive to planting a garden outside, you might have each group plant seeds in pots, place them in a sunny window, and chart their growth.

Adaptations and Variations

The following are some ideas on how this investigation may be modified depending on student population.

LD
- Assist in planning for their spot.
- Monitor data collection to ensure accuracy.
- Simplify the charting process if necessary by using a computer or wall chart.

PH
- Assign a supervisory role in the group if student is unable to help plant or measure.
- Provide aid in charting if unable to do by hand.

CD
- Take a nonverbal role when groups share.

BD
- Monitor closely when planting or measuring.
- If problems arise, prohibit these students from collecting data or tending to the plot.

HI
- Give directions in signing or writing.
- Have a student sign when groups share data.

VI
- Assist in planting and measuring.
- Enlarge graphs for these students.

 39 *Mathematics: Applications and Connections*

Theme: Roller Coasters

In the past 100 years, roller coasters at Cedar Point have undergone a lot of changes. Its earliest coaster, the Switchback Railway in 1892, was a wooden roller coaster 25 feet tall, which moved at a maximum speed of 10 mph. Cedar Point's newest wooden roller coaster, the Mean Streak, opened in 1991 and is 161 feet tall, zipping along at about 65 mph.

Question of the Day How many times larger than the Switchback Railway is the Mean Streak? How many times faster? 6.44; 6.5

Assess Prerequisite Skills

Ask students to read through the list of objectives presented in "What you'll learn in Chapter 6." You may wish to ask them what each of the objectives means or if they have experienced or used any of these math concepts before.

Building Portfolios

Encourage students to revise their portfolios as they study this chapter. They might want to include new ways of expressing quantities and operations or new ways of solving problems.

Math and the Family

In the *Family Letters and Activities* booklet (pp. 37–38), you will find a letter to the parents explaining what students will study in Chapter 6. An activity appropriate for the whole family is also available.

CHAPTER 6 Algebra: Exploring Equations and Functions

What you'll learn in Chapter 6

- to solve addition, subtraction, and multiplication equations,
- to write simple algebraic expressions and equations,
- to solve inequalities,
- to graph functions and linear equations by plotting points, and
- to solve problems by working backward.

CD-ROM Program

- Chapter 6 Introduction
- Interactive Lessons 6-1, 6-2, 6-3, 6-7
- Extended Activity 6-6
- Assessment Game
- Resource Lessons 6-1 through 6-7

CHAPTER Project

AMERICA'S SCREAM MACHINES

Cedar Point, a world-famous amusement park on the coast of Lake Erie in Ohio, has earned the nickname "America's Roller Coast." The park built its first roller coaster in 1892 and has continued to add roller coasters ever since.

In this project, you'll use equations to find which of Cedar Point's roller coasters has the fastest average speed. You'll also choose one of the roller coasters and graph the distance it travels and the number of riders it can carry. Finally, you'll do research about your roller coaster and prepare a display of statistics and information.

Getting Started

- Look at the table. Which roller coaster travels the greatest distance? Which takes the least amount of time?
- Which roller coaster can accommodate the most riders per hour?

Roller Coasters at Cedar Point

Name	Track Length (feet)	Time of Ride	Rider Capacity (per hour)
Blue Streak	2,558	1 min 45 s	1,400
Cedar Creek	2,540	2 min 42 s	2,400
Corkscrew	2,050	2 min	1,800
Gemini	3,935	2 min 20 s	3,300
Iron Dragon	2,800	2 min	2,000
Magnum	5,106	2 min	2,000
Mantis	3,900	2 min 40 s	1,800
Mean Streak	5,427	2 min 45 s	1,600
Raptor	3,790	2 min 16 s	1,800
Wildcat	1,837	1 min 25 s	900

Technology Tips

- Use a **spreadsheet** to find the average speed of each roller coaster.
- Use **computer software** to make graphs.
- Use a **graphing calculator** to make tables and graphs.

Data Update For up-to-date information on Cedar Point, visit:

www.glencoe.com/sec/math/mac/mathnet

Working on the Project

You can use what you'll learn in Chapter 6 to help you find the average speeds and make your graphs.

Page	Exercise
236	32
252	8
257	30
261	Alternative Assessment

CHAPTER Project NOTES

Objectives Students should
- use equations to determine average speed from distance and time measurements.
- be able to use graphs and charts to compare quantities.

Project Pointer You may suggest that students begin a *Project Folder* to keep their work as they complete each stage of the Chapter Project. The completed project may also be added to their portfolios.

Students may want to make illustrations of roller coasters, drawn to scale, to compare the sizes, speeds, or capacities of different rides.

Using the Table Students may need guidance in converting track length and time of ride into rate of speed in feet per second. Remind them to convert minutes to seconds and divide distance by time $\left(r = \frac{d}{t}\right)$.

***Investigations and Projects Masters,* p. 40**

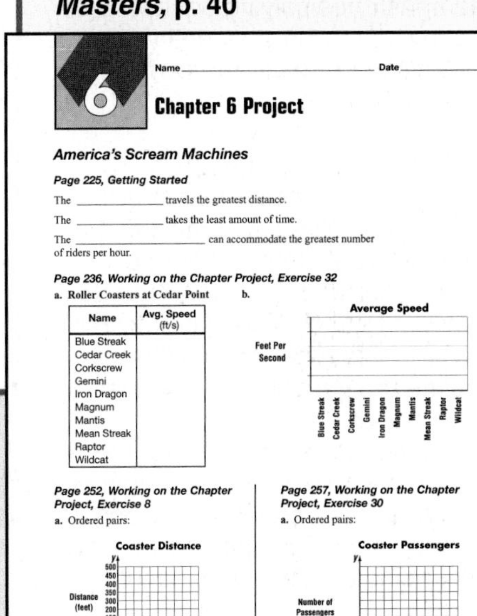
Name ______ Date ______

Chapter 6 Project

America's Scream Machines

Page 225, Getting Started

The ______ travels the greatest distance.

The ______ takes the least amount of time.

The ______ can accommodate the greatest number of riders per hour.

Page 236, Working on the Chapter Project, Exercise 32

a. Roller Coasters at Cedar Point

Name	Avg. Speed (ft/s)
Blue Streak	
Cedar Creek	
Corkscrew	
Gemini	
Iron Dragon	
Magnum	
Mantis	
Mean Streak	
Raptor	
Wildcat	

b.

Page 252, Working on the Chapter Project, Exercise 8

a. Ordered pairs:

b.

Page 257, Working on the Chapter Project, Exercise 30

a. Ordered pairs:

b.

 40 *Mathematics: Applications and Connections, Course 2*

Glencoe has made every effort to ensure that the website links for *Mathematics: Applications and Connections* at **www.glencoe.com/sec/math/mac/mathnet** are current and contain appropriate content. However, these website links are not under Glencoe's control.

Instructional Resources ▶▶▶

A recording sheet to help students organize their data for the Chapter Project is shown at the right and is available in the *Investigations and Projects Masters,* p. 40.

6-1A HANDS-ON LAB Notes

GET READY

Objective Students use models to solve equations.

Optional Resources
Hands-On Lab Masters
- integer counters, p. 6
- pattern for cup, p. 7
- equation mat, p. 9
- worksheet, p. 49

Overhead Manipulative Resources
- cups
- counters
- equation mat

Manipulative Kit
- cups
- counters
- equation mat

MANAGEMENT TIPS

Recommended Time
30 minutes

Getting Started Have students model an equation using a ruler as a balance scale. Balancing the ruler at its midpoint on a pencil or eraser, point out that the two sides are equal when the same quantity (of inches) is on both sides.

Activity 1 on page 226 demonstrates solving equations by removing the same quantity from each side to isolate the variable on one side.

In **Activity 2** on page 227, students encounter equations that cannot be solved by removing the same quantity from each side. They learn to add the appropriate amount to each side to create zero pairs that can be removed to isolate the variable on one side.

Teaching Tip Remind students that they can use any operation on one side of an equation, as long as they do the same operation on the other side to keep it in balance.

HANDS-ON LAB

COOPERATIVE LEARNING

6-1A Solving Equations Using Models

A Preview of Lesson 6-1

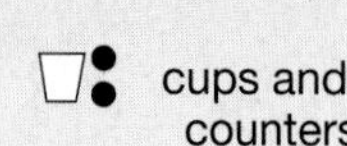
cups and counters

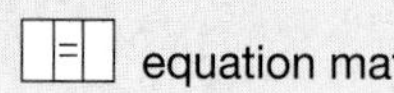
equation mat

If you have ever balanced on a seesaw, you've used a simple machine called a lever. When a seesaw is balanced, the forces on the left side and right side are equal. A seesaw is also a model for an equation.

In this lab, you will use models to solve simple equations.

TRY THIS

Work with a partner.

1 Solve the equation $x + 3 = 5$ using models.

- Use a cup to represent the unknown value, x. Place 1 cup and 3 yellow counters on the left side of an equation mat. Place 5 yellow counters on the right side of the mat.

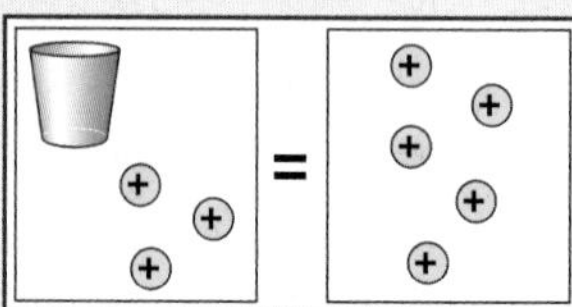

- The goal is to determine what's in the cup. To do so, get the cup by itself on one side of the mat. Then the counters on the other side will be the value of the cup, or x.
- To find the value of x, remove 3 counters from the left side and 3 counters from the right side. *You need to remove the same amount from both sides to maintain the balance.*

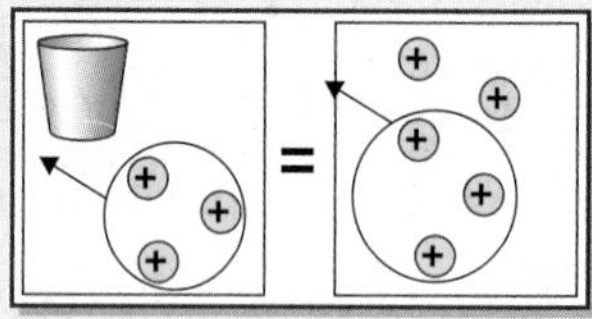

- The cup is by itself on one side of the mat. There are two counters on the other side. Therefore, the solution is 2.

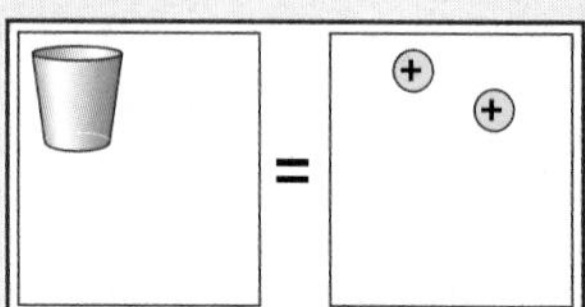

ON YOUR OWN

Solve each equation using models. **1–6. See Answer Appendix for models.**

1. $x + 1 = 6$ **5**
2. $x + 2 = 5$ **3**
3. $x + 5 = 10$ **5**
4. $x + 4 = 7$ **3**
5. $x + 0 = 3$ **3**
6. $x + 3 = 3$ **0**
7. In what way is a balanced seesaw like an equation? **See margin.**
8. Explain how solving equations using cups and counters is similar to keeping a seesaw in balance. **See margin.**

Additional Answers

7. Sample answer: The forces on each arm of the seesaw are equal; each side of an equation has the same value.
8. Sample answer: If you add the force on one arm of the seesaw, you need to add an equal force to the other arm; in an equation, whatever operation you perform on one side, you need to perform on the other.

Some equations are solved by using *zero pairs.* A zero pair consists of a positive counter and a negative counter. You may add or subtract a zero pair from either side of an equation without changing its value. Remember, yellow counters represent positive integers, and red counters represent negative integers.

TRY THIS

2 Solve the equation $x + 2 = -1$ using models.

- Place 1 cup and 2 yellow counters on the left side of an equation mat. Place 1 red counter on the right side.

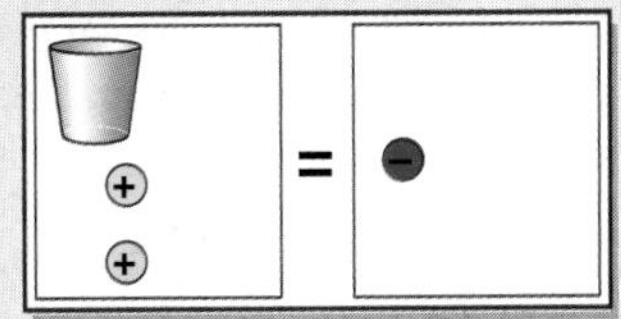

- The goal is to get the cup by itself on one side of the mat. However, it is not possible to remove 2 yellow counters from each side of the mat. Instead, add 2 red counters to each side of the mat, which forms zero pairs.

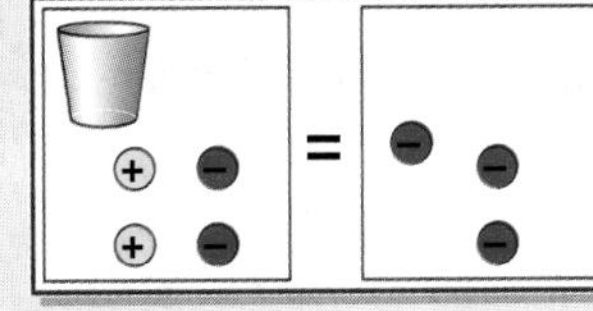

- Now, remove 2 zero pairs from the left side.

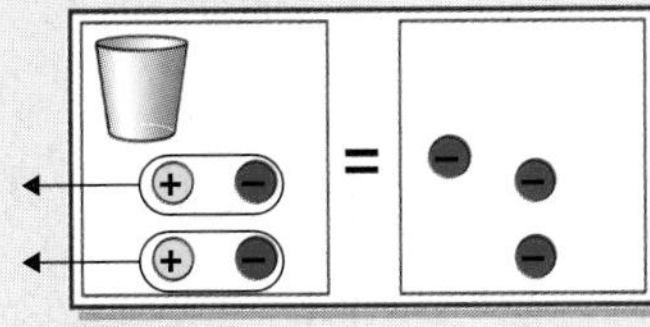

- The cup is by itself on one side of the mat. There are 3 negative counters on the other side. Therefore, the solution is -3.

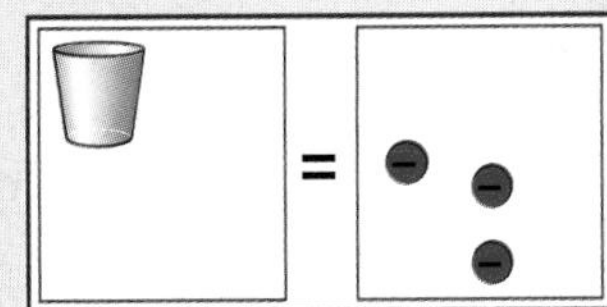

ON YOUR OWN

Solve each equation using models. **9–14. See Answer Appendix for models.**

9. $x + 3 = -2$ **−5** **10.** $x + 4 = 1$ **−3** **11.** $-2 = x + 1$ **−3**

Write each subtraction expression as an addition expression. Then solve the equation. For example, write $x - 3 = -2$ as $x + (-3) = -2$.

12. $x - 3 = -2$ **1** **13.** $x - 1 = -3$ **−2** **14.** $4 = x - 2$ **6**

15. Explain why you can remove a zero pair from one side of a mat without changing the value of the equation. **See margin.**

Have students write a paragraph explaining what a "solution" of an equation is, and how removing the same number of counters from each mat provides the solution of the equation.

ASSESS

As students complete Exercises 1–6 and 9–11, make sure they add or remove the same number of counters from both sides of the mat. If students have difficulty identifying the empty cup as the unknown, place the correct number of counters in the cup as the (hidden) solution to the problem, against which they can check their answers.

Additional Answer

15. Sample answer: A zero pair has a value of 0. So, adding or subtracting a zero pair is like adding or subtracting zero.

***Hands-On Lab Masters,* p. 49**

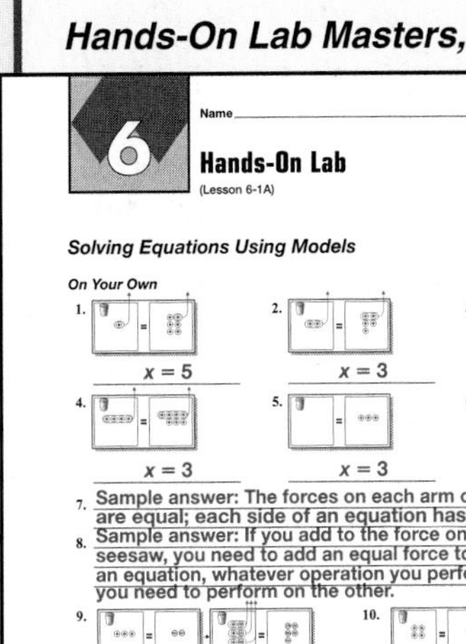

Name ______ Date ______

6 **Hands-On Lab** (Lesson 6-1A)

Solving Equations Using Models

On Your Own

1. $x = 5$
2. $x = 3$
3. $x = 5$
4. $x = 3$
5. $x = 3$
6. $x = 0$
7. Sample answer: The forces on each arm of the seesaw are equal; each side of an equation has the same value.
8. Sample answer: If you add to the force on one arm of the seesaw, you need to add an equal force to the other arm; in an equation, whatever operation you perform on one side, you need to perform on the other.

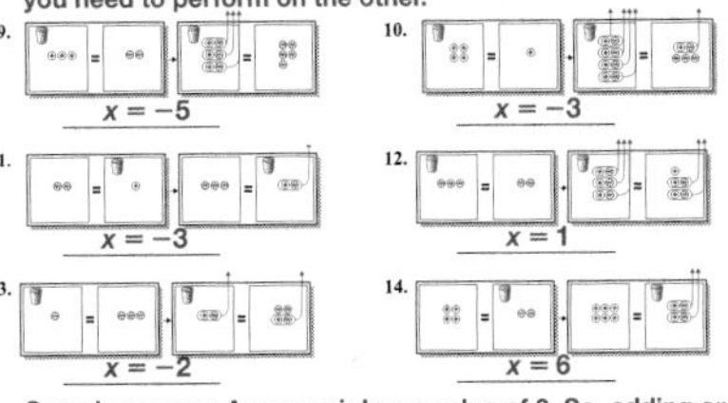

9. $x = -5$
10. $x = -3$
11. $x = -3$
12. $x = 1$
13. $x = -2$
14. $x = 6$
15. Sample answer: A zero pair has a value of 0. So, adding or subtracting a zero pair is like adding or subtracting a zero.

 49 *Mathematics: Applications and Connections, Course 2*

6-1 Lesson Notes

Instructional Resources

- *Study Guide Masters,* p. 42
- *Practice Masters,* p. 42
- *Enrichment Masters,* p. 42
- Transparencies 6-1, A and B
- *Technology Masters,* p. 37

- CD-ROM Program
  - Resource Lesson 6-1
  - Interactive Lesson 6-1

Recommended Pacing	
Standard	Days 2 & 3 of 14
Honors	Day 2 of 13
Block	Day 2 of 7

1 FOCUS

5-Minute Check
(Chapter 5)

1. Replace ● with <, >, or = to make -5 ● 1 a true sentence. <

Solve each equation.

2. $3 + (-5) = a$ -2
3. $-10 - 4 = b$ -14
4. $c = -7(-3)$ 21
5. $d = -16 \div 4$ -4

The 5-Minute Check is also available on **Transparency 6-1A** for this lesson.

Motivating the Lesson

Hands-On Activity Construct an array showing the location on a green of four golf balls shot from a tee 150 meters from the hole. Ball *a* is 5 meters short of the hole, ball *b* is 3 meters short, ball *c* is 4 meters past the hole, and ball *d* is 9 meters past. Have students use an equation to calculate the length of each tee shot.

6-1 Solving Addition and Subtraction Equations

What you'll learn

You'll learn to solve addition and subtraction equations.

When am I ever going to use this?

In geometry, you'll use equations to find missing angle measures.

Word Wise

subtraction property of equality
addition property of equality

On April 13, 1997, golfer Tiger Woods broke the course record for the Masters Championship with a final score of 18 under par, or -18. For each of the first three rounds, his scores were -2, -6, and -7. What was his score for the fourth round? *This problem will be solved in Example 4.*

You have solved equations by using models or by using mental math skills. However, you may not be able to solve all equations using these methods. The following examples describe methods you can use to solve all addition and subtraction equations.

Did you know Tiger Woods is also the youngest golfer ever to win the Masters Championship.

Example 1 Solve $x + 4 = 6$.

Method 1 Use symbols.

$x + 4 = 6$

$x + 4 - 4 = 6 - 4$

Subtracting 4 from each side of the equation is like removing 4 yellow counters from each side of the equation mat.

$x = 2$

The solution is 2.

Method 2 Use models.

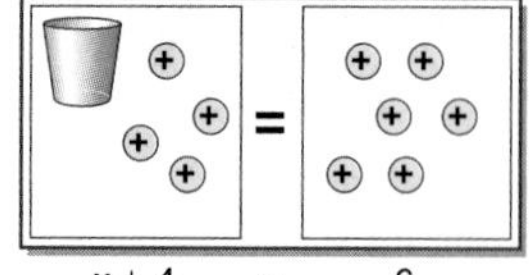

$x + 4 = 6$

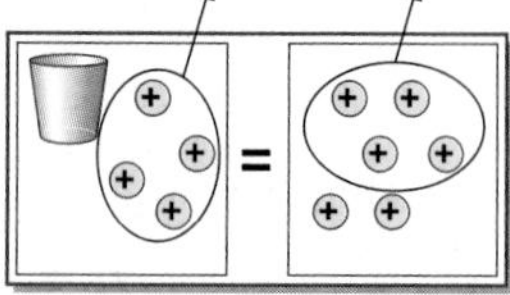

$x + 4 - 4 = 6 - 4$

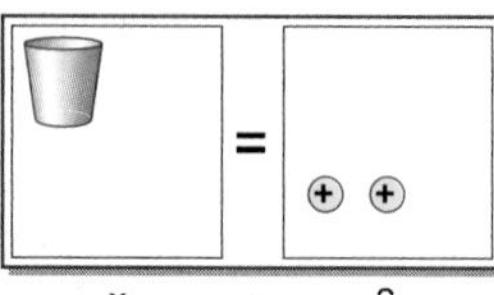

$x = 2$

In Example 1, you used the **subtraction property of equality**.

Subtraction Property of Equality	
Words:	If you subtract the same number from each side of an equation, then the two sides remain equal.
Symbols:	**Arithmetic**: $4 = 4$, $4 - 3 = 4 - 3$, $1 = 1$ — **Algebra**: $a = b$, $a - c = b - c$

Classroom Vignette

"To reinforce the Addition and Subtraction Properties of Equality, I use the example of a teeter-totter. You and a friend are perfectly balanced on a teeter-totter. What happens if your friend jumps off? Or what happens if someone else jumps on with your friend?"

JoEllyn Heinkel, Teacher
Sabish Junior High
Fond du Lac, WI

There is a similar property when addition is used.

Addition Property of Equality	**Words:** If you add the same number to each side of an equation, then the two sides remain equal. **Symbols:** **Arithmetic** $5 = 5$, $5 + 4 = 5 + 4$, $9 = 9$ — **Algebra** $a = b$, $a + c = b + c$

Examples

2 **Solve $x - 2 = 3$. Check your solution.**

Method 1 Use symbols.

$x - 2 = 3$

$x - 2 + 2 = 3 + 2$

Adding 2 to each side of the equation is like adding 2 yellow counters to each side of the equation mat.

$x = 5$

When you remove zero pairs, you are simplifying the expressions.

Method 2 Use models.

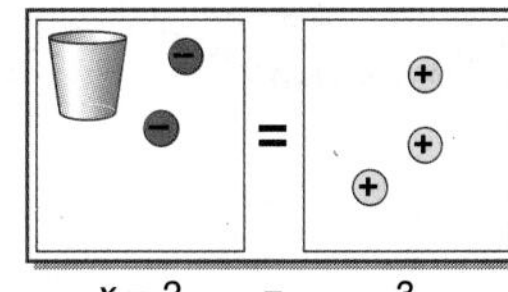

$x - 2 = 3$

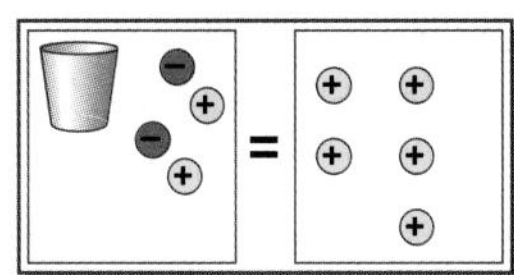

$x - 2 + 2 = 3 + 2$

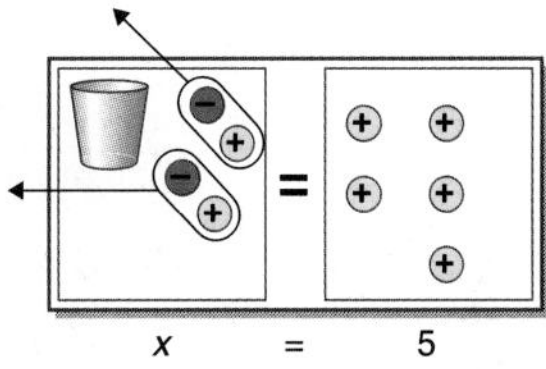

$x = 5$

To check your solution, replace x with 5 in the original equation.

$x - 2 = 3$

$5 - 2 \stackrel{?}{=} 3$ *Is this sentence true?*

$3 = 3$ ✓ The solution is 5.

Study Hint

Mental Math It is always wise to check your solution. You can often use arithmetic facts to check the solutions of simple equations.

3 **Solve $x - 5.7 = 6.3$. Check your solution.**

$x - 5.7 = 6.3$

$x - 5.7 + 5.7 = 6.3 + 5.7$ *Add 5.7 to each side of the equation.*

6.3 [+] 5.7 [=] 12

$x = 12$

Check: $x - 5.7 = 6.3$

$12 - 5.7 \stackrel{?}{=} 6.3$ *Replace x with 12.*

$6.3 = 6.3$ ✓ The solution is 12.

2 TEACH

Transparency 6-1B contains a teaching aid for this lesson.

Thinking Algebraically Ask students what information in the opening problem is given and what is unknown. Have them write a sentence expressing this information in the form of an addition problem.

In-Class Examples

For Example 1
Solve $14 + y = 20$. 6

For Example 2
Solve $z - 8 = -12$. -4

For Example 3
Solve $x + 4.2 = 11.1$. 6.9

For Example 4
If Tiger Woods had scores of -1, -4, and -3 on his first three rounds, what would his fourth round need to be if his final score was -18? -10

Teaching Tip In Examples 1 and 2, remind students that adding a negative number is equivalent to subtracting its absolute value and that subtracting a negative number is equivalent to adding its absolute value.

Multiple Learning Styles

Kinesthetic Ask students to construct a balance scale from a ruler and two cups with an equal number of counters in each cup. Ask the following questions:

- What would happen if you removed two counters from the right side? **Right side of scale will be higher than left.**
- What can you do to the left side of the scale to make the scale in balance again? **Remove two counters.**

3 PRACTICE/APPLY

Check for Understanding

If students need additional practice or instruction after completing Exercises 1–11, one of these options may be helpful.

- Extra Practice, see p. 583
- Reteaching Activity
- *Study Guide Masters,* p. 42
- *Practice Masters,* p. 42
- Interactive Mathematics Tools Software

Additional Answers

1. 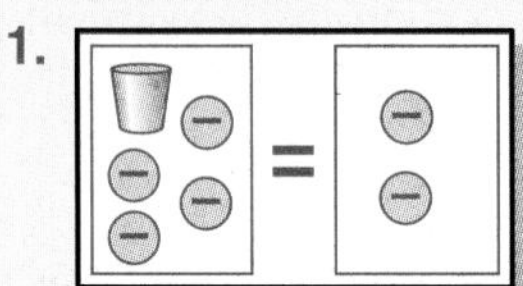

2. **Substitute the solution back into the original equation to see if a true statement results.**

Study Guide Masters, p. 42

Name________________ Date________

6-1 Study Guide

Solving Addition and Subtraction Equations

Remember, equations must always remain balanced. If you add the same number to each side of an equation, the two sides remain equal.

Example 1 **Solve $t - 12.2 = 15.3$. Check your solution.**

$t - 12.2 + 12.2 = 15.3 + 12.2$ *Add 12.2 to each side of the equation.*

$t = 27.5$

Check: $t - 12.2 = 15.3$

$27.5 - 12.2 \stackrel{?}{=} 15.3$ *Replace t with 27.5.*

$15.3 = 15.3$ ✔

If you subtract the same number from each side of an equation, the two sides remain equal.

Example 2 **Solve $5\frac{2}{5} + v = 7\frac{1}{2}$. Check your solution.**

$5\frac{2}{5} - 5\frac{2}{5} + v = 7\frac{1}{2} - 5\frac{2}{5}$ *Subtract $5\frac{2}{5}$ from each side of the equation.*

$v = 7\frac{5}{10} - 5\frac{4}{10}$

$v = 2\frac{1}{10}$

Check: $5\frac{2}{5} + v = 7\frac{1}{2}$

$5\frac{2}{5} + 2\frac{1}{10} \stackrel{?}{=} 7\frac{1}{2}$ *Replace v with $2\frac{1}{10}$.*

$5\frac{4}{10} + 2\frac{1}{10} \stackrel{?}{=} 7\frac{1}{2}$

$7\frac{5}{10} \stackrel{?}{=} 7\frac{1}{2}$

$7\frac{1}{2} = 7\frac{1}{2}$ ✔

Solve each equation. Check your solution.

1. $17 + k = 62$ **45**
2. $j - 4.5 = 1.7$ **6.2**
3. $8.9 = p - 3.3$ **12.2**
4. $n + 2\frac{1}{3} = 4\frac{2}{3}$ **$2\frac{1}{3}$**
5. $17.2 = h + 4.9$ **12.3**
6. $y - 9 = 29$ **38**
7. $133 = v + 70$ **63**
8. $x - 7\frac{1}{2} = 15$ **$22\frac{1}{2}$**
9. $146 + j = 199$ **53**
10. $m - 9.4 = 15.7$ **25.1**
11. $89.6 = c + 62.2$ **27.4**
12. $f - 19 = 77$ **96**

 T42 *Mathematics: Applications and Connections, Course 2*

Example 4 — Real World APPLICATION

Golf **Refer to the beginning of the lesson. Find Tiger Woods' score for the fourth round.**

Explore You know that the scores for the first three rounds were -2, -6, and -7. You know that the final score was -18. You need to find his score for the fourth round.

Plan Let s represent the fourth round score. The final score is the sum of the scores for each round. You can write an equation for this problem.

$$\underbrace{(-2) + (-6) + (-7)}_{\text{scores for first three rounds}} + \underbrace{s}_{\text{score for fourth round}} = \underbrace{-18}_{\text{final score}}$$

LOOK BACK
You can refer to Lesson 5-4 to review adding integers.

Solve $(-2) + (-6) + (-7) + s = -18$

$(-15) + s = -18$

$(-15) + 15 + s = -18 + 15$ *Add 15 to each side.*

$s = -3$

Tiger's score for the fourth round was -3.

Examine Check the solution by adding.

$-2 + (-6) + (-7) + (-3) = -18$ ✓

CHECK FOR UNDERSTANDING

Communicating Mathematics

Read and study the lesson to answer each question. **1–2. See margin.**

1. ***Draw*** a model that shows the equation $x - 4 = -2$.
2. ***Tell*** how to check your solution to an equation.
3. ***Write*** the equation shown by the model. Then explain how to solve the equation by using models and by using the properties of equality. **See Answer Appendix.**

Math Journal

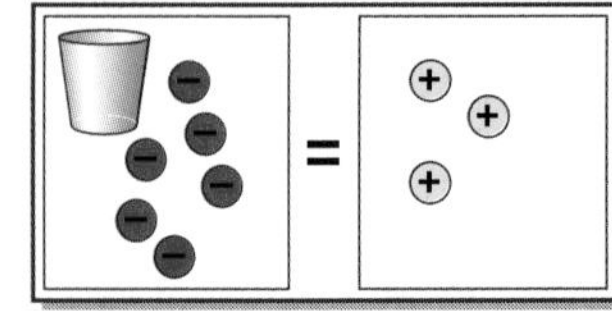

Guided Practice

Solve each equation. Use models if necessary. Check your solution.

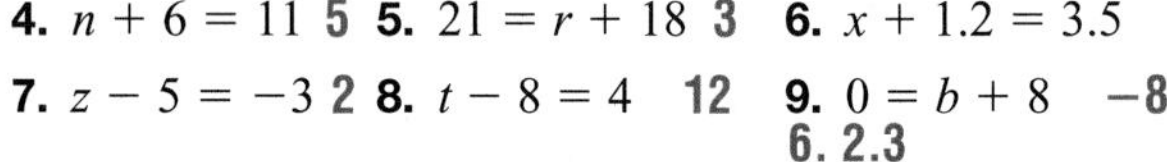

4. $n + 6 = 11$ **5**
5. $21 = r + 18$ **3**
6. $x + 1.2 = 3.5$ **6. 2.3**
7. $z - 5 = -3$ **2**
8. $t - 8 = 4$ **12**
9. $0 = b + 8$ **−8**
10. The sum of a number and 3 is -2. This means $n + 3 = -2$. Solve the equation to find the number. **−5**
11. ***Tourist Attractions*** The Gateway to the West Arch in St. Louis, Missouri, is 630 feet tall. It is 75 feet higher than the Washington Monument in Washington, D.C. Use the equation $t + 75 = 630$ to find the height of the Washington Monument. **555 feet**

Reteaching the Lesson

Activity Have students work with partners to model each example. Have them solve every equation by adding the proper quantity to make zero pairs on the side with the variable. Explain that this will work for any type of addition/subtraction equation.

Error Analysis
Watch for students who reverse the positive or negative sign when attempting to simplify an expression.
Prevent by emphasizing that a number added to one side of an equation must also be added to the other side (not subtracted).

EXERCISES

Practice

Solve each equation. Check your solution.

12. $a + 3 = 12$ **9**　**13.** $m - 8 = 13$ **21**　**14.** $27 = 18 + g$ **9**

15. $32 + c = 24$ **−8**　**16.** $34 = m + 18$ **16**　**17.** $y + 43 = 68$ **25**

18. $k - 7.2 = 4.5$ **11.7**　**19.** $-5 + v = 3$ **8**　**20.** $m - 5 = -9$ **−4**

21. $-9 = 3 + r$ **−12**　**22.** $-8 = y - 7$ **−1**　**23.** $-34 = t + 9$ **−43**

24. $-9 + w = -12$ **−3**　**25.** $a + 3.9 = 5.6$ **1.7**　**26.** $e + 11.8 = 13.1$ **1.3**

27. $13.2 = p + 4.7$ **8.5**　**28.** $s - 5.9 = 4.8$ **10.7**　**29.** $y - 16 = -5$ **11**

30. If you decrease a number by 4, the result is −5. This means $n - 4 = -5$. Solve the equation to find the number. **−1**

31. Negative 10 is the sum of a number and −6. Solve $-10 = n + (-6)$ to find the number. **−4**

Applications and Problem Solving

32. ***Aviation*** Orville and Wilbur Wright flew their airplane called *Flyer I* in Kitty Hawk, North Carolina, on December 17, 1903. Wilbur's flight was 364 feet, which was 120 feet longer than Orville's flight. Solve the equation $f + 120 = 364$ to find the length of his flight. **244 feet**

33. ***Geometry*** The sum of the measures of the angles of a triangle is 180°. Find the missing measure. **$a + 50 + 75 = 180$; 55°**

$a°$, 50°, 75°

34. ***Write an Equation*** Write about a real-life situation involving the photo at the left that can be represented by the equation $x - 3 = 7$.

34. See students' work.

35. ***Critical Thinking*** Write two different equations that have −2 as a solution. **Sample answer: $x - 5 = -7$, $x + 4 = 2$**

Mixed Review

36. **Standardized Test Practice** Which graph shows a translation of the letter *Z*? *(Lesson 5-8)* **C**

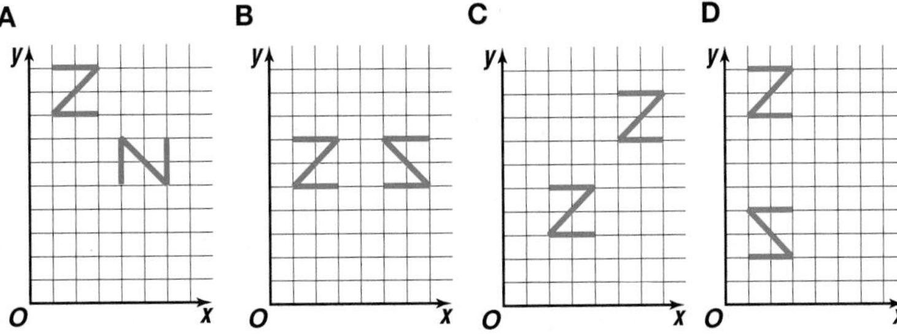

37. Find $12 - (-4)$. *(Lesson 5-5)* **16**

38. On his most recent math test, Ricardo scored 84 out of 100 points. Express his score as a fraction in simplest form. *(Lesson 4-5)* $\frac{21}{25}$

39. ***Statistics*** The mean income for a group of accountants was $26,266.67. Their incomes were $17,500, $26,100, $19,800, $23,400, $21,300, and $49,500. In what way is the mean misleading? *(Lesson 3-7)*

39. The one very high salary increases the mean.

For **Extra Practice,** see page 583.

Assignment Guide

Core: 13–33 odd, 35–39
Enriched: 12–30 even, 32–39

4 ASSESS

Closing Activity

Writing Have students write two equations—one that can be solved by using the Addition Property of Equality and one that can be solved using the Subtraction Property of Equality.

***Practice Masters,* p. 42**

Name______ Date______

6-1 Practice

Solving Addition and Subtraction Equations

Solve each equation. Check your solution.

1. $y + 18 = 39$ **21**　2. $m - 23 = 17$ **40**　3. $74 = d + 37$ **37**
4. $w + 6 = 19$ **13**　5. $n - 4.7 = 8.4$ **13.1**　6. $s - 5 = 12$ **17**
7. $m + 18 = 78$ **60**　8. $12\frac{3}{4} + y = 32\frac{1}{8}$ **$19\frac{3}{8}$**　9. $18.42 + t = 63$ **44.58**
10. $p - 12 = 34$ **46**　11. $b - 43 = 18$ **61**　12. $48 = t - 63$ **111**
13. $d + 2.6 = 7.1$ **4.5**　14. $h - 32\frac{3}{5} = 44$ **$76\frac{3}{5}$**　15. $e - 0.9 = 17.4$ **18.3**
16. $26 = y - 87$ **113**　17. $13.2 + f = 17.4$ **4.2**　18. $25\frac{2}{3} = k - 2\frac{1}{6}$ **$27\frac{5}{6}$**
19. $104 = a - 14$ **118**　20. $a + 34 = 90$ **56**　21. $e + 12.2 = 40$ **27.8**

T42　*Mathematics: Applications and Connections, Course 2*

Extending the Lesson

***Enrichment Masters,* p. 42**

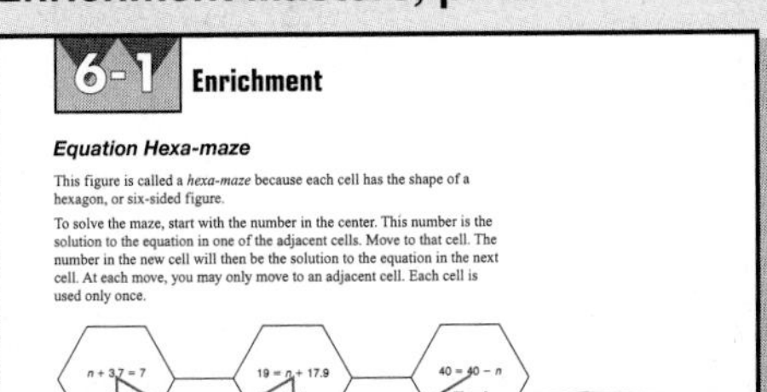

6-1 Enrichment

Equation Hexa-maze

This figure is called a *hexa-maze* because each cell has the shape of a hexagon, or six-sided figure.

To solve the maze, start with the number in the center. This number is the solution to the equation in one of the adjacent cells. Move to that cell. The number in the new cell will then be the solution to the equation in the next cell. At each move, you may only move to an adjacent cell. Each cell is used only once.

$n + 3.7 = 7$　$19 = n + 17.9$　$40 = 40 - n$

Activity Working in small groups, have each student write an addition or subtraction equation and read it to the group. Each member must write a word problem that can be solved by using the equation.

6-1B THINKING LAB Notes

Objective Students solve problems by working backward.

Recommended Pacing	
Standard	Day 4 of 14
Honors	Day 3 of 13
Block	Day 2 of 7

1 FOCUS

Getting Started Have students work backward to solve the following problem. To catch a 7:30 bus, Carla needs 30 minutes to get dressed, 30 minutes for breakfast, and 15 minutes to walk to the bus stop. What time should she wake up? **6:15 A.M.**

2 TEACH

Teaching Tip Suggest that students use a number line to make a timeline from 1900 to 1996 to help solve the problem. Start at 1996 and use arcs to move backward on the timeline to mark the date of each event.

In-Class Example

Rico and Lena went to a movie. Each ticket cost $4.50. If they each bought a $2.50 popcorn and a $1.50 drink, and had $3.00 left, how much did they have to spend? **$20**

PROBLEM SOLVING

6-1B Work Backward

A Follow-Up of Lesson 6-1

Mike and Heather found a puzzle about famous toys in a magazine at the school library. How would you solve it?

- In the early 1900s, a toy company names its stuffed bears Teddy Bears after President Teddy Roosevelt.
- Forty-nine years later, wire coil toys start rolling down stairs everyw
- Four years later, England exports miniature toy cars to the Unitec States.
- Forty years pass until 1996, when small beanbag animals captur everyone's attention.

In what year was the Teddy Bear named?

I suppose we could just guess the year and see if it's right.

Mike

That might work. But we can find the answer another way. Small beanbag animals were in 1996, and miniature toy cars were 40 years before. So, 1996 - 40 is 1956.

I get it. We'll keep working backward until we get to the Teddy Bear!

Heather

THINK ABOUT IT

Work with a partner.

1. In what year was the wire coil toy introduced? **1952**
2. In what year was the Teddy Bear named? **1903**
3. ***Explain*** why the guess-and-check strategy isn't the best choice for solving this problem. **Sample answer: There are too many guesses you might make; it would take less time to work backward.**
4. Apply the **work backward** strategy to solve this problem.

   Jaime rented 3 times as many videotapes as Phyllis last month. Phyllis rented 4 fewer than Marva, but 4 more than Paloma. Marva rented 10 videotapes. How many videotapes did each person rent? **Jaime, 18; Phyllis, 6; Marva, 10; Paloma, 2**

Reteaching the Lesson

Activity Marcel and Dieter bought Eurail passes in Paris and rode the train for 1 day to spend 2 days in Zurich, traveled another 1 day to spend 3 days in Florence, rode another train 1 day to spend 2 days in Vienna, rode 1 day to spend 4 days in Prague, and 1 day to arrive back in Paris on July 14. When did they leave? **June 29**

For **Extra Practice,** see page 583.

ON YOUR OWN

5. See margin.

5. ***Explain*** how you would solve the equation $x + 13 = 25$ by working backward.
6. ***Write a Problem*** that can be solved by working backward. **See students' work.**
7. ***Explain*** how you can find the answer to Exercise 32 on page 231 by working backward. **Sample answer: Subtract 120 from 364.**

10. 1,024 cartons

MIXED PROBLEM SOLVING

STRATEGIES
- Look for a pattern.
- Solve a simpler problem.
- Act it out.
- Guess and check.
- Draw a diagram.
- Make a chart.
- Work backward.

Solve. Use any strategy.

8. ***Numbers*** I'm thinking of a number. If I multiply it by 5 and add 17, the result is 67. What is the number? **10**
9. ***Money Matters*** Antoine is on vacation and is planning to send postcards and letters to his friends. He has $2.66 to spend on postage. A stamp for a letter costs 33¢, and a stamp for a postcard costs 20¢. If he is going to spend the entire $2.66 on postage, how many postcards and letters can he send? **See margin.**
10. ***Food*** Mr. Roberts is delivering cartons of cereal to supermarkets. At the first market, he drops off half of the cartons he has in the truck. At each of the other markets, he drops off half of the cartons he has left. Then, at the eleventh market, he drops off one carton, which is the last one in the truck. How many cartons were originally in the truck?
11. ***Food*** When a certain chocolate bar was first introduced, it was not wrapped in paper. Two years later, in 1896, rolled chocolate candy became the first paper-wrapped candy bars. In what year was the chocolate bar introduced? **1894**
12. ***Money Matters*** Crystal and her sister, Ebony, each own an equal number of shares of stock. Crystal sells one third of her shares for $2,700. What was the total value of Crystal's and Ebony's stock before the sale? **$16,200**
13. ***Patterns*** Look at the model of the triangular numbers. How many dots would be in a triangle that has 10 dots on a side? **55**

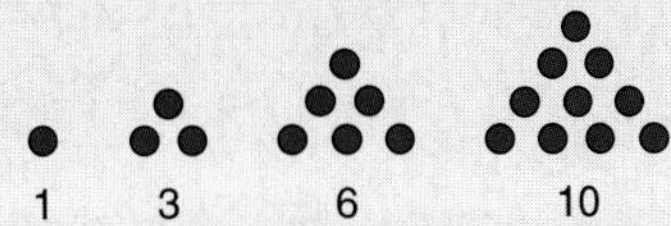

14. ***Games*** In a popular board game, players make words from tiles printed with letters of the alphabet. The squares on the board are pink, dark blue, light blue, red, or gray.

- There are 8 less pink than light blue.
- There are twice as many light blue as dark blue.
- There are $\frac{1}{6}$ as many dark blue as red.
- There are 28 fewer red than gray.

There are 100 gray squares on the board. How many are pink? **16 pink squares**

15. ***Standardized Test Practice*** The #6 bus runs every 8 minutes, the #9 bus runs every 10 minutes, and the #10 bus runs every 12 minutes. If all three buses leave the station at 8:00 A.M., when is the next time all three buses leave the station at the same time? **B**
    A 9:00 A.M.
    B 10:00 A.M.
    C 11:00 A.M.
    D 12:00 P.M.

3 PRACTICE/APPLY

Check for Understanding

Review the steps students went through to solve Exercise 4 and what mathematical operation (addition, subtraction, multiplication, or division) is appropriate for each step.

Extra Practice If students need additional practice in problem solving, extra practice is available on the following pages.
- Work Backward, see p. 583
- Mixed Problem Solving, see pp. 605–606

Assignment Guide
All: 5–15

4 ASSESS

Closing Activity

Writing Ask students to imagine what they would do with $100. Have them write a budget, working backward from $100, and include the costs of items they would buy: tickets to events, food, and other expenses.

Additional Answers

5. Sample answer: Since 13 was added to x to get 25, subtract 13 from 25. The solution is 12.
9. 2 letters and 10 postcards

Extending the Lesson

Activity Have students create four-person 3,200-m relays in which each team member runs a different distance. Have them do the same for a 100-km bicycle relay and an 800-m swimming relay.

Sample answer:
1,600 + 800 + 600 + 200 = 3,200 m (run)
10 + 20 + 30 + 40 = 100 km (bicycle)
50 + 150 + 250 + 350 = 800 m (swim)

6-2 Lesson Notes

Instructional Resources

- *Study Guide Masters,* p. 43
- *Practice Masters,* p. 43
- *Enrichment Masters,* p. 43
- Transparencies 6-2, A and B
- *Assessment and Evaluation Masters,* p. 155
- *Diversity Masters,* p. 19
- *Hands-On Lab Masters,* p. 77

 CD-ROM Program
- Resource Lesson 6-2
- Interactive Lesson 6-2

Recommended Pacing	
Standard	Day 5 of 14
Honors	Day 4 of 13
Block	Day 3 of 7

1 FOCUS

5-Minute Check

Solve each equation. Check your solution.

1. $b + 7 = 22$ **15**
2. $8.4 = t - 5.6$ **14**
3. $p - 23.8 = 35.7$ **59.5**
4. $11.5 = 0.4 + r$ **11.1**
5. Wayne bought 1,000 pine seedlings for $400 and planted them. Five years later, he sold 300 of the trees for $5 each. How much did Wayne gain? **$1,100**

 The 5-Minute Check is also available on **Transparency 6-2A** for this lesson.

Motivating the Lesson

Problem Solving Tell students that in a community there are 201 televisions, and each household has 3. This fact can be represented by the equation $3m = 201$. How can this equation be used to find the number of households?

6-2 Solving Multiplication Equations

What **you'll learn**

You'll learn to solve multiplication equations.

When **am I ever going to use this?**

In physical science, you'll use the formula $d = rt$ to study velocity.

Word Wise

coefficient
division property of equality

Equations like $2x = -8$ are called multiplication equations because the expression $2x$ means *2 times the value of x*. You can also use models to solve multiplication equations.

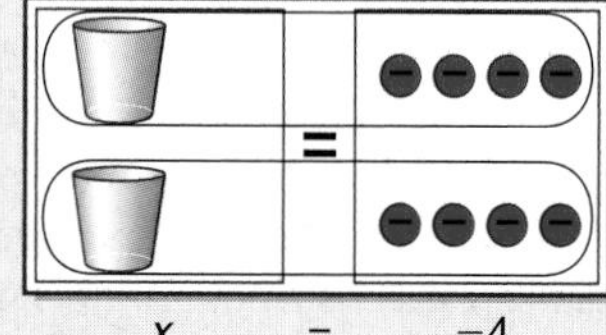

MINI-LAB

Work with a partner. cups and counters, equation mat

Solve $2x = -8$.

- Place two cups on the left side of an equation mat. Place 8 red counters on the right side of the mat.

$2x = -8$

- Each cup must contain the same number of counters. Arrange the counters into two equal groups to correspond to the two cups.

$x = -4$

The solution is -4.

Try This

1. Solve each equation using models. **See Answer Appendix for models.**
 a. $5x = 20$ **4** **b.** $-12 = 4x$ **−3** **c.** $3x = 3$ **1**

Talk About It

2. What operation did you use to find each solution? **division**
3. The **coefficient** of an expression like $3x$ is the numerical part, 3. How can you use the coefficient to solve the equation $3x = 12$?
4. How would you solve $2x = 5$ without using models?

3. Divide each side by the coefficient, 3.
4. Divide 5 by 2.

In the Mini-Lab, you placed an equal number of counters in each cup. This suggests the operation of division.

Division Property of Equality			
	Words:	If you divide each side of an equation by the same nonzero number, then the two sides remain equal.	
	Symbols:	**Arithmetic**	**Algebra**
		$8 = 8$	$a = b$
		$\frac{8}{2} = \frac{8}{2}$	$\frac{a}{c} = \frac{b}{c}, c \neq 0$
		$4 = 4$	

Notice that the division problem $8 \div 2$ is written as the fraction $\frac{8}{2}$.

Multiple Learning Styles

 **Interpersonal** Ask students to divide the class (n) into any number of teams (x) of equal numbers (y) and express it as an equation, such as $n = xy$. If necessary, add or subtract to make teams come out even ($n + 3 = xy$, for example.)

Examples

Solve each equation. Check your solution.

1 $12 = 3x$

Method 1

Use symbols.

$12 = 3x$

$\frac{12}{3} = \frac{3x}{3}$ *Divide each side of the equation by 3.*

$4 = x$ *$12 \div 3 = 4$*

Check: $12 = 3x$

$12 \stackrel{?}{=} 3 \cdot 4$

$12 = 12$ ✓

The solution is 4.

Method 2

Use models.

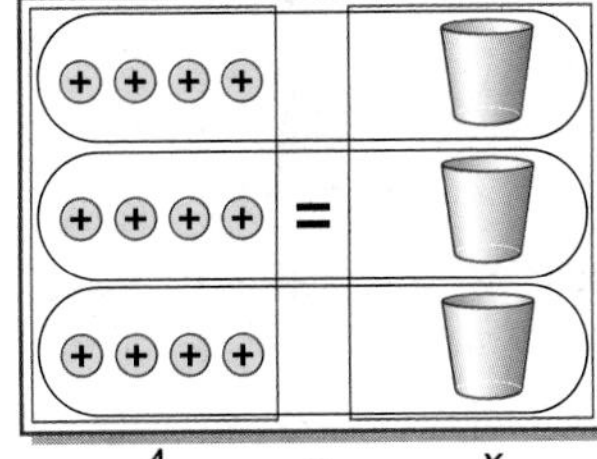

Dividing each side of the equation by 3 is like placing an equal number of counters in each cup.

2 $-5y = 15$

$-5y = 15$

$\frac{-5y}{-5} = \frac{15}{-5}$ *Divide each side of the equation by −5.*

$y = -3$ *$15 \div (-5) = -3$*

Check: $-5y = 15$

$-5(-3) \stackrel{?}{=} 15$

$15 = 15$ ✓

The solution is −3.

APPLICATION

3 **Kites** You can make a simple kite with newspaper, bendable sticks, and some string. The longer stick must be 1.5 times the length of the shorter stick. If 36 inches is the length of the longer stick, what should be the length of the shorter stick? Use the equation $1.5s = 36$, where s is the length of the shorter stick.

$1.5s = 36$

$\frac{1.5s}{1.5} = \frac{36}{1.5}$ *Divide each side of the equation by 1.5.*

$36 \div 1.5 = 24$

$s = 24$

Check: $1.5 \times 24 = 36$ ✓

The shorter stick should be 24 inches long.

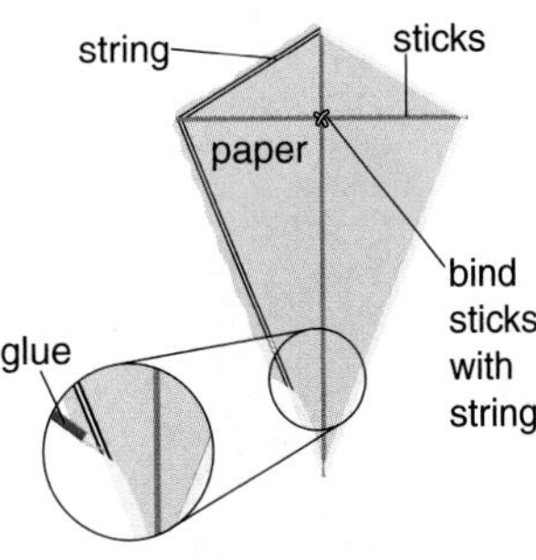

Fold paper over string and glue.

Cultural Kaleidoscope

Kites were originally used for military purposes. Around 1200 B.C., the Chinese used kites to send secret codes between army camps. The Chinese were also the first to fly kites for fun.

2 TEACH

Transparency 6-2B contains a teaching aid for this lesson.

Using the Mini-Lab Point out that multiplication and division are inverse operations, where one can "undo" the other. Model the division of counters into two, three, four, or five equal groups, depending on the multiplier in the equation.

In-Class Examples

For Example 1
Solve $141 = 3x$. **47**

For Example 2
Solve $-4y = 60$. **−15**

For Example 3
If the length of the longer stick of your kite was 99 inches, what would be the length of the shorter stick? Use the equation $1.5s = 99$, where s is the length of the shorter stick. **$s = 66$ in.**

Teaching Tip Before doing Example 3, encourage students to determine whether their solution is reasonable by estimating it using compatible numbers.

Investigations for the Special Education Student

This blackline master booklet helps you plan for the needs of your special education students by providing long-term projects along with teacher notes. Investigation 13, *How Does Your Garden Grow?*, may be used with this chapter.

3 PRACTICE/APPLY

Check for Understanding

If students need additional practice or instruction after completing Exercises 1–10, one of these options may be helpful.

- Extra Practice, see p. 584
- Reteaching Activity
- *Study Guide Masters*, p. 43
- *Practice Masters*, p. 43

Assignment Guide

Core: 11–33 odd, 34–38
Enriched: 12–30 even, 31, 33–38

Exercise 32 asks students to advance to the next stage of work on the Chapter Project. Encourage students to look for patterns when solving each equation.

Additional Answer

32a. Blue Streak, 24 ft/s; Cedar Creek, 16 ft/s; Corkscrew, 17 ft/s; Gemini, 28 ft/s; Iron Dragon, 23 ft/s; Magnum, 43 ft/s; Mantis, 24 ft/s; Mean Streak, 33 ft/s; Raptor, 28 ft/s; Wildcat, 22 ft/s

***Study Guide Masters*, p. 43**

Name________________ Date________

6-2 **Study Guide**

Solving Multiplication Equations

If you divide each side of an equation by the same nonzero number, the two sides remain equal.

Example 1 **Solve 48.6 = 6*c*. Check your solution.**

$\frac{48.6}{6} \stackrel{?}{=} \frac{6c}{6}$ *Divide each side of the equation by 6.*

$8.1 = c$

Check: $48.6 = 6c$

$48.6 \stackrel{?}{=} 6 \times 8.1$ *Replace c with 8.1.*

$48.6 = 48.6$ ✔

If you multiply each side of an equation by the same number, the two sides remain equal.

Example 2 **Solve $\frac{w}{5} = 2.3$. Check your solution.**

$\frac{w}{5} \cdot 5 = 2.3 \times 5$ *Multiply each side of the equation by 5.*

$w = 11.5$

Check: $\frac{w}{5} = 2.3$

$\frac{11.5}{5} \stackrel{?}{=} 2.3$ *Replace w with 11.5.*

$2.3 = 2.3$ ✔

Solve each equation. Check your solution.

1. $5r = 45$ 9
2. $\frac{y}{7} = 3.5$ 24.5
3. $180 = 9v$ 20
4. $21 = \frac{n}{3}$ 63
5. $\frac{1}{5}x = 4$ 20
6. $\frac{f}{1.1} = 7$ 7.7
7. $\frac{1}{2} = \frac{1}{8} \cdot c$ 4
8. $17v = 289$ 17
9. $3.5 = \frac{m}{4}$ 14
10. $\frac{y}{5} = 2.4$ 12
11. $5.1p = 61.2$ 12
12. $0.6 = \frac{a}{9}$ 5.4
13. $\frac{x}{10} = 4.9$ 49
14. $6.4t = 64$ 10
15. $\frac{s}{8} = 9.6$ 76.8

 T43 *Mathematics: Applications and Connections, Course 2*

CHECK FOR UNDERSTANDING

Communicating Mathematics

Read and study the lesson to answer each question.

1. ***Write*** the equation shown by the model. Then find the solution. **$3x = -15$; -5**

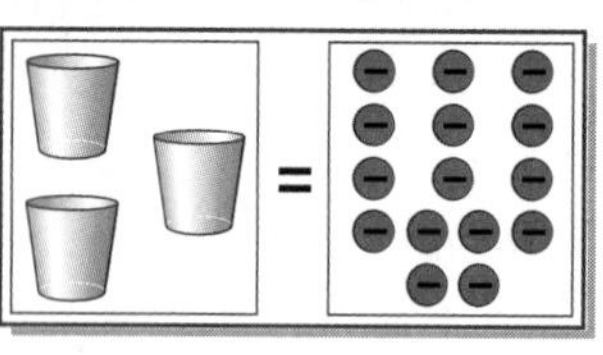

2. ***Tell*** whether 3 is a solution of $-7b = 21$.

2. no; $-7(3) \neq 21$

HANDS-ON MATH

3. ***Use models*** or make a drawing to solve $12 = 2t$. **6; see Answer Appendix for models.**

Guided Practice

Solve each equation. Use models if necessary. Check your solution.

4. $7c = 49$ **7**	**5.** $9e = -54$ **−6**	**6.** $36 = -4m$ **−9**
7. $-10x = -120$ **12**	**8.** $5z = 4.5$ **0.9**	**9.** $1.2c = 7.2$ **6**

10. ***Life Science*** An elephant, going at a steady speed of about 5 miles per hour, can walk faster than a human. A herd of elephants can easily cover 50 miles in one day. Find the time it takes for the herd to cover 50 miles. Use the formula $d = rt$, where d represents distance traveled, r represents the rate or average speed, and t represents the time. **10 hours**

EXERCISES

Practice

Solve each equation. Check your solution.

11. $3c = 21$ **7**	**12.** $12y = 60$ **5**	**13.** $34 = -2g$ **−17**
14. $-5m = 35$ **−7**	**15.** $-8n = -16$ **2**	**16.** $-24 = 6r$ **−4**
17. $-196 = 4s$ **−49**	**18.** $-168 = 3w$ **−56**	**19.** $6 = 1.2s$ **5**
20. $1.3x = 1.56$ **1.2**	**21.** $-15s = -225$ **15**	**22.** $-4d = 64$ **−16**
23. $3.9y = 18.33$ **4.7**	**24.** $4x = 9.2$ **2.3**	**25.** $1.8a = 9.72$ **5.4**
26. $2.6b = 2.08$ **0.8**	**27.** $5.4 = 0.3p$ **18**	**28.** $0.792 = 0.6c$ **1.32**

29. When a number is multiplied by −9, the result is 45. This can be represented by the equation $-9n = 45$. Solve to find the number. **−5**

30. Four tenths times a number is 16. Find the solution of $0.4n = 16$. **40**

Applications and Problem Solving

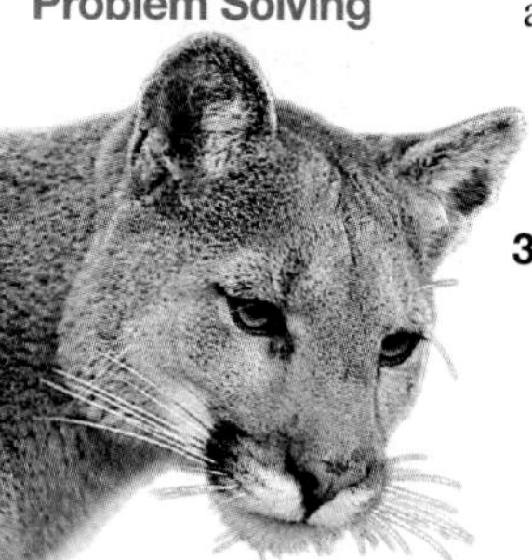

31. ***Life Science*** The cougars that are found in the colder regions of North and South America are about 75 inches long. They are about 1.5 times longer than the cougars that are found in the tropical jungles of Central America. Use the equation $1.5c = 75$ to find c, the length of the tropical cougar. **50 inches**

32. ***Working on the CHAPTER Project*** Refer to the table on page 225.

a. Use the formula $d = rt$ to find the average speed of each roller coaster in feet per second. In the formula, d represents distance in feet, t represents time in seconds, and r represents the rate or average speed in feet per second. Round each speed to the nearest whole number. **See margin.**

b. Make a graph that shows the average speed of each roller coaster. **See students' work.**

Reteaching the Lesson

Activity Have students use counters to model equations such as $4n = 24$. Have them distribute the counters so that each cup has the same amount. Have students repeat this solution process with several equations until they realize that equations involving multiplication can be solved by dividing.

Error Analysis

Watch for students who try to solve an equation like $-2x = 12$ by adding.

Prevent by reminding them that the number before the variable is *multiplied*, not subtracted.

33. ***Earth Science*** Scientists determine the epicenter of an earthquake by measuring the time it takes for surface waves to travel between two places. How long would it take surface waves to travel from Los Angeles to Phoenix, which is a distance of 600 km, if they travel about 6 km/s through Earth's crust? Use the formula $d = rt$. (See Exercise 32.) **100 seconds**

34. ***Critical Thinking*** Solve $3|x| = 6$. **2, −2**

Mixed Review

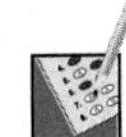

35. ***Algebra*** Solve $t - 3.6 = 4$. *(Lesson 6-1)* **7.6**

36. **Standardized Test Practice** The owner of a pie shop buys bags of apples every day for apple pie. There are between 15 and 18 apples in a bag, and he always gets 9 bags. Which is a reasonable total for the number of apples that the shop owner buys every day? *(Lesson 5-6)* **C**

A 100 **B** 120 **C** 150 **D** 170 **E** Not Here

37. Solve $y = 18 + (-17)$. *(Lesson 5-4)* **1**

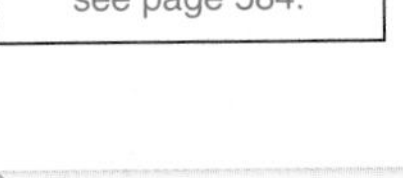

For **Extra Practice,** see page 584.

38. ***Statistics*** Find the mean, median, and mode for this set of data. \$10, \$18, \$15, \$6, \$13, \$12, \$10 *(Lesson 3-4)* **\$12, \$12, \$10**

Math-0

Math Skill
Solving Equations

Get Ready This game is for two, three, or four players. scissors

26 index cards 4 different-colored markers

Get Set Cut each index card in half, making 52 cards. To make a set of four cards, use the markers to put a different-colored stripe at the top of each card. Then write a different equation on each card. The solution of each equation should be 1. Continue to make sets of four cards having equations with solutions of 2, 3, 4, 5, 6, 0, −1, −2, −3, −4, and −5. Mark the remaining set of four cards "Wild".

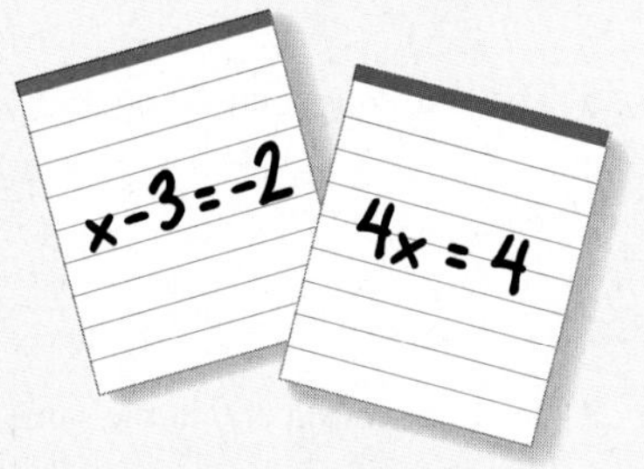

Go

- The dealer shuffles the cards and deals five to each person. The remaining cards are placed in a pile facedown in the middle of the table. The dealer turns the top card faceup.
- The player to the left of the dealer plays a card with the same color or solution as the faceup card. Wild cards can be played any time. If the player cannot play a card, he or she takes a card from the pile and plays it, if possible. If it is not possible to play, the player places the card in his or her hand, and it is the next player's turn.
- The winner is the first person to play all cards in his or her hand.

Visit www.glencoe.com/sec/math/mac/mathnet for more games.

4 ASSESS

Closing Activity

Speaking Have students describe how to solve multiplication equations as if they were explaining it to a student who has missed the lesson.

Chapter 6, Quiz A (Lessons 6-1 and 6-2) is available in the *Assessment and Evaluation Masters,* p. 155.

***Practice Masters,* p. 43**

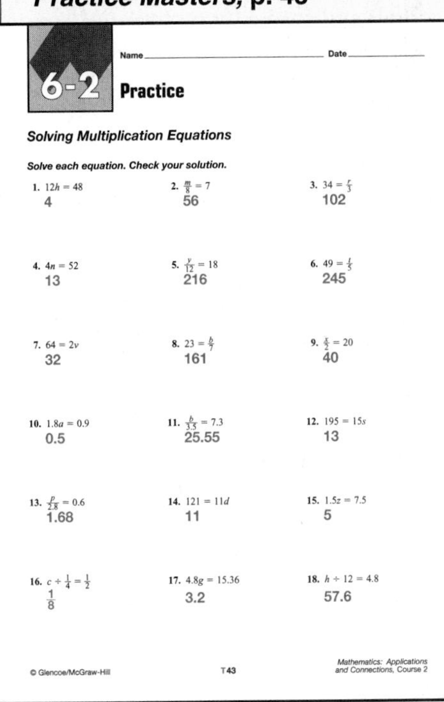

Name ____________ Date ________

6-2 Practice

Solving Multiplication Equations

Solve each equation. Check your solution.

1. $12h = 48$ **4**
2. $\frac{m}{8} = 7$ **56**
3. $34 = \frac{r}{3}$ **102**
4. $4n = 52$ **13**
5. $\frac{y}{12} = 18$ **216**
6. $49 = \frac{t}{5}$ **245**
7. $64 = 2v$ **32**
8. $23 = \frac{b}{7}$ **161**
9. $\frac{x}{2} = 20$ **40**
10. $1.8a = 0.9$ **0.5**
11. $\frac{b}{3.5} = 7.3$ **25.55**
12. $195 = 15s$ **13**
13. $\frac{p}{2.8} = 0.6$ **1.68**
14. $121 = 11d$ **11**
15. $1.5z = 7.5$ **5**
16. $c \div \frac{1}{4} = \frac{1}{2}$ **$\frac{1}{8}$**
17. $4.8g = 15.36$ **3.2**
18. $h \div 12 = 4.8$ **57.6**

© Glencoe/McGraw-Hill T43 *Mathematics: Applications and Connections, Course 2*

Extending the Lesson

***Enrichment Masters,* p. 43**

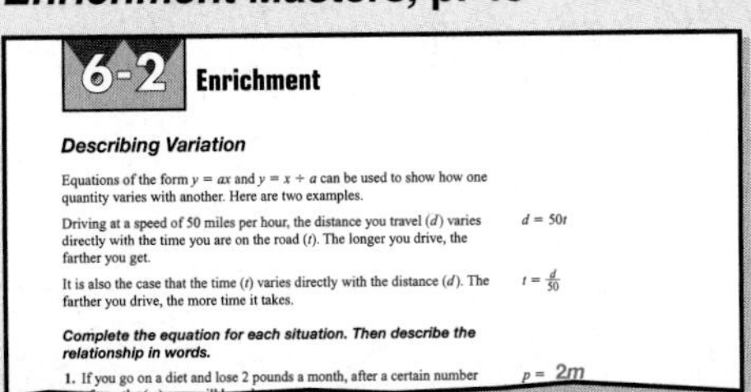

6-2 Enrichment

Describing Variation

Equations of the form $y = ax$ and $y = x \div a$ can be used to show how one quantity varies with another. Here are two examples.

Driving at a speed of 50 miles per hour, the distance you travel (d) varies directly with the time you are on the road (t). The longer you drive, the farther you get. $d = 50t$

It is also the case that the time (t) varies directly with the distance (d). The farther you drive, the more time it takes. $t = \frac{d}{50}$

Complete the equation for each situation. Then describe the relationship in words.

1. If you go on a diet and lose 2 pounds a month, after a certain number $p =$ **2m**

After students complete Lesson 6-3, have them revise their decks by adding two-step equation cards. Then have them play the game again.

GET READY

Objective Students use models to solve two-step equations.

Optional Resources
Hands-On Lab Masters
- integer counters, p. 6
- pattern for cup, p. 7
- equation mat, p. 9
- worksheet, p. 50

Overhead Manipulative Resources
- cups
- counters
- equation mat

Manipulative Kit
- cups
- counters
- equation mat

MANAGEMENT TIPS

Recommended Time
30 minutes

Getting Started Model the equation $3x - 4 = 5$ by placing 3 cups and 4 negative counters on the left side of the mat, and placing 5 counters on the right side of the mat. Ask students to tell what equation you have modeled and what operations are involved.

For the **Activity,** demonstrate the additional step in two-step equations, first adding to create zero pairs and then dividing to find the unknown. Have students check their answers by placing two positive counters in each cup and emptying the cups at the end of the equation to show that $2(2) = 1 + 3$.

ASSESS

Have students complete Exercises 1–8. Watch for students who follow the normal order of operations, solving the division portion of the equation before creating zero pairs. Make sure they do the addition or subtraction operation first, creating zero pairs before doing the division to find x.

HANDS-ON LAB

COOPERATIVE LEARNING

6-3A Solving Two-Step Equations

A Preview of Lesson 6-3

cups and counters

equation mat

In this lab, you will use what you know about solving one-step equations like $x + 3 = -4$ and $2x = 52$ to solve two-step equations like $2x - 3 = 1$.

TRY THIS

Work with a partner.

- First, let's build the equation $2x - 3 = 1$ using models. On the left side of the mat, place 2 cups and 3 negative counters. On the right side, place 1 positive counter.

  Remember, the goal is to get the cups by themselves on one side of the mat.

- Add 3 positive counters to each side of the equation to create zero pairs on the left side. Remove the zero pairs, since their value is 0.

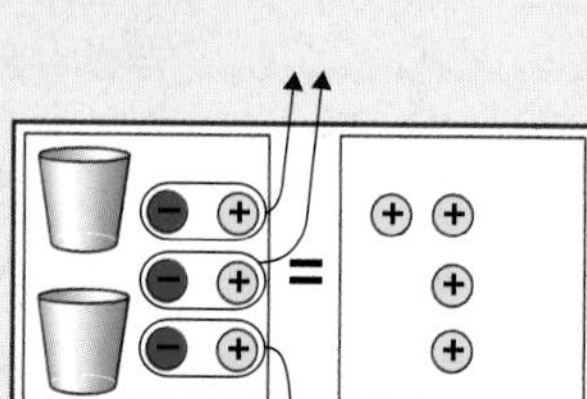

- The new equation is $2x = 4$.

- Each cup must contain the same number of counters. Divide the counters evenly. Therefore, the solution is 2.

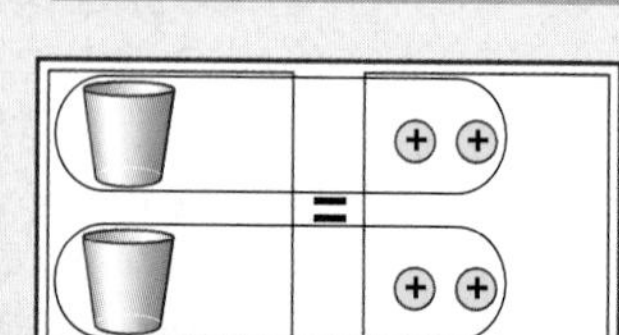

ON YOUR OWN

Solve each equation using models. **1–6. See Answer Appendix for models.**

1. $3x + 1 = 7$ **2**
2. $2x - 4 = 2$ **3**
3. $9 = 4x + 1$ **2**
4. $5 = 3x - 4$ **3**
5. $2x - 3 = -3$ **0**
6. $2x + 3 = -3$ **−3**

7. Why is an equation like $2x + 3 = 7$ called a two-step equation? **See margin.**

8. ***Look Ahead*** Solve $2x + 3 = 7$ without using models. **2**

Additional Answer

7. It is made up of two operations and takes two steps to solve.

Have students write a paragraph explaining how adding or subtracting creates zero pairs.

6-3 Solving Two-Step Equations

What you'll learn

You'll learn to solve two-step equations.

When am I ever going to use this?

You can use two-step equations to change temperatures from Celsius to Fahrenheit and vice versa.

Word Wise

term

In a popular movie, a young girl and her father lead a flock of orphaned geese from their home in Canada to the geese's winter home in North Carolina. In order to return to Canada on their own in the spring, the geese had to remember their original flight path and fly it in reverse order.

In algebra, you face a similar task when you solve a two-step equation like $2x + 1 = 17$. This is a two-step equation because it has two **terms**, $2x$ and 1. It involves two different operations, multiplication and addition. To solve the equation, "undo" the operations in reverse order.

Here's how to solve the equation.

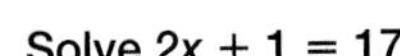

1 Solve $2x + 1 = 17$.

Method 1

Use symbols.

$$2x + 1 = 17$$

$$2x + 1 - 1 = 17 - 1$$ *Subtract 1 from each side.*

$$2x = 16$$

$$\frac{2x}{2} = \frac{16}{2}$$ *Divide each side by 2.*

$$x = 8$$

Check: $2x + 1 = 17$

$2 \cdot 8 + 1 \stackrel{?}{=} 17$ *Replace x with 8.*

$16 + 1 \stackrel{?}{=} 17$

$17 = 17$ ✓

The solution is 8.

Method 2

Use models.

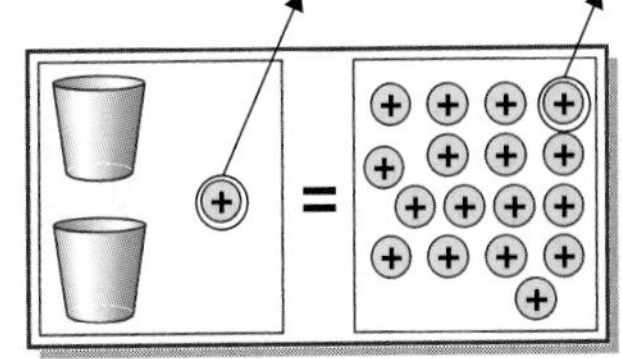

$2x + 1 - 1 = 17 - 1$

Notice the cups are by themselves on the left side of the mat.

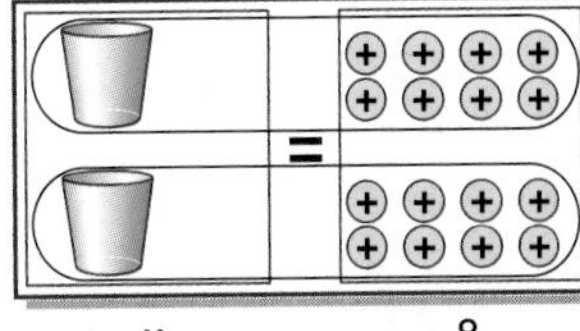

$x = 8$

6-3 Lesson Notes

Instructional Resources

- *Study Guide Masters,* p. 44
- *Practice Masters,* p. 44
- *Enrichment Masters,* p. 44
- Transparencies 6-3, A and B
- *School to Career Masters,* p. 19
- CD-ROM Program
  - Resource Lesson 6-3
  - Interactive Lesson 6-3

Recommended Pacing	
Standard	Days 6 & 7 of 14
Honors	Days 5 & 6 of 13
Block	Day 4 of 7

1 FOCUS

5-Minute Check
(Lesson 6-2)

Solve each equation. Check your solution.

1. $4t = 36$ **9**
2. $0.6n = 72$ **120**
3. $48 = 1.2y$ **40**
4. $4r = 220$ **55**
5. Manuel is paid 52 times a year for an annual salary of \$23,400. Use the formula $52p = \$23{,}400$ to find his weekly pay. **\$450**

The 5-Minute Check is also available on **Transparency 6-3A** for this lesson.

Motivating the Lesson

Communication Ask students to explain why they "undo" operations to solve equations. **Undo operations to isolate the variable on one side of the equals sign.**

2 TEACH

Transparency 6-3B contains a teaching aid for this lesson.

Reading Mathematics Ask students to define what it means to "work backward" or to follow the "order of operations."

Classroom Vignette

"I put masking tape down the center of the students' desks to represent an equals sign. Then I give students three colors of dots to represent positive numbers, negative numbers, and variables. Then I have them work through several two-step equations to solve for the variable dot."

Tim A. Klein, Teacher
Wamego Middle School
Wamego, KS

Tim A. Klein

In-Class Examples

For Example 1
Solve $-3t + 9 = 3$. 2

For Example 2
Solve $-9 = 7r + 5$. -2

For Example 3
On a July day in Detroit, Michigan, the temperature rose to 80°F. Find this temperature in degrees Celsius. about 26.7°C

3 PRACTICE/APPLY

Check for Understanding

If students need additional practice or instruction after completing Exercises 1–10, one of these options may be helpful.

- Extra Practice, see p. 584
- Reteaching Activity
- *Study Guide Masters,* p. 44
- *Practice Masters,* p. 44
- Interactive Mathematics Tools Software

Examples

2 Solve $-3r + 8 = -4$.

$$-3r + 8 = -4$$
$$-3r + 8 - 8 = -4 - 8 \quad \textit{Subtract 8 from each side.}$$
$$-3r = -12 \quad -4 - 8 = -4 + (-8) \text{ or } -12$$
$$\frac{-3r}{-3} = \frac{-12}{-3} \quad \textit{Divide each side by } -3.$$
$$r = 4 \quad \textit{Check the solution.}$$

The solution is 4.

INTEGRATION

3 **Measurement** Temperature is usually measured on the Fahrenheit scale (°F) or the Celsius scale (°C). The highest temperature ever recorded in Orlando, Florida, was 102°F in May, 1945. Find this temperature in degrees Celsius by using the formula $F = 1.8C + 32$.

$$F = 1.8C + 32$$
$$102 = 1.8C + 32 \quad \textit{Replace F with 102.}$$
$$102 - 32 = 1.8C + 32 - 32 \quad \textit{Subtract 32 from each side.}$$
$$70 = 1.8C$$
$$\frac{70}{1.8} = \frac{1.8C}{1.8} \quad \textit{Divide each side by 1.8.}$$

70 [÷] 1.8 [=] 38.88888889

$38.9 \approx C$ *Check the solution.*

The temperature was about 39°C.

CHECK FOR UNDERSTANDING

Communicating Mathematics

Read and study the lesson to answer each question. 1. See Answer Appendix for model.

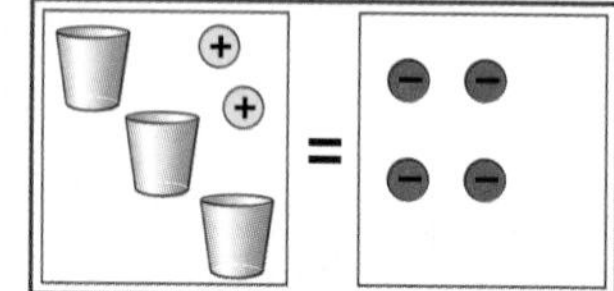

1. ***Show*** how to use the model to solve the equation $3x + 2 = -4$. $3x + 2 = -4; -2$
2. ***Explain*** how the work backward strategy is used in solving two-step equations.
3. ***You Decide*** Sherita says that the first step in solving $5x - 4 = 16$ with models is to put 5 counters in each cup. Hector says it is to add 4 counters to each side of the mat. Who is correct? Explain your reasoning. Hector; the first step is to create zero pairs.

2. You undo the operations in reverse order.

Guided Practice

Solve each equation. Check your solution. 9. 2.1

4. $3n - 5 = 16$ 7
5. $2t + 7 = -1$ -4
6. $2x - 3 = 7$ 5
7. $-11 = 3m + 1$ -4
8. $16 = 0.5r - 8$ 48
9. $5w + 9.2 = 19.7$
10. Three times a number plus 8 is -7. This can be represented by $3n + 8 = -7$. Solve the equation to find the number. -5

Reteaching the Lesson

Activity Guide students to undo operations in reverse of the order of operations. Point out how this is done in each of the examples. Reinforce this concept by modeling solutions to equations using envelopes and pennies, or file folders and index cards, instead of cups and counters.

MathPASS CD-ROM

This CD-ROM offers a complete, self-paced mathematics curriculum. Each lesson includes a pretest, tutorial, guided practice, and posttest. MathPASS Lesson 16 is correlated to this Student Edition lesson.

For Windows & Macintosh

***Study Guide Masters,* p. 44**

Name____________________ Date__________

Study Guide

Solving Two-Step Equations

To solve two-step equations, you need to add or subtract first.
You also need to multiply or divide.

Examples *1* **Solve $7v - 3 = 25$.**

$$7v - 3 = 25$$
$$7v - 3 + 3 = 25 + 3 \quad \textit{Add 3 to each side of the equation.}$$
$$7v = 28$$
$$\frac{7v}{7} = \frac{28}{7} \quad \textit{Divide each side of the equation by 7.}$$
$$v = 4$$

2 **Solve $\frac{1}{6}(r - 3) = -5$.**

$$\frac{1}{6}(r - 3) = -5$$
$$6 \times \frac{1}{6}(r - 3) = 6(-5) \quad \textit{Multiply each side by 6.}$$
$$r - 3 = -30$$
$$r - 3 + 3 = -30 + 3 \quad \textit{Add 3 to each side of the equation.}$$
$$r = -27$$

Solve each equation. Check your solution.

1. $\frac{1}{3}(s + 6) = 3$ 3
2. $\frac{1}{5}(t - 2) = 0$ 2
3. $\frac{2}{3}(a - 18) = -6$ 9
4. $12 - 4n = 4$ 2
5. $7 + \frac{k}{4} = 9$ 8
6. $\frac{1}{2}y - 7 = -9$ -4
7. $\frac{2}{3}(b + 6) = -2$ -9
8. $\frac{3}{8}(c + 8) = -\frac{3}{2}$ -12
9. $\frac{5}{7}(d + 20) = -10$ -34
10. $14 + \frac{t}{5} = 10$ -20
11. $\frac{-h}{6} + 1 = -1$ 12
12. $-5t - 5 = -5$ 0

 T44 *Mathematics: Applications and Connections, Course 2*

EXERCISES

Practice

Solve each equation. Check your solution.

11. $4x + 5 = 13$ **2**	**12.** $3w - 4 = 8$ **4**	**13.** $8m - 12 = -36$ **−3**
14. $2y + 1 = -3$ **−2**	**15.** $13 = 4s + 1$ **3**	**16.** $2x + 5 = -13$ **−9**
17. $2r - 3.1 = 1.7$ **2.4**	**18.** $-2y - 7 = 3$ **−5**	**19.** $-3n - 8 = 7$ **−5**
20. $21 = 13w - 5$ **2**	**21.** $16b - 6.5 = 9.5$ **1**	**22.** $85 = 4d + 5$ **20**
23. $19 = -4y + 3$ **−4**	**24.** $0.2n + 3 = 8.6$ **28**	**25.** $17 = 17 + 8z$ **0**
26. $-2x - 7.2 = 18.2$	**27.** $28 = 7.5s - 2$ **4**	**28.** $1.5x - 16 = 8$ **16**

26. −12.7

29. Add 3 to the product of a number and 4. The result is 15. Solve $3 + 4n = 15$ to find the number. **3**

30. Multiply a number by −2 and then subtract 5. The result is 9. Find the solution of $-2n - 5 = 9$ to find the number. **−7**

Applications and Problem Solving

31. ***Money Matters*** Benny's Balloons charges \$2 for each balloon in an arrangement. There is also a \$5 fee for making the arrangement. If you have \$15 to spend, how many balloons would you get? Solve the equation $15 = 2b + 5$, where b is the number of balloons. **5 balloons**

32. ***Measurement*** Travelers to the 2000 Olympics in Sydney, Australia, will find that Australians measure temperature in degrees Celsius. Find the high temperature in your city yesterday and convert it to degrees Celsius using the formula $F = 1.8C + 32$. Is your answer warmer or cooler than the average high temperature for this month in Sydney? **See students' work.**

Temperatures for Sydney, Australia (degrees Celsius)

49°
38°
27°
16°
4°
−7°
Record high
Avg. high
Avg. low
Record low
J F M A M J J A S O N D
Month

Source: *The Weather Almanac*

33. ***Modeling*** Show how you could use cups and counters to solve the equation $4x - 3 = x + 6$. **See Answer Appendix.**

34. ***Critical Thinking*** Write two different two-step equations that have 1.2 as their solution. **Sample answer: $2x + 5 = 7.4$; $3x - 2 = 1.6$**

Mixed Review

35. **Standardized Test Practice** Use the formula $A = bh$ to find the height of a parallelogram with a base of 34 mm and an area of 612 mm^2. *(Lesson 6-2)*

A 20,800 mm **B** 646 mm **C** 578 mm **D** 18 mm **D**

36. ***Algebra*** Solve $p - 14 = 27$. *(Lesson 6-1)* **41**

37. Express 9,800 in scientific notation. *(Lesson 2-9)* **9.8×10^3**

38. Divide 0.0081 by 0.09. *(Lesson 2-6)* **0.09**

For **Extra Practice,** see page 584.

Assignment Guide

Core: 11–33 odd, 34–38
Enriched: 12–30 even, 31–38

4 ASSESS

Closing Activity

Writing Have each student write a quiz that assesses solving two-step equations. The quiz should contain word problems as well as exercises. Have students exchange quizzes and test each other.

Practice Masters, p. 44

Name____________ Date________

6-3 Practice

Solving Two-Step Equations

Solve each equation. Check your solution.

1. $6n - 2 = 22$ 4	**2.** $0.5(y - 3) = 12$ 27	**3.** $4x - 5 = 15$ 5
4. $\frac{w}{-3} + 14 = 5$ 27	**5.** $1.5s - 8 = 19$ 18	**6.** $24 = 17 - 2c$ −3.5
7. $6 - 3b = -9$ 5	**8.** $-5h - 6 = 24$ −6	**9.** $\frac{n}{3} - 6 = 12$ 54
10. $3n + 12 = -12$ −8	**11.** $7x + 2 = 23$ 3	**12.** $9 = 16d + 51$ $-2\frac{5}{8}$
13. $3 = -3y - 15$ −6	**14.** $174 = 75 + 55t$ $1\frac{4}{5}$	**15.** $2n + 35 = 106$ $35\frac{1}{2}$
16. $1.2x + 3.7 = 34.6$ 25.75	**17.** $3q + 7 = 13$ 2	**18.** $-12 = 7s - 5$ −1
19. $7t - 3 = 10$ $\frac{13}{7}$	**20.** $9y + 4 = 4$ 0	**21.** $8w + 2 = -2$ $-\frac{1}{2}$

 T44 *Mathematics: Applications and Connections, Course 2*

Extending the Lesson

Enrichment Masters, p. 44

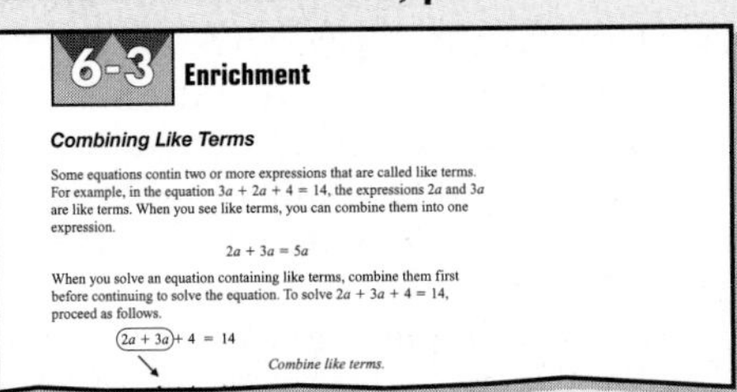

6-3 Enrichment

Combining Like Terms

Some equations contin two or more expressions that are called like terms. For example, in the equation $3a + 2a + 4 = 14$, the expressions $2a$ and $3a$ are like terms. When you see like terms, you can combine them into one expression.

$$2a + 3a = 5a$$

When you solve an equation containing like terms, combine them first before continuing to solve the equation. To solve $2a + 3a + 4 = 14$, proceed as follows.

$(2a + 3a) + 4 = 14$ *Combine like terms.*

Activity Have students work in pairs to use an equation mat to create equations like Exercise 33. In these equations the unknown is on both sides of the mat, for example: $7x - 5 = x - 2$.

6-4 Lesson Notes

Instructional Resources

- *Study Guide Masters,* p. 45
- *Practice Masters,* p. 45
- *Enrichment Masters,* p. 45
- Transparencies 6-4, A and B
- *Assessment and Evaluation Masters,* pp. 154, 155
- *Classroom Games,* pp. 17–20

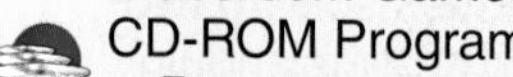

CD-ROM Program
- Resource Lesson 6-4

Recommended Pacing	
Standard	Day 8 of 13
Honors	Day 7 of 12
Block	Day 4 of 7

1 FOCUS

5-Minute Check
(Lesson 6-3)

Solve each equation. Check your solution.

1. $-3t + 5 = -10$ **5**
2. $15 = 4w + 7$ **2**
3. $6y - 6 = 30$ **6**
4. $77 = 4.5z + 14$ **14**
5. Add 7 to the product of a number and 11. The result is 40. Solve $7 + 11n = 40$ to find the number. **3**

The 5-Minute Check is also available on **Transparency 6-4A** for this lesson.

Motivating the Lesson

Problem Solving Pablo is making a 1-hour film about four students' experiences in a new school. He estimates he will need to shoot 40 hours of film to edit. If he shoots 8 hours of film a week and spends another 3 weeks editing, how long should he plan to work on the project? $\frac{40}{8} + 3 = t$; $t = 8$ **weeks**

6-4 Writing Expressions and Equations

What you'll learn

You'll learn to write simple algebraic expressions and equations from verbal phrases and sentences.

When am I ever going to use this?

You'll use algebraic expressions when you work with spreadsheets.

Word Wise

defining the variable

Did you ever feel like these characters from *Peanuts*?

In this lesson, you will learn how to translate verbal phrases such as *three years older than the daughter* into algebraic expressions.

Words and phrases often suggest addition, subtraction, multiplication, and division. Here are some examples.

Addition or Subtraction		Multiplication or Division	
plus sum more than increased by total	minus difference less than less decreased by	times product multiplied of twice	divided quotient

Example 1 Write each phrase as an algebraic expression.

a. **three runs less than the Pirates scored**

Let r represent the number of runs the Pirates scored. The words *less than* suggest subtraction. So, the expression is $r - 3$.

b. **twice as many tomatoes as last year**

Let t represent the number of tomatoes last year. The word *twice* suggests multiplication by two. So, the expression is $2t$.

Multiple Learning Styles

Auditory/Musical Have students work with a partner to translate algebraic equations into verbal sentences. Make sure they use the appropriate words or phrases for the operations involved. One student can convert a written equation into a spoken sentence, and their partner can translate that sentence into a written equation.

MathPASS CD-ROM

This CD-ROM offers a complete, self-paced mathematics curriculum. Each lesson includes a pretest, tutorial, guided practice, and posttest. MathPASS Lesson 17 is correlated to this Student Edition lesson.
For Windows & Macintosh

Remember, an equation is a sentence in mathematics that contains an equals sign. When you write a sentence as an equation, the word *equals* or *is* can be represented by the equals sign.

Example 2 Write each sentence as an algebraic equation.

a. Five more than a number is 25.

Five more than a number is 25.

$$5 \quad + \quad n \quad = 25$$

The equation is $5 + n = 25$.

b. 17 is equal to four less than three times a number.

17 is equal to three times a number minus four.

$$17 \quad = \quad 3 \quad \times \quad n \quad - \quad 4$$

The equation is $17 = 3n - 4$.

One strategy you can use to solve a real-life problem is to solve an equation. First, choose a variable to represent one of the unknowns in a problem. This is called **defining the variable**. Then use the variable to write and solve an equation.

Example 3 Real World APPLICATION

Money Matters Shopping networks on television are a popular way to shop. In addition to the cost of the items, you usually pay a shipping fee. Koko wants to order several pairs of running shorts that cost $12 each. The total shipping fee is $7. How many shorts can she order with $55?

Explore You know that the shorts cost $12 each. There will be an additional fee of $7. You need to find how many shorts she can order for $55.

Plan Define a variable. Then write and solve an equation.

Solve Let s represent the number of shorts.
Then $12s$ represents the cost of the shorts.

cost of shorts plus shipping fee is total cost of order

$$12s \quad + \quad 7 \quad = \quad 55$$

$$12s + 7 = 55$$

$$12s + 7 - 7 = 55 - 7 \quad \textit{Subtract 7 from each side.}$$

$$12s = 48$$

$$\frac{12s}{12} = \frac{48}{12} \quad \textit{Divide each side by 12.}$$

$$s = 4$$

Examine Koko can order 4 pairs of running shorts.
Examine this solution.

Study Hint
Reading Math Before writing the equation, it may be helpful to restate the problem in a simple sentence.

2 TEACH

Transparency 6-4B contains a teaching aid for this lesson.

Reading Mathematics Have students identify the verbal phrases in the Peanuts cartoon and in Example 3 that signify mathematical operations, and translate them into algebraic expressions. Brainstorm with students to find more synonyms to add to the examples in the chart.

In-Class Examples

For Example 1
Write each phrase as an algebraic expression.
a. 6 fewer hours than her sister **$s - 6$**
b. half the population of Tulsa **$\frac{P}{2}$**

For Example 2
Write each sentence as an algebraic equation.
a. Seven times the cost is $63. **$7c = 63$**
b. He weighs 180 pounds, which is 22 pounds less than double her weight. **$180 = 2z - 22$**

For Example 3
If Tammy, Gary, and Luanda have $70 and they want to buy lamps that cost $18, plus $5 for the shipping cost, how many lamps can they purchase? **3 lamps**

Teaching Tip Have students begin a chart that they can use here and in subsequent lessons. The chart will have two columns: one for word phrases and one for the algebraic expressions having the same meaning.

Cross-Curriculum Cue

Inform the other teachers on your team that your classes are studying how to write algebraic expressions. Suggestions for curriculum integration are:
Science: temperature variations and their effect on cricket chirping
Civics: congressional representation for each state as a variable based on population (for House) plus two (for Senate)
Language Arts: words and phrases implying addition, subtraction, multiplication, and division

3 PRACTICE/APPLY

Check for Understanding

If students need additional practice or instruction after completing Exercises 1–11, one of these options may be helpful.

- Extra Practice, see p. 584
- Reteaching Activity
- *Study Guide Masters,* p. 45
- *Practice Masters,* p. 45

Assignment Guide

Core: 13–35 odd, 36–41
Enriched: 12–32 even, 33–41
All: Self Test, 1–10

4 ASSESS

Closing Activity

Writing Have students write a paragraph describing the steps in writing an algebraic expression. **Sample answer: Determine what is known; define the variable to represent the unknown number; figure out what operations and numbers are needed to find the unknown.**

***Study Guide Masters,* p. 45**

Name______________________ Date__________

Study Guide

Writing Expressions and Equations

The table below shows phrases written as mathematical expressions.

Phrases	Expression	Phrases	Expression
9 more than a number the sum of 9 and a number a number plus 9 a number increased by 9 the total of x and 9	$x + 9$	4 subtracted from a number a number minus 4 4 less than a number a number decreased by 4 the difference of h and 4	$h - 4$
Phrases	**Expression**	**Phrases**	**Expression**
6 multiplied by g 6 times a number the product of g and 6	$6g$	a number divided by 5 the quotient of t and 5 divide a number by 5	$\frac{t}{5}$

The table below shows sentences written as an equation.

Sentences	Equation
Sixty less than three times the amount is $59. Three times the amount less 60 is equal to 59. 59 is equal to 60 subtracted from three times a number. A number times three minus 60 equals 59.	$3n - 60 = 59$

Write each phrase as an algebraic expression.

1. 7 less than m $m - 7$
2. the quotient of 3 and y $\frac{3}{y}$
3. the total of 5 and c $5 + c$
4. the difference of 6 and r $6 - r$
5. n divided by 2 $\frac{n}{2}$
6. the product of k and 9 $9k$

Write each sentence as an algebraic equation.

7. A number increased by 7 is 11. $n + 7 = 11$
8. The price decreased by $4 is $29. $p - 4 = 29$
9. Twice as many points as Bob would be 18 points. $2b = 18$
10. After dividing the money 5 ways, each person got $67. $\frac{m}{5} = 67$
11. Three more than 8 times as many trees is 75 trees. $8t + 3 = 75$
12. Seven less than a number is 15. $n - 7 = 15$

 T45 *Mathematics: Applications and Connections, Course 2*

CHECK FOR UNDERSTANDING

Communicating Mathematics

Read and study the lesson to answer each question.

1. ***Choose*** the algebraic expression for the phrase *5 less than a number.* **c**
   a. $5 - n$ **b.** $5 + n$ **c.** $n - 5$ **d.** $n \div 5$

2. ***Explain*** what it means to define the variable. **See margin.**
3. ***Write*** a sentence explaining the meaning of the expression $a + 3$, if a represents someone's age. **See margin.**

Guided Practice

Write each phrase as an algebraic expression.

4. seven more than t $t + 7$
5. eight less than p $p - 8$
6. 4 times as many bees $4b$
7. –9 increased by some number $-9 + n$

Write each sentence as an algebraic equation.

8. Ten more than a number is 25.
9. The product of a number and 20 is 120.
10. If you double the number of eggs, the result is 6. $2e = 6$
11. ***Statistics*** The median age of people in the United States was 33.0 years in 1990. This is 10.1 years more than the median age in 1900. Write and solve an equation to find the median age in 1900.

8. $10 + n = 25$
9. $20n = 120$
11. $m + 10.1 = 33.0$; $m = 22.9$

EXERCISES

Practice

Write each phrase as an algebraic expression.

12. the difference of g and 4 $g - 4$
13. the product of x and two $x \cdot 2$ or $2x$
14. the quotient of b and 5
15. nine increased by x $9 + x$
16. seventeen less than p $p - 17$
17. your age divided by 3 $a \div 3$ or $\frac{a}{3}$
18. five years older than Paul
19. twice as many apples $2a$
20. Jamila's salary plus $1,100
21. Sue's score increased by 10 $s + 10$
22. a number decreased by $\frac{1}{2}$
23. the square of some number divided by 10

14. $b \div 5$ or $\frac{b}{5}$
18. $p + 5$
20. $s + 1{,}100$
22. $n - \frac{1}{2}$
23. $\frac{n^2}{10}$

Write each sentence as an algebraic equation.

24. The sum of a number and three is −8. $n + 3 = -8$
25. The product of a number and 8 is −64. $8n = -64$
26. Three more than twice a number is 13. $3 + 2n = 13$
27. Five less than seven times a number is 37.
28. Six less than the number of cookies is 18.
29. The number of students increased by 15 is 220.
30. His allowance less $3 is $12. $a - 3 = 12$
31. Eight more than twice her age is 60.
32. Ten inches less than her height is 50 inches.

27. $7n - 5 = 37$
28. $c - 6 = 18$
29. $s + 15 = 220$
31. $8 + 2a = 60$
32. $h - 10 = 50$

Applications and Problem Solving

33. ***Snacks*** Potato chips were the top snack food in 1995, with 1.9 billion pounds consumed. This was 0.2 billion pounds more than the pounds consumed in 1992. Write and solve an equation to find the amount consumed in 1992. $p + 0.2 = 1.9$; $p = 1.7$

Reteaching the Lesson

Activity Have students copy each phrase or sentence on their paper. Then have them use geometric figures or different colors to highlight the words that indicate numerical values, unknowns, or operations. Then write the algebraic equivalent.

Additional Answers

2. choosing a variable to represent one of the unknowns in a problem
3. Sample answer: the age of a person 3 years older; the person's age in 3 years

Find yesterday's high and low temperature from a newspaper or television report. Let t represent the low temperature. Write an expression for the high temperature.

34. ***Greeting Cards*** The graph shows the average number of greeting cards purchased yearly by the average person in the United States. Let c represent the number of cards purchased by Americans ages 35 to 44.

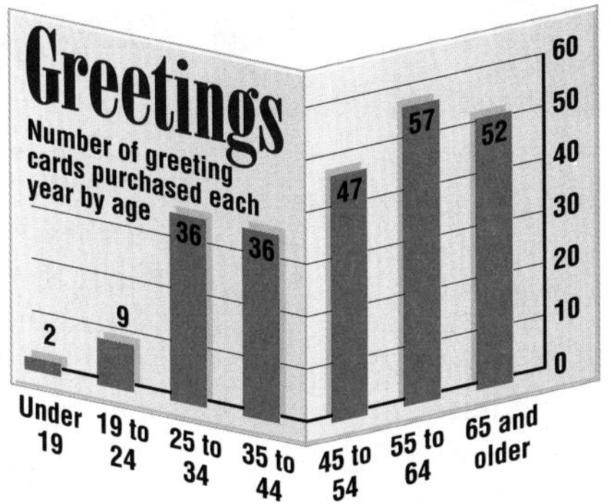

Source: American Greetings Corporation

a. Write an expression using c to represent the number of cards purchased by Americans ages 45 to 54. **$c + 11$**

b. Which age group would be represented by the expression $\frac{c}{4}$? **19 to 24**

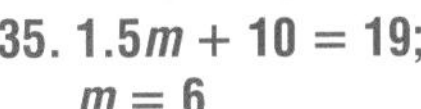

35. $1.5m + 10 = 19$; $m = 6$

35. ***Money Matters*** A taxi company charges \$1.50 per mile, plus a \$10 fee. Suppose Eva can afford to spend \$19 for a taxi ride from her apartment to the mall. Write and solve an equation to find the distance she can travel, so she will know whether to take this taxi or try to find a cheaper one.

36. ***Critical Thinking*** If x is an odd number, how would you represent the odd number immediately following it? preceding it? **$x + 2$, $x - 2$**

Mixed Review

37. ***Algebra*** Solve the equation $2q + 6 = -20$. *(Lesson 6-3)* **-13**

38. **Standardized Test Practice** Mark had several baseball cards. He sold 15 of the cards and had 46 cards left. To find the number of cards he started with, Mark wrote the equation $c - 15 = 46$. How many cards did Mark start with? *(Lesson 6-1)* **B**

A 690 **B** 61 **C** 31 **D** 26

39. Solve $m = 6 - (-12)$. *(Lesson 5-5)* **18**

40. ***Geometry*** Find the area of a parallelogram having a base of 2.3 centimeters and a height of 1.6 centimeters. *(Lesson 1-7)* **3.68 cm²**

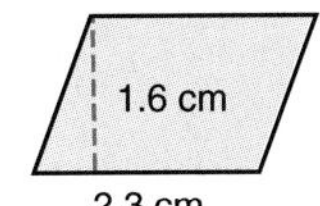

For **Extra Practice,** see page 584.

41. ***Algebra*** Evaluate b^5 if $b = 3$. *(Lesson 1-4)* **243**

CHAPTER 6 Mid-Chapter Self Test

Solve each equation. Check your solution. *(Lessons 6-1, 6-2, and 6-3)*

1. $41 + w = 71$ **30**
2. $s - 5 = -11$ **-6**
3. $z + 3.5 = 8.7$ **5.2**
4. $11b = 121$ **11**
5. $1.5y = 18$ **12**
6. $-24 = -6c$ **4**
7. $2m - 7 = -5$ **1**
8. $5x + 11 = 26$ **3**
9. $-8 = 6m + 16$ **-4**

10. ***Aviation*** An airplane is flying at an altitude of t feet before it increases its altitude by 1,000 feet to avoid a thunderstorm. Write an expression for its new altitude. *(Lesson 6-4)* **$t + 1{,}000$**

Encourage students to write algebraic expressions comparing high and low temperatures for each day of the week or for different cities on a particular day, and then to graph their findings. Challenge them to write an equation comparing the temperature variations (high minus low) of different cities.

Mid-Chapter Self Test

The Mid-Chapter Self Test reviews the concepts in Lessons 6-1 through 6-4. Lesson references are given so students can review concepts not yet mastered.

Mid-Chapter Test (Lessons 6-1 through 6-4) is available in the *Assessment and Evaluation Masters,* p. 154.

Chapter 6, Quiz B (Lessons 6-3 and 6-4) is available in the *Assessment and Evaluation Masters,* p. 155.

Extending the Lesson

Enrichment Masters, p. 45

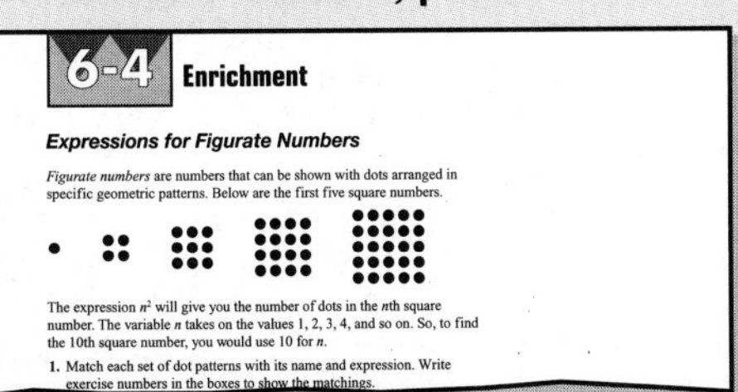

6-4 Enrichment

Expressions for Figurate Numbers

Figurate numbers are numbers that can be shown with dots arranged in specific geometric patterns. Below are the first five square numbers.

The expression n^2 will give you the number of dots in the nth square number. The variable n takes on the values 1, 2, 3, 4, and so on. So, to find the 10th square number, you would use 10 for n.

1. Match each set of dot patterns with its name and expression. Write exercise numbers in the boxes to show the matchings.

Activity At Milt's Sporting Goods store, bats cost \$35 each, and gloves are \$55 each. Write an algebraic expression for the total cost of x bats and y gloves. **$35x + 55y$** Discuss examples of equipment another sports team might need, and write an algebraic expression for each total cost.

Practice Masters, p. 45

Name ______ Date ______

6-4 Practice

Writing Expressions and Equations

Write each phrase as an algebraic expression.

1. thirteen plus v $13 + v$
2. three times d $3d$
3. six less w $6 - w$
4. the product of 5 and a number $5n$
5. g divided by 6 $\frac{g}{6}$
6. the difference of h and 8 $h - 8$
7. three more hits than Bob $3 + b$
8. 23 divided into y $\frac{y}{23}$
9. twice Michael's age $2m$
10. \$18 less than the sale price $p - 18$
11. three higher than Kyra's score $3 + k$
12. the quotient of n and 12 $\frac{n}{12}$

Write each sentence as an algebraic equation.

13. Juan's salary plus \$125 is \$600. $j + 125 = 600$
14. Fourteen divided by a number is 21. $\frac{14}{n} = 21$
15. Four times the number of feet is 12 feet. $4f = 12$
16. Six times as many visitors is 120 visitors. $6v = 120$
17. Twenty-seven is seven fewer students than last year. $27 = s - 7$
18. The number of cats decreased by 17 is 19. $c - 17 = 19$
19. Two and one-half times the amount of interest is \$2,500. $2\frac{1}{2}i = 2{,}500$
20. One hundred increased by a number is 537. $100 + n = 537$

 T45 *Mathematics: Applications and Connections, Course 2*

6-5 Lesson Notes

Instructional Resources

- *Study Guide Masters,* p. 46
- *Practice Masters,* p. 46
- *Enrichment Masters,* p. 46
- Transparencies 6-5, A and B

CD-ROM Program
- Resource Lesson 6-5

Recommended Pacing	
Standard	Day 9 of 14
Honors	Day 8 of 13
Block	Day 5 of 7

1 FOCUS

5-Minute Check

Write each phrase as an algebraic expression.

1. three fewer runs than the Tigers **$t - 3$**
2. eight increased by m **$8 + m$**

Write each sentence as an algebraic equation.

3. Twelve divided by y is 48. **$12 \div y = 48$**
4. Dan's score decreased by 9 is 51. **$n - 9 = 51$**
5. The product of w and 7 is 56. **$7w = 56$**

The 5-Minute Check is also available on **Transparency 6-5A** for this lesson.

Motivating the Lesson

Communication Have students make lists of words that might be represented by the symbols $<$, $>$, $\geq$, and $\leq$. Post the lists and add to them as students work through this lesson.

2 TEACH

Transparency 6-5B contains a teaching aid for this lesson.

Using the Mini-Lab Remind students that the actual solution of $x > 6$ includes numbers greater than 10. For Exercise 7, discuss with students the idea that all numbers less than 5 are included in the set.

6-5 Inequalities

What **you'll learn**

You'll learn to solve inequalities.

When **am I ever going to use this?**

You'll use inequalities when you try to determine whether you have enough money to buy an item.

Word Wise

inequality

At age 14, Tara Lipinski became the youngest winner of the Ladies' World Figure Skating Championship. The ages of Tara and two other previous winners are graphed below.

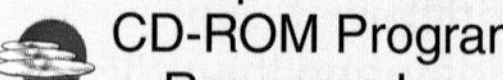

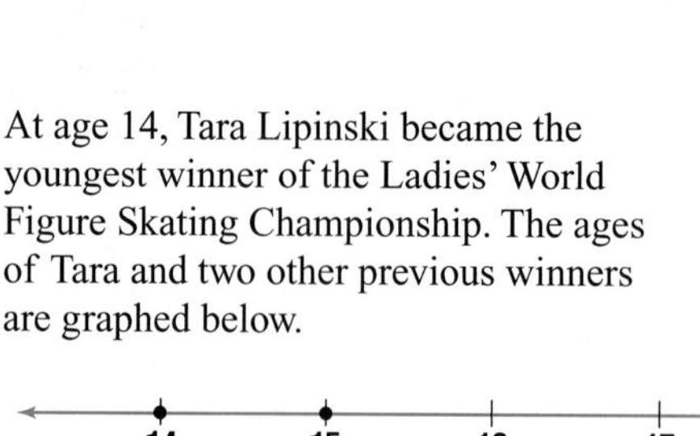

All of the other winners were older than Tara. Their ages are graphed to the right of Tara's age. If a represents any of those ages, you can use the inequality $a > 14$ to show the relationship between their ages and Tara's age.

An **inequality** is a mathematical sentence that contains the symbols $<$, $>$, $\leq$, or $\geq$.

Words	Symbols
x is greater than 4.	$x > 4$
y is less than 10.	$y < 10$
m is greater than or equal to -5.	$m \geq -5$
r is less than or equal to 8.	$r \leq 8$

Inequalities may have many solutions.

MINI-LAB

Work with a partner. sheet of paper

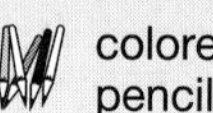
colored pencils

The number line shows whole numbers from 0 through 10. The large dots show whole number solutions of $x > 6$.

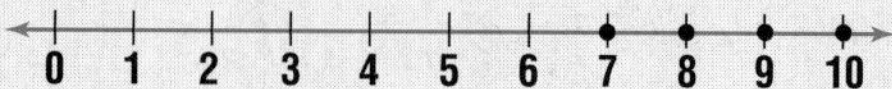

LOOK BACK You can refer to Lesson 1-5 to review solutions and replacement sets.

Try This 1–4. See margin.

Draw a number line with the whole numbers 0 to 10. Draw a large dot at each number that is a solution of the inequality.

1. $x \geq 2$ **2.** $x + 2 > 3$ **3.** $2x > 3$ **4.** $x + 5 \leq 6$

Talk About It

5. Number lines include all numbers, not just whole numbers. How could you show all of the solutions of the inequality $x < 5$?

5. Sample answer: You could shade a thick line instead of circles.

Additional Answers for the Mini-Lab

1.
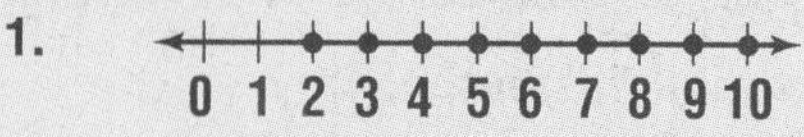

2.

3.

4.
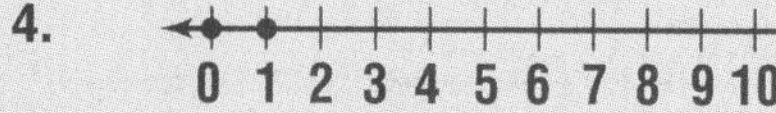

All numbers, not just whole numbers, are included in the graph of an inequality on a number line.

Example 1 **CONNECTION**

Health **According to the *Mayo Clinic Health Letter,* a healthful breakfast cereal contains less than 3 grams of fat, at least 3 grams of fiber, and no more than 5 grams of sugar per serving. Write an inequality for each situation. Then graph the solution on a number line.**

In Example 1, the number lines start at 0 because real-world quantities like the number of grams of fat cannot have a negative value.

a. less than 3 grams of fat

The inequality is $f < 3$, where f is the number of grams of fat.

To show the solution, draw an open circle at 3. Then draw a thick arrow over the numbers to the left.

An open circle shows that this point is not included.

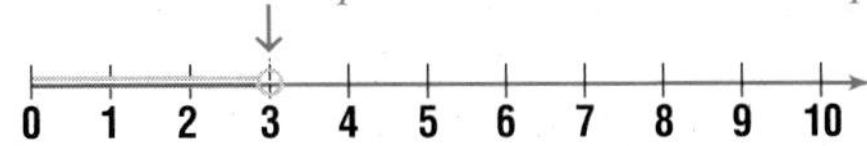

b. at least 3 grams of fiber

At least 3 grams means 3 grams or more. Use the symbol $\geq$.

The inequality is $g \geq 3$, where g is the number of grams of fiber.

To show the solution, fill in a circle at 3. Then draw a thick arrow over the numbers to the right.

A filled-in circle shows that this point is included.

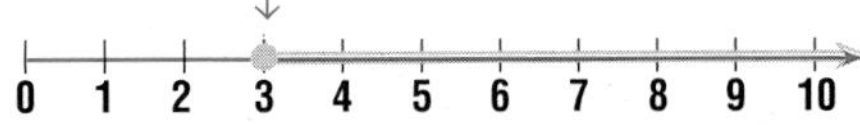

c. no more than 5 grams of sugar

No more than means 5 grams or less. Use the symbol $\leq$.

The inequality is $s \leq 5$, where s is the number of grams of sugar.

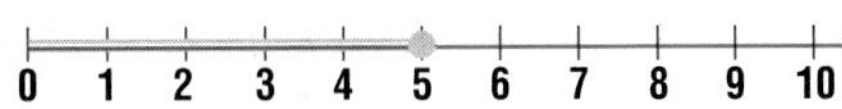

Inequalities and equations are solved in a similar manner.

Example 2

Solve $x - 4 > 3$. Check your solution. Then graph the solution.

$$x - 4 > 3$$

$$x - 4 + 4 > 3 + 4 \quad \textit{Add 4 to each side of the inequality.}$$

$$x > 7$$

Check: Try 10, a number greater than 7.

$$x - 4 > 3$$

$$10 - 4 > 3 \quad \textit{Replace x with 10.}$$

$$6 > 3 \ \checkmark$$

The solution is $x > 7$, all numbers greater than 7.

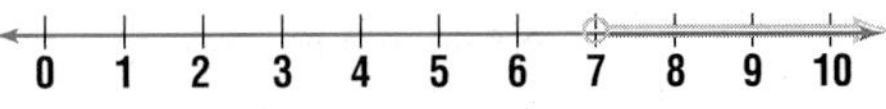

In-Class Examples

For Example 1

Write an inequality for each situation. Then graph the solution on a number line.

a. weight less than 6 ounces **$w < 6$**

0 1 2 3 4 5 6 7 8 9 10

b. at least 8 gallons **$g \geq 8$**

2 3 4 5 6 7 8 9 10

c. no more than 4 feet **$f \leq 4$**

0 1 2 3 4 5

For Example 2

Solve $y - 2 > 6$. Check your solution. Then graph the solution. **$y > 8$**

3 4 5 6 7 8 9 10

Teaching Tip A different procedure is used to solve problems like $-4x > 12$. In Course 3, students learn to do this type of problem.

***Study Guide Masters,* p. 46**

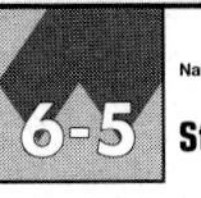

Name______ Date______

Study Guide

Inequalities

An inequality is a mathematical sentence that contains the symbols $<$, $>$, $\leq$, or $\geq$.

Words	Symbols
m is greater than 7.	$m > 7$
r is less than −4.	$r < -4$
t is greater than or equal to 6.	$t \geq 6$
y is less than or equal to 1.	$y \leq 1$

Solve inequalities just like you solve equations.
You can use a number line to show solutions to inequalities.

Examples 1 **Solve $v + 3 < 5$. Then graph the solution.**

$$v + 3 < 5$$
$$v + 3 - 3 < 5 - 3$$
$$v < 2$$

This point is not included.

−2 −1 0 1 2 3

2 **Solve $\frac{k}{4} \geq 2$. Then graph the solution.**

$$\frac{k}{4} > 2$$
$$\frac{k}{4} \times 4 \geq 2 \times 4$$
$$k \geq 8$$

This point is included.

6 7 8 9 10 11

Solve each inequality. Graph the solution on the number line.

1. $c - 1 < 4$ (−2 −1 0 1 2 3 4 5 6 7 8)
2. $4 + t > -1$ (−7 −6 −5 −4 −3 −2 −1 0 1 2 3)
3. $\frac{r}{2} > 5$ (7 8 9 10 11 12 13 14 15 16 17)
4. $3w < -3$ (−7 −6 −5 −4 −3 −2 −1 0 1 2 3)
5. $2p \geq 6$ (−2 −1 0 1 2 3 4 5 6 7 8)
6. $v - 4 \leq 3$ (0 1 2 3 4 5 6 7 8 9 10)

 T46 *Mathematics: Applications and Connections,* Course 2

Reteaching the Lesson

Activity Have students draw scales to show $>$, $<$, $\leq$, and $\geq$ for quantities *A* and *B*.

$B > A$ / $A < B$ — A, B (scale)

$A \geq B$, $A \leq B$ / $B \leq A$, $B \geq A$ / $A = B$ — A, B (scale)

MathPASS CD-ROM

This CD-ROM offers a complete, self-paced mathematics curriculum. Each lesson includes a pretest, tutorial, guided practice, and posttest. MathPASS Lesson 18 is correlated to this Student Edition lesson.

For Windows & Macintosh

3 PRACTICE/APPLY

Check for Understanding

If students need additional practice or instruction after completing Exercises 1–8, one of these options may be helpful.

- Extra Practice, see p. 584
- Reteaching Activity, see p. 247
- *Study Guide Masters,* p. 46
- *Practice Masters,* p. 46

Assignment Guide

Core: 9–23 odd, 25–28
Enriched: 10–22 even, 23–28

4 ASSESS

Closing Activity

Writing Have students work with a partner to write three statements from their everyday lives that can be rewritten as inequalities.

Additional Answers

2. The solution of $x < 10$ does not include 10, but $x \leq 10$ does.

3. 

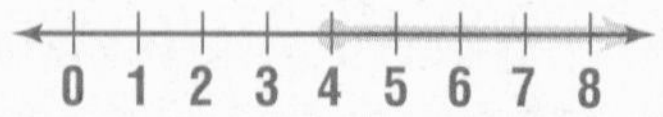

Practice Masters, p. 46

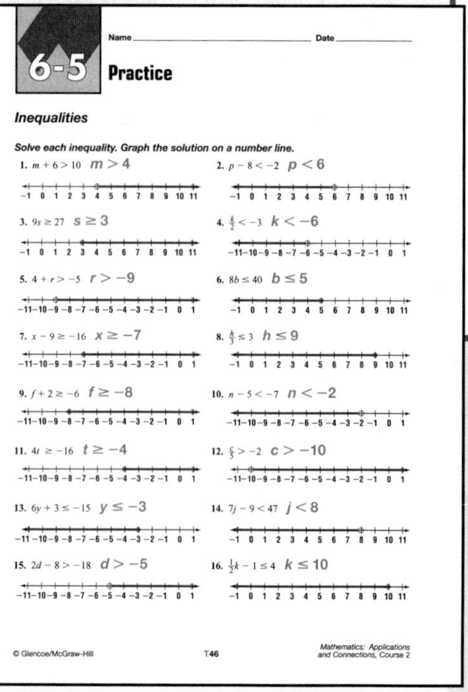

6-5 **Practice**

Name__________ Date__________

Inequalities

Solve each inequality. Graph the solution on a number line.

1. $m + 6 > 10$ $m > 4$
2. $p - 8 < -2$ $p < 6$
3. $9s \geq 27$ $s \geq 3$
4. $\frac{k}{2} < -3$ $k < -6$
5. $4 + r > -5$ $r > -9$
6. $8b \leq 40$ $b \leq 5$
7. $x - 9 \geq -16$ $x \geq -7$
8. $\frac{h}{3} \leq 3$ $h \leq 9$
9. $f + 2 \geq -6$ $f \geq -8$
10. $n - 5 < -7$ $n < -2$
11. $4t \geq -16$ $t \geq -4$
12. $\frac{c}{5} > -2$ $c > -10$
13. $6y + 3 \leq -15$ $y \leq -3$
14. $7j - 9 < 47$ $j < 8$
15. $2d - 8 > -18$ $d > -5$
16. $\frac{1}{2}k - 1 \leq 4$ $k \leq 10$

 T46 *Mathematics: Applications and Connections, Course 2*

CHECK FOR UNDERSTANDING

Communicating Mathematics

Read and study the lesson to answer each question. 2–3. See margin.

1. ***Write*** the inequality graphed on the number line at the right. $x \leq -1$ 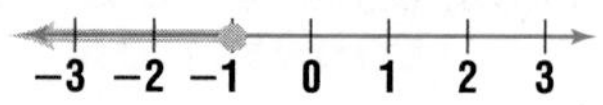
   (number line: −3 −2 −1 0 1 2 3)
2. ***Explain*** the difference between $x < 10$ and $x \leq 10$.
3. ***Draw*** a number line that shows *all numbers greater than or equal to 4.*

HANDS-ON MATH

Guided Practice 4–7. See Answer Appendix.

Solve each inequality. Graph the solution on a number line.

4. $5 + y < 13$
5. $a - 3 \geq -5$
6. $3t > 12$
7. $x + 6 \leq 0$
8. ***Food*** One dozen jumbo eggs must weigh at least 30 ounces. Write this sentence as an inequality. $e \geq 30$

EXERCISES

Practice 9–20. See Answer Appendix.

Solve each inequality. Graph the solution on a number line.

9. $x + 3 > -4$
10. $g - 5 > 2$
11. $6d \geq 24$
12. $t - 3 < -2$
13. $5 + p > 3$
14. $2y \leq 15$
15. $3r < 24$
16. $b + 4 \leq 3$
17. $y + 1.3 < 4.5$
18. $3x + 8 < 23$
19. $2a - 5 > 9$
20. $9d + 4 \geq 22$

Write an inequality for each sentence. Then solve the inequality.

21. Five times a number is greater than 60. $5n > 60$, $n > 12$
22. The sum of a number and 5 is less than or equal to −9. $n + 5 \leq -9$, $n \leq -14$

Applications and Problem Solving

24. $4h \geq 115$, $h \geq 28.75$

23. ***Civics*** The 26th amendment to the United States Constitution guarantees the right to vote to citizens who are eighteen years of age or older. Write an inequality showing the age of all voters. $a \geq 18$ 
24. ***Money Matters*** Luther earns \$4 an hour doing yard work so he can buy a portable CD player that costs \$115. Write an inequality for the least number of hours he needs to work to reach his goal. Then solve the inequality.
25. ***Critical Thinking*** Sandstone is formed by grains of sand that have become cemented together. These grains are between 0.06 millimeter and 2 millimeters in size. Write an inequality for the size of a grain of sand. $0.06 < s < 2$

For **Extra Practice,** see page 585.

Mixed Review

26. ***Algebra*** Write an algebraic expression for the phrase *6 less than w.* *(Lesson 6-4)* $w - 6$

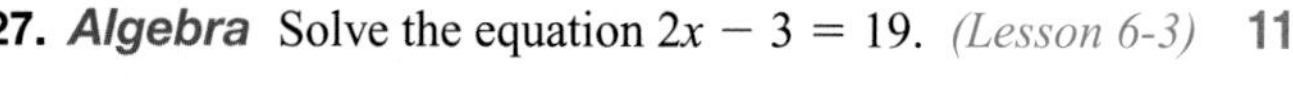

27. ***Algebra*** Solve the equation $2x - 3 = 19$. *(Lesson 6-3)* 11

28. **Standardized Test Practice** Lou has a section of tubing that is 83 inches long. What is the greatest number of 9-inch pieces that he can cut from the tubing? *(Lesson 5-7)* E

A 3 **B** 5 **C** 7 **D** 8 **E** Not Here

Extending the Lesson

Enrichment Masters, p. 46

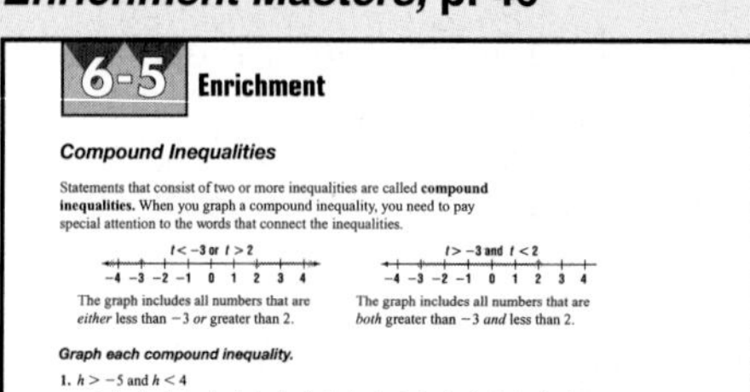

6-5 **Enrichment**

Compound Inequalities

Statements that consist of two or more inequalities are called **compound inequalities.** When you graph a compound inequality, you need to pay special attention to the words that connect the inequalities.

$t < -3$ or $t > 2$ — The graph includes all numbers that are *either* less than −3 *or* greater than 2.

$t > -3$ and $t < 2$ — The graph includes all numbers that are *both* greater than −3 *and* less than 2.

Graph each compound inequality.

1. $h > -5$ and $h < 4$

Activity An electrician charges \$36 per hour. How many hours can she work without exceeding her estimate of \$150? Show the formula for finding the answer. $36x \leq 150$ or 4 hours

6-6 Functions and Graphs

What **you'll learn**

You'll learn to represent functions as ordered pairs.

When **am I ever going to use this?**

In social studies, you'll use graphs to study recent trends in population.

Word Wise

function

When Christian Laettner played basketball for Duke University, he was 83 inches, or 211 centimeters, tall. Certainly this is taller than the average 18-year-old. The chart shows the average height for males ages 8 to 18.

Average Height for Males	
Age (yr)	**Height (cm)**
8	124
9	130
10	135
11	140
12	145
13	152
14	161
15	167
16	172
17	174
18	178

This information can be represented by using an ordered pair (age, height). You can then graph the ordered pairs on a coordinate plane. Age is graphed on the horizontal axis, and height is graphed on the vertical axis.

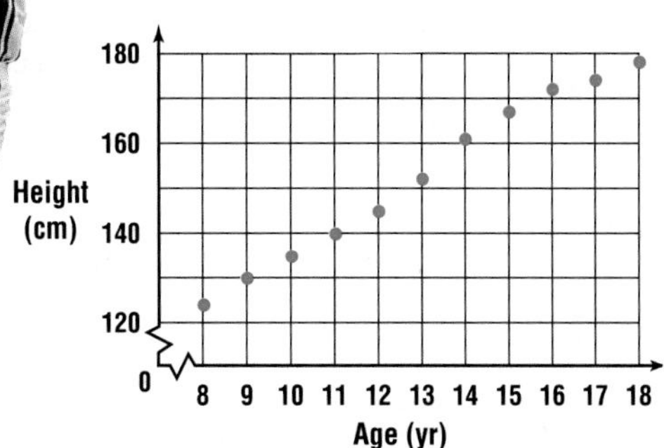

It is clear from the graph that height increases with age. Height is a **function** of age, which means that height *depends* on age. A function describes a relationship between two quantities.

1 **Law Enforcement** The Pennsylvania Bureau of Highway Safety and Traffic Engineering reports these data for cars.

a. Graph the ordered pairs (speed, distance) on a coordinate plane.

b. Describe how the stopping distance is related to the speed.

Dry Pavement Stopping Distance for Cars	
Speed (mph)	**Distance (feet)**
55	289
60	332
65	378
70	426

a.

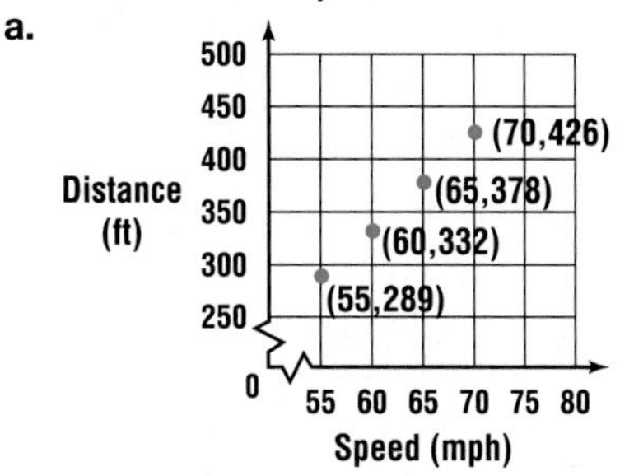

b. The stopping distance depends on the speed. So stopping distance is a function of the speed.

Teaching Tip Make sure the data in the first column is graphed on the horizontal (x-axis) and the data in the second column is graphed on the vertical (y-axis) so that students understand y as a function of x.

Motivating the Lesson

Communication Use statistics about books, movies, or music gathered over several weeks. Ask students to graph the data and discuss any patterns they observe.

6-6 Lesson Notes

Instructional Resources

- *Study Guide Masters,* p. 47
- *Practice Masters,* p. 47
- *Enrichment Masters,* p. 47
- Transparencies 6-6, A and B
- *Assessment and Evaluation Masters,* p. 156
- *Science and Math Lab Manual,* pp. 33–36
- *Technology Masters,* p. 38

CD-ROM Program
- Resource Lesson 6-6
- Extended Activity 6-6

Recommended Pacing	
Standard	Day 10 of 14
Honors	Days 9 & 10 of 13
Block	Day 6 of 7

1 FOCUS

5-Minute Check (Lesson 6-5)

Solve each inequality. Graph the solution on a number line.

1. $b - 18 > -3$ $b > 15$

   11 12 13 14 15 16 17 18

2. $10 \geq 3 + x$ $7 \geq x$

   0 1 2 3 4 5 6 7 8 9 10

3. $x + 11 < 6$ $x < -5$

   −8 −7 −6 −5 −4 −3 −2

4. $4c - 3 \leq 13$ $c \leq 4$

   0 1 2 3 4 5 6

5. $-9 + d > 9$ $d > 18$

   14 15 16 17 18 19 20

The 5-Minute Check is also available on **Transparency 6-6A** for this lesson.

2 TEACH

Transparency 6-6B contains a teaching aid for this lesson.

In-Class Examples

For Example 1

a. Graph the ordered pairs (distance from Sun, length of year) on a coordinate plane.

Planet	Distance from Sun (million miles)	Length of Year (Earth days)
Mercury	36	88
Venus	67	225
Earth	93	365
Mars	142	687

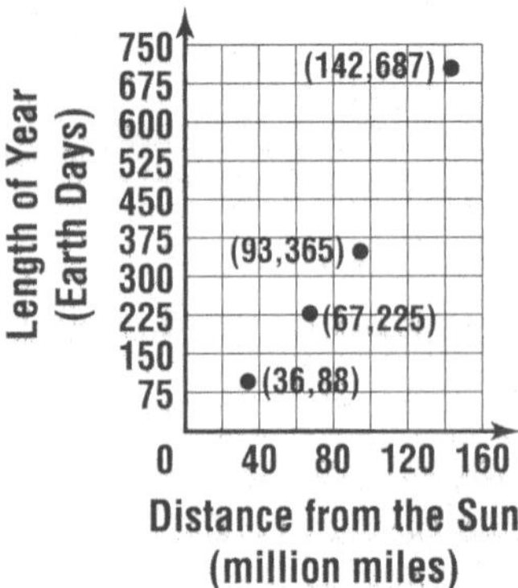

b. Describe the length of the year related to the distance from the Sun. **The farther away from the Sun, the longer the year; length of year is a function of the distance from the Sun.**

For Example 2

a. Graph the ordered pairs (length, depth) on a coordinate plane.

Lake	Length (mi)	Maximum Depth (ft)
Reindeer	143	720
Huron	206	750
Michigan	307	923
Superior	350	1,330

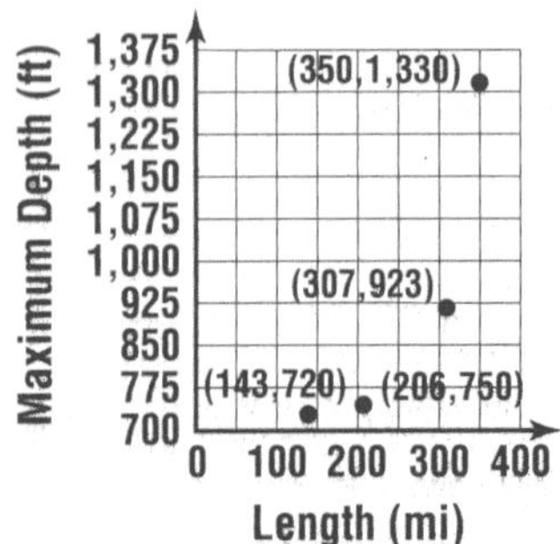

b. What appears to be the relationship between the length of each lake and its maximum depth? **The longer the lake, the deeper it is; maximum depth is a function of length.**

Example CONNECTION

2 **Life Science** A scientist was studying how temperature affects viruses. The chart at the right shows the results.

Viruses	
Temperature (°C)	**Number (millions)**
36.9	1.0
37.2	1.0
37.5	0.5
37.8	0.25
38.3	0.10
38.9	0.05

a. Graph the ordered pairs (temperature, number) on a coordinate plane.

b. What appears to be the relationship between temperature and viruses?

a.

Number (millions): 1.0, 0.75, 0.5, 0.25, 0
Temperature (°C): 36°, 37°, 38°, 39°

b. The graph shows that the number of viruses decreases as the temperature increases. The number of viruses is a function of the temperature.

How long would it take all of the students in your school to complete one cycle of "the wave"? In the Mini-Lab, you will do an experiment to estimate the time.

MINI-LAB

Work as a class.

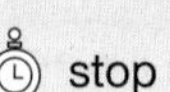 stop watch

Try This

- Begin with five students, sitting in a row.
- At the timer's signal, the first student stands up, waves his or her arms overhead, and sits down. Each student repeats the wave. When the last student sits down, the timer records the time in seconds.
- Repeat for 10, 15, 20, and 25 students.

Talk About It

1. Graph the ordered pairs (number of students, time) on a coordinate plane. **1–2. See students' work.**
2. How long would it take 30 students to complete the wave? 50 students? the number of students in your school?
3. Complete the sentence: The time it takes to do the wave is a function of __?__. **the number of students**

Using the Mini-Lab Make sure students stand and wave sequentially (not simultaneously) when doing "the wave." Encourage them to speed up or slow down the sequence when going through a second set of trials, beginning again with 5 students, then 10, and so on. Is time still a function of number of participants?

CHECK FOR UNDERSTANDING

Communicating Mathematics

Read and study the lesson to answer each question.

1. ***Describe*** a function. **a relationship between two quantities**
2. ***Name*** two ways to represent functions. **a table, graph of ordered pairs**
3. HANDS-ON MATH Refer to the Mini-Lab. How would your graph change if each student clapped twice and turned around before doing the wave?

Guided Practice

3. Sample answer: It would take longer for each student, so the graph would be above the original graph.

For Exercises 4 and 5, graph the ordered pairs in each table on a coordinate plane. Then write a sentence describing each relationship as a function.

4. ***Health*** The table shows the average number of heartbeats per minute for an adult who is working to improve aerobic conditioning. **See Answer Appendix.**

Age	25	30	35	40	45	50	55	60	65
Beats per Minute	147	143	139	135	131	127	124	120	115

Source: *The Heart Rate Monitor Book*

5. ***Geography*** The population of the state of Arizona over the last several decades is given in the table. **See Answer Appendix.**

Year	1930	1940	1950	1960	1970	1980	1990
Population (millions)	0.4	0.5	0.7	1.3	1.8	2.7	3.7

Source: U.S. Census

EXERCISES

Applications and Problem Solving

6. ***Sports*** Starting in 1991, NCAA Division I Men's Basketball instituted three-point shooting. The table shows the average number of attempts per game and the accuracy of the shots.

Three-point Shots		
Year	**Attempts**	**Accuracy**
1991	28.0	0.355
1992	29.8	0.354
1993	33.0	0.345
1994	34.3	0.345
1995	34.0	0.341

Source: NCAA

   a. Graph the ordered pairs (year, attempts) on one coordinate plane and (year, accuracy) on another coordinate plane. **See Answer Appendix.**
   b. Write a statement that describes the trends in attempts and accuracy.
   c. Graph the ordered pairs (attempts, accuracy) on a third coordinate plane. What is the relationship between attempts and accuracy? **See Answer Appendix.**

6b. The number of attempts has increased while the accuracy has decreased.

3 PRACTICE/APPLY

Check for Understanding

If students need additional practice or instruction after completing Exercises 1–5, one of these options may be helpful.

- Extra Practice, see p. 585
- Reteaching Activity
- *Study Guide Masters,* p. 47
- *Practice Masters,* p. 47

Assignment Guide

Core: 6, 7, 9, 11–13
Enriched: 6, 7, 9–13

Reteaching the Lesson

Activity Have students graph the following ordered pairs and describe their functional relationship. Ask them why a president's year of birth would not be a function of his first year in office.

President	Year of Birth	1st Year in Office
Washington	1732	1789
Adams	1735	1797
Jefferson	1743	1801
Madison	1751	1809
Monroe	1758	1817

Study Guide Masters, p. 47

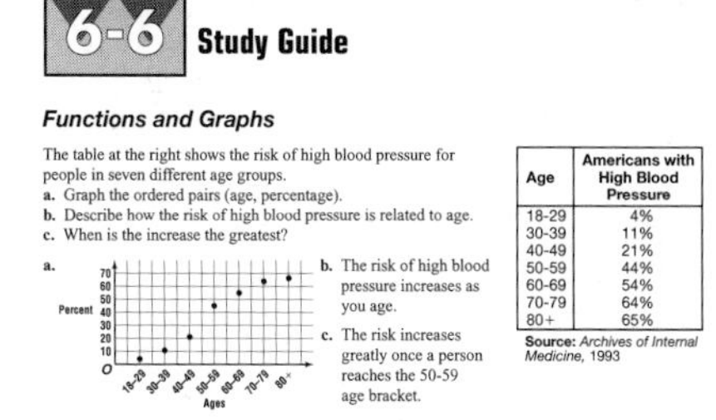

Name ______ Date ______

6-6 **Study Guide**

Functions and Graphs

The table at the right shows the risk of high blood pressure for people in seven different age groups.
a. Graph the ordered pairs (age, percentage).
b. Describe how the risk of high blood pressure is related to age.
c. When is the increase the greatest?

Age	Americans with High Blood Pressure
18-29	4%
30-39	11%
40-49	21%
50-59	44%
60-69	54%
70-79	64%
80+	65%

Source: *Archives of Internal Medicine,* 1993

a.

b. The risk of high blood pressure increases as you age.
c. The risk increases greatly once a person reaches the 50-59 age bracket.

Solve.

1. The table below shows the number of adult memberships at sport clubs.
   a. Graph the ordered pairs (year, memberships) on the coordinate plane.
   b. Write a statement that describes the trend in memberships. **Memberships are increasing over time.**

Year	Memberships (in millions)
1987	14
1989	16
1991	16
1993	18
1995	19

Source: International Health, Racquet, and Sportsclub Association

2. The table below shows the average monthly household cable bill for 1990-1996.
   a. Graph the ordered pairs (year, bill) on the coordinate plane.
   b. Describe the trend of cable bills over time. **Except for a one-year drop, cable bills are increasing.**

Year	Average Cable Bill
1990	$17.60
1991	$19.20
1992	$20.62
1993	$22.49
1994	$21.60
1995	$23.07
1996	$25.50

Source: *USA TODAY*

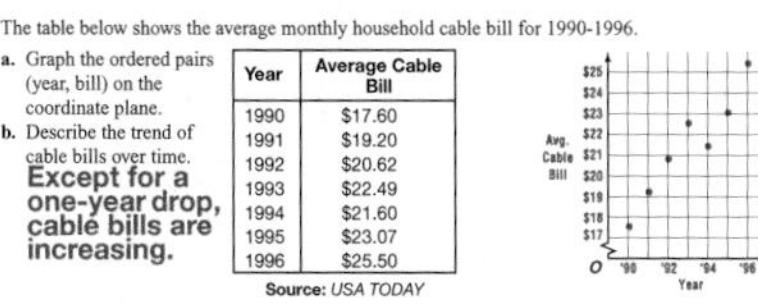

 T47 *Mathematics: Applications and Connections, Course 2*

Exercise 8 asks students to advance to the next stage of work on the Chapter Project. Ask students who have ridden a roller coaster to explain why the average distance traveled per second is not really what happens.

4 ASSESS

Closing Activity

Modeling Have students use a balance scale to compare the relative weights of various objects (a book, a hairbrush, a pen, or a brick.) Once they have established which objects are heavier, challenge them to discern what properties of those objects make them heavy, and to complete the sentence: *Weight is a function of. . . .*

Chapter 6, Quiz C (Lessons 6-5 and 6-6) is available in the *Assessment and Evaluation Masters,* p. 156.

***Practice Masters,* p. 47**

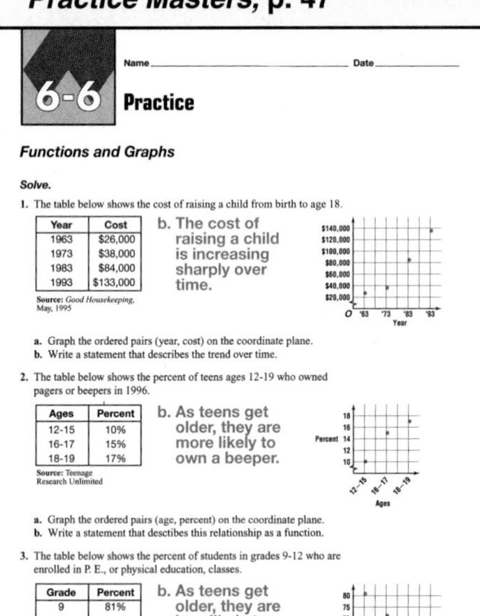
Name__________ Date__________

6-6 Practice

Functions and Graphs

Solve.

1. The table below shows the cost of raising a child from birth to age 18.

Year	Cost
1963	$26,000
1973	$38,000
1983	$84,000
1993	$133,000

Source: *Good Housekeeping,* May, 1995

b. The cost of raising a child is increasing sharply over time.

a. Graph the ordered pairs (year, cost) on the coordinate plane.
b. Write a statement that describes the trend over time.

2. The table below shows the percent of teens ages 12-19 who owned pagers or beepers in 1996.

Ages	Percent
12-15	10%
16-17	15%
18-19	17%

Source: Teenage Research Unlimited

b. As teens get older, they are more likely to own a beeper.

a. Graph the ordered pairs (age, percent) on the coordinate plane.
b. Write a statement that desctibes this relationship as a function.

3. The table below shows the percent of students in grades 9-12 who are enrolled in P. E., or physical education, classes.

Grade	Percent
9	81%
10	72%
11	47%
12	42%

Source: U. S. Dept. of Health and Human Services

b. As teens get older, they are less likely to take P. E.

a. Graph the ordered pairs (grade, percent) on the coordinate plane.
b. Write a statement that describes this relationship as a function.

 T47 *Mathematics: Applications and Connections, Course 2*

7b. Production costs have increased.

8a. See students' work.

8b. Yes; average distance depends on the amount of time.

9. As you grow older, you are more likely to snore and less likely to talk in your sleep.

7. ***Entertainment*** The table shows average production costs per film for several years.

Year	1	2	3	4	5
Production Cost (millions of dollars)	42.3	44.0	50.4	54.1	59.7

Source: Motion Picture Association of America

a. Graph the ordered pairs (year, cost). **See Answer Appendix.**
b. Write a statement that describes the trend in production costs.

8. ***Working on the*** CHAPTER Project Refer to the table on page 225.
a. Select one of the ten roller coasters. Find the average distance traveled by the roller coaster after 1, 2, 3, and up through 10 seconds. Write ordered pairs (time, distance) and graph them on a coordinate plane.
b. Is distance a function of the time? Explain your reasoning.

9. ***Health*** The graph shows the percent of people who snore or talk in their sleep. Write a statement that tells how the chances of doing either change as you grow older.

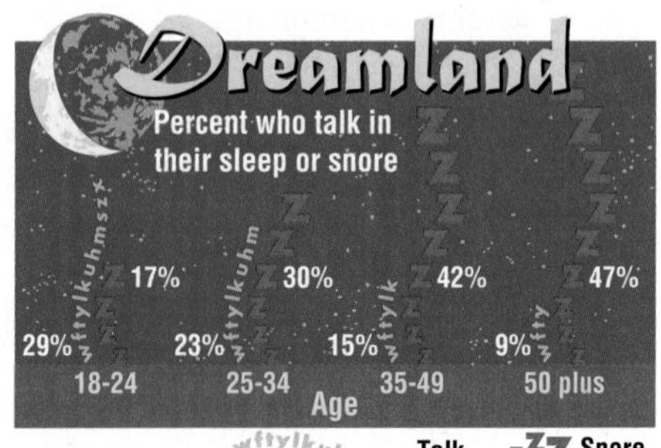

Source: The Better Sleep Council

10. ***Current Events*** Find data in a recent newspaper or magazine that can be expressed as ordered pairs. Graph the data and write a statement explaining the relationship of the values. **See students' work.**

11. ***Critical Thinking*** Refer to the beginning of the lesson. For which ages is the rate of growth fastest? Explain your reasoning. **Between 12 and 14; the line connecting the points is steeper for these years.**

Mixed Review

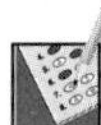

12. **Standardized Test Practice** Choose the graph that is the solution of $x \geq 1$. *(Lesson 6-5)* **D**

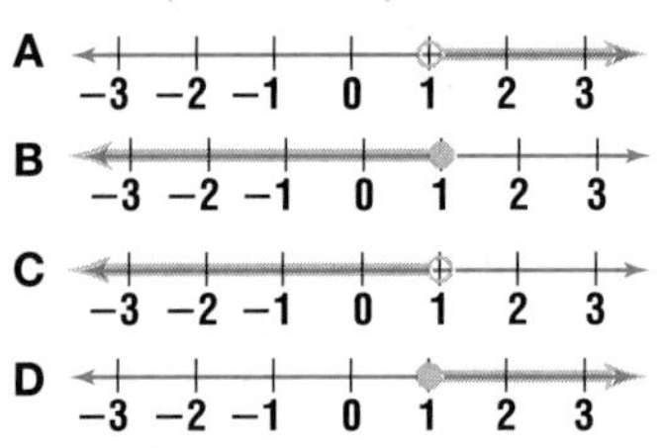

For **Extra Practice,** see page 585.

13. ***Algebra*** Evaluate $15(xy) - (x + y)$ if $x = 4$ and $y = 1$. *(Lesson 1-3)* **55**

Extending the Lesson

***Enrichment Masters,* p. 47**

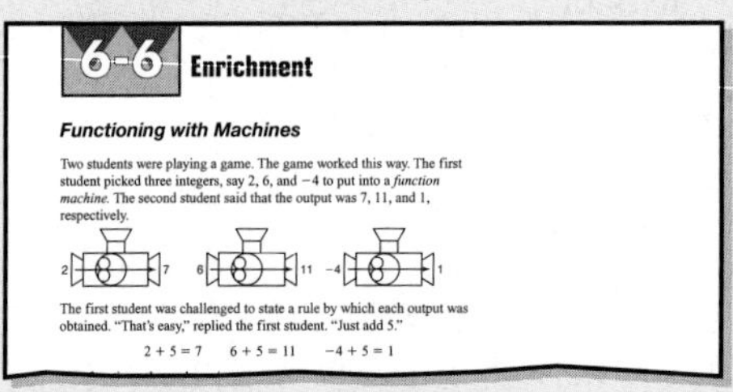
6-6 Enrichment

Functioning with Machines

Two students were playing a game. The game worked this way. The first student picked three integers, say 2, 6, and −4 to put into a *function machine.* The second student said that the output was 7, 11, and 1, respectively.

The first student was challenged to state a rule by which each output was obtained. "That's easy," replied the first student. "Just add 5."

$2 + 5 = 7 \quad 6 + 5 = 11 \quad -4 + 5 = 1$

Activity Ask students how they would determine which data to graph on the *x*-axis and which on the *y*-axis for each example covered. What difference does it make if *y* is a function of *x* or *x* is a function of *y*? **The set of data that depends upon the other data belongs on the *y*-axis in order to graph an ordered pair according to the form (*x*, *y*), where *y* is a function of *x*.**

COOPERATIVE LEARNING

6-7A A Function of Time

A Preview of Lesson 6-7

stopwatch or watch with second hand

grid paper

On a cold morning, you may "see" your breath as the water vapor condenses when you exhale. But otherwise, you probably don't think much about breathing. Breathing is something we do naturally, without even thinking about it. In this lab, you will learn how breathing is a function of time.

TRY THIS

Work with a partner.

- One person does the breathing, and the other is the timer. When the timer says "Go," the first student begins to count the number of times he or she breathes *out*. After one minute, the timer says "Stop," and the first student records the number of breaths.
- Repeat five more times and record each result.
- Find the mean of the six results. This is the average number of breaths per minute.
- Copy the table and use this average to complete it.

Minutes	Minutes × Average Breaths per Minute	Total Breaths
1	1 × ?	?
2	2 × ?	?
3	3 × ?	?
4	4 × ?	?
5	5 × ?	?
6	6 × ?	?

In this table, the minutes are called *input* values, and the total breaths are called *output* values. The middle column contains the *function rule*. When you input a value into the function rule, you get an output value. On what does the total number of breaths depend? In this case, the total number of breaths depends on the number of minutes. So, the number of breaths is a function of time.

ON YOUR OWN

1. Graph the ordered pairs (minutes, breaths) on a coordinate plane. **See students' work.**
2. Describe any patterns in the graph. **The points should be in a line.**
3. How can you use the graph to estimate the number of breaths you take in 8 minutes? **Extend the line.**
4. Let m be the number of minutes. Write an expression for the total number of breaths you take in m minutes. **See margin.**
5. Repeat this lab using number of heartbeats per minute. **See students' work.**

Math Journal Have students write a paragraph describing the connection between input values, output values, and a function rule.

Additional Answer

4. **Sample answer: If you take 20 breaths in one minute, the expression is $20m$.**

6-7A HANDS-ON LAB Notes

GET READY

Objective Students use a function rule to find the output of a function.

Optional Resources

Hands-On Lab Masters
- grid paper, p. 11
- worksheet, p. 51

Overhead Manipulative Resources
- coordinate grid

Manipulative Kit
- coordinate grid stamp

MANAGEMENT TIPS

Recommended Time
30 minutes

Getting Started Ask students to record their guesses about how many times per minute they blink. Test the guesses by demonstrating how to determine the number of blinks per minute.

For the **Activity,** you can suggest that students save time by counting the number of breaths in 15 or 30 seconds and then multiplying by 4 or 2 to find the number of breaths per minute. You can also graph the entire class' results and ask students to look for a pattern in the plotted points.

ASSESS

Use Exercises 3 and 4 to determine whether students understand the function rule. Substitute other input values that require further computation.

6-7 Lesson Notes

Instructional Resources

- *Study Guide Masters,* p. 48
- *Practice Masters,* p. 48
- *Enrichment Masters,* p. 48
- Transparencies 6-7, A and B
- *Assessment and Evaluation Masters,* p. 156

CD-ROM Program
- Resource Lesson 6-7
- Interactive Lesson 6-7

Recommended Pacing	
Standard	Days 11 & 12 of 14
Honors	Day 11 of 13
Block	Day 6 of 7

1 FOCUS

5-Minute Check (Lesson 6-6)

In four straight baseball games, Andy pitched 1, 2, 4, and 3 innings, giving up 0, 1, 5, and 2 runs in each game.

1. Graph the ordered pairs (innings, runs).

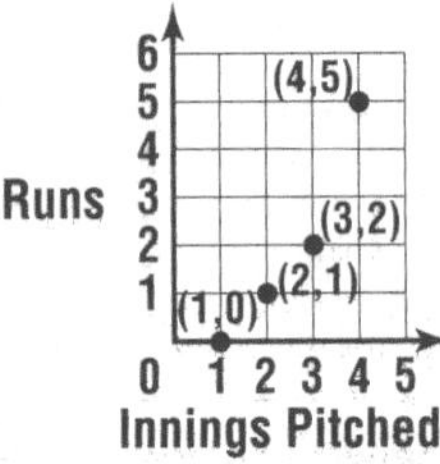

2. Write a statement describing a tendency. **The more innings he pitches, the more runs he gives up.**

The 5-Minute Check is also available on **Transparency 6-7A** for this lesson.

Motivating the Lesson

Hands-On Activity Provide a recipe for trail mix, and have students write an equation to increase the recipe to serve the number of students in the class. To serve 8: mix 2 cups peanuts, 1 cup cashews, 1 cup raisins, 1 cup chocolate-covered raisins. Have students mix both recipes, one for 8 and one for *n* students, in quart jars and compare the amount.

6-7 Functions and Equations

What you'll learn
You'll learn to solve equations with two variables and graph the solution.

When am I ever going to use this?
When you do experiments in science, you will use more than one variable.

Word Wise
linear equation

At the end of each summer, the Westerville Band performs at Cedar Point in Sandusky, Ohio. Each band member pays an admission price of \$15, which allows them to ride all of Cedar Point's twelve roller coasters.

The band's total admission cost is a function of the number of members who go to Cedar Point. There are several ways to represent the function.

Method 1 Use a verbal description.
\$15 times the number of members equals the total cost.

Method 2 Make a table of values.
The table lists the total cost for various numbers of members.

Number of Members	Multiply by 15	Total Cost
1	15 × 1	15
2	15 × 2	30
3	15 × 3	45
4	15 × 4	60

Method 3 Write an equation.
It's not convenient to list all of the possibilities in a table, so you can use variables. Let x represent the number of members and y represent the total cost.

number of members → ← *total cost*

$$15x = y$$

Method 4 Draw a graph.
The solution of an equation with two variables consists of two numbers, one for each variable. The solution is usually written as an ordered pair, (x, y).

Based on the table above, four solutions of the equation $15x = y$ are (1, 15), (2, 30), (3, 45), and (4, 60). Graph the ordered pairs on a coordinate plane.

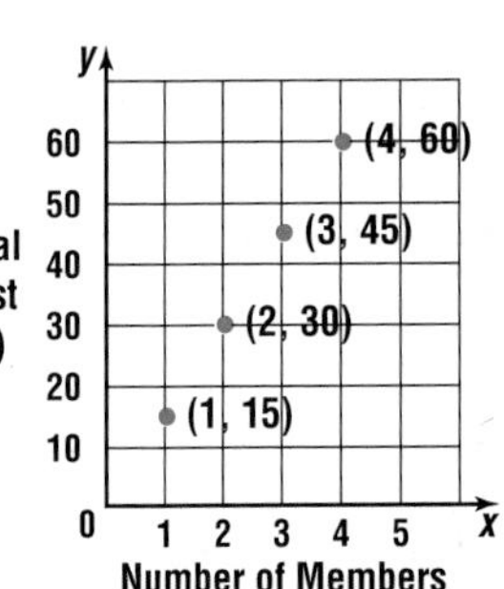

Notice that all four points lie on a line.

Example **1** **Find four solutions of $y = 2x - 1$. Write the solutions as ordered pairs and graph them.**

Select any four values for x. We chose 2, 1, 0, and -1. Substitute these values for x to find y and complete the table of values.

x	$2x - 1$	y	(x, y)
2	$2(2) - 1$	3	(2, 3)
1	$2(1) - 1$	1	(1, 1)
0	$2(0) - 1$	-1	(0, -1)
-1	$2(-1) - 1$	-3	(-1, -3)

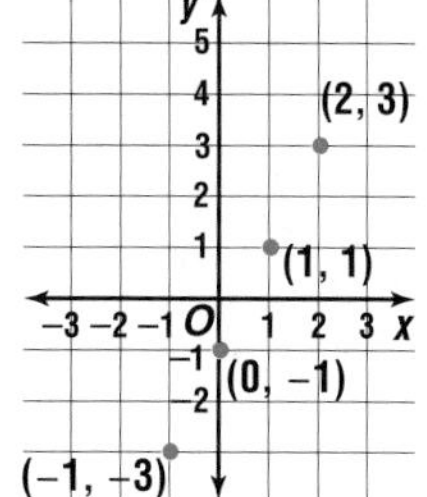

LOOK BACK
You can refer to Lesson 5-3 to review how to graph ordered pairs.

Four solutions are (2, 3), (1, 1), (0, -1), and (-1, -3).

Notice that all four points in the graph above lie on a line. Draw a line through the points to graph *all* solutions of the equation $y = 2x - 1$.

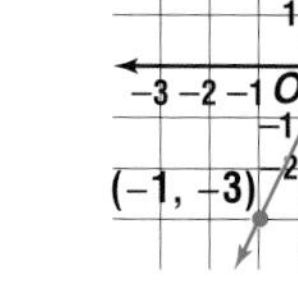

The graph of (3, 5) is on the line. Let's check whether (3, 5) is also a solution.

$y = 2x - 1$

$5 = 2(3) - 1$ *Replace x with 3 and y with 5.*

$5 = 5$ ✓

(3, 5) is a solution.

An equation like $y = 2x - 1$ is called a **linear equation** because its graph is a straight line. Only two points are needed to graph the line. However, graph more points to check accuracy.

Example **2** **INTEGRATION**

Geometry **The equation $A = 5w$, where A is the area and w is the width, can be used to show the area of all rectangles whose length is 5 units. Graph the equation $A = 5w$.**

Select any four values for w. Since w represents the width of a rectangle, choose only positive numbers. We chose 1, 2, 3, and 4.

Make a table of values.

w	$5w$	A	(w, A)
1	5(1)	5	(1, 5)
2	5(2)	10	(2, 10)
3	5(3)	15	(3, 15)
4	5(4)	20	(4, 20)

Graph the ordered pairs and draw a line through the points.

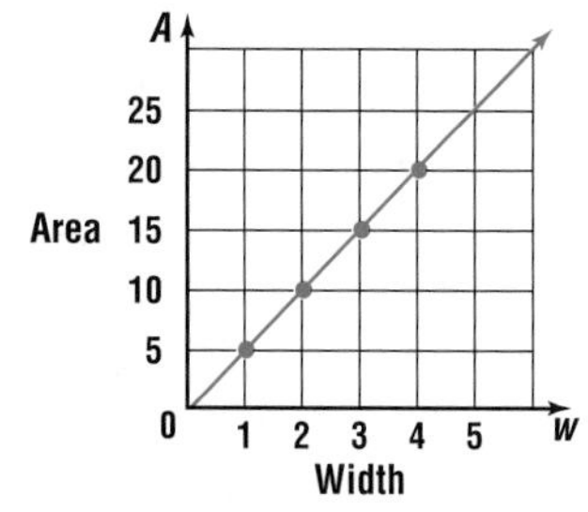

2 TEACH

Transparency 6-7B contains a teaching aid for this lesson.

Thinking Algebraically Being able to write an expression that describes a pattern shows a real understanding of a functional relationship. Give students situations and have them write expressions to represent them.

In-Class Examples

For Example 1

Find four solutions for $x = y$. Write the solutions as ordered pairs and graph them.

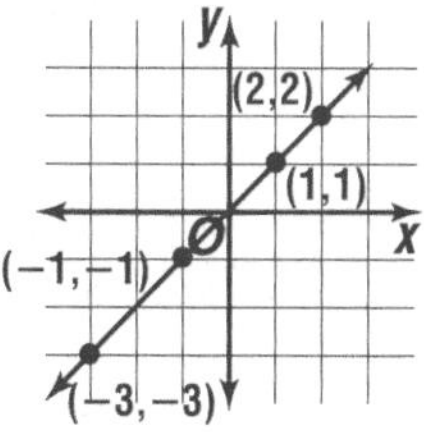

For Example 2

Use the equation $y = 10x$ to find how much money Ms. Ivanoff will earn teaching a one-hour ballet class, where x is the number of students who pay $10 per class. Graph the equation for 5, 10, 15, and 20 students.

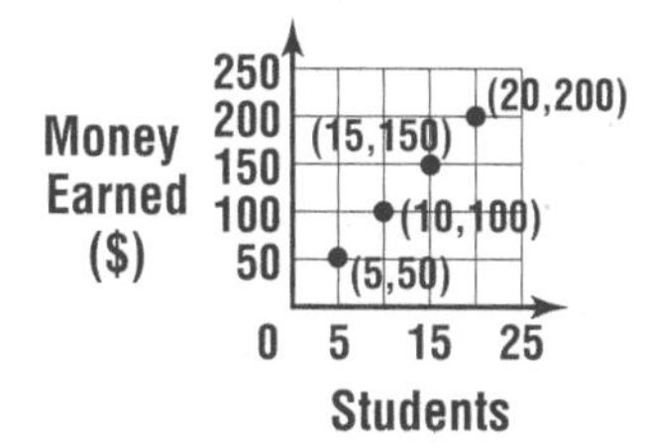

3 PRACTICE/APPLY

Check for Understanding

If students need additional practice or instruction after completing Exercises 1–11, one of these options may be helpful.

- Extra Practice, see p. 585
- Reteaching Activity
- *Study Guide Masters,* p. 48
- *Practice Masters,* p. 48
- Interactive Mathematics Tools Software

Assignment Guide

Core: 13–31 odd, 33–37
Enriched: 12–28 even, 29, 31–37

Additional Answers

11a.

Hours	Earnings
3	18
5	30
7	42
9	54

11c.

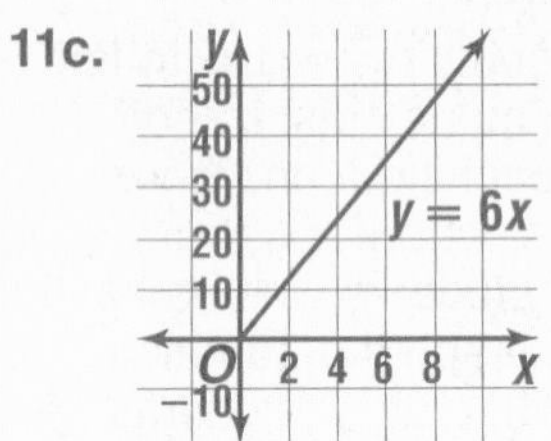

***Study Guide Masters,* p. 48**

Name ______ Date ______

Study Guide

Functions and Equations

If the graph of the solutions for an equation is a straight line, the equation is a linear equation.

Example Graph $y = \frac{1}{2}x + 1$.

Select any four values for x. We chose −2, 0, 2, and 4. Substitute these values for x to find y and complete the table of values.

x	$\frac{1}{2}x + 1$	y	(x, y)
−2	$\frac{1}{2}(-2) + 1$	0	(−2, 0)
0	$\frac{1}{2}(0) + 1$	1	(0, 1)
2	$\frac{1}{2}(2) + 1$	2	(2, 2)
4	$\frac{1}{2}(4) + 1$	3	(4, 3)

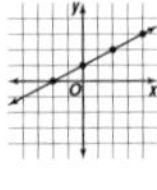

Graph the ordered pairs. Draw a line through all the points.

Graph each equation.

1. $y = 2x$
2. $y = x + 2$
3. $y = -\frac{1}{2}x$
4. $y = -x + 1$
5. $y = x - 1$
6. $y = -x$

 T48 *Mathematics: Applications and Connections, Course 2*

CHECK FOR UNDERSTANDING

Communicating Mathematics

Read and study the lesson to answer each question.

1. ***Choose*** the equation for the graph. d
   a. $y = 2x$ b. $y = x$
   c. $y = x - 1$ d. $y = 2x - 2$

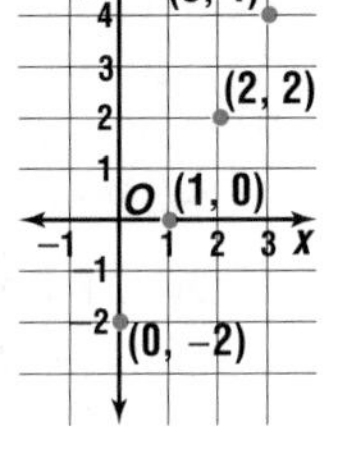

2. ***List*** four ways to show the relationship between two variables. **2. verbally, table of values, equation, graph**
3. ***You Decide*** Beatriz thinks (1, −1) is a solution of $y = 2x - 1$. Grace thinks it is *not* a solution. Who is correct? Explain your reasoning.
   Grace; $2(1) - 1 \neq -1$

Guided Practice

Copy and complete each table. Then graph the ordered pairs. **4–6. See Answer Appendix.**

4. $y = 2x + 1$

x	$2x + 1$	y
1		
2		
3		
4		

5. $y = 3x$

x	$3x$	y
−1		
0		
1		
2		

6. $y = -2x + 3$

x	$-2x + 3$	y
−1		
0		
1		
2		

Graph each equation. **7–10. See Answer Appendix.**

7. $y = 3x - 1$
8. $y = x - 2$
9. $y = -2x$
10. $y = 1.5x$
11. ***Money Matters*** Angel earns $6 per hour at the Ice Cream Shop.
    a. Make a table that shows her total earnings for working 3, 5, 7, and 9 hours.
    b. Write an equation in which x represents the number of hours and y represents Angel's total earnings. **$y = 6x$**
    c. Graph the equation. **a, c. See margin.**

EXERCISES

Practice

Graph each equation. **12–23. See Answer Appendix.**

12. $y = 2x + 3$
13. $y = 4x - 1$
14. $y = 0.25x$
15. $y = 0.5x - 1$
16. $y = x - 3$
17. $y = -2x + 2$
18. $y = -3x - 1$
19. $y = x + 0.5$
20. $y = 2x - 1.5$
21. $y = 2x - 5$
22. $y = 6x$
23. $y = 0.1x$

Make a table of values for each sentence. Then write an equation. Let x represent the first number and y represent the second number.

24. The second number is three more than the first. **$y = x + 3$**
25. The second number is twice the first. **$y = 2x$**
26. The second number is the product of −3 and the first number. **$y = -3x$**
27. The sum of the numbers is 10. **$x + y = 10$**

Reteaching the Lesson

Activity Provide groups of students with an ordered pair. Have them list several equations the ordered pair will satisfy. Repeat with other ordered pairs.

Error Analysis

Watch for students who confuse x- and y-variables.

Prevent by emphasizing the use of a table to list ordered pairs of x- and y-values.

Applications and Problem Solving

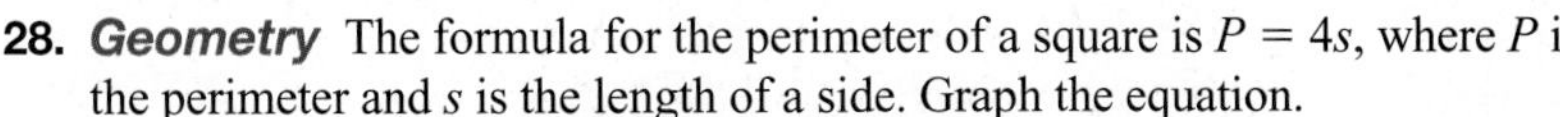

28. ***Geometry*** The formula for the perimeter of a square is $P = 4s$, where P is the perimeter and s is the length of a side. Graph the equation.

29. ***Age*** The table shows how Jared's age and his sister Emily's age are related.

Jared's age	1	2	3	4	5
Emily's age	7	8	9	10	11

   a. Write a verbal expression to describe how the ages are related.
   b. Write an equation for the verbal expression. Let x represent Jared's age and y represent Emily's age. **$y = x + 6$**
   c. Predict how old Emily will be when Jared is 10. **16**
   d. Graph the equation. **See Answer Appendix.**

28. See Answer Appendix.

29a. Sample answer: Emily is 6 years older than Jared.

interNET CONNECTION For the latest amusement park statistics, visit: www.glencoe.com/sec/math/mac/mathnet

30. ***Working on the CHAPTER Project*** Refer to the table on page 225.
   a. Select one of the ten roller coasters. Find the total number of passengers that could have ridden the roller coaster after 1, 2, 3, and up through 12 hours. Write the ordered pairs (time, number of passengers) and graph them on a coordinate plane. **See students' work.**
   b. Write an equation for the graph. Let x represent the time in hours and y represent the total number of passengers. **See students' work.**

31. ***Scuba Diving*** When you swim underwater, the pressure you feel in your ears is a function of the depth at which you are swimming. The equation that gives the pressure p, in lb/in^2, as a function of the depth d, in feet, is $p = 0.43d$.
   a. Find the pressure at a depth of 10 feet. **4.3 lb/in^2**
   b. Graph the equation. **See Answer Appendix.**
   c. Use your graph to predict the pressure at 30 feet.

32. ***Write a Problem*** about a real-life situation that can be represented by the equation $y = 3x$.

33. ***Critical Thinking*** Refer to the beginning of the lesson. Explain whether it makes sense to draw a line joining the points on the graph. **No; the number of members of the band can only be represented with whole numbers.**

Mixed Review

31c. about 12 or 13 lb/in^2

32. See students' work.

For **Extra Practice,** see page 585.

34. ***Recreation*** The graphs show recent trends in tennis and softball. Which activity has had the greatest decrease in recent years? *(Lesson 6-6)* **tennis**

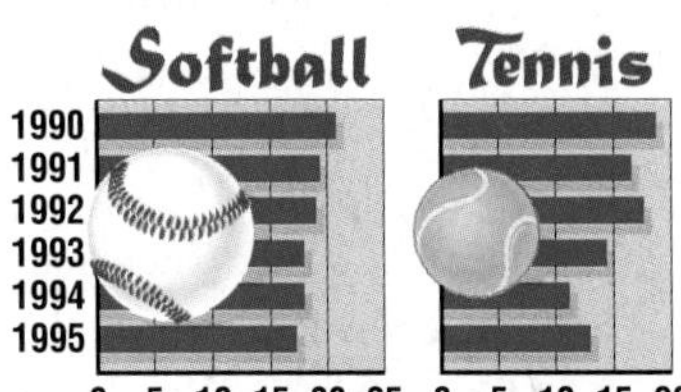

Source: National Sporting Goods Association

35. ***Algebra*** Solve $6p = 72$. *(Lesson 6-2)* **12**

36. ***Measurement*** Complete the sentence 2.33 km = _?_ m. *(Lesson 2-8)* **2,330**

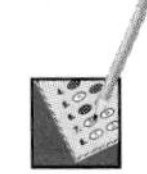

37. **Standardized Test Practice** Eduardo bought a 2-liter bottle of cola. He drank 0.735 liter for lunch. How much cola was left? *(Lesson 2-3)* **B**

   A 0.652 L **B** 1.265 L **C** 1.652 L **D** 1.865 L **E** Not Here

Exercise 30 asks students to advance to the next stage of work on the Chapter Project. You may want to demonstrate by filling in the number of passengers for 1 hour and have students proceed for 2–12 hours.

4 ASSESS

Closing Activity

Speaking Have students explain how a graph of a linear equation shows solutions of that equation. **Sample answer: It is a line connecting all points indicated by the ordered pairs that are solutions of the equation.**

Chapter 6, Quiz D (Lesson 6-7) is available in the *Assessment and Evaluation Masters,* p. 156.

Practice Masters, p. 48

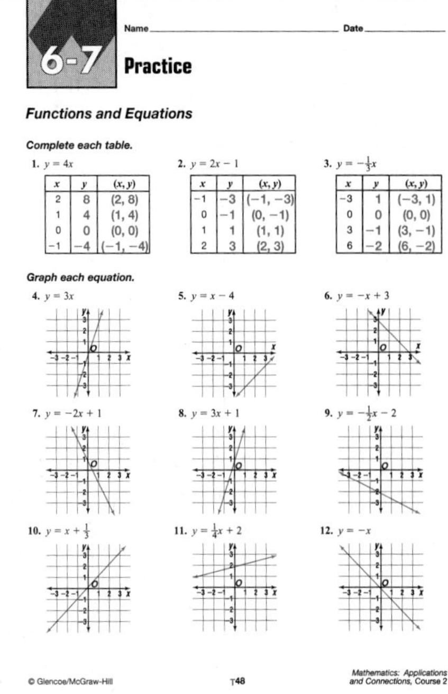

Name__________ Date__________

6-7 Practice

Functions and Equations

Complete each table.

1. $y = 4x$

x	y	(x, y)
2	8	(2, 8)
1	4	(1, 4)
0	0	(0, 0)
−1	−4	(−1, −4)

2. $y = 2x - 1$

x	y	(x, y)
−1	−3	(−1, −3)
0	−1	(0, −1)
1	1	(1, 1)
2	3	(2, 3)

3. $y = -\frac{1}{3}x$

x	y	(x, y)
−3	1	(−3, 1)
0	0	(0, 0)
3	−1	(3, −1)
6	−2	(6, −2)

Graph each equation.

4. $y = 3x$
5. $y = x - 4$
6. $y = -x + 3$
7. $y = -2x + 1$
8. $y = 3x + 1$
9. $y = -\frac{1}{2}x - 2$
10. $y = x + \frac{1}{3}$
11. $y = \frac{1}{4}x + 2$
12. $y = -x$

© Glencoe/McGraw-Hill T48 *Mathematics: Applications and Connections,* Course 2

Extending the Lesson

Enrichment Masters, p. 48

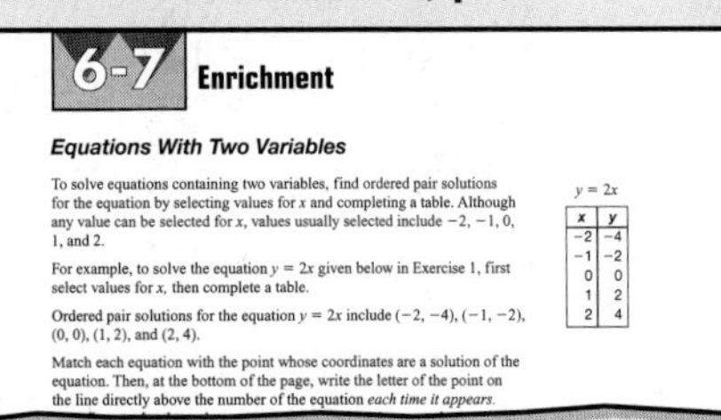

6-7 Enrichment

Equations With Two Variables

To solve equations containing two variables, find ordered pair solutions for the equation by selecting values for x and completing a table. Although any value can be selected for x, values usually selected include −2, −1, 0, 1, and 2.

For example, to solve the equation $y = 2x$ given below in Exercise 1, first select values for x, then complete a table.

Ordered pair solutions for the equation $y = 2x$ include (−2, −4), (−1, −2), (0, 0), (1, 2), and (2, 4).

$y = 2x$

x	y
−2	−4
−1	−2
0	0
1	2
2	4

Match each equation with the point whose coordinates are a solution of the equation. Then, at the bottom of the page, write the letter of the point on the line directly above the number of the equation *each time it appears.*

Activity Have students write an equation that relates the following ordered pairs. **$y = 2.5x$**

x	y
−4	−10
2	5
6	15

Vocabulary

This section provides a listing of the new terms, properties, and phrases that were introduced in this chapter. Have students define each term and provide an example or two of it, if appropriate.

Understanding and Using the Vocabulary

These exercises check students' understanding of the terms by using a variety of verbal formats including matching, completion, and true/false.

Glossaries A complete glossary of terms appears on pages 656–663. The glossary also appears in Spanish on pages 664–672.

Additional Answer

11. If you add the same number to each side of an equation, the two sides will still be equal.

CHAPTER 6 Study Guide and Assessment

Chapter Review For additional lesson-by-lesson review, visit: www.glencoe.com/sec/math/mac/mathnet

Vocabulary

After completing this chapter, you should be able to define each term, concept, or phrase and give an example or two of each.

Algebra
addition property of equality (p. 229)
coefficient (p. 234)
defining the variable (p. 243)
division property of equality (p. 234)
inequality (p. 246)
linear equation (p. 255)
subtraction property of equality (p. 228)
term (p. 239)
zero pairs (p. 227)

Problem Solving
work backward (p. 232)

Patterns and Functions
function (p. 249)
function rule (p. 253)
input (p. 253)
output (p. 253)

2. false, addition or subtraction

Understanding and Using the Vocabulary

State whether each sentence is *true* or *false.* If *false,* replace the underlined word or number to make a true sentence.

1. Choosing a number to represent an unknown in a problem is called defining the variable. false, variable
2. The words "more than" suggest the operation of multiplication.
3. An inequality is a mathematical sentence that contains the symbols $<$, $>$, $\leq$, or $\geq$. true
4. When graphing $t < 2$ on a number line, an open circle should be used to show that 2 is not included in the solution. true
5. A function describes a relationship between two quantities. true
6. An equation is called a linear equation if its graph is a point. false, line
7. The solution of $m + 5 = 12$ is 17. false, 7
8. The solution of $g - 4 = 18$ is 22. true
9. The solution of $-8w = 48$ is 6. false, -6
10. The solution of $2y \leq 18$ is $y \leq 16$. false, 9

In Your Own Words

11. ***Explain*** the addition property of equality. See margin.

MindJogger Videoquizzes

MindJogger Videoquizzes provide an alternative review of concepts presented in this chapter. Students work in teams to answer questions, gaining points for correct answers. The questions are presented in three rounds.
Round 1 Concepts–5 questions
Round 2 Skills–4 questions
Round 3 Problem Solving–4 questions

Objectives & Examples

Upon completing this chapter, you should be able to:

- solve addition and subtraction equations *(Lesson 6-1)*

Solve $c - 32 = 112$.

$$c - 32 = 112$$
$$c - 32 + 32 = 112 + 32 \quad \text{Add 32 to each side.}$$
$$c = 144$$

Review Exercises

Use these exercises to review and prepare for the chapter test.

Solve each equation. Check your solution.

12. $x + 15 = 14$ **−1** **13.** $w + 13 = -25$
14. $10.9 + r = 11$ **0.1** **15.** $54 = m - 9$ **63**
16. $t - 3.6 = 10.1$ **13.7** **17.** $s + 3.75 = 5.25$ **1.5**
13. −38

- solve multiplication equations *(Lesson 6-2)*

Solve $33y = 132$.

$$33y = 132$$
$$\frac{33y}{33} = \frac{132}{33} \quad \text{Divide each side by 33.}$$
$$y = 4$$

Solve each equation. Check your solution.

18. $4b = 32$ **8** **19.** $64 = 16a$ **4**
20. $-4q = 48$ **−12** **21.** $-8w = -72$ **9**
22. $5.9r = 0.59$ **0.1** **23.** $-1.3t = 3.9$ **−3**

- solve two-step equations *(Lesson 6-3)*

Solve $6t - 5 = 19$.

$$6t - 5 = 19$$
$$6t - 5 + 5 = 19 + 5 \quad \text{Add 5 to each side.}$$
$$6t = 24$$
$$\frac{6t}{6} = \frac{24}{6} \quad \text{Divide each side by 6.}$$
$$t = 4$$

27. −2 29. −10

Solve each equation. Check your solution.

24. $3p - 4 = 8$ **4** **25.** $2x + 5 = 3$ **−1**
26. $8 - 6w = 50$ **−7** **27.** $5m + 6 = -4$
28. $6 = 3y - 12$ **6** **29.** $-15 = 5 + 2t$
30. $-4y + 5.1 = 8.3$ **−0.8** **31.** $-1.5b + 1 = 7$ **−4**

- write simple algebraic expressions and equations from verbal phrases and sentences *(Lesson 6-4)*

Translate "4 times the price" into an algebraic expression.

Let p represent the price. The algebraic expression is $4p$.

35. $14n = 56$ **36.** $5n - 4 = 19$

Write each phrase as an algebraic expression.

32. the sum of x and 5 **$x + 5$**
33. 13 less than s **$s - 13$**
34. the quotient of z and 15 **$z \div 15$**

Write each sentence as an algebraic equation.

35. The product of 14 and a number is 56.
36. Four less than 5 times a number is 19.

Objectives & Examples

This section reviews the skills and concepts of the chapter and shows completely worked examples.

Review Exercises

These exercises provide practice for the corresponding objectives.

***Assessment and Evaluation Masters*, pp. 143–144**

Name ______ Date ______

Chapter 6 Test, Form 1B

Solve each equation. Check your solution.

1. $19 + b = 44$ — 1. **D**
   A. 63 B. −25 C. 836 D. 25
2. $k + 4.8 = 11.3$ — 2. **A**
   A. 6.5 B. 16.1 C. 54.2 D. −6.5

Solve. Use any strategy.

3. Edwin's mother is 57 years old. Her age is three years more than twice Edwin's age. What is Edwin's age? — 3. **B**
   A. 30 years B. 27 years C. 15 years D. 37 years

Solve each equation. Check your solution.

4. $81 = 3k$ — 4. **A**
   A. 27 B. 243 C. 78 D. 84
5. $3j = 2.7$ — 5. **C**
   A. 8.1 B. 0.3 C. 0.9 D. −0.3
6. $-3m - 21 = -6$ — 6. **D**
   A. −45 B. 81 C. 9 D. −5
7. $2y - 1.7 = 3.3$ — 7. **C**
   A. 3.2 B. 0.8 C. 2.5 D. 10

Choose the correct algebraic expression for each phrase.

8. 15 less than w — 8. **B**
   A. $w + 15$ B. $w - 15$ C. $15 - w$ D. $15 + w$
9. twelve times a number — 9. **D**
   A. $12 + x$ B. $12 - x$ C. $12 \div x$ D. $12x$
10. 17 divided by q — 10. **D**
    A. $17 + q$ B. $17q$ C. $17 - q$ D. $17 \div q$

Choose the correct algebraic expression for each sentence.

11. Twelve plus six times a number is −7. — 11. **A**
    A. $12 + 6d = -7$ B. $6d - 12 = -7$
    C. $12d - 6 = -7$ D. $12d + 6 = -7$
12. Sixteen times a number minus four and one tenth is 13. — 12. **C**
    A. $16j + 4.1 = 13$ B. $16 - 4.1j = 13$
    C. $16j - 4.1 = 13$ D. $16 + 4.1j = 13$

 143 *Mathematics: Applications and Connections, Course 2*

Chapter 6 Test, Form 1B (continued)

Solve each inequality.

13. $16x + 3 \le 19$ — 13. **B**
    A. $x \le 1.375$ B. $x \le 1$ C. $x \le 256$ D. $x < 352$
14. $2n > 16$ — 14. **C**
    A. $n < 32$ B. $n > 14$ C. $n > 8$ D. $n < 18$

Write an inequality for each sentence. Then solve the inequality.

15. Two times a number is less than or equal to −50. — 15. **A**
    A. $2s \le -50; s \le -25$ B. $2s \le 50; s \le 25$
    C. $2 + s \le -50; s \le -48$ D. $2 + s \le 50; s \le 52$
16. Four plus 3 times a number is greater than 7. — 16. **C**
    A. $4n + 3 < 7; n < 1$ B. $7n + 4 > 3; n > -1$
    C. $4 + 3n > 7; n > 1$ D. $n - 4 > 7; n > 3$
17. Choose the sentence which best shows the relationship between the number of cars in the parking lot and the time of day. — 17. **C**
    Number of Cars / Time of Day (A.M.)
    A. The number of cars is a function of the number of people in the cars.
    B. The time of day is a function of the number of cars.
    C. The number of cars is a function of the time of day.
    D. The time of day is a function of the number of people in the cars.
18. Which line is the graph of $y = x - 2$? — 18. **D**
    A. line k B. line l C. line m D. line n

Charles charges $3.00 an hour to baby-sit. He also charges an extra $10 for families with more than three children. Use this information for Questions 19 and 20.

19. Write an equation for what Charles charges to baby-sit a family of 4 children. — 19. **D**
    A. $y = 3x - 10$ B. $y = 3x + 10x$
    C. $y = 30x$ D. $y = 3x + 10$
20. How much will Charles charge to baby-sit 4 children for 4 hours? — 20. **C**
    A. $2 B. $120 C. $22 D. $43

 144 *Mathematics: Applications and Connections, Course 2*

Assessment and Evaluation

Six forms of Chapter 6 Test are available in the *Assessment and Evaluation Masters* as shown in the chart.

1A	Multiple Choice	Honors
1B	Multiple Choice	Average
1C	Multiple Choice	Basic
2A	Free Response	Honors
2B	Free Response	Average
2C	Free Response	Basic

Chapter 6 Test, Form 1B, is shown at the right. Chapter 6 Test, Form 2B, is shown on the next page.

Objectives & Examples

Review Exercises

- solve inequalities *(Lesson 6-5)*

Solve $d - 5 \geq 7$. Graph the solution on a number line.

$$d - 5 \geq 7$$
$$d - 5 + 5 \geq 7 + 5 \quad \text{Add 5 to each side.}$$
$$d \geq 12$$

8 9 10 11 12 13 14

Solve each inequality. Graph the solution on a number line.

37. $8 + g \leq 10$ $g \leq 2$

38. $4j < 28$ $j < 7$

39. $m - 7 \geq -10$ $m \geq -3$

40. $3h + 2 > 17$ $h > 5$

37–40. See Answer Appendix for graphs.

- represent functions as ordered pairs *(Lesson 6-6)*

Infant's Age (months)	1	2	3	4
Weight (pounds)	10.5	12.3	14.5	16.2

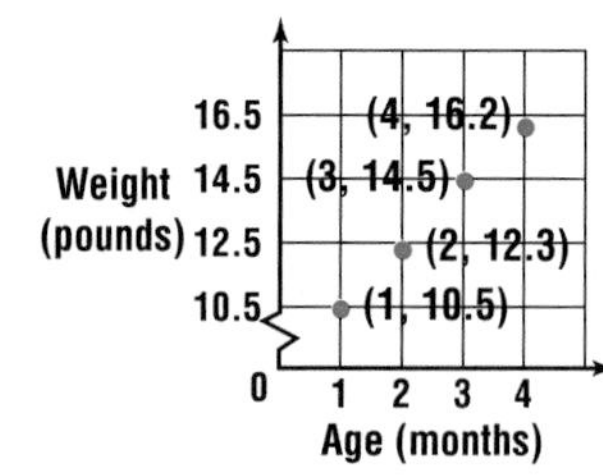

As the age increases, the weight also increases.

Graph the ordered pairs in each table on a coordinate plane. Then write a sentence describing each relationship as a function. 41–42. See Answer Appendix.

41.

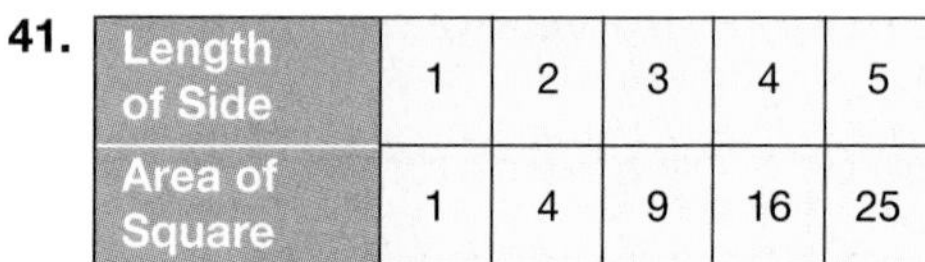

Length of Side	1	2	3	4	5
Area of Square	1	4	9	16	25

42.

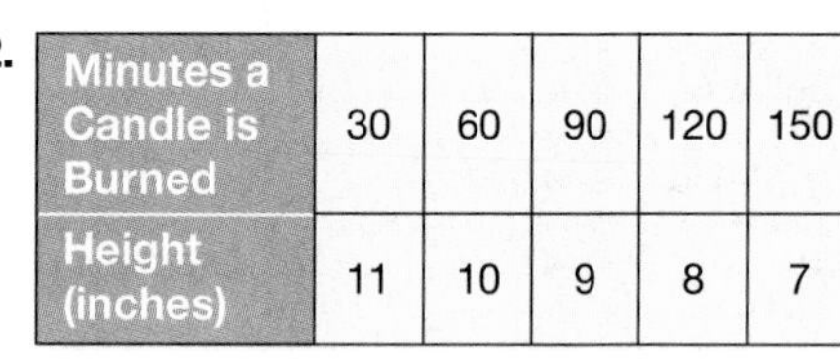

Minutes a Candle is Burned	30	60	90	120	150
Height (inches)	11	10	9	8	7

- solve equations with two variables and graph the solution *(Lesson 6-7)*

Graph $y = x + 3$.

x	$x + 3$	y
−1	−1 + 3	2
1	1 + 3	4
2	2 + 3	5

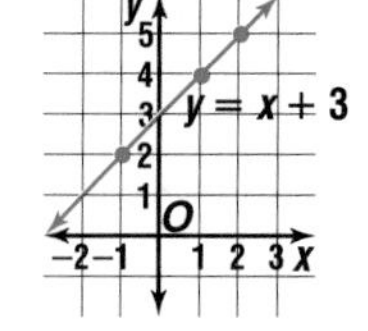

Three solutions are $(-1, 2)$, $(1, 4)$, and $(2, 5)$.

Graph each equation. 43–46. See Answer Appendix.

43. $y = 2x$

44. $y = -0.5x$

45. $y = 3x + 2$

46. $y = x + 4$

Test and Review Software

You may use this software, a combination of an item generator and item bank, to create your own tests or worksheets. Types of items include free response, multiple choice, short answer, and open ended.

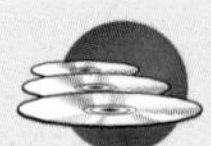

CD-ROM Program

The CD-ROM Program contains an Assessment Game whose questions review the concepts in this chapter.

***Assessment and Evaluation Masters*, pp. 149–150**

Name______________ Date______________

Chapter 6 Test, Form 2B

Solve each equation. Check your solution.

1. $12 + w = -4$ 1. −16
2. $11 = 3.5 + b$ 2. 7.5
3. $16 - m = -4$ 3. 20

Solve. Use any strategy.

4. The Leungs sold a valuable painting for $55,000. This price is $1,000 more than twice the amount they originally paid for it. How much did they originally pay? 4. $27,000

Solve each equation. Check your solution.

5. $6x = -48$ 5. −8
6. $2.7a = 13.5$ 6. 5
7. $2.8t = -47.6$ 7. −17
8. $37 = 18q + 1$ 8. 2
9. $-12 = 4.7k + 11.5$ 9. −5

Write each phrase as an algebraic equation.

10. seven hits more than Maile 10. $m + 7$
11. a number decreased by 3.8 11. $c - 3.8$
12. six point one times a number 12. $6.1v$
13. a number divided by thirteen 13. $s \div 13$

Write each sentence as an algebraic equation.

14. Seventeen plus four times a number is −3. 14. $17 + 4q = -3$
15. Nine minus sixteen multiplied by a number is 23. 15. $9 - 16p = 23$

Solve each inequality.

16. $16 + j \leq -21$ 16. $j \leq -37$
17. $2n - 11 > 11$ 17. $n > 11$
18. $3.5f + 4 < 14.5$ 18. $f < 3$

 149 *Mathematics: Applications and Connections, Course 2*

Chapter 6 Test, Form 2B (continued)

Write an inequality for each sentence. Then solve the inequality.

19. Four times a number minus 2.4 is greater than −50.4. 19. $4n - 2.4 > -50.4$; $n > -12$
20. A number minus twelve is less than negative three. 20. $n - 12 < -3$; $n < 9$
21. Sixteen is greater than or equal to six plus five times a number. 21. $16 \geq 6 + 5n$; $2 \geq n$

Maddy likes to rake leaves. The table shows the number of bags of leaves she collects with that day's wind speed. Refer to this information for Questions 22 and 23.

Wind Speed (miles per hour)	10	20	30	40	50	60
Number of Bags	6	9	10	10	14	15

22. On a separate sheet of paper, graph the ordered pairs (leaves, hour). 22. See graph.
23. Write a sentence that describes the trend in leaf fall. 23. Leaf fall is a function of wind speed.

At recess Mrs. Miller's class decided to play dodgeball. The table shows how the number of throws of the ball is related to the number of players remaining inside the circle.

Number of Throws	2	10	15	18	20	25
Number of Players Remaining	26	18	13	10	8	3

24. Write the ordered pairs (throws, players) and graph them on a coordinate plane. Use a separate sheet of paper. 24. See graph.
25. Write an equation for the graph. Let x represent the number of throws and y represent the number of players remaining. 25. $y = -x + 28$

 150 *Mathematics: Applications and Connections, Course 2*

Applications & Problem Solving

47. ***Work Backward*** Four friends collect stamps. They are comparing how many Mexican stamps they each have. Jeff has 3 times as many as Fina. Mario has 4 fewer stamps than Danielle, but 3 more than Fina. Fina has 9 stamps. How many stamps does each friend have? *(Lesson 6-1B)* **See margin.**

48. ***Money Matters*** Pedro earned $65 in January shoveling snow. The total was 4 times more than his January earnings last winter. How much did he earn last January? *(Lesson 6-4)* **$16.25**

49. ***Catering*** Christina's Catering Service charges $12.50 per person for a sit-down dinner. *(Lesson 6-7)*

a. Write an equation that represents the cost, y, for x people. $y = 12.50x$

b. What is the cost for 40 people? **$500**

50. ***Earth Science*** The graph shows one factor of the Fujita scale, which rates the intensity of tornados. Graph the ordered pairs (F-scale, maximum wind) on a coordinate plane. Then write a statement that describes the relationship as a function. *(Lesson 6-6)* **See Answer Appendix.**

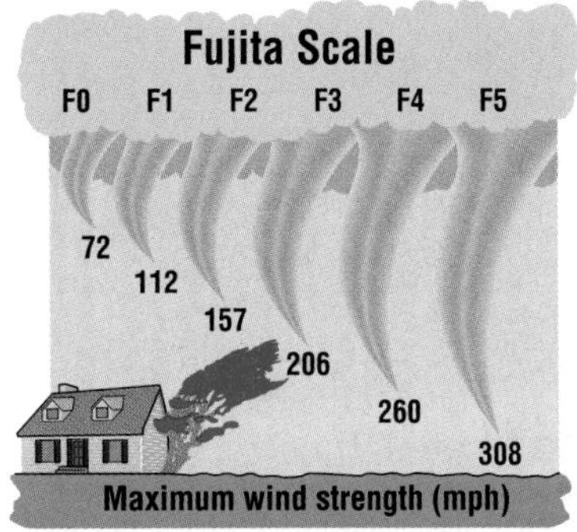

Source: National Audubon Society Field Guide to North American Weather

Alternative Assessment

Open Ended

Suppose your family is moving to a new home. Two moving companies are called so rates can be compared. The first company charges a flat rate of $150 plus $12 per hour for a 2-person crew. The second company charges $28 per hour for a 2-person crew. If it should take 8 hours for the move, how can you determine which company is less expensive? **See margin.**

Suppose the move actually took 12 hours. Which company would have charged the least? **See margin.**

A practice test for Chapter 6 is provided on page 612.

Completing the CHAPTER Project

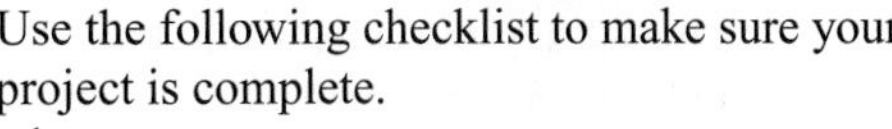

Use the following checklist to make sure your project is complete.

- ☑ You have included a graph with the average speed of each roller coaster.
- ☑ You have graphed the distance it travels and number of riders for one of the roller coasters.
- ☑ You have included some interesting facts about your roller coaster.

Select an item from this chapter that shows your creativity and place it in your portfolio.

Applications & Problem Solving

This section provides additional practice in solving real-world problems that involve the skills of this chapter.

Alternative Assessment

The ***Open Ended*** section provides students with a performance assessment opportunity to evaluate their work and understanding.

Students should complete the final stages of their project and prepare a class demonstration of their results. A scoring guide for the project is available in the *Investigations and Projects Masters,* p. 39.

Students should add to their portfolios at this time.

Additional Answer

47. Jeff: 27, Fina: 9, Mario: 12, Danielle: 16

***Assessment and Evaluation Masters,* p. 153**

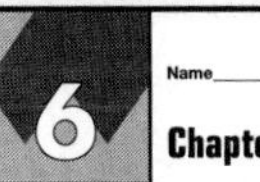

Name________________ Date________

Chapter 6 Performance Assessment

Instructions: Demonstrate your knowledge by giving a clear, concise solution to each problem. Be sure to include all relevant drawings and justify your answers. You may show your solutions in more than one way or investigate beyond the requirements of the problems.

1. The Ortiz family will travel from Indianapolis to Denver this summer. The driving distance between the two cities is 1,058 miles. They need to find out about how much the gas for the round trip will cost. Their car gets about 20 miles per gallon. They usually spend about $1.20 per gallon.
   - **a.** Write and solve an algebraic equation to find out how many miles they will travel. Explain your steps.
   - **b.** Write and solve an algebraic equation to find out how many gallons of gas they will use. Explain your steps.
   - **c.** Write and solve an algebraic equation to find out how much the Ortiz's will spend on gas for the round trip. Explain your steps.
   - **d.** Write and solve an inequality for the least amount they will spend on gas.
   - **e.** Suppose you know the total cost of the gas, but do not know the price per gallon. Explain how you would work backward to solve the problem.
2. Every winter, students at Camden Middle School go on a class ski trip. For every inch of snow that falls, an additional 25 students sign up. When no snow falls, no students attend.
   - **a.** Use a verbal model to show the function.
   - **b.** Make a table of values to show the function.
   - **c.** Write an equation to show the functions.
   - **d.** Graph the function. Explain your steps.

 153 *Mathematics: Applications and Connections, Course 2*

Additional Answers for the Open Ended item

- Write an equation to represent each company's charge. Then use each equation to find the cost of an 8-hour move.
- For a 12-hour move, the first company would charge $294, and the second company would charge $336. The first company would be less expensive.

Performance Assessment

Additional performance assessment tasks for this chapter are included in the *Assessment and Evaluation Masters* on page 153. A scoring guide is also provided on page 165.

Standardized Test Practice

The Standardized Test Practice may be used to help students prepare for standardized tests. The test items are written in the same style as those in state proficiency tests and standardized tests like CAT, CTBS, ITBS, MAT, SAT and Terra Nova. The test items cover skills and concepts covered up to this point in the text.

The pages can be used as an overnight assessment. After students have completed the pages, discuss how each problem can be solved, or provide copies of the solutions from the *Solutions Manual.*

***Assessment and Evaluation Masters,* p. 159**

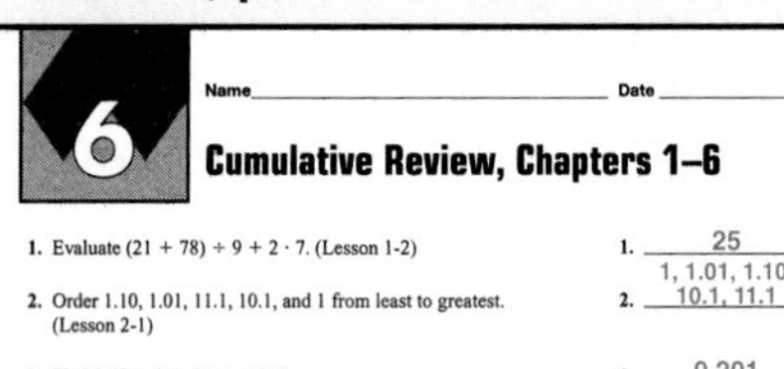

6 Name____________ Date________

Cumulative Review, Chapters 1–6

1. Evaluate $(21 + 78) \div 9 + 2 \cdot 7$. (Lesson 1-2) — 1. 25
2. Order 1.10, 1.01, 11.1, 10.1, and 1 from least to greatest. (Lesson 2-1) — 2. 1, 1.01, 1.10, 10.1, 11.1
3. Find 0.67×0.3. (Lesson 2-4) — 3. 0.201
4. Write 2,070,000,000 in scientific notation. (Lesson 2-9) — 4. 2.07×10^9
5. Make a line plot of laundry detergent prices: \$5.50, \$8.50, \$7, \$6, \$5.50, \$8, \$6. (Lesson 3-3) — 5. 5.5 6.5 7.5 8.5
6. Use the divisibility rules to determine if 420 is divisible by 2, 3, 5, 6, 9, or 10. (Lesson 4-1) — 6. 2, 3, 5, 6, 10

Use a factor tree to find the prime factorization of each number. (Lesson 4-2)

7. 108 — 7. $2^2 \times 3^3$
8. 328 — 8. $2^3 \times 41$

Write an integer for each situation. (Lesson 5-1)

9. 9°F below 0 — 9. −9
10. a gain of 6 pounds — 10. 6
11. Find $23 - (-8)$. (Lesson 5-5) — 11. 31
12. Solve $-6t = 1.8$. (Lesson 6-2) — 12. −0.3
13. Solve $6x - 2 = 19$. (Lesson 6-3) — 13. 3.5

Solve each equation. Check your solution. (Lesson 6-3)

14. $4.3x - 1 = 11.9$ — 14. 3
15. $-2y - 19 = -43$ — 15. 12

Write each sentence as an algebraic equation. (Lesson 6-4)

16. Three minus six times a is 21. — 16. $3 - 6a = 21$
17. A number plus fifteen is −3. — 17. $x + 15 = -3$

Solve each inequality. Graph the solution on the number line. (Lesson 6-5)

18. $2k + 1 \le 5$ — 18. −3 −1 0 1 3
19. $m - 5 > 6$ — 19. 10 11 12 13 14 15
20. On a separate sheet of paper, graph $y = 2x - 4$. (Lesson 6-7) — 20. See students' graphs.

 159 *Mathematics: Applications and Connections, Course 2*

CHAPTERS 1–6

Standardized Test Practice

Assessing Knowledge & Skills

Section One: Multiple Choice

There are eleven multiple-choice questions in this section. Choose the best answer. If a correct answer is *not here* choose the letter for Not Here.

1. Which is equivalent to $3m < 39$? D
   - A $m > 13$
   - B $m > 36$
   - C $m = 13$
   - D $m < 13$
2. What is the least common multiple of 30 and 45? H
   - F 15
   - G 75
   - H 90
   - J 1,350
3. Viho performed a probability experiment by rolling a cube that has its faces colored blue, yellow, and red, 120 times. The results of his experiment follow.

Color	Number of Rolls
blue	20
yellow	60
red	40

   How many sides of the cube would you expect to be colored yellow? B
   - A 2
   - B 3
   - C 4
   - D 5
4. Which decimal is equivalent to $\frac{19}{25}$? J
   - F 1.31
   - G 1.11
   - H 0.96
   - J 0.76
5. Which is the graph of the equation $y = 3x + 2$? A

A
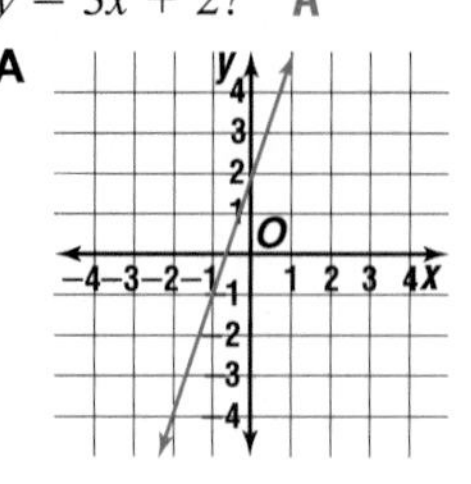

B
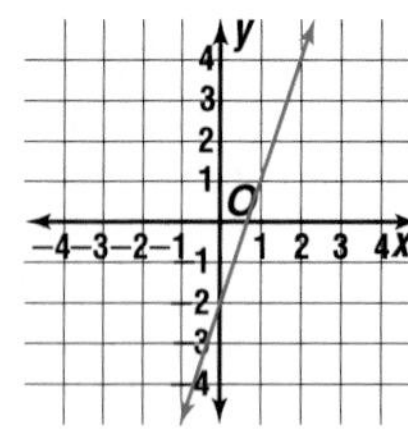

C
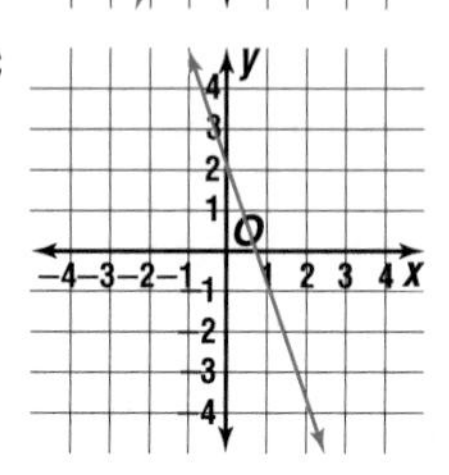

D
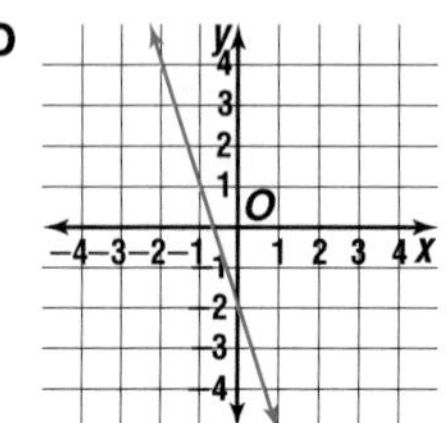

Please note that Questions 6–11 have five answer choices.

6. Tickets for a musical cost \$9.50 for adults and \$6.75 for children. Which equation could be used to find the total cost in dollars, d, of tickets for any number of adults, a, and children, c? K
   - F $d = 9.50 + 6.75 + a + c$
   - G $d = (9.50 + 6.75) \times (a + c)$
   - H $d = (9.50 \times 6.75) + (a \times c)$
   - J $d = (9.50 \times c) + (6.75 \times a)$
   - K $d = (9.50 \times a) + (6.75 \times c)$
7. The range of points that can be earned on a single lab in physical science is from 5 to 9 points. Lenora has turned in 7 labs. What is a reasonable estimate of the number of points she has earned so far in physical science lab? C
   - A less than 14
   - B between 14 and 35
   - C between 35 and 63
   - D between 63 and 90
   - E greater than 90

262 Chapters 1–6 Standardized Test Practice

◀◀◀ Instructional Resources

Another cumulative review is shown at the left and is available in the *Assessment and Evaluation Masters,* p. 159.

8. The stem-and-leaf plot shows the number of points scored by the Bears in each of their basketball games this season. H

Stem	Leaf
1	8 9
2	0 2 3 3 6 8 8 9
3	0 1 4 4 5 6 8 9
4	0 1 2 *1|8 = 18 points*

In how many games did they score at least 30 points?

F 8 **G** 9
H 11 **J** 20
K Not Here

9. The student council collected a total of \$1,100 during the last 4 years for a charity donation. What is the average yearly amount collected over the 4-year period? B

A \$225
B \$275
C \$450
D \$675
E Not Here

10. Jack packed 396 crayons into 18 boxes. If each box contains the same number of crayons, how many are in each box? K

F 20
G 23
H 25
J 52
K Not Here

11. Domingo earned \$50 in one week by working 6.25 hours. How much was Domingo paid per hour? E

A \$6.25
B \$6.50
C \$8.50
D \$10.50
E Not Here

Test-Taking Tip THE PRINCETON REVIEW

As part of your preparation for a standardized test, review basic definitions. For example:

- A number is prime if it has no factors except itself and one.
- 7 is a prime number. 8 is not prime because it has factors other than one and itself.

Section Two: Free Response

This section contains six questions for which you will provide short answers. Write your answers on your paper.

12. Write three numbers less than 10 that are factors of 1,215. **Sample answer: 1, 3, 5, 9**

13. Let $y = wx$. If $y = 15$ and $w = 5$, find the value of x. **3**

14. Write an expression to represent the phrase *eight more than a number.* **$8 + n$**

15. Claire worked 20 hours last week. She earned \$6.00 per hour. Write an equation to find her total earnings, E. **$E = 6(20)$**

16. Kyung is reading a 258-page novel. If he reads 8 pages an hour, about how long will it take him to read the entire book? **Sample answer: $240 \div 8 = 30$ hours**

17. What number should replace y in the table? **−1**

x	$2x - 5$
1	−3
2	y
4	3
8	11
16	27

Test Practice For additional test practice questions, visit:

www.glencoe.com/sec/math/mac/mathnet

Instructional Resources ▶▶▶

Additional standardized test practice is shown at the right and is available in the *Assessment and Evaluation Masters,* pp. 157–158.

Test-Taking Tip

Students can prepare for taking standardized tests by working through practice tests such as this one. The more students work with questions in a format similar to the actual test, the more skilled they become in test taking.

Assessment and Evaluation Masters, pp. 157–158

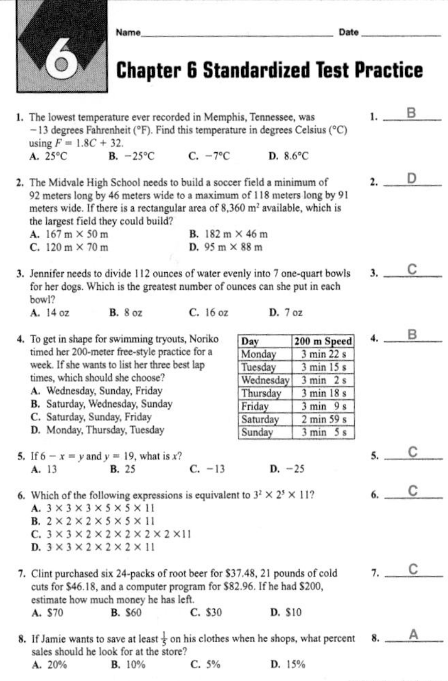

Name__________ Date________

Chapter 6 Standardized Test Practice

1\. The lowest temperature ever recorded in Memphis, Tennessee, was −13 degrees Fahrenheit (°F). Find this temperature in degrees Celsius (°C) using $F = 1.8C + 32$. 1. B
A. 25°C B. −25°C C. −7°C D. 8.6°C

2\. The Midvale High School needs to build a soccer field a minimum of 92 meters long by 46 meters wide to a maximum of 118 meters long by 91 meters wide. If there is a rectangular area of 8,360 m^2 available, which is the largest field they could build? 2. D
A. 167 m × 50 m B. 182 m × 46 m
C. 120 m × 70 m D. 95 m × 88 m

3\. Jennifer needs to divide 112 ounces of water evenly into 7 one-quart bowls for her dogs. Which is the greatest number of ounces can she put in each bowl? 3. C
A. 14 oz B. 8 oz C. 16 oz D. 7 oz

4\. To get in shape for swimming tryouts, Noriko timed her 200-meter free-style practice for a week. If she wants to list her three best lap times, which should she choose? 4. B
A. Wednesday, Sunday, Friday
B. Saturday, Wednesday, Sunday
C. Saturday, Sunday, Friday
D. Monday, Thursday, Tuesday

Day	200 m Speed
Monday	3 min 22 s
Tuesday	3 min 15 s
Wednesday	3 min 2 s
Thursday	3 min 18 s
Friday	3 min 9 s
Saturday	2 min 59 s
Sunday	3 min 5 s

5\. If $6 - x = y$ and $y = 19$, what is x? 5. C
A. 13 B. 25 C. −13 D. −25

6\. Which of the following expressions is equivalent to $3^2 \times 2^5 \times 11$? 6. C
A. $3 \times 3 \times 3 \times 5 \times 5 \times 11$
B. $2 \times 2 \times 2 \times 5 \times 5 \times 11$
C. $3 \times 3 \times 2 \times 2 \times 2 \times 2 \times 2 \times 11$
D. $3 \times 3 \times 2 \times 2 \times 2 \times 11$

7\. Clint purchased six 24-packs of root beer for \$37.48, 21 pounds of cold cuts for \$46.18, and a computer program for \$82.96. If he had \$200, estimate how much money he has left. 7. C
A. \$70 B. \$60 C. \$30 D. \$10

8\. If Jamie wants to save at least $\frac{1}{5}$ on his clothes when he shops, what percent sales should he look for at the store? 8. A
A. 20% B. 10% C. 5% D. 15%

© Glencoe/McGraw-Hill 157 *Mathematics: Applications and Connections, Course 2*

Chapter 6 Standardized Test Practice (continued)

The table lists the results of a poll of 7th grade students about how many cacti are owned per teacher's class. Use this information for Questions 9 and 10.

Number of Students in Class	Number of Cacti Owned
25	7
22	9
23	4
18	11
21	12
17	11

9\. What is the mean number of cacti owned per class? 9. D
A. 11 B. 10 C. 8 D. 9

10\. What is the range of the number of students in the class? 10. A
A. 8 B. 3 C. 13 D. 6

11\. Which of the following equations is equivalent to *two times a number plus seventeen is nine*? 11. B
A. $2n + 9 = 17$ B. $2n + 17 = 9$ C. $2n - 9 = 17$ D. $2n - 17 = 9$

12\. Eiko wants to read 10 books over her summer vacation. Each book has a minimum of 200 pages and Eiko can read 1 page per minute. Which is a reasonable length of time it will take her to read all 10 books? 12. A
A. 40 hours B. 10 hours C. 200 hours D. 25 hours

13\. If Josh gave his friend 6 rubber bands and now Josh has 25 rubber bands, how many rubber bands did he have before? 13. D
A. 19 B. 13 C. 30 D. 31

14\. Gary has 124 pieces of gum to last him 17 days. Can he chew the same number of pieces of gum each day? 14. A
A. no B. yes C. cannot determine

15\. Emile gives 35¢ to Lauren who has \$1.75. How much money does Lauren have now? 15. B
A. \$2.00 B. \$2.10 C. \$1.10 D. \$2.15

16\. Haley has 8 cans of tennis balls with 3 tennis balls in each can. How many tennis balls does Haley have? 16. B
A. 11 B. 24 C. 16 D. 20

© Glencoe/McGraw-Hill 158 *Mathematics: Applications and Connections, Course 2*

Interdisciplinary Investigation

GET READY

This optional investigation is designed to be completed by a group of 3 or 4 students over several days or several weeks.

Mathematical Overview

This investigation utilizes the mathematical skills and concepts presented in Chapters 4–6.

- tallying scores
- writing ratios
- converting ratios to percent

Time Management	
Gathering Data	30 minutes
Calculations	45 minutes
Summarizing Data	15 minutes
Preparing Letter Sets	15 minutes
Presentation	15 minutes

Instructional Resources

- *Investigations and Projects Masters,* pp. 5–8

***Investigations and Projects Masters,* p. 8**

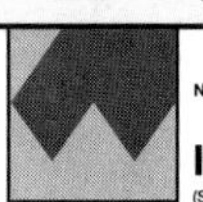

Name__________________ Date__________

Interdisciplinary Investigation

(Student Edition, Pages 264–265)

"A" is for Apple

2.

Letter	Number of Times in Text	Ratio Out of ____ Letters	Ratio as %
A			
B			
C			
D			
E			
F			
G			
H			
I			
J			
K			
L			
M			
N			
O			
P			
Q			
R			
S			
T			
U			
V			
W			
X			
Y			
Z			

3. Most common:
Least common:

 8 *Mathematics: Applications and Connections, Course 2*

Interdisciplinary Investigation

"A" IS FOR APPLE

Have you ever played games where you must build words? Did you groan when you drew a Q or an X? Did you ever say to yourself, "What word can I make with that letter? Now I can't possibly win!" Are some letters used more than others in our language?

What You'll Do

In this investigation, you will collect data using printed materials you read every day. You will determine which letters are most common and design your own letter set.

Materials 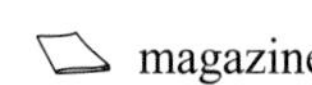 magazine 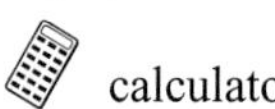 calculator  photocopy machine highlighters

Procedure

1. Work in a group of three or four. Have each member select a page of written text from a different source like newspapers, magazines, novels, or textbooks. Photocopy the page and highlight with a marker about 80 to 100 consecutive words. This is your text sample.
2. Work individually. Tally the number of each letter in your text sample and find the total number of letters in the sample. Write a ratio comparing the number of each letter to the total number of letters. Express each ratio as a percent.
3. Work in your group. Combine the information from all of the text samples into one large sample. Which letters are most common? least common?
4. Work in your group. Some businesses use signs with removable letters to advertise their products. Suppose you are going to make a letter set to sell to these businesses. The set should have at least 100, but no more than 150 letters. As a group, decide which letters and how many of each to include.

Technology Tips

- Use a **spreadsheet** to calculate the percent for each letter.
- Use a **spreadsheet** to help you plan the letter set.
- Surf the **Internet** as a research tool.

◀◀◀Instructional Resources

A recording sheet to help students organize their data for this investigation is shown at the left and is available in the *Investigations and Projects Masters,* p. 8.

Cooperative Learning

This investigation offers an excellent opportunity for using cooperative learning groups. For more information on cooperative learning strategies and group management, see *Cooperative Learning in the Mathematics Classroom.*

Making the Connection

Use the data collected from your text samples as needed to help in these investigations.

Language Arts

You may be studying a language such as Spanish or French in school or speak a language other than English at home. Repeat steps 1 through 3 of the investigation using a text sample from another language. Which letters are most common?

Music

A musical score is made up of notes, just as words are made up of letters. Count the number of each note in a page of a musical piece. Find the percent each note represents of the total notes in the score.

Social Studies

Research the history of the English alphabet. Investigate *alphabetic writing* and *Phoenician writing*.

Go Further

- Compare the percent of letters in a word game to the percent of letters you found in your text samples.
- Investigate the lengths of words. Use different types of printed material. What word length is most common?

interNET CONNECTION Research **For current information on frequency distributions of letters in the alphabet, visit the following website.**

Data Collection and Comparison **To share and compare your data with other students in the U.S., visit:**

www.glencoe.com/sec/math/mac/mathnet

PORTFOLIO You may want to place your work on this investigation in your portfolio.

MANAGEMENT TIPS

Working in Teams Have each group organize their individual data into one table. Each group member can be responsible for creating part of the table. For example, one student can count the total number of tallies, one student can convert the total to a ratio, and one student can convert the ratio to a percent.

Making the Connection
You may wish to alert other teachers on your team that your students may need their assistance in this investigation. ***Language*** Students may need to be reminded that in Spanish, for example, *n* and *ñ* are different letters, as are *r* and *rr* and *l* and *ll*. ***Music*** Students may choose not to count octaves, flats, and sharps. ***Social Studies*** Students may use an interactive encyclopedia on CD-ROM to find more information on the English alphabet.

ASSESS

You may require each group to give an oral presentation to support the choices they have made for Exercise 4. After all groups have given their presentation, discuss similarities and differences in the decisions of each group.

Instructional Resources ▶▶▶
Sample solutions for this investigation are provided in the *Investigations and Projects Masters* on p. 6. The scoring guide for assessing student performance shown at the right is also available on p. 7.

***Investigations and Projects Masters*, p. 7**

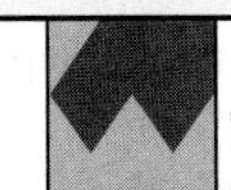

SCORING GUIDE

Interdisciplinary Investigation
(Student Edition, Pages 264–265)

"A" is for Apple

Level	Specific Criteria
3 Superior	• Shows a thorough understanding of the concept of *ratio*. • Uses appropriate strategies to solve problems. • Computations are correct. • Written explanations are exemplary. • Letter set is appropriate and sensible. • Goes beyond the requirements of some or all problems.
2 Satisfactory, with minor flaws	• Shows understanding of the concept of *ratio*. • Uses appropriate strategies to solve problems. • Computations are mostly correct. • Written explanations are effective. • Letter set is appropriate and sensible. • Satisfies the requirements of problems.
1 Nearly Satisfactory, with obvious flaws	• Shows understanding of most of the concept of *ratio*. • May not use appropriate strategies to solve problems. • Computations are mostly correct. • Written explanations are satisfactory. • Letter set is appropriate and sensible. • Satisfies the requirements of problems.
0 Unsatisfactory	• Shows little or no understanding of the concept of *ratio*. • Does not use appropriate strategies to solve problems. • Computations are incorrect. • Written explanations are not satisfactory. • Letter set is not appropriate or sensible. • Does not satisfy the requirements of the problems.

 7 *Mathematics: Applications and Connections, Course 2*

Applying Fractions

Previewing the Chapter

Overview

This chapter focuses first on operations with fractions and then on integrating both measurements and geometry. Students use fractions and mixed numbers in finding perimeter and circumference and apply the associative, commutative, identity, distributive, and reciprocal properties of real numbers. Students also practice solving problems by eliminating possibilities.

Lesson (pages)	Lesson Objectives	NCTM Standards 2000	Standardized Tests	State/Local Objectives
7-1 (268–271)	Estimate sums, differences, products, and quotients of fractions and mixed numbers.	1, 6–10	CTBS, TN	
7-2 (272–275)	Add and subtract fractions.	1, 4, 6–10	CAT, CTBS, ITBS, MAT, SAT, TN	
7-3 (276–279)	Add and subtract mixed numbers.	1, 4, 6–10	CTBS, SAT, TN	
7-3B (280–281)	Solve problems by eliminating possibilities.	1, 6–9	MAT, SAT	
7-4A (282–283)	Use models to multiply fractions and mixed numbers.	1, 6–10	CTBS, TN	
7-4 (284–287)	Multiply fractions and mixed numbers.	1, 2, 4, 6–10	CAT, CTBS, ITBS, MAT, SAT, TN	
7-4B (288)	Examine fractal patterns by multiplying fractions and mixed numbers.	1, 2, 7, 8, 10		
7-5 (289–291)	Change units in the customary system.	1, 4, 6–10	CTBS, MAT, SAT, TN	
7-6 (292–295)	Find perimeter.	1, 3, 4, 6–10	CAT, CTBS, MAT, SAT, TN	
7-7 (297–300)	Find the circumference of circles.	1–4, 6–10	SAT	
7-8 (301–304)	Use addition and multiplication properties to solve problems.	1, 2, 6–10	CAT, CTBS, ITBS, MAT, SAT, TN	
7-9 (305–307)	Divide fractions and mixed numbers.	1, 4, 6–10	CAT, CTBS, ITBS, MAT, SAT, TN	

CAT = California Achievement Tests, CTBS = Comprehensive Tests of Basic Skills, ITBS = Iowa Tests of Basic Skills, MAT = Metropolitan Achievement Tests, SAT = Stanford Achievement Tests, TN = Terra Nova
For the key to numbering of NCTM Standards 2000, see page T6.

Organizing the Chapter

The **Interactive Lesson Planner** contains all of the blackline masters and transparencies. This CD-ROM also includes an easy-to-use lesson planning calendar.

LESSON PLANNING GUIDE

		BLACKLINE MASTERS (PAGE NUMBERS)										
Lesson	Extra Practice (Student Edition)	Study Guide	Practice	Enrichment	Assessment & Evaluation	Classroom Games	Diversity	Hands-On Lab	School to Career	Science and Math Lab Manual	Technology	Transparencies A and B
7-1	p. 586	49	49	49								7-1
7-2	p. 586	50	50	50								7-2
7-3	p. 586	51	51	51	183							7-3
7-3B	p. 587											
7-4A								52				
7-4	p. 587	52	52	52								7-4
7-4B								53				
7-5	p. 587	53	53	53	182, 183							7-5
7-6	p. 588	54	54	54				78	20			7-6
7-7	p. 588	55	55	55	184		20				39, 40	7-7
7-8	p. 588	56	56	56								7-8
7-9	p. 589	57	57	57	184	21–22						7-9
Study Guide/ Assessment					169–181, 185–187							

OTHER CHAPTER RESOURCES

Student Edition

Chapter Project, pp. 267, 271, 287, 307, 311
School to Career, p. 296
Let the Games Begin, p. 285

Technology

 MathPASS CD-ROM

 Interactive Mathematics Tools Software

Teacher's Classroom Resources

Applications

Family Letters and Activities, pp. 39–40
Investigations and Projects Masters, pp. 41–44

Meeting Individual Needs

Transition Booklet, pp. 27–34
Investigations for the Special Education Student, pp. 15–20

Teaching Aids

Answer Key Masters
Block Scheduling Booklet
Lesson Planning Guide
Solutions Manual

Professional Publications

Glencoe Mathematics Professional Series

Planning the Chapter

MindJogger Videoquizzes provide a unique format for reviewing concepts presented in the chapter.

Assessment Resources

Student Edition

Mixed Review, pp. 271, 275, 279, 287, 291, 295, 300, 304, 307
Mid-Chapter Self Test, p. 287
Math Journal, pp. 277, 293
Study Guide and Assessment, pp. 308–311
Performance Task, p. 311
Portfolio Suggestion, p. 311
Standardized Test Practice, pp. 312–313
Chapter Test, p. 613

Assessment and Evaluation Masters

Multiple-Choice Tests (Forms 1A, 1B, 1C), pp. 169–174
Free-Response Tests (Forms 2A, 2B, 2C), pp. 175–180
Performance Assessment, p. 181
Mid-Chapter Test, p. 182
Quizzes A–D, pp. 183–184
Standardized Test Practice, pp. 185–186
Cumulative Review, p. 187

Teacher's Wraparound Edition

5-Minute Check, pp. 268, 272, 276, 284, 289, 292, 297, 301, 305
Building Portfolios, p. 266
Math Journal, pp. 283, 288
Closing Activity, pp. 271, 275, 279, 281, 287, 291, 295, 300, 304, 307

Technology

Test and Review Software
MindJogger Videoquizzes
CD-ROM Program

Materials and Manipulatives

Lesson 7-2
grid paper†
markers

Lesson 7-4A
paper
markers

Lesson 7-4
spinners*†

Lesson 7-4B
dot paper†

Lesson 7-6
rulers*†

Lesson 7-7
rulers*†
string
circular objects

*Glencoe Manipulative Kit

†Glencoe Overhead Manipulative Resources

Pacing Chart

See pages T25–T27 for the Course Planning Calendar.

COURSE	DAY 1	DAY 2	DAY 3	DAY 4	DAY 5	DAY 6	DAY 7
Standard	Chapter Project	Lesson 7-1	Lesson 7-2	Lesson 7-3	Lesson 7-3B	Lessons 7-4A & 7-4	
Honors	Chapter Project	Lesson 7-1	Lesson 7-2	Lesson 7-3	Lesson 7-3B	Lessons 7-4 & 7-4B	
Block	Chapter Project & Lesson 7-1	Lessons 7-2 & 7-3	Lessons 7-3B & 7-4A	Lessons 7-4 & 7-5	Lesson 7-6	Lesson 7-7	Lessons 7-8 & 7-9

The *Transition Booklet* (Skills 12-15) can be used to review adding and subtracting functions and mixed numbers and measuring with customary units of measure.

Interactive Mathematics:
Activities and Investigations

is an activity-based program that may be used as an enhancement for chapters in ***Mathematics: Applications and Connections.***

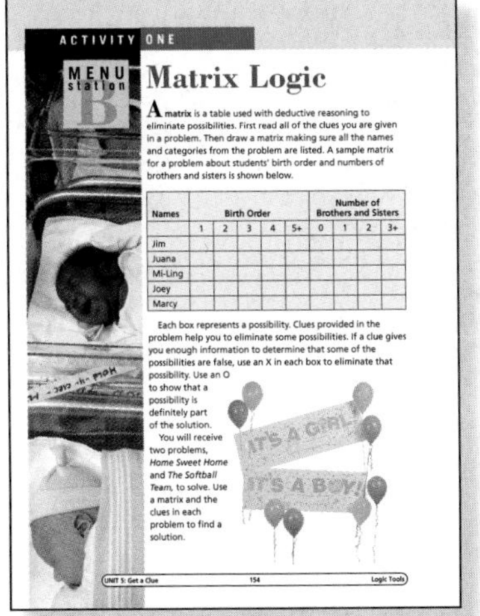

ACTIVITY ONE

MENU station B

Matrix Logic

A **matrix** is a table used with deductive reasoning to eliminate possibilities. First read all of the clues you are given in a problem. Then draw a matrix making sure all the names and categories from the problem are listed. A sample matrix for a problem about students' birth order and numbers of brothers and sisters is shown below.

Names	Birth Order					Number of Brothers and Sisters			
	1	2	3	4	5+	0	1	2	3+
Jim									
Juana									
Mi-Ling									
Joey									
Marcy									

Each box represents a possibility. Clues provided in the problem help you to eliminate some possibilities. If a clue gives you enough information to determine that some of the possibilities are false, use an X in each box to eliminate that possibility. Use an O to show that a possibility is definitely part of the solution.

You will receive two problems, *Home Sweet Home* and *The Softball Team*, to solve. Use a matrix and the clues in each problem to find a solution.

UNIT 5: Get a Clue 154 Logic Tools

Unit 5, Activity One, Menu B
Use with Lesson 7-3B.

Summary Students use tables and matrix logic to solve problems from clues given about various individuals and their characteristics.

Math Connection By using the table and deductive thinking, students eliminate the possibilities as they analyze each clue of the puzzle.

Unit 3, Activity Six, Menu B
Use with Lesson 7-7.

Summary Students measure the circumference and diameter of five round objects. They graph the recorded ordered pairs comparing the diameter with the circumference and looking for a pattern in the points graphed.

Math Connection Students compare the circumference and diameter as a ratio. When the ratio of the circumference to the diameter is divided to find a decimal form, the result is always pi (π) or approximately 3.14.

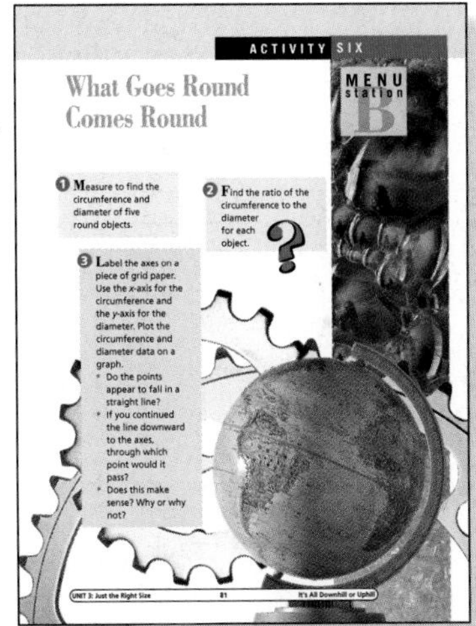

ACTIVITY SIX

MENU station B

What Goes Round Comes Round

1. **M**easure to find the circumference and diameter of five round objects.
2. **F**ind the ratio of the circumference to the diameter for each object.
3. **L**abel the axes on a piece of grid paper. Use the *x*-axis for the circumference and the *y*-axis for the diameter. Plot the circumference and diameter data on a graph.
   * Do the points appear to fall in a straight line?
   * If you continued the line downward to the axes, through which point would it pass?
   * Does this make sense? Why or why not?

UNIT 3: Just the Right Size 81 It's All Downhill or Uphill

DAY 8	DAY 9	DAY 10	DAY 11	DAY 12	DAY 13	DAY 14	DAY 15
Continue from Day 7	Lesson 7-5	Lesson 7-6	Lesson 7-7	Lesson 7-8	Lesson 7-9	Study Guide and Assessment	Chapter Test
Lesson 7-5	Lesson 7-6	Lesson 7-7	Lesson 7-8	Lesson 7-9	Study Guide and Assessment	Chapter Test	
Study Guide and Assessment, Chapter Test							

Enhancing the Chapter

APPLICATIONS

Classroom Games, pp. 21–22

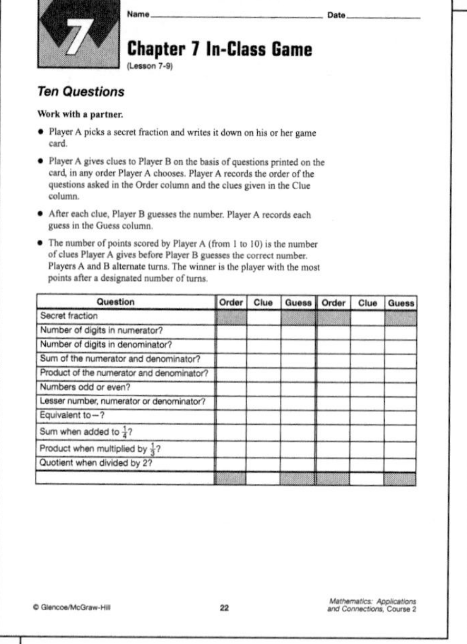

Name ______ Date ______

Chapter 7 In-Class Game
(Lesson 7-9)

Ten Questions

Work with a partner.

- Player A picks a secret fraction and writes it down on his or her game card.
- Player A gives clues to Player B on the basis of questions printed on the card, in any order Player A chooses. Player A records the order of the questions asked in the Order column and the clues given in the Clue column.
- After each clue, Player B guesses the number. Player A records each guess in the Guess column.
- The number of points scored by Player A (from 1 to 10) is the number of clues Player A gives before Player B guesses the correct number. Players A and B alternate turns. The winner is the player with the most points after a designated number of turns.

Question	Order	Clue	Guess	Order	Clue	Guess
Secret fraction						
Number of digits in numerator?						
Number of digits in denominator?						
Sum of the numerator and denominator?						
Product of the numerator and denominator?						
Numbers odd or even?						
Lesser number, numerator or denominator?						
Equivalent to –?						
Sum when added to $\frac{1}{4}$?						
Product when multiplied by $\frac{1}{3}$?						
Quotient when divided by 2?						

© Glencoe/McGraw-Hill 22 *Mathematics: Applications and Connections, Course 2*

Diversity Masters, p. 20

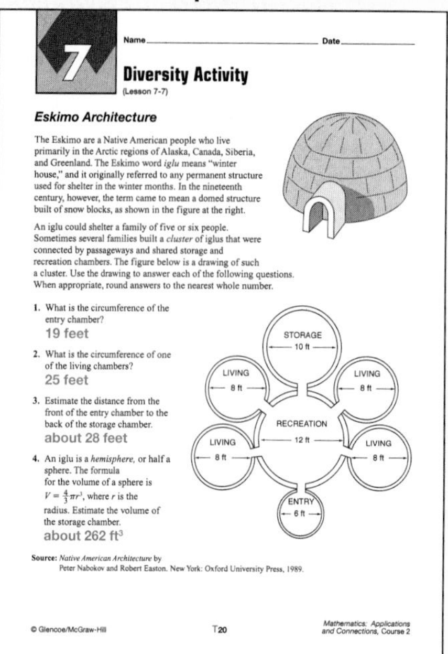

Name ______ Date ______

Diversity Activity
(Lesson 7-7)

Eskimo Architecture

The Eskimo are a Native American people who live primarily in the Arctic regions of Alaska, Canada, Siberia, and Greenland. The Eskimo word *iglu* means "winter house," and it originally referred to any permanent structure used for shelter in the winter months. In the nineteenth century, however, the term came to mean a domed structure built of snow blocks, as shown in the figure at the right.

An iglu could shelter a family of five or six people. Sometimes several families built a *cluster* of iglus that were connected by passageways and shared storage and recreation chambers. The figure below is a drawing of such a cluster. Use the drawing to answer each of the following questions. When appropriate, round answers to the nearest whole number.

1. What is the circumference of the entry chamber? 19 feet
2. What is the circumference of one of the living chambers? 25 feet
3. Estimate the distance from the front of the entry chamber to the back of the storage chamber. about 28 feet
4. An iglu is a *hemisphere,* or half a sphere. The formula for the volume of a sphere is $V = \frac{4}{3}\pi r^3$, where r is the radius. Estimate the volume of the storage chamber. about 262 ft^3

Source: *Native American Architecture* by Peter Nabokov and Robert Easton. New York: Oxford University Press, 1989.

© Glencoe/McGraw-Hill T20 *Mathematics: Applications and Connections, Course 2*

School to Career Masters, p. 20

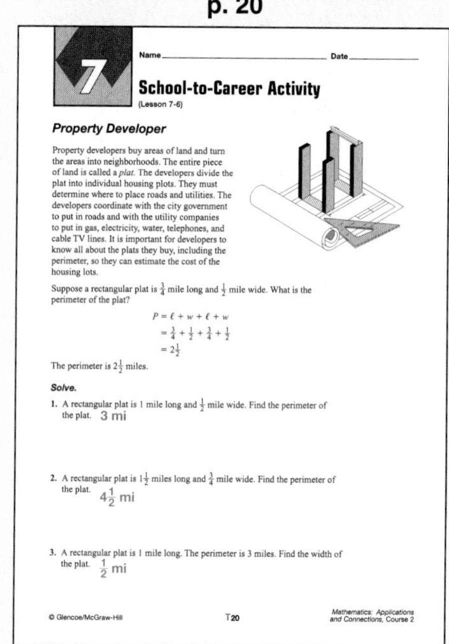

Name ______ Date ______

School-to-Career Activity
(Lesson 7-6)

Property Developer

Property developers buy areas of land and turn the areas into neighborhoods. The entire piece of land is called a *plat.* The developers divide the plat into individual housing plots. They must determine where to place roads and utilities. The developers coordinate with the city government to put in roads and with the utility companies to put in gas, electricity, water, telephones, and cable TV lines. It is important for developers to know all about the plats they buy, including the perimeter, so they can estimate the cost of the housing lots.

Suppose a rectangular plat is $\frac{3}{4}$ mile long and $\frac{1}{2}$ mile wide. What is the perimeter of the plat?

$$P = \ell + w + \ell + w$$
$$= \frac{3}{4} + \frac{1}{2} + \frac{3}{4} + \frac{1}{2}$$
$$= 2\frac{1}{2}$$

The perimeter is $2\frac{1}{2}$ miles.

Solve.

1. A rectangular plat is 1 mile long and $\frac{1}{2}$ mile wide. Find the perimeter of the plat. 3 mi
2. A rectangular plat is $1\frac{1}{2}$ miles long and $\frac{3}{4}$ mile wide. Find the perimeter of the plat. $4\frac{1}{2}$ mi
3. A rectangular plat is 1 mile long. The perimeter is 3 miles. Find the width of the plat. $\frac{1}{2}$ mi

© Glencoe/McGraw-Hill T20 *Mathematics: Applications and Connections, Course 2*

Family Letters and Activities, pp. 39–40

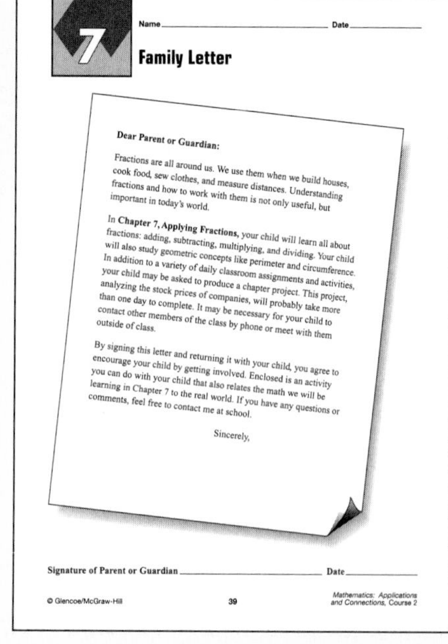

Name ______ Date ______

Family Letter

Dear Parent or Guardian:

Fractions are all around us. We use them when we build houses, cook food, sew clothes, and measure distances. Understanding fractions and how to work with them is not only useful, but important in today's world.

In **Chapter 7, Applying Fractions,** your child will learn all about fractions: adding, subtracting, multiplying, and dividing. Your child will also study geometric concepts like perimeter and circumference. In addition to a variety of daily classroom assignments and activities, your child may be asked to produce a chapter project. This project, analyzing the stock prices of companies, will probably take more than one day to complete. It may be necessary for your child to contact other members of the class by phone or meet with them outside of class.

By signing this letter and returning it with your child, you agree to encourage your child by getting involved. Enclosed is an activity you can do with your child that also relates the math we will be learning in Chapter 7 to the real world. If you have any questions or comments, feel free to contact me at school.

Sincerely,

Signature of Parent or Guardian ______ **Date** ______

© Glencoe/McGraw-Hill 39 *Mathematics: Applications and Connections, Course 2*

Name ______ Date ______

Family Activity

Changing Units in the Customary System

Work with a family member. Select four cans of food, four boxes of food, and two beverages. Find the net weight on each item. It is usually located at the bottom of the container. Use the chart to convert the unit on your food to a different unit.

1 pound (lb)	16 ounces (oz)
1 cup (c)	8 fluid ounces (fl oz)
1 pint (pt)	2 cups
1 quart (qt)	2 pints
1 gallon (gal)	4 quarts

Example: The net weight of an individual serving of apple sauce is 4 ounces: 4 ounces = $\frac{1}{2}$ cup.

1. Item:
   Net weight:
2. Item:
   Net weight:
3. Item:
   Net weight:
4. Item:
   Net weight:
5. Item:
   Net weight:
6. Item:
   Net weight:
7. Item:
   Net weight:
8. Item:
   Net weight:
9. Item:
   Net weight:
10. Item:
    Net weight:

© Glencoe/McGraw-Hill 40 *Mathematics: Applications and Connections, Course 2*

MANIPULATIVES/MODELING

Hands-On Lab Masters, p. 78

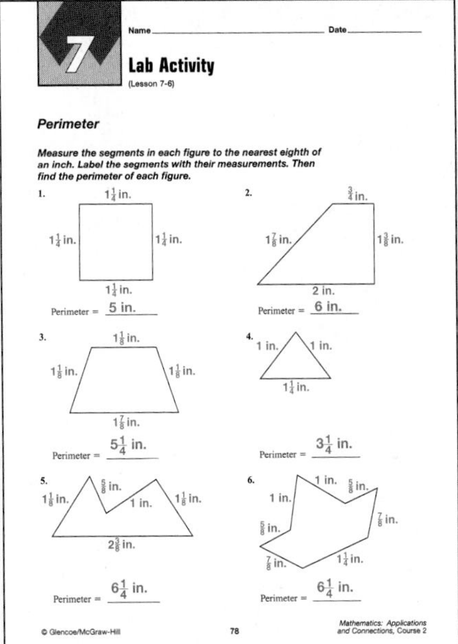

Name________ Date________

Lab Activity
(Lesson 7-6)

Perimeter

Measure the segments in each figure to the nearest eighth of an inch. Label the segments with their measurements. Then find the perimeter of each figure.

1. Perimeter = 5 in.
2. Perimeter = 6 in.
3. Perimeter = $5\frac{1}{4}$ in.
4. Perimeter = $3\frac{1}{4}$ in.
5. Perimeter = $6\frac{1}{4}$ in.
6. Perimeter = $6\frac{1}{4}$ in.

© Glencoe/McGraw-Hill 78 *Mathematics: Applications and Connections, Course 2*

ASSESSMENT/EVALUATION

Assessment and Evaluation Masters, pp. 182–184

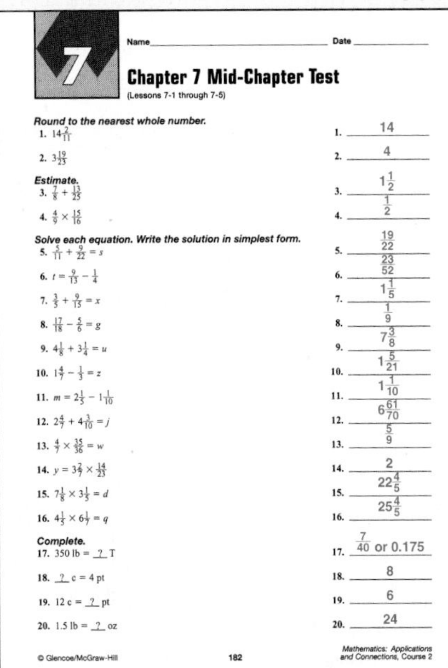

Name________ Date________

Chapter 7 Mid-Chapter Test
(Lessons 7-1 through 7-5)

Round to the nearest whole number.

1. $14\frac{2}{11}$ — 1. 14
2. $3\frac{19}{23}$ — 2. 4

Estimate.

3. $\frac{7}{8} + \frac{13}{25}$ — 3. $1\frac{1}{2}$
4. $\frac{4}{9} \times \frac{15}{16}$ — 4. $\frac{1}{2}$

Solve each equation. Write the solution in simplest form.

5. $\frac{5}{11} + \frac{9}{22} = s$ — 5. $\frac{19}{22}$
6. $t = \frac{9}{13} - \frac{1}{4}$ — 6. $\frac{23}{52}$
7. $\frac{3}{5} + \frac{9}{15} = x$ — 7. $1\frac{1}{5}$
8. $\frac{17}{18} - \frac{5}{6} = g$ — 8. $\frac{1}{9}$
9. $4\frac{1}{8} + 3\frac{1}{4} = u$ — 9. $7\frac{3}{8}$
10. $1\frac{4}{7} - \frac{1}{3} = z$ — 10. $1\frac{5}{21}$
11. $m = 2\frac{1}{5} - 1\frac{1}{10}$ — 11. $1\frac{1}{10}$
12. $2\frac{4}{7} + 4\frac{3}{10} = j$ — 12. $6\frac{61}{70}$
13. $\frac{4}{7} \times \frac{35}{36} = w$ — 13. $\frac{5}{9}$
14. $y = 3\frac{2}{7} \times \frac{14}{23}$ — 14. 2
15. $7\frac{1}{8} \times 3\frac{1}{5} = d$ — 15. $22\frac{4}{5}$
16. $4\frac{1}{5} \times 6\frac{1}{7} = q$ — 16. $25\frac{4}{5}$

Complete.

17. 350 lb = _?_ T — 17. $\frac{7}{40}$ or 0.175
18. _?_ c = 4 pt — 18. 8
19. 12 c = _?_ pt — 19. 6
20. 1.5 lb = _?_ oz — 20. 24

© Glencoe/McGraw-Hill 182 *Mathematics: Applications and Connections, Course 2*

Name________ Date________

Chapter 7 Quiz A
(Lessons 7-1 through 7-3)

Estimate.

1. $8\frac{2}{3} + 7\frac{1}{4}$ — 1. 16
2. $11\frac{7}{8} \div 3\frac{5}{6}$ — 2. 3
3. $4\frac{1}{8} - 2\frac{3}{4}$ — 3. 1
4. $3\frac{1}{5} \times 2\frac{4}{5}$ — 4. 9

Solve each equation. Write the solution in simplest form.

5. $\frac{5}{7} + \frac{3}{4} = r$ — 5. $1\frac{13}{28}$
6. $\frac{4}{5} - \frac{1}{8} = l$ — 6. $\frac{27}{40}$
7. $m = 5\frac{3}{8} - \frac{3}{4}$ — 7. $4\frac{5}{8}$
8. $2\frac{1}{2} + 1\frac{2}{9} = v$ — 8. $3\frac{13}{18}$
9. $4\frac{1}{8} - 2\frac{1}{2} = k$ — 9. $1\frac{5}{8}$
10. $j = 3\frac{3}{5} + 1\frac{1}{6}$ — 10. $4\frac{23}{30}$

Name________ Date________

Chapter 7 Quiz B
(Lessons 7-4 and 7-5)

Multiply. Write the product in simplest form.

1. $\frac{8}{9} \times 16\frac{1}{2}$ — 1. $14\frac{2}{3}$
2. $5 \times 2\frac{3}{5}$ — 2. 13
3. $\frac{4}{7} \times 7\frac{7}{8}$ — 3. $4\frac{1}{2}$

Complete.

4. 14 qt = _?_ gal — 4. 3.5
5. $3\frac{1}{2}$ lb = _?_ oz — 5. 56

© Glencoe/McGraw-Hill 183 *Mathematics: Applications and Connections, Course 2*

TECHNOLOGY/MULTIMEDIA

Technology Masters, pp. 39–40

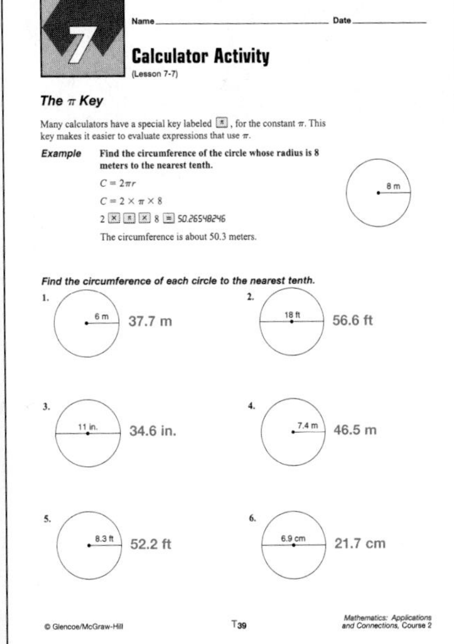

Name________ Date________

Calculator Activity
(Lesson 7-7)

The π Key

Many calculators have a special key labeled [π], for the constant π. This key makes it easier to evaluate expressions that use π.

Example **Find the circumference of the circle whose radius is 8 meters to the nearest tenth.**

$C = 2\pi r$

$C = 2 \times \pi \times 8$

2 [×] [π] [×] 8 [=] 50.26548246

The circumference is about 50.3 meters.

Find the circumference of each circle to the nearest tenth.

1. 6 m — 37.7 m
2. 18 ft — 56.6 ft
3. 11 in. — 34.6 in.
4. 7.4 m — 46.5 m
5. 8.3 ft — 52.2 ft
6. 6.9 cm — 21.7 cm

© Glencoe/McGraw-Hill T39 *Mathematics: Applications and Connections, Course 2*

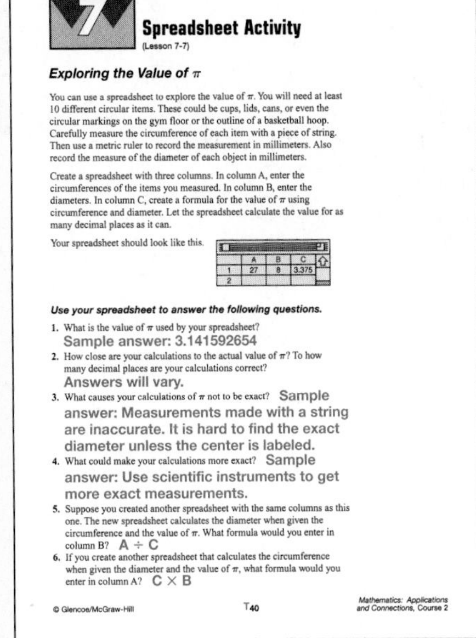

Name________ Date________

Spreadsheet Activity
(Lesson 7-7)

Exploring the Value of π

You can use a spreadsheet to explore the value of π. You will need at least 10 different circular items. These could be cups, lids, cans, or even the circular markings on the gym floor or the outline of a basketball hoop. Carefully measure the circumference of each item with a piece of string. Then use a metric ruler to record the measurement in millimeters. Also record the measure of the diameter of each object in millimeters.

Create a spreadsheet with three columns. In column A, enter the circumferences of the items you measured. In column B, enter the diameters. In column C, create a formula for the value of π using circumference and diameter. Let the spreadsheet calculate the value for as many decimal places as it can.

Your spreadsheet should look like this.

	A	B	C
1	27	8	3.375
2			

Use your spreadsheet to answer the following questions.

1. What is the value of π used by your spreadsheet?
   Sample answer: 3.141592654
2. How close are your calculations to the actual value of π? To how many decimal places are your calculations correct?
   Answers will vary.
3. What causes your calculations of π not to be exact? Sample answer: Measurements made with a string are inaccurate. It is hard to find the exact diameter unless the center is labeled.
4. What could make your calculations more exact? Sample answer: Use scientific instruments to get more exact measurements.
5. Suppose you created another spreadsheet with the same columns as this one. The new spreadsheet calculates the diameter when given the circumference and the value of π. What formula would you enter in column B? A ÷ C
6. If you create another spreadsheet that calculates the circumference when given the diameter and the value of π, what formula would you enter in column A? C × B

© Glencoe/McGraw-Hill T40 *Mathematics: Applications and Connections, Course 2*

MEETING INDIVIDUAL NEEDS

Investigations for the Special Education Student, pp. 15–20

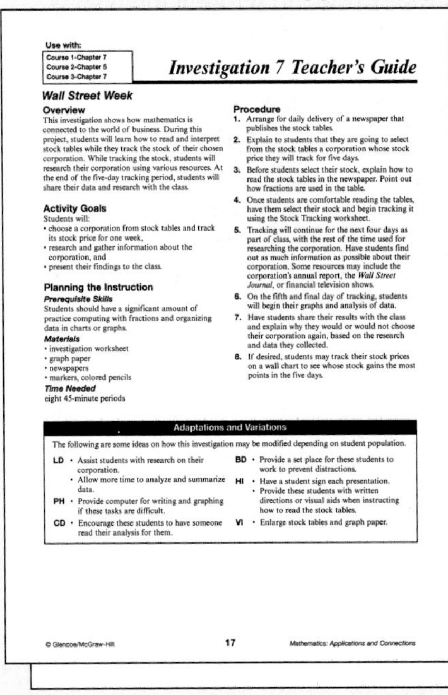

Use with:
Course 1-Chapter 7
Course 2-Chapter 5
Course 3-Chapter 7

Investigation 7 Teacher's Guide

Wall Street Week

Overview

This investigation shows how mathematics is connected to the world of business. During this project, students will learn how to read and interpret stock tables while they track the stock of their chosen corporation. While tracking the stock, students will research their corporation using various resources. At the end of the five-day tracking period, students will share their data and research with the class.

Activity Goals

Students will:
- choose a corporation from stock tables and track its stock price for one week,
- research and gather information about the corporation, and
- present their findings to the class.

Planning the Instruction

Prerequisite Skills
Students should have a significant amount of practice computing with fractions and organizing data in charts or graphs.

Materials
- investigation worksheet
- graph paper
- newspapers
- markers, colored pencils

Time Needed
eight 45-minute periods

Procedure

1. Arrange for daily delivery of a newspaper that publishes the stock tables.
2. Explain to students that they are going to select from the stock tables a corporation whose stock price they will track for five days.
3. Before students select their stock, explain how to read the stock tables in the newspaper. Point out how fractions are used in the table.
4. Once students are comfortable reading the tables, have them select their stock and begin tracking it using the Stock Tracking worksheet.
5. Tracking will continue for the next four days as part of class, with the rest of the time used for researching the corporation. Have students find out as much information as possible about their corporation. Some resources may include the corporation's annual report, the *Wall Street Journal*, or financial television shows.
6. On the fifth and final day of tracking, students will begin their graphs and analysis of data.
7. Have students share their results with the class and explain why they would or would not choose their corporation again, based on the research and data they collected.
8. If desired, students may track their stock prices on a wall chart to see whose stock gains the most points in the five days.

Adaptations and Variations

The following are some ideas on how this investigation may be modified depending on student population.

LD • Assist students with research on their corporation.
• Allow more time to analyze and summarize data.

PH • Provide computer for writing and graphing if these tasks are difficult.

CD • Encourage these students to have someone read their analysis for them.

BD • Provide a set place for these students to work to prevent distractions.

HI • Have a student sign each presentation.
• Provide these students with written directions or visual aids when instructing how to read the stock tables.

VI • Enlarge stock tables and graph paper.

© Glencoe/McGraw-Hill 17 *Mathematics: Applications and Connections*

CHAPTER 7 NOTES

Theme: Stock Market

The New York Stock Exchange plans to begin trading in dollars and cents rather than in fractions by January 1, 2000. The change was decided because price movements are occurring in smaller and smaller fractions, and decimals are easier for many consumers to understand.

Question of the Day If you own 12 shares of stock in the Veggie Soup Company and the price of the stock closes up $\frac{1}{8}$ of a dollar, how much money did you make on your shares for that day? **$1.50**

Assess Prerequisite Skills

Ask students to read through the list of objectives presented in "What you'll learn in Chapter 7." You may wish to ask them what each of the objectives means or if they have experienced or used any of these math concepts before.

Building Portfolios

Encourage students to revise their portfolios as they study this chapter. Work chosen for the portfolio should represent the student's increasing understanding of how to apply fractions.

Math and the Family

In the *Family Letters and Activities* booklet (pp. 39–40), you will find a letter to the parents explaining what students will study in Chapter 7. An activity appropriate for the whole family is also available.

CHAPTER 7 Applying Fractions

What you'll learn in Chapter 7

- to estimate with fractions and mixed numbers,
- to add, subtract, multiply, and divide fractions and mixed numbers,
- to solve problems by eliminating possibilities,
- to change units in the customary system, and
- to find perimeter and circumference.

CD-ROM Program

Activities for Chapter 7

- Chapter 7 Introduction
- Interactive Lessons 7-2, 7-4, 7-6
- Extended Activity 7-7
- Assessment Game
- Resource Lessons 7-1 through 7-9

UPS AND DOWNS

In this project, you will use fractions in a report summarizing the stock prices of four companies. To do this, you will research the stock history of each company and keep track of the value of their stocks.

Getting Started

- Research what it means to own stock in a company.
- Choose the stocks of four companies to track. Include at least one from the table.
- Create a table that you can use to keep track of your stocks for one month on a daily basis.

Company	Close	Change
A	$39\frac{1}{16}$	$-\frac{3}{4}$
B	$58\frac{3}{4}$	$-1\frac{5}{16}$
C	12	$+\frac{1}{8}$
D	$76\frac{5}{8}$	$-2\frac{1}{4}$
E	$43\frac{1}{16}$	$-\frac{9}{16}$
F	$93\frac{13}{16}$	$-\frac{3}{8}$
G	$22\frac{11}{16}$	$+\frac{1}{16}$
H	$33\frac{13}{16}$	$-\frac{7}{8}$
I	50	$-1\frac{17}{16}$
J	$59\frac{1}{2}$	$-2\frac{11}{16}$
K	$35\frac{3}{4}$	$-\frac{1}{2}$
L	$99\frac{1}{16}$	$+\frac{9}{16}$

Technology Tips

- Use an **electronic encyclopedia** to do your research.
- Use a **word processor** to write your report.
- Surf the **Internet** for stock prices.

Data Update **For up-to-date information on the stock market, visit:**

www.glencoe.com/sec/math/mac/mathnet

Working on the Project

You can use what you'll learn in Chapter 7 to help you complete your report.

Page	Exercise
271	51
287	36
307	35
311	Alternative Assessment

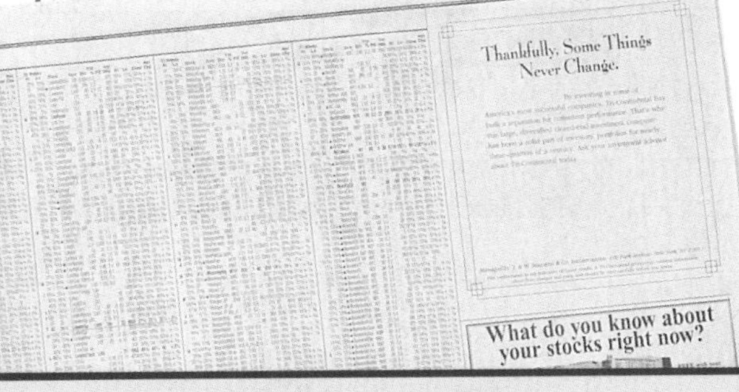

Thankfully, Some Things Never Change.
What do you know about your stocks right now?

CHAPTER Project NOTES

Objectives Students should
- learn what it means to own stock in a company.
- track the movement of four companies' stocks for one month.
- learn how fractions are used in stock tables.

Project Pointer You may suggest that students begin a *Project Folder* to keep their work as they complete each stage of the Chapter Project. The completed project may also be added to their portfolios.

Using the Table Explain that the fractions in the table represent parts of a dollar. The price of Nike stock, for example, closed at $59\frac{1}{2}$, down $2\frac{11}{16}$. Tell students this translates to $59.50, down $2.6875 per share. The actual stock tables in the newspaper may also have additional information, such as the overall gain or loss for the year-to-date, total trading volume, and the highest/lowest price from the previous day.

***Investigations and Projects Masters,* p. 44**

7 Name ______ Date ______

Chapter 7 Project

Ups and Downs

Page 267, Getting Started

Make your own table on a separate sheet of paper.

Page 271, Working on the Chapter Project, Exercise 51

The estimated cost of buying 32 shares of ______ stock on August 18, 1997, was ______.

Page 287, Working on the Chapter Project, Exercise 36

a.

Company	Cost for 100 Shares (First Day)	Cost for 100 Shares (Yesterday)

b.

Page 307, Working on the Chapter Project, Exercise 35

a.

b.

 44 *Mathematics: Applications and Connections, Course 2*

internet CONNECTION

Glencoe has made every effort to ensure that the website links for *Mathematics: Applications and Connections* at **www.glencoe.com/sec/math/mac/mathnet** are current and contain appropriate content. However, these website links are not under Glencoe's control.

Instructional Resources ▶▶▶

A recording sheet to help students organize their data for the Chapter Project is shown at the right and is available in the *Investigations and Projects Masters,* p. 44.

7-1 Lesson Notes

Instructional Resources

- *Study Guide Masters,* p. 42
- *Practice Masters,* p. 42
- *Enrichment Masters,* p. 42
- Transparencies 7-1, A and B

CD-ROM Program
- Resource Lesson 7-1

Recommended Pacing	
Standard	Day 2 of 15
Honors	Day 2 of 14
Block	Day 1 of 8

1 FOCUS

5-Minute Check (Chapter 6)

1. Write *14 less than y* as an algebraic expression. $y - 14$

Solve each equation.

2. $12m = 84$ 7
3. $6w - 9 = 57$ 11
4. $r + 32 = 45.5$ 13.5
5. Graph $y = 2x - 0.5$.

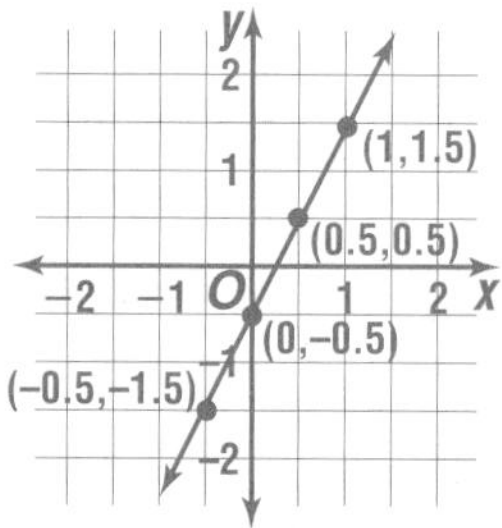

The 5-Minute Check is also available on **Transparency 7-1A** for this lesson.

Motivating the Lesson

Problem Solving Shawn bought $\frac{3}{4}$ pound of apples, $\frac{15}{16}$ pound of bananas, and $\frac{7}{8}$ pound of grapes. Ask students how they would use estimation to determine whether Shawn bought more or less than 2 pounds of fruit.

7-1 Estimating with Fractions

What **you'll learn**

You'll learn to estimate sums, differences, products, and quotients of fractions and mixed numbers.

When **am I ever going to use this?**

Knowing how to estimate with fractions will help you approximate the amount of ingredients needed for a recipe.

In August, 1996, an article in a kid's magazine described how kids turned their hobbies into dream jobs. Boaz Frankel earns $5 per hour for computer tutoring in Oregon. If he tutors $9\frac{3}{4}$ hours one month, estimate how much money he will make.

To estimate the sum, difference, or product of mixed numbers, round each mixed number to the nearest whole number. Estimate the product of 5 and $9\frac{3}{4}$.

$5 \times 9\frac{3}{4} \rightarrow 5 \times 10 = 50$

Boaz will make *about* $50. *Since $9\frac{3}{4} < 10$, he will make a little less than $50.*

Example 1

When a mixed number contains $\frac{1}{2}$, the number is usually rounded up.

Estimate the sum of $4\frac{1}{5}$ and $1\frac{1}{2}$.

$4\frac{1}{5} + 1\frac{1}{2} \rightarrow 4 + 2 = 6$

$4\frac{1}{5} + 1\frac{1}{2}$ is *about* 6. *Is the actual sum more or less than 6?*

To estimate the sum or difference of fractions, round each fraction to 0, $\frac{1}{2}$, or 1, whichever is closest. Sometimes fraction models can help you decide how to round.

Fractions Close to 0	Fractions Close to $\frac{1}{2}$	Fractions Close to 1
$\frac{1}{5}$	$\frac{2}{3}$	$\frac{5}{6}$
$\frac{1}{6}$	$\frac{5}{8}$	$\frac{6}{7}$
$\frac{1}{12}$	$\frac{7}{12}$	$\frac{11}{12}$

Cross-Curriculum Cue

Inform the other teachers on your team that your students are studying estimating with fractions. Suggestions for curriculum integration are:

Family and Consumer Science: recipes and sewing
Art: graphic design
Physical Education: field event heights or lengths

Examples

Estimate.

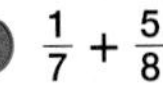

2 $\frac{1}{7} + \frac{5}{8}$

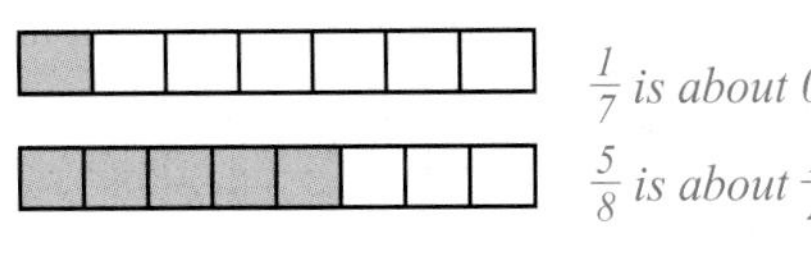

$\frac{1}{7}$ is about 0.

$\frac{5}{8}$ is about $\frac{1}{2}$.

$\frac{1}{7} + \frac{5}{8} \rightarrow 0 + \frac{1}{2} = \frac{1}{2}$

$\frac{1}{7} + \frac{5}{8}$ is *about* $\frac{1}{2}$.

3 $\frac{5}{6} - \frac{1}{2}$

$\frac{5}{6} - \frac{1}{2} \rightarrow 1 - \frac{1}{2} = \frac{1}{2}$ *$\frac{5}{6}$ is about 1.*

$\frac{5}{6} - \frac{1}{2}$ is *about* $\frac{1}{2}$.

4 $\frac{1}{8} \times 15$ *$\frac{1}{8} \times 15$ means $\frac{1}{8}$ of 15.*

$\frac{1}{8} \times 15 \rightarrow \frac{1}{8}$ of 16 or 2 *Round 15 to 16, since 16 is divisible by 8.*

$\frac{1}{8}$ of 15 is *about* 2.

APPLICATION

5 **Baking** **Katrina made $7\frac{1}{4}$ pounds of chocolate fudge that she wants to split into $1\frac{1}{2}$-pound portions to give away as gifts. About how many gifts of fudge can she give away?**

Explore You want to estimate how many $1\frac{1}{2}$-pound portions Katrina can get from $7\frac{1}{4}$ pounds of fudge.

Plan To find the number of portions, divide $7\frac{1}{4}$ by $1\frac{1}{2}$. First, round $1\frac{1}{2}$ to 2. Then replace the dividend with a number that is easy to divide mentally.

Solve $7\frac{1}{4} \div 1\frac{1}{2} \rightarrow 7\frac{1}{4} \div 2$ *Round $1\frac{1}{2}$ to 2.*

$\rightarrow 8 \div 2$ or 4 *8 is divisible by 2.*

Katrina can give away about 4 gifts of fudge.

Examine Since four 2-pound gifts would equal 8 pounds of fudge, the estimate is reasonable.

2 TEACH

Transparency 7-1B contains a teaching aid for this lesson.

Using Calculators In addition to the methods presented in this lesson, students can use calculators to estimate fractions. If they divide the numerator of a fraction by the denominator, they can use the answer to estimate whether the fraction is closer to 0, $\frac{1}{2}$, or 1.

In-Class Examples

For Example 1

Estimate the sum of $5\frac{3}{4}$ and $7\frac{4}{5}$. **$6 + 8 = 14$**

For Example 2

Estimate $\frac{2}{5} + \frac{7}{8}$. **$\frac{1}{2} + 1 = 1\frac{1}{2}$**

For Example 3

Estimate $\frac{6}{7} - \frac{1}{2}$. **$1 - \frac{1}{2} = \frac{1}{2}$**

For Example 4

Estimate $\frac{1}{4} \times 19$. **$\frac{1}{4} \times 20 = 5$**

For Example 5

Jeron made $2\frac{1}{2}$ quarts of lemonade for himself and seven friends. About how much lemonade does each get to drink? **$3 \div 8 = \frac{3}{8}$ qt**

Teaching Tip Remind students that they can check their estimates of sums and differences by using number sense to determine the two whole numbers between which the answer will fall.

Investigations for the Special Education Student

This blackline master booklet helps you plan for the needs of your special education students by providing long-term projects along with teacher notes. Investigation 6, *Read All About Us,* Investigation 7, *Wall Street Week,* and Investigation 8, *Weather Report,* may be used with this chapter.

3 PRACTICE/APPLY

Check for Understanding

If students need additional practice or instruction after completing Exercises 1–15, one of these options may be helpful.

- Extra Practice, see p. 586
- Reteaching Activity
- *Study Guide Masters*, p. 49
- *Practice Masters*, p. 49
- Interactive Mathematics Tools Software

Assignment Guide

Core: 17–49 odd, 52–58
Enriched: 16–46 even, 48–50, 52–58

Additional Answer

2. 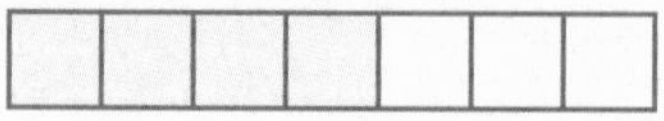

CHECK FOR UNDERSTANDING

Communicating Mathematics

1b. $\frac{6}{7}$, 1

Read and study the lesson to answer each question.

1. ***Write*** each fraction modeled and tell if it is closest to 0, $\frac{1}{2}$, or 1.
   a. 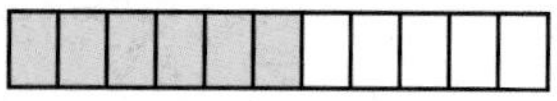 $\frac{6}{11}$, $\frac{1}{2}$
   b. 
2. ***Draw*** an illustration representing $\frac{4}{7}$ and use it to round the fraction to 0, $\frac{1}{2}$, or 1. $\frac{1}{2}$; See margin for drawing.

Guided Practice

Round each fraction to 0, $\frac{1}{2}$, or 1.

3. $\frac{1}{8}$ 0
4. $\frac{10}{11}$ 1
5. $\frac{2}{5}$ $\frac{1}{2}$

Round to the nearest whole number.

6. $3\frac{1}{2}$ 4
7. $9\frac{1}{3}$ 9
8. $12\frac{6}{7}$ 13

Estimate. 9–14. Sample answers are given.

9. $\frac{1}{2} + \frac{5}{6}$ $\frac{1}{2} + 1 = 1\frac{1}{2}$
10. $\frac{5}{8} - \frac{1}{10}$ $\frac{1}{2} - 0 = \frac{1}{2}$
11. $\frac{7}{8} \times 11$ $1 \times 11 = 11$
12. $4 + 3\frac{4}{5}$ $4 + 4 = 8$
13. $5\frac{1}{3} \times 2\frac{2}{3}$ $5 \times 3 = 15$
14. $8\frac{1}{2} \div 3\frac{1}{4}$ $9 \div 3 = 3$
15. ***Horticulture*** Carmen uses $\frac{3}{4}$ cup of liquid fertilizer for each shrub in her plant nursery. Estimate how much liquid fertilizer she will need for 24 shrubs. Sample answer: $1 \times 24 = 24$ cups

EXERCISES

Practice

Round each fraction to 0, $\frac{1}{2}$, or 1.

16. $\frac{1}{6}$ 0
17. $\frac{3}{5}$ $\frac{1}{2}$
18. $\frac{9}{10}$ 1
19. $\frac{4}{5}$ 1
20. $\frac{2}{5}$ $\frac{1}{2}$
21. $\frac{1}{7}$ 0
22. $\frac{3}{10}$ $\frac{1}{2}$
23. $\frac{5}{6}$ 1

Round to the nearest whole number.

24. $9\frac{1}{6}$ 9
25. $2\frac{1}{2}$ 3
26. $11\frac{2}{3}$ 12
27. $4\frac{1}{10}$ 4
28. $7\frac{1}{3}$ 7
29. $5\frac{3}{4}$ 6
30. $10\frac{2}{9}$ 10
31. $6\frac{7}{8}$ 7

Estimate. 32–50. Sample answers are given.

32. $\frac{1}{2} + \frac{7}{8}$ $\frac{1}{2} + 1 = 1\frac{1}{2}$
33. $\frac{3}{8} - \frac{1}{10}$ $\frac{1}{2} - 0 = \frac{1}{2}$
34. $\frac{1}{8} \times \frac{3}{4}$ $0 \times 1 = 0$
35. $\frac{4}{5} \div \frac{7}{8}$ $1 \div 1 = 1$
36. $\frac{1}{3} + \frac{1}{8}$ $\frac{1}{2} + 0 = \frac{1}{2}$
37. $5\frac{1}{3} - 2\frac{3}{4}$ $5 - 3 = 2$
38. $9\frac{7}{8} + 2\frac{3}{4}$ (38. $10 + 3 = 13$)
39. $\frac{1}{2} \times 17$ $\frac{1}{2} \times 18 = 9$
40. $5\frac{5}{7} \times 8\frac{2}{3}$ $6 \times 9 = 54$
41. $11\frac{1}{2} - 1\frac{5}{6}$ (41. $12 - 2 = 10$)
42. $2\frac{4}{5} \times \frac{8}{9}$ $3 \times 1 = 3$
43. $21\frac{1}{2} \div 1\frac{3}{4}$ $22 \div 2 = 11$

***Study Guide Masters*, p. 49**

Name ______________________ Date ____________

7-1 Study Guide

Estimating with Fractions

Use rounding or patterns to estimate with fractions.

Rounding: For mixed numbers, round to the nearest whole number.
$4\frac{1}{6} + 3\frac{7}{8} \rightarrow 4 + 4 = 8$
$4\frac{1}{6} + 3\frac{7}{8}$ is about 8.

For proper fractions, round to 0, $\frac{1}{2}$ or 1.
$\frac{11}{12} - \frac{4}{9} \rightarrow 1 - \frac{1}{2} = \frac{1}{2}$
$\frac{11}{12} - \frac{4}{9}$ is about $\frac{1}{2}$.

Compatible Numbers: $\frac{1}{4} \times 19\frac{1}{2} \rightarrow \frac{1}{4} \times 20 = 5$
20 is divisible by 4.
$\frac{1}{4} \times 19\frac{1}{2}$ is about 5.

$29\frac{1}{3} \div 3\frac{9}{10} \rightarrow 28 \div 4 = 7$
28 is divisible by 4.
$29\frac{1}{3} \div 3\frac{9}{10}$ is about 7.

Round each fraction to 0, $\frac{1}{2}$, or 1.

1. $\frac{7}{8}$ 1
2. $\frac{1}{5}$ 0
3. $\frac{11}{12}$ 1
4. $\frac{3}{7}$ $\frac{1}{2}$
5. $\frac{4}{9}$ $\frac{1}{2}$

Round to the nearest whole number.

6. $6\frac{3}{4}$ 7
7. $7\frac{2}{5}$ 7
8. $4\frac{7}{9}$ 5
9. $12\frac{2}{11}$ 12
10. $1\frac{1}{7}$ 1

Estimate.

11. $\frac{3}{5} + \frac{1}{4}$ $\frac{1}{2} + \frac{1}{2} = 1$
12. $\frac{7}{9} - \frac{2}{5}$ $1 - \frac{1}{2} = \frac{1}{2}$
13. $5\frac{1}{8} + 6\frac{9}{11}$ $5 + 7 = 12$
14. $3\frac{9}{10} - 2\frac{1}{8}$ $4 - 2 = 2$
15. $\frac{4}{5} \times \frac{7}{8}$ $1 \times 1 = 1$
16. $3\frac{5}{6} \times 2\frac{1}{9}$ $4 \times 2 = 8$
17. $\frac{1}{10} \times 27\frac{1}{2}$ $\frac{1}{10} \times 30 = 3$
18. $\frac{6}{7} \div \frac{11}{12}$ $1 \div 1 = 1$
19. $16\frac{1}{3} \div 3\frac{7}{9}$ $16 \div 4 = 4$

 T49 *Mathematics: Applications and Connections, Course 2*

Reteaching the Lesson

Activity Provide fraction strips to help students visually round mixed numbers to the nearest half or whole number. Have them shade the strip to show the fraction modeled and fold the strip in half twice. They can determine whether the shaded part is closer to 0, $\frac{1}{2}$, or 1.

44. $14 - 1 = 13$
45. $\frac{1}{2} \times \frac{1}{2} = \frac{1}{4}$
46. $6 \div 3 = 2$

Applications and Problem Solving

47. $2 + 1 + 6 = 9$

Interview a family member who cooks, sews, or does carpentry work about how they use fractions. Make a list of the situations where they might estimate fractional amounts.

44. Estimate $14\frac{1}{7}$ minus $\frac{5}{6}$.

45. Estimate the product of $\frac{1}{3}$ and $\frac{4}{9}$.

46. Estimate $5\frac{5}{6}$ divided by 3.

47. Estimate the sum of $1\frac{7}{9}$, $\frac{4}{5}$, and $6\frac{1}{8}$.

48. ***Construction*** *About* how many $3\frac{1}{2}$-foot shelves can a carpenter cut from a 12-foot board for a bookcase? **about 3 shelves**

49. ***Life Science*** Komodo dragons are the largest lizards ever to have lived. A 250-pound komodo dragon can eat enough in one sitting to increase its weight by $\frac{3}{4}$. Estimate $\frac{3}{4} \times 250$ to find how much weight a komodo dragon would gain after eating. **$1 \times 250 = 250$ pounds**

Komodo dragon

50. ***Technology*** The advertised diagonal size of a computer monitor is larger than the actual viewing diagonal.

Computer Monitor (as advertised)	Actual Diagonal Measure (in.)
17-inch	$15\frac{4}{5}$
15-inch	$13\frac{1}{2}$
14-inch	$13\frac{1}{10}$

a. Estimate the difference between the sizes for each computer monitor. **1, 1, 1**

b. What conjecture could you make, based on your estimates? **See margin.**

51. ***Working on the CHAPTER Project*** Refer to the table on page 267. For each of the companies that you have chosen to track, estimate the cost of buying 32 shares of stock on August 18, 1997. **See students' work.**

52. ***Critical Thinking*** If the number being divided is rounded up and the divisor is rounded down, what is the effect on the answer? **It will be greater.**

Mixed Review

53. ***Algebra*** Find four solutions of $y = 3x + 1$. Write the solutions as ordered pairs. *(Lesson 6-7)* **Sample answer: (1, 4), (2, 7), (3, 10), (4, 13)**

54. ***Algebra*** Translate the phrase *65 less than w* into an algebraic expression. *(Lesson 6-4)* **$w - 65$**

55. ***Algebra*** Solve $18 = m - 5$. *(Lesson 6-1)* **23**

For **Extra Practice,** see page 586.

56. Solve $s = -5(12)$. *(Lesson 5-6)* **-60**

57. Replace ● in $\frac{1}{4}$ ● $\frac{2}{7}$ with $<$, $>$, or $=$ to make a true sentence. *(Lesson 4-10)* **$<$**

58. **Standardized Test Practice** A pair of jeans is on sale for 30% off the regular price. What fraction of the regular price is this? *(Lesson 4-7)* **B**

A $\frac{3}{100}$ **B** $\frac{3}{10}$ **C** $\frac{3}{5}$ **D** $\frac{1}{3}$

Extending the Lesson

Enrichment Masters, p. 49

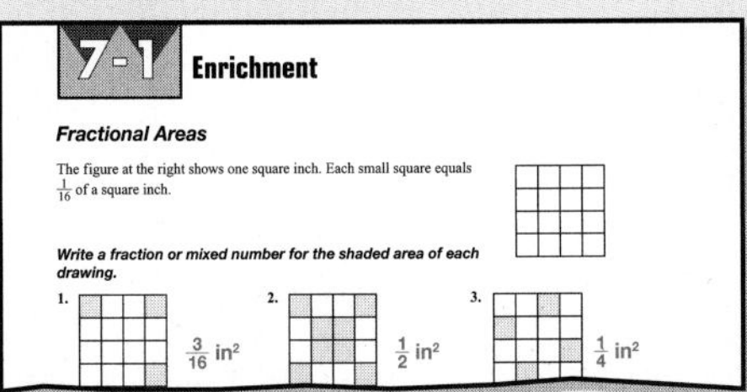
7-1 Enrichment

Fractional Areas

The figure at the right shows one square inch. Each small square equals $\frac{1}{16}$ of a square inch.

Write a fraction or mixed number for the shaded area of each drawing.

1. $\frac{3}{16}$ in²
2. $\frac{1}{2}$ in²
3. $\frac{1}{4}$ in²

Activity Have students choose a whole number and write four problems using fractions or mixed numbers that when rounded, yield an estimate equal to the number chosen. One should be an addition problem, one subtraction, one multiplication, and one a division problem.

Exercise 51 asks students to advance to the next stage of work on the Chapter Project. You may have students who selected the same stock work in groups to complete this problem.

4 ASSESS

Closing Activity

Speaking Have students explain how estimating with fractions is similar to and different from estimating with whole numbers and decimals.

Ask students to share with the class the results of their interviews. You may wish to combine their lists to illustrate how fractions are used in the situations they described.

Additional Answer

50b. The actual viewing area of a computer monitor is about 1 inch less than the advertised size.

Practice Masters, p. 49

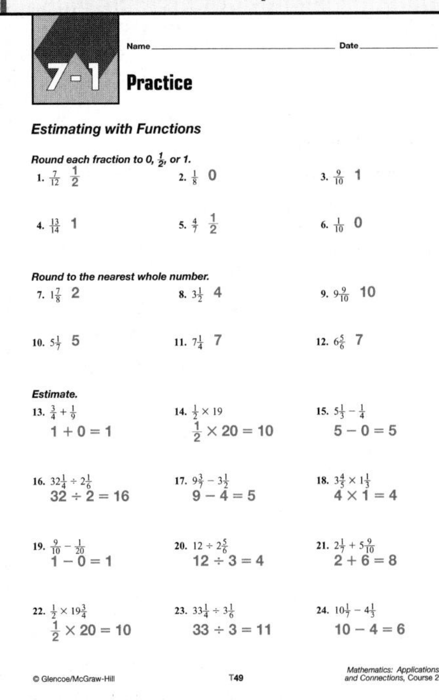
Name ____________ Date ________

7-1 **Practice**

Estimating with Functions

Round each fraction to 0, $\frac{1}{2}$, or 1.

1. $\frac{7}{12}$ $\frac{1}{2}$
2. $\frac{1}{8}$ 0
3. $\frac{9}{10}$ 1
4. $\frac{13}{14}$ 1
5. $\frac{4}{7}$ $\frac{1}{2}$
6. $\frac{1}{10}$ 0

Round to the nearest whole number.

7. $1\frac{7}{8}$ 2
8. $3\frac{1}{2}$ 4
9. $9\frac{9}{10}$ 10
10. $5\frac{1}{7}$ 5
11. $7\frac{1}{4}$ 7
12. $6\frac{5}{6}$ 7

Estimate.

13. $\frac{3}{4} + \frac{1}{9}$ — $1 + 0 = 1$
14. $\frac{1}{2} \times 19$ — $\frac{1}{2} \times 20 = 10$
15. $5\frac{1}{3} - \frac{1}{4}$ — $5 - 0 = 5$
16. $32\frac{1}{4} \div 2\frac{1}{6}$ — $32 \div 2 = 16$
17. $9\frac{3}{7} - 3\frac{1}{2}$ — $9 - 4 = 5$
18. $3\frac{4}{5} \times 1\frac{1}{3}$ — $4 \times 1 = 4$
19. $\frac{9}{10} - \frac{1}{20}$ — $1 - 0 = 1$
20. $12 \div 2\frac{5}{6}$ — $12 \div 3 = 4$
21. $2\frac{1}{7} + 5\frac{9}{10}$ — $2 + 6 = 8$
22. $\frac{1}{2} \times 19\frac{3}{4}$ — $\frac{1}{2} \times 20 = 10$
23. $33\frac{1}{4} \div 3\frac{1}{6}$ — $33 \div 3 = 11$
24. $10\frac{1}{7} - 4\frac{1}{3}$ — $10 - 4 = 6$

 T49 *Mathematics: Applications and Connections, Course 2*

7-2 Lesson Notes

Instructional Resources

- *Study Guide Masters,* p. 50
- *Practice Masters,* p. 50
- *Enrichment Masters,* p. 50
- Transparencies 7-2, A and B

- CD-ROM Program
  - Resource Lesson 7-2
  - Interactive Lesson 7-2

Recommended Pacing	
Standard	Day 3 of 15
Honors	Day 3 of 14
Block	Day 2 of 8

1 FOCUS

5-Minute Check *(Lesson 7-1)*

Round each fraction to 0, $\frac{1}{2}$, or 1.

1. $\frac{2}{7}$ $\frac{1}{2}$
2. $\frac{7}{8}$ 1
3. Round $8\frac{5}{8}$ to the nearest whole number. 9

Estimate.

4. $\frac{1}{5} + \frac{5}{6}$ $0 + 1 = 1$
5. $4\frac{3}{8} \times 3\frac{1}{4}$ $4 \times 3 = 12$

The 5-Minute Check is also available on **Transparency 7-2A** for this lesson.

Motivating the Lesson

Hands-On Activity Show students two clear measuring cups partially filled with colored water $\left(\text{for example, } \frac{2}{3}, \frac{1}{4}\right)$. Ask them how much there would be if they were combined. Combine the two into one cup and ask them to estimate the quantity.

7-2 Adding and Subtracting Fractions

What **you'll learn**

You'll learn to add and subtract fractions.

When **am I ever going to use this?**

Knowing how to add and subtract fractions can help you determine how much paint you need to buy in order to paint a room in your home.

The graph shows the different times of the year that people join health clubs. What fraction of the people join during the first six months of the year? *This problem will be solved in Example 1.*

To add or subtract fractions, the denominators must be the same.

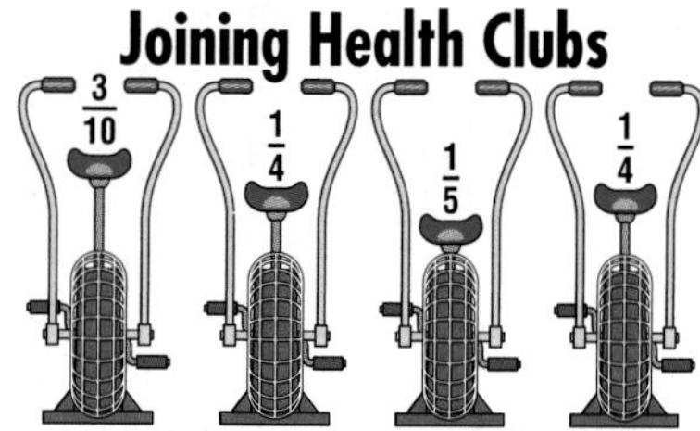

Source: National Health Club Association

4. Find the LCM of the denominators and draw the models using that number of squares.
5. First, find a common denominator. Then add and simplify if necessary.

HANDS-ON MINI-LAB

Work with a partner.  grid paper 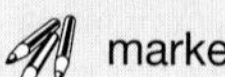 markers

Use squares to model each fraction.

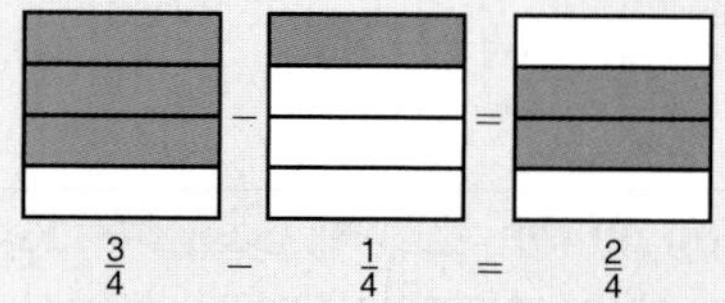

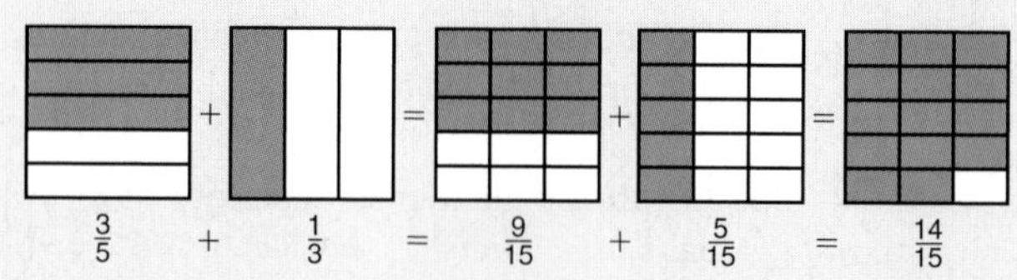

Try This

Model each sum or difference. 1–3. See Answer Appendix.

1. $\frac{4}{5} - \frac{2}{5}$
2. $\frac{1}{3} + \frac{1}{2}$
3. $\frac{5}{6} - \frac{3}{4}$

Talk About It

4. Explain how to take two fractions with different denominators and draw them so that they have the same denominator.
5. Explain how to add two fractions that have different denominators.

Multiple Learning Styles

Logical Use $\frac{1}{6}, \frac{5}{12}, \frac{2}{6}, \frac{3}{4}, \frac{3}{12}, \frac{2}{3}$, and $\frac{1}{4}$, to fill in the blanks to form true statements.

___ + ___ = ___. $\frac{1}{6} + \frac{1}{4} = \frac{5}{12}$

___ ÷ ___ = 2. $\frac{2}{3} \div \frac{2}{6} = 2$

3 · ___ = ___. $3 \cdot \frac{3}{12} = \frac{3}{4}$

1 **Health** Refer to the beginning of the lesson. Find the fraction of the people who join health clubs during the first six months of the year.

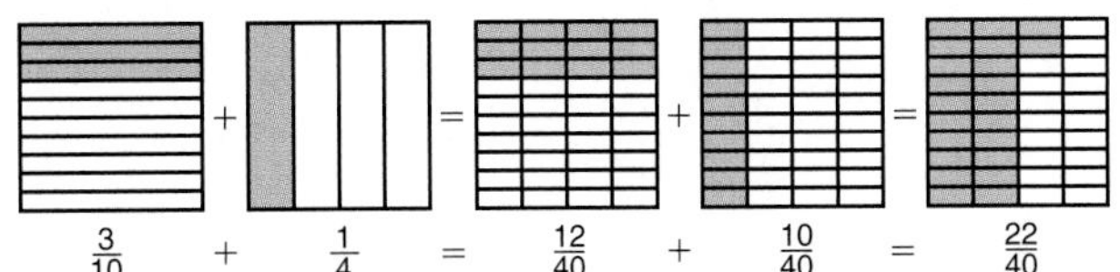

$\frac{3}{10} + \frac{1}{4} = \frac{12}{40} + \frac{10}{40} = \frac{22}{40}$

You need to find the sum of $\frac{3}{10}$ and $\frac{1}{4}$.

So, $\frac{22}{40}$ or $\frac{11}{20}$ of the people who join health clubs do so during the first six months of the year.

Study Hint

Technology You can use a calculator to add and subtract fractions. To find $\frac{3}{10} + \frac{1}{4}$ enter: 3 [/] 10 [+] 1 [/] 4 [=]. To get an answer in simplest form, press [SIMP] [=] until N/D → n/d no longer appears on the screen.

LOOK BACK Refer to Lesson 4-10 to review LCD.

Adding and Subtracting Fractions with Unlike Denominators	To add or subtract fractions: 1. Rename the fractions with a common denominator as necessary. 2. Add or subtract the numerators. 3. Simplify.

The least common denominator (LCD) can be used to rename fractions for addition and subtraction. Remember that the LCD is the LCM of the denominators.

Example

2 Find $\frac{5}{6} - \frac{3}{8}$. Write the difference in simplest form.

Estimate: $1 - \frac{1}{2} = \frac{1}{2}$

$$\begin{array}{lcccc} \frac{5}{6} & \text{LCD: } 24 & \frac{5 \times 4}{6 \times 4} & \rightarrow & \frac{20}{24} \\ -\frac{3}{8} & \rightarrow & \frac{3 \times 3}{8 \times 3} & \rightarrow & -\frac{9}{24} \\ \hline & & & & \frac{11}{24} \end{array}$$

So, $\frac{5}{6} - \frac{3}{8} = \frac{11}{24}$. *$\frac{11}{24}$ is close to the estimate, $\frac{1}{2}$.*

2 TEACH

Transparency 7-2B contains a teaching aid for this lesson.

Using the Mini-Lab You may wish to have students use the fraction bar models from the *Hands-On Lab Masters* to model each fraction. They should place the bars end to end to find a sum and one on top of the other to find the difference. They may use other fraction bars to determine the results when the fractions have unlike denominators.

In-Class Examples

For Example 1

Find the sum of $\frac{3}{5} + \frac{5}{6}$ and express in simplest form. $1\frac{13}{30}$

For Example 2

Find $\frac{7}{8} - \frac{1}{3}$. Write the difference in simplest form. $\frac{13}{24}$

For Example 3

Solve $w = \frac{4}{7} + \frac{2}{3}$. Write the solution in simplest form. $1\frac{5}{21}$

Teaching Tip Before beginning the examples, review the relationship between adding fractions and finding the least common multiple (LCM). Review ways to find the least common denominator (LCD) of two fractions.

MathPASS CD-ROM

This CD-ROM offers a complete, self-paced mathematics curriculum. Each lesson includes a pretest, tutorial, guided practice, and posttest. MathPASS Lessons 19 and 20 are correlated to this Student Edition lesson.
For Windows & Macintosh

3 PRACTICE/APPLY

Check for Understanding

If students need additional practice or instruction after completing Exercises 1–11, one of these options may be helpful.

- Extra Practice, see p. 586
- Reteaching Activity
- *Transition Booklet,* pp. 29–32
- *Study Guide Masters,* p. 50
- *Practice Masters,* p. 50
- Interactive Mathematics Tools Software

Assignment Guide

Core: 13–33 odd, 35–39
Enriched: 12–30 even, 32–39

Example 3 Solve $\frac{4}{9} + \frac{11}{12} = a$. Write the solution in simplest form.

Estimate: $\frac{1}{2} + 1 = 1\frac{1}{2}$

$$\frac{4}{9} + \frac{11}{12} = a$$

$$\frac{4 \times 4}{9 \times 4} + \frac{11 \times 3}{12 \times 3} = a \quad \textit{The LCD is 36.}$$

$$\frac{16}{36} + \frac{33}{36} = a$$

$$\frac{49}{36} = a$$

Rename $\frac{49}{36}$ as $1\frac{13}{36}$.

So, $\frac{4}{9} + \frac{11}{12} = 1\frac{13}{36}$. *Compare to the estimate,* $1\frac{1}{2}$.

CHECK FOR UNDERSTANDING

Communicating Mathematics

Read and study the lesson to answer each question.

1. ***Tell*** why you must have a common denominator to add or subtract fractions. **The units of measure must be the same.**
2. ***Describe*** a common unit of measure that can be used to add 4 inches and 1 yard. **inches**
3. ***Model*** $\frac{3}{8} + \frac{1}{6}$ using grid paper and find the sum. **See Answer Appendix.**

HANDS-ON MATH

Guided Practice

Add or subtract. Write each sum or difference in simplest form.

4. $\frac{1}{7} + \frac{3}{7}$ **$\frac{4}{7}$**
5. $\frac{3}{5} + \frac{1}{15}$ **$\frac{2}{3}$**
6. $\frac{5}{6} - \frac{1}{9}$ **$\frac{13}{18}$**
7. $\frac{3}{8} - \frac{1}{8}$ **$\frac{1}{4}$**
8. $\frac{7}{10} - \frac{1}{6}$ **$\frac{8}{15}$**
9. $\frac{5}{9} + \frac{5}{6}$ **$1\frac{7}{18}$**
10. Solve $\frac{1}{2} + \frac{5}{12} = d$. Write the solution in simplest form. **$\frac{11}{12}$**
11. ***Transportation*** When Ke Min started his trip to his sister's house, he had $\frac{1}{2}$ of a tank of gas. When he arrived, he had $\frac{1}{8}$ of a tank. How much gasoline did Ke Min use during his trip? **$\frac{3}{8}$ tank**

EXERCISES

Practice

Add or subtract. Write each sum or difference in simplest form.

12. $\frac{4}{9} + \frac{2}{9}$ **$\frac{2}{3}$**
13. $\frac{9}{10} - \frac{1}{6}$ **$\frac{11}{15}$**
14. $\frac{5}{8} - \frac{1}{2}$ **$\frac{1}{8}$**
15. $\frac{3}{7} + \frac{4}{5}$ **$1\frac{8}{35}$**
16. $\frac{3}{7} + \frac{9}{14}$ **$1\frac{1}{14}$**
17. $\frac{2}{6} - \frac{1}{6}$ **$\frac{1}{6}$**
18. $\frac{7}{15} + \frac{5}{9}$ **$1\frac{1}{45}$**
19. $\frac{4}{5} - \frac{1}{6}$ **$\frac{19}{30}$**
20. $\frac{5}{8} - \frac{7}{12}$ **$\frac{1}{24}$**
21. $\frac{4}{9} + \frac{2}{15}$ **$\frac{26}{45}$**

Reteaching the Lesson

Activity Have students find the LCM and common denominators, then use fraction strips to show equivalent fractions.

Error Analysis

Watch for students who add or subtract both the numerators and the denominators.

Prevent by verbalizing each problem (for example, one-seventh plus five-sevenths equals how many sevenths?). Only the numerator tells how many.

***Study Guide Masters,* p. 50**

Name ______ Date ______

Study Guide

Adding and Subtracting Fractions

To add and subtract fractions, rename the fractions with a common denominator as necessary. Then add or subtract the numerators and simplify.

Examples **Add or subtract. Write each sum or difference in simplest form.**

	Find the least common multiple (LCM).	*Rename the fractions with a common denominator.*	*Add numerators. Simplify.*
1 $\frac{7}{8} + \frac{7}{12}$	$8 = 2 \times 2 \times 2$ $12 = 2 \times 2 \times 3$ The LCM of 8 and 12 is $2 \times 2 \times 2 \times 3$, or 24.	$\frac{7}{8} = \frac{21}{24}$ $+\frac{7}{12} = \frac{14}{24}$	$\frac{21}{24} + \frac{14}{24}$ $\frac{35}{24} = 1\frac{11}{24}$
	Find the LCM.	*Rename.*	*Subtract. Simplify.*
2 $\frac{7}{9} - \frac{1}{6}$	$9 = 3 \times 3$ $6 = 2 \times 3$ The LCM of 6 and 9 is $2 \times 3 \times 3$, or 18.	$\frac{7}{9} = \frac{14}{18}$ $-\frac{1}{6} = \frac{3}{18}$	$\frac{14}{18} - \frac{3}{18}$ $\frac{11}{18}$

Add or subtract. Write each sum or difference in simplest form.

1. $\frac{5}{8} + \frac{1}{8}$ $\frac{3}{4}$
2. $\frac{7}{9} - \frac{2}{9}$ $\frac{5}{9}$
3. $\frac{1}{2} + \frac{3}{4}$ $1\frac{1}{4}$
4. $\frac{2}{5} - \frac{1}{6}$ $\frac{7}{30}$
5. $\frac{4}{7} + \frac{1}{2}$ $1\frac{1}{14}$
6. $\frac{11}{12} - \frac{2}{3}$ $\frac{1}{4}$
7. $\frac{4}{9} + \frac{5}{6}$ $1\frac{5}{18}$
8. $\frac{5}{6} - \frac{5}{8}$ $\frac{5}{24}$
9. $\frac{1}{4} + \frac{3}{8}$ $\frac{5}{8}$
10. $\frac{8}{15} - \frac{2}{5}$ $\frac{2}{15}$
11. $\frac{7}{12} - \frac{3}{10}$ $\frac{17}{60}$
12. $\frac{1}{2} + \frac{1}{6}$ $\frac{2}{3}$

 T50 *Mathematics: Applications and Connections, Course 2*

22. Find $\frac{5}{8}$ minus $\frac{5}{12}$. $\frac{5}{24}$

23. Find the sum of $\frac{9}{10}$ and $\frac{4}{15}$. $1\frac{1}{6}$

Solve each equation. Write the solution in simplest form.

24. $\frac{19}{24} - \frac{1}{4} = c$ $\frac{13}{24}$

25. $x = \frac{8}{9} + \frac{7}{15}$ $1\frac{16}{45}$

26. $\frac{5}{8} - \frac{5}{36} = k$ $\frac{35}{72}$

27. $t = \frac{3}{8} - \frac{1}{12}$ $\frac{7}{24}$

28. $\frac{3}{4} + \frac{7}{20} = p$ $1\frac{1}{10}$

29. $\frac{7}{9} + \frac{5}{6} = w$ $1\frac{11}{18}$

30. ***Algebra*** Evaluate $b + \frac{11}{12}$ if $b = \frac{9}{20}$. $1\frac{11}{30}$

31. ***Algebra*** Find the value of $\frac{3}{4} - c$ if $c = \frac{3}{11}$. $\frac{21}{44}$

Applications and Problem Solving

32. ***Earth Science*** Carbon dioxide gas is said to be responsible for $\frac{1}{2}$ of the greenhouse effect, which is the warming of Earth's surface. Chlorofluorocarbons are said to account for another $\frac{1}{6}$ of it. Together, how much are these two gases responsible for the greenhouse effect? $\frac{2}{3}$

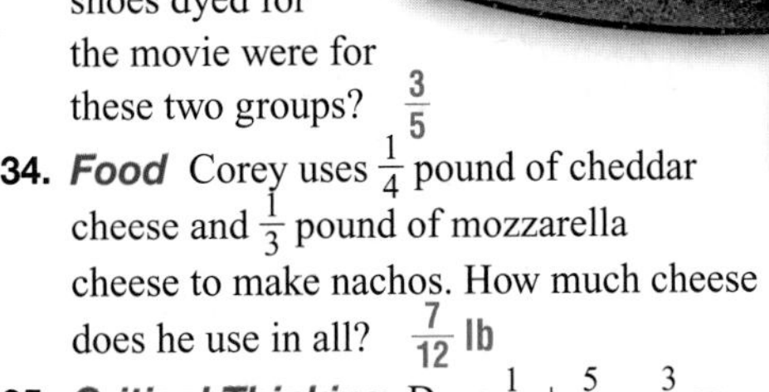

33. ***Entertainment*** For a popular movie, shoes were dyed emerald green for the residents of Emerald City. If $\frac{1}{3}$ of the shoes dyed were for the townspeople and $\frac{4}{15}$ were for the shopkeepers, what part of the shoes dyed for the movie were for these two groups? $\frac{3}{5}$

34. ***Food*** Corey uses $\frac{1}{4}$ pound of cheddar cheese and $\frac{1}{3}$ pound of mozzarella cheese to make nachos. How much cheese does he use in all? $\frac{7}{12}$ lb

35. ***Critical Thinking*** Does $\frac{1}{4} + \frac{5}{7} - \frac{3}{8} = \frac{5}{7} + \frac{3}{8} - \frac{1}{4}$? Explain. **No; commutative property does not hold for subtraction.**

Mixed Review

36. Round $\frac{2}{15}$ to 0, $\frac{1}{2}$, or 1. *(Lesson 7-1)* **0**

37. ***Algebra*** Solve $23 = 14w - 5$. *(Lesson 6-3)* **2**

38. 14 ft

38. ***Scuba Diving*** Find the distance between two divers if one diver is 27 feet below sea level and the other diver is 13 feet below sea level. *(Lesson 5-5)*

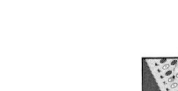

39. **Standardized Test Practice** Which percent represents the shaded area? *(Lesson 4-6)* **A**

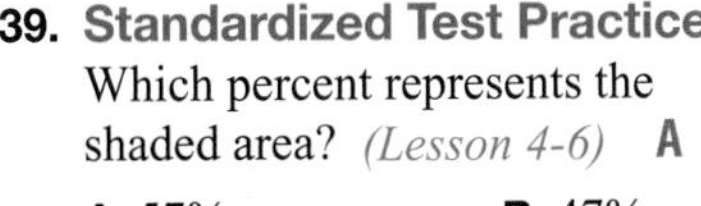

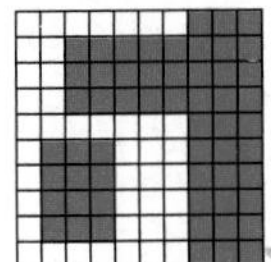

A 57% B 47%
C 43% D 38%

For **Extra Practice**, see page 586.

4 ASSESS

Closing Activity

Modeling Have students use different pattern blocks to make a large triangle or quadrilateral. Ask them to assign a value of 1 to the figure and then find the fractional values of the pattern block pieces they used. Have students use these values to write addition and subtraction exercises and their solutions. Students can check each other's work.

***Practice Masters*, p. 50**

Name______ Date______

7-2 Practice

Adding and Subtracting Fractions

Add or subtract. Write each sum or difference in simplest form.

1. $\frac{1}{7} + \frac{3}{7}$ $\frac{4}{7}$
2. $\frac{3}{4} - \frac{1}{4}$ $\frac{1}{2}$
3. $\frac{11}{12} - \frac{1}{3}$ $\frac{7}{12}$
4. $\frac{8}{15} - \frac{2}{5}$ $\frac{2}{15}$
5. $\frac{17}{25} + \frac{3}{10}$ $\frac{49}{50}$
6. $\frac{7}{8} + \frac{2}{3}$ $1\frac{13}{24}$
7. $\frac{6}{7} - \frac{1}{7}$ $\frac{5}{7}$
8. $\frac{9}{10} + \frac{1}{5}$ $1\frac{1}{10}$
9. $\frac{2}{3} + \frac{6}{7}$ $1\frac{11}{21}$
10. $\frac{11}{15} + \frac{3}{5}$ $1\frac{1}{3}$
11. $\frac{4}{5} - \frac{1}{10}$ $\frac{7}{10}$
12. $\frac{17}{18} - \frac{2}{9}$ $\frac{13}{18}$
13. $\frac{3}{4} + \frac{1}{9}$ $\frac{31}{36}$
14. $\frac{7}{8} - \frac{1}{3}$ $\frac{13}{24}$
15. $\frac{7}{9} + \frac{1}{3}$ $1\frac{1}{9}$
16. $\frac{3}{4} - \frac{2}{5}$ $\frac{7}{20}$
17. $\frac{2}{5} + \frac{12}{13}$ $1\frac{21}{65}$
18. $\frac{3}{20} + \frac{3}{10}$ $\frac{9}{20}$

 T50 *Mathematics: Applications and Connections*, Course 2

Extending the Lesson

***Enrichment Masters*, p. 50**

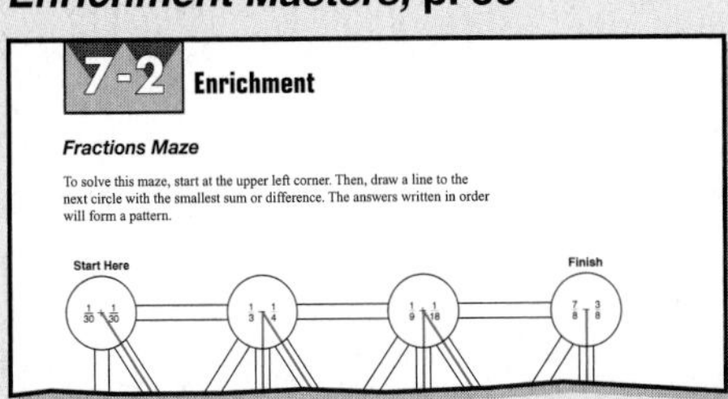

7-2 Enrichment
Fractions Maze
To solve this maze, start at the upper left corner. Then, draw a line to the next circle with the smallest sum or difference. The answers written in order will form a pattern.
Start Here
Finish

Activity Tell students that $a = \frac{1}{3}$, $b = \frac{3}{4}$, $c = \frac{4}{5}$, and $d = \frac{5}{6}$. Ask them to evaluate expressions such as $a + b$, $(b + c) - d$, $b + (d - a)$ and so on. Ask students to make up their own expressions for classmates to evaluate.

7-3 Lesson Notes

Instructional Resources

- *Study Guide Masters,* p. 51
- *Practice Masters,* p. 51
- *Enrichment Masters,* p. 51
- Transparencies 7-3, A and B
- *Assessment and Evaluation Masters,* p. 183

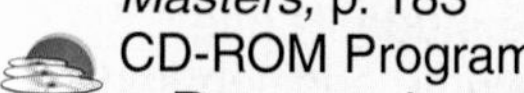

CD-ROM Program
- Resource Lesson 7-3

Recommended Pacing	
Standard	Day 4 of 15
Honors	Day 4 of 14
Block	Day 2 of 8

1 FOCUS

5-Minute Check
(Lesson 7-2)

Add or subtract. Write each sum or difference in simplest form.

1. $\frac{3}{8} + \frac{5}{8}$ 1
2. $\frac{2}{9} + \frac{3}{5}$ $\frac{37}{45}$
3. $\frac{9}{10} - \frac{3}{4}$ $\frac{3}{20}$
4. $1\frac{1}{12} + \frac{5}{9}$ $1\frac{23}{36}$
5. To make a salad, Henry used $\frac{3}{4}$ pound of Boston lettuce and $\frac{2}{3}$ pound of red lettuce. How much lettuce did he use in all? $1\frac{5}{12}$ pounds

The 5-Minute Check is also available on **Transparency 7-3A** for this lesson.

2 TEACH

Transparency 7-3B contains a teaching aid for this lesson.

Using Discussion Focus on two key elements of adding and subtracting mixed numbers—finding common denominators and renaming. Have students compare renaming of mixed numbers with renaming in subtraction of whole numbers.

7-3 Adding and Subtracting Mixed Numbers

What you'll learn

You'll learn to add and subtract mixed numbers.

When am I ever going to use this?

Knowing how to add and subtract mixed numbers can help you make alterations when sewing.

Leathersmith "Wild" Bill Cleaver of Vashon Island, Washington, makes frontier jeans, cowboy shirts, gloves, and vests using designs from the 1800s. If Bill has a shirt pattern for a back measurement of $18\frac{1}{2}$ inches, but his his client's back measures $16\frac{5}{8}$ inches, how much smaller than the pattern does he need to make the shirt? *This problem will be solved in Example 4.*

Adding and Subtracting Mixed Numbers	To add or subtract mixed numbers: 1. Add or subtract the fractions. If necessary, rename the fractions first. 2. Add or subtract the whole numbers. 3. Simplify.

Examples

Add or subtract. Write each sum or difference in simplest form.

1 $9\frac{4}{5} - 2\frac{1}{5}$

Estimate: 10 − 2 = 8

$$\begin{array}{r} 9\frac{4}{5} \\ -2\frac{1}{5} \\ \hline 7\frac{3}{5} \end{array}$$

The difference, $7\frac{3}{5}$, is close to the estimate.

2 $14\frac{5}{6} + 17\frac{9}{10}$

Estimate: 15 + 18 = 33

$$\begin{array}{r} 14\frac{5}{6} \\ +\ 17\frac{9}{10} \\ \hline \end{array} \rightarrow \begin{array}{r} 14\frac{25}{30} \\ +\ 17\frac{27}{30} \\ \hline 31\frac{52}{30} \end{array}$$

$$\begin{aligned} 31\frac{52}{30} &= 31 + \frac{52}{30} \\ &= 31 + 1\frac{22}{30} \\ &= 32\frac{22}{30} \text{ or } 32\frac{11}{15} \end{aligned}$$

Study Hint

Technology You can use a calculator to add and subtract mixed numbers. To find $12\frac{1}{5} + 6\frac{3}{4}$, enter:

12 [UNIT] 1 [/] 5 [+] 6 [UNIT] 3 [/] 4 [=] [Ab/c] 18U19/20. The answer is $18\frac{19}{20}$.

Sometimes, when you subtract two mixed numbers, the fraction in the first mixed number is less than the fraction in the second. In this case, you need to rename the first mixed number before subtracting.

Examples

3 Find $4\frac{1}{3} - 2\frac{2}{3}$.

Estimate: 4 − 3 = 1

$\frac{1}{3}$ is less than $\frac{2}{3}$, so you need to rename $4\frac{1}{3}$.

Think: $4\frac{1}{3} = 3\frac{■}{3}$

Motivating the Lesson

Communication Have students read the opening paragraph. Ask them how adding mixed numbers is similar to adding fractions and how it is different.

Use circle diagrams.

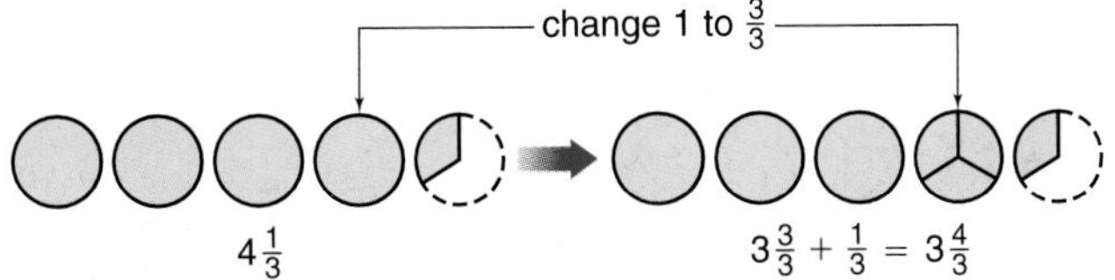

Now find the difference.

$3\frac{4}{3} - 2\frac{2}{3} = 1\frac{2}{3}$

So, $4\frac{1}{3} - 2\frac{2}{3} = 1\frac{2}{3}$. *Compare to the estimate.*

APPLICATION

4 **Sewing** **Refer to the beginning of the lesson. Find how much smaller than the pattern Bill must make the shirt.**

Explore You need to find $18\frac{1}{2} - 16\frac{5}{8}$. *Estimate: 19 − 17 = 2*

Plan Rename $18\frac{1}{2}$ as $18\frac{4}{8}$. So, $18\frac{4}{8} - 16\frac{5}{8}$. Since $\frac{4}{8}$ is less than $\frac{5}{8}$, you need to rename $18\frac{4}{8}$.

$18\frac{4}{8} = 17\frac{8}{8} + \frac{4}{8} = 17\frac{12}{8}$

Solve $17\frac{12}{8} - 16\frac{5}{8} = 1\frac{7}{8}$

The shirt needs to be $1\frac{7}{8}$ inches smaller than the pattern.

Examine Compare to the estimate. The answer is reasonable.

CHECK FOR UNDERSTANDING

Communicating Mathematics

Read and study the lesson to answer each question.

1. ***Show*** that $3\frac{1}{4} = 2\frac{5}{4}$ using circle models. **See margin.**
2. ***Explain*** whether $5\frac{2}{3} + 1\frac{3}{4}$ is greater than, less than, or equal to $4\frac{1}{3} + \frac{5}{8}$. How do you know? **greater than, since 6 + 2 > 4 + 1**

3. ***Write*** an explanation comparing renaming of mixed numbers with renaming of whole numbers in subtraction. **See margin.**

Guided Practice

Complete. Use circle diagrams if necessary.

4. $3\frac{6}{4} = 4\frac{■}{2}$ **1**
5. $5\frac{1}{6} = 4\frac{■}{6}$ **7**
6. $2\frac{12}{9} = ■\frac{1}{3}$ **3**

■ Reteaching the Lesson ■

Activity Provide pairs of students with inch rulers to use as number lines. Have them use the rulers to model addition of mixed numbers by locating the first addend and then *counting forward.* They can model subtraction by locating the first mixed number and then *counting backward.*

In-Class Examples

Add or subtract. Write each sum or difference in simplest form.

For Example 1

$7\frac{5}{6} - 4\frac{2}{9}$ **$3\frac{11}{18}$**

For Example 2

$14\frac{5}{8} + 18\frac{3}{10}$ **$32\frac{37}{40}$**

For Example 3

$4\frac{1}{4} - 2\frac{3}{8}$ **$1\frac{7}{8}$**

For Example 4

Bob's hat size is $6\frac{3}{4}$. Betty's hat size is $7\frac{1}{8}$. How much larger is Betty's size than Bob's? **$\frac{3}{8}$ of a size**

Teaching Tip Remind students that the first step in solving problems with mixed numbers is to find a common denominator for the fractions.

3 PRACTICE/APPLY

Check for Understanding

If students need additional practice or instruction after completing Exercises 1–11, one of these options may be helpful.

- Extra Practice, see p. 586
- Reteaching Activity
- *Transition Booklet,* pp. 27–28
- *Study Guide Masters,* p. 51
- *Practice Masters,* p. 51

Additional Answers

1.

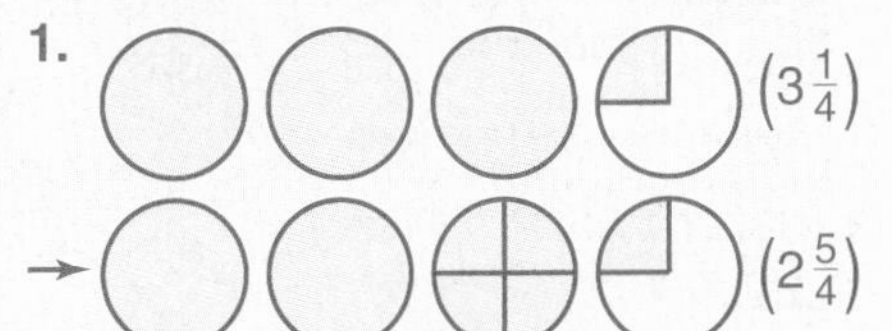

3. **Renaming of mixed numbers is used when the fraction in the first mixed number is less than the fraction in the second. Renaming of whole numbers is used when the digit in the first number is less than the digit in the same place value in the second number.**

Assignment Guide

Core: 13–37 odd, 39–44
Enriched: 12–34 even, 36–44

Add or subtract. Write each sum or difference in simplest form.

7. $3\frac{1}{6} + 5\frac{1}{6}$ $8\frac{1}{3}$
8. $8\frac{7}{9} - 3\frac{1}{9}$ $5\frac{2}{3}$
9. $3\frac{1}{2} - 1\frac{3}{4}$ $1\frac{3}{4}$
10. Solve $g = 7\frac{3}{8} + 9\frac{1}{6}$. Write the solution in simplest form. $16\frac{13}{24}$
11. ***Jewels*** In 1908, the world's largest diamond was cut. Two of the gems that came from the cutting were Cullinan I, which weighed $530\frac{1}{5}$ carats, and Cullinan II, which weighed $317\frac{2}{5}$ carats. How much more did Cullinan I weigh than Cullinan II? $212\frac{4}{5}$ carats

EXERCISES

Practice

Complete. Use circle diagrams if necessary.

12. $3\frac{10}{7} = 4\frac{■}{7}$ 3
13. $6\frac{1}{2} = 5\frac{■}{2}$ 3
14. $7\frac{14}{10} = 8\frac{■}{10}$ 4
15. $8\frac{3}{5} = 7\frac{■}{5}$ 8
16. $9\frac{9}{8} = 10\frac{■}{8}$ 1
17. $4\frac{5}{6} = 3\frac{■}{6}$ 11
18. $9\frac{2}{3} = ■\frac{5}{3}$ 8
19. $12\frac{9}{5} = ■\frac{4}{5}$ 13

Add or subtract. Write each sum or difference in simplest form.

20. $9\frac{1}{8} + 2\frac{5}{8}$ $11\frac{3}{4}$
21. $7\frac{5}{6} - 3\frac{1}{6}$ $4\frac{2}{3}$
22. $7\frac{5}{6} + 9\frac{3}{8}$ $17\frac{5}{24}$
23. $6\frac{5}{6} - 2\frac{1}{3}$ $4\frac{1}{2}$
24. $9\frac{4}{5} - 2\frac{3}{10}$ $7\frac{1}{2}$
25. $13\frac{7}{8} + 15\frac{7}{10}$ $29\frac{23}{40}$
26. $3\frac{7}{12} + 8\frac{3}{4}$ $12\frac{1}{3}$
27. $7\frac{1}{3} - 3\frac{5}{9}$ $3\frac{7}{9}$
28. $8\frac{3}{4} - 1\frac{7}{10}$ $7\frac{1}{20}$
29. What is the sum of $2\frac{1}{6}$, $3\frac{1}{2}$, and $5\frac{7}{8}$? $11\frac{13}{24}$
30. Find $13\frac{1}{8}$ minus $1\frac{7}{10}$. $11\frac{17}{40}$

Solve each equation. Write the solution in simplest form.

31. $5\frac{5}{6} - 3\frac{2}{3} = a$ $2\frac{1}{6}$
32. $6\frac{13}{15} + 2\frac{3}{5} = y$ $9\frac{7}{15}$
33. $q = 4\frac{3}{10} - 1\frac{3}{4}$ $2\frac{11}{20}$
34. ***Algebra*** Evaluate $k + 8\frac{5}{12}$ if $k = 11\frac{1}{4}$. $19\frac{2}{3}$
35. ***Algebra*** Find the value of $6\frac{1}{2} - m$ if $m = 3\frac{4}{9}$. $3\frac{1}{18}$

***Study Guide Masters*, p. 51**

Name__________ Date__________

7-3 Study Guide

Adding and Subtracting Mixed Numbers

To add or subtract mixed number:
1. Add or subtract the fractions. Rename if necessary.
2. Add or subtract the whole numbers.
3. Rename and simplify.

Examples

1. $14\frac{1}{2} + 18\frac{2}{3} \rightarrow 14\frac{3}{6} + 18\frac{4}{6} \rightarrow \frac{7}{6} \rightarrow 32\frac{7}{6} = 33\frac{1}{6}$

2. $21 - 12\frac{5}{8} \rightarrow 20\frac{8}{8} - 12\frac{5}{8} \rightarrow \frac{3}{8} \rightarrow 8\frac{3}{8}$

Complete.

1. $7\frac{1}{6} = 6\frac{□}{6}$ 7
2. $5\frac{2}{5} = 4\frac{□}{5}$ 7
3. $8\frac{1}{2} = 7\frac{□}{2}$ 3
4. $9 = 8\frac{□}{7}$ 7
5. $4\frac{12}{9} = □\frac{1}{3}$ 5
6. $7\frac{10}{8} = 8\frac{□}{4}$ 1

Add or subtract. Write each sum or difference in simplest form.

7. $8\frac{1}{7} + 5\frac{3}{7}$ $13\frac{4}{7}$
8. $9\frac{3}{4} - 2\frac{1}{4}$ $7\frac{1}{2}$
9. $6\frac{5}{8} + 3\frac{3}{8}$ 10
10. $5\frac{1}{2} - 3\frac{1}{4}$ $2\frac{1}{4}$
11. $6\frac{1}{3} + 2\frac{1}{6}$ $8\frac{1}{2}$
12. $9 - 3\frac{2}{5}$ $5\frac{3}{5}$
13. $2\frac{3}{4} + 7\frac{3}{4}$ $10\frac{1}{2}$
14. $6\frac{1}{2} - 6\frac{1}{3}$ $\frac{1}{6}$
15. $18\frac{1}{2} + 5\frac{5}{8}$ $24\frac{1}{8}$
16. $13\frac{2}{9} - 7\frac{1}{3}$ $5\frac{8}{9}$
17. $15\frac{14}{15} + 13\frac{1}{2}$ $29\frac{13}{30}$
18. $26 - 6\frac{12}{13}$ $19\frac{1}{13}$

 T51 *Mathematics: Applications and Connections*, Course 2

MathPASS CD-ROM

This CD-ROM offers a complete, self-paced mathematics curriculum. Each lesson includes a pretest, tutorial, guided practice, and posttest. MathPASS Lessons 21 and 22 are correlated to this Student Edition lesson.
For Windows & Macintosh

Applications and Problem Solving

36. ***Stock Market*** The table shows the 52-week high and low prices of airline stocks as of April, 1997. Find the difference between the high and low price of each stock.
    a. Airline A $28\frac{5}{8}$
    b. Airline B $16\frac{1}{16}$
    c. Airline C $12\frac{5}{8}$

Airline Stocks Soar

COMPANY	52-week high / low
Airline A	$95\frac{3}{8}$ / $66\frac{3}{4}$
Airline B	$21\frac{3}{8}$ / $5\frac{5}{16}$
Airline C	$33\frac{1}{4}$ / $20\frac{5}{8}$

37. ***Measurement*** You can make your own window-washing solution by mixing $1\frac{1}{3}$ cups of ammonia and $1\frac{1}{2}$ cups of vinegar with baking soda and water. Will the solution fit in a $\frac{1}{2}$-quart pan?

37. No, the ammonia and vinegar make $2\frac{5}{6}$ cups. A $\frac{1}{2}$-quart pan holds only 2 cups.

38. ***Life Science*** Female anglerfish are larger than males, and they have glowing lures that attract prey. If a female is $2\frac{1}{2}$ inches long, and a male is only $\frac{2}{5}$ of an inch long, how much longer is the female than the male? **$2\frac{1}{10}$ in.**

Anglerfish

39. ***Critical Thinking*** A string is cut in half, and one of the halves is used to bundle newspapers. Then one-fifth of the remaining string is cut off and used to tie a balloon. The piece left is 8 feet long. How long was the string originally? **20 ft**

Mixed Review

40. Add $\frac{5}{6}$ and $\frac{2}{3}$. *(Lesson 7-2)* **$1\frac{1}{2}$**

41. ***Algebra*** Find four solutions of $y = -3x + 7$. Write the solutions as ordered pairs. *(Lesson 6-7)* **Sample answers: (−1, 10), (0, 7), (1, 4), (2, 1)**

42. **Standardized Test Practice** Martin's job is to pack calculators into boxes. One day, Martin packed 448 calculators into 16 boxes. If each box contains the same number of calculators, how many calculators did Martin put into each box? *(Lesson 5-7)* **C**

    A 10 **B** 25 **C** 28 **D** 52 **E** 57

43. ***Food*** The graph shows what percent of Americans chose the given pizza toppings as their favorite. Express the percent of people who chose each topping as a fraction in simplest form. *(Lesson 4-7)*
    a. onions $\frac{1}{25}$
    b. vegetables $\frac{13}{100}$
    c. mushrooms $\frac{7}{50}$

What's On Top?

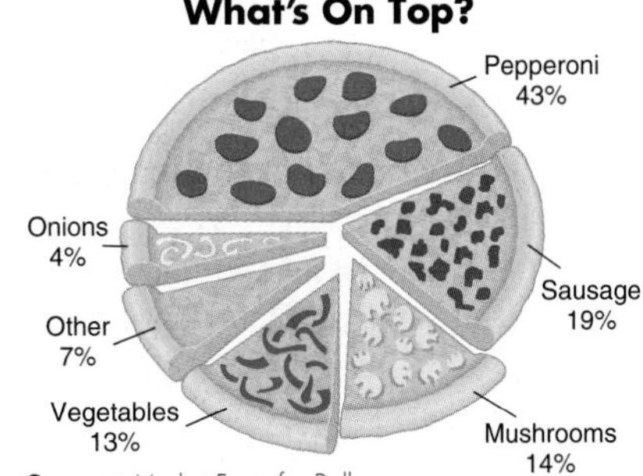

Source: Market Facts for Bolla

44. Express $\frac{7}{25}$ as a decimal. *(Lesson 2-7)* **0.28**

For **Extra Practice,** see page 586.

Teaching Tip In Exercise 36, the *high* and *low* refers to the extremes in prices for the past 52 weeks ending that day.

4 ASSESS

Closing Activity

Writing Ask students to write and solve two problems involving mixed numbers, one in which renaming is necessary and one in which it is not. Have students present the solutions in simplest form.

Chapter 7, Quiz A (Lessons 7-1 through 7-3) is available in the *Assessment and Evaluation Masters,* p. 183.

Practice Masters, p. 51

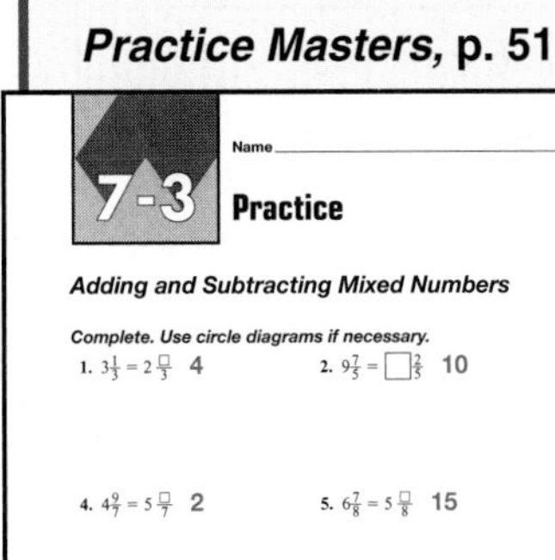

Name________ Date________

7-3 Practice

Adding and Subtracting Mixed Numbers

Complete. Use circle diagrams if necessary.

1. $3\frac{1}{3} = 2\frac{\square}{3}$ **4**
2. $9\frac{7}{5} = \square\frac{2}{5}$ **10**
3. $7\frac{1}{2} = 6\frac{\square}{2}$ **3**
4. $4\frac{9}{7} = 5\frac{\square}{7}$ **2**
5. $6\frac{7}{8} = 5\frac{\square}{8}$ **15**
6. $12\frac{3}{4} = 11\frac{\square}{4}$ **7**

Add or subtract. Write each sum or difference in simplest form.

7. $2\frac{1}{3} + 5\frac{1}{3}$ **$7\frac{2}{3}$**
8. $9\frac{6}{7} - 6\frac{1}{7}$ **$3\frac{5}{7}$**
9. $3\frac{4}{5} + 1\frac{3}{5}$ **$5\frac{2}{5}$**
10. $8\frac{3}{4} - 5\frac{1}{8}$ **$3\frac{5}{8}$**
11. $7\frac{5}{6} - 2\frac{1}{3}$ **$5\frac{1}{2}$**
12. $9\frac{5}{12} - 5\frac{3}{4}$ **$3\frac{2}{3}$**
13. $12\frac{7}{10} - 5\frac{3}{4}$ **$6\frac{19}{20}$**
14. $6\frac{5}{6} + 7\frac{3}{8}$ **$14\frac{5}{24}$**
15. $9\frac{3}{8} - 1\frac{2}{3}$ **$7\frac{17}{24}$**
16. $10\frac{7}{9} + 4\frac{1}{4}$ **$15\frac{1}{36}$**
17. $8\frac{4}{15} - 6\frac{3}{5}$ **$1\frac{2}{3}$**
18. $2\frac{1}{4} + 3\frac{1}{2} + 5\frac{5}{8}$ **$11\frac{3}{8}$**

 T51 *Mathematics: Applications and Connections, Course 2*

Extending the Lesson

Enrichment Masters, p. 51

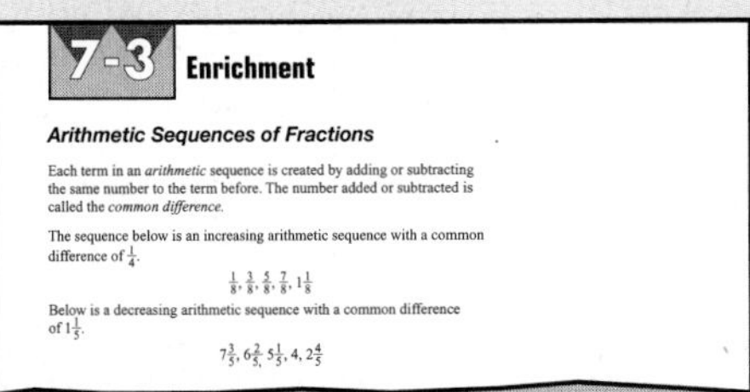

7-3 Enrichment

Arithmetic Sequences of Fractions

Each term in an *arithmetic* sequence is created by adding or subtracting the same number to the term before. The number added or subtracted is called the *common difference.*

The sequence below is an increasing arithmetic sequence with a common difference of $\frac{1}{4}$.

$\frac{1}{8}, \frac{3}{8}, \frac{5}{8}, \frac{7}{8}, 1\frac{1}{8}$

Below is a decreasing arithmetic sequence with a common difference of $1\frac{1}{5}$.

$7\frac{3}{5}, 6\frac{2}{5}, 5\frac{1}{5}, 4, 2\frac{4}{5}$

Activity Have students write the next three numbers in each sequence. Then ask them to make up sequences of their own for others to continue.

1. $2\frac{1}{4}, 3\frac{3}{4}, 5\frac{1}{4}, \ldots$ **$6\frac{3}{4}, 8\frac{1}{4}, 9\frac{3}{4}, \ldots$**

2. $20\frac{1}{3}, 17\frac{2}{3}, 15, \ldots$ **$12\frac{1}{3}, 9\frac{2}{3}, 7, \ldots$**

Objective Students solve problems by eliminating possibilities.

Recommended Pacing	
Standard	Day 5 of 15
Honors	Day 5 of 14
Block	Day 3 of 8

1 FOCUS

Getting Started Have students act out the situation presented at the beginning of the lesson. You may suggest they make a drawing of what they know about the problem. Ask them how eliminating possibilities will help them to make this decision. Have them work in groups to answer Exercises 1–3. They might model Exercise 3 using cups of water instead of gallons.

2 TEACH

Teaching Tip Ask students how the eliminating-possibilities strategy might help them when taking standardized tests. **Sample answers: saves time; could improve chances of correct answer if guessing.**

In-Class Example

Jeanine has to fill the children's pool with 15 gallons of water. She has already filled it with $9\frac{1}{8}$ gallons. How much more does she need to add? **B**

A. $5\frac{1}{8}$ **B.** $5\frac{7}{8}$

C. $4\frac{7}{8}$ **D.** $5\frac{3}{8}$

Teaching Tip In Exercise 2, some students may say C can be eliminated because 2 + 3 = 5 and the fractional parts would make it more than 5.

PROBLEM SOLVING

7-3B Eliminate Possibilities

A Follow-Up of Lesson 7-3

Look at this problem. What answer do you get?

Anne has a 5-gallon cooler that she fills with juice and takes to her softball games. If the cooler has $2\frac{1}{3}$ gallons of juice in it, how much juice does she need to add to fill it?

A $7\frac{1}{3}$ gal **B** $2\frac{2}{3}$ gal **C** $3\frac{1}{3}$ gal **D** $\frac{2}{3}$ gal

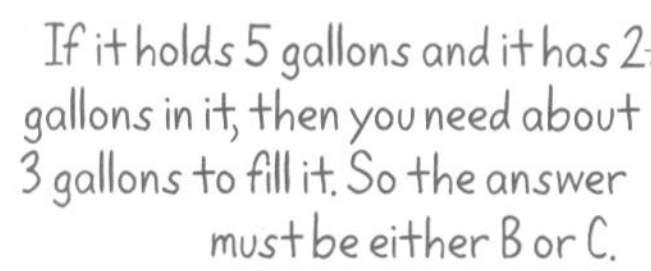

If it holds 5 gallons and it has $2\frac{1}{3}$ gallons in it, then you need about 3 gallons to fill it. So the answer must be either B or C.

Andy

I got Answer A, but that can't be right because it's too big! So, we can eliminate choice A.

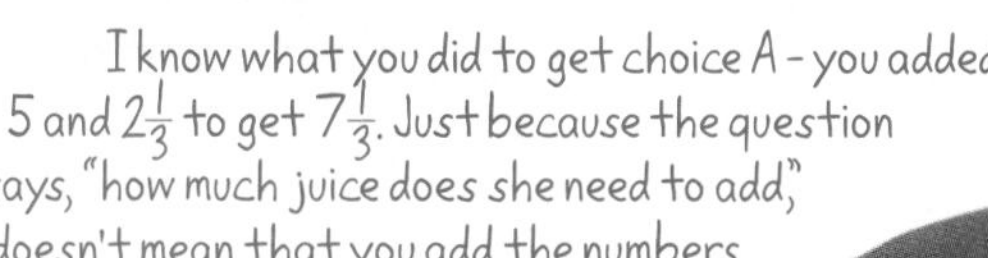

I know what you did to get choice A - you added 5 and $2\frac{1}{3}$ to get $7\frac{1}{3}$. Just because the question says, "how much juice does she need to add," doesn't mean that you add the numbers.

Neshawn

THINK ABOUT IT

Work with a partner.

1. ***List*** different ways to **eliminate possibilities** in solving problems.
2. ***Think*** of another answer that you could eliminate in the problem above.

1. Sample answer: Use estimation, work backward, draw a diagram. 2. Answer D could be eliminated because it is too small.

3. ***Apply*** what you have learned to solve the following problem.

A fishbowl holds $1\frac{1}{2}$ gallons of water. If there is $\frac{1}{3}$ gallon of water in the bowl, how many more gallons are needed to fill the bowl? **D**

A $1\frac{5}{6}$ *gal* *B* $\frac{2}{3}$ *gal*

C $2\frac{1}{6}$ *gal* *D* $1\frac{1}{6}$ *gal*

■ Reteaching the Lesson ■

Activity Have students work with a partner to try different strategies for eliminating possible answers as they work through the exercises in this lesson, making a note of which strategies work best for each problem.

For **Extra Practice,** see page 587.

ON YOUR OWN

4. The third step of the 4-step plan for problem solving asks you to *solve* the problem. ***Explain*** how you use the strategy of eliminating possibilities to solve a problem. **See margin.**

5. ***Write a Problem*** in which eliminating the possibilities would help you solve it. Explain your answer.
6. ***Reflect Back*** Explain how you eliminated possibilities in Exercise 3.
5–6. See students' work.

MIXED PROBLEM SOLVING

STRATEGIES
Look for a pattern.
Solve a simpler problem.
Act it out.
Guess and check.
Draw a diagram.
Make a chart.
Work backward.

Solve. Use any strategy.

7. ***Food*** You need $2\frac{1}{2}$ cups of flour and $1\frac{2}{3}$ cups of sugar in a chocolate chip cookie recipe. How many cups of flour and sugar are called for? **$4\frac{1}{6}$ c**

8. **Standardized Test Practice** Migina bought pencils, 2 for $0.49; felt-tipped pens, 3 for $1.39; and an eraser for $0.29. Choose the best estimate for the amount of change she will get from $5. **C**
A $0.30
B $1.80
C $2.80
D $3.30

9. ***Technology*** A videotape will record 6 hours of programming. Katherine has recorded $2\frac{5}{6}$ hours of a miniseries. She wants to record $3\frac{1}{2}$ hours more on the same tape. Can she do this? Explain your answer. **no; $2\frac{5}{6} + 3\frac{1}{2} > 6$**

10. ***Money Matters*** In 1965, Congress reduced the silver content of half-dollars from $\frac{9}{10}$ to $\frac{2}{5}$. How much less was the silver content after the reduction? **$\frac{1}{2}$**

11. Sample answer: about 98,000 thousand

11. ***Technology*** The cellular phone industry has grown by leaps and bounds since 1995. The graph shows the number of cellular phone antenna sites in thousands.

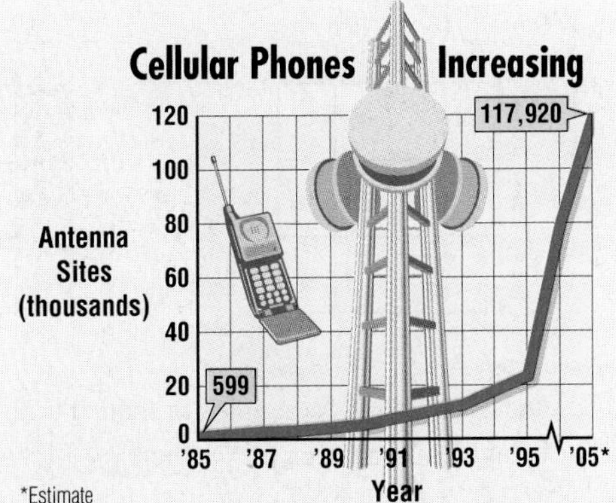

Source: Cellular Telecommunications Industry Association

Estimate the increase in the number of antenna sites from 1995 to 2005.

12. **Standardized Test Practice** A taxi charges $1.15 for the first 0.2 mile and $0.50 for each additional 0.2 mile. Find the cost of a 4-mile taxi ride. **B**
A $9.65
B $10.65
C $12.65
D $13.65
E $13.15

3 PRACTICE/APPLY

Check for Understanding

Use students' responses to Exercise 6 to determine whether they understand the eliminating-possibilities strategy.

Extra Practice If students need additional practice in problem solving, extra practice is available on the following pages.
- Eliminate Possibilities, see p. 587
- Mixed Problem Solving, see pp. 605–606

Assignment Guide

All: 7–12

4 ASSESS

Closing Activity

Writing Have students write their own problems with a set of possible answers. Ask them to include an explanation of how answers can be eliminated and the problem can be solved.

Additional Answer

4. **Sample answer: If you eliminate all but one possibility, the remaining possibility is the solution.**

Extending the Lesson

Activity Ask students which of the following is an accurate total of the handshakes six people can exchange among themselves: 36, 30, 15, or 6. Have six students act out the handshaking described, while another student records the number of handshakes. Make sure each person shakes every person's hand once. Have them revise their guesses and eliminate possibilities as the activity progresses.

GET READY

Objective Students use models to multiply fractions and mixed numbers.

Optional Resources
Hands-On Lab Masters
- worksheet, p. 52

MANAGEMENT TIPS

Recommended Time
30 minutes

Getting Started Have students work with area models to review multiplication and division of whole numbers. This will help them visually comprehend the process involving multiplication of fractions and mixed numbers.

Activities 1 and 2 on page 282 demonstrate how area models can be used to show products involving fractions and whole numbers. Color transparencies might help students visualize the process more easily.

Activity 3 on page 283 demonstrates how area models can be used to show products involving mixed numbers. Point out that it may be helpful for students to use different colored pencils while shading their models. This will help them to remember what portion of the model represents each fraction.

Teaching Tip Some students may interpret the results of Activity 2 incorrectly by saying the product is $\frac{4}{6}$, because 4 of 6 areas are shaded. Have students cut their models apart, keeping only the double shaded portions. Have them arrange the portions and compare them to the size of the unit square to check the accuracy of their interpretation.

COOPERATIVE LEARNING

7-4A Multiplying Fractions and Mixed Numbers

A Preview of Lesson 7-4

paper

markers

You can use area models to multiply fractions.

TRY THIS

Work with a partner.

1 Model $\frac{1}{4} \times \frac{1}{3}$.

Divide a unit square vertically into fourths and horizontally into thirds.

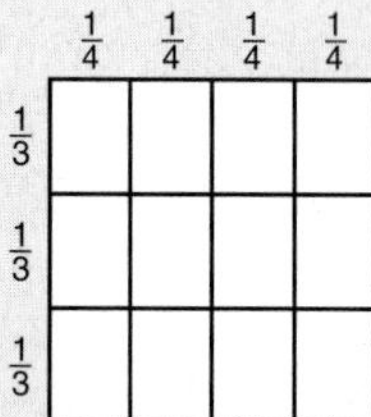

Color one fourth of the square one color.

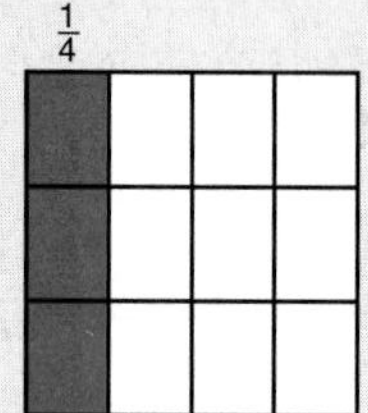

Color one third of the square another color. Count the small rectangles that are shaded both colors.

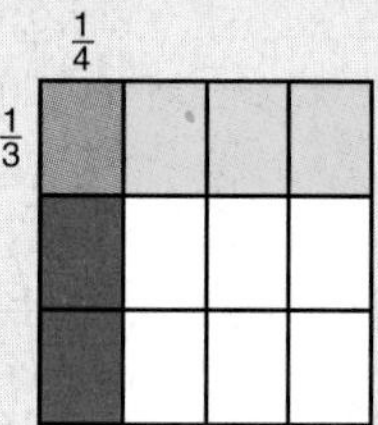

One of the small rectangles is shaded both colors. Since each small rectangle has an area of $\frac{1}{12}$, then $\frac{1}{4} \times \frac{1}{3} = \frac{1}{12}$.

2 Model $2 \times \frac{2}{3}$.

Draw 2 unit squares side by side. Divide them horizontally into thirds.

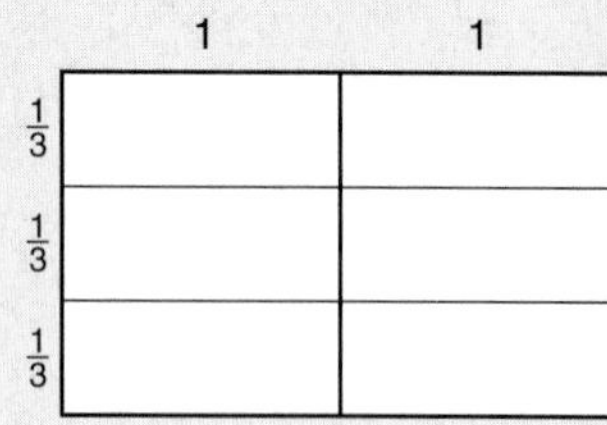

Color the 2 unit squares one color.

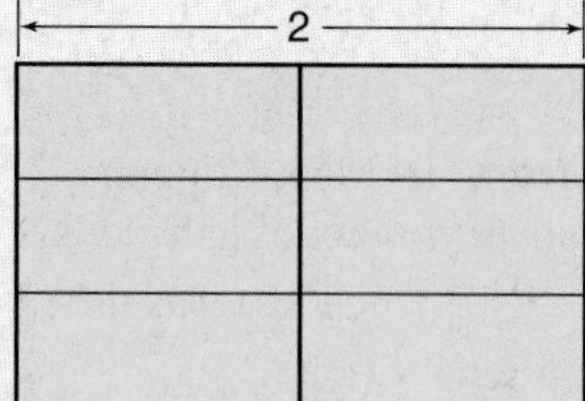

Have students write a paragraph that explains how area models are used to illustrate the multiplication of fractions and mixed numbers.

Color two-thirds of the squares another color. Count the small rectangles that are shaded both colors.

Four of the small rectangles are shaded both colors. Add their areas.

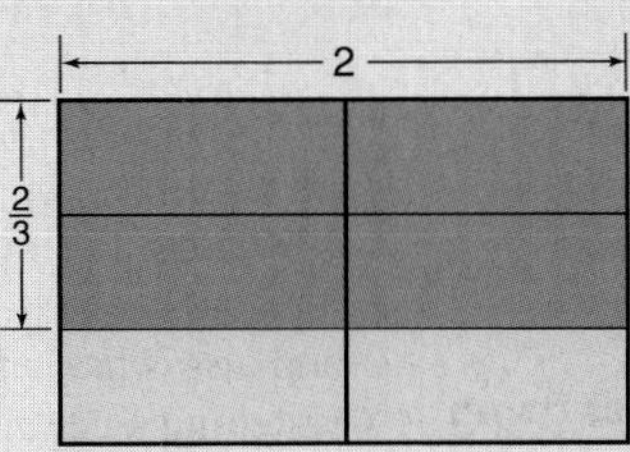

$\frac{1}{3} + \frac{1}{3} + \frac{1}{3} + \frac{1}{3} = \frac{4}{3}$ *Based on 1 unit square, each small rectangle has an area of $\frac{1}{3}$.*

So, $2 \times \frac{2}{3} = \frac{4}{3}$ or $1\frac{1}{3}$.

3 Model $1\frac{1}{2} \times \frac{2}{5}$.

Divide 2 unit squares vertically into halves and horizontally into fifths.

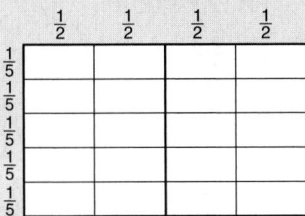

Color $1\frac{1}{2}$ of the squares one color.

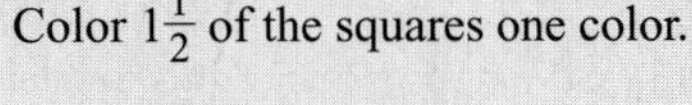

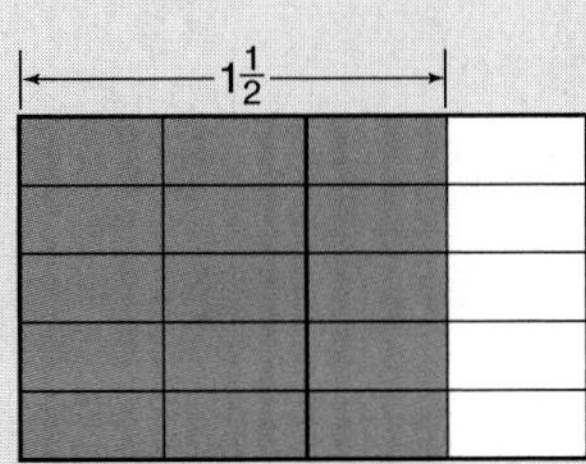

Color two-fifths of the squares another color.

Six of the small rectangles are shaded both colors. Add their areas.

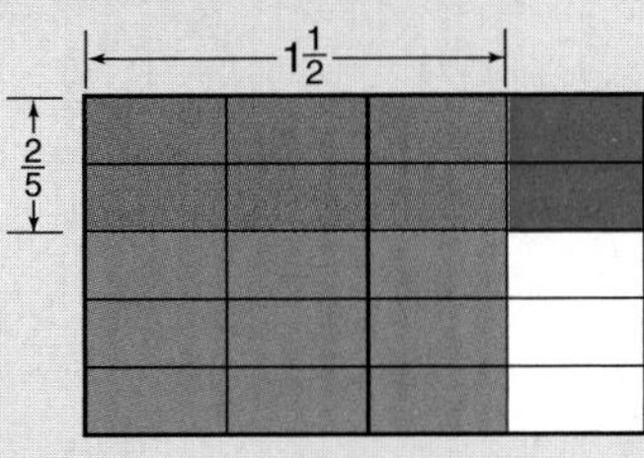

$\frac{1}{10} + \frac{1}{10} + \frac{1}{10} + \frac{1}{10} + \frac{1}{10} + \frac{1}{10} = \frac{6}{10}$ *Based on 1 unit square, each small rectangle has an area of $\frac{1}{10}$.*

So, $1\frac{1}{2} \times \frac{2}{5} = \frac{6}{10}$ or $\frac{3}{5}$.

ON YOUR OWN

Use area models to find each product. **1–6. See margin for models.**

1. $\frac{1}{2} \times \frac{1}{3}$ $\frac{1}{6}$
2. $\frac{2}{3} \times \frac{3}{4}$ $\frac{6}{12}$ or $\frac{1}{2}$
3. $3 \times \frac{1}{2}$ $\frac{3}{2}$ or $1\frac{1}{2}$
4. $2 \times \frac{3}{4}$ $\frac{6}{4}$ or $1\frac{1}{2}$
5. $1\frac{1}{3} \times \frac{1}{4}$ $\frac{4}{12}$ or $\frac{1}{3}$
6. $3\frac{1}{2} \times \frac{1}{2}$ $\frac{7}{4}$ or $1\frac{3}{4}$
7. ***Look Ahead*** Find $2\frac{1}{2} \times 1\frac{1}{3}$. Use area models if necessary. $\frac{20}{6}$ or $3\frac{1}{3}$

Additional Answers

3.

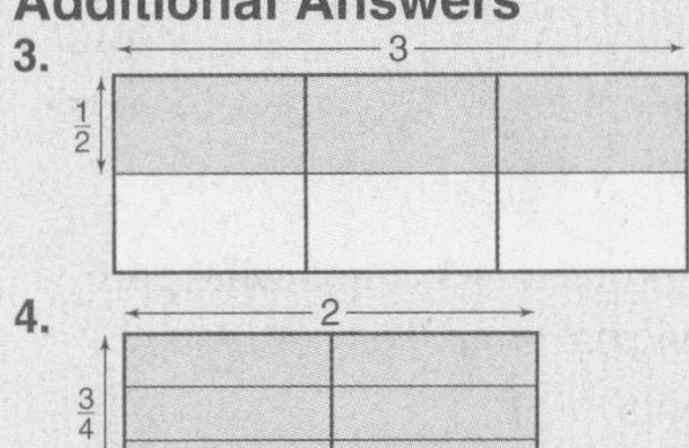

4.

5.

6.

ASSESS

Have students complete Exercises 1–6. Watch for students who may have difficulty dividing and shading their models to represent the appropriate fractions. Make sure they divide them evenly and count the sections carefully before shading.

Use Exercise 7 to determine whether students have mastered the multiplication of fractions and mixed numbers.

Additional Answers

1.

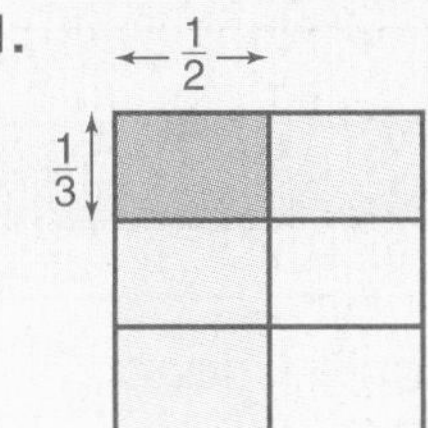

2.

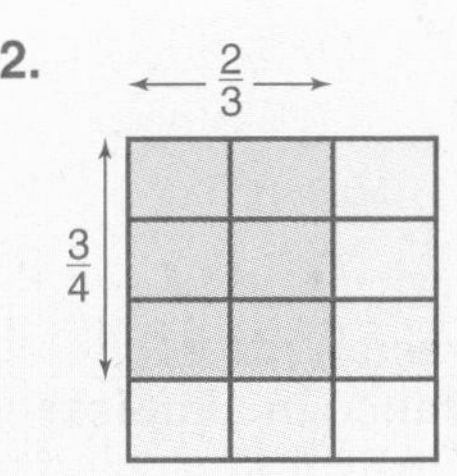

***Hands-On Lab Masters*, p. 52**

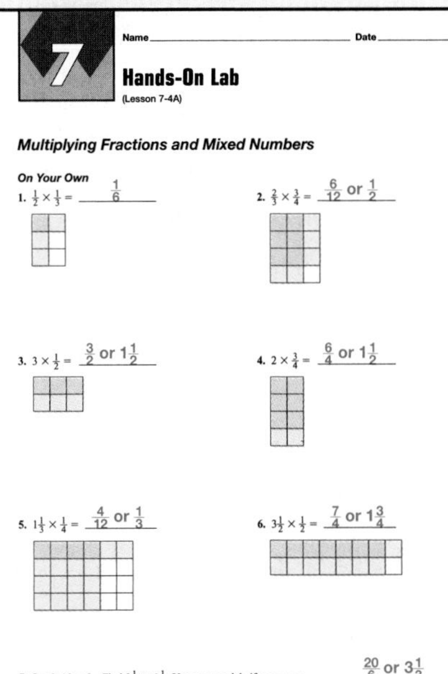

Name ____________ Date ________

7 **Hands-On Lab** (Lesson 7-4A)

Multiplying Fractions and Mixed Numbers

On Your Own

1. $\frac{1}{2} \times \frac{1}{3} =$ $\frac{1}{6}$
2. $\frac{2}{3} \times \frac{3}{4} =$ $\frac{6}{12}$ or $\frac{1}{2}$
3. $3 \times \frac{1}{2} =$ $\frac{3}{2}$ or $1\frac{1}{2}$
4. $2 \times \frac{3}{4} =$ $\frac{6}{4}$ or $1\frac{1}{2}$
5. $1\frac{1}{3} \times \frac{1}{4} =$ $\frac{4}{12}$ or $\frac{1}{3}$
6. $3\frac{1}{2} \times \frac{1}{2} =$ $\frac{7}{4}$ or $1\frac{3}{4}$
7. **Look Ahead** Find $2\frac{1}{2} \times 1\frac{1}{3}$. Use area models if necessary. $\frac{20}{6}$ or $3\frac{1}{3}$

© Glencoe/McGraw-Hill 52 *Mathematics: Applications and Connections, Course 2*

7-4 Lesson Notes

Instructional Resources

- *Study Guide Masters,* p. 52
- *Practice Masters,* p. 52
- *Enrichment Masters,* p. 52
- Transparencies 7-4, A and B

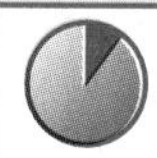

- CD-ROM Program
  - Resource Lesson 7-4
  - Interactive Lesson 7-4

Recommended Pacing	
Standard	Days 6 & 7 of 15
Honors	Days 6 & 7 of 14
Block	Day 4 of 8

1 FOCUS

5-Minute Check
(Lesson 7-3)

Complete.

1. $4\frac{1}{6} = 3\frac{\blacksquare}{6}$ 7
2. $6\frac{7}{5} = \blacksquare\frac{2}{5}$ 7

Add or subtract. Write each sum or difference in simplest form.

3. $3\frac{2}{3} + 5\frac{1}{3}$ 9
4. $6\frac{5}{8} + 8\frac{5}{6}$ $15\frac{11}{24}$
5. $7\frac{1}{5} - 2\frac{1}{2}$ $4\frac{7}{10}$

The 5-Minute Check is also available on **Transparency 7-4A** for this lesson.

Motivating the Lesson

Problem Solving Ask students how they would determine how far a giant tortoise could travel in $3\frac{1}{2}$ hours at a rate of $1\frac{1}{6}$ miles per hour. Multiply $3\frac{1}{2}$ times $1\frac{1}{6}$.

7-4 Multiplying Fractions and Mixed Numbers

***What** you'll learn*

You'll learn to multiply fractions and mixed numbers.

***When** am I ever going to use this?*

Knowing how to multiply fractions and mixed numbers can help you make adjustments in the ingredients in a recipe.

Media ratings measure what part of the U.S. households have their television turned on and also what part of those households were watching a certain program. Suppose $\frac{1}{2}$ of all households have their TV turned on, and $\frac{1}{5}$ of those were watching Program A. You can multiply $\frac{1}{5}$ and $\frac{1}{2}$ to find the part of all households that were watching Program A.

You can multiply fractions like $\frac{1}{2}$ and $\frac{1}{5}$ by using an area model.

$$\frac{1}{2} \times \frac{1}{5} = \frac{1}{10}$$

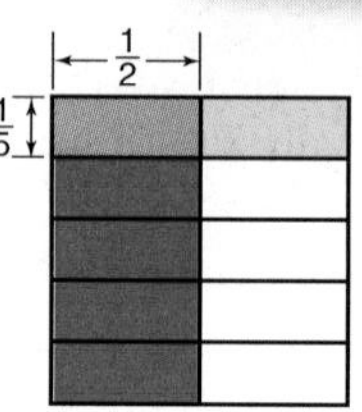

Multiplying Fractions	
Words:	To multiply fractions, multiply the numerators and then multiply the denominators.
Symbols:	**Arithmetic** $\frac{1}{2} \times \frac{1}{5} = \frac{1}{10}$ **Algebra** $\frac{a}{b} \times \frac{c}{d} = \frac{ac}{bd}$ $b, d \neq 0$

Example 1 Find $\frac{1}{3} \times \frac{3}{4}$.

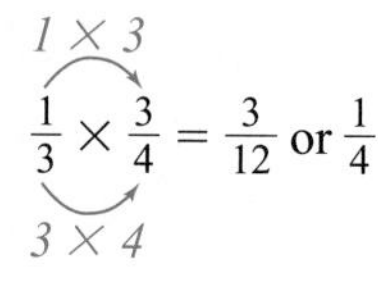

1 × 3

$$\frac{1}{3} \times \frac{3}{4} = \frac{3}{12} \text{ or } \frac{1}{4}$$

3 × 4

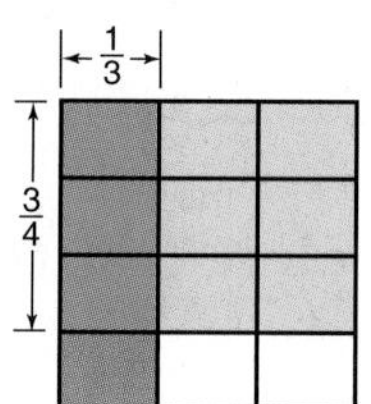

When the numerator and denominator of either fraction have a common factor, you can simplify before you multiply.

Example 2 Multiply $\frac{1}{6} \times \frac{3}{5}$. *Estimate: $0 \times \frac{1}{2} = 0$*

The GCF of 3 and 6 is 3.

$$\frac{1}{6} \times \frac{3}{5} = \frac{1}{\cancel{6}_2} \times \frac{\cancel{3}^1}{5} \quad \textit{Divide 3 and 6 by 3.}$$

$$= \frac{1}{10}$$

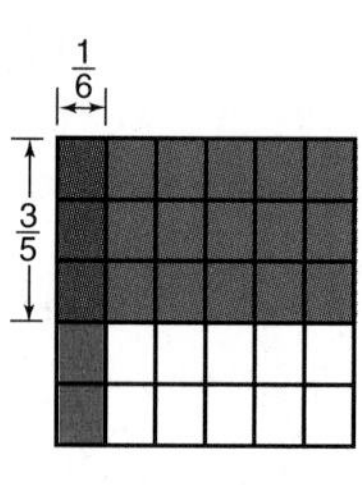

LOOK BACK
Refer to Lesson 4-4 to review GCF.

Multiple Learning Styles

Visual/Spatial Have students model products by using groups of objects separated into subgroups. For example, to multiply $\frac{1}{3}$ and $\frac{3}{4}$, give students 24 counters. First have them find $\frac{1}{3}$ of the counters. 8 Put the rest of the counters aside. Then have them find $\frac{3}{4}$ of the pile representing $\frac{1}{3}$ of the original group. 6 Ask them what part of the original group this subgroup represents. $\frac{6}{24}$ or $\frac{1}{4}$

Example 3 Solve $a = \frac{3}{8} \times \frac{10}{27}$.

$a = \frac{\overset{1}{\cancel{3}}}{\underset{4}{\cancel{8}}} \times \frac{\overset{5}{\cancel{10}}}{\underset{9}{\cancel{27}}}$ *The GCF of 3 and 27 is 3. The GCF of 8 and 10 is 2.*

$a = \frac{5}{36}$

Multiplying Mixed Numbers	To multiply mixed numbers, rename each mixed number as an improper fraction. Then multiply the fractions.

Example 4 CONNECTION **Life Science** Every minute, you inhale about $10\frac{1}{5}$ liters of air. About how much air do you take in each hour?

Estimate: $10 \times 60 = 600$

$10\frac{1}{5} \times 60 = \frac{51}{5} \times 60$ *1 hour = 60 minutes*

$= \frac{51}{\underset{1}{\cancel{5}}} \times \frac{\overset{12}{\cancel{60}}}{1}$ *The GCF of 5 and 60 is 5.*

$= 612$

So, you take in about 612 liters of air each hour.

Let the Games Begin

Totally Mental

Get Ready This game is for two players.  spinner

Get Set Each player should have a game sheet like the one shown at the right. Use a spinner with the digits 1 through 9.

Go • Each player chooses one of the boxes on his or her sheet and writes the number from the spinner in it. After 4 spins, the player with the greatest product is the winner.

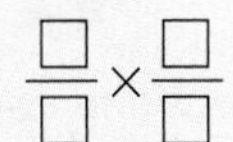

Math Skill
Multiplying Fractions

interNET CONNECTION Visit www.glencoe.com/sec/math/mac/mathnet for more games.

CHECK FOR UNDERSTANDING

Communicating Mathematics

Read and study the lesson to answer each question. 1–3. See margin.

1. ***Explain*** the steps you would use to find $16\frac{2}{3} \times 9\frac{5}{9}$.
2. ***Write*** the multiplication sentence shown by the area model.

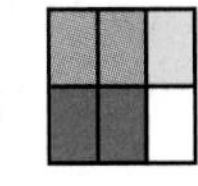

HANDS-ON MATH 3. Use area models to show $\frac{4}{5} \times \frac{1}{4}$.

2 TEACH

Transparency 7-4B contains a teaching aid for this lesson.

Thinking Algebraically As students work through the examples and exercises, have them look for patterns in the products, comparing the result with the two fractions or mixed numbers that are multiplied. When would the product be smaller than a factor? When would it be larger?

In-Class Examples

For Example 1
Find $\frac{2}{3} \times \frac{5}{8}$. $\frac{5}{12}$

For Example 2
Multiply $\frac{3}{4} \times \frac{2}{3}$. $\frac{1}{2}$

For Example 3
Solve $n = \frac{7}{8} \times \frac{4}{5}$. $n = \frac{7}{10}$

For Example 4
Jonas drinks $\frac{3}{4}$ liter of water every time he plays tennis. If he plays 8 times this month, how many liters will he drink? 6

Before playing, ask students how they will decide where to write each digit they spin. After they have played a game, ask them what strategy they used. **Sample answer: write larger digits in numerator position and smaller digits in denominator.**

*Additional resources for this game can be found on pages 43–44 of the **Classroom Games.***

3 PRACTICE/APPLY

Check for Understanding

If students need additional practice or instruction after completing Exercises 1–11, one of these options may be helpful.

- Extra Practice, see p. 587
- Reteaching Activity, see p. 286
- *Study Guide Masters,* p. 52
- *Practice Masters,* p. 52
- Interactive Mathematics Tools Software

Additional Answers

1. Rename each mixed number as an improper fraction. Multiply the numerators and the denominators. Simplify.
2. $\frac{2}{3} \times \frac{1}{2} = \frac{2}{6}$ or $\frac{1}{3}$
3. $\frac{4}{5} \times \frac{1}{4} = \frac{4}{20}$ or $\frac{1}{5}$

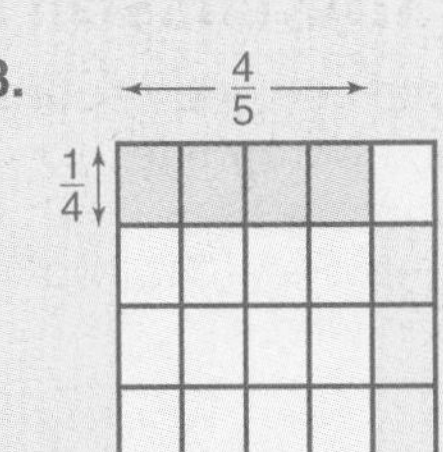

Assignment Guide

Core: 13–35 odd, 37–42
Enriched: 12–34 even, 35, 37–42
All: Self Test, 1–10

Guided Practice

Multiply. Write each product in simplest form.

4. $\frac{1}{5} \times \frac{1}{2}$ **$\frac{1}{10}$**
5. $\frac{3}{7} \times \frac{2}{3}$ **$\frac{2}{7}$**
6. $2 \times \frac{3}{4}$ **$1\frac{1}{2}$**
7. $\frac{2}{3} \times \frac{3}{8}$ **$\frac{1}{4}$**
8. $2\frac{1}{2} \times 2\frac{2}{3}$ **$6\frac{2}{3}$**
9. $5\frac{1}{3} \times \frac{4}{5}$ **$4\frac{4}{15}$**
10. Solve $\frac{6}{25} \times \frac{5}{8} = h$. Write the solution in simplest form. **$\frac{3}{20}$**
11. ***Government*** By law, the length of an official United States flag must be $1\frac{9}{10}$ times its width. If the width of a flag is $3\frac{1}{2}$ feet, what is its length? **$6\frac{13}{20}$ ft**

EXERCISES

Practice

Multiply. Write each product in simplest form.

12. $\frac{3}{5} \times \frac{1}{2}$ **$\frac{3}{10}$**
13. $\frac{1}{8} \times \frac{3}{4}$ **$\frac{3}{32}$**
14. $\frac{2}{3} \times \frac{5}{6}$ **$\frac{5}{9}$**
15. $4 \times \frac{2}{5}$ **$1\frac{3}{5}$**
16. $\frac{3}{5} \times \frac{10}{11}$ **$\frac{6}{11}$**
17. $\frac{5}{6} \times \frac{3}{5}$ **$\frac{1}{2}$**
18. $\frac{4}{5} \times \frac{1}{8}$ **$\frac{1}{10}$**
19. $\frac{3}{8} \times \frac{4}{5}$ **$\frac{3}{10}$**
20. $6 \times \frac{4}{5}$ **$4\frac{4}{5}$**
21. $\frac{3}{5} \times \frac{10}{21}$ **$\frac{2}{7}$**
22. $\frac{3}{7} \times \frac{5}{6}$ **$\frac{5}{14}$**
23. $2\frac{1}{2} \times \frac{5}{8}$ **$1\frac{9}{16}$**
24. $\frac{4}{7} \times 4\frac{2}{3}$ **$2\frac{2}{3}$**
25. $3\frac{2}{3} \times 9$ **33**
26. $3\frac{1}{4} \times 2\frac{2}{3}$ **$8\frac{2}{3}$**
27. $4\frac{1}{2} \times 1\frac{1}{3}$ **6**
28. Find the product of $1\frac{1}{6}$, $\frac{3}{7}$, and $\frac{1}{3}$. **$\frac{1}{6}$**
29. What is the product of $4\frac{7}{12}$ and $9\frac{1}{5}$? **$42\frac{1}{6}$**

Solve each equation. Write the solution in simplest form.

30. $3 \times 2\frac{1}{7} = s$ **$6\frac{3}{7}$**
31. $a = 1\frac{4}{7} \times 4\frac{2}{3}$ **$7\frac{1}{3}$**
32. $r = 2\frac{1}{4} \times \frac{9}{10}$ **$2\frac{1}{40}$**
33. ***Algebra*** Evaluate $q \times \frac{2}{9}$ if $q = 1\frac{1}{8}$. **$\frac{1}{4}$**
34. ***Algebra*** Find the value of $6\frac{2}{3} \times w$ if $w = \frac{3}{4}$. **5**

Applications and Problem Solving

35. ***History*** In 1513, Juan Ponce de León discovered Florida. His route from Puerto Rico to Florida measures about $2\frac{1}{4}$ inches on the map. If 1 inch represents 667 miles, find the approximate length of his route. **$1{,}500\frac{3}{4}$ mi**

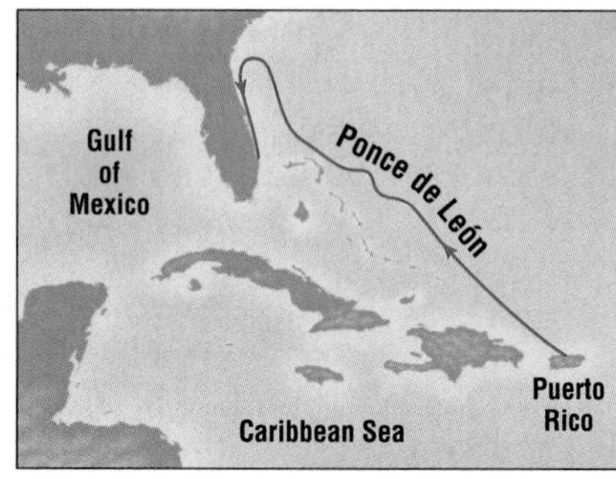

***Study Guide Masters*, p. 52**

Name__________ Date________

7-4 Study Guide

Multiplying Fractions and Mixed Numbers

To multiply fractions: Multiply the numerators. Then multiply the denominators.

$\frac{5}{6} \times \frac{3}{5} = \frac{5 \times 3}{6 \times 5} = \frac{15}{30} = \frac{1}{2}$

To multiply mixed numbers: Rename each mixed number as a fraction. Multiply the fractions.

$7 \times 1\frac{1}{4} = \frac{7}{1} \times \frac{5}{4} = \frac{35}{4} = 8\frac{3}{4}$

Multiply. Write each product in simplest form.

1. $\frac{2}{3} \times \frac{1}{4}$ $\frac{1}{6}$
2. $\frac{3}{7} \times \frac{1}{2}$ $\frac{3}{14}$
3. $\frac{1}{3} \times \frac{3}{5}$ $\frac{1}{5}$
4. $\frac{1}{2} \times \frac{6}{7}$ $\frac{3}{7}$
5. $\frac{3}{8} \times 4$ $1\frac{1}{2}$
6. $\frac{7}{10} \times \frac{5}{7}$ $\frac{1}{2}$
7. $\frac{4}{9} \times 3$ $1\frac{1}{3}$
8. $\frac{1}{4} \times \frac{1}{4}$ $\frac{1}{16}$
9. $1\frac{1}{2} \times 6$ 9
10. $\frac{3}{4} \times 1\frac{2}{3}$ $1\frac{1}{4}$
11. $3\frac{1}{3} \times 2\frac{1}{2}$ $8\frac{1}{3}$
12. $4\frac{1}{5} \times \frac{1}{7}$ $\frac{3}{5}$
13. $1\frac{1}{9} \times \frac{3}{5}$ $\frac{2}{3}$
14. $6 \times \frac{11}{12}$ $5\frac{1}{2}$
15. $\frac{1}{2} \times 2\frac{2}{3}$ $1\frac{1}{3}$

 T52 *Mathematics: Applications and Connections, Course 2*

Reteaching the Lesson

Activity Have students use grid paper to draw rectangles of the appropriate number of columns and rows to represent the denominators of the two fractions. Then proceed with simple multiplications.

MathPASS CD-ROM

This CD-ROM offers a complete, self-paced mathematics curriculum. Each lesson includes a pretest, tutorial, guided practice, and posttest. MathPASS Lesson 23 is correlated to this Student Edition lesson.
For Windows & Macintosh

36. ***Working on the***  Suppose that on your first day of tracking stock prices you had purchased 100 shares of stock in each of your four companies. **a–b. See students' work.**

a. For each company, how much would you have paid for 100 shares?

b. How much money would you have received if you had sold all your shares at yesterday's closing price?

37. ***Critical Thinking*** Observe that $3 \times \frac{1}{3} = 1$, $4 \times \frac{1}{4} = 1$, and $8 \times \frac{1}{8} = 1$. What number times $1\frac{1}{2}$ equals 1? What number times $2\frac{1}{2}$ equals 1? $\frac{2}{3}, \frac{2}{5}$

Mixed Review

38. Find the sum of $6\frac{3}{4}$ and $9\frac{7}{8}$. *(Lesson 7-3)* $16\frac{5}{8}$

39. ***Algebra*** Solve the inequality $r + 3 > -5$. *(Lesson 6-5)* $r > -8$

40. **Standardized Test Practice** Desiree is driving cross-country. If she expects to drive between 350 and 450 miles per day, which number of days is reasonable for her to drive 3,800 miles? *(Lesson 5-7)* **C**

A fewer than 6 days
B between 6 and 8 days
C between 9 and 11 days
D between 14 and 16 days
E more than 16 days

41. ***Earth Science*** The low temperatures for 10 cities on January 23 are −3, 27, 13, −6, −14, 36, 47, 52, −2, and 0. Order these temperatures from greatest to least. *(Lesson 5-2)* **52, 47, 36, 27, 13, 0, −2, −3, −6, −14**

For **Extra Practice,** see page 587.

42. ***Music*** In a survey, 12 out of 78 people preferred classical music to jazz. Write this ratio as a fraction in simplest form. *(Lesson 4-5)* $\frac{2}{13}$

CHAPTER 7 Mid-Chapter Self Test

Estimate. *(Lesson 7-1)*

1. $\frac{3}{8} + \frac{6}{7}$ $\frac{1}{2} + 1 = 1\frac{1}{2}$
2. $\frac{4}{5} - \frac{1}{2}$ $1 - \frac{1}{2} = \frac{1}{2}$
3. $\frac{1}{3} \times 14$ $\frac{1}{2} \times 14 = 7$

Add or subtract. Write each sum or difference in simplest form. *(Lessons 7-2 and 7-3)*

4. $\frac{5}{8} - \frac{1}{6}$ $\frac{11}{24}$
5. $\frac{7}{9} + \frac{5}{12}$ $1\frac{7}{36}$
6. $\frac{4}{5} - \frac{3}{7}$ $\frac{13}{35}$
7. $8\frac{3}{4} - 2\frac{5}{12}$ $6\frac{1}{3}$
8. $5\frac{1}{8} + 3\frac{3}{8}$ $8\frac{1}{2}$
9. $18\frac{3}{10} + 13\frac{5}{6}$ $32\frac{2}{15}$
10. ***History*** In 1986, *Voyager* became the first plane to fly nonstop around the world without refueling in midair. *Voyager* weighed 2,000 pounds, but at take-off it carried about $3\frac{1}{2}$ times its weight in fuel. How many pounds of fuel did *Voyager* carry at take-off? *(Lesson 7-4)* **about 7,000 lb**

CHAPTER Project

Exercise 36 asks students to advance to the next stage of work on the Chapter Project. You may wish to have students work in groups to answer the question.

4 ASSESS

Closing Activity

Modeling Have students use area models to find a fraction that represents the number of yards of fabric needed for 6 costumes if each costume requires $3\frac{1}{4}$ yards. $19\frac{1}{2}$ yd

Mid-Chapter Self Test

The Mid-Chapter Self Test reviews the concepts in Lessons 7-1 through 7-4. Lesson references are given so students can review concepts not yet mastered.

Extending the Lesson

Enrichment Masters, p. 52

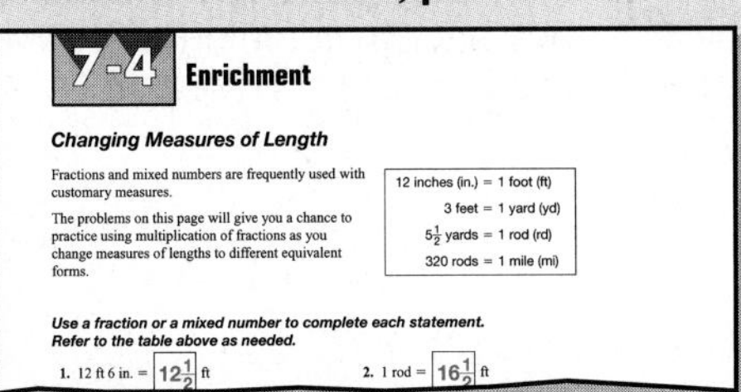

7-4 **Enrichment**

Changing Measures of Length

Fractions and mixed numbers are frequently used with customary measures.

The problems on this page will give you a chance to practice using multiplication of fractions as you change measures of lengths to different equivalent forms.

12 inches (in.) = 1 foot (ft)
3 feet = 1 yard (yd)
$5\frac{1}{2}$ yards = 1 rod (rd)
320 rods = 1 mile (mi)

Use a fraction or a mixed number to complete each statement. Refer to the table above as needed.

1. 12 ft 6 in. = $12\frac{1}{2}$ ft
2. 1 rod = $16\frac{1}{2}$ ft

Activity Have students use a cookbook to find a recipe for a dessert they would like to make. Ask them to rewrite the recipe, giving the amount of each ingredient that will be needed to serve the entire class.

Practice Masters, p. 52

Name ____________ Date ________

Practice

Multiplying Fractions and Mixed Numbers

Multiply. Write each product in simplest form.

1. $\frac{2}{3} \times \frac{1}{2}$ $\frac{1}{3}$
2. $\frac{3}{4} \times \frac{1}{9}$ $\frac{1}{12}$
3. $3 \times \frac{4}{9}$ $1\frac{1}{3}$
4. $\frac{1}{5} \times \frac{1}{4}$ $\frac{1}{20}$
5. $\frac{1}{4} \times \frac{4}{5}$ $\frac{1}{5}$
6. $\frac{4}{9} \times \frac{3}{4}$ $\frac{1}{3}$
7. $\frac{13}{21} \times \frac{7}{13}$ $\frac{1}{3}$
8. $\frac{7}{8} \times \frac{4}{9}$ $\frac{7}{18}$
9. $\frac{5}{7} \times \frac{7}{10}$ $\frac{1}{2}$
10. $\frac{4}{5} \times \frac{5}{14}$ $\frac{2}{7}$
11. $\frac{1}{4} \times \frac{5}{8}$ $\frac{5}{32}$
12. $\frac{2}{3} \times \frac{5}{9}$ $\frac{10}{27}$
13. $\frac{4}{5} \times 7$ $5\frac{3}{5}$
14. $2\frac{2}{5} \times 1\frac{3}{7}$ $3\frac{3}{7}$
15. $6 \times \frac{2}{3}$ 4
16. $3\frac{3}{4} \times 12$ 45
17. $1\frac{5}{9} \times 2\frac{4}{7}$ 4
18. $4\frac{1}{3} \times \frac{1}{2}$ $2\frac{1}{6}$

 T52 *Mathematics: Applications and Connections,* Course 2

GET READY

Objective Students examine fractal patterns by multiplying fractions and mixed numbers.

Optional Resources
Hands-On Lab Masters
- square dot paper, p. 14
- worksheet, p. 53

Overhead Manipulative Resources
- rectangular dot paper

MANAGEMENT TIPS

Recommended Time
30 minutes

Getting Started Have students fold a blank sheet of paper in half and draw a large X covering one side. Then have them fold it in half again, blank side out, and draw an X on one side; fold it in half again, blank side out, draw an X on one side; fold again and draw an X. Ask students what fraction of one side of the paper remains blank. $\frac{1}{16}$

The **Activity** uses shading to show a fractal pattern in which the area of each stage is $\frac{8}{9}$ that of the previous stage.

ASSESS

Have students complete Exercises 1–5. Watch for students who include the shaded area in their calculations.

HANDS-ON LAB

COOPERATIVE LEARNING

7-4B Fractal Patterns

A Follow-Up of Lesson 7-4

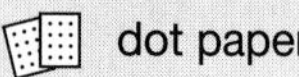

In Lesson 1-6, you learned about fractal patterns. You can use multiplication of fractions and mixed numbers to examine these patterns.

TRY THIS

Work with a partner.

Step 1
Draw a square with sides measuring 9 units.

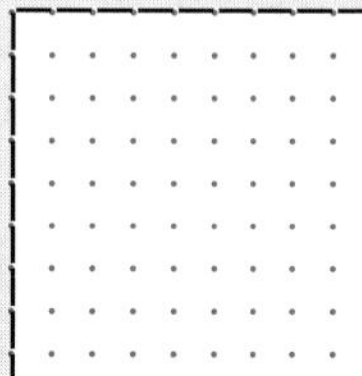

Stage 0

Step 2
Divide each side into 3 equal lengths to form 9 smaller squares. Shade the middle square.

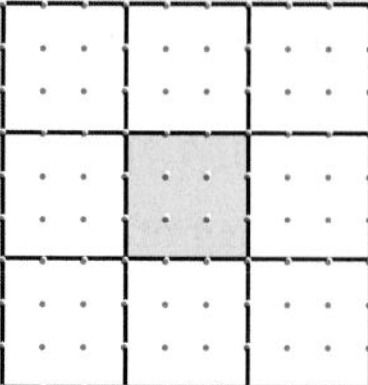

Stage 1

Step 3
Divide each unshaded square into 9 smaller squares and shade the middle squares.

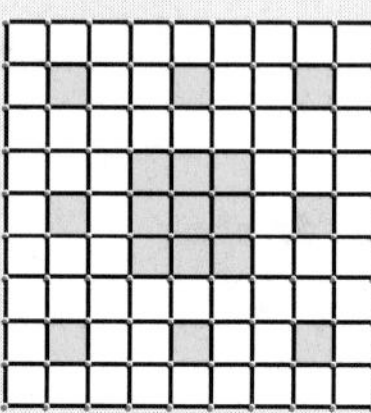

Stage 2

ON YOUR OWN

1. Think of the shaded squares as holes. The area of Stage 0 is 81 square units. Find the areas of Stage 1 and Stage 2. *Do not include the holes.* **72 sq units; 64 sq units**
2. Write the areas of Stages 0–2. Study the pattern. You can multiply each area by what fraction to get the next area? **81 sq units, 72 sq units, 64 sq units; $\frac{8}{9}$**
3. ***Make a conjecture*** about the area of each fractal stage. **See margin.**
4. Use your conjecture to find the area of Stage 3. **$56\frac{8}{9}$ sq units**
5. ***Reflect Back*** Refer to Example 1 in Lesson 1–6. In the Sierpinski triangle, the area of Stage 0 is 1 square unit. Use the equations to find the areas of each stage.

   a. (area of Stage 0) × $\frac{3}{4}$ = area of Stage 1 **$\frac{3}{4}$ sq units**

   b. (area of Stage 1) × $\frac{3}{4}$ = area of Stage 2 **$\frac{9}{16}$ sq units**

   c. (area of Stage 2) × $\frac{3}{4}$ = area of Stage 3 **$\frac{27}{64}$ sq units**

Additional Answer

3. You can multiply the area of each stage by $\frac{8}{9}$ to get the area of the next stage.

Ask students what connection they can see between fractions and fractal patterns. What could they have in common with other terms, such as "fracture" or "refract"?

7-5 Integration: Measurement
Changing Customary Units

What you'll learn

You'll learn to change units in the customary system.

When am I ever going to use this?

Knowing how to change units will help you compare prices of grocery items.

Word Wise

ounce, pound, ton, cup, pint, quart, gallon

In 1996, the *Olmec Art of Ancient Mexico* exhibit was on display at the National Gallery of Art in Washington, D.C. Included among the 3,000 year-old works was a sculpture of a head that weighed $9\frac{1}{2}$ tons. How many pounds did the sculpture weigh? *This problem will be solved in Example 1.*

Customary units of weight are **ounce**, **pound**, and **ton**. The relationships among these units is shown in the table.

1 pound (lb) = 16 ounces (oz)
1 ton (T) = 2,000 pounds

When you change from a larger unit to a smaller unit, multiply. *There will be more smaller units than larger units.*

Example 1 CONNECTION

Art In the beginning of the lesson, how many pounds did the sculpture weigh?

You need to change $9\frac{1}{2}$ tons to pounds.

$9\frac{1}{2}$ T = ? lb — *larger unit → smaller unit*

$9\frac{1}{2} \times 2{,}000 = 19{,}000$ — *Since 2,000 lb = 1 ton, multiply by 2,000.*

The sculpture weighed 19,000 pounds.

Study Hint

Estimation $9\frac{1}{2}$ is about 10. Since there are 2,000 lb in 1 ton, the answer should be close to 10 × 2,000 or 20,000 lb.

Sometimes you will need to convert from a smaller unit to a larger unit. In this case, divide. *There will be fewer larger units than smaller units.*

Example 2

How many pounds is 72 ounces?

72 oz = ? lb — *smaller unit → larger unit*

72 ÷ 16 = 4.5 — *Since 16 oz = 1 lb, divide by 16.*

72 ounces is equal to 4.5 pounds.

MathPASS CD-ROM

This CD-ROM offers a complete, self-paced mathematics curriculum. Each lesson includes a pretest, tutorial, guided practice, and posttest. MathPASS Lesson 24 is correlated to this Student Edition lesson.

For Windows & Macintosh

Motivating the Lesson

Hands-On Activity Provide newspapers, catalogues, and magazines. Have students read through them to find several examples of customary measurements. Ask them to list the items measured and convert their measurements to either larger or smaller units.

7-5 Lesson Notes

Instructional Resources

- *Study Guide Masters,* p. 53
- *Practice Masters,* p. 53
- *Enrichment Masters,* p. 53
- Transparencies 7-5, A and B
- *Assessment and Evaluation Masters,* pp. 182, 183

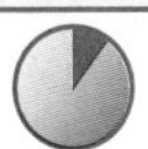

CD-ROM Program
- Resource Lesson 7-5

Recommended Pacing	
Standard	Day 9 of 15
Honors	Day 8 of 14
Block	Day 4 of 8

1 FOCUS

5-Minute Check *(Lesson 7-4)*

Multiply. Write each product in simplest form.

1. $\frac{2}{5} \times \frac{1}{2}$ $\frac{1}{5}$
2. $\frac{2}{3} \times \frac{5}{8}$ $\frac{5}{12}$
3. $6 \times 2\frac{3}{4}$ $16\frac{1}{2}$
4. $2\frac{1}{4} \times 1\frac{1}{6}$ $2\frac{5}{8}$
5. $2\frac{4}{7} \times \frac{8}{9}$ $2\frac{2}{7}$

The 5-Minute Check is also available on **Transparency 7-5A** for this lesson.

2 TEACH

Transparency 7-5B contains a teaching aid for this lesson.

Reading Mathematics The abbreviations for customary units may not be obvious to all students. For example, *lb* comes from the Latin word *libra,* which was a pound equaling 12 ounces. *Ounce* comes from the Latin word meaning "one-twelfth." The pound and the foot were both divided into units of 12 for consistency.

In-Class Examples

For Example 1
How many pounds can an elevator safely hold if its sign says "Weight Limit: $1\frac{1}{2}$ tons"?
3,000 lb

For Example 2
How many pounds is 56 ounces? **3.5 lb**

For Example 3
Gino's canteen holds 4 fluid ounces more than 4 cups. How many fluid ounces does it hold?
36 oz

For Example 4
How many cups are in 2 quarts?
8 c

Customary units of liquid capacity are **cup**, **pint**, **quart**, and **gallon**. The relationships among these units is shown in the table.

1 cup (c) = 8 fluid ounces (fl oz)
1 pint (pt) = 2 cups
1 quart (qt) = 2 pints
1 gallon (gal) = 4 quarts

Examples Real World **APPLICATION**

3 **Fish** **A fish tank contains 2 quarts less water than 9 gallons. How many quarts of water are in the tank?**

$9 \cdot 4 = 36$ *Multiply by 4 since there are 4 quarts in a gallon.*

There are 36 quarts in 9 gallons. So, the tank contains 36 − 2, or 34 quarts of water.

4 **Food** **A popular drink contains 64 ounces of soda. How many cups is this?**

64 fl oz = __?__ c *smaller unit → larger unit*
$64 \div 8 = 8$ *Divide by 8 since there are 8 fl oz in a cup.*

There are 8 cups of soda in the drink.

3 PRACTICE/APPLY

Check for Understanding

If students need additional practice or instruction after completing Exercises 1–9, one of these options may be helpful.

- Extra Practice, see p. 587
- Reteaching Activity
- *Transition Booklet,* pp. 33–34
- *Study Guide Masters,* p. 53
- *Practice Masters,* p. 53

CHECK FOR UNDERSTANDING

Communicating Mathematics

Read and study the lesson to answer each question.

1. ***Tell*** which operation is needed to convert from cups to pints. Explain how you know. **Division; pints are larger than cups.**
2. ***Write*** about a real-life situation in which you would need to change units in the customary system. **See margin.**

Guided Practice

Complete. **5. 9 8. $\frac{1}{2}$**

3. 5 lb = __?__ oz **80**	**4.** 12 qt = __?__ gal **3**	**5.** 4.5 pt = __?__ c
6. 4,000 lb = __?__ T **2**	**7.** 3 c = __?__ fl oz **24**	**8.** 1 pt = __?__ qt

9. ***Life Science*** A newborn hooded seal pup gains about 56 ounces per day for the first four days of its life. How many pounds will the average pup gain in one day? **3.5 lb**

EXERCISES

Practice

Complete. **11. 10,000**

10. 2 gal = __?__ qt **8**	**11.** 5 T = __?__ lb	**12.** 128 oz = __?__ lb **8**
13. 12 c = __?__ pt **6**	**14.** 16 qt = __?__ gal **4**	**15.** 8 pt = __?__ qt **4**
16. 96 oz = __?__ lb **6**	**17.** 3 lb = __?__ oz **48**	**18.** 5 pt = __?__ c **10**
19. 2.5 qt = __?__ pt **5**	**20.** 15 pt = __?__ qt **7.5**	**21.** 2.5 lb = __?__ oz **40**
22. 2 T = __?__ lb **4,000**	**23.** 4.5 pt = __?__ c **9**	**24.** 6,000 lb = __?__ T **3**
25. 2 fl oz = __?__ c $\frac{1}{4}$	**26.** 5 c = __?__ pt **2.5**	**27.** 0.5 gal = __?__ qt **2**

***Study Guide Masters,* p. 53**

Name____________ Date________

7-5 Study Guide

Integration: Measurement
Changing Customary Units

Customary Units	
Weight	**Liquid Capacity**
1 pound (lb) = 16 ounces (oz) 1 ton (T) = 2,000 pounds	1 cup (c) = 8 fluid ounces (fl oz) 1 pint (pt) = 2 cups 1 quart (qt) = 2 pints 1 gallon (1 gal) = 4 quarts

To change from larger units to smaller units, multiply.

Example 1 $5\frac{1}{2}$ lb = ____ oz *larger unit → smaller unit*
$5\frac{1}{2} \times 16 = 88$ *Multiply to change from pounds to ounces.*
$5\frac{1}{2}$ lb = 88 oz

To change from smaller units to larger units, divide.

Example 2 28 fl oz = ____ c *smaller unit → larger unit*
$28 \div 8 = 3\frac{1}{2}$ *Divide to change from quarts to gallons.*
28 fl oz = $3\frac{1}{2}$ c

Complete.

1. 4 lb = ____ oz 64	2. 3 T = ____ lb 6,000	3. 5 c = ____ fl oz 40
4. 40 oz = ____ lb $2\frac{1}{2}$	5. 5,000 lb = ____ T $2\frac{1}{2}$	6. 2 pt = ____ c 4
7. 1.5 lb = ____ oz 24	8. 10 pt = ____ qt 5	9. 12 qt = ____ gal 3
10. 2.5 pt = ____ c 5	11. 1.5 gal = ____ qt 6	12. 3.5 qt = ____ pt 7
13. 12 fl oz = ____ c $1\frac{1}{2}$	14. 24 oz = ____ lb $1\frac{1}{2}$	15. 7 c = ____ fl oz 56
16. 3 gal = ____ qt 12	17. 5.5 T = ____ lb 11,000	18. 48 fl oz = ____ c 6

 T53 *Mathematics: Applications and Connections, Course 2*

Reteaching the Lesson

Activity Provide students with opportunities to handle and use some of the measures to get an idea of their size. For example, provide students with a quart measuring cup so they can see how pints and ounces compare in capacity with a quart and with each other.

Additional Answer

2. Sample answer: finding whether a container is big enough to hold juice, finding correct measures in cooking and baking

28. How many tons are in 4,200 pounds? $2\frac{1}{10}$ T

29. If 4 cups = 1 quart, then 9 cups = __?__ quarts? $2\frac{1}{4}$ qt

30. If 36 inches = 1 yard, then 2.3 yards = __?__ inches? 82.2 in.

31. ***Write an Equation*** that you can use to change c cups to fluid ounces. Use f for fluid ounces. Then use the equation to find the number of fluid ounces in 6.5 cups. **See students' work; $f=8c$; 52 fl oz**

Applications and Problem Solving

32. ***Life Science*** An adult has about 5 quarts of blood. If a person donates 1 pint of blood, how many pints are left? **9 pt**

33. ***Life Science*** Mammoths have been discovered deep-frozen in the ice of the Arctic tundra. When these animals lived over 10,000 years ago, they weighed up to 15,500 pounds. How many tons did they weigh? **33. $7\frac{3}{4}$T**

34. ***Safety*** A bridge has a $3\frac{1}{2}$-ton weight limit. If a truck and its cargo weigh 6,800 pounds, can the truck cross over the bridge? Explain.

35. ***Food*** Is a 2-quart pitcher large enough to hold 1 batch of cherry punch?

Cherry Punch
$2\frac{1}{2}$ c cherry juice
2 c orange juice
$1\frac{1}{2}$ c pineapple juice
3 c ginger ale

36. ***Critical Thinking*** Make a table that shows the number of ounces in 1, 2, 3, and 4 pounds. Graph the ordered pairs (pounds, ounces) on a coordinate plane. Describe the graph. **See margin.**

34. Yes; the truck weighs 200 pounds less than the limit of $3\frac{1}{2}$ tons.

35. No, the recipe makes 9 cups of punch and the pitcher holds only 2 quarts, or 8 cups.

Mixed Review

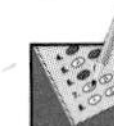

37. **Standardized Test Practice** A box of books weighs $8\frac{2}{3}$ pounds. How much do $4\frac{1}{2}$ boxes weigh? *(Lesson 7-4)* **D**

A 19 pounds **B** $27\frac{2}{3}$ pounds **C** $32\frac{1}{2}$ pounds **D** 39 pounds

38. ***Employment*** Mallory gets paid a flat rate of \$75 plus \$4.50 per hour for cleaning. The equation $4.5h + 75 = 165$, where h is the number of hours, describes the number of hours she must work to make \$165. How many hours must she work to make \$165? *(Lesson 6-3)* **20 hours**

39. Find the LCM of 16 and 20. *(Lesson 4-9)* **80**

40. ***Statistics*** Rainfall is rarest in the southwest region of the nation. The data show nine southwestern cities and their average number of days with rain per year. Find the mean, mode, and median of these data. *(Lesson 3-4)* **31.56, none, 32**

It Rarely Rains

Rainfall (days)

Yuma, Ariz.	17
Las Vegas, Nev.	26
Bishop, Calif	29
Santa Barbara, Calif.	30
Long Beach, Calif.	32
Los Angeles, Calif.	35
Phoenix, Ariz.	36
Bakersfield, Calif.	37
San Diego, Calif.	42

Source: *USA TODAY Weather Almanac*

interNET CONNECTION
For the latest statistics on rainfall in the United States, visit: www.glencoe.com/sec/math/mac/mathnet

For **Extra Practice,** see page 587.

Assignment Guide

Core: 11–35 odd, 36–40
Enriched: 10–30 even, 32–40

4 ASSESS

Closing Activity

Modeling Provide ingredients for the punch in Exercise 35, and have students make the punch to verify their solution. Then have them work in groups to measure and mix enough for the whole class, converting each amount into fluid ounces and fractions of a quart.

Chapter 7, Quiz B (Lessons 7-4 and 7-5) is available in the *Assessment and Evaluation Masters,* p. 183.

Mid-Chapter Test (Lessons 7-1 through 7-5) is available in the *Assessment and Evaluation Masters,* p. 182.

Additional Answer

36. See students' work. The graph is a straight line. For each x-value increase of 1, the y-value increases by 16.

Practice Masters, p. 53

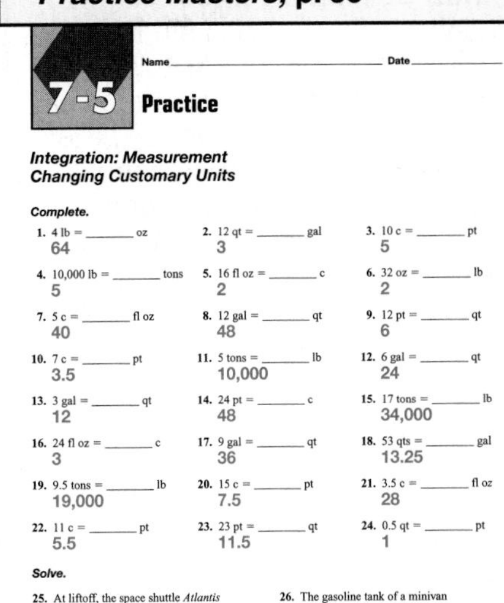

Name________ Date________

7-5 Practice

Integration: Measurement Changing Customary Units

Complete.

1. 4 lb = ____ oz **64**
2. 12 qt = ____ gal **3**
3. 10 c = ____ pt **5**
4. 10,000 lb = ____ tons **5**
5. 16 fl oz = ____ c **2**
6. 32 oz = ____ lb **2**
7. 5 c = ____ fl oz **40**
8. 12 gal = ____ qt **48**
9. 12 pt = ____ qt **6**
10. 7 c = ____ pt **3.5**
11. 5 tons = ____ lb **10,000**
12. 6 gal = ____ qt **24**
13. 3 gal = ____ qt **12**
14. 24 pt = ____ c **48**
15. 17 tons = ____ lb **34,000**
16. 24 fl oz = ____ c **3**
17. 9 gal = ____ qt **36**
18. 53 qts = ____ gal **13.25**
19. 9.5 tons = ____ lb **19,000**
20. 15 c = ____ pt **7.5**
21. 3.5 c = ____ fl oz **28**
22. 11 c = ____ pt **5.5**
23. 23 pt = ____ qt **11.5**
24. 0.5 qt = ____ pt **1**

Solve.

25. At liftoff, the space shuttle *Atlantis* weighed 100 tons. How many pounds is this? **200,000 lb**
26. The gasoline tank of a minivan holds 18 gallons. How many quarts is this? **72 qt**
27. The average weight of a baby at birth is 7 pounds. How many ounces is this? **112 oz**
28. Portable telephones can weigh as little as 8 ounces. How many pounds is this? **0.5 lb**
28. Milk is sold in 8 fl oz, 16 fl oz, 32 fl oz, and 64 fl oz cardboard containers. Change these sizes to cups. **1 c, 2 c, 4 c, and 8 c**
30. The United States exports over 200 billion pounds of coal. How many tons is this? **100 million**

 T53 *Mathematics: Applications and Connections, Course 2*

Extending the Lesson

Enrichment Masters, p. 53

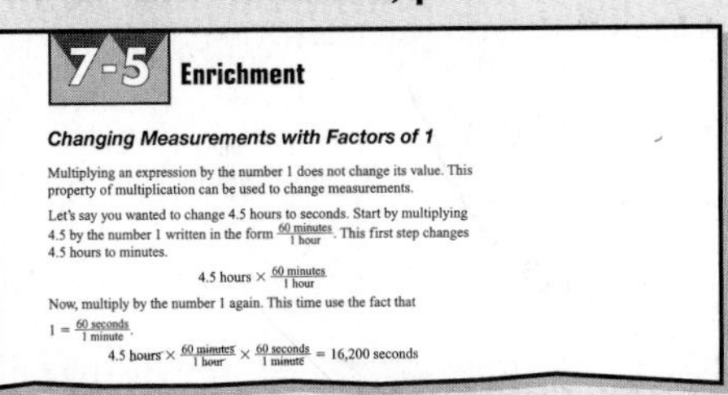

7-5 Enrichment

Changing Measurements with Factors of 1

Multiplying an expression by the number 1 does not change its value. This property of multiplication can be used to change measurements.

Let's say you wanted to change 4.5 hours to seconds. Start by multiplying 4.5 by the number 1 written in the form $\frac{60 \text{ minutes}}{1 \text{ hour}}$. This first step changes 4.5 hours to minutes.

$$4.5 \text{ hours} \times \frac{60 \text{ minutes}}{1 \text{ hour}}$$

Now, multiply by the number 1 again. This time use the fact that $1 = \frac{60 \text{ seconds}}{1 \text{ minute}}$.

$$4.5 \text{ hours} \times \frac{60 \text{ minutes}}{1 \text{ hour}} \times \frac{60 \text{ seconds}}{1 \text{ minute}} = 16{,}200 \text{ seconds}$$

Activity Have students use an almanac or other reference books to research additional customary weights and measures, such as gills (4 per pt), pecks (8 dry qt), bushels (4 pecks), drams (8 per fl oz), bales (500 lb of cotton), barrels (42 gal of oil, 31.5 gal of wine), and tablespoons (2 per oz).

7-6 Lesson Notes

Instructional Resources

- *Study Guide Masters,* p. 54
- *Practice Masters,* p. 54
- *Enrichment Masters,* p. 54
- Transparencies 7-6, A and B
- *School to Career Masters,* p. 20
- *Hands-On Lab Masters,* p. 78

- CD-ROM Program
  - Resource Lesson 7-6
  - Interactive Lesson 7-6

Recommended Pacing	
Standard	Day 10 of 15
Honors	Day 9 of 14
Block	Day 5 of 8

1 FOCUS

5-Minute Check (Lesson 7-5)

Complete.

1. 4 lb = ? oz 64
2. 2.5 qt = ? pt 5
3. 7 c = ? pt 3.5
4. 3,000 lb = ? T 1.5
5. 4 fl oz = ? c 0.5

The 5-Minute Check is also available on **Transparency 7-6A** for this lesson.

Motivating the Lesson

Hands-On Activity Provide students with lengths of string and a yardstick or meterstick. Ask them to use the string to model the distance representing the perimeter of several classroom objects, such as a desktop or a book. Point out that perimeters can be either regular geometric figures, like rectangles, or irregular shapes.

7-6 Integration: Geometry
Perimeter

What **you'll learn**

You'll learn to find perimeter.

When **am I ever going to use this?**

Knowing how to find perimeter can help you frame pictures.

Word Wise

perimeter

In Washington, D.C., the Capitol and the White House are $1\frac{1}{2}$ miles apart. This symbolizes the separation of powers between Congress and the President. The Jefferson and Lincoln Memorials are also arranged in a symbolic position. Find the **perimeter** around these four historical structures.

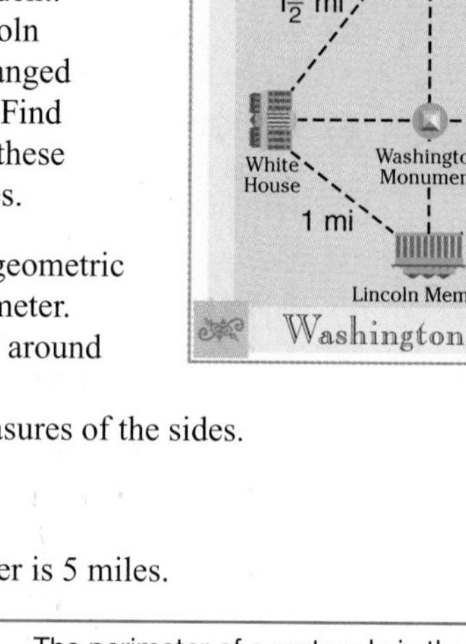

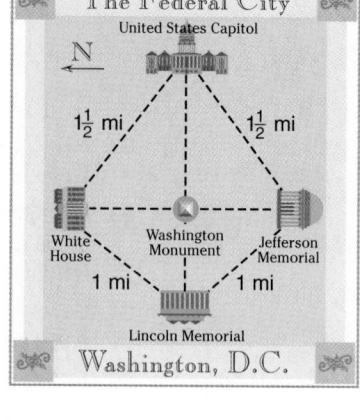

The distance around a geometric figure is called its perimeter. To find the perimeter P around these Washington, D.C. landmarks, add the measures of the sides.

$$P = 1\frac{1}{2} + 1\frac{1}{2} + 1 + 1$$

$P = 5$ The perimeter is 5 miles.

Perimeter of a Rectangle

Words: The perimeter of a rectangle is the sum of the measures of the sides. It can also be expressed as two times the length (ℓ) plus two times the width (w).

Symbols: $P = \ell + w + \ell + w$
$P = 2\ell + 2w$

Model: rectangle with sides ℓ, w, ℓ, w

Examples

Find the perimeter of each rectangle.

1 length = 9 meters
width = 5 meters

$P = 2\ell + 2w$ *Replace ℓ with 9*
$P = 2(9) + 2(5)$ *and w with 5.*
$P = 18 + 10$ or 28

The perimeter is 28 meters.

2 length = 2 feet
width = 18 inches

$P = 2\ell + 2w$
$P = 2(2) + 2(1.5)$ *18 in. = 1.5 ft*
$P = 4 + 3$ or 7

The perimeter is 7 feet.

Multiple Learning Styles

Kinesthetic Ask students to estimate how far it is around the classroom, the school building, the playground, or the block. Then have them pace those distances to determine what the perimeters are in number of steps. Then have them convert their paces to feet, yards, or meters.

Examples

3 Find the perimeter of the figure.

Estimate: 3 + 5 + 1 + 4 + 4 + 8 = 25

$P = 2\frac{2}{3} + 4\frac{1}{2} + 1 + 3\frac{1}{2} + 3\frac{2}{3} + 8$

$P = 23\frac{1}{3}$ The perimeter is $23\frac{1}{3}$ feet. This is close to the estimate of 25 feet.

INTEGRATION

4 **Measurement** Find the perimeter of the rectangle. Measure to the nearest eighth inch.

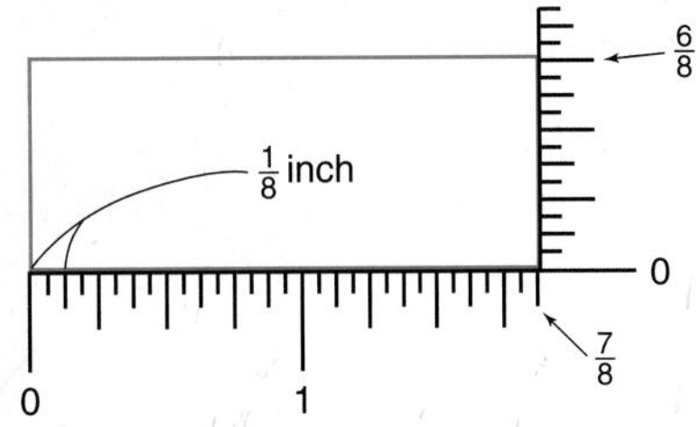

To the nearest eighth inch, the width is $\frac{6}{8}$ inch.

To the nearest eighth inch, the length is $1\frac{7}{8}$ inches.

Estimate: 2 + 1 + 2 + 1 = 6

$P = 2\ell + 2w$

$= \left(2 \times 1\frac{7}{8}\right) + \left(2 \times \frac{6}{8}\right)$ *Replace ℓ with $1\frac{7}{8}$ and w with $\frac{6}{8}$.*

$= \left(2 \times \frac{15}{8}\right) + \left(2 \times \frac{6}{8}\right)$ *Change $1\frac{7}{8}$ to $\frac{15}{8}$.*

$= \frac{30}{8} + \frac{12}{8}$ *Multiply within each set of parentheses.*

$= \frac{42}{8}$ *Add.*

$= 5\frac{2}{8}$ or $5\frac{1}{4}$ The perimeter is $5\frac{1}{4}$ inches.

CHECK FOR UNDERSTANDING

Communicating Mathematics

Read and study the lesson to answer each question.

1. ***Show*** where $8\frac{3}{8}$ is located on a ruler. **See students' work.**
2. ***Write,*** in your own words, how to find the perimeter of a square figure. **2. Multiply the length of a side by 4.**
3. ***Write*** about a situation in which you would need to find the perimeter of an object. **Sample answer: wallpaper border around bedroom**

Math Journal

Guided Practice

Find the perimeter of each figure shown or described. Estimate to check your answer.

4. **$52\frac{1}{5}$ in.**

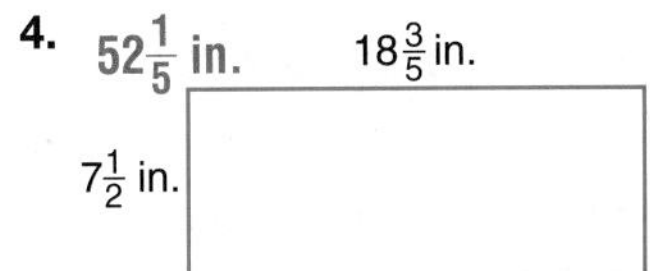

5. **56 cm**

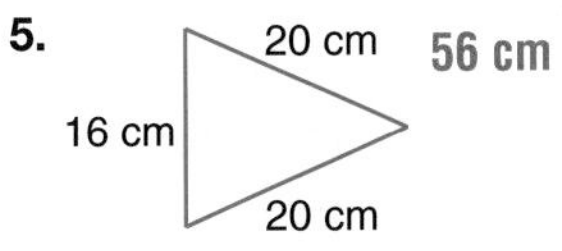

2 TEACH

Transparency 7-6B contains a teaching aid for this lesson.

Thinking Algebraically The formula for the perimeter of a rectangle may also be given as $P = 2(\ell + w)$. Ask students to find several perimeters using this formula. Then ask them to make a conjecture about why this is equivalent to the formula given in the lesson.

In-Class Examples

For Example 1
Find the perimeter of a rectangle with length 12 miles and width 7 miles. **38 miles**

For Example 2
Find the perimeter of a rectangle 1 meter long and 50 centimeters wide. **3 m**

For Example 3
Find the perimeter of the figure. **180 m**

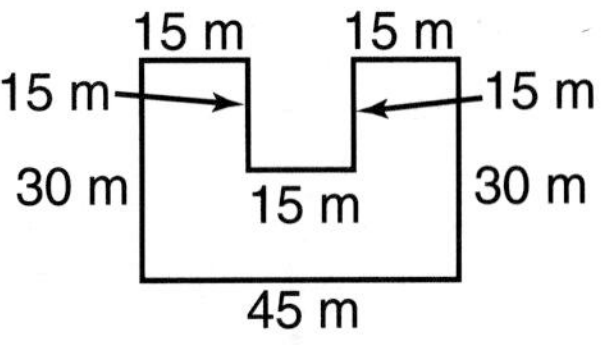

For Example 4
Find the perimeter of the top cover of your math textbook. Measure to the nearest fourth inch. **$39\frac{3}{4}$ in.**

3 PRACTICE/APPLY

Check for Understanding

If students need additional practice or instruction after completing Exercises 1–9, one of these options may be helpful.

- Extra Practice, see p. 588
- Reteaching Activity
- *Study Guide Masters,* p. 54
- *Practice Masters,* p. 54

Reteaching the Lesson

Activity Have students draw various shapes on centimeter grid paper and calculate the lengths of each side. Then find the perimeter. A centimeter ruler may be needed for any diagonal lines drawn.

Error Analysis
Watch for students who add the given length and width to find only half the perimeter of a rectangle.
Prevent by reminding students that the distance around a figure must include both sides and both ends.

Assignment Guide

Core: 11–29 odd, 31–35
Enriched: 10–26 even, 28–35

6. rectangle: $\ell = 2\frac{1}{2}$ feet, $w = 15$ inches **$7\frac{1}{2}$ ft**

7. rectangle: $\ell = 1.7$ yards, $w = 3.5$ yards **10.4 yd**

8. Find the perimeter of the figure. Use a ruler to measure to the nearest fourth inch. **$3\frac{1}{4}$ in.**

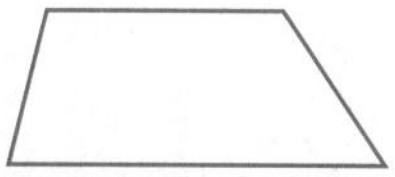

9. ***Flag Day*** A giant cake decorated as an American flag was displayed in front of Independence Hall in Philadelphia. The rectangular cake, zwhich was created to commemorate Flag Day, measured 60 feet by 90 feet. What was the perimeter of the cake? **300 ft**

EXERCISES

Practice

Find the perimeter of each figure shown or described.

10. **$17\frac{7}{8}$ in.** 11. **18.8 ft**

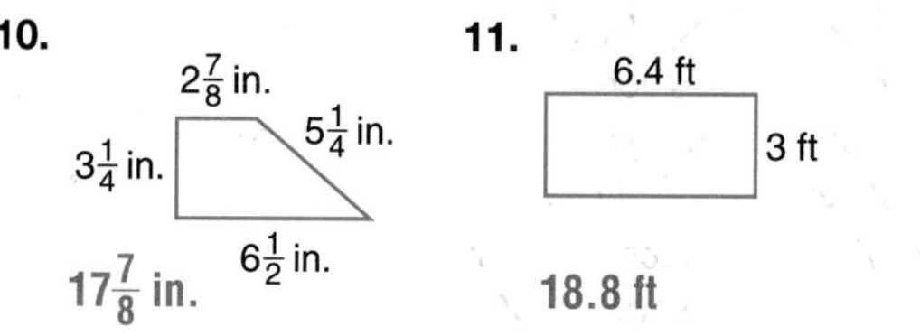

12. **84 mm**

13. **50 mi**

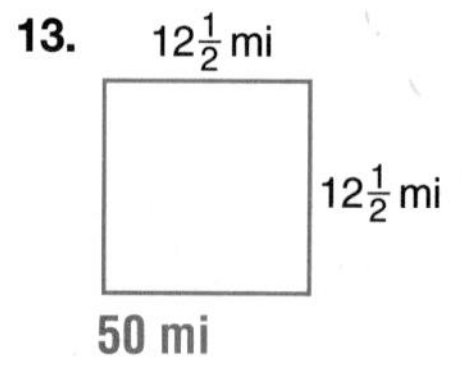

14. $13\frac{1}{3}$ in., 7 in., $9\frac{2}{3}$ in., 10 in., $15\frac{1}{6}$ in. **$55\frac{1}{6}$ in.**

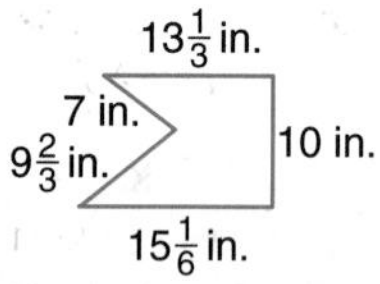

15. **110 m**

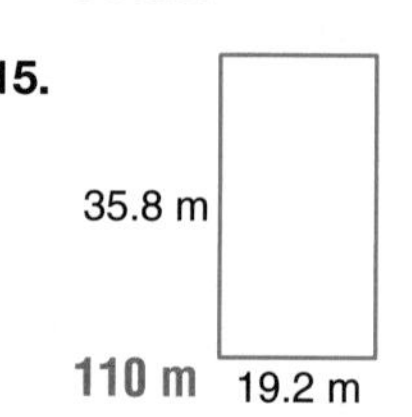

16. rectangle: $\ell = 9\frac{1}{4}$ feet, $w = 36$ inches **$24\frac{1}{2}$ ft**

17. rectangle: $\ell = 6\frac{1}{2}$ inches, $w = 4\frac{3}{8}$ inches **$21\frac{3}{4}$ in.**

18. rectangle: $\ell = 13\frac{1}{2}$ yards, $w = 7\frac{3}{4}$ yards **$42\frac{1}{2}$ yd**

19. rectangle: $\ell = 4.8$ meters, $w = 7.2$ meters **24 m**

20. Find the perimeter in feet of a triangle with sides that measure 7 inches, 10 inches, and 1 foot. **$2\frac{5}{12}$ ft**

21. Find the perimeter of a rectangle with length 17 cm and width 9.1 cm. **21. 52.2 cm**

22. Find the perimeter of a square with side 21 yards. **84 yd**

23. A rectangle is made with 9 feet of string. One side is $2\frac{5}{16}$ feet long. What is the length of the other side? **23. $2\frac{3}{16}$ ft**

Study Guide Masters, p. 54

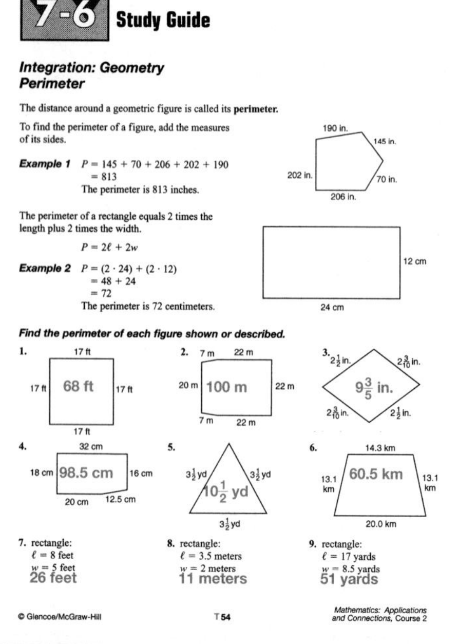

Name________ Date________

7-6 Study Guide

Integration: Geometry Perimeter

The distance around a geometric figure is called its **perimeter**.

To find the perimeter of a figure, add the measures of its sides.

Example 1 $P = 145 + 70 + 206 + 202 + 190 = 813$
The perimeter is 813 inches.

The perimeter of a rectangle equals 2 times the length plus 2 times the width.

$P = 2\ell + 2w$

Example 2 $P = (2 \cdot 24) + (2 \cdot 12) = 48 + 24 = 72$
The perimeter is 72 centimeters.

Find the perimeter of each figure shown or described.

1. 17 ft, 17 ft, 17 ft, 17 ft — **68 ft**
2. 7 m, 22 m, 20 m, 22 m, 7 m, 22 m — **100 m**
3. $2\frac{1}{2}$ in., $2\frac{3}{10}$ in., $2\frac{3}{10}$ in., $2\frac{1}{2}$ in. — **$9\frac{3}{5}$ in.**
4. 32 cm, 18 cm, 16 cm, 20 cm, 12.5 cm — **98.5 cm**
5. $3\frac{1}{2}$ yd, $3\frac{1}{2}$ yd, $3\frac{1}{2}$ yd — **$10\frac{1}{2}$ yd**
6. 14.3 km, 13.1 km, 13.1 km, 20.0 km — **60.5 km**
7. rectangle: $\ell = 8$ feet, $w = 5$ feet — **26 feet**
8. rectangle: $\ell = 3.5$ meters, $w = 2$ meters — **11 meters**
9. rectangle: $\ell = 17$ yards, $w = 8.5$ yards — **51 yards**

 T54 *Mathematics: Applications and Connections, Course 2*

Classroom Vignette

"To assess students, they were asked to make rectangles that had a perimeter of 24 inches. Some made their rectangles with tape on the floor while others constructed them on paper. Some had only whole number dimensions while others included the use of fractions and mixed numbers."

Joy Metzger

Joy Metzger, Teacher
Buckeye Valley Middle School
Radnor, OH

Find the perimeter of each figure. Use a ruler to measure to the nearest fourth inch.

24. 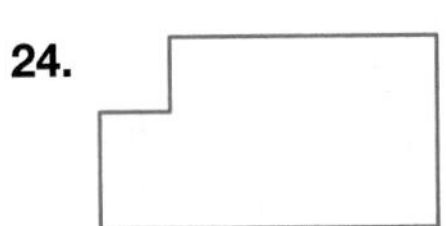 $3\frac{1}{2}$ in.

25. 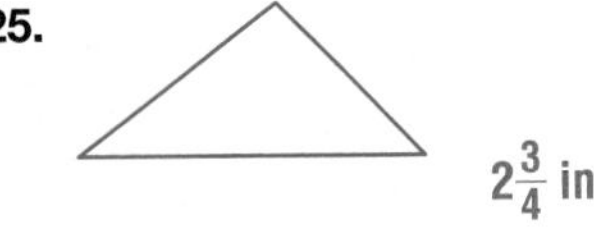 $2\frac{3}{4}$ in.

26. 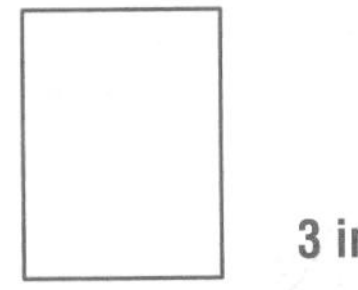 3 in.

27. 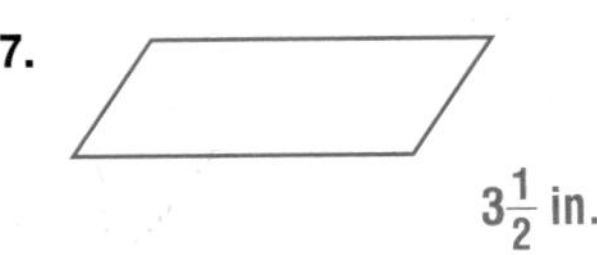 $3\frac{1}{2}$ in.

Applications and Problem Solving

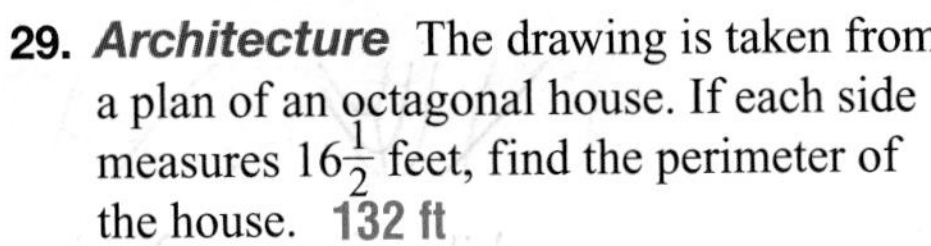

28. ***Pets*** Jamal has 38 feet of fencing for a rectangular dog pen. He plans to use 24 feet of the garage wall for one side of the pen.

a. Draw and label a diagram of the pen. **See margin.**

b. Find the width of the pen. **7 ft**

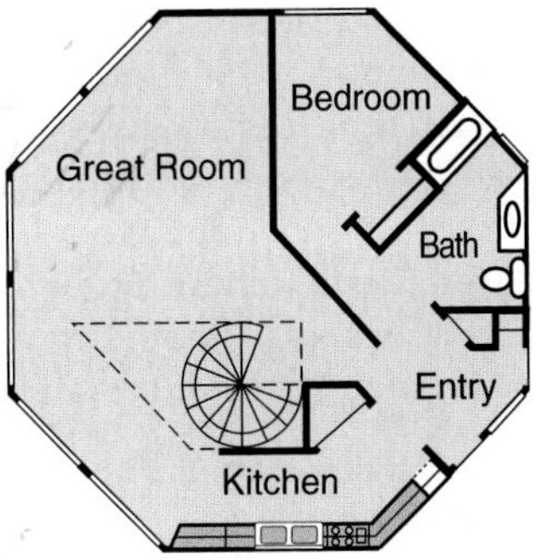

29. ***Architecture*** The drawing is taken from a plan of an octagonal house. If each side measures $16\frac{1}{2}$ feet, find the perimeter of the house. **132 ft**

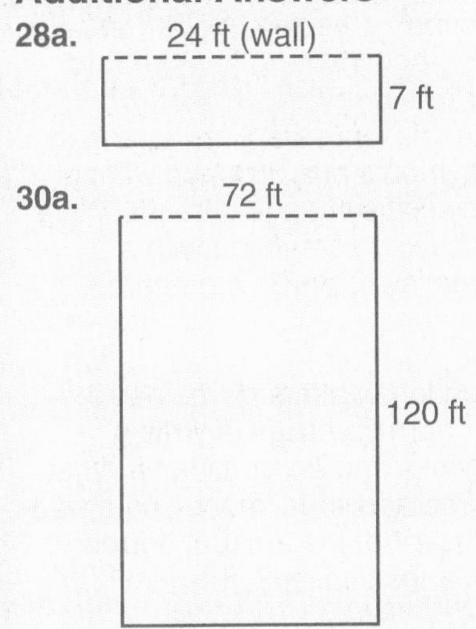

30. ***Landscaping*** Ms. Williams is going to plant shrubs across the back and down two sides of her yard. Her yard is 72 feet wide and 120 feet deep.

a. Draw and label a diagram of Ms. Williams' yard. **See margin.**

b. How many shrubs will she need to buy if she plants them 4 feet apart? **79 shrubs**

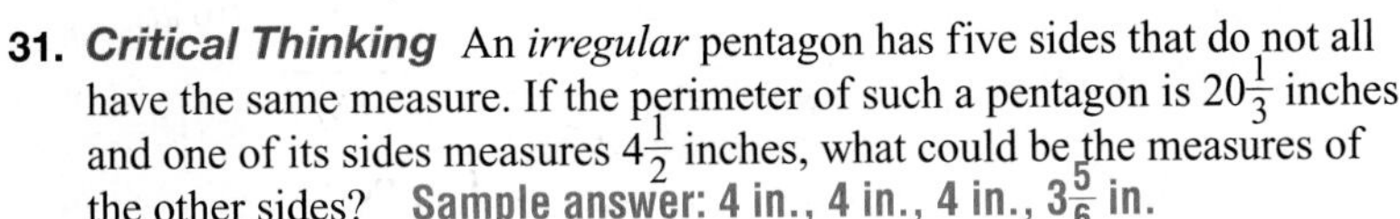

31. ***Critical Thinking*** An *irregular* pentagon has five sides that do not all have the same measure. If the perimeter of such a pentagon is $20\frac{1}{3}$ inches and one of its sides measures $4\frac{1}{2}$ inches, what could be the measures of the other sides? **Sample answer: 4 in., 4 in., 4 in., $3\frac{5}{6}$ in.**

Mixed Review

32. ***Measurement*** Complete: 40 oz = __?__ lb. *(Lesson 7-5)* $2\frac{1}{2}$

33. ***Algebra*** Solve $p - 25.5 = 74.4$. *(Lesson 6-1)* **99.9**

For **Extra Practice,** see page 588.

34. ***Probability*** A box of pencils contains 7 red, 2 orange, 4 blue, and 3 yellow pencils. If you reach in the box and choose one pencil at random, what is the probability that you will select a blue pencil? Express your answer as both a fraction and a percent. *(Lesson 4-8)* $\frac{1}{4}$, **25%**

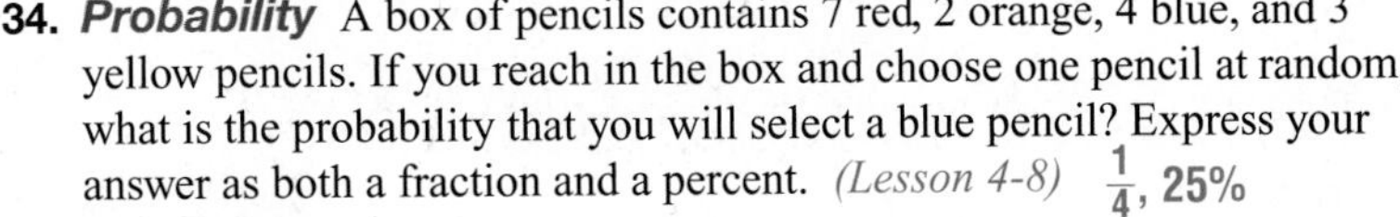

35. **Standardized Test Practice** If Addie has 1,000 nickels, how much money does she have? *(Lesson 2-4)* **A**

A \$50 **B** \$500 **C** \$1,000 **D** \$20,000

4 ASSESS

Closing Activity

Modeling Have students use graph paper to sketch a floor plan of their ideal apartment or one-story house, including measurements, using Exercise 29 as an example. Have students exchange completed plans and then determine the perimeter of each other's homes.

Additional Answers

28a. 24 ft (wall); 7 ft

30a. 72 ft; 120 ft

Extending the Lesson

***Enrichment Masters,* p. 54**

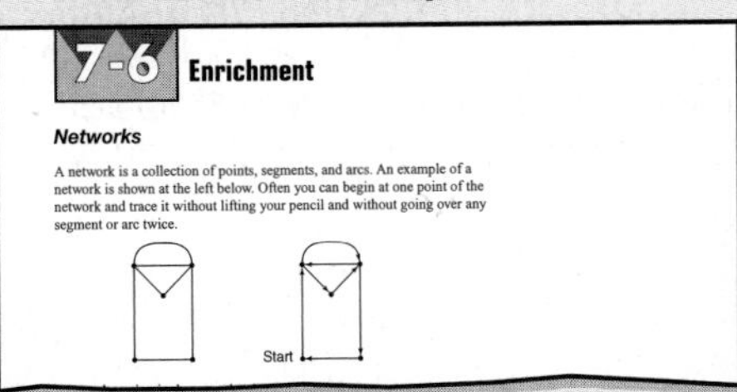

7-6 Enrichment

Networks

A network is a collection of points, segments, and arcs. An example of a network is shown at the left below. Often you can begin at one point of the network and trace it without lifting your pencil and without going over any segment or arc twice.

Start

Activity Challenge students to research sports in which distance around is an important concept. Ask students what other perimeters can be observed in sports, such as a tennis, basketball, or volleyball court and a football or soccer field. Ask why these distances are important.

***Practice Masters,* p. 54**

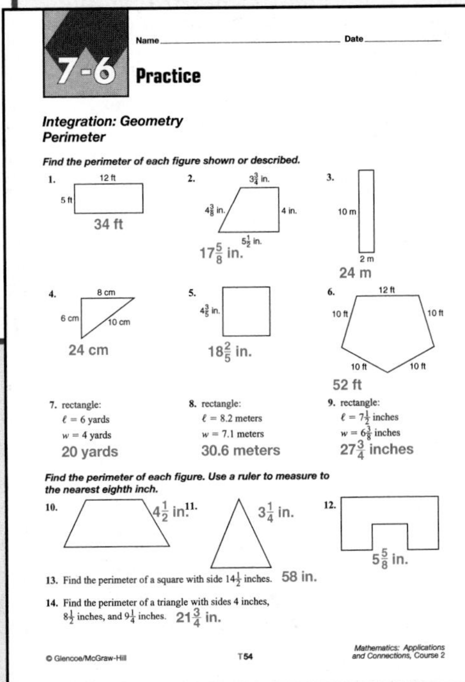

Name ______ Date ______

7-6 **Practice**

Integration: Geometry
Perimeter

Find the perimeter of each figure shown or described.

1. 12 ft, 5 ft — 34 ft
2. $3\frac{3}{4}$ in., $4\frac{3}{8}$ in., 4 in., $5\frac{1}{2}$ in. — $17\frac{5}{8}$ in.
3. 10 m, 2 m — 24 m
4. 8 cm, 6 cm, 10 cm — 24 cm
5. $4\frac{3}{5}$ in. — $18\frac{2}{5}$ in.
6. 12 ft, 10 ft, 10 ft, 10 ft, 10 ft — 52 ft
7. rectangle: ℓ = 6 yards, w = 4 yards — 20 yards
8. rectangle: ℓ = 8.2 meters, w = 7.1 meters — 30.6 meters
9. rectangle: $\ell = 7\frac{1}{4}$ inches, $w = 6\frac{5}{8}$ inches — $27\frac{3}{4}$ inches

Find the perimeter of each figure. Use a ruler to measure to the nearest eighth inch.

10. $4\frac{1}{2}$ in.
11. $3\frac{1}{4}$ in.
12. $5\frac{5}{8}$ in.

13. Find the perimeter of a square with side $14\frac{1}{2}$ inches. 58 in.

14. Find the perimeter of a triangle with sides 4 inches, $8\frac{1}{4}$ inches, and $9\frac{1}{2}$ inches. $21\frac{3}{4}$ in.

© Glencoe/McGraw-Hill T54 *Mathematics: Applications and Connections, Course 2*

Motivating Students

To begin the discussion about a career as a banker, you may want to give students an overview of the history of banking.

- Early banks exchanged the coins of one kingdom for another. How could you find how many German marks, for example, equal an English pound? **Use the exchange rate posted in some newspapers or at a bank.**
- Renaissance bankers arranged payments at a distance without any coins changing hands. What is buying something with a promise to pay in the future? **buying on credit or getting a loan**
- London bankers developed the modern practices of writing checks and making loans. What is the additional money paid as a percent of the amount borrowed for a loan called? **interest**

Making the Math Connection

Bankers must maintain a balance sheet showing that the bank's assets equal its liabilities. Using computer spreadsheets, bankers calculate large and small amounts with care for accuracy.

Working on *Your Turn*

Students may want to work in pairs to complete their posters. One student may describe the relationship between deposits and loans, while the other student illustrates the steps involved in those transactions.

An additional School to Career activity is available on page 20 of the ***School to Career Masters.***

FINANCE

Elouise C. Cobell
BANKER

Elouise Cobell helped found Blackfeet National Bank in Browning, Montana. It is the only national bank located on an Indian reservation and owned by an Indian tribe. She received a "genius grant," which is a fellowship awarded to people who show exceptional creativity and to those who make a significant difference in human thought and action. Today, Ms. Cobell directs a project that is working to improve the management of Indian trust funds.

To work in a bank as a financial manager, you'll need a bachelor's degree in accounting, finance, or business administration. You should have a solid background in mathematics and good computer skills. Financial managers must be able to communicate well, think quickly, and analyze data accurately.

For more information

American Bankers Association
Center for Banking Information
1120 Connecticut Ave. NW.
Washington, DC 20036

interNET CONNECTION
www.glencoe.com/sec/math/mac/mathnet

I put money in my savings account every week. I'd like to work in a bank someday!

Your Turn

Suppose you started your own bank. Make a poster displaying the various products and services that your bank would provide for its customers.

More About Elouise Cobell

- As an advocate for Native American self-determination, Elouise Cobell has inspired many Native American women to seek influence and leadership within their own communities.
- Ms. Cobell served as national spokesperson for the Native American trust funds, comptroller for the Blackfeet Indian Nation, and chair of the Intertribal Monitoring Association.
- Elouise Cobell attended Great Falls Commercial College, Montana State University, U.S. Army-SACOM, Northern Montana State University, and Blackfeet Community College.

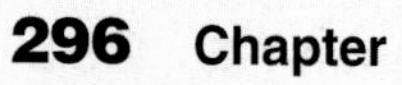

7-7 Integration: Geometry
Circles and Circumference

What you'll learn

You'll learn to find the circumference of circles.

When am I ever going to use this?

You can use circumference to find the distance you travel while riding a bicycle.

Word Wise

circle
center
diameter
radius
circumference

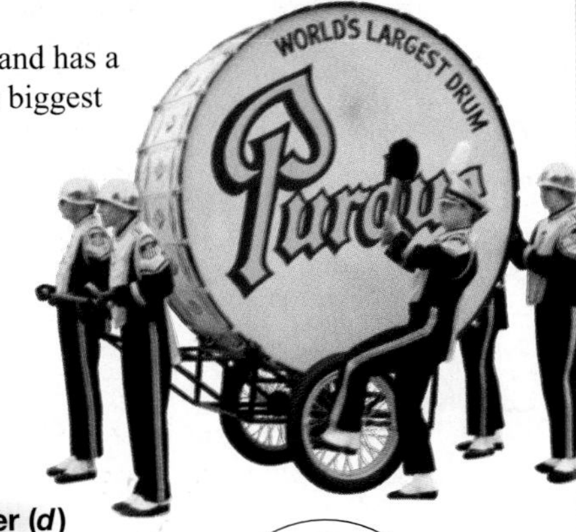

Purdue University's marching band has a bass drum that they claim is the biggest in the world. It takes four band members to pull it and two to pound on it. If the diameter of the drum is 8 feet, what is its circumference? *This problem will be solved in Example 1.*

A **circle** is the set of all points in a plane that are the same distance from a given point called the **center**. The **diameter (d)** is the distance across the circle through its center. The **radius (r)** is the distance from the center to any point on the circle. The **circumference (C)** is the distance around the circle.

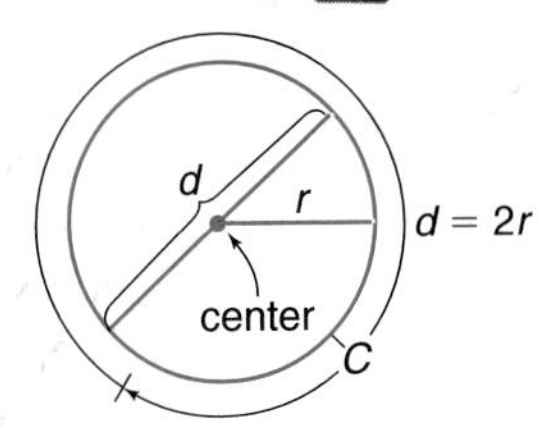

MINI-LAB

Work with a partner.

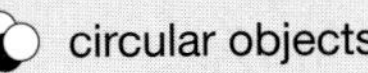

You can use circular objects to find the relationship between circumference and diameter.

Try This

- Use a ruler to measure the diameter of a circular object. Record your finding.
- Wrap a string around the circular object once. Mark the string where it meets itself.
- Measure the length of the string with your ruler. Record your finding. This is the circumference of the circle.
- Repeat this activity with circular objects of various sizes.

Talk About It

1. For each circular object, graph the ordered pair (diameter, circumference) on a coordinate plane. What do you find?
2. For each object, divide the circumference by the diameter. Compare the results. $\frac{C}{d} \approx 3.14$
3. How is the circumference related to the diameter? $C \approx 3.14d$

LOOK BACK

Refer to Lesson 6-7 to review graphing on a coordinate plane.

1. See students' graphs. All points will lie on a diagonal line.

7-7 Lesson Notes

Instructional Resources

- *Study Guide Masters,* p. 55
- *Practice Masters,* p. 55
- *Enrichment Masters,* p. 55
- Transparencies 7-7, A and B
- *Assessment and Evaluation Masters,* p. 184
- *Diversity Masters,* p. 20
- *Technology Masters,* pp. 39–40

CD-ROM Program
- Resource Lesson 7-7
- Extended Activity 7-7

Recommended Pacing	
Standard	Day 11 of 15
Honors	Day 10 of 14
Block	Day 6 of 8

1 FOCUS

5-Minute Check (Lesson 7-6)

Find the perimeter of each figure shown or described.

1.

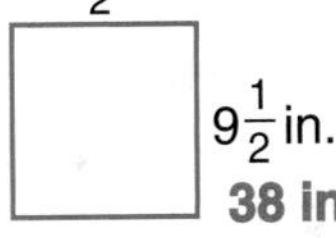

38 in.

2.

49 in.

3. ℓ = 2.5 meters
   w = 3.8 meters **12.6 m**
4. Find the perimeter of a square with a side $12\frac{3}{8}$ inches long. **$49\frac{1}{2}$ in.**
5. Find the perimeter of any rectangular object in the classroom. Measure to the nearest eighth of an inch.

The 5-Minute Check is also available on **Transparency 7-7A** for this lesson.

Motivating the Lesson

Problem Solving Ask students how they would solve this problem if they didn't know the formula for the distance around a circle. *If Inez takes her dog to the park on an 18-foot leash, what is the greatest distance the dog can run in one circle around Inez?*

MathPASS CD-ROM

This CD-ROM offers a complete, self-paced mathematics curriculum. Each lesson includes a pretest, tutorial, guided practice, and posttest. MathPASS Lesson 25 is correlated to this Student Edition lesson.
For Windows & Macintosh

2 TEACH

Transparency 7-7B contains a teaching aid for this lesson.

Using the Mini-Lab Before measuring any circles, have students guess what their findings will be. After they conclude the activity, ask them how the rim of a bicycle wheel is related to a spoke. Then ask students to use what they know about the relationship between the diameter and circumference to design a device for measuring the length of their school building.

In-Class Examples

For Example 1
The free-throw line on a basketball court is 12 feet long. Find the circumference of the circle whose diameter is the free-throw line. Use 3.14 for π. **37.68 ft**

For Example 2
Find the circumference of a circle with a radius of 21 meters. Use $\frac{22}{7}$ for π. **about 132 m**

For Example 3
Find the circumference of a circle with a radius of 12.5 miles. Use your calculator. **about 78.5 mi**

Teaching Tip Ask students when they think they should use $\frac{22}{7}$ for π. Point out that this estimate is often used when the radius is divisible by 7.

The Greek letter π is used to represent the circumference divided by the diameter $\frac{C}{d}$. Approximations often used for π are 3.14 and $\frac{22}{7}$.

The diameter of a circle is twice the radius.

Circumference of a Circle

Words: The circumference of a circle is equal to π times its diameter or π times twice the radius.

Symbols: $C = \pi d$ or $C = 2\pi r$

Model:

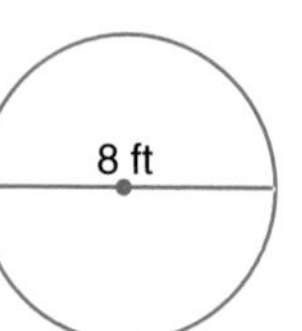

Example 1 Real World APPLICATION

Music **Refer to the beginning of the lesson. Find the circumference of the drum to the nearest tenth.**

Since you know the diameter, use the formula $C = \pi d$.

$C = \pi d$

$C \approx 3.14(8)$ *Use 3.14 for π. Replace d with 8.*

$C \approx 25.12$

The circumference of the drum is about 25.1 feet.

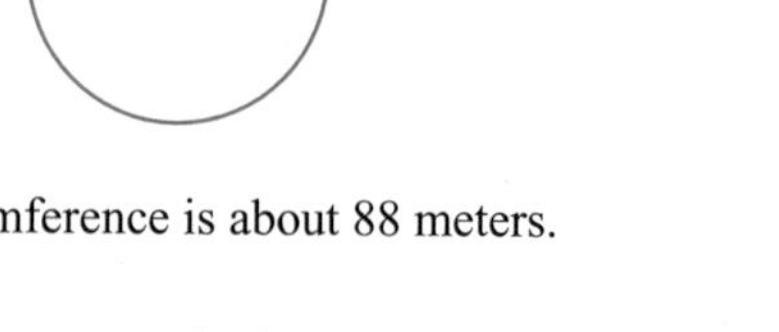

Study Hint
Reading Math
$\approx$ means *is approximately equal to.*

One approximate value for π is the fraction $\frac{22}{7}$. Use this value for π when the radius or diameter of the circle is a multiple of 7 or has a multiple of 7 in its numerator.

Example 2 **Find the circumference of a circle with a radius of 14 meters.**

$C = 2\pi r$

$C \approx 2\left(\frac{22}{7}\right)(14)$

$C \approx 2\left(\frac{22}{\cancel{7}_1}\right)\left(\frac{\cancel{14}^2}{1}\right)$

$C \approx 2 \times \frac{22}{1} \times \frac{2}{1}$

$C \approx 88$ The circumference is about 88 meters.

14 m

π usually has its own key on a calculator. You can use this key to find the circumference of a circle. *What is displayed on your calculator when you press* [π]*?*

Example 3 **Find the circumference of a circle with a radius of 4.5 inches.**

$C = 2\pi r$

$C \approx 2\pi(4.5)$ *Estimate: $2 \times 3 \times 5 = 30$*

2 [×] [π] [×] 4.5 [=] 28.27433388

$C \approx 28.3$ *Round to the nearest tenth since the original measurement was only to the tenths place.*

The circumference is about 28.3 inches.

4.5 in.

Classroom Vignette

"I bring several different sized circular objects into the classroom. Each group of students uses a tape measure to find the circumference and diameter of each object. Then we divide to find a pattern and thus discover *pi*."

Judy Dexter, Teacher
Lathrop Middle School
Lathrop, MO

CHECK FOR UNDERSTANDING

Communicating Mathematics

Read and study the lesson to answer each question.

1. ***Describe*** real-life situations in which finding the circumference of a circle would be useful. **See students' work.**
2. ***Describe*** what is meant by an *approximation* when finding the circumference of a circle. **See margin.**

Guided Practice

Answers are calculated using 3.14 and then rounded unless otherwise noted.

Find the circumference of each circle to the nearest tenth. Use $\frac{22}{7}$ or 3.14 for π.

3. 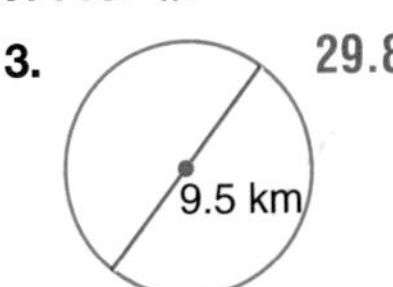

29.8 km

4. $1\frac{3}{4}$ ft   **$\pi = \frac{22}{7}$; 11 ft**

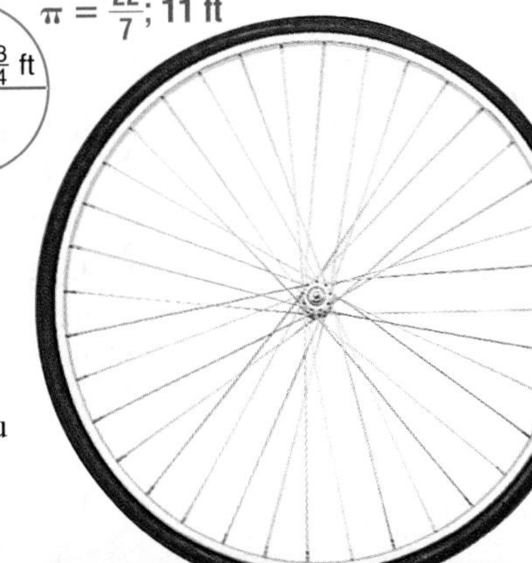

5. $r = 1.5$ yd **9.4 yd**
6. $d = 17$ ft **53.4 ft**
7. $d = 10.3$ cm **32.3 cm**
8. ***Cycling*** The diameter of a bicycle wheel is 26 inches. How far will you travel after one complete turn of the wheel? **81.6 in.**

EXERCISES

Practice

Find the circumference of each circle to the nearest tenth. Use $\frac{22}{7}$ or 3.14 for π.

9. 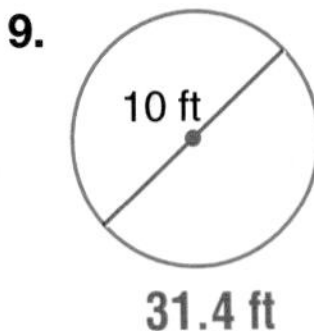

31.4 ft

10. 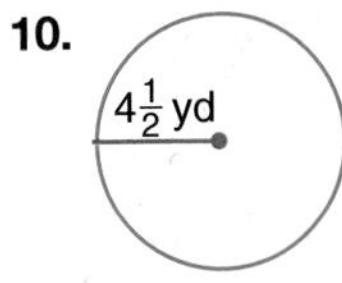

28.3 yd

11. 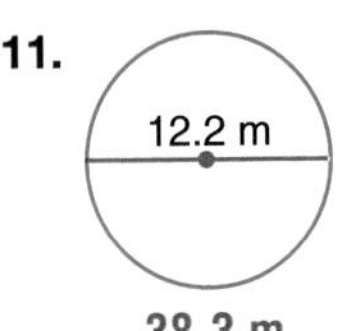

38.3 m

12. 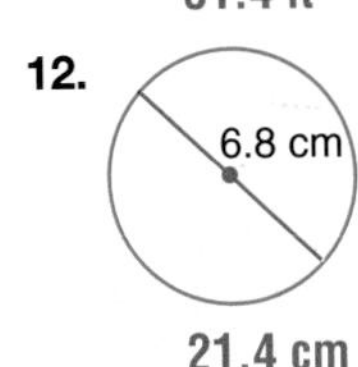

21.4 cm

13. 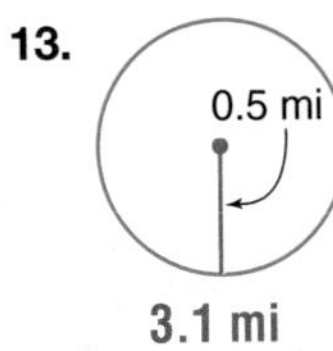

3.1 mi

14. 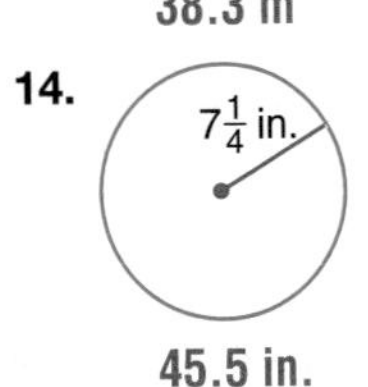

45.5 in.

15. $d = 14$ m
16. $r = 10\frac{1}{2}$ in.
17. $r = 6.2$ cm
18. $d = 8\frac{1}{4}$ ft

15. $\pi = \frac{22}{7}$; 44 m
16. 65.9 in.
17. 38.9 cm
18. 25.9 ft

19. Find the circumference of a circle whose radius is $\frac{2}{5}$ yard. **$2\frac{18}{35}$ or 2.5 yd**
20. What is the radius of a circle whose diameter is 7 meters? **3.5 m**
21. Find the circumference of a circle whose radius is $8\frac{3}{4}$ feet. **$\pi = \frac{22}{7}$; 55 ft**
22. If the radius of the circle in Exercise 21 is doubled, is the circumference doubled? Why or why not? **Yes, the circumference is 110 ft.**

Reteaching the Lesson

Activity Provide students with compasses, rulers, and string with which to draw and measure circles. Measure each circle to find the relationship between the radius and the diameter, the radius and the circumference, and the diameter and the circumference.

Error Analysis

Watch for students who forget to double the radius when finding circumference. **Prevent by** reinforcing that the formula is $C = \pi d$ and $d = 2r$.

3 PRACTICE/APPLY

Check for Understanding

If students need additional practice or instruction after completing Exercises 1–8, one of these options may be helpful.

- Extra Practice, see p. 588
- Reteaching Activity
- *Study Guide Masters,* p. 56
- *Practice Masters,* p. 56

Assignment Guide

Core: 9–25 odd, 27–31
Enriched: 10–22 even, 23–31

Additional Answer

2. It means that the value of the circumference is not exact since the value of π is a rounded number.

***Study Guide Masters,* p. 55**

Name__________ Date________

7-7 Study Guide

Integration: Geometry
Circles and Circumference

A **circle** is the set of all points in a plane that are the same distance from a given point called the **center.**

The **diameter** (*d*) is the distance across the circle through its center.

The **radius** (*r*) is the distance from the center to any point on the circle.

The **circumference** (*C*) is the distance around the circle.

Examples **1** **Find the circumference of a circle with a diameter of 7.5 inches.**

$C = \pi d$
$C \approx 3.14 \times 7.5$ *Use 3.14 for π.*
$C \approx 23.55$ The circumference of the circle is about 23.55 inches.

2 **If the radius of a circle is 14 inches, what is its circumference?**

$C = 2\pi r$
$C = 2 \times \frac{22}{7} \times 14$ *Use $\frac{22}{7}$ for π.*
$C = 88$ The circumference of the circle is about 88 inches.

Find the circumference of each circle to the nearest tenth. Use $\frac{22}{7}$ or 3.14 for π.

1. 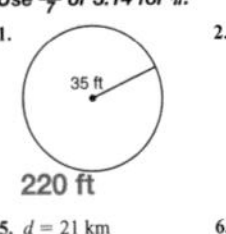

220 ft

2. 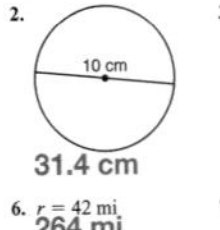

31.4 cm

3. 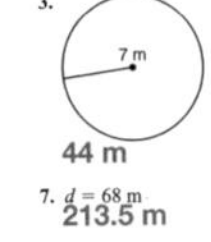

44 m

4. 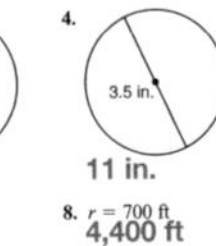

11 in.

5. $d = 21$ km **66 km**
6. $r = 42$ mi **264 mi**
7. $d = 68$ m **213.5 m**
8. $r = 700$ ft **4,400 ft**
9. $r = 91$ cm **572 cm**
10. $d = 5$ km **15.7 km**
11. $r = 90$ ft **$565\frac{1}{5}$ ft**
12. $d = 6.3$ m **19.8 m**

 T55 *Mathematics: Applications and Connections, Course 2*

4 ASSESS

Closing Activity

Speaking Have students use the measurements 10 feet and 62.8 feet and the terms *circle, circumference,* and either *diameter* or *radius* in a true sentence. **Sample answer: A circle with radius 10 feet has a circumference of about 62.8 feet.**

Chapter 7, Quiz C (Lessons 7-6 and 7-7) is available in the *Assessment and Evaluation Masters,* p. 184.

Practice Masters, p. 55

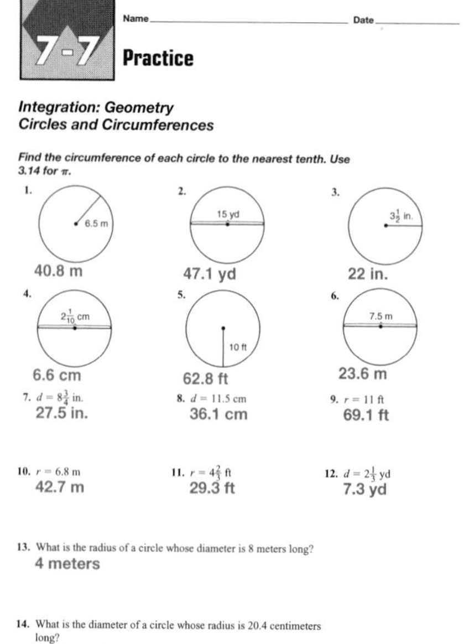

Name________ Date________

7-7 Practice

Integration: Geometry
Circles and Circumferences

Find the circumference of each circle to the nearest tenth. Use 3.14 for π.

1. (6.5 m) 40.8 m
2. (15 yd) 47.1 yd
3. ($3\frac{1}{2}$ in.) 22 in.
4. ($2\frac{1}{10}$ cm) 6.6 cm
5. (10 ft) 62.8 ft
6. (7.5 m) 23.6 m
7. $d = 8\frac{3}{4}$ in. 27.5 in.
8. $d = 11.5$ cm 36.1 cm
9. $r = 11$ ft 69.1 ft
10. $r = 6.8$ m 42.7 m
11. $r = 4\frac{2}{3}$ ft 29.3 ft
12. $d = 2\frac{1}{3}$ yd 7.3 yd

13. What is the radius of a circle whose diameter is 8 meters long? 4 meters

14. What is the diameter of a circle whose radius is 20.4 centimeters long? 40.8 centimeters

© Glencoe/McGraw-Hill T55 Mathematics: Applications and Connections, Course 2

Applications and Problem Solving

23. ***Recreation*** The pedals on a bicycle from the 1870s were on the front wheel. For speed, the front wheel was large, with a diameter of about 64 inches. The back wheel diameter was about 12 inches.

a. How far did a cyclist travel each time the pedals made a complete turn?

b. How many times does the back wheel go around for each complete turn of the front wheel? **5.3 times**

23a. 201.0 in.

24. ***Sports*** A basketball hoop has a diameter of $18\frac{1}{2}$ inches. Estimate the circumference. **58.1 in.**

25. ***Life Science*** The rafflesia plant, found in the rain forests of Malaysia, produces the world's largest flower. It gives off a smell of rotting meat to attract flies and promote pollination. If the center of the flower has a radius of $\frac{3}{4}$ foot, find the circumference. **4.7 ft**

26. ***Life Science*** The largest bird nest on record was built by bald eagles near St. Petersburg, Florida. Its estimated weight is more than 2 tons, and it has a diameter of $9\frac{1}{2}$ feet. What is the circumference of the nest? **29.8 ft**

27. ***Critical Thinking*** How many segments x will fit on the circumference of the circle? **2π**

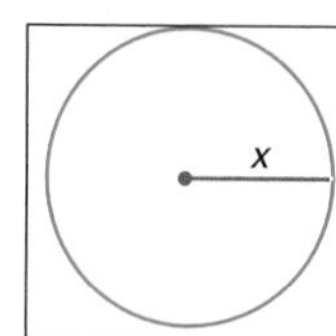

Mixed Review

28. ***Physical Fitness*** Every evening, Alicia walks around a neighborhood block, which is a rectangle 0.75 mile long and 0.2 mile wide. How far does Alicia walk each evening? *(Lesson 7-6)* **1.9 miles**

29. **Standardized Test Practice** Belinda had $4\frac{2}{3}$ pounds of chopped walnuts. She used $1\frac{1}{4}$ pounds in a recipe. How much of the chopped walnuts did she have left? *(Lesson 7-3)* **A**

A $3\frac{5}{12}$ **B** $2\frac{5}{12}$ **C** $3\frac{1}{2}$ **D** $2\frac{1}{3}$

30. ***Geometry*** In which quadrant do ordered pairs with a positive x-coordinate and a negative y-coordinate lie? *(Lesson 5-3)* **IV**

31. ***Environment*** The graph shows the percent of materials that make up landfills. Express each percent as a fraction in simplest form. *(Lesson 4-7)*

31. $16\% = \frac{4}{25}$, $35\% = \frac{7}{20}$, $49\% = \frac{49}{100}$

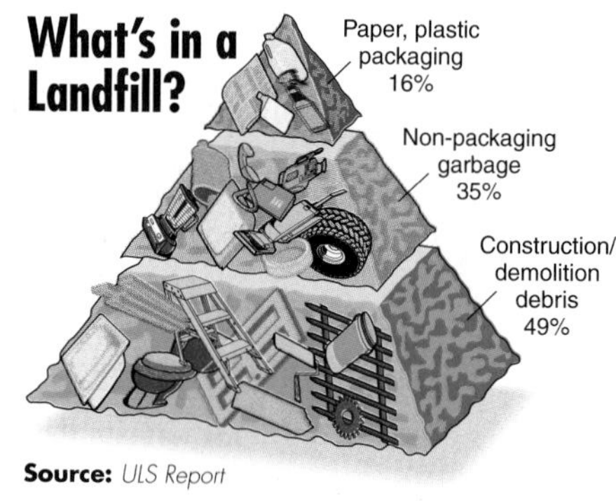

For **Extra Practice,** see page 588.

Extending the Lesson

Enrichment Masters, p. 55

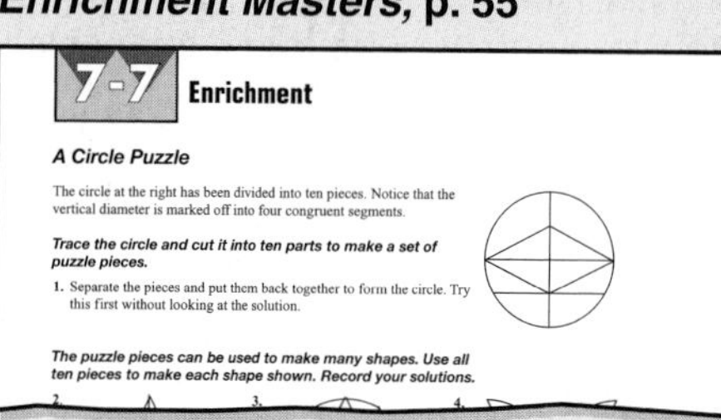

7-7 Enrichment

A Circle Puzzle

The circle at the right has been divided into ten pieces. Notice that the vertical diameter is marked off into four congruent segments.

Trace the circle and cut it into ten parts to make a set of puzzle pieces.

1. Separate the pieces and put them back together to form the circle. Try this first without looking at the solution.

The puzzle pieces can be used to make many shapes. Use all ten pieces to make each shape shown. Record your solutions.

Activity Have students research the history of π. They may also want to access the Internet to see what some of the latest research on π has revealed.

7-8 Properties

What you'll learn

You'll learn to use addition and multiplication properties to solve problems.

When am I ever going to use this?

Knowing how to use properties can help you find how much money you can earn each month.

Word Wise

commutative
associative
identity
multiplicative inverse
reciprocal
distributive

According to Wildlife Fact File, one Siberian tiger traveled 620 miles in search of food. If the tiger traveled an average of $28\frac{1}{5}$ miles each day, how long did it travel before finding food? *This problem will be solved in Example 4.*

Addition and multiplication of fractions have the same properties you learned for addition and multiplication of whole numbers.

Property	Arithmetic	Algebra
Commutative	$\frac{2}{3} + \frac{1}{8} = \frac{1}{8} + \frac{2}{3}$ $\frac{2}{3} \times \frac{1}{8} = \frac{1}{8} \times \frac{2}{3}$	$a + b = b + a$ $a \times b = b \times a$
Associative	$\left(\frac{1}{5} + \frac{2}{5}\right) + \frac{3}{4} = \frac{1}{5} + \left(\frac{2}{5} + \frac{3}{4}\right)$ $\left(\frac{1}{5} \times \frac{2}{5}\right) \times \frac{3}{4} = \frac{1}{5} \times \left(\frac{2}{5} \times \frac{3}{4}\right)$	$(a + b) + c = a + (b + c)$ $(a \times b) \times c = a \times (b \times c)$
Identity	$\frac{1}{2} + 0 = \frac{1}{2}$ $\frac{1}{2} \times 1 = \frac{1}{2}$	$a + 0 = a$ $a \times 1 = a$

Zero has no reciprocal because any number times 0 is 0.

Two numbers whose product is 1 are **multiplicative inverses**, or **reciprocals**.

Multiplicative Inverse Property

Words: The product of a number and its multiplicative inverse is 1.

Symbols: **Arithmetic** $\frac{2}{7} \times \frac{7}{2} = 1$

Algebra For all fractions $\frac{a}{b}$, where $a, b \neq 0$, $\frac{a}{b} \times \frac{b}{a} = 1$.

Example 1 Name the multiplicative inverse of $3\frac{1}{4}$.

$3\frac{1}{4} = \frac{13}{4}$ *Rename the mixed number as an improper fraction.*

$\frac{13}{4} \times \blacksquare = 1$ *What number can you multiply by $\frac{13}{4}$ to get 1?*

$\frac{13}{4} \times \frac{4}{13} = 1$

The multiplicative inverse of $3\frac{1}{4}$ is $\frac{4}{13}$.

7-8 Lesson Notes

Instructional Resources

- *Study Guide Masters,* p. 56
- *Practice Masters,* p. 56
- *Enrichment Masters,* p. 56
- Transparencies 7-8, A and B
- CD-ROM Program
  - Resource Lesson 7-8

Recommended Pacing	
Standard	Day 12 of 15
Honors	Day 11 of 14
Block	Day 7 of 8

1 FOCUS

5-Minute Check
(Lesson 7-7)

Find the circumference of each circle to the nearest tenth.

1.

3.8 m

2.

about 71.0 ft

3. $d = 14\frac{1}{2}$ mi **45.5 mi**

4. $r = 4.5$ km **28.3 km**

5. Use $\pi = \frac{22}{7}$ to find the circumference of a circle whose radius is 28 yards. **176 yd**

The 5-Minute Check is also available on **Transparency 7-8A** for this lesson.

Motivating the Lesson

Problem Solving A world-class marathon runner ran the 26-mile race in 2 hours and 10 minutes, or 130 minutes. To find his average time per mile, divide 130 by 26, or $\frac{130}{26} = t$. **5 min**

2 TEACH

Transparency 7-8B contains a teaching aid for this lesson.

Reading Mathematics Discuss with students the meaning of the root words from which the terms *identity*, *commutative*, *associative*, *distributive*, and *inverse* are derived, such as "the same," "change places," "grouping," "spread out," and "upside-down." Encourage students to explain how the properties work using these or similar words.

Teaching Tip Some students may have difficulty with the wording of the distributive property. You may wish to express this more simply as "you can add first and then multiply or multiply and then add—the result is the same.

In-Class Examples

For Example 1
Name the multiplicative inverse of $\frac{4}{5}$. **$\frac{5}{4}$ or $1\frac{1}{4}$**

For Example 2
Find $\frac{1}{3} \times 9\frac{3}{8}$. **$3\frac{1}{8}$**

For Example 3
Solve each equation.

a. $\frac{b}{12} = 7.6$ **91.2**

b. $\frac{3}{4}y = 60$ **80**

The **distributive property** ties addition and multiplication together.

Distributive Property	**Words:**	The sum of two addends multiplied by a number is the sum of the product of each addend and the number.
	Symbols:	**Arithmetic** $\frac{1}{5} \times \left(\frac{2}{5} + \frac{3}{4}\right) = \frac{1}{5} \times \frac{2}{5} + \frac{1}{5} \times \frac{3}{4}$
		Algebra $a \times (b + c) = a \times b + a \times c$

You can use the distributive property to solve multiplication problems involving mixed numbers.

Example 2 Find $\frac{1}{2} \times 4\frac{2}{5}$.

Estimate: $\frac{1}{2} \times 4 = 2$

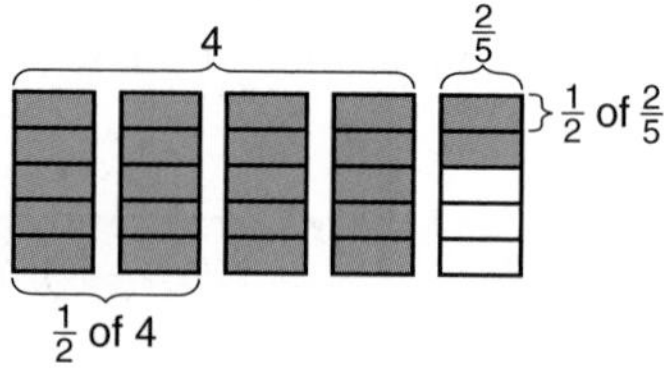

$$\frac{1}{2} \times 4\frac{2}{5} = \frac{1}{2} \times \left(4 + \frac{2}{5}\right) \quad \textit{Distributive property}$$

$$= \left(\frac{1}{2} \times 4\right) + \left(\frac{1}{2} \times \frac{2}{5}\right)$$

$$= 2 + \frac{1}{5} \text{ or } 2\frac{1}{5} \quad 2\tfrac{1}{5} \textit{ is close to the estimate.}$$

You can "undo" division in an equation by multiplying each side of the equation by the same number.

Multiplication Property of Equality	**Words:**	If you multiply each side of an equation by the same nonzero number, the two sides remain equal.	
	Symbols:	**Arithmetic**	**Algebra**
		$7 = 7$	$a = b$
		$7 \cdot 2 = 7 \cdot 2$	$ac = bc$
		$14 = 14$	

Example 3 INTEGRATION

Algebra Solve each equation.

a. $\frac{a}{3.2} = 5$

$$\frac{a}{3.2} = 5$$

$$\frac{a}{3.2} \cdot 3.2 = 5 \cdot 3.2$$

$$a = 16$$

Multiply each side by 3.2 to undo the division.

b. $\frac{2}{3}t = 8$

$$\frac{2}{3}t = 8$$

$$\frac{2}{3}t\left(\frac{3}{2}\right) = 8\left(\frac{3}{2}\right)$$

$$t = 12$$

Multiply each side by the reciprocal of $\frac{2}{3}$.

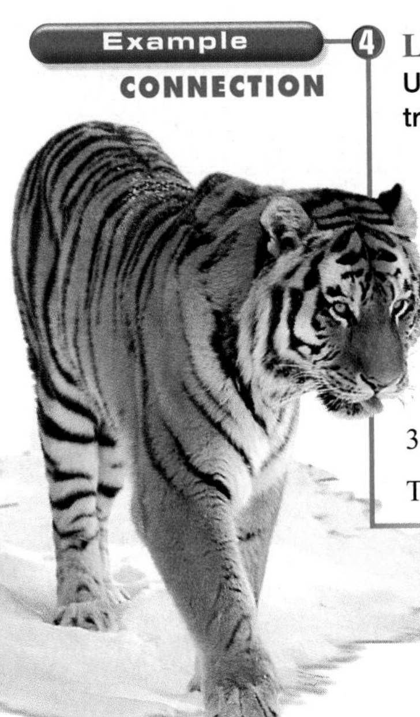

Example CONNECTION

4 **Life Science** Refer to the beginning of the lesson. Use $28\frac{1}{5}d = 620$ to find d, the number of days that the tiger traveled before finding food.

$$28\frac{1}{5}d = 620$$

$$\frac{141}{5}d = 620 \qquad \textit{Rename } 28\tfrac{1}{5} \textit{ as } \tfrac{141}{5}.$$

$$\left(\frac{5}{141}\right)\frac{141}{5}d = \left(\frac{5}{141}\right)620 \qquad \textit{Multiply each side by } \tfrac{5}{141} \textit{ to undo the multiplication by } \tfrac{141}{5}.$$

$$d = \frac{3{,}100}{141}$$

3100 [÷] 141 [=] 21.9858156 *Use a calculator.*

The tiger traveled about 22 days before finding food.

CHECK FOR UNDERSTANDING

Communicating Mathematics

Read and study the lesson to answer each question.

1. ***Tell*** whether 5 is a solution of $\frac{t}{4} = 20$. **no; $4 \cdot 20 \neq 5$**
2. ***You Decide*** *True* or *false*? Explain. $(12 + 27) \times 3 = 12 + 27 \times 3$
3. ***Simplify*** each of the following. Then tell the properties you used.
   a. $80 + 276 + 20$ b. $-26 + 54 + 26$
   c. $\left(-\frac{5}{9}\right)\left(\frac{11}{11}\right)$ d. $(-7)(3)(-15)(-9 + 9)$
   a-d. See margin.

2. false; $(12 + 27) \times 3 = 117$; $12 + 27 \times 3 = 93$; $117 \neq 93$

Guided Practice

Name the property shown by each statement.

4. $\frac{5}{9} \times \frac{1}{3} = \frac{1}{3} \times \frac{5}{9}$ **commutative (×)**
5. $\frac{3}{5} + 0 = \frac{3}{5}$ **identity (+)**

Name the multiplicative inverse of each number.

6. $\frac{8}{11}$ $\frac{11}{8}$
7. $4\frac{2}{5}$ $\frac{5}{22}$
8. 14 $\frac{1}{14}$

Solve each equation. Write the solution in simplest form.

9. $\frac{3}{4}a = 24$ **32**
10. $\frac{c}{16} = 2$ **32**
11. $r = 2 \times 5\frac{1}{2}$ **11**

12. ***Earth Science*** In 1996, astronomers discovered a huge planet where they once thought it was impossible for any planet to form. Earth's diameter is only $\frac{5}{86}$ the size of this unnamed planet's diameter. Use the equation $\frac{5}{86}d = 7{,}970$ to find d, the diameter of the new planet in miles. *7,970 miles is the diameter of Earth.* **137,084 miles**

In-Class Example

For Example 4

Jill runs for $1\frac{3}{4}$ as long as Eva. Find Eva's running time if Jill runs for 84 minutes. **48 min**

3 PRACTICE/APPLY

Check for Understanding

If students need additional practice or instruction after completing Exercises 1–12, one of these options may be helpful.

- Extra Practice, see p. 588
- Reteaching Activity
- *Study Guide Masters,* p. 56
- *Practice Masters,* p. 56

Additional Answers

3a. $80 + 276 + 20 = 80 + 20 + 276 = 100 + 276 = 376$; commutative

3b. $-26 + 54 + 26 = -26 + 26 + 54 = 0 + 54 = 54$; commutative; additive inverse; identity (+)

3c. $\left(-\frac{5}{9}\right)\left(\frac{11}{11}\right) = \left(-\frac{5}{9}\right)(1) = -\frac{5}{9}$; identity (×)

3d. $(-7)(3)(-15)(-9 + 9) = (-7)(3)(-15)(0) = 0$; additive inverse; multiplicative prop. of 0.

***Study Guide Masters,* p. 56**

Name ______ Date ______

Study Guide

Properties

The table shows the properties for addition and multiplication of fractions.

Property	Examples
Commutative The sum or product of two fractions is the same regardless of the order in which they are added or multiplied.	$\frac{1}{2} + \frac{1}{4} = \frac{1}{4} + \frac{1}{2}$ $\frac{2}{3} \times \frac{1}{5} = \frac{1}{5} \times \frac{2}{3}$
Associative The sum or product of three or more fractions is the same regardless of the way in which they are grouped.	$\left(\frac{1}{2} + \frac{5}{6}\right) + \frac{7}{8} = \frac{1}{2} + \left(\frac{5}{6} + \frac{7}{8}\right)$ $\frac{1}{8} \times \left(\frac{3}{4} \times \frac{6}{7}\right) = \left(\frac{1}{8} \times \frac{3}{4}\right) \times \frac{6}{7}$
Identity The sum of any fraction and 0 is the fraction. The product of any fraction and 1 is the fraction.	$\frac{7}{8} + 0 = \frac{7}{8}$ $\frac{5}{9} \times 1 = \frac{5}{9}$
Inverse (Reciprocal) The product of a fraction and its reciprocal is 1.	$\frac{7}{8} \times \frac{8}{7} = 1$
Distributive The sum of two fractions multiplied by a number is equal to the sum of the products of each fraction and the number.	$\frac{2}{3}\left(\frac{1}{2} + \frac{3}{7}\right) = \left(\frac{2}{3} \times \frac{1}{2}\right) + \left(\frac{2}{3} \times \frac{3}{7}\right)$

Name the property shown by each statement.

1. $\frac{11}{12} \times 1 = \frac{11}{12}$ identity
2. $\left(\frac{1}{5} + \frac{2}{3}\right) + \frac{5}{9} = \frac{1}{5} + \left(\frac{2}{3} + \frac{5}{9}\right)$ associative
3. $\frac{3}{4} \times \frac{5}{6} = \frac{5}{6} \times \frac{3}{4}$ commutative
4. $\frac{3}{5} \times \left(\frac{1}{3} + \frac{5}{7}\right) = \left(\frac{3}{5} \times \frac{1}{3}\right) + \left(\frac{3}{5} \times \frac{5}{7}\right)$ distributive
5. $\frac{9}{4} \times \frac{4}{9} = 1$ inverse
6. $\frac{4}{5} + \frac{3}{4} = \frac{3}{4} + \frac{4}{5}$ commutative
7. $0 + \frac{17}{18} = \frac{17}{18}$ identity
8. $\frac{2}{9} \times \left(\frac{1}{4} \times \frac{9}{10}\right) = \left(\frac{2}{9} \times \frac{1}{4}\right) \times \frac{9}{10}$ associative

Name the multiplicative inverse of each number.

9. $\frac{6}{11}$ $\frac{11}{6}$
10. $\frac{19}{3}$ $\frac{3}{19}$
11. $\frac{1}{8}$ 8
12. 9 $\frac{1}{9}$

 T56 *Mathematics: Applications and Connections, Course 2*

Reteaching the Lesson

Activity Use base-ten blocks or counters to illustrate the commutative, associative, and distributive properties for whole-number expressions, such as, $5 \times 3 = 3 \times 5$, $3 \times (4 \times 5) = (3 \times 4) \times 5$, and $3 \times (4 + 5) = 3 \times 4 + 3 \times 5$.

Assignment Guide

Core: 13–33 odd, 35–39
Enriched: 14–32 even, 33–39

4 ASSESS

Closing Activity

Writing Have students write an arithmetic sentence that shows the distributive property.

Practice Masters, p. 56

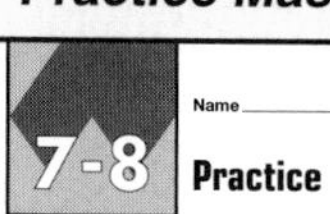

Name__________ Date________

7-8 Practice

Properties

Name the property shown by each statement.

1. $\frac{3}{8} + 0 = \frac{3}{8}$ identity (+)
2. $\frac{3}{4} \times \left(\frac{1}{2} \times \frac{1}{3}\right) = \left(\frac{3}{4} \times \frac{1}{2}\right) \times \frac{1}{3}$ associative (×)
3. $\frac{1}{3} \times \left(\frac{1}{4} + \frac{3}{5}\right) = \frac{1}{3} \times \frac{1}{4} + \frac{1}{3} \times \frac{3}{5}$ distributive
4. $\frac{3}{5} + \frac{5}{9} = \frac{5}{9} + \frac{3}{5}$ commutative (+)
5. $\frac{1}{6} \times \frac{3}{4} = \frac{3}{4} \times \frac{1}{6}$ commutative (×)
6. $1\frac{7}{9} \times 1 = 1\frac{7}{9}$ identity (×)

Name the multiplicative inverse of each number.

7. 5 $\frac{1}{5}$
8. $1\frac{3}{4}$ $\frac{4}{7}$
9. $\frac{7}{9}$ $\frac{9}{7}$ or $1\frac{2}{7}$
10. 1 1
11. $2\frac{1}{2}$ $\frac{2}{5}$
12. $\frac{3}{13}$ $\frac{13}{3}$ or $4\frac{1}{3}$

Solve each equation. Write the solution in simplest form.

13. $\frac{3}{2}h = 6$ 4
14. $3 \times 1\frac{1}{5} = p$ $3\frac{3}{5}$
15. $7\frac{1}{10} \times 8 = d$ $56\frac{4}{5}$

Compute mentally.

16. $\frac{1}{2} \times 6\frac{2}{7}$ $3\frac{1}{7}$
17. $9\frac{9}{24} \times \frac{1}{3}$ $3\frac{1}{8}$
18. $8\frac{4}{9} \times \frac{1}{4}$ $2\frac{1}{9}$

 T56 *Mathematics: Applications and Connections, Course 2*

EXERCISES

Practice **Name the property shown by each statement.**

13. commutative (+)
14. associative (+)
16. distributive
17. multiplication (=)
18. multiplicative inverse

13. $\frac{1}{5} + \frac{3}{5} = \frac{3}{5} + \frac{1}{5}$
14. $\frac{2}{9} + \left(\frac{1}{9} + \frac{6}{4}\right) = \left(\frac{2}{9} + \frac{1}{9}\right) + \frac{6}{4}$
15. $\frac{8}{9} \times 1 = \frac{8}{9}$ **identity (×)**
16. $\frac{1}{2} \times \left(\frac{1}{5} + \frac{1}{4}\right) = \frac{1}{2} \times \frac{1}{5} + \frac{1}{2} \times \frac{1}{4}$
17. $\frac{1}{2}b = 4$, so $b = 8$
18. $\frac{3}{5} \times 1\frac{2}{3} = 1$

Name the multiplicative inverse of each number.

19. $\frac{2}{3}$ **$\frac{3}{2}$ or $1\frac{1}{2}$**
20. $\frac{1}{9}$ **9**
21. 12 **$\frac{1}{12}$**
22. $6\frac{2}{3}$ **$\frac{3}{20}$**

Solve each equation. Write the solution in simplest form.

26. $2\frac{1}{3}$
29. $24\frac{1}{2}$
30. 2.88

23. $\frac{a}{12} = 3$ **36**
24. $\frac{1}{2}t = \frac{2}{5}$ **$\frac{4}{5}$**
25. $\frac{7}{8}x = 21$ **24**
26. $2 \times 1\frac{1}{6} = b$
27. $28 = \frac{g}{4}$ **112**
28. $\frac{4}{9}r = 84$ **189**
29. $4 \times 6\frac{1}{8} = q$
30. $\frac{s}{3.6} = 0.8$
31. What is the reciprocal of $1\frac{1}{4}$? **$\frac{4}{5}$**
32. Solve $\frac{5}{6}m = 35.1$. **42.12**

Applications and Problem Solving

33. ***Food*** Nick is serving a 12-pound turkey at a dinner party. As a rule, you should allow about $\frac{3}{4}$ of a pound of meat per person. If he invited 15 people, will he have enough turkey? Use the equation $\frac{3}{4}p = 12$, where p is the number of people.

33. Yes; there is enough turkey for 16 people.

34. ***Engineering*** In designing gasoline storage tanks, engineers multiply the government-required minimum thickness by a factor of $\frac{5}{2}$ for added safety. Fill in the blank with the appropriate fraction: The minimum thickness of gasoline storage tanks is __?__ as thick as the engineers use. **$\frac{2}{5}$**
35. ***Critical Thinking*** Use the properties of addition and multiplication to compute $60\left(4\frac{7}{8}\right) + 60\left(2\frac{1}{8}\right)$ mentally. **420**

Mixed Review

36. ***Geometry*** Find the circumference to the nearest tenth of a circle whose radius is 21 meters. *(Lesson 7-7)* **131.9 m**

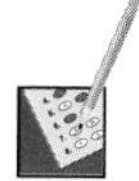

37. **Standardized Test Practice** A jug contains 3 quarts less water than 4 gallons. How many quarts is this? *(Lesson 7-5)* **D**

    A 12 qt **B** 16 qt **C** 1 qt **D** 13 qt
38. Write an integer to represent decreasing the length by 11 inches. *(Lesson 5-1)* **−11**
39. ***Statistics*** Find the range for 45, 29, 31, 38, and 25. Choose an appropriate scale and an interval. *(Lesson 3-1)* **20; Sample answer: 20-50; 5**

For **Extra Practice,** see page 588.

Extending the Lesson

Enrichment Masters, p. 56

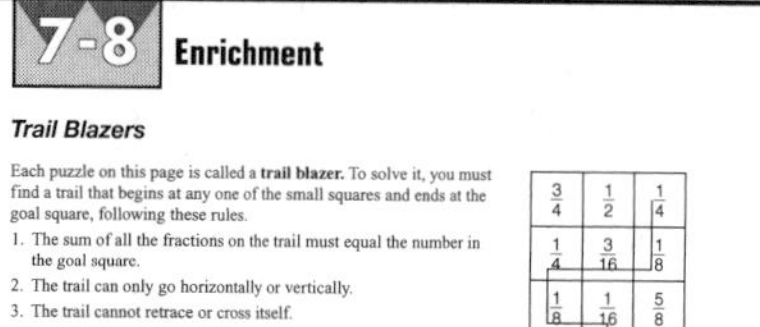

7-8 Enrichment

Trail Blazers

Each puzzle on this page is called a **trail blazer.** To solve it, you must find a trail that begins at any one of the small squares and ends at the goal square, following these rules.

1. The sum of all the fractions on the trail must equal the number in the goal square.
2. The trail can only go horizontally or vertically.
3. The trail cannot retrace or cross itself.

When you are solving a trail blazer, try to eliminate possibilities. For instance, in the puzzle at the right, you know that you cannot include $\frac{3}{4}$: $\frac{3}{4} + \frac{1}{4} = 1$ and $\frac{3}{4} + \frac{1}{2} = 1\frac{1}{4}$, while the goal for the entire trail is only 1. **Answers may vary.**

Activity Have students show by counterexample that subtraction of fractions is neither commutative nor associative. Then have students express remainders in absolute value and see if subtraction is commutative. **It is.**

7-9 Dividing Fractions and Mixed Numbers

What **you'll learn**

You'll learn to divide fractions and mixed numbers.

When **am I ever going to use this?**

Knowing how to divide fractions and mixed numbers can help you find equal food portions.

A silkworm's cocoon is made up of a single thread about $\frac{1}{2}$ mile long. A thread that is strong enough for spinning contains 3 miles of silkworm threads twisted together. How many cocoons does it take to make a 3-mile long thread for spinning?

To solve this problem, we need to find how many $\frac{1}{2}$ miles are in 3 miles.

Method 1 Use models.

Divide 3 by $\frac{1}{2}$.

So, $3 \div \frac{1}{2} = 6$.

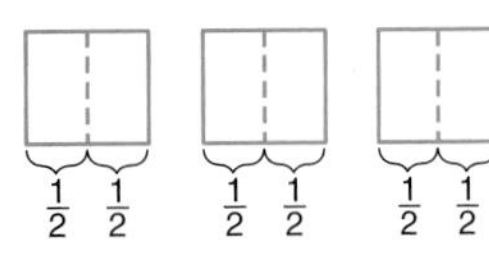

Method 2 Use the multiplicative inverse.

We can also divide by a fraction or mixed number. To do this, multiply by its multiplicative inverse.

$3 \div \frac{1}{2} = \frac{3}{1} \div \frac{1}{2}$ *Rename 3 as $\frac{3}{1}$.*

$= \frac{3}{1} \times \frac{2}{1}$ *Dividing by $\frac{1}{2}$ is the same as multiplying by $\frac{2}{1}$.*

$= \frac{6}{1}$ or 6

So, it takes 6 cocoons to make a thread 3 miles long for spinning.

Division of Fractions and Mixed Numbers		
Words:	To divide by a fraction, multiply by its multiplicative inverse.	
Symbols:	**Arithmetic**	$\frac{5}{6} \div \frac{3}{4} = \frac{5}{6} \cdot \frac{4}{3}$
	Algebra	$\frac{a}{b} \div \frac{c}{d} = \frac{a}{b} \cdot \frac{d}{c}$, where b, c, and $d \neq 0$.

Example CONNECTION

1 Life Science **During the first year, a baby whale gains about $27\frac{3}{5}$ tons. What is the average weight gain per month?**

Estimate: 28 ÷ 14 = 2

$27\frac{3}{5} \div 12 = \frac{138}{5} \div \frac{12}{1}$ *Rename $27\frac{3}{5}$ as $\frac{138}{5}$ and 12 as $\frac{12}{1}$.*

$= \frac{\cancel{138}^{23}}{5} \times \frac{1}{\cancel{12}_{2}}$ *Dividing by $\frac{12}{1}$ is the same as multiplying by $\frac{1}{12}$.*

$= \frac{23}{10}$ or $2\frac{3}{10}$

So, a whale gains an average of $2\frac{3}{10}$ tons per month during the first year. *This is close to the estimate of 2 tons.*

7-9 Lesson Notes

Instructional Resources

- *Study Guide Masters,* p. 57
- *Practice Masters,* p. 57
- *Enrichment Masters,* p. 57
- Transparencies 7-9, A and B
- *Assessment and Evaluation Masters,* p. 184
- *Classroom Games,* pp. 21–22

CD-ROM Program
- Resource Lesson 7-9

Recommended Pacing	
Standard	Day 13 of 15
Honors	Day 12 of 14
Block	Day 7 of 8

1 FOCUS

5-Minute Check
(Lesson 7-8)

1. Name the multiplicative inverse of $\frac{2}{5}$. $\frac{5}{2}$

Name the property shown by each statement.

2. $\frac{3}{4} \times \frac{2}{3} = \frac{2}{3} \times \frac{3}{4}$ **commutative (×)**
3. $\frac{1}{2} \times \left(\frac{2}{3} + \frac{2}{5}\right) = \frac{1}{2} \times \frac{2}{3} + \frac{1}{2} \times \frac{2}{5}$ **distributive**

Solve each equation.

4. $\frac{x}{7} = 14$ **98**
5. $\frac{5}{8}y = 1{,}100$ **1,760**

The 5-Minute Check is also available on **Transparency 7-9A** for this lesson.

2 TEACH

Transparency 7-9B contains a teaching aid for this lesson.

Using Logical Reasoning Give students the complex fraction $\frac{\frac{1}{2}}{\frac{2}{3}}$. Tell them this is a way to write $\frac{1}{2} \div \frac{2}{3}$. Ask them what number they could multiply both the numerator and denominator by so the denominator equals 1. $\frac{3}{2}$ The numerator becomes $\frac{1}{2} \times \frac{3}{2}$.

Motivating the Lesson

Communication Have students work with a partner to make up number sequences of fractions, mixed numbers, or both, using division in the rule for the sequences. One partner should create a sequence, and the other should solve it, stating the rule in words and in symbols.

MathPASS CD-ROM

This CD-ROM offers a complete, self-paced mathematics curriculum. Each lesson includes a pretest, tutorial, guided practice, and posttest. MathPASS Lessons 26 and 27 are correlated to this Student Edition lesson.
For Windows & Macintosh

In-Class Examples

For Example 1

Mr. Gomez had $\frac{3}{4}$ of a cake to divide among 6 guests. What part of a cake will each guest receive? $\frac{1}{8}$ **cake**

For Example 2

Find $\frac{5}{6} \div 2\frac{1}{2}$. Write in simplest form. $\frac{1}{3}$

For Example 3

Solve $12\frac{1}{2} \div 1\frac{1}{4} = d$. 10

3 PRACTICE/APPLY

Check for Understanding

If students need additional practice or instruction after completing Exercises 1–10, one of these options may be helpful.

- Extra Practice, see p. 589
- Reteaching Activity
- *Study Guide Masters,* p. 57
- *Practice Masters,* p. 57

***Study Guide Masters,* p. 57**

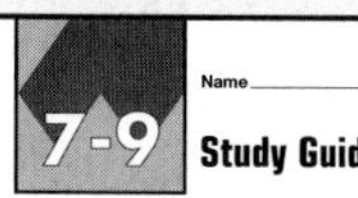

Name________________ Date________

Study Guide

Dividing Fractions and Mixed Numbers

To divide fractions and mixed numbers:
1. Write any mixed numbers as improper fractions.
2. Find the reciprocal of the divisor.
3. Multiply the dividend by the reciprocal of the divisor.

Examples **1** $\frac{5}{8} + \frac{5}{12}$ *The reciprocal of $\frac{5}{12}$ is $\frac{12}{5}$.*

$\frac{5}{8} \div \frac{5}{12} = \frac{5}{8} \times \frac{12}{5}$

$= \frac{60}{40}$ or $1\frac{1}{2}$

2 $7 \div 3\frac{1}{2} \rightarrow \frac{7}{1} \div \frac{7}{2}$ *The reciprocal of $\frac{7}{2}$ is $\frac{2}{7}$.*

$7 \div 3\frac{1}{2} = \frac{7}{1} \times \frac{2}{7}$

$= \frac{14}{7}$ or 2

Name the reciprocal of each number.

1. $\frac{6}{11}$ $\frac{11}{6}$ 2. $\frac{14}{5}$ $\frac{5}{14}$ 3. 8 $\frac{1}{8}$ 4. $\frac{1}{5}$ 5

Divide. Write each quotient in simplest form.

5. $n = \frac{7}{8} \div \frac{1}{4}$ $3\frac{1}{2}$ 6. $p = \frac{2}{5} \div \frac{5}{8}$ $\frac{16}{25}$ 7. $y = \frac{1}{3} \div \frac{1}{6}$ 2

8. $8 \div \frac{1}{3} = k$ 24 9. $\frac{5}{9} \div 5 = v$ $\frac{1}{9}$ 10. $24 \div 1\frac{1}{2} = t$ 16

11. $c = 2\frac{1}{2} \div 5$ $\frac{1}{2}$ 12. $z = 3\frac{1}{3} \div \frac{2}{9}$ 15 13. $m = \frac{5}{8} \div 2\frac{1}{2}$ $\frac{1}{4}$

14. $1\frac{1}{3} \div 2\frac{1}{2} = t$ $\frac{8}{15}$ 15. $3\frac{1}{3} \div 1\frac{2}{5} = f$ $2\frac{8}{21}$ 16. $\frac{9}{10} \div 5\frac{2}{5} = k$ $\frac{1}{6}$

 T57 *Mathematics: Applications and Connections, Course 2*

Examples

2 **Find $\frac{1}{2} \div 2\frac{3}{4}$. Write in simplest form.**

Estimate: $\frac{1}{2} \div 3 = \frac{1}{6}$

$\frac{1}{2} \div 2\frac{3}{4} = \frac{1}{2} \div \frac{11}{4}$ *Rename $2\frac{3}{4}$ as $\frac{11}{4}$.*

$= \frac{1}{2} \times \frac{4}{11}$ *Dividing by $\frac{11}{4}$ is the same as multiplying by $\frac{4}{11}$.*

$= \frac{2}{11}$ *Compare to the estimate.*

3 **Solve $4\frac{1}{3} \div 1\frac{1}{2} = d$. Write in simplest form.**

$4\frac{1}{3} \div 1\frac{1}{2} = d$ *Estimate: $4 \div 2 = 2$*

$\frac{13}{3} \div \frac{3}{2} = d$ *Rename $4\frac{1}{3}$ as $\frac{13}{3}$ and $1\frac{1}{2}$ as $\frac{3}{2}$.*

$\frac{13}{3} \times \frac{2}{3} = d$ *Dividing by $\frac{3}{2}$ is the same as multiplying by $\frac{2}{3}$.*

$\frac{26}{9} = d$ *Rename as a mixed number.*

The solution is $\frac{26}{9}$ or $2\frac{8}{9}$. *How does this compare to the estimate?*

CHECK FOR UNDERSTANDING

Communicating Mathematics

Read and study the lesson to answer each question.

1. ***Write*** the steps you would use to find $1\frac{1}{9} \div \frac{8}{9}$.
2. ***Draw*** a figure or fold a piece of paper to show $4 \div 1\frac{1}{3}$. Explain how to use the figure or paper to find the answer. **3; See Answer Appendix for drawing.**
3. ***You Decide*** For a camping trip, Joshua has $2\frac{1}{4}$ pounds of trail mix to split among three friends and himself. He figures each person will get about 1.8 pounds. Omar says that each person will get less than a pound. Who is right? Explain.

1. Rename $1\frac{1}{9}$ as $\frac{10}{9}$, and multiply by the inverse of $\frac{8}{9}$.
3. Omar; each person will get $2\frac{1}{4} \div 4 = \frac{9}{16}$ or 0.5625 pound.

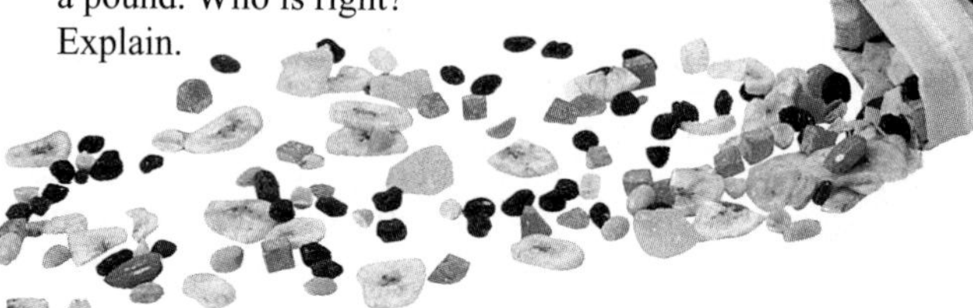

Guided Practice

Divide. Write each quotient in simplest form.

4. $\frac{2}{3} \div \frac{1}{2}$ $1\frac{1}{3}$
5. $6 \div \frac{1}{2}$ 12
6. $2\frac{2}{3} \div 4$ $\frac{2}{3}$
7. $4\frac{2}{3} \div \frac{7}{8}$ $5\frac{1}{3}$

Solve each equation.

8. $1\frac{2}{3} \div 3 = a$ $\frac{5}{9}$
9. $k = \frac{3}{5} \div 2\frac{1}{4}$ $\frac{4}{15}$
10. ***Consumerism*** A box of laundry detergent contains 35 cups. If you use $1\frac{1}{4}$ cups per load of laundry, how many loads do you get from 1 box? **28 loads**

Reteaching the Lesson

Activity Have students model division of fractions on a number line by counting intervals. For example, in the lesson opener, they would count off groups of $\frac{1}{2}$ until they reach 3.

Error Analysis

Watch for students who forget to invert the divisor before multiplying, or invert the dividend instead.

Prevent by reminding students that changing the division operation to multiplication requires inverting (or "flipping") the second number in a division equation rather than the first.

EXERCISES

Practice

Divide. Write each quotient in simplest form.

11. $\frac{3}{8} \div \frac{6}{7}$ **$\frac{7}{16}$**
12. $\frac{3}{4} \div \frac{1}{2}$ **$1\frac{1}{2}$**
13. $\frac{3}{5} \div \frac{1}{4}$ **$2\frac{2}{5}$**
14. $\frac{4}{9} \div 2$ **$\frac{2}{9}$**
15. $\frac{5}{6} \div \frac{2}{3}$ **$1\frac{1}{4}$**
16. $\frac{5}{9} \div \frac{5}{6}$ **$\frac{2}{3}$**
17. $\frac{3}{4} \div \frac{3}{8}$ **2**
18. $3 \div \frac{6}{7}$ **$3\frac{1}{2}$**
19. $\frac{1}{8} \div \frac{1}{3}$ **$\frac{3}{8}$**
20. $\frac{3}{4} \div 1\frac{1}{2}$ **$\frac{1}{2}$**
21. $\frac{2}{3} \div 2\frac{1}{2}$ **$\frac{4}{15}$**
22. $5 \div 1\frac{1}{3}$ **$3\frac{3}{4}$**
23. What is $1\frac{1}{9}$ divided by $\frac{2}{3}$? **$1\frac{2}{3}$**
24. Divide $\frac{5}{6}$ by $\frac{8}{9}$. **$\frac{15}{16}$**

Solve each equation.

25. $b = 5\frac{1}{4} \div 3$ **$1\frac{3}{4}$**
26. $\frac{9}{10} \div 2\frac{1}{4} = h$ **$\frac{2}{5}$**
27. $2\frac{1}{4} \div \frac{2}{3} = r$ **$3\frac{3}{8}$**
28. $f = 4\frac{1}{2} \div 6\frac{3}{4}$ **$\frac{2}{3}$**
29. $p = 1\frac{1}{4} \div 3\frac{1}{2}$ **$\frac{5}{14}$**
30. $6\frac{2}{7} \div 3\frac{1}{7} = s$ **2**
31. ***Algebra*** Evaluate $k \div 1\frac{1}{8}$ if $k = \frac{6}{7}$. **$\frac{16}{21}$**
32. Solve $m = \left(\frac{1}{4} + \frac{1}{10}\right) \div 2\frac{1}{3}$. **$\frac{3}{20}$**

Applications and Problem Solving

33. 20 packages

33. ***Food*** Nancy has 5 pounds of mints from which she wants to make $\frac{1}{4}$-pound packages for party favors. How many packages can she make?

34. ***Housing*** A contractor has 15 acres of land that she is going to sell as $\frac{3}{4}$-acre lots. How many lots can she sell? **20 lots**

35a–b. See students' work.

35. ***Working on the* CHAPTER Project** Refer to the table on page 267.
    a. For each of the companies that you have chosen to track, find how many shares you could have purchased for $1,000 on August 18, 1997.
    b. Using yesterday's closing price for the same companies, how much money would the shares that you purchased in 1997 be worth now?

40. 2, 3, 4, 5, 6, 10

36. ***Critical Thinking*** Will the quotient $6\frac{1}{5} \div 2\frac{3}{4}$ be a proper fraction or a mixed number? Why? **mixed number, since $6\frac{1}{5} > 2\frac{3}{4}$**

Mixed Review

37. Name the multiplicative inverse of $3\frac{5}{8}$. *(Lesson 7-8)* **$\frac{8}{29}$**
38. ***Geometry*** Find the perimeter of a rectangle if the length is 6.4 inches and the width is 5 inches. *(Lesson 7-6)* **22.8 in.**
39. Express 18 out of 100 as a percent. *(Lesson 4-6)* **18%**
40. Tell whether 240 is divisible by 2, 3, 4, 5, 6, 9, or 10. *(Lesson 4-1)*

For **Extra Practice,** see page 589.

41. **Standardized Test Practice** Estimate 29.78 − 7.21 by rounding. *(Lesson 2-3)* **C**

    A 20 **B** 22 **C** 23 **D** 24

Assignment Guide

Core: 11–33 odd, 36–41
Enriched: 12–32 even, 33, 34, 36–41

CHAPTER Project

Exercise 35 asks students to advance to the next stage of work on the Chapter Project. You may wish to bring in a current newspaper and compare the price of the same stocks today. Have students compare how much their shares would be worth today if they had purchased them in 1997.

4 ASSESS

Closing Activity

Writing Have students write a word problem that can be solved by dividing fractions or mixed numbers. Ask students to exchange problems with classmates.

Chapter 7, Quiz D (Lessons 7-8 and 7-9) is available in the *Assessment and Evaluation Masters,* p. 184.

***Practice Masters,* p. 57**

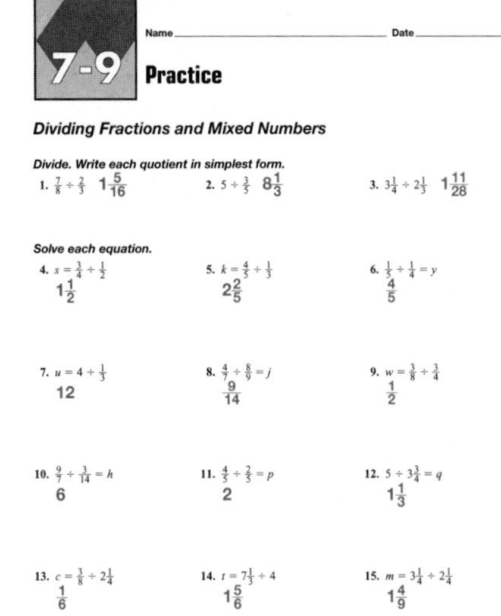

Name __________ Date __________

7-9 Practice

Dividing Fractions and Mixed Numbers

Divide. Write each quotient in simplest form.

1. $\frac{7}{8} \div \frac{2}{3}$ $1\frac{5}{16}$
2. $5 \div \frac{3}{5}$ $8\frac{1}{3}$
3. $3\frac{1}{4} \div 2\frac{1}{3}$ $1\frac{11}{28}$

Solve each equation.

4. $s = \frac{3}{4} \div \frac{1}{2}$ $1\frac{1}{2}$
5. $k = \frac{4}{5} \div \frac{1}{3}$ $2\frac{2}{5}$
6. $\frac{1}{5} \div \frac{1}{4} = y$ $\frac{4}{5}$
7. $u = 4 \div \frac{1}{3}$ 12
8. $\frac{4}{7} \div \frac{8}{9} = j$ $\frac{9}{14}$
9. $w = \frac{3}{8} \div \frac{3}{4}$ $\frac{1}{2}$
10. $\frac{9}{7} \div \frac{3}{14} = h$ 6
11. $\frac{4}{5} \div \frac{2}{5} = p$ 2
12. $5 \div 3\frac{3}{4} = q$ $1\frac{1}{3}$
13. $c = \frac{3}{8} \div 2\frac{1}{4}$ $\frac{1}{6}$
14. $t = 7\frac{1}{3} \div 4$ $1\frac{5}{6}$
15. $m = 3\frac{1}{4} \div 2\frac{1}{4}$ $1\frac{4}{9}$
16. $n = 1\frac{2}{7} \div 1\frac{13}{14}$ $\frac{2}{3}$
17. $1\frac{1}{5} \div \frac{3}{10} = r$ 4
18. $7\frac{1}{2} \div 2\frac{5}{6} = w$ $2\frac{11}{17}$

T57 *Mathematics: Applications and Connections, Course 2*

Extending the Lesson

***Enrichment Masters,* p. 57**

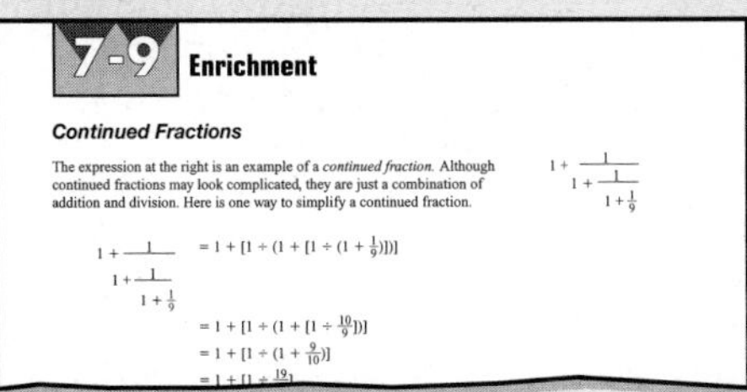

7-9 Enrichment

Continued Fractions

The expression at the right is an example of a *continued fraction.* Although continued fractions may look complicated, they are just a combination of addition and division. Here is one way to simplify a continued fraction.

$$1 + \cfrac{1}{1 + \cfrac{1}{1 + \frac{1}{9}}}$$

$$1 + \cfrac{1}{1 + \cfrac{1}{1 + \frac{1}{9}}} = 1 + [1 \div (1 + [1 \div (1 + \tfrac{1}{9})])]$$

$$= 1 + [1 \div (1 + [1 \div \tfrac{10}{9}])]$$

$$= 1 + [1 \div (1 + \tfrac{9}{10})]$$

$$= 1 + [1 \div \tfrac{19}{...}]$$

Activity Bring in several empty food containers to further demonstrate how fractions are used in everyday life. Compare a $\frac{1}{3}$ cup serving size to larger or smaller amounts and discuss how this relates to other nutrition information given on the labels.

Study Guide and Assessment

Vocabulary

This section provides a listing of the new terms, properties, and phrases that were introduced in this chapter. Have students define each term and provide an example or two of it, if appropriate.

Understanding and Using the Vocabulary

These exercises check students' understanding of the terms by using a variety of verbal formats including matching, completion, and true/false.

Glossaries A complete glossary of terms appears on pages 656–663. The glossary also appears in Spanish on pages 664–672.

CHAPTER 7

Study Guide and Assessment

interNET CONNECTION **Chapter Review For additional lesson-by-lesson review, visit: www.glencoe.com/sec/math/mac/mathnet**

Vocabulary

After completing this chapter, you should be able to define each term, concept, or phrase and give an example or two of each.

Number and Operations
associative (p. 301)
commutative (p. 301)
distributive property (p. 302)
identity (p. 301)
multiplicative inverse (p. 301)
multiplication property of equality (p. 302)
reciprocal (p. 301)

Geometry
center (p. 297)
circle (p. 297)
circumference (p. 297)
diameter (p. 297)
perimeter (p. 292)
radius (p. 297)

Measurement
cup (p. 290)
gallon (p. 290)
ounce (p. 289)
pint (p. 290)
pound (p. 289)
quart (p. 290)
ton (p. 289)

Problem Solving
eliminate possibilities (p. 280)

Understanding and Using the Vocabulary

Choose the letter of the term that best matches each phrase.

1. the property that states $a \times b = b \times a$ **e**
2. the multiplicative inverse of a number **a**
3. the property that states that $a + 0 = a$ **c**
4. the distance around a rectangle **b**
5. the distance across a circle through the center **j**
6. the property that states that $(a + b) + c = a + (b + c)$ **k**
7. the distance around a circle **d**
8. what to do to convert from a smaller unit of measure to a larger unit **i**
9. what to do to convert from a larger unit of measure to a smaller unit **g**

a. reciprocal
b. perimeter
c. identity
d. circumference
e. commutative
f. inverse
g. multiply
h. radius
i. divide
j. diameter
k. associative
l. distributive

In Your Own Words

10. ***Explain*** how the distributive property can be used to compute the product of a mixed number and a whole number. **Answers will vary.**

MindJogger Videoquizzes

MindJogger Videoquizzes provide an alternative review of concepts presented in this chapter. Students work in teams to answer questions, gaining points for correct answers. The questions are presented in three rounds.
Round 1 Concepts–5 questions
Round 2 Skills–4 questions
Round 3 Problem Solving–4 questions

Objectives & Examples

Upon completing this chapter, you should be able to:

- estimate sums, differences, products, and quotients of fractions and mixed numbers *(Lesson 7-1)*

Estimate $15\frac{7}{9} + 3\frac{1}{6}$.

$16 + 3 = 19$

12. $6 + 12 = 18$ **13.** $12 \div 1 = 12$
14. $3 \div 1 = 3$ **16.** $90 - 8 = 82$
17. $2 \times 16 = 32$ **18.** $6 \times 3 = 18$

Review Exercises

Use these exercises to review and prepare for the chapter test.

Estimate. 11–18. Sample answers are given.

11. $\frac{3}{4} + \frac{8}{9}$ $1 + 1 = 2$ **12.** $5\frac{4}{5} + 12\frac{1}{6}$

13. $12 \div \frac{2}{3}$ **14.** $2\frac{9}{10} \div 1\frac{1}{8}$

15. $\frac{13}{15} - \frac{1}{4}$ $1 - 0 = 1$ **16.** $89\frac{9}{10} - 7\frac{4}{5}$

17. $1\frac{12}{13} \times 16\frac{1}{12}$ **18.** $6\frac{1}{9} \times 2\frac{5}{6}$

- add and subtract fractions *(Lesson 7-2)*

$$\frac{11}{12} - \frac{1}{6} = \frac{11}{12} - \frac{2}{12}$$
$$= \frac{9}{12} \text{ or } \frac{3}{4}$$

Add or subtract. Write each sum or difference in simplest form.

19. $\frac{3}{5} + \frac{3}{7}$ $1\frac{1}{35}$ **20.** $\frac{5}{6} - \frac{1}{2}$ $\frac{1}{3}$

21. $\frac{3}{4} - \frac{3}{20}$ $\frac{3}{5}$ **22.** $\frac{3}{8} + \frac{1}{3}$ $\frac{17}{24}$

- add and subtract mixed numbers *(Lesson 7-3)*

$$5\frac{3}{4} + 10\frac{1}{3} = 5\frac{9}{12} + 10\frac{4}{12}$$
$$= 15\frac{13}{12} \text{ or } 16\frac{1}{12}$$

Add or subtract. Write each sum or difference in simplest form.

23. $8 + 5\frac{5}{9}$ $13\frac{5}{9}$ **24.** $5\frac{1}{12} + 2\frac{5}{6}$ $7\frac{11}{12}$

25. $3\frac{7}{8} - \frac{5}{6}$ $3\frac{1}{24}$ **26.** $5\frac{2}{7} - 4\frac{1}{2}$ $\frac{11}{14}$

- multiply fractions and mixed numbers *(Lesson 7-4)*

$$\frac{3}{5} \times \frac{1}{2} = \frac{3}{10} \qquad 4\frac{3}{4} \times 2\frac{2}{3} = \frac{19}{\underset{1}{4}} \times \frac{\overset{2}{8}}{3}$$
$$= \frac{38}{3} \text{ or } 12\frac{2}{3}$$

Multiply. Write each product in simplest form.

27. $\frac{5}{9} \times \frac{3}{5}$ $\frac{1}{3}$ **28.** $4\frac{1}{5} \times 3\frac{1}{3}$ 14

29. $5\frac{1}{2} \times 6\frac{2}{7}$ $34\frac{4}{7}$ **30.** $6 \times 2\frac{3}{8}$ $14\frac{1}{4}$

- change units in the customary system *(Lesson 7-5)*

Complete: 14 lb = __?__ oz

Since 1 lb = 16 oz, multiply by 16.

$14 \cdot 16 = 224$

14 lb = 224 oz

Complete.

31. 4 qt = __?__ pt 8
32. 6 gal = __?__ qt 24
33. 8,000 lb = __?__ T 4
34. 48 oz = __?__ lb 3
35. 48 fl oz = __?__ c 6
36. 9 c = __?__ pt $4\frac{1}{2}$

Assessment and Evaluation

Six forms of Chapter 7 Test are available in the *Assessment and Evaluation Masters* as shown in the chart.

1A	Multiple Choice	Honors
1B	Multiple Choice	Average
1C	Multiple Choice	Basic
2A	Free Response	Honors
2B	Free Response	Average
2C	Free Response	Basic

Chapter 7 Test, Form 1B, is shown at the right. Chapter 7 Test, Form 2B, is shown on the next page.

Objectives & Examples

This section reviews the skills and concepts of the chapter and shows completely worked examples.

Review Exercises

These exercises provide practice for the corresponding objectives.

Assessment and Evaluation Masters, pp. 171–172

7

Name__________ Date__________

Chapter 7 Test, Form 1B

Round to the nearest whole number.

1. $2\frac{2}{7}$
   A. 0 B. 2 C. 1 D. 3 — 1. B
2. $5\frac{1}{9}$
   A. $5\frac{1}{2}$ B. 6 C. $5\frac{1}{4}$ D. 5 — 2. D

Estimate.

3. $\frac{7}{8} + 3\frac{1}{16}$
   A. 5 B. 2 C. 4 D. 3 — 3. C
4. $11\frac{2}{3} \div 1\frac{4}{5}$
   A. 11 B. 12 C. 10 D. 6 — 4. D

Add or subtract. Write each sum or difference in simplest form.

5. $\frac{2}{3} + \frac{3}{8}$
   A. $\frac{5}{11}$ B. $\frac{5}{24}$ C. $\frac{1}{4}$ D. $1\frac{1}{24}$ — 5. D
6. $\frac{9}{11} - \frac{1}{2}$
   A. $\frac{7}{22}$ B. $\frac{10}{13}$ C. $\frac{29}{13}$ D. $\frac{9}{22}$ — 6. A
7. $2\frac{1}{8} + 1\frac{5}{12}$
   A. $3\frac{3}{10}$ B. $3\frac{5}{96}$ C. $3\frac{1}{4}$ D. $3\frac{13}{24}$ — 7. D
8. $10\frac{1}{6} - 4\frac{3}{14}$
   A. $5\frac{20}{21}$ B. $6\frac{1}{4}$ C. $6\frac{1}{10}$ D. $5\frac{1}{4}$ — 8. A
9. Usually Emory rides his bicycle $5\frac{4}{5}$ miles a day. Today he didn't have much time, so he rode half his usual distance. How far did he ride?
   A. $2\frac{7}{10}$ B. $2\frac{9}{10}$ C. $2\frac{4}{10}$ D. $3\frac{4}{10}$ — 9. B

Multiply. Write each product in simplest form.

10. $1\frac{1}{2} \times 4\frac{1}{3}$
    A. $6\frac{1}{2}$ B. $\frac{3}{13}$ C. 6 D. $\frac{16}{5}$ — 10. A
11. $\frac{3}{5} \times 5\frac{5}{8}$
    A. $3\frac{3}{8}$ B. $5\frac{1}{8}$ C. $6\frac{3}{8}$ D. $3\frac{1}{8}$ — 11. A

Solve each equation. Write the solution in simplest form.

12. $p = 2\frac{5}{6} \times \frac{1}{3}$
    A. $3\frac{1}{6}$ B. $1\frac{8}{9}$ C. $\frac{17}{9}$ D. $\frac{17}{18}$ — 12. D

 171 *Mathematics: Applications and Connections, Course 2*

7

Chapter 7 Test, Form 1B (continued)

Solve each equation. Write the solution in simplest form.

13. $3\frac{1}{3} \times 4\frac{1}{2} = q$
    A. $7\frac{5}{6}$ B. 15 C. $\frac{19}{5}$ D. $3\frac{4}{5}$ — 13. B
14. $1\frac{1}{7} \times 2\frac{1}{3} = s$
    A. $\frac{15}{21}$ B. $\frac{8}{3}$ C. $2\frac{2}{3}$ D. $3\frac{10}{21}$ — 14. C

Complete.

15. $4\frac{1}{2}$ pt = __?__ c
    A. 2.25 B. 8 C. 10 D. 9 — 15. D
16. __?__ gal = 18 qt
    A. 16 B. 2.25 C. 4.5 D. 9 — 16. C

Name the property shown by each statement.

17. $\left(\frac{7}{8} \times \frac{1}{9}\right) \times \frac{2}{3} = \frac{7}{8} \times \left(\frac{1}{9} \times \frac{2}{3}\right)$
    A. commutative B. associative
    C. identity D. multiplicative inverse — 17. B
18. $\frac{2}{8} \times \frac{1}{7} = \frac{1}{7} \times \frac{2}{8}$
    A. commutative B. associative
    C. identity D. multiplicative inverse — 18. A

Solve each equation. Write the solution in simplest form.

19. $\frac{1}{3}t = \frac{5}{6}$
    A. $\frac{5}{18}$ B. $2\frac{1}{2}$ C. $\frac{1}{2}$ D. $3\frac{5}{6}$ — 19. B
20. $u = 2 \times 2\frac{1}{3}$
    A. $1\frac{1}{6}$ B. $4\frac{1}{3}$ C. 3 D. $4\frac{2}{3}$ — 20. D
21. $r = 3\frac{3}{7} \div 2\frac{2}{9}$
    A. $1\frac{19}{35}$ B. $7\frac{13}{21}$ C. $2\frac{43}{63}$ D. $1\frac{2}{7}$ — 21. A
22. $2\frac{3}{4} \div \frac{7}{8} = x$
    A. 3 B. $\frac{7}{22}$ C. $3\frac{1}{7}$ D. $\frac{88}{28}$ — 22. C
23. $w = 4\frac{1}{4} \div 2\frac{1}{2}$
    A. $1\frac{5}{8}$ B. $1\frac{7}{10}$ C. $6\frac{3}{4}$ D. $1\frac{3}{4}$ — 23. B
24. Find the perimeter of a rectangle 4 feet wide by $16\frac{1}{2}$ feet long.
    A. 41 ft B. $20\frac{1}{2}$ ft C. 66 ft D. 648 ft — 24. A
25. Find the circumference of a circle whose radius is 2.75 feet. Round to the nearest tenth.
    A. 8.6 ft B. 17.3 ft C. 17 ft D. 8 ft — 25. B

 172 *Mathematics: Applications and Connections, Course 2*

Study Guide and Assessment

Assessment and Evaluation Masters, pp. 177–178

Name______________________ Date __________

Chapter 7 Test, Form 2B

Round to the nearest whole number.

1. $4\frac{7}{11}$	1.	5
2. $2\frac{2}{19}$	2.	2

Estimate.

3. $10\frac{7}{8} - 6\frac{1}{5}$	3.	5
4. $10\frac{1}{5} \div 4\frac{3}{4}$	4.	2

Add or subtract. Write each sum or difference in simplest form.

5. $\frac{2}{5} + \frac{5}{8}$	5.	$1\frac{1}{40}$
6. $\frac{4}{5} - \frac{8}{15}$	6.	$\frac{4}{15}$
7. $\frac{3}{5} + \frac{5}{7}$	7.	$1\frac{11}{35}$
8. $\frac{2}{3} - \frac{4}{9}$	8.	$\frac{2}{9}$
9. $1\frac{9}{10} + \frac{14}{15}$	9.	$2\frac{5}{6}$
10. $3\frac{1}{5} - 1\frac{5}{6}$	10.	$1\frac{11}{30}$
11. $1\frac{1}{5} + 5\frac{1}{4}$	11.	$6\frac{9}{20}$
12. $3\frac{1}{6} - 2\frac{1}{8}$	12.	$1\frac{1}{24}$
13. After school, Patsy spends $\frac{1}{2}$ of an hour on the telephone, $\frac{5}{8}$ of an hour exercising, and $\frac{3}{4}$ of an hour studying. What is the total time Patsy spends in these activities?	13.	$1\frac{7}{8}$ hours or 1 h $52\frac{1}{2}$ min

Multiply. Write each product in simplest form.

14. $3\frac{1}{4} \times 8$	14.	26
15. $\frac{5}{6} \times 12\frac{3}{5}$	15.	$10\frac{1}{2}$

© Glencoe/McGraw-Hill 177 *Mathematics: Applications and Connections, Course 2*

Chapter 7 Test, Form 2B (continued)

Solve each equation. Write the solution in simplest form.

16. $t = 1\frac{4}{5} \times 3\frac{2}{9}$	16.	$5\frac{4}{5}$
17. $m = 6\frac{2}{5} \times 3\frac{1}{8}$	17.	20
18. $4\frac{1}{2} \times 5\frac{5}{6} = r$	18.	$26\frac{1}{4}$
19. $2\frac{2}{3} \times 4\frac{1}{2} = p$	19.	12

Complete.

20. $5\frac{1}{2}$ lb = _?_ oz	20.	88
21. 2.5 pt = _?_ c	21.	5
22. _?_ c = 3 qt	22.	12
23. _?_ oz = 1 pt	23.	16

Name the property shown by each statement.

24. $\frac{6}{2} \times \frac{2}{6} = 1$	24.	multiplicative inverse
25. $\frac{1}{3} + \left(\frac{2}{5} + \frac{1}{8}\right) = \left(\frac{1}{3} + \frac{2}{5}\right) + \frac{1}{8}$	25.	associative

Solve each equation. Write the solution in simplest form.

26. $q = \frac{24}{25} \times \frac{1}{3}$	26.	$\frac{8}{25}$
27. $7 = \frac{t}{4}$	27.	28
28. $1\frac{3}{5} \div \frac{7}{15} = s$	28.	$3\frac{3}{7}$
29. $t = 3\frac{3}{7} \div 2\frac{5}{8}$	29.	$1\frac{15}{49}$
30. $k = 1\frac{7}{8} \div \frac{5}{6}$	30.	$2\frac{1}{4}$
31. $2\frac{2}{7} \div \frac{8}{21} = v$	31.	6
32. Find the perimeter of a rectangle with a length of $8\frac{1}{2}$ inches and a width of $5\frac{3}{4}$ inches.	32.	$28\frac{1}{2}$ in.
33. Find the circumference of a circle with a radius of $\frac{7}{8}$ mile. (Use $\pi \approx \frac{22}{7}$.)	33.	$2\frac{3}{4}$ mi

© Glencoe/McGraw-Hill 178 *Mathematics: Applications and Connections, Course 2*

Objectives & Examples | **Review Exercises**

find perimeter *(Lesson 7-6)*

Find the perimeter of a rectangle $4\frac{3}{4}$ feet long and $3\frac{1}{3}$ feet wide.

$P = 4\frac{3}{4} + 4\frac{3}{4} + 3\frac{1}{3} + 3\frac{1}{3}$

$P = 16\frac{2}{12}$ or $16\frac{1}{6}$ feet

The perimeter is $16\frac{1}{6}$ feet.

Find the perimeter of each figure shown or described.

37. (rectangle: 4.8 m by 3.5 m) 16.6 m

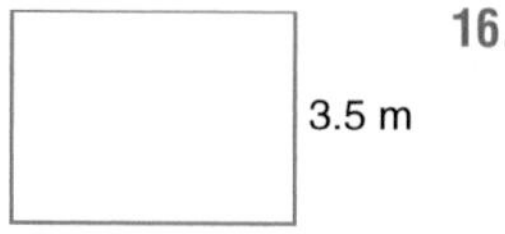

38. rectangle: $\ell = 25\frac{1}{6}$ ft, $w = 10\frac{2}{3}$ ft $71\frac{2}{3}$ ft

find the circumference of circles *(Lesson 7-7)*

If the diameter of a circle is $2\frac{1}{3}$ feet, then find its circumference.

$C = \pi d$

$C \approx \frac{22}{7} \times 2\frac{1}{3}$ *Use $\frac{22}{7}$ because the diameter has a numerator of 7.*

$C \approx \frac{22}{7} \times \frac{7}{3}$

$C \approx 7\frac{1}{3}$

The circumference is about $7\frac{1}{3}$ or 7.3 feet.

Find the circumference of each circle to the nearest tenth. Use $\frac{22}{7}$ or 3.14 for π.

39.

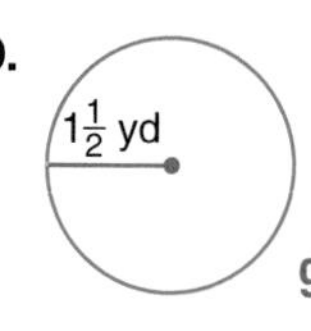

9.4 yd

40. (circle, diameter 10.4 m)

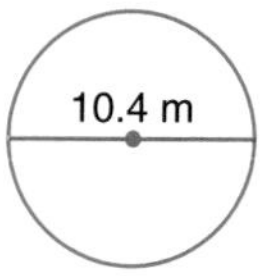

41. $d = 14$ in.

42. $r = 1.4$ cm 8.8 cm

43. $r = \frac{7}{11}$ ft

44. $d = 6\frac{2}{5}$ ft 20.1 ft

40. 32.7 m 41. $\pi = \frac{22}{7}$; 44 in. 43. $\pi = \frac{22}{7}$; 4 ft

use addition and multiplication properties to solve problems *(Lesson 7-8)*

$\frac{1}{4} \times 8\frac{2}{3} = \frac{1}{4}\left(8 + \frac{2}{3}\right)$

$= 2 + \frac{2}{12}$ or $2\frac{1}{6}$

Solve each equation.

45. $6 \times 3\frac{1}{8} = a$ $18\frac{3}{4}$

46. $\frac{1}{3}t = \frac{1}{5}$ $\frac{3}{5}$

47. $\frac{5}{6}r = 5$ 6

48. $c = 5\frac{5}{6} \times 2$ $11\frac{2}{3}$

divide fractions and mixed numbers *(Lesson 7-9)*

$2\frac{4}{5} \div \frac{7}{10} = \frac{\overset{2}{\cancel{14}}}{\underset{1}{\cancel{5}}} \times \frac{\overset{2}{\cancel{10}}}{\underset{1}{\cancel{7}}} = \frac{4}{1}$ or 4

Divide. Write each quotient in simplest form.

49. $\frac{3}{5} \div \frac{1}{10}$ 6

50. $\frac{5}{8} \div \frac{3}{4}$ $\frac{5}{6}$

51. $3\frac{1}{7} \div \frac{2}{5}$ $7\frac{6}{7}$

52. $1\frac{5}{6} \div 3\frac{2}{9}$ $\frac{33}{58}$

Test and Review Software

You may use this software, a combination of an item generator and item bank, to create your own tests or worksheets. Types of items include free response, multiple choice, short answer, and open ended.

CD-ROM Program

The CD-ROM Program contains an Assessment Game whose questions review the concepts in this chapter.

Applications & Problem Solving

53. ***Cooking*** A recipe calls for $2\frac{1}{2}$ cups of flour, $1\frac{3}{4}$ cups of sugar, and $1\frac{2}{3}$ cups of brown sugar. How many cups are in the mixture? *(Lesson 7-3)* **$5\frac{11}{12}$ cups**

54. ***Eliminate Possibilities*** On a map, 1 inch represents 200 miles. A trip you are planning is $4\frac{1}{2}$ inches on the map. How long is your trip? *(Lesson 7-3B)* **A**
    - **A** 900 miles
    - **B** 450 miles
    - **C** $4\frac{1}{2}$ miles
    - **D** 90 miles
    - **E** 800 miles

55. ***Driving*** A bridge has a weight limit of 5 tons. If a truck weighs 4,125 pounds, is it safe for the truck to cross the bridge if no other vehicles are on the bridge? *(Lesson 7-5)* **yes**

56. ***Gardening*** Celia wants to fence in her garden whose dimensions are shown in the diagram below. How much fencing will she need? *(Lesson 7-6)* **$131\frac{1}{2}$ ft**

$40\frac{1}{2}$ ft

$25\frac{1}{4}$ ft

Alternative Assessment

Open Ended

Suppose you want to build a deck around a circular swimming pool. The swimming pool has a radius of 66 inches and you want the deck to be 4 feet wide. If you put a fence around the outside of the deck, about how much fencing will you need to the nearest foot? Show your work. **See Answer Appendix.**

Suppose you decide to put a fence around just the pool instead of the deck. If you save $375 by doing this instead of putting a fence around the outside of the deck, about how much does one foot of fencing cost? Explain. **See Answer Appendix.**

Select one of the problems you solved in this chapter and place the problem and its solution in your portfolio. Attach a note explaining why you selected it.

Completing the CHAPTER Project

Suppose you had purchased 100 shares of stock on the first day of tracking stock prices. In your report, explain which stock would have made you the most money if you had sold all your shares on the last day. Also, pick the day on which each stock should have been sold to make the most money during the month.

Use the following checklist to make sure your project is complete.

- ☑ You have a report that includes your table of stock prices.
- ☑ You have a graph of the price for each stock.
- ☑ You have a brief explanation of the price trend for each stock over the month.

A practice test for Chapter 7 is provided on page 613.

Applications & Problem Solving

This section provides additional practice in solving real-world problems that involve the skills of this chapter.

Alternative Assessment

The ***Open Ended*** section provides students with a performance assessment opportunity to evaluate their work and understanding.

Students should complete the final stages of their project and prepare a class demonstration of their results. A scoring guide for the project is available in the *Investigations and Projects Masters,* p. 43.

Students should add to their portfolios at this time.

***Assessment and Evaluation Masters,* p. 181**

Name______________________ Date __________

Chapter 7 Performance Assessment

Instructions: Demonstrate your knowledge by giving a clear, concise solution to each problem. Be sure to include all relevant drawings and justify your answers. You may show your solutions in more than one way or investigate beyond the requirements of the problems.

1. Maria is shopping for food for her party.
   - **a.** Maria bought $1\frac{1}{2}$ pounds of bologna and $2\frac{1}{4}$ pounds of turkey breast. How much more turkey breast than bologna did she buy? Find the answer two ways.
   - **b.** Draw a model that illustrates $2\frac{1}{2} \times \frac{1}{2}$.
   - **c.** If a recipe for punch calls for $\frac{1}{2}$ gallon of fruit drink, how much fruit drink will Maria need to make $2\frac{1}{2}$ recipes?
   - **d.** Write a word problem that uses mixed numbers and asks to find the unit price of an item.
   - **e.** Find the unit price for part d.
   - **f.** Maria can't decide on the best value for popcorn. If one brand costs $2.00 for 1 lb 9 oz and the second brand costs $2.10 for 1 lb 14 oz, which is the better buy? Why? (*Hint:* What is the cost per ounce?)

2. Will and Steve want to draw a target for playing darts. Will wants to draw a circle, and Steve wants to draw a rectangle. Neither can have a perimeter or circumference larger than 12 centimeters.
   - **a.** Estimate the dimensions of the rectangle and the radius of the circle if the circumference and perimeter both equal 12 centimeters.
   - **b.** The perimeter of the rectangle equals the circumference of the circle. The length of the sides is $6\frac{1}{2}$ centimeters. The width is $2\frac{2}{3}$ centimeters. What is the radius of the circle?

 181 *Mathematics: Applications and Connections, Course 2*

Performance Assessment

Additional performance assessment tasks for this chapter are included in the *Assessment and Evaluation Masters* on page 181. A scoring guide is also provided on page 193.

Standardized Test Practice

The Standardized Test Practice may be used to help students prepare for standardized tests. The test items are written in the same style as those in state proficiency tests and standardized tests like CAT, CTBS, ITBS, MAT, SAT, and Terra Nova. The test items cover skills and concepts covered up to this point in the text.

The pages can be used as an overnight assessment. After students have completed the pages, discuss how each problem can be solved, or provide copies of the solutions from the *Solutions Manual.*

Assessment and Evaluation Masters, p. 187

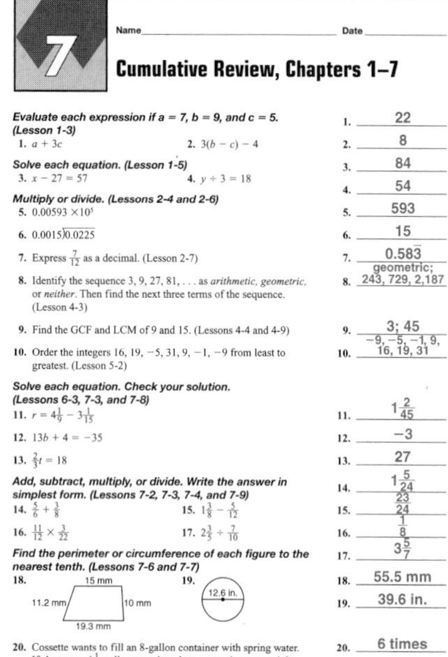

7

Name__________ Date__________

Cumulative Review, Chapters 1–7

Evaluate each expression if a = 7, b = 9, and c = 5. (Lesson 1-3)

1. $a + 3c$ 2. $3(b - c) - 4$

Solve each equation. (Lesson 1-5)

3. $x - 27 = 57$ 4. $y \div 3 = 18$

Multiply or divide. (Lessons 2-4 and 2-6)

5. 0.00593×10^5

6. $0.0015\overline{)0.0225}$

7. Express $\frac{7}{12}$ as a decimal. (Lesson 2-7)

8. Identify the sequence 3, 9, 27, 81, . . . as *arithmetic, geometric,* or *neither*. Then find the next three terms of the sequence. (Lesson 4-3)

9. Find the GCF and LCM of 9 and 15. (Lessons 4-4 and 4-9)

10. Order the integers 16, 19, −5, 31, 9, −1, −9 from least to greatest. (Lesson 5-2)

Solve each equation. Check your solution. (Lessons 6-3, 7-3, and 7-8)

11. $r = 4\frac{1}{9} - 3\frac{1}{15}$

12. $13b + 4 = -35$

13. $\frac{2}{3}t = 18$

Add, subtract, multiply, or divide. Write the answer in simplest form. (Lessons 7-2, 7-3, 7-4, and 7-9)

14. $\frac{5}{6} + \frac{3}{8}$ 15. $1\frac{3}{8} - \frac{5}{12}$

16. $\frac{11}{12} \times \frac{3}{22}$ 17. $2\frac{3}{5} \div \frac{7}{10}$

Find the perimeter or circumference of each figure to the nearest tenth. (Lessons 7-6 and 7-7)

18. (trapezoid: 15 mm, 11.2 mm, 10 mm, 19.3 mm) 19. (circle: 12.6 in.)

20. Cossette wants to fill an 8-gallon container with spring water. If she uses a $1\frac{1}{2}$-gallon container, how many times must it be filled? (Lesson 7-9)

Answers:
1. 22
2. 8
3. 84
4. 54
5. 593
6. 15
7. $0.58\overline{3}$
8. geometric; 243, 729, 2,187
9. 3; 45
10. −9, −5, −1, 9, 16, 19, 31
11. $1\frac{2}{45}$
12. −3
13. 27
14. $1\frac{5}{24}$
15. $\frac{23}{24}$
16. $\frac{1}{8}$
17. $3\frac{5}{7}$
18. 55.5 mm
19. 39.6 in.
20. 6 times

 187 *Mathematics: Applications and Connections, Course 2*

CHAPTERS 1–7

Standardized Test Practice

Assessing Knowledge & Skills

Section One: Multiple Choice

There are eleven multiple-choice questions in this section. Choose the best answer. If a correct answer is *not here,* choose the letter for Not Here.

1. Which is the equation for the line graphed? A

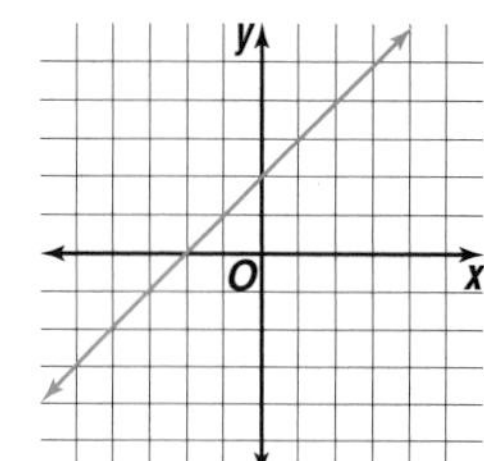

A $y = x + 2$
B $y = x - 2$
C $y = 2x$
D $y = 2x + 2$

2. Change $3\frac{5}{8}$ to an improper fraction. J

F $\frac{35}{8}$
G $\frac{20}{8}$
H $\frac{15}{8}$
J $\frac{29}{8}$

3. Which expression is equivalent to $3.2 \times (2.4 \times 5.8)$? B

A $(3.2 \times 2.4) + (3.2 \times 5.8)$
B $(3.2 \times 2.4) \times 5.8$
C $3.2 \times (2.4 + 5.8)$
D $2.4 + (3.2 \times 5.8)$

4. A doorway is 5 inches less than 8 feet tall. How many *inches* is this? H

F 101 inches
G 96 inches
H 91 inches
J 40 inches

Please note that Questions 5–11 have five answer choices.

5. Margaret can earn tips ranging from \$3–\$5 per table at a steak restaurant. If she has 9 tables, which is a reasonable estimate of the tips she will earn? B

A less than \$27
B between \$27 and \$45
C between \$45 and \$70
D between \$70 and \$90
E more than \$90

6. Which expression represents *three less than a number*? F

F $n - 3$
G $3 - n$
H n
J $\frac{n}{3}$
K $3n - 3$

7. Forest Park Middle School's 52 band students and 7 adult sponsors are planning a trip to an amusement park. Each school bus will carry at most 31 people. Each ticket to the park costs \$19.75, but schools get a \$3.00 discount per ticket. Which piece of information is *not* needed for the school principal to determine the amount of money required for the amusement park tickets? C

A There are 52 students in the band.
B There are 7 adult sponsors.
C Each school bus will carry at most 31 people.
D The price of each ticket is \$19.75.
E The discount per ticket is \$3.00.

◄◄◄ Instructional Resources

Another cumulative review is shown at the left and is available in the *Assessment and Evaluation Masters,* p. 187.

8. Nate had $\frac{7}{8}$ of a tank of gas in the lawn mower. After mowing the grass, he had $\frac{1}{4}$ of a tank. How much gas did Nate use mowing the lawn? **F**

F $\frac{5}{8}$ of a tank
G $\frac{3}{4}$ of a tank
H $\frac{3}{8}$ of a tank
J $\frac{1}{8}$ of a tank
K Not Here

9. A recycling group at Thompson Middle School collected cans for a service project. They collected 122.4 pounds, 88.9 pounds, and 117.02 pounds in the last three weeks. What was the total amount of cans collected for that period? **C**

A 248.15 pounds　B 211.13 pounds
C 328.32 pounds　D 328.5 pounds
E Not Here

10. The regular price of 3 packages of batteries is \$8.85 without tax. Before tax is added, how much can be saved by buying 3 packages on sale for \$6.49? **G**

F \$3.36　G \$2.36
H \$2.26　J \$1.06
K Not Here

11. In 1996, Donovan Bailey set a world record of 9.84 seconds for the 100-meter dash. A honeybee can fly the same distance in 20.706 seconds. How many times faster than a honeybee is Donovan Bailey? **D**

A 10.2 times
B 10.9 times
C 4.8 times
D 2.1 times
E Not Here

Test-Taking Tip
THE PRINCETON REVIEW

When taking a standardized test, you may be able to eliminate answer choices through estimating. Also, look to see which answers are not reasonable for the information given in the problem.

Section Two: Free Response

This section contains five questions for which you will provide short answers. Write your answers on your paper.

12. $\frac{3}{4} + \frac{1}{2} =$ $1\frac{1}{4}$

13. $\frac{1}{4} \times 2\frac{1}{2} =$ $\frac{5}{8}$

14. Solve $3x + 10 < 28$. $x < 6$

15. Name the ordered pairs for points Q, R, and S. Then tell in which quadrant each point lies. **$Q(-6, 3)$, II; $R(-3\frac{1}{2}, -4)$, III; $S(2, 0)$, x-axis**

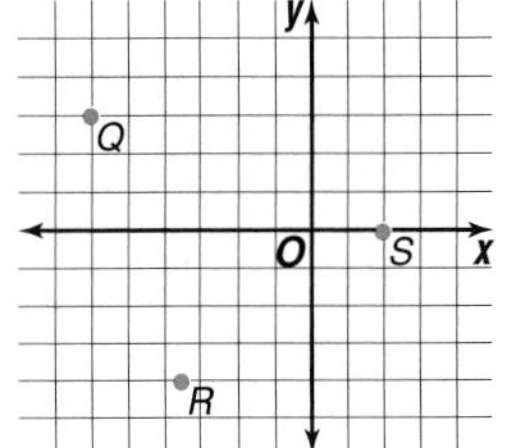

16. The McCanns make cookies for their carpool. If they buy a 12-pound bag of flour and they use $1\frac{1}{3}$ cups of flour per batch of cookies, how many batches of cookies do they get from one bag of flour? **9 batches**

Test Practice **For additional test practice questions, visit:**

www.glencoe.com/sec/math/mac/mathnet

Test-Taking Tip

Have students use estimation to eliminate wrong answers and to check their own answers. Remind them to reduce all answers to simplest form.

Instructional Resources ▶▶▶

Additional standardized test practice is shown at the right and is available in the *Assessment and Evaluation Masters,* pp. 185–186.

Assessment and Evaluation Masters, pp. 185–186

7

Name______________ Date__________

Chapter 7 Standardized Test Practice

1. Mr. Martin has a bag containing $16\frac{1}{2}$ cups of flour. If he uses $3\frac{2}{3}$ cups in a recipe, how much flour will he have left? 1. C
A. 13 cups　B. $11\frac{3}{4}$ cups　C. $12\frac{5}{6}$ cups　D. $12\frac{1}{3}$ cups

2. Which algebraic expression best represents *sixteen times a number plus four is negative eleven*? 2. C
A. $16 + 4n = -11$　B. $16n + 4 = 11$
C. $16n + 4 = -11$　D. $16 + 4n = 11$

3. Julia needs to mix 2 quarts of water with every 4 tablespoons of lemonade mix. If she has 40 ounces of water, how many tablespoons of lemonade mix should she mix in? 3. B
A. 1.5　B. 2.5　C. 3　D. 2

Each graph compares Brady Anderson and Kenny Lofton's stolen bases from 1994–1996. Use this information for Questions 4 and 5.

Graph A　Graph B

4. Which graph is misleading? 4. B
A. Graph A　B. Graph B　C. neither　D. both

5. Predict the total bases stolen by Brady Anderson in 1997. 5. D
A. 30　B. 85　C. 10　D. 15

6. Kevin Jones has 6 cats and 6 cat food bowls. If he has $4\frac{4}{5}$ cups of cat food, how much can go in each bowl if he divides the food evenly? 6. A
A. $\frac{4}{5}$　B. $\frac{13}{30}$　C. $\frac{11}{15}$　D. $\frac{5}{6}$

7. Belva has 6 containers of food she has to place on a shelf in order from lightest to heaviest. Which is the correct order? 7. D
A. rice, noodles, flour, vinegar, chips, beans
B. chips, beans, vinegar, rice, noodles, flour
C. chips, rice, beans, vinegar, flour, noodles
D. chips, beans, rice, vinegar, noodles, flour

Food Item	Weight (oz)
can of beans	8.3
box of rice	12.6
bag of flour	80
box of noodles	23.5
bottle of vinegar	17
bag of chips	2.25

8. Jodi deposits $\frac{1}{5}$ of her pay into a savings account. What percent of her pay is this? 8. A
A. 20%　B. 40%　C. 50%　D. 10%

7

Chapter 7 Standardized Test Practice (continued)

9. Mali had \$900 to spend on a TV and VCR. When she was finished shopping she had \$195 left. How much did she spend? 9. C
A. \$805　B. \$635　C. \$705　D. \$895

10. José has 14 baseball cards to trade with his friends. If he gives 6 to Todd and gets 8 from Jeanie, how many does he have now? 10. B
A. 14　B. 16　C. 15　D. 17

11. Jerome knows that the bus comes every $12\frac{1}{2}$ minutes. Assuming that the bus is on time and its been $4\frac{3}{4}$ minutes since the last bus came, about how much longer does Jerome have to wait? 11. B
A. 9 minutes　B. 8 minutes　C. 7 minutes　D. 6 minutes

Sixteen-year-old Jeri wants to know how regular her heartbeat is during her aerobic workouts. So she created the table using the following formulas: $220 - \text{age} = 204$, $204 \cdot \text{intensity } \% = x$ beats per minute, $x \div 6 = y$ beats per 10 seconds. Use this information for Questions 12–14.

12. If Jeri wants to work out at 75% of her heart's capacity, what would the beats per minute be? 12. D

Intensity	x	y
90%	184	31
80%	163	27
70%	143	24
60%	122	20

A. 140　B. 147　C. 151　D. 153

13. What percent intensity of her workout is 194 beats per minute? 13. A
A. 95%　B. 85%　C. 75%　D. 65%

14. What is the mean beats per 10 seconds in column y of the table? 14. C
A. 25　B. 20　C. 25.5　D. 23.5

15. Which of the following expressions is equivalent to $2^3 \times 5 \times 11^2$? 15. C
A. $2 \times 2 \times 5 \times 11 \times 11$　B. $3 \times 5 \times 11$
C. $2 \times 2 \times 2 \times 5 \times 11 \times 11$　D. $2 \times 3 \times 5 \times 11 \times 12$

16. Brittany has 3 kilograms of oatmeal and she needs 4,000 milligrams of oatmeal for a recipe. How much oatmeal does she have left? 16. A
A. 2.996 kg　B. 2.6 kg　C. 1 kg　D. 2.96 kg

CHAPTER 8

Using Proportional Reasoning

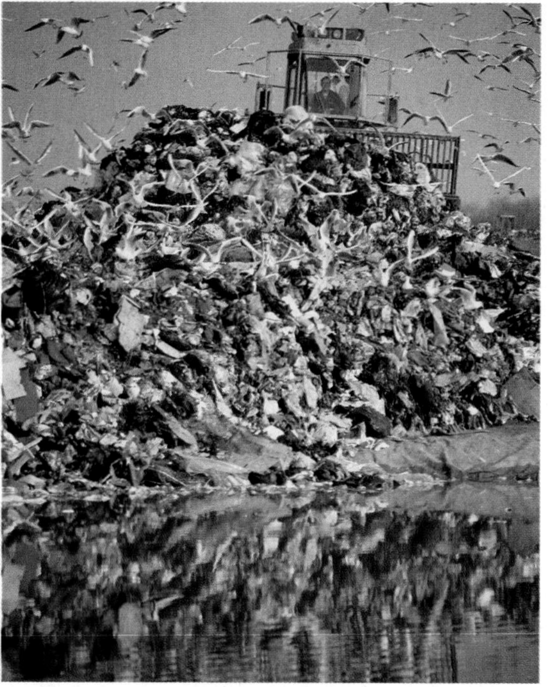

Previewing the Chapter

Overview

This chapter explores ratios, proportions, and percents. Students learn to relate fractions, decimals, and percents. After a survey of ratios, rates, and proportions, students apply the concept of proportion to geometric figures and scale drawings. Students also learn to draw diagrams to solve problems. Percents are introduced as a kind of ratio, and various problems are solved. Students are also introduced to percents greater than 100% and less than 1%. Finally, students practice finding the percent of a number and explore the connection between percent and proportion.

Lesson (pages)	Lesson Objectives	NCTM Standards 2000	Standardized Tests	State/Local Objectives
8-1A (316)	Explore the meaning of *ratio* and *proportion.*	1, 6–10		
8-1 (317–320)	Express ratios as fractions and determine whether two ratios are equivalent.	1–3, 5–10	ITBS, MAT, SAT, TN	
8-2 (321–324)	Determine unit rates.	1, 6–9	CAT	
8-3 (325–328)	Solve proportions.	1, 2, 4, 6–10	CAT, CTBS, MAT, SAT, TN	
8-3B (329)	Use the capture-recapture technique to estimate.	1, 6–9		
8-4A (330–331)	Solve problems by drawing a diagram.	1, 6–9	CTBS, TN	
8-4 (332–335)	Solve problems involving scale drawings.	1, 2, 6–10	CTBS, TN	
8-5 (336–338)	Express fractions as percents and vice versa.	1, 6–10	CAT, CTBS, ITBS, SAT, TN	
8-6 (339–341)	Express decimals as percents and vice versa.	1, 6–10	CAT, CTBS, ITBS, SAT, TN	
8-7 (342–345)	Express percents greater than 100% and percents less than 1% as fractions and as decimals, and vice versa.	1, 5–10		
8-8 (346–348)	Find the percent of a number.	1, 2, 6–10	CAT, ITBS	
8-9 (349–351)	Solve problems using the percent proportion.	1, 6–10		

CAT = California Achievement Tests, CTBS = Comprehensive Tests of Basic Skills, ITBS = Iowa Tests of Basic Skills, MAT = Metropolitan Achievement Tests, SAT = Stanford Achievement Tests, TN = Terra Nova
For the key to numbering of NCTM Standards 2000, see page T6.

Organizing the Chapter

The **Interactive Lesson Planner** contains all of the blackline masters and transparencies. This CD-ROM also includes an easy-to-use lesson planning calendar.

LESSON PLANNING GUIDE

Lesson	Extra Practice (Student Edition)	Blackline Masters (page numbers)										Transparencies A and B
		Study Guide	Practice	Enrichment	Assessment & Evaluation	Classroom Games	Diversity	Hands-On Lab	School to Career	Science and Math Lab Manual	Technology	
8-1A								54				
8-1	p. 589	58	58	58								8-1
8-2	p. 589	59	59	59								8-2
8-3	p. 590	60	60	60	211					37–40		8-3
8-3B								55				
8-4A	p. 590											
8-4	p. 590	61	61	61				79	21			8-4
8-5	p. 591	62	62	62	210, 211						41	8-5
8-6	p. 591	63	63	63						81–84		8-6
8-7	p. 591	64	64	64	212	23–25						8-7
8-8	p. 592	65	65	65								8–8
8-9	p. 592	66	66	66	212		21				42	8-9
Study Guide/ Assesment					197–209, 213–215							

Other Chapter Resources

Student Edition

Chapter Project, pp. 315, 320, 345, 355
Math in the Media, p. 324
Let the Games Begin, p. 328

Technology

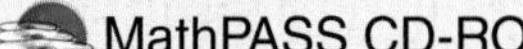
MathPASS CD-ROM
Interactive Mathematics Tools Software

Teacher's Classroom Resources

Applications
Family Letters and Activities, pp. 41–42
Investigations and Projects Masters, pp. 45–48

Meeting Individual Needs
Investigations for the Special Education Student, pp. 21–28

Teaching Aids
Answer Key Masters
Block Scheduling Booklet
Lesson Planning Guide
Solutions Manual

Professional Publications
Glencoe Mathematics Professional Series

Planning the Chapter

MindJogger Videoquizzes provide a unique format for reviewing concepts presented in the chapter.

Assessment Resources

Student Edition
Mixed Review, pp. 320, 324, 328, 335, 338, 341, 345, 348, 351
Mid-Chapter Self Test, p. 335
Math Journal, pp. 318, 340
Study Guide and Assessment, pp. 352–355
Performance Task, p. 355
Portfolio Suggestion, p. 355
Standardized Test Practice, pp. 356–357
Chapter Test, p. 614

Assessment and Evaluation Masters
Multiple-Choice Tests (Forms 1A, 1B, 1C), pp. 197–202
Free-Response Tests (Forms 2A, 2B, 2C), pp. 203–208
Performance Assessment, p. 209
Mid-Chapter Test, p. 210
Quizzes A–D, pp. 211–212
Standardized Test Practice, pp. 213–214
Cumulative Review, p. 215

Teacher's Wraparound Edition
5-Minute Check, pp. 317, 321, 325, 332, 336, 339, 342, 346, 349
Building Portfolios, p. 314
Math Journal, pp. 316, 329
Closing Activity, pp. 320, 324, 328, 335, 338, 341, 345, 348, 351

Technology
Test and Review Software
MindJogger Videoquizzes
CD-ROM Program

Materials and Manipulatives

Lesson 8-1A
counters*

Lesson 8-3
spinner*†
counters*

Lesson 8-3B
small bowl
dried beans
markers
paper cup

Lesson 8-4
tape measure*
ruler*†
$\frac{1}{4}$-inch grid paper

Lesson 8-7
grid paper
colored pencils

*Glencoe Manipulative Kit

†Glencoe Overhead Manipulative Resources

Pacing Chart

See pages T25–T27 for the Course Planning Calendar.

COURSE	DAY 1	DAY 2	DAY 3	DAY 4	DAY 5	DAY 6	DAY 7
Standard	Chapter Project	Lessons 8-1A & 8-1		Lesson 8-2	Lesson 8-3	Lesson 8-4A	Lesson 8-4
Honors	Chapter Project	Lesson 8-1	Lesson 8-2	Lessons 8-3 & 8-3B		Lesson 8-4A	Lesson 8-4
Block	Chapter Project & Lesson 8-1A	Lessons 8-1 & 8-2	Lessons 8-3 & 4A	Lessons 8-4 & 8-5	Lessons 8-6 & 8-7	Lessons 8-8 & 8-9	Study Guide and Assessment, Chapter Test

Interactive Mathematics:
Activities and Investigations

is an activity-based program that may be used as an enhancement for chapters in ***Mathematics: Applications and Connections.***

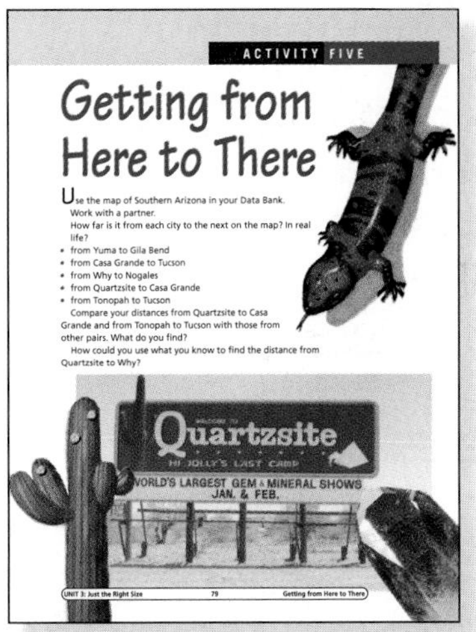

ACTIVITY FIVE

Getting from Here to There

Use the map of Southern Arizona in your Data Bank. Work with a partner.
How far is it from each city to the next on the map? In real life?
- from Yuma to Gila Bend
- from Casa Grande to Tucson
- from Why to Nogales
- from Quartzsite to Casa Grande
- from Tonopah to Tucson

Compare your distances from Quartzsite to Casa Grande and from Tonopah to Tucson with those from other pairs. What do you find?
How could you use what you know to find the distance from Quartzsite to Why?

UNIT 3: Just the Right Size 79 Getting from Here to There

Unit 3, Activity Five
Use with Lesson 8-4.

Summary Students use the map and scale provided in the Data Bank to find the distances between selected cities in Arizona. They then compare their results for the distances between a pair of selected cities with the results of other pairs.

Math Connection Students may use various methods to determine the distance on a map. They might measure the distance between two cities and use the scale to determine the actual distance. They can also copy the scale on paper and use it to measure the mileage.

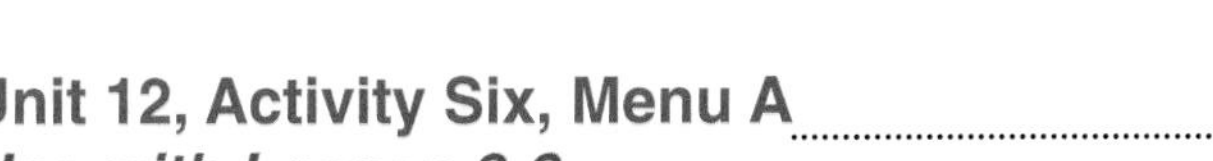

Unit 12, Activity Six, Menu A
Use with Lesson 8-9.

Summary Students use information on frequency of letter use in text material to help them decipher a coded message. They describe their strategies and explain how the activity used proportions.

Math Connection Students become involved with the concepts of proportionality, frequency tables, and looking for patterns. They will use their knowledge of the English language, the guess-and-check strategy, and the comparison of the frequency of letters in the text material to a frequency table to decipher a message using a simple substitution code.

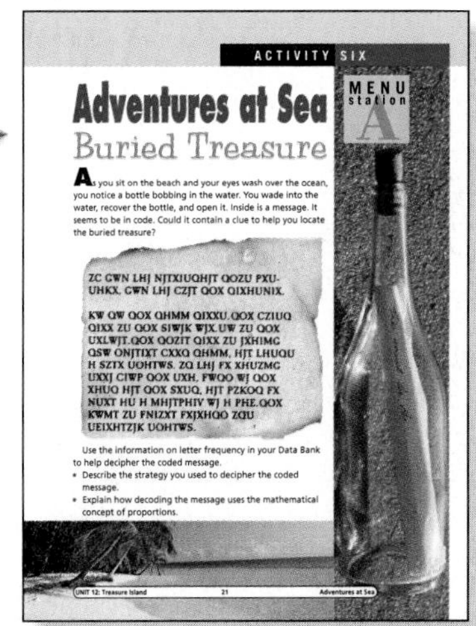

ACTIVITY SIX

MENU station A

Adventures at Sea

Buried Treasure

As you sit on the beach and your eyes wash over the ocean, you notice a bottle bobbing in the water. You wade into the water, recover the bottle, and open it. Inside is a message. It seems to be in code. Could it contain a clue to help you locate the buried treasure?

Use the information on letter frequency in your Data Bank to help decipher the coded message.
- Describe the strategy you used to decipher the coded message.
- Explain how decoding the message uses the mathematical concept of proportions.

UNIT 12: Treasure Island 21 Adventures at Sea

DAY 8	DAY 9	DAY 10	DAY 11	DAY 12	DAY 13	DAY 14	DAY 15
Lesson 8-5	Lesson 8-6	Lesson 8-7	Lesson 8-8	Lesson 8-9	Study Guide and Assessment	Chapter Test	
Lesson 8-5	Lesson 8-6	Lesson 8-7	Lesson 8-8	Lesson 8-9	Study Guide and Assessment	Chapter Test	

Enhancing the Chapter

APPLICATIONS

Classroom Games, pp. 23–25

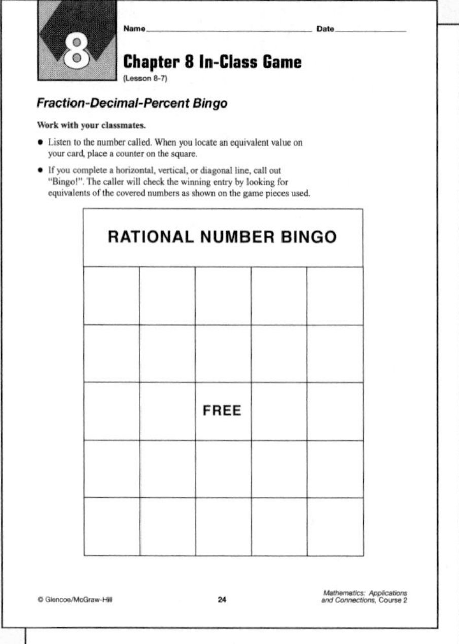

8 Name ______ Date ______

Chapter 8 In-Class Game
(Lesson 8-7)

Fraction-Decimal-Percent Bingo

Work with your classmates.

- Listen to the number called. When you locate an equivalent value on your card, place a counter on the square.
- If you complete a horizontal, vertical, or diagonal line, call out "Bingo!". The caller will check the winning entry by looking for equivalents of the covered numbers as shown on the game pieces used.

RATIONAL NUMBER BINGO				
		FREE		

© Glencoe/McGraw-Hill 24 *Mathematics: Applications and Connections, Course 2*

Diversity Masters, p. 21

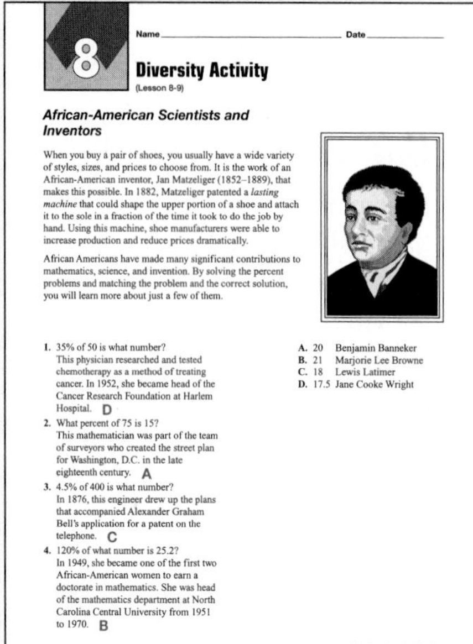

8 Name ______ Date ______

Diversity Activity
(Lesson 8-9)

African-American Scientists and Inventors

When you buy a pair of shoes, you usually have a wide variety of styles, sizes, and prices to choose from. It is the work of an African-American inventor, Jan Matzeliger (1852–1889), that makes this possible. In 1882, Matzeliger patented a *lasting machine* that could shape the upper portion of a shoe and attach it to the sole in a fraction of the time it took to do the job by hand. Using this machine, shoe manufacturers were able to increase production and reduce prices dramatically.

African Americans have made many significant contributions to mathematics, science, and invention. By solving the percent problems and matching the problem and the correct solution, you will learn more about just a few of them.

1. 35% of 50 is what number?
   This physician researched and tested chemotherapy as a method of treating cancer. In 1952, she became head of the Cancer Research Foundation at Harlem Hospital. D
2. What percent of 75 is 15?
   This mathematician was part of the team of surveyors who created the street plan for Washington, D.C. in the late eighteenth century. A
3. 4.5% of 400 is what number?
   In 1876, this engineer drew up the plans that accompanied Alexander Graham Bell's application for a patent on the telephone. C
4. 120% of what number is 25.2?
   In 1949, she became one of the first two African-American women to earn a doctorate in mathematics. She was head of the mathematics department at North Carolina Central University from 1951 to 1970. B

A. 20 Benjamin Banneker
B. 21 Marjorie Lee Browne
C. 18 Lewis Latimer
D. 17.5 Jane Cooke Wright

© Glencoe/McGraw-Hill T21 *Mathematics: Applications and Connections, Course 2*

School to Career Masters, p. 21

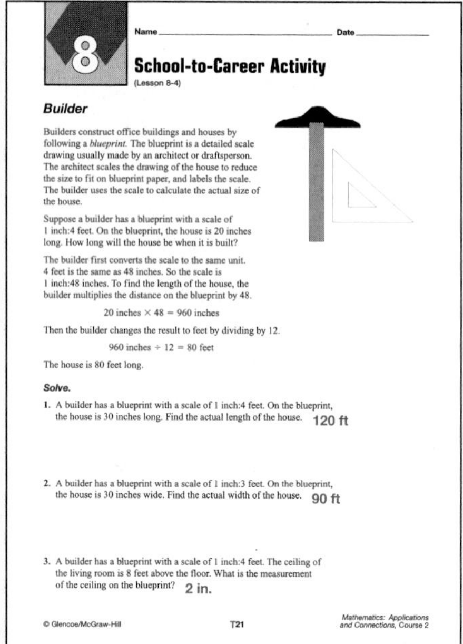

8 Name ______ Date ______

School-to-Career Activity
(Lesson 8-4)

Builder

Builders construct office buildings and houses by following a *blueprint*. The blueprint is a detailed scale drawing usually made by an architect or draftsperson. The architect scales the drawing of the house to reduce the size to fit on blueprint paper, and labels the scale. The builder uses the scale to calculate the actual size of the house.

Suppose a builder has a blueprint with a scale of 1 inch:4 feet. On the blueprint, the house is 20 inches long. How long will the house be when it is built?

The builder first converts the scale to the same unit. 4 feet is the same as 48 inches. So the scale is 1 inch:48 inches. To find the length of the house, the builder multiplies the distance on the blueprint by 48.

$$20 \text{ inches} \times 48 = 960 \text{ inches}$$

Then the builder changes the result to feet by dividing by 12.

$$960 \text{ inches} \div 12 = 80 \text{ feet}$$

The house is 80 feet long.

Solve.

1. A builder has a blueprint with a scale of 1 inch:4 feet. On the blueprint, the house is 30 inches long. Find the actual length of the house. 120 ft
2. A builder has a blueprint with a scale of 1 inch:3 feet. On the blueprint, the house is 30 inches wide. Find the actual width of the house. 90 ft
3. A builder has a blueprint with a scale of 1 inch:4 feet. The ceiling of the living room is 8 feet above the floor. What is the measurement of the ceiling on the blueprint? 2 in.

© Glencoe/McGraw-Hill T21 *Mathematics: Applications and Connections, Course 2*

Family Letters and Activities, pp. 41–42

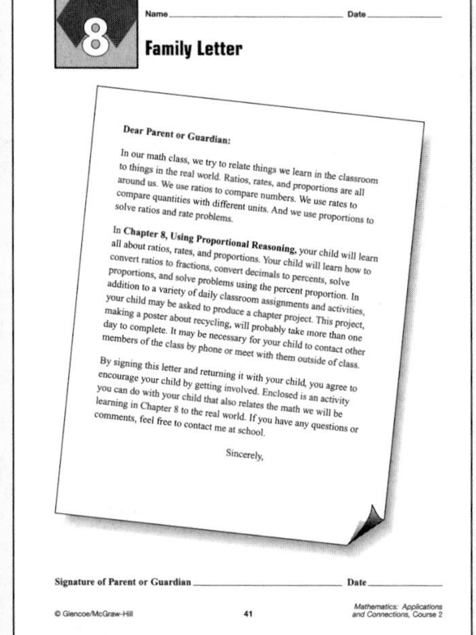

8 Name ______ Date ______

Family Letter

Dear Parent or Guardian:

In our math class, we try to relate things we learn in the classroom to things in the real world. Ratios, rates, and proportions are all around us. We use ratios to compare numbers. We use rates to compare quantities with different units. And we use proportions to solve ratios and rate problems.

In **Chapter 8, Using Proportional Reasoning,** your child will learn all about ratios, rates, and proportions. Your child will learn how to convert ratios to fractions, convert decimals to percents, solve proportions, and solve problems using the percent proportion. In addition to a variety of daily classroom assignments and activities, your child may be asked to produce a chapter project. This project, making a poster about recycling, will probably take more than one day to complete. It may be necessary for your child to contact other members of the class by phone or meet with them outside of class.

By signing this letter and returning it with your child, you agree to encourage your child by getting involved. Enclosed is an activity you can do with your child that also relates the math we will be learning in Chapter 8 to the real world. If you have any questions or comments, feel free to contact me at school.

Sincerely,

Signature of Parent or Guardian ______ **Date** ______

© Glencoe/McGraw-Hill 41 *Mathematics: Applications and Connections, Course 2*

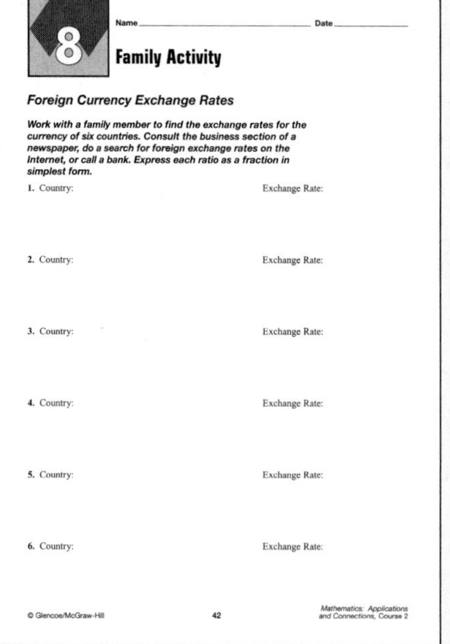

8 Name ______ Date ______

Family Activity

Foreign Currency Exchange Rates

Work with a family member to find the exchange rates for the currency of six countries. Consult the business section of a newspaper, do a search for foreign exchange rates on the Internet, or call a bank. Express each ratio as a fraction in simplest form.

1. Country: Exchange Rate:
2. Country: Exchange Rate:
3. Country: Exchange Rate:
4. Country: Exchange Rate:
5. Country: Exchange Rate:
6. Country: Exchange Rate:

© Glencoe/McGraw-Hill 42 *Mathematics: Applications and Connections, Course 2*

Science and Math Lab Manual, pp. 37–40, 81–84

10 Name ______ Date ______

Science and Mathematics Lab
(Course 2, Lesson 8-3)

Relating Ratios to Dinosaurs

INTRODUCTION

Dinosaurs inhabited Earth until about 65 million years ago. Some dinosaurs were very large, while others were quite small. In this lab, you will measure toy dinosaurs and compare these measurements to those of actual dinosaurs using ratios and proportions.

OBJECTIVES

In this lab, you will:

- measure the length and height of toy dinosaurs.
- compare these measurements to actual measurements using ratios and proportions.

MATERIALS

- toy dinosaurs in a variety of types and sizes
- metric ruler
- calculator

PROCEDURE

1. Select three dinosaurs of different sizes.
2. Measure the height and length of each dinosaur and record the data in the table. To find the height of the dinosaur, measure from its hip (the top of the hind leg) to the bottom of its hind foot. To find the length of the dinosaur, measure from its nose to the tip of its tail.

Height at hip
Length

DATA AND OBSERVATIONS

Dinosaur	Height (mm)	Length (mm)

© Glencoe/McGraw-Hill 39 *Mathematics: Applications and Connections*

MANIPULATIVES/MODELING

Hands-On Lab Masters, p. 79

Name____________________ Date__________

8 **Lab Activity**
(Lesson 8-4)

Scale Drawings

The Room of Your Dreams

What if you could build a room of any size and put anything you wanted in it?

Use the grid as a blueprint. Title your drawing and choose a scale. Then sketch the things you would put in your room, such as a bed, a desk, closet, TV, windows, a door. You can make the furnishings larger or smaller than usual. Make sure you draw everything to scale. Label everything in the room.

1. List the objects in your room and their actual size.
   See students' work. Make sure drawings are the correct scale based on this information and the scale of the grid.
2. Why did you want these things in your room? Answers will vary.
3. Why did you choose these sizes? Answers will vary.

© Glencoe/McGraw-Hill 79 *Mathematics: Applications and Connections, Course 2*

ASSESSMENT/EVALUATION

Assessment and Evaluation Masters, pp. 210–212

Name____________________ Date__________

8 **Chapter 8 Mid-Chapter Test**
(Lessons 8-1 through 8-5)

1. Express the ratio 6 inches to 2 feet as a fraction in simplest form. — 1. $\frac{1}{4}$
2. Express the ratio 12 centimeters to 5 meters as a fraction in simplest form. — 2. $\frac{3}{125}$
3. Are the ratios 5:8 and 20:32 equivalent? Show your answer by simplifying. — 3. yes; $\frac{5}{8} = \frac{20}{32}$
4. Express the unit rate of $14.30 for 11 glow-in-the-dark pencils. — 4. $1.30 per pencil
5. Express the unit rate of 27,460 books in a 860-square-foot library. — 5. about 32 books per sq. foot
6. Express the unit rate of 192 crayons for 8 boxes. — 6. 24 crayons per box

Solve each proportion and state the solution in simplest form.

7. $\frac{5}{8} = \frac{3}{x}$ — 7. 4.8
8. $\frac{9}{5} = \frac{n}{10}$ — 8. 18
9. $\frac{g}{12} = \frac{8}{16}$ — 9. 6
10. $\frac{6}{y} = \frac{2}{9}$ — 10. 27
11. If Jyoti wants to arrange her spoon collection of 16 spoons on a spoon rack that holds 22 spoons, how could she do so in the most regular shape? Fill in the diagram with spoons that hang from the dots. — 11.
12. If the scale for a model train is 1 inch for every 10 feet of a real train, how big is the model for an 83-foot train? — 12. 8.3 in.
13. Express $\frac{17}{19}$ as a percent. — 13. 89.5%
14. Express $\frac{2}{13}$ as a percent. — 14. 15.4%
15. Express 14% as a fraction. — 15. $\frac{7}{50}$
16. Express 96% as a fraction. — 16. $\frac{24}{25}$

© Glencoe/McGraw-Hill 210 *Mathematics: Applications and Connections, Course 2*

Name____________________ Date__________

Chapter 8 Quiz A (Lessons 8-1 through 8-3)

Express each ratio as a fraction in simplest form.

1. 54:9 — 1. $\frac{6}{1}$
2. 21 to 91 — 2. $\frac{3}{13}$
3. Are the ratios $\frac{3}{7}$ and $\frac{15}{35}$ equivalent? — 3. yes
4. Write a ratio that is equivalent to $\frac{7}{9}$. — 4. Sample answer: $\frac{14}{18}$

Express each rate as a unit rate.

5. $1.16 for 4 pounds — 5. $0.29 per lb
6. 320 meters in 20 seconds — 6. 16 m/s
7. 128 pounds of dog food for 16 dogs — 7. 8 lbs per dog

Solve each proportion.

8. $\frac{25}{n} = \frac{40}{8}$ 9. $\frac{z}{10} = \frac{15}{75}$ 10. $\frac{8}{5} = \frac{12}{c}$

8. 5
9. 2
10. 7.5

Name____________________ Date__________

Chapter 8 Quiz B (Lessons 8-4 and 8-5)

On a map, the scale is $\frac{1}{2}$ inch:25 miles. For each map distance, find the actual distance.

1. 3 inches — 1. 150 mi
2. $10\frac{1}{2}$ inches — 2. 525 mi
3. Express the fraction $\frac{7}{12}$ as a percent. — 3. $58\frac{1}{3}$%
4. Express $15\frac{1}{2}$% as a fraction in simplest form. — 4. $\frac{31}{200}$
5. Express 48% as a fraction in simplest form. — 5. $\frac{12}{25}$

© Glencoe/McGraw-Hill 211 *Mathematics: Applications and Connections, Course 2*

TECHNOLOGY/MULTIMEDIA

Technology Masters, pp. 41–42

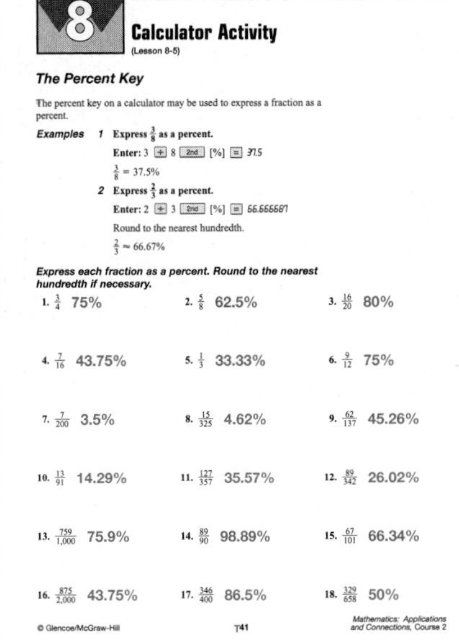

Name____________________ Date__________

8 **Calculator Activity**
(Lesson 8-5)

The Percent Key

The percent key on a calculator may be used to express a fraction as a percent.

Examples ***1*** **Express $\frac{3}{8}$ as a percent.**

Enter: 3 [÷] 8 [2nd] [%] [=] 37.5

$\frac{3}{8} = 37.5\%$

2 **Express $\frac{2}{3}$ as a percent.**

Enter: 2 [÷] 3 [2nd] [%] [=] 66.666667

Round to the nearest hundredth.

$\frac{2}{3} \approx 66.67\%$

Express each fraction as a percent. Round to the nearest hundredth if necessary.

1. $\frac{3}{4}$ 75% 2. $\frac{5}{8}$ 62.5% 3. $\frac{16}{20}$ 80%
4. $\frac{7}{16}$ 43.75% 5. $\frac{1}{3}$ 33.33% 6. $\frac{9}{12}$ 75%
7. $\frac{7}{200}$ 3.5% 8. $\frac{15}{325}$ 4.62% 9. $\frac{62}{137}$ 45.26%
10. $\frac{13}{91}$ 14.29% 11. $\frac{127}{357}$ 35.57% 12. $\frac{89}{342}$ 26.02%
13. $\frac{759}{1,000}$ 75.9% 14. $\frac{89}{90}$ 98.89% 15. $\frac{67}{101}$ 66.34%
16. $\frac{875}{2,000}$ 43.75% 17. $\frac{346}{400}$ 86.5% 18. $\frac{329}{658}$ 50%

© Glencoe/McGraw-Hill T41 *Mathematics: Applications and Connections, Course 2*

Name____________________ Date__________

8 **Spreadsheet Activity**
(Lesson 8-9)

The Percent Proportion

You can use a spreadsheet to help solve the three types of percent problems. Create a spreadsheet with three columns. Label the first column P for the percentage, the second column B for base, and the third column r for rate.

If you have values in any two columns, you can find the third value by entering the correct formula in the third column.

The formula for column P is (B × C) / 100.

The formula for column B is (A × 100) / C.

The formula for column r is (A × 100) / B.

Use the spreadsheet to find what number is 25% of 64.

	A	B	C
1	P	B	r
2	16	64	25
3			

16 is 25% of 64.

Use your knowledge of percents and spreadsheets to answer each question.

1. Suppose you want to use a spreadsheet to solve "21 is 35% of what number?" Which columns would you use for each number?
   Column A: 21; Column C: 35; calculate to find Column B: 60
2. Suppose you want to use a spreadsheet to solve "What percent of 125 is 20?" Which columns would you use for each number?
   Column A: 20; Column B: 125; calculate to find Column C: 16%

Use the spreadsheet to solve each problem. Round answers to the nearest tenth if necessary.

3. 9 is what percent of 20? 45% 4. What number is 37% of 52? 19.2
5. 75% of 63 is what number? 47.3 6. What percent of 62 is 31? 50%
7. 16 is 32% of what number? 50 8. 20 is 58% of what number? 34.5

© Glencoe/McGraw-Hill T42 *Mathematics: Applications and Connections, Course 2*

MEETING INDIVIDUAL NEEDS

Investigations for the Special Education Student, pp. 21–28

Use with:
Course 1-Chapter 10
Course 2-Chapter 11
Course 3-Chapter 9

Investigation 9 Teacher's Guide

Park It!

Overview
Students will work in groups of four to design a park according to preset criteria. During this investigation, students will experience firsthand how measurement, proportions, and decimal operations are necessary for careers that involve design. Each student is responsible for a certain job in the group: engineer, draftsperson, finance officer, or public relations person. The culminating point of the investigation is a videotaped, oral presentation of the designs.

Activity Goals
Students will:
- design a park to scale using proportions,
- use decimal operations for budgeting, and
- work cooperatively and responsibly with a group.

Planning the Instruction
Prerequisite Skills
Students should have a significant amount of practice measuring, solving proportions, using scales, and computing with decimals.
Materials
- investigation worksheets
- calculators
- rulers, measuring tape
- drawing paper
- crayons, colored pencils, markers
- video camera and videotape

Time Needed
ten 45-minute periods

Procedure
1. Discuss the investigation with the class. Explain that their task is to design a park to scale that will fit on a 200-foot by 300-foot piece of land. The investigation will end with a videotaped, oral presentation to the class.
2. Brainstorm with the entire class a list of features they would like to include in their designs.
3. Set up student groups.
4. Have each group meet and compile their own list of features, using ideas from the class list.
5. Describe the different jobs to the class. Then have the groups discuss and sign the Group Job Contract worksheet according to their responsibilities.
6. Have students begin their designated jobs according to their Job Specification worksheets.
7. Monitor student progress through observations and group meetings. In addition, be available to answer questions when necessary.
8. Set a date for the presentations.
9. Conduct and videotape presentations while students evaluate each other.
10. Collect evaluations and have students view the recorded presentations.

Adaptations and Variations

The following are some ideas on how this investigation may be modified depending on student population.

LD • Allow more time.
• If measuring is difficult, allow students to use nonstandard units such as their hands.
• If converting measurements is difficult using scale factors and proportions, allow students to convert using nonstandard scale units such as one hand in real length equals one paper clip in drawing length.

PH • For students who have trouble drawing, allow them to use computer graphics.

CD • If a communicably-troubled student should choose to be the public relations person, have each group member say several lines of the speech.

BD • Assign job specification tasks one at a time, with a reward system in place for each one completed in an appropriate manner.

HI • Have another student sign each presentation.

VI • Make sure students give a detailed description of their designs when presenting.

© Glencoe/McGraw-Hill 21 *Mathematics: Applications and Connections*

CHAPTER 8 NOTES

Theme: Recycling
Green Valley Recycling of Los Gatos, California, began in 1918 when a local hog farmer made an agreement with grocery merchants to haul away their trash if he could feed their leftover greens to his animals. By 1996, it was also collecting Christmas trees, telephone books, yard clippings, cardboard, metal, paper, plastic, and glass.

Question of the Day Of the 6,563,000 metric tons of aluminum used in 1995, 3,188,000 metric tons were recycled. What percent of the total was recycled? about 48.6%

Assess Prerequisite Skills

Ask students to read through the list of objectives presented in "What you'll learn in Chapter 8." You may wish to ask them what each of the objectives means or if they have experienced or used any of these math concepts before.

Building Portfolios

Encourage students to revise their portfolios as they study this chapter. Have them include examples of both the easiest and the most challenging problems, reflecting their individual strengths and improvement.

Math and the Family

In the *Family Letters and Activities* booklet (pp. 41–42), you will find a letter to the parents explaining what students will study in Chapter 8. An activity appropriate for the whole family is also available.

CHAPTER 8 Using Proportional Reasoning

What you'll learn in Chapter 8

- to express ratios as fractions,
- to solve proportions,
- to solve problems by drawing a diagram,
- to solve problems involving scale drawings,
- to express percents as fractions and decimals, and
- to find the percent of a number.

314 Chapter 8 Using Proportional Reasoning

CD-ROM Program

Activities for Chapter 8
- Chapter 8 Introduction
- Interactive Lessons 8-1, 8-3, 8-8
- Extended Activity 8-4
- Assessment Game
- Resource Lessons 8-1 through 8-9

CHAPTER Project

WASTE NOT, WANT NOT

In this project, you will use percents to make a poster about trash. You will determine the steps you can take to reduce the amount of trash by increasing the amount of material that is recycled.

Getting Started

- Keep track of the trash your family throws away for one week. Make a chart showing the type and amount of trash you throw away each day. Use fractions to estimate what part of the day's trash each type represents. For example, aluminum cans may be about $\frac{1}{4}$ of your trash on a certain day.
- Find recent statistics about what materials are recycled and what the recycled material becomes.
- Research the recycling programs in your area.

Technology Tips

- Use a **spreadsheet** to keep track of the data you collect.
- Use **graphing software** to make statistical graphs to represent the data.
- Use a **word processor** to make the text for your poster.

Research For up-to-date information on recycling, visit:

www.glencoe.com/sec/math/mac/mathnet

Working on the Project

You can use what you learn in Chapter 8 to study trash and recycling.

Page	Exercise
320	42
345	50
355	Alternative Assessment

CHAPTER Project NOTES

Objectives Students should
- investigate the various kinds of materials that can be recycled by households.
- compare the amounts of different materials using ratios and percents.

Project Pointer You may suggest that students begin a *Project Folder* to keep their work as they complete each stage of the Chapter Project. The completed project may also be added to their portfolios.

Students may want to use photographs or create visuals for their posters. Remind them to include information about what can and cannot be recycled. Students may also want to compare a recycling program in their community with one in a nearby community.

***Investigations and Projects Masters*, p. 48**

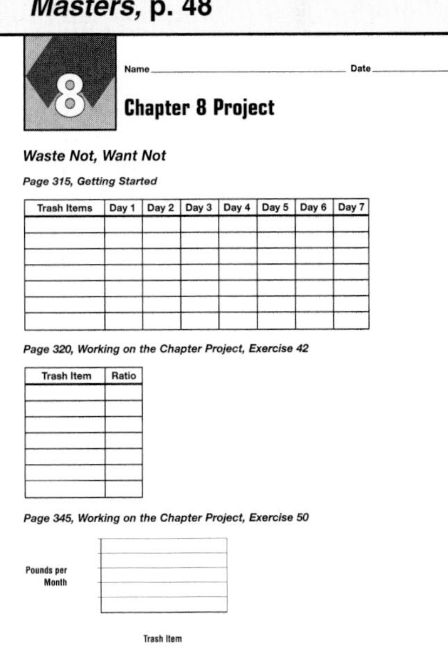

8 Name______ Date______

Chapter 8 Project

Waste Not, Want Not

Page 315, Getting Started

Trash Items	Day 1	Day 2	Day 3	Day 4	Day 5	Day 6	Day 7

Page 320, Working on the Chapter Project, Exercise 42

Trash Item	Ratio

Page 345, Working on the Chapter Project, Exercise 50

© Glencoe/McGraw-Hill 48 *Mathematics: Applications and Connections, Course 2*

interNET CONNECTION

Glencoe has made every effort to ensure that the website links for *Mathematics: Applications and Connections* at **www.glencoe.com/sec/math/mac/mathnet** are current and contain appropriate content. However, these website links are not under Glencoe's control.

Instructional Resources ▶▶▶
A recording sheet to help students organize their data for the Chapter Project is shown at the right and is available in the *Investigations and Projects Masters,* p. 48.

GET READY

Objective Students explore the meaning of *ratio* and *proportion.*

Optional Resources
Hands-On Lab Masters
- counters, p. 6
- worksheet, p. 54

Overhead Manipulative Resources
- counters

Manipulative Kit
- counters

MANAGEMENT TIPS

Recommended Time
30 minutes

Getting Started Have students use counters to model fractions using their pencil as the fraction bar. Have them model families of equivalent fractions such as $\frac{1}{2}$, $\frac{2}{4}$, $\frac{3}{6}$, $\frac{4}{8}$, and so on. Ask them to look for patterns in how these are related.

For the **Activity**, demonstrate how equal ratios are formed using different quantities. Before students place any counters in V, note that for every 2 counters in C there are 3 in D.

ASSESS

Have students complete Exercises 1–3. In Exercise 2, watch for students who mistake 84 for the first term in the ratio *W*:*X*. Remind them that $W < X$.

COOPERATIVE LEARNING

8-1A Equal Ratios

A Preview of Lesson 8-1

counters

A *ratio* is the comparison of two numbers. Ratios are often used to show how large one quantity is compared to another. For example, for every four counters in pile A there is one counter in pile B. So we can say that piles A and B have the ratio 4 to 1.

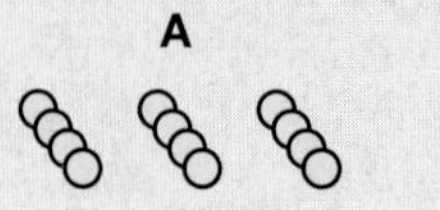

TRY THIS

Work in pairs.

Step 1 Fold a sheet of paper into eighths. Then unfold it and label and place the counters in the sections as shown.

Step 2 Place the counters in sections V, W, and Z so that the ratio of the counters in each column is equal to the ratio of the counters in C and D.

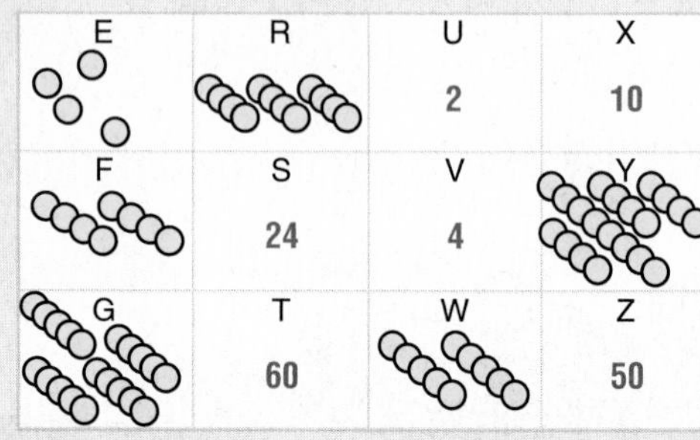

ON YOUR OWN

1. See margin.

1. Describe how you decided how many counters to place in sections V, W, and Z.
2. If there were 84 counters in section X, how many counters would you have placed in section W? **56**
3. Fold another piece of paper into twelve sections. Then label and place the counters in the sections as shown. Place the counters in the empty sections so that the ratios in each column are equal to the ratio of E to F to G. **See table.**

E	R	U 2	X 10
F	S 24	V 4	Y
G	T 60	W	Z 50

Additional Answer

1. Sample answer: Make equivalent fractions. $\frac{2}{3} = \frac{4}{6} = \frac{6}{9} = \frac{10}{15}$

Have students write a paragraph describing how they solved Exercise 3.

8-1 Ratios

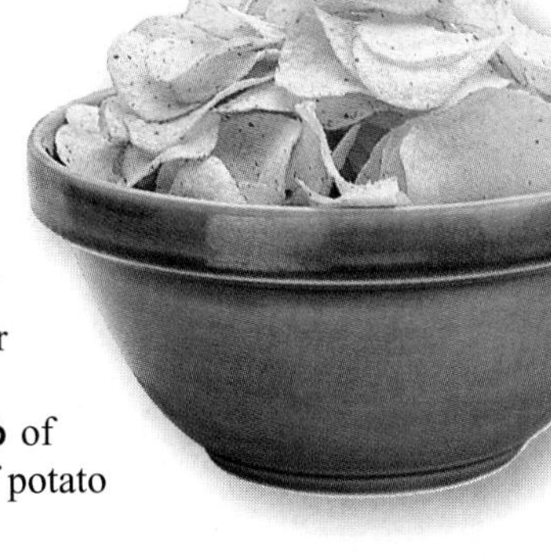

***What* you'll learn**

You'll learn to express ratios as fractions and determine whether two ratios are equivalent.

***When* am I ever going to use this?**

Ratios are used to report foreign currency exchange rates in the newspaper.

Word Wise

ratio
equivalent ratios

Are potato chips on your list of favorite snacks? Americans eat about 606 million pounds of chips each summer! It takes four pounds of potatoes to make one pound of potato chips. The **ratio** of pounds of potatoes to pounds of potato chips is 4 to 1.

Ratio		
	Words:	A ratio is a comparison of two numbers by division.
	Symbols:	**Arithmetic** 4 to 1 4:1 $\frac{4}{1}$
		Algebra a to b a:b $\frac{a}{b}$

A ratio can be written as a fraction. Often, ratios are written as fractions in simplest form.

Example 1 — Real World APPLICATION

Recycling **For every 207 pounds of waste that is generated in the United States, 45 pounds are recycled into new products. Write the ratio of the pounds of recycled material to the total pounds of waste in simplest form.**

$$\frac{\text{pounds recycled}}{\text{pounds of waste}} \rightarrow \frac{45}{207} = \frac{45 \div 9}{207 \div 9} = \frac{5}{23}$$ *The GCF of 45 and 207 is 9.*

The ratio in simplest form is $\frac{5}{23}$, 5 to 23, or 5:23.

Study Hint

Reading Math The ratio of 5 to 23 means that for every 5 pounds of recycled material, there was 23 pounds of waste.

You can also write a ratio as a decimal. The ratio in Example 1 can be expressed as a decimal in the following way.

5 [÷] 23 [=] 0.217391304

When you simplify a ratio that compares measurements, be sure that the measurements have the same unit of measure.

8-1 Lesson Notes

Instructional Resources

- *Study Guide Masters,* p. 58
- *Practice Masters,* p. 58
- *Enrichment Masters,* p. 58
- Transparencies 8-1, A and B

CD-ROM Program
- Resource Lesson 8-1
- Interactive Lesson 8-1

Recommended Pacing	
Standard	Days 2 & 3 of 14
Honors	Day 2 of 14
Block	Day 2 of 7

1 FOCUS

5-Minute Check *(Chapter 7)*

Solve each equation. Write the solution in simplest form.

1. $\frac{2}{3} + \frac{5}{6} = x$ $1\frac{1}{2}$
2. $t = \frac{3}{4} - \frac{1}{9}$ $\frac{23}{36}$
3. $2\frac{5}{12} + \frac{7}{8} = y$ $3\frac{7}{24}$
4. $a = 25 \div 3\frac{1}{8}$ 8
5. Find the circumference of a circle whose radius is $\frac{7}{8}$ inch. Use $\pi \approx \frac{22}{7}$. $5\frac{1}{2}$ in.

The 5-Minute Check is also available on **Transparency 8-1A** for this lesson.

Motivating the Lesson

Communication Ask students to work with a partner to describe how much time they spend per day on their homework. Then have them write a ratio predicting the number of hours per week their partner spends on homework compared to the number of hours they spend in school. Have students compare their ratios.

Cross-Curriculum Cue

Inform the other teachers on your team that your classes are studying ratio, proportion, and percent. Suggestions for curriculum integration are:

Physical Science: mixing chemicals, gear ratios
Civics: surveys, population changes, demographics
Music: time signatures, notes in an octave

2 TEACH

Transparency 8-1B contains a teaching aid for this lesson.

Reading Mathematics After students calculate the ratios in the examples, have them describe what the quantities represent. For Example 2, for every 7 inches in the shortest deer's height, the tallest deer is 46 inches tall.

Teaching Tip In Example 1, point out that the ratio compares a part to the whole.

In-Class Examples

For Example 1
A store sold 360 newspapers last week and 440 this week. Write a ratio in simplest form comparing last week's sales to this week's sales. **$\frac{9}{11}$, 9 to 11, or 9:11**

For Example 2
Write the ratio of the height of an oak seedling 6 inches tall to the height of another seedling 3 feet tall in simplest form. **$\frac{1}{6}$ or 1:6**

For Example 3
Tell whether 10:12 and 24:30 are equivalent ratios. **No; $\frac{5}{6} \neq \frac{4}{5}$**

3 PRACTICE/APPLY

Check for Understanding

If students need additional practice or instruction after completing Exercises 1–12, one of these options may be helpful.
- Extra Practice, see p. 589
- Reteaching Activity
- *Study Guide Masters,* p. 58
- *Practice Masters,* p. 58

Additional Answers

1. **$\frac{15}{20}$, 15:20, 15 to 20**
2. **$\frac{18}{64}$, $\frac{18 \div 2}{64 \div 2} = \frac{9}{32}$**
3. **Sample answer: Write both ratios as fractions in simplest form. If the fractions are equal, then the ratios are equivalent.**

Example CONNECTION 2

LOOK BACK
Refer to Lesson 7-5 for information on changing measurements.

Life Science The shortest member of the deer family is the southern puda, which is about 14 inches tall. The Alaskan moose is the tallest deer. The tallest Alaskan moose recorded was 7 feet 8 inches tall. Write the ratio of the height of the shortest deer to the height of the tallest deer in simplest form.

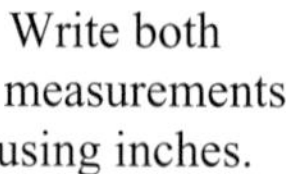

Write both measurements using inches.

$$\frac{14 \text{ inches}}{7 \text{ feet } 8 \text{ inches}} = \frac{\overset{7}{\cancel{14}} \text{ inches}}{\underset{46}{\cancel{92}} \text{ inches}} \quad \textit{7 feet 8 inches = 92 inches}$$

$$= \frac{7}{46} \quad \textit{The GCF of 14 and 92 is 2.}$$

The ratio in simplest form is $\frac{7}{46}$, or 7:46.

Two ratios that have the same value are **equivalent ratios**.

Example 3 **Tell whether 4:9 and 36:81 are equivalent ratios.**

Express each ratio as a fraction in simplest form.

The GCF of 4 and 9 is 1. So $\frac{4}{9}$ is in simplest form.

$$\frac{36}{81} = \frac{36 \div 9}{81 \div 9} = \frac{4}{9} \quad \textit{The GCF of 36 and 81 is 9.}$$

The ratios in simplest form are equal. So 4:9 and 36:81 are equivalent ratios.

CHECK FOR UNDERSTANDING

Communicating Mathematics

Read and study the lesson to answer each question. **1–3. See margin.**

1. ***Express*** the ratio *15 out of 20 cars* in three different ways.
2. ***Demonstrate*** how to simplify the ratio 18:64.
3. ***Write*** how you can determine whether two ratios are equivalent.

Math Journal

Guided Practice

Express each ratio as a fraction in simplest form.

4. $\frac{5}{35}$ **$\frac{1}{7}$**
5. 16 to 42 **$\frac{8}{21}$**
6. 36:9 **$\frac{4}{1}$**
7. 8 hours in a week **$\frac{1}{21}$**
8. 3 pounds: 12 ounces **$\frac{4}{1}$**

Reteaching the Lesson

Activity Have students group differently colored counters or centimeter cubes to represent boys and girls in the class, or other pairs of quantities. Ask them to write ratios in simplest form to compare the groups. Give students simple ratios for them to model using the counters.

Error Analysis
Watch for students who reverse the terms of a ratio when writing it.
Prevent by having students write the words for each term and then substitute quantities. For Example 2, they might write $\frac{\text{southern puda}}{\text{Alaskan moose}} = \frac{14}{92}$.

Tell whether the ratios are equivalent. Show your answer by simplifying. **9–11. See margin.**

9. $\frac{12}{16}$ and $\frac{21}{28}$

10. $\frac{5}{8}$ and $\frac{65}{100}$

11. \$15 for 6 pounds and \$90 for 36 pounds

12. ***Sports*** In baseball, a player's batting average is the ratio of his hits to times at bat. The table shows the hits and times at bat for various professional players in 1999. Find each player's batting average as a fraction in simplest form and as a decimal to the nearest thousandth. **See margin.**

Player	Hits	Times At Bat
Juan Gonzalez, Texas Rangers	183	562
Ken Griffey, Jr., Seattle Mariners	173	606
Kenny Lofton, Cleveland Indians	140	465
Jim Thome, Cleveland Indians	137	494

Source: *Major League Baseball*

EXERCISES

Practice

Express each ratio as a fraction in simplest form.

13. $\frac{21}{45}$ $\frac{7}{15}$
14. 9 to 12 $\frac{3}{4}$
15. 49:14 $\frac{7}{2}$
16. 24:4 $\frac{6}{1}$
17. 125 to 25 $\frac{5}{1}$
18. 27:36 $\frac{3}{4}$
19. 35 to 36 $\frac{35}{36}$
20. 27:15 $\frac{9}{5}$
21. 155 to 220 $\frac{31}{44}$
22. 11 teachers to 275 students $\frac{1}{25}$
23. 64 inches to $1\frac{1}{2}$ feet $\frac{32}{9}$
24. 45 minutes to 8 hours $\frac{3}{32}$
25. 14 ounces to 5 pounds $\frac{7}{40}$
26. 65¢ to \$4.50 $\frac{13}{90}$
27. 18 weeks to one year $\frac{9}{26}$

28–36. See margin.

Tell whether the ratios are equivalent. Show your answer by simplifying.

28. $\frac{12}{9}$ and $\frac{15}{12}$
29. 150:15 and 3:1
30. $\frac{6}{39}$ and $\frac{2}{13}$
31. $\frac{65}{5}$ and $\frac{1}{13}$
32. $\frac{6}{12}$ and $\frac{0.5}{1}$
33. 14:42 and 58:1,218
34. 6 pounds:72 ounces and 2 pounds:24 ounces
35. 3 days to 4 hours and 9 days to 12 hours
36. 5 miles to 100 feet and 15 miles to 100 yards
37. Write 180 days of school in one year as a fraction in simplest form. $\frac{36}{73}$
38. Are the ratios 14 inches to 9 feet and 16 feet to 12 yards equivalent? **See margin.**

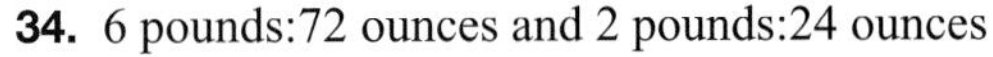

Applications and Problem Solving

39. ***Collectibles*** Do you have any small beanbag animals? In 1997, you could buy one of the retired styles, Peanut the Elephant, for about \$1,500 at trade shows. The retail price of a small beanbag animal then was \$5. Write the ratio of the retail price to Peanut's price as a fraction in simplest form. $\frac{1}{300}$

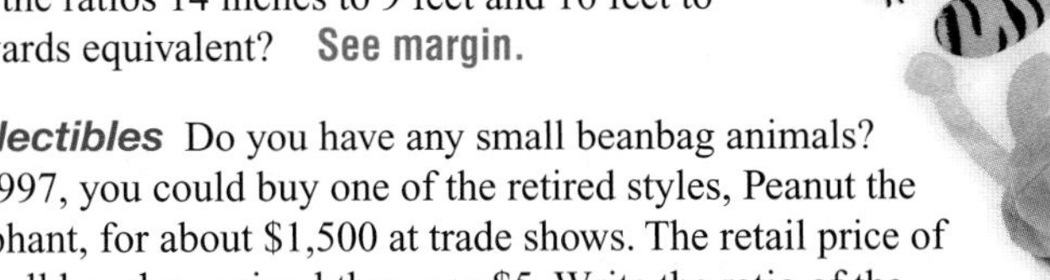

Investigations for the Special Education Student

This blackline master booklet helps you plan for the needs of your special education students by providing long-term projects along with teacher notes. Investigation 9, *Park It!,* may be used with this chapter.

Assignment Guide

Core: 13–41 odd, 43–48
Enriched: 14–38 even, 39–41, 43–48

Additional Answers

9. Yes; $\frac{12}{16} = \frac{3}{4}$ and $\frac{21}{28} = \frac{3}{4}$
10. No; $\frac{65}{100} = \frac{13}{20}$
11. Yes; $\frac{15}{6} = \frac{5}{2}$ and $\frac{90}{36} = \frac{5}{2}$
12. Gonzalez: $\frac{183}{562}$; 0.326; Griffey: $\frac{173}{606}$; 0.285; Lofton: $\frac{140}{465}$; 0.301; Thome: $\frac{137}{494}$; 0.277
28. No; $\frac{12}{9} = \frac{4}{3}$ and $\frac{15}{12} = \frac{5}{4}$
29. No; 150:15 = 10:1
30. Yes; $\frac{6}{39} = \frac{2}{13}$
31. No; $\frac{65}{5} = \frac{13}{1}$
32. Yes; $\frac{6}{12} = \frac{1}{2}$ and $\frac{0.5}{1} = \frac{1}{2}$
33. No; 14:42 = 1:3 and 58:1,218 = 1:21
34. Yes; 6 lb:72 oz = 4:3 and 2 lb:24 oz = 4:3
35. Yes; 3 d:4 h = 18:1 and 9 d to 12 h = 18:1
36. Yes; 5 mi to 100 ft = 264:1 and 15 mi to 100 yd = 264:1
38. No; 14 in.:9 ft = 7:54 and 16 ft: 12 yd = 4:9

***Study Guide Masters,* p. 58**

Name ______ Date ______

8-1 Study Guide

Ratios

A **ratio** is a comparison of two numbers by division.

Example 1 **Ron made 10 out of 16 foul shots. Write a ratio of the shots Ron made to his total shots.**

The ratio of foul shots made to total foul shots is: 10 to 16, 10:16, or $\frac{10}{16}$.

Since a ratio can be written as a fraction, ratios are often written in simplest form.

foul shots made → / *total foul shots* → $\frac{10}{16} = \frac{10}{16}$ or $\frac{5}{8}$

The ratio can also be expressed as a decimal: $10 \div 16 = 0.625$.

Two ratios are equivalent if the simplest form of the ratios are equal.

Example 2 **Tell whether 12:18 and 14:21 are equivalent ratios.**

Express each ratio as a fraction in simplest form.

$\frac{12}{18} = \frac{12 \div 6}{18 \div 6} = \frac{2}{3}$ $\frac{14}{21} = \frac{14 \div 7}{21 \div 7} = \frac{2}{3}$

Since $\frac{2}{3} = \frac{2}{3}$, the ratios are equivalent.

Express each ratio as a fraction in simplest form.

1. 16 to 20 $\frac{4}{5}$
2. 35:40 $\frac{7}{8}$
3. 27 feet to 24 feet $\frac{9}{8}$
4. 13 hours:52 hours $\frac{1}{4}$
5. 25 to 90 $\frac{5}{18}$
6. 45 minutes to 75 minutes $\frac{3}{5}$
7. 2 hours:1 day $\frac{1}{12}$
8. 96:18 $\frac{16}{3}$
9. $\frac{24}{40}$ $\frac{3}{5}$

Tell whether the ratios are equivalent. Show your answer by simplifying.

10. $\frac{64}{80}$ and $\frac{20}{25}$ yes
11. 42 to 49 and 54 to 63 yes
12. 18:42 and 20:44 no
13. 35 to 15 and 49 to 21 yes
14. 144:36 and 72:32 no
15. 16 to 96 and 1 to 6 yes

 T58 *Mathematics: Applications and Connections, Course 2*

Exercise 42 asks students to advance to the next stage of work on the Chapter Project. You may also have students write the ratio of one material to another on each day to see how it changed.

4 ASSESS

Closing Activity

Modeling Have students toss a coin 50 times and write a ratio in simplest form that compares the number of heads to the total number of coin tosses.

Additional Answer

40. 21,098,000:95,900,000 = 11:50 and 29,040,000:85,900,000 = 1,452:4,295

Practice Masters, p. 58

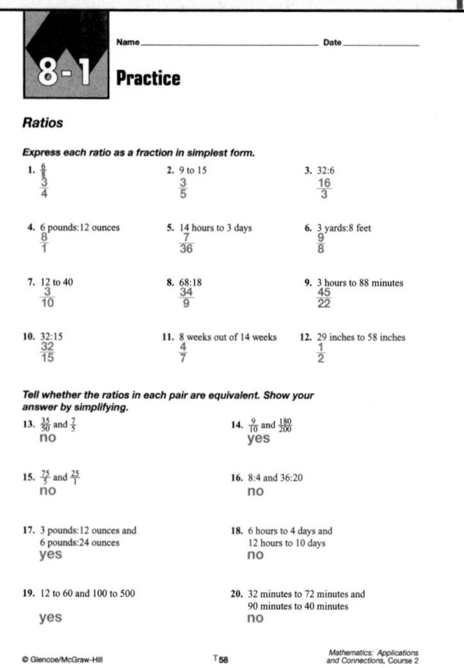

8-1 Practice

Name________________ Date________

Ratios

Express each ratio as a fraction in simplest form.

1. $\frac{6}{8}$ — $\frac{3}{4}$
2. 9 to 15 — $\frac{3}{5}$
3. 32:6 — $\frac{16}{3}$
4. 6 pounds:12 ounces — $\frac{8}{1}$
5. 14 hours to 3 days — $\frac{7}{36}$
6. 3 yards:8 feet — $\frac{9}{8}$
7. 12 to 40 — $\frac{3}{10}$
8. 68:18 — $\frac{34}{9}$
9. 3 hours to 88 minutes — $\frac{45}{22}$
10. 32:15 — $\frac{32}{15}$
11. 8 weeks out of 14 weeks — $\frac{4}{7}$
12. 29 inches to 58 inches — $\frac{1}{2}$

Tell whether the ratios in each pair are equivalent. Show your answer by simplifying.

13. $\frac{35}{50}$ and $\frac{7}{5}$ — no
14. $\frac{9}{10}$ and $\frac{180}{200}$ — yes
15. $\frac{75}{5}$ and $\frac{25}{1}$ — no
16. 8:4 and 36:20 — no
17. 3 pounds:12 ounces and 6 pounds:24 ounces — yes
18. 6 hours to 4 days and 12 hours to 10 days — no
19. 12 to 60 and 100 to 500 — yes
20. 32 minutes to 72 minutes and 90 minutes to 40 minutes — no

 T58 *Mathematics: Applications and Connections, Course 2*

40. ***Entertainment*** In the 1995-1996 television season, the highest-rated show had 21,098,000 of the 95,900,000 television-owning households tuning in. The highest-rated show in the 1985-1986 season had 29,040,000 of the 85,900,000 television-owning households tuned in. Are the ratios of viewers to total TV households for these shows equivalent? Explain. **No; see margin for explanation.**

41. ***Geography*** The Tobu World Square in Nikko, Japan, has 102 of the world's most recognized landmarks recreated at a fraction of their actual size. The table shows the height of the model and the actual height of a few of the buildings. **a.** $\frac{1}{25}$

Landmark	Model Height	Actual Height
Arch de Triomphe, Paris, France	1.98 m	49.5 m
Great Sphinx, Giza, Egypt	2.64 ft	66 ft
Parthenon, Athens, Greece	72 cm	18 m
White House, Washington, D.C.	40.8 in.	85 ft

a. Find the ratio of the model height to the actual height for each building.
b. Are the models all in the same ratio? Explain. **yes; they are all 1:25.**

42. ***Working on the CHAPTER Project*** Refer to the data you have gathered about your family's trash. Write the ratio of the amount of trash in each category to the total amount of trash. **See students' work.**

43. ***Critical Thinking*** Find the next number in the pattern 5,400, 2,700, 900, 225, ____. Explain your reasoning. (*Hint:* Look at the ratios of consecutive numbers.) **45; The ratios of successive terms decrease by 1.**

Mixed Review

44. Find $\frac{4}{5} \div 1\frac{1}{2}$. Write the quotient in simplest form. *(Lesson 7-9)* $\frac{8}{15}$

45. ***Algebra*** Solve $18x = 54$. Check your solution. *(Lesson 6-2)* **3**

46. **Standardized Test Practice** Melissa is writing a report on these events.

Year	Event
1200 B.C.	A calendar of 18 months of 20 days developed by the Olemecs in Mesomenia.
46 B.C.	Julius Caesar reforms the Roman calendar to use 365 days per year, plus one extra day every four years.
A.D. 1948	The atomic clock is invented.
8000 B.C.	The Egyptians use a calendar with 12 months of 30 days each.

If she wants to list the events in order from least recent to most recent, which order should she choose? *(Lesson 5-2)* **B**

A Egyptian calendar, atomic clock, Olemec calendar, Roman calendar
B Egyptian calendar, Olemec calendar, Roman calendar, atomic clock
C Egyptian calendar, Roman calendar, Olemec calendar, atomic clock
D Roman calendar, Olemec calendar, atomic clock, Egyptian calendar

47. ***Patterns*** Determine whether 3,498 is divisible by 2, 3, 4, 5, 6, 9, or 10. *(Lesson 4-1)* **2, 3, 6**

For **Extra Practice,** see page 589.

48. Find 0.65×2.4. *(Lesson 2-4)* **1.56**

Extending the Lesson

Enrichment Masters, p. 58

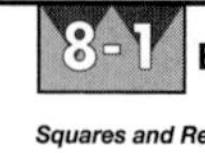

Enrichment

Squares and Rectangles

The perimeter and area of a square are found by using the formulas $P = 4s$ and $A = s^2$. The perimeter and area of a rectangle are found by using formulas $P = 2l + 2w$ and $A = lw$.

Use these formulas to help answer the following questions.

1. A piece of rope 72 inches long must be cut into two pieces. Each piece of rope will be used to form a square. Where should the rope be cut if the perimeter of one square must be $\frac{1}{3}$ of the perimeter of the other square?
18 in. from the end

Activity Have students write a ratio of the number of teachers and the number of students in your class. Then have them write another ratio of the total number of teachers in the school to the total number of students in the school. Ask them to compare the ratios.

8-2 Rates

***What** you'll learn*

You'll learn to determine unit rates.

***When** am I ever going to use this?*

You can use unit rates to compare prices of different brands of soft drinks at the grocery.

Word Wise

rate
unit rate
population density

The first fountains were built in ancient Greece above natural springs. In Renaissance Europe, elaborate pump systems made complicated fountains possible. Many modern fountains use computers to control the water flow and lights. The Prometheus Fountain in Rockefeller Center in New York City is one of the most photographed fountains in the world. It pumps one million gallons of water every 250 minutes.

You often need to compare two quantities with different units. For example, the ratio *one million gallons of water every 250 minutes* compares a number of gallons to a number of minutes. A ratio of this type is called a **rate**.

Rate	A rate is a ratio of two measurements with different units.

How many gallons of water does the Prometheus Fountain pump every minute? To answer this question, you need to find a **unit rate**.

Unit Rate	A unit rate is a rate in which the denominator is 1 unit.

Example 1 **Real World APPLICATION**

Architecture **Refer to the beginning of the lesson. How many gallons of water does the Prometheus Fountain pump every minute?**

Write the rate as a fraction. Then find an equivalent rate with a denominator of 1.

$$\frac{\text{gallons} \rightarrow}{\text{minute} \rightarrow} \quad \frac{1{,}000{,}000}{250} = \frac{1{,}000{,}000 \div 250}{250 \div 250} = \frac{4{,}000}{1}$$

The Prometheus Fountain pumps 4,000 gallons each minute, or 4,000 gallons *per minute.*

8-2 Lesson Notes

Instructional Resources

- *Study Guide Masters,* p. 59
- *Practice Masters,* p. 59
- *Enrichment Masters,* p. 59
- Transparencies 8-2, A and B

CD-ROM Program
- Resource Lesson 8-2

Recommended Pacing	
Standard	Day 4 of 14
Honors	Day 3 of 14
Block	Day 2 of 7

1 FOCUS

5-Minute Check *(Lesson 8-1)*

Express each ratio as a fraction in simplest form.

1. 30 to 12 $\frac{5}{2}$
2. 15:50 $\frac{3}{10}$
3. 2 feet:6 yards $\frac{1}{9}$

Tell whether the ratios are equivalent. Show your answer by simplifying.

4. $\frac{4}{15}$ and $\frac{12}{45}$ Yes; $\frac{4}{15} = \frac{4}{15}$
5. 6 hours to 4 days and 8 hours to 6 days. No; $\frac{6h}{4d} = \frac{1}{16}, \frac{8h}{6d} = \frac{1}{18}$

The 5-Minute Check is also available on **Transparency 8-2A** for this lesson.

Motivating the Lesson

Problem Solving A driver can go the 318 miles from the south rim of the Grand Canyon to Durango, Colorado, in 6 hours. Ask students to describe the average rate of speed for the trip in miles per hour.

Multiple Learning Styles

Kinesthetic Have students work with a partner to find their heart rate in beats per minute. While one student acts as timekeeper, the other finds their own pulse, counts the number of heartbeats in 15 seconds, and with their partner calculates the unit rate.

2 TEACH

Transparency 8-2B contains a teaching aid for this lesson.

Thinking Algebraically Have students write an equation for each example, such as $r = \frac{g}{m}$ for Example 1. Then challenge students to solve the equation for *g*. $g = rm$ Encourage them to rewrite the equations for miles per gallon, miles per hour, price per pound, and meters per second.

In-Class Examples

For Example 1
There are 168 Calories in an 8-ounce serving of yogurt. How many Calories are there in a 1-ounce serving of yogurt?
21 Calories

For Example 2
Express reading 30 pages in 45 minutes as a unit rate.
$\frac{2}{3}$ **page per minute**

For Example 3
Find the population density of a county with 56,000 residents and an area of 636 square miles. **about 88 people per square mile**

Teaching Tip Remind students that if they switch the numerator and denominator when finding a unit rate, it will provide very different information. For example, gallons per mile (instead of mpg) or pounds per dollar (instead of dollars per pound).

3 PRACTICE/APPLY

Check for Understanding

If students need additional practice or instruction after completing Exercises 1–10, one of these options may be helpful.

- Extra Practice, see p. 589
- Reteaching Activity
- *Study Guide Masters,* p. 59
- *Practice Masters,* p. 59

Additional Answers

1a. No; the denominator is not 1.
1b. Yes; the denominator is 1.
1c. Yes; the denominator is 1.

In Example 1, the unit rate is found by writing the rate with a denominator of 1. You can simplify this process by dividing. For example, to find miles per gallon, divide the number of miles driven by the number of gallons of gas used.

Example 2 **Express selling 150 tickets in 5 days as a unit rate.**

Divide the number of tickets by the number of days to find tickets per day.

$150 \div 5 = 30$

The unit rate is 30 tickets per day.

The table shows some of the common unit rates you know.

Unit Rate	Abbreviation
miles per gallon	mi/gal (or mpg)
miles per hour	mi/h (or mph)
price per pound	dollars/lb
meters per second	m/s

The U.S. Bureau of the Census studies the changes in the population. One rate they find is the **population density**, which is the population per square mile.

Example 3 INTEGRATION

Statistics **The U.S. Bureau of the Census recently estimated the population of Virginia to be 6,791,345. If the land area of Virginia is 39,598 square miles, find the population density.**

Explore You know the population and the area of Virginia. You need to find the population density.

Plan Divide the population by the land area to find the population per square mile.

Solve $\frac{6{,}791{,}345 \text{ people}}{39{,}598 \text{ square miles}}$

6791345 [÷] 39598 [=] 171.5072731

Virginia had a population density of about 172 people per square mile.

Examine Check the answer by estimating. The population is about 6,800,000, and the area is about 40,000. So the population density should be about 170 people per square mile. The answer is reasonable.

The country of Monaco, located on the Mediterranean coast near France, has the greatest population density with 41,076 people per square mile. Mongolia in east central Asia has the least at 4 people per square mile.

CHECK FOR UNDERSTANDING

Communicating Mathematics

Read and study the lesson to answer each question.

1. ***State*** whether each rate is a unit rate. Explain why or why not.
   a. 35 miles in 1.5 gallons **a–c. See margin.**
   b. $1.99 per pound
   c. 155 people per square mile

Reteaching the Lesson

Activity Have students model a unit rate, using counters as the numerator and denominator and a pencil as the fraction bar. With 4 counters above the bar and 2 below, tell students to model the unit rate based on 1 group of 2 in the denominator and 2 groups of 2 in the numerator. $\frac{2}{1}$

Error Analysis
Watch for students who have trouble determining which quantities should be the numerator and the denominator in a unit rate.
Prevent by pointing out that the quantity after *per* is the denominator when they read the unit rate as miles *per* gallon.

2. ***Explain*** the difference between a ratio and a rate. **2–3. See margin.**

3. ***You Decide*** Marta says that \$3.99 for a 16-ounce bag of candy is a better buy than \$2.99 for a 12-ounce bag. April disagrees. Who is correct and why?

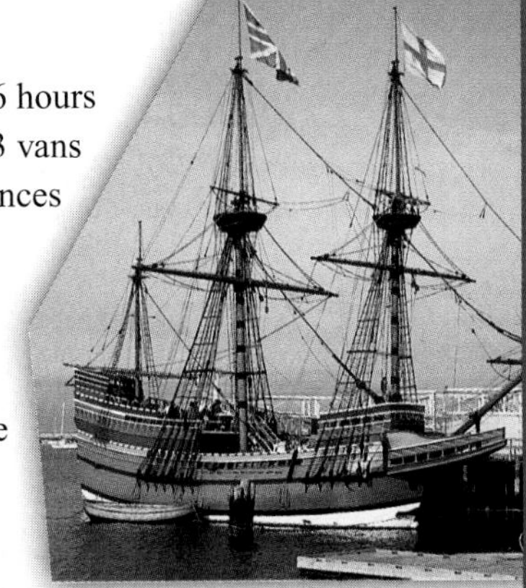

Guided Practice

Express each rate as a unit rate.

4. \$6.99 for 4 pounds
5. 360 miles in 6 hours
6. 410 miles in 16 gallons
7. 45 people in 3 vans
8. \$42 for 8 hours
9. 99¢ for 16 ounces

4. \$1.7475 per pound
5. 60 miles per hour
6. 25.625 miles per gallon
7. 15 people per van
8. \$5.25 per hour
9. 6.1875¢ per ounce

10. ***History*** The *Mayflower* set sail from Plymouth, England, on September 16, 1620 bound for America. The tiny ship completed its 3,000-nautical mile journey 67 days later. On the average, what was the *Mayflower's* unit rate of travel per day? **about 44.8 nautical miles**

EXERCISES

Practice

Express each rate as a unit rate. **17–29. See margin.**

11. 200 miles in 5 hours
12. 2 cups for 36 cookies
13. \$350 for 5 days **\$70 per day**
14. 90,000 seats in 36 sections
15. 18 pounds in 6 weeks
16. 14,960 visitors in 55 days
17. 200 meters in 40 seconds
18. 245,000 people in 1,750 sq mi
19. \$1.89 for 6.5 ounces
20. \$960 for 16 days
21. \$6.20 for 5 pounds
22. 480 miles in 6 days
23. 24 people in 8 cars
24. 1,500 words in 25 minutes
25. 228 feet in 24 seconds
26. 450 Calories in 3 servings
27. 1,080 rotations in 12 minutes
28. 205 students to 8 teachers
29. Find the unit price for a 16-ounce box of cereal that costs \$3.92.
30. What is the population density of a city with 425,000 people in 1,872 square miles? **227.0 people per square mile**

11. 40 miles per hour
12. $\frac{1}{18}$ cup per cookie
14. 2,500 seats per section
15. 3 pounds per week
16. 272 people per day

Applications and Problem Solving

31. ***Manufacturing*** In its first 25 years of business, a company made 54,000,000 of one of the most popular children's toys. On average, how many toys were made each of those years? **2,160,000 toys per year**

32. ***Money Matters*** Aspirin is sold in boxes of 24 for \$3.69, 50 for \$5.49, 100 for \$8.29, and 150 for \$11.99. Which box has the best unit price? **the box with 150**

33. ***Life Science*** The average heart rate of an adult human is 72 beats per minute. For an adult elephant, the average heart rate is 35 beats per minute.
    a. Whose heart beats more times in one hour? **adult human**
    b. Whose heart makes 1,000,000 beats in less time? **adult human**

Assignment Guide

Core: 11–35 odd, 36–39
Enriched: 12–30 even, 31–39

Additional Answers

2. **Sample answer: A ratio is a comparison of two numbers by division. A rate is a comparison of two measurements with unlike units.**
3. **April is correct. The \$3.99 bag has a unit price of about 24.94¢ and the \$2.99 bag has a unit price of about 24.92¢.**
17. **5 meters per second**
18. **140 people per square mile**
19. **about 29.08¢ per ounce**
20. **\$60 per day**
21. **\$1.24 per pound**
22. **80 miles per day**
23. **3 people per car**
24. **60 words per minute**
25. **9.5 feet per second**
26. **150 Calories per serving**
27. **90 rotations per minute**
28. **25.625 students per teacher**
29. **24.5¢ per ounce**

***Study Guide Masters*, p. 59**

Name ______________ Date ______________

Study Guide

Rates

A **rate** is a ratio of two measurements with different units.

Example 1 **Six bottles of mineral water cost \$2.59.**

The ratio 6 bottles for \$2.59 is a rate.

A rate in which the denominator is 1 is a **unit rate.**

Example 2 **Express 6 bottles for \$2.59 as a unit rate.**

$$\frac{price \rightarrow}{bottles \rightarrow}\ \frac{\$2.59}{6} = \frac{\$2.59 \div 6}{6 \div 6} \approx \frac{\$0.4317}{1}$$

The unit rate is about \$0.43 per bottle.

Express each rate as a unit rate.

1. 120 miles in 3 hours — 40 miles per hour
2. 72 apples for 12 people — 6 apples per person
3. \$1 for 3 pounds of bananas — \$0.33 per pound
4. 36 breaths in 3 minutes — 12 breaths per minute
5. \$1.69 for 12 muffins — \$0.14 per muffin
6. 45 kilometers in 5 hours — 9 kilometers per hour
7. 352 steps in 4 minutes — 88 steps per minute
8. \$9.96 for 6 roses — \$1.66 per rose
9. 279 students for 9 teachers — 31 students per teacher
10. 1,520 people in 5 square miles — 304 people per square mile
11. \$450 for 6 days — \$75 per day
12. 7 inches of rain in 4 days — 1.75 inches per day

T59 *Mathematics: Applications and Connections, Course 2*

MathPASS CD-ROM

This CD-ROM offers a complete, self-paced mathematics curriculum. Each lesson includes a pretest, tutorial, guided practice, and posttest. MathPASS Lesson 28 is correlated to this Student Edition lesson.
For Windows & Macintosh

4 ASSESS

Closing Activity

Writing Have students work in groups to list some of their favorite canned or frozen foods and estimate the unit price for each. Then have them find the actual prices and unit prices of these items and compare them to their estimates.

Have students compare the rates of wasted water they calculated. Ask them what the average rate per household would be.

Additional Answer for Math in the Media

3. Sample answer: As the pressure increases or decreases, your ears readjust to equalize the pressure inside and outside of your eardrum.

Practice Masters, p. 59

Name ____________ Date ____________

Practice

Rates

Express each rate as a unit rate.

1. $3.24 for 3 pounds **$1.08 per pound**
2. $75 for 6 compact discs **$12.50 per compact disc**
3. 100 people in 4 rows **25 people per row**
4. 2.5 pounds for $7.50 **$3 per pound**
5. $900 for 5 days **$180 per day**
6. 14 pounds in 7 weeks **2 pounds per week**
7. 385 miles in 7 hours **55 miles per hour**
8. $47.00 for 4 shirts **$11.75 for 1 shirt**
9. 4 cups for 3 recipes **$1\frac{1}{3}$ cups for one recipe**
10. 2,500 tickets in 10 days **250 tickets per day**
11. 9 cups for 3 pounds **3 cups for 1 pound**
12. 12 ounces for 3 cups **4 ounces for 1 cup**
13. 18 people in 6 cars **3 people in one car**
14. $32.00 for 10 floppy disks **$3.20 for one floppy disk**
15. $14.00 for 7 minutes **$2.00 per minute**
16. $12.00 for 3 hours **$4 per hour**
17. The Main Street Market sells oranges at $3.00 for five pounds and apples at $3.99 for three pounds. The Off Street Market sells oranges at $2.59 for four pounds and apples at $1.98 for two pounds.
   a. Find the unit price for each item at each store. **Main Street: oranges are $0.60 per pound and apples are $1.33 per pound. Off Street: oranges are $0.65 per pound and apples are $0.99 per pound.**
   b. Which store has the better buy for oranges? for apples? **Main Street has the better buy for oranges. Off Street has the better buy for apples.**

 T59 *Mathematics: Applications and Connections, Course 2*

Let a faucet slowly drip for 15 minutes into a measuring cup. Then calculate how much water would be wasted per hour and per day for a similar drip.

34. ***Statistics*** Find the population density for each country.

Country	Population	Area (square miles)	people per sq mile
Australia	18,260,863	2,966,200	**6.16**
Belize	219,296	8,867	**24.73**
Japan	125,449,703	145,850	**860.13**
Zaire	46,498,539	905,354	**51.36**

Source: *World Almanac*, 1997

35. ***Critical Thinking*** A train goes 65 miles per hour and travels 320 miles. How many hours will it take for the train to reach its destination? **about 4.9 hours**

Mixed Review

36. Write the ratio 45:81 as a fraction in simplest form. *(Lesson 8-1)* $\frac{5}{9}$
37. ***Civics*** The United States Constitution states that no person who is not at least 25 years old and a citizen of the United States for 7 years may serve as a U.S. Representative. Write an inequality showing the age of a person who may be a U.S. Representative. *(Lesson 6-5)* $a \geq 25$
38. ***Statistics*** Find the mean, mode(s), and median for the data: 2.1, 2.2, 2.2, 2.4, 2.4, 2.4, 2.7, 2.8, 3.0, 3.0, 3.4. *(Lesson 3-4)* **2.6; 2.4; 2.4**

39. **Standardized Test Practice** Which is equivalent to 6×8^4? *(Lesson 1-4)* **D**
   A 6×64
   B $48 \times 48 \times 48 \times 48$
   C $6 \times 8 \times 6 \times 8 \times 6 \times 8 \times 6 \times 8$
   D $6 \times 8 \times 8 \times 8 \times 8$

For **Extra Practice,** see page 589.

MATH IN THE MEDIA

B.C.
by johnny hart
I'M BORED.
HEY, HERE'S SOMETHING INTERESTING!
THERE'S 14.7 POUNDS OF PRESSURE ON EVERY SQUARE INCH OF YOUR BODY!
I'M DEPRESSED.
©1997 CREATORS SYNDICATE, INC
1-27

1. Is the rate stated a unit rate? Explain. **Yes; the denominator is 1.**
2. In 20 feet of freshwater, a scuba diver whose body has an area of 2,880 square inches experiences about 67,104 pounds of pressure. Find the unit rate. **23.3 pounds per sq in.**
3. Research what pressure has to do with your ears popping when you drive up or down a big hill. **See margin.**

Extending the Lesson

Enrichment Masters, p. 59

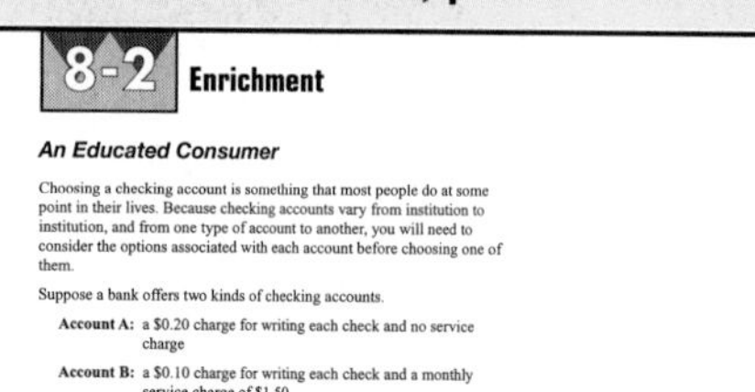
8-2 **Enrichment**

An Educated Consumer

Choosing a checking account is something that most people do at some point in their lives. Because checking accounts vary from institution to institution, and from one type of account to another, you will need to consider the options associated with each account before choosing one of them.

Suppose a bank offers two kinds of checking accounts.

Account A: a $0.20 charge for writing each check and no service charge

Account B: a $0.10 charge for writing each check and a monthly service charge of $1.50

MATH IN THE MEDIA

For Exercise 2, ask students how many pounds of pressure the scuba diver would experience on his or her whole body while on land. **42,336 pounds**

8-3 Solving Proportions

What **you'll learn**

You'll learn to solve proportions.

When **am I ever going to use this?**

You can use proportions to change the number of servings made using a recipe.

Word Wise

proportion
cross products

How much lemonade can you drink when you're really thirsty? How about 2,250 liters! In 1994, a company made a giant bottle of lemonade to mark its 200th year. It held 2,250 liters or 9,000 servings of lemonade! A standard bottle holds 2 liters or 8 servings of lemonade.

If you find the ratios of the number of liters to the number of servings of lemonade in each bottle, how do they compare?

Giant bottle: $\frac{\text{liters}}{\text{servings}} \rightarrow \frac{2{,}250}{9{,}000} = \frac{2{,}250 \div 2{,}250}{9{,}000 \div 2{,}250} = \frac{1}{4}$

Standard bottle: $\frac{\text{liters}}{\text{servings}} \rightarrow \frac{2}{8} = \frac{2 \div 2}{8 \div 2} = \frac{1}{4}$

The ratios $\frac{2{,}250}{9{,}000}$ and $\frac{2}{8}$ are equivalent. So, we can write $\frac{2{,}250}{9{,}000} = \frac{2}{8}$. This equation is an example of a **proportion**.

Proportion	
Words:	A proportion is an equation that shows that two ratios are equivalent.
Symbols:	**Arithmetic** $\frac{2}{3} = \frac{4}{6}$ **Algebra** $\frac{a}{b} = \frac{c}{d}, b \neq 0, d \neq 0$

Study Hint

Reading Math $\frac{2}{3} = \frac{8}{12}$ is sometimes read as 2 is to 3 as 8 is to 12.

When two ratios form a proportion, the **cross products** are equal. The cross products in the proportion below are 2×12 and 3×8.

$\frac{2}{3} = \frac{8}{12}$ 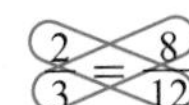 $2 \times 12 = 24$, $3 \times 8 = 24$

Property of Proportions	
Words:	The cross products of a proportion are equal.
Symbols:	If $\frac{a}{b} = \frac{c}{d}$, then $ad = bc$. $(b \neq 0, d \neq 0)$

You can use cross products to find a missing term in a proportion. This is known as *solving the proportion*. Solving a proportion is similar to solving an equation.

Multiple Learning Styles

Naturalist Have students collect leaves from three kinds of trees, measure the length and width of each leaf, and record these measurements as the ratio $\frac{\ell}{w}$. Ask students if they think the ratio of length and width of a leaf is equal to the ratio of height and width of the tree. Have them measure the widths of the 3 trees, estimate the heights, and write these measurements as the ratio $\frac{h}{w}$. Compare the ratio of each leaf's length and width to the ratio of the tree's height and width to see if they make a proportion.

8-3 Lesson Notes

Instructional Resources

- *Study Guide Masters,* p. 60
- *Practice Masters,* p. 60
- *Enrichment Masters,* p. 60
- Transparencies 8-3, A and B
- *Assessment and Evaluation Masters,* p. 211
- *Science and Math Lab Manual,* pp. 37–40

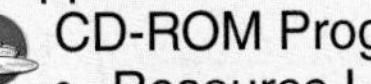 CD-ROM Program
- Resource Lesson 8-3
- Interactive Lesson 8-3

Recommended Pacing	
Standard	Day 5 of 14
Honors	Days 4 & 5 of 14
Block	Day 3 of 7

1 FOCUS

5-Minute Check *(Lesson 8-2)*

Express each rate as a unit rate.

1. 315 miles in 7 hours **45 mph**
2. \$42.00 for 6 tapes **\$7.00 per tape**
3. 1,500 tickets in 6 days **250 tickets per day**
4. Mike's Market sells Kittie Treats at \$2.00 for 5 boxes. At Donna's Deli, a 6-pack of the same product sells for \$2.30. Which store has the better unit price? **Donna's Deli**

The 5-Minute Check is also available on **Transparency 8-3A** for this lesson.

Motivating the Lesson

Hands-On Activity Provide students with centimeter cubes. If each cube represents 25 students, have students build a model to represent 250 students, another for 500 students, and another for 1,000 students.

2 TEACH

Transparency 8-3B contains a teaching aid for this lesson.

Using Problem Solving Tell students a photograph 3 inches wide and 5 inches long is being enlarged to fit in a frame $7\frac{1}{2}$ inches wide. How long should the frame be? **$12\frac{1}{2}$ in.**

In-Class Examples

For Example 1

Solve $\frac{n}{5} = \frac{36}{60}$. **3**

For Example 2

Charlotte made a pottery bowl $2\frac{1}{2}$ inches deep and 6 inches wide. She wants to make another bowl in the same shape but $3\frac{3}{4}$ inches deep. How wide should the bowl be? **9 inches**

Teaching Tip Encourage students to look for a ratio that can be simplified before solving the proportion.

Examples

INTEGRATION

1 Algebra Solve $\frac{n}{7} = \frac{18}{42}$.

$\frac{n}{7} = \frac{18}{42}$

$n \times 42 = 7 \times 18$ *Find the cross products.*

$42n = 126$

$\frac{42n}{42} = \frac{126}{42}$ *Divide each side by 42.*

$n = 3$

The solution is 3.

APPLICATION

2 Models A toy car is 7.6 centimeters long and 3.2 centimeters wide. A real car is 4.788 meters long. How wide is the real car?

Explore The length and width of the model car are 7.6 centimeters and 3.2 centimeters. The length of the real car is 4.788 meters or 478.8 centimeters.

Plan Use w to represent the width of the real car. Then you can write a proportion.

	Model		**Real Car**	
length →	7.6	=	478.8	← *length*
width →	3.2		w	← *width*

Find the cross products. Then solve the proportion.

Solve $\frac{7.6}{3.2} = \frac{478.8}{w}$

$7.6w = 3.2 \times 478.8$ *Find the cross products.*

$w = \frac{3.2 \times 478.8}{7.6}$

3.2 [×] 478.8 [÷] 7.6 [=] 201.6

The width of the real car is 201.6 centimeters or 2.016 meters.

Examine Express each ratio as a decimal and compare.

$\frac{7.6}{3.2}$ → 7.6 [÷] 3.2 [=] 2.375

$\frac{478.8}{201.6}$ → 478.8 [÷] 201.6 [=] 2.375

Because the decimals are equal, the ratios are equivalent. So, 201.6 centimeters or 2.016 meters is correct.

Study Hint

Problem Solving More than one proportion can be used to solve a problem. Here's another proportion for Example 2.

	length		*width*	
model→	7.6	=	3.2	←model
real car→	478.8		w	←real car

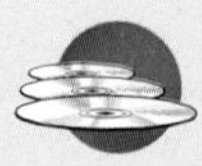

MathPASS CD-ROM

This CD-ROM offers a complete, self-paced mathematics curriculum. Each lesson includes a pretest, tutorial, guided practice, and posttest. MathPASS Lesson 29 is correlated to this Student Edition lesson.

For Windows & Macintosh

CHECK FOR UNDERSTANDING

Communicating Mathematics

Read and study the lesson to answer each question. **1–2. See margin.**

1. ***Explain*** how you can determine whether two ratios are equivalent.
2. ***Demonstrate*** how to solve $\frac{8}{12} = \frac{a}{3}$.

Guided Practice

Solve each proportion.

3. $\frac{6}{9} = \frac{4}{x}$ **6**
4. $\frac{2}{6} = \frac{5}{n}$ **15**
5. $\frac{a}{8} = \frac{3}{4}$ **6**
6. $\frac{10}{y} = \frac{2.5}{4}$ **16**
7. a. If there are 12 wheels, how many bicycles are there? **6 bicycles**
   b. If there are 35 toes, how many feet are there? **7 feet**

EXERCISES

Practice

Solve each proportion. **18. 200**

8. $\frac{2}{3} = \frac{16}{n}$ **24**
9. $\frac{a}{36} = \frac{15}{24}$ **22.5**
10. $\frac{15}{9} = \frac{10}{z}$ **6**
11. $\frac{18}{27} = \frac{t}{3}$ **2**
12. $\frac{3}{d} = \frac{9}{5}$ **$1\frac{2}{3}$**
13. $\frac{8}{20} = \frac{30}{x}$ **75**
14. $\frac{n}{12} = \frac{12}{4}$ **36**
15. $\frac{5}{g} = \frac{6}{3}$ **2.5**
16. $\frac{2.6}{13} = \frac{8}{m}$ **40**
17. $\frac{21}{b} = \frac{10}{20}$ **42**
18. $\frac{6}{1} = \frac{1{,}200}{t}$
19. $\frac{0.2}{y} = \frac{3}{5}$ **$\frac{1}{3}$**
20. In the sixth grade, the ratio of boys to girls is 5:6. If there are 88 sixth-grade students, how many are boys? **40**
21. Nikki can word process 7 words in 6 seconds. At this rate, how many words can she word process in 3 minutes? **210 words**

Applications and Problem Solving

22. ***Models*** The first jumbo jet was the Boeing 747, which is 70.5 meters long. The wingspan of a 747 is 60 meters. A model 747 has a wingspan of 80 centimeters. What should the length of the model be? **94 cm**

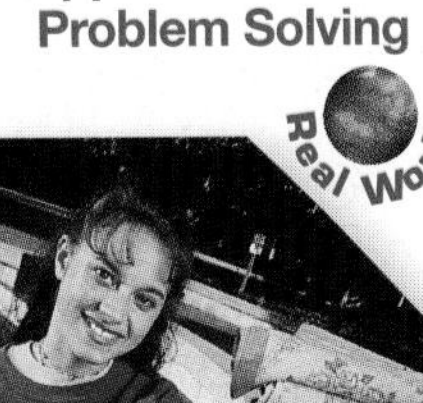

Amber Coffman

23. ***Cooking*** Every Saturday, Amber Coffman and her friends make 600 sack lunches for the homeless in Glen Burnie, Maryland.
   a. Use proportions to find the amount of each ingredient Amber would need to make 600 tuna pitas. **See margin.**
   b. ***Write a Problem*** that can be solved using a proportion and the information in the recipe. **See students' work.**

Tuna Pitas

$6\frac{1}{8}$ oz tuna	2 pita breads
$\frac{1}{4}$ tsp dill	$\frac{1}{3}$ c plain yogurt
$\frac{1}{8}$ c diced celery	$1\frac{1}{2}$ tsp mustard
4 lettuce leaves	1 tomato, sliced

Combine tuna, yogurt, celery, mustard and dill. Line pitas with lettuce leaves and tomatoes. Divide tuna mixture among pitas. (Serves 4.)

Reteaching the Lesson

Activity Have students find the factor that relates the two ratios making up a proportion. For example, in $\frac{2}{5} = \frac{a}{15}$, $5 \times 3 = 15$, so to find a, multiply 2×3. Therefore $a = 6$.

Error Analysis

Watch for students who forget to divide once they cross multiply to solve a proportion.

Prevent by reminding students that a proportion, being an equation, is not solved until the variable is alone on one side of the equals sign.

3 PRACTICE/APPLY

Check for Understanding

If students need additional practice or instruction after completing Exercises 1–7, one of these options may be helpful.

- Extra Practice, p. 590
- Reteaching Activity
- *Study Guide Masters,* p. 60
- *Practice Masters,* p. 60
- Interactive Mathematics Tools Software

Assignment Guide

Core: 9–23 odd, 25–28
Enriched: 8–20 even, 22–28

Additional Answers

1. **Compare the cross products. If they are equal, the ratios are equivalent.**
2. $$\frac{8}{12} = \frac{a}{3}$$
   $$8 \times 3 = 12a$$
   $$24 = 12a$$
   $$2 = a$$

23a. **tuna: $918\frac{3}{4}$ oz; pita breads: 300; dill: $37\frac{1}{2}$ t; yogurt: 50 c; celery: $18\frac{3}{4}$ c; mustard: 225 t; lettuce: 600 leaves; tomatoes: 150**

***Study Guide Masters,* p. 60**

Name______________ Date______________

Study Guide

Solving Proportions

A **proportion** is an equation that shows that two ratios are equivalent. The **cross products** of a proportion are equal. If one term of a proportion is not known, you can use cross products to find the term. This is called **solving the proportion.**

Example 1 Solve $\frac{2}{3} = \frac{f}{18}$.

$\frac{2}{3} = \frac{f}{18}$

$2 \times 18 = 3 \times f$ *Find the cross products.*

$36 = 3f$

$\frac{36}{3} = \frac{3f}{3}$ *Divide each side by 3.*

$12 = \frac{3}{f}$

Example 2 Solve $\frac{r}{24} = \frac{7}{8}$.

$\frac{r}{24} = \frac{7}{8}$

$r \times 8 = 24 \times 7$ *Find the cross products.*

$8r = 168$

$\frac{8r}{8} = \frac{168}{8}$ *Divide each side by 8.*

$r = 21$

Solve each proportion.

1. $\frac{2}{n} = \frac{5}{10}$ **4**
2. $\frac{5}{8} = \frac{m}{24}$ **15**
3. $\frac{12}{20} = \frac{k}{15}$ **9**
4. $\frac{y}{7} = \frac{7}{49}$ **1**
5. $\frac{21}{f} = \frac{9}{12}$ **28**
6. $\frac{10}{12} = \frac{15}{v}$ **18**
7. $\frac{3.5}{m} = \frac{16}{32}$ **7**
8. $\frac{6}{20} = \frac{n}{50}$ **15**
9. $\frac{75}{r} = \frac{6}{2}$ **25**
10. $\frac{f}{0.8} = \frac{2}{8}$ **0.2**
11. $\frac{15}{120} = \frac{t}{16}$ **2**
12. $\frac{7}{9} = \frac{c}{36}$ **28**

 T60 *Mathematics: Applications and Connections,* Course 2

4 ASSESS

Closing Activity

Writing Have students write and solve a proportion to find the number of people who voted for Ms. Gomez in a mayoral election, given that two-thirds of the 375 voters voted for her. **250**

Chapter 8, Quiz A (Lessons 8-1 through 8-3) is available in the *Assessment and Evaluation Masters,* p. 211.

***Practice Masters,* p. 60**

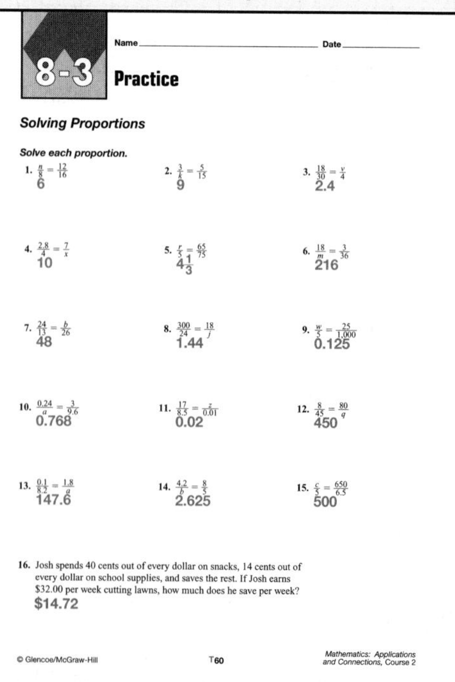

Name ____________ Date ____________

8-3 Practice

Solving Proportions

Solve each proportion.

1. $\frac{n}{8} = \frac{12}{16}$ **6**
2. $\frac{3}{k} = \frac{5}{15}$ **9**
3. $\frac{18}{30} = \frac{y}{4}$ **2.4**
4. $\frac{2.8}{4} = \frac{7}{x}$ **10**
5. $\frac{r}{5} = \frac{65}{75}$ **$4\frac{1}{3}$**
6. $\frac{18}{m} = \frac{3}{36}$ **216**
7. $\frac{24}{13} = \frac{b}{26}$ **48**
8. $\frac{300}{24} = \frac{18}{j}$ **1.44**
9. $\frac{w}{5} = \frac{25}{1{,}000}$ **0.125**
10. $\frac{0.24}{a} = \frac{3}{9.6}$ **0.768**
11. $\frac{17}{8.5} = \frac{z}{0.01}$ **0.02**
12. $\frac{8}{45} = \frac{80}{q}$ **450**
13. $\frac{0.1}{8.2} = \frac{1.8}{a}$ **147.6**
14. $\frac{4.2}{b} = \frac{8}{5}$ **2.625**
15. $\frac{c}{5} = \frac{650}{6.5}$ **500**
16. Josh spends 40 cents out of every dollar on snacks, 14 cents out of every dollar on school supplies, and saves the rest. If Josh earns $32.00 per week cutting lawns, how much does he save per week? **$14.72**

 T60 *Mathematics: Applications and Connections, Course 2*

24. ***Money*** Suppose that one French franc is worth 20¢. In Paris, France, a quart of milk costs 9 francs. In Los Angeles, a quart of milk cost $1.65. In which city is the quart of milk more expensive? **Paris**

25. ***Critical Thinking*** In some proportions, such as $\frac{3}{6} = \frac{6}{12}$, the same number appears in two of the diagonal positions. In that case, the repeated number is called the *geometric mean* of the other two. Find a pair of numbers other than 3 and 12 for which 6 is the geometric mean. **Sample answers: 1 and 36; 2 and 18; 4 and 9**

Mixed Review

26. ***Travel*** On her summer vacation, Luanda drove 250 miles in 5 hours on the first day. She continued driving at the same rate the second day and drove for 8 hours. How many miles did Luanda drive the second day of her vacation? *(Lesson 8-2)* **400 miles**

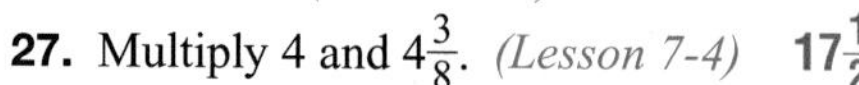

27. Multiply 4 and $4\frac{3}{8}$. *(Lesson 7-4)* **$17\frac{1}{2}$**

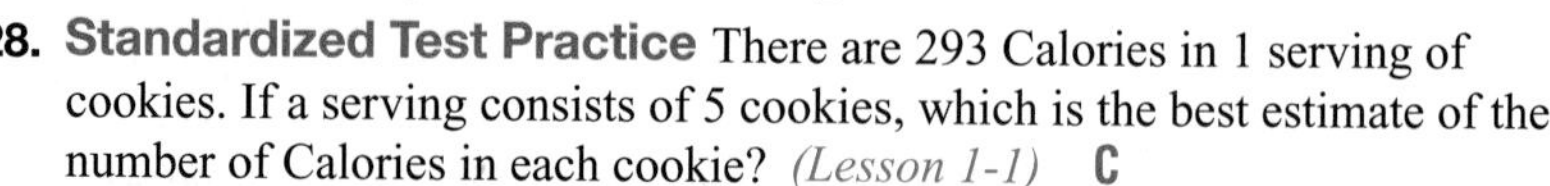

28. **Standardized Test Practice** There are 293 Calories in 1 serving of cookies. If a serving consists of 5 cookies, which is the best estimate of the number of Calories in each cookie? *(Lesson 1-1)* **C**

A 20 **B** 40 **C** 60 **D** 80 **E** 100

For **Extra Practice,** see page 590.

Left from the Start

Math Skill
Solving Proportions

Get Ready This game is for two players. spinner counters

Get Set Copy the game board shown onto one or more pieces of paper. Make sure that a counter will fit inside each square on the board.

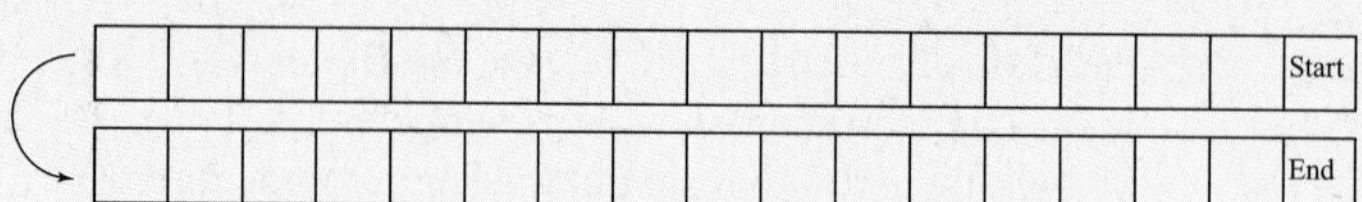

Label equal sections of a spinner with 10, 12, 15, 20, 24, 30, 40, and 60.

Go

- Each player places a counter on the *Start* square.
- One player spins the spinner and substitutes the number on the spinner for x in the proportion $\frac{y}{15} = \frac{8}{x}$. The player solves the proportion and moves his or her counter y spaces. Then the other player spins the spinner and substitutes the number on the spinner for y in the given proportion. He or she solves the proportion and moves his or her counter x spaces.
- Trade roles and continue play. The first person to reach the *End* square wins the round. It is not necessary to land on *End* with an exact roll.

Visit www.glencoe.com/sec/math/mac/mathnet for more games.

Extending the Lesson

***Enrichment Masters,* p. 60**

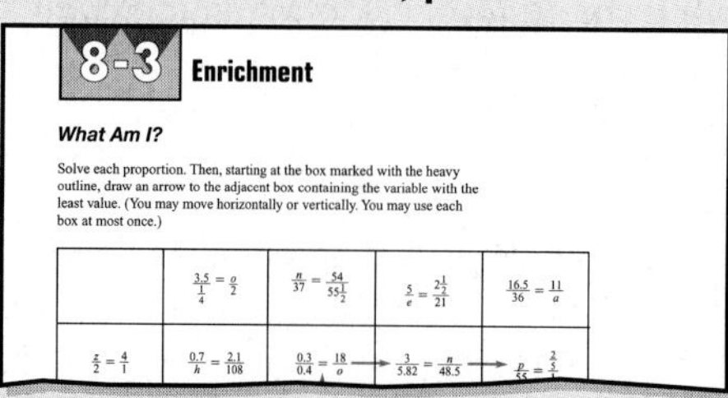

8-3 Enrichment

What Am I?

Solve each proportion. Then, starting at the box marked with the heavy outline, draw an arrow to the adjacent box containing the variable with the least value. (You may move horizontally or vertically. You may use each box at most once.)

	$\frac{3.5}{\frac{1}{4}} = \frac{o}{2}$	$\frac{n}{37} = \frac{54}{55\frac{1}{2}}$	$\frac{5}{e} = \frac{2\frac{1}{2}}{21}$	$\frac{16.5}{36} = \frac{11}{a}$
$\frac{z}{2} = \frac{4}{1}$	$\frac{0.7}{h} = \frac{2.1}{108}$	$\frac{0.3}{0.4} = \frac{18}{o}$ →	$\frac{3}{5.82} = \frac{n}{48.5}$ →	$\frac{p}{55} = \frac{2}{5}$

You can also use the Spinner Tool on the CD-ROM Program to simulate this game. *Additional resources for this game can be found on pages 45–46 of the **Classroom Games.***

COOPERATIVE LEARNING

8-3B Wildlife Sampling

A Follow-Up of Lesson 8-3

- small bowl
- dried beans
- markers
- paper cup

In planning for the care of a park or wildlife preserve, it is often important for naturalists to know the size of an animal population. One method used to estimate this is the *capture-recapture* technique. You will model this technique to see how naturalists make reasonable estimates. Dried beans represent deer in a forest and a bowl will represent the forest.

TRY THIS

Work in groups.

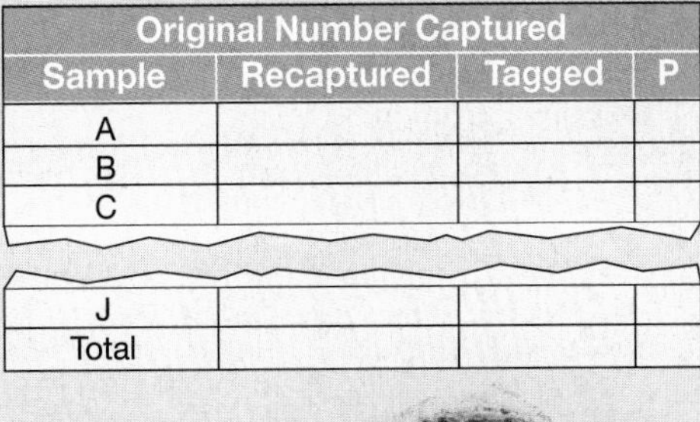

Original Number Captured			
Sample	Recaptured	Tagged	P
A			
B			
C			
J			
Total			

Step 1 Fill a small bowl with dried beans.

Step 2 Use the paper cup to scoop some of the beans. Count the beans selected and record in a table like the one at the right. These represent the captured deer. Mark each bean with an X on both sides.

Step 3 Return the beans to the bowl and mix well with the rest.

Step 4 Scoop another cupful of beans from the bowl. Count the beans selected. This is the first *sample* which represents the deer that are recaptured. Count the beans marked with an X. This is the tagged deer recaptured. Record both numbers.

Step 5 Use the proportion below to estimate the total number of beans in the bowl. Then record the value of *P.*

$$\frac{\text{original number captured}}{\text{total population}} = \frac{\text{tagged in sample}}{\text{recaptured}}$$

Step 6 Return the beans to the bowl.

Step 7 Repeat Steps 4–6 nine times.

ON YOUR OWN

1. Find the average of the estimates. Do you think this is a good estimate of the number of beans in the bowl? Explain your reasoning.
2. Count the number of beans in the bowl. How does the actual count compare to the estimates? **See students' work.**
3. Why is it important to return the beans to the bowl and mix well after taking each sample? **1, 3, 4. See margin.**
4. What would happen to the estimates if one or more of the marks wore off during sampling? What does this represent with deer in the field?

Have students write a paragraph describing the capture-recapture process and its results.

Additional Answers

1. See students' work.
3. The sample needs to be a random handful of the total number of beans.
4. The estimates would decrease. Some of the deer could lose their tags.

8-3B HANDS-ON LAB Notes

GET READY

Objective Students use the capture-recapture technique to estimate.

Optional Resources
Hands-On Lab Masters
- worksheet, p. 55

MANAGEMENT TIPS

Recommended Time
30 minutes

Getting Started Ask students how they would estimate the number of fish in an aquarium if the fish move around too fast to count. Have students imagine that a certain number of fish are distinctively marked, and with a net they randomly captured a few fish. Then the ratio of marked fish captured to the total number captured would roughly equal the ratio of the number captured to the total.

The **Activity** simulates the capture-recapture technique used in estimating wildlife populations. After several trials, ask students how a greater number of trials might affect their estimates. Encourage them to repeat the process 10 or more times.

ASSESS

Have students complete Exercises 1–4. Watch for students who expect every sample to be an accurate representation of the total population, or who see a sample as no indication of the total population. Remind both to observe the effects of repeated trials on the average.

8-4A THINKING LAB Notes

Objective Students solve problems by drawing a diagram.

Recommended Pacing	
Standard	Day 6 of 14
Honors	Day 6 of 14
Block	Day 3 of 7

1 FOCUS

Getting Started If Amanda's cat has a litter of 4 kittens and 2 are females, each of which has a litter of 4 kittens, and 2 of each of those litters are females who later have litters of 4 kittens, how many cats will Amanda have? 29

2 TEACH

Teaching Tip Guide students to see that different kinds of diagrams can be used to solve different problems. Ask what sorts of people might use this strategy to do their jobs. Encourage them to use their imagination when choosing a diagram.

In-Class Example
There is going to be a single-elimination chess tournament with 32 entrants. Figure out how many matches must be played to determine a winner. 31

Additional Answer

2. **Answers will vary. Sample answer: It is often easier to solve a problem by drawing a diagram than by writing an equation or solving mentally.**

PROBLEM SOLVING

8-4A Draw a Diagram

A Preview of Lesson 8-4

Charmaine and Lisa are the president and vice-president of the Grove City 4-H Club. They are discussing the club's service project to shovel snow for elderly people in their community. When it snows, they need to organize quickly. Let's listen in!

Lisa: We have 40 members in the club. If you and I are the only ones calling members, it will take forever to get our act together. I think we should call a few and then have them call some to get everyone together faster.

Charmaine: Good idea. We won't have to say much on each call, so let's guess that it will take about 1 minute each. How about if I call you, the secretary and the treasurer? Then each of you can call three people, and so on.

Lisa: That makes sense. If I draw a diagram we can make sure everyone gets called and figure out how long the calling will take.

Charmaine: That looks good! And there are 40 people on it. At a minute a call, each person will be on the phone about 3 minutes. So each level of the tree is 3 minutes.

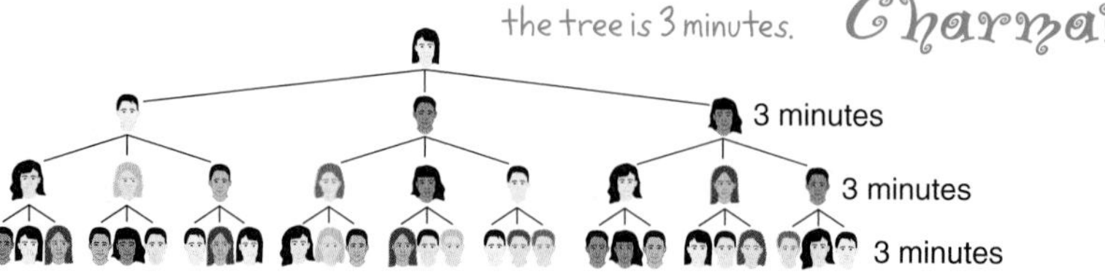

Lisa: So, it's 3 × 3 or 9 minutes to activate the troops!

Charmaine: Not bad! Operation "Snow Shovel" is ready for duty!

THINK ABOUT IT

Work with a partner.

1. ***Tell*** how many people are contacted in the last 3 minutes of the telephone tree. **27 people**
2. ***Write*** one or two sentences explaining why **drawing a diagram** can be a useful problem-solving strategy. **See margin.**
3. ***Draw*** a diagram to find the number of people that could be contacted if the telephone tree was extended to 12 minutes. **121 people**

Reteaching the Lesson

Activity Discuss how drawing diagrams, such as a football coach might diagram a play, can be an effective strategy for solving problems. Ask students to describe situations in which they or other family members have drawn diagrams to solve problems, such as building, plumbing, or wiring projects.

For **Extra Practice,** see page 590.

ON YOUR OWN

4. The last step of the 4-step plan for problem solving is to *examine* the solution. ***Describe*** one or two things that Lisa and Charmaine assumed when they made the telephone tree that could change the solution if the assumptions were wrong. **See margin.**

5. A map is a diagram of a location. ***Draw*** a map of your route to school. **See students' work.**

MIXED PROBLEM SOLVING

STRATEGIES
- Look for a pattern.
- Solve a simpler problem.
- Act it out.
- Guess and check.
- Draw a diagram.
- Make a chart.
- Work backward.

Solve. Use any strategy.

6. ***Money Matters*** Jill bought some folders for 79¢ each and some spiral-bound notebooks for $1.19 each. If she spent $5.54, how many of each item did Jill buy? **See margin.**

7. ***Education*** The scores on a Social Studies test are found by adding 8 points for each correct answer, subtracting 4 points for each incorrect answer, and subtracting 2 points for each unanswered question. There were 15 questions on the test. If Kenji's score was 86, how many of his answers were correct, wrong, and blank? **12 right, 2 wrong, 1 unanswered**

8. ***Standardized Test Practice*** If 4 computers are needed for every 6 students in a class, how many computers are needed for a class of 54 students? **C**

   A 18 **B** 27
   C 36 **D** 5

9. ***Civics*** Chief Justice Melville W. Fuller began the tradition of the "conference handshake" in the U.S. Supreme Court in the late 1800s. Before they take their seats, each justice shakes hands with the others to show that they have a common purpose. If there are nine justices, how many handshakes take place? **36 handshakes**

10. ***Sports*** Sixteen softball teams are participating in a single-elimination tournament; that means that if a team loses one game it is eliminated. How many games will the winning team have played? **4 games**

11. ***Physics*** A ball is dropped from 10 feet above the ground. It hits the ground and bounces up half as high as it fell.
    a. What height does the ball reach on the fourth bounce? **a–b. See margin.**
    b. Find the total distance up and down that the ball has traveled when it hits the ground the fifth time.

12. ***Puzzles*** Copy the grid below. Start at the 0 and draw a line 1 square long to a 1. Then continue the line 2 squares to a 2, three squares to a 3, and so on. You can move horizontally and vertically, but not diagonally. Find a path to the 8 without revisiting any square.

0	1	3	2	5	5	4	6
1	3	2	4	3	5	6	4
3	3	4	4	5	6	4	5
5	3	5	4	5	7	5	6
5	4	5	6	4	5	6	7
7	7	4	5	7	5	6	7
6	7	4	6	5	4	6	5
6	7	6	7	5	7	6	8

3 PRACTICE/APPLY

Check for Understanding

Use the results of Exercise 3 to determine if students understand how to use a diagram to solve a problem. In Exercise 5 suggest to students that their route to school does not necessarily have to be accurately drawn to scale.

Extra Practice If students need additional practice in problem solving, extra practice is available on the following pages.
- Draw a Diagram, see p. 590
- Mixed Problem Solving, see pp. 605–606

Assignment Guide

All: 4–12

4 ASSESS

Closing Activity

Writing Have students draw a diagram to solve this problem. *Jack's house, the post office, the bank, and the library are on the same road. Jack lives 3.5 miles from the library, which is 2.25 miles farther from his house than the bank. The post office is between the bank and the library and 0.75 mile from the bank. How far is it from Jack's house to the post office?* **2 miles**

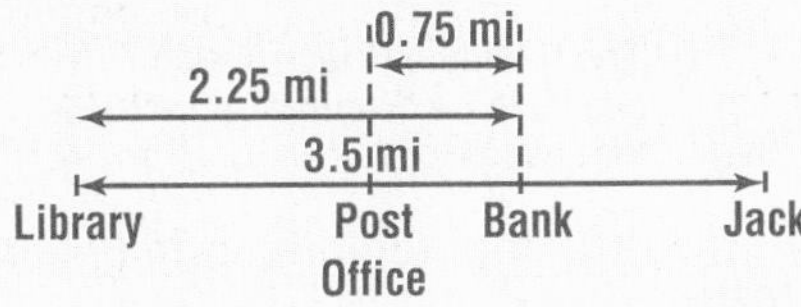

Additional Answers

4. Sample answers: each call takes 1 minute; none of the calls result in a busy signal. If either of these assumptions are wrong, the calling would take more time.

6. 4 folders and 2 spiral-bound notebooks

11a. $\frac{5}{8}$ feet

11b. $28\frac{3}{4}$ feet or 345 inches

Extending the Lesson

Activity Provide partners with a street map of a nearby neighborhood. Have them imagine that a treasure is buried on one of the street corners. Have each set of partners choose a location for the treasure, write clues for finding it, and trade clues with another pair of students. Both sets of partners must then make a diagram and use the clues to find the treasure.

Sample problem: *Suppose the choice is a street corner with a gas station on it, 4 blocks north and 2 blocks east of the school. There is a 4-way stop sign and a house on each of the other 3 corners. Possible clues are:*
- *The treasure is near a school.*
- *You must stop here.*
- *There is food for cars here.*

8-4 Lesson Notes

Instructional Resources

- *Study Guide Masters,* p. 61
- *Practice Masters,* p. 61
- *Enrichment Masters,* p. 61
- Transparencies 8-4, A and B
- *Hands-On Lab Masters,* p. 79
- *School to Career Masters,* p. 21

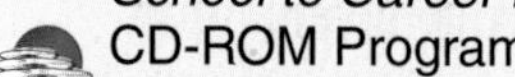

CD-ROM Program
- Resource Lesson 8-4
- Extended Activity 8-4

Recommended Pacing	
Standard	Day 7 of 14
Honors	Day 7 of 14
Block	Day 4 of 7

1 FOCUS

5-Minute Check
(Lesson 8-3)

Solve each proportion.

1. $\frac{4}{9} = \frac{6}{n}$ $13\frac{1}{2}$
2. $\frac{26}{m} = \frac{2}{3}$ 39
3. $\frac{900}{600} = \frac{x}{14}$ 21
4. $\frac{y}{40} = \frac{2.5}{8}$ 12.5
5. Elena saves 15 cents of every dollar of her weekly allowance. She gets $5.00. How much does she save each week? $0.75

The 5-Minute Check is also available on **Transparency 8-4A** for this lesson.

Motivating the Lesson

Hands-On Activity Ask students to draw a "bird's-eye view" of the school building and school yard showing the relationship of their sizes. Have them guess how much larger the actual school yard is than their drawings and convert that guess to a scale (for example, 1 foot = 100 yards).

8-4 Scale Drawings

What you'll learn
You'll learn to solve problems involving scale drawings.

When am I ever going to use this?
You can use a scale to find distances between cities on a map.

Word Wise
scale drawing
scale

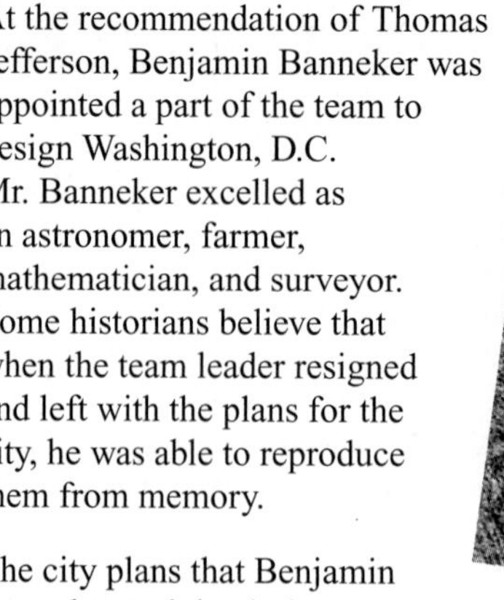

At the recommendation of Thomas Jefferson, Benjamin Banneker was appointed a part of the team to design Washington, D.C. Mr. Banneker excelled as an astronomer, farmer, mathematician, and surveyor. Some historians believe that when the team leader resigned and left with the plans for the city, he was able to reproduce them from memory.

The city plans that Benjamin Banneker and the design team developed are an example of a **scale drawing**. A scale drawing is used to represent something that is too large or too small for an actual-size drawing to be useful.

You have probably used a map before. A map is a scale drawing. The **scale** on a map is the ratio of the distance on the map to the actual distance. When you know the scale of a map, you can find actual distances by writing and solving proportions.

Example 1 — Real World APPLICATION

Travel **Set-Su and Amy are helping plan a field trip to the Johnson Space Center in Houston from their school in Austin. They measured the distance their map shows from Austin to Houston as about 3.25 inches. The scale on the map says that 1 inch represents 55 miles. What is the actual distance between the cities?**

Let n represent the actual distance between the cities. Write and solve a proportion.

	key		Austin to Houston	
map distance → *actual distance* →	$\frac{1 \text{ inch}}{55 \text{ miles}}$	=	$\frac{3.25 \text{ inches}}{n \text{ miles}}$	← *map distance* ← *actual distance*

$1 \times n = 55 \times 3.25$ *Estimate: $60 \times 3 = 180$*

$n = 178.75$

The actual distance between Austin and Houston is about 179 miles.

Classroom Vignette

"Students use centimeter grid paper to make scale drawings of their 'dream house.' The first drawing's scale is 1 cm = 3 ft. Then they make a second drawing with a scale of 1 cm = 10 ft. They can include anything they want, but the square footage of each area has to be listed and there must be at least one bathroom."

Greg Rusnak

Greg Rusnak, Teacher
Madison Middle School
Madison, OH

2 **Architecture** **Architects draw buildings to scale in blueprints. A room in a new home will be 4.6 meters long and 3.3 meters wide. If the scale of the blueprint is 1 centimeter = 2.5 meters, what should the dimensions be in the scale drawing?**

Use ℓ for the length and w for the width.

Length

scale → / *actual* → $\frac{1 \text{ cm}}{2.5 \text{ m}} = \frac{\ell \text{ cm}}{4.6 \text{ m}}$ ← *scale* / ← *actual*

$1 \times 4.6 = 2.5 \times \ell$ *Find the cross products.*

$\frac{1 \times 4.6}{2.5} = \ell$

$4.6 \div 2.5 = 1.84$

Width

scale → / *actual* → $\frac{1 \text{ cm}}{2.5 \text{ m}} = \frac{w \text{ cm}}{3.3 \text{ m}}$ ← *scale* / ← *actual*

$1 \times 3.3 = 2.5 \times w$ *Find the cross products.*

$\frac{1 \times 3.3}{2.5} = w$

$3.3 \div 2.5 = 1.32$

The scale drawing should be 1.84 cm long and 1.32 cm wide.

You can use proportions to make your own scale drawing.

Did you know

Archaeologists have found an ancient blueprint for the Pantheon in Rome, Italy, in which the scale is 1:1.

HANDS-ON MINI-LAB

Work with a partner. 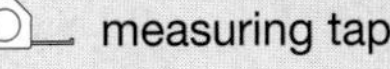 measuring tape  ruler $\frac{1}{4}$-inch grid paper

Try This

- Measure the length of each wall, door, window, and chalkboard in your classroom.
- Round each length to the nearest inch. Record the lengths.
- Make a scale drawing like the one at the right on a piece of grid paper. Use the scale $\frac{1}{4}$-inch:12 inches.

chalkboard

window

door

Talk About It

1. Write the proportion you used to find the length of the chalkboard for your scale drawing. **See students' work.**
2. How would a scale drawing that used a scale of $\frac{1}{4}$-inch:24 inches compare to your scale drawing? **It would be half as large.**

2 TEACH

Transparency 8-4B contains a teaching aid for this lesson.

In-Class Examples

For Example 1

A pocket atlas has a scale of 1 in. represents 110 mi. What distance on the map represents 179 miles between Louisville, KY, and Nashville, TN? **$1\frac{5}{8}$ in.**

For Example 2

A room is 18 meters long and 10 meters wide. On a scale drawing, 1 centimeter represents 3 meters. What are the length and width of the room in the scale drawing?

6 cm, $3\frac{1}{3}$ cm

Teaching Tip For Example 2, make sure students are consistent in making the scale measurement the numerator and the actual measurement the denominator for both length and width.

Using the Mini-Lab Have students work cooperatively to share the measuring, recording, drawing, and labeling tasks in creating their drawing.

3 PRACTICE/APPLY

Check for Understanding

If students need additional practice or instruction after completing Exercises 1–8, one of these options may be helpful.

- Extra Practice, see p. 590
- Reteaching Activity
- *Study Guide Masters,* p. 61
- *Practice Masters,* p. 61

Assignment Guide

Core: 9–21 odd, 23–26
Enriched: 10–20 even, 21–26
All: Self Test, 1–10

Additional Answer

2. Find the distance on the drawing and write a proportion using the measure and the scale.

CHECK FOR UNDERSTANDING

Communicating Mathematics

Read and study the lesson to answer each question.

1. ***Tell*** what important information must be given on a scale drawing in orde: to use it. **the scale**
2. ***Explain*** how to find an actual distance using a scale drawing. **See margin.**
3. ***Draw*** a scale drawing of a room in your home. Use $\frac{1}{4}$-inch grid paper and a scale of 1 inch = 3 feet. **See students' work.** (HANDS-ON MATH)

Guided Practice

Find the distance between each pair of cities, given the map distance and the scale.

4. Charlotte, North Carolina and Knoxville, Tennessee; $12\frac{4}{5}$ inches; 1 inch:18 miles **230.4 miles**
5. Cape Town, South Africa and London, England; 19.3 cm; 1 cm:500 km **9,650 km**

Find the length of each object on a scale drawing with the given scale.

6. a patio door 72 inches wide; 1 inch:2 feet **3 inches**
7. a room 50 feet long; $\frac{1}{2}$ inch:6 inches **50 inches**
8. ***City Planning*** When the Brazilian government moved its capital from Rio de Janeiro, they held a contest to design the city of Brasilia. The winner was Lucio Costa, who designed the city to resemble the curved wings of a jet airplane. A map of Brasilia has a scale of 1 inch to 5 miles. If the city is $2\frac{7}{16}$ inches across on the map, how far is it across the actual city? Use estimation to check your answer. **$12\frac{3}{16}$ miles**

Lucio Costa

EXERCISES

Practice

Find the distance between each pair of cities, given the map distance and the scale.

	Cities	Map Distance	Scale	
9.	Spokane and Richland, Washington	$6\frac{1}{10}$ inches	1 inch: 22 miles	**$134\frac{1}{5}$ mi**
10.	Baltimore, Maryland and Washington, D.C.	$2\frac{7}{8}$ inches	$\frac{1}{2}$ inch: 6 miles	**$34\frac{1}{2}$ mi**
11.	Dallas, Texas and Montgomery, Alabama	$4\frac{5}{8}$ inches	$\frac{1}{4}$ inch: 35 miles	**$647\frac{1}{2}$ mi**
12.	Chicago, Illinois and Mexico City, Mexico	10.9 cm	1 cm: 250 km	**2,725 km**
13.	Singapore and New Delhi, India	9.9 cm	3 cm: 1,250 km	**4,125 km**
14.	Paris, France and Montreal, Canada	16.2 cm	2.2 cm: 750 km	**about 5,522.7 km**

***Study Guide Masters,* p. 61**

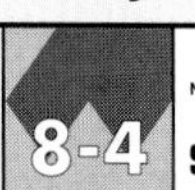

Name ________ Date ________

Study Guide

Scale Drawings

A **scale drawing** is used to present something that is too large or too small to be drawn to actual size. The **scale** is the ratio of the distance on the drawing to the actual distance.

Example **Chuck is making a scale drawing of Detroit's Tiger Stadium. He is using the scale $\frac{1}{4}$ inch:25 feet. The home-run distance from home plate to right field is 325 feet. What length should Chuck make this distance on his drawing?**

Use the scale $\frac{1}{4}$ inch:25 feet. Solve a proportion.

$$\frac{\frac{1}{4}}{25} = \frac{x}{325} \quad \frac{\text{drawing length}}{\text{actual length}}$$

$$\frac{1}{4} \times 325 = 25x \quad \text{Find cross products.}$$

$$81\frac{1}{4} = 25x$$

$$\frac{81\frac{1}{4}}{25} = \frac{25x}{25}$$

$$3\frac{1}{4} = x$$

On Chuck's drawing, the length should be $3\frac{1}{4}$inches.

On a map, the scale is 1 inch:160 miles. For each map distance, find the actual distance.

1. 3 inches **480 miles**
2. $1\frac{1}{2}$ inches **240 miles**
3. $2\frac{5}{8}$ inches **420 miles**
4. $4\frac{1}{4}$ inches **680 miles**
5. $2\frac{3}{4}$ inches **440 miles**
6. 7 inches **1,120 miles**
7. $1\frac{7}{8}$ inches **300 miles**
8. $5\frac{1}{2}$ inches **880 miles**

On a scale drawing, the scale is $\frac{1}{2}$ inch:1 foot. Find the dimensions of each room in the scale drawing.

9. 10 feet by 20 feet **5 in. by 10 in.**
10. 15 feet by 12 feet **$7\frac{1}{2}$ in. by 6 in.**
11. 14 feet by 11 feet **7 in. by $5\frac{1}{2}$ in.**
12. 9 feet by 13 feet **$4\frac{1}{2}$ in. by $6\frac{1}{2}$ in.**

 T61 *Mathematics: Applications and Connections, Course 2*

Reteaching the Lesson

Activity Have students model a polygon on a geoboard, measure the sides, and make a larger version of the polygon on graph paper. Help students prepare a scale showing the ratio of the board version to the graph-paper version. Use the scale to find the lengths of the sides of the graph-paper polygon by solving proportions.

Error Analysis

Watch for students who confuse the units of measure for the actual object with the units for the scale drawing.

Prevent by verbal association in writing a proportion; small is to large as small is to large.

Find the length of each object on a scale drawing with the given scale.

15. a garage door 16 feet wide; 2 inches:1 foot **32 inches**
16. a bridge 26 meters wide; 1 centimeter:5.5 meters **about 4.7 cm**
17. a elevator shaft 3 meters wide; 0.5 centimeter:2.5 meters **0.6 cm**
18. a surgical instrument $5\frac{7}{8}$ inches long; 1 inch:$\frac{1}{2}$ inch **$11\frac{3}{4}$ inches**
19. a computer circuit board 4 centimeters wide; 1 centimeter: 0.2 centimeter
20. a gear $3\frac{5}{8}$ inches across; 4 inches:$\frac{1}{2}$ inch **29 inches**

19. 20 cm

Applications and Problem Solving

21. ***Technology*** Have you ever wished your television showed three-dimensional images? An invention by NASA engineer Valerie Thomas may make that possible. A drawing for her patent of the illusion transmitter is 8.4 centimeters tall. If the scale is 1 cm:2.2 cm, what will the actual height of the transmitter be? **18.48 cm**

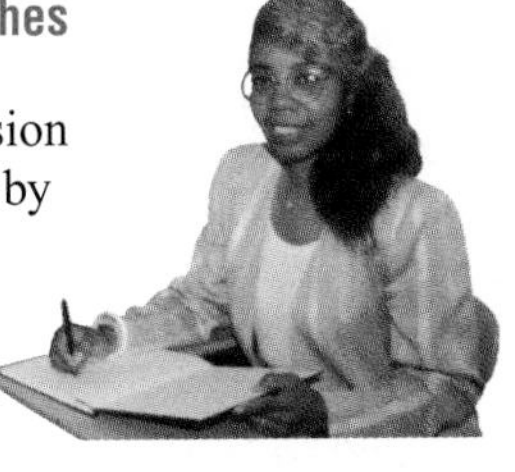
Valerie Thomas

22. ***Civil Engineering*** The Natchez Trace Bridge in Franklin, Tennessee, is the first and longest bridge of its kind in the United States. A scale drawing of the bridge has a scale of 1 inch:25 feet. How long is the drawing of the bridge if the actual bridge spans 1,500 feet? **60 inches**
23. ***Critical Thinking*** The distance between Huntington, West Virginia, and Cincinnati, Ohio, is 148 miles. If a map shows the distance as about $9\frac{1}{4}$ inches, what is the scale of the map? **1 inch:16 miles**

Mixed Review

For **Extra Practice,** see page 590.

24. **Standardized Test Practice** Inali earned \$157.50 one week by working 30 hours. If he works 35 hours the next week, how much will he earn? *(Lesson 8-3)* **C**

    A \$135.00 **B** \$160.50 **C** \$183.75 **D** \$210.25 **E** Not Here
25. ***Geometry*** On graph paper, draw coordinate axes. Then graph the point $B(-4, 4)$. *(Lesson 5-3)* **See margin.**
26. Find the GCF of 345, 253, and 115. *(Lesson 4-4)* **23**

CHAPTER 8 Mid-Chapter Self Test

Express each ratio as a fraction in simplest form. *(Lesson 8-1)*

1. 4 to 36 $\frac{1}{9}$
2. $\frac{60}{12}$ $\frac{5}{1}$
3. 5 pounds to 10 ounces $\frac{8}{1}$

Express each rate as a unit rate. *(Lesson 8-2)*

4. 640 miles in 5 hours **128 mph**
5. \$11.90 for 10 disks **\$1.19 per disk**
6. 5 million people in 410 square miles **about 12,195 people per square mile**

Solve each proportion. *(Lesson 8-3)*

7. $\frac{3}{4} = \frac{9}{n}$ **12**
8. $\frac{9}{36} = \frac{x}{48}$ **12**
9. $\frac{5}{y} = \frac{1}{0.5}$ **2.5**
10. On a scale drawing, 1 centimeter represents 2 meters. What length on the drawing should be used to represent 3.2 meters? *(Lesson 8-4)* **1.6 cm**

4 ASSESS

Closing Activity

Writing Have students use a road atlas and its map scale to write a proportion problem. It should involve finding either a map distance or the actual distance.

Mid-Chapter Self Test

The Mid-Chapter Self Test reviews the concepts in Lessons 8-1 through 8-4. Lesson references are given so students can review concepts not yet mastered.

Additional Answer

25.

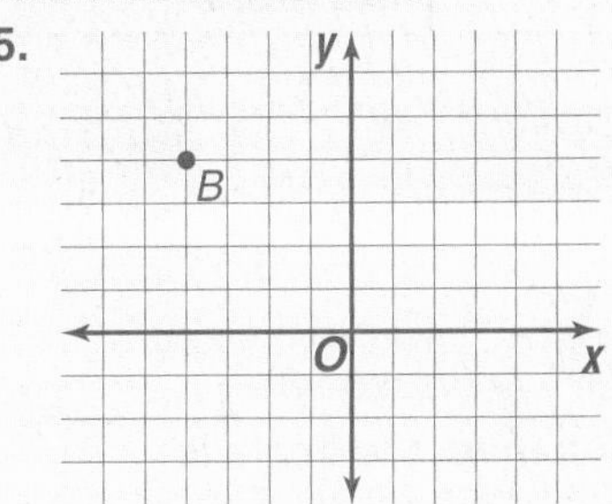

Extending the Lesson

Enrichment Masters, p. 61

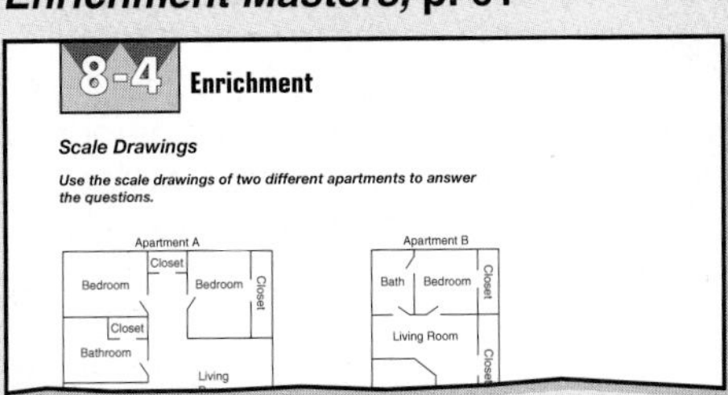
8-4 Enrichment

Scale Drawings

Use the scale drawings of two different apartments to answer the questions.

Activity Have students play a game with a road map of their state in which each student chooses a "base town" and three destinations. Students calculate the actual distance to each destination by using the map's scale. Given the base town and actual distances, students try to find each other's destinations.

Practice Masters, p. 61

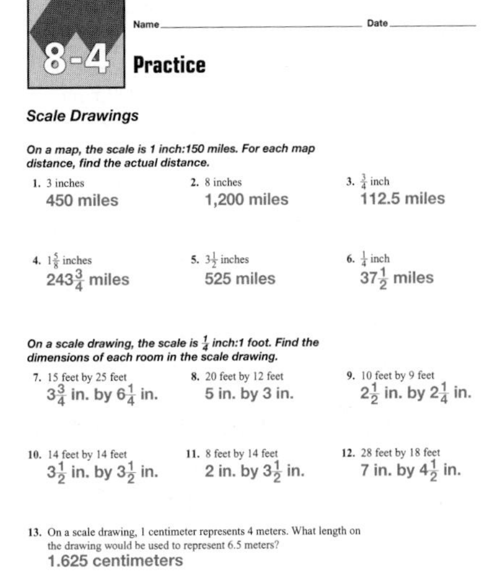
Name________ Date________

8-4 **Practice**

Scale Drawings

On a map, the scale is 1 inch:150 miles. For each map distance, find the actual distance.

1. 3 inches 450 miles
2. 8 inches 1,200 miles
3. $\frac{3}{4}$ inch 112.5 miles
4. $1\frac{5}{8}$ inches $243\frac{3}{4}$ miles
5. $3\frac{1}{2}$ inches 525 miles
6. $\frac{1}{4}$ inch $37\frac{1}{2}$ miles

On a scale drawing, the scale is $\frac{1}{4}$ inch:1 foot. Find the dimensions of each room in the scale drawing.

7. 15 feet by 25 feet $3\frac{3}{4}$ in. by $6\frac{1}{4}$ in.
8. 20 feet by 12 feet 5 in. by 3 in.
9. 10 feet by 9 feet $2\frac{1}{2}$ in. by $2\frac{1}{4}$ in.
10. 14 feet by 14 feet $3\frac{1}{2}$ in. by $3\frac{1}{2}$ in.
11. 8 feet by 14 feet 2 in. by $3\frac{1}{2}$ in.
12. 28 feet by 18 feet 7 in. by $4\frac{1}{2}$ in.
13. On a scale drawing, 1 centimeter represents 4 meters. What length on the drawing would be used to represent 6.5 meters? 1.625 centimeters
14. On a scale drawing, 1 inch represents 8 feet. What are the dimensions on the scale drawing that represent a 32 feet by 24 feet room? 4 in. by 3 in.

 T61 *Mathematics: Applications and Connections, Course 2*

8-5 Lesson Notes

Instructional Resources

- *Study Guide Masters,* p. 62
- *Practice Masters,* p. 62
- *Enrichment Masters,* p. 62
- Transparencies 8-5, A and B
- *Assessment and Evaluation Masters,* pp. 210, 211
- *Technology Masters,* p. 41

CD-ROM Program
- Resource Lesson 8-5

Recommended Pacing	
Standard	Day 8 of 14
Honors	Day 8 of 14
Block	Day 4 of 7

1 FOCUS

5-Minute Check
(Lesson 8-4)

On a map, the scale is 1 inch:150 miles. For each map distance, find the actual distance.

1. 5 inches **750 miles**
2. $3\frac{1}{2}$ inches **525 miles**

On a scale drawing, the scale is $\frac{1}{4}$ inch:1 foot. Find the dimensions of each room in the scale drawing.

3. 20 feet by 25 feet
   5 in. by $6\frac{1}{4}$ in.
4. 16 feet by 12 feet
   4 in. by 3 in.
5. A model of a dinosaur built to a scale of 3 cm:1 m is 24 centimeters tall. How tall was the actual dinosaur? **8 m**

The 5-Minute Check is also available on **Transparency 8-5A** for this lesson.

2 TEACH

Transparency 8-5B contains a teaching aid for this lesson.

Reading Mathematics Ask students to explain the difference between fractions and percents. Guide them to see that "percent" simply means "divided by 100," or a fraction with a denominator of 100.

8-5 Percents and Fractions

What you'll learn
You'll learn to express fractions as percents, and vice versa.

When am I ever going to use this?
You can express your test and homework scores using percents.

Scuba divers wear belts with lead weights so that they will be able to spend time beneath the surface of the water more easily. An average diver's belt should weigh about $\frac{1}{10}$ of his or her weight. What is $\frac{1}{10}$ written as a percent?

Remember that percent means per hundred. Any fraction can also be written as a percent. One way to express a fraction as a percent is to find an equivalent fraction with a denominator of 100.

$$\frac{1}{10} = \frac{1}{10} \times \frac{10}{10}$$
$$= \frac{10}{100} \text{ or } 10\%$$

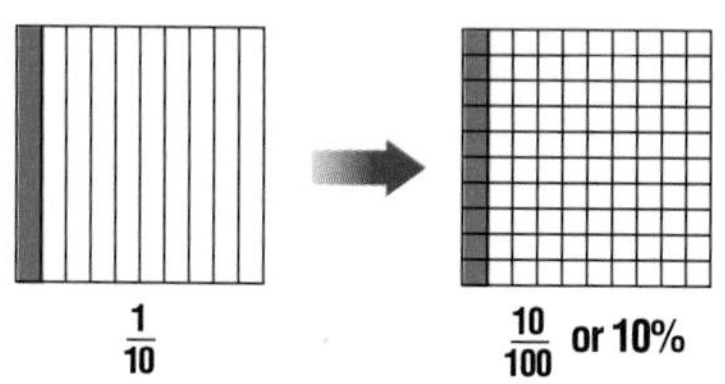

So, a diver's belt should be 10% of his or her weight.

You can also use a proportion to express a fraction as a percent.

Examples

Express each fraction as a percent.

1 $\frac{7}{8}$

$\frac{7}{8} = \frac{n}{100}$ *Find the cross products.*

$700 = 8n$

$\frac{700}{8} = \frac{8n}{8}$ *Divide each side by 8.*

$87.5 = n$

So, $\frac{7}{8} = 87.5\%$.

2 $\frac{20}{48}$

$\frac{20}{48} = \frac{n}{100}$ *Find the cross products.*

$2{,}000 = 48n$

2000 [÷] 48 [=] 41.6666667

So, $\frac{20}{48}$ is about 41.7%.

Study Hint
Estimation Notice that $\frac{7}{8}$ is close to 1. So the percent should be close to 100%. $\frac{20}{48}$ is close to $\frac{1}{2}$. So the percent should be close to 50%.

When you want to write a percent as a fraction, begin with a fraction that has a denominator of 100. Then write the fraction in simplest form.

Motivating the Lesson
Problem Solving Tell students that in one basketball game, Tina made 7 of her 8 free-throw attempts. Ask them to express her free-throw shooting as a percent.

Multiple Learning Styles

Visual/Spatial Have students use graph paper to draw several 10 × 10 squares. Give students a series of fractions to express as percents, and ask them to color a portion of each square to correspond to the percent, or "how many squares out of 100?"

Examples

Express each percent as a fraction in simplest form.

3 45%

Estimate: 45% is about 50%, which is $\frac{1}{2}$.

$$45\% = \frac{45}{100}$$
$$= \frac{45 \div 5}{100 \div 5} \quad \textit{The GCF is 5.}$$
$$= \frac{9}{20}$$

So, $45\% = \frac{9}{20}$. *Compare to the estimate.*

4 $83\frac{1}{3}\%$

$$83\frac{1}{3}\% = \frac{83\frac{1}{3}}{100}$$
$$= 83\frac{1}{3} \div 100$$
$$= \frac{250}{3} \div 100$$
$$= \frac{250}{3} \times \frac{1}{100} \quad \textit{To divide by 100, multiply by } \frac{1}{100}.$$
$$= \frac{250}{300} \text{ or } \frac{5}{6}$$

So, $83\frac{1}{3}\% = \frac{5}{6}$.

Some percents are used often in everyday situations. It is helpful to memorize these percents and their equivalent fractions.

$20\% = \frac{1}{5}$	$25\% = \frac{1}{4}$	$12\frac{1}{2}\% = \frac{1}{8}$	$16\frac{2}{3}\% = \frac{1}{6}$
$40\% = \frac{2}{5}$	$50\% = \frac{1}{2}$	$37\frac{1}{2}\% = \frac{3}{8}$	$33\frac{1}{3}\% = \frac{1}{3}$
$60\% = \frac{3}{5}$	$75\% = \frac{3}{4}$	$62\frac{1}{2}\% = \frac{5}{8}$	$66\frac{2}{3}\% = \frac{2}{3}$
$80\% = \frac{4}{5}$		$87\frac{1}{2}\% = \frac{7}{8}$	$83\frac{1}{3}\% = \frac{5}{6}$
$100\% = 1$			

5 **Economics** In 1996, $5\frac{2}{5}\%$ of the American workforce was unemployed. Write the percent as a fraction.

$$5\frac{2}{5}\% = \frac{5\frac{2}{5}}{100}$$
$$= 5\frac{2}{5} \div 100 \quad \textit{Write the fraction as a division problem.}$$
$$= \frac{27}{5} \times \frac{1}{100} \quad \textit{Rewrite } 5\tfrac{2}{5} \textit{ as an improper fraction.}$$
$$= \frac{27}{500}$$

In 1996, $\frac{27}{500}$ of the workforce was unemployed.

CHECK FOR UNDERSTANDING

Communicating Mathematics

Read and study the lesson to answer each question.

1. ***Demonstrate*** how to write $\frac{3}{16}$ as a percent. **1. See Answer Appendix.**
2. ***Write*** a fraction and a percent to represent the shaded portion of the model at the right. **35%, $\frac{7}{20}$**

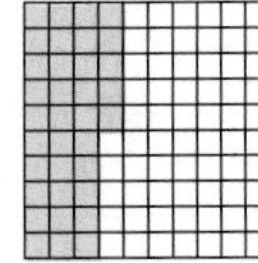

In-Class Examples

Express each fraction as a percent.

For Example 1
$\frac{2}{25}$ 8%

For Example 2
$\frac{3}{16}$ 18.75%

Express each percent as a fraction in simplest form.

For Example 3
52% $\frac{13}{25}$

For Example 4
$17\frac{1}{3}\%$ $\frac{13}{75}$

For Example 5
A football player catches 36% of the passes thrown to him. Write this percent as a fraction. $\frac{9}{25}$

3 PRACTICE/APPLY

Check for Understanding

If students need additional practice or instruction after completing Exercises 1–9, one of these options may be helpful.

- Extra Practice, see p. 591
- Reteaching Activity
- *Study Guide Masters,* p. 62
- *Practice Masters,* p. 62

***Study Guide Masters,* p. 62**

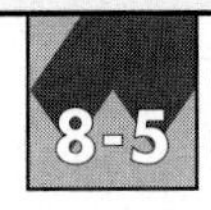

Name________________ Date________

8-5 Study Guide

Percents and Fractions

To write a fraction as a percent, use a proportion.

Examples **1** Express $\frac{5}{8}$ as a percent.

$\frac{5}{8} = \frac{x}{100}$

$500 = 8x$

$\frac{500}{8} = \frac{8x}{8}$

$62.5 = x$

$\frac{5}{8}$ is 62.5%.

2 Express $\frac{15}{16}$ as a percent.

$\frac{15}{16} = \frac{m}{100}$

$1{,}500 = 16m$

$\frac{1{,}500}{16} = \frac{16m}{16}$

$93.75 = m$

$\frac{15}{16}$ is 93.75%.

To write a percent as a fraction, write a fraction with a denominator of 100. Then write the fraction is simplest form.

Examples **3** Express 24% as a fraction.

$24\% = \frac{24}{100} = \frac{24 \div 4}{100 \div 4} = \frac{6}{25}$

4 Express $87\frac{1}{2}\%$ as a fraction.

$87\frac{1}{2}\% = \frac{87\frac{1}{2}}{100} = \frac{\frac{175}{2}}{100} = \frac{175}{2} \times \frac{1}{100} = \frac{175}{200} = \frac{7}{8}$

Express each fraction as a percent.

1. $\frac{1}{2}$ 50%
2. $\frac{3}{5}$ 60%
3. $\frac{7}{10}$ 70%
4. $\frac{9}{20}$ 45%
5. $\frac{19}{25}$ 76%
6. $\frac{1}{8}$ 12.5%
7. $\frac{1}{6}$ $16\frac{2}{3}\%$
8. $\frac{3}{4}$ 75%

Express each percent as a fraction in simplest form.

9. 40% $\frac{2}{5}$
10. 30% $\frac{3}{10}$
11. 85% $\frac{17}{20}$
12. 56% $\frac{14}{25}$
13. $37\frac{1}{2}\%$ $\frac{3}{8}$
14. $33\frac{1}{3}\%$ $\frac{1}{3}$
15. 4% $\frac{1}{25}$
16. 17% $\frac{17}{100}$

 T62 *Mathematics: Applications and Connections, Course 2*

Reteaching the Lesson

Activity Have students first estimate the percent of students in the class who are left-handed. Count the actual number of left-handed students, writing it as a fraction of the total number of students. Ask students to write that as a fraction of 100.

MathPASS CD-ROM

This CD-ROM offers a complete, self-paced mathematics curriculum. Each lesson includes a pretest, tutorial, guided practice, and posttest. MathPASS Lesson 30 is correlated to this Student Edition lesson.

For Windows & Macintosh

Assignment Guide

Core: 11–33 odd, 34–38
Enriched: 10–30 even, 32–38

4 ASSESS

Closing Activity

Modeling Have students work with a partner to model and write percents using counters. One student will express the fraction as a percent of the total number of counters designated by the other student.

Chapter 8, Quiz B (Lessons 8-4 and 8-5) is available in the *Assessment and Evaluation Masters,* p. 211.

Mid-Chapter Test (Lessons 8-1 through 8-5) is available in the *Assessment and Evaluation Masters,* p. 210.

***Practice Masters,* p. 62**

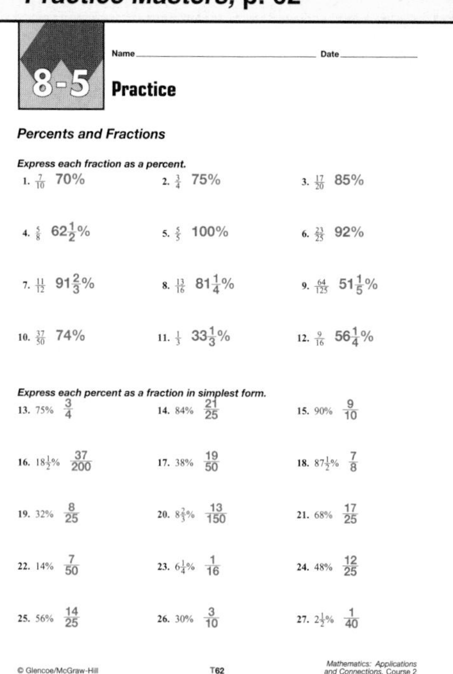

Name ______ Date ______

8-5 Practice

Percents and Fractions

Express each fraction as a percent.

1. $\frac{7}{10}$ 70%
2. $\frac{3}{4}$ 75%
3. $\frac{17}{20}$ 85%
4. $\frac{5}{8}$ $62\frac{1}{2}$%
5. $\frac{5}{5}$ 100%
6. $\frac{23}{25}$ 92%
7. $\frac{11}{12}$ $91\frac{2}{3}$%
8. $\frac{13}{16}$ $81\frac{1}{4}$%
9. $\frac{64}{125}$ $51\frac{1}{5}$%
10. $\frac{37}{50}$ 74%
11. $\frac{1}{3}$ $33\frac{1}{3}$%
12. $\frac{9}{16}$ $56\frac{1}{4}$%

Express each percent as a fraction in simplest form.

13. 75% $\frac{3}{4}$
14. 84% $\frac{21}{25}$
15. 90% $\frac{9}{10}$
16. $18\frac{1}{2}$% $\frac{37}{200}$
17. 38% $\frac{19}{50}$
18. $87\frac{1}{2}$% $\frac{7}{8}$
19. 32% $\frac{8}{25}$
20. $8\frac{2}{3}$% $\frac{13}{150}$
21. 68% $\frac{17}{25}$
22. 14% $\frac{7}{50}$
23. $6\frac{1}{4}$% $\frac{1}{16}$
24. 48% $\frac{12}{25}$
25. 56% $\frac{14}{25}$
26. 30% $\frac{3}{10}$
27. $2\frac{1}{2}$% $\frac{1}{40}$

 T62 *Mathematics: Applications and Connections, Course 2*

Guided Practice

Express each fraction as a percent.

3. $\frac{3}{10}$ **30%**
4. $\frac{7}{20}$ **35%**
5. $\frac{5}{16}$ **31.25%**

Express each percent as a fraction in simplest form.

6. 85% $\frac{17}{20}$
7. 72% $\frac{18}{25}$
8. $17\frac{1}{2}$% $\frac{7}{40}$
9. ***Life Science*** A banana is 75% water. Write 75% as a fraction in simplest form. $\frac{3}{4}$

EXERCISES

Practice

Express each fraction as a percent. **11. 43.75% 13. 11.5% 15. about 41.7% 17. about 36.4% 19. about 3.3%**

10. $\frac{9}{20}$ **45%**
11. $\frac{7}{16}$
12. $\frac{18}{25}$ **72%**
13. $\frac{23}{200}$
14. $\frac{5}{5}$ **100%**
15. $\frac{5}{12}$
16. $\frac{14}{20}$ **70%**
17. $\frac{4}{11}$
18. $\frac{1}{16}$ **6.25%**
19. $\frac{1}{30}$

Express each percent as a fraction in simplest form. **23. $\frac{69}{200}$ 26. $\frac{141}{400}$ 27. $\frac{901}{2,000}$ 28. $\frac{7}{16}$**

20. 55% $\frac{11}{20}$
21. 40% $\frac{2}{5}$
22. 18% $\frac{9}{50}$
23. 34.5%
24. 6.2% $\frac{31}{500}$
25. $62\frac{1}{2}$% $\frac{5}{8}$
26. $35\frac{1}{4}$%
27. 45.05%
28. $43\frac{3}{4}$%
29. 100% **1**
30. Write $33\frac{1}{3}$% as a fraction. $\frac{1}{3}$
31. What percent is equivalent to $\frac{40}{125}$? **32%**

Applications and Problem Solving **32. $\frac{3}{100}$**

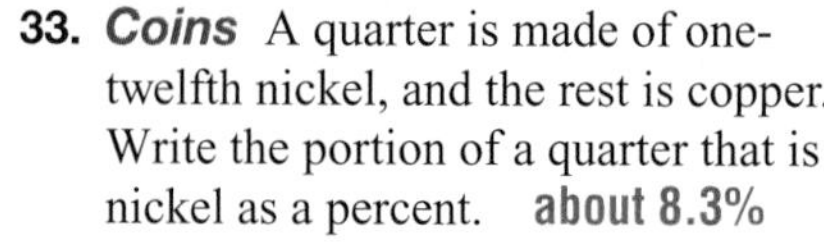

32. ***Careers*** Only 3% of the people who work in the space industry work for NASA. Write 3% as a fraction in simplest form.
33. ***Coins*** A quarter is made of one-twelfth nickel, and the rest is copper. Write the portion of a quarter that is nickel as a percent. **about 8.3%**
34. ***Critical Thinking*** For what value of x is $\frac{1}{x} = x$%? **10**

Mixed Review

35. **Standardized Test Practice** Choose the distance between Chattanooga and Memphis if they are 1.75 inches apart on the map and the scale is 1 inch:152 miles. *(Lesson 8-4)* **A**

 A 266 miles **B** 86.8 miles **C** 188 miles **D** 322 miles

36. ***Measurement*** Change 56 ounces to pounds. *(Lesson 7-5)* $3\frac{1}{2}$ **lb**
37. Solve $-9 - (-6) = t$. *(Lesson 5-5)* **−3**
38. Find the least common multiple of 28 and 74. *(Lesson 4-9)* **1,036**

For **Extra Practice,** see page 591.

Extending the Lesson

***Enrichment Masters,* p. 62**

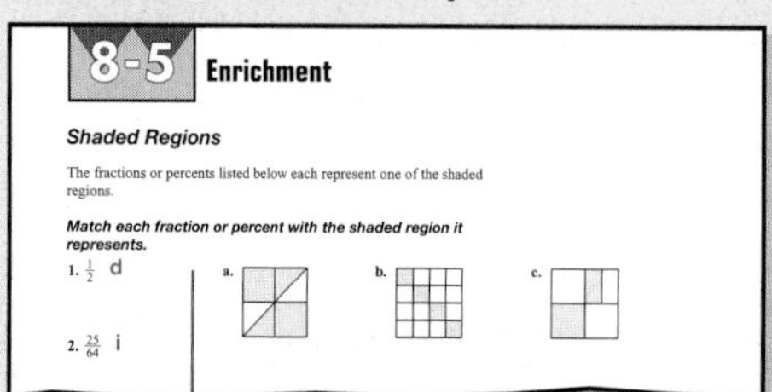

8-5 Enrichment

Shaded Regions

The fractions or percents listed below each represent one of the shaded regions.

Match each fraction or percent with the shaded region it represents.

1. $\frac{1}{2}$ d
2. $\frac{25}{64}$ i

a. b. c.

Activity Have students express the fraction of the total number of students in the class who are 13 years or older as a percent. Challenge students to collect other demographic data to express in both fraction and percent form.

8-6 Percents and Decimals

What **you'll learn**

You'll learn to express decimals as percents, and vice versa.

When **am I ever going to use this?**

You can write your batting average as a decimal and a percent.

Did you know that jellyfish aren't really fish? They are invertebrates, which means they have no backbone. In fact, jellyfish have no bones at all. A jellyfish's body is made up of 95% water. What is 95% written as a decimal? *This question will be answered in Example 3.*

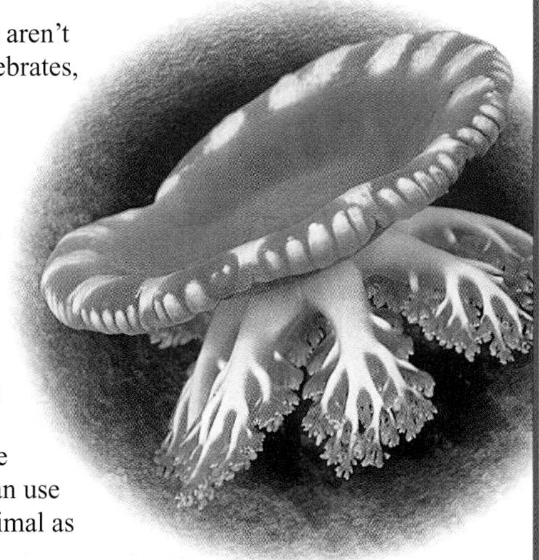

When you studied fractions in Chapter 4, you learned that any decimal can also be written as a fraction. You can use that fact to express any decimal as a percent.

Examples

Express each decimal as a percent.

1 0.12

$0.12 = \frac{12}{100}$ *Write as a fraction.*

$= 12\%$

So, $0.12 = 12\%$.

2 0.119

$0.119 = \frac{119}{1{,}000}$ *Write as a fraction.*

$= \frac{119 \div 10}{1{,}000 \div 10}$ *Divide to make the denominator 100.*

$= \frac{11.9}{100}$ or 11.9%

So, $0.119 = 11.9\%$.

Study the pattern in the decimals and the equivalent percents in Examples 1 and 2. Notice that you can write the percent by multiplying the decimal number by 100 and adding the percent symbol.

Writing a Decimal as a Percent	
Words:	To write a decimal as a percent, multiply the decimal by 100 and add the percent symbol.
Symbols:	0.56 = 0.56 = 56%

When you want to write a percent as a decimal, reverse the process.

Writing a Percent as a Decimal	
Words:	To write a percent as a decimal, divide the percent by 100 and remove the percent symbol.
Symbols:	68% = 68 = 0.68

8-6 Lesson Notes

Instructional Resources

- *Study Guide Masters,* p. 63
- *Practice Masters,* p. 63
- *Enrichment Masters,* p. 63
- Transparencies 8-6, A and B
- *Science and Math Lab Manual,* pp. 81–84

CD-ROM Program
- Resource Lesson 8-6

Recommended Pacing	
Standard	Day 9 of 14
Honors	Day 9 of 14
Block	Day 5 of 7

1 FOCUS

5-Minute Check *(Lesson 8-5)*

Express each fraction as a percent.

1. $\frac{21}{25}$ 84% **2.** $\frac{7}{10}$ 70%

Express each percent as a fraction in simplest form.

3. 35% $\frac{7}{20}$ **4.** $16\frac{2}{3}\%$ $\frac{1}{6}$

5. Express *twenty-eight percent* as a fraction in simplest form. $\frac{7}{25}$

The 5-Minute Check is also available on **Transparency 8-6A** for this lesson.

Motivating the Lesson

Problem Solving Tell students that the highest major league batting average since 1900 occurred in 1924 when Rogers Hornsby hit 0.424. Ask them to give the percent of his times at bat that Hornsby got hits. 42.4%

2 TEACH

Transparency 8-6B contains a teaching aid for this lesson.

Using Calculators Have students practice expressing decimals as percents by multiplying given decimal numbers by 100 and noticing that the decimal point moves right 2 spaces. Reverse this process to express percents as decimals.

Multiple Learning Styles

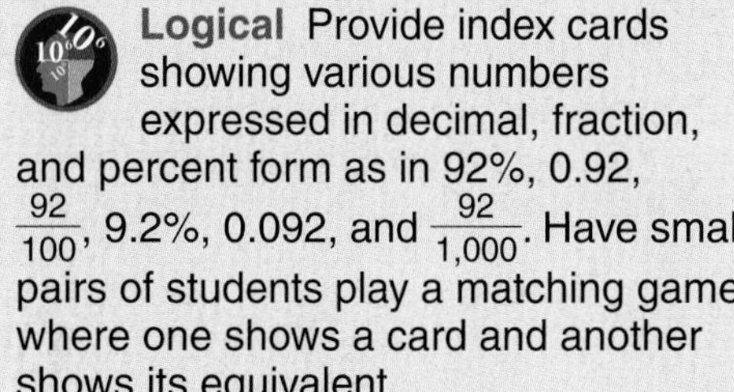

Logical Provide index cards showing various numbers expressed in decimal, fraction, and percent form as in 92%, 0.92, $\frac{92}{100}$, 9.2%, 0.092, and $\frac{92}{1{,}000}$. Have small pairs of students play a matching game where one shows a card and another shows its equivalent.

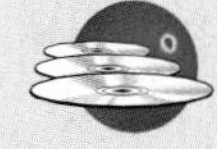

MathPASS CD-ROM

This CD-ROM offers a complete, self-paced mathematics curriculum. Each lesson includes a pretest, tutorial, guided practice, and posttest. MathPASS Lesson 31 is correlated to this Student Edition lesson.

For Windows & Macintosh

In-Class Examples

Express each decimal as a percent.

For Example 1
0.27 **27%**

For Example 2
0.439 **43.9%**

For Example 3
In Pakistan, 41% of the population in 1997 was under 15 years of age. Write 41% as a decimal. **0.41**

Express each percent as a decimal.

For Example 4
16.7% **0.167**

For Example 5
$13\frac{1}{5}\%$ **0.132**

3 PRACTICE/APPLY

Check for Understanding

If students need additional practice or instruction after completing Exercises 1–10, one of these options may be helpful.

- Extra Practice, see p. 591
- Reteaching Activity
- *Study Guide Masters,* p. 63
- *Practice Masters,* p. 63

Examples CONNECTION

3 **Life Science** **Refer to the beginning of the lesson. Write 95% as a decimal.**

95% = 95 = 0.95

A jellyfish's body is 0.95 water.

Jellyfish

Express each percent as a decimal.

4 **44.9%**

44.9% = 44.9 = 0.449

So, 44.9% = 0.449.

5 $\mathbf{23\frac{1}{4}\%}$

$23\frac{1}{4}\% = 23.25\%$ *Write $\frac{1}{4}$ as 0.25.*

$= 23.25 = 0.2325$

So, $23\frac{1}{4}\% = 0.2325$.

CHECK FOR UNDERSTANDING

Communicating Mathematics

Read and study the lesson to answer each question.

1. ***Choose*** the percent that is equivalent to 0.67. **b**
   a. 6.7%   **b.** 67%   **c.** 0.67%
2. ***Tell*** the steps used to write a percent as a decimal. **See margin.**
3. ***Write*** an explanation of how the diagram illustrates that any number can be expressed in three ways. **See margin.**

Math Journal

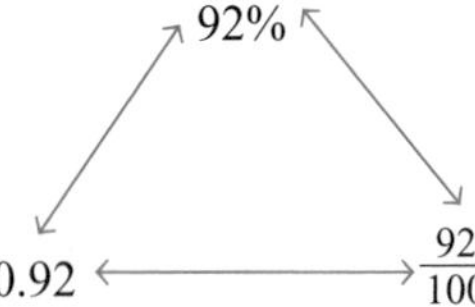

Guided Practice

Express each decimal as a percent.

4. 0.23 **23%**   5. 0.06 **6%**   6. 0.785 **78.5%**

Express each percent as a decimal.

7. 65% **0.65**   8. 42% **0.42**   9. $18\frac{1}{2}\%$ **0.185**

10. ***Food*** What is your favorite vegetable? In a survey, 19.7% of adults said broccoli was their favorite. Write 19.7% as a decimal. **0.197**

EXERCISES

Practice

Express each decimal as a percent. **14. 67.5%** **16. 4.44%**

11. 0.17 **17%** 12. 0.08 **8%** 13. 0.85 **85%** 14. 0.675 15. 0.099 **9.9%**
16. 0.0444 17. 0.01 **1%** 18. 0.025 **2.5%** 19. 0.009 **0.9%** 20. 1.0 **100%**

Reteaching the Lesson

Activity Have students use combinations of coins to make different money amounts. Help students add various denominations, such as quarters and dimes, as percents of a dollar, and then convert them to dollar-and-cents notation.

Additional Answers

2. Sample answer: Divide the number by 100 and remove the % symbol.
3. Sample answer: A number can be expressed as a fraction, a decimal, or a percent.

***Study Guide Masters,* p. 63**

Name________________ Date________

Study Guide

Percents and Decimals

To write a decimal as a percent, multiply the decimal by 100 and add the percent symbol.

Examples **1 Express 0.77 as a percent.**
0.77 = 0.77
= 77%

2 Express 0.323 as a percent.
0.323 = 0.323
= 32.3%

To write a percent as a decimal, divide the percent by 100 and remove the percent symbol.

Examples **3 Express 51% as a decimal.**
51% = 51.
= 0.51

4 Express 90.2% as a decimal.
90.2% = 90.2
= 0.902

Express each decimal as a percent.

1. 0.67 67%   2. 0.14 14%   3. 0.2 20%   4. 0.345 34.5%
5. 0.09 9%   6. 0.084 8.4%   7. 0.02 2%   8. 0.89 89%

Express each percent as a decimal.

9. 95% 0.95   10. 12% 0.12   11. 4% 0.04   12. 100% 1
13. 14.4% 0.144   14. 80% 0.8   15. 7.5% 0.075   16. $10\frac{1}{2}\%$ 0.105

 T63 *Mathematics: Applications and Connections, Course 2*

Express each percent as a decimal. 21. 0.45 24. 0.645 25. 0.081

21. 45% 22. 70% 0.7 23. 16% 0.16 24. 64.5% 25. 8.1%

26. $78\frac{1}{2}$% 27. $14\frac{1}{4}$% 28. 12.35% 0.1235 29. $94\frac{3}{4}$% 30. 100% 1.00

26. 0.785
27. 0.1425
29. 0.9475

31. Write the percent that is equivalent to 0.848. 84.8%

32. What decimal is equivalent to $25\frac{1}{4}$%? 0.2525

Applications and Problem Solving

33. ***Sports*** In 1971, 0.04 of high school girls played sports. In 1994, the number had risen to 0.33. Write each decimal as a percent. 4%; 33%

34. ***Technology*** The graph shows the Internet users who find websites from different sources. Write each percent as a decimal.

34. friends: 0.44; reading: 0.39; browsing: 0.32; links: 0.1; on-line directory: 0.07; e-mail: 0.03; on-line advertising: 0.02

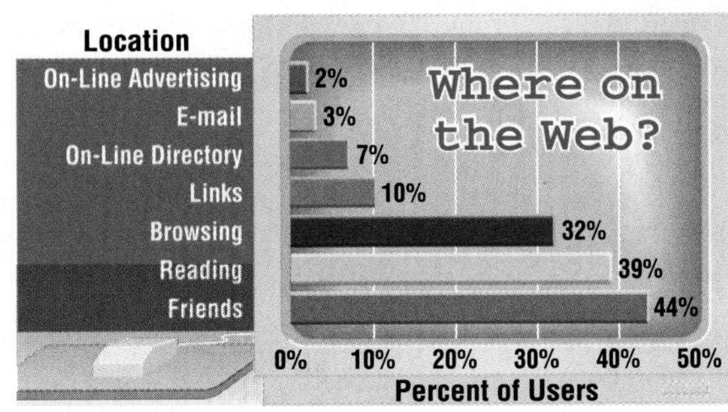

Source: *Electronic Access*

35. ***Critical Thinking*** Choose the greater number of each pair.
a. 35%, 3.5 b. $1\frac{3}{4}$%, 0.175 c. $\frac{23}{40}$, 0.60

Mixed Review

36. **Standardized Test Practice** Antonia and Luis bought a new stereo that was on sale for 38% off. What is this percent written as a fraction? *(Lesson 8-5)* C
A $\frac{1}{38}$ B $\frac{9}{25}$ C $\frac{19}{50}$ D $\frac{38}{75}$

37. ***Algebra*** Translate *t divided by 8* into an algebraic expression. *(Lesson 6-4)*

37. $t \div 8$ or $\frac{t}{8}$

38. Express $\frac{28}{98}$ in simplest form. *(Lesson 4-5)* $\frac{2}{7}$

39. ***Statistics*** Use the graph. In what age category are most officers of the U.S. military? *(Lesson 3-2)* 26–30 and 31–35

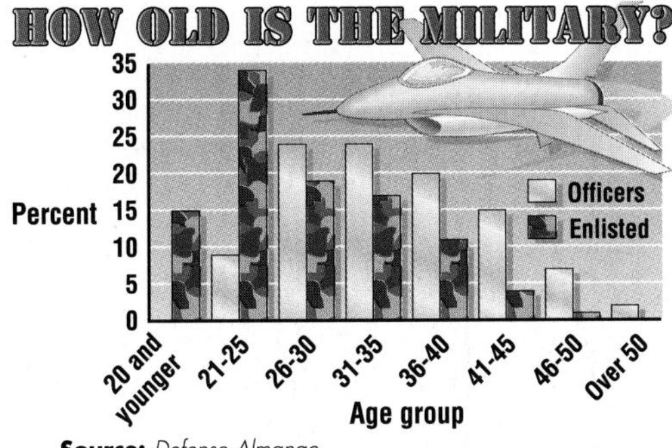

Source: *Defense Almanac*

For **Extra Practice**, see page 591.

Assignment Guide

Core: 11–33 odd, 35–39
Enriched: 12–32 even, 33–39

4 ASSESS

Closing Activity

Speaking Have students work in small groups to explain how to express a percent as a decimal and a decimal as a percent. Encourage them to paraphrase the textbook's explanation.

Extending the Lesson

Enrichment Masters, p. 63

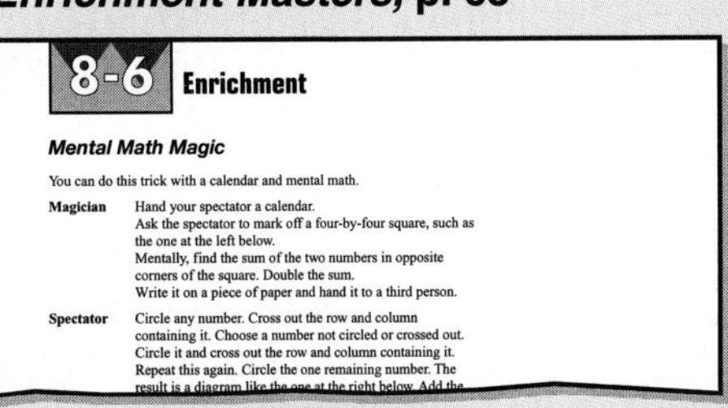

8-6 Enrichment

Mental Math Magic

You can do this trick with a calendar and mental math.

Magician Hand your spectator a calendar.
Ask the spectator to mark off a four-by-four square, such as the one at the left below.
Mentally, find the sum of the two numbers in opposite corners of the square. Double the sum.
Write it on a piece of paper and hand it to a third person.

Spectator Circle any number. Cross out the row and column containing it. Choose a number not circled or crossed out. Circle it and cross out the row and column containing it. Repeat this again. Circle the one remaining number. The result is a diagram like the one at the right below. Add the

Activity Have students survey the class, their families, or other students about sports participation to see how the percents compare to the data in Exercise 33.

Practice Masters, p. 63

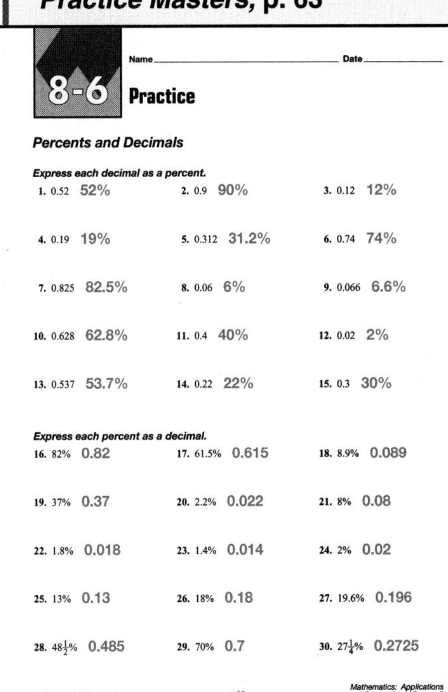

Name______ Date______

8-6 Practice

Percents and Decimals

Express each decimal as a percent.

1. 0.52 52%	2. 0.9 90%	3. 0.12 12%
4. 0.19 19%	5. 0.312 31.2%	6. 0.74 74%
7. 0.825 82.5%	8. 0.06 6%	9. 0.066 6.6%
10. 0.628 62.8%	11. 0.4 40%	12. 0.02 2%
13. 0.537 53.7%	14. 0.22 22%	15. 0.3 30%

Express each percent as a decimal.

16. 82% 0.82	17. 61.5% 0.615	18. 8.9% 0.089
19. 37% 0.37	20. 2.2% 0.022	21. 8% 0.08
22. 1.8% 0.018	23. 1.4% 0.014	24. 2% 0.02
25. 13% 0.13	26. 18% 0.18	27. 19.6% 0.196
28. $48\frac{1}{2}$% 0.485	29. 70% 0.7	30. $27\frac{1}{4}$% 0.2725

 T63 *Mathematics: Applications and Connections, Course 2*

8-7 Lesson Notes

Instructional Resources

- *Study Guide Masters,* p. 64
- *Practice Masters,* p. 64
- *Enrichment Masters,* p. 64
- Transparencies 8-7, A and B
- *Assessment and Evaluation Masters,* p. 212
- *Classroom Games,* pp. 23–25

CD-ROM Program
- Resource Lesson 8-7

Recommended Pacing	
Standard	Day 10 of 14
Honors	Day 10 of 14
Block	Day 5 of 7

1 FOCUS

5-Minute Check (Lesson 8-6)

Express each decimal as a percent.

1. 0.52 52%
2. 0.835 83.5%

Express each percent as a decimal.

3. 8% 0.08
4. $32\frac{1}{4}$% 0.3225
5. In South Dakota, 91.4% of public high school students graduate. Write this as a decimal. 0.914

The 5-Minute Check is also available on **Transparency 8-7A** for this lesson.

Motivating the Lesson

Communication Ask students to write two statements, one that is reasonable and one that is not, using the number 125%. Have students share and justify their choices. Repeat the process with the number 0.25%.

8-7 Percents Greater Than 100% and Percents Less Than 1%

What you'll learn

You'll learn to express percents greater than 100% and percents less than 1% as fractions and as decimals, and vice versa.

When am I ever going to use this?

Changes over time, like population growth, are often reported as percents greater than 100% or less than 1%.

The North African ostrich is the largest bird living on Earth today. An ostrich can grow as tall as 9 feet! This is 150% the height of an average man. How many times taller than a man is an ostrich? *This question will be answered in Example 1.*

A percent greater than 100% represents a number greater than 1. Percents less than 1% represent numbers less than 0.01 or $\frac{1}{100}$.

HANDS-ON MINI-LAB

Work with a partner. 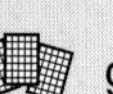 grid paper  colored pencils

Try This

- Draw three 10 × 10 squares on a piece of grid paper. Each large square represents 100% and each small square represents 1%.
- Use two of the models to shade 120 small squares.
- On the third model, shade half of one small square.

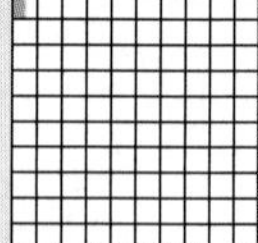

Talk About It

1. Which model represents a percent greater than 100%? What is the percent? **first model; 120%**
2. Which model represents a percent less than 1%? What is the percent? **second model; $\frac{1}{2}$%**

Example CONNECTION

1 **Life Science** **Refer to the beginning of the lesson. Express 150% as a decimal and as a fraction to find how many times taller the ostrich is than an average man.**

Make a model.

$150\% = 1.50$ or 1.5

$= 1\frac{1}{2}$

So, the ostrich is 1.5 or $1\frac{1}{2}$ times as tall as a man.

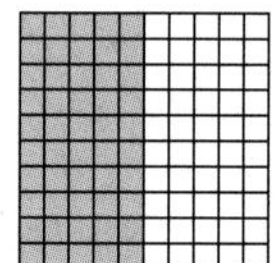

You can use the same method for writing a decimal as a percent to write decimals greater than 1 and decimals less than 0.01 as percents.

Examples

Express each number as a percent.

2 **1.45**

$1.45 = 145 = 145\%$

So, $1.45 = 145\%$.

3 **0.0016**

$0.0016 = 00016 = 0.16\%$

So, $0.0016 = 0.16\%$.

An alternative way to write a mixed number or a fraction as a percent is to first write the number as a decimal. Then write the decimal as a percent.

Fraction → Decimal → Percent

Examples

Express each number as a percent.

4 $7\frac{1}{2}$

$7\frac{1}{2} = 7.5$

$7.5 = 750 = 750\%$

So, $7\frac{1}{2} = 750\%$.

5 $\frac{2}{500}$

Use a calculator.

2 [÷] 500 [=] 0.004

$0.004 = 0004 = 0.4\%$

So, $\frac{2}{500} = 0.4\%$.

APPLICATION

6 **Recreation** **The National Sporting Goods Association estimates that in a recent year, the total sales of equipment for water skiing was $51 million. That same year, all of the sporting goods sold in the United States totaled $48,732 million! What percent of the sporting goods sales was related to water skiing? Round to the nearest hundredth of a percent.**

Use a calculator.

51 [÷] 48732 [=] 0.00104654

$0.00104654 = 000104654$

$= 0.104654\%$

So, about 0.10% of the sporting goods were related to water skiing.

2 TEACH

Transparency 8-7B contains a teaching aid for this lesson.

Using the Mini-Lab Have students explain how they know that one model represents a percent greater than 100% and the other represents a percent less than 1%. Ask students how they would use models to express percents greater than 200%.

In-Class Examples

For Example 1
Horses live about 286% as long as kangaroos. Express 286% as a decimal and as a fraction. **2.86, $2\frac{43}{50}$**

Express each number as a percent.

For Example 2
3.92 **392%**

For Example 3
0.00025 **0.025%**

For Example 4
$6\frac{2}{3}$ **667%**

For Example 5
$\frac{3}{125}$ **2.4%**

For Example 6
The California Redwood grows to be about 366 feet tall. The Saguaro cactus grows to be about 52 feet tall. What percent of the redwood's height is a Saguaro? Round to the nearest tenth of a percent. **14.2%**

3 PRACTICE/APPLY

Check for Understanding

If students need additional practice or instruction after completing Exercises 1–14, one of these options may be helpful.

- Extra Practice, see p. 591
- Reteaching Activity
- *Study Guide Masters,* p. 64
- *Practice Masters,* p. 64

Assignment Guide

Core: 15–51 odd, 52–57
Enriched: 16–46 even, 47–49, 51–57

Additional Answers

1. 150% is greater than 100%.
2. It is less than $\frac{1}{100}$.
12. No; The most any candidate could receive is 100% of the votes.
13. Yes; This means that they can expect a price higher than the minimum guaranteed.

***Study Guide Masters,* p. 64**

Name________________ Date________

8-7 Study Guide

Percents Greater Than 100% and Percents Less Than 1%

You can express a percent greater than 100% or less than 1% as a decimal.

Examples **1 Express 725% as a decimal.** **2 Express 0.015% as a decimal.**

$725\% = 725 = 7.25$ $0.015\% = 00.015 = 0.00015$

You can use percents to represent numbers that are greater than 1.

Examples **3 Express 5.75 as a percent.** **4 Express $8\frac{9}{10}$ as a percent.**

$5.75 = 5.75 = 575\%$ $8\frac{9}{10} = 8.9 = 8.90 = 890\%$

You can use percents to represent numbers that are less than 0.01 or $\frac{1}{100}$.

Examples **5 Express 0.007 as a percent.** **6 Express $\frac{1}{400}$ as a percent.**

$0.007 = 0.007 = 0.7\%$ $\frac{1}{400} = 1 \div 400 = 0.0025 = 0.0025 = 0.25\%$

Express each percent as a decimal.

1. 115% 1.15
2. 300% 3
3. 540% 5.4
4. 758% 7.58
5. 0.2% 0.002
6. 0.57% 0.0057
7. 0.125% 0.00125
8. 0.0006% 0.000006

Express each number as a percent.

9. 5.79 579%
10. $4\frac{1}{2}$ 450%
11. 2.4 240%
12. 95 9,500%
13. 0.001 0.1%
14. $\frac{6}{1,200}$ 0.5%
15. 0.0016 0.16%
16. $\frac{4}{1,600}$ 0.25%

 T64 *Mathematics: Applications and Connections, Course 2*

CHECK FOR UNDERSTANDING

Communicating Mathematics

Read and study the lesson to answer each question. 1–2. See margin.

1. ***Explain*** why 150% of the height of a person is taller than the person.
2. ***Describe*** a fraction that is equivalent to a percent less than 1%.
3. **HANDS-ON MATH** ***Draw*** a model to represent each percent. See Answer Appendix.
   a. 175% b. 0.75%

Guided Practice

Express each percent as a decimal.

4. 800% 8
5. 0.55% 0.0055
6. 240% 2.4
7. $\frac{1}{5}\%$ 0.002

Express each number as a percent. 11. about 0.29%

8. 4.3 430%
9. $15\frac{1}{2}$ 1,550%
10. 0.005 0.5%
11. $\frac{1}{350}$

Tell whether each of the following is reasonable. Explain why or why not. 12–13. See margin.

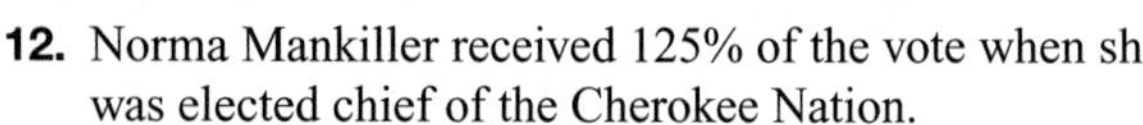

12. Norma Mankiller received 125% of the vote when she was elected chief of the Cherokee Nation.
13. The demand for Egyptian cotton rose in 1996. A popular newspaper reported that farmers there could expect prices to be 120% of the minimum guaranteed by the state.
Source: *USA TODAY*

Norma Mankiller

14. ***Education*** Recently, 8,753 of the 1,136,553 bachelor's degrees earned were in architecture. Use a calculator to find the ratio of the degrees in architecture to the degrees earned as a percent. Round your answer to the nearest hundredth of a percent. 0.77%

EXERCISES

Practice

Express each percent as a decimal.

15. 500% 5
16. 310% 3.1
17. 115% 1.15
18. 270% 2.7
19. 100.5%
20. 1,000% 10
21. 0.068%
22. 0.012%
23. 0.0025%
24. 0.75%
25. 0.032%
26. $\frac{1}{8}\%$

19. 1.005
21. 0.00068
22. 0.00012
23. 0.000025
24. 0.0075
25. 0.00032
26. 0.00125

Express each number as a percent. 36. about 0.89%

27. 9 900%
28. $3\frac{1}{2}$ 350%
29. $7\frac{3}{4}$ 775%
30. 6.25 625%
31. 34 3,400%
32. 2.9 290%
33. 0.009 0.9%
34. 0.0018 0.18%
35. $\frac{4}{1,000}$ 0.4%
36. $\frac{8}{900}$
37. 0.0001 0.01%
38. $\frac{12}{5,000}$ 0.24%
39. Express 1.8 as a percent. 180%
40. Write 925% as a decimal. 9.25

Reteaching the Lesson

Activity Use money to guide students to see that a penny is 1% of \$1.00 and 0.5% of \$2.00. Use coins to help them see that any amount greater than a coin is more than 100% than that of a coin.

Error Analysis
Watch for students who see 100% as an absolute maximum, and therefore see 150% as an impossibility.
Prevent by explaining that some percents greater than 100 are impossible, such as "110% effort," but others are quite possible, such as "150% of last year's income."

Tell whether each of the following is reasonable. Explain why or why not. **41–46. See Answer Appendix.**

41. Your height now is 0.1% of your height at 1 year old.

42. Central High School's 1998 enrollment is 105% of its 1997 enrollment.

43. Teenagers are 120% of the attendance at an amusement park.

44. Josefina gave away 130% of her stamp collection.

45. The U.S. population in 1990 is 0.5% of its population in 1790.

46. In 1994, 0.3% of the population of Pittsburgh moved out of the area.

Applications and Problem Solving

47. ***Economics*** In 1994, the price of consumer goods in Brazil increased to 2,669% of their 1993 prices. How many times the 1993 prices were the 1994 prices? **26.69**

48. ***Earth Science*** The diameter of the Sun is 865,500 miles. The diameter of Earth is about 0.9% of the Sun's diameter. Write 0.9% as a fraction in simplest form. $\frac{9}{1,000}$

49. ***Life Science*** The blue whale is the largest mammal that has ever lived. It has been known to reach a length of 110 feet! The smallest mammal is the pygmy shrew, with a total length of just 2.9 inches, including its tail. What percent of a whale's size is a shrew? **about 0.22%**

50. ***Working on the CHAPTER Project*** Use the information that you gathered about material that is recycled in your community. Write a paragraph and make a graph showing the amounts of different available materials that are recycled. **See students' work.**

51. ***Critical Thinking*** In 1995, there were 69,036,000 people under the age of 18 in the United States. The U.S. Bureau of the Census predicts that in 2010, the number of people under 18 will be 106.6% of that number. What is the estimated number of people under 18 for 2010? **73,592,376**

Mixed Review

52. Express 43% as a decimal. *(Lesson 8-6)* **0.43**

53. Tell whether the ratios 13 to 39 and 26 to 78 are equivalent. Show your answer by simplifying. *(Lesson 8-1)*

53. yes; 13 to 39 = $\frac{1}{3}$ and 26 to 78 = $\frac{1}{3}$

54. **Standardized Test Practice** The maximum capacity of an elevator is 3,000 pounds. Which number line shows this capacity? *(Lesson 6-5)* **B**

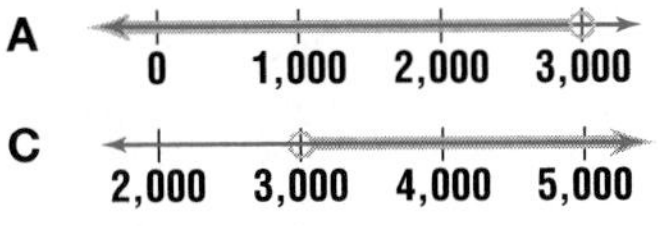

B 0 1,000 2,000 3,000

D 2,000 3,000 4,000 5,000

55. ***Geometry*** Graph $\triangle XYZ$ with vertices $X(2, 4)$, $Y(1, -1)$, and $Z(3, 5)$ and its reflection over the x-axis. Write the ordered pairs for the vertices of the new figure. *(Lesson 5-8)* **See Answer Appendix.**

56. ***Patterns*** Find the next three terms in the sequence 2, 5, 12.5, 31.25, ... *(Lesson 4-3)* **78.125, 195.3125, 488.28125**

For **Extra Practice,** see page 591.

57. ***Statistics*** Construct a stem-and-leaf plot for the data: 95, 83, 66, 81, 92, 85, 62, 90. *(Lesson 3-5)* **See Answer Appendix.**

Exercise 50 asks students to advance to the next stage of work on the Chapter Project. You may want to remind students that percents for some materials may have increased or decreased from day to day, so the changes should be marked as either positive or negative.

4 ASSESS

Closing Activity

Speaking Have students explain what it means to meet 100% of a goal, 150% of a goal, 200% of a goal, and 300% of a goal. Ask them how much time they would spend doing homework if teachers were to give them assignments requiring 150%, 200%, or 300% of the time they ordinarily take to complete their work.

Chapter 8, Quiz C (Lessons 8-6 and 8-7) is available in the *Assessment and Evaluation Masters,* p. 212.

***Practice Masters,* p. 64**

Name______ Date______

Practice

Percents Greater Than 100% and Percents Less Than 1%

Express each percent as a decimal.

1. 520% 5.2	2. 140% 1.4	3. 235% 2.35
4. 0.32% 0.0032	5. 0.015% 0.00015	6. $\frac{1}{4}$% 0.0025
7. $\frac{2}{5}$% 0.004	8. 1,000% 10	9. 0.125% 0.00125
10. 240% 2.4	11. 550% 5.5	12. 8,200% 82

Express each number as a percent.

13. 3.4 340%	14. 0.0026 0.26%	15. $3\frac{1}{5}$ 320%
16. 1.9 190%	17. 8 800%	18. 0.0002 0.02%
19. 1 100%	20. 1.95 195%	21. 35 3,500%
22. 0.00112 0.112%	23. 63 6,300%	24. $5\frac{3}{4}$ 575%

 T64 *Mathematics: Applications and Connections, Course 2*

Extending the Lesson

***Enrichment Masters,* p. 64**

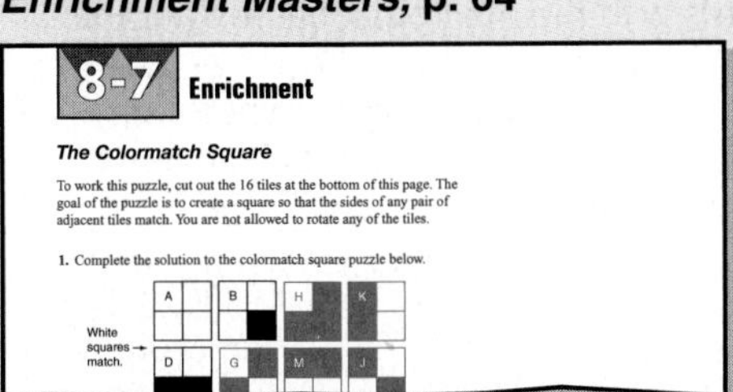

8-7 **Enrichment**

The Colormatch Square

To work this puzzle, cut out the 16 tiles at the bottom of this page. The goal of the puzzle is to create a square so that the sides of any pair of adjacent tiles match. You are not allowed to rotate any of the tiles.

1. Complete the solution to the colormatch square puzzle below.

Activity Refer students to Exercises 41–46. Challenge them to rewrite the reasonable statements so that they will no longer make sense, and to rewrite those that are unreasonable so that they do make sense.

8-8 Lesson Notes

Instructional Resources

- *Study Guide Masters,* p. 65
- *Practice Masters,* p. 65
- *Enrichment Masters,* p. 65
- Transparencies 8-8, A and B
- CD-ROM Program
  - Resource Lesson 8-8
  - Interactive Lesson 8-8

Recommended Pacing	
Standard	Day 11 of 14
Honors	Day 11 of 14
Block	Day 6 of 7

1 FOCUS

5-Minute Check (Lesson 8-7)

Express each percent as a decimal.

1. 1,063% 10.63
2. $\frac{1}{16}$% 0.000625

Express each number as a percent.

3. $9\frac{3}{5}$ 960%
4. 0.0033 0.33%
5. Tell whether *your fingers are $\frac{1}{10}$ the size of your fingers at 2 years old* is a reasonable statement. Explain why or why not. Not reasonable; your fingers are longer now than at age 2.

The 5-Minute Check is also available on **Transparency 8-8A** for this lesson.

Motivating the Lesson

Communication Ask students to describe how they could figure out the savings on a car stereo system that is selling for 15% off the regular price of $300.

8-8 Percent of a Number

What **you'll learn**

You'll learn to find the percent of a number.

When **am I ever going to use this?**

You'll use percents to find the sale price of an item.

You can learn a lot by reading the back of a packet of seeds. A new gardener can learn how deep to plant the seeds, how far apart to plant the seeds, and how many are expected to germinate or sprout. For example, one packet of beans guarantees that 95% of its 200 seeds will germinate. How many beans are expected to germinate?

In this problem, 95% means that 95 out of every 100 seeds are expected to germinate. There are several ways to solve this problem.

Method 1 Use a model.

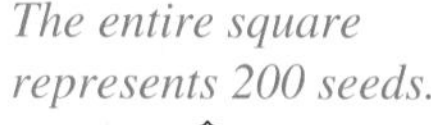

The entire square represents 200 seeds.

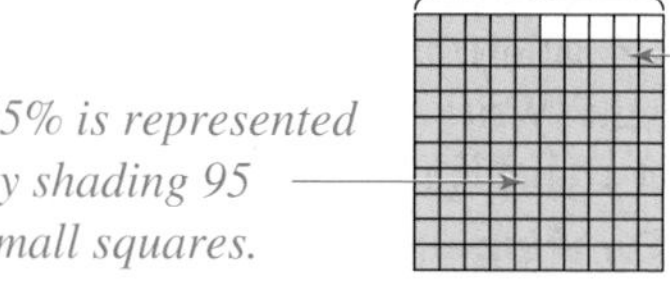

95% is represented by shading 95 small squares.
Each small square represents 200 ÷ 100 or 2 seeds.

95% of 200 is represented by 95 × 2 or 190.
So, 190 seeds are expected to germinate.

Method 2 Use a proportion.

Let n represent the number of seeds that are expected to germinate.

$$\frac{n}{200} = \frac{95}{100}$$ *germinating seeds → n; total seeds in packet → 200; percent germinating ← 95; total percent in packet ← 100*

$n \cdot 100 = 200 \cdot 95$ *Find the cross products.*

$100n = 19{,}000$

$\frac{100n}{100} = \frac{19{,}000}{100}$ *Divide each side by 100.*

$n = 190$

Method 3 Use multiplication.

First express the percent as a decimal. Then multiply.

95% of 200 = 0.95 × 200 *95% = 0.95*
= 190

All three methods give the same result, 190 seeds.

> **Study Hint**
> **Technology** You can find a percent of a number with a calculator. To find 95% of 200, enter
> 95 [2nd] [%] [×] 200 [=] 190

Classroom Vignette

"Students can act as servers with menus from local restaurants. Students switch from the role of server (where they total the bills and calculate the tax) to the role of customer (where they check the total and determine the tip). This is a practical use of percents that everyone needs to practice."

Virginia P. Healy, Teacher
Thomas Harrison Middle School
Harrisburg, VA

Examples

1 **Find 18.5% of 500 by using a proportion.**

Let n represent the number.

$$\frac{n}{500} = \frac{18.5}{100}$$

$$n \cdot 100 = 500 \cdot 18.5 \quad \textit{Find the cross products.}$$

$$\frac{n \cdot 100}{100} = \frac{500 \cdot 18.5}{100} \quad \textit{Divide each side by 100.}$$

$$n = 92.5$$

18.5% of 500 is 92.5.

> **Study Hint**
> **Mental Math** You can find 25% of 120 mentally by using the fraction $\frac{1}{4}$. $\frac{1}{4}$ of 120 is 30.

2 **What number is 25% of 120? Find the number by multiplying.**

$$25\% \text{ of } 120 = 0.25 \times 120 \quad \textit{25\% = 0.25}$$
$$= 30$$

25% of 120 is 30.

INTEGRATION

3 **Statistics** **A magazine recently surveyed 603 students to find what fast-food restaurants they preferred. The results are shown in the circle graph. Of the 603 students surveyed, how many preferred restaurant E?**

Favorite Fast-Food Restaurants

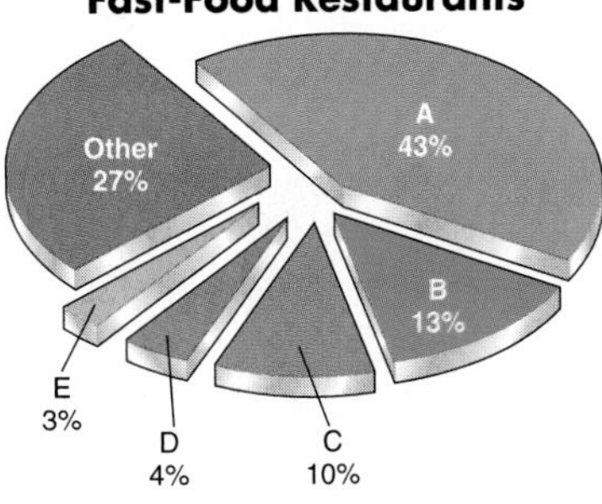

Find 3% of 603.

$$3\% \text{ of } 603 = 0.03 \times 603$$
$$= 18.09$$

About 18 of the students surveyed prefer restaurant E.

CHECK FOR UNDERSTANDING

Communicating Mathematics

Read and study the lesson to answer each question.

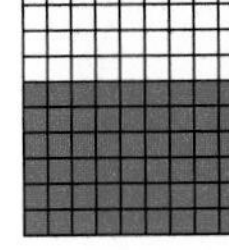

1. ***Explain*** how the model at the right can be used to find 60% of 300. **See margin.**
2. ***Write*** a proportion that can be used to find 42% of 386.

2. $\frac{n}{386} = \frac{42}{100}$

Guided Practice

Find each number. Round to the nearest tenth if necessary.

3. Find 93% of 215. **200.0**
4. Find 64% of 88. **56.3**
5. What number is 140% of 220? **308**
6. 0.5% of 350 is what number? **1.8**
7. ***Money Matters*** The purchase price of a bicycle is \$140. The state tax rate is 6.5% of the purchase price. How much state tax is charged? **\$9.10**

2 TEACH

Transparency 8-8B contains a teaching aid for this lesson.

Modeling Mathematics When using a 10×10 grid to model percent problems, students should think of the percent number as the numerator and 100 squares as the denominator of a fraction.

In-Class Examples

For Example 1
Find 12.3% of 230 by using a proportion. **28.29**

For Example 2
What number is 16% of 350? Find the number by multiplying. **56**

For Example 3
The highest-rated TV show of 1996 was watched by 22% of the 95,900,000 TV-owning households in the U.S. How many households watched the show? **21,098,000**

Additional Answer

1. Sample answer: Each square represents 3. Sixty squares are shaded. So, 60% of 300 is 60×3 or 180.

***Study Guide Masters*, p. 65**

Name________________ Date________

Study Guide

Percent of a Number

A **percent** is a ratio that compares a number to 100.

Example 1 **3 out of 4 is what percent?**

$$\frac{3}{4} = \frac{r}{100}$$
$$3 \times 100 = 4r \quad \textit{Find the cross products.}$$
$$\frac{300}{4} = \frac{4r}{4} \quad \textit{Divide each side by 4.}$$
$$75 = r$$

3 out of 4 is 75%.

Examples **2 What number is 20% of 180?**

Let n represent the number.

$$\frac{n}{180} = \frac{20}{100}$$
$$n \cdot 100 = 180 \cdot 20 \quad \textit{Find the cross products.}$$
$$\frac{100n}{100} = \frac{3,600}{100} \quad \textit{Divide each side by 100.}$$
$$n = 36$$

20% of 180 is 36.

3 40% of 48 is what number?

Let n represent the number.

$$\frac{n}{48} = \frac{40}{100}$$
$$n \cdot 100 = 48 \cdot 40$$
$$\frac{100n}{100} = \frac{1,920}{100}$$
$$n = 19.2$$

40% of 48 is 19.2.

Find each number. Round to the nearest tenth if necessary.

1. What number is 10% of 230? 23
2. 25% of 38 is what number? 9.5
4. Find 15% of 160. 24
5. What number is 24% of 20? 4.8
7. 50% of 74 is what number? 37
8. What number is 40% of 250? 100
10. 36% of 75 is what number? 27
11. 36% of 18 is what number? 6.5
13. What is 15% of 200? 30
14. Find 19% of 87. 16.5
16. Find 725% of 3.4. 24.7
17. What is 0.05% of 2999? 1.5

 T65 *Mathematics: Applications and Connections, Course 2*

■ Reteaching the Lesson ■

Activity Survey class members to find out how many of their homes have telephone-answering machines. Use the data to write a ratio and a percent proportion.

MathPASS CD-ROM

This CD-ROM offers a complete, self-paced mathematics curriculum. Each lesson includes a pretest, tutorial, guided practice, and posttest. MathPASS Lesson 32 is correlated to this Student Edition lesson.
For Windows & Macintosh

3 PRACTICE/APPLY

Check for Understanding

If students need additional practice or instruction after completing Exercises 1–7, one of these options may be helpful.

- Extra Practice, see p. 592
- Reteaching Activity, see p. 347
- *Study Guide Masters,* p. 65
- *Practice Masters,* p. 65

Assignment Guide

Core: 9–23 odd, 24–27
Enriched: 8–18 even, 20–27

4 ASSESS

Closing Activity

Writing Have students write a quiz for classmates consisting of 5 problems to solve by finding a percent of a number. If possible, students should use actual information from a newspaper, magazine, or catalogue to formulate their problems.

Additional Answer

20. never–207,770 consumers; regularly–7,890 consumers; occasionally–47,340 consumers

***Practice Masters,* p. 65**

Name______________ Date______________

8-8 Practice

Percent of a Number

Find each number. Round to the nearest tenth if necessary.

1. What number is 18% of 450? 81
2. Find 92% of 120. 110.4
3. $37\frac{1}{2}$ is 30% of what number? 125
4. 45% of 156 is what number? 70.2
5. 96 is 30% of what number? 320
6. Forty percent of 80 is what number? 32
7. What number is 58% of 200? 116
8. $33\frac{1}{3}$% of 249 is what number? 83
9. What number is 12% of 150? 18
10. Find $82\frac{1}{2}$% of 400. 330
11. What number is 72% of 1,024? 737.3
12. Find 12% of 12. 1.4
13. What number is 60% of 264? 158.4
14. 96% of 72 is what number? 69.1
15. 380% of 30 is what number? 114
16. $37\frac{1}{2}$% of 18 is what number? 6.8
17. Find 70% of 1,760. 1232
18. What number is 24% of 294? 70.6

 T65 *Mathematics: Applications and Connections, Course 2*

EXERCISES

Practice **Find each number. Round to the nearest tenth if necessary.**

8. What number is 25% of 560? **140**
9. Find 37.5% of 64. **24**
10. 50% of 128 is what number? **64**
11. What number is 25% of 36? **9**
12. Find 80% of 90.5. **72.4**
13. What number is 75% of 92? **69**
14. 12% of 16.5 is what number? **2.0**
15. 130% of 96 is what number? **124.8**
16. 0.25% of 400 is what number? **1**
17. What number is 20% of twenty? **4**
18. What number is $33\frac{1}{3}$% of 18? **6**
19. Find $16\frac{2}{3}$% of 60. **10**

Applications and Problem Solving

20. ***Shopping*** A company surveyed 263,000 consumers ages 14 years and older to find how often they buy products from TV shopping shows. How many consumers fall into each category of the circle graph? **See margin.**

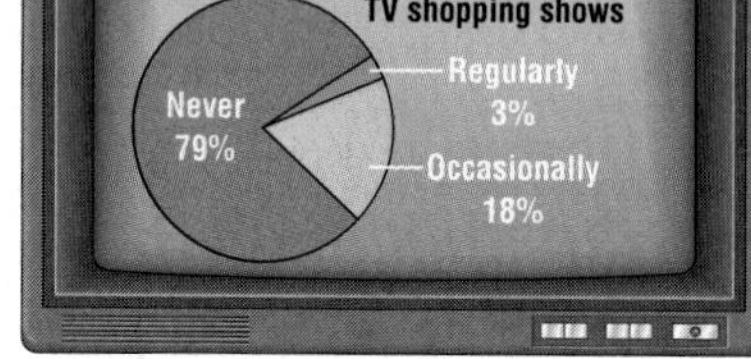

Source: Impact Resources

21. ***Money Matters*** The standard rate for tipping in a restaurant is 15% of your total bill. A family of six has a bill of $74.80 at a restaurant. What should their tip be? **$11.22**

22. ***Civics*** On an average day, 1,648 persons immigrate to the United States. Nearly 41% of them will become naturalized American citizens. How many of the daily immigrants to the United States are likely to become citizens? **676 immigrants**

23. ***Business*** The leading brand of cosmetics in the United States had about 20% of the total sales in the industry. The total sales were $2.6 billion. Find the leading brand's sales. **$0.52 billion or $520 million**

24. ***Critical Thinking*** Suppose you add 10% of a number to the number. Then you subtract 10% of the total. How does the result compare to your original number? Explain your reasoning. **See Answer Appendix.**

Mixed Review

25. Express 0.6% as a decimal. *(Lesson 8-7)* **0.006**

26. **Standardized Test Practice** Which of the following has the best unit price? *(Lesson 8-2)* **B**
    A 18 ounces for $5.40 **B** 16 ounces for $4.64
    C 12 ounces for $3.72 **D** 10 ounces for $3.30

For **Extra Practice,** see page 592.

27. ***Measurement*** How many $\frac{1}{2}$-cup servings of ice cream are there in a gallon of chocolate ice cream? *(Lesson 7-5)* **32 servings**

Extending the Lesson

***Enrichment Masters,* p. 65**

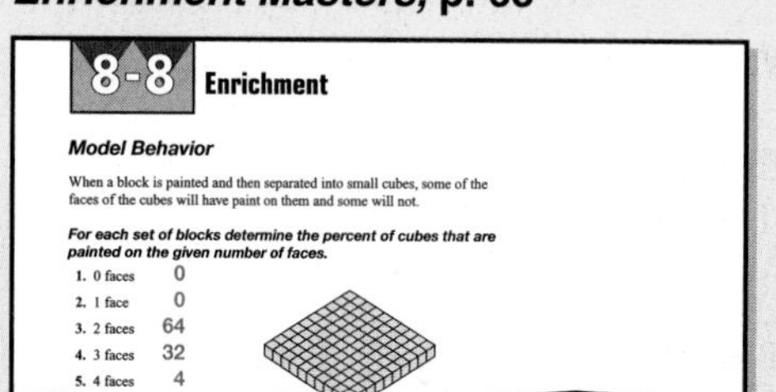

8-8 Enrichment

Model Behavior

When a block is painted and then separated into small cubes, some of the faces of the cubes will have paint on them and some will not.

For each set of blocks determine the percent of cubes that are painted on the given number of faces.

1. 0 faces 0
2. 1 face 0
3. 2 faces 64
4. 3 faces 32
5. 4 faces 4

Activity Have students write a paragraph explaining what happens to a percent of a number as the base number increases. Ask them what happens to the percent when the base number decreases.

8-9 The Percent Proportion

***What** you'll learn*

You'll learn to solve problems using the percent proportion.

***When** am I ever going to use this?*

You'll use the percent proportion to make and analyze circle graphs.

Word Wise

percentage
base
rate
percent proportion

Arthropods

Insects 88%
Spiders 7%
Crustaceans 4%
Millipedes and Centipedes 1%

Are you afraid of spiders? Do insects give you the creeps? It's no wonder, because there are about 854,000 different species of spiders, insects, crustaceans, millipedes, and centipedes on Earth. The graph shows that 88% of the total number of species of arthropods are insects. How many species are insects?

Let n represent the number of species of insects.

$$\frac{n}{854{,}000} = \frac{88}{100}$$

$$n \cdot 100 = 854{,}000 \cdot 88$$

$$\frac{n \cdot 100}{100} = \frac{854{,}000 \cdot 88}{100}$$

$$n = \frac{854{,}000 \cdot 88}{100}$$

854000 [×] 88 [÷] 100 [=] 751520

There are about 752,000 species of insects on Earth.

In the problem above, 752,000 is the **percentage (*P*)**. The number 854,000 is the **base (*B*)**. The ratio $\frac{88}{100}$ is the **rate (*r*)**. The percentage, base, and rate are related in the **percent proportion**.

Percent Proportion	The percent proportion is $\frac{P}{B} = \frac{r}{100}$, where *P* represents the percentage, *B* represents the base, and *r* represents the number per hundred.

There are three basic kinds of percent problems that can be solved using the percent proportion. Using the proportion $\frac{1}{2} = \frac{50}{100}$, you can see that the types are related as shown below.

Find the percentage.	What number is 50% of 2? (*Percentage*: What number)	$\frac{■}{2} = \frac{50}{100}$
Find the rate.	1 is what percent of 2? (*Rate*: what percent)	$\frac{1}{2} = \frac{■}{100}$
Find the base.	1 is 50% of what number? (*Base*: what number)	$\frac{1}{■} = \frac{50}{100}$

8-9 Lesson Notes

Instructional Resources

- *Study Guide Masters,* p. 66
- *Practice Masters,* p. 66
- *Enrichment Masters,* p. 66
- Transparencies 8-9, A and B
- *Assessment and Evaluation Masters,* p. 212
- *Diversity Masters,* p. 21
- *Technology Masters,* p. 42
- CD-ROM Program
  - Resource Lesson 8-9

Recommended Pacing	
Standard	Day 12 of 14
Honors	Day 12 of 14
Block	Day 6 of 7

1 FOCUS

5-Minute Check
(Lesson 8-8)

1. Find $62\frac{1}{2}$% of 32. 20
2. What number is 60% of 180? 108
3. 75% of 72 is what number? 54
4. 85 is 35% of what number? 242.9
5. Find 38% of 50. 19

The 5-Minute Check is also available on **Transparency 8-9A** for this lesson.

Motivating the Lesson

Problem Solving Have students use an almanac or other source to compare Olympic track and field results. For example, by what percent did the winning times change in the women's 100-meter and the men's 100-meter dash from 1992 to 1996?

2 TEACH

Transparency 8-9B contains a teaching aid for this lesson.

Thinking Algebraically Some students may wish to manipulate the percent proportion to yield a formula for each type of problem: $P = \frac{Br}{100}$, $r = \frac{100P}{B}$, and $B = \frac{100P}{r}$

In-Class Examples

For Example 1
Thirty-seven is 25% of what number? 148

For Example 2
According to the graph, the number of cars made in 1995 was 49.869 million. What percent of the total was made in Japan? 20.4%

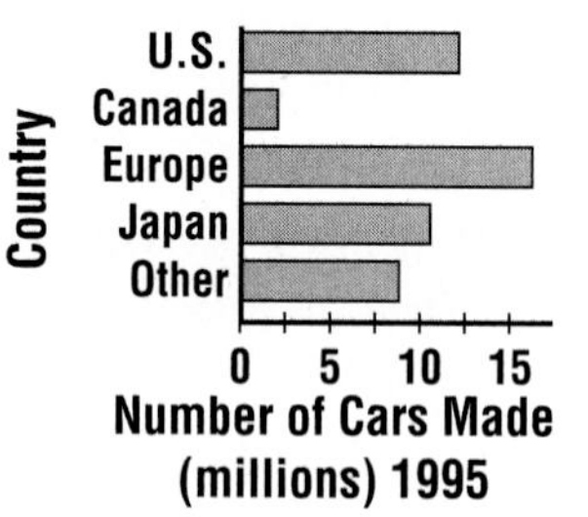

3 PRACTICE/APPLY

Check for Understanding

If students need additional practice or instruction after completing Exercises 1–10, one of these options may be helpful.

- Extra Practice, see p. 592
- Reteaching Activity
- *Study Guide Masters,* p. 66
- *Practice Masters,* p. 66

***Study Guide Masters,* p. 66**

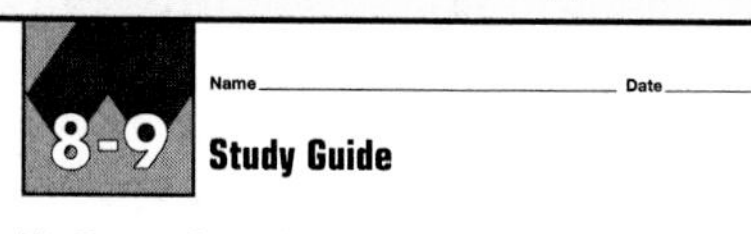

Name__________ Date__________

8-9 Study Guide

The Percent Proportion

Use the percent proportion to solve problems.

$\frac{P}{B} = \frac{r}{100}$, where P = percentage, B = base, and $\frac{r}{100}$ = rate.

Examples **1 12 is what percent of 96?**

$\frac{P}{B} = \frac{r}{100}$ *Replace P with 12 and B with 96.*

$\frac{12}{96} = \frac{r}{100}$

$12 \times 100 = 96r$ *Find the cross products.*

$\frac{1{,}200}{96} = \frac{96r}{96}$

$12.5 = r$

So, 12 is 12.5% of 96.

2 What number is 120% of 55?

$\frac{P}{B} = \frac{r}{100}$ *Replace B with 55 and r with 120.*

$\frac{P}{55} = \frac{120}{100}$

$100P = 55 \times 120$ *Find the cross products.*

$\frac{100P}{100} = \frac{6{,}600}{100}$

$P = 66$

So, 66 is 120% of 55.

Find each number. Round to the nearest tenth if necessary.

1. 12 is what percent of 14? 85.7%
2. 50% of what number is 9? 18
3. What percent of 50 is 75? 150%
4. Find 12.5% of 16. 2
5. What percent of 80 is 16? 20%
6. 40% of what number is 32? 80
7. Find 90% of 68. 61.2
8. 72 is what percent of 60? 120%
9. What number is 75% of 128? 96
10. $12\frac{1}{2}$ percent of what number is 2? 16

 T66 *Mathematics: Applications and Connections, Course 2*

Examples

Study Hint
Reading Math In a percent problem, the base usually follows the word *of.*

1 Twenty-five is 20% of what number?

$\frac{P}{B} = \frac{r}{100}$ *Write the percent proportion.*

$\frac{25}{B} = \frac{20}{100}$ *Replace P with 25 and r with 20.*

$25 \cdot 100 = B \cdot 20$ *Find the cross products.*

$2{,}500 = 20B$

$\frac{2{,}500}{20} = \frac{20B}{20}$ *Divide each side by 20.*

$125 = B$ 25 is 20% of 125.

APPLICATION

2 Sports Refer to the graph at the right. What percent of the athletes trying out for the U.S. swimming team earned positions on the team?

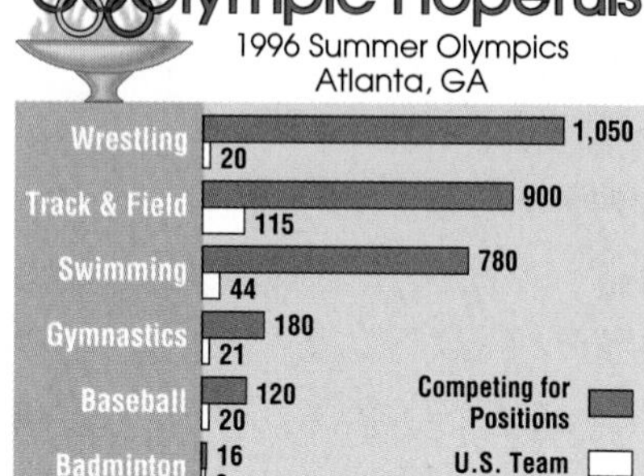

Source: SportsTicker Enterprises

Find what percent 44 is of 780.

$\frac{P}{B} = \frac{r}{100}$

$\frac{44}{780} = \frac{r}{100}$

$44 \cdot 100 = 780r$

$\frac{44 \cdot 100}{780} = r$ 44 [×] 100 [÷] 780 [=] 5.641025641

$5.6 \approx r$

About 5.6% of the athletes who tried out made the team.

CHECK FOR UNDERSTANDING

Communicating Mathematics

Read and study the lesson to answer each question.

1. ***Tell*** what P, B, and r represent in the percent proportion. **See margin.**
2. ***Write*** a proportion that can be used to find the rate if the percentage is 18 and the base is 54. $\frac{18}{54} = \frac{r}{100}$
3. ***You Decide*** Jackson is trying to find what percent 30 is of 20. He uses the proportion $\frac{20}{30} = \frac{r}{100}$. Meredith uses $\frac{30}{20} = \frac{r}{100}$. Who is correct? **Meredith; 30 is being compared to 20, so 20 is the base.**

Guided Practice

Find each number. Round to the nearest tenth if necessary.

4. What number is 45% of 60? **27**
5. 3 is what percent of 40? **7.5%**
6. 80 is 75% of what number? **106.7**
7. What percent of 24 is 12? **50%**
8. Find 42.5% of 48. **20.4**
9. 20% of what number is 25? **125**
10. ***School*** A class picture included 95% of the students. Seven students were missing. How many students were in the class? **140 students**

Reteaching the Lesson

Activity Focus on what the problem asks and what information is given, in terms of the percent, base *(B),* and percentage *(P).* Remind students that $\frac{r}{100}$ always represents the percent. You may wish to have students write the problem and color code each number to identify *P, B,* and *r* before writing the proportion.

Additional Answer

1. ***P*** **is the percentage,** ***B*** **is the base, and** ***r*** **is the number per hundred.**

EXERCISES

Practice

Find each number. Round to the nearest tenth if necessary.

11. 8 is what percent of 16? **50%**
12. 20% of what number is 18? **90**
13. 58.2% of 50 is what number? **29.1**
14. What number is 105% of 36? **37.8**
15. What number is 38% of 70? **26.6**
16. 14 is what percent of 49? **28.6%**
17. 61 is 35% of what number? **174.3**
18. 7.5% of 48 is what number? **3.6**
19. What percent of 180 is 30? **16.7%**
20. 12.5% of what number is 24? **192**
21. 63 is what percent of 42? **150%**
22. 50% of what number is 15.8? **31.6**
23. $6\frac{1}{4}$% of 235 is what number? **14.7**
24. 5% of what number is $6\frac{1}{2}$? **130**
25. What percent of 250 is 25? **10%**
26. What number is 40% of 86? **34.4**
27. 20% of what number is 12? **60**
28. Find 125% of 48. **60**

interNET CONNECTION For the latest recommended daily allowances, visit: www.glencoe.com/sec/math/mac/mathnet

Applications and Problem Solving

29. 50 grams
31. See students' work.
32. Baseball, gymnastics, wrestling; if the percentage stays the same, the percent decreases as the base increases.

29. ***Health*** A nutritional label from a bag of pretzels is shown at the right. One serving of pretzels contains 1.5 grams of fat, which is 3% of the daily amount recommended for a 2,000-Calorie diet. How many grams of fat are recommended?

Nutrition Facts
Serving Size 1 package (46.8g)
Servings per container 1

Amount per serving	
Calories 190 Calories from Fat 15	
	% Daily Value
Total Fat 1.5g	3%
Saturated Fat 0g	0%
Cholesterol 0mg	0%
Sodium 760mg	32%
Total Carbohydrate 37g	12%
Dietary Fiber less than 1g	2%
Sugars 2g	
Protein 5g	
Vitamin A 0% •	Vitamin C 0%
Calcium 0% •	Iron 3%

*Percent Daily Values are based on a 2,000 calorie diet. Your daily values may be higher or lower depending on your calorie needs.

Calories per gram:
Fat 9 • Carbohydrates 4 • Protein 4

30. ***Civics*** Recently, there were 6,954 cases filed in the U.S. Supreme Court. Of these cases, only 82 of them were decided in the Supreme Court. What percent of the cases that were filed were actually decided by the Supreme Court? **1.2%**
31. ***Write a Problem*** that can be solved by finding 75% of $245.59.
32. ***Critical Thinking*** Refer to Example 2. The wrestling, baseball, and gymnastics teams had almost the same number of competitors. Order the sports from greatest to least percent of hopefuls who made the cut. Explain how you can determine the order without determining the actual percents.

Mixed Review

33. Find 22% of 85 by multiplying. *(Lesson 8-8)* **18.7**
34. Express 0.00065 as a percent. *(Lesson 8-7)* **0.065%**
35. **Standardized Test Practice** A mechanic charges a $35 initial fee and $32.50 for each hour he works. Which equation could be used to find the cost, c, of a repair job that lasts h hours? *(Lesson 6-4)* **B**
    A $c = 32.5 + 35h$ **B** $c = 35 + 32.5h$ **C** $c = 32.5 - 35h$
    D $c = 35 - 32.5h$ **E** $c = 32.5(35 - h)$
36. ***Algebra*** Find the solution of $g - 6.9 = 13.3$. *(Lesson 6-1)* **20.2**

For **Extra Practice**, see page 592.

Assignment Guide

Core: 11–31 odd, 32–36
Enriched: 12–28 even, 29–36

4 ASSESS

Closing Activity

Speaking Have students explain how to use the percent proportion to solve problems.

Chapter 8, Quiz D (Lessons 8-8 and 8-9) is available in the *Assessment and Evaluation Masters,* p. 212.

Practice Masters, p. 66

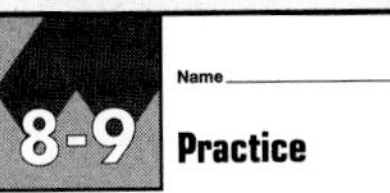

Name ______ Date ______

8-9 Practice

The Percent Proportion

Find each number. Round to the nearest tenth if necessary.

1. 12 is what percent of 30? 40%
2. 40% of what number is 82? 205
3. What percent of 49 is 7? 14.3%
4. 6.25% of 190 is what number? 11.9
5. 64.2% of 84 is what number? 53.9
6. What percent of 76 is 14? 18.4%
7. What number is 32% of 1,000? 320
8. What is 84% of 180? 151.2
9. $12\frac{1}{2}$ is 25% of what number? 50
10. 85% of 190 is what number? 161.5
11. What percent of 128 is 24? 18.8%
12. 25 is what percent of 365? 6.8%
13. What number is 20% of 625? 125
14. $33\frac{1}{3}$% of 900 is what number? 300
15. 40% of what number is 36? 90
16. 8.25% of 180 is what number? 14.9
17. 73 is 20% of what number? 365
18. What percent of 185 is 35? 18.9%
19. What number is 36% of 96? 34.6
20. 56% of 109 is what number? 61.0

 T66 *Mathematics: Applications and Connections, Course 2*

Extending the Lesson

Enrichment Masters, p. 66

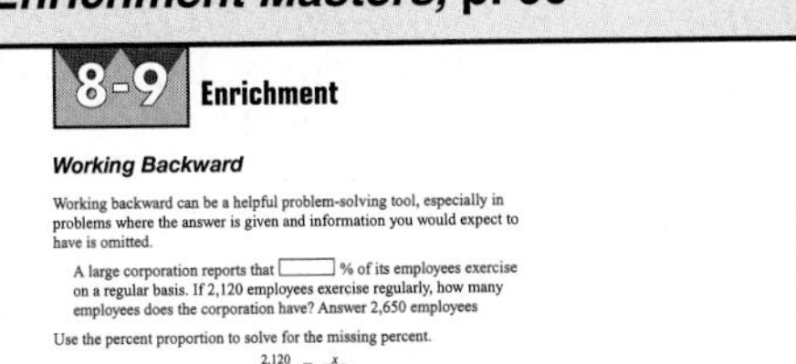

8-9 Enrichment

Working Backward

Working backward can be a helpful problem-solving tool, especially in problems where the answer is given and information you would expect to have is omitted.

A large corporation reports that ☐ % of its employees exercise on a regular basis. If 2,120 employees exercise regularly, how many employees does the corporation have? Answer 2,650 employees

Use the percent proportion to solve for the missing percent.

$$\frac{2,120}{2,650} = \frac{x}{100}$$
$$2,120 \times 100 = 2,650x$$
$$x = 80$$

Activity Challenge students to explain how they would go about finding the percent of a percent of a number, such as 25% of 25% of 24. Ask students to write a problem of this kind for classmates to solve.

Study Guide and Assessment

Vocabulary

This section provides a listing of the new terms, properties, and phrases that were introduced in this chapter. Have students define each term and provide an example or two of it, if appropriate.

Understanding and Using the Vocabulary

These exercises check students' understanding of the terms by using a variety of verbal formats including matching, completion, and true/false.

Glossaries A complete glossary of terms appears on pages 656–663. The glossary also appears in Spanish on pages 664–672.

Additional Answers

11. $\frac{5}{2}$
12. $\frac{1}{5}$
13. $\frac{1}{6}$
14. $\frac{3}{16}$
15. $\frac{30}{11}$
16. $\frac{1}{2}$
19. 4 cups per person
20. 30 people per class
21. $4.75 per pound
22. 90 miles per day
23. $9.50 per hour
24. 8 gerbils per cage

CHAPTER 8 Study Guide and Assessment

interNET CONNECTION Chapter Review For additional lesson-by-lesson review, visit: www.glencoe.com/sec/math/mac/mathnet

Vocabulary

After completing this chapter, you should be able to define each term, concept, or phrase and give an example or two of each.

Number and Operations
base (p. 349)
cross products (p. 325)
equivalent ratios (p. 318)
percent proportion (p. 349)
percentage (p. 349)
population density (p. 322)
property of proportions (p. 325)
proportion (p. 325)
rate (pp. 321, 349)
ratio (p. 317)
unit rate (p. 321)

Geometry
scale (p. 332)
scale drawing (p. 332)

Statistics and Probability
capture-recapture technique (p. 329)
sample (p. 329)

Problem Solving
draw a diagram (p. 330)

10. Find the cross products; 6×4 and $12 \times n$. Multiply to produce the equation $24 = 12n$. Divide each side by 12 and the result is $n = 2$.

Understanding and Using the Vocabulary

Choose the letter of the term that best matches each phrase.

1. a comparison of two numbers by division e
2. two ratios that have the same value i
3. a ratio of two measurements with different units a
4. an equation that shows that two ratios are equivalent h
5. used to present something that is too large or too small for actual-size drawing c
6. the ratio of the distance on a map to the actual distance f
7. a ratio that compares a number to 100 d
8. the name for 60 in the percent proportion $\frac{15}{25} = \frac{60}{100}$ a
9. the name for 25 in the percent proportion $\frac{15}{25} = \frac{60}{100}$ b

a. rate
b. base
c. scale drawing
d. percent
e. ratio
f. scale
g. unit rate
h. proportion
i. equivalent ratios
j. cross products
k. percentage

In Your Own Words

10. ***Explain*** how to solve $\frac{6}{12} = \frac{n}{4}$.

MindJogger Videoquizzes

MindJogger Videoquizzes provide an alternative review of concepts presented in this chapter. Students work in teams to answer questions, gaining points for correct answers. The questions are presented in three rounds.

Round 1 Concepts–5 questions
Round 2 Skills–4 questions
Round 3 Problem Solving–4 questions

Objectives & Examples

Upon completing this chapter, you should be able to:

- express ratios as fractions and determine whether two ratios are equivalent *(Lesson 8-1)*

Express 6:18 as a fraction in simplest form.

$$\frac{6}{18} = \frac{6 \div 6}{18 \div 6} = \frac{1}{3}$$

The simplest form is $\frac{1}{3}$.

Review Exercises

Use these exercises to review and prepare for the chapter test.

Express each ratio as a fraction in simplest form. **11–16. See margin.**

11. 25 to 10 **12.** 14:70 **13.** 11:66

14. 12 to 64 **15.** 90 to 33 **16.** 50:100

Tell whether the ratios are equivalent. Show your answer by simplifying.

17. $\frac{63}{9}$ and $\frac{21}{14}$ **no** **18.** $\frac{5}{10}$ and $\frac{12}{24}$ **yes**

- to determine unit rates *(Lesson 8-2)*

Find the unit price for a 16-ounce box of pasta on sale for 96 cents.

$$\frac{cents}{ounces} \rightarrow \frac{96}{16} = \frac{96 \div 16}{16 \div 16} = \frac{6}{1}$$

The unit price is 6 cents per ounce.

Express each rate as a unit rate. **19–24. See margin.**

19. 16 cups for 4 people

20. 150 people for 5 classes

21. $23.75 for 5 pounds

22. 810 miles in 9 days

23. $38 in 4 hours

24. 24 gerbils in 3 cages

- to solve proportions *(Lesson 8-3)*

Solve $\frac{6}{9} = \frac{x}{12}$

$$\frac{6}{9} = \frac{x}{12}$$

$$6 \times 12 = 9 \times x$$

$$72 = 9x$$

$$8 = x$$ The solution is 8.

Solve each proportion.

25. $\frac{13}{25} = \frac{39}{m}$ **75** **26.** $\frac{w}{6} = \frac{12}{8}$ **9**

27. $\frac{350}{p} = \frac{2}{10}$ **1,750** **28.** $\frac{45}{5} = \frac{x}{7}$ **63**

29. ***Algebra*** Find the value of x that makes $\frac{5}{x} = \frac{6}{3}$ a proportion. **2.5**

- to solve problems involving scale drawings *(Lesson 8-4)*

A map scale is 1 inch:80 miles. Find the actual distance for a map distance of $3\frac{1}{4}$ inches.

$$\begin{matrix} map \rightarrow \\ actual \rightarrow \end{matrix} \frac{1 \text{ inch}}{80 \text{ miles}} = \frac{3\frac{1}{4} \text{ inches}}{n \text{ miles}} \begin{matrix} \leftarrow map \\ \leftarrow actual \end{matrix}$$

$$1 \times n = 80 \times 3\frac{1}{4}$$

$$n = 260$$

The actual distance is 260 miles.

30. Find the distance between Atlanta and Savannah, Georgia if the map distance is $3\frac{1}{2}$ inches and the scale is 1 inch:70 miles.

31. Find the length of a building 20 yards wide on a scale drawing with a scale of $\frac{1}{2}$ in. = 1 yd. **10 inches**

30. 245 miles

Objectives & Examples

This section reviews the skills and concepts of the chapter and shows completely worked examples.

Review Exercises

These exercises provide practice for the corresponding objectives.

***Assessment and Evaluation Masters*, pp. 199–200**

Name__________ Date__________

Chapter 8 Test, Form 1B

1. Express the ratio 8 feet to 12 yards as a fraction in simplest form. 1. D
   A. $\frac{8}{12}$ B. $\frac{3}{2}$ C. $\frac{1}{2}$ D. $\frac{2}{9}$

2. Are the ratios 4:9 and 12:18 equivalent? Choose the simplified answer. 2. C
   A. Yes; $\frac{12}{18} = \frac{4}{9}$. B. Yes; $\frac{4}{9} = \frac{12}{18}$.
   C. No; $\frac{12}{18} = \frac{2}{3}$. D. No; $\frac{18}{12} = \frac{3}{2}$.

3. Express the rate of $1.35 for 45 pieces of paper as a unit rate. 3. C
   A. 30¢ per piece B. 0.03¢ per piece
   C. 3¢ per piece D. 9¢ per piece

4. What is the unit rate of 232 people in 8 classrooms? 4. A
   A. 29 people per classroom B. 58 people per classroom
   C. 19 people per classroom D. 32 people per classroom

5. Solve the proportion $\frac{30}{42} = \frac{55}{d}$. 5. B
   A. 39.3 B. 77 C. 67 D. 23

6. Solve the proportion $\frac{w}{11} = \frac{8}{7}$. 6. A
   A. 12.57 B. 5.09 C. 9.63 D. 2.18

7. Eleven tennis players are playing in a single-elimination tournament (if a player loses one match he or she is eliminated). Choose the diagram that accurately shows the number of matches played in the tournament. 7. D
   A. B. C. D.

8. On a map, the scale is 1 inch:125 miles. What is the actual distance if the map distance is $2\frac{3}{4}$ inches? 8. A
   A. $343\frac{3}{4}$ miles B. $281\frac{1}{4}$ miles
   C. 257 miles D. 325 miles

9. On a scale drawing, the scale is $\frac{1}{4}$ inch:1 foot. What are the dimensions in the scale drawing for a room that is 16 feet by 24 feet? 9. A
   A. 4 inches by 6 inches B. 7 inches by 12 inches
   C. 1 inch by 2 inches D. 1 inch by 2 inches

© Glencoe/McGraw-Hill 199 *Mathematics: Applications and Connections, Course 2*

Chapter 8 Test, Form 1B (continued)

10. Express the fraction $\frac{5}{8}$ as a percent. 10. A
    A. 62.5% B. 0.625% C. 625% D. 6.25%

11. Express 12% as a fraction in simplest form. 11. C
    A. $\frac{12}{1}$ B. $\frac{12}{100}$ C. $\frac{3}{25}$ D. $\frac{6}{50}$

12. Express 0.047 as a percent. 12. B
    A. 47% B. 4.7% C. 0.47% D. 0.047%

13. Express 3% as a decimal. 13. A
    A. 0.03 B. 3.0 C. 0.3 D. 30.0

14. Express 0.02% as a decimal. 14. C
    A. 2.0 B. 0.02 C. 0.0002 D. 0.002

15. Express 155% as a decimal. 15. B
    A. 15.5 B. 1.55 C. 155.0 D. 0.155

16. Express $1\frac{3}{5}$ as a percent. 16. C
    A. 13.5% B. 135% C. 160% D. 1.6%

17. What percent of 55 is 10? Round to the nearest whole percent. 17. B
    A. 6% B. 18% C. 2% D. 550%

18. Write a proportion and solve to find what number is 64% of 25. 18. D
    A. $\frac{x}{25} = \frac{64}{100}; x = 15$ B. $\frac{25}{x} = \frac{100}{64}; x = 2.6$
    C. $\frac{25}{x} = \frac{64}{100}; x = 39.1$ D. $\frac{x}{25} = \frac{64}{100}; x = 16$

19. Anita sent out invitations to a party and received an RSVP from every invitation. Thirteen of the RSVPs came back with a yes response and six RSVPs came back with a no response. What percent of the people that Anita invited to her party are not coming? 19. A
    A. 31.58% B. 46.15% C. 68.42% D. 1.46%

20. Angie wants to put a winter coat in layaway at a store. To do so, she must pay the store 20% of the cost of the coat so they will hold it. If the coat costs $48.99, about how much of a deposit does Angie need to pay the store? 20. B
    A. $2.50 B. $10 C. $15 D. $5

© Glencoe/McGraw-Hill 200 *Mathematics: Applications and Connections, Course 2*

Assessment and Evaluation

Six forms of Chapter 8 Test are available in the *Assessment and Evaluation Masters* as shown in the chart.

1A	Multiple Choice	Honors
1B	Multiple Choice	Average
1C	Multiple Choice	Basic
2A	Free Response	Honors
2B	Free Response	Average
2C	Free Response	Basic

Chapter 8 Test, Form 1B, is shown at the right. Chapter 8 Test, Form 2B, is shown on the next page.

Study Guide and Assessment

Assessment and Evaluation Masters, pp. 205–206

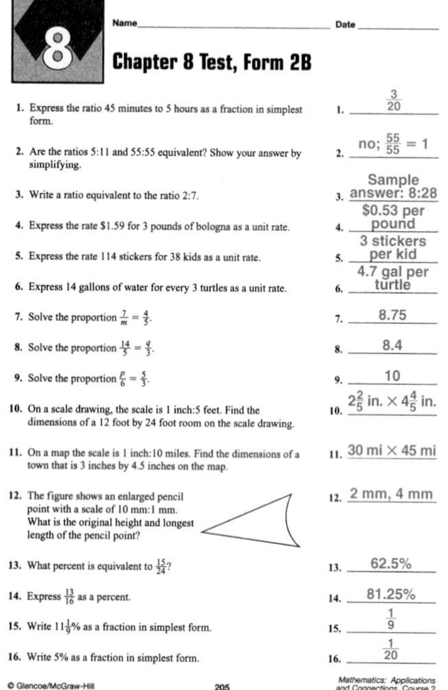

Name__________ Date__________

8 Chapter 8 Test, Form 2B

1. Express the ratio 45 minutes to 5 hours as a fraction in simplest form. 1. $\frac{3}{20}$
2. Are the ratios 5:11 and 55:55 equivalent? Show your answer by simplifying. 2. no; $\frac{55}{55} = 1$
3. Write a ratio equivalent to the ratio 2:7. 3. Sample answer: 8:28
4. Express the rate \$1.59 for 3 pounds of bologna as a unit rate. 4. \$0.53 per pound
5. Express the rate 114 stickers for 38 kids as a unit rate. 5. 3 stickers per kid
6. Express 14 gallons of water for every 3 turtles as a unit rate. 6. 4.7 gal per turtle
7. Solve the proportion $\frac{7}{m} = \frac{4}{5}$. 7. 8.75
8. Solve the proportion $\frac{14}{5} = \frac{q}{3}$. 8. 8.4
9. Solve the proportion $\frac{p}{6} = \frac{5}{3}$. 9. 10
10. On a scale drawing, the scale is 1 inch:5 feet. Find the dimensions of a 12 foot by 24 foot room on the scale drawing. 10. $2\frac{2}{5}$ in. × $4\frac{4}{5}$ in.
11. On a map the scale is 1 inch:10 miles. Find the dimensions of a town that is 3 inches by 4.5 inches on the map. 11. 30 mi × 45 mi
12. The figure shows an enlarged pencil point with a scale of 10 mm:1 mm. What is the original height and longest length of the pencil point? 12. 2 mm, 4 mm
13. What percent is equivalent to $\frac{15}{24}$? 13. 62.5%
14. Express $\frac{13}{16}$ as a percent. 14. 81.25%
15. Write $11\frac{1}{9}$% as a fraction in simplest form. 15. $\frac{1}{9}$
16. Write 5% as a fraction in simplest form. 16. $\frac{1}{20}$

 205 *Mathematics: Applications and Connections, Course 2*

8 Chapter 8 Test, Form 2B (continued)

17. Express 0.085 as a percent. 17. 8.5%
18. What percent is equivalent to 0.9134? 18. 91.34%
19. Write 19.7% as a decimal. 19. 0.197
20. Write the decimal that is equivalent to 7.3%. 20. 0.073
21. Express $4\frac{2}{3}$ as a percent. 21. 466.7%
22. What percent is equivalent to 0.00036? 22. 0.036%
23. Write $2\frac{1}{3}$% as a decimal. 23. 2.33
24. Write 577% as a fraction. 24. $5\frac{77}{100}$
25. 19% of what number is 31? Round your answer to the nearest tenth. 25. 163.2
26. Find 35% of 80. 26. 28
27. What number is 45% of 60? 27. 27
28. Write a proportion and solve to find what number is 36% of 19. 28. $\frac{x}{19} = \frac{36}{100}$; $x = 6.84$
29. Use a proportion to find what number is 78% of 78. 29. 60.84
30. 33% of what number is 33? 30. 100
31. What percent of 120 is 15? 31. 12.5%
32. A mother cat had 2 kittens in one litter. Each of these kittens grew up and had 2 litters of 2 kittens each. Then each of these kittens, her "grandkittens," had 2 litters of 2 kittens each. On a separate sheet of paper, draw a diagram to show how many "great-grandkittens" the mother cat has. 32. 32 great-grand kittens;
33. A family of four went out to eat at a restaurant. Their total bill was \$46.69 plus 15% of the bill as a tip. How much did the family spend at the restaurant? 33. \$53.69

 206 *Mathematics: Applications and Connections, Course 2*

- to express fractions as percents, and vice versa *(Lesson 8-5)*

Express $\frac{18}{20}$ as a percent.

$\frac{18}{20} = \frac{n}{100}$ *Find cross products.*

$1,800 = 20n$ *Divide each side by 20.*

$90 = n$

So, $\frac{18}{20} = 90\%$.

Express each fraction as a percent.

32. $\frac{3}{5}$ **60%**
33. $\frac{5}{8}$ **62.5%**

Express each percent as a fraction in simplest form.

34. 65% $\frac{13}{20}$
35. $13\frac{1}{2}$% $\frac{27}{200}$
36. $78\frac{3}{4}$% $\frac{63}{80}$
37. 43.5% $\frac{87}{200}$

- to express decimals as percents, and vice versa *(Lesson 8-6)*

Express 48% as a decimal.

48% = 048 = 0.48

Express each decimal as a percent.

38. 0.87 **87%**
39. 0.325 **32.5%**

Express each percent as a decimal.

40. 42% **0.42**
41. $15\frac{3}{4}$% **0.1575**

- to express percents greater than 100% and percents less than 1% as fractions and as decimals, and vice versa *(Lesson 8-7)*

Write 2.35 as a percent.

$2.35 = 2\frac{35}{100}$

$= \frac{235}{100}$ or 235%

Express each percent as a decimal.

42. 125% **1.25**
43. 0.25% **0.0025**
44. 0.05% **0.0005**
45. 563% **5.63**

Express each number as a percent.

46. 0.002 **0.2%**
47. 4.75 **475%**
48. $7\frac{1}{2}$ **750%**
49. 0.0095 **0.95%**

- find the percent of a number *(Lesson 8-8)*

Find 45% of 400.

$\frac{n}{400} = \frac{45}{100}$

$100n = 18,000$

$n = 180$

Find each number. Round to the nearest tenth if necessary.

50. What number is 68% of 320? **217.6**
51. Find 18% of 90. **16.2**
52. 0.75% of 80 is what number? **0.6**
53. What number is 280% of 18? **50.4**

- solve problems using the percent proportion *(Lesson 8-9)*

What percent of 90 is 18?

$\frac{P}{B} = \frac{r}{100}$

$\frac{18}{90} = \frac{r}{100}$

$1,800 = 90r$

$20 = r$

Find each number. Round to the nearest tenth if necessary.

54. 6 is what percent of 120? **5%**
55. Find 0.8% of 35. **0.3**
56. What percent of 375 is 40? **10.7%**
57. 15% of what number is 900? **6,000**

Test and Review Software

You may use this software, a combination of an item generator and item bank, to create your own tests or worksheets. Types of items include free response, multiple choice, short answer, and open ended.

CD-ROM Program

The CD-ROM Program contains an Assessment Game whose questions review the concepts in this chapter.

Applications & Problem Solving

58. ***Geography*** Brookville has a population of 4,312 people and an area of 127 square miles. To the nearest whole number, how many people per square mile are there in Brookville? *(Lesson 8-2)*

59. ***Draw a Diagram*** The advisor for the Spanish Club tells three students about a club meeting. It takes 1 minute for her to tell three students and 1 minute for each of those three students to tell three other students, and so on. How many students will know about the meeting in three minutes? *(Lesson 8-4A)* **39 students**

58. 34 people per sq mi

60. ***Statistics*** Of the 100 teens who answered a survey, 21 owned a cat. What percent of those who answered the survey own a cat? *(Lesson 8-5)* **21%**

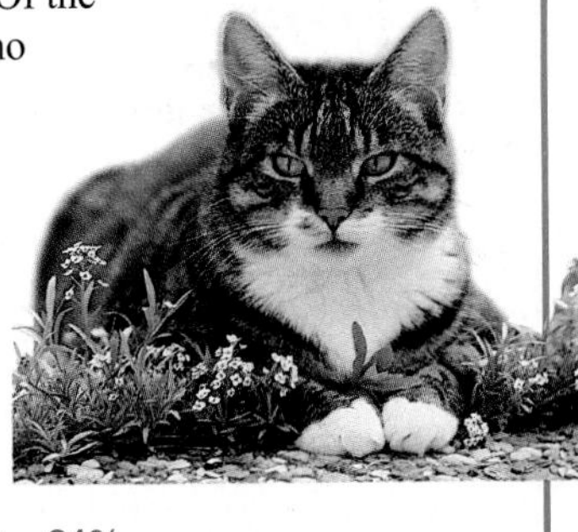

61. ***Life Science*** Did you know that humans are outnumbered on Earth? There are so many insects that the weight of all humans together is just $\frac{1}{3}\%$ of the weight of all the insects! What is $\frac{1}{3}\%$ written as a decimal? *(Lesson 8-7)* **$0.00\overline{3}$**

Alternative Assessment

Open Ended

A manager of a telephone sales force found that last month her team sold 436 magazine subscriptions. The team made 15,265 calls that month. How many calls should the manager have her team make if the goal for this month is to sell 550 subscriptions? **about 19,256 calls**

One salesperson can make a call every five minutes. A full-time salesperson works forty hours in a week, and a part-time salesperson works 20 hours in a week. How many full-time and part-time salespeople should the manager have on the team to meet the 550 subscription goal?

Sample answer: about 40 full-time salespeople and one part-time salesperson

Completing the 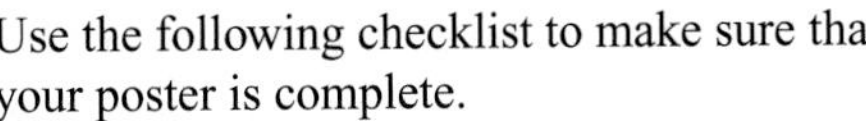

Use the following checklist to make sure that your poster is complete.

- ☑ The chart for the type and amount of trash thrown away each day is clear and easy to read.
- ☑ The recent statistics about the items you can recycle and local recycling programs are complete and easy to understand.
- ☑ The percents describing the amount of trash that can be recycled and the decrease in the total amount of trash are included.

Select an item from this chapter that you found challenging. Place it in your portfolio.

A practice test for Chapter 8 is provided on page 614.

Applications and Problem Solving

This section provides additional practice in solving real-world problems that involve the skills of this chapter.

Alternative Assessment

The ***Open Ended*** section provides students with a performance assessment opportunity to evaluate their work and understanding.

Students should complete the final stages of their project and prepare a class demonstration of their results. A scoring guide for the project is available in the *Investigations and Projects Masters,* p. 47.

Students should add to their portfolios at this time.

Performance Assessment

Additional performance assessment tasks for this chapter are included in the *Assessment and Evaluation Masters* on page 209. A scoring guide is also provided on page 221.

***Assessment and Evaluation Masters,* p. 209**

Name__________ Date_______

Chapter 8 Performance Assessment

Instructions: Demonstrate your knowledge by giving a clear, concise solution to each problem. Be sure to include all relevant drawings and justify your answers. You may show your solutions in more than one way or investigate beyond the requirements of the problems.

1. a. Explain what is meant by two ratios being equivalent.
   b. Give 3 sets of ratios that are equivalent.
   c. Explain what is meant by a *proportion.*
   d. Draw counters in each box to complete each proportion.
   e. A rectangular house is 64 feet long and 32 feet wide. Draw a scale drawing of the house. Let 1 millimeter represent 1 foot.

2. Many rates are used in baseball to indicate a player's or team's performance.
   a. A player's batting average is the ratio of the number of hits to the number of official times at bat. Julian has 27 hits in 72 times at bat. Write his batting average as a fraction, as a decimal, and as a percent. Show and explain your work.
   b. Pitcher Pedro Sanchez won 125 of his games during his career. If he pitched 200 games, explain how you would use mathematics to show his career performance. Show his career performance as a percent, as a decimal, and as a fraction.
   c. If a team is winning about 50% of their games, it's called a 500 team (0.500 = 50%). If a team ends the season as a 325 team and there are 240 games in a season, how many games did they lose? What percent of the season did they lose? Show and explain your work.

 209 *Mathematics: Applications and Connections, Course 2*

Standardized Test Practice

The Standardized Test Practice may be used to help students prepare for standardized tests. The test items are written in the same style as those in state proficiency tests and standardized tests like CAT, CTBS, ITBS, MAT, SAT, and Terra Nova. The test items cover skills and concepts covered up to this point in the text.

The pages can be used as an overnight assessment. After students have completed the pages, discuss how each problem can be solved, or provide copies of the solutions from the *Solutions Manual.*

CHAPTERS 1–8

Standardized Test Practice

Assessing Knowledge & Skills

Section One: Multiple Choice

There are ten multiple-choice questions in this section. Choose the best answer. If a correct answer is *not here*, choose the letter for Not Here.

1. In a stem-and-leaf plot of the data below, what numbers would be used for the stems? **C**

Height (Inches)

52	75	49	51	57	66	69
58	59	62	61	61	73	68
76	74	78	49			

A 0–9
B 1–9
C 4–7
D 4–9

2. There are twenty pieces of candy in a jar on the counter at the bank. Four are orange, seven are root beer, three are lemon, and six are strawberry. If a customer chooses one at random, what is the probability that it will *not* be root beer? **H**

E $\frac{1}{4}$
F $\frac{1}{20}$
G $\frac{7}{20}$
H $\frac{13}{20}$

3. If 10 overhead projectors are needed for every 14 teachers, how many overhead projectors are needed for 112 teachers? **B**

A 140
B 80
C 60
D 25

Please note that Questions 4–10 have five answer choices.

4. People were asked to choose a favorite newscast. The graph shows the results of the survey. **J**

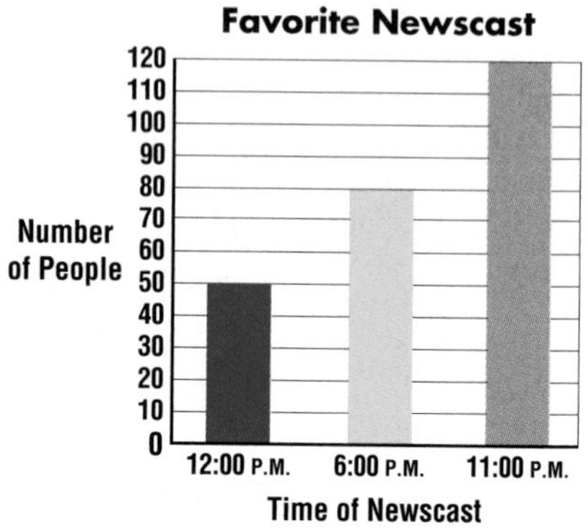

What were the total number of people who were surveyed about the newscasts?

F 180
G 210
H 220
J 250
K 280

5. A symphony orchestra held a series of special concerts to raise money for the restoration of the theater where they perform. Sixty percent of the price of each ticket was donated. Each ticket sold for \$35. What else do you need to know to find how much money was donated to the theater restoration? **D**

A the amount of profit on each ticket
B the number of seats in the theater
C the number of performances in the series
D the total number of tickets sold
E the operating cost of the orchestra

356 **Chapters 1–8** Standardized Test Practice

◀◀◀ Instructional Resources

Another cumulative review is shown at the left and is available in the *Assessment and Evaluation Masters,* p. 215.

***Assessment and Evaluation Masters,* p. 215**

8

Name________________ Date________

Cumulative Review, Chapters 1–8

1. Find the area of a parallelogram with $b = 12.2$ cm and $h = 8.5$ cm. (Lesson 1-7) — 1. 103.7 cm²
2. Complete 1.27 L = _?_ mL. (Lesson 2-8) — 2. 1,270
3. Find the mean for the set of data 13, 14, 12, 15, 11, 16, 21, and 18. (Lesson 3-1) — 3. 15
4. Write $\frac{65}{78}$ in simplest form. (Lesson 4-5) — 4. $\frac{5}{6}$
5. Name the integer represented by P. Then find its opposite and absolute value. (Lesson 5-1) — 5. −5; 5; 5

6. Translate *the quotient of c and 11* into an algebraic expression. (Lesson 6-4) — 6. $\frac{c}{11}$
7. How many quarts are in $6\frac{1}{4}$ gallons? (Lesson 7-5) — 7. 25
8. Find the perimeter of a rectangle with $\ell = 3\frac{1}{4}$ feet and $w = 2\frac{2}{3}$ feet. (Lesson 7-6) — 8. $11\frac{5}{6}$ ft
9. Express the ratio 24:33 as a fraction in simplest form. (Lesson 8-1) — 9. $\frac{8}{11}$
10. Find the unit price for one blank videotape if 8 videotapes in a box cost \$24.40. (Lesson 8-2) — 10. \$3.05
11. Solve the proportion $\frac{a}{6} = \frac{25}{30}$. (Lesson 8-3) — 11. 5
12. Gil made a slide from a photo. The photo is 4 inches wide and 7 inches long. If the width of the slide is 1 inch, what is the length of the slide? (Lesson 8-4) — 12. 1.75 inches
13. Express the fraction $\frac{17}{44}$ as a percent. Round to the nearest hundredth. (Lesson 8-5) — 13. 38.64%
14. Express 3.45% as a decimal. (Lesson 8-6) — 14. 0.0345
15. Express 424% as a decimal. (Lesson 8-7) — 15. 4.24
16. What percent of 85 is 21? Round to the nearest tenth. (Lesson 8-9) — 16. 24.7%

 215 *Mathematics: Applications and Connections, Course 2*

6. The coach paid $476.60 for thirty soccer balls without tax. How much could be saved by buying the thirty soccer balls on sale for $381.36? F
   - F $95.24
   - G $85.24
   - H $125.54
   - J $114.34
   - K $75.54

7. Jay bought a bag of flour for making bread in his bread machine. Each loaf of bread uses $2\frac{1}{2}$ cups of flour. If the bag contains 20 cups of flour, how many loaves will Jay get from the bag? D

   A 5 B 6
   C 7 D 8
   E Not Here

8. What is the value of $8 + x^2$ if $x = 12$? G

   F 32 G 152
   H 400 J 420
   K Not Here

9. There was $244.87 in the cash register at a video store. The manager removed $150 to deposit in the bank. How much money was left in the cash register? A

   A $94.87 B $88.87
   C $84.87 D $74.87
   E Not Here

10. Golf balls are on sale for $9.98 per box of 3. What is the cost of 7 boxes of golf balls before sales tax is added? J

   F $29.64 G $29.94
   H $45.86 J $69.86
   K $71.86

Test-Taking Tip THE PRINCETON REVIEW

When taking a long test, work carefully but quickly through the problems. Skip those problems that take more than the average amount of time allotted for doing a problem. Mark these in the test booklet and come back to them after you have completed the problems that you could easily do.

11. Associative property of equality

Section Two: Free Response

This section contains five questions for which you will provide short answers. Write your answers on your paper.

11. What property allows you to say that $\frac{1}{3} + \left(\frac{2}{3} + \frac{4}{5}\right) = \left(\frac{1}{3} + \frac{2}{3}\right) + \frac{4}{5}$?

12. Carol pays $185.55 each month for her car payment. What is this amount rounded to the nearest ten dollars? **$190**

13. Astronomers use angles to describe the positions of objects in the sky. On April 25, 1997, the angle of Comet Hale-Bopp was 30°. The angle of the comet was −10° on July 24, 1997. Find the difference between these angle measures. **−40°**

14. Find the next three terms in the sequence 6, −12, 18, −24, 30, −36, … . Is the sequence arithmetic, geometric, or neither? **42, −48, 54; neither**

15. Soft drinks are sold in 2-liter bottles. How many milliliters are in a 2-liter bottle? **2,000 mL**

Test Practice For additional test practice questions, visit:

www.glencoe.com/sec/math/mac/mathnet

Test-Taking Tip

Remind students to listen carefully to the instructions given by the test administrator. If they are not allowed to mark in the test booklets, they can make a list of skipped problems on scrap paper.

Assessment and Evaluation Masters, pp. 213–214

Name ______ Date ______

8 Chapter 8 Standardized Test Practice

1. If 3 litter boxes are needed for every 5 cats, how many litter boxes are needed for 25 cats? 1. B

   A. 16 B. 15 C. 3 D. 8

2. Choose the next two figures that continue the pattern. 2. D

   A. B. C. D.

The table shows the average high and low temperatures in April for various cities around the world. Use this information for Questions 3–5.

City	April Average High (°F)	April Average Low (°F)
Beijing*	70	45
Buenos Aires	72	53
Cairo	83	57
Frankfurt	60	42
Hong Kong*	75	67
Jerusalem*	73	50
London	56	42
Los Angeles	70	50
Moscow*	50	34
San Juan	82	72
Sydney	71	58

*cities in Asia

3. How much warmer is it in Sydney during April than in London? 3. A

   A. about 15°F B. about 20°F
   C. about 25°F D. about 10°F

4. Find the mean (average) low temperature of the cities in Asia. 4. A

   A. 49°F B. 67°F
   C. 40.5°F D. 54°F

5. If you had to list these cities from coldest low temperature to warmest high temperature, which city would be first on the list and which city would be last? 5. B

   A. London and Frankfurt/San Juan B. Moscow/Cairo
   C. London and Frankfurt/Cairo D. Moscow/San Juan

6. If a store advertises a pair of shoes for 35% off the regular price, what fraction of the regular price is this? 6. D

   A. $\frac{7}{25}$ B. $\frac{5}{21}$ C. $\frac{5}{14}$ D. $\frac{7}{20}$

7. The length of a piece of poster board is 42 inches and it has an area of 1,176 square inches. What is the width? 7. C

   A. 1,134 in. B. 34.3 in. C. 28 in. D. 42 in.

8. Natane is working quiz by quiz through a chapter of her self-paced math course. She has taken 4 of the 10 quizzes, each worth 5 to 10 points. Which of these is a reasonable estimate of the number of points Natane has earned? 8. C

   A. less than 5 B. between 5 and 20
   C. between 25 and 40 D. between 45 and 60

© Glencoe/McGraw-Hill 213 *Mathematics: Applications and Connections, Course 2*

8 Chapter 8 Standardized Test Practice (continued)

9. Samantha has a toy fire engine that is $\frac{1}{30}$ the size of a real fire engine. If her toy fire engine is 2.5 inches wide by 6 inches long, how large would the equivalent real fire engine be? 9. B

   A. 6 ft by 12 ft B. 6.25 ft by 15 ft
   C. 7.5 ft by 18 ft D. 75 ft by 180 ft

10. Annie needs to cut two $3\frac{4}{5}$-foot-long pieces of pipe from a 30-foot-long pipe? How much pipe will she have left? 10. A

   A. $22\frac{2}{5}$ feet B. 24 feet C. 23 feet D. $21\frac{4}{5}$ feet

The table lists the top 10 best cities for baseball players to play in according to Baseball Weekly, Nov. 26–Dec. 2, 1997. Use this information for Questions 11 and 12.

Rating	City	Ratings Point Total
1	Atlanta	85
2	Arizona	80
3	Colorado	80
4	Cleveland	77
5	Baltimore	76
tie (5)	Seattle	76
7	Los Angeles	75
tie (7)	New York Yankees	75
9	Texas	74
10	Anaheim	73
tie (10)	San Diego	73
tie (10)	Tampa Bay	73

11. What is the mean (average) rating for the top ten cities? 11. A

   A. 76.4 B. 79.6
   C. 76.9 D. 72.6

12. What two cities have the greatest difference in points? 12. B

   A. Anaheim and Tampa Bay
   B. Atlanta and Cleveland
   C. Arizona and San Diego
   D. Colorado and Los Angeles

13. Blake decides how long to watch the football game by rolling two number cubes, where each side is 15 minutes times that number. What is the probability that he will watch the game for only 30 minutes? 13. A

   A. $\frac{1}{6}$ B. $\frac{2}{3}$ C. $\frac{1}{12}$ D. $\frac{1}{3}$

14. Which of the following expressions is equivalent to $4n - 3 \leq -2$? 14. D

   A. $n \leq -1\frac{1}{4}$ B. $n \leq 4$ C. $n \leq -20$ D. $n \leq \frac{1}{4}$

© Glencoe/McGraw-Hill 214 *Mathematics: Applications and Connections, Course 2*

Instructional Resources ▶▶▶

Additional standardized test practice is shown at the right and is available in the *Assessment and Evaluation Masters*, pp. 213–214.

CHAPTER 9

Geometry: Investigating Patterns

Previewing the Chapter

Overview

This chapter explores some concepts of geometry, including angles, characteristics of polygons, tessellations, translations, and reflections. Students learn how to construct bisectors of segments and angles, perpendiculars, and regular polygons. Applications include art, with an emphasis on the work of the Dutch artist M. C. Escher. Students also use logical reasoning to solve problems involving classification.

Lesson (pages)	Lesson Objectives	NCTM Standards 2000	Standardized Tests	State/Local Objectives
9-1A (360–361)	Measure angles by using a protractor.	2, 4, 6, 8–10		
9-1 (362–365)	Classify angles.	1–4, 6, 8, 10	CTBS, ITBS, MAT, SAT, TN	
9-1B (366–367)	Construct perpendicular and parallel lines.	1, 4, 6, 8, 10	CTBS, TN	
9-2A (369)	Find the sum of the angle measures of polygons.	1–4, 6, 8, 10		
9-2 (370–373)	Identify polygons and regular polygons.	1–4, 6, 8–10	CAT, SAT	
9-2B (374–375)	Inscribe triangles, squares, and hexagons in circles.	3, 4, 6, 8, 10	CTBS, TN	
9-3 (376–379)	Determine whether polygons are similar and find a missing length in a pair of similar polygons.	1–4, 6–8, 10	CTBS, MAT, TN	
9-3B (380)	Enlarge a figure on a coordinate plane.	3, 4, 6, 8, 10		
9-4A (381)	Discover characteristics of various kinds of triangles and quadrilaterals.	3, 4, 6, 8, 10		
9-4 (382–385)	Classify triangles and quadrilaterals.	1–4, 6–10	CTBS, ITBS, SAT, TN	
9-4B (386–387)	Solve problems by using logical reasoning.	6–8	MAT	
9-5 (388–391)	Determine which regular figures can be used to form a tessellation.	2–4, 8–10		
9-6 (392–394)	Create Escher-like drawings by using translations.	2, 3, 8–10		
9-7 (395–397)	Create Escher-like drawings by using reflections.	2, 3, 8–10		

CAT = California Achievement Tests, CTBS = Comprehensive Tests of Basic Skills, ITBS = Iowa Tests of Basic Skills, MAT = Metropolitan Achievement Tests, SAT = Stanford Achievement Tests, TN = Terra Nova

For the key to numbering of NCTM Standards 2000, see page T6.

Organizing the Chapter

The **Interactive Lesson Planner** contains all of the blackline masters and transparencies. This CD-ROM also includes an easy-to-use lesson planning calendar.

LESSON PLANNING GUIDE

Lesson	Extra Practice (Student Edition)	Blackline Masters (Page Numbers)										Transparencies A and B
		Study Guide	Practice	Enrichment	Assessment & Evaluation	Classroom Games	Diversity	Hands-On Lab	School to Career	Science and Math Lab Manual	Technology	
9-1A								56				
9-1	p. 592	67	67	67						41–44		9-1
9-1B								57				
9-2A								58				
9-2	p. 593	68	68	68	239						43	9-2
9-2B								59				
9-3	p. 593	69	69	69							44	9-3
9-3B								60				
9-4A								61				
9-4	p. 593	70	70	70	238, 239							9-4
9-4B	p. 594											
9-5	p. 594	71	71	71		26–28		80				9-5
9-6	p. 594	72	72	72	240							9-6
9-7	p. 595	73	73	73	240		22		22			9-7
Study Guide/ Assessment					225–237, 241–243							

Other Chapter Resources

Student Edition
Chapter Project, pp. 359, 391, 394, 397, 401
School to Career, p. 368
Let the Games Begin, p. 391

Technology
 MathPASS CD-ROM
 Interactive Mathematics Tools Software

Teacher's Classroom Resources

Applications
Family Letters and Activities, pp. 43–44
Investigations and Projects Masters, pp. 49–52

Meeting Individual Needs
Investigations for the Special Education Student, p. 29

Teaching Aids
Answer Key Masters
Block Scheduling Booklet
Lesson Planning Guide
Solutions Manual

Professional Publications
Glencoe Mathematics Professional Series

Planning the Chapter

MindJogger Videoquizzes provide a unique format for reviewing concepts presented in the chapter.

Assessment Resources

Student Edition

Mixed Review, pp. 365, 373, 379, 385, 391, 394, 397
Mid-Chapter Self Test, p. 379
Math Journal, pp. 372, 384
Study Guide and Assessment, pp. 398–401
Performance Task, p. 401
Portfolio Suggestion, p. 401
Standardized Test Practice, pp. 402–403
Chapter Test, p. 615

Assessment and Evaluation Masters

Multiple-Choice Tests (Forms 1A, 1B, 1C), pp. 225–230
Free-Response Tests (Forms 2A, 2B, 2C), pp. 231–236
Performance Assessment, p. 237
Mid-Chapter Test, p. 238
Quizzes A–D, pp. 239–240
Standardized Test Practice, pp. 241–242
Cumulative Review, p. 243

Teacher's Wraparound Edition

5-Minute Check, pp. 362, 370, 376, 382, 388, 392, 395
Building Portfolios, p. 358
Math Journal, pp. 361, 367, 369, 375, 380, 381
Closing Activity, pp. 365, 373, 379, 385, 387, 391, 394, 397

Technology

Test and Review Software
MindJogger Videoquizzes
CD-ROM Program

Materials and Manipulatives

Lesson 9-1A
protractor*†
dot paper†
colored pencils

Lesson 9-1
protractor*†
dot paper†

Lesson 9-1B
compass*†
straightedge*†

Lesson 9-2A
protractor*†
scissors*

Lesson 9-2B
compass*†
straightedge*†
scissors*
ruler*†
protractor*†

Lesson 9-3
dot paper†
protractor*†

Lesson 9-3B
cartoon
grid paper†
straightedge*†
colored pencils
white paper

Lesson 9-4A
4" × 6" index cards
scissors*
brass fasteners
protractors*†

Lesson 9-5
pattern blocks*
counters*†
dot paper†

*Glencoe Manipulative Kit

†Glencoe Overhead Manipulative Resources

Pacing Chart

See pages T25–T27 for the Course Planning Calendar.

COURSE	DAY 1	DAY 2	DAY 3	DAY 4	DAY 5	DAY 6	DAY 7
Standard	Chapter Project	Lessons 9-1A & 9-1			Lessons 9-2A & 9-2		Lesson 9-3
Honors	Chapter Project	Lessons 9-1 & 9-1B		Lessons 9-2 & 9-2B		Lessons 9-3 & 9-3B	
Block	Chapter Project & Lesson 9-1A	Lessons 9-1 & 9-2A	Lessons 9-2 & 9-3	Lessons 9-4A & 9-4	Lessons 9-4B & 9-5	Lesson 9-6	Lesson 9-7

Interactive Mathematics:
Activities and Investigations

is an activity-based program that may be used as an enhancement for chapters in ***Mathematics: Applications and Connections.***

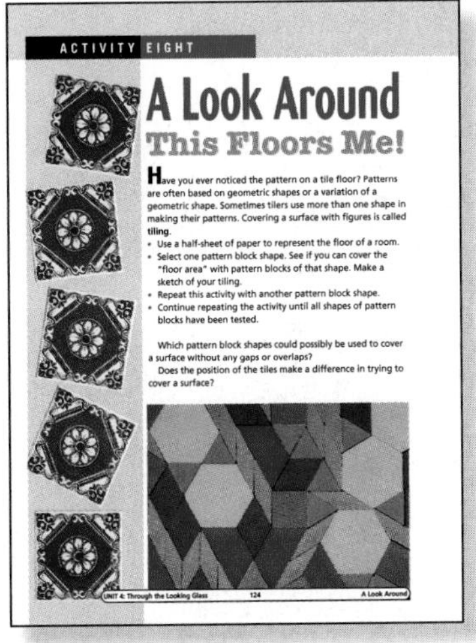

ACTIVITY EIGHT

A Look Around

This Floors Me!

Have you ever noticed the pattern on a tile floor? Patterns are often based on geometric shapes or a variation of a geometric shape. Sometimes tilers use more than one shape in making their patterns. Covering a surface with figures is called **tiling**.

- Use a half-sheet of paper to represent the floor of a room.
- Select one pattern block shape. See if you can cover the "floor area" with pattern blocks of that shape. Make a sketch of your tiling.
- Repeat this activity with another pattern block shape.
- Continue repeating the activity until all shapes of pattern blocks have been tested.

Which pattern block shapes could possibly be used to cover a surface without any gaps or overlaps?

Does the position of the tiles make a difference in trying to cover a surface?

UNIT 4: Through the Looking Glass 124 A Look Around

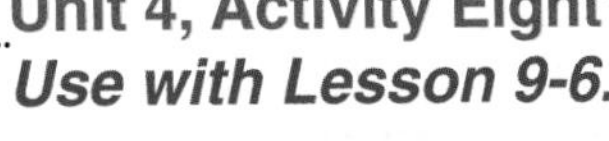

Unit 4, Activity Eight
Use with Lesson 9-6.

Summary Students select a pattern block and arrange blocks of like kind to cover a given area. They study the patterns associated with the block and how it tiles to cover the area. Then they determine which angles of which pattern blocks can fit together around a given point. This process is repeated with two or more types of blocks.

Math Connection Students explore tilings and tessellations using pattern blocks. They determine which pattern blocks will fit together at a given point. The angles of the pieces that fit together around a point must add up to 360°.

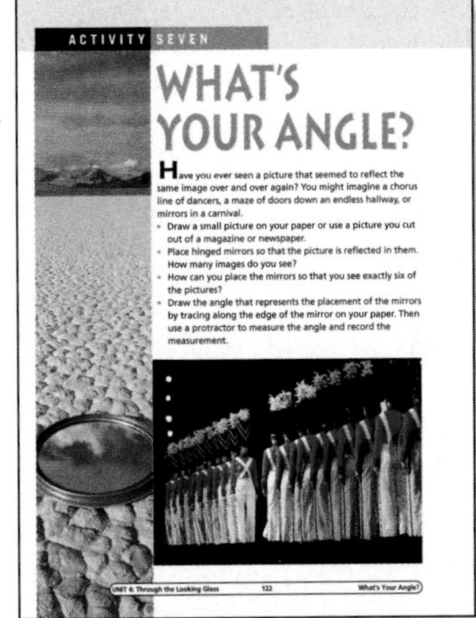

ACTIVITY SEVEN

WHAT'S YOUR ANGLE?

Have you ever seen a picture that seemed to reflect the same image over and over again? You might imagine a chorus line of dancers, a maze of doors down an endless hallway, or mirrors in a carnival.

- Draw a small picture on your paper or use a picture you cut out of a magazine or newspaper.
- Place hinged mirrors so that the picture is reflected in them. How many images do you see?
- How can you place the mirrors so that you see exactly six of the pictures?
- Draw the angle that represents the placement of the mirrors by tracing along the edge of the mirror on your paper. Then use a protractor to measure the angle and record the measurement.

UNIT 4: Through the Looking Glass 122 What's Your Angle?

Unit 4, Activity Seven
Use with Lesson 9-8.

Summary Students experiment with hinged mirrors to determine the angle of reflection for a given number of images. They trace the position of the mirror, which forms an angle, and summarize their findings in a report.

Math Connection Students explore angles of reflection using hinged mirrors. The angle of the hinge and the number or images seen are related. If you see six images, including the original image, the angle of reflection is 360 ÷ 6, or 60°.

DAY 8	DAY 9	DAY 10	DAY 11	DAY 12	DAY 13	DAY 14	DAY 15
Lessons 9-4A & 9-4		Lesson 9-4B	Lesson 9-5	Lesson 9-6	Lesson 9-7	Study Guide and Assessment	Chapter Test
Lesson 9-4	Lesson 9-4B	Lesson 9-5	Lesson 9-6	Lesson 9-7	Study Guide and Assessment	Chapter Test	
Study Guide and Assessment, Chapter Test							

APPLICATIONS

Classroom Games, pp. 26–28

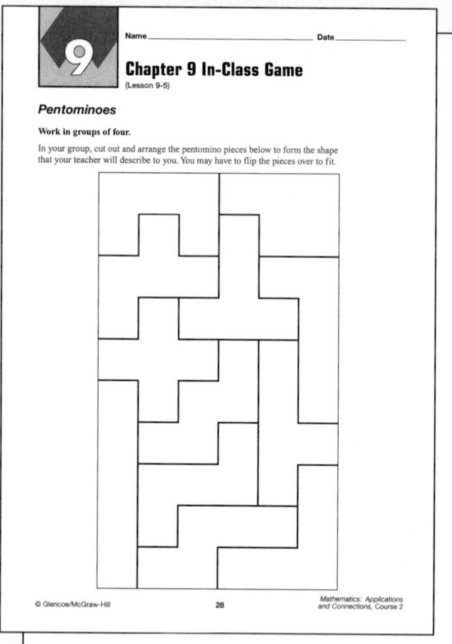

Name ______ Date ______

Chapter 9 In-Class Game
(Lesson 9-5)

Pentominoes

Work in groups of four.

In your group, cut out and arrange the pentomino pieces below to form the shape that your teacher will describe to you. You may have to flip the pieces over to fit.

© Glencoe/McGraw-Hill 28 *Mathematics: Applications and Connections, Course 2*

Diversity Masters, p. 22

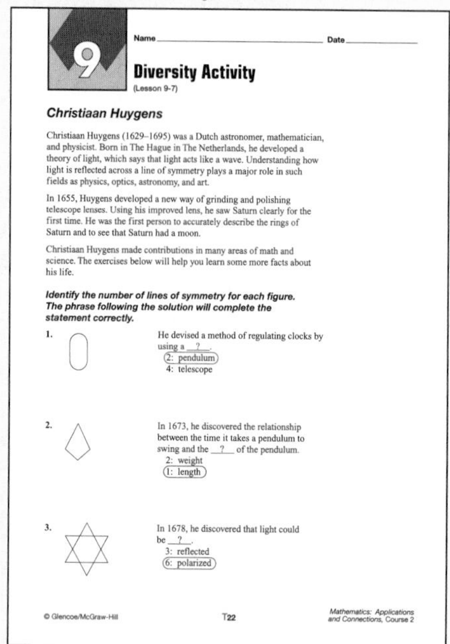

Name ______ Date ______

Diversity Activity
(Lesson 9-7)

Christiaan Huygens

Christiaan Huygens (1629–1695) was a Dutch astronomer, mathematician, and physicist. Born in The Hague in The Netherlands, he developed a theory of light, which says that light acts like a wave. Understanding how light is reflected across a line of symmetry plays a major role in such fields as physics, optics, astronomy, and art.

In 1655, Huygens developed a new way of grinding and polishing telescope lenses. Using his improved lens, he saw Saturn clearly for the first time. He was the first person to accurately describe the rings of Saturn and to see that Saturn had a moon.

Christiaan Huygens made contributions in many areas of math and science. The exercises below will help you learn some more facts about his life.

Identify the number of lines of symmetry for each figure. The phrase following the solution will complete the statement correctly.

1. He devised a method of regulating clocks by using a __?__.
   (2: pendulum)
   4: telescope
2. In 1673, he discovered the relationship between the time it takes a pendulum to swing and the __?__ of the pendulum.
   2: weight
   (1: length)
3. In 1678, he discovered that light could be __?__.
   3: reflected
   (6: polarized)

© Glencoe/McGraw-Hill T22 *Mathematics: Applications and Connections, Course 2*

School to Career Masters, p. 22

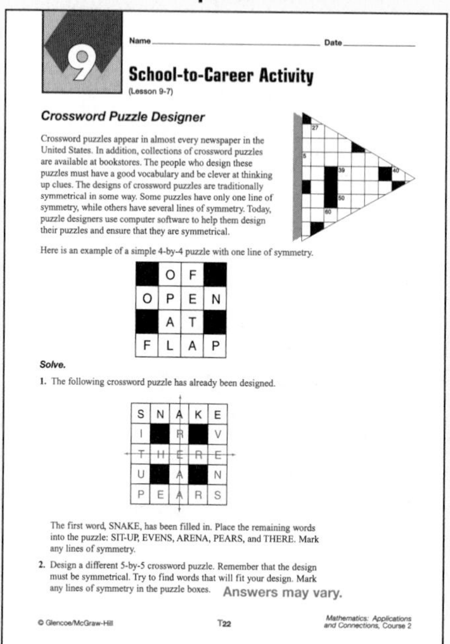

Name ______ Date ______

School-to-Career Activity
(Lesson 9-7)

Crossword Puzzle Designer

Crossword puzzles appear in almost every newspaper in the United States. In addition, collections of crossword puzzles are available at bookstores. The people who design these puzzles must have a good vocabulary and be clever at thinking up clues. The designs of crossword puzzles are traditionally symmetrical in some way. Some puzzles have only one line of symmetry, while others have several lines of symmetry. Today, puzzle designers use computer software to help them design their puzzles and ensure that they are symmetrical.

Here is an example of a simple 4-by-4 puzzle with one line of symmetry.

■	O	F	■
O	P	E	N
■	A	T	■
F	L	A	P

Solve.

1. The following crossword puzzle has already been designed.

S	N	A	K	E
I	■	R	■	V
T	H	E	R	E
U	■	A	■	N
P	E	A	R	S

The first word, SNAKE, has been filled in. Place the remaining words into the puzzle: SIT-UP, EVENS, ARENA, PEARS, and THERE. Mark any lines of symmetry.

2. Design a different 5-by-5 crossword puzzle. Remember that the design must be symmetrical. Try to find words that will fit your design. Mark any lines of symmetry in the puzzle boxes. **Answers may vary.**

© Glencoe/McGraw-Hill T22 *Mathematics: Applications and Connections, Course 2*

Family Letters and Activities, pp. 43–44

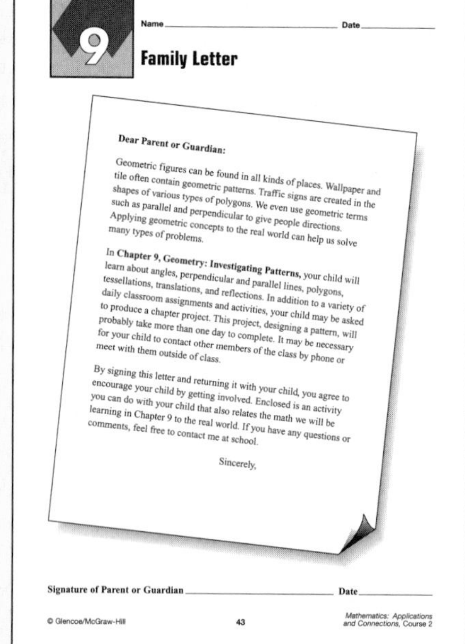

Name ______ Date ______

Family Letter

Dear Parent or Guardian:

Geometric figures can be found in all kinds of places. Wallpaper and tile often contain geometric patterns. Traffic signs are created in the shapes of various types of polygons. We even use geometric terms such as parallel and perpendicular to give people directions. Applying geometric concepts to the real world can help us solve many types of problems.

In **Chapter 9, Geometry: Investigating Patterns,** your child will learn about angles, perpendicular and parallel lines, polygons, tessellations, translations, and reflections. In addition to a variety of daily classroom assignments and activities, your child may be asked to produce a chapter project. This project, designing a pattern, will probably take more than one day to complete. It may be necessary for your child to contact other members of the class by phone or meet with them outside of class.

By signing this letter and returning it with your child, you agree to encourage your child by getting involved. Enclosed is an activity you can do with your child that also relates the math we will be learning in Chapter 9 to the real world. If you have any questions or comments, feel free to contact me at school.

Sincerely,

Signature of Parent or Guardian ______ **Date** ______

© Glencoe/McGraw-Hill 43 *Mathematics: Applications and Connections, Course 2*

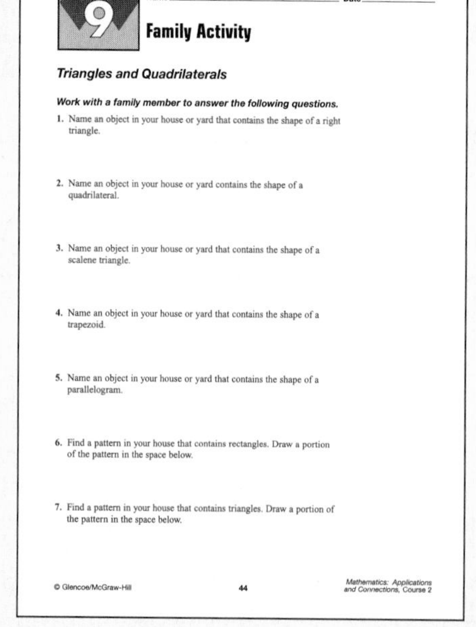

Name ______ Date ______

Family Activity

Triangles and Quadrilaterals

Work with a family member to answer the following questions.

1. Name an object in your house or yard that contains the shape of a right triangle.
2. Name an object in your house or yard contains the shape of a quadrilateral.
3. Name an object in your house or yard that contains the shape of a scalene triangle.
4. Name an object in your house or yard that contains the shape of a trapezoid.
5. Name an object in your house or yard that contains the shape of a parallelogram.
6. Find a pattern in your house that contains rectangles. Draw a portion of the pattern in the space below.
7. Find a pattern in your house that contains triangles. Draw a portion of the pattern in the space below.

© Glencoe/McGraw-Hill 44 *Mathematics: Applications and Connections, Course 2*

Science and Math Lab Manual, pp. 41–44

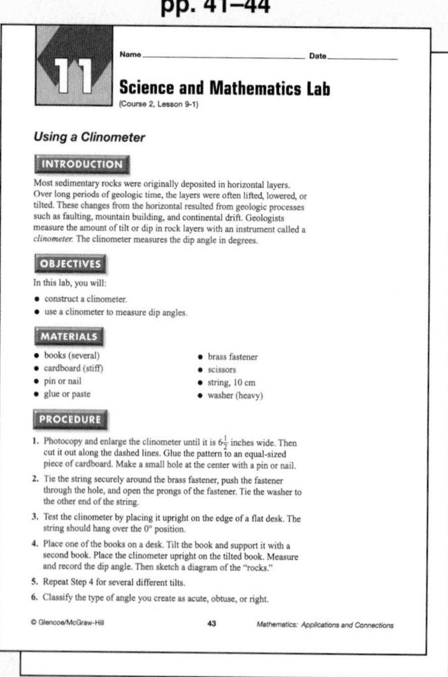

Name ______ Date ______

11 Science and Mathematics Lab
(Course 2, Lesson 9-1)

Using a Clinometer

INTRODUCTION

Most sedimentary rocks were originally deposited in horizontal layers. Over long periods of geologic time, the layers were often lifted, lowered, or tilted. These changes from the horizontal resulted from geologic processes such as faulting, mountain building, and continental drift. Geologists measure the amount of tilt or dip in rock layers with an instrument called a *clinometer.* The clinometer measures the dip angle in degrees.

OBJECTIVES

In this lab, you will:

- construct a clinometer.
- use a clinometer to measure dip angles.

MATERIALS

- books (several)
- cardboard (stiff)
- pin or nail
- glue or paste
- brass fastener
- scissors
- string, 10 cm
- washer (heavy)

PROCEDURE

1. Photocopy and enlarge the clinometer until it is $6\frac{1}{2}$ inches wide. Then cut it out along the dashed lines. Glue the pattern to an equal-sized piece of cardboard. Make a small hole at the center with a pin or nail.
2. Tie the string securely around the brass fastener, push the fastener through the hole, and open the prongs of the fastener. Tie the washer to the other end of the string.
3. Test the clinometer by placing it upright on the edge of a flat desk. The string should hang over the 0° position.
4. Place one of the books on a desk. Tilt the book and support it with a second book. Place the clinometer upright on the tilted book. Measure and record the dip angle. Then sketch a diagram of the "rocks."
5. Repeat Step 4 for several different tilts.
6. Classify the type of angle you create as acute, obtuse, or right.

© Glencoe/McGraw-Hill 43 *Mathematics: Applications and Connections*

MANIPULATIVES/MODELING

Hands-On Lab Masters, p. 80

9

Name ______________________ Date __________

Lab Activity

(Lesson 9-5)

Quadrilateral Tessellations

1. A convex polygon is a polygon whose diagonals lie entirely within the polygon. Draw a convex quadrilateral with four different angles.
   Sample answer:
2. Measure the angles of your quadrilateral with a protractor. Write the measure of each angle on the drawing. 2–5. See students' work.
3. Use tracing paper to make at least 8 copies of your quadrilateral.
4. Use scissors to carefully cut out your 8 quadrilaterals.
5. Rearrange the quadrilaterals until they form a tessellation pattern.
6. Sketch the tessellation pattern you found. Sample answer:
7. What is the sum of the angles of your quadrilateral? 360°
8. Do you think any convex quadrilateral will tessellate? yes
   Why or why not? The sum of the angles of a convex quadrilateral is 360°. This means the vertices can be put together so there are no gaps. This is what we need to make a tessellation.

© Glencoe/McGraw-Hill 80 *Mathematics: Applications and Connections, Course 2*

ASSESSMENT/EVALUATION

Assessment and Evaluation Masters, pp. 238–240

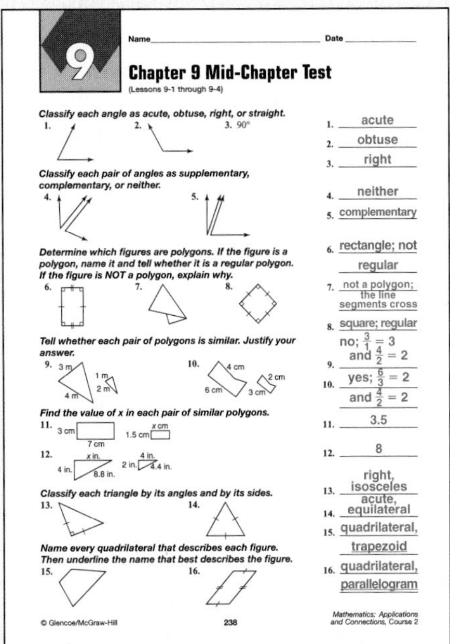
9

Name ______________________ Date __________

Chapter 9 Mid-Chapter Test

(Lessons 9-1 through 9-4)

Classify each angle as acute, obtuse, right, or straight.

1. 2. 3. 90°

Classify each pair of angles as supplementary, complementary, or neither.

4. 5.

Determine which figures are polygons. If the figure is a polygon, name it and tell whether it is a regular polygon. If the figure is NOT a polygon, explain why.

6. 7. 8.

Tell whether each pair of polygons is similar. Justify your answer.

9. 3 m, 4 m; 1 m, 2 m
10. 4 cm, 6 cm; 2 cm, 3 cm

Find the value of x in each pair of similar polygons.

11. 3 cm, 7 cm; 1.5 cm, x cm
12. x in., 4 in., 8.8 in.; 4 in., 2 in., 4.4 in.

Classify each triangle by its angles and by its sides.

13. 14.

Name every quadrilateral that describes each figure. Then underline the name that best describes the figure.

15. 16.

1. acute
2. obtuse
3. right
4. neither
5. complementary
6. rectangle; not regular
7. not a polygon; the line segments cross
8. square; regular
9. no; $\frac{3}{1} = 3$ and $\frac{4}{2} = 2$
10. yes; $\frac{6}{3} = 2$ and $\frac{4}{2} = 2$
11. 3.5
12. 8
13. right, isosceles
14. acute, equilateral
15. quadrilateral, trapezoid
16. quadrilateral, parallelogram

© Glencoe/McGraw-Hill 238 *Mathematics: Applications and Connections, Course 2*

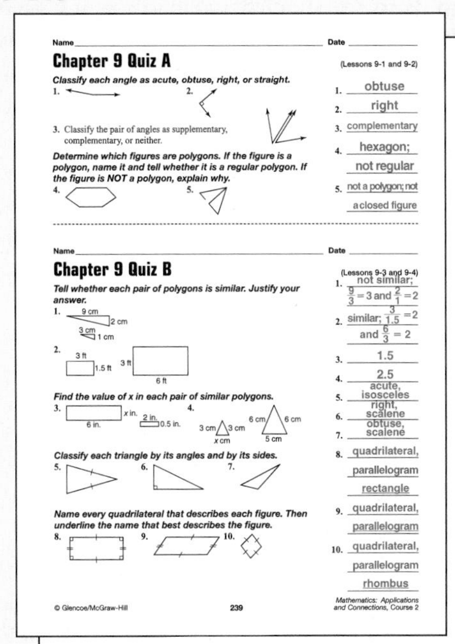
Name ______________________ Date __________

Chapter 9 Quiz A

(Lessons 9-1 and 9-2)

Classify each angle as acute, obtuse, right, or straight.

1. 2.
3. Classify the pair of angles as supplementary, complementary, or neither.

Determine which figures are polygons. If the figure is a polygon, name it and tell whether it is a regular polygon. If the figure is NOT a polygon, explain why.

4. 5.

1. obtuse
2. right
3. complementary
4. hexagon; not regular
5. not a polygon; not a closed figure

Name ______________________ Date __________

Chapter 9 Quiz B

(Lessons 9-3 and 9-4)

Tell whether each pair of polygons is similar. Justify your answer.

1. 9 cm, 2 cm; 3 cm, 1 cm
2. 3 ft, 1.5 ft; 3 ft, 6 ft

Find the value of x in each pair of similar polygons.

3. 6 in., x in.; 2 in., 0.5 in.
4. 3 cm, 3 cm, x cm; 6 cm, 6 cm, 5 cm

Classify each triangle by its angles and by its sides.

5. 6. 7.

Name every quadrilateral that describes each figure. Then underline the name that best describes the figure.

8. 9. 10.

1. not similar; $\frac{9}{3} = 3$ and $\frac{2}{1} = 2$
2. similar; $\frac{3}{1.5} = 2$ and $\frac{6}{3} = 2$
3. 1.5
4. 2.5
5. acute, isosceles
6. right, scalene
7. obtuse, scalene
8. quadrilateral, parallelogram, rectangle
9. quadrilateral, parallelogram
10. quadrilateral, parallelogram, rhombus

© Glencoe/McGraw-Hill 239 *Mathematics: Applications and Connections, Course 2*

TECHNOLOGY/MULTIMEDIA

Technology Masters, pp. 43–44

Name ______________________ Date __________

Calculator Activity

(Lesson 9-2)

Parentheses

What is the sum of the measures of the interior angles of an octagon? The solution is (8 − 2) × 180°, or 1,080°. If the octagon is regular, what is the measure of each of its angles? The solution is (8 − 2) × 180° ÷ 8, or 135°.

For any polygon, the sum of the interior angles is $(n - 2) \times 180°$, where n is the number of sides. If a polygon is regular, each angle has a measure given by the expression below.

$$(n - 2) \times 180° \div n$$

Use the parentheses keys, (and), on a calculator to complete the chart below for each polygon listed.

Number of Sides	Name of Polygon	Sum of Interior Angles	Each Angle (Regular Polygon)
3	triangle	(3 − 2) × 180° = 180°	180° ÷ 3 = 60°
4	quadrilateral	360°	90°
5	pentagon	540°	108°
6	hexagon	720°	120°
7	heptagon	900°	≈ 128.57°
8	octagon	1,080°	135°
9	nonagon	1,260°	140°
10	decagon	1,440°	144°
11	undecagon	1,620°	≈ 147.27°
12	dodecagon	1,800°	150°
15	pentadecagon	2,340°	156°
n	n-gon	(n − 2) × 180°	(n − 2) × 180° ÷ n

© Glencoe/McGraw-Hill T43 *Mathematics: Applications and Connections, Course 2*

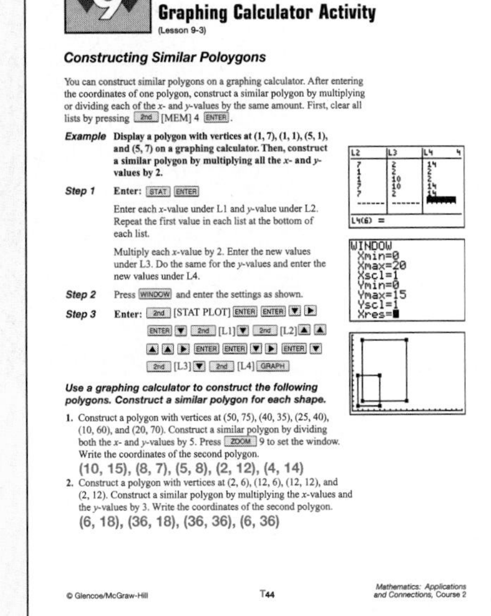
9

Name ______________________ Date __________

Graphing Calculator Activity

(Lesson 9-3)

Constructing Similar Poloygons

You can construct similar polygons on a graphing calculator. After entering the coordinates of one polygon, construct a similar polygon by multiplying or dividing each of the x- and y-values by the same amount. First, clear all lists by pressing 2nd [MEM] 4 ENTER.

Example **Display a polygon with vertices at (1, 7), (1, 1), (5, 1), and (5, 7) on a graphing calculator. Then, construct a similar polygon by multiplying all the x- and y-values by 2.**

Step 1 Enter: STAT ENTER

Enter each x-value under L1 and y-value under L2. Repeat the first value in each list at the bottom of each list.

Multiply each x-value by 2. Enter the new values under L3. Do the same for the y-values and enter the new values under L4.

Step 2 Press WINDOW and enter the settings as shown.

Step 3 Enter: 2nd [STAT PLOT] ENTER ENTER ▼ ▶ ENTER ▼ 2nd [L1] ▼ 2nd [L2] ▲ ▲ ▲ ▲ ▶ ENTER ENTER ▼ ▶ ENTER ▼ 2nd [L3] ▼ 2nd [L4] GRAPH

Use a graphing calculator to construct the following polygons. Construct a similar polygon for each shape.

1. Construct a polygon with vertices at (50, 75), (40, 35), (25, 40), (10, 60), and (20, 70). Construct a similar polygon by dividing both the x- and y-values by 5. Press ZOOM 9 to set the window. Write the coordinates of the second polygon.
   (10, 15), (8, 7), (5, 8), (2, 12), (4, 14)
2. Construct a polygon with vertices at (2, 6), (12, 6), (12, 12), and (2, 12). Construct a similar polygon by multiplying the x-values and the y-values by 3. Write the coordinates of the second polygon.
   (6, 18), (36, 18), (36, 36), (6, 36)

© Glencoe/McGraw-Hill T44 *Mathematics: Applications and Connections, Course 2*

MEETING INDIVIDUAL NEEDS

Investigations for the Special Education Student, p. 29

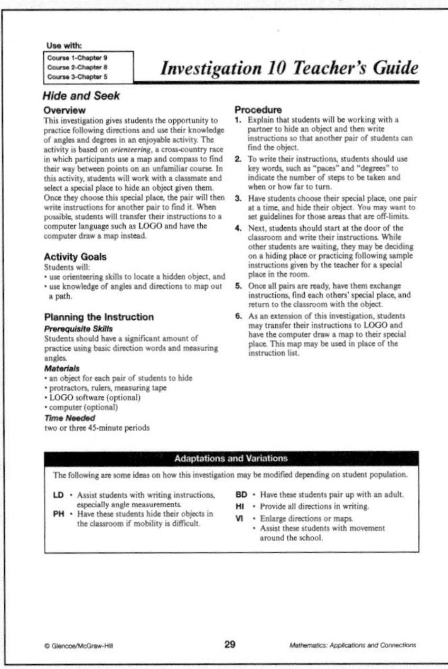
Use with:
Course 1-Chapter 9
Course 2-Chapter 8
Course 3-Chapter 5

Investigation 10 Teacher's Guide

Hide and Seek

Overview

This investigation gives students the opportunity to practice following directions and use their knowledge of angles and degrees in an enjoyable activity. The activity is based on *orienteering*, a cross-country race in which participants use a map and compass to find their way between points on an unfamiliar course. In this activity, students will work with a classmate and select a special place to hide an object given them. Once they choose this special place, the pair will then write instructions for another pair to find it. When possible, students will transfer their instructions to a computer language such as LOGO and have the computer draw a map instead.

Activity Goals

Students will:
- use orienteering skills to locate a hidden object, and
- use knowledge of angles and directions to map out a path.

Planning the Instruction

Prerequisite Skills

Students should have a significant amount of practice using basic direction words and measuring angles.

Materials
- an object for each pair of students to hide
- protractors, rulers, measuring tape
- LOGO software (optional)
- computer (optional)

Time Needed

two or three 45-minute periods

Procedure

1. Explain that students will be working with a partner to hide an object and then write instructions so that another pair of students can find the object.
2. To write their instructions, students should use key words, such as "paces" and "degrees" to indicate the number of steps to be taken and when or how far to turn.
3. Have students choose their special place, one pair at a time, and hide their object. You may want to set guidelines for those areas that are off-limits.
4. Next, students should start at the door of the classroom and write their instructions. While other students are waiting, they may be deciding on a hiding place or practicing following sample instructions given by the teacher for a special place in the room.
5. Once all pairs are ready, have them exchange instructions, find each others' special place, and return to the classroom with the object.
6. As an extension of this investigation, students may transfer their instructions to LOGO and have the computer draw a map to their special place. This map may be used in place of the instruction list.

Adaptations and Variations

The following are some ideas on how this investigation may be modified depending on student population.

LD • Assist students with writing instructions, especially angle measurements.
PH • Have these students hide their objects in the classroom if mobility is difficult.
BD • Have these students pair up with an adult.
HI • Provide all directions in writing.
VI • Enlarge directions or maps.
• Assist these students with movement around the school.

© Glencoe/McGraw-Hill 29 *Mathematics: Applications and Connections*

CHAPTER 9 NOTES

Theme: Art

New software and computers have revolutionized what artists can do with images. Computer Aided Design (CAD) allows artists to make drawings electronically in a fraction of the time it would take to draw them with paper and pencil. This allows an artist to quickly try out, alter, combine, rearrange, and refine new ideas.

Question of the Day If all snowflakes are complex six-sided crystals, could a flat surface be covered with snowflakes lying edge-to-edge? **Yes; hexagons make a tessellation.**

Assess Prerequisite Skills

Ask students to read through the list of objectives presented in "What you'll learn in Chapter 9." You may wish to ask them what each of the objectives means or if they have experienced or used any of these math concepts before.

Building Portfolios

Encourage students to revise their portfolios as they study this chapter. Encourage students to include concepts and operations that are new to them even if they are difficult at first.

Math and the Family

In the *Family Letters and Activities* booklet (pp. 43–44), you will find a letter to the parents explaining what students will study in Chapter 9. An activity appropriate for the whole family is also available.

CHAPTER 9 Geometry: Investigating Patterns

- to classify angles and polygons,
- to use proportions to express the relationship between corresponding parts of similar figures,
- to use logical reasoning to solve problems,
- to classify triangles and quadrilaterals, and
- to create patterns using tessellations, translations, and reflections.

CD-ROM Program

Activities for Chapter 9

- Chapter 9 Introduction
- Interactive Lessons 9-1, 9-7
- Extended Activity 9-6
- Assessment Game
- Resource Lessons 9-1 through 9-7

CHAPTER Project

GEOMETRIC ART

In this project, you will use geometric concepts to design a pattern for a wall-hanging, poster, tie, or T-shirt. You will create three designs: one with a tessellation, another with a translation, and a third with a reflection. To complete your project, you will choose one of your designs to present to the class.

Getting Started

- Look for examples of geometric patterns in fabrics you find in your home. Describe the patterns.
- Do research about geometric patterns that may be common in your ethnic heritage. The patterns can be modern designs or may date back many centuries.

Technology Tips

- Use an **electronic encyclopedia** to do your research.
- Use ***Geometer's Sketchpad*** or other drawing software to complete your basic design.

Research For up-to-date information on tessellations, visit:

www.glencoe.com/sec/math/mac/mathnet

Working on the Project

You can use what you'll learn in Chapter 9 to help you create your geometric design.

Page	Exercise
391	14
394	12
397	11
401	Alternative Assessment

Glencoe has made every effort to ensure that the website links for *Mathematics: Applications and Connections* at **www.glencoe.com/sec/math/mac/mathnet** are current and contain appropriate content. However, these website links are not under Glencoe's control.

Instructional Resources ▶▶▶

A recording sheet to help students organize their data for the Chapter Project is shown at the right and is available in the *Investigations and Projects Masters,* p. 52.

CHAPTER Project NOTES

Objectives Students should

- recognize and name various kinds of polygons based on the number of sides and the relationship of the sides and angles.
- measure the sides and angles of polygons and use logical reasoning to make predictions about how polygons can be combined in geometric patterns.

Project Pointer You may suggest that students begin a *Project Folder* to keep their work as they complete each stage of the Chapter Project. The completed project may also be added to their portfolios.

Using Drawing Software Students may want to experiment with different methods of drawing geometric patterns, including freehand sketches, compass and straightedge, protractor, grid paper, dot paper, and computer graphics programs. Encourage students to copy and save figures they construct on the computer so they can return to the drawing and make changes later.

***Investigations and Projects Masters,* p. 52**

Name ______ Date ______

Chapter 9 Project

Geometric Art

Page 391, Working on the Chapter Project, Exercise 14

Page 394, Working on the Chapter Project, Exercise 12

Page 397, Working on the Chapter Project, Exercise 11

 52 *Mathematics: Applications and Connections, Course 2*

9-1A HANDS-ON LAB Notes

GET READY

Objective Students measure angles by using a protractor.

Optional Resources
Hands-On Lab Masters
- square dot paper, p. 12
- worksheet, p. 56

Manipulative Kit
- protractor

MANAGEMENT TIPS

Recommended Time
30 minutes

Getting Started Have students estimate the measures of the angles of several objects. Then have them practice placing a protractor correctly by measuring the right angles on books, papers, or desks. Guide them to see that when the center of the protractor is on the corner of a book, then the top (90°) is on the adjacent side of the book.

Activity 1 demonstrates how to read both scales of a protractor. Help students to locate the appropriate scale for the angle they want to measure, pointing out that the angle measures should increase as they read up the scale.

HANDS-ON LAB

COOPERATIVE LEARNING

9-1A Measuring Angles

A Preview of Lesson 9-1

 protractor

 dot paper

 colored pencils

When you want to measure a line, you can use a ruler. When you want to measure an angle, you can use a *protractor*. Angles are measures of rotation and are measured in units called *degrees*.

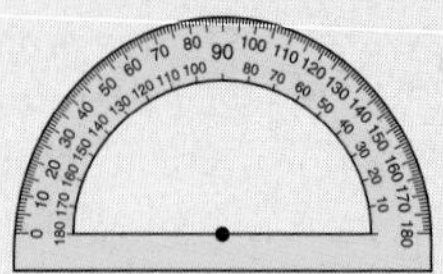

Notice that the protractor has two scales. The outer scale goes from 0 to 180 from left to right. The inner scale goes from 0 to 180 from right to left.

TRY THIS

1 Follow these steps to measure an angle.

- Place the protractor on the angle so that the center is on the vertex of the angle and one side goes through 0° on the protractor.
- In this case, 0° is on the inner scale. Follow the inner scale to the point where the other side of the angle meets the protractor. Find the inner number. This is the angle's measure. The measure of this angle is 110°.

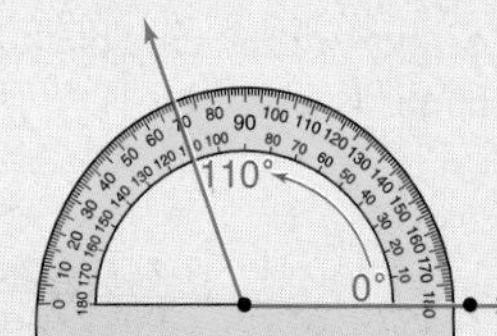

ON YOUR OWN

Copy each angle onto dot paper. Then use a protractor to find its measure. You may need to extend the sides of the angle in order to measure it.

1. 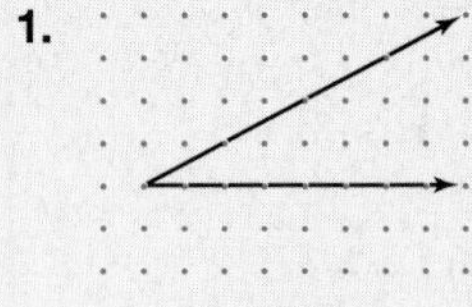 27°

2. 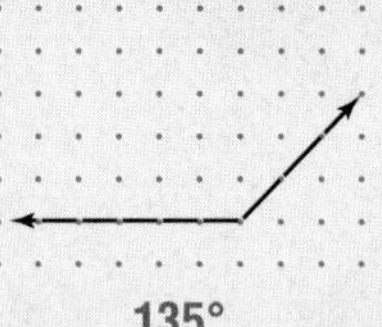 135°

3. 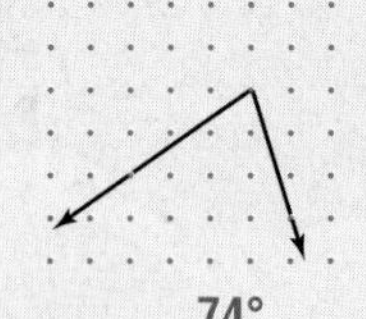 74°

4. How do you know which scale on the protractor to read? **See margin.**
5. Why do you think there are two scales on the protractor? **See margin.**

Additional Answers

4. **Find the scale where 0° intersects the side of the angle. If 0° is on the inner scale, use the inner scale. If 0° is on the outer scale, use the outer scale.**
5. **You can conveniently read the measure of an acute or obtuse angle from one scale or the other.**

TRY THIS

❷ The figure at the right shows parallel lines. The line that intersects the parallel lines is called a *transversal.*

- Copy the figure onto dot paper and label the angles as shown.
- Measure each angle with your protractor and record each measure.
- Using colored pencils, shade any angles with the same measure one color. For example, angle 1 and angle 4 have the same measure, and they are shaded yellow. If there are other angles with a different measure, shade them a second color. Angle 6 is shaded blue because it has a different measure. Continue shading using this pattern.

In the figure above, certain pairs of angles have special names. The angles that make up each pair have the same measure.

alternate interior angles	∠3 and ∠6, ∠4 and ∠5
alternate exterior angles	∠1 and ∠8, ∠2 and ∠7
corresponding angles	∠1 and ∠5, ∠2 and ∠6, ∠3 and ∠7, ∠4 and ∠8
vertical angles	∠1 and ∠4, ∠2 and ∠3, ∠5 and ∠8, ∠6 and ∠7

ON YOUR OWN

Copy each figure onto dot paper. Then use a protractor to find the measure of each angle. Shade angles with equal measures as you did above. **6–7. See margin.**

6.

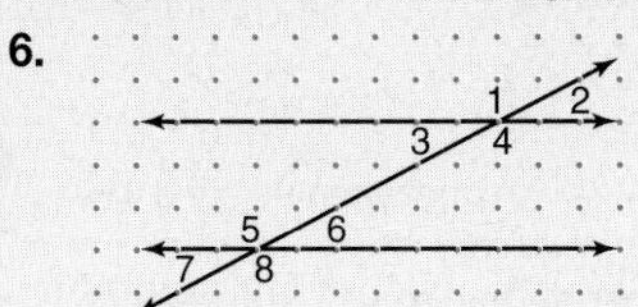

7.

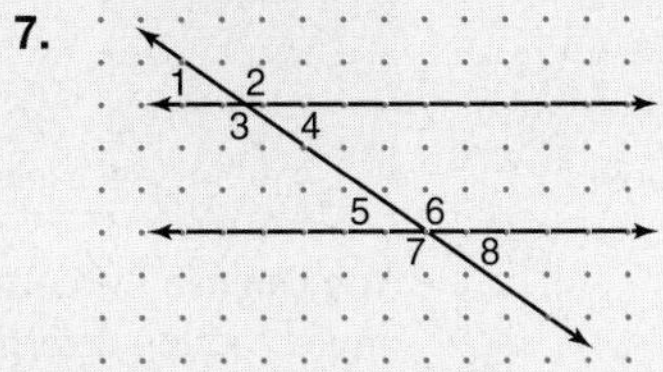

8. Look for a pattern in the shading of your parallel lines. Make a conjecture about the measure of the angles formed when a transversal intersects a pair of parallel lines. **See margin.**

9. In the figure at the right, the measure of angle 2 is 45°. Predict the measure of the other angles in the figure. Then copy the figure onto dot paper and check by using a protractor. **45°:∠3, ∠6, ∠7; 135°:∠1, ∠4, ∠5, ∠8**

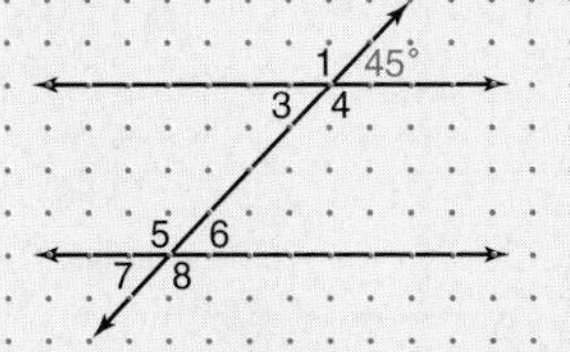

Activity 2 shows the relationship between angles created by a transversal. Encourage students to measure each angle twice, placing the base line of the protractor on a different line each time and comparing the measurements.

ASSESS

Have students complete Exercises 1–9. Guide students to recognize that angles smaller than the corner of a book measure less than 90° and those that are larger measure more than 90°. If they are able to recognize this distinction, students will know whether they are reading the correct scale.

Additional Answers

6. **27°: ∠2, ∠3, ∠6, ∠7; 153°: ∠1, ∠4, ∠5, ∠8**

7. **34°: ∠1, ∠4, ∠5, ∠8; 146°: ∠2, ∠3, ∠6, ∠7**

8. **Sample answer: Of the eight angles that are formed, "alternate" angles are equal.**

***Hands-On Lab Masters,* p. 56**

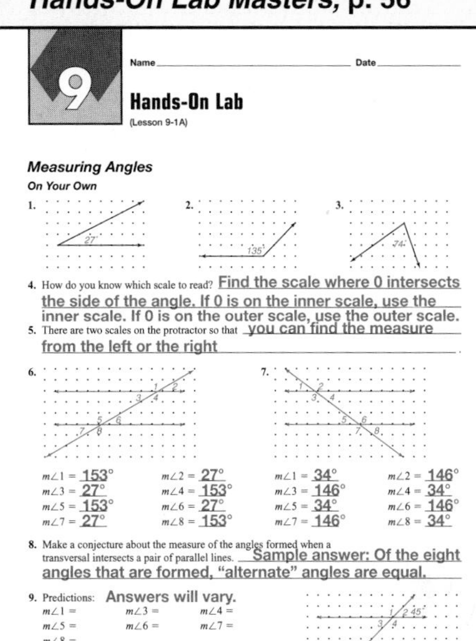

9 Name ______ Date ______

Hands-On Lab
(Lesson 9-1A)

Measuring Angles
On Your Own

1. 27° 2. 135° 3. 74°

4. How do you know which scale to read? Find the scale where 0 intersects the side of the angle. If 0 is on the inner scale, use the inner scale. If 0 is on the outer scale, use the outer scale.

5. There are two scales on the protractor so that you can find the measure from the left or the right.

6.

m∠1 = 153° m∠2 = 27°
m∠3 = 27° m∠4 = 153°
m∠5 = 153° m∠6 = 27°
m∠7 = 27° m∠8 = 153°

7.

m∠1 = 34° m∠2 = 146°
m∠3 = 146° m∠4 = 34°
m∠5 = 34° m∠6 = 146°
m∠7 = 146° m∠8 = 34°

8. Make a conjecture about the measure of the angles formed when a transversal intersects a pair of parallel lines. Sample answer: Of the eight angles that are formed, "alternate" angles are equal.

9. Predictions: Answers will vary.
m∠1 = m∠3 = m∠4 =
m∠5 = m∠6 = m∠7 =
m∠8 =

Actual measures:
m∠1 = 135° m∠3 = 45° m∠4 = 135°
m∠5 = 135° m∠6 = 45° m∠7 = 45°
m∠8 = 135°

© Glencoe/McGraw-Hill 56 *Mathematics: Applications and Connections, Course 2*

Have students describe the various relationships among the eight angles formed by two parallel lines and a transversal.

9-1 Lesson Notes

Instructional Resources

- *Study Guide Masters,* p. 67
- *Practice Masters,* p. 67
- *Enrichment Masters,* p. 67
- Transparencies 9-1, A and B
- *Science and Math Lab Manual,* pp. 41–44

CD-ROM Program
- Resource Lesson 9-1
- Interactive Lesson 9-1

Recommended Pacing	
Standard	Days 2–4 of 15
Honors	Days 2 & 3 of 14
Block	Day 2 of 8

1 FOCUS

5-Minute Check
(Chapter 8)

1. Find the unit price for 15 cards on sale for $0.75. **$0.05 per card**
2. Solve $\frac{3}{4} = \frac{x}{24}$. **18**
3. On a map, the scale is 1 inch:120 miles. Find the actual distance for a map distance of $3\frac{1}{2}$ inches. **420 miles**
4. Express $\frac{7}{8}$ as a percent. **$87\frac{1}{2}\%$**
5. Express $\frac{1}{5}\%$ as a decimal. **0.002**

The 5-Minute Check is also available on **Transparency 9-1A** for this lesson.

Motivating the Lesson

Hands-On Activity Provide cardboard disks for students to model slicing a pizza pie. Have them locate the center and draw lines indicating where they would slice their pies to make some pieces larger than others. Ask students to describe the difference in the angles at the center between larger and smaller pieces.

9-1 Angles

What you'll learn
You'll learn to classify angles.

When am I ever going to use this?
You'll use angles when you study about Earth's rotation and revolution.

Word Wise
angle
vertex
degrees
right angle
straight angle
acute angle
obtuse angle
supplementary
complementary

Many families celebrate Thanksgiving with delicious pies like sweet potato, pumpkin, or apple. The next time you enjoy a piece of pie, think of geometry. A piece of pie is a model of an **angle**.

An angle is made up of two rays with a common endpoint. The rays are called the *sides* of the angle, and the point where they meet is called the **vertex**.

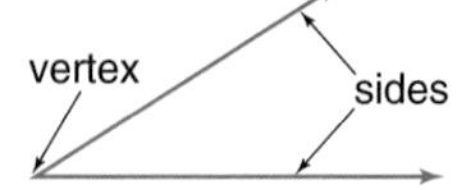

An angle is not measured by the length of its sides, but in units called **degrees**. Imagine that you cut a whole pie into 360 equal-sized pieces. The angle of each piece measures 1 degree.

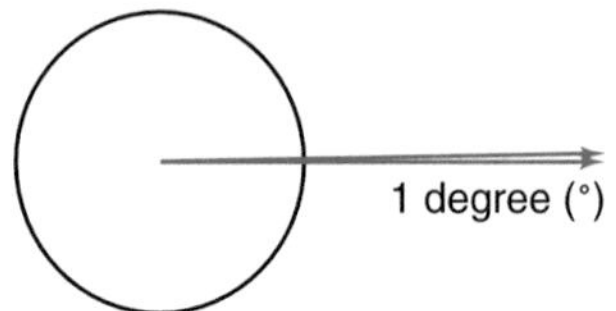

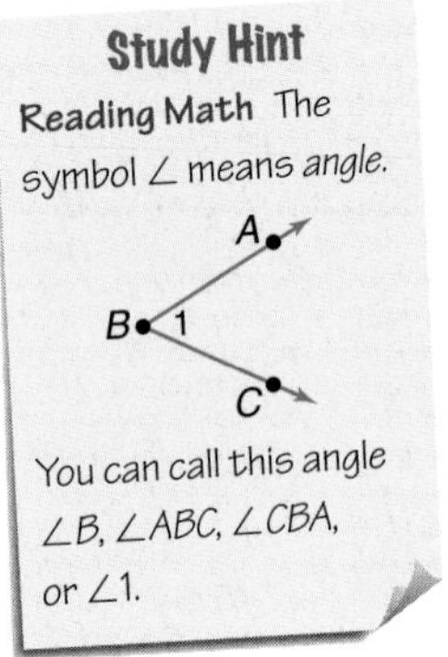

Study Hint
Reading Math The symbol ∠ means angle.
A
B
1
C
You can call this angle ∠B, ∠ABC, ∠CBA, or ∠1.

Angles are classified according to their measure.

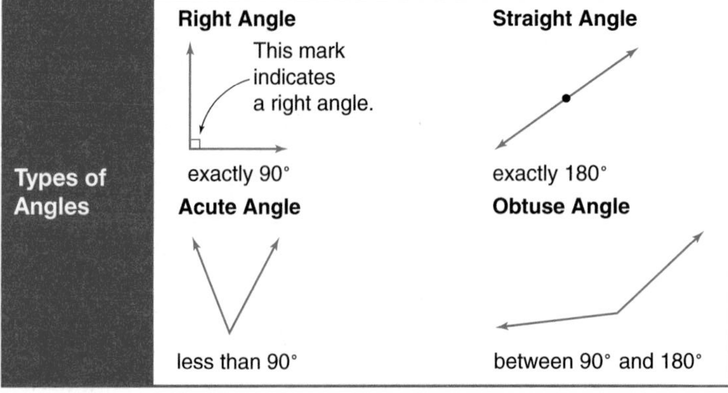

You can use the corner of a sheet of notebook paper, which is a right angle, to help determine whether an angle is right, acute, or obtuse. The edge of the paper can be used to determine straight angles.

Example 1 Classify each angle as right, acute, obtuse, or straight.

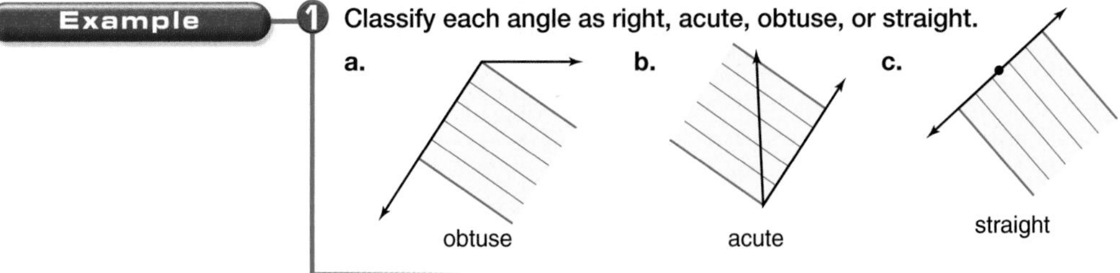

Cross-Curriculum Cue

Inform the other teachers on your team that your classes are studying geometry. Suggestions for curriculum integration are:
Art: architecture and design, space art, dance choreography
Physical Science: machines and work, astronomy
Physical Education: gymnastics, baseball
Geography: mapping, navigation

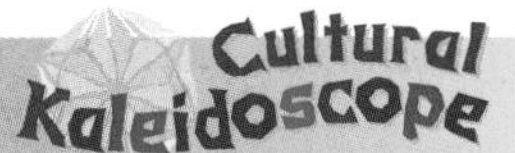

Mathematicians believe that the Babylonians were the first to divide a circle into 360°.

1–6. Approximate answers given.
1. $m\angle 1 = 135°$; $m\angle 2 = 45°$
2. $m\angle 3 = 27°$; $m\angle 4 = 45°$
3. $m\angle 5 = 62°$; $m\angle 6 = 118°$
4. $m\angle 7 = 62°$; $m\angle 8 = 28°$
5. $m\angle 9 = 62°$; $m\angle 10 = 28°$
6. $m\angle 11 = 45°$; $m\angle 12 = 118°$

Some pairs of angles are **supplementary** or **complementary**.

MINI-LAB

Work with a partner.  protractor  dot paper

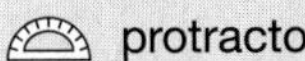

Try This

Copy each pair of angles onto dot paper and measure each angle with a protractor. Look for a pattern.

1. 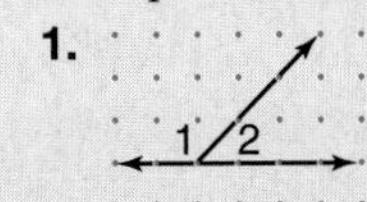
supplementary

2. 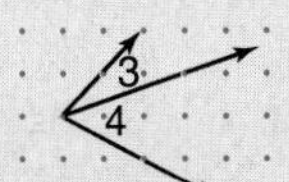
not supplementary

3. 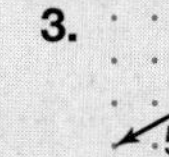
supplementary

4. complementary

5. 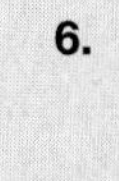
complementary

6. *not* complementary

Talk About It

Tell whether each pair of angles is supplementary.

7. 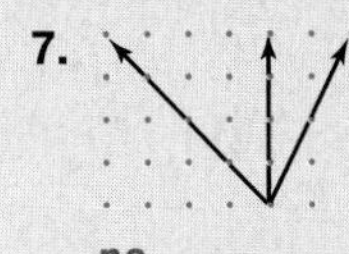
no

8. 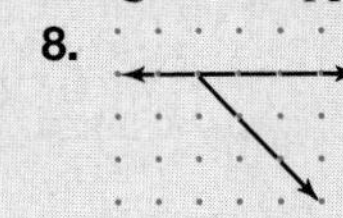
yes

9. 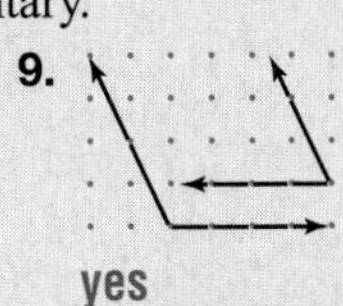
yes

10. What is true about supplementary angles? **Sum is 180°.**

Tell whether each pair of angles is complementary.

11. 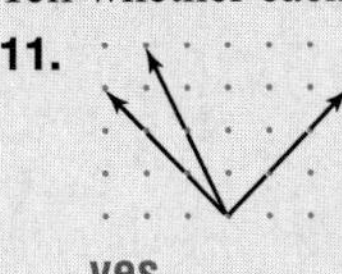
yes

12. 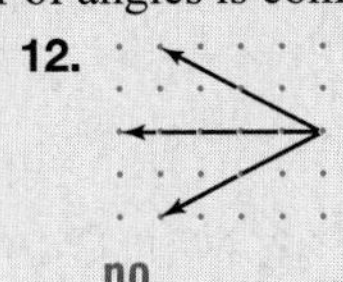
no

13. 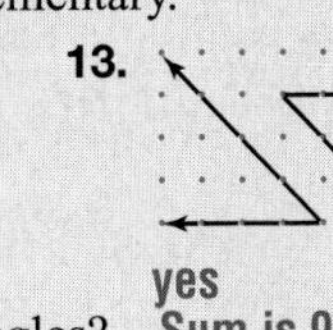
yes

14. What is true about complementary angles? **Sum is 90°.**

Study Hint

Reading Math The symbol $m\angle 1$ means the measure of angle 1.

If the sum of the measures of two angles is 180°, the angles are supplementary. If the sum of the measures of two angles is 90°, the angles are complementary.

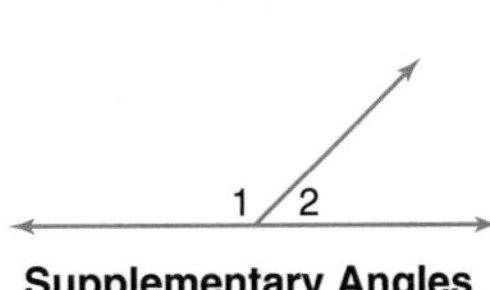
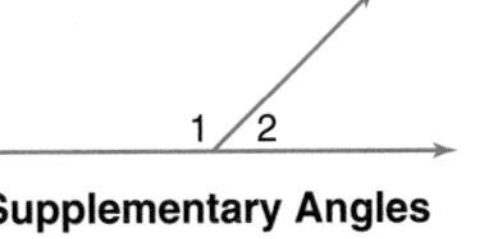

Supplementary Angles
$m\angle 1 + m\angle 2 = 180°$

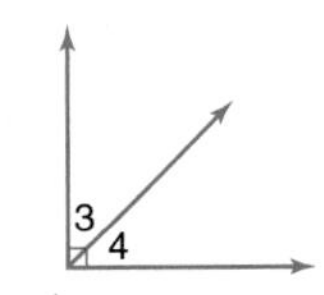

Complementary Angles
$m\angle 3 + m\angle 4 = 90°$

2 TEACH

Transparency 9-1B contains a teaching aid for this lesson.

In-Class Example

For Example 1
Classify each angle as right, acute, obtuse, or straight.

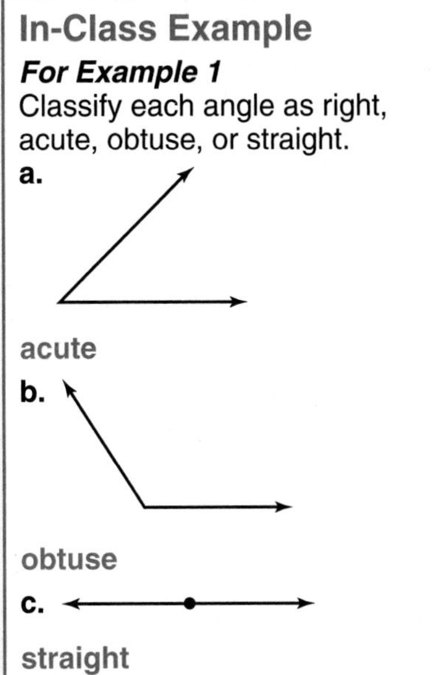

Using the Mini-Lab Ask students what the supplementary angles have in common and what the complementary angles have in common. Have students use a protractor to measure and draw their own supplementary and complementary angles, checking their partner's work to make sure they fit the pattern.

Multiple Learning Styles

Logical Have students work with a partner to answer the following questions. *How many pieces of pie are formed by a straight angle? How many pieces with right angles can be cut from one pie? with obtuse angles? What is the least number of pieces with acute angles that can be cut from one pie?*
2; 4; 3; 5

Teaching Tip In Example 2, encourage students to refer to the definition of supplementary angles and draw angles *A* and *B* with a common vertex.

In-Class Example

For Example 2
Angles *X* and *Y* are complementary. If $m\angle X = 45°$, find $m\angle Y$. **45°**

3 PRACTICE/APPLY

Check for Understanding

If students need additional practice or instruction after completing Exercises 1–9, one of these options may be helpful.

- Extra Practice, see p. 592
- Reteaching Activity
- *Study Guide Masters,* p. 67
- *Practice Masters,* p. 67

Assignment Guide

Core: 11–25 odd, 26–29
Enriched: 10–24 even, 25–29

Additional Answer

2. Sample art:

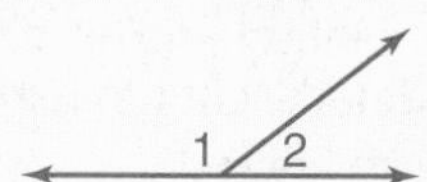

They form a straight angle.

***Study Guide Masters,* p. 67**

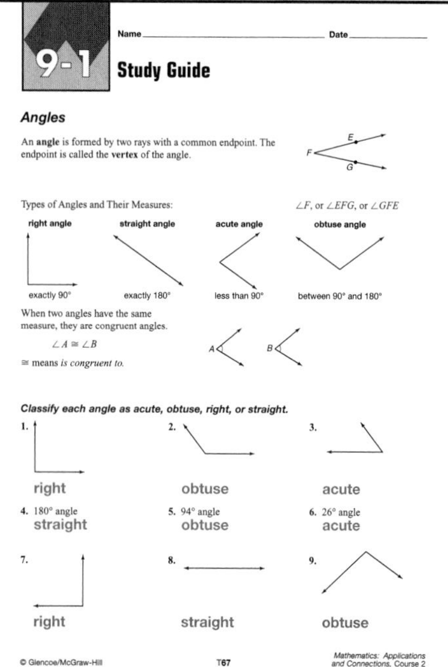

Name ____________ Date ____________

9-1 Study Guide

Angles

An **angle** is formed by two rays with a common endpoint. The endpoint is called the **vertex** of the angle.

$\angle F$, or $\angle EFG$, or $\angle GFE$

Types of Angles and Their Measures:

right angle	straight angle	acute angle	obtuse angle
exactly 90°	exactly 180°	less than 90°	between 90° and 180°

When two angles have the same measure, they are congruent angles.

$\angle A \cong \angle B$

$\cong$ means *is congruent to.*

Classify each angle as acute, obtuse, right, or straight.

1. right
2. obtuse
3. acute
4. 180° angle straight
5. 94° angle obtuse
6. 26° angle acute
7. right
8. straight
9. obtuse

© Glencoe/McGraw-Hill T67 *Mathematics: Applications and Connections, Course 2*

Example 2 **INTEGRATION**

Algebra Angles *A* and *B* are supplementary. If $m\angle A = 70°$, find $m\angle B$.

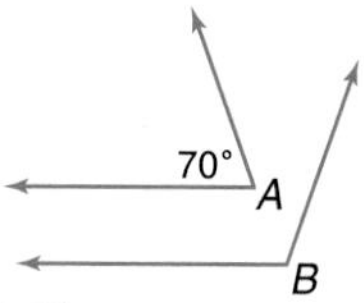

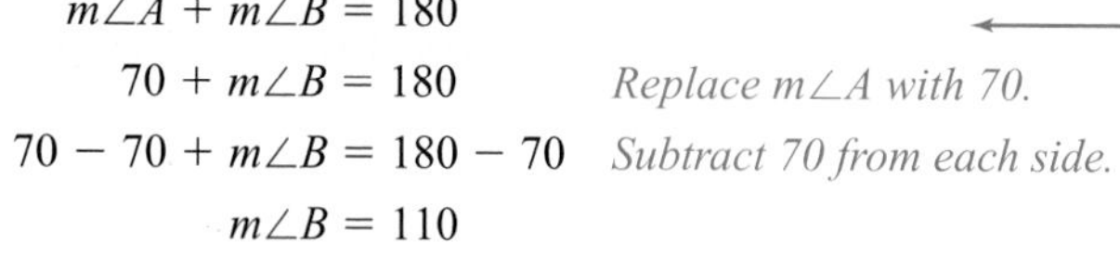

$$m\angle A + m\angle B = 180$$
$$70 + m\angle B = 180 \quad \textit{Replace } m\angle A \textit{ with 70.}$$
$$70 - 70 + m\angle B = 180 - 70 \quad \textit{Subtract 70 from each side.}$$
$$m\angle B = 110$$

The measure of $\angle B$ is 110°.

CHECK FOR UNDERSTANDING

Communicating Mathematics 1. See students' work.

Read and study the lesson to answer each question.

1. ***Show*** how you can classify an angle using the corner of your paper.
2. ***Draw*** an example of supplementary angles. Explain how you know they are supplementary. **See margin.**

HANDS-ON MATH

3. The figure at the right shows two intersecting lines. They form two pairs of "opposite" angles called *vertical angles*. Angles 1 and 3 are vertical angles, and angles 2 and 4 are vertical angles. Copy and measure each angle. Make a conjecture about the measures of vertical angles. Test your conjecture with other vertical angles. **Vertical angles are congruent.**

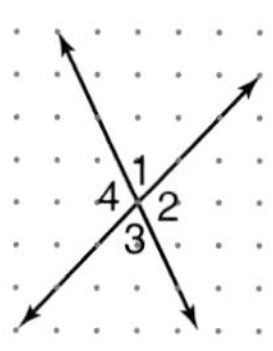

Guided Practice

Classify each angle as *acute*, *obtuse*, *right*, or *straight*.

4. **right**

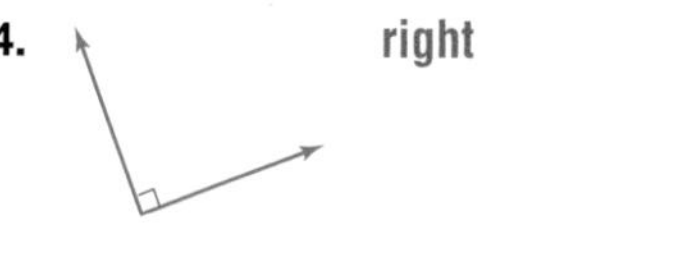

5. **acute**

6. 165° **obtuse**

7. 180° **straight**

8. Classify the angles at the right as *complementary*, *supplementary*, or *neither*. **neither**

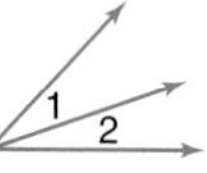

9. ***Algebra*** Angles *X* and *Y* are complementary. If $m\angle X = 15°$, find $m\angle Y$. **75°**

EXERCISES

Practice

Classify each angle as *acute*, *obtuse*, *right*, or *straight*.

10. **obtuse**

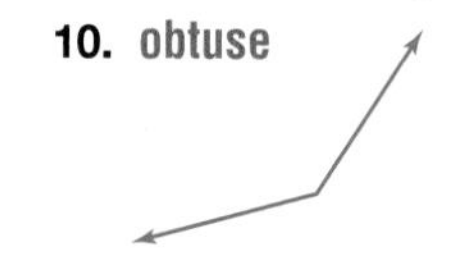

11. 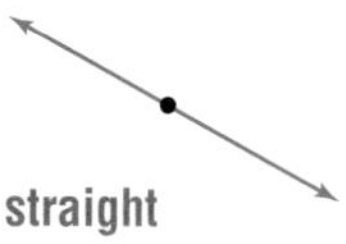 **straight**

12. 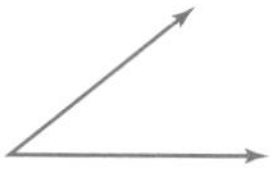 **acute**

Reteaching the Lesson

Activity In a diagram of a baseball diamond, including the outfield, use home plate as the vertex. Guide students to see that a right angle is formed by rays going from home plate toward the foul poles along the left-field and right-field foul lines.

Error Analysis

Watch for students who haven't grasped the difference between measuring degrees and measuring distance.
Prevent by comparing degrees to the minute marks on a circular clock. Ask students how many minutes there are to the circle and how many degrees there are to a minute.

13. 36° acute **14.** 170° obtuse **15.** 60° acute

16. 1° acute **17.** 91.5° obtuse **18.** 179.5° obtuse

Classify each pair of angles as *supplementary*, *complementary*, or *neither*.

19. **20.** **21.**

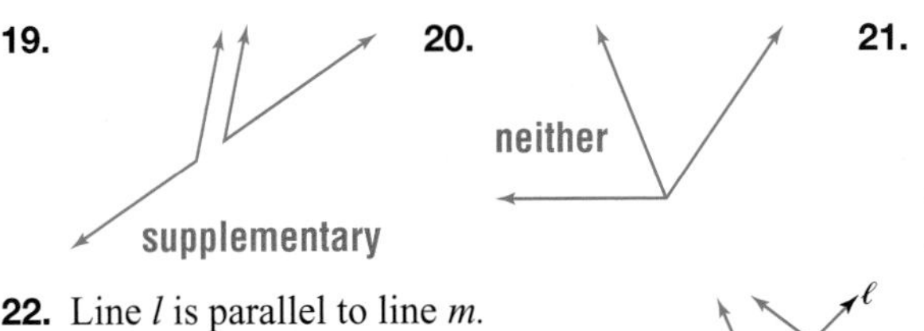

complementary

22. Line l is parallel to line m. Find the missing angles.
$a = 70°$, $b = 80°$, $c = 100°$, $d = 110°$

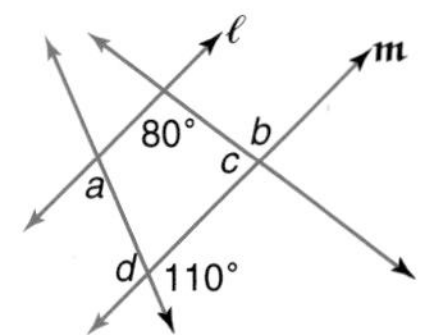

23. *Algebra* Angles A and B are supplementary. If $m\angle A = 25°$, find $m\angle B$. 155°

Applications and Problem Solving

24. *Geography* Earth rotates 360° degrees in one day. Through how many degrees does it rotate in one hour? 15°

25. *Earth Science* The Big Dipper is the best known group of stars in the sky. The figures below show how the Big Dipper probably looked 100,000 years ago, how it looks today, and how it will look 100,000 years from now.

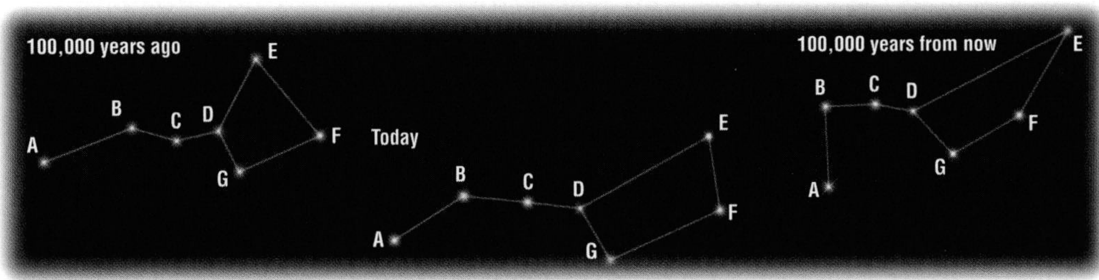

a. Which angle was obtuse 100,000 years ago and will be acute 100,000 years from now? $\angle EDG$

b. Identify an angle that appears to be a right angle.

25b. $\angle ABC$ in 100,000 years or $\angle DGF$ and $\angle EDG$ today

26. *Critical Thinking* Suppose two angles are supplementary. If each angle below represents one angle of the pair, what kind of angle is its supplement? d. not possible

a. acute obtuse **b.** right right **c.** obtuse acute **d.** straight

Mixed Review

27. Standardized Test Practice 95 of the 273 seventh-graders have turned in permission slips for the field trip. About what percent of the seventh-graders have not turned in a permission slip? *(Lesson 8-9)* A

A 65% **B** 55% **C** 45% **D** 35%

For **Extra Practice,** see page 592.

28. Find 45% of 1,600. *(Lesson 8-8)* 720

29. Subtract $1\frac{1}{3}$ from $4\frac{3}{4}$. *(Lesson 7-3)* $3\frac{5}{12}$

4 ASSESS

Closing Activity

Speaking Have students randomly draw and define a word from a stack of index cards on which the words *angle, vertex, degrees, right, straight, acute, obtuse, supplementary,* and *complementary* have been written.

***Practice Masters,* p. 67**

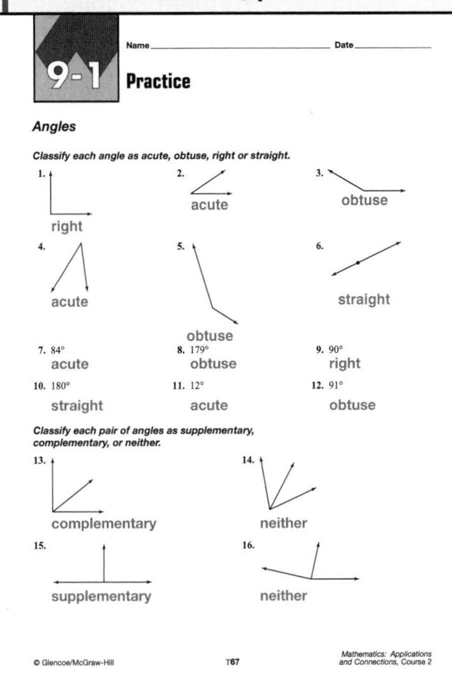

9-1 Practice

Name________ Date________

Angles

Classify each angle as acute, obtuse, right or straight.

1. right 2. acute 3. obtuse
4. acute 5. obtuse 6. straight
7. 84° acute 8. 179° obtuse 9. 90° right
10. 180° straight 11. 12° acute 12. 91° obtuse

Classify each pair of angles as supplementary, complementary, or neither.

13. complementary 14. neither
15. supplementary 16. neither

 T67 *Mathematics: Applications and Connections, Course 2*

Extending the Lesson

***Enrichment Masters,* p. 67**

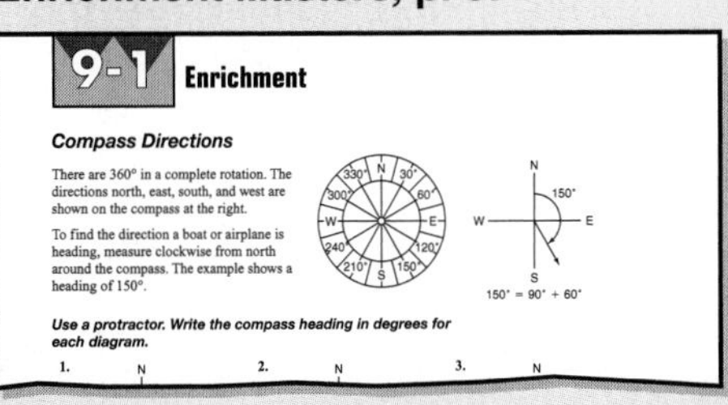

9-1 Enrichment

Compass Directions

There are 360° in a complete rotation. The directions north, east, south, and west are shown on the compass at the right.

To find the direction a boat or airplane is heading, measure clockwise from north around the compass. The example shows a heading of 150°.

Use a protractor. Write the compass heading in degrees for each diagram.

1. N 2. N 3. N

Activity Have students work in groups to draw two large circles on poster paper, representing the northern and southern hemispheres of Earth as seen from above. After completing Exercise 24, ask students to measure and draw 24 congruent angles from the north and south poles to show time zones, and refer to a globe to draw in the continents.

GET READY

Objective Students construct perpendicular and parallel lines.

Optional Resources
Hands-On Lab Masters
- worksheet, p. 57

Manipulative Kit
- compass

MANAGEMENT TIPS

Recommended Time
25 minutes

Getting Started Have students experiment with using a compass. Tell them that they can use a compass together with a straightedge to make geometric constructions. Have students practice drawing circles and arcs with their compasses.

Activity 1 demonstrates the use of a compass and straightedge to construct perpendicular lines. Remind students that their compasses must open wider to draw the arcs above the line, and the second arc must be drawn with the compass at the same setting as the first arc.

HANDS-ON LAB

COOPERATIVE LEARNING

9-1B Perpendicular and Parallel Lines

A Follow-Up of Lesson 9-1

compass

straightedge

Perpendicular lines are lines that form right angles when they intersect. In the figure, line ℓ is perpendicular to line m. This can also be written as $\ell \perp m$.

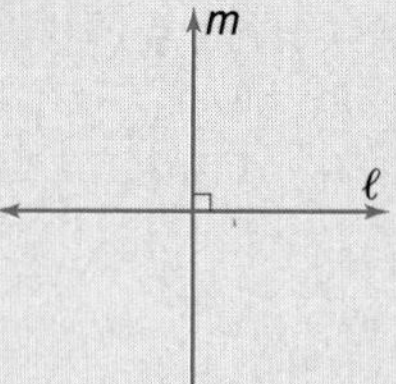

You can use a compass and straightedge to construct perpendicular lines.

TRY THIS

1 Construct a line perpendicular to line m through point P.

- Draw a line and label it m. Draw a dot on the line and label it point P.
- Place the compass point on P and draw equal arcs to intersect line m twice. Label these points Q and R. *An arc is part of a circle.*

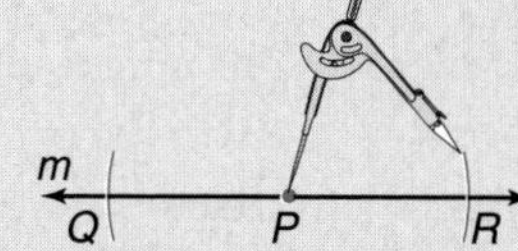

- Open your compass wider. Put the compass point at Q and draw an arc above line m.

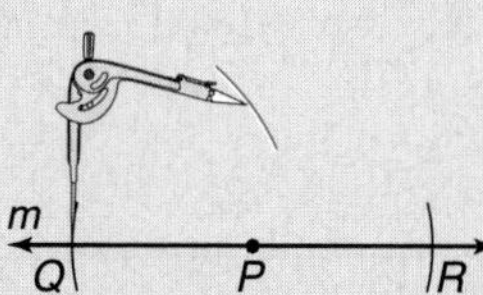

- With the same setting, put the compass point at R and draw an arc to intersect the one you just drew. Label this intersection point S.

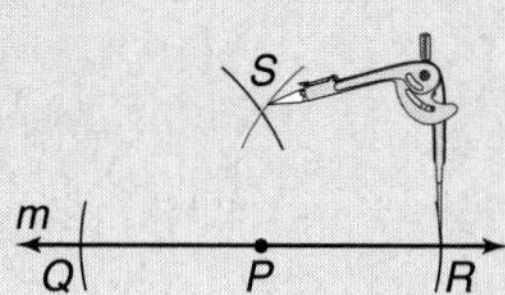

- Use a straightedge to draw a line through S and P. Line PS is perpendicular to line m.

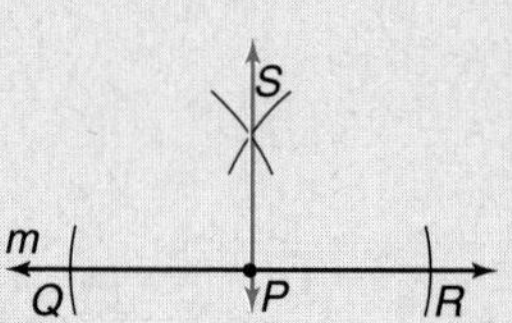

ON YOUR OWN

1. Construct a rectangle by constructing perpendiculars. **See margin.**

Additional Answer

1.
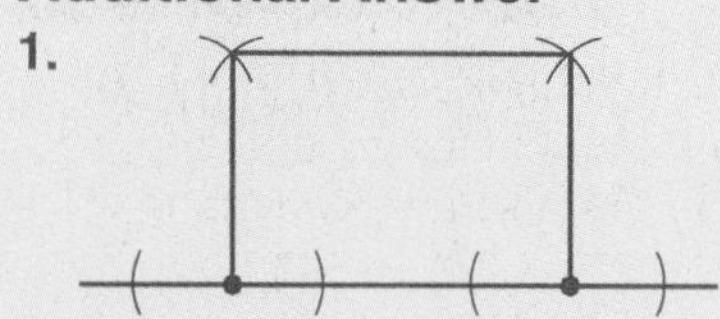

In Lesson 9-1A, you learned that some of the angle pairs formed when a transversal intersects parallel lines have the same measure. For example, in the figure at the right, line ℓ is parallel to line m. Angle 1 and angle 2 have the same measure.

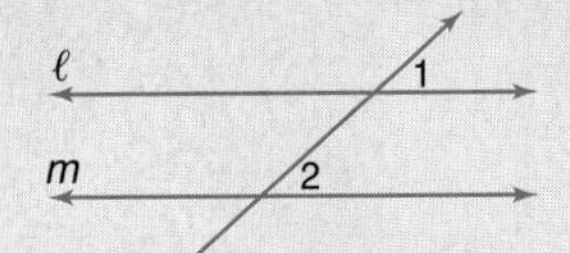

You can use a compass and a straightedge to construct a line parallel to a given line.

TRY THIS

2 Construct a line parallel to line ℓ through point P.

- Draw a line and label it ℓ. Choose any point P, not on the line.
- Draw a line through P that intersects ℓ. Label the point of intersection Q.

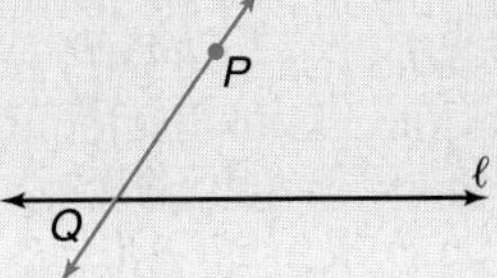

- Place your compass point at Q and draw an arc. Label the points R and S.
- With the same setting, place the compass point point at P and draw an arc. Label the point T.

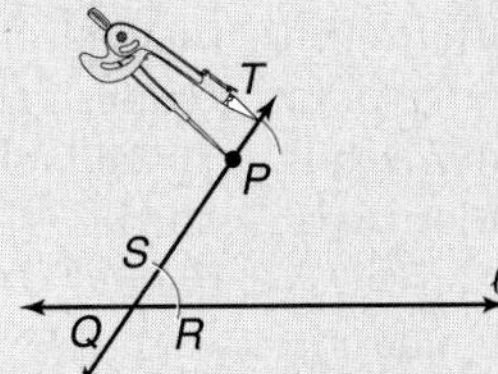

- Use your compass to measure the distance from R to S.
- With the same setting, place your compass at T and draw an arc to intersect the one already drawn. Label this point U.

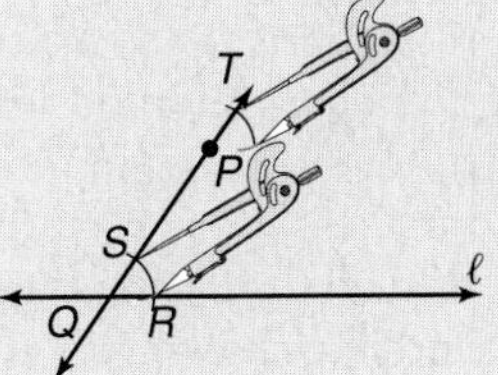

- Draw a line through P and U. Label it m. Line m is parallel to line ℓ.

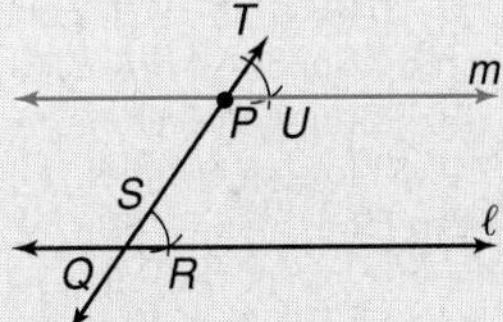

ON YOUR OWN

2. Name angles in the construction that have the same measure. **$\angle TPU$ and $\angle SQR$**
3. A parallelogram is a figure with opposite sides parallel. Use a compass and straightedge to construct a parallelogram. **See margin.**

Math Journal Have students write a paragraph describing the process by which a compass makes it possible to draw perpendicular and parallel lines.

Activity 2 demonstrates the use of a compass and straightedge to construct parallel lines. Have students repeat the activity with a different point P to show that any line that intersects ℓ will help them to draw a line parallel to ℓ.

ASSESS

Have students complete Exercises 1–3. Encourage students to work together on Exercise 1 to see that constructing a rectangle entails constructing three different perpendicular lines.

Additional Answer

3.

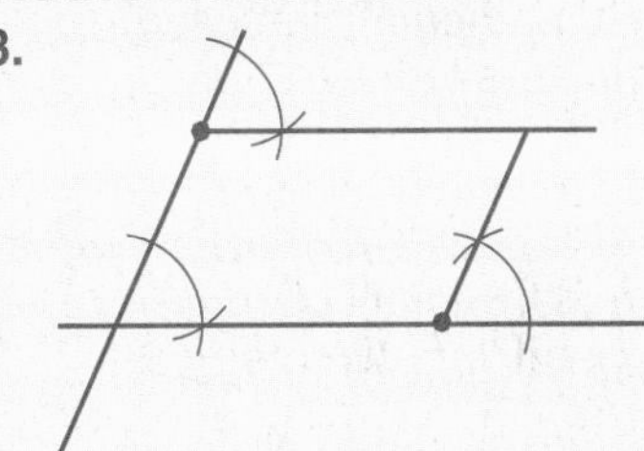

***Hands-On Lab Masters*, p. 57**

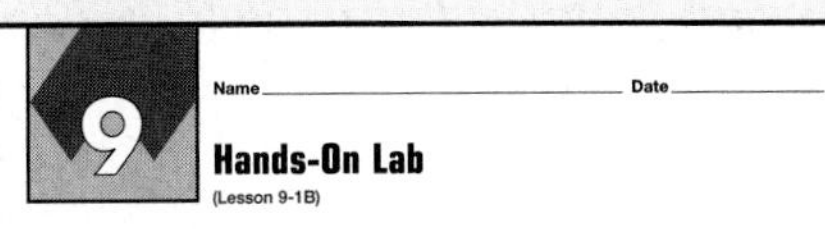

9 Name ______ Date ______

Hands-On Lab
(Lesson 9-1B)

Perpendicular and Parallel Lines

On Your Own

1. Construct a rectangle by constructing perpendiculars.
Sample answer:

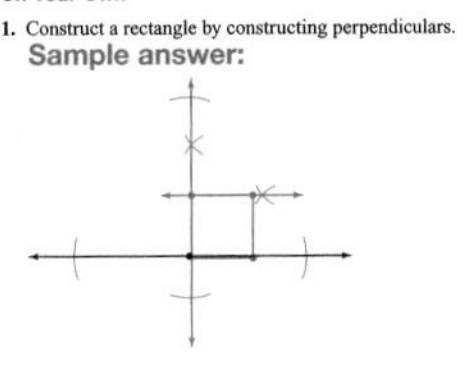

2. The angles with the same measure are $\angle TPU$ and $\angle SQR$.

3. A parallelogram is a figure with opposite sides parallel. Use a compass and straightedge to construct a parallelogram.
Sample answer:

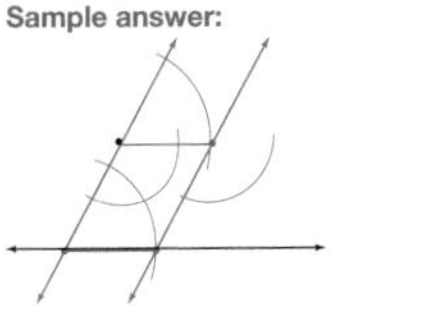

 57 *Mathematics: Applications and Connections, Course 2*

Motivating Students

As students learned in the Chapter Project on page 359, artists create and manipulate a variety of geometric figures in designing buildings, furniture, landscape, videos, magazines, and clothing. As computer technology advances, more opportunities open up for imaginative people who know how to draw, measure, analyze, and combine geometric shapes. Students might not know:

- What mathematician used computers to make breakthroughs in understanding and creating fractals? Dr. Benoit Mandelbrot
- How many kinds of mathematical symmetry are there? 17

Making the Math Connection

Jhane Barnes finds inspiration in the symmetry she sees in architecture, nature, and mathematics. Using a computer aided design (CAD) system with an air-powered loom, she weaves fabrics using graphics created by mathematical software. Ms. Barnes's latest collections of sweaters, jackets, pants, socks, and ties are based on fractals, the hottest "trend" in the world of mathematics.

Working on *Your Turn*

Students may enjoy research on the use of tessellations, translations, and reflections in fabric, wallpaper, rug, tile, or game designs. Have students look for examples where the designer created either symmetrical or asymmetrical patterns.

*An additional School to Career activity is available on page 22 of the **School to Career Masters.***

Someday, I'd like to be a famous fashion designer like Jhane Barnes.

Jhane Barnes
FASHION DESIGNER

Did you ever think that you could use geometry to become a successful fashion designer? Jhane Barnes did! While still a student at New York's Fashion Institute of Technology, she started her own business. More than twenty years later, her company remains at the leading edge of fashion design. Along the way, Ms. Barnes has won numerous awards, including a Coty American Fashion Critics' Menswear Award in 1980. At that time, she was the youngest person, and the only female, to win this award.

Ms. Barnes designs textiles that start with a basic geometric element and grow into unique designs through translations, reflections, and rotations. She also uses fractals in her designs. To be a fashion designer, you'll need to take courses in mathematics, business, design, and art. You should be artistically creative, imaginative, and like challenges.

For more information:
International Association of Clothing Designers
240 Madison Avenue
12th Floor
New York, NY 10016

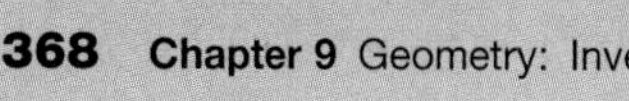

www.glencoe.com/sec/math/mac/mathnet

Your Turn
Design a brochure that describes how geometry is used in fashion design. Include sketches of your designs.

More About Jhane Barnes

- By working with mathematicians to design fabrics using computer graphics software, Ms. Barnes discovered how creative and visually exciting math can be.
- Ms. Barnes organized a symposium in New York for scientists and fashion designers to share their ideas about art, mathematics, and geometric shapes found in nature.

COOPERATIVE LEARNING

9-2A Angles of a Polygon

A Preview of Lesson 9-2

protractor

scissors

In this lab, you will look for a pattern among the angles of a triangle and use the pattern to find the sum of the angle measures of any figure with more than three sides.

TRY THIS

Work with a partner.

1 • Draw three triangles. One triangle should have three acute angles, one should have an obtuse angle, and the last should have a right angle. Cut out the triangles.
• For each triangle, tear off the angles and arrange as shown.

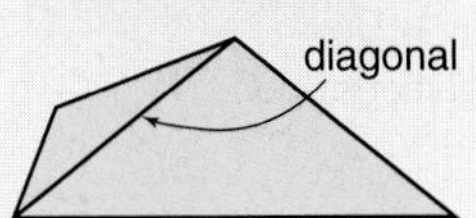

2 • Draw any four-sided figure and cut it out.
• Pick one vertex and draw the diagonal to the opposite vertex. Cut along the diagonal.

ON YOUR OWN

1. For each triangle in Activity 1, what kind of angle is formed where the vertices meet? **straight**
2. What is the measure of this type of angle? **180°**
3. Complete this statement: The sum of the measures of the angles of a triangle is __?__. **180°**
4. How many triangles were formed when you cut along the diagonal of the four-sided figure in Activity 2? **2**
5. Predict the sum of the measures of the angles in your four-sided figure. Explain your reasoning. **See margin.**
6. Devise a way to check your prediction. **See margin.**
7. Find the sum of the measures of the angles of a figure with the following number of sides.
   a. 5 **540°** **b.** 6 **720°** **c.** 8 **1,080°** **d.** 10 **1,440°**
8. ***Algebra*** If n is the number of sides of a figure, write an algebraic expression that tells the sum of the measures of the angles of the figure. **$180(n - 2)$**

Additional Answers

5. **Sample answer: 360°; Since the sum of the measures of each triangle is 180°, there should be 2 × 180° or 360°.**
6. **Sample answer: Tear off the angles and place vertices together. They will form a circle, which is 360°.**

Math Journal Have students write a paragraph describing the pattern they observe in the sums of the measures of the angles of polygons.

9-2A HANDS-ON LAB Notes

GET READY

Objective Students find the sum of the angle measures of polygons.

Optional Resources
Hands-On Lab Masters
• worksheet, p. 58
Overhead Manipulative Resources
• protractor
Manipulative Kit
• scissors
• protractor

MANAGEMENT TIPS

Recommended Time
30 minutes

Getting Started Have students draw several differently shaped triangles, including some with obtuse angles. Ask students to guess the approximate measure of each angle and the sum of the angles in each triangle.

Activity 1 shows that the sum of the measures of the angles of a triangle is 180°. Encourage students to tear apart and reassemble several triangles and observe the results.

Activity 2 reveals a pattern in adding the measures of the angles of different polygons. Ask students what observations they can make about the sums of the angle measures of three-, four-, five-, and six-sided figures.

ASSESS

Have students complete Exercises 1–8. Invite them to make hypotheses about the angles of polygons, and have them test their hypotheses by measuring the angles with a protractor.

9-2 Lesson Notes

Instructional Resources

- *Study Guide Masters,* p. 68
- *Practice Masters,* p. 68
- *Enrichment Masters,* p. 68
- Transparencies 9-2, A and B
- *Assessment and Evaluation Masters,* p. 239
- *Technology Masters,* p. 43
- CD-ROM Program
  - Resource Lesson 9-2

Recommended Pacing	
Standard	Days 5 & 6 of 15
Honors	Days 4 & 5 of 14
Block	Day 3 of 8

1 FOCUS

5-Minute Check
(Lesson 9-1)

Classify each angle as *right, acute, obtuse,* or *straight.*

1.

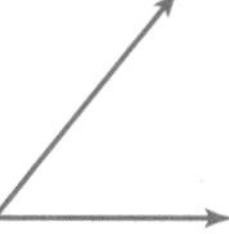

acute

2. 98° angle obtuse
3. Classify the angles as *supplementary, complementary,* or *neither.*

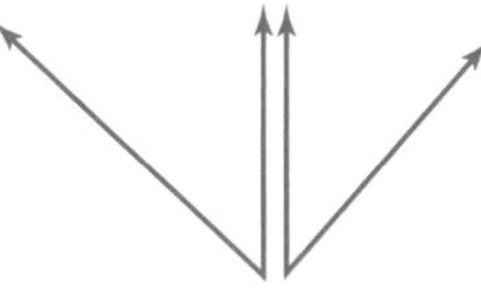

complementary

The 5-Minute Check is also available on **Transparency 9-2A** for this lesson.

Motivating the Lesson

Communication Have students list as many words as possible that begin with the prefixes *poly-, tri-, quad-, penta-, hexa-, hepta-, octa-, nona-,* and *deca-*. Discuss how these words can be used.

9-2 Polygons

What you'll learn

You'll learn to identify polygons and regular polygons.

When am I ever going to use this?

You can identify many types of traffic signs by their shape.

Word Wise

polygon
triangle
quadrilateral
pentagon
hexagon
heptagon
octagon
nonagon
decagon
congruent
regular polygon

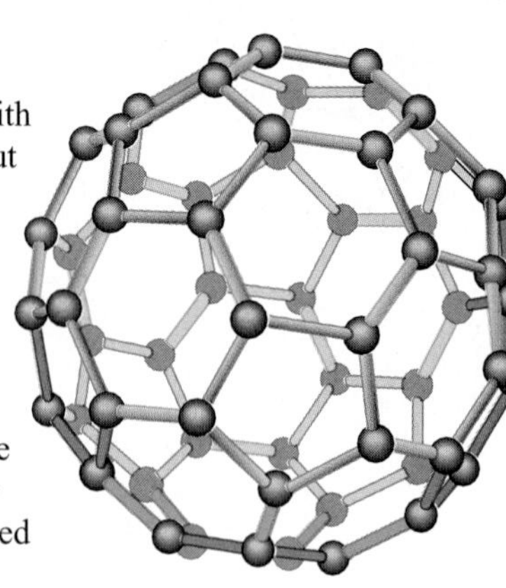

If you love soccer, you are familiar with the unique shapes on a soccer ball. But did you know there is a molecule of carbon with the same shapes? In the early 1990s, scientists discovered that when they fired lasers at carbon molecules, the molecules sometimes formed tiny structures that resembled hollow soccer balls. They named these structures "Buckyballs," because they resembled the geodesic domes designed by Buckminster Fuller.

The five- and six-sided shapes on a soccer ball or Buckyball are examples of **polygons**. A polygon is a *simple closed* figure formed by three or more line segments. *Simple* means that the line segments don't cross each other, and *closed* means that, when you draw the polygon, your pencil ends up where it started. Since the segments meet to form angles and angles have vertices, polygons also have vertices.

Polygons	*Not* Polygons

A polygon is named by the number of its sides or by the number of its angles. The word **triangle** means *three angles*. The word **quadrilateral** means *four sides*. Other common polygons are shown below. Each of these figures is only one example of that type of figure.

pentagon
5 sides

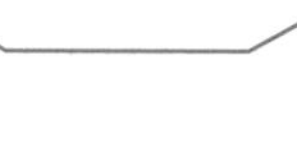

hexagon
6 sides

heptagon
7 sides

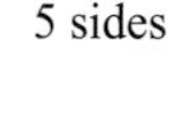

octagon
8 sides

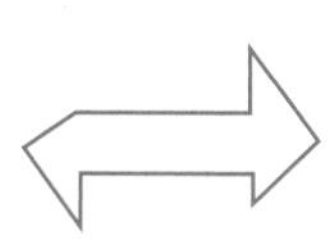

nonagon
9 sides

decagon
10 sides

Classroom Vignette

"In order to identify polygons, students are given laminated pictures of buildings. Students work in groups and use water-based markers to outline polygons found in the pictures. Then they must name these polygons and list their properties."

Suetta Gladfelter, Department Chair
Caroline Middle School
Milford, VA

Suetta Gladfelter

The red slash marks indicate congruent sides, and the red arcs indicate congruent angles.

When two angles or two line segments have the same measure, they are **congruent**. The hexagon at the right has all sides congruent and all angles congruent. This figure is an example of a **regular polygon**.

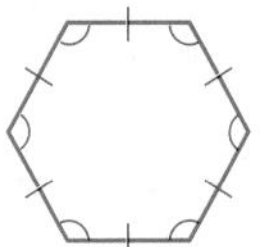

Examples

Determine which figures are polygons. If the figure is a polygon, name it and tell whether it is a regular polygon. If the figure is *not* a polygon, explain why.

1

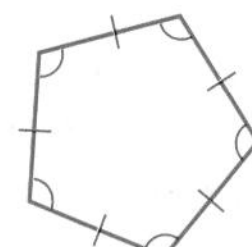

The figure is a polygon. It is a regular pentagon.

2

The figure is *not* a polygon because one of its sides is *not* a line segment.

3

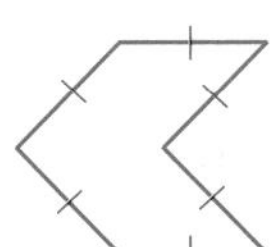

The figure is a polygon. It is a hexagon. It is *not* regular because its angles are not congruent.

4

The figure is a polygon. It is a decagon. It is *not* regular because its sides and angles are *not* congruent.

Study Hint

Reading Math The word polygon comes from the prefix poly- meaning *many* and the suffix -gon meaning *angle*. So, a polygon is a many-angled figure.

In Lesson 9-2A, you found the sum of the measures of the angles of a polygon by drawing all of the diagonals from one vertex and counting the triangles. Then you multiplied that number by 180°. In a hexagon, there are 4 triangles, so the sum of the measures of the angles of a hexagon is $4 \cdot 180°$ or 720°.

Example

INTEGRATION

5 **Algebra** **Use an equation to find the measure of each angle of a regular hexagon.**

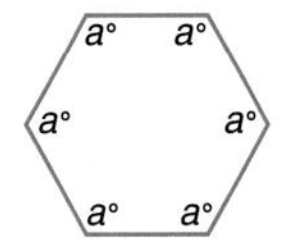

In a regular hexagon, all of the angles have the same measure. Let a represent the measure of one angle.

The sum of the measures of the six angles is 720°. So, solve the equation $6a = 720$.

$6a = 720$

$\frac{6a}{6} = \frac{720}{6}$ *Divide each side of the equation by 6.*

$a = 120$ Each angle of a regular hexagon measures 120°.

■ Reteaching the Lesson ■

Activity Make two hexagons—one that is regular and one that is not. Ask students to examine both figures and list their similarities and differences. Have them measure the sides and the angles. Repeat the process with a pentagon. Ask students to write a definition of a regular polygon based on their investigation.

2 TEACH

Transparency 9-2B contains a teaching aid for this lesson.

Reading Mathematics Write the terms from the Word Wise list on page 370 on index cards. Have students take turns drawing a card, defining the term, and drawing an example of that kind of figure on the chalkboard.

In-Class Examples

Is the figure a polygon? If so, is it a regular polygon? If not, explain why.

For Example 1

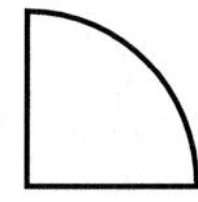

No; one side is not a line segment.

For Example 2

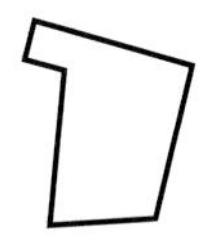

polygon; not regular

For Example 3

No; the figure is not closed.

For Example 4

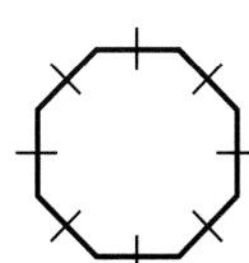

polygon; regular

For Example 5

Find the measure of each angle in a regular octagon. The sum of the angles' measures is 1,080°. **135°**

Teaching Tip In Example 5, students can use the formula $180(n - 2)$, where n is the number of sides, to find the sum of the measures of the angles of any polygon.

3 PRACTICE/APPLY

Check for Understanding

If students need additional practice or instruction after completing Exercises 1–6, one of these options may be helpful.

- Extra Practice, see p. 593
- Reteaching Activity, see p. 371
- *Study Guide Masters,* p. 68
- *Practice Masters,* p. 68
- Interactive Mathematics Tools Software

Assignment Guide

Core: 7–15 odd, 17–20
Enriched: 8–12 even, 14–20

Have students share their drawings of the shapes of signs and architectural objects with the class. Encourage students to create a classroom display of polygons found in everyday environments.

***Study Guide Masters,* p. 68**

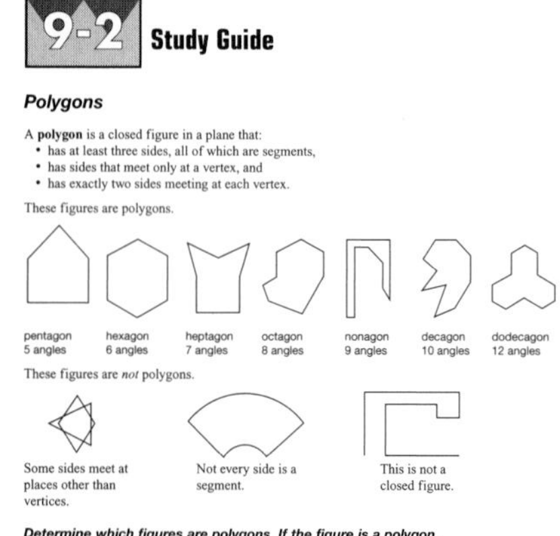

Name ______________ Date ______

9-2 **Study Guide**

Polygons

A **polygon** is a closed figure in a plane that:
- has at least three sides, all of which are segments,
- has sides that meet only at a vertex, and
- has exactly two sides meeting at each vertex.

These figures are polygons.

pentagon 5 angles; hexagon 6 angles; heptagon 7 angles; octagon 8 angles; nonagon 9 angles; decagon 10 angles; dodecagon 12 angles

These figures are *not* polygons.

Some sides meet at places other than vertices. Not every side is a segment. This is not a closed figure.

Determine which figures are polygons. If the figure is a polygon, name it and tell whether it is a regular polygon. If a figure is not a polygon, explain why.

1. pentagon
2. not a closed figure
3. Some parts are not segments
4. octagon
5. hexagon, regular
6. Segments meet at points other than vertices.

© Glencoe/McGraw-Hill T68 *Mathematics: Applications and Connections, Course 2*

CHECK FOR UNDERSTANDING

Communicating Mathematics

Read and study the lesson to answer each question.

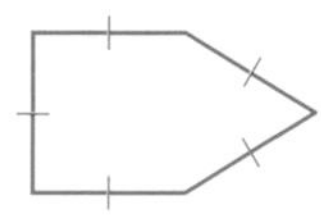

1. ***Tell*** whether the figure is a regular polygon. Explain your reasoning. **No; angles are not congruent.**
2. ***Draw*** a figure that is not a polygon and explain why it is not. **See margin.**

3. ***Draw and label*** a pentagon, hexagon, heptagon, octagon, nonagon, and decagon so that three of the figures are regular and three are *not* regular. **See students' work.**

Guided Practice

Determine which figures are polygons. If the figure is a polygon, name it and tell whether it is a regular polygon. If the figure is *not* a polygon, explain why.

Draw the shape of some other signs or objects you see everyday. Name each shape and identify which type of polygon it is, if any.

4. 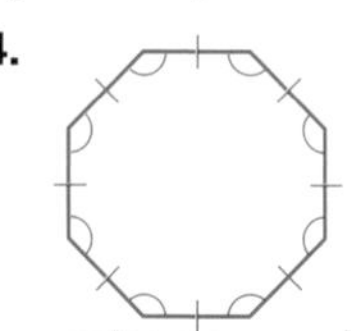
octagon, regular

5. 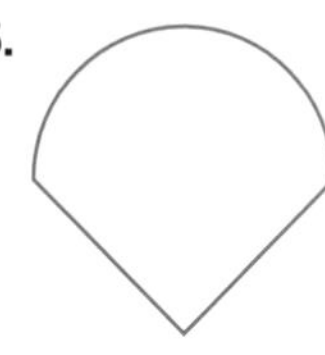
Not a polygon; sides are not line segments.

6. ***Traffic Safety*** Part of the exam you'll take to earn a driver's license asks you to identify road signs. Name the shape of each sign below and tell whether the sign represents a regular polygon.

a. STOP — **octagon, regular**

b. 
quadrilateral, regular

c. YIELD — **triangle, regular**

d. SPEED LIMIT 50 — **quadrilateral, not regular**

EXERCISES

Practice

Determine which figures are polygons. If the figure is a polygon, name it and tell whether it is a regular polygon. If the figure is *not* a polygon, explain why.

7. 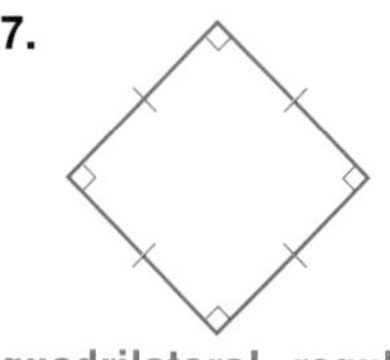
quadrilateral, regular

8. 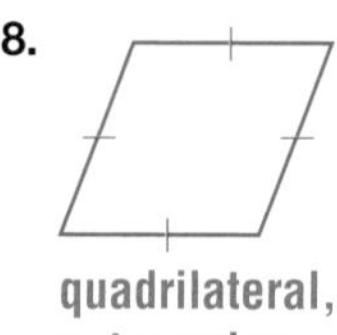
quadrilateral, not regular

9. **Not a polygon; figure is not closed.**

10. 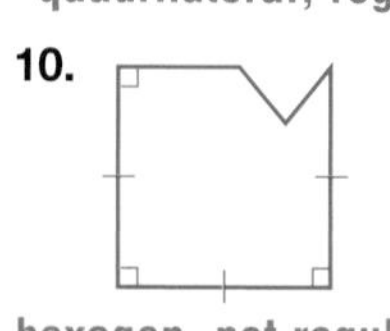
hexagon, not regular

11. **Not a polygon; figure is not closed.**

12. 
quadrilateral, not regular

Additional Answer

2. Sample answer:

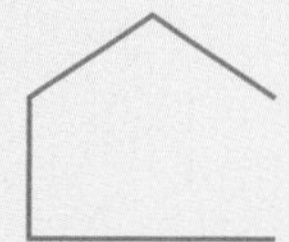

The figure is not closed.

13. A *dodecagon* is a polygon with 12 angles. Draw a dodecagon. **See margin.**

Applications and Problem Solving

14. ***Algebra*** The sum of the measures of the angles of a regular decagon is 1,440°. Write and solve an equation to find the measure of one of its angles. $10x = 1{,}440$; $x = 144$

15. ***Clothing*** If you've bought a new T-shirt or pair of pants recently, you may notice something different on the label. Words are no longer used to describe how to care for the garment. Instead, they have been replaced by symbols. Which of the symbols are polygons? **bleach, dry**

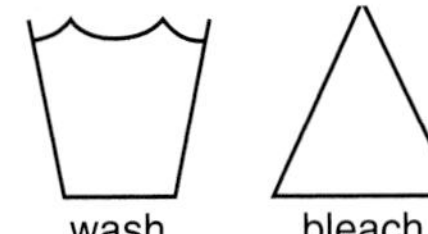

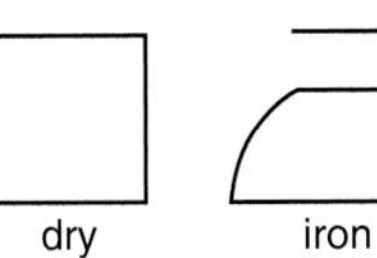

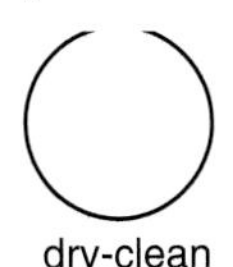

16. ***Earth Science*** In about 135 B.C., Chinese author Han Ying recognized that snowflakes are always six-pointed. Name the figure formed by connecting the points of a snowflake. **hexagon**

17. ***Critical Thinking*** Line l is perpendicular to line m. Line p is parallel to line n. Find each of the following angles.
    - **a.** complementary *e, f*
    - **b.** supplementary *a, b* or *b, c*
    - **c.** vertical *a, c*
    - **d.** alternate interior *c, d*
    - **e.** corresponding *a, d*
    - **f.** acute *e* or *f*
    - **g.** right *g*

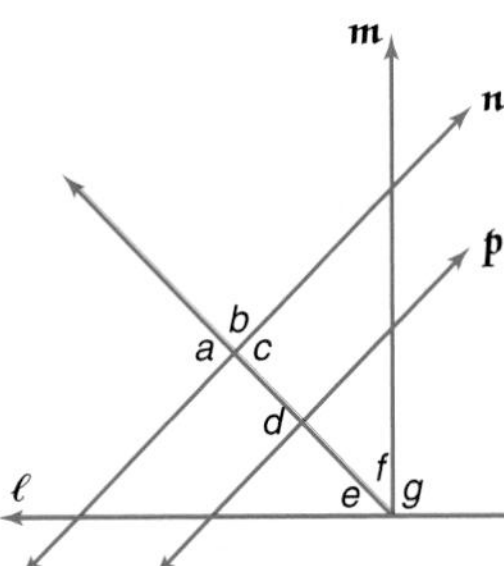

Mixed Review

18. Classify the angles as *supplementary*, *complementary*, or *neither*. *(Lesson 9-1)* **neither**

19. about 4.5 billion pounds

19. ***Food*** The United States produced about 11 billion pounds of apples in a recent year. Use the information in the graph to find how many pounds of apples were used to make juice. *(Lesson 8-8)*

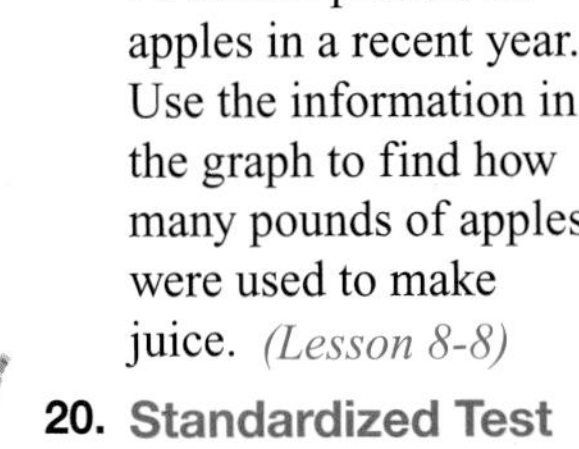

Source: International Apple Institute, 1995

20. **Standardized Test Practice** Alberta is 3 inches less than 6 feet tall. How tall is she in inches? *(Lesson 7-5)* **B**
    - **A** 67 in.
    - **B** 69 in.
    - **C** 72 in.
    - **D** 75 in.

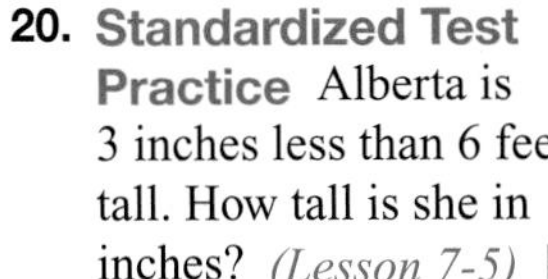

For **Extra Practice,** see page 593.

4 ASSESS

Closing Activity

Writing Have students write a definition of *regular polygon* and explain how to find the degree measure of each of its angles. Then have them trade papers with a partner and critique each other's definitions.

Chapter 9, Quiz A (Lessons 9-1 and 9-2) is available in the *Assessment and Evaluation Masters,* p. 239.

Additional Answer

13.

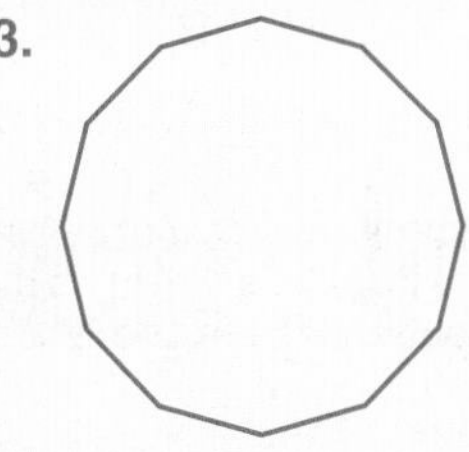

***Practice Masters,* p. 68**

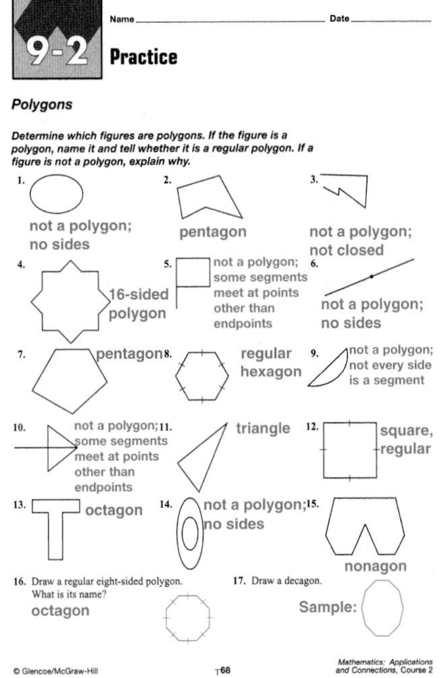

Name______ Date______

9-2 Practice

Polygons

Determine which figures are polygons. If the figure is a polygon, name it and tell whether it is a regular polygon. If a figure is not a polygon, explain why.

1. not a polygon; no sides
2. pentagon
3. not a polygon; not closed
4. 16-sided polygon
5. not a polygon; some segments meet at points other than endpoints
6. not a polygon; no sides
7. pentagon
8. regular hexagon
9. not a polygon; not every side is a segment
10. not a polygon; some segments meet at points other than endpoints
11. triangle
12. square, regular
13. octagon
14. not a polygon; no sides
15. nonagon
16. Draw a regular eight-sided polygon. What is its name? octagon
17. Draw a decagon. Sample:

© Glencoe/McGraw-Hill T68 *Mathematics: Applications and Connections, Course 2*

Extending the Lesson

***Enrichment Masters,* p. 68**

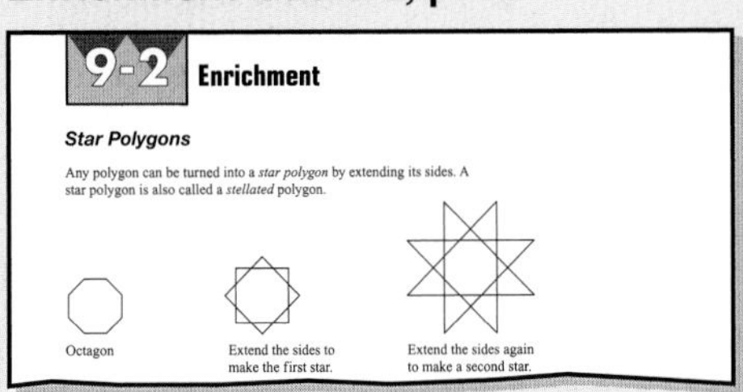

9-2 Enrichment

Star Polygons

Any polygon can be turned into a *star polygon* by extending its sides. A star polygon is also called a *stellated* polygon.

Octagon | Extend the sides to make the first star. | Extend the sides again to make a second star.

Activity Ask students to draw a row of figures, some of which are polygons and some of which are not. Have students exchange papers and decide which drawings are not polygons and why. Then ask them to modify those figures to make them polygons.

9-2B HANDS-ON LAB Notes

GET READY

Objective Students inscribe triangles, squares, and hexagons in circles.

Optional Resources
Hands-On Lab Masters
- worksheet, p. 59

Overhead Manipulative Resources
- compass
- ruler

Manipulative Kit
- compass
- scissors
- ruler

MANAGEMENT TIPS

Recommended Time
20 minutes

Getting Started Ask students how they would use a circle to construct a regular polygon. Have them describe and demonstrate their ideas, either with a drawing or with a circle cut out of paper.

Activities 1 and 2 demonstrate the steps in two methods (with a compass and folding paper) of constructing an inscribed square. Have students work together in two groups, one using each method, and discuss their results.

HANDS-ON LAB

COOPERATIVE LEARNING

9-2B Inscribed Polygons

A Follow-Up of Lesson 9-2

 compass

 straightedge

 scissors

 ruler

 protractor

A polygon is an *inscribed* polygon if each of its vertices lies on a circle. You can inscribe a square in a circle by using some simple paper folding or by using a compass and straightedge.

TRY THIS

1 To use paper folding, follow these steps.

- Use your compass to draw a circle. Then cut out the circle.
- Fold the circle in half and in half again.

- Open the circle. Use your straightedge to draw line segments that connect the points where the paper folds meet the circle. Connect the points in order.

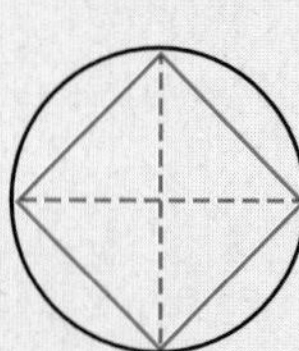

2 To use a compass and straightedge, follow these steps.

- Use your compass to draw a circle.

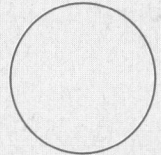

- Draw a diameter through the center of the circle. Then, draw a line perpendicular to the diameter through the center of the circle.

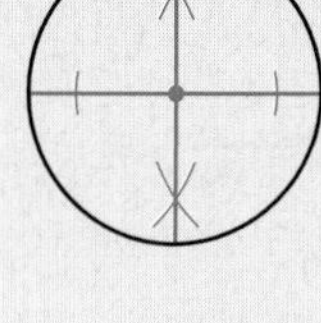

- Use your straightedge to connect the points where the diameter and its perpendicular meet the circle. Connect the points in order.

1. The angles are 90° and the sides are congruent.
2. Sample answer: Folding the circle once is like drawing a diameter; folding it the second time is like drawing the perpendicular line.

ON YOUR OWN

1. Use your protractor to measure the angles of the quadrilaterals. You may need to extend the sides. Use a ruler to measure the sides. What do you find?
2. Explain how the paper folding method is similar to using a compass and straightedge.
3. Use paper folding to inscribe an octagon in a circle. Explain the steps you used. **See margin.**

Additional Answer

3. **Sample answer: Follow the same steps as inscribing a square, but fold the circle in half one more time.**

You can also inscribe other regular polygons in a circle using a compass and straightedge.

TRY THIS

3 To inscribe a regular hexagon in a circle, follow these steps.

- Use your compass to draw a circle. Leave the compass at the same setting.

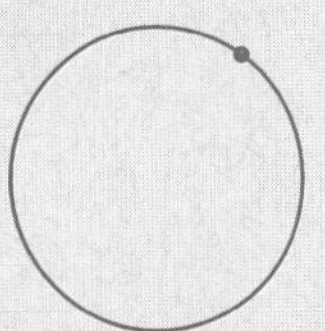

- Put a point on the circle and place your compass on that point. Draw a small arc that intersects the circle.

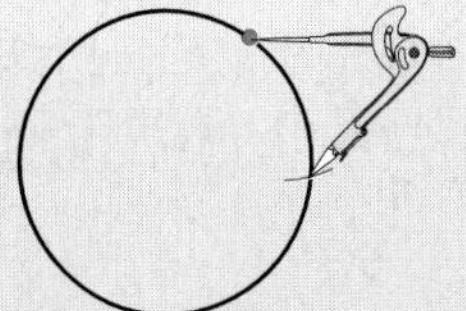

- Place the compass on the point where the arc intersects the circle. Draw another small arc to intersect the circle.

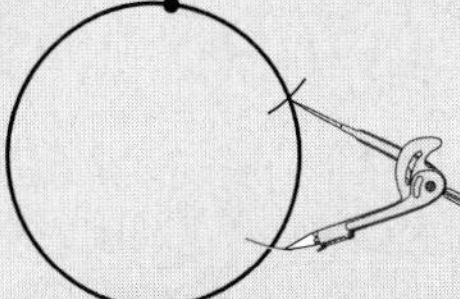

- Continue the process until you come back to the first point. Use the ruler to connect the intersection points in order as shown.

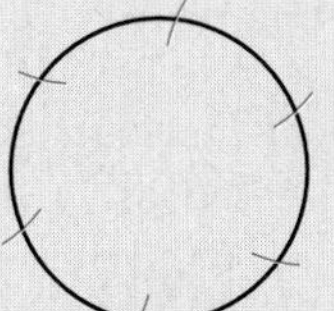

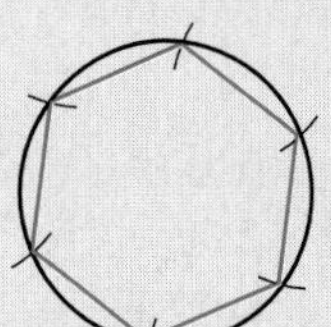

ON YOUR OWN

4. Use your protractor to measure the angles of your hexagon. You may need to extend the sides. Use a ruler to measure the sides. What do you find? Is the hexagon regular? **The angles are 120°; the sides are congruent; yes.**
5. Inscribe an equilateral triangle in a circle. Explain the steps you used. (*Hint*: Modify the steps you used to inscribe a hexagon in a circle.) **See margin.**

Have students write a paragraph explaining how they performed the operation in Exercise 5. Ask what conclusion they can make about diameter, radius, and polygons.

Activity 3 demonstrates the steps in using a compass to construct an inscribed regular hexagon. Caution students to make sure they keep the compass at the same setting throughout.

ASSESS

Have students complete Exercises 1–5. If students need help, review the procedure for using a compass to draw a perpendicular line. Ask students what kind of triangles would be formed by drawing radii from the center of the circle to each vertex of the hexagon in Activity 3. **equilateral**

Additional Answer

5. **Sample answer: Follow the same steps to inscribe a hexagon in a circle, but connect every other intersection point with a line segment.**

***Hands-On Lab Masters,* p. 59**

Name__________ Date__________

Hands-On Lab
(Lesson 9-2B)

Inscribed Polygons

On Your Own

1. When you use a protractor to measure the angles of the quadrilaterals and a ruler to measure the sides, you find **the angles are 90° and the sides are congruent**.
2. Explain how the paper folding method is similar to using a compass and a straightedge. **Sample answer: Folding the circle once is like drawing a diameter. Folding it the second time is like drawing the perpendicular line.**
3. Use paper folding to inscribe an octagon in a circle. Explain the steps you used. **See students' work. Fold the circle in half a third time.**

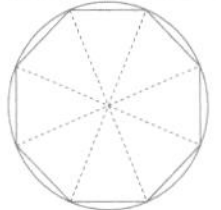

4. When you use a protractor to measure the angles of your hexagon and a ruler to measure the sides, you find **the angles are 120°; the sides are congruent. Yes, the hexagon is regular**.
5. Inscribe an equilateral triangle in a circle. Explain the steps you used. **See students' work. Connect every other point with a line segment.**

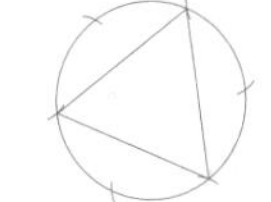

 59 *Mathematics: Applications and Connections,* Course 2

9-3 Lesson Notes

Instructional Resources

- *Study Guide Masters,* p. 69
- *Practice Masters,* p. 69
- *Enrichment Masters,* p. 69
- Transparencies 9-3, A and B
- *Technology Masters,* p. 44

CD-ROM Program
- Resource Lesson 9-3

Recommended Pacing	
Standard	Day 7 of 15
Honors	Days 6 & 7 of 14
Block	Day 3 of 8

1 FOCUS

5-Minute Check (Lesson 9-2)

Determine which figures are polygons. If a figure is a polygon, name it and tell whether it is a regular polygon. If the figure is *not* a polygon, explain why.

1. 
polygon; pentagon; not regular

2. 
Not a polygon; one side is not a line segment.

3. triangle; not regular

4. 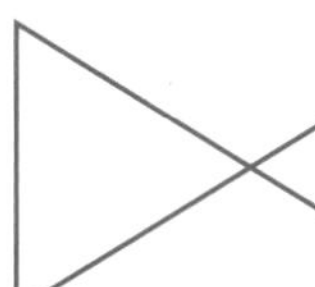
Not a polygon; some sides do not meet at vertices.

The 5-Minute Check is also available on **Transparency 9-3A** for this lesson.

9-3 Integration: Algebra Similar Polygons

What you'll learn
You'll learn to determine whether polygons are similar and find a missing length in a pair of similar polygons.

When am I ever going to use this?
You'll use similar polygons when you enlarge or reduce drawings.

Word Wise
similar
indirect measurement

Have you ever seen a photograph of the United States taken from space? The photo is an example of a **similar** figure. It has the same shape as the United States but is a different size.

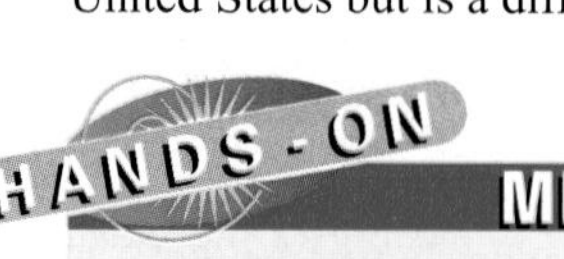

MINI-LAB

Work with a partner.  dot paper 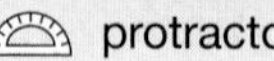 protractor

Try This

- Copy each pair of polygons onto dot paper.

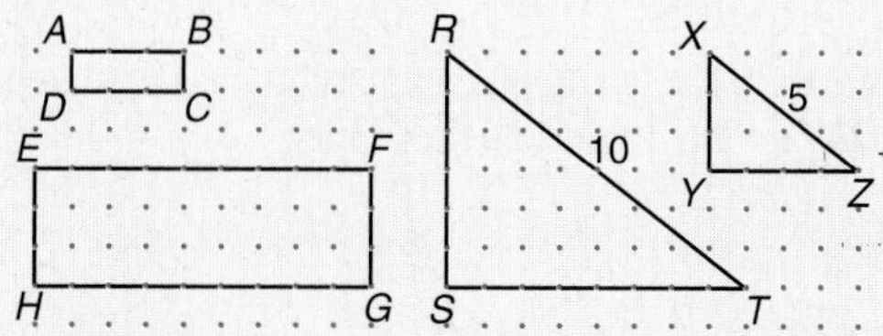

- Measure each angle in degrees and each side in units.

Talk About It 2–3. They are equal.

1. Express each ratio in simplest form. *Letters such as AB refer to the measure of the segment with those endpoints.*
   a. $\frac{AB}{EF}, \frac{BC}{FG}, \frac{DC}{HG}, \frac{AD}{EH}$ **b.** $\frac{RS}{XY}, \frac{ST}{YZ}, \frac{RT}{XZ}$ 2, 2, 2
2. The rectangles are similar and the triangles are similar. What do you notice about the ratios of their corresponding sides?
3. In the triangles above, find corresponding angles. What do you notice about the measure of corresponding angles?
4. Write a definition of similar polygons.

1a. $\frac{1}{3}, \frac{1}{3}, \frac{1}{3}, \frac{1}{3}$
4. Angles are congruent and ratios of sides are equal.

Study Hint
Reading Math Parts of similar figures that "match" are called *corresponding parts.* In the triangles above, ∠R and ∠X are corresponding angles.

The pattern in the Mini-Lab suggests the following definition.

Similar Polygons

Words: Two polygons are similar if their corresponding angles are congruent and their corresponding sides are in proportion.

Symbols: $\triangle ABC \sim \triangle XYZ$
The symbol ~ means is similar to.

Model:

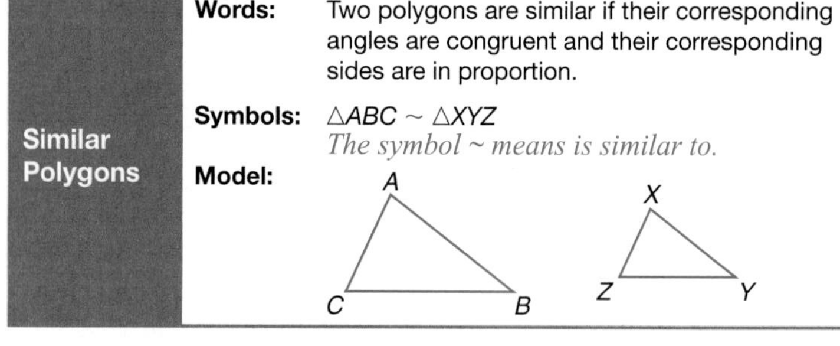

Proportions are useful in finding the missing length of a side in any pair of similar polygons.

Example 1 **If $\triangle ABC \sim \triangle DEF$, find the length of $\overline{EF}$.**

The symbol $\overline{EF}$ means line segment EF.

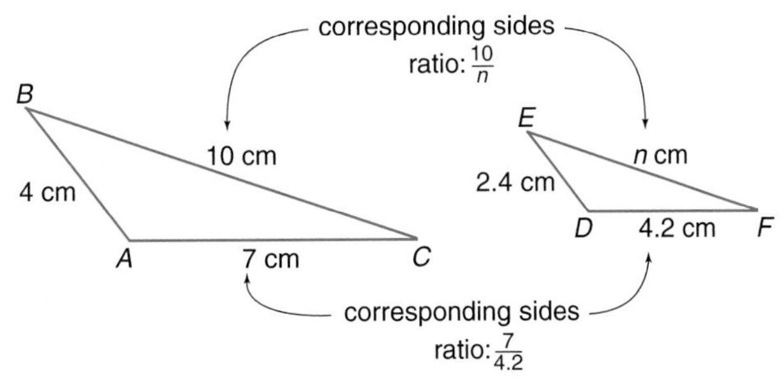

In similar polygons, these two ratios are equal. So, you can write and solve a proportion to find the missing measure.

Let n represent the missing measure.

$$\frac{7}{4.2} = \frac{10}{n}$$

$7n = 4.2(10)$ *Find the cross products.*

$7n = 42$

$n = 6$ *Divide each side by 7.*

The length of $\overline{EF}$ is 6 centimeters.

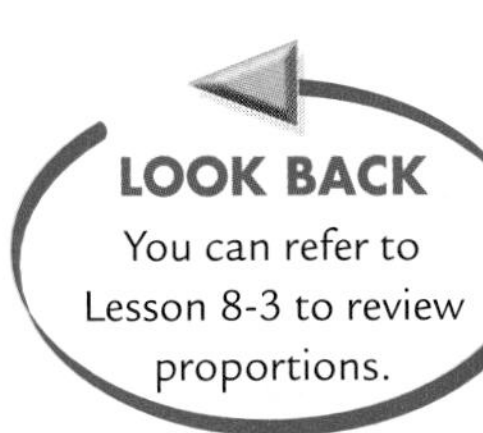

LOOK BACK
You can refer to Lesson 8-3 to review proportions.

You can use similar triangles to find the height of objects like flagpoles that are too difficult to measure directly. This kind of measurement is called **indirect measurement**.

Example 2 **INTEGRATION**

Measurement **The height of a flagpole and the length of its shadow are proportional to the height of another object and the length of its shadow. The objects and their shadows form two sides of similar triangles. Find the height of the flagpole shown below.**

Let x represent the height of the flagpole.

height of tree → / *length of shadow* → $\frac{6}{4} = \frac{x}{18}$ ← *height of flagpole* / ← *length of shadow*

$6(18) = 4x$

$108 = 4x$

$27 = x$

The height of the flagpole is 27 feet.

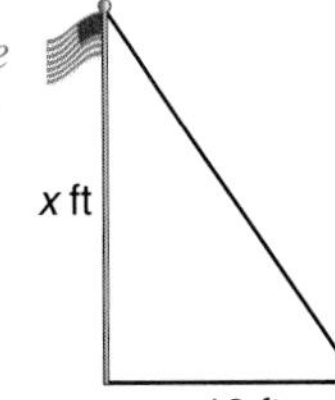

Study Hint
Estimation After setting up the proportion, you can estimate to help you solve the problem.
$5 \times 20 = 4x$
$100 = 4x$
$25 = x$

Motivating the Lesson

Problem Solving Ask students how they would determine how wide an enlargement of a photo is if the original is 5 inches wide and 7 inches long and the enlargement is 21 inches long.

2 TEACH

Transparency 9-3B contains a teaching aid for this lesson.

Using the Mini-Lab Point out to students that the word *similar* has a specific mathematical meaning that is not necessarily the same as in everyday use.

Teaching Tip In Example 1, ask students if another ratio besides $\frac{7}{4.2}$ could be used to find *n*. **yes;** $\frac{4}{2.4}$

In-Class Examples

For Example 1
If $\triangle ABC \sim \triangle DEF$, find the length of $\overline{DF}$. **15**

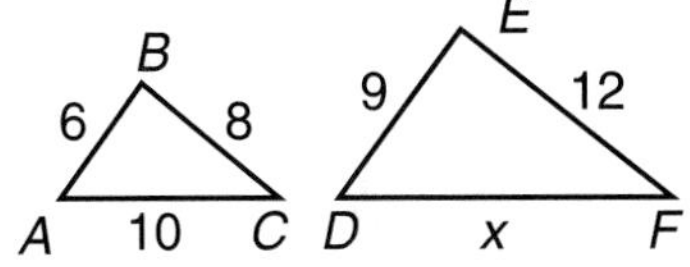

For Example 2
The basketball hoop in a school yard is 10 feet high, and its shadow is 2 feet long. The shadow of the sycamore tree next to the hoop in the school yard is 8 feet long. How tall is the tree? **40 feet**

MathPASS CD-ROM

This CD-ROM offers a complete, self-paced mathematics curriculum. Each lesson includes a pretest, tutorial, guided practice, and posttest. MathPASS Lesson 33 is correlated to this Student Edition lesson.
For Windows & Macintosh

3 PRACTICE/APPLY

Check for Understanding

If students need additional practice or instruction after completing Exercises 1–8, one of these options may be helpful.

- Extra Practice, see p. 593
- Reteaching Activity
- *Study Guide Masters,* p. 69
- *Practice Masters,* p. 69

Assignment Guide

Core: 9–17 odd, 18–20
Enriched: 10–14 even, 16–20
All: Self Test, 1–5

CHECK FOR UNDERSTANDING

Communicating Mathematics

1. $\frac{4}{2.4} = \frac{10}{n}$

3. Nikki; $\frac{2}{3} \neq \frac{3}{4}$

Read and study the lesson to answer each question.

1. ***Write*** another proportion that could have been used to find the value of n in Example 1 on page 377.
2. ***Draw*** two similar rectangles whose corresponding sides are in the ratio of 3:5. Label the sides. **See students' work.**
3. ***You Decide*** Lorena thinks the rectangles at the right are similar. Nikki thinks they are *not* similar. Who is correct? Explain your reasoning.

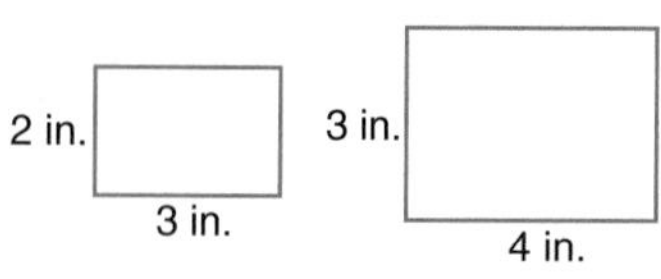

Guided Practice

4. No; $\frac{3}{6} = \frac{1}{2}$ and $\frac{4}{7} = \frac{4}{7}$

5. Yes; $\frac{2}{6} = \frac{1}{3}$ and $\frac{3}{9} = \frac{1}{3}$

Tell whether each pair of polygons is similar. Justify your answer.

4.

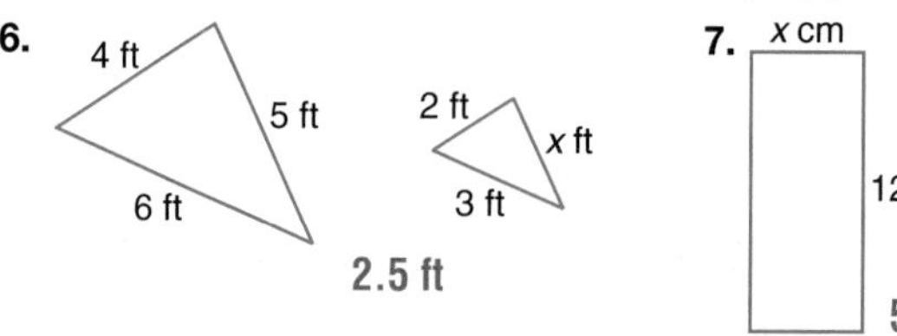

5. 2 cm, 3 cm; 6 cm, 9 cm

Find the value of x in each pair of similar polygons.

6. 4 ft, 5 ft, 6 ft; 2 ft, x ft, 3 ft **2.5 ft**

7. x cm, 12 cm; 1.25 cm, 3 cm **5 cm**

8. Rectangles F and G are similar. The ratio of rectangle F's width to rectangle G's width is 2:3. The length of rectangle F is 15 inches, and its width is 10 inches. Find the perimeter of rectangle G. **75 inches**

EXERCISES

Practice

10. No; $\frac{10}{5} = \frac{2}{1}$ and $\frac{12}{7} = \frac{12}{7}$

Tell whether each pair of polygons is similar. Justify your answer.

9. 1 yd, 2 yd; 3 yd, 6 yd
Yes; $\frac{2}{6} = \frac{1}{3}$

10.

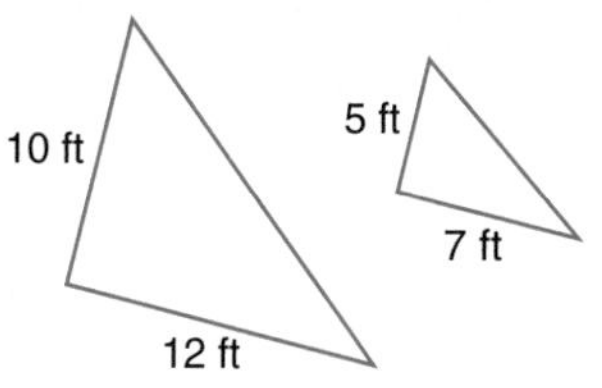

Find the value of x in each pair of similar polygons.

11. 3 m, 6 m, 4 m; 6 m, 12 m, x m **8 m**

12. 21 in., x in.; 7 in., 1 in. **3 in.**

Study Guide Masters, p. 69

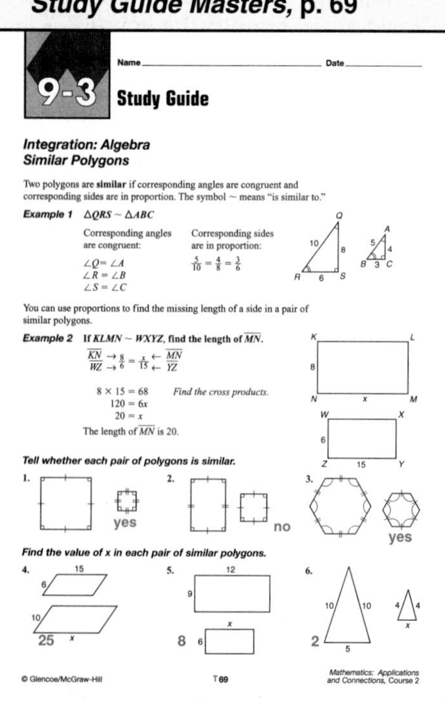

Name ______ Date ______

9-3 **Study Guide**

Integration: Algebra
Similar Polygons

Two polygons are **similar** if corresponding angles are congruent and corresponding sides are in proportion. The symbol ~ means "is similar to."

Example 1 $\triangle QRS \sim \triangle ABC$

Corresponding angles are congruent:
$\angle Q = \angle A$
$\angle R = \angle B$
$\angle S = \angle C$

Corresponding sides are in proportion:
$\frac{5}{10} = \frac{4}{8} = \frac{3}{6}$

You can use proportions to find the missing length of a side in a pair of similar polygons.

Example 2 If $KLMN \sim WXYZ$, find the length of $\overline{MN}$.

$\frac{\overline{KN} \rightarrow 8}{\overline{WZ} \rightarrow 6} = \frac{x \leftarrow \overline{MN}}{15 \leftarrow \overline{YZ}}$

$8 \times 15 = 68$ *Find the cross products.*
$120 = 6x$
$20 = x$

The length of $\overline{MN}$ is 20.

Tell whether each pair of polygons is similar.

1. yes
2. no
3. yes

Find the value of x in each pair of similar polygons.

4. 15, 6; 10, x — 25
5. 12, 9; x, 6 — 8
6. 10, 10, 5; 4, 4, x — 2

 T69 *Mathematics: Applications and Connections, Course 2*

Reteaching the Lesson

Activity Have students use geoboards to form the similar figures shown in the lesson examples. Have them measure the angles and then the lengths of the sides whose measurements are not given. Ask them what they notice about the corresponding angles and sides.

Error Analysis
Watch for students who inadvertently invert the ratio of two sides of similar polygons.
Prevent by making sure the numerator of each ratio represents a side of one figure and the denominator of each ratio represents a corresponding side of the other figure.

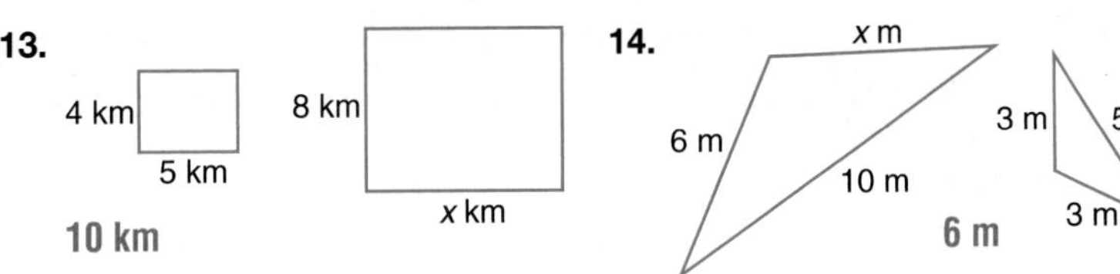

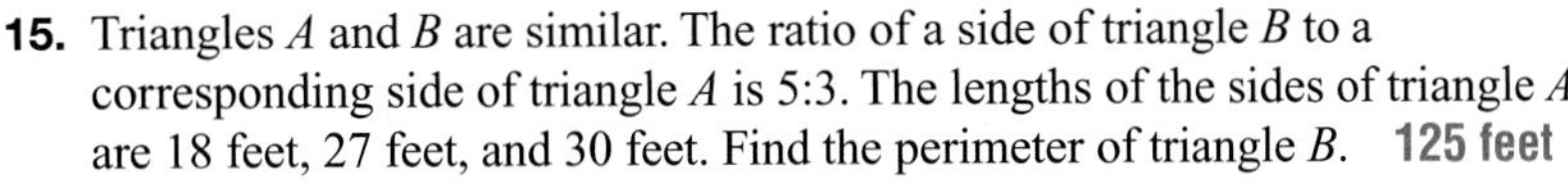

15. Triangles A and B are similar. The ratio of a side of triangle B to a corresponding side of triangle A is 5:3. The lengths of the sides of triangle A are 18 feet, 27 feet, and 30 feet. Find the perimeter of triangle B. **125 feet**

Applications and Problem Solving

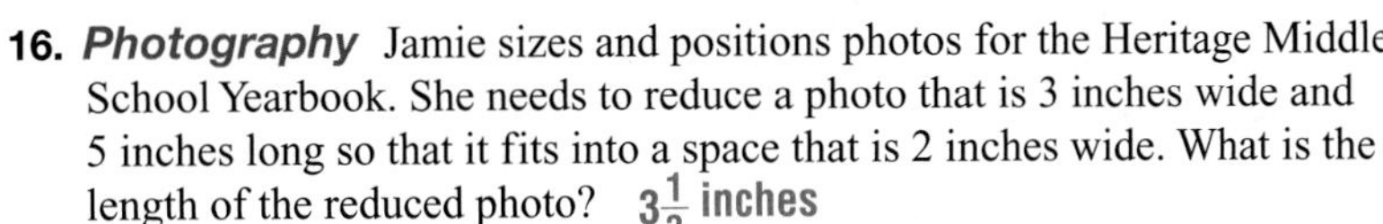

16. ***Photography*** Jamie sizes and positions photos for the Heritage Middle School Yearbook. She needs to reduce a photo that is 3 inches wide and 5 inches long so that it fits into a space that is 2 inches wide. What is the length of the reduced photo? **$3\frac{1}{3}$ inches**

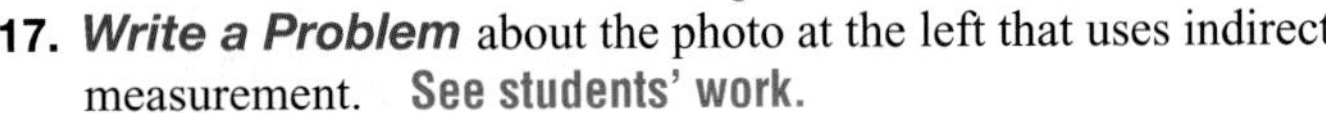

17. ***Write a Problem*** about the photo at the left that uses indirect measurement. **See students' work.**

18. ***Critical Thinking*** Two rectangles are similar. The ratio of their corresponding sides is 1:2.

a. Find the ratio of their perimeters. **1:2**

b. Find the ratio of their areas. **1:4**

Mixed Review

19. **Standardized Test Practice** Which is *not* a polygon? *(Lesson 9-2)* **D**

A  **B** 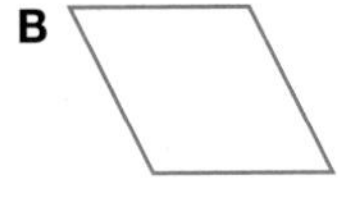 **C**  **D** 

For **Extra Practice,** see page 593.

20. Evaluate 5^3. *(Lesson 1-4)* **125**

Mid-Chapter Self Test

Classify each angle as *acute, obtuse, right,* or *straight.* *(Lesson 9-1)*

1. **obtuse**

2. **right**

Determine which figures are polygons. If the figure is a polygon, name it and tell whether it is a regular polygon. If the figure is *not* a polygon, explain why. *(Lesson 9-2)*

3. **No; figure is not closed.**

4. **Yes; hexagon, not regular**

5. Find the value of x in the similar triangles at the right. *(Lesson 9-3)* **5.25 cm**

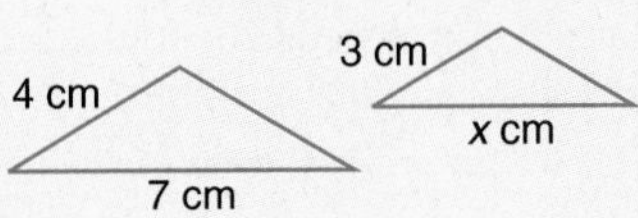

4 ASSESS

Closing Activity

Modeling Have students draw and label the lengths of the sides of a pair of similar figures, providing all but one length. Students should exchange papers and find the missing length.

Mid-Chapter Self Test

The Mid-Chapter Self Test reviews the concepts in Lessons 9-1 through 9-3. Lesson references are given so students can review concepts not yet mastered.

***Practice Masters,* p. 69**

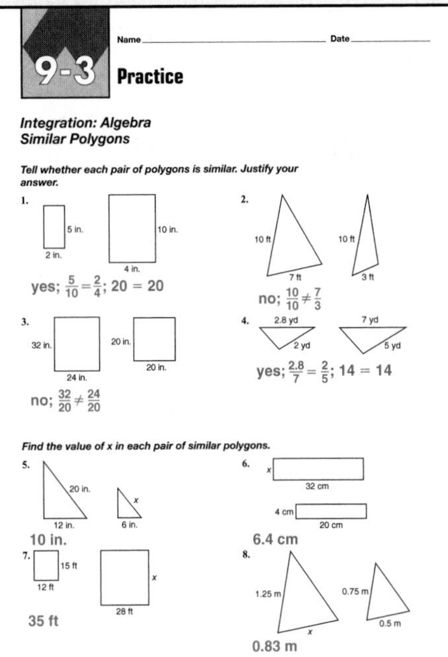

Name______________ Date__________

9-3 Practice

Integration: Algebra
Similar Polygons

Tell whether each pair of polygons is similar. Justify your answer.

1. 5 in., 2 in.; 10 in., 4 in. **yes; $\frac{5}{10} = \frac{2}{4}$; 20 = 20**

2. 10 ft, 7 ft; 10 ft, 3 ft **no; $\frac{10}{10} \neq \frac{7}{3}$**

3. 32 in., 24 in.; 20 in., 20 in. **no; $\frac{32}{20} \neq \frac{24}{20}$**

4. 2.8 yd, 2 yd; 7 yd, 5 yd **yes; $\frac{2.8}{7} = \frac{2}{5}$; 14 = 14**

Find the value of x in each pair of similar polygons.

5. 20 in., 12 in.; x, 6 in. **10 in.**

6. x, 32 cm; 4 cm, 20 cm **6.4 cm**

7. 15 ft, 12 ft; x, 28 ft **35 ft**

8. 1.25 m, x; 0.75 m, 0.5 m **0.83 m**

© Glencoe/McGraw-Hill T 69 *Mathematics: Applications and Connections, Course 2*

Extending the Lesson

***Enrichment Masters,* p. 69**

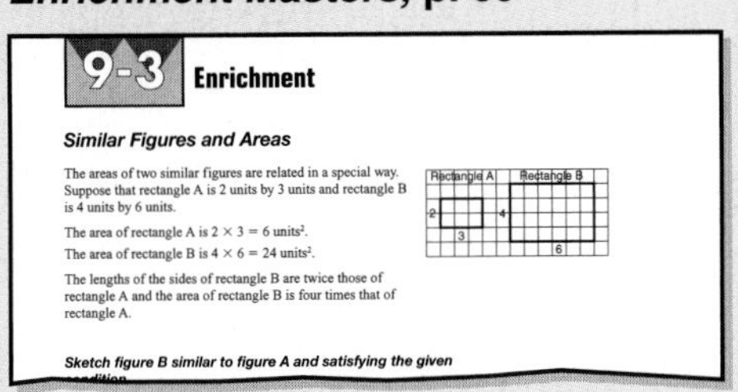

9-3 Enrichment

Similar Figures and Areas

The areas of two similar figures are related in a special way. Suppose that rectangle A is 2 units by 3 units and rectangle B is 4 units by 6 units.

The area of rectangle A is $2 \times 3 = 6$ units^2.

The area of rectangle B is $4 \times 6 = 24$ units^2.

The lengths of the sides of rectangle B are twice those of rectangle A and the area of rectangle B is four times that of rectangle A.

Sketch figure B similar to figure A and satisfying the given condition.

Activity There are three seventh grade classes. Class A has 12 boys and 15 girls, class B has 33 students, of which 18 are girls, and class C has 22 students, with two more girls than boys. Ask students which two classes have identical boy-girl ratios. **classes B and C**

GET READY

Objective Students enlarge a figure on a coordinate plane.

Optional Resources
Hands-On Lab Masters
- grid paper, p. 10
- worksheet, p. 60

Overhead Manipulative Resources
- grid paper
- straightedge

Manipulative Kit
- straightedge

MANAGEMENT TIPS

Recommended Time
25 minutes

Getting Started Ask students to list examples they have seen of enlargements and reductions of images. Have them suggest possible methods of reproducing original designs either smaller for storage or larger for display.

The **Activity** shows how to make a drawing similar to and twice the size of a picture. Tell students to expect some inaccuracies when sketching onto the larger squares and to correct them when tracing the final draft onto white paper. Encourage them to try drawing a second cartoon that is tripled in size.

ASSESS

Have students complete Exercises 1–3. Ask students what would happen if they doubled the height but not the width of the grid, or if they doubled the width but not the height.

HANDS-ON LAB COOPERATIVE LEARNING

9-3B Dilations

A Follow-Up of Lesson 9-3

- cartoon
- grid paper
- straightedge
- colored pencils
- white paper

Some copy machines can reduce and enlarge images. In mathematics, the process of reducing and enlarging a figure is a transformation called a *dilation*.

TRY THIS

- Place a piece of grid paper over a cartoon or picture you want to enlarge. Trace the picture. It may help to put the paper against a window to see the image more clearly.

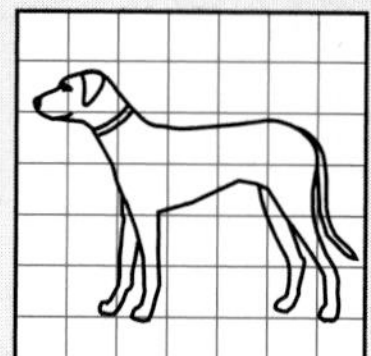

- On another piece of grid paper, use a colored pencil to draw horizontal lines every two squares. Then draw vertical lines every two squares.
- Now sketch the parts of the figure contained in each small square of your original picture onto each large square of the grid you created.
- Place a piece of white paper over your new drawing. Trace the picture and then color it.

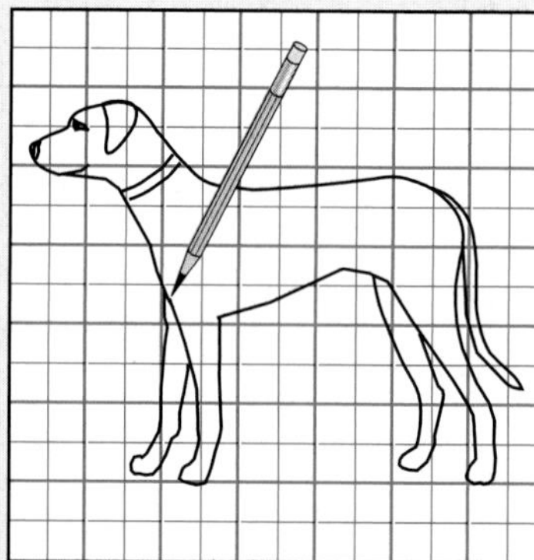

ON YOUR OWN

1. Has the figure been enlarged or reduced? By how much has the height changed? **enlarged; doubled** **2. Yes; each part of the drawing is proportional to the enlargement.**
2. Is the enlargement similar to the original drawing? Explain your reasoning.
3. What type of grid would you use to *reduce* a picture? **one with smaller squares**

Have students write a paragraph explaining what is the same and what is different about two similar drawings.

COOPERATIVE LEARNING

9-4A Investigating Triangles and Quadrilaterals

A Preview of Lesson 9-4

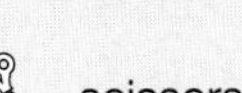 4 × 6 index cards

scissors

brass fasteners

protractor

In this lab, you will investigate the characteristics of special triangles and quadrilaterals. Before you begin the lab, cut $\frac{1}{2}$-inch wide strips from the index cards. You will need four 3-inch long strips, four 5-inch long strips, and four 6-inch long strips.

TRY THIS

Work with a partner.

1
- Use your paper strips and fasteners to make three triangles *A*, *B*, and *C*.
  Triangle *A* has three congruent sides.
  Triangle *B* has exactly two congruent sides.
  Triangle *C* has no congruent sides.
- Measure the angles of your triangles.
- Compare your triangles with those of other groups.
- What conclusions can you draw about the angles of a triangle with three congruent sides? two congruent sides? no congruent sides?

2
- Choose four congruent paper strips. Join them with brass fasteners to form a quadrilateral with four right angles. This is quadrilateral *D*.
- Shift your figure into a different-shaped quadrilateral. Call it quadrilateral *E*. Measure its angles. What pattern do you notice?
- Make quadrilateral *F* from two congruent paper strips and two other congruent paper strips. Form a quadrilateral with four right angles.
- Shift your figure into a different-shaped quadrilateral. This is quadrilateral *G*. Measure its angles. What pattern do you notice?
- Compare your findings with those of other groups. What conclusions can you draw about the angles of quadrilaterals like quadrilateral *E*? like quadrilateral *G*?

ON YOUR OWN

1. You were able to shift your quadrilaterals so that the angles changed. Are you able to shift a triangle into a different triangle? Try it by making several different triangles. **no**
2. Suppose you were building a bookcase. The outside is in the shape of a rectangle.
   a. Would you expect the rectangle to be rigid or would you expect it to shift? **shift**
   b. How could you make the bookcase more rigid? **See margin.**
3. ***Make a conjecture*** about why triangles are often used in the construction of buildings. **See margin.**

Additional Answers

2b. Add a diagonal support, which make two triangles.

3. Triangles are rigid shapes and do not shift.

Have students write a paragraph describing details about different kinds of triangles and quadrilaterals. Then ask them to write a more general statement about triangles and a general statement about quadrilaterals.

9-4A HANDS-ON LAB Notes

GET READY

Objective Students discover characteristics of various kinds of triangles and quadrilaterals.

Optional Resources

Hands-On Lab Masters
- worksheet, p. 61

Overhead Manipulative Resources
- protractor

Manipulative Kit
- protractor
- scissors

MANAGEMENT TIPS

Recommended Time
30 minutes

Getting Started Ask students to describe examples of triangles and quadrilaterals used in architecture. Consider different shapes used for the roofs and walls of buildings and what effect each shape might have on the structure.

Activity 1 shows how the relationship between the sides of a triangle affects the relationship between the angles. Ask students what relationship they can observe between an angle and the opposite side.

Activity 2 shows how changing the angles of a quadrilateral affects the relationship of the angles to each other and the kind of polygon it is. Ask students what relationship they can observe between adjacent angles.

ASSESS

Have students complete Exercises 1–3. For Exercise 2, encourage students to reinforce their paper-strip quadrilaterals with paper-strip triangles and note the results. For Exercise 3, ask students what problems might be solved by using triangles in construction.

9-4 Lesson Notes

Instructional Resources

- *Study Guide Masters,* p. 70
- *Practice Masters,* p. 70
- *Enrichment Masters,* p. 70
- Transparencies 9-4, A and B
- *Assessment and Evaluation Masters,* pp. 238, 239

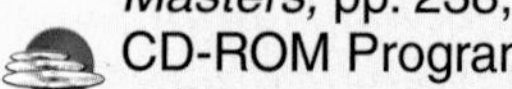
CD-ROM Program
- Resource Lesson 9-4

Recommended Pacing	
Standard	Days 8 & 9 of 15
Honors	Day 8 of 14
Block	Day 4 of 8

1 FOCUS

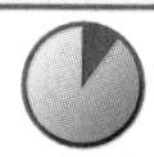

5-Minute Check
(Lesson 9-3)

Tell whether each pair of polygons is similar. Justify your answer.

1.

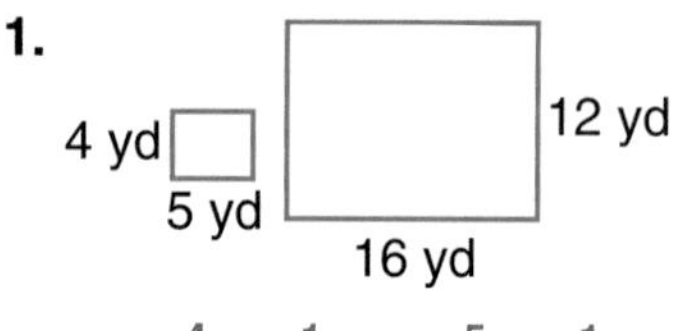

no; $\frac{4}{12} = \frac{1}{3}$ and $\frac{5}{16} \neq \frac{1}{3}$

2.

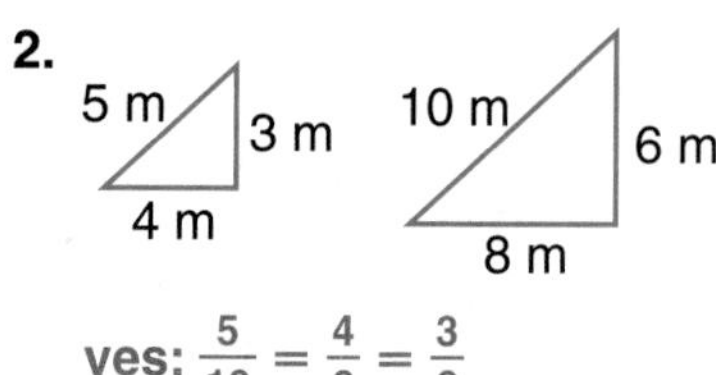

yes; $\frac{5}{10} = \frac{4}{8} = \frac{3}{6}$

Find the value of *x* in each pair of similar polygons.

3.

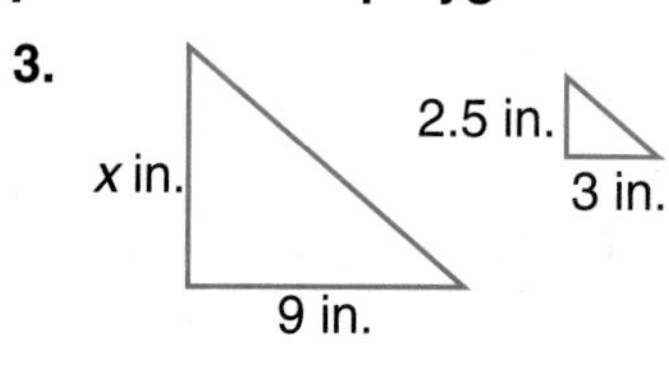

7.5

4.

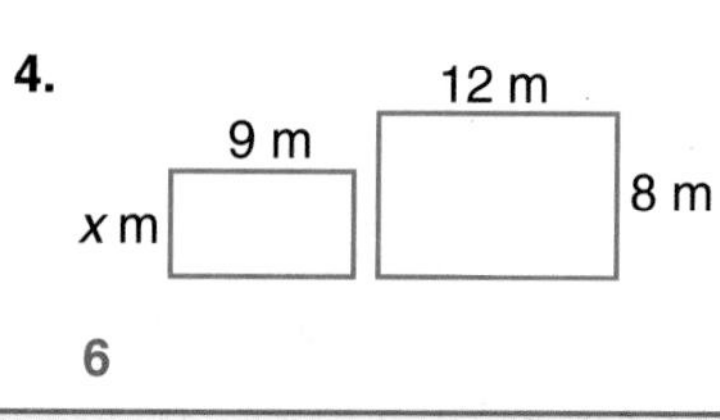

6

The 5-Minute Check is also available on **Transparency 9-4A** for this lesson.

9-4 Triangles and Quadrilaterals

What you'll learn

You'll learn to classify triangles and quadrilaterals.

When am I ever going to use this?

You'll use the properties of triangles and quadrilaterals when you do sewing or carpentry projects.

Word Wise

acute triangle
right triangle
obtuse triangle
scalene triangle
isosceles triangle
equilateral triangle
rhombus
trapezoid

The drawing shows how scientists classify living things. An organism is a single individual. A population is all of the individuals of one species with the same characteristics. A community is made up of populations of different species.

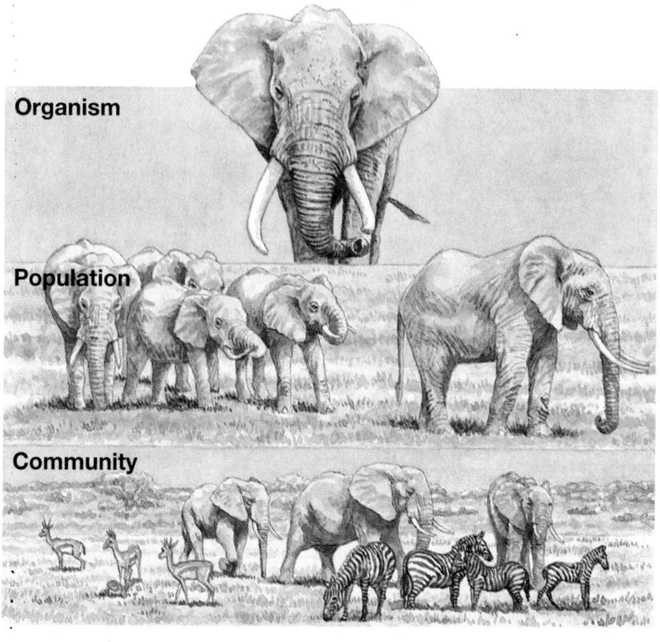

In geometry, you can classify polygons in a similar manner. For example, triangles can be classified by their angle measures. Every triangle has two acute angles. You can classify a triangle using the third angle.

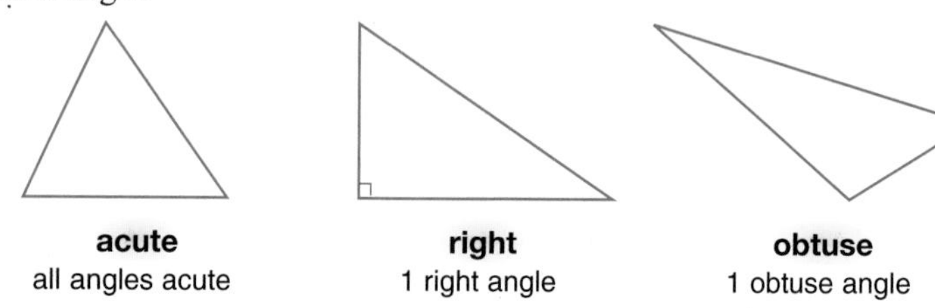

acute all angles acute | **right** 1 right angle | **obtuse** 1 obtuse angle

Triangles can also be classified by the number of congruent sides they have.

scalene
no congruent sides

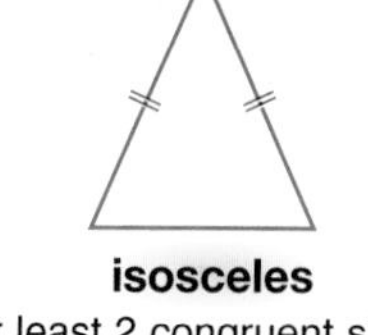

isosceles
at least 2 congruent sides

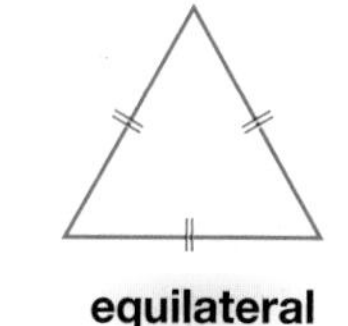

equilateral
3 congruent sides

Motivating the Lesson

Communication Have students look about the room to find examples of shapes that are triangles or quadrilaterals. Ask them to work with partners to think of ways to describe these figures individually and as members of categories.

1 **Architecture** Triangles are used in the design of many office buildings to secure them in case of high winds or earthquakes. Classify each triangle by its angles and by its sides.

a. $\triangle ABC$

$\triangle ABC$ is acute and isosceles.

b. $\triangle BCD$

$\triangle BCD$ is obtuse and scalene.

c. $\triangle ACE$

$\triangle ACE$ is right and scalene.

A E B

Study Hint

Reading Math The symbol $\triangle ABC$ means the triangle with vertices A, B, and C.

You are already familiar with three types of quadrilaterals. They are squares, rectangles, and parallelograms. Two other types of quadrilaterals are the **rhombus** and the **trapezoid**. The chart below shows one way to classify quadrilaterals.

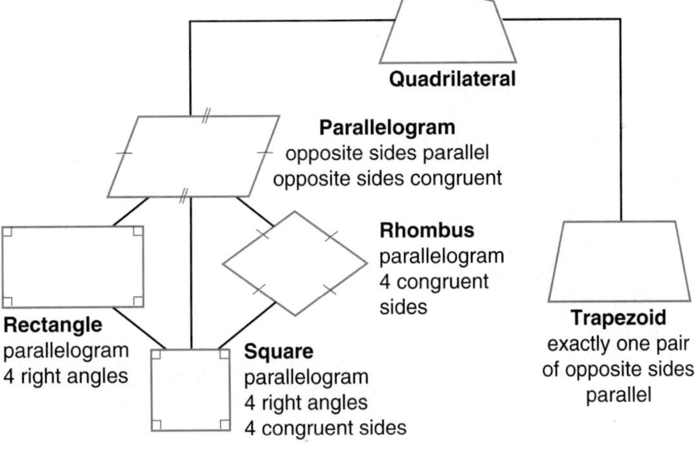

The best description of a quadrilateral is the one that is the most specific.

Examples

Name every quadrilateral that describes each figure. Then state which name best describes the figure.

2 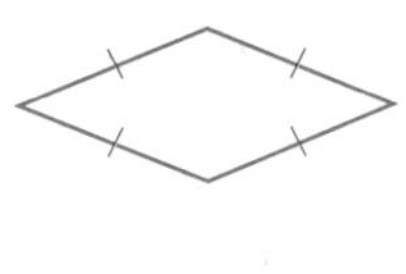

quadrilateral
parallelogram
rhombus

Rhombus best describes this figure.

3 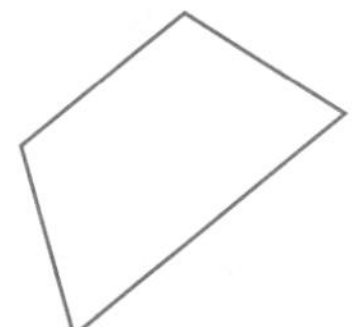

quadrilateral
trapezoid

Trapezoid best describes this figure.

4 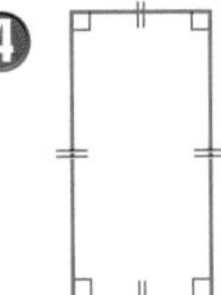

quadrilateral
parallelogram
rectangle

Rectangle best describes this figure.

2 TEACH

Transparency 9-4B contains a teaching aid for this lesson.

Modeling Mathematics Have students work in small groups to construct a Venn diagram showing how squares, rectangles, parallelograms, rhombuses, trapezoids, and quadrilaterals are related. Have them include accurately drawn examples of the figures in each area of the diagram.

In-Class Examples

For Example 1

Classify each triangle by its angles and by its sides.

a. right, scalene

b.

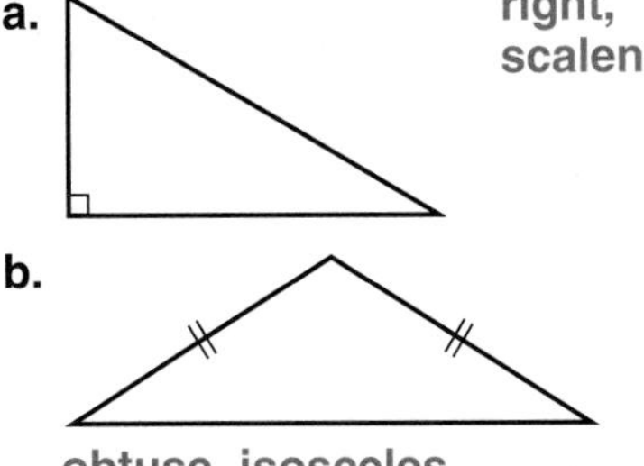

obtuse, isosceles

c. acute, isosceles

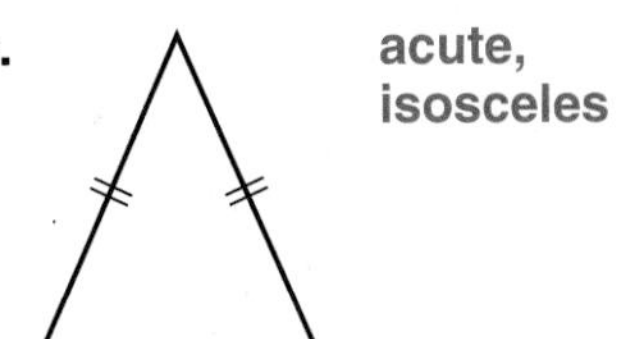

Name every quadrilateral that describes each figure. Then underline the name that best describes the figure.

For Example 2

parallelogram; <u>rhombus</u>

For Example 3

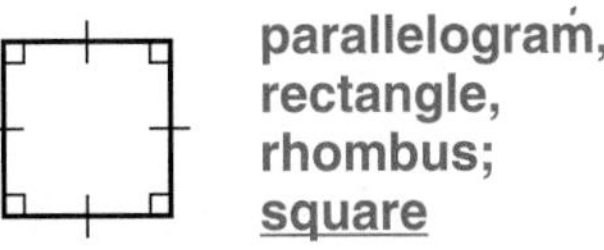

parallelogram, rectangle, rhombus; <u>square</u>

For Example 4

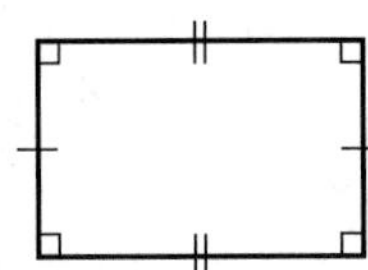

parallelogram; <u>rectangle</u>

Classroom Vignette

"To help students master the vocabulary of mathematics, I have an oral 'Math Bee' from time to time. We continually use the terms from our master vocabulary list all year. As we come to specific terms in the textbook, we spend more time discussing them. I try to show students how knowing these terms can help on standardized tests."

Carol Anne Thornton

Carol Thornton, Teacher
Purks Middle School
Cedartown, GA

3 PRACTICE/APPLY

Check for Understanding

If students need additional practice or instruction after completing Exercises 1–8, one of these options may be helpful.

- Extra Practice, see p. 593
- Reteaching Activity
- *Study Guide Masters,* p. 70
- *Practice Masters,* p. 70

Assignment Guide
Core: 9–19 odd, 21–24 **Enriched:** 10–18 even, 19–24

Additional Answers

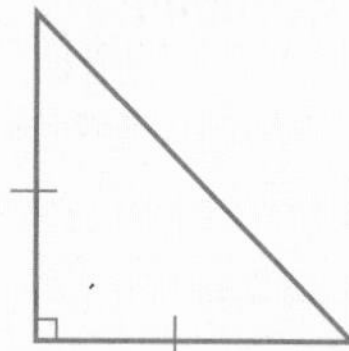

2. All squares are rectangles because they have opposite sides parallel and congruent and have four right angles; all rectangles are not squares because some rectangles do not have all sides congruent.
3. Sample answer: Both a rhombus and a square are parallelograms; they are different because a square has 4 right angles and a rhombus may not.

***Study Guide Masters,* p. 70**

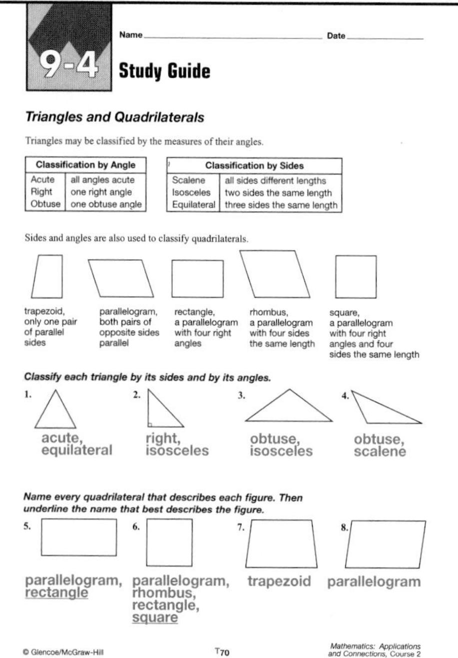

Name ______ Date ______

9-4 Study Guide

Triangles and Quadrilaterals

Triangles may be classified by the measures of their angles.

Classification by Angle	
Acute	all angles acute
Right	one right angle
Obtuse	one obtuse angle

Classification by Sides	
Scalene	all sides different lengths
Isosceles	two sides the same length
Equilateral	three sides the same length

Sides and angles are also used to classify quadrilaterals.

trapezoid, only one pair of parallel sides

parallelogram, both pairs of opposite sides parallel

rectangle, a parallelogram with four right angles

rhombus, a parallelogram with four sides the same length

square, a parallelogram with four right angles and four sides the same length

Classify each triangle by its sides and by its angles.

1. acute, equilateral
2. right, isosceles
3. obtuse, isosceles
4. obtuse, scalene

Name every quadrilateral that describes each figure. Then underline the name that best describes the figure.

5. parallelogram, <u>rectangle</u>
6. parallelogram, rhombus, rectangle, <u>square</u>
7. trapezoid
8. parallelogram

 T70 *Mathematics: Applications and Connections, Course 2*

CHECK FOR UNDERSTANDING

Communicating Mathematics

Math Journal

Read and study the lesson to answer each question.

1. ***Draw*** a sketch of an isosceles right triangle. **1–3. See margin.**
2. ***Tell*** why all squares are rectangles, but not all rectangles are squares.
3. ***Write*** a short paragraph that tells how a rhombus and a square are alike and how they are different.

Guided Practice

Classify each triangle by its angles and by its sides.

4. 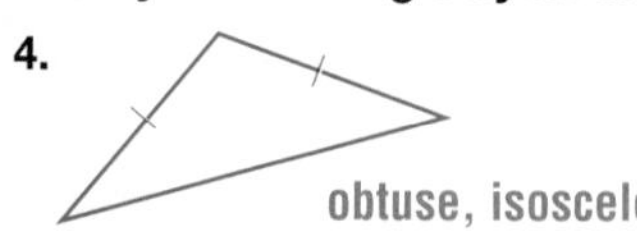 obtuse, isosceles
5.  acute, equilateral

Name every quadrilateral that describes each figure. Then underline the name that best describes the figure.

6. 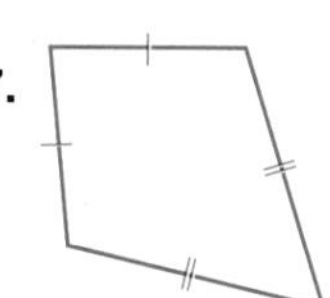 quadrilateral, parallelogram, rectangle, rhombus, square
7. quadrilateral

8. ***Architecture*** The figure at the right shows the basic design for a geodesic dome. What kinds of triangles are found in the figure? obtuse, equilateral, isosceles

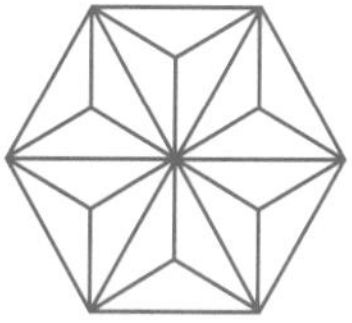

EXERCISES

Practice

Classify each triangle by its angles and by its sides.

9. acute, isosceles,
10. 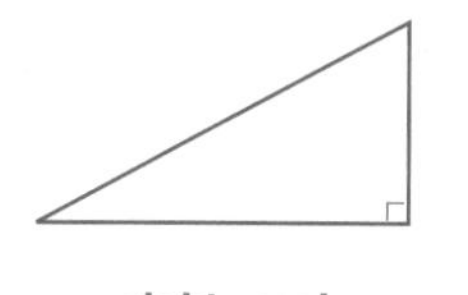 right, scalene
11. obtuse, scalene

Name every quadrilateral that describes each figure. Then underline the name that best describes the figure.

12. 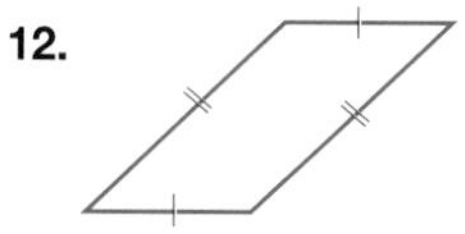
13. 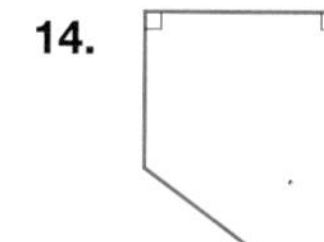
14.

12. quadrilateral, parallelogram
13. quadrilateral, parallelogram, rhombus
14. quadrilateral, trapezoid

Reteaching the Lesson

Activity Have students use dot paper and a straightedge to draw an example of each type of triangle and quadrilateral. Ask students to identify the defining characteristics of each figure and to make additional examples of each.

Error Analysis

Watch for students who omit one or more classifications when describing a particular kind of quadrilateral.

Prevent by focusing on how quadrilaterals are related according to the chart on page 383. Ask students to compare quadrilaterals.

15. See margin.

15. Draw a quadrilateral that is a rhombus, but not a rectangle.

16. Which quadrilaterals have four right angles? **rectangles, squares**

17. Three angles of a triangle measure 30°, 60°, and 90°. Classify the triangle by its angles. **right**

18. Three sides of a triangle measure 5 inches, 8 inches, and 8 inches. Classify the triangle by its sides. **isosceles**

Applications and Problem Solving

19c. $a = 55°$, $b = 65°$, $c = 60°$, $d = 30°$

19. ***Algebra*** The sum of the measures of the angles of a triangle is 180°. Find the missing measure(s) in each figure.

a.

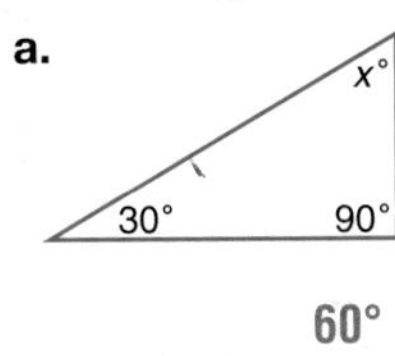

60°

b.

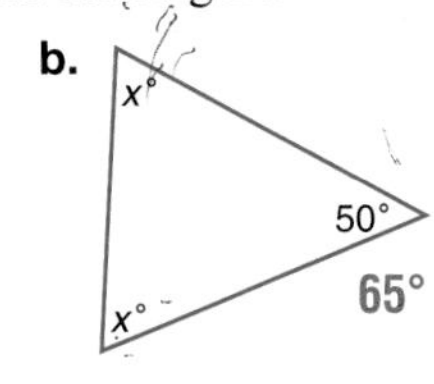

65°

c. 125° a° b c d 60°

20. ***Sewing*** Quilting has become a popular art form, but it began for practical purposes. In the American colonies, new fabric was scarce. So, quilt makers stitched together scraps of worn-out clothing to make patterned quilt tops.

20a. square, isosceles triangle, trapezoid

20b. Sample answer: You would know how to cut out the various shapes so that they fit together.

a. Classify the triangles and quadrilaterals you see in the photo at the right.

b. Explain how knowing the characteristics of different shapes can help in making a quilt.

21. ***Critical Thinking*** Determine whether each statement is *always*, *sometimes*, or *never* true.

a. A trapezoid is a quadrilateral. **always**

b. A quadrilateral is a trapezoid. **sometimes**

c. A rectangle is a parallelogram. **always**

d. A rectangle is a square. **sometimes**

e. A square is an equilateral triangle. **never**

Mixed Review

22. **Standardized Test Practice** Which best represents a pair of similar figures? *(Lesson 9-3)* **A**

A

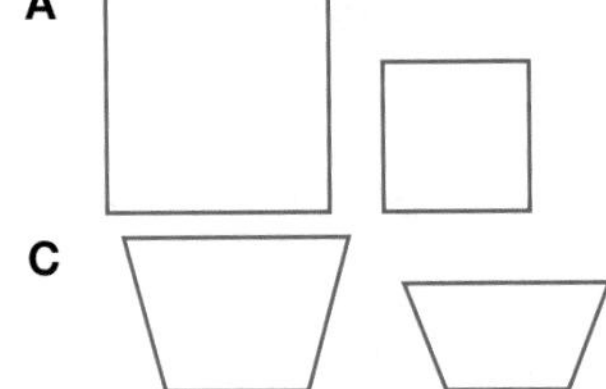

B

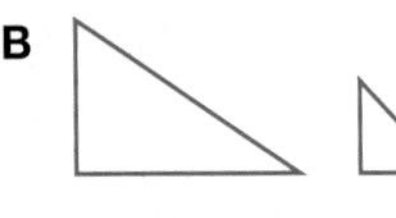

C

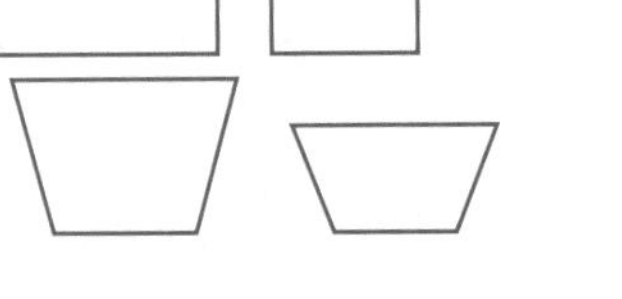

D

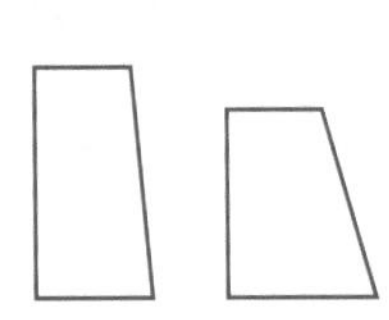

23. Estimate $1\frac{7}{12} \times 12\frac{1}{5}$. *(Lesson 7-1)* $2 \times 12 = 24$

24. ***Algebra*** The temperature in Buffalo, N.Y. dropped to −5°F. Find this temperature in degrees Celsius by using the formula $F = \frac{9}{5}C + 32$. *(Lesson 6-3)* **−20.6°C**

For **Extra Practice,** see page 593.

4 ASSESS

Closing Activity

Speaking Have students work with partners to formulate questions such as "I am a 3-sided polygon with 3 congruent angles. What figure am I?" The partner should name the correct polygon and draw it.

Chapter 9, Quiz B (Lessons 9-3 and 9-4) is available in the *Assessment and Evaluation Masters,* p. 239.

Mid-Chapter Test (Lessons 9-1 through 9-4) is available in the *Assessment and Evaluation Masters,* p. 238.

Additional Answer

15.

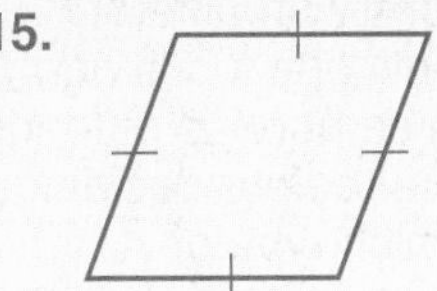

***Practice Masters,* p. 70**

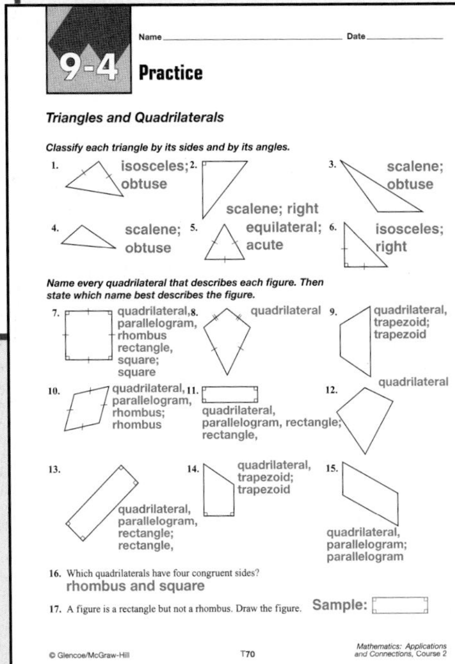

Name ______ Date ______

9-4 Practice

Triangles and Quadrilaterals

Classify each triangle by its sides and by its angles.

1. isosceles; obtuse
2. scalene; right
3. scalene; obtuse
4. scalene; obtuse
5. equilateral; acute
6. isosceles; right

Name every quadrilateral that describes each figure. Then state which name best describes the figure.

7. quadrilateral, parallelogram, rhombus rectangle, square; square
8. quadrilateral
9. quadrilateral, trapezoid; trapezoid
10. quadrilateral, parallelogram, rhombus; rhombus
11. quadrilateral, parallelogram, rectangle; rectangle,
12. quadrilateral
13. quadrilateral, parallelogram, rectangle; rectangle,
14. quadrilateral, trapezoid; trapezoid
15. quadrilateral, parallelogram; parallelogram

16. Which quadrilaterals have four congruent sides? rhombus and square

17. A figure is a rectangle but not a rhombus. Draw the figure. Sample:

© Glencoe/McGraw-Hill T70 *Mathematics: Applications and Connections, Course 2*

Extending the Lesson

***Enrichment Masters,* p. 70**

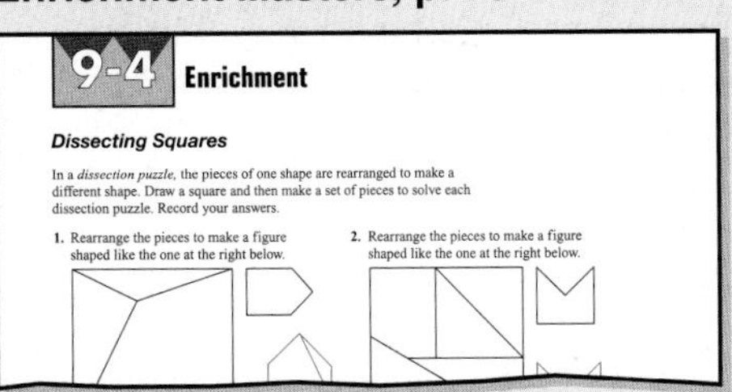

9-4 Enrichment

Dissecting Squares

In a *dissection puzzle,* the pieces of one shape are rearranged to make a different shape. Draw a square and then make a set of pieces to solve each dissection puzzle. Record your answers.

1. Rearrange the pieces to make a figure shaped like the one at the right below.

2. Rearrange the pieces to make a figure shaped like the one at the right below.

Activity Have students connect the midpoints of the three sides of a triangle. Ask them whether the four small triangles formed have the same size and shape. **yes** Have students repeat the activity with triangles of different shapes and check for congruence by using tracing paper.

Objective Students solve problems by using logical reasoning.

Recommended Pacing	
Standard	Day 10 of 15
Honors	Day 9 of 14
Block	Day 5 of 8

1 FOCUS

Getting Started Ask students whether they are more likely to: follow a recipe exactly or experiment with ingredients; wear only colors they know will look good together or try on different combinations until one looks right; eat only certain categories of foods or sample several before deciding. Ask students which type of reasoning is more evident in each case, and if both, how they go together.

2 TEACH

In-Class Example

Bobby's coach told him to run one mile every day, so Bobby ran a mile today. Dean ran a different distance each day last week and then decided a mile a day is best for him. Compare and contrast Bobby's and Dean's reasoning. **Bobby reasoned deductively; Dean reasoned inductively.**

Teaching Tip In Exercise 4, ask students to analyze situations *a* and *b* to determine whether they use a set of facts to establish a rule or use a rule to establish a fact.

Additional Answer

1. **Sample answer: Vince is making a rule from a pattern; Carlos has a rule.**

PROBLEM SOLVING

9-4B Using Logical Reasoning

A Follow-Up of Lesson 9-4

It's Friday morning before school, and Vince and Carlos are both studying for quizzes. How do they know they'll be having quizzes? Let's listen in!

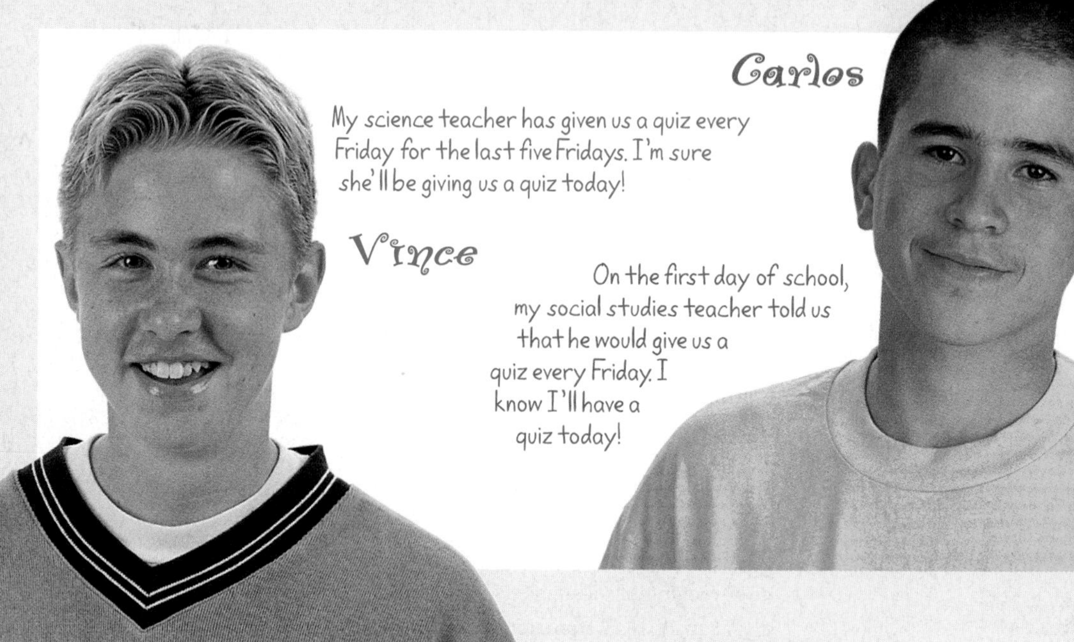

Carlos
My science teacher has given us a quiz every Friday for the last five Fridays. I'm sure she'll be giving us a quiz today!
Vince
On the first day of school, my social studies teacher told us that he would give us a quiz every Friday. I know I'll have a quiz today!

THINK ABOUT IT

Work with a partner.

1. ***Compare and contrast*** Vince's and Carlos' reasoning. **See margin.**
2. When you use *inductive reasoning,* you make a rule after seeing several examples. Who was using inductive reasoning? **Vince**
3. When you use *deductive reasoning,* you use a rule to make a decision. Who was using deductive reasoning? **Carlos**
4. ***Use logical reasoning*** to decide whether each situation is an example of inductive or deductive reasoning. **a. deductive**
   a. *A number is divisible by 4 if its last two digits make a number that is divisible by 4. So, 15,624 is divisible by 4.*
   b. *For many years, the swallows of San Juan Capistrano have returned to the mission on March 19. So, every year, a celebration is planned for March 19.* **inductive**

Reteaching the Lesson

Activity Have students use grid paper and a straightedge to draw a square, a rhombus, and a trapezoid. Divide the class into two groups. Tell both groups to determine which figures are parallelograms, one by consulting the chart on page 383, and the other by measuring the lines and angles. Ask students whether their reasoning was inductive or deductive.

For **Extra Practice,** see page 594.

ON YOUR OWN

5. ***Draw*** several rectangles and measure their diagonals.
   a. What can you conclude about the diagonals of rectangles?
   b. Did you use deductive or inductive reasoning? **inductive** **5a. The diagonals are congruent.**
6. ***Explain*** how the problem-solving strategy *look for a pattern* is like inductive reasoning.
7. ***Write*** about a situation in which you use either inductive or deductive reasoning.
See students' work. 6. Each one bases a conclusion on a pattern.

MIXED PROBLEM SOLVING

Strategies
Look for a pattern.
Solve a simpler problem.
Act it out.
Guess and Check.
Draw a diagram.
Make a chart.
Work backward.

Solve. Use any strategy.

8. ***Puzzles*** Brett, Conrad, and Alton play safety, running back, and quarterback on a football team, but not necessarily in that order. Brett and the quarterback drove Alton to practice on Saturday. Brett does not play safety. Who is the safety?
9. ***Number Theory*** The figures represent triangular numbers. Use the pattern to draw figures for the next two triangular numbers.

• • • • • • • • • •
   •   • •   • • •
         •   • •
                 •

See margin.

10. ***Geometry*** Trisha reads in a geometry book that the diagonals of a square are perpendicular to each other.
    a. If Trisha draws a square and its diagonals, what should she expect to be true about the diagonals? **See margin.**
    b. Is this an example of inductive or deductive reasoning? **deductive**
    c. Suppose Trisha had drawn several squares before reading her geometry book and found that their diagonals were perpendicular. Was she using inductive or deductive reasoning? **inductive**
11. Is the average of 96.8, 68.3, 79.3, 125.2, 138.7, and 101.5 about 101.7 or 10.17? Explain your reasoning. **See margin.**

8. Alton

12. ***Physical Science*** Luisa was trying to find the relationship between the time it took a pendulum to swing back and forth and its length. The data are listed in the table.

Time (seconds)	Length (units)
1	1
2	4
3	9
4	16

Apply inductive reasoning to predict the length of a pendulum if its time is 5 seconds. **25 units**

13. ***Standardized Test Practice*** Which construction is shown in the drawing? **C**

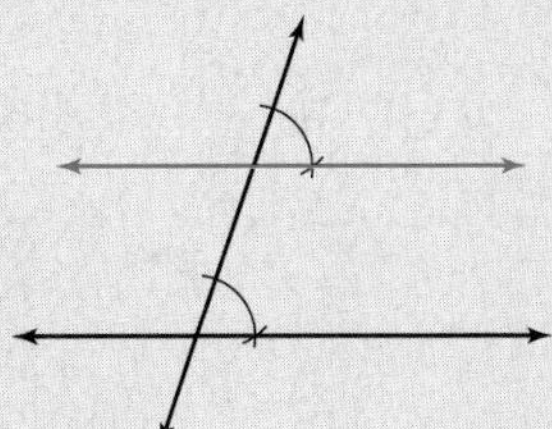

A bisect an angle
B construct a perpendicular line through a point on a given line segment
C construct a line parallel to a given line through a point not on the line
D construct a segment congruent to a given line segment

3 PRACTICE/APPLY

Check for Understanding

Use the results of Exercise 4 to determine whether students understand the difference between induction and deduction.

Extra Practice If students need additional practice in problem solving, extra practice is available on the following pages.

- Logical Reasoning, see p. 594
- Mixed Problem Solving, see pp. 605–606

Assignment Guide

All: 5–13

4 ASSESS

Closing Activity

Writing Have students write definitions of deductive reasoning and inductive reasoning in their own words.

Additional Answers

9.
• • • • •   • • • • • •
• • • •   • • • • •
• • •   • • • •
• •   • • •
•   • •
            •

10a. They will be perpendicular.

11. 101.7; All of the data are greater than 10.17.

Extending the Lesson

Activity Have students solve the following problem and explain how they solved it. Mr. Wang awoke to find the gerbil loose in the den. He questioned his four children to find out who left the cage open. Ed said that Tom left it open. Tom said Lian did it. Chen said, "I didn't do it." Lian said that Tom was lying. Only one child is telling the truth. Who left the door open? **Chen**

9-5 Lesson Notes

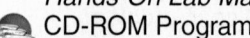

Instructional Resources

- *Study Guide Masters,* p. 71
- *Practice Masters,* p. 71
- *Enrichment Masters,* p. 71
- Transparencies 9-5, A and B
- *Classroom Games,* pp. 26–28
- *Hands-On Lab Masters,* p. 80

 CD-ROM Program
- Resource Lesson 9-5

Recommended Pacing	
Standard	Day 11 of 15
Honors	Day 10 of 14
Block	Day 5 of 8

1 FOCUS

5-Minute Check
(Lesson 9-4)

Classify each triangle by its angles and by its sides.

1. 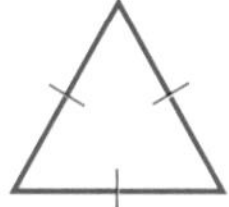

acute, equilateral

2. 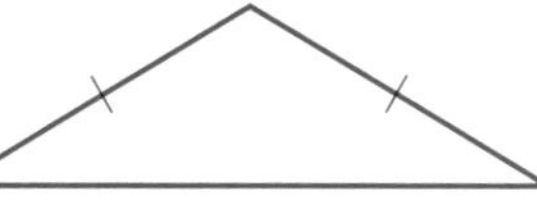

obtuse, isosceles

Name every quadrilateral that describes each figure, and underline the name that best describes the figure.

3. 

quadrilateral, <u>trapezoid</u>

4. 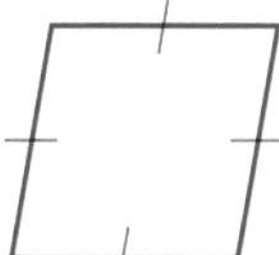

quadrilateral, parallelogram, <u>rhombus</u>

 The 5-Minute Check is also available on **Transparency 9-5A** for this lesson.

9-5 Tessellations

What you'll learn

You'll learn to determine which regular figures can be used to form a tessellation.

When am I ever going to use this?

You'll use tessellations to make designs in art class.

Word Wise

tessellation

Checkmate! In 1997, a supercomputer nicknamed "Deep Blue" stunned the world of chess by beating Garry Kasparov. This was the first time a computer was able to defeat the best human player in a chess match.

Although computer chess is a recent development, historians believe that the game of chess was invented in India almost 1,500 years ago. Even though the rules of chess are very complicated, the game is played on a simple game board made of squares. In a chessboard, the squares cover the entire surface without any overlaps or gaps. In mathematics, this is called a **tesselation**. A tessellation can be made of one kind of polygon or several kinds of polygons.

In the Mini-Lab, you'll investigate which regular polygons can be used to make a tessellation.

Did you know Deep Blue is a customized RS/6000 SP supercomputer which weighs 1.4 tons, costs $2 million, and processes 200 million chess moves each second.

MINI-LAB

Work with a partner. 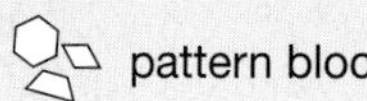 pattern blocks

Try This 1. See students' work.

1. Arrange the triangles so that they make a tessellation.
2. Make a sketch of the pattern. See students' work.
3. Find the measure of each angle of the triangle. 60°
4. Find a point in your pattern where the vertices of several triangles meet. How many triangles are around this point? 6
5. Do equilateral triangles make a tessellation? yes
6. Repeat Steps 1–5 using squares and then hexagons.
7. Organize your data in a table. 6. See table below.

Polygon	Measure of Angle	How Many Polygons Around a Point?	Make a Tessellation?
Triangle	60°	6	yes
Square	90°	4	yes
Hexagon	120°	3	yes

Talk About It

8. Find the sum of the measures of the angles of the polygons whose vertices meet at a point. 360°
9. Predict whether a regular pentagon will make a tessellation. Explain your reasoning.

9. No; the sum of the measures of the angles at a point is not 360°.

Multiple Learning Styles

 **Kinesthetic** Provide bricks, tiles, or pave stones for students to use in building a wall or path. Have students find as many different patterns as possible in which to place bricks, tiles, or stones in a tessellation.

In the Mini-Lab, you found that the sum of the measures of the angles where the vertices meet is 360°.

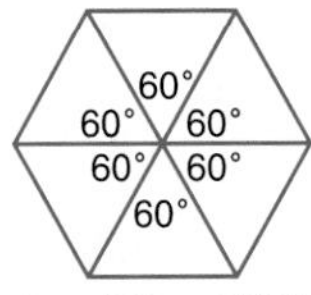

$6 \times 60° = 360°$

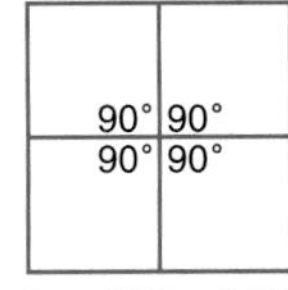

$4 \times 90° = 360°$

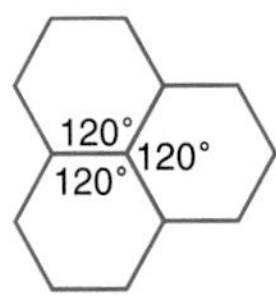

$3 \times 120° = 360°$

Example 1 **INTEGRATION**

Algebra **The sum of the measures of the angles of a pentagon is 540°. Can a regular pentagon make a tessellation?**

Explore You know that the sum of the measures of the angles of a pentagon is 540°. You need to find if regular pentagons can make a tessellation.

Plan Each angle of a regular pentagon has a measure of $540 \div 5$ or 108°.

To find out if a pentagon tessellates, solve $108n = 360$, where n is the number of angles at a vertex.

Solve $108n = 360$ 360 ÷ 108 = *3.333333333*

$n \approx 3.33$

The solution is not a whole number. So, a regular pentagon will not make a tessellation.

Examine Check your answer by making a drawing.

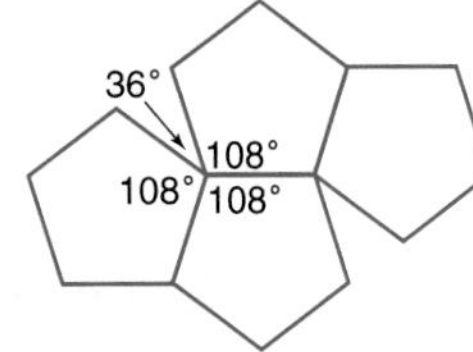

It is often possible to make a tessellation with a combination of polygons.

Example 2

Make a tessellation with hexagons and triangles.

Each angle of a regular hexagon measures 120°. Use 1 hexagon.

total at vertex	−	*one angle of hexagon*		
360°	−	120°	=	240°

Now determine how many triangles will fit in 240°. Each angle of an equilateral triangle measures 60°.

240° = ? triangles

240° = 4 triangles *60° × 4 = 240°*

In the tessellation, there are four triangles touching each vertex of each hexagon.

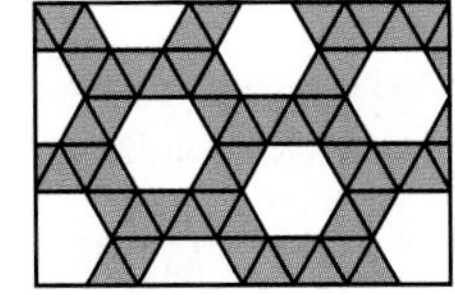

Motivating the Lesson

Hands-On Activity Provide students with graph paper. Ask them to choose a shape and to try to completely cover the paper by drawing the shape repeatedly. Encourage students to try again with both a regular and an irregular polygon.

2 TEACH

Transparency 9-5B contains a teaching aid for this lesson.

Using the Mini-Lab Encourage students to experiment to see whether they can tessellate a surface using any triangle or quadrilateral. Ask them what they discover. **All triangles and quadrilaterals tessellate.**

In-Class Examples

For Example 1

The sum of the measures of the angles of an 11-sided polygon is 1,620°. Can you tessellate a regular 11-sided polygon by itself? **no**

For Example 2

To make a tessellation with regular hexagons and equilateral triangles where 2 hexagons meet at a vertex, how many triangles are needed at each vertex? **2**

Teaching Tip In Example 2, have students try different arrangements of 1 hexagon with 4 triangles (or 2 hexagons with 2 triangles) to show that they can tessellate in more than one way.

3 PRACTICE/APPLY

Check for Understanding

If students need additional practice or instruction after completing Exercises 1–5, one of these options may be helpful.

- Extra Practice, see p. 594
- Reteaching Activity
- *Study Guide Masters,* p. 71
- *Practice Masters,* p. 71

Assignment Guide
Core: 7–13 odd, 15–17
Enriched: 6–12 even, 13, 15–17

Exercise 14 asks students to advance to the next stage of work on the Chapter Project. You may want students to create several different designs, experimenting with various combinations of polygons and colors.

Additional Answer

3a.

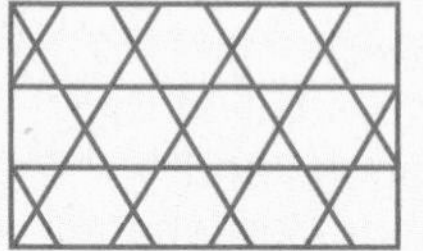

***Study Guide Masters,* p. 71**

Name________________ Date________

Study Guide

Tessellations

A **tessellation,** or tiling, is an arrangement of polygons that completely covers a plane surface without leaving gaps or overlapping.

The sum of the angle measures at any vertex of a tessellation is 360°. To determine whether a regular polygon tessellates, divide 360 by the measure of any angle of the polygon. If the quotient is a whole number, the polygon tessellates.

Examples *1* **hexagon** The measure of an angle is 120°. $360 \div 120 = 3$. A hexagon can be used to form a tessellation.

2 **pentagon** The measure of an angle is 108°. $360 \div 108 = 3.\overline{3}$. A pentagon cannot be used to form a tessellation.

To determine how a combination of regular polygons tessellates, find a way that the sum of the angles at each vertex equals 360°. There may be more than one way.

Example 3 **If an equilateral triangle, a square, and a regular hexagon are used in a tessellation, how many of each do you need at a vertex?**

Each angle of an equilateral triangle measures 60°.
Each angle of a square measures 90°.
Each angle of a regular hexagon measures 120°. Try one of each: $60 + 90 + 120 = 270$. That is not enough.
Try 1 triangle, 2 squares and 1 hexagon:
$60 + 90 + 90 + 120 = 360$.
One possibility is 1 triangle, 2 squares, and 1 hexagon.

Assume that each polygon is regular. Determine whether it can be used by itself to make a tessellation.

1. triangle yes
2. octagon no
3. heptagon no

The following regular polygons tessellate. Determine how many of each polygon you need at each vertex. Then sketch the tessellation.

4. dodecagon, triangle 2 dodecagons, 1 triangle

5. triangle, square 3 triangles, 2 squares

 T71 *Mathematics: Applications and Connections, Course 2*

CHECK FOR UNDERSTANDING

Communicating Mathematics

Read and study the lesson to answer the following.

1. ***Tell*** how you know when a regular polygon can be used by itself to make a tessellation. **The angle measure is a factor of 360°.**
2. ***Explain*** how you know that the rhombus at the right can be used to make a tessellation.

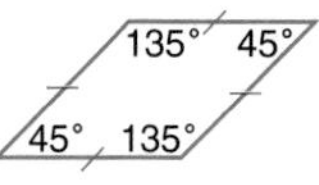

2. 45° + 135° + 45° + 135° = 360°

HANDS-ON MATH

3. In Example 2 on page 389, you made a tessellation with 1 hexagon and 4 triangles.
   a. Use pattern blocks to find a different tessellation made with hexagons and triangles. **See margin.**
   b. Write an addition problem showing that the sum of the measures of the angles where the vertices meet is 360°. **120° + 60° + 120° + 60° = 360°**

Guided Practice

4. The sum of the measures of the angles of a regular octagon is 1,080°.
   a. Determine whether an octagon can be used by itself to make a tessellation. **no**
   b. Verify your results by finding the number of angles at a vertex. **about 2.67**
5. ***Design*** Describe a tessellation that you have seen. **See students' work.**

EXERCISES

Practice

Determine whether each polygon can be used by itself to make a tessellation. Verify your results by finding the measures of the angles at a vertex. The sum of the measures of the angles of each polygon is given.

6. heptagon; 900°
7. nonagon; 1,260°
8. decagon; 1,440°
9. Sketch a tessellation made with right triangles. **See students' work.**

6. no; 128.6°
7. no; 140°
8. no; 144°
10. 2 squares, 3 triangles
11. 1 square, 2 octagons
12. squares

10–11. See Answer Appendix for drawings.

The following regular polygons tessellate. Determine how many of each polygon you need at each vertex. Then sketch the tessellation.

10. triangles and squares
11. squares and octagons

Applications and Problem Solving

Real World

12. ***Art*** Ancient Greeks used marble, alabaster, and granite for the designs in their mosaics. Identify the shapes in the mosaic shown at the right.

Reteaching the Lesson

Activity Review both methods for finding the measure of each angle of a regular polygon. Guide students to see that this number must be a factor of 360 for the polygon to tessellate.

Error Analysis

Watch for students who infer from the examples that only regular polygons can tessellate.

Prevent by using graph paper to draw isosceles and scalene triangles that tessellate, demonstrating that the sides of a polygon in a tessellation need not be congruent.

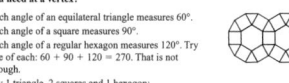

13. ***Life Science*** One of the most famous tessellations found in nature is a bee's honeycomb. Explain one advantage of using hexagons in a honeycomb. **Sample answer: There are no gaps.**

14. See students' work.
15. See margin.

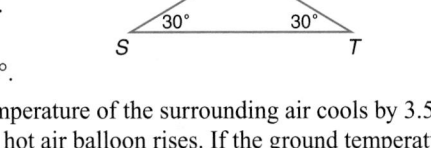

14. ***Working on the CHAPTER Project*** Create a tessellation on isometric dot paper. Use various colors to make a geometric design.

15. ***Critical Thinking*** You can make a tessellation with equilateral triangles. Can you make a tessellation with any isosceles or scalene triangle? If so, explain your reasoning and make a drawing of your tessellation.

Mixed Review

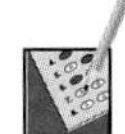

16. **Standardized Test Practice** Which procedure could best be used to find the measure of angle R? *(Lesson 9-4)* **B**

A Add 30° to 180°.
B Subtract 60° from 180°.
C Subtract 30° from 90°.
D Add 30° to 90°.
E Subtract 180° from 60°.

R, S, T, 30°, 30°

17. ***Earth Science*** The temperature of the surrounding air cools by 3.5°F for each 1,000 feet that a hot air balloon rises. If the ground temperature is 65°F, the equation $y = -3.5x + 65$ gives the air temperature. In the equation, x is the height of the balloon in thousands of feet and y is the air temperature. Make a table of values for heights of 1,000, 2,000, and 3,000 feet. *(Lesson 6-7)* **See margin.**

For **Extra Practice,** see page 594.

Let the Games Begin

Tic-Tac Squares

Math Skill
Tessellations

Get Ready This game is for two players.

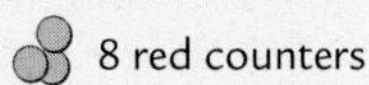 8 red counters  8 yellow counters  dot paper

Get Set Copy the game board onto dot paper.

Go
- The first player covers any black dot with a counter. Then, players alternate turns.
- The object of the game is to be the first player to cover the four vertices of a square. Note that the sides of a square don't have to be vertical or horizontal. The square can be "tilted" to one side.

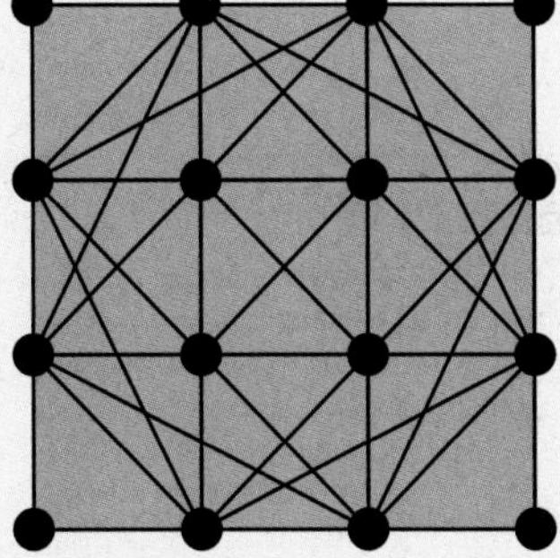

Visit www.glencoe.com/sec/math/mac/mathnet for more games.

4 ASSESS

Closing Activity

Speaking Have students explain how to determine whether a regular polygon can be used by itself or in combination with another to tessellate a surface. The sum of the angle measures at each vertex must be 360°.

Additional Answers

15. **Yes; the sum of the measures of angles of any triangle is 180°, which is a**

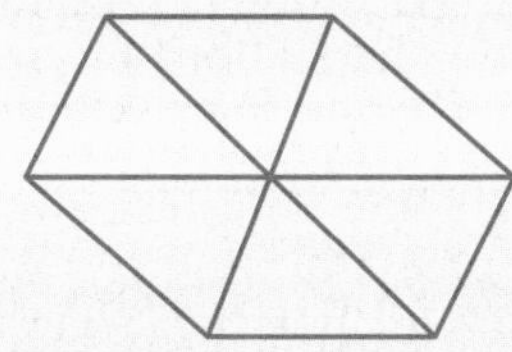

17.

Height (thousand feet)	Temperature (°F)
1	61.5
2	58.0
3	54.5

***Practice Masters,* p. 71**

Name ____________ Date ________

9-5 Practice

Tessellations

Determine whether each polygon can be used by itself to make a tessellation. Verify your results by finding the number of angles at a vertex. The sum of the measures of the angles of each polygon is given.

1. triangle; 180° yes
2. decagon; 1,440° no
3. pentagon; 540° no
4. heptagon; 900° no
5. nonagon; 1,260° no
6. quadrilateral; 360° yes
7. hexagon; 720° yes
8. dodecagon; 1,800° no
9. octagon; 1,080° no

10. Sketch a tessellation made with regular triangles and regular hexagons.

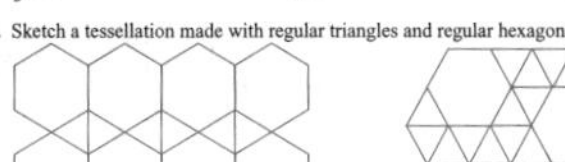

The following regular polygons tessellate. Determine how many of each polygon you need at each vertex. Then sketch the tessellation.

11. triangle, square — 3 triangles, 2 squares
12. triangle, square, dodecagon — 2 triangles, 1 square, 1 dodecagon

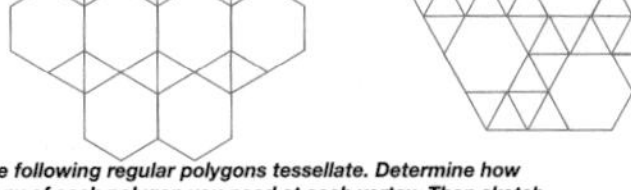

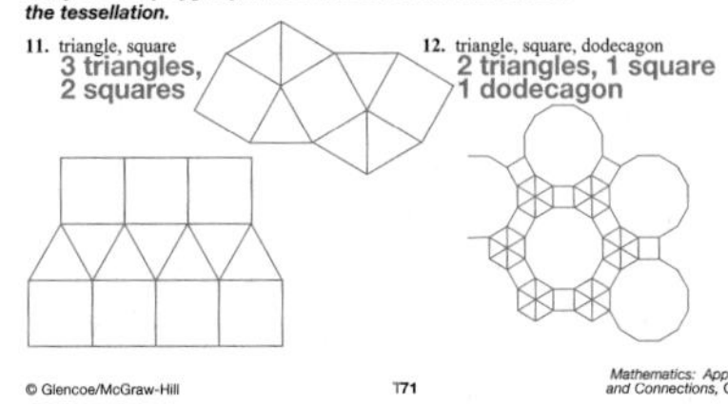

© Glencoe/McGraw-Hill T71 *Mathematics: Applications and Connections, Course 2*

Extending the Lesson

***Enrichment Masters,* p. 71**

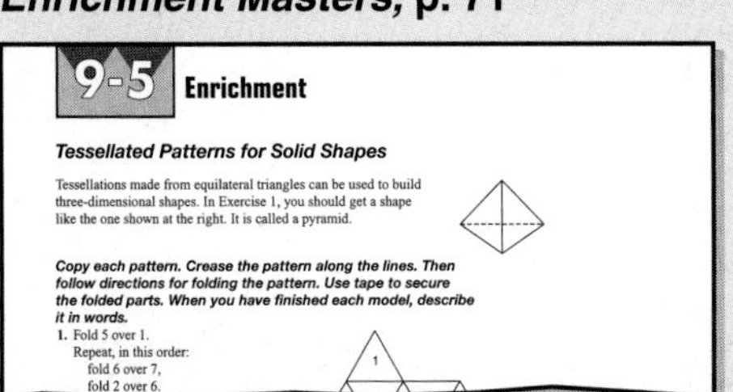

9-5 Enrichment

Tessellated Patterns for Solid Shapes

Tessellations made from equilateral triangles can be used to build three-dimensional shapes. In Exercise 1, you should get a shape like the one shown at the right. It is called a pyramid.

Copy each pattern. Crease the pattern along the lines. Then follow directions for folding the pattern. Use tape to secure the folded parts. When you have finished each model, describe it in words.

1. Fold 5 over 1. Repeat, in this order: fold 6 over 7, fold 2 over 6.

Let the Games Begin

Remind students to look for both small and large squares, and squares with diagonal lines, as they play.

Additional resources for this game can be found on page 47 of the ***Classroom Games.***

9-6 Lesson Notes

Instructional Resources

- *Study Guide Masters,* p. 72
- *Practice Masters,* p. 72
- *Enrichment Masters,* p. 72
- Transparencies 9-6, A and B
- *Assessment and Evaluation Masters,* p. 240

CD-ROM Program
- Resource Lesson 9-6
- Extended Activity 9-6

Recommended Pacing	
Standard	Day 12 of 15
Honors	Day 11 of 14
Block	Day 6 of 8

1 FOCUS

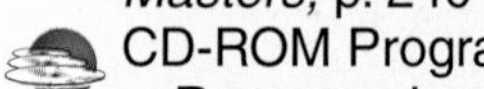

5-Minute Check (Lesson 9-5)

1. Determine whether a regular hexagon can be used by itself to tessellate. **yes**
2. Regular hexagons tessellate with equilateral triangles. Determine how many of each you need at each vertex, and sketch the tessellation. **4 triangles, 1 hexagon**

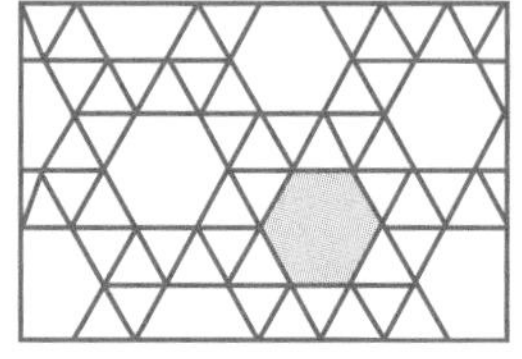

The 5-Minute Check is also available on **Transparency 9-6A** for this lesson.

2 TEACH

Transparency 9-6B contains a teaching aid for this lesson.

Reading Mathematics Refer students to the definition of *translation* on page 392 and to a dictionary definition. Explain that the term comes from Latin words meaning to "carry across." Ask students how a geometric translation is related to translating a statement from one language to another.

9-6 Translations

What you'll learn
You'll learn to create Escher-like drawings by using translations.

When am I ever going to use this?
You'll use translations when you make designs.

Word Wise
translation

Maurits Cornelis Escher (1898–1972), a Dutch artist, spent many days studying the Alhambra, a thirteenth century palace in Spain. He was inspired to create recognizable figures to fill space like the pieces of stone that filled the surface of the mosaic walls in the Alhambra. His figures were often in the shapes of birds, fish, or reptiles.

Source: ©M.C. Escher/Cordon Art–Baam–Holland Collection Haags Gemeentemuseum–The Hauge

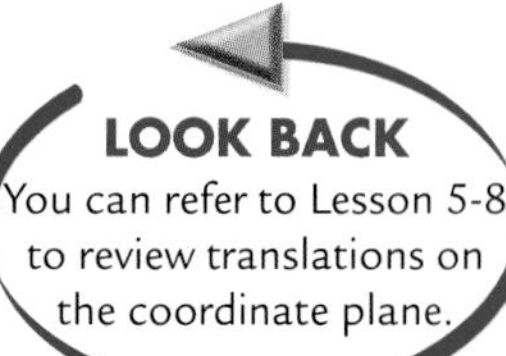

LOOK BACK
You can refer to Lesson 5-8 to review translations on the coordinate plane.

Many of Escher's sketches began as tessellations of polygons. You can make Escher-like drawings by making changes in the polygons of the tessellation. One way to do this is by using a **translation**.

A translation is sliding part of a drawing to another place without turning it. The square below has the left side changed. To make sure the pieces, or pattern units, will tessellate, slide or translate that change to the opposite side and copy it.

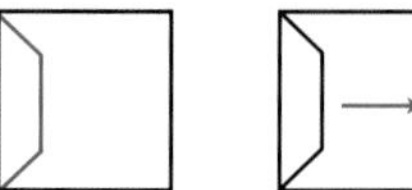

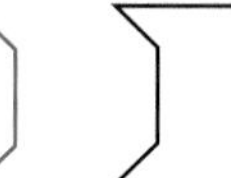

interNET CONNECTION For more information about Escher designs, visit: www.glencoe.com/sec/math/mac/mathnet

Now change all of the squares in a tessellation the same way. The tessellation takes on Escher-like qualities when you use different colors or designs.

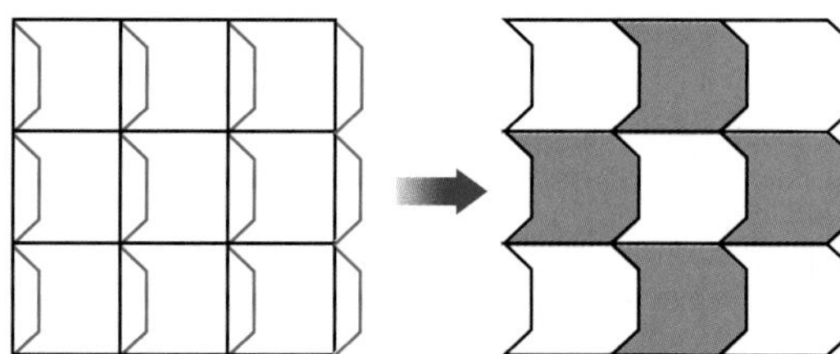

Motivating the Lesson

Hands-On Activity Obtain a book of Escher prints to share with the class. Have students suggest any connections between Escher's work and tessellations and try to recognize what polygons he turned into animals or other figures. Then have them try to create Escher-like drawings by beginning with a tessellation.

Example CONNECTION

1 **Art** Draw a tessellation using the change shown at the right.

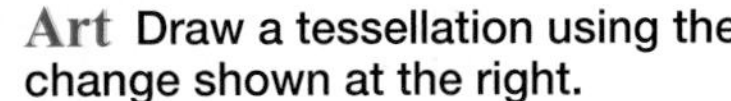

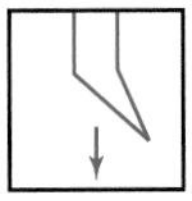

A cardboard pattern unit can help in creating the tessellation.

First, complete the pattern unit.

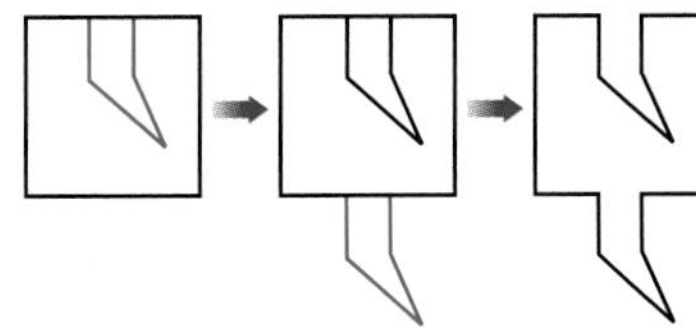

Translate the change to all squares in the tessellation. Use color to complete the effect.

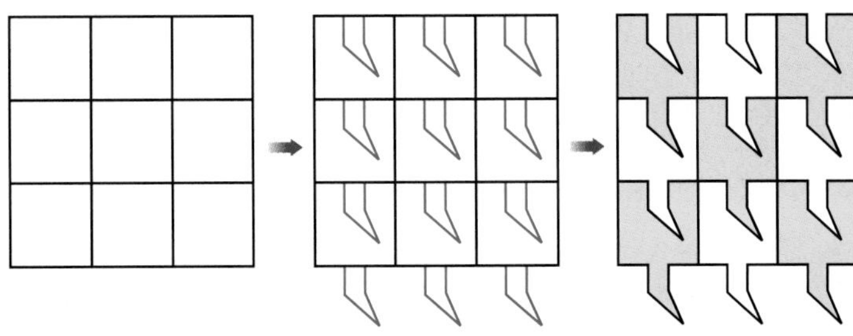

You can make more complex tessellations by doing two translations.

Example CONNECTION

2 **Art** Draw a tessellation using both changes shown at the right.

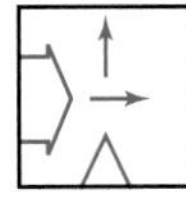

First, complete the pattern unit.

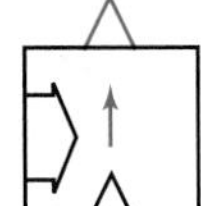

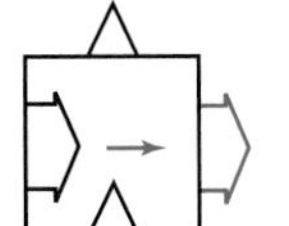

Then complete the tessellation.

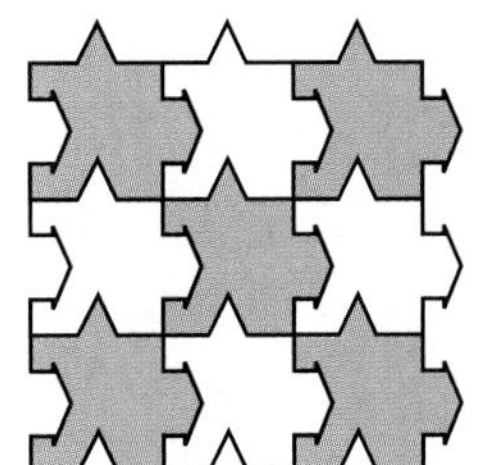

Study Hint

Reading Math When a figure is translated, the original figure and the translated figure have the same size and shape. They are called *congruent figures*.

In-Class Examples

For Example 1

Draw a tessellation using the change shown below.

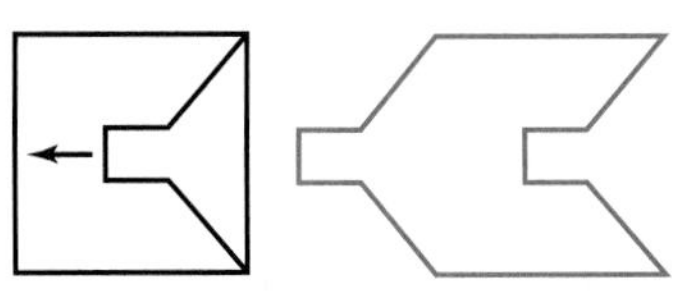

For Example 2

Draw a tessellation using both changes shown below.

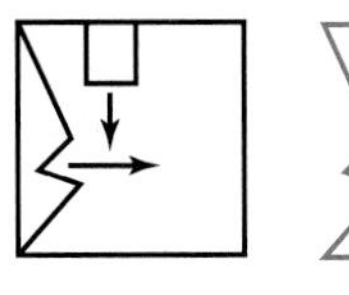

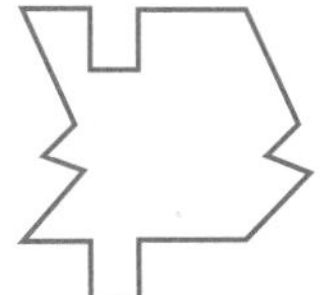

3 PRACTICE/APPLY

Check for Understanding

If students need additional practice or instruction after completing Exercises 1–5, one of these options may be helpful.

- Extra Practice, see p. 594
- Reteaching Activity
- *Study Guide Masters,* p. 72
- *Practice Masters,* p. 72

***Study Guide Masters,* p. 72**

Name ______________________ Date __________

9-6 Study Guide

Translations

You can make changes in the polygons that tessellate to create new pattern units that will tessellate. One way to do this is by using a **translation,** or a slide.

Example 1 **Change the square by sliding a piece from the left to the right to make a new pattern piece.**

Then change all the squares in a tessellation the same way.

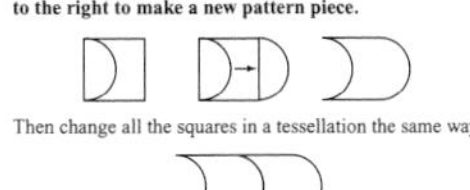

You can make more complex tessellations by doing two translations.

Example 2 **Make two changes to create a pattern unit.** **Then complete the tessellation.**

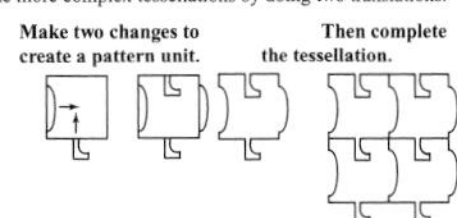

Complete the pattern unit for each translation. Then draw the tessellation.

1. 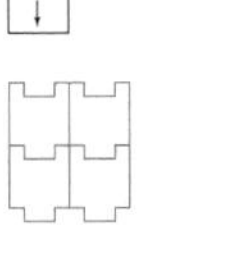

2. 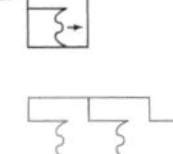

3. 

Reteaching the Lesson

Activity Have students work in groups of 3 or more to collaborate on translations. Each student should draw a square on graph paper, change one side of it, and then pass it on to another student, who translates the change to the opposite side. The next student reproduces the translated square in a tessellation, and the next student shades or colors the tessellation. Encourage groups to embellish their designs with animal or other shapes.

Assignment Guide

Core: 7–11 odd, 13–15
Enriched: 6–10 even, 11, 13–15

Exercise 12 asks students to advance to the next stage of work on the Chapter Project. Suggest that students work with a partner and exchange ideas.

4 ASSESS

Closing Activity

Writing Have students write a paragraph explaining translations to a student who has missed the lesson.

Chapter 9, Quiz C (Lessons 9-5 and 9-6) is available in the *Assessment and Evaluation Masters,* p. 240.

Additional Answers

2. Use a translation to make changes in the polygons of a tessellation.
10. Translations can be used to show motion in one direction.
11. Sample answer: birds, fish
14. No, the measure of one angle is 144°, which is not a

***Practice Masters,* p. 72**

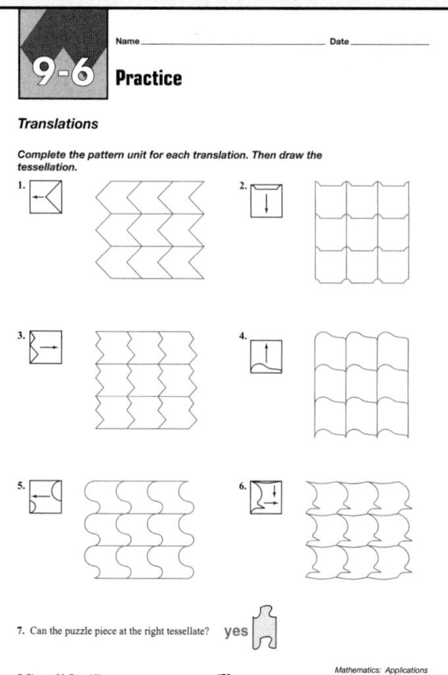

9-6 **Practice**

Name ______________ Date ______________

Translations

Complete the pattern unit for each translation. Then draw the tessellation.

1. 2. 3. 4. 5. 6.

7. Can the puzzle piece at the right tessellate? yes

© Glencoe/McGraw-Hill T72 *Mathematics: Applications and Connections, Course 2*

CHECK FOR UNDERSTANDING

Communicating Mathematics

Read and study the lesson to answer each question. 2. See margin.

1. ***Write*** a definition of a translation. 1. sliding a figure without turning it
2. ***Tell*** how a translation can be used to form an Escher-like drawing.
3. ***You Decide*** Omar thinks that the puzzle piece will make a tessellation. Talutah disagrees. Who is correct? Explain your reasoning. Talutah; the patterns on the top and bottom will not tessellate.

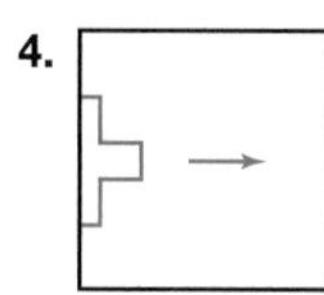

Guided Practice

Complete the pattern unit for each translation. Then draw the tessellation. 4–5. See Answer Appendix.

4. 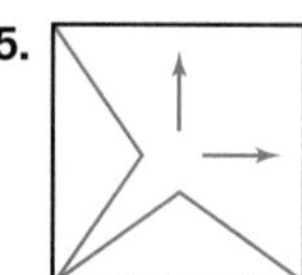

5. 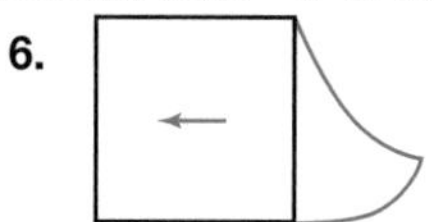

EXERCISES

Practice

Complete the pattern unit for each translation. Then draw the tessellation. 6–8. See Answer Appendix.

6. 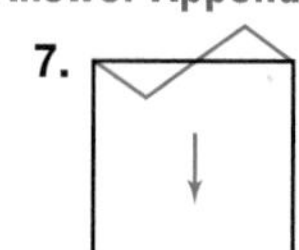

7. 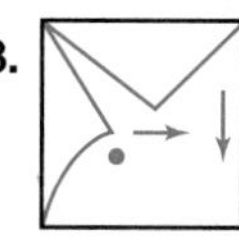

8.

9. Draw a pattern unit that has a parallelogram as the basic tessellation. See students' work.

Applications and Problem Solving

10. ***Animation*** In the first full-length film made completely with computer graphics, animators first draw the characters to look like wire skeletons and then change the figures with computers. Explain how translations can be used in computer graphics. See margin.
11. ***Art*** Animals frequently appear in Escher designs. Research Mr. Escher and identify one animal that was used in his designs. Tell what polygon might have been used as the basis for the design. See margin.
12. ***Working on the* Chapter Project** Use translations to design a pattern for an Escher-like drawing. Then draw the tessellation. Use different colors or textures to create an interesting design. See students' work.
13. ***Critical Thinking*** Is it possible to make a tessellation with translations by using equilateral triangles? Explain your reasoning. No; There is no opposite side to translate the change.

For **Extra Practice,** see page 594.

Mixed Review

14. ***Art*** Marlene wishes to construct a tessellation for a wall-hanging made only from regular decagons. Is this possible? *(Lesson 9-5)* See margin.

15. **Standardized Test Practice** Jarina had 4.65 pounds of sugar. She used 0.86 pound in a recipe. How much sugar did she have left? *(Lesson 1-1)* A

A 3.79 lb **B** 4.35 lb **C** 4.62 lb **D** 5.51 lb **E** Not Here

Extending the Lesson

***Enrichment Masters,* p. 72**

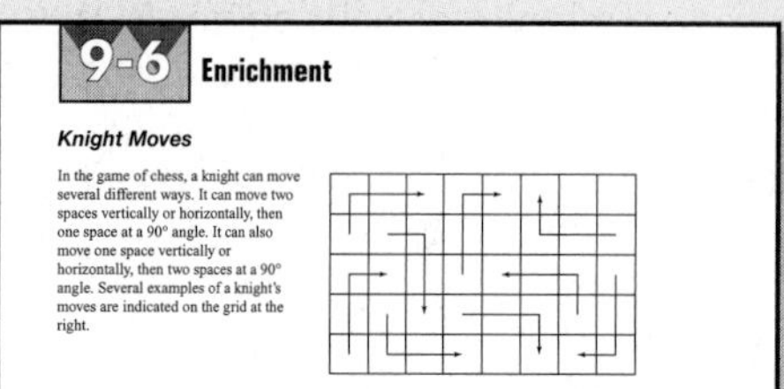

9-6 **Enrichment**

Knight Moves

In the game of chess, a knight can move several different ways. It can move two spaces vertically or horizontally, then one space at a 90° angle. It can also move one space vertically or horizontally, then two spaces at a 90° angle. Several examples of a knight's moves are indicated on the grid at the right.

Activity Give students the coordinates of the vertices of a polygon and ask them to draw it on graph paper. Then ask which coordinates would be affected by a horizontal translation and which would be affected by a vertical translation. only *x*-coordinates; only *y*-coordinates

9-7 Reflections

What you'll learn

You'll learn to create Escher-like drawings by using reflections.

When am I ever going to use this?

You'll use symmetry when you classify animals in science.

Word Wise

line symmetry
line of symmetry
reflection

Most animals have bodies that look the same on both sides. They can be divided into right and left halves by drawing an imaginary line down the length of the body. Each half is a mirror image of the other half. Scientists call this bilateral symmetry.

Bilateral means "two sides".

In mathematics, figures that match exactly when folded in half have **line symmetry**. The figures below have line symmetry. Some figures can be folded in more than one way to show symmetry. Each fold line is called a **line of symmetry**.

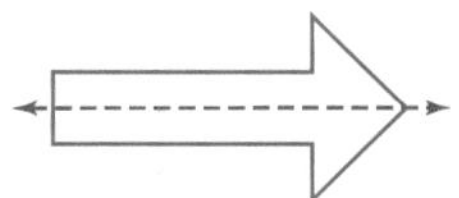 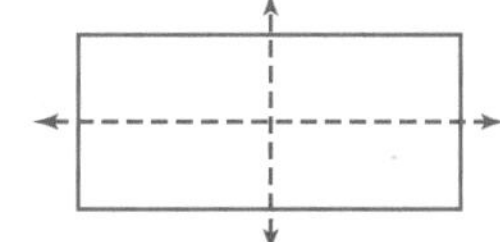 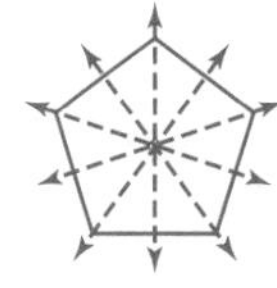

Examples

Determine which figures have line symmetry. Draw all of the lines of symmetry.

1 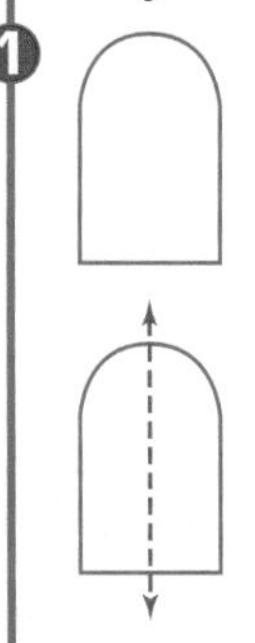

2 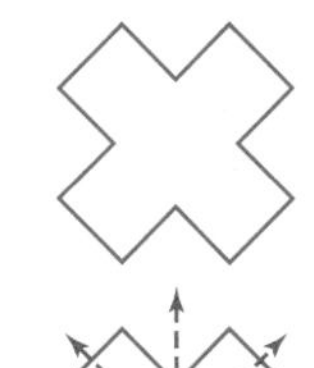

3 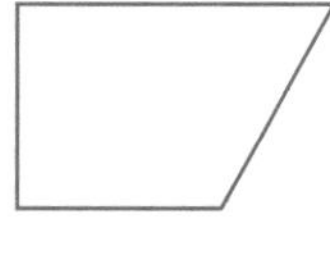

no symmetry

You can create figures that have line symmetry by using a **reflection**. A reflection is a mirror image of a figure across a line of symmetry.

9-7 Lesson Notes

Instructional Resources

- *Study Guide Masters,* p. 73
- *Practice Masters,* p. 73
- *Enrichment Masters,* p. 73
- Transparencies 9-7, A and B
- *Assessment and Evaluation Masters,* p. 240
- *Diversity Masters,* p. 22
- *School to Career Masters*, p. 22
- CD-ROM Program
  - Resource Lesson 9-7

Recommended Pacing	
Standard	Day 13 of 15
Honors	Day 12 of 14
Block	Day 7 of 8

1 FOCUS

5-Minute Check
(Lesson 9-6)

Complete the pattern unit for each translation. Then draw the tessellation.

1.  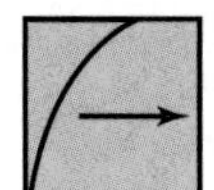 

2.  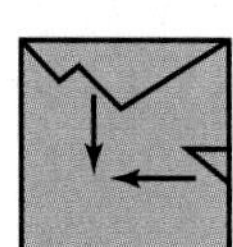 

See students' work for tessellations.

The 5-Minute Check is also available on **Transparency 9-7A** for this lesson.

2 TEACH

Transparency 9-7B contains a teaching aid for this lesson.

Using Discussion Have students describe the relationship between lines of symmetry and reflections. **Reflection is a mirror image across a line of symmetry**

Multiple Learning Styles

Naturalist Have students research biological organisms (plants, animals, micro-organisms) and group them into those that are bilaterally symmetrical, those that are radially symmetrical, and those that are asymmetrical.

Motivating the Lesson

Problem Solving Have students work with partners to determine which letters of the alphabet have a horizontal line of symmetry, a vertical line of symmetry, both a horizontal and a vertical line of symmetry, or no line of symmetry. Have groups compare results, and demonstrate how they did it.

In-Class Examples

Determine which figures have line symmetry. Draw all lines of symmetry.

For Example 1

For Example 2
No lines of symmetry

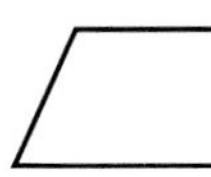

For Example 3

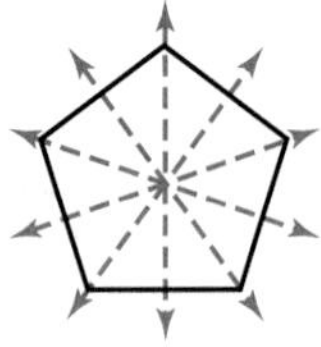

For Example 4
Complete an Escher-like drawing using the change shown.

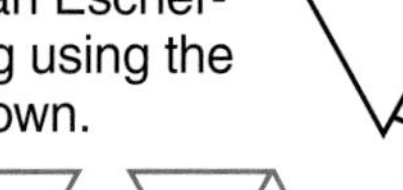

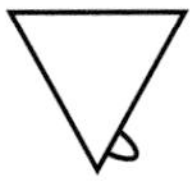

***Study Guide Masters,* p. 73**

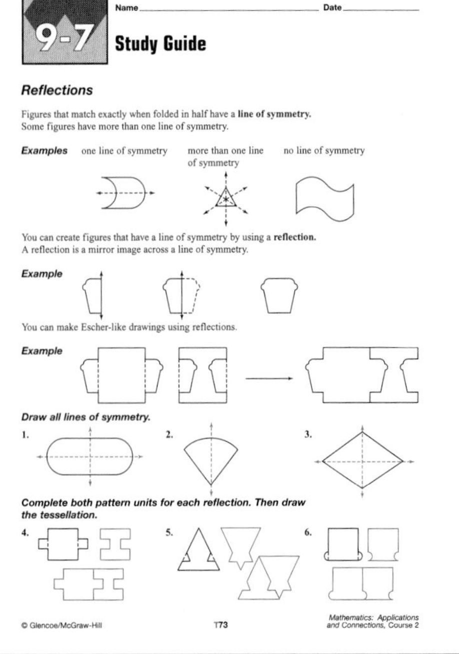

Name ______ Date ______

9-7 **Study Guide**

Reflections

Figures that match exactly when folded in half have a **line of symmetry.** Some figures have more than one line of symmetry.

Examples one line of symmetry | more than one line of symmetry | no line of symmetry

You can create figures that have a line of symmetry by using a **reflection.** A reflection is a mirror image across a line of symmetry.

Example

You can make Escher-like drawings using reflections.

Example

Draw all lines of symmetry.

1. 2. 3.

Complete both pattern units for each reflection. Then draw the tessellation.

4. 5. 6.

© Glencoe/McGraw-Hill T73 *Mathematics: Applications and Connections, Course 2*

Mr. Escher also used reflections in some of his works. You can create different types of drawings using reflections. However, in these tessellations, two pattern units are used.

Example CONNECTION

4 **Art** **Complete an Escher-like drawing using the change shown at the right.**

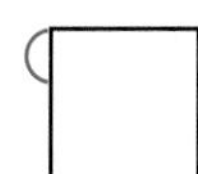

Complete the first pattern unit by drawing the reflection of the design on another side of the square.

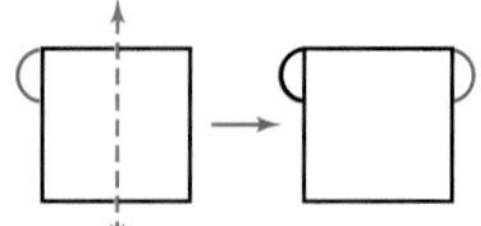

Now add another square. Reflect the new pattern in the second square.

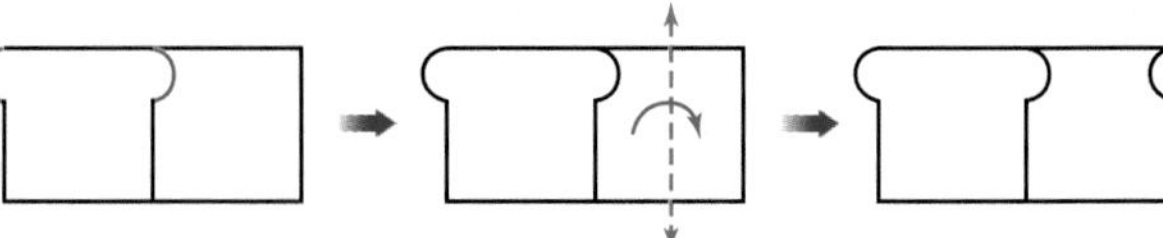

Continue this process to complete the tessellation.

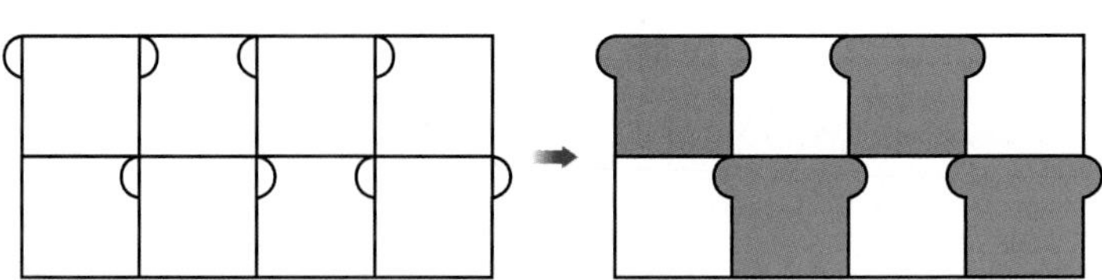

Study Hint
Problem Solving Look for a pattern to determine the two different units of the tessellation.

CHECK FOR UNDERSTANDING

Communicating Mathematics

Read and study the lesson to answer each question.

1. ***Tell*** how a line of symmetry is related to a reflection. **See Answer Appendix.**
2. ***Explain*** how a reflection is different from a translation. **See Answer Appendix.**

Guided Practice

3. The figure below is a regular hexagon. Copy the figure and draw all lines of symmetry.

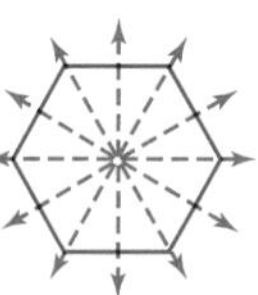

4. ***Art*** Complete both pattern units for the reflection shown below. Then draw the tessellation. **See Answer Appendix.**

■ Reteaching the Lesson ■

Activity Have students draw triangles, rectangles, and circles using graph paper or a compass and a straightedge. Have them cut out the figures and try to fold each to create two matching halves.

Exercise 11 asks students to advance to the next stage of work on the Chapter Project. Discuss with students how their designs might be used or displayed.

EXERCISES

Practice

Copy each figure. Draw all lines of symmetry.

5. 
no lines of symmetry

6. 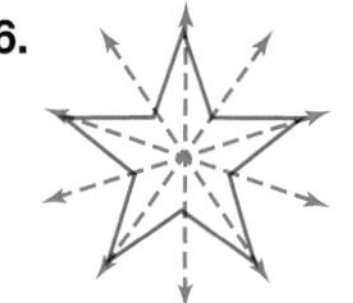

7. 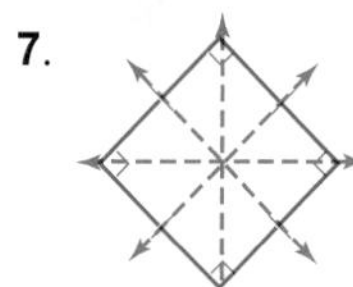

8. How many lines of symmetry does an equilateral triangle have? 3

Applications and Problem Solving

9. ***Art*** Complete the tessellation described by the pattern shown at the right. See Answer Appendix.

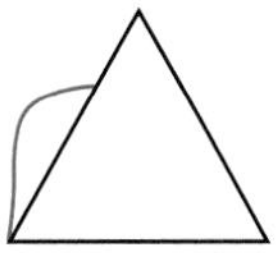

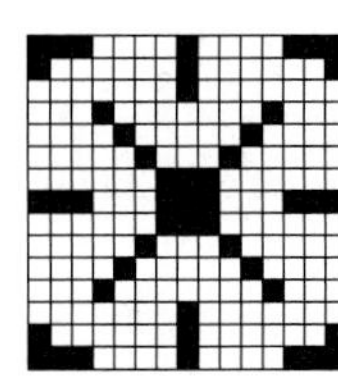

10. ***Crossword Puzzles*** Some crossword puzzles are designed so that the pattern of black and white squares looks the same upside down as right-side up. These puzzles have *half-turn symmetry*. In addition, some puzzles also have line symmetry. How many lines of symmetry are there in the puzzle at the right? 4

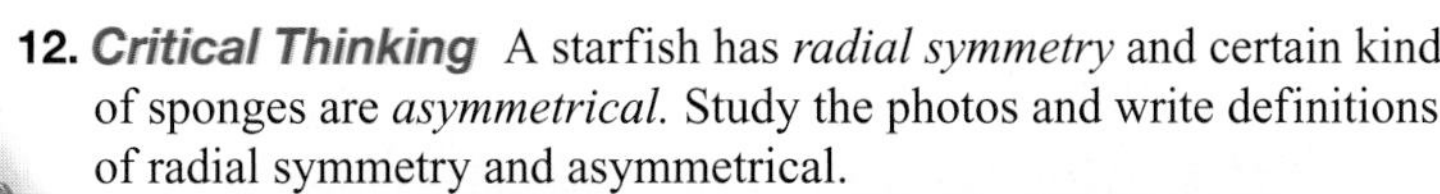

11. ***Working on the CHAPTER Project*** Use reflections to design a pattern for an Escher-like drawing. Then draw the tessellation. Use colors and/or textures to create an interesting pattern. See students' work.

12. ***Critical Thinking*** A starfish has *radial symmetry* and certain kinds of sponges are *asymmetrical.* Study the photos and write definitions of radial symmetry and asymmetrical.

12. In radial symmetry, parts are arranged in a circle around a central point. If a figure is asymmetrical, it has no symmetry.

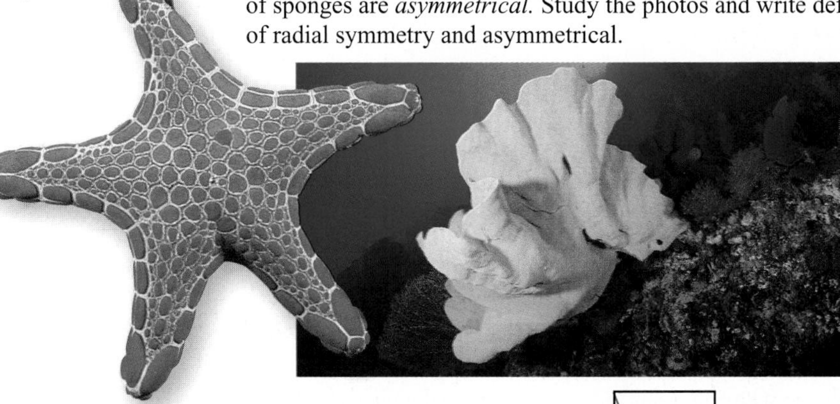

Mixed Review

13. ***Art*** Complete the pattern unit for the translation at the right. Then draw the tessellation. *(Lesson 9-6)*

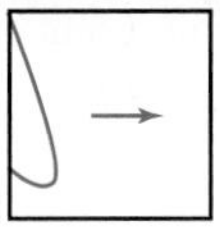

13. See Answer Appendix.

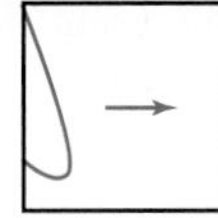

14. **Standardized Test Practice** The Wee Folk Furniture Company produces furniture for children that is a reduced version of adult furniture. The top of a full-sized desk measures 54 inches long by 36 inches wide. If the top of the child's desk is 24 inches wide, what is the length? *(Lesson 9-3)* B

A 16 in. **B** 36 in. **C** 48 in. **D** 54 in. **E** 60 in.

For **Extra Practice,** see page 595.

3 PRACTICE/APPLY

Check for Understanding

If students need additional practice or instruction after completing Exercises 1–4, one of these options may be helpful.

- Extra Practice, see p. 595
- Reteaching Activity
- *Study Guide Masters,* p. 73
- *Practice Masters,* p. 73

Assignment Guide

Core: 5–9 odd, 12–14
Enriched: 6–8 even, 9, 10, 12–14

4 ASSESS

Closing Activity

Modeling Have students draw regular polygons on their paper. Ask if there is a relationship between a regular polygon and how many lines of symmetry it has. **A regular polygon has as many lines of symmetry as it has sides.**

Chapter 9, Quiz D (Lesson 9-7) is available in the *Assessment and Evaluation Masters,* p. 240.

***Practice Masters,* p. 73**

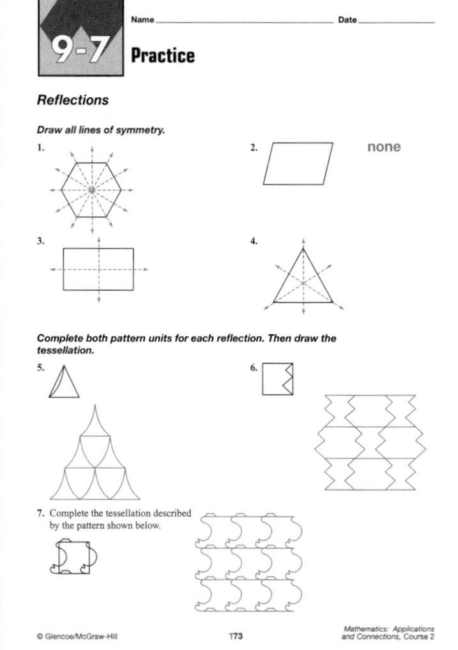
Name ______ Date ______

9-7 Practice

Reflections

Draw all lines of symmetry.

1.

2. none

3.

4.

Complete both pattern units for each reflection. Then draw the tessellation.

5.

6.

7. Complete the tessellation described by the pattern shown below.

© Glencoe/McGraw-Hill T73 *Mathematics: Applications and Connections, Course 2*

Extending the Lesson

***Enrichment Masters,* p. 73**

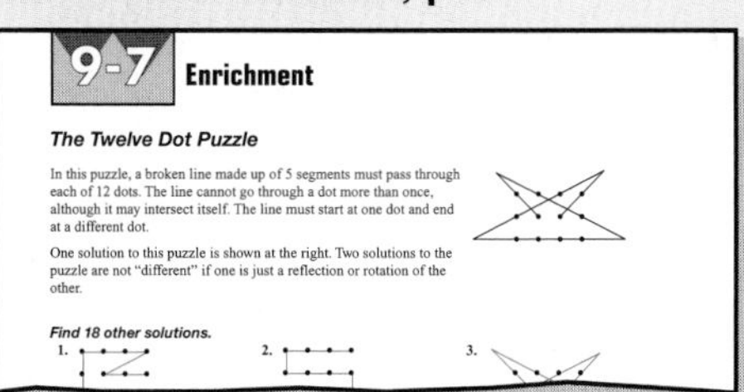
9-7 Enrichment

The Twelve Dot Puzzle

In this puzzle, a broken line made up of 5 segments must pass through each of 12 dots. The line cannot go through a dot more than once, although it may intersect itself. The line must start at one dot and end at a different dot.

One solution to this puzzle is shown at the right. Two solutions to the puzzle are not "different" if one is just a reflection or rotation of the other.

Find 18 other solutions.

1. 2. 3.

Activity Have students collect examples of the use of line symmetry in art, architecture, interior design, industrial design, clothing design, and advertising. Ask students how each object's symmetrical design may have made it more beautiful or functional.

Study Guide and Assessment

Vocabulary

This section provides a listing of the new terms, properties, and phrases that were introduced in this chapter. Have students define each term and provide an example or two of it, if appropriate.

Understanding and Using the Vocabulary

These exercises check students' understanding of the terms by using a variety of verbal formats including matching, completion, and true/false.

Glossaries A complete glossary of terms appears on pages 656–663. The glossary also appears in Spanish on pages 664–672.

Additional Answers

11. **A translation is a slide of the same pattern over and over. Translating an image that can cover an entire surface creates a tessellation**
18. **quadrilateral, not regular**
19. **not a polygon; More than 2 sides meet at a vertex.**
20. **pentagon, regular**
21. **heptagon, not regular**
22. **yes;** $\frac{5}{10} = \frac{8}{16}$
23. **yes;** $\frac{3}{2} = \frac{3}{2}$

CHAPTER 9 Study Guide and Assessment

interNET CONNECTION Chapter Review **For additional lesson-by-lesson review, visit: www.glencoe.com/sec/math/mac/mathnet**

Vocabulary

After completing this chapter, you should be able to define each term, concept, or phrase and give an example or two of each.

Geometry
acute angle (p. 362)
acute triangle (p. 382)
angle (p. 362)
complementary (p. 363)
congruent (p. 371)
decagon (p. 370)
degree (p. 362)
dilation (p. 380)
equilateral (p. 382)
heptagon (p. 370)
hexagon (p. 370)
indirect measurement (p. 377)
inscribed (p. 374)
isosceles (p. 382)
line of symmetry (p. 395)
line symmetry (p. 395)
nonagon (p. 370)
obtuse angle (p. 362)
obtuse triangle (p. 382)
octagon (p. 370)
pentagon (p. 370)
polygon (p. 370)
protractor (p. 360)
quadrilateral (p. 370)
reflection (p. 395)
regular polygon (p. 371)
rhombus (p. 383)
right angle (p. 362)
right triangle (p. 382)
scalene (p. 382)
similar (p. 376)
straight angle (p. 362)
supplementary (p. 363)
tessellation (p. 388)
translation (p. 392)
transversal (p. 361)
trapezoid (p. 383)
triangle (p. 370)
vertex (p. 362)

Problem Solving
use logical reasoning (p. 386)

Understanding and Using the Vocabulary

Choose the correct term or number to complete each sentence.

1. The point where the sides of an angle meet is called the (ray, vertex).
2. An (acute, obtuse) angle has a measure less than 90°.
3. If the sum of the measures of two angles is (90°, 180°), the angles are supplementary
4. A polygon with six sides is called a (heptagon, hexagon).
5. A polygon with congruent sides and congruent angles is called a (regular, similar) polygon.
6. A scalene triangle has (2, 0) congruent sides.
7. An (isosceles, equilateral) triangle has three congruent sides.
8. The sum of the angle measures at the vertex of any tessellation is (180°, 360°).
9. Figures that match exactly when folded in half have (translation, line symmetry).
10. A (reflection, tessellation) is a mirror image of a figure across a line of symmetry.

In Your Own Words

11. ***Explain*** how a translation can be used in constructing a tessellation. **See margin.**

MindJogger Videoquizzes

MindJogger Videoquizzes provide an alternative review of concepts presented in this chapter. Students work in teams to answer questions, gaining points for correct answers. The questions are presented in three rounds.
Round 1 Concepts–5 questions
Round 2 Skills–4 questions
Round 3 Problem Solving–4 questions

Objectives & Examples

Upon completing this chapter, you should be able to:

- classify angles *(Lesson 9-1)*

Classify the angle.

The angle above is an acute angle because its measure is less than 90°.

Review Exercises

Use these exercises to review and prepare for the chapter test.

Classify each angle as *acute*, *obtuse*, *right*, or *straight*.

12. 49° acute **13.** 90° right

14. 180° straight **15.** 113° obtuse

16. obtuse **17.** acute

Objectives & Examples

- identify polygons and regular polygons *(Lesson 9-2)*

Name the figure and tell whether it is regular.

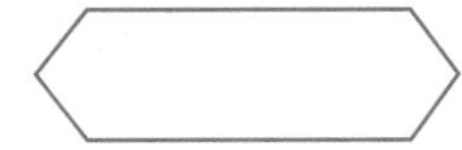

The figure above is a six-sided polygon. It is a hexagon. It is not regular because its sides are not congruent.

Review Exercises

Determine which figures are polygons. If the figure is a polygon, name it and tell whether it is regular. If the figure is *not* a polygon, explain why. 18–21. See margin.

18.

19.

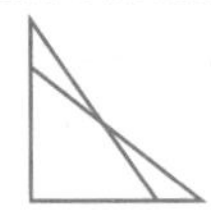

20.

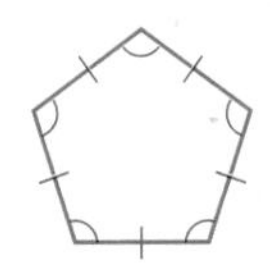

21.

Objectives & Examples

- determine whether polygons are similar and find a missing length in a pair of similar polygons *(Lesson 9-3)*

Tell whether the pair of polygons is similar.

3 cm, 1 cm; 6 cm, 2 cm

The polygons above are similar because corresponding angles are congruent and corresponding lengths are in proportion.

$$\frac{1}{2} = \frac{3}{6}$$

Review Exercises

Tell whether each pair of polygons is similar. Justify your answer.

22. 10 cm, 16 cm; 5 cm, 8 cm **23.** 3 ft, 3 ft; 2 ft, 2 ft

22–23. See margin.

Find the value of *x* in each pair of similar polygons.

24. **25.**

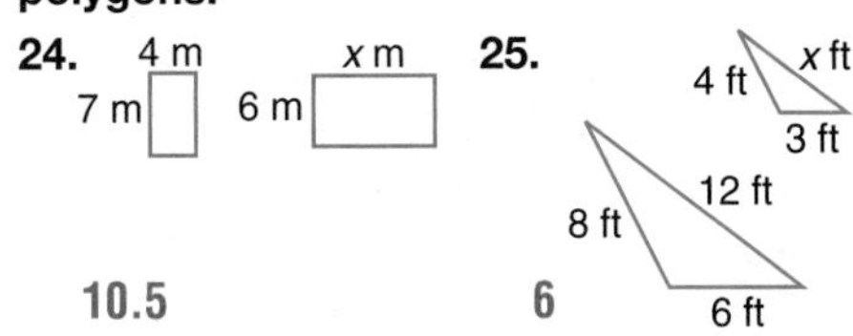

10.5 6

Assessment and Evaluation

Six forms of Chapter 9 Test are available in the *Assessment and Evaluation Masters* as shown in the chart.

1A	Multiple Choice	Honors
1B	Multiple Choice	Average
1C	Multiple Choice	Basic
2A	Free Response	Honors
2B	Free Response	Average
2C	Free Response	Basic

Chapter 9 Test, Form 1B, is shown at the right. Chapter 9 Test, Form 2B, is shown on the next page.

Objectives & Examples

This section reviews the skills and concepts of the chapter and shows completely worked examples.

Review Exercises

These exercises provide practice for the corresponding objectives.

***Assessment and Evaluation Masters*, pp. 227–228**

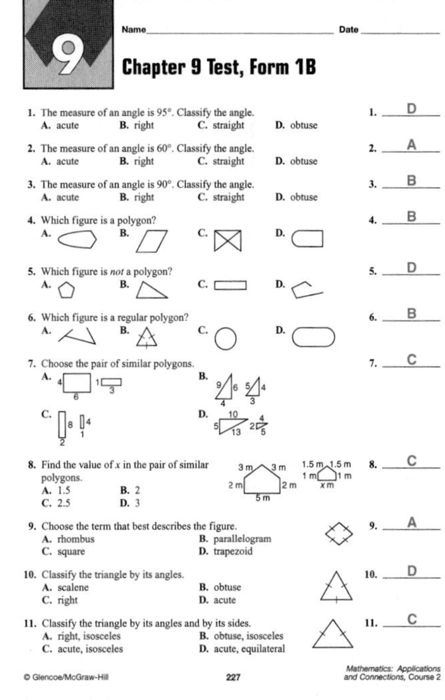

Name__________ Date__________

Chapter 9 Test, Form 1B

1. The measure of an angle is 95°. Classify the angle. — 1. D
   A. acute B. right C. straight D. obtuse
2. The measure of an angle is 60°. Classify the angle. — 2. A
   A. acute B. right C. straight D. obtuse
3. The measure of an angle is 90°. Classify the angle. — 3. B
   A. acute B. right C. straight D. obtuse
4. Which figure is a polygon? — 4. B
   A. B. C. D.
5. Which figure is *not* a polygon? — 5. D
   A. B. C. D.
6. Which figure is a regular polygon? — 6. B
   A. B. C. D.
7. Choose the pair of similar polygons. — 7. C
   A. 4, 6; 1, 3 B. 9, 6, 4; 5, 4, 3
   C. 8, 2; 4, 1 D. 10, 5, 13; 4, 2, 5
8. Find the value of *x* in the pair of similar polygons. (3 m, 3 m, 2 m, 2 m, 5 m; 1.5 m, 1.5 m, 1 m, 1 m, x m) — 8. C
   A. 1.5 B. 2
   C. 2.5 D. 3
9. Choose the term that best describes the figure. — 9. A
   A. rhombus B. parallelogram
   C. square D. trapezoid
10. Classify the triangle by its angles. — 10. D
    A. scalene B. obtuse
    C. right D. acute
11. Classify the triangle by its angles and by its sides. — 11. C
    A. right, isosceles B. obtuse, isosceles
    C. acute, isosceles D. acute, equilateral

© Glencoe/McGraw-Hill 227 *Mathematics: Applications and Connections, Course 2*

Chapter 9 Test, Form 1B (continued)

12. Classify the quadrilateral. — 12. B
    A. square B. parallelogram
    C. trapezoid D. rectangle
13. Which regular polygon can be used by itself to make a tessellation? — 13. B
    A. octagon B. equilateral triangle
    C. decagon D. circle
14. Which regular polygon *cannot* be used by itself to make a tessellation? — 14. D
    A. square B. equilateral triangle
    C. hexagon D. octagon
15. At the right is a pattern unit for a translation. Identify the tessellation. — 15. C
    A. B. C. D.
16. At the right is a pattern unit for a translation. Identify the tessellation. — 16. A
    A. B. C. D.
17. At the right is a pattern unit for a reflection. Identify the tessellation. — 17. A
    A. B. C. D.
18. Choose the figure that shows all lines of symmetry drawn correctly. — 18. B
    A. B. C. D.

Choose the type of logical reasoning used in Questions 19 and 20.

19. Joni and Cedric want to join a club that takes a trip to New York City. Since the chess club goes to New York every year for a tournament, they join the chess club. — 19. A
    A. deductive B. inductive C. circular D. none
20. Ms. Yong needs to create a trivia question for her students to research. She regularly sees trivia facts on the front page of each section of *USA Today,* so she bought a copy to get some ideas. — 20. B
    A. deductive B. inductive C. circular D. none

© Glencoe/McGraw-Hill 228 *Mathematics: Applications and Connections, Course 2*

Additional Answer

32. 2 squares, 3 triangles

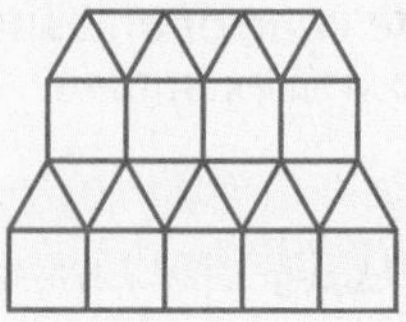

Assessment and Evaluation Masters, pp. 233–234

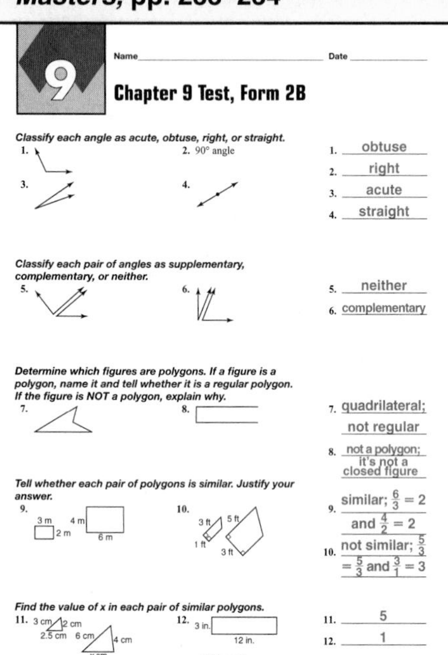

Name________________ Date________

Chapter 9 Test, Form 2B

Classify each angle as acute, obtuse, right, or straight.

1. [angle] 2. 90° angle 3. [angle] 4. [angle]

1. obtuse
2. right
3. acute
4. straight

Classify each pair of angles as supplementary, complementary, or neither.

5. [angles] 6. [angles]

5. neither
6. complementary

Determine which figures are polygons. If a figure is a polygon, name it and tell whether it is a regular polygon. If the figure is NOT a polygon, explain why.

7. [figure] 8. [figure]

7. quadrilateral; not regular
8. not a polygon; it's not a closed figure

Tell whether each pair of polygons is similar. Justify your answer.

9. 3 m, 2 m; 4 m, 6 m 10. 3 ft, 1 ft; 5 ft, 3 ft

9. similar; $\frac{6}{3} = 2$ and $\frac{4}{2} = 2$
10. not similar; $\frac{5}{3} = \frac{5}{3}$ and $\frac{3}{1} = 3$

Find the value of x in each pair of similar polygons.

11. 3 cm, 2 cm, 2.5 cm; 6 cm, 4 cm, x cm 12. 3 in., 12 in.; x in., 4 in.

11. 5
12. 1

© Glencoe/McGraw-Hill 233 *Mathematics: Applications and Connections, Course 2*

Chapter 9 Test, Form 2B (continued)

Classify each triangle by its angles and by its sides.

13. [triangle] 14. [triangle]

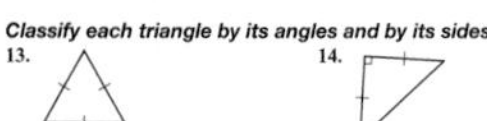

13. acute, equilateral
14. right, isosceles

Name every quadrilateral that best describes each figure. Then underline the name that best describes the figure.

15. [figure] 16. [figure]

15. quadrilateral
16. quadrilateral, rhombus, parallelogram

Assume each polygon is regular. Determine if it can be used by itself to make a tessellation.

17. octagon 18. square

17. no
18. yes

Complete the pattern unit for each translation.

19. [figure] 20. [figure]

Complete the pattern unit for each reflection.

21. [figure] 22. [figure]

23. Draw all lines of symmetry for a square. How many lines of symmetry are there?
24. Clair was in line to get lunch at the cafeteria. She wanted to get macaroni and cheese but did not know if it was on the menu. She saw 4 friends pass her with macaroni and cheese on their plates so she thought how good it would taste as she waited in line. What type of logical reasoning did she use?
25. Four students have birthdays in January, July, October, and December. Bucky's birthday is nearest to Independence Day. Amy was not born in the winter. Lucy's is the month after Jamie's. In what month was each born? What type of reasoning is used to solve this question?

23. 4
24. inductive
25. Amy, Oct.; Bucky, July; Lucy, Jan.; Jamie, Dec.; deductive

© Glencoe/McGraw-Hill 234 *Mathematics: Applications and Connections, Course 2*

Objectives & Examples	Review Exercises

- **classify triangles and quadrilaterals** *(Lesson 9-4)*

Classify the triangle.

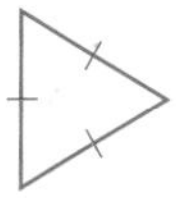

The figure above has 3 congruent sides, and all of its angles are acute. It is an acute equilateral triangle.

Classify each triangle by its angles and by its sides.

26.

right, scalene

27.

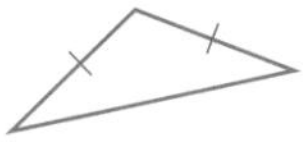

obtuse, isosceles

Name every quadrilateral that describes each figure. Then underline the name that best describes the figure.

28.

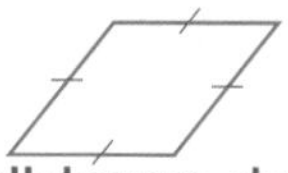

parallelogram, rhombus

29.

trapezoid

- **determine which regular figures can be used to form a tessellation** *(Lesson 9-5)*

Determine whether regular pentagons (540°) can be used to make a tessellation.

$$540 \div 5 = 108$$

No, because each angle measures 108° and 108 is not a factor of 360.

Determine whether each polygon can be used by itself to make a tessellation. Verify your results by finding the measures of the angles at a vertex.

30. hexagon; 720° yes; 120°

31. octagon; 1,080° no; 135°

32. Equilateral triangles and squares tessellate. Determine how many of each polygon are needed at each vertex. Then sketch the tessellation. **See margin.**

- **create Escher-like drawings by using translations** *(Lesson 9-6)*

Complete the pattern and then the tessellation.

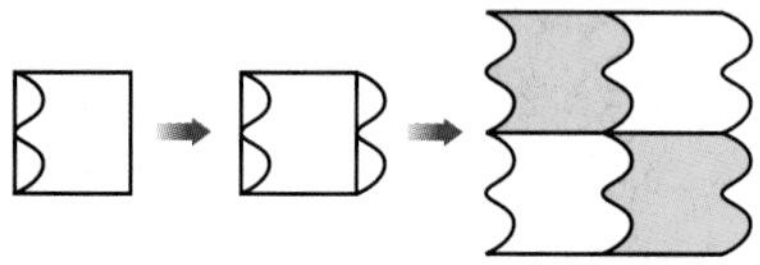

Complete the pattern unit for each translation. Then draw the tessellation.

33.

34.

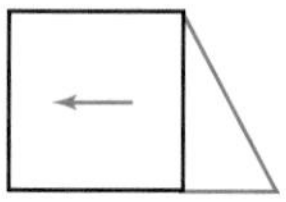

33–34. See Answer Appendix.

- **create Escher-like drawings by using reflections** *(Lesson 9-7)*

Draw all lines of symmetry in the figure.

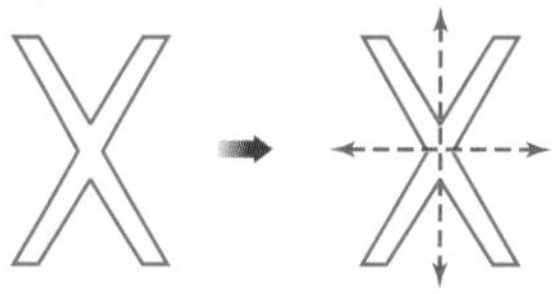

Copy each figure. Draw all lines of symmetry.

35.

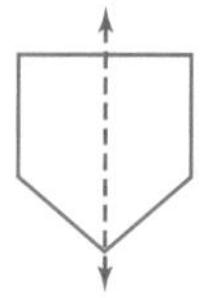

36.

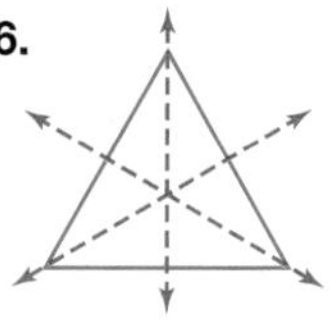

Test and Review Software

You may use this software, a combination of an item generator and item bank, to create your own tests or worksheets. Types of items include free response, multiple choice, short answer, and open ended.

CD-ROM Program

The CD-ROM Program contains an Assessment Game whose questions review the concepts in this chapter.

Applications & Problem Solving

37. ***Food*** Angelo's Pizza Parlor shapes its pizzas as squares. After baking, the pizzas are cut along one diagonal into two triangles. Describe completely the triangles that result. *(Lesson 9-4)* **isosceles, right**

38. ***Logical Reasoning*** Use the pattern below to draw the next two figures in the sequence. *(Lesson 9-4B)* **See Answer Appendix.**

1

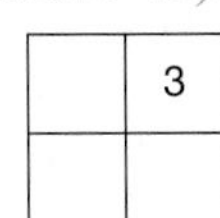

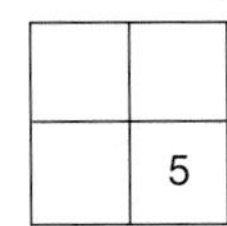

39. ***Crafts*** Edwyna is piecing together a quilt from fabric pieces in the shapes of hexagons and equilateral triangles. How many of each of the shapes will she need at each vertex in the tessellation created by the fabric pieces? Sketch the tessellation. *(Lesson 9-5)* **See Answer Appendix.**

40. ***Sports*** A tennis court and a badminton court are shaped like rectangles. Their dimensions are shown in the graph. Determine whether the rectangles are similar. *(Lesson 9-3)*

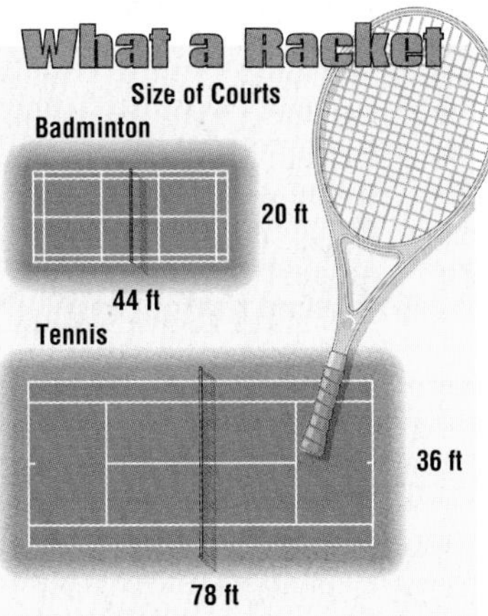

No; $\frac{36}{20} = \frac{9}{5}$ and $\frac{78}{44} = \frac{39}{22}$

Alternative Assessment

Open Ended

Suppose you want to find the height of a tall tree. It is not possible to climb the tree to measure it, but you notice the tree is casting a shadow. You also notice that there is a 4-foot fence post next to it casting a shadow. How can you determine the height of the tree? What other information do you need? **See margin.**

If the shadow of the tree is 36 feet long and the shadow of the fence post is 3 feet long, how tall is the tree? **48 feet**

Completing the Chapter Project

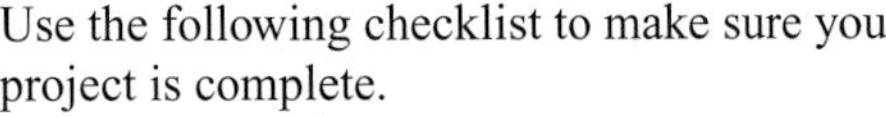

Use the following checklist to make sure your project is complete.

- ☑ You have created three designs.
- ☑ Your presentation includes an explanation of the mathematics that is used in your design.

Add any finishing touches you would like to make your design more attractive.

Select some of your work from this chapter that shows your creativity. Place it in your portfolio.

A practice test for Chapter 9 is provided on page 615.

Applications & Problem Solving

This section provides additional practice in solving real-world problems that involve the skills of this chapter.

Alternative Assessment

The ***Open Ended*** section provides students with a performance assessment opportunity to evaluate their work and understanding.

Students should complete the final stages of their project and prepare a class demonstration of their results. A scoring guide for the project is available in the *Investigations and Projects Masters,* p. 51.

Students should add to their portfolios at this time.

Additional Answer for the Open Ended item

You can use indirect measurement. Find the length of the shadow of the tree and the shadow of the fence post. Use these measurements in a proportion to find the height of the tree. 48 feet

Performance Assessment

Additional performance assessment tasks for this chapter are included in the *Assessment and Evaluation Masters* on page 237. A scoring guide is also provided on page 249.

***Assessment and Evaluation Masters,* p. 237**

Name________________ Date________

Chapter 9 Performance Assessment

Instructions: Demonstrate your knowledge by giving a clear, concise solution to each problem. Be sure to include all relevant drawings and justify your answers. You may show your solutions in more than one way or investigate beyond the requirements of the problems.

1. a. Draw a figure that is a polygon and another figure that is not a polygon. Explain how the figures are different.
   b. Explain how to classify triangles by the measure of their angles. Draw an example of each classification.
   c. Describe at least four classifications of quadrilaterals. Give an example of each.
   d. Is a trapezoid ever a rhombus? Explain your reasoning.
   e. Explain what is meant by *regular polygon*.
   f. Draw a right angle, obtuse angle, straight angle, and acute angle. Explain how the figures are different.
   g. Draw an example of supplementary angles. Explain how supplementary angles are different from complementary angles.

2. a. Explain why you think honeycombs are tessellated with hexagons instead of octagons.

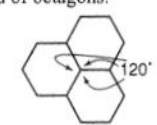

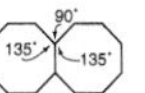

   b. Tile a rectangular area with squares. Then use at least two translations to create an Escher-like drawing. Explain each step.

3. a. Draw a figure that has two or more lines of symmetry. Draw all the lines of symmetry.
   b. Draw a figure that has no lines of symmetry.
   c. Draw a pattern unit for a reflection. Then tile a rectangular area with the pattern unit.

 237 *Mathematics: Applications and Connections, Course 2*

Standardized Test Practice

The Standardized Test Practice may be used to help students prepare for standardized tests. The test items are written in the same style as those in state proficiency tests and standardized tests like CAT, CTBS, ITBS, MAT, SAT, and Terra Nova. The test items cover skills and concepts covered up to this point in the text.

The pages can be used as an overnight assessment. After students have completed the pages, discuss how each problem can be solved, or provide copies of the solutions from the *Solutions Manual.*

***Assessment and Evaluation Masters,* p. 243**

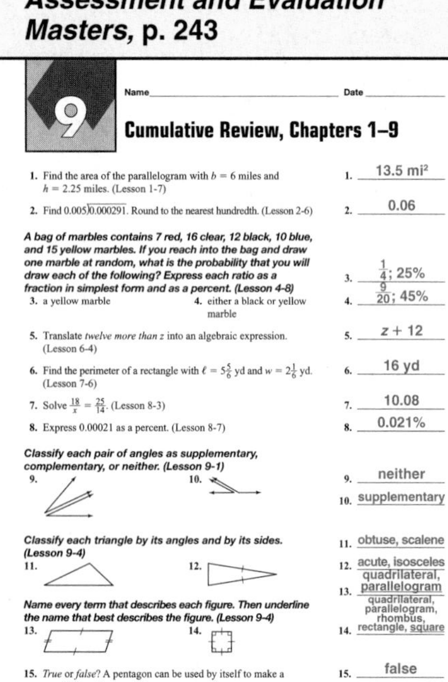

9

Name________________ Date________

Cumulative Review, Chapters 1–9

1. Find the area of the parallelogram with $b = 6$ miles and $h = 2.25$ miles. (Lesson 1-7) — 1. 13.5 mi²
2. Find $0.005\overline{)0.000291}$. Round to the nearest hundredth. (Lesson 2-6) — 2. 0.06

A bag of marbles contains 7 red, 16 clear, 12 black, 10 blue, and 15 yellow marbles. If you reach into the bag and draw one marble at random, what is the probability that you will draw each of the following? Express each ratio as a fraction in simplest form and as a percent. (Lesson 4-8)

3. a yellow marble — 3. $\frac{1}{4}$; 25%
4. either a black or yellow marble — 4. $\frac{9}{20}$; 45%
5. Translate *twelve more than z* into an algebraic expression. (Lesson 6-4) — 5. $z + 12$
6. Find the perimeter of a rectangle with $\ell = 5\frac{5}{6}$ yd and $w = 2\frac{1}{6}$ yd. (Lesson 7-6) — 6. 16 yd
7. Solve $\frac{18}{x} = \frac{25}{14}$. (Lesson 8-3) — 7. 10.08
8. Express 0.00021 as a percent. (Lesson 8-7) — 8. 0.021%

Classify each pair of angles as supplementary, complementary, or neither. (Lesson 9-1)

9. — 9. neither
10. — 10. supplementary

Classify each triangle by its angles and by its sides. (Lesson 9-4)

11. — 11. obtuse, scalene
12. — 12. acute, isosceles

Name every term that describes each figure. Then underline the name that best describes the figure. (Lesson 9-4)

13. — 13. quadrilateral, parallelogram
14. — 14. quadrilateral, parallelogram, rhombus, rectangle, square

15. *True* or *false*? A pentagon can be used by itself to make a tessellation. (Lesson 9-5) — 15. false
16. Complete the pattern unit for the reflection. (Lesson 9-7) — 16.

 243 *Mathematics: Applications and Connections, Course 2*

CHAPTERS 1–9 Standardized Test Practice

Assessing Knowledge & Skills

Section One: Multiple Choice

There are ten multiple choice questions in this section. Choose the best answer. If a correct answer is *not here,* choose the letter for Not Here.

1. Which is the equation for the line graphed? **A**

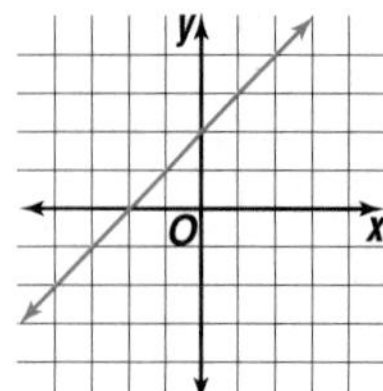

A $y = x + 2$ **B** $y = x - 2$
C $y = 2x$ **D** $y = 2x + 2$

2. Which word does not have a vertical line of symmetry? **G**

F H O W **G** B O Y
H M A T T **J** W H O

3. A doorway is 5 inches less than 8 feet tall. How many inches is this? **C**

A 101 inches
B 96 inches
C 91 inches
D 40 inches

4. Which expression represents *three less than a number*? **F**

F $n - 3$
G $3 - n$
H $3n$
J $\frac{n}{3}$

5. The triangles below are congruent. The measures of some of the angles and some of the sides are shown.

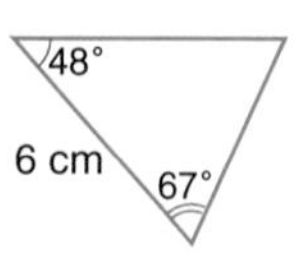

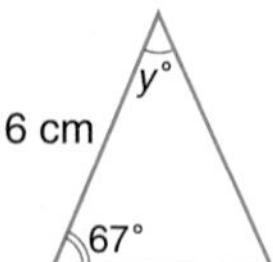

What is the value of y? **C**

A 55 **B** 67
C 48 **D** 65

Please note that Questions 6–10 have five answer choices.

6. The stem-and-leaf plot shows the prices for tickets to the summer concerts at a local amphitheater.

Stem	Leaf
1	5 9
2	2 4 7 8 9
3	0 2 2
4	1
5	
6	2 5 *1|5 = $15*

Into which price range do most of the tickets fall? **G**

F \$10–\$19
G \$20–\$29
H \$30–\$39
J \$40–\$49
K \$50–\$59

7. Which expression is equivalent to $3.2 \times (2.4 \times 5.8)$? **B**

A $(3.2 \times 2.4) + (3.2 \times 5.8)$
B $(3.2 \times 2.4) \times 5.8$
C $3.2 \times (2.4 + 5.8)$
D $2.4 + (3.2 \times 5.8)$
E Not Here

◀◀◀Instructional Resources

Another cumulative review is shown at the left and is available in the *Assessment and Evaluation Masters,* p. 243.

8. Colin had $\frac{7}{8}$ of a tank of gas in the lawn mower. After mowing the lawn, he had $\frac{1}{4}$ of a tank. How much gas did Colin use mowing the lawn? **H**

F $\frac{6}{4}$ of a tank

G $\frac{3}{4}$ of a tank

H $\frac{5}{8}$ of a tank

J $\frac{3}{8}$ of a tank

K $\frac{1}{8}$ of a tank

9. A recycling group at the middle school collected cans for a service project. They collected 122.4 pounds, 88.9 pounds, and 117.02 pounds in the last three weeks. What was the total amount collected for that period? **C**

A 248.15 lb

B 211.13 lb

C 328.32 lb

D 328.5 lb

E Not Here

10. On Monday, Fiona worked $5\frac{7}{12}$ hours. On Wednesday, she worked $6\frac{3}{4}$ hours. How many hours did Fiona work altogether? **G**

F $13\frac{5}{8}$ h

G $12\frac{1}{3}$ h

H $11\frac{5}{8}$ h

J $11\frac{1}{3}$ h

K Not Here

Test Practice For additional test practice questions, visit:

www.glencoe.com/sec/math/mac/mathnet

Test-Taking Tip
THE PRINCETON REVIEW

When taking a standardized test, you may be able to eliminate answer choices through estimating. Also, look to see which answers are *not* reasonable for the information given in the problem.

Section Two: Free Response

This section contains four questions for which you will provide short answers. Write your answers on your paper.

11. The table shows the values of p and q, where the values of p and q form a proportion.

p	5	10	Z
q	9	Y	63

What are the values of Y and Z? **18, 35**

12. In the figure, line a is parallel to line b. Name two supplementary angles.
Sample answer: ∠1, ∠2

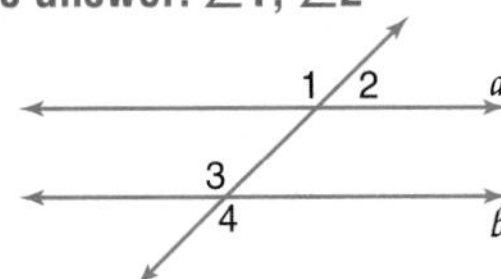

13. Triangles XYZ and RST are similar. Find the value of x. **11**

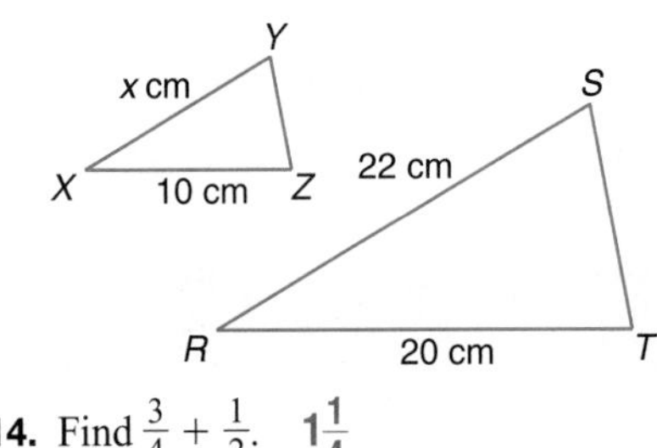

14. Find $\frac{3}{4} + \frac{1}{2}$. **$1\frac{1}{4}$**

Test-Taking Tip

Caution students to be sure to compare the answer with the original figure when considering which figure is correct. Eliminating the figures with the wrong characteristics often leads to the correct answer.

***Assessment and Evaluation Masters*, pp. 241–242**

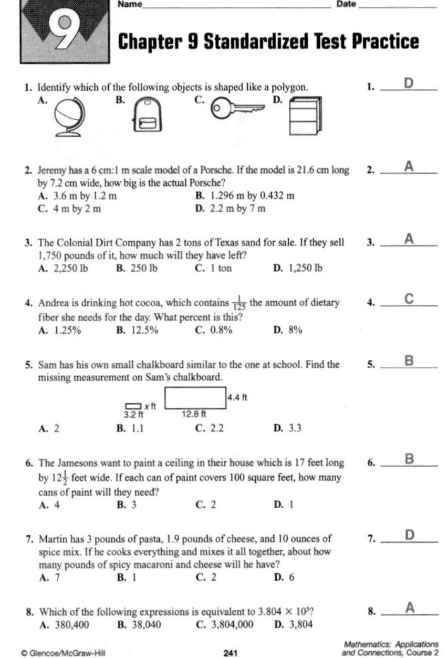

Name______________ Date__________

Chapter 9 Standardized Test Practice

1. Identify which of the following objects is shaped like a polygon. 1. D
A. B. C. D.

2. Jeremy has a 6 cm:1 m scale model of a Porsche. If the model is 21.6 cm long by 7.2 cm wide, how big is the actual Porsche? 2. A
A. 3.6 m by 1.2 m B. 1.296 m by 0.432 m
C. 4 m by 2 m D. 2.2 m by 7 m

3. The Colonial Dirt Company has 2 tons of Texas sand for sale. If they sell 1,750 pounds of it, how much will they have left? 3. A
A. 2,250 lb B. 250 lb C. 1 ton D. 1,250 lb

4. Andrea is drinking hot cocoa, which contains $\frac{1}{125}$ the amount of dietary fiber she needs for the day. What percent is this? 4. C
A. 1.25% B. 12.5% C. 0.8% D. 8%

5. Sam has his own small chalkboard similar to the one at school. Find the missing measurement on Sam's chalkboard. 5. B
x ft, 3.2 ft, 4.4 ft, 12.8 ft
A. 2 B. 1.1 C. 2.2 D. 3.3

6. The Jamesons want to paint a ceiling in their house which is 17 feet long by $12\frac{1}{2}$ feet wide. If each can of paint covers 100 square feet, how many cans of paint will they need? 6. B
A. 4 B. 3 C. 2 D. 1

7. Martin has 3 pounds of pasta, 1.9 pounds of cheese, and 10 ounces of spice mix. If he cooks everything and mixes it all together, about how many pounds of spicy macaroni and cheese will he have? 7. D
A. 7 B. 1 C. 2 D. 6

8. Which of the following expressions is equivalent to 3.804×10^5? 8. A
A. 380,400 B. 38,040 C. 3,804,000 D. 3,804

© Glencoe/McGraw-Hill 241 *Mathematics: Applications and Connections, Course 2*

Chapter 9 Standardized Test Practice (continued)

9. Mrs. Romano has various lengths of silverware she has to organize. She has 4.5 inch forks, $7\frac{1}{8}$ inch forks, $9\frac{1}{4}$ spoons, 5.8 inch spoons, and $9\frac{2}{5}$ inch knives. Which of the following lists the sizes from smallest to largest? 9. D
A. 4.5, 5.8, $7\frac{1}{8}$, $9\frac{2}{5}$, $9\frac{1}{4}$ B. 5.8, $7\frac{1}{8}$, 4.5, $9\frac{2}{5}$, $9\frac{1}{4}$
C. 4.5, $7\frac{1}{8}$, 5.8, $9\frac{1}{4}$, $9\frac{2}{5}$ D. 4.5, 5.8, $7\frac{1}{8}$, $9\frac{1}{4}$, $9\frac{2}{5}$

10. The French Connection Restaurant usually serves 18 pounds of escargot per week. They have $3\frac{3}{5}$ pounds left and the escargot comes in 5-pound boxes. Which is a reasonable amount of escargot to order if they order 2 weeks worth at a time? 10. D
A. 11 boxes B. 9 boxes C. 5 boxes D. 7 boxes

11. At Fairfield High School, about 25 cartons of chocolate milk are purchased from the vending machine daily. If James is stocking the machine for the week on Monday morning, how many cartons of chocolate milk should he put in the machine? 11. C
A. 75 B. 100 C. 125 D. 50

12. Carrie has 30 6-pound bags of cotton candy to hand out to 4 classes of 18 students each. How much cotton candy will each student receive? 12. B
A. 3 lb B. 2.5 lb C. 2 lb D. 1.5 lb

13. There is an oddly shaped street corner in Pennsburg, Pennsylvania, which forms a 30 degree angle. Is this an obtuse, acute, straight, or right angle? 13. A
A. acute B. obtuse C. right D. straight

14. Which figure completes the reflection? 14. A

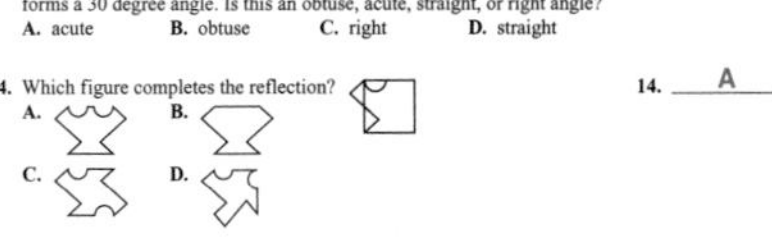

15. Jeannie purchased a skirt for $25.80 (before sales tax) that originally cost $43.00. What was the sale percent? 15. C
A. 60% B. 50% C. 40% D. 30%

16. Which of the following expressions is equivalent to $y = -4x - 9$ if $x = -3$? 16. B
A. $y = -21$ B. $y = 3$ C. $y = -16$ D. $y = 21$

© Glencoe/McGraw-Hill 242 *Mathematics: Applications and Connections, Course 2*

Instructional Resources ▶▶▶

Additional standardized test practice is shown at the right and is available in the *Assessment and Evaluation Masters*, pp. 241–242.

Interdisciplinary Investigation

GET READY

This optional investigation is designed to be completed by a group of 4 students over several days or several weeks.

Mathematical Overview

This investigation utilizes the concepts from Chapters 6–9.

- solving two-step equations
- finding perimeter
- finding circumference
- identifying regular polygons

Time Management	
Drawing figures	30 minutes
Calculations	40 minutes
Summarizing Data	40 minutes
Presentation	10 minutes

Instructional Resources

- *Investigations and Projects Masters,* pp. 9–12
- *Manipulative Kit*
  - protractor
  - ruler
  - compass

***Investigations and Projects Masters,* p. 12**

Name____________ Date________

Interdisciplinary Investigation
(Student Edition, Pages 404–405)

Pi for Polygons

Use this table to record your data.

3.

Polygon	Number of Sides	Perimeter, P	Radius, r	$2r$	$\frac{P}{2r}$
	3				
	4				
	5				
	6				
	7				
	8				
	9				
	10				

 12 *Mathematics: Applications and Connections, Course 2*

Interdisciplinary Investigation

Pi for Polygons

You have already learned that circles have a special ratio called *pi.* Pi is the ratio of the circumference of a circle to twice its radius. Could there be a special ratio for polygons that compares the perimeter of a polygon to its "radius"?

What You'll Do

In this investigation, you will construct and measure regular polygons to decide whether regular polygons have a special ratio like pi.

Materials 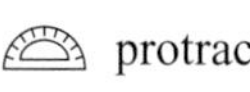 protractor  ruler compass  construction paper  calculator

Procedure

1. Work in groups of four. Assign each member of your group one pair of these numbers: 3 and 10, 4 and 9, 5 and 8, or 6 and 7. These numbers will represent the number of sides of regular polygons.
2. Work alone. Construct large regular polygons for your pair of numbers. Find the center of each polygon. This is the point in the interior that is equal in distance from each vertex. Measure the distance from the center to a vertex. This length will be called the *radius* of the polygon.
3. Work in your group. Prepare a table similar to the one below for all of the polygons from your group. Use a calculator to find the values in the last two columns.
4. Compare the tables from all of the groups. How do the values in the last column compare?
5. Write expressions for the perimeter of each regular polygon using P for the perimeter and $2r$.

radius

Polygon	Number of Sides	Perimeter (P)	Radius (r)	$2r$	$\frac{P}{2r}$

Instructional Resources

A recording sheet to help students organize their data for this investigation is shown at the left and is available in the *Investigations and Projects Masters,* p. 12.

Cooperative Learning

This investigation offers an excellent opportunity for using cooperative learning groups. For more information on cooperative learning strategies and group management, see *Cooperative Learning in the Mathematics Classroom.*

Making the Connection

Use the information from your table as needed to help in these investigations.

Language Arts

Design a poster to display your polygons, table, and formulas. Explain how you found the formulas for the regular polygons.

Social Studies

Research Carl Friedrich Gauss and his theory about constructing regular polygons. How did a heptadecagon affect his life?

Science

Honeycombs contain regular hexagons. Investigate other occurrences of regular polygons in nature.

Technology Tips

- Use a **spreadsheet** to calculate the values for the last two columns of the table.
- Use **geometry software** to construct and measure regular polygons.

Go Further

- Using geometry software, construct regular polygons with more than ten sides. Make a conjecture about the ratio of the perimeter of a polygon to twice its radius.
- Investigate the measure of one interior angle of a regular polygon as the number of sides of the polygon increases. Make a conjecture about the angle measure.

interNET CONNECTION For more information on π, visit: www.glencoe.com/sec/math/mac/mathnet

PORTFOLIO You may want to place your work on this investigation in your portfolio.

MANAGEMENT TIPS

Working in Teams Have each student write his or her findings in the table. Then the team can try to identify a pattern in their own results before comparing their table with the tables of other groups.

Making the Connection
You may wish to alert other teachers on your team that your students may need their assistance in this investigation.
Language Arts Students may research the names of certain geometric figures, such as *heptadecagon.*
Social Studies Students may find out how Gauss divided a circle into 17 equal parts, or learn about his work in astronomy and magnetism.
Science Students may investigate how the chemical structure of minerals determines the shape of a rock crystal.

ASSESS

Have students present their formulas for each polygon. Ask if they notice a pattern.

***Investigations and Projects Masters,* p. 11**

SCORING GUIDE

Interdisciplinary Investigation
(Student Edition, Pages 404–405)

Pi for Polygons

Level	Specific Criteria
3 Superior	• Shows a thorough understanding of the concepts of *constructing regular polygons* and *working with ratios.* • Uses appropriate strategies to solve problems. • Computations are correct. • Written explanations are exemplary. • Charts, model, and any statements included are appropriate and sensible. • Goes beyond the requirements of some or all problems.
2 Satisfactory, with minor flaws	• Shows understanding of the concepts of *constructing regular polygons* and *working with ratios.* • Uses appropriate strategies to solve problems. • Computations are mostly correct. • Written explanations are effective. • Charts, model, and any statements included are appropriate and sensible. • Satisfies the requirements of problems.
1 Nearly Satisfactory, with obvious flaws	• Shows understanding of most of the concepts of *constructing regular polygons* and *working with ratios.* • May not use appropriate strategies to solve problems. • Computations are mostly correct. • Written explanations are satisfactory. • Charts, model, and any statements included are appropriate and sensible. • Satisfies the requirements of problems.
0 Unsatisfactory	• Shows little or no understanding of the concepts of *constructing regular polygons* and *working with ratios.* • Does not use appropriate strategies to solve problems. • Computations are incorrect. • Written explanations are not satisfactory. • Charts, model, and any statements included are not appropriate or sensible. • Does not satisfy the requirements of the problems.

 11 *Mathematics: Applications and Connections,* Course 2

Instructional Resources ▶▶▶

Sample solutions for this investigation are provided in the *Investigations and Projects Masters* on p. 10. The scoring guide for assessing student performance shown at the right is also available on p. 11.

CHAPTER 10

Geometry: Exploring Area

Previewing the Chapter

Overview

In this chapter, students explore the concept of area. Students learn to find and estimate square roots by relating the area of a square to the length of its side. They also learn to solve problems by using guess and check and by using the Pythagorean Theorem. Students also learn to estimate and find the area of triangles, trapezoids, circles, and irregular figures. Probability is studied using area models.

Lesson (pages)	Lesson Objectives	NCTM Standards 2000	Standardized Tests	State/Local Objectives
10-1A (408–409)	Solve problems by using the guess-and-check strategy.	1, 6–9		
10-1 (410–414)	Find squares of numbers and square roots of perfect squares.	1, 3, 6–10	MAT, SAT	
10-2 (415–417)	Estimate square roots.	1, 3, 6–10		
10-3A (418)	Find the relationship among the sides of a right triangle.	1, 3, 6–10		
10-3 (419–422)	Find length using the Pythagorean Theorem.	1, 3, 6–10		
10-4 (423–426)	Estimate the area of irregular figures.	1, 3, 6–10	SAT	
10-5A (427)	Find the area of a triangle.	1, 3, 6–10	CAT, MAT, SAT	
10-5 (428–431)	Find the areas of triangles and trapezoids.	1, 3, 6–10	CAT, MAT, SAT	
10-6 (432–435)	Find the area of circles.	1, 3, 6–10	CAT, MAT, SAT	
10-7A (436–437)	Estimate the area of a figure using probability.	1, 3, 5–10		
10-7 (438–441)	Find probability using area models.	1, 3, 5–9	CTBS, TN	

CAT = California Achievement Tests, CTBS = Comprehensive Tests of Basic Skills, ITBS = Iowa Tests of Basic Skills, MAT = Metropolitan Achievement Tests, SAT = Stanford Achievement Tests, TN = Terra Nova
For the key to numbering of NCTM Standards 2000, see page T6.

Organizing the Chapter

CD-ROM

The **Interactive Lesson Planner** contains all of the blackline masters and transparencies. This CD-ROM also includes an easy-to-use lesson planning calendar.

LESSON PLANNING GUIDE

		Blackline Masters (page numbers)										
Lesson	**Extra Practice (Student Edition)**	**Study Guide**	**Practice**	**Enrichment**	**Assessment & Evaluation**	**Classroom Games**	**Diversity**	**Hands-On Lab**	**School to Career**	**Science and Math Lab Manual**	**Technology**	**Transparencies A and B**
10-1A	p. 595											
10-1	p. 595	74	74	74							45	10-1
10-2	p. 596	75	75	75	267							10-2
10-3A								62				
10-3	p. 596	76	76	76			23				46	10-3
10-4	p. 596	77	77	77	266, 267							10-4
10-5A								63				
10-5	p. 597	78	78	78		29–30						10-5
10-6	p. 597	79	79	79	268			81	23			10-6
10-7A								64				
10-7	p. 597	80	80	80	268							10-7
Study Guide/ Assessment					253–265, 269–271							

Other Chapter Resources

Student Edition

Chapter Project, p. 407, 426, 431, 441, 445

Let the Games Begin, p. 414

Technology

 MathPASS CD-ROM

 Interactive Mathematics Tools Software

Teacher's Classroom Resources

Applications

Family Letters and Activities, pp. 45–46

Investigations and Projects Masters, pp. 53–56

Meeting Individual Needs

Investigations for the Special Education Student, pp. 35–38

Teaching Aids

Answer Key Masters

Block Scheduling Booklet

Lesson Planning Guide

Solutions Manual

Professional Publications

Glencoe Mathematics Professional Series

Planning the Chapter

MindJogger Videoquizzes provide a unique format for reviewing concepts presented in the chapter.

Assessment Resources

Student Edition

Mixed Review, pp. 413, 417, 422, 426, 431, 435, 441
Mid-Chapter Self Test, p. 426
Math Journal, p. 440
Study Guide and Assessment, pp. 442–445
Performance Task, p. 445
Portfolio Suggestion, p. 445
Standardized Test Practice, pp. 446–447
Chapter Test, p. 616

Assessment and Evaluation Masters

Multiple-Choice Tests (Forms 1A, 1B, 1C), pp. 253–258
Free-Response Tests (Forms 2A, 2B, 2C), pp. 259–264
Performance Assessment, p. 265
Mid-Chapter Test, p. 266
Quizzes A–D, pp. 267–268
Standardized Test Practice, pp. 269–270
Cumulative Review, p. 271

Teacher's Wraparound Edition

5-Minute Check, pp. 410, 415, 419, 423, 428, 432, 438
Building Portfolios, p. 406
Math Journal, pp. 418, 427, 437
Closing Activity, pp. 409, 413, 417, 422, 426, 431, 435, 441

Technology

Test and Review Software
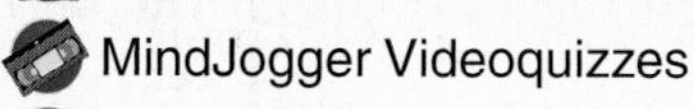
MindJogger Videoquizzes
CD-ROM Program

Materials and Manipulatives

Lesson 10-1
grid paper†
calculator
index cards

Lesson 10-2
grid paper†
calculator

Lesson 10-3A
centimeter grid paper†
ruler*†
scissors*

Lesson 10-3
calculator

Lesson 10-4
centimeter grid paper†

Lesson 10-5A
grid paper†
scissors*

Lesson 10-5
grid paper†
scissors*
tape
calculator

Lesson 10-6
compass*†
straightedge*†
scissors*
calculator

Lesson 10-7A
inch grid paper
ruler*†
compass*†
small counters*†

Lesson 10-7
calculator

*Glencoe Manipulative Kit

†Glencoe Overhead Manipulative Resources

Pacing Chart

See pages T25–T27 for the Course Planning Calendar.

COURSE	DAY 1	DAY 2	DAY 3	DAY 4	DAY 5	DAY 6	DAY 7
Standard	Chapter Project	Lesson 10-1A	Lesson 10-1	Lesson 10-2	Lessons 10-3A & 10-3		Lesson 10-4
Honors	Chapter Project	Lesson 10-1A	Lesson 10-1	Lesson 10-2	Lessons 10-3A & 10-3		Lesson 10-4
Block	Chapter Project & Lesson 10-1A	Lessons 10-1 & 10-2	Lessons 10-3A & 10-3	Lessons 10-4 & 10-5A	Lessons 10-5 & 10-6	Lessons 10-7A & 10-7	Study Guide and Assessment, Chapter Test

Interactive Mathematics:
Activities and Investigations

is an activity-based program that may be used as an enhancement for chapters in ***Mathematics: Applications and Connections.***

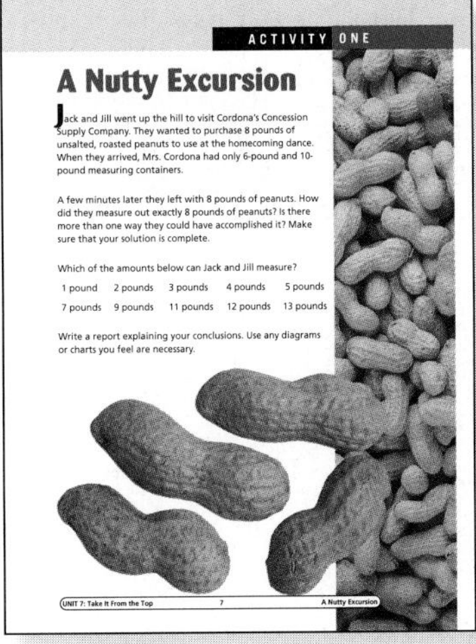

ACTIVITY ONE

A Nutty Excursion

Jack and Jill went up the hill to visit Cordona's Concession Supply Company. They wanted to purchase 8 pounds of unsalted, roasted peanuts to use at the homecoming dance. When they arrived, Mrs. Cordona had only 6-pound and 10-pound measuring containers.

A few minutes later they left with 8 pounds of peanuts. How did they measure out exactly 8 pounds of peanuts? Is there more than one way they could have accomplished it? Make sure that your solution is complete.

Which of the amounts below can Jack and Jill measure?

1 pound	2 pounds	3 pounds	4 pounds	5 pounds
7 pounds	9 pounds	11 pounds	12 pounds	13 pounds

Write a report explaining your conclusions. Use any diagrams or charts you feel are necessary.

UNIT 7: Take It From the Top 7 A Nutty Excursion

Unit 7, Activity One
Use with Lesson 10-1A.

Summary Students use the guess-and-check strategy to determine how to get exactly 8 pounds of peanuts using only 10-pound and 6-pound containers. Then students write a one-page report that explains their conclusions and discusses their methods.

Math Connection Students use the guess-and-check strategy to solve a problem. Then they communicate their mathematical understanding by writing about how the problem was solved.

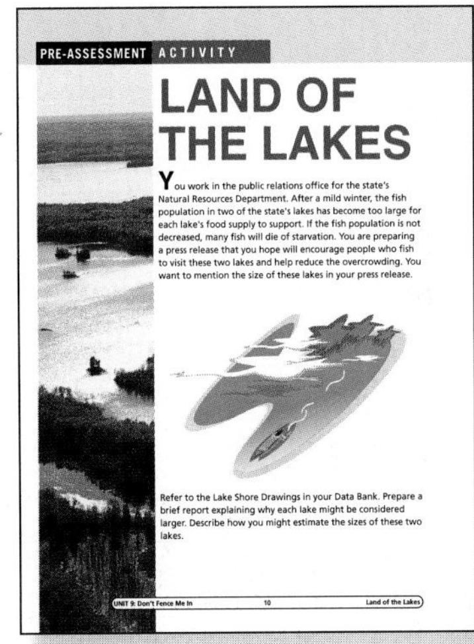

PRE-ASSESSMENT ACTIVITY

LAND OF THE LAKES

You work in the public relations office for the state's Natural Resources Department. After a mild winter, the fish population in two of the state's lakes has become too large for each lake's food supply to support. If the fish population is not decreased, many fish will die of starvation. You are preparing a press release that you hope will encourage people who fish to visit these two lakes and help reduce the overcrowding. You want to mention the size of these lakes in your press release.

Refer to the Lake Shore Drawings in your Data Bank. Prepare a brief report explaining why each lake might be considered larger. Describe how you might estimate the sizes of these two lakes.

UNIT 9: Don't Fence Me In 10 Land of the Lakes

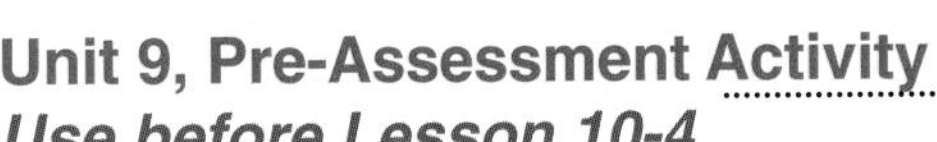

Unit 9, Pre-Assessment Activity
Use before Lesson 10-4.

Summary Students work in pairs using maps to determine which of two lakes is larger. Each pair gives an oral presentation of their findings.

Math Connection Students use their knowledge of geometry to estimate the areas and perimeters of two figures. They need to use proportional reasoning and the key to convert map measures to actual mearures.

DAY 8	DAY 9	DAY 10	DAY 11	DAY 12	DAY 13	DAY 14	DAY 15
Lessons 10-5A & 10-5		Lesson 10-6	Lessons 10-7A & 10-7		Study Guide and Assessment	Chapter Test	
Lesson 10-5		Lesson 10-6	Lesson 10-7	Study Guide and Assessment	Chapter Test		

Enhancing the Chapter

APPLICATIONS

Classroom Games, pp. 29–30

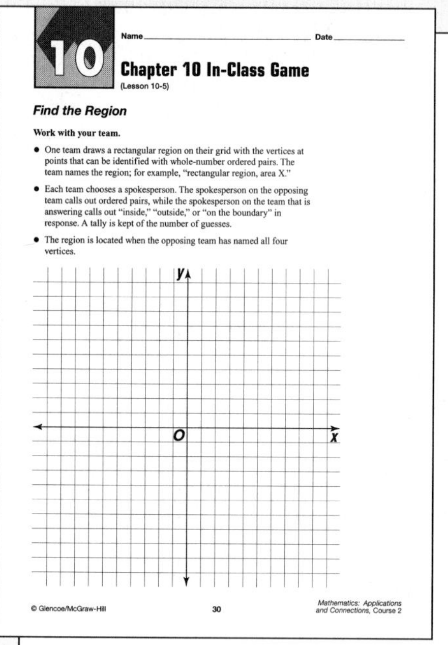

Name ____________ Date ________

Chapter 10 In-Class Game
(Lesson 10-5)

Find the Region

Work with your team.

- One team draws a rectangular region on their grid with the vertices at points that can be identified with whole-number ordered pairs. The team names the region; for example, "rectangular region, area X."
- Each team chooses a spokesperson. The spokesperson on the opposing team calls out ordered pairs, while the spokesperson on the team that is answering calls out "inside," "outside," or "on the boundary" in response. A tally is kept of the number of guesses.
- The region is located when the opposing team has named all four vertices.

© Glencoe/McGraw-Hill 30 *Mathematics: Applications and Connections, Course 2*

Diversity Masters, p. 23

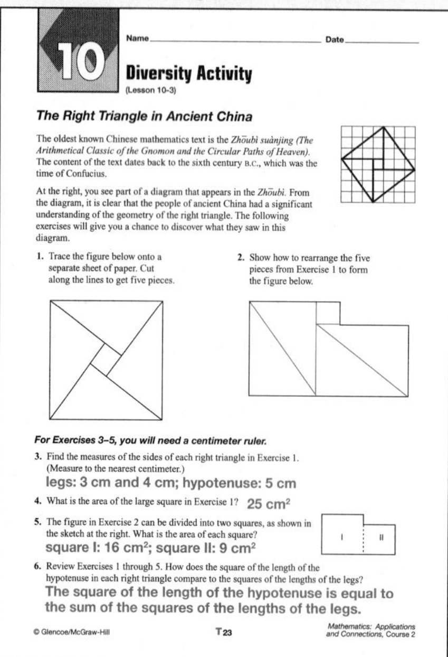

Name ____________ Date ________

Diversity Activity
(Lesson 10-3)

The Right Triangle in Ancient China

The oldest known Chinese mathematics text is the *Zhōubì suànjing (The Arithmetical Classic of the Gnomon and the Circular Paths of Heaven).* The content of the text dates back to the sixth century B.C., which was the time of Confucius.

At the right, you see part of a diagram that appears in the *Zhōubì.* From the diagram, it is clear that the people of ancient China had a significant understanding of the geometry of the right triangle. The following exercises will give you a chance to discover what they saw in this diagram.

1. Trace the figure below onto a separate sheet of paper. Cut along the lines to get five pieces.
2. Show how to rearrange the five pieces from Exercise 1 to form the figure below.

For Exercises 3–5, you will need a centimeter ruler.

3. Find the measures of the sides of each right triangle in Exercise 1. (Measure to the nearest centimeter.)
   legs: 3 cm and 4 cm; hypotenuse: 5 cm
4. What is the area of the large square in Exercise 1? **25 cm^2**
5. The figure in Exercise 2 can be divided into two squares, as shown in the sketch at the right. What is the area of each square?
   square I: 16 cm^2; square II: 9 cm^2
6. Review Exercises 1 through 5. How does the square of the length of the hypotenuse in each right triangle compare to the squares of the lengths of the legs?
   The square of the length of the hypotenuse is equal to the sum of the squares of the lengths of the legs.

© Glencoe/McGraw-Hill T23 *Mathematics: Applications and Connections, Course 2*

School to Career Masters, p. 23

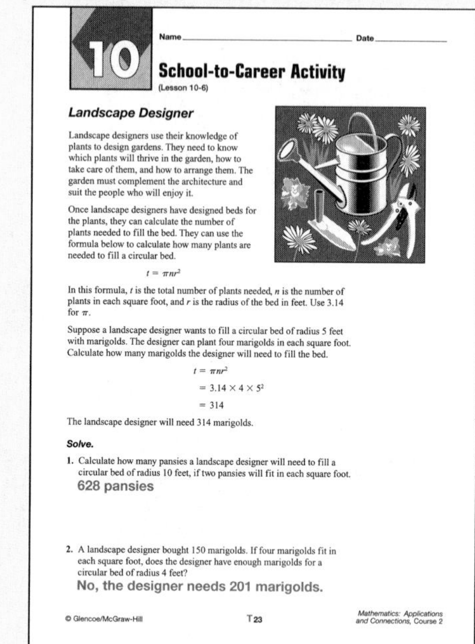

Name ____________ Date ________

School-to-Career Activity
(Lesson 10-6)

Landscape Designer

Landscape designers use their knowledge of plants to design gardens. They need to know which plants will thrive in the garden, how to take care of them, and how to arrange them. The garden must complement the architecture and suit the people who will enjoy it.

Once landscape designers have designed beds for the plants, they can calculate the number of plants needed to fill the bed. They can use the formula below to calculate how many plants are needed to fill a circular bed.

$$t = \pi n r^2$$

In this formula, t is the total number of plants needed, n is the number of plants in each square foot, and r is the radius of the bed in feet. Use 3.14 for π.

Suppose a landscape designer wants to fill a circular bed of radius 5 feet with marigolds. The designer can plant four marigolds in each square foot. Calculate how many marigolds the designer will need to fill the bed.

$$\begin{aligned} t &= \pi n r^2 \\ &= 3.14 \times 4 \times 5^2 \\ &= 314 \end{aligned}$$

The landscape designer will need 314 marigolds.

Solve.

1. Calculate how many pansies a landscape designer will need to fill a circular bed of radius 10 feet, if two pansies will fit in each square foot.
   628 pansies
2. A landscape designer bought 150 marigolds. If four marigolds fit in each square foot, does the designer have enough marigolds for a circular bed of radius 4 feet?
   No, the designer needs 201 marigolds.

© Glencoe/McGraw-Hill T23 *Mathematics: Applications and Connections, Course 2*

Family Letters and Activities, pp. 45–46

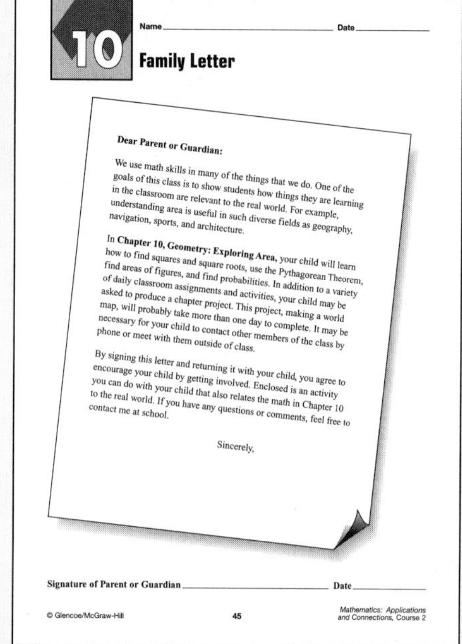

Name ____________ Date ________

Family Letter

Dear Parent or Guardian:

We use math skills in many of the things that we do. One of the goals of this class is to show students how things they are learning in the classroom are relevant to the real world. For example, understanding area is useful in such diverse fields as geography, navigation, sports, and architecture.

In **Chapter 10, Geometry: Exploring Area,** your child will learn how to find squares and square roots, use the Pythagorean Theorem, find areas of figures, and find probabilities. In addition to a variety of daily classroom assignments and activities, your child may be asked to produce a chapter project. This project, making a world map, will probably take more than one day to complete. It may be necessary for your child to contact other members of the class by phone or meet with them outside of class.

By signing this letter and returning it with your child, you agree to encourage your child by getting involved. Enclosed is an activity you can do with your child that also relates the math in Chapter 10 to the real world. If you have any questions or comments, feel free to contact me at school.

Sincerely,

Signature of Parent or Guardian ____________ **Date** ________

© Glencoe/McGraw-Hill 45 *Mathematics: Applications and Connections, Course 2*

Name ____________ Date ________

Family Activity

Estimating Areas

With a family member, find four small objects around the house. Put each one on the centimeter grid and draw an outline of one side of the object. Estimate the area of the outline.

1. name of object:
2. name of object:
3. name of object:
4. name of object:
5. Choose one of your objects. Give a reason why you might want to find the area of the object. Work with your family member to get ideas.

© Glencoe/McGraw-Hill 46 *Mathematics: Applications and Connections, Course 2*

MANIPULATIVES/MODELING

Hands-On Lab Masters, p. 81

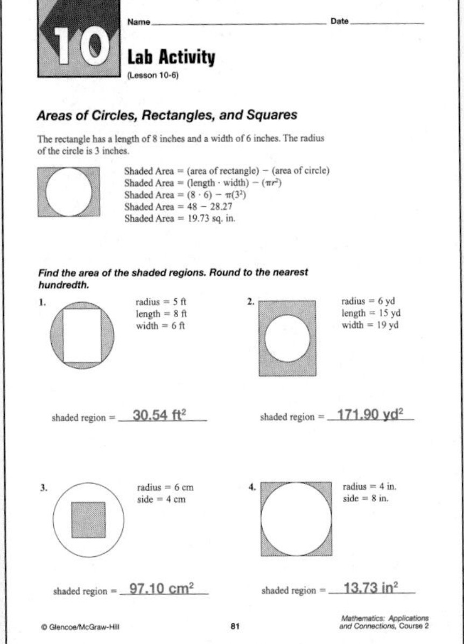

10

Name ____________ Date ____________

Lab Activity

(Lesson 10-6)

Areas of Circles, Rectangles, and Squares

The rectangle has a length of 8 inches and a width of 6 inches. The radius of the circle is 3 inches.

Shaded Area = (area of rectangle) − (area of circle)
Shaded Area = (length · width) − (πr^2)
Shaded Area = (8 · 6) − $\pi(3^2)$
Shaded Area = 48 − 28.27
Shaded Area = 19.73 sq. in.

Find the area of the shaded regions. Round to the nearest hundredth.

1. radius = 5 ft, length = 8 ft, width = 6 ft — shaded region = 30.54 ft²
2. radius = 6 yd, length = 15 yd, width = 19 yd — shaded region = 171.90 yd²
3. radius = 6 cm, side = 4 cm — shaded region = 97.10 cm²
4. radius = 4 in., side = 8 in. — shaded region = 13.73 in²

© Glencoe/McGraw-Hill 81 *Mathematics: Applications and Connections, Course 2*

ASSESSMENT/EVALUATION

Assessment and Evaluation Masters, pp. 266–268

10

Name ____________ Date ____________

Chapter 10 Mid-Chapter Test

(Lessons 10-1 through 10-4)

1. Jobeth is thinking of two numbers. The sum of the numbers is 100. The difference of the numbers is 20. What are the numbers? — 1. 40, 60

Find the square of each number.

2. 9 — 81
3. 16 — 256
4. 11 — 121

Find each square root.

5. $\sqrt{225}$ — 15
6. $\sqrt{324}$ — 18

Estimate to the nearest whole number.

7. $\sqrt{289}$ — 17
8. $\sqrt{407}$ — 20
9. $\sqrt{183}$ — 14

Find the missing measure for each right triangle. Round to the nearest tenth.

10. a = 12 cm; c = 13 cm — 5 cm
11. a = 14 ft; b = 19 ft — 23.6 ft
12. a = 11 m; c = 23 m — 20.2 m
13. b = 10 in.; c = 18 in. — 15.0 in.

Estimate the area of each figure.

14. 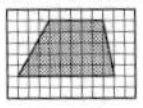 — about 35 units²
15. 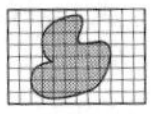 — about 36 units²
16. 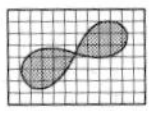 — about 21 units²

© Glencoe/McGraw-Hill 266 *Mathematics: Applications and Connections, Course 2*

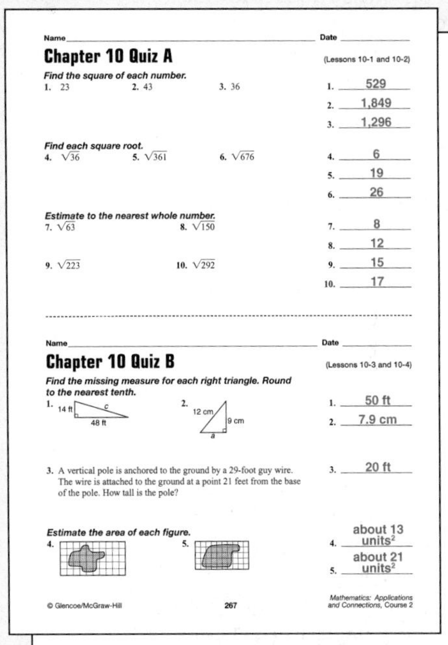

Name ____________ Date ____________

Chapter 10 Quiz A (Lessons 10-1 and 10-2)

Find the square of each number.

1. 23 — 529
2. 43 — 1,849
3. 36 — 1,296

Find each square root.

4. $\sqrt{36}$ — 6
5. $\sqrt{361}$ — 19
6. $\sqrt{676}$ — 26

Estimate to the nearest whole number.

7. $\sqrt{63}$ — 8
8. $\sqrt{150}$ — 12
9. $\sqrt{223}$ — 15
10. $\sqrt{292}$ — 17

Name ____________ Date ____________

Chapter 10 Quiz B (Lessons 10-3 and 10-4)

Find the missing measure for each right triangle. Round to the nearest tenth.

1. 14 ft, 48 ft, c — 50 ft
2. 12 cm, 9 cm, a — 7.9 cm
3. A vertical pole is anchored to the ground by a 29-foot guy wire. The wire is attached to the ground at a point 21 feet from the base of the pole. How tall is the pole? — 20 ft

Estimate the area of each figure.

4. — about 13 units²
5. — about 21 units²

© Glencoe/McGraw-Hill 267 *Mathematics: Applications and Connections, Course 2*

TECHNOLOGY/MULTIMEDIA

Technology Masters, pp. 45–46

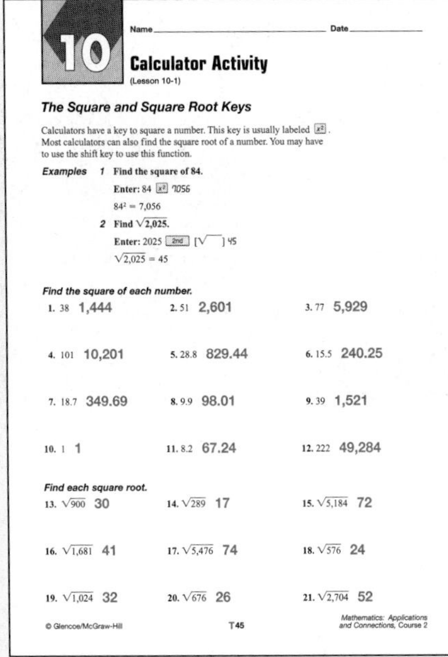

10

Name ____________ Date ____________

Calculator Activity

(Lesson 10-1)

The Square and Square Root Keys

Calculators have a key to square a number. This key is usually labeled [x²]. Most calculators can also find the square root of a number. You may have to use the shift key to use this function.

Examples 1 **Find the square of 84.**
Enter: 84 [x²] 7056
$84^2 = 7,056$

2 **Find $\sqrt{2,025}$.**
Enter: 2025 [2nd] [√] 45
$\sqrt{2,025} = 45$

Find the square of each number.

1. 38 1,444
2. 51 2,601
3. 77 5,929
4. 101 10,201
5. 28.8 829.44
6. 15.5 240.25
7. 18.7 349.69
8. 9.9 98.01
9. 39 1,521
10. 1 1
11. 8.2 67.24
12. 222 49,284

Find each square root.

13. $\sqrt{900}$ 30
14. $\sqrt{289}$ 17
15. $\sqrt{5,184}$ 72
16. $\sqrt{1,681}$ 41
17. $\sqrt{5,476}$ 74
18. $\sqrt{576}$ 24
19. $\sqrt{1,024}$ 32
20. $\sqrt{676}$ 26
21. $\sqrt{2,704}$ 52

© Glencoe/McGraw-Hill T45 *Mathematics: Applications and Connections, Course 2*

10

Name ____________ Date ____________

Graphing Calculator Activity

(Lesson 10-3)

The Pythagorean Theorem

The square and square root functions on a graphing calculator can help you solve problems involving the Pythagorean Theorem.

Examples 1 **Find the measure of the hypotenuse.**

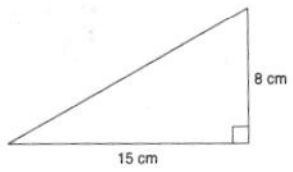

$a^2 + b^2 = c^2$
$15^2 + 8^2 = c^2$

Enter: 15 [x²] [+] 8 [x²] [ENTER] 289

$c^2 = 289$

Enter: [2nd] [√] 289 [ENTER] 17

The hypotenuse of the triangle measures 17 centimeters.

(Figure: right triangle with legs 15 cm and 8 cm)

2 **Find the measure of the remaining side of a right triangle if one side measures 14 feet and the hypotenuse measures 21 feet. Round to the nearest tenth.**

$a^2 + b^2 = c^2$
$14^2 + b^2 = 21^2$
$14^2 - 14^2 + b^2 = 21^2 - 14^2$
$b^2 = 21^2 - 14^2$

Enter: 21 [x²] [−] 14 [x²] [ENTER] 245

$b^2 = 245$

Enter: [2nd] [√] 245 [ENTER] 15.65247584

Rounded to the nearest tenth, the remaining side measures 15.7 feet.

Find the missing measure for each right triangle. Round to the nearest tenth.

1. a: 5 cm; b: 7 cm — 8.6 cm
2. a: 16 in.; b: 11 in. — 19.4 in.
3. b: 10 m; c: 15 m — 11.2 m
4. a: 21 ft; c: 25 ft — 13.6 ft
5. b: 13.7 mm; c: 17.1 mm — 10.2 mm
6. a: 7.8 m; c: 9.9 m — 6.1 m

© Glencoe/McGraw-Hill T46 *Mathematics: Applications and Connections, Course 2*

MEETING INDIVIDUAL NEEDS

Investigations for the Special Education Student, pp. 35–38

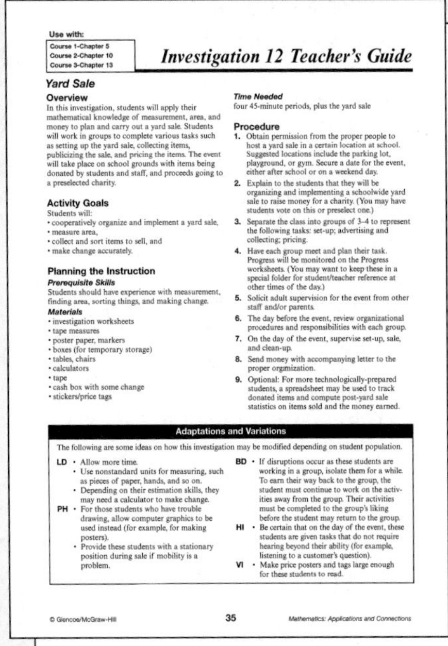

Use with:
Course 1-Chapter 5
Course 2-Chapter 10
Course 3-Chapter 13

Investigation 12 Teacher's Guide

Yard Sale

Overview

In this investigation, students will apply their mathematical knowledge of measurement, area, and money to plan and carry out a yard sale. Students will work in groups to complete various tasks such as setting up the yard sale, collecting items, publicizing the sale, and pricing the items. The event will take place on school grounds with items being donated by students and staff, and proceeds going to a preselected charity.

Activity Goals

Students will:
- cooperatively organize and implement a yard sale,
- measure area,
- collect and sort items to sell, and
- make change accurately.

Planning the Instruction

Prerequisite Skills

Students should have experience with measurement, finding area, sorting things, and making change.

Materials

- investigation worksheets
- tape measures
- poster paper, markers
- boxes (for temporary storage)
- tables, chairs
- calculators
- tape
- cash box with some change
- stickers/price tags

Time Needed

four 45-minute periods, plus the yard sale

Procedure

1. Obtain permission from the proper people to host a yard sale in a certain location at school. Suggested locations include the parking lot, playground, or gym. Secure a date for the event, either after school or on a weekend day.
2. Explain to the students that they will be organizing and implementing a schoolwide yard sale to raise money for a charity. (You may have students vote on this or preselect one.)
3. Separate the class into groups of 3-4 to represent the following tasks: set-up; advertising and collecting; pricing.
4. Have each group meet and plan their task. Progress will be monitored on the Progress worksheets. (You may want to keep these in a special folder for student/teacher reference at other times of the day.)
5. Solicit adult supervision for the event from other staff and/or parents.
6. The day before the event, review organizational procedures and responsibilities with each group.
7. On the day of the event, supervise set-up, sale, and clean-up.
8. Send money with accompanying letter to the proper orgamization.
9. Optional: For more technologically-prepared students, a spreadsheet may be used to track donated items and compute post-yard sale statistics on items sold and the money earned.

Adaptations and Variations

The following are some ideas on how this investigation may be modified depending on student population.

LD • Allow more time.
• Use nonstandard units for measuring, such as pieces of paper, hands, and so on.
• Depending on their estimation skills, they may need a calculator to make change.

PH • For those students who have trouble drawing, allow computer graphics to be used instead (for example, for making posters).
• Provide these students with a stationary position during sale if mobility is a problem.

BD • If disruptions occur as these students are working in a group, isolate them for a while. To earn their way back to the group, the student must continue to work on the activities away from the group. Their activities must be completed to the group's liking before the student may return to the group.

HI • Be certain that on the day of the event, these students are given tasks that do not require hearing beyond their ability (for example, listening to a customer's question).

VI • Make price posters and tags large enough for these students to read.

© Glencoe/McGraw-Hill 35 *Mathematics: Applications and Connections*

CHAPTER 10 NOTES

Theme: Geography

The Inter-governmental Panel for Climate Change (IPCC) says that global warming is causing glaciers and small ice caps to slowly melt. As a result, sea level is rising. By the year 2030, global sea level will be about 18 centimeters higher than it is today.

Question of the Day The circular island of Gutenacht has a radius of 19 miles. By the year 2030, it is predicted to lose 200 square miles of area due to the rising sea level. If Ravi plants a tree at random on Gutenacht, what is the probability that it will be on dry ground in 2030? **about $\frac{934}{1,134}$ or $\frac{467}{567}$**

Assess Prerequisite Skills

Ask students to read through the list of objectives presented in "What you'll learn in Chapter 10." You may wish to ask them what each of the objectives means or if they have experienced or used any of these math concepts before.

Building Portfolios

Encourage students to revise their portfolios as they study this chapter. They should select work that demonstrates their grasp of the concepts and skills learned in the chapter. Portfolio work provides a good basis for review of the chapter content.

Math and the Family

In the *Family Letters and Activities* booklet (pp. 45–46), you will find a letter to the parents explaining what students will study in Chapter 10. An activity appropriate for the whole family is also available.

CHAPTER 10 Geometry: Exploring Area

What you'll learn in Chapter 10

- to solve problems by using guess and check,
- to find the squares and square roots of numbers,
- to find length using the Pythagorean Theorem,
- to find the areas of irregular figures, triangles, trapezoids, and circles, and
- to find probability using area models.

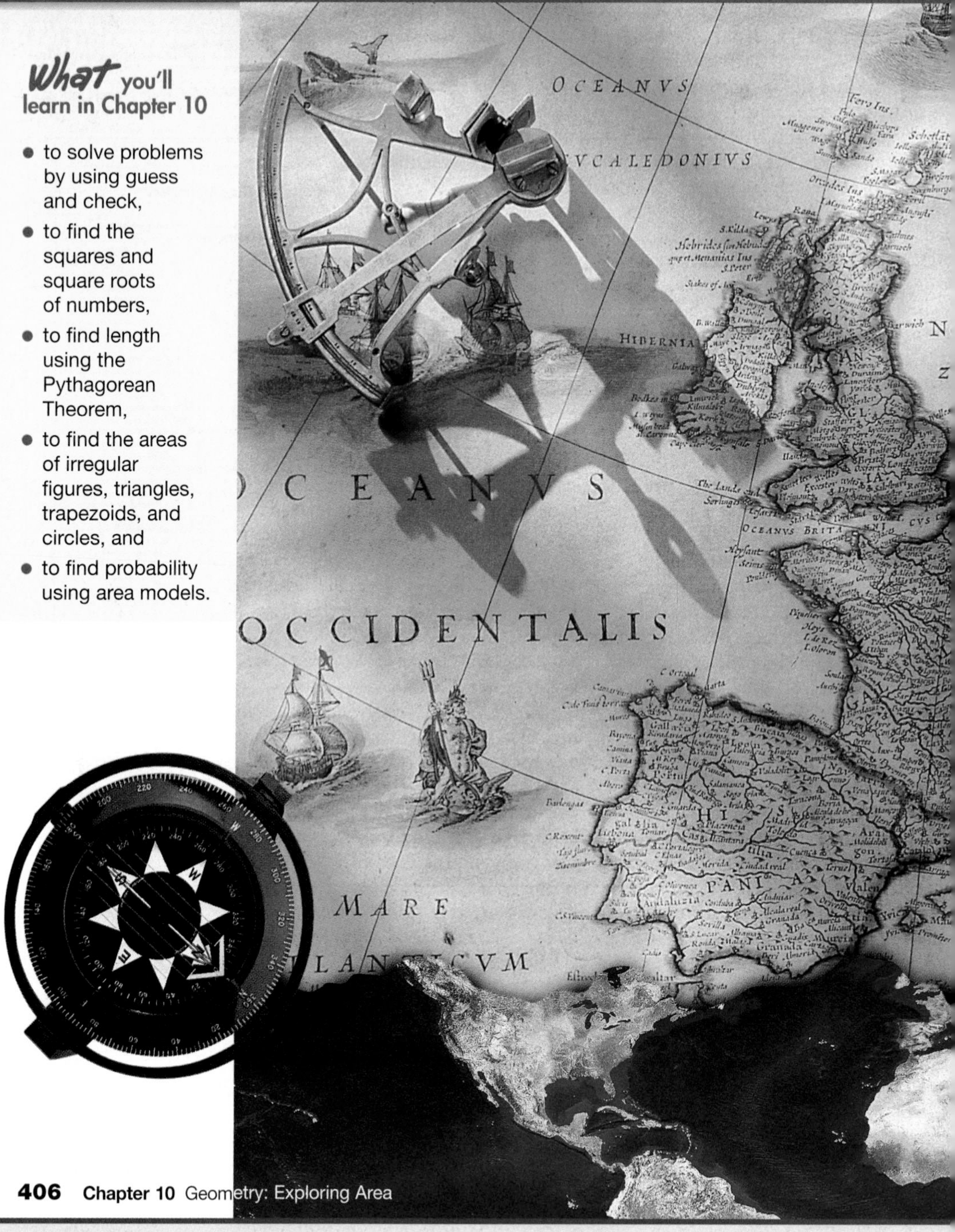

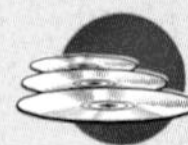

CD-ROM Program

Activities for Chapter 10

- Chapter 10 Introduction
- Interactive Lessons 10-2, 10-3, 10-5, 10-7
- Assessment Game
- Resource Lessons 10-1 through 10-7

IT'S A SMALL WORLD

In this project, you will make a simple map of Earth and use geometry to approximate the area of landmasses and bodies of water. You will determine what part of Earth is covered in water. You can use colored pencils to draw your map on poster board or a large sheet of paper.

Getting Started

- Find a world map. Using the map as a guideline, sketch the outlines of the landmasses on your poster board or paper. Keep in mind that the existing map may be a different size than the one you are drawing. Be sure to make any necessary adjustments.
- Label the landmasses and the bodies of water with their names.

Technology Tips

- Use an **electronic encyclopedia** to find a map.
- Use a **calculator** to help you approximate the areas of the landmasses and the bodies of water.
- Use a **word processor** to write information about the map.

Research For information on world maps, visit:

www.glencoe.com/sec/math/mac/mathnet

Working on the Project

You can use what you'll learn in Chapter 10 to help you make your map.

Page	Exercise
426	16
431	24
441	18
445	Alternative Assessment

interNET CONNECTION

Glencoe has made every effort to ensure that the website links for *Mathematics: Applications and Connections* at **www.glencoe.com/sec/math/mac/mathnet** are current and contain appropriate content. However, these website links are not under Glencoe's control.

Instructional Resources ▶▶▶

A recording sheet to help students organize their data for the Chapter Project is shown at the right and is available in the *Investigations and Projects Masters,* p. 56.

CHAPTER Project NOTES

Objectives Students should
- use geometry to approximate the area of landmass and bodies of water on Earth.
- determine what part of Earth is covered in water.

Project Pointer You may suggest that students begin a *Project Folder* to keep their work in as they complete each stage of the Chapter Project. The completed project may also be added to their portfolios.

***Investigations and Projects Masters,* p. 56**

Name ______________________ Date ____________

Chapter 10 Project

It's a Small World

Page 426, Working on the Chapter Project, Exercise 16

Landmass	Estimate of Area (sq. mi)	Actual Area (sq. mi)
North America		
South America		
Europe/Asia		
Africa		
Australia		
Antarctica		
Body of Water	**Estimated**	**Actual**
Pacific Ocean		
Atlantic Ocean		
Indian Ocean		
Arctic Ocean		

Page 431, Working on the Chapter Project, Exercise 24

Triangles and Trapezoids		
Name	Area	
	Estimated	Actual
Australia		
Africa		
South America		

Page 441, Working on the Chapter Project, Exercise 18

The probability that the meteor will land in water is about:

 56 *Mathematics: Applications and Connections, Course 2*

10-1A THINKING LAB Notes

Objective Students solve problems by using the guess-and-check strategy.

Recommended Pacing	
Standard	Day 2 of 14
Honors	Day 2 of 13
Block	Day 1 of 7

1 FOCUS

Getting Started Have students describe in their own words what the opening problem requires. For example, of the 16 shots Willie Arriago made, how many were for two points and how many were for one point?

2 TEACH

Teaching Tip Have students suggest ways to fine tune their guessing process. You may suggest that they use a table to record the guesses and look for a pattern.

In-Class Example
A mother is 28 years older than her son. The sum of their ages totals 70 years. How old is each? **49; 21**

Additional Answers

1. **Sample answer: Charo picked six 1-point shots and ten 2-point shots because it is easy to see that 6 + 10 = 16. The guess results in 26 points which is less than 30. She should decrease the number of 1-point shots and increase the number of 2-point shots.**
2. **Willie made two 1-point shots and fourteen 2-point shots. See Answer Appendix for table.**

PROBLEM SOLVING

10-1A Guess and Check

A Preview of Lesson 10-1

The Los Angeles Kodiaks played the Massachusetts Chariots in the Second National Junior Wheelchair Basketball Tournament. The leading scorer was Willie Arriago with 30 points. He missed 20 of his 36 attempts. All of his shots were worth either one or two points. Quesone and Charo wonder how many one-point shots and how many two-point shots Willie made. Let's listen in!

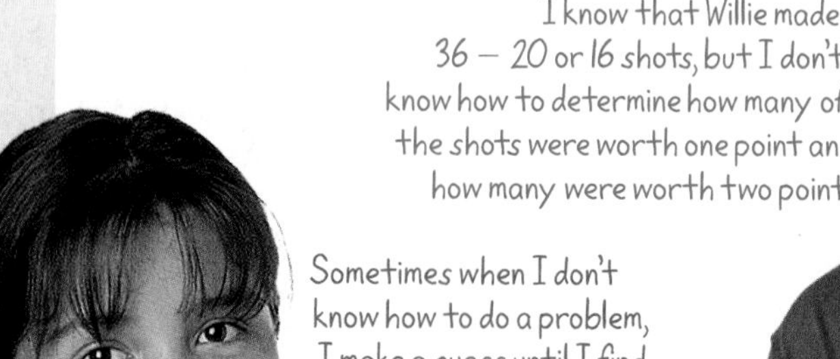

I know that Willie made 36 − 20 or 16 shots, but I don't know how to determine how many of the shots were worth one point and how many were worth two points.
Sometimes when I don't know how to do a problem, I make a guess until I find one that works.
Charo
Quesone

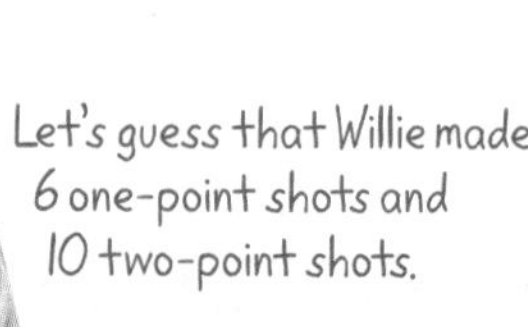

What do you mean?
Let's guess that Willie made 6 one-point shots and 10 two-point shots.

THINK ABOUT IT

Work with a partner.

1. ***Analyze*** Charo's thinking. How do you think she came up with her two numbers? Does this guess result in 30 points? If not, how should Charo adjust her guess? **See margin.**
2. ***Make*** a table to show different guesses to solve this problem. How many one-point shots and two-point shots did Willie make? **See margin.**
3. ***Apply*** the **guess and check** strategy to solve the following problem.
   The Pike's Peak souvenir shop sells standard-sized postcards in packages of 5 and large-sized postcards in packages of 3. If Iku bought 16 postcards, how many packages of each did she buy? **two 5-card packages and two 3-card packages**

Reteaching the Lesson

Activity Have students use play money to act out and solve this problem. *Together, Ray and Kate have $1.10. Kate has $0.60 more than Ray. How much money does each have?* **Ray has $0.25 and Kate has $0.85.**

For **Extra Practice,** see page 595.

ON YOUR OWN

4. The third step of the 4-step plan for problem solving tells you to *solve* the problem. ***Tell*** why, during this step in the guess and check strategy, you must keep a careful record of each of your guesses and their results.
5. ***Write a Problem*** which you could solve using the guess and check strategy.
6. ***Look Ahead*** Explain how the guess and check strategy could be used to find a number that when multiplied by itself produces a product of 256.
4–6. See margin.

MIXED PROBLEM SOLVING

STRATEGIES
Look for a pattern.
Solve a simpler problem.
Act it out.
Guess and check.
Draw a diagram.
Make a chart.
Work backward.

Solve. Use any strategy.

7. ***Number Theory*** Three consecutive integers have a sum of 12 and a product of 60. What are the integers? **3, 4 and 5**
8. ***Football*** In football, if a team makes a 6-point touchdown, it has a chance to try for either 1 or 2 extra points. If the team cannot make a touchdown, it can attempt to kick a 3-point field goal. Suppose 2-point safeties are excluded. List the number of points less than 20 that a football team can accumulate.

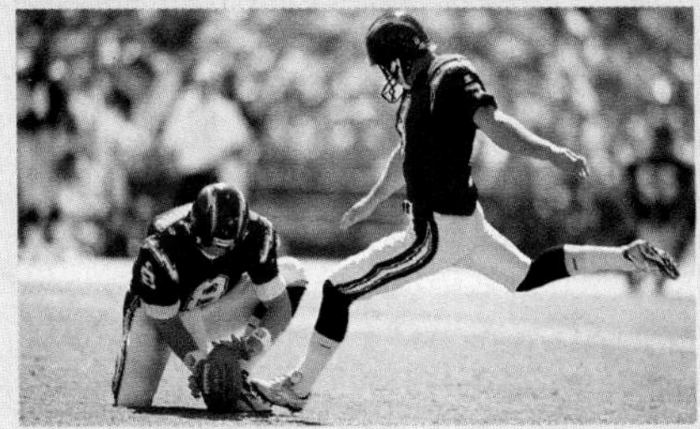

See margin.

9. ***Transportation*** Mr. Cardona has agreed to drive 4 students to the concert. If he can put one student in the front seat and three students in the back, how many ways can the 4 students be arranged in the car? **24 ways**
10. ***Ticket Sales*** Kelsey sold tickets to the school musical. She had 12 bills worth $175 for the tickets she sold. If all the money was in $5 bills, $10 bills, and $20 bills, how many of each bill did she have? **See margin.**
11. ***Geometry*** The large square below has been divided into 9 squares. The lengths of the sides of two squares are given. Find the area of the large square. **441 units^2**

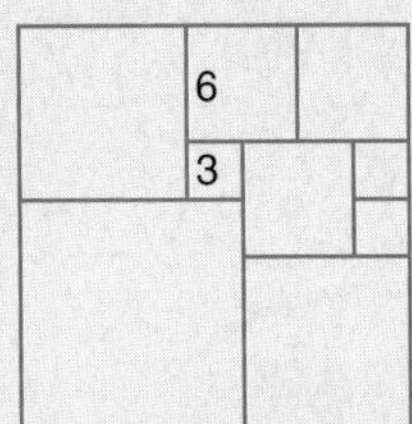

12.  ***Standardized Test Practice*** Derrick used his calculator to divide 5,762,664 by 2,113.6. Which number is a good estimate for the quotient? **C**
A 30
B 300
C 3,000
D 30,000
E 300,000

Extending the Lesson

Activity Present the following problem for students to solve by using the guess-and-check strategy.
Louise has the same number of quarters, dimes, and nickels. In all she has $4 in change. How many of each coin does she have? **10**

3 PRACTICE/APPLY

Check for Understanding

Use the results of Exercise 3 to determine how well students are able to adjust their own guesses.

Extra Practice If students need additional practice in problem solving, extra practice is available on the following pages.
- Guess and Check, see p. 595
- Mixed Problem Solving, see pp. 605–606.

Assignment Guide
All: 4–12

4 ASSESS

Closing Activity

Writing Have students write a problem for others to solve by using the guess-and-check strategy.

Additional Answers

4. You need to keep track of what numbers you have already guessed, so that you do not make the same guess twice. You also need to know what numbers produce answers that are too large or too small, so you can make better guesses.
5. Sample answer: The car wash to raise money for band uniforms charged $4 for a car and $6 for a van or truck. During the first hour, they washed 16 vehicles and earned $78. How many cars did they wash? answer: 9 cars
6. Guess a number and multiply it by itself. If the product is less than 256, choose a greater number. If the product is greater than 256, choose a lesser number. Continue this process until the product is 256. The answer is 16.
8. 3, 6, 7, 8, 9, 10, 11, 12, 13, 14, 15, 16, 17, 18, 19
10. 3 $5-bills, 2 $10-bills, and 7 $20-bills or 1 $5-bill, 5 $10-

10-1 Lesson Notes

Instructional Resources

- *Study Guide Masters,* p. 74
- *Practice Masters,* p. 74
- *Enrichment Masters,* p. 74
- Transparencies 10-1, A and B
- *Technology Masters,* p. 45

CD-ROM Program
- Resource Lesson 10-1

Recommended Pacing	
Standard	Day 3 of 14
Honors	Day 3 of 13
Block	Day 1 of 7

1 FOCUS

5-Minute Check
(Chapter 9)

1. Classify the angle as *acute, obtuse, right,* or *straight.* **acute**

2. Tell whether each pair of polygons is similar. Justify your answer.

a.

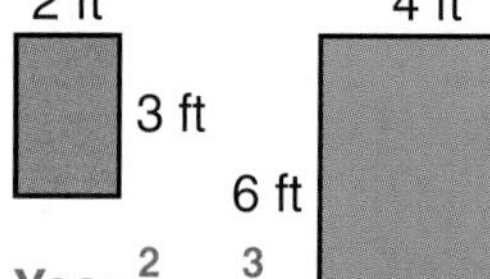

Yes; $\frac{2}{4} = \frac{3}{6}$.

b.

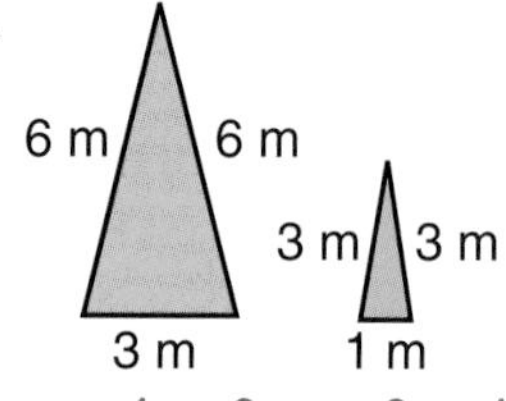

No; $\frac{1}{3} = \frac{2}{6}$ and $\frac{3}{6} = \frac{1}{2}$.

3. Classify the triangle by its angles and sides.

obtuse isosceles triangle

The 5-Minute Check is also available on **Transparency 10-1A** for this lesson.

10-1 Squares and Square Roots

What you'll learn
You'll learn to find squares of numbers and square roots of perfect squares.

When am I ever going to use this?
Knowing how to find squares of numbers can help you find the amount of floor covering needed for a square room.

Word Wise
square
perfect square
square root
radical sign

There are many rectangles that have a perimeter of 12 units. Which of these rectangles has the greatest area? One way to solve this problem is to use the guess-and-check strategy.

Work with a partner.

The following rectangle has a perimeter of 12 units and an area of 5 square units.

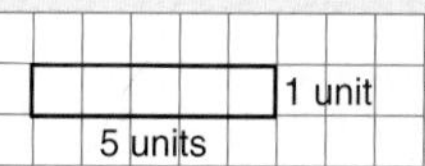

Try This

1. On grid paper, draw other rectangles that have a perimeter of 12 units.
2. Complete the following chart so that it shows all of your rectangles.

Drawing	Perimeter	Area
[rectangle]	12 units	5 square units

3. Repeat Steps 1–2 for a rectangle with a perimeter of 16 units.

Talk About It

4. For each perimeter, which rectangle has the greatest area?
5. What do you notice about the rectangles with the greatest areas?

1–3. See Answer Appendix.
4. 3 by 3 rectangle; 4 by 4 rectangle
5. They are squares.

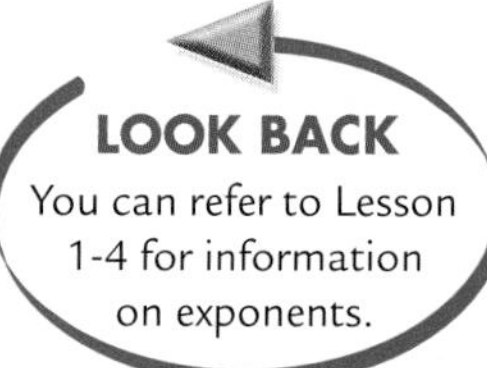

LOOK BACK
You can refer to Lesson 1-4 for information on exponents.

Consider the 6-by-6 square at the right. Its area is 6×6 or 36 square units.

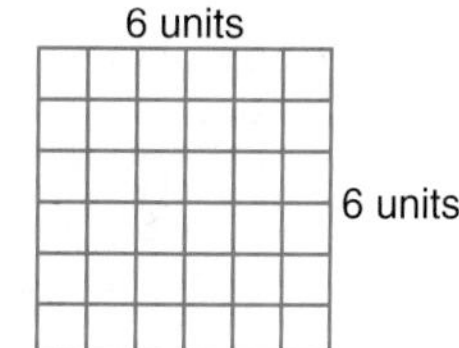

Remember that an *exponent* tells how many times a number, called the *base,* is used as a *factor.* In the expression 6×6, 6 is used as a factor twice. When you compute 6×6 or 6^2, you are finding the **square** of 6.

$$6^2 = 6 \times 6$$
$$= 36 \quad \textit{The square of 6 is 36.}$$

Examples

1. Evaluate 7^2.

$7 \times 7 = 49$

2. Evaluate 23^2.

23 [x^2] 529

Motivating the Lesson

Hands-On Activity Have students use square tiles to form squares of various sizes. Have them record the dimensions of the square and how many tiles they used. Ask students what they notice about the totals. **Total is the square of the side.**

Numbers such as 36, 49, and 529 are called **perfect squares** because they are squares of whole numbers.

The 6-by-6 square on page 410 has an area of 36 square units. One way to find the length of a side of a square with an area of 36 square units is to count the number of units on one side of the square. Another way is to find the **square root** of 36.

Square Root	If $a^2 = b$, then a is a square root of b.

Study Hint
Reading Math $\sqrt{36} = 6$ is read as the square root of 36 is 6.

Since $6^2 = 36$, one square root of 36 is 6. It is also true that $(-6)^2 = 36$, so another square root of 36 is -6. *Since the length of a side of a square with an area of 36 square units must be positive, each side of the square is 6 units long.*

The symbol $\sqrt{\ }$, called a **radical sign**, is used to represent a nonnegative square root.

$$\sqrt{36} = 6$$

Examples

3 Find $\sqrt{64}$.

Since $8^2 = 64$, $\sqrt{64} = 8$.

4 Find $\sqrt{961}$.

961 [2nd] [$\sqrt{\ }$] 31

APPLICATION

5 **Ballooning** On a clear day, the distance you can see from a location above Earth can be estimated using the formula $V = 1.22 \times \sqrt{A}$, where V is the distance in miles and A is the altitude in feet. Catalina is riding in a hot air balloon about 196 feet above the ground. She looks off to the horizon and can just see her school in the distance. About how far is she from the school?

$V = 1.22 \times \sqrt{A}$

$V = 1.22 \times \sqrt{196}$ *Replace A with 196.*

$V = 1.22 \times 14$ *196* [2nd] [$\sqrt{\ }$] *14*

$V = 17.08$

Catalina is about 17 miles from her school.

Study Hint
Technology Some calculators may have a square root key. In this case, just enter the number and press the key to find the square root.

1. The area of the square is 16 units and each side is 4 units long.

CHECK FOR UNDERSTANDING

Communicating Mathematics

Read and study the lesson to answer each question.

1. ***Tell*** why the model shows $\sqrt{16} = 4$.

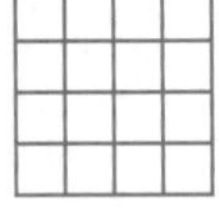

2. ***Explain*** how finding the square of a number is like finding the area of a square. **See margin.**

2 TEACH

Transparency 10-1B contains a teaching aid for this lesson.

Using the Mini-Lab Have students look for a pattern in the decreasing length of rectangles as the width increases. Point out that for every additional unit wider, a rectangle of a given perimeter becomes one unit shorter.

In-Class Examples

For Example 1
Evaluate 9^2. **81**

For Example 2
Evaluate 18^2. **324**

For Example 3
Find $\sqrt{25}$. **5**

For Example 4
Find $\sqrt{625}$. **25**

For Example 5
If Catalina's hot-air balloon rises to an altitude of 256 feet, about how far can she see? Use the formula $V = 1.22 \times \sqrt{A}$. **about 19.5 miles**

Teaching Tip In Example 5, have students interpret the formula verbally before calculating the answer. For example, "Visibility equals about one and one-fifth miles times the square root of the altitude."

3 PRACTICE/APPLY

Check for Understanding

If students need additional practice or instruction after completing Exercises 1–10, one of these options may be helpful.

- Extra Practice, see p. 595
- Reteaching Activity
- *Study Guide Masters,* p. 74
- *Practice Masters,* p. 74
- Interactive Mathematics Tools Software

Additional Answer

2. The square of a number is the product of the number times itself. The area of a square equals the length of a side times itself.

Reteaching the Lesson

Activity Have students work in pairs using base-ten blocks to form perfect squares. Ask them to start with the smallest possible square and build larger squares. Have them record the length, width, area, and perimeter of each. Ask students what areas are perfect squares. **1, 4, 9, 16, 25, 36...**

Assignment Guide

Core: 11–35 odd, 36–40
Enriched: 12–32 even, 33–40

Additional Answers

3a. 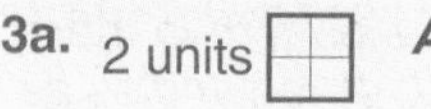

$A = 4$ units²

3b. 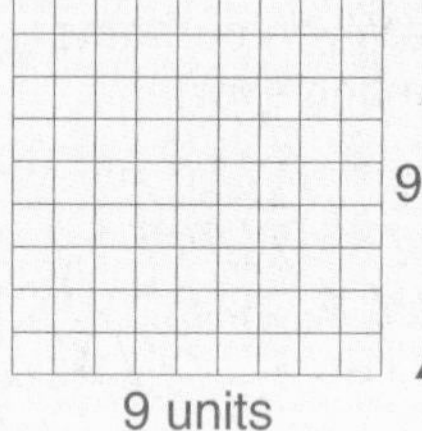

$A = 81$ units²

32a–b. 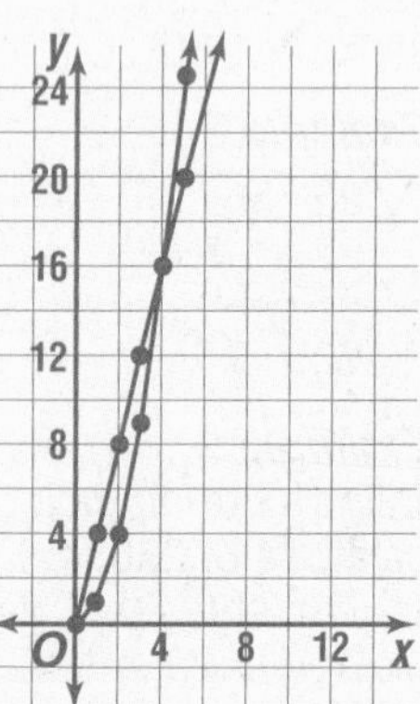

32e. The length of the sides, the area, and the perimeter cannot be negative.

***Study Guide Masters,* p. 74**

Name ____________ Date ______

10-1 Study Guide

Squares and Square Roots

When you multiply a number by itself, you are finding the square of the number.

Examples

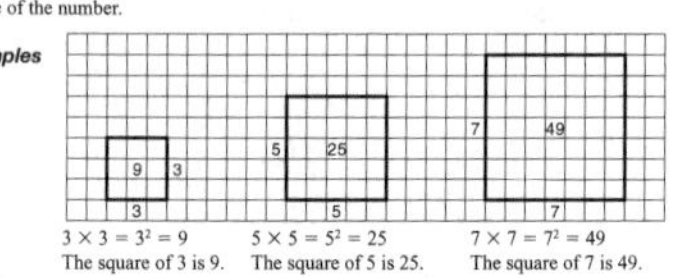

$3 \times 3 = 3^2 = 9$ The square of 3 is 9. $5 \times 5 = 5^2 = 25$ The square of 5 is 25. $7 \times 7 = 7^2 = 49$ The square of 7 is 49.

If $a^2 = b$, then a is the square root of b. The symbol, $\sqrt{\ }$ called a **radical sign,** is used to represent a nonnegative square root. Read $\sqrt{9}$ as "the square root of 9."

Examples **Find $\sqrt{9}$.** Since $3^2 = 9$, $\sqrt{9} = 3$. **Find $\sqrt{16} = 4$.** Since $4^2 = 16$, $\sqrt{16} = 4$. **Find $\sqrt{64}$.** Since $8^2 = 64$, $\sqrt{64} = 8$.

Find the square of each number.

1. 9 **81**
2. 4 **16**
3. 10 **100**
4. 8 **64**
5. 24 **576**
6. 30 **900**
7. 15 **225**
8. 40 **1,600**

Find each square root.

9. 4 **2**
10. 64 **8**
11. 16 **4**
12. 121 **11**
13. 400 **20**
14. 2,500 **50**
15. 144 **12**
16. 169 **13**
17. 1 **1**
18. 36 **6**
19. 3,600 **60**
20. 100 **10**

 T74 *Mathematics: Applications and Connections, Course 2*

HANDS-ON MATH **3.** ***Make a model*** to show each of the following.
a. $2^2 = 4$ **See margin.** **b.** $\sqrt{81} = 9$ **See margin.**

Guided Practice **Find the square of each number.**

4. 10 **100** **5.** 15 **225** **6.** 33 **1,089**

Find each square root.

7. $\sqrt{144}$ **12** **8.** $\sqrt{1{,}225}$ **35** **9.** $\sqrt{324}$ **18**

10. ***Skydiving*** Sky divers leap from airplanes at heights up to 15,000 feet and fall freely at speeds of more than 100 miles per hour. In accuracy skydiving competitions, participants try to land on a square target that may measure only 5 centimeters across. Find the area of such a target. **25 cm²**

EXERCISES

Practice **Find the square of each number.**

11. 1 **1** **12.** 13 **169** **13.** 32 **1,024** **14.** 16 **256**
15. 40 **1,600** **16.** 55 **3,025** **17.** 27 **729** **18.** 200 **40,000**

Find each square root.

19. $\sqrt{121}$ **11** **20.** $\sqrt{625}$ **25** **21.** $\sqrt{289}$ **17** **22.** $\sqrt{900}$ **30**
23. $\sqrt{1{,}089}$ **33** **24.** $\sqrt{2{,}601}$ **51** **25.** $\sqrt{576}$ **24** **26.** $\sqrt{90{,}000}$ **300**

27. What is the square of 38? **1,444**
28. Find the positive square root of 361. **19**
29. Find the length of a side of a square whose area is 484 square inches. **22 in.**
30. The area of a square is 1,024 square centimeters. Find its perimeter. **128 cm**
31. Find the greatest possible area for a rectangle whose perimeter is 96 feet. **576 ft²**
32. ***Algebra*** Use graphs to study area and perimeter.
a. Let the x-axis of a coordinate plane represent the length of a side of a square and the y-axis represent the area of the square. Graph the points that represent squares with sides 0, 1, 2, 3, 4, and 5 units long. Draw a line or curve that goes through each point. **See margin.**
b. On the same coordinate plane, let the x-axis represent the length of a side of a square and the y-axis represent the perimeter of the square. Graph the points that represent squares with sides 0, 1, 2, 3, 4, and 5 units long. Draw a line or curve that goes through each point. **See margin.**
c. Compare and contrast the two graphs.
d. When is the value of the perimeter greater than the value of the area? When are the values equal?
e. Why do these graphs only make sense in the first quadrant? **See margin.**

32c. Both graphs increase as the length of the sides increase. The graph for the area is a curve and the graph for the perimeter is a straight line.
32d. when the length of a side is greater than 0 and less than 4; when the length of a side equals 0 or 4

Cross-Curriculum Cue

Inform the other teachers on your team that your classes are studying area. Suggestions for curriculum integration are:
Art: architecture principles, sewing, quilting, framing
Social Studies: geography, urban planning
Physical Education: basketball, football
Science: physics, ecology

Applications and Problem Solving

33a. a square house that is 40 ft by 40 ft
33b. a square house that is 35 ft by 35 ft

33. ***Architecture*** Because a square house has the least outside wall space for the area, it is the most energy-efficient type of house to build. A house in the shape of an H is the least energy efficient.
   a. Describe the most energy-efficient one-story house you could build with an area of 1,600 square feet.
   b. A two-story home is more energy-efficient than a one-story home, because there is less roof space. Describe the most energy-efficient two-story house you could build with a total area of 2,450 square feet.

34. ***Sports*** A boxing ring is actually a square with an area of 400 square feet. What are the dimensions of the ring? **20 ft by 20 ft**

35. ***Landscaping*** Gro-Fast fertilizer comes in bags that cover 2,500 square feet.
   a. What are the dimensions of the largest square that could be covered by one bag of fertilizer? **50 ft by 50 ft**
   b. How many bags of fertilizer would you need to buy to cover a square whose side is 75 feet? **3 bags**

36. ***Critical Thinking*** The states of Wisconsin, Michigan, Illinois, Indiana, and Ohio made up the Northwest Territory. The Land Ordinance of 1785 divided this territory into townships. Each township was a square 6 miles on a side and was divided into 36 sections. One of these sections, the 16th, was reserved to support public schools. If a square piece of land contained 2,304 square miles, how many sections were reserved for public schools? **64 sections**

Mixed Review

37. **Standardized Test Practice** Which word, written as shown, does *not* have a vertical line of symmetry? *(Lesson 9-7)* **C**

A	B	C	D
H	M	B	W
I	O	A	H
T	T	T	O
	H		

38. ***Algebra*** Solve $\frac{3}{x} = \frac{25}{15}$. *(Lesson 8-3)* **1.8**

39. ***Algebra*** Solve the equation $d = -3 + (-2)$. *(Lesson 5-4)* **−5**

40. ***Statistics*** Refer to the graph of shoe sales. Which color of shoe would you consider to be the least popular? *(Lesson 3-2)* **red**

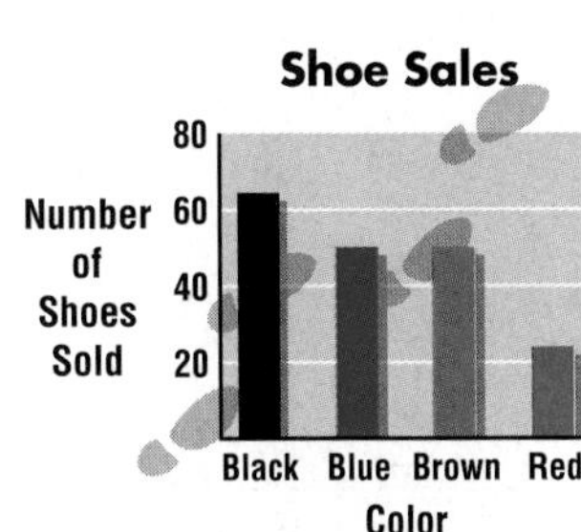

For **Extra Practice,** see page 595.

4 ASSESS

Closing Activity

Writing Have students research data on the habitat of selected animal species, such as the bald eagle, timberwolf, or manatee. Have them calculate the area of land or water needed to support an individual or small group and find the dimensions of that area.

Practice Masters, p. 74

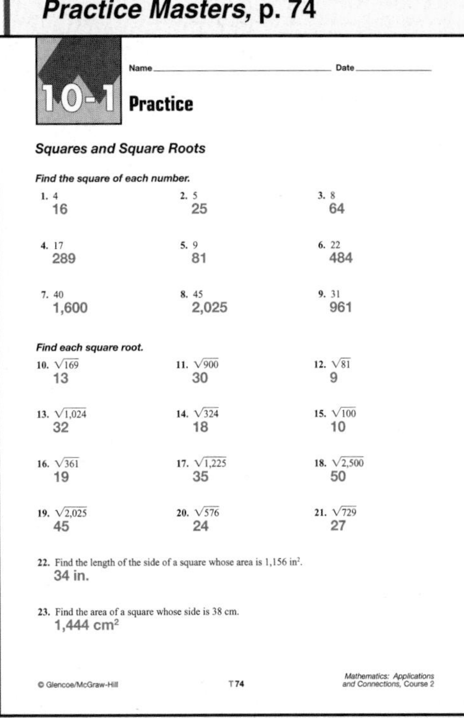

Name______ Date______

10-1 Practice

Squares and Square Roots

Find the square of each number.

1. 4 — 16	2. 5 — 25	3. 8 — 64
4. 17 — 289	5. 9 — 81	6. 22 — 484
7. 40 — 1,600	8. 45 — 2,025	9. 31 — 961

Find each square root.

10. $\sqrt{169}$ — 13	11. $\sqrt{900}$ — 30	12. $\sqrt{81}$ — 9
13. $\sqrt{1{,}024}$ — 32	14. $\sqrt{324}$ — 18	15. $\sqrt{100}$ — 10
16. $\sqrt{361}$ — 19	17. $\sqrt{1{,}225}$ — 35	18. $\sqrt{2{,}500}$ — 50
19. $\sqrt{2{,}025}$ — 45	20. $\sqrt{576}$ — 24	21. $\sqrt{729}$ — 27

22. Find the length of the side of a square whose area is 1,156 in^2. 34 in.

23. Find the area of a square whose side is 38 cm. 1,444 cm^2

© Glencoe/McGraw-Hill T74 *Mathematics: Applications and Connections, Course 2*

Extending the Lesson

Enrichment Masters, p. 74

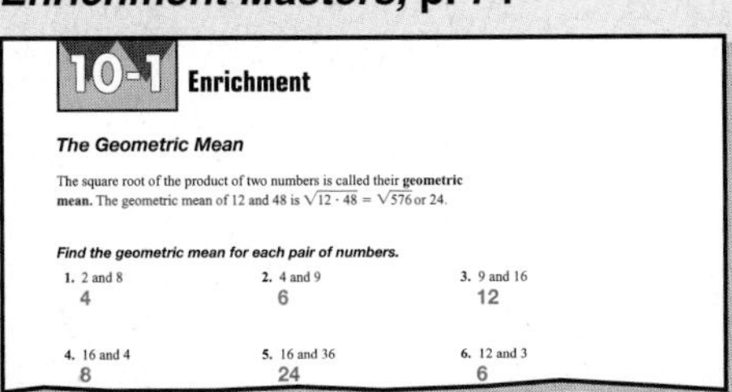

10-1 Enrichment

The Geometric Mean

The square root of the product of two numbers is called their **geometric mean.** The geometric mean of 12 and 48 is $\sqrt{12 \cdot 48} = \sqrt{576}$ or 24.

Find the geometric mean for each pair of numbers.

1. 2 and 8 — 4	2. 4 and 9 — 6	3. 9 and 16 — 12
4. 16 and 4 — 8	5. 16 and 36 — 24	6. 12 and 3 — 6

Activity Tell students that Marcia's quilt is a large square made from 100 small squares. The entire border of the quilt is blue. Ask students how many blue squares are in the border. **36**

Let the Games Begin

Encourage students to write a wide range of numbers on their tic-tac-toe boards. Using a calculator may help to speed the game along.

You may suggest that students create and play several boards "bingo-style" until a winner is found.

To save squares for future games, you can use counters to cover the numbers instead of marking them with an X. You can also place the squares in page protectors and use dry markers to draw the Xs. Then wipe clean for the next game. *Additional resources for this game can be found on pages 48–50 of the* ***Classroom Games.***

Tic Tac Root

Math Skill
Finding Square Roots

Get Ready This game is for two to four players.

 index cards

Get Set Use 20 index cards. On each card, write one of the following square roots.

$\sqrt{1}$	$\sqrt{4}$	$\sqrt{9}$	$\sqrt{16}$
$\sqrt{25}$	$\sqrt{36}$	$\sqrt{49}$	$\sqrt{64}$
$\sqrt{81}$	$\sqrt{100}$	$\sqrt{121}$	$\sqrt{144}$
$\sqrt{169}$	$\sqrt{196}$	$\sqrt{225}$	$\sqrt{256}$
$\sqrt{289}$	$\sqrt{324}$	$\sqrt{361}$	$\sqrt{400}$

Each player should draw a tic-tac-toe board on a piece of paper. In each square, place a number from 1 to 20, but do not use any number more than once. See the sample board at the right.

6	13	18
8	12	5
3	17	9

Go

- The dealer shuffles the index cards and places them facedown on the table.
- The player to the left of the dealer chooses the top index card and places it faceup. Any player with the matching square root on his or her board places an X on the appropriate square.
- The next player chooses the top index card and places it faceup on the last card chosen. Players mark their boards accordingly.
- The game continues until a player has three Xs in a row. The other players use the cards in the chosen pile to check the tic-tac-toe.
- The first player to get a correct tic-tac-toe wins the game.

Visit www.glencoe.com/sec/math/mac/mathnet for more games.

10-2 Estimating Square Roots

What you'll learn

You'll learn to estimate square roots.

When am I ever going to use this?

Knowing how to estimate square roots can help you to solve problems involving car accident investigations.

Does your family have a vegetable garden? The graph shows how the average size of family vegetable gardens decreased in one decade.

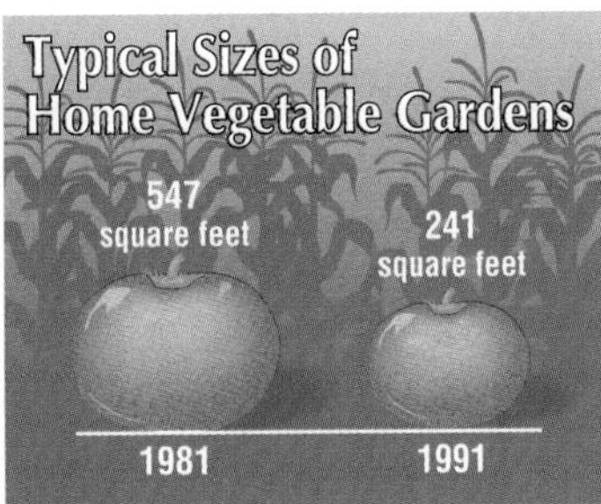

Source: National Garden Association/Gallup Inc.

Suppose a vegetable garden is planted on a square plot of ground. What is the approximate length of the side of a typical garden for 1981 and for 1991? *This problem will be solved in Exercise 29.*

You know that the square root of a perfect square, such as 25, is a whole number. You can estimate the square root when the number is not a perfect square.

MINI-LAB

Work with a partner.

 grid paper

Try This

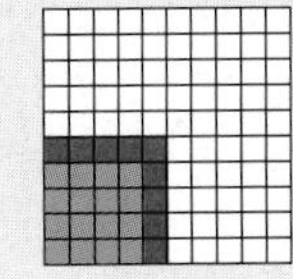

- On grid paper, draw the largest possible square using no more than 22 small squares.
- On grid paper, draw the smallest possible square using at least 22 small squares.

Talk About It **3. See margin.**

1. The value of $\sqrt{22}$ is between two consecutive whole numbers. What are these numbers? **4 and 5**
2. Which whole number would be the better estimate for $\sqrt{22}$? Why? **5; 22 is closer to 25 than 16.**
3. Explain how you could use grid paper to estimate $\sqrt{39}$.

Since 22 is not a perfect square, estimate $\sqrt{22}$ by finding the two perfect squares closest to 22. List some perfect squares.

$$1, 4, 9, \underbrace{16, 25}, 36, 49, \ldots$$

22 is between 16 and 25.

How does this method of estimating square roots compare to the one in the Mini-Lab?

$$16 < 22 < 25$$

$$\sqrt{16} < \sqrt{22} < \sqrt{25} \quad \textit{Find the square root of each number.}$$

$$4 < \sqrt{22} < 5 \quad \textit{This means that } \sqrt{22} \textit{ is between 4 and 5.}$$

So $\sqrt{22}$, is between 4 and 5. Since 22 is closer to 25 than 16, $\sqrt{22}$ is closer to 5 than to 4. The best whole number estimate for $\sqrt{22}$ is 5.

Multiple Learning Styles

Logical Ask students if they can draw a square on grid paper using exactly 22 small squares. Then ask if they can draw a square using 20, 28, 30, or other nonperfect-square numbers. Emphasize that an estimate is needed to find a whole-number square root.

Additional Answer for the Mini-Lab

3. **Draw the largest possible square using no more than 39 small squares. Draw the smallest possible square using at least 39 small squares. Since 39 is between 36 and 49, $\sqrt{39}$ is between 6 and 7. Since 39 is closer to 36 than 49,**

10-2 Lesson Notes

Instructional Resources

- *Study Guide Masters,* p. 75
- *Practice Masters,* p. 75
- *Enrichment Masters,* p. 75
- Transparencies 10-2, A and B
- *Assessment and Evaluation Masters,* p. 267

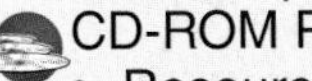

CD-ROM Program
- Resource Lesson 10-2
- Interactive Lesson 10-2

Recommended Pacing	
Standard	Day 4 of 14
Honors	Day 4 of 13
Block	Day 2 of 7

1 FOCUS

5-Minute Check
(Lesson 10-1)

Find the square of each number.

1. 12 **144** **2.** 27 **729**

Find each square root.

3. $\sqrt{256}$ **16** **4.** $\sqrt{1{,}156}$ **34**

5. Find the area of a square whose side is 18 meters. **324 m^2**

The 5-Minute Check is also available on **Transparency 10-2A** for this lesson.

Motivating the Lesson

Problem Solving Ask students to explain how they would determine the length of each side, if they had to paint a 150-square meter checkerboard in the school yard.

2 TEACH

Transparency 10-2B contains a teaching aid for this lesson.

Using the Mini-Lab Point out that except for perfect squares, all square roots are nonrepeating decimals best expressed as estimates. Use a calculator to demonstrate this by finding $\sqrt{5}$, $\sqrt{6}$, $\sqrt{8}$, and $\sqrt{10}$.

In-Class Examples

For Example 1
Estimate $\sqrt{75}$ to the nearest whole number. 9

For Example 2
Using the formula $s = \sqrt{30df}$, what was the approximate speed of a car that crashed after skidding 25 feet when f is 1.2? 30 mph

3 PRACTICE/APPLY

Check for Understanding

If students need additional practice or instruction after completing Exercises 1–10, one of these options may be helpful.

- Extra Practice, see p. 596
- Reteaching Activity
- *Study Guide Masters,* p. 75
- *Practice Masters,* p. 75

Additional Answers

1. 34 is between 25 and 36. Since 34 is closer to 36 than 25, $\sqrt{34}$ is closer to 6 than 5.

3. 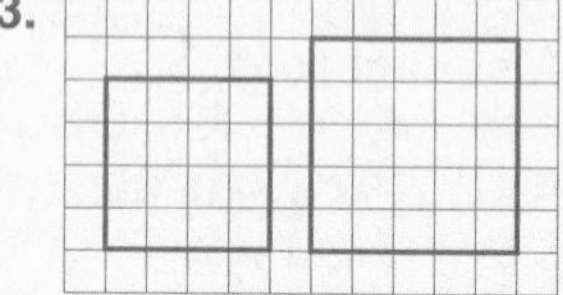

***Study Guide Masters,* p. 75**

Name__________ Date__________

Study Guide

Estimating Square Roots

Estimate to find the square root of a number that is not a perfect square.

Example **Estimate $\sqrt{95}$.**

$81 < 95 < 100$	Find the last perfect square less than 95 and the first perfect square greater than 95.
$\sqrt{81} < \sqrt{95} < \sqrt{100}$	Take the square root of each number. The square root of 95 is between the square root of 81 and the square root of 100.
$9 < \sqrt{95} < 10$	Find the square roots. The square root of 95 is between 9 and 10.

Since 95 is closer to 100 than to 81, $\sqrt{95}$ is closer to 10 than to 9.

The best whole number estimate for $\sqrt{95}$ is 10.

Estimate each square root to the nearest whole number.

1. $\sqrt{46}$ 7	2. $\sqrt{15}$ 4	3. $\sqrt{78}$ 9	4. $\sqrt{97}$ 10
5. $\sqrt{10}$ 3	6. $\sqrt{50}$ 7	7. $\sqrt{62}$ 8	8. $\sqrt{33}$ 6

Use a calculator to find each square root to the nearest tenth.

9. $\sqrt{150}$ 12.2	10. $\sqrt{391}$ 19.8	11. $\sqrt{84}$ 9.2	12. $\sqrt{5}$ 2.2
13. $\sqrt{87}$ 9.3	14. $\sqrt{200}$ 14.1	15. $\sqrt{185}$ 13.6	16. $\sqrt{787}$ 28.1

 T75 *Mathematics: Applications and Connections, Course 2*

Example 1 **Estimate $\sqrt{85}$ to the nearest whole number.**

List some perfect squares.

1, 4, 9, 16, 25, 36, 49, 64, 81, 100, ...

85 is between 81 and 100.

$81 < 85 < 100$	
$\sqrt{81} < \sqrt{85} < \sqrt{100}$	*Find the square root of each number.*
$9 < \sqrt{85} < 10$	*This means that $\sqrt{85}$ is between 9 and 10.*

Since 85 is closer to 81 than 100, the best whole number estimate is 9.

In real-life situations, calculators are used to find square roots.

Example 2 **Real World APPLICATION**

Accident Investigations **After an accident, police officers can determine the speed of a car before it skidded to a stop. They use the formula $s = \sqrt{30df}$, where s is the speed in miles per hour, d is the length of the skid marks in feet, and f is a value that depends on weather conditions. What was the approximate speed of a car if the skid marks are 90 feet long and f is 1.2?**

$s = \sqrt{30df}$	
$s = \sqrt{30 \times 90 \times 1.2}$	*Replace d with 90 and f with 1.2.*
$s = \sqrt{3{,}240}$	*3240* [2nd] [√] 56.92099788
$s \approx 56.9$	*≈ means "is approximately equal to."*

The car was traveling about 57 miles per hour.

CHECK FOR UNDERSTANDING

Communicating Mathematics

Read and study the lesson to answer each question.

1. ***Explain***, in your own words, why 6 is the best whole number estimate for $\sqrt{34}$. **See margin.**
2. ***Name*** three numbers that have square roots between 3 and 4. **Sample answer: 10, 11, 12**

HANDS-ON 

3. ***Draw*** the largest possible square using no more than 18 small squares on a piece of grid paper. Then draw the smallest possible square using at least 18 small squares. Which whole number would be the better estimate for $\sqrt{18}$? **See margin for drawing; 4.**

Guided Practice

Estimate each square root to the nearest whole number.

4. $\sqrt{10}$ **3**
5. $\sqrt{47}$ **7**
6. $\sqrt{194}$ **14**

Use a calculator to find each square root to the nearest tenth.

7. $\sqrt{15}$ **3.9**
8. $\sqrt{89}$ **9.4**
9. $\sqrt{230}$ **15.2**

■ Reteaching the Lesson ■

Activity Have students model the activity in the Mini-Lab on p. 415 using centimeter cubes. Emphasize that the sides of their squares must be equal.

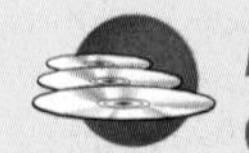

MathPASS CD-ROM

This CD-ROM offers a complete, self-paced mathematics curriculum. Each lesson includes a pretest, tutorial, guided practice, and posttest. MathPASS Lesson 34 is correlated to this Student Edition lesson.

For Windows & Macintosh

10. ***Accident Investigations*** Refer to Example 2. Estimate the speed of a car if the skid marks are 60 feet long and f is 1.4. **about 50 mph**

EXERCISES

Practice

Estimate each square root to the nearest whole number.

11. $\sqrt{8}$ **3**
12. $\sqrt{50}$ **7**
13. $\sqrt{65}$ **8**
14. $\sqrt{79}$ **9**
15. $\sqrt{140}$ **12**
16. $\sqrt{230}$ **15**
17. $\sqrt{115}$ **11**
18. $\sqrt{580}$ **24**

Use a calculator to find each square root to the nearest tenth.

19. $\sqrt{20}$ **4.5**
20. $\sqrt{55}$ **7.4**
21. $\sqrt{72}$ **8.5**
22. $\sqrt{88}$ **9.4**
23. $\sqrt{125}$ **11.2**
24. $\sqrt{99}$ **9.9**
25. $\sqrt{645}$ **25.4**
26. $\sqrt{1,380}$ **37.1**
27. Which is closer to 6, $\sqrt{34}$ or $\sqrt{44}$? **$\sqrt{34}$**
28. Which is closer to $\sqrt{55}$, 7 or 8? **7**

Applications and Problem Solving

29. ***Gardening*** Refer to the beginning of the lesson. Assume the gardens are square. **a. about 23.4 ft b. about 15.5 ft**
    a. Find the approximate length of a side of a typical vegetable garden in 1981.
    b. Find the approximate length of a side of a typical vegetable garden in 1991.
30. ***Geometry*** You can use Heron's formula to find the area of a triangle if you know the measures of its sides. If the measures of the sides are a, b, and c, the area A equals $\sqrt{s(s-a)(s-b)(s-c)}$, where s is half of the perimeter. Suppose a triangle has sides 15 meters, 20 meters, and 27 meters long.

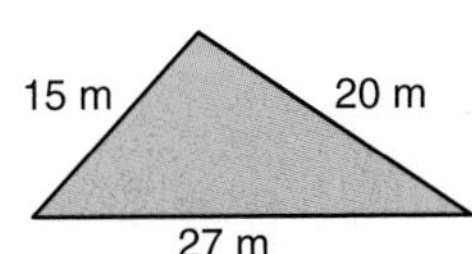

    a. What is the value of s? **31**
    b. Find the area of the triangle.

30b. about 147.7 m²

31. ***Critical Thinking*** The equation $R = \frac{s^2}{A}$ is used to design hang gliders. In this equation, R represents the aspect ratio, s the wingspan, and A the area of the wing. If R is 2.5 and A is 100 square feet, find the wingspan. **about 15.8 ft**

Mixed Review

32. 22

32. Find $\sqrt{484}$. *(Lesson 10-1)*
33. Express 35% as a fraction in simplest form. *(Lesson 8-5)* **$\frac{7}{20}$**

34. **Standardized Test Practice** The wheel on Namid's bicycle has a diameter of 11 inches. About how far does Namid travel in 150 revolutions of the wheel? Use 3.14 for π. *(Lesson 7-7)* **D**
    A 34.54 in. B 286 in. C 2,590.5 in.
    D 5,181 in. E Not Here
35. Evaluate $2(3 + 5) \div 4 - 2$. *(Lesson 1-2)* **2**

For **Extra Practice,** see page 596.

Assignment Guide

Core: 11–31 odd, 32–35
Enriched: 12–28 even, 29–35

4 ASSESS

Closing Activity

Modeling Have students draw a plan for a square community garden whose area is four times the area of the average home garden in 1991, as described at the beginning of the lesson. Ask students to label the length of the sides. **31 feet**

Chapter 10, Quiz A (Lessons 10-1 and 10-2) is available in the *Assessment and Evaluation Masters,* p. 267.

Practice Masters, p. 75

Name ____________ Date ________

10-2 Practice

Estimating Square Roots

Estimate each square root to the nearest whole number.

1. $\sqrt{13}$ 4
2. $\sqrt{27}$ 5
3. $\sqrt{60}$ 8
4. $\sqrt{84}$ 9
5. $\sqrt{101}$ 10
6. $\sqrt{72}$ 8
7. $\sqrt{97}$ 10
8. $\sqrt{47}$ 7
9. $\sqrt{35}$ 6
10. $\sqrt{58}$ 8
11. $\sqrt{145}$ 12
12. $\sqrt{10}$ 3

Use a calculator to find each square root to the nearest tenth.

13. $\sqrt{800}$ 28.3
14. $\sqrt{189}$ 13.7
15. $\sqrt{850}$ 29.2
16. $\sqrt{123}$ 11.1
17. $\sqrt{50}$ 7.1
18. $\sqrt{369}$ 19.2
19. $\sqrt{450}$ 21.2
20. $\sqrt{399}$ 20.0
21. $\sqrt{150}$ 12.2
22. $\sqrt{220}$ 14.8
23. $\sqrt{1,200}$ 34.6
24. $\sqrt{37}$ 6.1
25. $\sqrt{1,869}$ 43.2
26. $\sqrt{24}$ 4.9
27. $\sqrt{296}$ 17.2

 T75 *Mathematics: Applications and Connections, Course 2*

Extending the Lesson

Enrichment Masters, p. 75

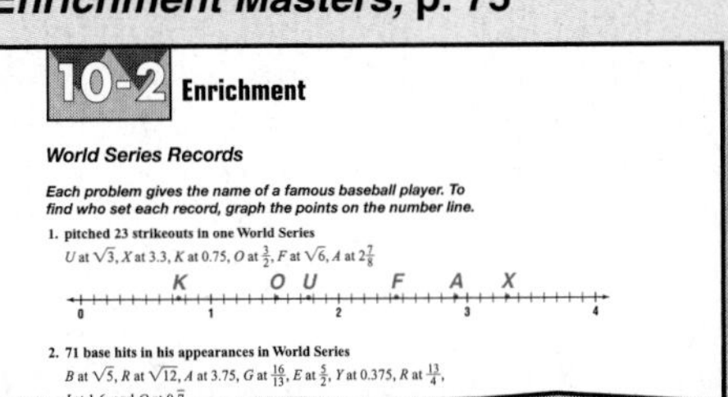

10-2 Enrichment

World Series Records

Each problem gives the name of a famous baseball player. To find who set each record, graph the points on the number line.

1. **pitched 23 strikeouts in one World Series**
   U at $\sqrt{3}$, X at 3.3, K at 0.75, O at $\frac{3}{2}$, F at $\sqrt{6}$, A at $2\frac{7}{8}$

2. **71 base hits in his appearances in World Series**
   B at $\sqrt{5}$, R at $\sqrt{12}$, A at 3.75, G at $\frac{16}{13}$, E at $\frac{5}{2}$, Y at 0.375, R at $\frac{13}{4}$,

Activity Ask students to explain how they would find the square root of a number to the nearest tenth or hundredth without using a calculator. Have them demonstrate their method.

10-3A HANDS-ON LAB Notes

GET READY

Objective Students find the relationship among the sides of a right triangle.

Optional Resources
Hands-On Lab Masters
- centimeter grid paper, p. 11
- worksheet, p. 62

Overhead Manipulative Resources
- centimeter grid transparency

Manipulative Kit
- ruler
- scissors

MANAGEMENT TIPS

Recommended Time
20 minutes

Getting Started Use a 12-foot knotted rope to show how the ancient Egyptians discovered the 3-4-5 right triangle. Have three students hold the knotted rope while standing at the angles and observe the length of the sides.

The **Activity** shows students how the squares of the measures of the legs of a right triangle compare to the square of the measure of the hypotenuse. Ask students how the areas of the three squares will compare, then have them find the areas.

ASSESS

Have students complete Exercises 1–4. Make it clear that other right triangles need not have side measures that are proportional to the 3-4-5 triangle for the Pythagorean Theorem to hold true.

Have students write a paragraph explaining why an equilateral triangle cannot be a right triangle.

HANDS-ON LAB

COOPERATIVE LEARNING

10-3A The Pythagorean Theorem

centimeter grid paper

ruler

scissors

A Preview of Lesson 10-3

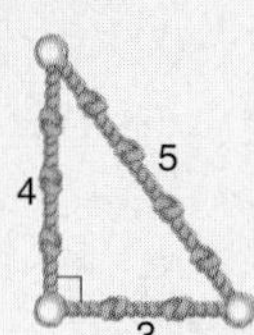

The ancient Egyptians used mathematics to lay out their fields with square corners. About 2000 B.C., they discovered a 3-4-5 right triangle. They took a piece of rope and knotted it into 12 equal spaces. Taking three stakes, they stretched the rope around the stakes to form a right triangle. The sides of the triangle had lengths of 3, 4, and 5 units.

In this lab, you will investigate the relationship that exists among the sides of a right triangle.

TRY THIS

Work with a partner.

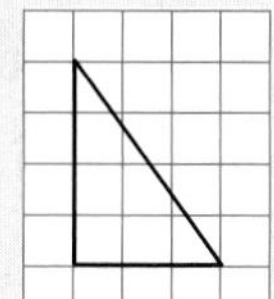

Step 1 On grid paper, draw a segment that is 3 centimeters long. At one end of this segment, draw a perpendicular segment that is 4 centimeters long. Draw a third segment to form a triangle. Cut out the triangle.

Step 2 Measure the length of the longest side in centimeters.

Step 3 Cut out three squares: one with 3 centimeters on a side, one with 4 centimeters on a side, and one with 5 centimeters on a side.

Step 4 Place the edges of the squares against the corresponding sides of the right triangle.

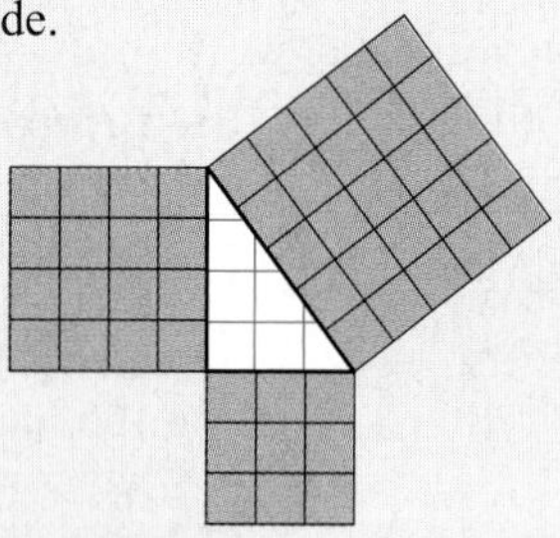

Step 5 Find the area of each square.

ON YOUR OWN

1. What relationship exists among the areas of the three squares? **1–3. See margin.**
2. Do you think the relationship you described in Exercise 1 is true for any right triangle? Repeat the activity for each right triangle whose perpendicular sides have the following measures.
   a. 6 centimeters, 8 centimeters **b.** 5 centimeters, 12 centimeters
3. ***Write*** one or more sentences that summarize your findings.
4. ***Look Ahead*** Suppose the perpendicular sides of a right triangle are 9 inches and 12 inches long. Find the length of the other side. **15 in.**

Additional Answers

1. The sum of the area of the two smaller squares equals the area of the largest square.
2. yes

2a. See students' work.
$36 \text{ cm}^2 + 64 \text{ cm}^2 = 100 \text{ cm}^2$

2b. See students' work.
$25 \text{ cm}^2 + 144 \text{ cm}^2 = 169 \text{ cm}^2$

3. The sum of the squares of the lengths of the perpendicular sides of a right triangle equals the square of the length of the side opposite the right angle.

10-3 The Pythagorean Theorem

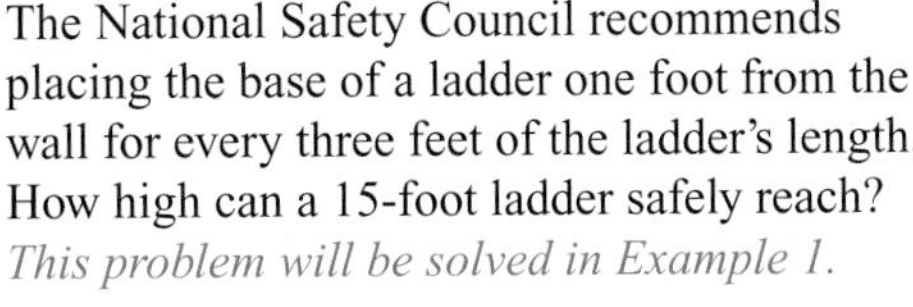

What you'll learn
You'll learn to find length using the Pythagorean Theorem.

When am I ever going to use this?
Knowing how to use the Pythagorean Theorem can help you find lengths of sides of right triangles.

Word Wise
hypotenuse
leg
Pythagorean Theorem

The National Safety Council recommends placing the base of a ladder one foot from the wall for every three feet of the ladder's length. How high can a 15-foot ladder safely reach? *This problem will be solved in Example 1.*

Look at the diagram of the ladder. A right triangle is formed. The longest side of a right triangle is called the **hypotenuse**. It is opposite the right angle. The other two sides, called **legs**, form the right angle.

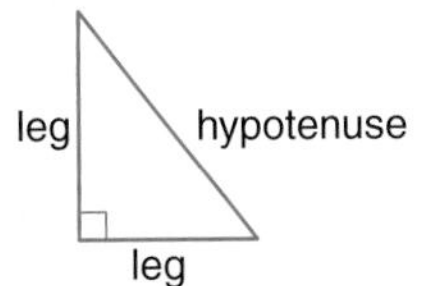

About 2,500 years ago, a Greek mathematician, Pythagoras, formalized a relationship among the sides of any right triangle. It has become known as the **Pythagorean Theorem**.

Pythagoras

Pythagorean Theorem

Words: In a right triangle, the sum of the squares of the lengths of the legs (a and b) is equal to the square of the length of the hypotenuse (c).

Symbols:
Arithmetic $3^2 + 4^2 = 5^2$
Algebra $a^2 + b^2 = c^2$

Model:

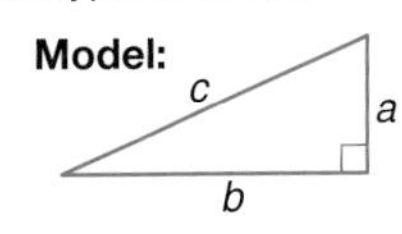

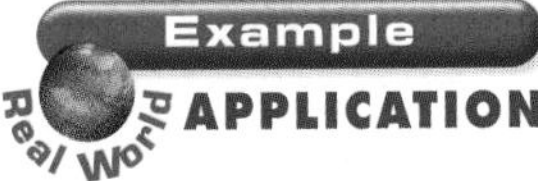

1 **Safety** Refer to the beginning of the lesson. How high can a 15-foot ladder safely reach?

Explore You know that the National Safety Council recommends the base of a ladder be placed one foot from the wall for every three feet of the ladder's length. You also know the ladder is 15 feet long. You need to know how high the ladder can safely reach.

Plan The base of the ladder should be placed 15 ÷ 3 or 5 feet from the wall. Use the Pythagorean Theorem to find how high the ladder can reach.

15 ft
?
5 ft

(continued on the next page)

10-3 Lesson Notes

Instructional Resources

- *Study Guide Masters,* p. 76
- *Practice Masters,* p. 76
- *Enrichment Masters,* p. 76
- Transparencies 10-3, A and B
- *Diversity Masters,* p. 23
- *Technology Masters,* p. 46
- CD-ROM Program
  - Resource Lesson 10-3
  - Interactive Lesson 10-3

Recommended Pacing	
Standard	Days 5 & 6 of 14
Honors	Days 5 & 6 of 13
Block	Day 3 of 7

1 FOCUS

5-Minute Check
(Lesson 10-2)

Estimate each square root to the nearest whole number.

1. $\sqrt{14}$ 4 **2.** $\sqrt{35}$ 6

Use a calculator to find each square root to the nearest tenth.

3. $\sqrt{118}$ 10.9 **4.** $\sqrt{395}$ 19.9

5. Which is closer to 5, $\sqrt{23}$ or $\sqrt{32}$? $\sqrt{23}$

The 5-Minute Check is also available on **Transparency 10-3A** for this lesson.

Motivating the Lesson

Communication Ask students to explain what guidelines they would use to design a ramp to improve wheelchair access to a building entrance that is 18 inches above ground level. Inform them of regulations that say the ramp must be a little over 1 foot long for every inch of height.

Multiple Learning Styles

Kinesthetic Have students work in pairs to calculate the length of a "human hypotenuse." Have one student stand an arm's length from a wall and lean forward until his or her arms reach as high on the wall as possible. The other student marks the spot lightly in pencil, measures its height, and measures the distance from the wall to their partner's heels. Students then use the Pythagorean Theorem to calculate the length of the "human hypotenuse."

2 TEACH

Transparency 10-3B contains a teaching aid for this lesson.

Thinking Algebraically Have students use what they know about equations to rewrite the formula for finding the square of the hypotenuse so that it can be used to find the square of either leg. $c^2 - b^2 = a^2$ or $c^2 - a^2 = b^2$

In-Class Examples

For Example 1
Alma's desk faces a corner of her rectangular room. If the desk is 51 inches long and one side is about 36 inches from the corner, how far is the other side of the desk from the corner? about 36 in.

Given the lengths of the sides of a triangle, determine whether each triangle is a right triangle.

For Example 2
8 inches, 13 inches, 16 inches no

For Example 3
30 meters, 40 meters, 50 meters yes

Teaching Tip In Example 3, have students draw the triangle described to show it is not a right triangle.

3 PRACTICE/APPLY

Check for Understanding

If students need additional practice or instruction after completing Exercises 1–10, one of these options may be helpful.

- Extra Practice, see p. 596
- Reteaching Activity
- *Study Guide Masters,* p. 76
- *Practice Masters,* p. 76

Study Hint
Estimation
$196 < 200 < 225$
$14 < \sqrt{200} < 15$

Solve

$a^2 + b^2 = c^2$ *Pythagorean Theorem*
$5^2 + b^2 = 15^2$ *Replace a with 5 and c with 15.*
$25 + b^2 = 225$
$25 - 25 + b^2 = 225 - 25$ *Subtract 25 from each side.*
$b^2 = 200$
$b = \sqrt{200}$ *Definition of square root*
$b \approx 14.14$ 200 [2nd] [√] 14.14213562

The ladder can safely reach 14.14 feet above the ground.

Examine Use the Pythagorean Theorem to check the answer.

$a^2 + b^2 = c^2$ *a = 5, b ≈ 14.14, c = 15*
$5^2 + 14.14^2 \stackrel{?}{=} 15^2$
$25 + 199.9396 \stackrel{?}{=} 225$
$224.9396 \approx 225$ ✓

You can also use the Pythagorean Theorem to determine whether a triangle is a right triangle.

Examples

Given the lengths of the sides of a triangle, determine whether each triangle is a right triangle.

Remember the hypotenuse is always the longest side.

2 **0.7 meters, 2.4 meters, 2.5 meters**

$a^2 + b^2 = c^2$
$0.7^2 + 2.4^2 \stackrel{?}{=} 2.5^2$
$0.49 + 5.76 \stackrel{?}{=} 6.25$
$6.25 = 6.25$ ✓

It is a right triangle.

3 **9 inches, 15 inches, 18 inches**

$a^2 + b^2 = c^2$
$9^2 + 15^2 \stackrel{?}{=} 18^2$
$81 + 225 \stackrel{?}{=} 324$
$306 \neq 324$

It is *not* a right triangle.

2. Square the lengths of the two legs and find the sum of the resulting numbers. The square root of the sum is the length of the hypotenuse.

CHECK FOR UNDERSTANDING

Communicating Mathematics

Read and study the lesson to answer each question. 1. $4^2 + 3^2 = 5^2$

1. ***Write*** an equation that describes the relationship among the three large squares in the figure.
2. ***Describe*** how you would use the Pythagorean Theorem to find the length of the hypotenuse of a right triangle when you are given the lengths of its two legs.

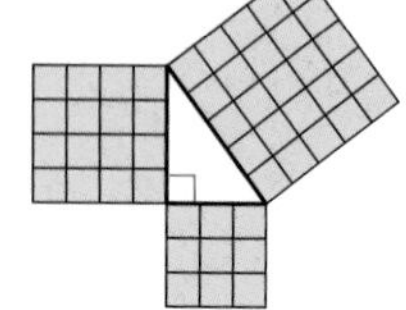

Reteaching the Lesson

Activity Have students use centimeter graph paper to draw one of the triangles in the Guided Practice Exercises. Have them work through the equation step by step with a partner, and then check their results by actually measuring with a centimeter ruler.

Error Analysis
Watch for students who neglect to find the square root of the length of the leg or hypotenuse.
Prevent by encouraging students to estimate the answer first and to compare their answers to their estimate.

3. Ricardo; the length of the hypotenuse is 8 m, so the sum of the squares of the other two sides equals 8^2.

3. ***You Decide*** Ms. Egan asked two students from her class to come to the board and write an equation that can be used to find x in the triangle. Who wrote the correct answer? Explain your reasoning.

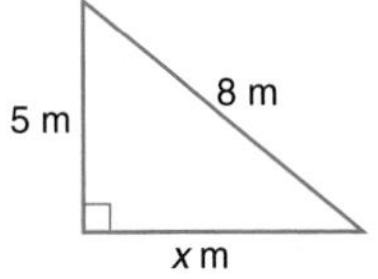

Brian	**Ricardo**
$5^2 + 8^2 = x^2$	$5^2 + x^2 = 8^2$

Guided Practice

Find the missing measure for each right triangle. Round to the nearest tenth.

4. a: 2 ft; b: 5 ft **5.4 ft**
5. a: 13 cm; c: 27 cm **23.7 cm**

Write an equation to solve for x. Then solve. Round to the nearest tenth.

6. 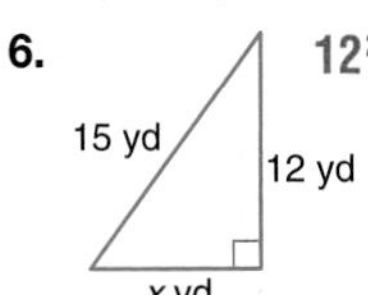

$12^2 + x^2 = 15^2$; 9 yd

7. 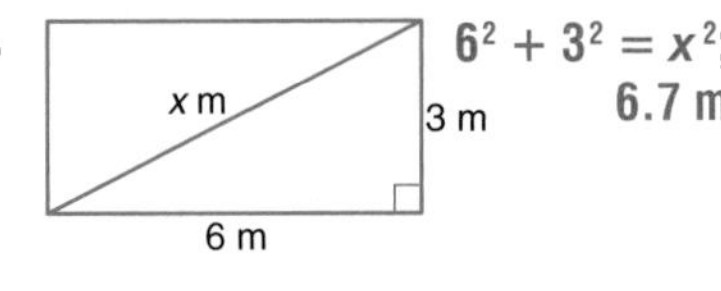

$6^2 + 3^2 = x^2$; 6.7 m

Given the lengths of the sides of a triangle, determine whether each triangle is a right triangle. Write *yes* or *no*.

8. 2 m, 3 m, 4 m **no**
9. 7 ft, 24 ft, 25 ft **yes**

10. ***Technology*** The sizes of television and computer monitors are given in inches. However, these dimensions are actually the diagonal measures of the rectangular screens. Suppose a 14-inch computer monitor has an actual screen length of 11 inches. What is the height of the screen? **about 8.7 in.**

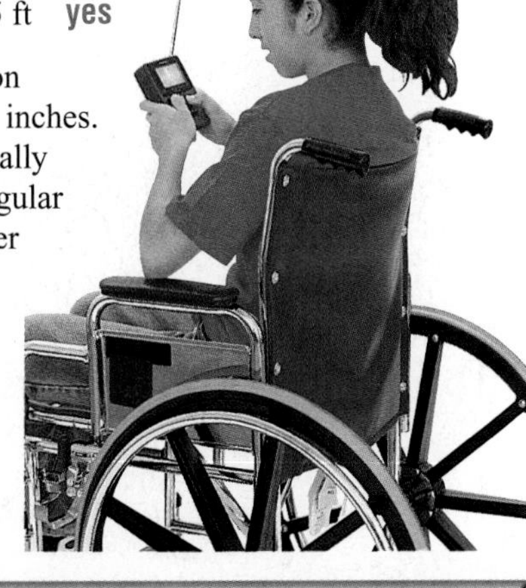

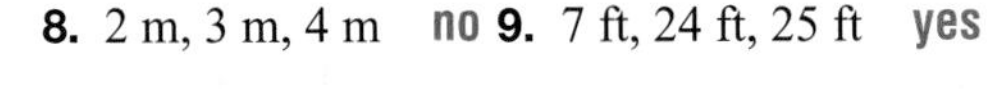

Practice

Find the missing measure for each right triangle. Round to the nearest tenth.

11. a: 13 mm; b: 9 mm **15.8 mm**
12. a: 14 ft; b: 8 ft **16.1 ft**
13. a: 8.2 m; b: 15.6 m **17.6 m**
14. a: 5 cm; c: 13 cm **12 cm**
15. b: 24 m; c: 25 m **7 m**
16. a: 8 in.; c: 14 in. **11.5 in.**

Write an equation to solve for x. Then solve. Round to the nearest tenth.

17. 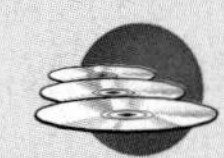

18. 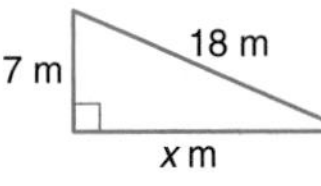

19. 7 m, 18 m, x m

17. $12^2 + 5^2 = x^2$; 13 cm
18. $10^2 + x^2 = 25^2$; 22.9 ft
19. $7^2 + x^2 = 18^2$; 16.6 m

Assignment Guide

Core: 11–31 odd, 32–35
Enriched: 12–28 even, 29–35

Study Guide Masters, p. 76

Name__________ Date________

Study Guide

The Pythagorean Theorem

The longest side of a right triangle is the **hypotenuse.** The hypotenuse is the side opposite the right angle. The other two sides of the triangle are the **legs.**

The **Pythagorean Theorem** relates the lengths of the sides of a right triangle.

For any right triangle, the sum of the squares of the lengths of the legs (a and b) is equal to the square of the length of the hypotenuse (c).

hypotenuse, a, c, legs, b: $a^2 + b^2 = c^2$

You can use the Pythagorean Theorem to find the length of a side of a right triangle if the lengths of the other two sides are known.

Example **Find the length of the leg.**

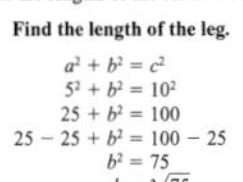

$$a^2 + b^2 = c^2$$
$$5^2 + b^2 = 10^2$$
$$25 + b^2 = 100$$
$$25 - 25 + b^2 = 100 - 25$$
$$b^2 = 75$$
$$b = \sqrt{75}$$
$$b \approx 8.660254038$$

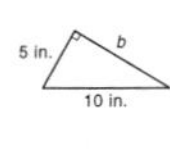

The length of the leg (to the nearest tenth of an inch) is 8.7 in.

If the lengths of the sides of a right triangle can be substituted into the Pythagorean Theorem so that $a^2 + b^2 = c^2$, then the triangle is a right triangle.

Find the missing measure for each right triangle. Round to the nearest tenth.

1. a: 8 m; b: 15 m **17 m**
2. a: 6 ft; b: 9 ft **10.8 ft**
3. a: 10 km; c: 26 km **24 km**
4. b: 7 yd; c: 12 yd **9.7 yd**
5. a: 7 in.; b: 10 in. **12.2 in.**
6. a: 9 yd; b: 40 yd **41 yd**
7. a: 12 cm; c: 20 cm **16 cm**
8. b: 5 ft; c: 9 ft **7.5 ft**

Given the lengths of the sides of a triangle, determine whether each triangle is a right triangle. Write yes or no.

9. 20 in., 21 in., 29 in. **yes**
10. 8 ft, 11 ft, 13 ft **no**
11. 7 yd, 24 yd, 25 yd **yes**
12. 7 cm, 9 cm, 12 cm **no**

 T76 *Mathematics: Applications and Connections, Course 2*

Investigations for the Special Education Student

This blackline master booklet helps you plan for the needs of your special education students by providing long-term projects along with teacher notes, Investigation 12, *Yard Sale,* may be used with this chapter.

MathPASS CD-ROM

This CD-ROM offers a complete, self-paced mathematics curriculum. Each lesson includes a pretest, tutorial, guided practice, and posttest. MathPASS Lesson 35 is correlated to this Student Edition lesson.
For Windows & Macintosh

4 ASSESS

Closing Activity

Writing Have students draw a right triangle and label two of its sides with dimensions. Ask students to exchange drawings and use the Pythagorean Theorem to find the length of the third side.

20. $25^2 + 25^2 = x^2$; 35.4 mm

21. $13^2 + x^2 = 18^2$; 12.4 in.

Write an equation to solve for *x*. Then solve. Round to the nearest tenth.

20. 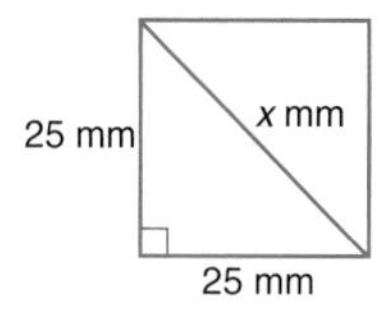

21. 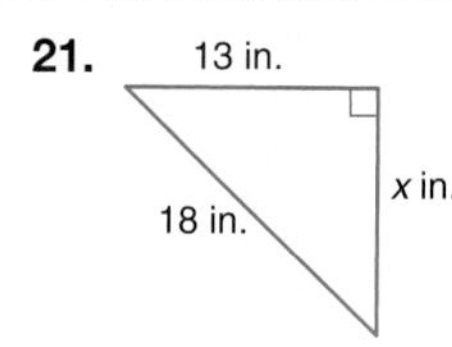

22. 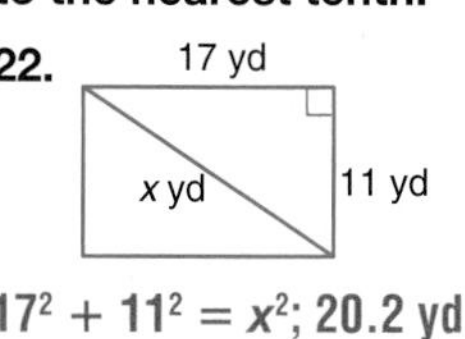

$17^2 + 11^2 = x^2$; 20.2 yd

Given the lengths of the sides of a triangle, determine whether each triangle is a right triangle. Write *yes* or *no*.

23. 8 in., 11 in., 19 in. **no**
24. 9 cm, 40 cm, 41 cm **yes**
25. 30 yd, 40 yd, 50 yd **yes**
26. 5 ft, 7 ft, 9 ft **no**
27. The lengths of the sides of a triangle are 9 meters, 12 meters, and 15 meters. Is the triangle a right triangle? **yes**
28. A rectangle is 13 centimeters by 8 centimeters. Find the length of one of its diagonals to the nearest tenth of a centimeter. **15.3 cm**

Applications and Problem Solving

29. ***Forestry*** A tree was hit by lightning during a storm. The part of the tree still standing is 3 meters tall. The top of the tree is now resting 8 meters from the base of the tree. Assume the ground is level. How tall was the tree before it was hit by lightning? **about 11.5 m**

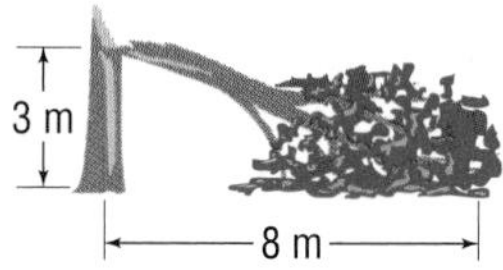

30. ***Sports*** A diamond used for baseball or softball is actually a square. The distance between bases on a major league field is 90 feet. If the catcher has to throw the ball to second base in an attempt to throw out a runner trying to steal the base, how long is the throw? **about 127.3 ft**

31. ***Critical Thinking*** Find the length of the diagonal of the cube. **about 8.7 ft**

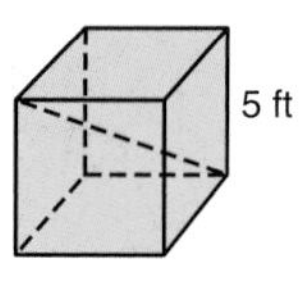

Mixed Review

32. Which is closer to $\sqrt{45}$, 6, or 7? *(Lesson 10-2)* **7**
33. **Standardized Test Practice** Is an angle that measures 87° *acute*, *obtuse*, *right*, or *straight*? *(Lesson 9-1)* **A**

    A acute **B** obtuse
    C right **D** straight

34. ***Carpentry*** The deck on a house is $25\frac{3}{4}$ feet long and $12\frac{1}{2}$ feet wide. One length of the deck is against the house. How many feet of wood does Jack need to buy to build a railing around the deck? *(Lesson 7-6)* **$50\frac{3}{4}$ ft**
35. Write the prime factorization for 36. *(Lesson 4-2)* **$2^2 \cdot 3^2$**

For **Extra Practice,** see page 596.

Practice Masters, p. 76

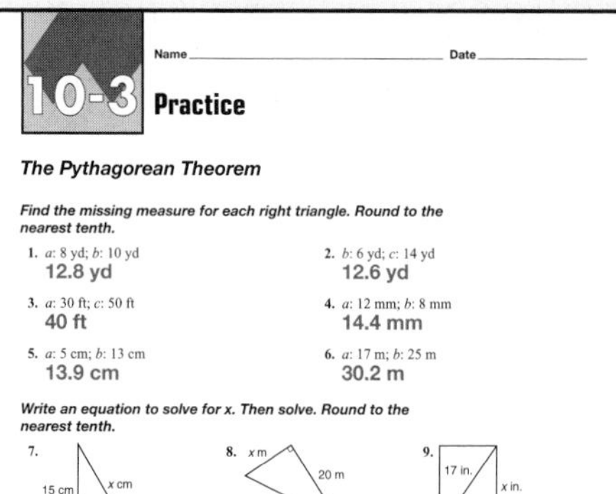

Name__________ Date__________

10-3 Practice

The Pythagorean Theorem

Find the missing measure for each right triangle. Round to the nearest tenth.

1. *a*: 8 yd; *b*: 10 yd **12.8 yd**
2. *b*: 6 yd; *c*: 14 yd **12.6 yd**
3. *a*: 30 ft; *c*: 50 ft **40 ft**
4. *a*: 12 mm; *b*: 8 mm **14.4 mm**
5. *a*: 5 cm; *b*: 13 cm **13.9 cm**
6. *a*: 17 m; *b*: 25 m **30.2 m**

Write an equation to solve for x. Then solve. Round to the nearest tenth.

7. (15 cm, 9 cm, x cm) $15^2 + 9^2 = x^2$; 17.5 cm
8. (x m, 20 m, 24 m) $x^2 + 20^2 = 24^2$; 13.3 m
9. (17 in., 10 in., x in.) $x^2 + 10^2 = 17^2$; 13.7 in.
10. (9 cm, 40 cm, x cm) $9^2 + 40^2 = x^2$; 41 cm
11. (12 cm, 16 cm, x cm) $12^2 + 16^2 = x^2$; 20 cm
12. (20 yd, 48 yd, x yd) $20^2 + 48^2 = x^2$; 52 yd

Given the lengths of the sides of a triangle, determine whether each triangle is a right triangle. Write yes or no.

13. 6 ft, 8 ft, 9 ft **no**
14. 24 m, 32 m, 40 m **yes**
15. 9 cm, 39 cm, 41 cm **no**

 T76 *Mathematics: Applications and Connections,* Course 2

Extending the Lesson

Enrichment Masters, p. 76

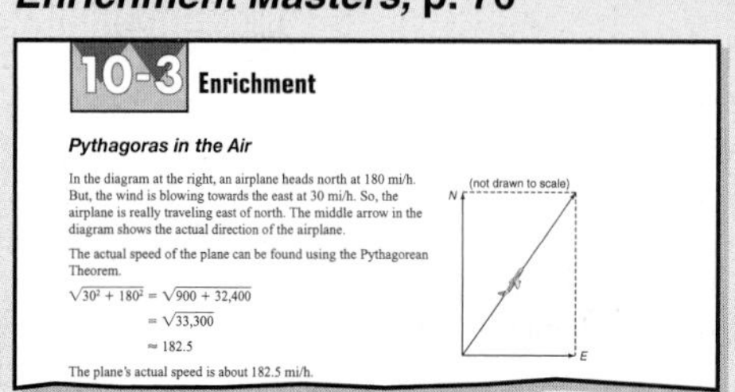

10-3 Enrichment

Pythagoras in the Air

In the diagram at the right, an airplane heads north at 180 mi/h. But, the wind is blowing towards the east at 30 mi/h. So, the airplane is really traveling east of north. The middle arrow in the diagram shows the actual direction of the airplane.

The actual speed of the plane can be found using the Pythagorean Theorem.

$$\sqrt{30^2 + 180^2} = \sqrt{900 + 32{,}400}$$
$$= \sqrt{33{,}300}$$
$$\approx 182.5$$

The plane's actual speed is about 182.5 mi/h.

Activity Tell students that Pythagorean triples are sets of three whole numbers, *a*, *b*, and *c*, for which $a^2 + b^2 = c^2$. Have them list as many as they can.

10-4 Area of Irregular Figures

What you'll learn You'll learn to estimate the area of irregular figures.

When am I ever going to use this? Knowing how to estimate the area of irregular figures can help you estimate the area of states.

Word Wise
irregular figure
inner measure
outer measure

You can find the area of a rectangle by multiplying its length by its width. Finding the area of an **irregular figure** is more difficult. Irregular figures do not necessarily have straight sides and square corners.

MINI-LAB

Work with a partner.  centimeter grid paper

Try This

Draw an outline of your foot on a piece of grid paper. If necessary, tape two pieces of grid paper together.

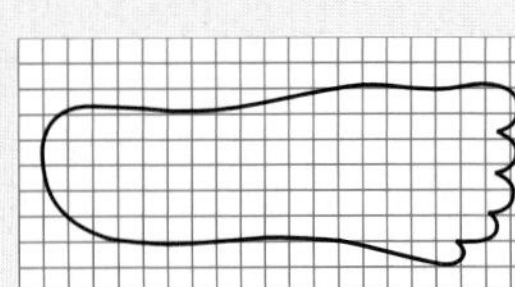

Talk About It

1. Find the number of whole squares within the outline of your foot. **1–3. See students' work.**
2. Find the number of whole squares within and containing part of the outline of your foot.
3. Estimate the area of your foot by finding the mean of the two numbers.
4. Describe another way you can estimate the area of the outline of your foot.

4. Sample answer: Count each square that is more than $\frac{3}{4}$ inside the outline as one. Count each square that is between $\frac{1}{4}$ and $\frac{3}{4}$ inside the outline as $\frac{1}{2}$. Do not count any square that is less than $\frac{1}{4}$ inside the outline. Find the total number of squares counted.

In the Mini-Lab, you estimated the area of an irregular figure by finding the mean of the **inner measure** and the **outer measure**. Inner measure is the number of whole squares within the figure. Outer measure is the number of squares within and containing part of the figure.

1 Skateboarding
Estimate the area of the skateboard.

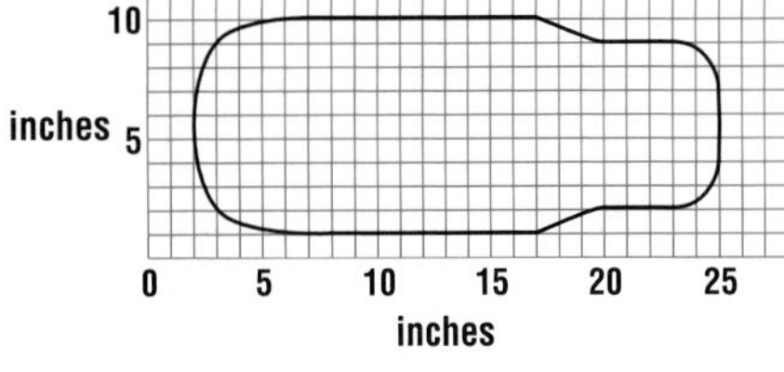

inner measure: 171 in^2

outer measure: 195 in^2

mean: $\frac{171 + 195}{2} = 183$

An estimate of the area of the skateboard is 183 square inches.

You may be able to divide some irregular figures into shapes that look like squares and rectangles. Then you can add the areas of those figures to estimate the area of the irregular figure.

10-4 Lesson Notes

Instructional Resources

- *Study Guide Masters,* p. 77
- *Practice Masters,* p. 77
- *Enrichment Masters,* p. 77
- Transparencies 10-4, A and B
- *Assessment and Evaluation Masters,* pp. 266, 267

 CD-ROM Program
- Resource Lesson 10-4

Recommended Pacing	
Standard	Day 7 of 14
Honors	Day 6 of 13
Block	Day 4 of 7

5-Minute Check
(Lesson 10-3)

Find the missing measure for each right triangle. Round to the nearest tenth.

1. *a*: 8 cm; *b*: 10 cm **12.8 cm**
2. *b*: 5 yd; *c*: 8 yd **6.2 yd**
3. *a*: 12 m; *c*: 20 m **16 m**
4. Given the following lengths, determine whether the triangle is a right triangle. 3 m, 8 m, 10 m **no**
5. A 12-foot ladder reaches a point on a wall that is 9 feet above the ground. How far from the wall is the base of the ladder? **about 8 feet**

 The 5-Minute Check is also available on **Transparency 10-4A** for this lesson.

Motivating the Lesson

Problem Solving Draw a curved figure, such as an oval running track or soccer stadium, on the chalkboard. Ask students to work in small groups to come up with a way to estimate the area of the figure. Have the class discuss the methods they have chosen and uses for knowing how to measure the area of irregular shapes.

Classroom Vignette

"I have students trace their hands on square centimeter paper and find the area of their handprints. That area represents about 1% of the skin on your body—a fact that burn units in the hospitals use all the time."

Kathy Kunkel

Kathy Kunkel, Teacher
Hastings Middle School
Hastings, MN

2 TEACH

Transparency 10-4B contains a teaching aid for this lesson.

Using the Mini-Lab Have students tell whether they think finding the mean of the inner and outer measures works for estimating the area of irregular figures. Encourage them to explore different methods or combinations of methods for making closer estimates.

Teaching Tip In Example 1, remind students that the outer measure includes the inner measure, as well as the squares around the edge.

In-Class Examples

For Example 1
Estimate the area of a boomerang. **Sample answer: 39 in^2**

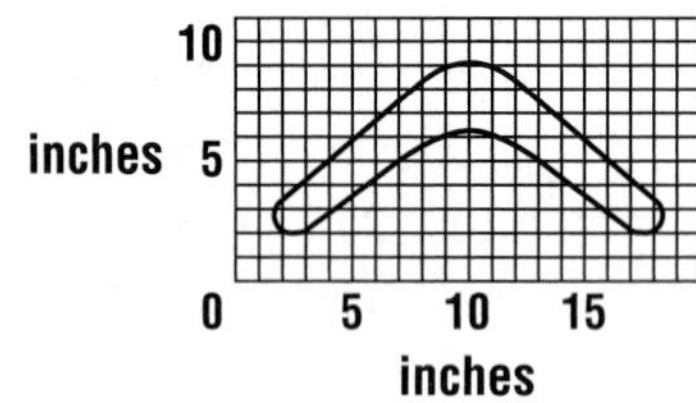

For Example 2
Find the area of the shaded region in the figure. **Sample answer: 44 units^2**

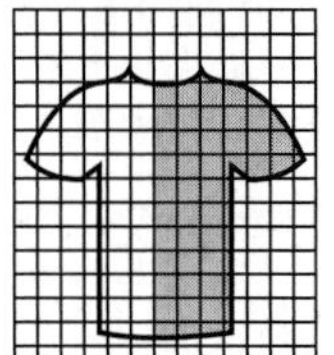

3 PRACTICE/APPLY

Check for Understanding

If students need additional practice or instruction after completing Exercises 1–6, one of these options may be helpful.

- Extra Practice, see p. 596
- Reteaching Activity, see p. 425
- *Study Guide Masters,* p. 77
- *Practice Masters,* p. 77
- Interactive Mathematics Tools Software

Example 2 Find the area of the shaded region in the figure.

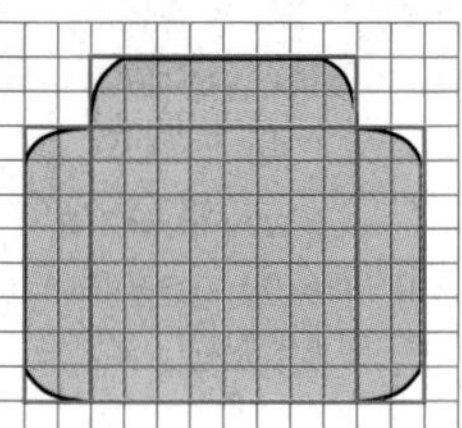

Method 1 Inner/Outer Measures

inner measure: 100 units^2
outer measure: 112 units^2
mean: $\frac{100 + 112}{2} = 106$

Method 2 Add the areas of the rectangles.

The irregular figure is made up of a square and three figures that look like rectangles.

square: $8 \times 8 = 64$
3 rectangles: $3(2 \times 8) = 48$

The area of the figure outlined in red is 64 + 48 or 112 square units. Since the shaded region is less than the figure outlined in red, the area of the shaded region is a little less than 112 square units.

The area of the shaded area is about 106 square units.

CHECK FOR UNDERSTANDING

Communicating Mathematics

Read and study the lesson to answer each question. **1–2. See margin.**

1. ***Tell*** why the area of some figures cannot be determined by using a formula.
2. ***Compare and contrast*** two methods to estimate the area of an irregular figure.

3. ***Draw*** an outline of a glove or mitten on a piece of centimeter grid paper. Estimate its area. **See students' work.**

Guided Practice

Estimate the area of each figure.

4. 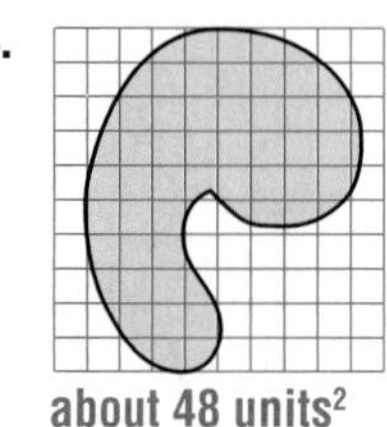
about 48 units^2

5. 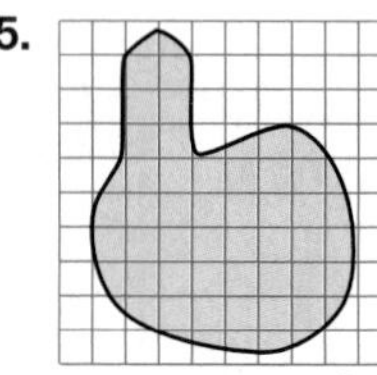
about 46 units^2

6. ***Baking*** Mr. Kim bakes cakes for special events. He is making a cake in the shape of a bunny for a child's birthday party. To determine how much icing he needs to make, he estimates the area of the top of the cake. What is a good estimate for this area? **about 28 units^2**

Additional Answers

1. Some figures are irregular with curved lines and corners that are not square.
2. Sample answer: One method is to find the mean of the inner measure and outer measure. Another method is to divide the figure into shapes that approximate the shapes of regular polygons, find the total area of these polygons, and make any necessary adjustments. Both methods only estimate the area of the irregular figure. The second method can only be used if the figure can be divided into shapes that approximate the shapes of regular polygons. The first method can always be used.

EXERCISES

Practice

Estimate the area of each figure.

7. 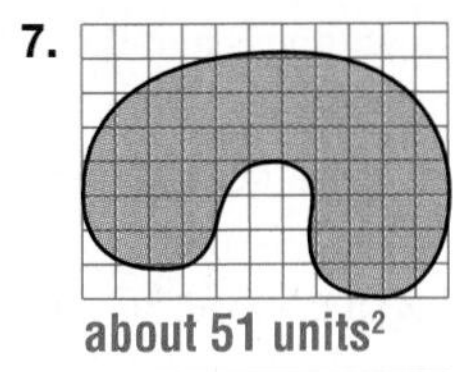
about 51 units²

8. 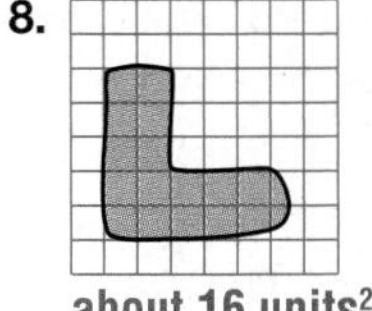
about 16 units²

9. 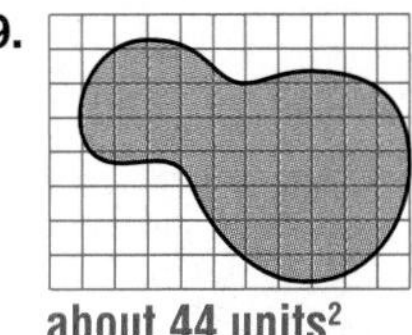
about 44 units²

10. 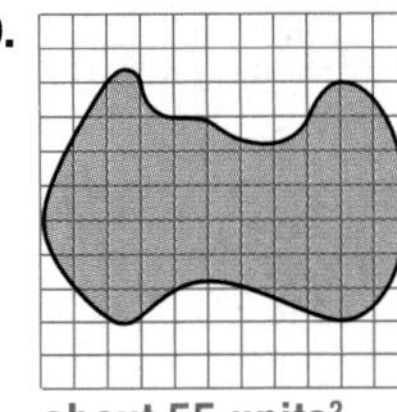
about 55 units²

11. 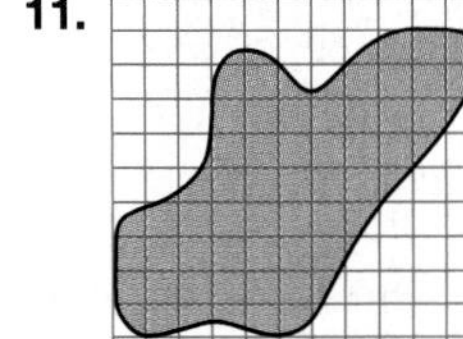
about 53 units²

12. 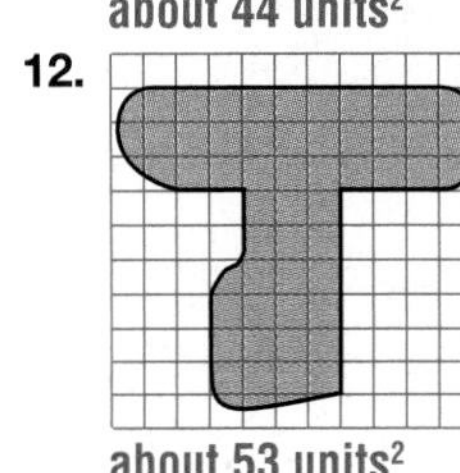
about 53 units²

13. Draw a spoon on a piece of centimeter grid paper. Estimate the area of the figure. **See students' work.**

14a. North Carolina, Arkansas, Mississippi

Applications and Problem Solving

14. ***Geography*** Refer to the maps of the states shown below.
   a. Which states most closely resemble a rectangle?
   b. Which states most closely resemble a triangle? **Idaho, Virginia**
   c. Use estimation to order the areas of the states below from greatest to least.

14c. Idaho, Arkansas, North Carolina, Mississippi, Virginia, West Virginia

Trace the outline of a family member's hand on grid paper. Estimate the area of the hand.

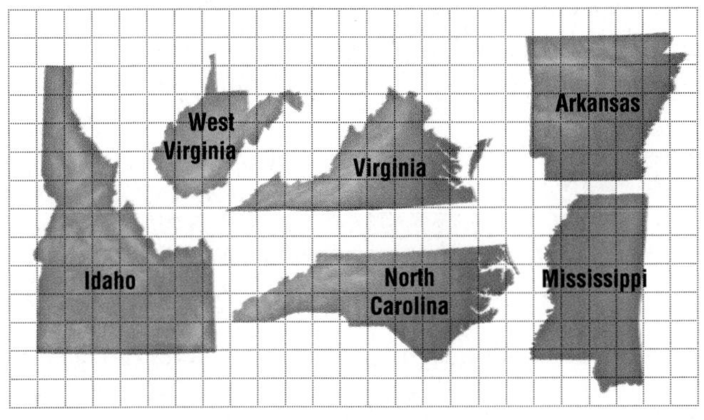

15. ***Heating and Air Conditioning (HVAC)*** Ann Merriman is an HVAC engineer who is designing a new duct system. Part of the template for her design is in the diagram. She needs to estimate the area to be sure it doesn't exceed 120 square inches. If each small square represents one square inch, will her design conform to the specifications? Explain. **See margin.**

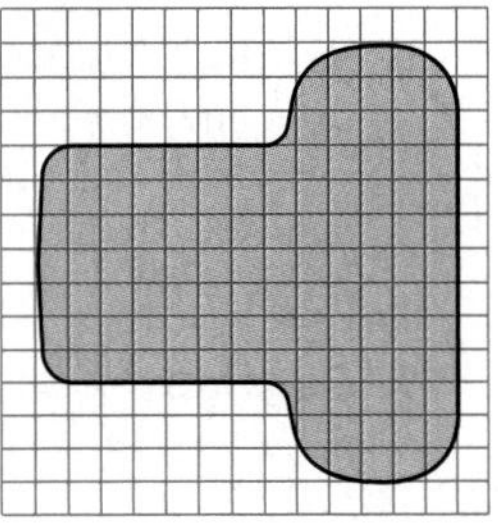

Assignment Guide

Core: 7–15 odd, 17–19
Enriched: 8–14 even, 15, 17–19
All: Self-Test, 1–10

Have students work in small groups to compare the hand sizes they've collected. If this is 1% of the skin on a person's body, what is the total area of skin on their body?

Additional Answer

15. Yes; if the figure is divided into shapes that include an 8-by-7 rectangle and a 5-by-13 rectangle, the area will be 121 in². However, the figure is at least 2 squares less than this area, so the area of the irregular shape will be less than 120 in².

■ Reteaching the Lesson ■

Activity Another way to estimate the area of an irregular figure is to separate it into a number of rectangles of various sizes and combine their areas. Guide students to see that the estimate improves as the number of rectangles into which a figure is separated increases.

***Study Guide Masters*, p. 77**

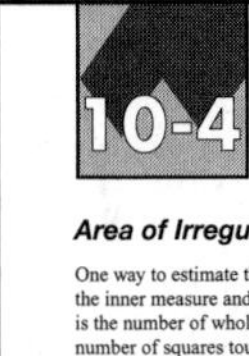

Name________ Date________

10-4 Study Guide

Area of Irregular Figures

One way to estimate the area of an irregular figure is to find the mean of the inner measure and the outer measure of the figure. The inner measure is the number of whole squares within the figure. The outer measure is the number of squares touching the figure anywhere plus the number of whole squares within the figure.

Example **Estimate the area of the irregular figure.**

inner measure (marked with dots): 68 units²

outer measure (shaded squares): 110 units²

mean: $\frac{68 + 110}{2} = 89$ units²

An estimate of the area of the irregular figure is 89 units².

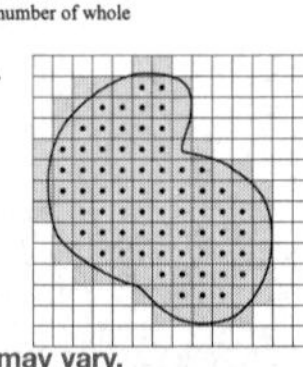

Estimate the area of each figure. Answers may vary.

1. $\frac{46 + 81}{2} = 63.5$ units²

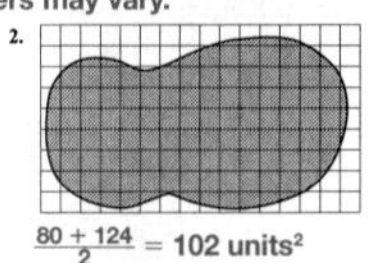

2. $\frac{80 + 124}{2} = 102$ units²

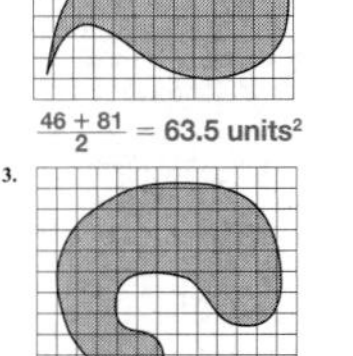

3. $\frac{45 + 86}{2} = 65.5$ units²

4. $\frac{38 + 75}{2} = 56.5$ units²

 T77 *Mathematics: Applications and Connections, Course 2*

Exercise 16 asks students to advance to the next stage of work on the Chapter Project. You may have students work in pairs, checking each other's work.

4 ASSESS

Closing Activity

Speaking Have students explain how they would estimate the area of the figure formed by a rubber band dropped on a sheet of centimeter grid paper.

Chapter 10, Quiz B (Lessons 10-3 and 10-4) is available in the *Assessment and Evaluation Masters,* p. 267.

Mid-Chapter Test (Lessons 10-1 through 10-4) is available in the *Assessment and Evaluation Masters,* p. 266.

Mid-Chapter Self Test

The Mid-Chapter Self Test reviews the concepts in Lessons 10-1 through 10-4. Lesson references are given so students can review concepts not yet mastered.

***Practice Masters,* p. 77**

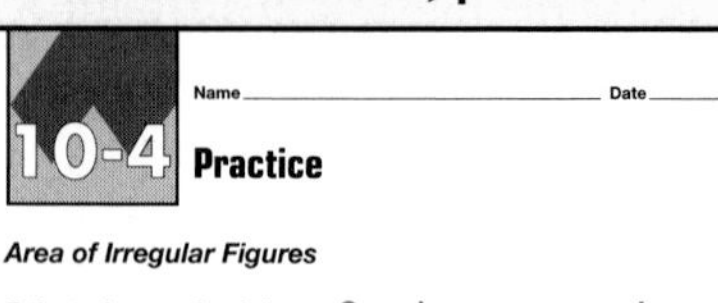

Name ______ Date ______

10-4 Practice

Area of Irregular Figures

Estimate the area of each figure. Sample answers are given.

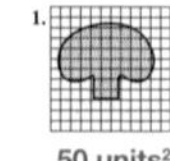
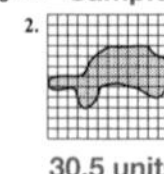
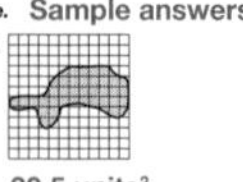
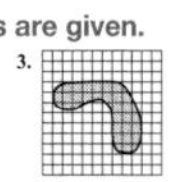
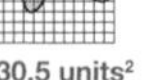

1. 50 units²
2. 30.5 units²
3. 26.5 units²
4. 41 units²
5. 63 units²
6. 50 units²

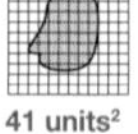
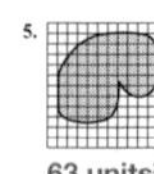
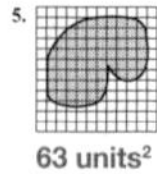
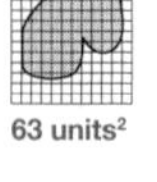

7. 44 units²
8. 36 units²
9. 46.5 units²

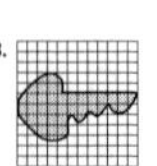
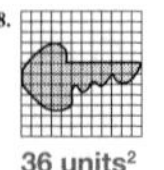
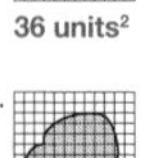
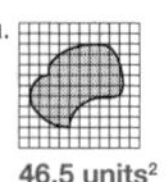
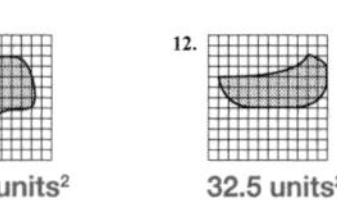

10. 69 units²
11. 46.5 units²
12. 32.5 units²

13. Draw the outline of a comb on a piece of centimeter grid paper. Estimate its area. Answers will vary.

© Glencoe/McGraw-Hill T77 *Mathematics: Applications and Connections, Course 2*

16. ***Working on the*** CHAPTER Project Refer to the map you drew on page 407. **a–b. See students' work.**
    a. Estimate the area of each landmass and body of water.
    b. Find the actual area of each landmass and body of water. Compare these numbers with your estimates. Make any necessary changes to your map.
17. ***Critical Thinking*** Suppose a figure has an inner measure of 10 square units and an outer measure of 20 square units. **a–c. See Answer Appendix.**
    a. Draw the figure so that the area is closer to 10 square units than 20 square units.
    b. Draw the figure so that the area is closer to 20 square units than 10 square units.
    c. Draw the figure so that the area is exactly 15 square units.

Mixed Review

18. ***Geometry*** Each side of a square is 7 inches long. Find the length of one of its diagonals to the nearest tenth of an inch. *(Lesson 10-3)* **9.9 in.**
19. **Standardized Test Practice** Translate the phrase *12 more than d* into an algebraic expression. *(Lesson 6-4)* **C**

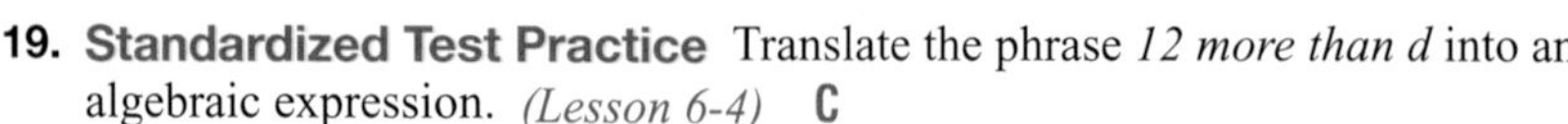

A $12d$ **B** $d - 12$ **C** $d + 12$ **D** $12 - d$ **E** $12 \div d$

For **Extra Practice,** see page 596.

CHAPTER 10 Mid-Chapter Self Test

Find the square of each number. *(Lesson 10-1)*

1. 18 **324**
2. 22 **484**

Find the square root of each number. *(Lesson 10-1)*

3. $\sqrt{256}$ **16**
4. $\sqrt{784}$ **28**

Estimate each square root to the nearest whole number. *(Lesson 10-2)*

5. $\sqrt{24}$ **5**
6. $\sqrt{140}$ **12**

Find the missing measure for each right triangle. Round to the nearest tenth. *(Lesson 10-3)*

7. a: 10 inches; b: 24 inches **26 in.**
8. a: 7 meters; c: 9 meters **5.7 m**
9. ***Football*** The mascot of Smith Middle School carried the school banner from one corner of the football field to the opposite corner of the field. A football field including the end zones is 360 feet long and 160 feet wide. How far did the mascot carry the banner? *(Lesson 10-3)* **about 394.0 ft**
10. ***Geometry*** Estimate the area of the figure. *(Lesson 10-4)* **about 18 units²**

Extending the Lesson

***Enrichment Masters,* p. 77**

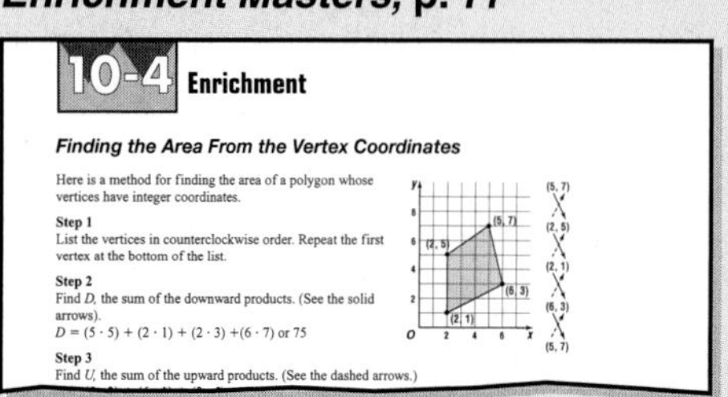

10-4 Enrichment

Finding the Area From the Vertex Coordinates

Here is a method for finding the area of a polygon whose vertices have integer coordinates.

Step 1
List the vertices in counterclockwise order. Repeat the first vertex at the bottom of the list.

Step 2
Find D, the sum of the downward products. (See the solid arrows.)
$D = (5 \cdot 5) + (2 \cdot 1) + (2 \cdot 3) + (6 \cdot 7)$ or 75

Step 3
Find U, the sum of the upward products. (See the dashed arrows.)

Activity Introduce students to Pick's Theorem for finding the area of an irregular-shaped polygon drawn on dot paper: $A = \frac{1}{2}b + (p - 1)$, where b = the number of points on the boundary of the figure, and p = the number of dots within the interior of the figure. Have students explore this theorem using their own figures.

COOPERATIVE LEARNING

10-5A Finding the Area of a Triangle

grid paper

scissors

A Preview of Lesson 10-5

You have learned that a triangle is a polygon with three sides. In this lab, you will find the area of a triangle.

TRY THIS

Work with a partner.

Step 1 Draw a parallelogram on a piece of grid paper. Your parallelogram can be of any size or shape.

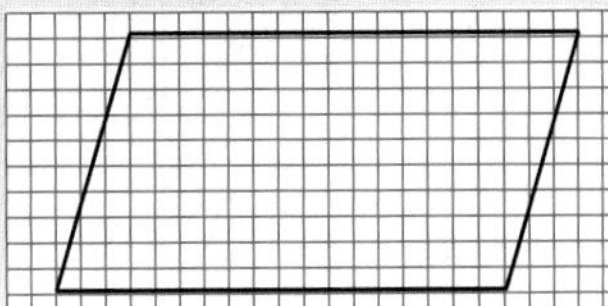

Step 2 Cut out your parallelogram.

Step 3 Draw a diagonal of the parallelogram.

Step 4 Cut along the diagonal.

5. The area of a triangle is half the base times the height.

ON YOUR OWN

1. What two shapes are formed? **2 triangles**
2. How do the two shapes compare? **They are the same size and shape.**
3. What is the area of the original parallelogram? **See students' work.**
4. What is the area of each triangle? **See students' work.**
5. What conclusions can you make about the areas of all triangles?
6. ***Look Ahead*** The formula for the area of a parallelogram is $A = bh$. Using this formula, write a formula for a triangle with the same base and height. $A = \frac{1}{2}bh$

Have students write a paragraph to explain how the area of any triangle can be found by using a parallelogram.

10-5A HANDS-ON LAB Notes

GET READY

Objective Students find the area of a triangle.

Optional Resources

Hands-On Lab Masters
- grid paper, p. 10
- worksheet, p. 63

Overhead Manipulative Resources
- centimeter grid transparency

Manipulative Kit
- scissors

MANAGEMENT TIPS

Recommended Time
20 minutes

Getting Started Remind students of the basic property of a parallelogram, which is a four-sided figure with opposite sides being parallel. Have them imagine what half of a parallelogram would look like.

For the **Activity,** have students measure the base and height of the parallelogram and calculate its area before they cut it.

ASSESS

Have students complete Exercises 1–6. Make sure the diagonal line along which students cut their parallelogram is drawn correctly. Guide them to see that both triangles can be described as having the same base and height as the parallelogram.

10-5 Lesson Notes

Instructional Resources

- *Study Guide Masters,* p. 78
- *Practice Masters,* p. 78
- *Enrichment Masters,* p. 78
- Transparencies 10-5, A and B
- *Classroom Games,* pp. 29–30

- CD-ROM Program
  - Resource Lesson 10-5
  - Interactive Lesson 10-5

Recommended Pacing	
Standard	Days 8 & 9 of 14
Honors	Days 8 & 9 of 13
Block	Day 5 of 7

1 FOCUS

5-Minute Check
(Lesson 10-4)

Estimate the area of each figure.

1.

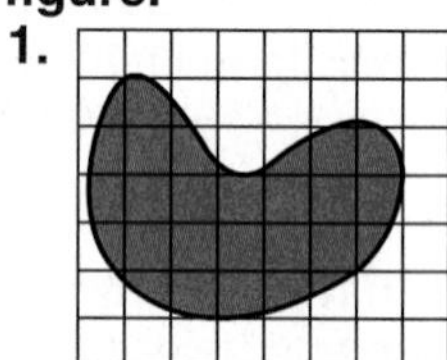

Sample answer: 20 units²

2.

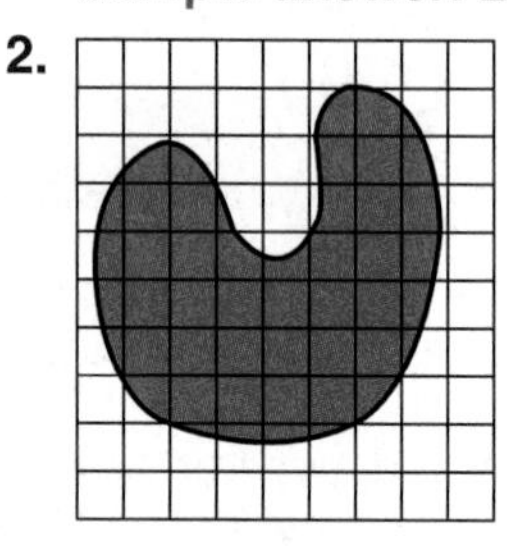

Sample answer: 35 units²

The 5-Minute Check is also available on **Transparency 10-5A** for this lesson.

Motivating the Lesson

Hands-On Activity Ask students to identify something in the classroom that has the shape of a triangle or trapezoid and estimate its area. After students complete the lesson, have them calculate the area and compare the result to their estimate.

10-5 Area of Triangles and Trapezoids

What you'll learn

You'll learn to find the areas of triangles and trapezoids.

When am I ever going to use this?

Knowing how to find the area of triangles and trapezoids can help you find the area of decks and rooms.

Word Wise

triangle
trapezoid

Nicaragua is a country in Central America. Its shape resembles a **triangle**. You can estimate the area of the country by using the formula for the area of a triangle.

The results of the Hands-On Lab on page 427 suggest the formula for the area of a triangle.

Area of a Triangle

Words: The area (A) of a triangle is equal to half the product of its base (b) and height (h).

Symbols: $A = \frac{1}{2}bh$

Model:

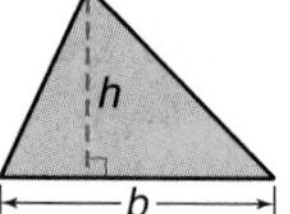

Example CONNECTION

1 **Geography** **The distance from the northern edge of Nicaragua to the southern edge is about 370 miles. The perpendicular distance from the western edge to the line along the eastern edge is about 268 miles. Estimate the area of Nicaragua.**

Consider the shape of Nicaragua to be a triangle. Identify the base and height of the triangle.

base: 370 miles

height: 268 miles

$A = \frac{1}{2}bh$ *Formula for the area of a triangle*

$A = \frac{1}{2} \times 370 \times 268$ *Replace b with 370 and h with 268.*

$A = 185 \times 268$

$A = 49{,}580$

The area of Nicaragua is about 49,580 square miles.

Use reference materials to check this estimate with the actual area.

Multiple Learning Styles

Visual/Spatial Have students use tangram pieces to create as many triangles and trapezoids as they can. Ask students if each new shape they create has a different area. Is the result different if not all of the pieces are used?

A **trapezoid** is a quadrilateral with exactly one pair of parallel sides.

MINI-LAB

Work with a partner.  grid paper 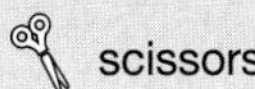 scissors tape

Try This

- Draw a trapezoid of any shape or size on a piece of grid paper.
- Cut out your trapezoid. Label the bases and height as shown.
- Measure the lengths of base 1 and base 2. Measure the height. Record the measurements.
- Fold base 1 onto base 2. Unfold.
- Cut the trapezoid on the fold line. Then form a parallelogram.

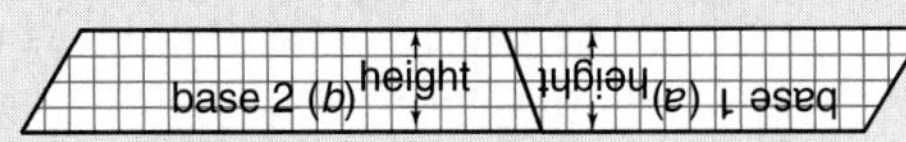

Talk About It

1. Find the length of the base of your parallelogram. How does it compare with the bases of your trapezoid?
2. Measure the height of your parallelogram. How does this height compare with the height of your trapezoid?
3. Find the area of your parallelogram. **See students' work.**
4. What is the area of your trapezoid? **See students' work.**
5. What conclusions can you make about the areas of all trapezoids?
6. Suppose you know the lengths of base 1 and base 2 and the height of a trapezoid. Write a formula for the area of the trapezoid.

1. See students' work; it equals the sum of the 2 bases of the trapezoid.
2. See students' work; it equals half the height of the trapezoid.
5. The area of a trapezoid is half the height times the sum of the bases.
6. $A = \frac{1}{2}h(a + b)$ where h is the height and a and b are the bases of the trapezoid.

The results of the Mini-Lab suggest the formula for the area of a trapezoid.

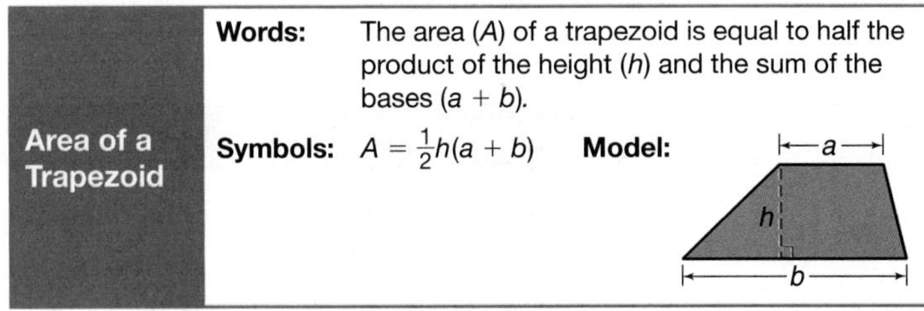

Area of a Trapezoid

Words: The area (A) of a trapezoid is equal to half the product of the height (h) and the sum of the bases ($a + b$).

Symbols: $A = \frac{1}{2}h(a + b)$ **Model:**

2 TEACH

Transparency 10-5B contains a teaching aid for this lesson.

Teaching Tip For Example 1, the actual area of Nicaragua is 50,838 square miles.

In-Class Example

For Example 1

The shape of New Hampshire resembles a right triangle with a base of 93 miles and a height of 180 miles. Estimate the area of New Hampshire. **8,370 mi²; actual area is 9,297 mi²**

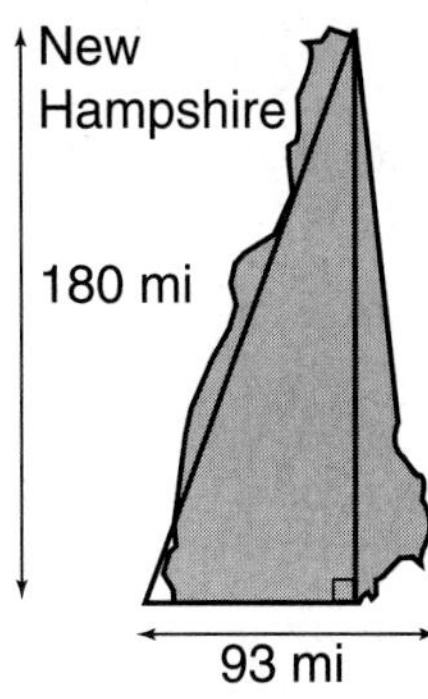

Source: *The World Book Encyclopedia*, vol. 14, 1989

Using the Mini-Lab Before completing Exercises 5 and 6 of the Mini-Lab, have students repeat the lab activity with other trapezoids. Are the results similar?

Teaching Tip When students are finding the area of a triangle, and either the height or the base is an even number, they can simplify their calculations by taking half the even number first, then multiplying it by the other number.

Reteaching the Lesson

Activity Have students use geoboards to form parallelograms. Challenge them to make trapezoids from their parallelograms by changing only one angle. Then have students make triangles from their trapezoids by changing one angle. They can compare areas by counting enclosed squares.

Error Analysis

Watch for students who use a side of either a triangle or a trapezoid for the height of the figure when finding its area.
Prevent by stressing that the height of a triangle is perpendicular to its base.

In-Class Example

For Example 2

Find the area of the trapezoid.

150 in^2

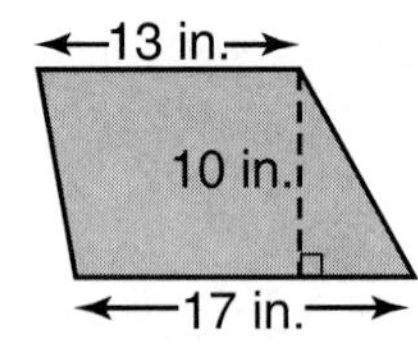

3 PRACTICE/APPLY

Check for Understanding

If students need additional practice or instruction after completing Exercises 1–8, one of these options may be helpful.

- Extra Practice, see p. 597
- Reteaching Activity, see p. 429
- *Study Guide Masters,* p. 78
- *Practice Masters,* p. 78

***Study Guide Masters*, p. 78**

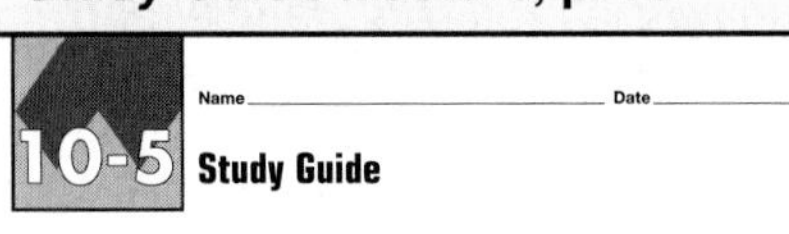

Name__________ Date__________

10-5 Study Guide

Area of Triangles and Trapezoids

A triangle is a polygon that has three sides. The area of a triangle is equal to one-half the product of its base and height.

$$A = \frac{1}{2}bh$$

Example 1 **Find the area of the triangle.**

$A = \frac{1}{2}bh$

$A = \frac{1}{2} \times 12 \times 5$

$A = 6 \times 5$

$A = 30$ The area of the triangle is 30 m^2.

A **trapezoid** is a quadrilateral with exactly one pair of parallel sides. The area of a trapezoid is equal to one-half the product of its height times the sum of its bases.

$$A = \frac{1}{2}h(a + b)$$

Example 2 **Find the area of the trapezoid.**

$A = \frac{1}{2}h(a + b)$

$A = \frac{1}{2}(8)(15 + 12)$

$A = \frac{1}{2}(8)(27)$

$A = 4(27)$

$A = 108$ The area of the trapezoid is 108 cm^2.

Find the area of each triangle to the nearest tenth.

1. base: 10 in. height: 20 in. **100 in^2**
2. base: 4 m height: 9 m **18 m^2**
3. base: 15 cm height: 12 cm **90 cm^2**
4. base: 2.4 cm height: 10 cm **12 cm^2**
5. base: 2.8 m height: 1.2 m **1.7 m^2**
6. base: $2\frac{1}{2}$ ft height: 6 ft **7.5 ft^2**

Find the area of each trapezoid to the nearest tenth.

7. bases: 6 m, 9 m height: 4 m **30 m^2**
8. bases: 10 ft, 15 ft height: 20 ft **250 ft^2**
9. bases: 7.6 cm, 10 cm height: 8 cm **70.4 cm^2**

 T78 *Mathematics: Applications and Connections,* Course 2

Example 2 **Find the area of the trapezoid.**

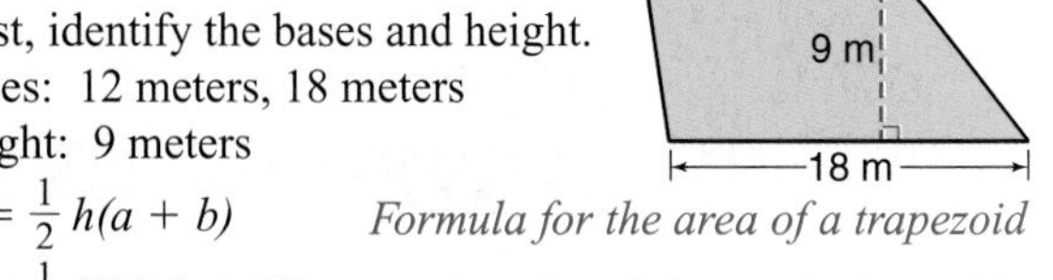

First, identify the bases and height.
bases: 12 meters, 18 meters
height: 9 meters

$A = \frac{1}{2}h(a + b)$ *Formula for the area of a trapezoid*

$A = \frac{1}{2}(9)(12 + 18)$ *Replace h with 9, a with 12, and b with 18.*

$A = \frac{1}{\cancel{2}_1}(9)(\cancel{30}^{15})$ or 135

The area of the trapezoid is 135 square meters.

CHECK FOR UNDERSTANDING

Communicating Mathematics

Read and study the lesson to answer each question. **1–2. See margin.**

1. ***Describe*** the relationship between the area of a parallelogram and the area of a triangle with the same height and base. Explain.
2. ***Draw*** a trapezoid and label the two bases and the height. In your own words, explain how to find the area of the trapezoid.

3. Use grid paper to ***draw*** a trapezoid with bases of 6 units and 12 units and a height of 4 units. Draw another trapezoid with bases of 6 units and 12 units and a height of 8 units. **See margin.**
   a. Find the area of each trapezoid. **36 units^2; 72 units^2**
   b. Write a ratio that compares the heights of the trapezoids. **1:2**
   c. Write a ratio that compares the areas of the trapezoids. **1:2**

Guided Practice

4. Find the area of the triangle.
   base: 7 ft **42 ft^2**
   height: 12 ft
5. Find the area of the trapezoid.
   bases: 5 cm, 14 cm **57 cm^2**
   height: 6 cm

Find the area of each figure to the nearest tenth.

6. **40 in^2**

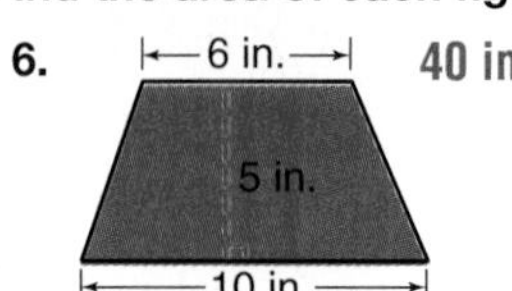

7. **7.5 m^2**

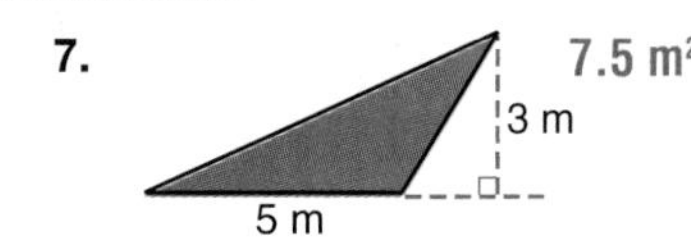

8. ***Construction*** The Deck and Porch Company has several designs for decks. One of them is shown at the right. Find the area of the deck. **82.5 ft^2**

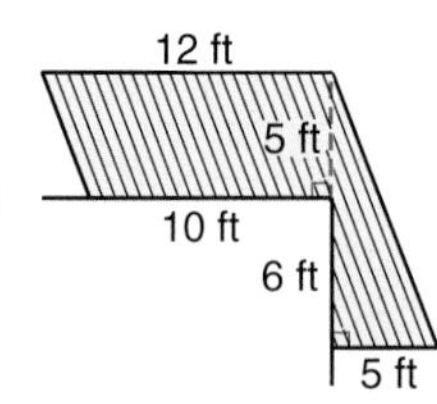

EXERCISES

Practice

Find the area of each triangle to the nearest tenth.

9. base: 16 yd height: 12 yd **96 yd^2**
10. base: 1.4 m height: 1.1 m **0.8 m^2**
11. base: 5 ft height: 12 ft **30 ft^2**

Additional Answers

1. The area of a triangle is $\frac{1}{2}$ the area of the parallelogram with the same base and height, because the two of these triangles can be formed by drawing a diagonal of the parallelogram.
2. See students' drawings; Multiply the sum of the bases and the height and take half of the product.
3.

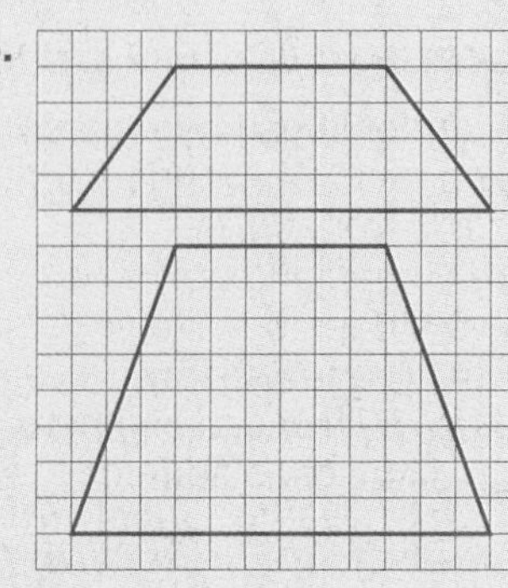

Find the area of each trapezoid to the nearest tenth.

12. bases: 4 m, 12 m height: 10 m **80 m²**
13. bases: 4 in., 8 in. height: 6 in. **36 in²**
14. bases: 7.3 cm, 9.5 cm height: 8.8 cm **73.9 cm²**

Find the area of each figure to the nearest tenth.

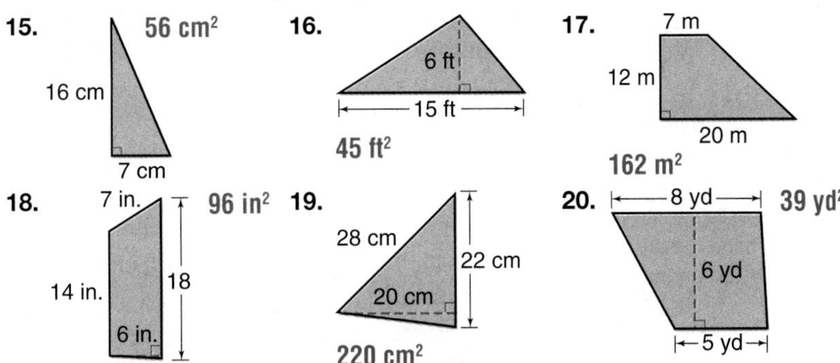

21. Find the area of a right triangle if one leg is 5 inches long and the hypotenuse is 13 inches long. **30 in²**

Applications and Problem Solving

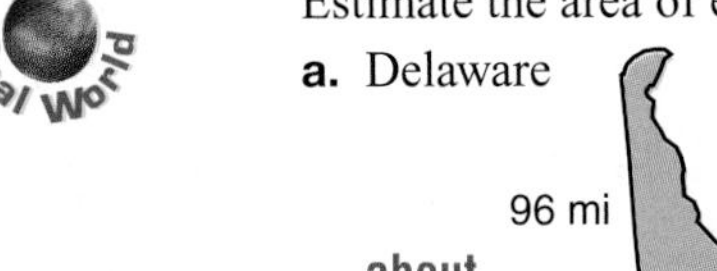

22. ***Geography*** Delaware is nicknamed the Diamond State, but its shape looks more like a triangle. Nevada has a shape that looks like a trapezoid. Estimate the area of each state.

a. Delaware

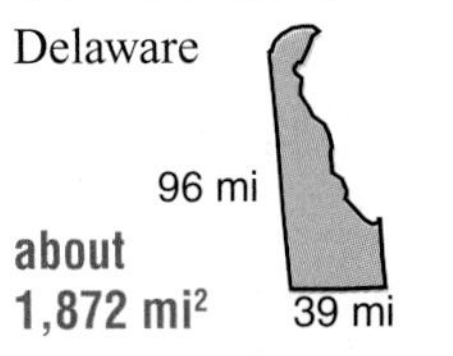

about 1,872 mi²

b. Nevada

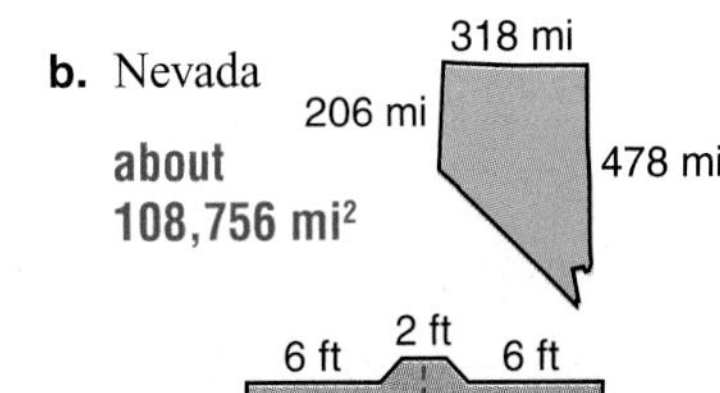

about 108,756 mi²

23. ***Interior Design*** The living room drawn at the right has a bay window. An interior designer is planning to have the hardwood floors in the room refinished. What is the total area that needs to be refinished? **195 ft²**

6 ft 2 ft 6 ft 13 ft 12 ft 16 ft

24. See students' work.

24. ***Working on the*** CHAPTER Project Refer to the map you drew on page 407. Are any of the landmasses or bodies of water shaped like a triangle or a trapezoid? If so, use the formulas to estimate the areas. How do these estimates compare with the actual areas?

25. ***Critical Thinking*** A triangle has height *h*. Its base is 4. Find the area of the triangle. (Express your answer in terms of *h*.) **$A = 2h$**

Mixed Review

26. ***Standardized Test Practice*** What is the best estimate of the area of the figure? *(Lesson 10-4)* **C**
    A 10 square units **B** 20 square units
    C 30 square units **D** 40 square units

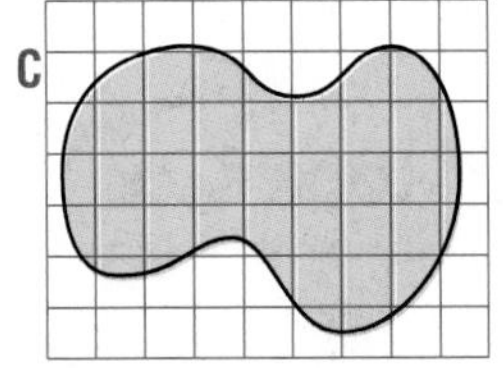

27. ***Geometry*** What is the name of a polygon with 6 sides? *(Lesson 9-2)* **hexagon**

28. ***Measurement*** Round 26.394 kilometers to the nearest kilometer. *(Lesson 2-2)* **26 km**

For **Extra Practice,** see page 597.

Assignment Guide

Core: 9–25 odd, 26–28
Enriched: 10–22 even, 23, 25–28

Exercise 24 asks students to advance to the next stage of work on the Chapter Project. You may want to have students check each others' work to see if they can make more accurate estimates of area.

4 ASSESS

Closing Activity

Speaking Have students draw both a triangle and a trapezoid. Then have them explain how they would find the area of each.

***Practice Masters,* p. 78**

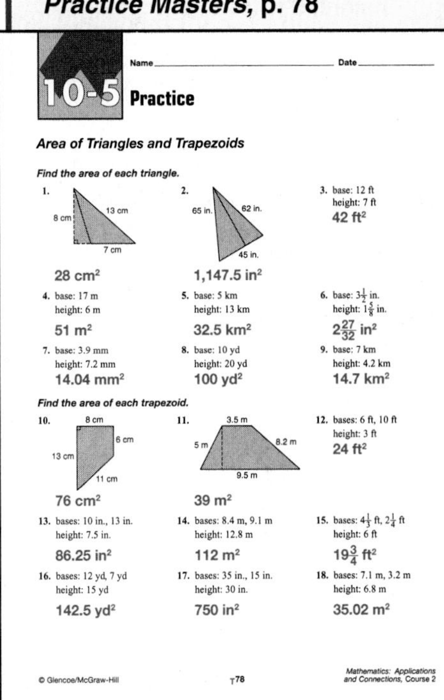

Name________ Date________

10-5 Practice

Area of Triangles and Trapezoids

Find the area of each triangle.

1. 8 cm, 13 cm, 7 cm **28 cm²**
2. 65 in., 62 in., 45 in. **1,147.5 in²**
3. base: 12 ft height: 7 ft **42 ft²**
4. base: 17 m height: 6 m **51 m²**
5. base: 5 km height: 13 km **32.5 km²**
6. base: $3\frac{1}{2}$ in. height: $1\frac{5}{8}$ in. **$2\frac{27}{32}$ in²**
7. base: 3.9 mm height: 7.2 mm **14.04 mm²**
8. base: 10 yd height: 20 yd **100 yd²**
9. base: 7 km height: 4.2 km **14.7 km²**

Find the area of each trapezoid.

10. 8 cm, 6 cm, 13 cm, 11 cm **76 cm²**
11. 3.5 m, 5 m, 8.2 m, 9.5 m **39 m²**
12. bases: 6 ft, 10 ft height: 3 ft **24 ft²**
13. bases: 10 in., 13 in. height: 7.5 in. **86.25 in²**
14. bases: 8.4 m, 9.1 m height: 12.8 m **112 m²**
15. bases: $4\frac{1}{2}$ ft, $2\frac{1}{4}$ ft height: 6 ft **$19\frac{3}{4}$ ft²**
16. bases: 12 yd, 7 yd height: 15 yd **142.5 yd²**
17. bases: 35 in., 15 in. height: 30 in. **750 in²**
18. bases: 7.1 m, 3.2 m height: 6.8 m **35.02 m²**

© Glencoe/McGraw-Hill T78 *Mathematics: Applications and Connections, Course 2*

Extending the Lesson

***Enrichment Masters,* p. 78**

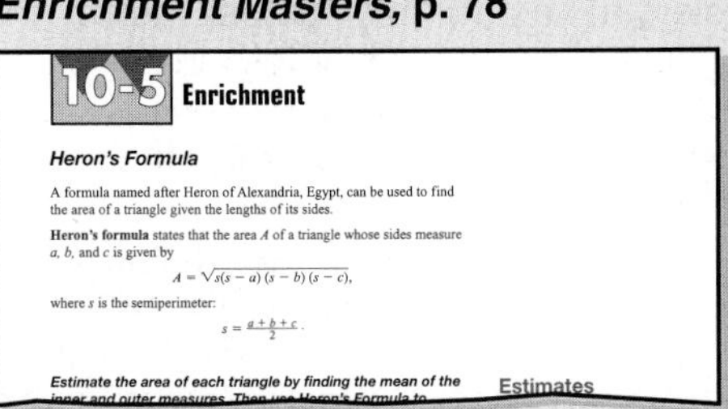

10-5 Enrichment

Heron's Formula

A formula named after Heron of Alexandria, Egypt, can be used to find the area of a triangle given the lengths of its sides.

Heron's formula states that the area *A* of a triangle whose sides measure *a*, *b*, and *c* is given by

$$A = \sqrt{s(s-a)(s-b)(s-c)},$$

where *s* is the semiperimeter:

$$s = \frac{a+b+c}{2}.$$

Estimate the area of each triangle by finding the mean of the inner and outer measures. Then use Heron's Formula to Estimates

Activity Ask students to predict what will happen to the area of a triangle if its height or base (but not both) is doubled. Ask them how the area will change if *both* the height and base are halved. Have them investigate to check their predictions. **It doubles; it is multiplied by $\frac{1}{4}$.**

10-6 Lesson Notes

Instructional Resources

- *Study Guide Masters,* p. 79
- *Practice Masters,* p. 79
- *Enrichment Masters,* p. 79
- Transparencies 10-6, A and B
- *Assessment and Evaluation Masters,* p. 268
- *Hands-On Lab Masters,* p. 81
- *School to Career Masters,* p. 23

CD-ROM Program
- Resource Lesson 10-6

Recommended Pacing	
Standard	Day 10 of 14
Honors	Day 10 of 13
Block	Day 5 of 7

1 FOCUS

5-Minute Check
(Lesson 10-5)

Find the area of each triangle to the nearest tenth.

1. base: 14 m, height: 9 m **63 m²**
2. base: 2.6 cm, height: 1.7 cm **2.2 cm²**

Find the area of each trapezoid to the nearest tenth.

3. bases: 4 in., 7 in. height: 5 in. **27.5 in²**
4. base: $3\frac{1}{2}$ feet, 8 ft height: 6 ft **34.5 ft²**

The 5-Minute Check is also available on **Transparency 10-6A** for this lesson.

Motivating the Lesson

Communication Ask students how they could determine which is larger, the pitcher's mound on a baseball field or the center circle of a basketball court.

10-6 Area of Circles

What **you'll learn**

You'll learn to find the area of circles.

When **am I ever going to use this?**

Knowing how to find the area of a circle can help you determine the area affected by an earthquake.

Model Ana Luque paraded through the streets of Torremolinos, Spain, in a very unusual dress. The dress was 28 feet in diameter and had a train 330 feet long. Assume the waist was 2 feet in diameter. What was the area of the skirt of the dress? *This problem will be solved in Example 1.*

To find the formula for the area of a circle, we can use the formula or the area of a parallelogram.

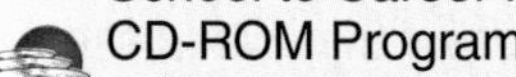

HANDS-ON MINI-LAB

Work with a partner.  compass straightedge scissors

Try This

- Draw a circle and several radii that separate the circle into equal-sized sections.
  Let r units represent the length of the radius of the circle. Let C units represent its circumference.
- Cut out each section of the circle.
- Reassemble the sections in the form of a parallelogram.

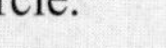
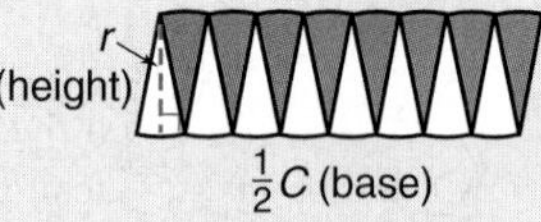

Talk About It

1. What is the height of this "parallelogram"? What is the length of the base?
2. What is the formula for the area of a parallelogram? ***A = bh***
3. How could you use this formula to find the area of a circle?

1. $r; \frac{1}{2}C$
3. Replace b with $\frac{1}{2}C$ and h with r to get $A = \left(\frac{1}{2}C\right)r$. Then replace C with $2\pi r$ and simplify to get $A = \pi r^2$.

The base of the parallelogram shown in the Mini-Lab is equal to one half of the circumference of the circle $\left(\frac{1}{2}C\right)$ The height of the parallelogram is r. Now, use the formula for the area of a parallelogram.

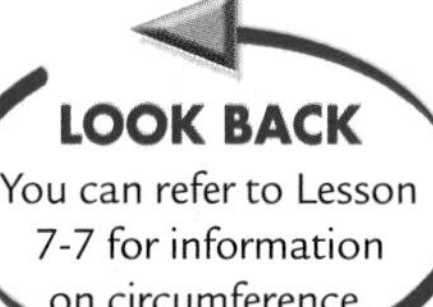
LOOK BACK
You can refer to Lesson 7-7 for information on circumference.

$A = bh$	*Formula for the area of a parallelogram*
$A = \left(\frac{1}{2}C\right)r$	*Substitute $\frac{1}{2}C$ for b and substitute r for h.*
$A = \left(\frac{1}{2} \times 2\pi r\right)r$	*Substitute $2\pi r$ for C. Why?*
$A = \pi r^2$	*Simplify: $\frac{1}{2} \times 2 = 1$, $r \times r = r^2$*

Classroom Vignette

"Have students draw a circle that has a whole number radius on grid paper using a compass. Use the method they learned in Lesson 10-4 about finding the area of irregular figures to find the area of the circle. Have your students compare this area with the calculated one."

Cindy J. Boyd, Teacher
Abilene High School
Abilene, TX

Area of a Circle	
Words:	The area (A) of a circle is equal to pi (π) times the square of the radius (r).
Symbols:	$A = \pi r^2$
Model:	

1 Fashion Refer to the beginning of the lesson. What is the area of the skirt of the dress?

Explore You are given the diameter of the dress and the diameter of the waist. You want to know the area of the skirt.

Plan Draw a figure to illustrate the skirt. The radius of the dress is $\frac{1}{2} \times 28$ or 14 feet. The radius of the waist is $\frac{1}{2} \times 2$ or 1 foot. To determine the area of the skirt, subtract the area of the waist from the area of a circle with a radius of 14 feet.

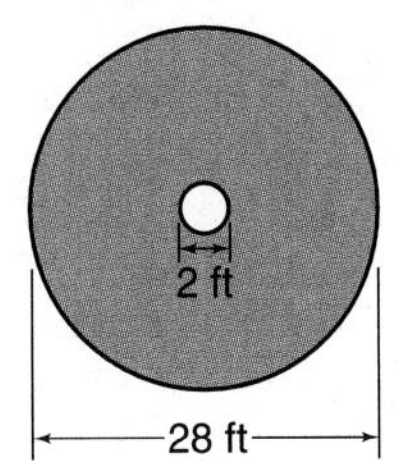

Solve

Area of 28-ft circle	**Area of 2-ft circle**
$A = \pi r^2$	$A = \pi r^2$
$A = \pi \cdot 14^2 \quad r = 14$	$A = \pi \cdot 1^2 \quad r = 1$
[π] [×] 14 [x²]	[π] [×] 1 [x²]
[=] 615.7521601	[=] 3.141592654
$A \approx 615.8$	$A \approx 3.1$

The area of the skirt is about 615.8 − 3.1 or 612.7 square feet.

Examine To estimate the area of the circles, use 3 for π.

$3 \times 14^2 = 588$ $\qquad$ $3 \times 1^2 = 3$

An estimate for the area of the skirt is 588 −3 or 585 square feet. The answer seems reasonable.

2 Find the length of the radius of a circle if its area is 40 square centimeters.

$A = \pi r^2$	*Formula for the area of a circle*
$40 = \pi r^2$	*Replace A with 40.*
$\frac{40}{\pi} = \frac{\pi r^2}{\pi}$	*Divide each side by π.*
$12.7 \approx r^2$	40 [÷] [π] [=] 12.73239545
$\sqrt{12.7} \approx r$	*Definition of square root*
$3.6 \approx r$	12.73239545 [2nd] [√] 3.568248232

The radius is about 3.6 centimeters.

2 TEACH

Transparency 10-6B contains a teaching aid for this lesson.

Using the Mini-Lab To divide the circle into equal-sized sections, suggest that students cut the circle out and fold it in half. Then continue folding it in half several times. Unfold the circle and cut along the folds to form congruent sections. Point out that although the figure formed by reassembling the sections resembles a parallelogram, the resemblance is only approximate.

In-Class Examples

For Example 1
Find the floor area of a ring in a circus if the diameter is 12 yards. **about 113.1 yd²**

For Example 2
Find the radius of a circle if its area is 176 square inches. **about 7.5 in.**

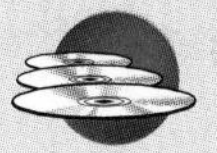

MathPASS CD-ROM

This CD-ROM offers a complete, self-paced mathematics curriculum. Each lesson includes a pretest, tutorial, guided practice, and posttest. MathPASS Lessons 36 and 37 are correlated to this Student Edition lesson.
For Windows & Macintosh

3 PRACTICE/APPLY

Check for Understanding

If students need additional practice or instruction after completing Exercises 1–11, one of these options may be helpful.

- Extra Practice, see p. 597
- Reteaching Activity
- *Study Guide Masters,* p. 79
- *Practice Masters,* p. 79
- Interactive Mathematics Tools Software

Assignment Guide

Core: 13–31 odd, 32–36
Enriched: 12–28 even, 30–36

Additional Answers

2. Sample answer:

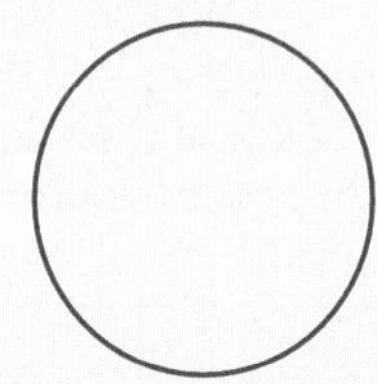

3. Briana; if the diameter is 20 centimeters, the radius is 10 centimeters. Since $\pi \times 100 \approx 314$, the area is about 314 square centimeters.

***Study Guide Masters,* p. 79**

Name________________ Date________

10-6 Study Guide

Area of Circles

The area of a circle is equal to pi (π) times the square of the radius of the circle.

$$A = \pi r^2$$

Example 1 **Find the area of the circle.**

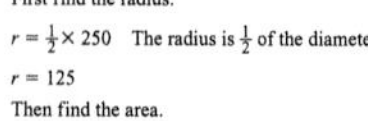

First find the radius.

$r = \frac{1}{2} \times 250$ The radius is $\frac{1}{2}$ of the diameter.

$r = 125$

Then find the area.

$A = \pi r^2$
$A \approx 3.14 \times 125^2$
$A \approx 3.14 \times 15{,}625$ *Replace π with 3.14 and r with 125.*
$A \approx 49{,}062.5$ The area of the circle is about 49,062.5 cm^2.

You can use the formula for the area of a circle to find the radius when the area is known.

Example 2 **Find the radius of a circle if its area is 452 ft^2.**

$A = \pi r^2$
$452 \approx 3.14 \times r^2$ *Replace A with 452 and π with 3.14.*
$452 \div 3.14 \approx (3.14 \times r^2) \div 3.14$ *Divide each side by 3.14.*
$143.9 \approx r^2$
$\sqrt{143.9} \approx r$
$12 \approx r$ The radius of the circle is about 12 ft.

Find the area of each circle to the nearest tenth.

1. 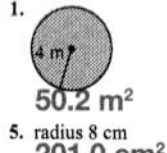

50.2 m^2

2. 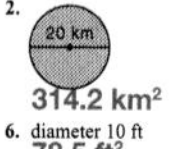

314.2 km^2

3. 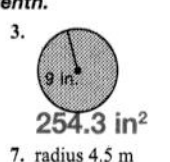

254.3 in^2

4. 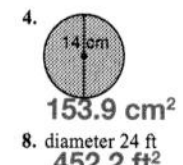

153.9 cm^2

5. radius 8 cm 201.0 cm^2
6. diameter 10 ft 78.5 ft^2
7. radius 4.5 m 63.6 m^2
8. diameter 24 ft 452.2 ft^2

Find the length of the radius of each circle given the following areas. Round answers to the nearest tenth.

9. 314 cm^2 10 cm
10. 113 ft^2 6 ft
11. 707 m^2 15 m
12. 1,256 in^2 20 in.

 T79 *Mathematics: Applications and Connections, Course 2*

CHECK FOR UNDERSTANDING

Communicating Mathematics

Read and study the lesson to answer each question.

1. ***Explain*** how to find the area of a circle if you know its radius. **1. Square the radius and multiply by π.**
2. ***Draw*** a circle with an area less than π square inches. **See margin.**
3. ***You Decide*** Briana says that the area of a circle with diameter of 20 centimeters is about 314 square centimeters. James says the area is about 1,257 square centimeters. Who is correct? Explain. **See margin.**

4. Use a compass to ***draw*** a circle on grid paper so that the center of the circle is at a place where two grid lines meet and the radius is a whole number. See the example at the right. **See students' work.**
   a. Estimate the area of the circle by finding the mean of the inner and outer measures. **4a. See students' work.**
   b. Find the area of the circle by using the formula. **See students' work.**
   c. Compare the areas found in parts a and b. **The areas are about the same.**

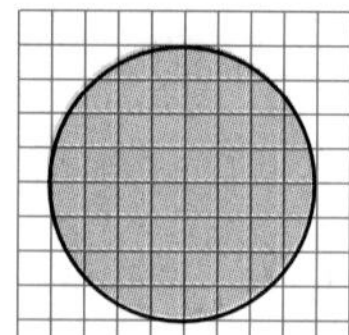

Guided Practice

Find the area of each circle to the nearest tenth.

5. 5 m **78.5 m^2**
6. 16 ft **201.1 ft^2**
7. radius: 9 in. **254.5 in^2**
8. diameter: 4.6 cm **16.6 cm^2**

Answers were calculated using the π key on a calculator and then rounded.

9. Find the length of the radius of a circle with an area of 28 square meters. Round to the nearest tenth. **3.0 m**
10. Find the length of the diameter of a circle with an area of 35 square feet. Round to the nearest tenth. **6.7 ft**
11. ***Architecture*** Many buildings have a circular shape.
    a. The Roman Pantheon was completed about 126 A.D. It is 142 feet in diameter. Find the area of the Pantheon. **about 15,836.8 ft^2**
    b. The Louisiana Superdome is the largest indoor stadium. It is 680 feet in diameter. Find the area of the Superdome.
    c. Compare the area of the Pantheon to the area of the Superdome. **The area of the Superdome is about 23 times the area of the Pantheon.**

11b. about 363,168.1 ft^2

interNET CONNECTION For more data about dome stadiums visit: www.glencoe.com/sec/math/mac/mathnet

EXERCISES

Practice

Find the area of each circle to the nearest tenth.

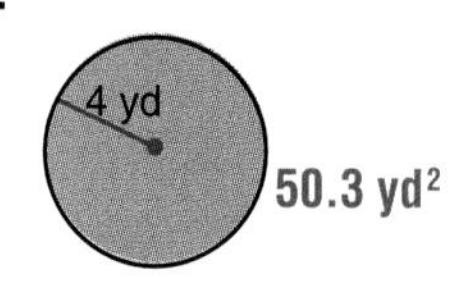

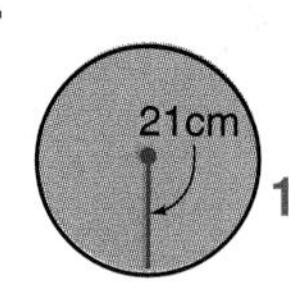

12. 4 yd **50.3 yd^2**
13. 21cm **1,385.4 cm^2**
14. 24 m **452.4 m^2**

Reteaching the Lesson

Activity Have students choose circular objects in the classroom and measure their radius or diameter. Encourage students to compute the area with calculators.

Error Analysis

Watch for students who confuse radius and diameter.

Prevent by pointing out that the radius *radiates* out from the center. It is also shorter than the diameter and is a shorter word than diameter.

Find the area of each circle to the nearest tenth. 17. 18.1 cm^2

15. 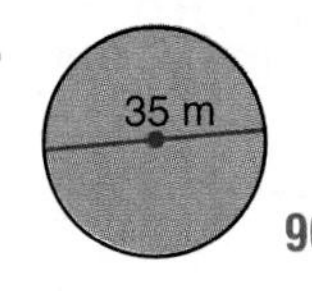

615.8 in^2

16. 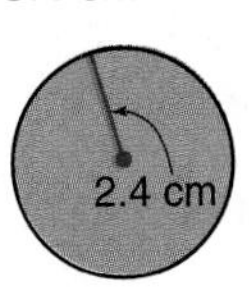

962.1 m^2

17. 2.4 cm

18. radius: 3 ft 28.3 ft^2 **19.** diameter: 34 m **20.** diameter: 17 cm

21. radius: 11 in. **22.** radius: 10.5 cm **23.** diameter: 13 yd

19. 907.9 m^2
20. 227.0 cm^2
21. 380.1 in^2
22. 346.4 cm^2
23. 132.7 yd^2

Find the length of the radius of each circle given the following areas. Round to the nearest tenth.

24. 14 m^2 2.1 m **25.** 70 in^2 4.7 in. **26.** 56 ft^2 4.2 ft

27. Find the length of the diameter of a circle with an area of 42 square centimeters. Round to the nearest tenth. 7.3 cm

28. Find the length of the radius of a circle with an area of 63 square meters. Round to the nearest tenth. 4.5 m

29. ***Algebra*** Let the x-axis of a coordinate plane represent the radius of a circle and the y-axis represent the area of the circle.

- **a.** Graph the points that represent circles with radii 0, 1, 2, and 3 units long. Draw a line or curve that goes through each point.
- **b.** Consider a circle with a radius of 1 unit and a circle with a radius of 2 units. Write a ratio comparing the radii. Write a ratio comparing the areas. Do these ratios form a proportion? Explain.
- **c.** What happens to the area of a circle when its diameter is doubled? Are the diameters and the areas of the two circles proportional?

29a. See Answer Appendix.
29b. 1:2; 1:4; No, $\frac{1}{2} \neq \frac{1}{4}$.
29c. The area is quadrupled; no.
30. penny, about 285.0 mm^2; nickel, about 353.3 mm^2; dime, about 251.9 mm^2; quarter, about 462.2 mm^2

Applications and Problem Solving

30. ***Coin Minting*** Refer to the chart. Find the area of one side of each coin.

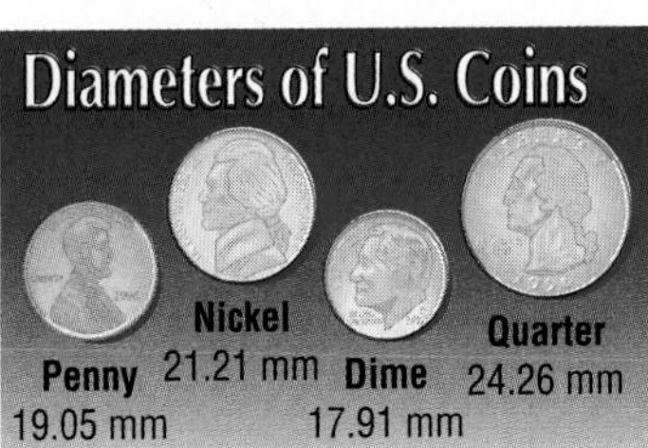

Source: Department of Treasury United States Mint

31. ***Money Matters*** Brittany is planning to order a pizza. She can buy a 12-inch pepperoni pizza for \$7.99 or a 14-inch pepperoni pizza for \$10.49. Which pizza is the better buy? 14-inch pizza

32. ***Critical Thinking*** What is the area of the largest circle that will fit inside a square with an area of 36 square centimeters? about 28.3 cm^2

Mixed Review

33. ***Geometry*** Find the area of a trapezoid with bases of 8 centimeters and 20 centimeters and a height of 11 centimeters. *(Lesson 10-5)* 154 cm^2

34. **Standardized Test Practice** A cake recipe calls for $2\frac{1}{3}$ cups of sugar and $3\frac{3}{4}$ cups of flour. About how many cups of sugar and flour are in the recipe? *(Lesson 7-1)* A

A 6 cups **B** 5 cups **C** 4 cups **D** 3 cups **E** Not Here

For **Extra Practice,** see page 597.

35. ***Algebra*** Graph the equation $y = -2x$. *(Lesson 6-7)* See margin.

36. Solve $r = -24 \div 8$. *(Lesson 5-7)* −3

4 ASSESS

Closing Activity

Modeling Clear a circular space in the classroom and have students stand at the circumference of the circle. Ask one or more students to walk through the center of the circle, and demonstrate how to find the area. Encourage students to use their own feet to measure the radius or diameter.

Chapter 10, Quiz C (Lessons 10-5 and 10-6) is available in the *Assessment and Evaluation Masters,* p. 268

Additional Answer

35.

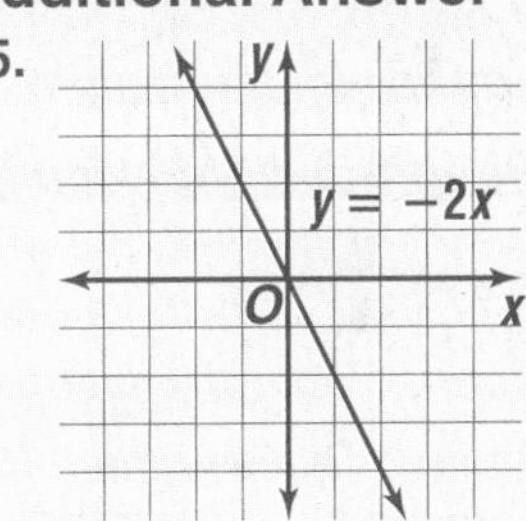

***Practice Masters,* p. 79**

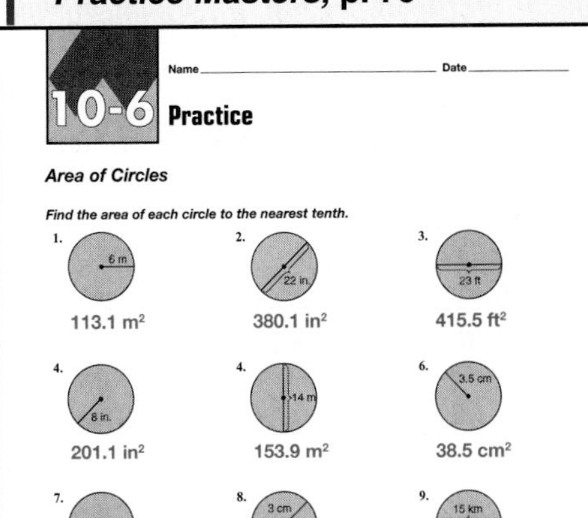

Name ______ Date ______

10-6 Practice

Area of Circles

Find the area of each circle to the nearest tenth.

1. 6 m 113.1 m^2
2. 22 in. 380.1 in^2
3. 23 ft 415.5 ft^2
4. 8 in. 201.1 in^2
4. 14 m 153.9 m^2
6. 3.5 cm 38.5 cm^2
7. 16 ft 804.2 ft^2
8. 3 cm 28.3 cm^2
9. 15 km 176.7 km^2
10. diameter 9 km 63.6 km^2
11. radius 24 ft 1,809.6 ft^2
12. radius 1 m 3.1 m^2

Find the radius of each circle given the following areas. Round to the nearest tenth.

13. 15 cm^2 2.2 cm
14. 100 m^2 5.6 m
15. 200 ft^2 8.0 ft
16. 12.4 in^2 2.0 in.
17. 2.25 km^2 0.8 km
18. 102.48 m^2 5.7 m

 T79 *Mathematics: Applications and Connections, Course 2*

Extending the Lesson

***Enrichment Masters,* p. 79**

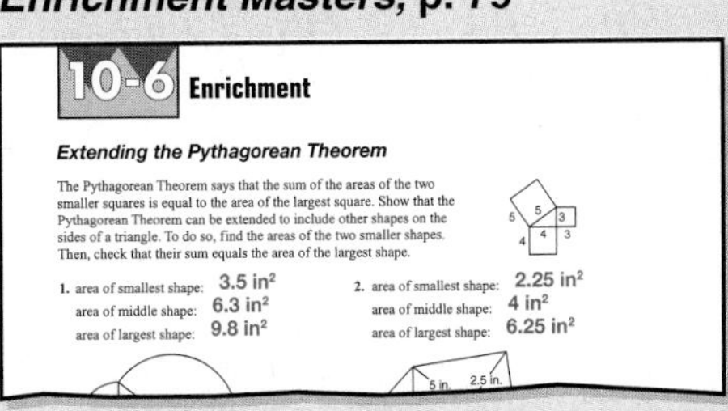

10-6 Enrichment

Extending the Pythagorean Theorem

The Pythagorean Theorem says that the sum of the areas of the two smaller squares is equal to the area of the largest square. Show that the Pythagorean Theorem can be extended to include other shapes on the sides of a triangle. To do so, find the areas of the two smaller shapes. Then, check that their sum equals the area of the largest shape.

1. area of smallest shape: 3.5 in^2
area of middle shape: 6.3 in^2
area of largest shape: 9.8 in^2

2. area of smallest shape: 2.25 in^2
area of middle shape: 4 in^2
area of largest shape: 6.25 in^2

Activity Ask students to describe the role mathematics plays in the work of a stained glass artist. Why would it be useful for the artist to find the areas of circles? **Many windows have curved sides, and other art objects are designed as circles or parts of circles.**

GET READY

Objective Students estimate the area of a figure by using probability.

Optional Resources
Hands-On Lab Masters
- grid paper, p. 10
- worksheet, p. 64

Overhead Manipulative Resources
- counters

Manipulative Kit
- ruler
- compass
- counters

MANAGEMENT TIPS

Recommended Time
30 minutes

Getting Started Discuss the difference between experimental and theoretical probability. Use experiments such as flipping a coin or spinning a spinner to demonstrate the distinction. Ask students whether it is possible to flip 10 heads in a row. Ask them to explain how doing this many trials of an experiment affects the relationship between experimental and theoretical probability. **The greater the number of trials, the closer the two probabilities are likely to become.**

For the **Activity**, the theoretical probability that the counters will land inside the circle is $\frac{\text{area of the circle}}{\text{area of the square}}$ or $\frac{6.25\pi}{64}$, which is a little less than $\frac{1}{3}$.

COOPERATIVE LEARNING

10-7A Probability and Area Models

A Preview of Lesson 10-7

 inch grid paper

 ruler

 compass

 small counters

In this lab, you will investigate the relationship between area and probability.

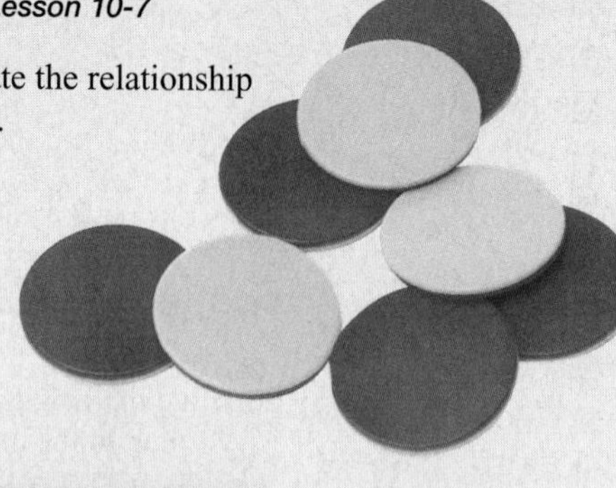

TRY THIS

Work in groups of three.

Step 1 On your grid paper, draw a square that has sides 8 inches long. Inside the square, draw a circle with a radius of 2.5 inches.

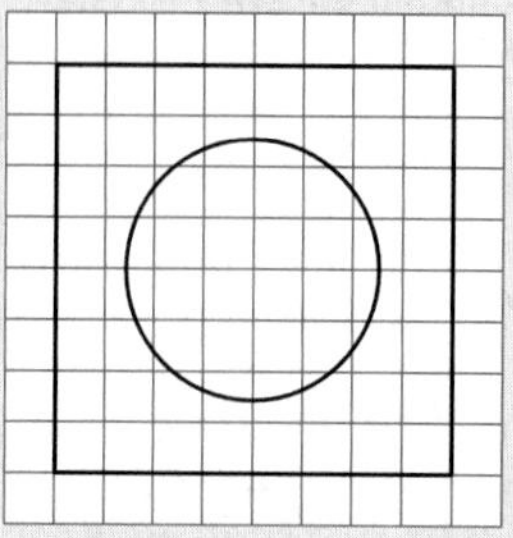

Step 2 Hold 20 counters about 5 inches above the paper and drop them onto the paper.

Step 3 Count the number of counters that landed completely within the square. (This includes those that landed within the circle.) Count the number that landed completely inside the circle. Do not count those that landed on the circle itself. These two numbers make up the first sample. Record your results.

Step 4 Repeat Steps 2 and 3 nine more times, recording your results each time.

Step 5 Add the results of your ten samples to find the total number of counters that fell within the square and the total number that fell within the circle.

Step 6 The probability that a counter will land inside the circle is expressed by the fraction:

$$\text{probability} = \frac{\text{total counters within the circle}}{\text{total counters within the square}}$$

Calculate the experimental probability based on your data.

Step 7 You can use experimental probability to estimate the area of the circle.

$$P(\text{probability}) = \frac{c\text{ (area of a circle)}}{s\text{ (area of square)}}$$

Substitute your experimental probability for P. Calculate the area of the square and substitute it for s. Then solve for c to find the approximate area of the circle.

ON YOUR OWN

1. Count the number of grid squares inside the circle to get an estimate of its area. Since many of the squares are not complete squares, you will need to combine two or three partial squares to get a better estimate of the equivalent number of complete squares. How does this estimate of the area compare with the experimental probability estimate you found in Step 7? **About 20 in^2; they are about the same.**
2. Using the radius of 2.5 inches and the formula $A = \pi r^2$, find the area of the circle. How does it compare with your experimental probability estimate? **About 19.6 in^2; they are about the same.**
3. Repeat this activity with a triangle inside your square. **See students' work.**

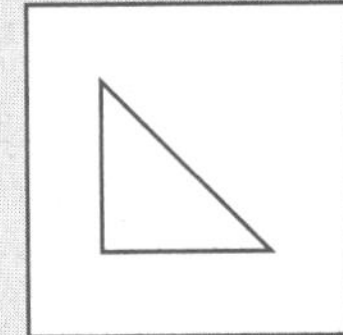

4. Repeat this activity with a trapezoid inside your square. **See students' work.**

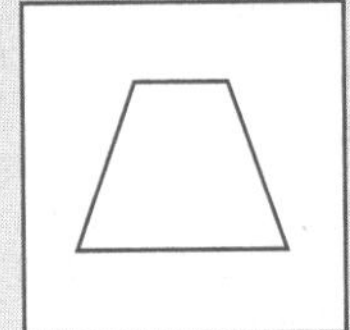

5. ***Look Ahead*** Find the probability that a randomly-dropped counter will fall in the shaded region. **$\frac{2}{7}$**

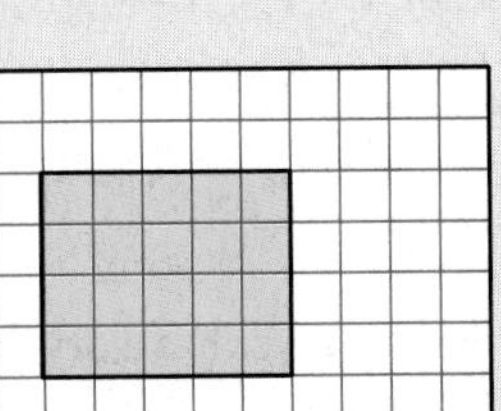

Have students write a paragraph describing when probability using area models could be used in a real-world situation.

ASSESS

Have students complete Exercises 1–5. Watch for students who confuse the area measurements with the probability ratios. Explain that they can either use probability to estimate one of the areas or use the ratio of the two areas to calculate the probability.

***Hands-On Lab Masters*, p. 64**

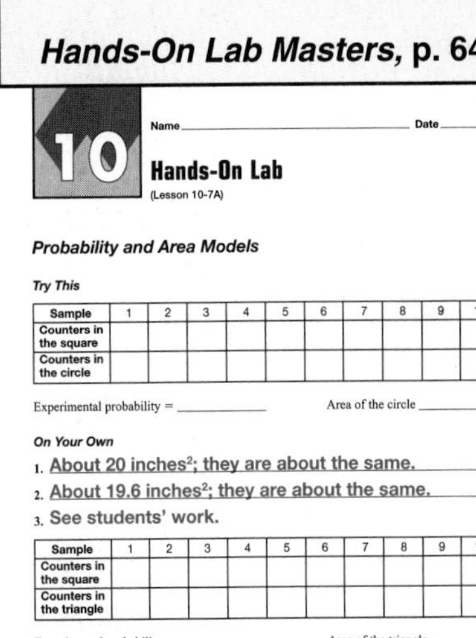

10 Name ______ Date ______

Hands-On Lab
(Lesson 10-7A)

Probability and Area Models

Try This

Sample	1	2	3	4	5	6	7	8	9	10	Sum
Counters in the square											
Counters in the circle											

Experimental probability = ______ Area of the circle ______

On Your Own

1. About 20 inches^2; they are about the same.
2. About 19.6 inches^2; they are about the same.
3. See students' work.

Sample	1	2	3	4	5	6	7	8	9	10	Sum
Counters in the square											
Counters in the triangle											

Experimental probability = ______ Area of the triangle ______

4. See students' work.

Sample	1	2	3	4	5	6	7	8	9	10	Sum
Counters in the square											
Counters in the trapezoid											

Experimental probability = ______ Area of the trapezoid ______

5. **Look Ahead** The probability that a randomly-dropped counter will fall in the shaded region is $\frac{2}{7}$.

© Glencoe/McGraw-Hill 64 *Mathematics: Applications and Connections, Course 2*

10-7 Lesson Notes

Instructional Resources

- *Study Guide Masters,* p. 80
- *Practice Masters,* p. 80
- *Enrichment Masters,* p. 80
- Transparencies 10-7, A and B
- *Assessment and Evaluation Masters,* p. 268

CD-ROM Program
- Resource Lesson 10-7
- Interactive Lesson 10-7

Recommended Pacing	
Standard	Days 11 & 12 of 14
Honors	Day 11 of 13
Block	Day 6 of 7

1 FOCUS

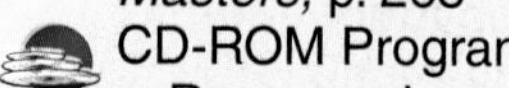

5-Minute Check *(Lesson 10-6)*

Find the area of each circle to the nearest tenth.

1. 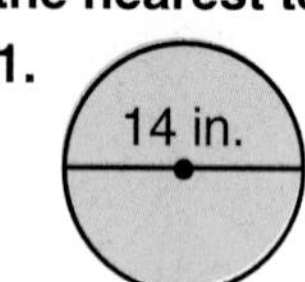

   153.9 in.²
2. radius: 3.4 m **36.3 m²**
3. diameter: 22 km **380.1 km²**
4. Find the radius of a circle whose area is 62 square feet. Round to the nearest tenth. **4.4 ft**

The 5-Minute Check is also available on **Transparency 10-7A** for this lesson.

Motivating the Lesson

Hands-On Activity Have students draw a target consisting of 4 concentric circles 1 inch apart. Have students discuss how to calculate the probability that a counter will land in each of the circles. Then have them perform the activity from Hands-On Lab 10-7A with the target.

10-7 Integration: Probability
Area Models

What **you'll learn**

You'll learn to find probability using area models.

When **am I ever going to use this?**

Knowing how to find the probability using area models can help you understand the game of darts.

At the age of 72, former president George Bush fulfilled a promise to himself. He went skydiving!

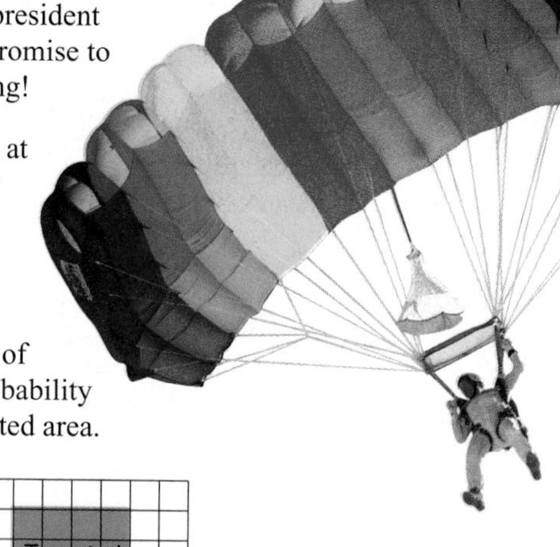

Suppose Mr. Bush landed at random in the rectangular field. What is the probability that he landed in the targeted area?

We can use the definition of probability to find the probability that he landed in the targeted area.

Targeted Area

$$\text{probability} = \frac{\text{number of ways to land in the targeted area}}{\text{number of ways to land in the field}}$$

In this case, the probability can be defined using area.

$$\text{probability} = \frac{\text{area of targeted area}}{\text{area of field}}$$

The area of the targeted area is 12 square units. The area of the field is 40 square units.

$$\text{probability} = \frac{12}{40} \quad \textit{The GCF of 12 and 40 is 4.}$$

$$= \frac{12 \div 4}{40 \div 4} \text{ or } \frac{3}{10}$$

The probability that George Bush landed in the targeted area is $\frac{3}{10}$.

1 **Skydiving** **A sky diver parachutes at random onto a square field that contains a pond. The field is 150 feet on a side, and the pond has an area of 750 square feet. What is the probability that the diver has a dry landing?**

area of field $= 150^2$ or 22,500 square feet

dry area of field $= 22{,}500 - 750$ or 21,750 square feet

$$\text{probability} = \frac{\text{dry area of field}}{\text{area of field}}$$

$$\text{probability} = \frac{21{,}750}{22{,}500} \text{ or } \frac{29}{30}$$

The probability that the diver has a dry landing is $\frac{29}{30}$.

Study Hint

Technology You can use a calculator to express $\frac{29}{30}$ as a decimal. $\frac{29}{30} = 0.9\overline{6}$ or $96.\overline{6}\%$

An *annulus* is the region bounded by two circles with the same center but different radii.

Example ② APPLICATION

Games **A dartboard has four annular rings surrounding a bull's-eye. The circles have radii of 1, 2, 3, 4, and 5 units. Suppose a dart is equally likely to hit any point on the board. Is the dart more likely to hit in the outermost ring or inside the region consisting of the bull's-eye and the two innermost rings?**

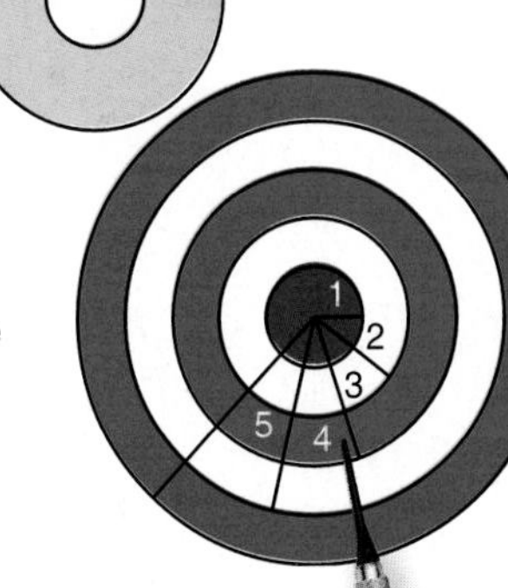

Step 1 Find the area of the target.

$A = \pi r^2$ *Formula for the area of a circle*

$A = \pi \cdot 5^2$ *Replace r with 5.*

[π] [×] 5 [x^2] [=] 78.53981634

The area of the target is about 78.5 square units.

Step 2 Find the area of the outermost ring.

The area of the outermost ring can be found by subtracting the area of a circle with radius of 4 units from the area of the target.

$A = \pi \cdot 5^2 - \pi \cdot 4^2$

[π] [×] 5 [x^2] [−] [π] [×] 4 [x^2] [=] 28.27433388

The area of the outermost ring is about 28.3 square units.

Step 3 Find the area of the region consisting of the bull's-eye and the two innermost rings.

$A = \pi \cdot 3^2$

[π] [×] 3 [x^2] [=] 28.27433388

The area of the region is about 28.3 square units.

In both cases, the probability is about $\frac{28.3}{78.5}$. The dart is as likely to hit in the outermost ring as it is to hit the bull's-eye and the two innermost rings.

Study Hint

Technology You can use a calculator to express $\frac{28.3}{78.5}$ as a decimal. $\frac{28.3}{78.5} \approx 0.361$ or about 36.1%.

CHECK FOR UNDERSTANDING

Communicating Mathematics

Read and study the lesson to answer each question.

1. ***Explain*** what is meant by a probability of a dry landing is $\frac{29}{30}$ in Example 1. Does the sky diver have a good chance for a dry landing? **See margin.**
2. ***Write*** the equation you would use to estimate the area of the trapezoid at the right if 4 out of 20 counters landed in the trapezoid. $\frac{4}{20} = \frac{a}{84}$

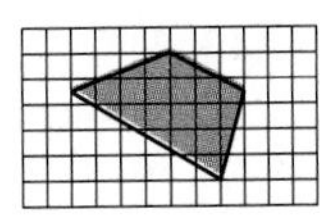

2 TEACH

Transparency 10-7B contains a teaching aid for this lesson.

Reading Mathematics The concept of probability may be difficult for students to grasp. Discuss it in contrast to *possibility* or *certainty*. Have students define *probability* in their own words and give examples of everyday situations involving probability, such as whether it will rain, whether Ken Griffey, Jr., will hit a home run, or whether a baby will be a boy or a girl.

In-Class Examples

For Example 1

Find the probability that a golf ball will land in the shaded region shown. $\frac{1}{6}$

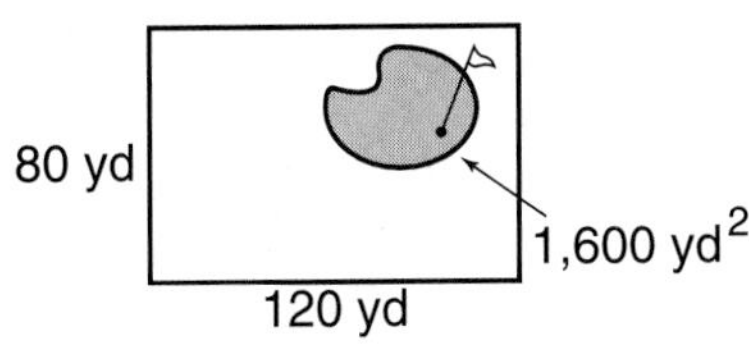

For Example 2

Mr. Ling is sitting in a dunking booth. What is the probability that one of his students will hit the circular dunking arm and dunk Mr. Ling? $\frac{7}{900}$

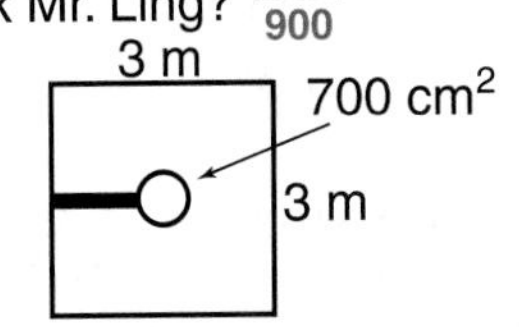

3 PRACTICE/APPLY

Check for Understanding

If students need additional practice or instruction after completing Exercises 1–6, one of these options may be helpful.

- Extra Practice, see p. 597
- Reteaching Activity
- *Study Guide Masters,* p. 80
- *Practice Masters,* p. 80

Additional Answer

1. **29 out of 30 random landings should be dry. The sky diver has a good chance of a dry landing.**

Reteaching the Lesson

Activity Point out that the total number of squares in a figure represents the number of possible outcomes and is expressed as the denominator of the fraction. Guide students to see that the shaded squares of the target represent favorable outcomes. Their sum is the numerator of the fraction.

Assignment Guide

Core: 7–19 odd, 20–22
Enriched: 8–16 even, 17, 19–22

Additional Answers

3a. Sample answer:

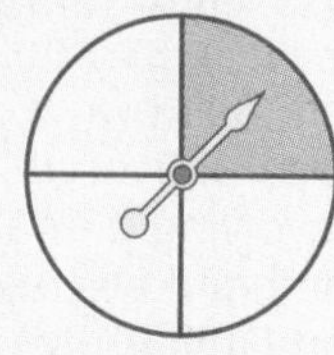

3b. Sample answer:

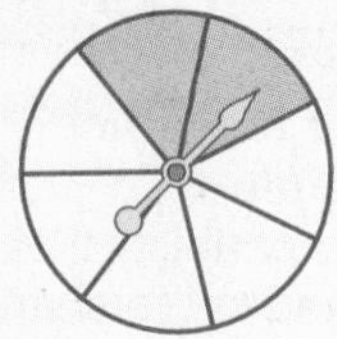

3c. Sample answer:

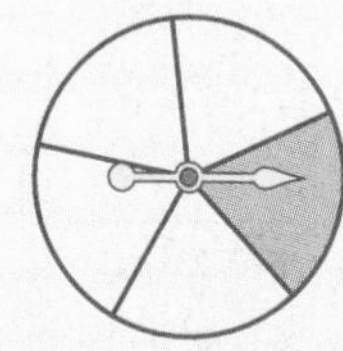

3d. The spinner in part b; since $\frac{1}{4} = \frac{35}{140}$, $\frac{2}{7} = \frac{40}{140}$, and $20\% = \frac{20}{100} = \frac{1}{5} = \frac{28}{140}$. $\frac{2}{7} > \frac{1}{4} > 20\%$.

***Study Guide Masters*, p. 80**

Name ______________ Date ______

10-7 Study Guide

Integration: Probability
Area Models

Determine the probability that a randomly-dropped counter will fall in the shaded area. Each small square has an area of 1 ft².

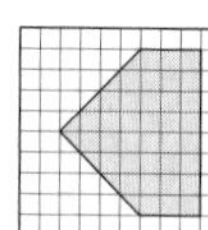

The area of the entire region is 100 ft².
The area of the shaded region is about 40 ft².

$\text{probability} = \frac{\text{number of ways an event can occur}}{\text{number of possible outcomes}}$

$= \frac{40}{100}$ or $\frac{2}{5}$

Find the probability that a randomly-dropped counter will fall in the shaded region.

1. 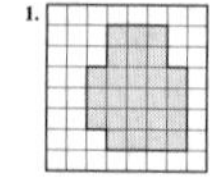 $\frac{25}{64}$

2. 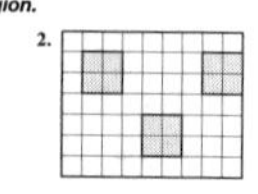 $\frac{12}{63} = \frac{4}{21}$

3. 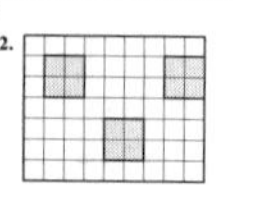 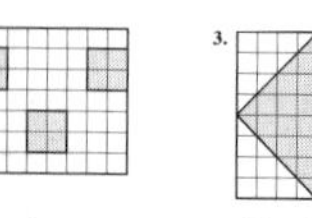 $\frac{40}{72} = \frac{5}{9}$

4. 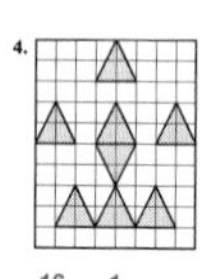 $\frac{16}{80} = \frac{1}{5}$

5. 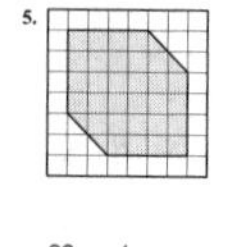 $\frac{32}{64} = \frac{1}{2}$

6. 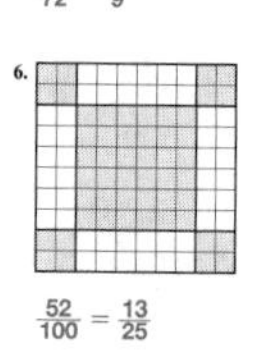 $\frac{52}{100} = \frac{13}{25}$

 T80 *Mathematics: Applications and Connections, Course 2*

Math Journal

3. Suppose that you are playing a game that uses a spinner and you need the spinner to stop on the red section for you to win the game.
   a. Draw a spinner where the probability of you winning is $\frac{1}{4}$.
   b. Draw a spinner where the probability of you winning is $\frac{2}{7}$.
   c. Draw a spinner where the probability of you winning is 20%.
   d. Write a short paragraph telling which spinner would give you a better chance of winning and why. **a–d. See margin.**

Guided Practice

Find the probability that a randomly-dropped counter will fall in the shaded region.

4. 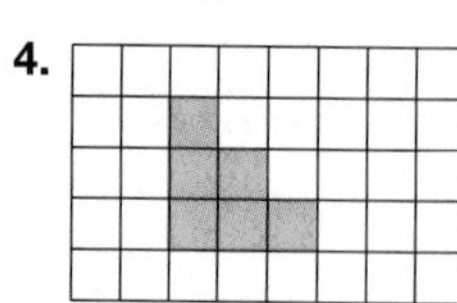 $\frac{3}{20}$ **or 0.15**

5. 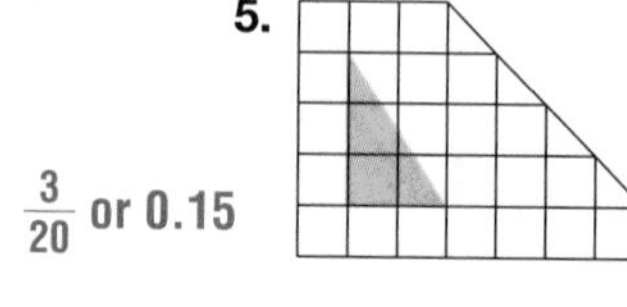 $\frac{6}{55}$ **or about 0.109**

6. ***Golf*** A golfer tees off and the ball lands in the rectangular region at the right. What is the probability that the ball lands on the green? $\frac{3}{8}$ **or 0.375**

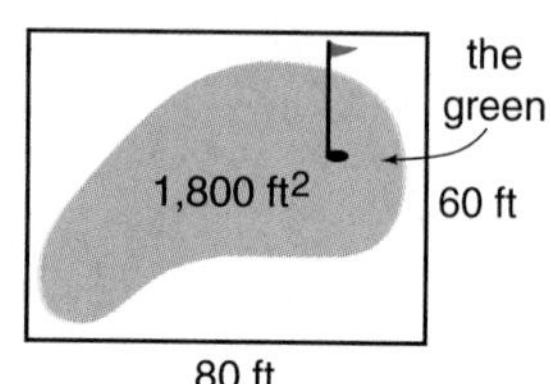

EXERCISES

Practice

Find the probability that a randomly-dropped counter will fall in the shaded region.

7. 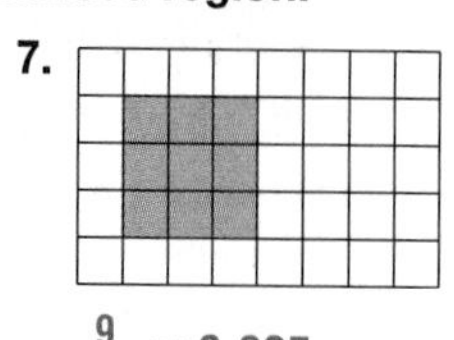 $\frac{9}{40}$ **or 0.225**

8. $\frac{12}{35}$ **or about 0.343**

9. 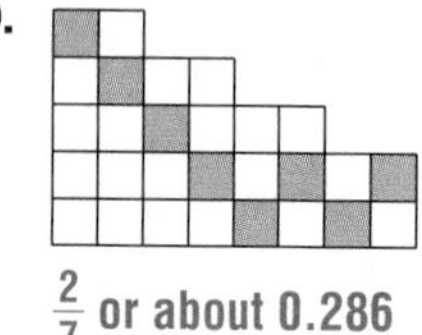 $\frac{2}{7}$ **or about 0.286**

10. **about 0.419**

11. $\frac{6}{35}$ **or about 0.171**

12. 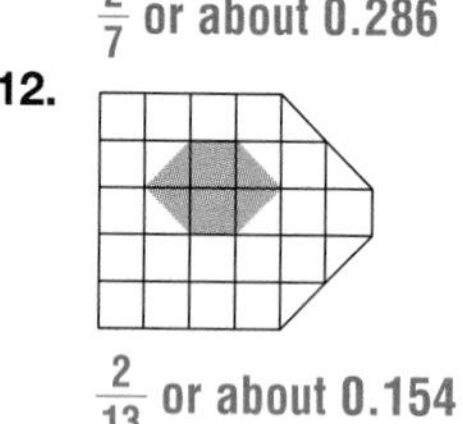 $\frac{2}{13}$ **or about 0.154**

13. Draw a square on a piece of grid paper that is 6 units on a side. Draw a triangle inside the square that has a base of 3 units and a height of 4 units. What is the probability that a randomly-dropped counter will fall in the triangle? **See margin for drawing;** $\frac{1}{6}$ **or about 0.167.**

Additional Answer

13. Sample answer:

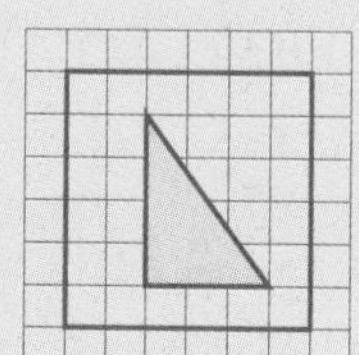

14. ***Draw*** a square on a piece of grid paper that is 10 units on a side. Draw a trapezoid inside the square so that the probability that a randomly-dropped counter will fall in the trapezoid is 24%. **See margin.**

15. ***Geometry*** A tangram, a puzzle that originated in China, consists of 7 pieces that form a square as shown. These pieces can be rearranged to form shapes of animals, people, and other objects. Suppose a counter is randomly dropped on the tangram. Find the probability that the counter will land on the small square. (*Hint:* The side of the small square is $\frac{1}{4}$ of the diagonal of the large square.) **$\frac{1}{8}$ or 0.125**

Applications and Problem Solving

16. ***Games*** A contestant throws a dart at a wall partially covered with balloons. If a balloon is popped, the contestant wins a prize. The wall has an area of 20 square feet. Eight square feet are covered with balloons. What is the probability that a contestant wins? **$\frac{2}{5}$ or 0.4**

17. ***Computer Technology*** A diskette contains 2,847 clusters of storage space. Suppose that 5 clusters are defective. What is the probability that information that needs to be saved will be saved to a portion of the diskette that is not defective? **$\frac{2,842}{2,847}$ or about 0.998**

18. ***Working on the CHAPTER Project*** Refer to the map you drew on page 407. Suppose a meteor heading toward Earth does not disintegrate as it passes through the atmosphere. What is the probability that the meteor will land in water? **about $\frac{7}{10}$**

19. ***Critical Thinking*** Odessa wins a prize by tossing a quarter onto a grid board so that it doesn't touch a line. The sides of the small squares of the grid are 40 millimeters long and the radius of a quarter is 12 millimeters long. What is the probability of winning? (*Hint:* Find the area where the center of the coin could land so that the edges don't touch a line.) **$\frac{4}{25}$ or 0.16**

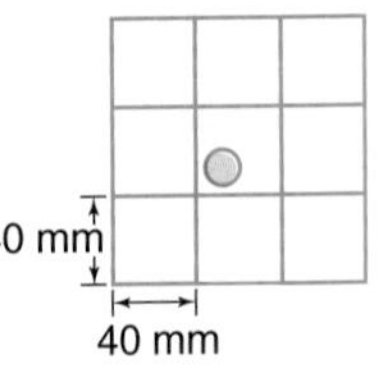

Mixed Review

20. ***Architecture*** The Connaught Centre building in Hong Kong has 1,748 circular windows. The diameter of each window is 2.4 meters. Find the total area of the glass in the windows. *(Lesson 10-6)* **about 7,907.8 m²**

21. **Standardized Test Practice** Which polygon is a regular polygon? *(Lesson 9-2)* **D**

A  **B**  **C** 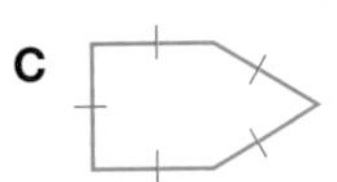 **D** 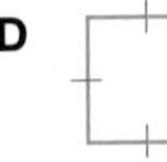

For **Extra Practice,** see page 597.

22. ***Algebra*** Solve $\frac{15}{32} = \frac{5}{p}$. *(Lesson 8-3)* **$10\frac{2}{3}$**

Exercise 18 asks students to advance to the next stage of work on the Chapter Project. You may want students to compare their probability calculations.

4 ASSESS

Closing Activity

Modeling Have students use grid paper to draw a model of a target for which the probability of landing an arrow in a shaded region is $\frac{3}{8}$. **Sample answer: 48-square unit target with an 18-square unit region shaded.**

Chapter 10, Quiz D (Lesson 10-7) is available in the *Assessment and Evaluation Masters,* p. 268.

Additional Answer

14. Sample answer:

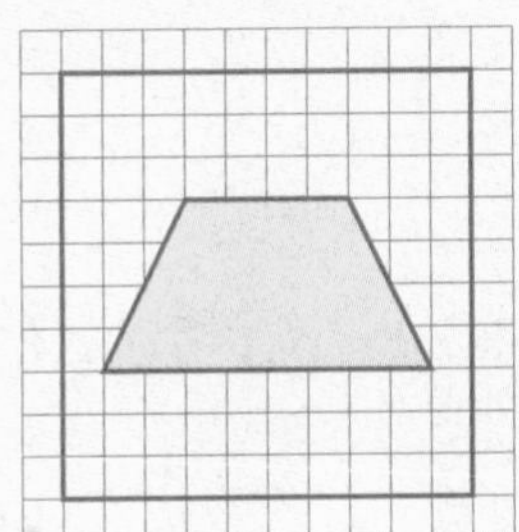

***Practice Masters,* p. 80**

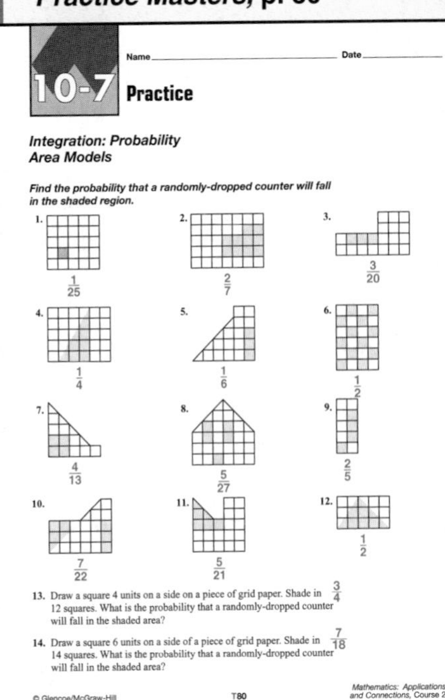

Name ________ Date ________

10-7 Practice

Integration: Probability
Area Models

Find the probability that a randomly-dropped counter will fall in the shaded region.

1. $\frac{1}{25}$ 2. $\frac{2}{7}$ 3. $\frac{3}{20}$
4. $\frac{1}{4}$ 5. $\frac{1}{6}$ 6. $\frac{1}{2}$
7. $\frac{4}{13}$ 8. $\frac{5}{27}$ 9. $\frac{2}{5}$
10. $\frac{7}{22}$ 11. $\frac{5}{21}$ 12. $\frac{1}{2}$

13. Draw a square 4 units on a side on a piece of grid paper. Shade in 12 squares. What is the probability that a randomly-dropped counter will fall in the shaded area? $\frac{3}{4}$

14. Draw a square 6 units on a side of a piece of grid paper. Shade in 14 squares. What is the probability that a randomly-dropped counter will fall in the shaded area? $\frac{7}{18}$

 T80 *Mathematics: Applications and Connections, Course 2*

Extending the Lesson

***Enrichment Masters,* p. 80**

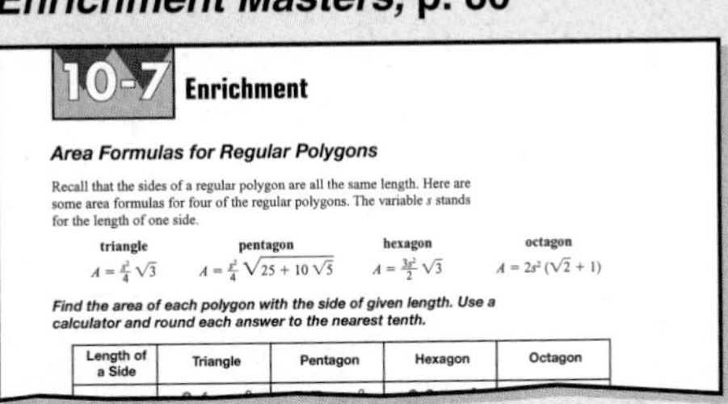

10-7 Enrichment

Area Formulas for Regular Polygons

Recall that the sides of a regular polygon are all the same length. Here are some area formulas for four of the regular polygons. The variable s stands for the length of one side.

triangle	pentagon	hexagon	octagon
$A = \frac{s^2}{4}\sqrt{3}$	$A = \frac{s^2}{4}\sqrt{25 + 10\sqrt{5}}$	$A = \frac{3s^2}{2}\sqrt{3}$	$A = 2s^2(\sqrt{2} + 1)$

Find the area of each polygon with the side of given length. Use a calculator and round each answer to the nearest tenth.

Length of a Side	Triangle	Pentagon	Hexagon	Octagon

Activity Have students obtain a state map. Ask them to imagine that scientists have predicted that an old satellite is going to land somewhere in the state, but they have no idea exactly where. Have students determine the probability that it will land in your county or in any other identifiable region.

Vocabulary

This section provides a listing of the new terms, properties, and phrases that were introduced in this chapter. Have students define each term and provide an example or two of it, if appropriate.

Understanding and Using the Vocabulary

These exercises check students' understanding of the terms by using a variety of verbal formats including matching, completion, and true/false.

Glossaries A complete glossary of terms appears on pages 656–663. The glossary also appears in Spanish on pages 664–672.

CHAPTER 10

Study Guide and Assessment

interNET CONNECTION **Chapter Review** For additional lesson-by-lesson review, visit: www.glencoe.com/sec/math/mac/mathnet

Vocabulary

After completing this chapter, you should be able to define each term, concept, or phrase and give an example or two of each.

Problem Solving
guess and check (p. 408)

Number and Operation
perfect square (p. 411)
radical sign (p. 411)
square (p. 410)
square root (p. 411)

Geometry
hypotenuse (p. 419)
inner measure (p. 423)
irregular figure (p. 423)
leg (p. 419)
outer measure (p. 423)
Pythagorean Theorem (p. 419)
trapezoid (p. 429)
triangle (p. 428)

13. $6^2 = 36$, $7^2 = 49$, and 45 is between 36 and 49. Since 45 is closer to 49 than 36, $\sqrt{45}$ is about 7.

Understanding and Using the Vocabulary

Choose the correct term or number to complete each sentence.

1. The number (64, 500) is a perfect square.
2. In a right triangle, the square of the length of the hypotenuse is (equal to, less than) the sum of the squares of the lengths of the legs.
3. A trapezoid is a quadrilateral with exactly one pair of (parallel, perpendicular) sides.
4. $A = \frac{1}{2}h(a + b)$ is the formula for the area of a (triangle, trapezoid).
5. $A = \pi r^2$ is the formula for the area of a (square, circle).
6. Probability can be expressed as a (radical, fraction).
7. The square of 9 is (3, 81).
8. A (square, square root) of 49 is 7.
9. The $\sqrt{\ }$ symbol is called a (radical, perfect square) sign.
10. The longest side of a right triangle is the (leg, hypotenuse).
11. The legs of a right triangle form a (right angle, hypotenuse).
12. A trapezoid (is, is not) an irregular figure.

In Your Own Words

13. ***Explain*** how you would estimate the square root of 45.

MindJogger Videoquizzes

MindJogger Videoquizzes provide an alternative review of concepts presented in this chapter. Students work in teams to answer questions, gaining points for correct answers. The questions are presented in three rounds.

Round 1 Concepts–5 questions
Round 2 Skills–4 questions
Round 3 Problem Solving–4 questions

Objectives & Examples

Upon completing this chapter, you should be able to:

- find squares of numbers and square roots of perfect squares *(Lesson 10-1)*

Evaluate $\sqrt{196}$.

Since $14^2 = 196$, $\sqrt{196} = 14$.

Review Exercises

Use these exercises to review and prepare for the chapter test.

Find the square of each number.

14. 9 **81**
15. 22 **484**
16. 43 **1,849**
17. 50 **2,500**

Find each square root.

18. $\sqrt{16}$ **4**
19. $\sqrt{0}$ **0**
20. $\sqrt{225}$ **15**
21. $\sqrt{256}$ **16**

- estimate square roots *(Lesson 10-2)*

Estimate $\sqrt{29}$ to the nearest whole number.

$$25 < 29 < 36$$
$$\sqrt{25} < \sqrt{29} < \sqrt{36}$$
$$5 < \sqrt{29} < 6$$

Since 29 is closer to 25 than 36, the best whole number estimate is 5.

Estimate each square root to the nearest whole number.

22. $\sqrt{6}$ **2**
23. $\sqrt{37}$ **6**
24. $\sqrt{99}$ **10**
25. $\sqrt{48}$ **7**
26. $\sqrt{90}$ **9**
27. $\sqrt{410}$ **20**

- find length using the Pythagorean Theorem *(Lesson 10-3)*

Find the missing measure.

$$a^2 + b^2 = c^2$$
$$4^2 + 12^2 = c^2$$
$$16 + 144 = c^2$$
$$160 = c^2$$
$$\sqrt{160} = c$$
$$12.6 \approx c$$

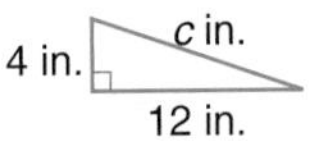

4 in.
c in.
12 in.

The missing measure is about 12.6 inches.

Find the missing measure for each right triangle. Round to the nearest tenth.

28. a: 5 ft; b: 6 ft **7.8 ft**
29. b: 10 yd; c: 12 yd **6.6 yd**
30. a: 12 in.; b: 4 in. **12.6 in.**
31. a: 7 m; c: 15 m **13.3 m**

- estimate the area of irregular figures *(Lesson 10-4)*

inner measure: 6
outer measure: 12
mean: $\frac{6 + 12}{2} = 9$
The area is about 9 square units.

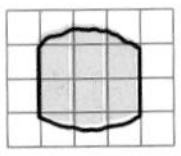

Estimate the area of each figure.

32. 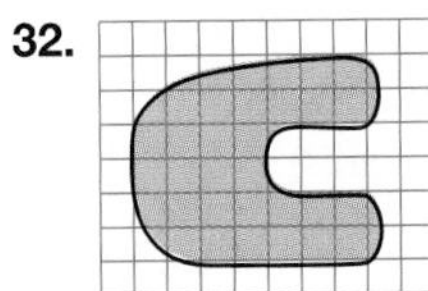
34 units²

33. 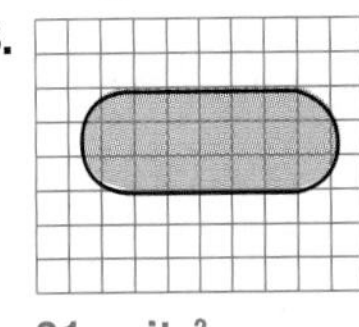
21 units²

Objectives & Examples

This section reviews the skills and concepts of the chapter and shows completely worked examples.

Review Exercises

These exercises provide practice for the corresponding objectives.

***Assessment and Evaluation Masters*, pp. 255–256**

Name ____________ Date ________

Chapter 10 Test, Form 1B

1. Camille is the youngest of four sisters. Each sister is four years older than the next youngest sister. The combined ages of Camille and her sisters is 68. How old is Camille?
A. 23 B. 15 C. 11 D. 12 — 1. C
2. Find 30^2.
A. 450 B. 30 C. 300 D. 900 — 2. D
3. Find $\sqrt{196}$.
A. 14 B. 98 C. 49 D. 16 — 3. A
4. Estimate $\sqrt{23}$ to the nearest whole number.
A. 4 B. 11 C. 6 D. 5 — 4. D
5. Estimate $\sqrt{102}$ to the nearest whole number.
A. 10 B. 11 C. 12 D. 10,404 — 5. A
6. Estimate $\sqrt{520}$ to the nearest whole number.
A. 20 B. 22 C. 23 D. 24 — 6. C
7. Estimate $\sqrt{173}$ to the nearest tenth.
A. 29,929 B. 13.2 C. 5.6 D. 13.1 — 7. B
8. The lengths of the legs of a right triangle are 16 feet and 30 feet. Which equation would you solve to find the length of the hypotenuse?
A. $16^2 + x^2 = 30$ B. $16^2 + 30^2 = x^2$
C. $30^2 + x^2 = 16$ D. $30^2 - 16^2 = x^2$ — 8. B
9. The length of one leg of a right triangle is 24 meters, and the length of the hypotenuse is 25 meters. Find the length of the other leg.
A. 7 m B. 35 m C. 49 m D. 1 m — 9. A
10. Which could be the lengths of the sides of a right triangle?
A. 7 cm, 8 cm, 10 cm B. 20 m, 30 m, 40 m
C. 12 ft, 15 ft, 20 ft D. 6 cm, 8 cm, 10 cm — 10. D
11. Estimate the area of the figure at the right.
A. about 28 units²
B. about 17 units²
C. about 39 units²
D. about 32 units² — 11. A

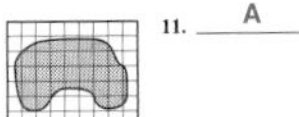

 255 *Mathematics: Applications and Connections*, Course 2

Chapter 10 Test, Form 1B (continued)

12. Estimate the area of the figure at the right.
A. about 8 units²
B. about 29 units²
C. about 20 units²
D. about 30 units² — 12. C

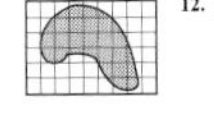

13. Find the area of the triangle at the right.
A. 225 m² B. 360 m²
C. 180 m² D. 90 m² — 13. C

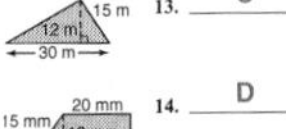

14. Find the area of the trapezoid at the right.
A. 348 mm² B. 588 mm²
C. 735 mm² D. 294 mm² — 14. D

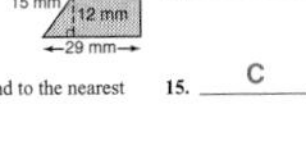

15. Find the area of a circle with a diameter of 24 feet. Round to the nearest tenth.
A. 1,809.6 ft² B. 37.7 ft²
C. 452.4 ft² D. 75.4 ft² — 15. C
16. Find the area of the circle shown at the right. Round to the nearest tenth.
A. 5026.5 m² B. 125.7 m²
C. 1,256.6 m² D. 62.8 m² — 16. C

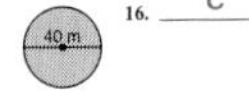

17. Find the probability that a randomly-dropped counter will fall in the shaded region shown at the right.
A. $\frac{1}{4}$ B. $\frac{1}{12}$
C. $\frac{1}{5}$ D. $\frac{5}{1}$ — 17. C

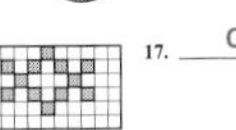

18. Find the probability that a randomly-dropped counter will fall in the shaded region shown at the right.
A. $\frac{4}{15}$ B. $\frac{4}{11}$
C. $\frac{1}{16}$ D. $\frac{15}{4}$ — 18. A

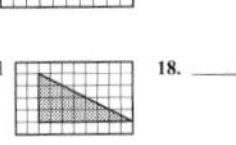

19. A 41-foot guy wire is used to brace an antenna. The wire is anchored 9 feet from the base of the antenna. How tall is the antenna?
A. 42 ft B. 40 ft C. 80 ft D. 22 ft — 19. B
20. The Garcias drove 24 miles east and then 7 miles north. At that point, what is the straight-line distance from their starting point?
A. 31 miles B. 625 miles C. 312.5 miles D. 25 miles — 20. D

 256 *Mathematics: Applications and Connections*, Course 2

Assessment and Evaluation

Six forms of the Chapter 10 Test are available in the *Assessment and Evaluation Masters* as shown in the chart.

1A	Multiple Choice	Honors
1B	Multiple Choice	Average
1C	Multiple Choice	Basic
2A	Free Response	Honors
2B	Free Response	Average
2C	Free Response	Basic

Chapter 10 Test, Form 1B, is shown at the right. Chapter 10 Test, Form 2B, is shown on the next page.

Study Guide and Assessment

Assessment and Evaluation Masters, **pp. 261–262**

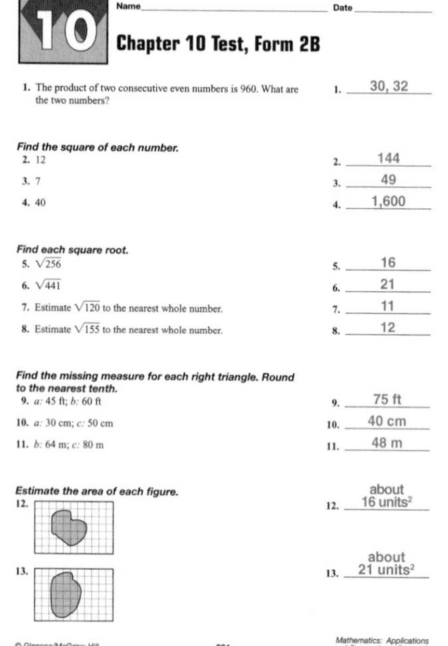

10 Name______________ Date______

Chapter 10 Test, Form 2B

1. The product of two consecutive even numbers is 960. What are the two numbers? — 1. 30, 32

Find the square of each number.

2. 12 — 2. 144
3. 7 — 3. 49
4. 40 — 4. 1,600

Find each square root.

5. $\sqrt{256}$ — 5. 16
6. $\sqrt{441}$ — 6. 21
7. Estimate $\sqrt{120}$ to the nearest whole number. — 7. 11
8. Estimate $\sqrt{155}$ to the nearest whole number. — 8. 12

Find the missing measure for each right triangle. Round to the nearest tenth.

9. *a*: 45 ft; *b*: 60 ft — 9. 75 ft
10. *a*: 30 cm; *c*: 50 cm — 10. 40 cm
11. *b*: 64 m; *c*: 80 m — 11. 48 m

Estimate the area of each figure.

12. — 12. about 16 units²
13. — 13. about 21 units²

 261 *Mathematics: Applications and Connections, Course 2*

10 **Chapter 10 Test, Form 2B (continued)**

Find the area of each figure.

14. — 14. 360 m²

15. — 15. 576 cm²

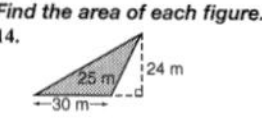

Find the area of each circle. Round to the nearest tenth.

16. radius: 18 cm — 16. 1,017.9 cm²

17. — 17. 907.9 in²

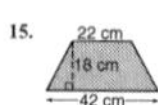

Solve.

18. Find the probability that a randomly-dropped counter will fall in the shaded region. — 18. $\frac{1}{5}$

19. A 15-foot ladder is propped against a wall. The base of the ladder is 9 feet from the base of the wall. How far up the wall does the ladder reach? — 19. 12 feet

20. Sally drives 10 miles east and then 10 miles south. At this point, what is the straight-line distance from her starting point? Estimate to the nearest whole number. — 20. 14 miles

 262 *Mathematics: Applications and Connections, Course 2*

Objectives & Examples

- find the areas of triangles and trapezoids *(Lesson 10-5)*

Area of a triangle: $A = \frac{1}{2}bh$

Area of a trapezoid: $A = \frac{1}{2}h(a + b)$

Find the area of the figure.

$$A = \frac{1}{2}h(a + b)$$
$$A = \frac{1}{2}(3)(2 + 8)$$
$$A = 15$$

The area of the figure is 15 cm².

Review Exercises

Find the area of each figure to the nearest tenth.

34.

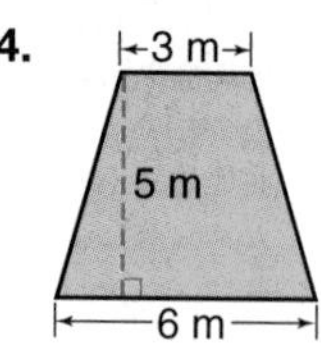

22.5 m²

35.

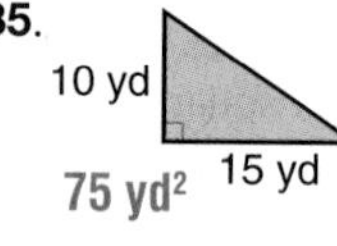

75 yd²

36. 5 in. 5 in. 10 in. 37.5 in²

37. 12 ft 6 ft 36 ft²

Objectives & Examples

- find the area of circles *(Lesson 10-6)*

Area of a circle: $A = \pi r^2$

Find the area of a circle with a radius of 5 inches.

$$A = \pi r^2$$
$$A = \pi \cdot 5^2$$
$$A \approx 78.5$$

The area of the circle is about 78.5 in².

Review Exercises

Find the area of each circle to the nearest tenth.

38. radius: 8 ft **201.1 ft²**

39. diameter: 14 mm **153.9 mm²**

40. diameter: 15 yd **176.7 yd²**

41. radius: 25 in. **1,963.5 in²**

38–41. Answers are calculated using the π key on a calculator and then rounded.

Objectives & Examples

- find probability using area models *(Lesson 10-7)*

probability of hitting a white square

$$= \frac{\text{area of white squares}}{\text{total area}}$$
$$= \frac{8}{25}$$

Review Exercises

Find the probability that a randomly-dropped counter will fall in the shaded region.

42.

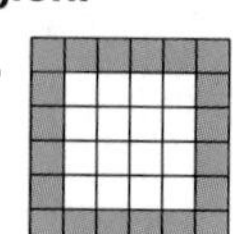

$\frac{5}{9}$

43.

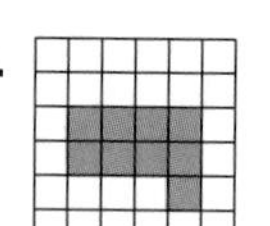

$\frac{1}{4}$

Test and Review Software

You may use this software, a combination of an item generator and item bank, to create your own tests or worksheets. Types of items include free response, multiple choice, short answer, and open ended.

CD-ROM Program

The CD-ROM Program contains an Assessment Game whose questions review the concepts in this chapter.

Applications & Problem Solving

44. ***Guess and Check*** Admission to the aquarium is $4 for adults, $1.50 for children under 12, and $2 for seniors. Ten people paid a total of $26.50. If the group included 4 adults, how many children and seniors were in the group? *(Lesson 10-1A)* **3 children, 3 seniors**

45. ***Communication*** A telephone pole has a wire attached from the top of the pole to a point 30 feet from the base of the pole. If the pole is 20 feet tall, find the length of the wire. Round to the nearest tenth. *(Lesson 10-3)* **36.1 ft**

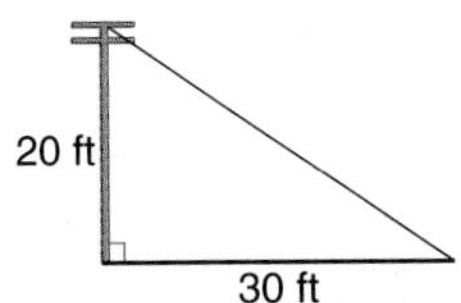

46. ***Gardening*** A lawn sprinkler can water a circular area with a radius of 20 feet. Find the area that can be watered with this sprinkler to the nearest tenth. *(Lesson 10-6)* **1,256.6 ft²**

47. ***Games*** A game at the state fair requires that a contestant throw a coin onto a board covered with different-colored squares. If the coin lands on a red square, the contestant wins. The board has an area of 15 square feet. Three square feet are covered with red squares. What is the probability of winning? *(Lesson 10-7)* $\frac{1}{5}$

Alternative Assessment

Open Ended

Suppose you want to build a patio that is in the shape of a trapezoid. You want the patio to have an area between 90 and 110 square feet. Draw a plan for the patio on grid paper. Show how to find the exact area of the patio.
See Answer Appendix.

Suppose you decide to replace part of the patio with a planter that is in the shape of a right triangle. The part of the patio that remains should still be a trapezoid. Add the planter to your plan. Show how to find the exact area of the planter and the exact area of the patio.
See Answer Appendix.

A practice test for Chapter 10 is provided on page 616.

Completing the CHAPTER Project

Use the following checklist to make sure your map is complete.

- ☑ The landmasses and bodies of water are the correct size.
- ☑ The estimates for the area of the landmasses and bodies of water are correct.
- ☑ A sentence describing the approximate part of Earth that is covered in water is included.

Add any finishing touches that you would like to make your map attractive.

Select one of the assignments from this chapter and place it in your portfolio. Attach a note to it explaining why you selected it.

Performance Assessment

Additional performance assessment tasks for this chapter are included in the *Assessment and Evaluation Masters* on page 265. A scoring guide is also provided on page 277.

Applications & Problem Solving

This section provides additional practice in solving real-world problems that involve the skills of this chapter.

Alternative Assessment

The ***Open Ended*** section provides students with a performance assessment opportunity to evaluate their work and understanding.

Students should complete the final stages of their project and prepare a class demonstration of their results. A scoring guide for the project is available in the *Investigations and Projects Masters,* p. 55.

Students should add to their portfolios at this time.

***Assessment and Evaluation Masters,* p. 265**

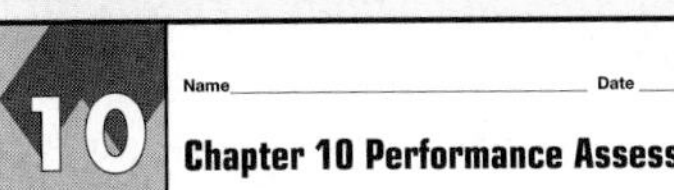

Instructions: Demonstrate your knowledge by giving a clear, concise solution to each problem. Be sure to include all relevant drawings and justify your answers. You may show your solutions in more than one way or investigate beyond the requirements of the problems.

1. a. Explain in your own words what is meant by the *square root* of a number.

b. Use a model to show that $\sqrt{17}$ is about 4.

c. State the Pythagorean Theorem in your own words.

d. Use a right triangle and squares to model $6^2 + 8^2 = 10^2$.

e. A carpenter is framing a house. The front of the house measures 48 feet. The width measures 36 feet. She measures diagonally across the house as shown. If the diagonal measurement is 62 feet, are the corners of the house square (right angles)? Explain your reasoning. Use a calculator.

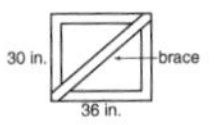

f. The carpenter is cutting a brace to keep a window frame square during installation. What is the length of the brace? Explain each step. Use a calculator.

30 in. brace 36 in.

2. Mrs. Cobel is preparing a bid for sodding a new city park. Her bid is for sodding all of the park except the fountain and garden areas. If she plans to submit a bid for $1.50 per square foot, tell what Mrs. Coble's bid will be. Show your work and explain your reasoning.

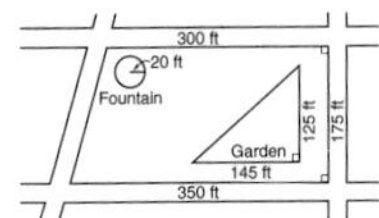

 265 *Mathematics: Applications and Connections, Course 2*

Standardized Test Practice

The Standardized Test Practice may be used to help students prepare for standardized tests. The test items are written in the same style as those in state proficiency tests and standardized tests like CAT, CTBS, ITBS, MAT, SAT, and Terra Nova. The test items cover skills and concepts covered up to this point in the text.

The pages can be used as an overnight assessment. After students have completed the pages, discuss how each problem can be solved, or provide copies of the solutions from the *Solutions Manual.*

***Assessment and Evaluation Masters*, p. 271**

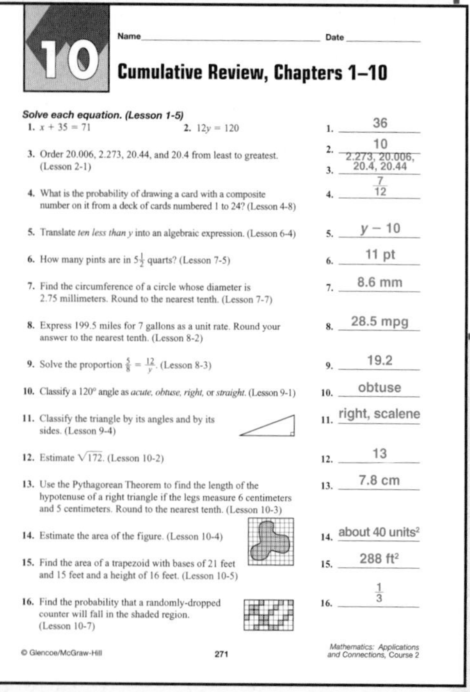

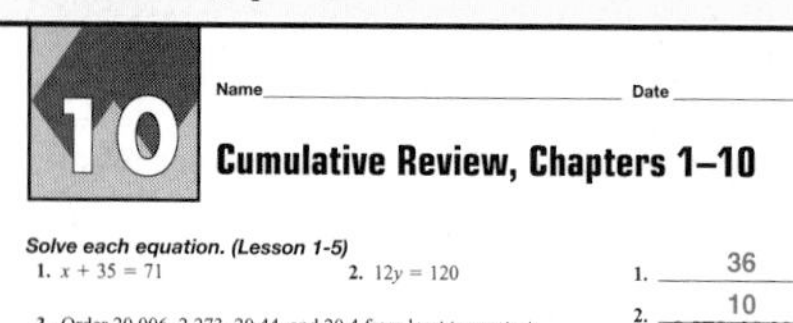

Name ______ Date ______

10 Cumulative Review, Chapters 1–10

Solve each equation. (Lesson 1-5)

1. $x + 35 = 71$ 2. $12y = 120$ — 1. 36 — 2. 10

3. Order 20.006, 2.273, 20.44, and 20.4 from least to greatest. (Lesson 2-1) — 3. 2.273, 20.006, 20.4, 20.44

4. What is the probability of drawing a card with a composite number on it from a deck of cards numbered 1 to 24? (Lesson 4-8) — 4. $\frac{7}{12}$

5. Translate *ten less than y* into an algebraic expression. (Lesson 6-4) — 5. $y - 10$

6. How many pints are in $5\frac{1}{2}$ quarts? (Lesson 7-5) — 6. 11 pt

7. Find the circumference of a circle whose diameter is 2.75 millimeters. Round to the nearest tenth. (Lesson 7-7) — 7. 8.6 mm

8. Express 199.5 miles for 7 gallons as a unit rate. Round your answer to the nearest tenth. (Lesson 8-2) — 8. 28.5 mpg

9. Solve the proportion $\frac{5}{8} = \frac{12}{y}$. (Lesson 8-3) — 9. 19.2

10. Classify a 120° angle as *acute, obtuse, right,* or *straight.* (Lesson 9-1) — 10. obtuse

11. Classify the triangle by its angles and by its sides. (Lesson 9-4) — 11. right, scalene

12. Estimate $\sqrt{172}$. (Lesson 10-2) — 12. 13

13. Use the Pythagorean Theorem to find the length of the hypotenuse of a right triangle if the legs measure 6 centimeters and 5 centimeters. Round to the nearest tenth. (Lesson 10-3) — 13. 7.8 cm

14. Estimate the area of the figure. (Lesson 10-4) — 14. about 40 units^2

15. Find the area of a trapezoid with bases of 21 feet and 15 feet and a height of 16 feet. (Lesson 10-5) — 15. 288 ft^2

16. Find the probability that a randomly-dropped counter will fall in the shaded region. (Lesson 10-7) — 16. $\frac{1}{3}$

 271 *Mathematics: Applications and Connections, Course 2*

Standardized Test Practice

Assessing Knowledge & Skills

Section One: Multiple Choice

There are eleven multiple choice questions in this section. Choose the best answer. If a correct answer is *not here*, choose the letter for Not Here.

1. Which regular polygon can be used by itself to make a tessellation? B

A pentagon
B hexagon
C heptagon
D nonagon

2. The maximum square footage of a storeroom is 1,500 square feet. What number line shows the range of square footage for this storeroom? J

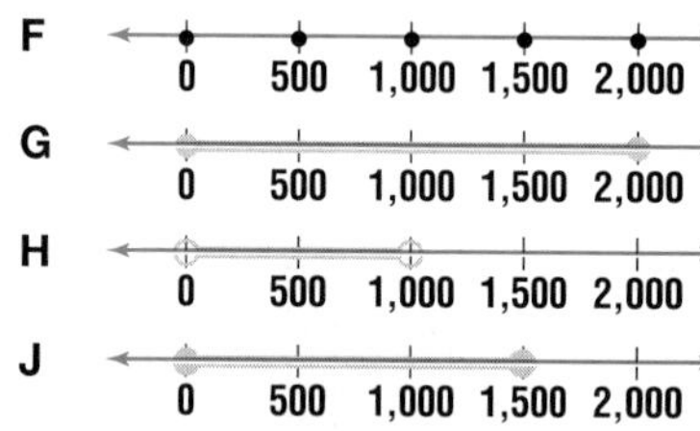

3. What is the probability that a randomly-dropped counter will fall in the shaded region? C

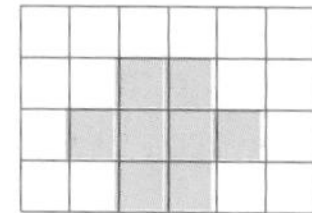

A $\frac{1}{8}$
B $\frac{1}{4}$
C $\frac{1}{3}$
D $\frac{1}{2}$

4. A coffee can contains 1 pound 10 ounces of coffee. How many ounces is this? H

F 18 oz
G 20 oz
H 26 oz
J 42 oz

Please note that Questions 5–11 have five answer choices.

5. How could you calculate the perimeter of an $8\frac{1}{2}$-by-11 piece of paper? C

A Add $8\frac{1}{2}$ and 11.
B Multiply 2 times $8\frac{1}{2}$ and add to 11.
C Add $8\frac{1}{2}$ and 11 and multiply the sum by 2.
D Multiply $8\frac{1}{2}$ and 11.
E Multiply 2 times 11 and add to $8\frac{1}{2}$.

6. There are 452 Calories in one handful of candy. If a handful of candy is 9 pieces, what is the best estimate of the number of Calories in each piece of candy? H

F 30 Calories
G 40 Calories
H 50 Calories
J 60 Calories
K 70 Calories

7. Tanya walks 5 kilometers east and 5 kilometers south. To the nearest kilometer, how far is she from her starting point? C

A 25 km
B 10 km
C 7 km
D 5 km
E 3 km

◀◀◀ Instructional Resources

Another cumulative review is shown at the left and is available in the *Assessment and Evaluation Masters,* p. 271.

8. The regular price of a compact disc player is \$279.83 without tax. Before tax is added, how much can be saved by buying a compact disc player on sale for \$225.65? H
   - F \$61.18
   - G \$57.18
   - H \$54.18
   - J \$54.08
   - K Not Here

9. Lyle's job is to pack textbooks into cartons. One day Lyle packed 504 textbooks into 36 cartons. If each carton contains the same number of textbooks, how many textbooks did Lyle put into each carton? B
   - A 12
   - B 14
   - C 28
   - D 50
   - E 56

10. A wall shaped like a trapezoid needs to be painted. The height of the wall is 12 feet, and the bases are 17 feet and 22 feet. If one can of paint covers 20 square feet, how many cans of paint will be needed to paint the wall? J
    - F 24 cans
    - G 21 cans
    - H 15 cans
    - J 12 cans
    - K Not Here

11. A fish tank holds 46.2 liters of water. If there should be 2.2 liters of water per fish, how many fish can be placed in the tank? C
    - A 2 fish
    - B 20 fish
    - C 21 fish
    - D 25 fish
    - E Not here

Test Practice For additional test practice questions, visit:

www.glencoe.com/sec/math/mac/mathnet

Test-Taking Tip THE PRINCETON REVIEW

You can prepare for standardized tests by working through practice tests such as this one. The more you work with questions in a format similar to the actual test, the better you become in the art of testing.

Section Two: Free Response

This section contains four questions for which you will provide short answers. Write your answers on your paper.

12. What are the vertices of $\triangle EFG$ after it is reflected over the y-axis?

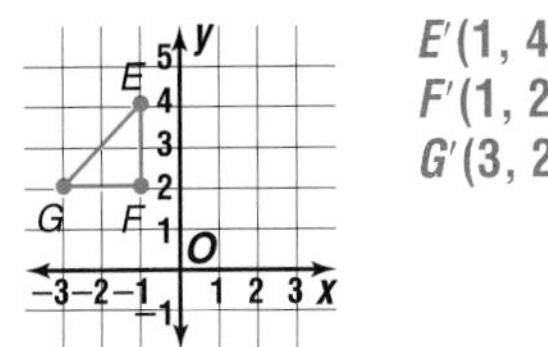

$E'(1, 4)$, $F'(1, 2)$, $G'(3, 2)$

13. Write the expression that represents five more than a number. $n + 5$

14. How many triangles of the shape and size of the shaded triangle can divide into the trapezoid evenly? 3

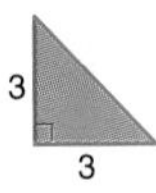

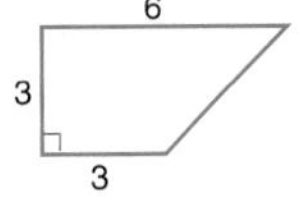

15. What is the area of the trapezoid? 120 ft²

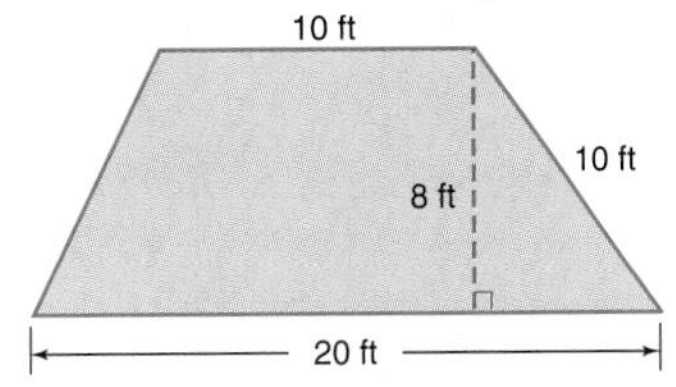

Instructional Resources ▶▶▶

Additional standardized test practice is shown at the right and is available in the *Assessment and Evaluation Masters,* pp. 269–270.

Test-Taking Tip

Knowing formulas for finding areas of various geometric figures can help students answer test questions more quickly. Encourage students to take practice tests without using reference materials for the formulas.

***Assessment and Evaluation Masters,* pp. 269–270**

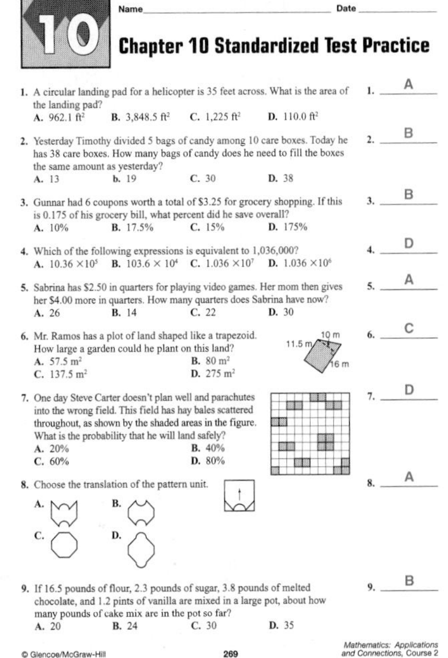

Name ______ Date ______

Chapter 10 Standardized Test Practice

1. A circular landing pad for a helicopter is 35 feet across. What is the area of the landing pad? 1. A
   A. 962.1 ft² B. 3,848.5 ft² C. 1,225 ft² D. 110.0 ft²
2. Yesterday Timothy divided 5 bags of candy among 10 care boxes. Today he has 38 care boxes. How many bags of candy does he need to fill the boxes the same amount as yesterday? 2. B
   A. 13 b. 19 C. 30 D. 38
3. Gunnar had 6 coupons worth a total of \$3.25 for grocery shopping. If this is 0.175 of his grocery bill, what percent did he save overall? 3. B
   A. 10% B. 17.5% C. 15% D. 175%
4. Which of the following expressions is equivalent to 1,036,000? 4. D
   A. 10.36×10^5 B. 103.6×10^4 C. 1.036×10^7 D. 1.036×10^6
5. Sabrina has \$2.50 in quarters for playing video games. Her mom then gives her \$4.00 more in quarters. How many quarters does Sabrina have now? 5. A
   A. 26 B. 14 C. 22 D. 30
6. Mr. Ramos has a plot of land shaped like a trapezoid. How large a garden could he plant on this land? (10 m, 11.5 m, 16 m) 6. C
   A. 57.5 m² B. 80 m² C. 137.5 m² D. 275 m²
7. One day Steve Carter doesn't plan well and parachutes into the wrong field. This field has hay bales scattered throughout, as shown by the shaded areas in the figure. What is the probability that he will land safely? 7. D
   A. 20% B. 40% C. 60% D. 80%
8. Choose the translation of the pattern unit. 8. A
   A. B. C. D.
9. If 16.5 pounds of flour, 2.3 pounds of sugar, 3.8 pounds of melted chocolate, and 1.2 pints of vanilla are mixed in a large pot, about how many pounds of cake mix are in the pot so far? 9. B
   A. 20 B. 24 C. 30 D. 35

© Glencoe/McGraw-Hill 269 *Mathematics: Applications and Connections, Course 2*

Chapter 10 Standardized Test Practice (continued)

10. Dr. Feldman wants to make a film for \$2,200. If he can earn \$265 each week toward his film costs, what is a reasonable length of time that it will take him to raise the \$2,200? 10. C
    A. 6 weeks B. 7 weeks C. 9 weeks D. 10 weeks
11. Paul Hill just purchased a new 27-inch TV. If the screen is 17 inches high and the diagonal length is 27 inches, what is the length of the screen rounded to the nearest tenth? 11. A
    A. 21.0 in. B. 20.1 in. C. 19.8 in. D. 31.9 in.
12. Ms. Suarez has $4\frac{2}{3}$ cases of toilet paper. If each case holds 24 rolls, how many rolls of toilet paper does she have? 12. D
    A. 72 B. 96 C. 28 D. 112
13. In order to make \$10 profit on a case of licorice sticks, the cost per stick, z, must be calculated. The cost per stick, z, is the cost of the case, x, plus the profit, \$10, divided by the number of licorice sticks in the case, y: $\frac{(x + 10)}{y} = z$. If a case containing 50 licorice sticks costs \$6, how much should be charged per stick? 13. B
    A. 50¢ B. 32¢ C. 20¢ D. 12¢
14. If Charmaine rolls a number cube, what is the probability that an odd number will come up? 14. C
    A. $\frac{1}{3}$ B. $\frac{1}{4}$ C. $\frac{1}{2}$ D. $\frac{1}{6}$
15. The bar graph indicates the number of roses sold each week for the last four weeks at Jimmy's Flowers in 1998. Predict how many roses will be sold next week. 15. C
    A. 100 B. 125 C. 150 D. 175

    Roses Sold Weekly (Amounts Sold: 0, 25, 50, 75, 100, 125, 150; Week: 1, 2, 3, 4)
16. Which expression is equivalent to $16x + 3(9 - 2)$? 16. A
    A. $27 - 6 + 16x$ B. $27 + 3x - 5$ C. $16x - 27 + 6$ D. $16x - 6 + 9$

© Glencoe/McGraw-Hill 270 *Mathematics: Applications and Connections, Course 2*

CHAPTER 11

Applying Percents

Previewing the Chapter

Overview

This chapter explores applications of percents, including estimating with percents, interpreting and making circle graphs, calculating percent of change, and working with discount, simple interest, and sales tax. Math connections include geometry, measurement, and statistics. Students solve problems by first solving a simpler problem, and explore the use of spreadsheets in calculating interest.

Lesson (pages)	Lesson Objectives	NCTM Standards 2000	Standardized Tests	State/Local Objectives
11-1 (450–453)	Estimate percents by using fractions and decimals.	1, 6–10	CTBS, SAT, TN	
11-1B (454–455)	Solve problems by solving a simpler problem.	1, 6–10	MAT	
11-2 (456–458)	Solve problems by using the percent equation.	1, 2, 6–10		
11-3A (459)	Make a circle graph.	1, 2, 5, 8–10	CTBS, TN	
11-3 (460–463)	Construct and interpret circle graphs.	1, 2, 5, 6, 8–10	CTBS, TN	
11-4 (464–467)	Predict actions of a larger group by using a sample.	1, 2, 5–9	CTBS, ITBS, SAT, TN	
11-5A (468)	Use dot paper to show percent of increase and percent of decrease.	1, 6, 8–10		
11-5 (469–472)	Find the percent of increase or decrease.	1, 2, 4–6, 8–10	ITBS	
11-6 (474–477)	Solve problems involving sales tax and discount.	1, 2, 6, 8,	CAT	
11-7 (478–480)	Solve problems involving simple interest.	1, 2, 6, 8, 9	ITBS	
11-7B (481)	Use a spreadsheet to find simple interest.	1, 2, 6, 8, 9		

CAT = California Achievement Tests, CTBS = Comprehensive Tests of Basic Skills, ITBS = Iowa Tests of Basic Skills, MAT = Metropolitan Achievement Tests, SAT = Stanford Achievement Tests, TN = Terra Nova
For the key to numbering of NCTM Standards 2000, see page T6.

Organizing the Chapter

The **Interactive Lesson Planner** contains all of the blackline masters and transparencies. This CD-ROM also includes an easy-to-use lesson planning calendar.

LESSON PLANNING GUIDE

Lesson	Extra Practice (Student Edition)	Blackline Masters (Page Numbers): Study Guide	Practice	Enrichment	Assessment & Evaluation	Classroom Games	Diversity	Hands-On Lab	School to Career	Science and Math Lab Manual	Technology	Transparencies A and B
11-1	p. 598	81	81	81				82				11-1
11-1B	p. 598											
11-2	p. 598	82	82	82	295				24	85–88		11-2
11-3A								65				
11-3	p. 599	83	83	83			24					11-3
11-4	p. 599	84	84	84	294, 295					45–48		11-4
11-5A								66				11-4
11-5	p. 599	85	85	85								11-5
11-6	p. 600	86	86	86	296	31–32					47	11-6
11-7	p. 600	87	87	87	296						48	11-7
11-7B												
Study Guide/ Assessment					281–293, 297–299							

Other Chapter Resources

Student Edition

Chapter Project, pp. 449, 458, 463, 467, 485
Math in the Media, p. 472
School to Career, p. 473
Let the Games Begin, p. 477

Technology

 MathPASS CD-ROM

 Interactive Mathematics Tools Software

Teacher's Classroom Resources

Applications

Family Letters and Activities, pp. 47–48
Investigations and Projects Masters, pp. 57–60

Meeting Individual Needs

Investigations for the Special Education Student, pp. 31–34

Teaching Aids

Answer Key Masters
Block Scheduling Booklet
Lesson Planning Guide
Solutions Manual

Professional Publications

Glencoe Mathematics Professional Series

Planning the Chapter

MindJogger Videoquizzes provide a unique format for reviewing concepts presented in the chapter.

Assessment Resources

Student Edition
Mixed Review, pp. 453, 458, 463, 467, 472, 477, 480
Mid-Chapter Self Test, p. 467
Math Journal, pp. 457, 475, 479
Study Guide and Assessment, pp. 482–485
Performance Task, p. 485
Portfolio Suggestion, p. 485
Standardized Test Practice, pp. 486–487
Chapter Test, p. 617

Assessment and Evaluation Masters
Multiple-Choice Tests (Forms 1A, 1B, 1C), pp. 281–286
Free-Response Tests (Forms 2A, 2B, 2C), pp. 287–292
Performance Assessment, p. 293
Mid-Chapter Test, p. 294
Quizzes A–D, pp. 295–296
Standardized Test Practice, pp. 297–298
Cumulative Review, p. 299

Teacher's Wraparound Edition
5-Minute Check, pp. 450, 456, 460, 464, 469, 474, 478
Building Portfolios, p. 485
Math Journal, pp. 459, 468, 481
Closing Activity, pp. 453, 455, 458, 463, 467, 472, 477, 480

Technology
Test and Review Software
MindJogger Videoquizzes
CD-ROM Program

Materials and Manipulatives

Lesson 11-1
grid paper†
markers

Lesson 11-3A
jelly beans
needle
thread
compass*†
straightedge*†

Lesson 11-3
compass*†
protractor*†

Lesson 11-5A
dot paper

Lesson 11-5
calculator
ruler*†

Lesson 11-6
index cards
spinners*†

*Glencoe Manipulative Kit

†Glencoe Overhead Manipulative Resources

Pacing Chart

See pages T25–T27 for the Course Planning Calendar.

COURSE	DAY 1	DAY 2	DAY 3	DAY 4	DAY 5	DAY 6	DAY 7
Standard	Chapter Project	Lesson 11-1	Lesson 11-1B	Lesson 11-2	Lessons 11-3A & 11-3		Lesson 11-4
Honors	Chapter Project	Lesson 11-1	Lesson 11-1B	Lesson 11-2	Lesson 11-3	Lesson 11-4	Lesson 11-5
Block	Chapter Project & Lesson 11-1	Lessons 11-1B & 11-2	Lessons 11-3A & 11-3	Lesson 11-4	Lessons 11-5A & 11-5	Lessons 11-6 & 11-7	Study Guide and Assessment, Chapter Test

Interactive Mathematics:
Activities and Investigations

is an activity-based program that may be used as an enhancement for chapters in ***Mathematics: Applications and Connections.***

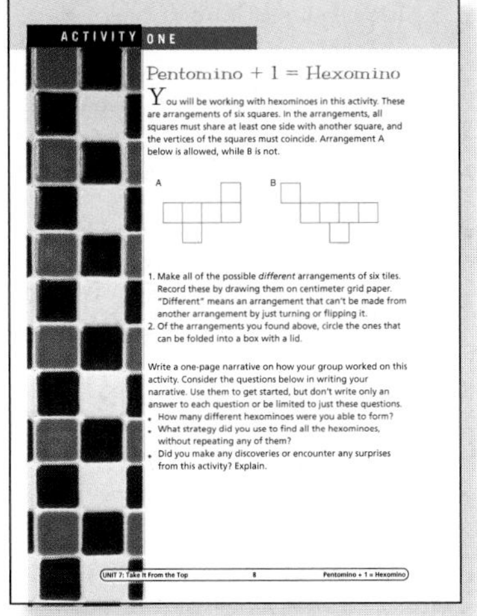
ACTIVITY ONE

Pentomino + 1 = Hexomino

You will be working with hexominoes in this activity. These are arrangements of six squares. In the arrangements, all squares must share at least one side with another square, and the vertices of the squares must coincide. Arrangement A below is allowed, while B is not.

1. Make all of the possible *different* arrangements of six tiles. Record these by drawing them on centimeter grid paper. "Different" means an arrangement that can't be made from another arrangement by just turning or flipping it.
2. Of the arrangements you found above, circle the ones that can be folded into a box with a lid.

Write a one-page narrative on how your group worked on this activity. Consider the questions below in writing your narrative. Use them to get started, but don't write only an answer to each question or be limited to just these questions.

- How many different hexominoes were you able to form?
- What strategy did you use to find all the hexominoes, without repeating any of them?
- Did you make any discoveries or encounter any surprises from this activity? Explain.

UNIT 7: Take It From the Top 8 Pentomino + 1 = Hexomino

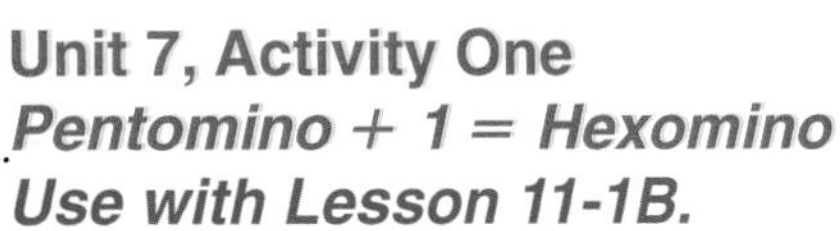

Unit 7, Activity One
Pentomino + 1 = Hexomino
Use with Lesson 11-1B.

Summary Students work in groups to form as many different hexominoes as they can. They record their formations on centimeter grid paper. Each student then writes a thorough explanation of the processes used in finding their solution.

Math Connection Students explore hexominoes, an arrangement of six squares in which all six squares must share at least one side with another square and the vertices of the squares coincide. They need to be aware that a flip or rotation of a hexomino represents the same shape.

Unit 16, Activity Four
Use with Lesson 11-7.

Summary Students use the simple interest formula, $I = prt$, to calculate both simple and compound interest. They also use a computer program written in BASIC to verify their findings and to calculate compound interest when it is compounded more than once annually.

Math Connection Students use the formula $I = prt$ to calculate interest. This formula is most often used to calculate simple interest, and the formula $A = P\left(1 + \frac{r}{n}\right)^{nt}$ is often used to calculate compound interest.

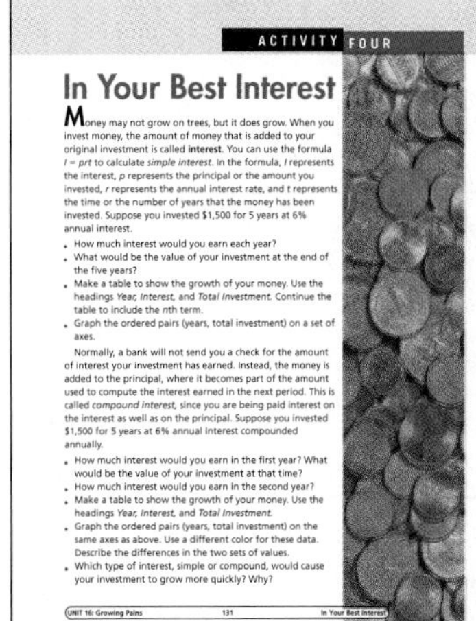
ACTIVITY FOUR

In Your Best Interest

Money may not grow on trees, but it does grow. When you invest money, the amount of money that is added to your original investment is called **interest**. You can use the formula $I = prt$ to calculate *simple interest*. In the formula, I represents the interest, p represents the principal or the amount you invested, r represents the annual interest rate, and t represents the time or the number of years that the money has been invested. Suppose you invested $1,500 for 5 years at 6% annual interest.

- How much interest would you earn each year?
- What would be the value of your investment at the end of the five years?
- Make a table to show the growth of your money. Use the headings *Year, Interest,* and *Total Investment.* Continue the table to include the *n*th term.
- Graph the ordered pairs (years, total investment) on a set of axes.

Normally, a bank will not send you a check for the amount of interest your investment has earned. Instead, the money is added to the principal, where it becomes part of the amount used to compute the interest earned in the next period. This is called *compound interest,* since you are being paid interest on the interest as well as on the principal. Suppose you invested $1,500 for 5 years at 6% annual interest compounded annually.

- How much interest would you earn in the first year? What would be the value of your investment at that time?
- How much interest would you earn in the second year?
- Make a table to show the growth of your money. Use the headings *Year, Interest,* and *Total Investment.*
- Graph the ordered pairs (years, total investment) on the same axes as above. Use a different color for these data. Describe the differences in the two sets of values.
- Which type of interest, simple or compound, would cause your investment to grow more quickly? Why?

UNIT 16: Growing Pains 131 In Your Best Interest

DAY 8	DAY 9	DAY 10	DAY 11	DAY 12	DAY 13	DAY 14	DAY 15
Lessons 11-5A & 11-5		Lesson 11-6	Lesson 11-7	Study Guide and Assessment	Chapter Test		
Lesson 11-6	Lessons 11-7 & 11-7B		Study Guide and Assessment	Chapter Test			

Enhancing the Chapter

APPLICATIONS

Classroom Games, pp. 31–32

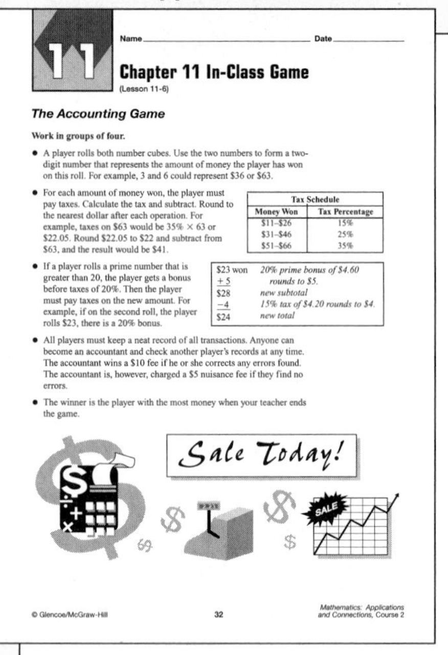

11

Name ______ Date ______

Chapter 11 In-Class Game
(Lesson 11-6)

The Accounting Game

Work in groups of four.

- A player rolls both number cubes. Use the two numbers to form a two-digit number that represents the amount of money the player has won on this roll. For example, 3 and 6 could represent \$36 or \$63.
- For each amount of money won, the player must pay taxes. Calculate the tax and subtract. Round to the nearest dollar after each operation. For example, taxes on \$63 would be 35% × 63 or \$22.05. Round \$22.05 to \$22 and subtract from \$63, and the result would be \$41.

Tax Schedule	
Money Won	**Tax Percentage**
\$11–\$26	15%
\$31–\$46	25%
\$51–\$66	35%

- If a player rolls a prime number that is greater than 20, the player gets a bonus before taxes of 20%. Then the player must pay taxes on the new amount. For example, if on the second roll, the player rolls \$23, there is a 20% bonus.

\$23 won	*20% prime bonus of \$4.60 rounds to \$5.*
+ 5	
\$28	*new subtotal*
−4	*15% tax of \$4.20 rounds to \$4.*
\$24	*new total*

- All players must keep a neat record of all transactions. Anyone can become an accountant and check another player's records at any time. The accountant wins a \$10 fee if he or she corrects any errors found. The accountant is, however, charged a \$5 nuisance fee if they find no errors.
- The winner is the player with the most money when your teacher ends the game.

© Glencoe/McGraw-Hill 32 *Mathematics: Applications and Connections, Course 2*

Diversity Masters, p. 24

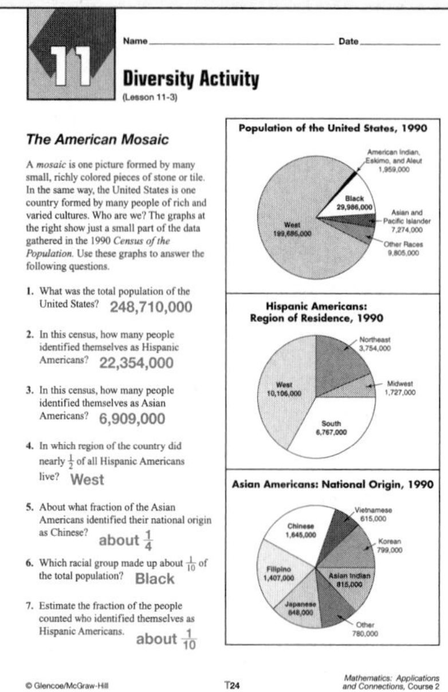

11

Name ______ Date ______

Diversity Activity
(Lesson 11-3)

The American Mosaic

A *mosaic* is one picture formed by many small, richly colored pieces of stone or tile. In the same way, the United States is one country formed by many people of rich and varied cultures. Who are we? The graphs at the right show just a small part of the data gathered in the 1990 *Census of the Population.* Use these graphs to answer the following questions.

1. What was the total population of the United States? 248,710,000
2. In this census, how many people identified themselves as Hispanic Americans? 22,354,000
3. In this census, how many people identified themselves as Asian Americans? 6,909,000
4. In which region of the country did nearly $\frac{1}{2}$ of all Hispanic Americans live? West
5. About what fraction of the Asian Americans identified their national origin as Chinese? about $\frac{1}{4}$
6. Which racial group made up about $\frac{1}{10}$ of the total population? Black
7. Estimate the fraction of the people counted who identified themselves as Hispanic Americans. about $\frac{1}{10}$

© Glencoe/McGraw-Hill T24 *Mathematics: Applications and Connections, Course 2*

School to Career Masters, p. 24

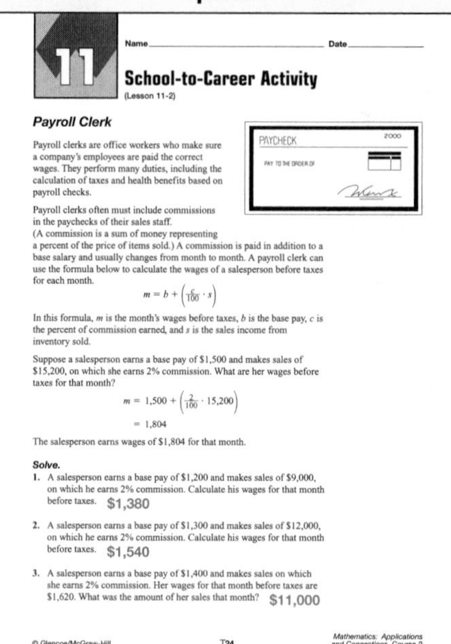

11

Name ______ Date ______

School-to-Career Activity
(Lesson 11-2)

Payroll Clerk

Payroll clerks are office workers who make sure a company's employees are paid the correct wages. They perform many duties, including the calculation of taxes and health benefits based on payroll checks.

Payroll clerks often must include commissions in the paychecks of their sales staff. (A commission is a sum of money representing a percent of the price of items sold.) A commission is paid in addition to a base salary and usually changes from month to month. A payroll clerk can use the formula below to calculate the wages of a salesperson before taxes for each month.

$$m = b + \left(\frac{c}{100} \cdot s\right)$$

In this formula, m is the month's wages before taxes, b is the base pay, c is the percent of commission earned, and s is the sales income from inventory sold.

Suppose a salesperson earns a base pay of \$1,500 and makes sales of \$15,200, on which she earns 2% commission. What are her wages before taxes for that month?

$$m = 1{,}500 + \left(\frac{2}{100} \cdot 15{,}200\right)$$
$$= 1{,}804$$

The salesperson earns wages of \$1,804 for that month.

Solve.

1. A salesperson earns a base pay of \$1,200 and makes sales of \$9,000, on which he earns 2% commission. Calculate his wages for that month before taxes. \$1,380
2. A salesperson earns a base pay of \$1,300 and makes sales of \$12,000, on which he earns 2% commission. Calculate his wages for that month before taxes. \$1,540
3. A salesperson earns a base pay of \$1,400 and makes sales on which she earns 2% commission. Her wages for that month before taxes are \$1,620. What was the amount of her sales that month? \$11,000

© Glencoe/McGraw-Hill T24 *Mathematics: Applications and Connections, Course 2*

Family Letters and Activities, pp. 47–48

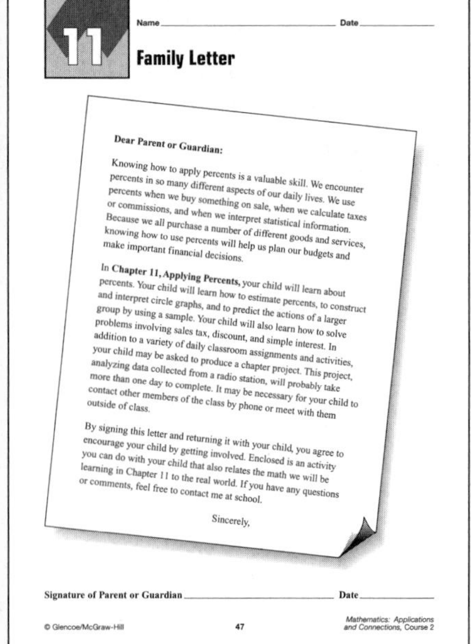

11

Name ______ Date ______

Family Letter

Dear Parent or Guardian:

Knowing how to apply percents is a valuable skill. We encounter percents in so many different aspects of our daily lives. We use percents when we buy something on sale, when we calculate taxes or commissions, and when we interpret statistical information. Because we all purchase a number of different goods and services, knowing how to use percents will help us plan our budgets and make important financial decisions.

In **Chapter 11, Applying Percents,** your child will learn about percents. Your child will learn how to estimate percents, to construct and interpret circle graphs, and to predict the actions of a larger group by using a sample. Your child will also learn how to solve problems involving sales tax, discount, and simple interest. In addition to a variety of daily classroom assignments and activities, your child may be asked to produce a chapter project. This project, analyzing data collected from a radio station, will probably take more than one day to complete. It may be necessary for your child to contact other members of the class by phone or meet with them outside of class.

By signing this letter and returning it with your child, you agree to encourage your child by getting involved. Enclosed is an activity you can do with your child that also relates the math we will be learning in Chapter 11 to the real world. If you have any questions or comments, feel free to contact me at school.

Sincerely,

Signature of Parent or Guardian ______ **Date** ______

© Glencoe/McGraw-Hill 47 *Mathematics: Applications and Connections, Course 2*

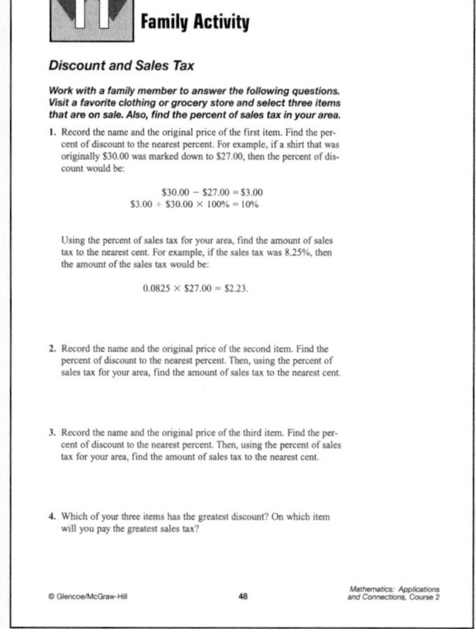

11

Name ______ Date ______

Family Activity

Discount and Sales Tax

Work with a family member to answer the following questions. Visit a favorite clothing or grocery store and select three items that are on sale. Also, find the percent of sales tax in your area.

1. Record the name and the original price of the first item. Find the percent of discount to the nearest percent. For example, if a shirt that was originally \$30.00 was marked down to \$27.00, then the percent of discount would be:

   \$30.00 − \$27.00 = \$3.00
   \$3.00 ÷ \$30.00 × 100% = 10%

   Using the percent of sales tax for your area, find the amount of sales tax to the nearest cent. For example, if the sales tax was 8.25%, then the amount of the sales tax would be:

   0.0825 × \$27.00 = \$2.23.

2. Record the name and the original price of the second item. Find the percent of discount to the nearest percent. Then, using the percent of sales tax for your area, find the amount of sales tax to the nearest cent.
3. Record the name and the original price of the third item. Find the percent of discount to the nearest percent. Then, using the percent of sales tax for your area, find the amount of sales tax to the nearest cent.
4. Which of your three items has the greatest discount? On which item will you pay the greatest sales tax?

© Glencoe/McGraw-Hill 48 *Mathematics: Applications and Connections, Course 2*

Science and Math Lab Manual, pp. 45–48, 85–88

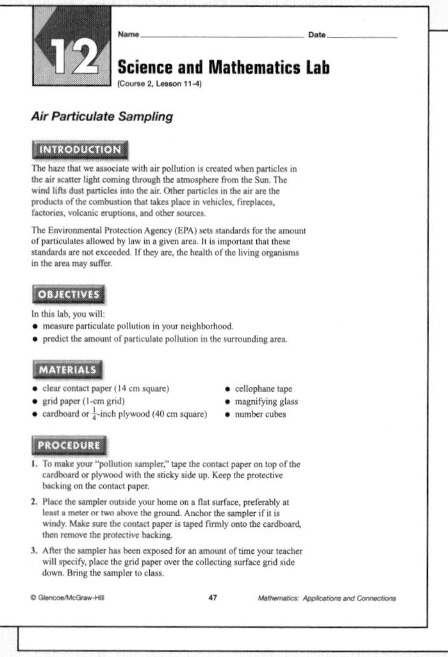

12

Name ______ Date ______

Science and Mathematics Lab
(Course 2, Lesson 11-4)

Air Particulate Sampling

INTRODUCTION

The haze that we associate with air pollution is created when particles in the air scatter light coming through the atmosphere from the Sun. The wind lifts dust particles into the air. Other particles in the air are the products of the combustion that takes place in vehicles, fireplaces, factories, volcanic eruptions, and other sources.

The Environmental Protection Agency (EPA) sets standards for the amount of particulates allowed by law in a given area. It is important that these standards are not exceeded. If they are, the health of the living organisms in the area may suffer.

OBJECTIVES

In this lab, you will:
- measure particulate pollution in your neighborhood.
- predict the amount of particulate pollution in the surrounding area.

MATERIALS

- clear contact paper (14 cm square)
- grid paper (1-cm grid)
- cardboard or $\frac{1}{4}$-inch plywood (40 cm square)
- cellophane tape
- magnifying glass
- number cubes

PROCEDURE

1. To make your "pollution sampler," tape the contact paper on top of the cardboard or plywood with the sticky side up. Keep the protective backing on the contact paper.
2. Place the sampler outside your home on a flat surface, preferably at least a meter or two above the ground. Anchor the sampler if it is windy. Make sure the contact paper is taped firmly onto the cardboard, then remove the protective backing.
3. After the sampler has been exposed for an amount of time your teacher will specify, place the grid paper over the collecting surface grid side down. Bring the sampler to class.

© Glencoe/McGraw-Hill 47 *Mathematics: Applications and Connections*

MANIPULATIVES/MODELING

Hands-On Lab Masters, p. 82

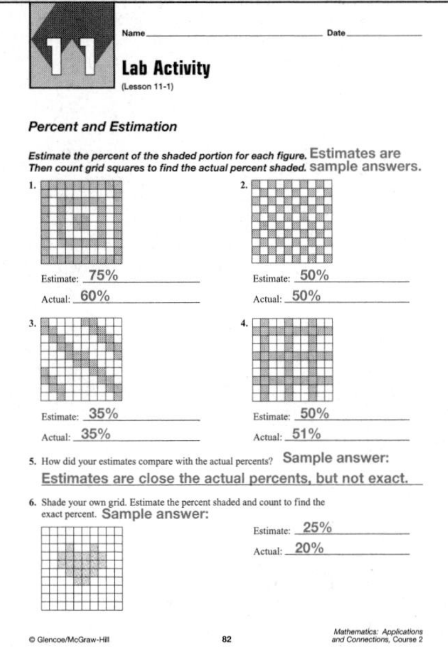

Name________________ Date________

11

Lab Activity

(Lesson 11-1)

Percent and Estimation

Estimate the percent of the shaded portion for each figure. Then count grid squares to find the actual percent shaded. Estimates are sample answers.

1. Estimate: 75%
   Actual: 60%
2. Estimate: 50%
   Actual: 50%
3. Estimate: 35%
   Actual: 35%
4. Estimate: 50%
   Actual: 51%
5. How did your estimates compare with the actual percents? Sample answer: Estimates are close the actual percents, but not exact.
6. Shade your own grid. Estimate the percent shaded and count to find the exact percent. Sample answer:
   Estimate: 25%
   Actual: 20%

© Glencoe/McGraw-Hill 82 *Mathematics: Applications and Connections, Course 2*

ASSESSMENT/EVALUATION

Assessment and Evaluation Masters, pp. 294–296

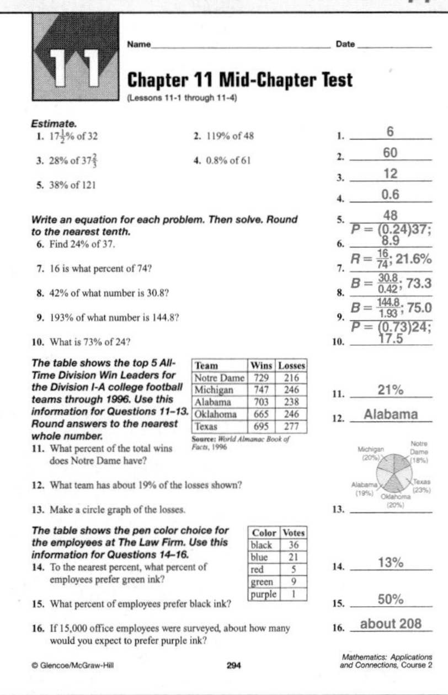

Name________________ Date________

11

Chapter 11 Mid-Chapter Test

(Lessons 11-1 through 11-4)

Estimate.

1. $17\frac{1}{2}$% of 32 — 1. 6
2. 119% of 48 — 2. 60
3. 28% of $37\frac{2}{3}$ — 3. 12
4. 0.8% of 61 — 4. 0.6
5. 38% of 121 — 5. 48

Write an equation for each problem. Then solve. Round to the nearest tenth.

6. Find 24% of 37. — 6. $P = (0.24)37$; 8.9
7. 16 is what percent of 74? — 7. $R = \frac{16}{74}$; 21.6%
8. 42% of what number is 30.8? — 8. $B = \frac{30.8}{0.42}$; 73.3
9. 193% of what number is 144.8? — 9. $B = \frac{144.8}{1.93}$; 75.0
10. What is 73% of 24? — 10. $P = (0.73)24$; 17.5

The table shows the top 5 All-Time Division Win Leaders for the Division I-A college football teams through 1996. Use this information for Questions 11–13. Round answers to the nearest whole number.

Team	Wins	Losses
Notre Dame	729	216
Michigan	747	246
Alabama	703	238
Oklahoma	665	246
Texas	695	277

Source: *World Almanac Book of Facts*, 1996

11. What percent of the total wins does Notre Dame have? — 11. 21%
12. What team has about 19% of the losses shown? — 12. Alabama
13. Make a circle graph of the losses. — 13. Michigan (20%), Notre Dame (18%), Texas (23%), Oklahoma (20%), Alabama (19%)

The table shows the pen color choice for the employees at The Law Firm. Use this information for Questions 14–16.

Color	Votes
black	36
blue	21
red	5
green	9
purple	1

14. To the nearest percent, what percent of employees prefer green ink? — 14. 13%
15. What percent of employees prefer black ink? — 15. 50%
16. If 15,000 office employees were surveyed, about how many would you expect to prefer purple ink? — 16. about 208

© Glencoe/McGraw-Hill 294 *Mathematics: Applications and Connections, Course 2*

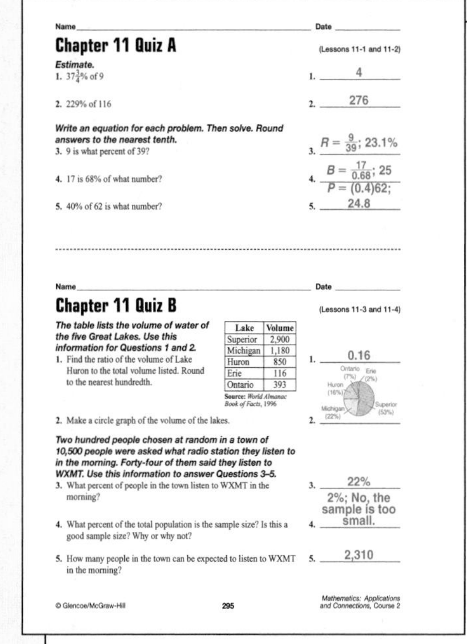

Name________________ Date________

Chapter 11 Quiz A

(Lessons 11-1 and 11-2)

Estimate.

1. $37\frac{3}{4}$% of 9 — 1. 4
2. 229% of 116 — 2. 276

Write an equation for each problem. Then solve. Round answers to the nearest tenth.

3. 9 is what percent of 39? — 3. $R = \frac{9}{39}$; 23.1%
4. 17 is 68% of what number? — 4. $B = \frac{17}{0.68}$; 25
5. 40% of 62 is what number? — 5. $P = (0.4)62$; 24.8

Name________________ Date________

Chapter 11 Quiz B

(Lessons 11-3 and 11-4)

The table lists the volume of water of the five Great Lakes. Use this information for Questions 1 and 2.

Lake	Volume
Superior	2,900
Michigan	1,180
Huron	850
Erie	116
Ontario	393

Source: *World Almanac Book of Facts*, 1996

1. Find the ratio of the volume of Lake Huron to the total volume listed. Round to the nearest hundredth. — 1. 0.16
2. Make a circle graph of the volume of the lakes. — 2. Ontario (7%), Erie (2%), Huron (16%), Michigan (22%), Superior (53%)

Two hundred people chosen at random in a town of 10,500 people were asked what radio station they listen to in the morning. Forty-four of them said they listen to WXMT. Use this information to answer Questions 3–5.

3. What percent of people in the town listen to WXMT in the morning? — 3. 22%
4. What percent of the total population is the sample size? Is this a good sample size? Why or why not? — 4. 2%; No, the sample is too small.
5. How many people in the town can be expected to listen to WXMT in the morning? — 5. 2,310

© Glencoe/McGraw-Hill 295 *Mathematics: Applications and Connections, Course 2*

TECHNOLOGY/MULTIMEDIA

Technology Masters, pp. 47–48

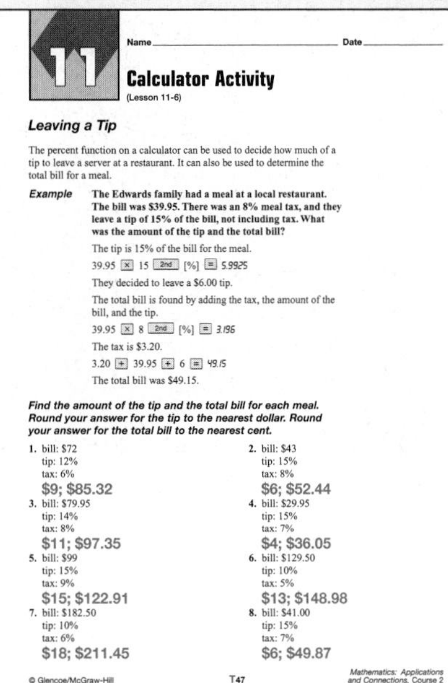

Name________________ Date________

11

Calculator Activity

(Lesson 11-6)

Leaving a Tip

The percent function on a calculator can be used to decide how much of a tip to leave a server at a restaurant. It can also be used to determine the total bill for a meal.

Example **The Edwards family had a meal at a local restaurant. The bill was $39.95. There was an 8% meal tax, and they leave a tip of 15% of the bill, not including tax. What was the amount of the tip and the total bill?**

The tip is 15% of the bill for the meal.

39.95 [×] 15 [2nd] [%] [=] 5.9925

They decided to leave a $6.00 tip.

The total bill is found by adding the tax, the amount of the bill, and the tip.

39.95 [×] 8 [2nd] [%] [=] 3.196

The tax is $3.20.

3.20 [+] 39.95 [+] 6 [=] 49.15

The total bill was $49.15.

Find the amount of the tip and the total bill for each meal. Round your answer for the tip to the nearest dollar. Round your answer for the total bill to the nearest cent.

1. bill: $72
   tip: 12%
   tax: 6%
   $9; $85.32
2. bill: $43
   tip: 15%
   tax: 8%
   $6; $52.44
3. bill: $79.95
   tip: 14%
   tax: 8%
   $11; $97.35
4. bill: $29.95
   tip: 15%
   tax: 7%
   $4; $36.05
5. bill: $99
   tip: 15%
   tax: 9%
   $15; $122.91
6. bill: $129.50
   tip: 10%
   tax: 5%
   $13; $148.98
7. bill: $182.50
   tip: 10%
   tax: 6%
   $18; $211.45
8. bill: $41.00
   tip: 15%
   tax: 7%
   $6; $49.87

© Glencoe/McGraw-Hill T47 *Mathematics: Applications and Connections, Course 2*

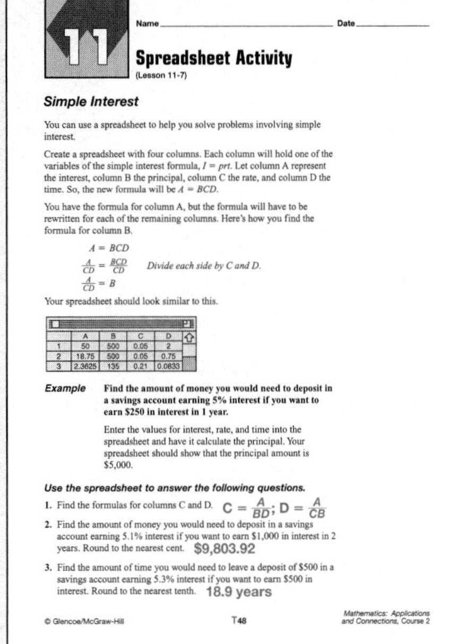

Name________________ Date________

11

Spreadsheet Activity

(Lesson 11-7)

Simple Interest

You can use a spreadsheet to help you solve problems involving simple interest.

Create a spreadsheet with four columns. Each column will hold one of the variables of the simple interest formula, $I = prt$. Let column A represent the interest, column B the principal, column C the rate, and column D the time. So, the new formula will be $A = BCD$.

You have the formula for column A, but the formula will have to be rewritten for each of the remaining columns. Here's how you find the formula for column B.

$$A = BCD$$

$$\frac{A}{CD} = \frac{BCD}{CD} \quad \textit{Divide each side by C and D.}$$

$$\frac{A}{CD} = B$$

Your spreadsheet should look similar to this.

	A	B	C	D
1	50	500	0.05	2
2	18.75	500	0.05	0.75
3	2.3625	135	0.21	0.0833

Example **Find the amount of money you would need to deposit in a savings account earning 5% interest if you want to earn $250 in interest in 1 year.**

Enter the values for interest, rate, and time into the spreadsheet and have it calculate the principal. Your spreadsheet should show that the principal amount is $5,000.

Use the spreadsheet to answer the following questions.

1. Find the formulas for columns C and D. $C = \frac{A}{BD}$; $D = \frac{A}{CB}$
2. Find the amount of money you would need to deposit in a savings account earning 5.1% interest if you want to earn $1,000 in interest in 2 years. Round to the nearest cent. $9,803.92
3. Find the amount of time you would need to leave a deposit of $500 in a savings account earning 5.3% interest if you want to earn $500 in interest. Round to the nearest tenth. 18.9 years

© Glencoe/McGraw-Hill T48 *Mathematics: Applications and Connections, Course 2*

MEETING INDIVIDUAL NEEDS

Investigations for the Special Education Student, pp. 31–34

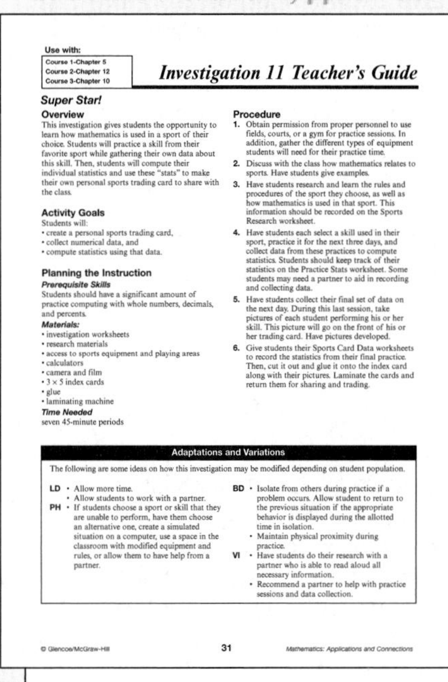

Use with:
Course 1-Chapter 5
Course 2-Chapter 12
Course 3-Chapter 10

Investigation 11 Teacher's Guide

Super Star!

Overview

This investigation gives students the opportunity to learn how mathematics is used in a sport of their choice. Students will practice a skill from their favorite sport while gathering their own data about this skill. Then, students will compute their individual statistics and use these "stats" to make their own personal sports trading card to share with the class.

Activity Goals

Students will:
- create a personal sports trading card,
- collect numerical data, and
- compute statistics using that data.

Planning the Instruction

Prerequisite Skills

Students should have a significant amount of practice computing with whole numbers, decimals, and percents.

Materials:
- investigation worksheets
- research materials
- access to sports equipment and playing areas
- calculators
- camera and film
- 3 × 5 index cards
- glue
- laminating machine

Time Needed

seven 45-minute periods

Procedure

1. Obtain permission from proper personnel to use fields, courts, or a gym for practice sessions. In addition, gather the different types of equipment students will need for their practice time.
2. Discuss with the class how mathematics relates to sports. Have students give examples.
3. Have students research and learn the rules and procedures of the sport they choose, as well as how mathematics is used in that sport. This information should be recorded on the Sports Research worksheet.
4. Have students each select a skill used in their sport, practice it for the next three days, and collect data from these practices to compute statistics. Students should keep track of their statistics on the Practice Stats worksheet. Some students may need a partner to aid in recording and collecting data.
5. Have students collect their final set of data on the next day. During this last session, take pictures of each student performing his or her skill. This picture will go on the front of his or her trading card. Have pictures developed.
6. Give students their Sports Card Data worksheets to record the statistics from their final practice. Then, cut it out and glue it onto the index card along with their pictures. Laminate the cards and return them for sharing and trading.

Adaptations and Variations

The following are some ideas on how this investigation may be modified depending on student population.

LD
- Allow more time.
- Allow students to work with a partner.

PH
- If students choose a sport or skill that they are unable to perform, have them choose an alternative one, create a simulated situation on a computer, use a space in the classroom with modified equipment and rules, or allow them to have help from a partner.

BD
- Isolate from others during practice if a problem occurs. Allow student to return to the previous situation if the appropriate behavior is displayed during the allotted time in isolation.
- Maintain physical proximity during practice.

VI
- Have students do their research with a partner who is able to read aloud all necessary information.
- Recommend a partner to help with practice sessions and data collection.

© Glencoe/McGraw-Hill 31 *Mathematics: Applications and Connections*

CHAPTER 11 NOTES

Theme: Radio

Much has changed since the days of orchestras broadcasting live performances from ballrooms. Computer technology has made it possible for a musician-technician to simulate the sound of many instruments with a synthesizer. And instead of a local disc jockey spinning records, listeners all over the U.S. might hear a whole day of programming planned and transmitted from a single studio and beamed by satellite to stations nationwide.

Question of the Day How might it help a modern musician or radio manager to be familiar with a calculator, spreadsheets, and statistics? **Sample answer: These tools help to keep track of income and expenses, programming, schedules, and data on audience likes and dislikes.**

Assess Prerequisite Skills

Ask students to read through the list of objectives presented in "What you'll learn in Chapter 11." You may wish to ask them what each of the objectives means or if they have experienced or used any of these math concepts before.

Building Portfolios

Encourage students to revise their portfolios as they study this chapter. They may want to include different ways of expressing the same information, such as in ratios, fractions, percents, and various kinds of graphs.

Math and the Family

In the *Family Letters and Activities* booklet (pp. 47–48), you will find a letter to the parents explaining what students will study in Chapter 11. An activity appropriate for the whole family is also available.

CHAPTER 11 Applying Percents

What you'll learn in Chapter 11

- to estimate percents and solve problems using the percent equation,
- to solve problems by solving a simpler problem,
- to construct and interpret circle graphs,
- to predict actions of a larger group by using a sample, and
- to solve problems involving sales tax, discount, and simple interest.

CD-ROM Program

Activities for Chapter 11

- Chapter 11 Introduction
- Interactive Lessons 11-1, 11-5
- Extended Activity 11-3
- Assessment Game
- Resource Lessons 11-1 through 11-7

CHAPTER Project

DON'T TURN THAT DIAL!

In this project, you will listen to a radio station and keep track of the types of programming. You will organize your results in a table and display your data in a circle graph. You will use the results to make predictions about the general format of the radio station. You will present your final results in a report that you will share with the class.

Getting Started

- Work in small groups. Your group should choose a local radio station.
- Choose 6 or 7 types of programming, such as news, commercials, weather reports, station identification, songs, traffic reports, and miscellaneous. For one hour, each person in your group should keep track of when they hear different types of programming and their length.
- Each person in your group should fill out a table like the one below.

Station: (name of station)
Format: (alternative, classic rock, country, jazz, all-news, top 40, classical, all-sports . . .)
Time: (date, day, hour)

Time	Type of Programming	Number of Minutes

Technology Tips

- Use a **calculator** to help you find percents.
- Use **computer software** to make graphs.
- Use a **word processor** to write your report.

Research For up-to-date information on radio broadcasting, visit:

www.glencoe.com/sec/math/mac/mathnet

Working on the Project

You can use what you'll learn in Chapter 11 to help you with your report.

Page	Exercise
458	25
463	9
467	10
485	Alternative Assessment

CHAPTER Project NOTES

Objectives Students should
- organize data from a survey and display it graphically.
- interpret data in terms of percents and make predictions based on these conclusions.

Project Pointer You may suggest that students begin a *Project Folder* to keep their work as they complete each stage of the Chapter Project. The completed project may also be added to their portfolios.

Using the Table Before beginning, students should decide the categories under "Type of Programming." Some examples are music, news, weather, sports, advertising, and chat. Encourage them to time each type accurately so the minutes total one hour.

***Investigations and Projects Masters,* p. 60**

Name ______ Date ______

Chapter 11 Project

Don't Turn That Dial!

Page 449, Getting Started

Station:
Format:
Time:

Time	Type of Programming	Number of Minutes

Page 458, Working on the Chapter Project, Exercise 25

Type of Programming	Percent of Total Hour

Page 463, Working on the Chapter Project, Exercise 9

Type of Programming

Page 467, Working on the Chapter Project, Exercise 10

On a separate sheet of paper, make an 8-hour programming schedule for the radio station you chose. To help organize your schedule, make a table with the following headings: Time, Type of Programming, and Number of Minutes.

 60 *Mathematics: Applications and Connections, Course 2*

interNET CONNECTION

Glencoe has made every effort to ensure that the website links for *Mathematics: Applications and Connections* at www.glencoe.com/sec/math/mac/mathnet are current and contain appropriate content. However, these website links are not under Glencoe's control.

Instructional Resources ▶▶▶

A recording sheet to help students organize their data for the Chapter Project is shown at the right and is available in the *Investigations and Projects Masters,* p. 60.

11-1 Lesson Notes

Instructional Resources

- *Study Guide Masters,* p. 81
- *Practice Masters,* p. 81
- *Enrichment Masters,* p. 81
- Transparencies 11-1, A and B
- *Hands-On Lab Masters,* p. 82

CD-ROM Program
- Resource Lesson 11-1
- Interactive Lesson 11-1

Recommended Pacing	
Standard	Day 2 of 13
Honors	Day 2 of 12
Block	Day 1 of 7

1 FOCUS

5-Minute Check (Chapter 10)

1. Find $\sqrt{169}$. 13
2. Estimate $\sqrt{80}$. about 9
3. For right triangle *ABC*, if the length of leg *a* is 6 m and the length of the hypotenuse *c* is 12 m, what is the length of leg *b*? Round to the nearest tenth. 10.4 m
4. Find the area of a trapezoid with bases of 12 cm and 4.5 cm, and a height of 8 cm. 66 cm^2
5. Find the area of a circular wading pool with a diameter of 18 feet. about 254 ft^2

The 5-Minute Check is also available on **Transparency 11-1A** for this lesson.

Motivating the Lesson

Problem Solving Athletic shoes that normally cost $49.95 are marked down 20 percent. What is the approximate sale price? $40

11-1 Percent and Estimation

What **you'll learn**

You'll learn to estimate percents by using fractions and decimals.

When **am I ever going to use this?**

Knowing how to estimate with percents will help you find out how much money you'll save when you buy something on sale.

In 1996, 14-year-old Subaru Takahashi became the youngest person to sail across the Pacific Ocean alone. He sailed about 47% of the 6,000-mile journey without outside communication after an engine died and the backup systems failed. For how many miles was he without communication?

You can estimate by rounding 47% to 50% and then finding 50% of 6,000.

Method 1

Use a fraction.

50% is the same as $\frac{1}{2}$.

$\frac{1}{2}$ of 6,000 is 3,000.

Method 2

Find 10% and multiply.

10% is the same as $\frac{1}{10}$ or 0.1.

10% of 6,000 is 0.1(6,000) or 600.

Now find 50% or 5 times (10% of 6,000).

$5 \times 600 = 3,000$

LOOK BACK
Refer to Lesson 2-5 to review multiplying by powers of ten.

Using either method, the estimate is 3,000. So, for about 3,000 miles, Subaru was without communication with the rest of the world.

HANDS-ON MINI-LAB

Work with a partner.

 grid paper 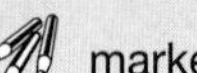 marker

You can use area models to estimate percent.

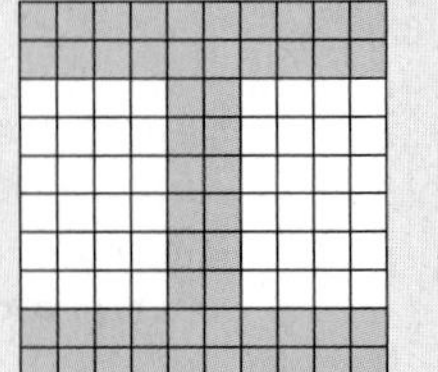
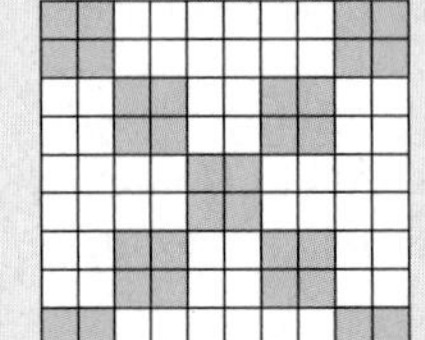
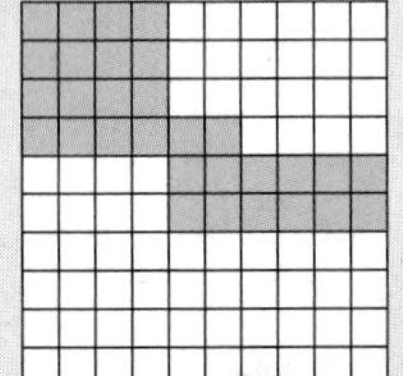

Try This 1. about 50%, about 30%, about 30%

1. Estimate the percent of the shaded portion of each figure.
2. Count grid squares to find the actual percent shaded.

Talk About It

3. How do the estimates compare with the actual percents?
4. Draw a design on a 10×10 grid and shade it. Estimate the percent shaded. Then count to find the exact percent.

2. 52%, 36%, 30%

3. They are close, but not exact.

4. See students' work.

Cross-Curriculum Cue

Inform the other teachers on your team that your classes are studying percents and their applications. Suggestions for curriculum integration are:

Life Science: ecology, relative sizes of animal body parts

Physical Education: sports statistics, body composition

Social Studies: consumer math, finances, population growth

Examples

1 Estimate 62% of 507.

62% is about 60%, and 60% = $\frac{60}{100}$ or $\frac{3}{5}$; 507 is about 500.

Method 1 Use a fraction.

$\frac{3}{5}$ of 500 is $\frac{3}{5} \times 500$ or 300.

So, 62% of 507 is *about* 300.

Method 2 Find 10% and multiply.

10% of 500 is 0.1(500) or 50. *10% = 0.1*

Now find 60% or 6 times (10% of 500).

6(50) = 300

So, 62% of 507 is *about* 300.

APPLICATION

2 Shopping Estimate how much money you would save on a $149 coat that is marked 30% off.

30% is about $\frac{1}{3}$ and $149 is about $150.

$\frac{1}{3}$ of 150 is $\frac{1}{3} \times 150$ or 50.

So, you would save about $50.

You can also estimate percents of numbers when the percent is less than 1 or the percent is greater than 100.

Examples

3 Estimate 113% of 42.

113% is more than 100%, so 113% of 42 is greater than 42.

113% is *about* 110%.

110% = 100% + 10%

$$42(100\% + 10\%) = 42(100\%) + 42(10\%) = 42 + 4.2 = 46.2$$

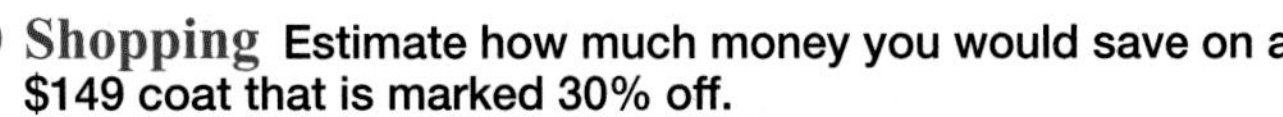

100% of 42 10% of 42

113% of 42 is *about* 46.

4 Estimate 0.5% of 223.

0.5% is half of 1%.

223 is about 200.

1% of 200 is 0.01 · 200 or 2. *1% = 0.01*

$\frac{1}{2}$ of 2 is 1.

0.5% of 223 is *about* 1.

2 TEACH

Transparency 11-1B contains a teaching aid for this lesson.

Using the Mini-Lab Encourage students to be creative with their grid designs. After they count their shaded squares, have students exchange papers with a partner and estimate the percent shaded on each other's designs.

Teaching Tip Ask students whether Method 1 or Method 2 in Example 1 makes more sense to them. Have students who prefer Method 1 work as a group and compete with students who prefer Method 2 to see which method works faster on Exercises 24–32.

In-Class Examples

For Example 1

Estimate 77% of 600.

$\frac{4}{5} \times 600 = 480$

For Example 2

Estimate the savings on a $289 item with 20% off.

$\frac{1}{5} \times \$300 = \$60$

For Example 3

Estimate 123% of $48.

(100% + 25%) · $48 = $48 + $12 or $60

For Example 4

Estimate 0.5% of 694.

$\frac{1}{2}(0.01 \cdot 700) = \frac{1}{2} \cdot 7$ or 3.5

3 PRACTICE/APPLY

Check for Understanding

If students need additional practice or instruction after completing Exercises 1–11, one of these options may be helpful.

- Extra Practice, see p. 598
- Reteaching Activity
- *Study Guide Masters*, p. 81
- *Practice Masters*, p. 81
- Interactive Mathematics Tools Software

Assignment Guide

Core: 13–37 odd, 38–43
Enriched: 12–34 even, 35–43

Additional Answers

1. Sample answer: You can estimate the percent of the shaded portion of the area model.
2. Yes, $0.3 \cdot 90 = 27$, which is about \$30.

10. $\frac{1}{100} \cdot 400 = 4, \frac{3}{10} \cdot 4 = 1.2$

***Study Guide Masters*, p. 81**

Name__________________ Date__________

11-1 Study Guide

Percent and Estimation

You can use these two methods to estimate with percents.

Example 1 **Estimate 77% of 800. Use a fraction.**
77% is about 75%, which is $\frac{3}{4}$.
$\frac{3}{4}$ of 800 = $\frac{3}{4} \times 800$ or 600
So, 77% of 800 is about 600.

Example 2 **Estimate 0.5% of 692. Find 1% and multiply.**
0.5% is half of 1%. *692 rounds to 700.*
Recall that 1% means $\frac{1}{100}$.
$\frac{1}{100} \times 700 = 7$
$\frac{1}{2}$ of 7 is 3.5. So, 0.5% of 692 is about 3.5.

Example 3 **Estimate 122% of 42. Use the meaning of percent method.**
122% is about 120%. *120% = 100% + 20%*
$42(100\% + 20\%) = 42(100\%) + 42(20\%)$ *20% means 2 × 10%.*
$= 42 + 8.4$
$= 50.4$
So, 122% of 42 is about 50.4.

Write the fraction, decimal, mixed number, or whole number equivalent of each percent that could be used to estimate. Estimates may vary.

1. 24% $\frac{1}{4}$
2. 35% $\frac{1}{3}$
3. 500% 5
4. 0.9% 0.01 or $\frac{1}{100}$
5. 37.2% $\frac{3}{8}$
6. $\frac{12}{13}$% 0.01 or $\frac{1}{100}$
7. 250% 2.5
8. 48.8% 0.5 or $\frac{1}{2}$

Estimate. Sample answers are given.

9. 11% of 67 $0.1 \times 67 = 6.7$
10. 50% of 78 $\frac{1}{2} \cdot 80 = 40$
11. 1% of 54 $0.01 \cdot 54 = 0.54$
12. 150% of 179 $180(100\% + 50\%) = 270$
13. 67% of 450 $\frac{2}{3} \cdot 450 = 300$
14. 79% of 590 $\frac{3}{4} \cdot 600 = 450$
15. 0.4% of 200 $0.01 \cdot 200 = 2, \frac{1}{2} \cdot 2 = 1$
16. 300% of 61 $3 \cdot 60 = 180$
17. 52% of 218 $\frac{1}{2} \cdot 200 = 100$

 T81 *Mathematics: Applications and Connections, Course 2*

CHECK FOR UNDERSTANDING

Communicating Mathematics

Read and study the lesson to answer each question. 1–2. See margin.

1. ***Explain*** how area models can be used to estimate a percent.
2. ***You Decide*** Tanika estimated that she would save about \$30 if she bought an \$86 dress on sale for 30% off. Is she right? Explain.

HANDS-ON MATH

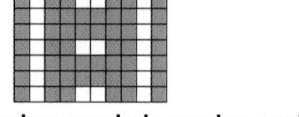

3. ***Draw*** a figure or design on a 10 × 10 grid. Shade $\frac{4}{10}$ of the figure or design. What percent is shaded? See students' work; 40%.

Guided Practice

4. Estimate the percent shaded. Then count to find the exact percent. about 80%, 72%

9. $56(100\% + 20\%) = 56 + 12$, or \$68

Write the fraction, decimal, mixed number, or whole number equivalent of each percent that could be used to estimate.

5. 38% 0.4
6. 300% 3
7. 25% $\frac{1}{4}$

Estimate. 8. $\frac{1}{4} \cdot 20 = 5$ 10. See margin.

8. 25% of 18
9. 121% of 56
10. 0.3% of 425

11. ***Geology*** Granite, often used for stone structures, is 0.8% water. About how many pounds of water are there in a 2,000-pound block of granite? $\frac{1}{100} \cdot 2{,}000 = 20$ lb

EXERCISES

Practice

12–32. Sample answers are given.
24. $0.2 \cdot 30 = 6$
25. $\frac{1}{4} \cdot 400 = 100$
26. $0.4 \cdot 60 = 24$
27. $\frac{3}{4} \cdot 120 = 90$
28. $0.01 \cdot 90 = 0.9$
29. $0.3 \cdot 50 = 15$
30. $\frac{5}{100} \cdot 200 = \frac{1}{20} \cdot 200 = 10$
31. $50(100\% + 50\%) = 50 + 25$, or 75
32. $0.01 \cdot 220 = 2.2, \frac{1}{2} \cdot 2.2 = 1.1$

Estimate the percent shaded. Then count to find the exact percent.

12.
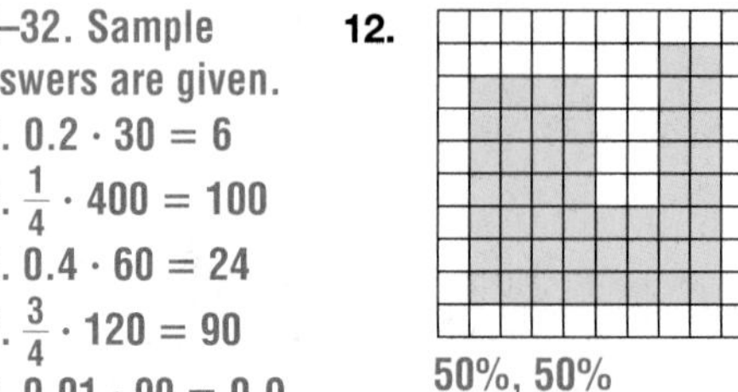
50%, 50%

13.
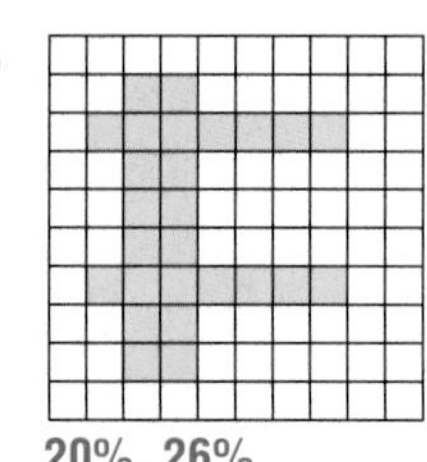
20%, 26%

14.
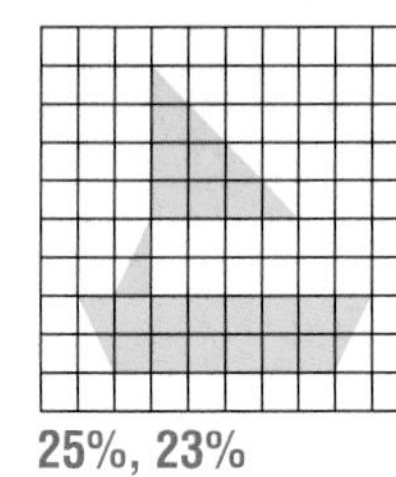
25%, 23%

Write the fraction, decimal, mixed number, or whole number equivalent of each percent that could be used to estimate.

15. 87% 0.9
16. 200% 2
17. 13% 0.1
18. 43.5% 0.4
19. 0.8% 0.01
20. 103% 1
21. 16.97% 0.2
22. $\frac{7}{8}$% 0.01
23. 350% 3.5

Estimate.

24. 16% of 32.6
25. 25% of 408
26. 40% of 62
27. 75% of 125
28. 1% of 89
29. 30.5% of 50
30. $6\frac{1}{2}$% of 236
31. 150% of 52
32. 0.6% of 220

Reteaching the Lesson

Activity On a 10 × 10 grid, have students make area models of a 160-acre farm. Tell students that 5 buyers will each receive 20% of the property. Have them estimate how many acres each will own. Invite students to estimate the number of acres in each parcel of land for different percents of 160.

33–34. Sample answers are given.

33. Estimate 20% of \$21.99. $\frac{1}{5} \cdot 20 = \$4$

34. ***Algebra*** Estimate 79% of x if $x = 304$. $\frac{4}{5} \cdot 300 = 240$

Applications and Problem Solving

Real World

35. ***Education*** In 1997, 70% of applicants to veterinary medical colleges were female. The College of Veterinary Medicine at Colorado State had 758 applicants in 1997. About how many of them might you estimate were females? $\frac{7}{10} \cdot 800 = 560$

36\. 56% − 14% ≈ 40%; 0.4 · 2,200 ≈ 880 schools

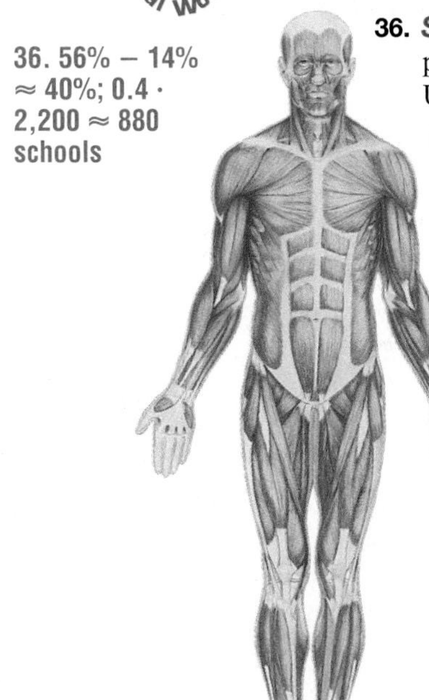

36. ***School*** About 2,200 public schools in the United States are in session all year. The graph shows the percent of these schools that are in various states. Estimate how many more schools have a year-round schedule in California than in Texas.

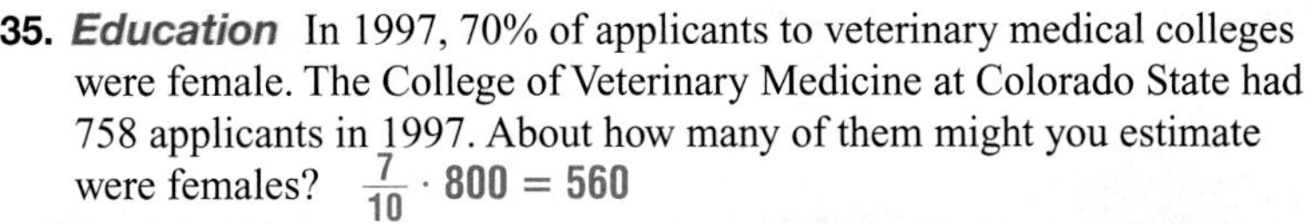

Source: Market Data Retrieval

37. ***Life Science*** The 639 muscles in your body make up about 40% of your total weight. If a person weighs 120 pounds, about how much of the weight is muscle? $\frac{2}{5} \cdot 120 = 48$ lb

38. ***Critical Thinking*** How could you find $\frac{1}{4}$% of a number? **Sample answer: Find 1% of a number, then divide by 4.**

Mixed Review

39. ***Probability*** Find the probability that a randomly-dropped counter will fall in the shaded region. *(Lesson 10-7)* $\frac{16}{40} = \frac{2}{5}$

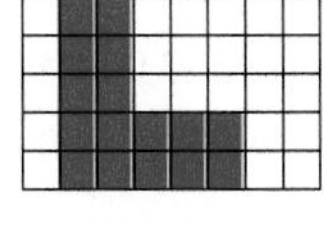

40. **Standardized Test Practice** Which procedure could be used to find the measure of angle G? *(Lesson 9-4)* **B**

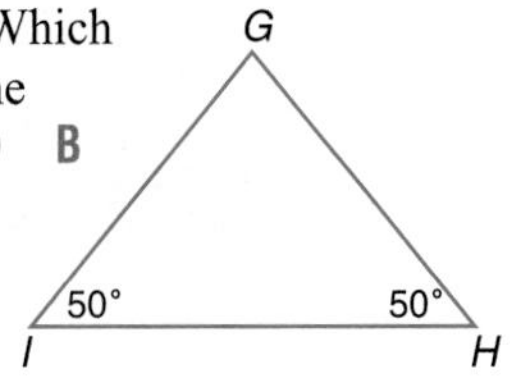

A Add 50° to 180°.
B Subtract 100° from 180°.
C Subtract 50° from 90°.
D Add 50° to 90°.
E Subtract 180° from 100°.

43\. $\frac{1}{16}, \frac{1}{2}, \frac{2}{3}, \frac{5}{6}, \frac{7}{8}$

41. Express 0.08 as a percent. *(Lesson 8-6)* **8%**

42. ***Algebra*** Solve $\frac{3}{5}a = 12$. *(Lesson 7-8)* **20**

43. Order $\frac{1}{2}, \frac{7}{8}, \frac{1}{16}, \frac{5}{6}$, and $\frac{2}{3}$ from least to greatest. *(Lesson 4-10)*

For **Extra Practice,** see page 598.

4 ASSESS

Closing Activity

Speaking Have students distinguish between the two methods for estimating percents and provide examples of each method.

Practice Masters, p. 81

Name ______ Date ______

11-1 Practice

Percent and Estimation

Estimate the percent shaded. Then count to find the exact percent.

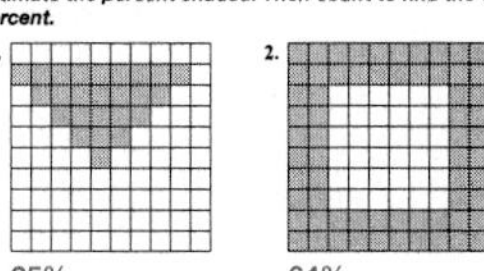

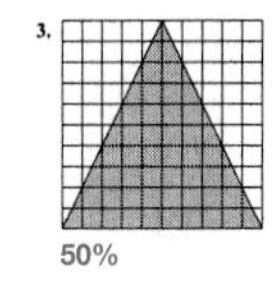

1\. 25% 2. 64% 3. 50%

Sample answers are given.

Write the fraction, decimal, mixed number, or whole number equivalent of each percent that could be used to estimate.

4. 42% $\frac{2}{5}$	5. 77% $\frac{3}{4}$	6. 9.2% $\frac{1}{10}$
7. 312% 3	8. 450% 4.5, $4\frac{1}{2}$	9. $\frac{4}{5}$% 0.01
10. $24\frac{1}{3}$% $\frac{1}{4}$	11. 0.1% $\frac{1}{1,000}$	12. 500% 5

Estimate. Sample answers are given.

13. 51% of 128 about 64	14. 310% of 500 about 1,500	15. 76% of 200 about 150
16. 0.49% of 10 about 0.05	17. 12% of $98\frac{1}{3}$ about 12	18. 32.9% of 90 about 30
19. 89% of 300 about 270	20. 153% of 20 about 30	21. 0.9% of 250 about 2.5
22. 19% of 450 about 90	23. 1% of 98 about 1	24. 24% of 8 about 2

 T81 *Mathematics: Applications and Connections, Course 2*

Extending the Lesson

Enrichment Masters, p. 81

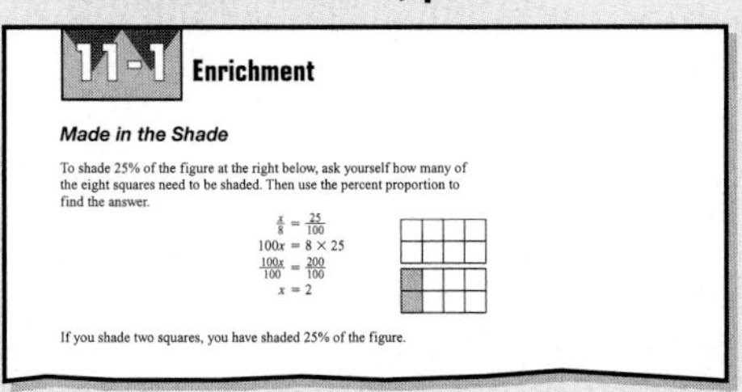

11-1 Enrichment

Made in the Shade

To shade 25% of the figure at the right below, ask yourself how many of the eight squares need to be shaded. Then use the percent proportion to find the answer.

$\frac{x}{8} = \frac{25}{100}$

$100x = 8 \times 25$

$\frac{100x}{100} = \frac{200}{100}$

$x = 2$

If you shade two squares, you have shaded 25% of the figure.

Activity Have students obtain advertisements for products. Ask them to select 3 or 4 items they estimate they can afford within a pre-determined budget. Students should include estimates of the sales tax and check their estimates with a calculator.

Objective Students solve problems by solving a simpler problem.

Recommended Pacing	
Standard	Day 3 of 13
Honors	Day 3 of 12
Block	Day 2 of 7

1 FOCUS

Getting Started Have students make area models on a 10 × 10 grid to estimate the number of acres of land cover in the chart. Ask them how many acres are not accounted for.

2 TEACH

Teaching Tip Challenge students to solve the problem by changing 20% to a fraction and using mental math to find $\frac{1}{5}$ of 2,000,000,000.

In-Class Example
Of Silver City's 26,488 voters, 24% voted for Kane for mayor. About how many people voted for Kane? **about 6,000 people**

PROBLEM SOLVING

11-1B Solve a Simpler Problem

A Follow-Up of Lesson 11-1

Jocelyn and Mi-Ling are studying land use in the United States in Earth Science class. Let's listen in!

I wonder how many acres of forests there are in the United States.

The table shows that 20.4% of the land is forests, but how much is that?

Mi-Ling

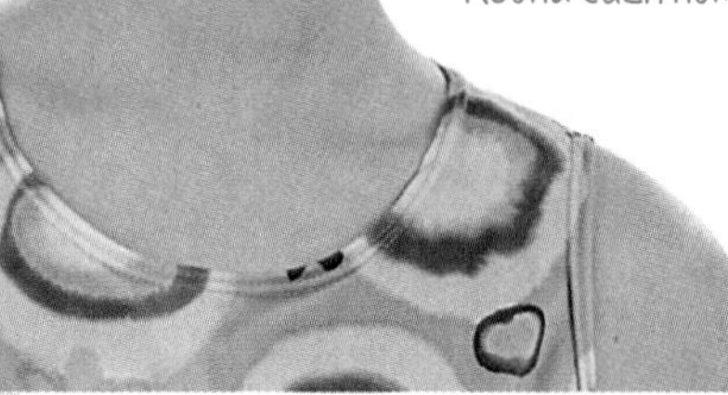

We need to find 20.4% of 1,940,011,000. We can estimate the number of acres by solving a simpler problem. Round each number to its greatest place value.

Land Cover	Percent
Crops	19.7
Pasture	6.5
Range	20.6
Forest	20.4
Total: 1,940,011,000 acres	

Source: *Statistical Abstract,* 1996

Jocelyn

Think: 20.4% → 20% *Nearest 10%*

1,940,011,000 → 2,000,000,000 *Nearest billion*

10% of 2,000,000,000 is 200,000,000.

So, 20% of 2,000,000,000 is 400,000,000.

So, about 400 million acres in the United States are forests.

THINK ABOUT IT

Work with a partner. **1. See students' work.**

1. ***Think*** of another way that Jocelyn and Mi-Ling could have estimated the number of forest acres in the United States.
2. ***Find*** the approximate number of pasture acres in the United States by **solving a simpler problem**. **0.07 · 2,000,000,000 = 140,000,000 acres**
3. ***Apply*** what you have learned to solve the following problem.

   In 1995, the United States imported $743.4 billion in goods from other countries. About 5% of this came from imported clothing. About how much in clothing did the United States import? **See margin.**

Reteaching the Lesson

Activity Have students estimate how many acres are in 1% of the total. Then have them multiply that number by each value in the percent column.

Additional Answer

3. $\frac{1}{20} \cdot 740 = \$37$ billion

For **Extra Practice,** see page 598.

ON YOUR OWN

4. The third step of the 4-step plan for problem solving asks you to *solve* the problem. ***Explain*** how you can solve problems by solving a simpler problem. **Solving a simpler problem often gives a pattern for solving a more complex problem.**

5. ***Write a Problem*** that you can solve by solving a simpler problem. Solve the problem and explain your answer. **See students' work.**

MIXED PROBLEM SOLVING

STRATEGIES
- Look for a pattern.
- Solve a simpler problem.
- Act it out.
- Guess and Check.
- Draw a diagram.
- Make a chart.
- Work backword.
- Make a list.

Solve. Use any strategy.

6. ***Photocopying*** Suppose you enlarge a drawing to 120% of its original size on the photocopy machine. If the drawing is 2 inches long and 3 inches wide,what are the dimensions of the copy? **2.4 in. by 3.6 in.**

7. ***Music*** The graph shows how current and former musicians learned to play their instruments.

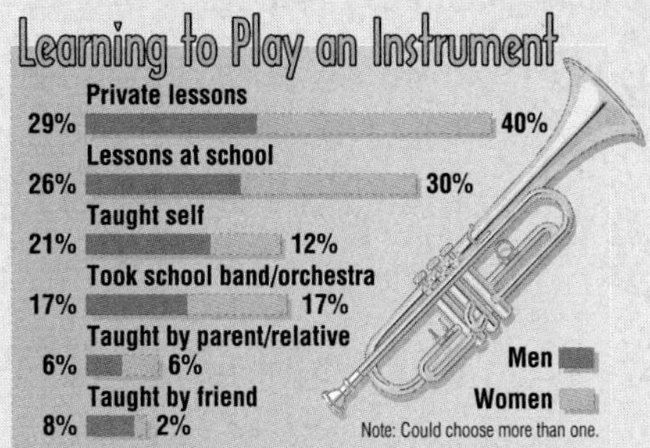

Source: Gallup for National Association for Music Merchants

Estimate how many women out of a group of 2,493 women musicians learned to play by taking band and/or orchestra in school. **$2,500 \cdot \frac{1}{5} = 500$ women**

8. ***Life Science*** The cheetah is the fastest land animal in the world. Its speed is $2\frac{1}{2}$ times that of the fastest human's speed. If the fastest recorded speed for a human is 28 miles per hour, how fast can the cheetah run? **70 mph**

9. ***Money Matters*** When the Glover family went out for pizza, their bill was $27.97. They wanted to leave a tip of approximately 15%. What is a reasonable estimate of the tip? **about $4**

10. ***Earth Science*** Earth's atmosphere exerts a pressure of 14.7 pounds per square inch at the ocean's surface. The pressure increases by 2.7 pounds per square inch for every 6 feet that you descend. Find the pressure at 18 feet below the surface. **22.8 pounds per sq in.**

11. **Standardized Test Practice** Alisa bought a new stereo. She made a 25% down payment and 12 monthly payments of $45. Which is a reasonable estimate for the total price of the stereo? **C**

A $590
B $620
C $700
D $840
E $900

3 PRACTICE/APPLY

Check for Understanding

Use the results of Exercise 3 to determine whether students grasp the concept of solving a simpler problem.

Extra Practice If students need additional practice in problem solving, extra practice is available on the following pages.
- Solve a Simpler Problem, p. 598
- Mixed Problem Solving, see pp. 605–606

Assignment Guide

All: 4–11

4 ASSESS

Closing Activity

Speaking Have students explain how to solve Exercise 9. Challenge students to solve it using two different methods.

Extending the Lesson

Activity Have students research land use in their home state and find the percents and areas for each major category.

11-2 Lesson Notes

Instructional Resources

- *Study Guide Masters,* p. 82
- *Practice Masters,* p. 82
- *Enrichment Masters,* p. 82
- Transparencies 11-2, A and B
- *Assessment and Evaluation Masters,* p. 295
- *School to Career Masters,* p. 24
- *Science and Math Lab Manual,* pp. 85–88

CD-ROM Program
- Resource Lesson 11-2

Recommended Pacing	
Standard	Day 4 of 13
Honors	Day 4 of 12
Block	Day 2 of 7

1 FOCUS

5-Minute Check *(Lesson 11-1)*

Write the fraction, decimal, mixed number, or whole number equivalent of each percent that could be used to estimate. All answers are sample answers.

1. 89% $\frac{9}{10}$

2. 13% $\frac{1}{8}$

Estimate.

3. 60% of 31 $0.6 \times 30 = 18$

4. 300% of 78 $3 \times 80 = 240$

5. 75% of 410 $\frac{3}{4} \times 400 = 300$

The 5-Minute Check is also available on **Transparency 11-2A** for this lesson.

Motivating the Lesson

Communication Have students discuss three ways in which the statement *15 percent of \$20 is \$3* could be written as an equation. $20 \times 0.15 = 3$; $\frac{3}{20} = 0.15$; $\frac{3}{0.15} = 20$

11-2 Integration: Algebra
The Percent Equation

What **you'll learn**

You'll learn to solve problems by using the percent equation.

When **am I ever going to use this?**

The percent equation is useful in calculating sales tax, discounts, and commissions.

LOOK BACK
Refer to Lesson 8-9 to review the percent proportion.

Ocean water contains about 3.5% salt. How much dissolved salt is in a 50-gallon tank of ocean water? You could solve this problem by using a percent proportion $\frac{P}{B} = \frac{r}{100}$, where P is the percentage, B is the base, and $\frac{r}{100}$ is the rate. Another method is to write an equation. Let R represent the ratio $\frac{r}{100}$.

$\frac{P}{B} = \frac{r}{100}$ *Percent proportion*

$\frac{P}{B} = R$ *Replace $\frac{r}{100}$ with R.*

$\frac{P}{B} \cdot B = R \cdot B$ *Multiply each side by B.*

$P = R \cdot B$

Thus, the percent proportion $\frac{P}{B} = \frac{r}{100}$ can be written as a percent equation $P = R \cdot B$.

Percent Equation	
Words:	The percentage (*P*) is equal to the rate (*R*) times the base (*B*).
Symbols:	$P = R \cdot B$

In the percent equation, the rate is usually expressed as a decimal.

In the problem above, the rate R is 3.5%, and the base B is 50.

$P = R \cdot B$

$P = 0.035 \cdot 50$ *$R = 3.5\% = \frac{3.5}{100}$ or 0.035, B = 50*

$P = 1.75$

So, 50 gallons of ocean water contains about 1.75 gallons of dissolved salt.

Example 1 **What number is 24% of 82?** *Estimate: $\frac{1}{4} \cdot 80 = 20$*

$P = R \cdot B$

$P = 0.24 \cdot 82$ *Replace R with 0.24 and B with 82.*

$P = 19.68$

24% of 82 is 19.68. *Compare to the estimate.*

Investigations for the Special Education Student

This blackline master booklet helps you plan for the needs of your special education students by providing long-term projects along with teacher notes. Investigation 11, *Super Star!,* may be used with this chapter.

Examples 

Real World APPLICATION

2 **Sports** **In a recent year, Alex Rodriguez had 215 hits in 601 times at bat. What percent of his times at bat were hits?**

Explore You need to find what percent of 601 is 215.

Estimate: $\frac{200}{600} = \frac{1}{3}$ *or about 33%.*

Plan Use the percent equation $P = R \cdot B$. The percentage, P, is 215, and the base, B, is 601.

Solve

$P = R \cdot B$

$215 = R \cdot 601$ *Replace P with 215 and B with 601.*

$\frac{215}{601} = R$ *Divide each side by 601.*

215 [÷] 601 [=] 0.357737105

So, about 36% of Mr. Rodriquez's times at bat were hits.

Examine Comparing the actual answer to the estimate, the answer is reasonable.

3 **42 is 56% of what number?** *Estimate: 42 is 50% or* $\frac{1}{2}$ *of 84.*

$P = R \cdot B$ *Use the percent equation.*

$42 = 0.56 \cdot B$ *Replace P with 42 and R with 0.56.*

$\frac{42}{0.56} = B$ *Divide each side by 0.56.*

42 [÷] .56 [=] 75

$B = 75$

42 is 56% of 75. *Compare to the estimate.*

CHECK FOR UNDERSTANDING

Communicating Mathematics

Read and study the lesson to answer each question. 1–2. See Answer Appendix.

1. ***Tell*** how the percent equation, $P = R \cdot B$, is related to the percent proportion, $\frac{P}{B} = \frac{r}{100}$.
2. ***Explain*** why the rate is the percent divided by 100.
3. ***Write*** when it is easier to use the percent equation rather than the percent proportion. **Sample answer: If the rate and the base are known, it is easier to use the percent equation.**

Guided Practice

Write an equation for each problem. Then solve. Round answers to the nearest tenth. 4. $22 = R \cdot 50$; 44.0% 5. $27 = 0.30 \cdot B$; 90.0

4. 22 is what percent of 50?
5. 30% of what number is 27?
6. 24 is 60% of what number? (6. $24 = 0.60 \cdot B$; 40.0)
7. Find 8% of 38. $P = 0.08 \cdot 38$; 3.0
8. ***Technology*** Scientists are trying to find energy-saving alternatives to electrical appliances. A microwave clothes dryer, which reduces drying time by 25%, is currently being developed. If normal drying time is 40 minutes, how much less time would it take a microwave clothes dryer to dry a load of clothes? **10 min**

2 TEACH

Transparency 11-2B contains a teaching aid for this lesson.

Using Calculators Encourage students to estimate the unknown factor in the percent equation first, then use a calculator to find the solution. They can multiply to find P and divide to find either R or B.

In-Class Examples

For Example 1
What number is 73% of 640? 467.2

For Example 2
Ricky threw 64 passes and completed 36 of them. What percent of his passes were complete? $56\frac{1}{4}$%

For Example 3
21 is 60% of what number? 35

3 PRACTICE/APPLY

Check for Understanding

If students need additional practice or instruction after completing Exercises 1–8, one of these options may be helpful.

- Extra Practice, see p. 598
- Reteaching Activity
- *Study Guide Masters,* p. 82
- *Practice Masters,* p. 82

***Study Guide Masters,* p. 82**

Name__________ Date__________

Study Guide

Integration: Algebra
The Percent Equation

In the percent proportion, $\frac{r}{100}$ is the rate. Let $R = \frac{r}{100}$.

Then $\frac{P}{B} = \frac{r}{100}$ becomes $\frac{P}{B} = R$.

Rewrite the equation at the right above to make it easier to solve equations when the rate and base are given.

$P = R \cdot B$

Examples *1* **What number is 35% of 480?**

$P = R \cdot B$ *Replace R with 0.35 and B with 480.*
$P = 0.35 \cdot 480$
$P = 168$
So, 35% of 480 is 168.

2 **56 is what percent of 224?**

$P = R \cdot B$ *Replace P with 56 and B with 224.*
$56 = 224R$
$\frac{56}{224} = \frac{224R}{224}$
$0.25 = R$

So, 56 is 25% of 224.

Write an equation for each problem. Then solve.

1. 63 is what percent of 42? 150%
2. 35% of what number is 49? 140
3. Find 12% of 225. 27
4. 198 is 60% of what number? 330
5. What percent of 360 is 108? 30%
6. 792 is 90% of what number? 880
7. 85% of 460 is what number? 391
8. 6% of what number is 9? 150
9. 95 is what percent of 50? 190%
10. What is 29% of $17? $4.93

 T82 *Mathematics: Applications and Connections, Course 2*

Reteaching the Lesson

Activity Have students shade 10 × 10 grids to model finding a percent of a number, finding what percent one number is of another, and finding a total when given a number and a percent.

Error Analysis

Watch for students who mistake *percentage* (P) for the *rate* (R) in the percent equation $P = R \cdot B$.

Prevent by explaining that P represents a certain portion of B in the percent proportion $\frac{P}{B} = R$, where R is written as a percent.

Assignment Guide

Core: 9–23 odd, 26–29
Enriched: 10–22 even, 23, 24, 26–29

Exercise 25 asks students to advance to the next stage of work on the Chapter Project. You may want each group to check that their percents add up to 100%.

4 ASSESS

Closing Activity

Writing Have students write an equation they could use to figure the amount of commission one would earn on sales of $5,500, if the commission rate is 3%. $c = 0.03 \times 5{,}500$

Chapter 11, Quiz A (Lessons 11-1 and 11-2) is available in the *Assessment and Evaluation Masters,* p. 295.

Additional Answers

16. $1.265 = 0.55 \cdot B$; 2.3
17. $P = 0.26 \cdot 48$; 12.5
18. $57 = R \cdot 87$; 65.5%
19. $30 = R \cdot 500$; 6%
20. $36 = 0.425 \cdot B$; 84.7

Practice Masters, p. 82

Name________________ Date________

11-2 Practice

Integration: Algebra
The Percent Equation

Write an equation for each problem. Then solve. Round answers to the nearest tenth.

1. 18 is 24% of what number? $18 = 0.24 \cdot B$; 75
2. 25% of 176 is what number? $P = 0.25 \cdot 176$; 44
3. 45% of what number is 121.5? $121.5 = 0.45 \cdot B$; 270
4. 80% of what number is 94? $94 = 0.80 \cdot B$; 117.5
5. 32.5% of 256 is what number? $P = 0.325 \cdot 256$; 83.2
6. What percent of 125 is 25? $25 = R \cdot 125$; 20%
7. $18\frac{3}{4}$ is 25% of what number? $18\frac{3}{4} = 0.25 \cdot B$; 75
8. 15% of 290 is what number? $P = 0.15 \cdot 290$; 43.5
9. What percent of 224 is 28? $28 = R \cdot 224$; 12.5%
10. 344.8 is what percent of 862? $344.8 = R \cdot 862$; 40%
11. What number is 60% of 605? $P = 0.60 \cdot 605$; 363
12. 32% of 250 is what number? $P = 0.32 \cdot 250$; 80

 T82 *Mathematics: Applications and Connections, Course 2*

EXERCISES

Practice

11. $75 = 0.78 \cdot B$; 96.2
12. $P = 0.26 \cdot 119$; 30.9
13. $45 = R \cdot 36$; 125%
14. $P = 0.2 \cdot 68$; 13.6
15. $17 = 0.4 \cdot B$; 42.5

16–20. See margin.

Write an equation for each problem. Then solve. Round answers to the nearest tenth. 9. $P = 0.16 \cdot 32$; 5.1 10. $17 = R \cdot 68$; 25%

9. 16% of 32 is what number?
10. 17 is what percent of 68?
11. 75 is 78% of what number?
12. Find 26% of 119.
13. 45 is what percent of 36?
14. Find 20% of 68.
15. 17 is 40% of what number?
16. 55% of what number is 1.265?
17. 26% of 48 is what number?
18. What percent of 87 is 57?
19. 30 is what percent of 500?
20. 42.5% of what number is 36?
21. Find 5.75% of $69. Round to the nearest cent. $3.97
22. ***Algebra*** If 70% of x is 42, find x. 60

Applications and Problem Solving

23. ***Pets*** The table shows the costs of owning a dog over an average 11-year lifespan, not including the initial price of the dog. What percent of the total cost is veterinary bills? 26.9%

Free(?) to a Good Home

Food	$4,020
Veterinary	$3,930
Grooming, toys, equipment, house	$2,960
Flea and tick treatment	$1,070
Training	$1,220
Other	$1,400

ROVER

Source: American Kennel Club, *USA TODAY* research

24. 1,440 to 1,470 cases

24. ***Life Science*** *Biometrics* is the science of verifying identities by biological characteristics. Researchers have developed a system that checks a person's identity by studying the iris of his or her eye. Currently, there are errors in only 2 to 4 percent of the identities checked by the system. If 1,500 people are tested using this system, about how many of the cases will be accurate?
25. ***Working on the CHAPTER Project*** Refer to your table of data for one hour of radio programming. Find the percent of the total hour for each type of programming. See students' work.
26. ***Critical Thinking*** Explain how you can predict when the percentage, P, will be less than, the same as, or greater than the base, B. See Answer Appendix.

Mixed Review

27. Estimate 18% of 40.5. *(Lesson 11-1)* $0.2 \cdot 40 = 8$
28. **Standardized Test Practice** A trapezoid has bases of 15 meters and 18 meters and a height of 10 meters. What is the area of the trapezoid? *(Lesson 10-5)* B

    A 30 m^2 **B** 165 m^2 **C** 60 m^2 **D** 330 m^2

29. ***Aviation*** A blimp starts a descent from 1,000 feet above the ground. After 10 minutes, the blimp is at 600 feet above the ground. Find the rate of its descent in feet per minute. *(Lesson 8-2)* 40 ft/min

For **Extra Practice,** see page 598.

Extending the Lesson

Enrichment Masters, p. 82

11-2 Enrichment

Just The Facts

Use the percent proportion and your calculator to help discover some interesting facts about the United States. Round your answers to the nearest tenth of a percent.

1. The United States produced 67,832 million eggs in 1990. The state of Indiana produced 5,445 million eggs—more than any other state. What percent of the eggs produced in the United States were produced outside Indiana? 92.0%
2. The population of the United States in 1990 was 248,709,873 people. Of these people, 121,239,418 were male. What percent of the population was female? 51.3%

Activity On a trip, George took 24 photos and Karin took 36. George says that he took $33\frac{1}{3}\%$ fewer pictures than Karin, who claims she took 50% more pictures than he. Ask students who is right. both are

HANDS-ON LAB

COOPERATIVE LEARNING

11-3A Jelly Bean Statistics

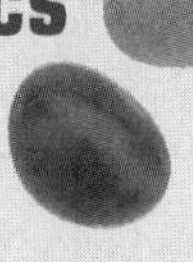

A Preview of Lesson 11-3

 jelly beans

needles

 thread

compass

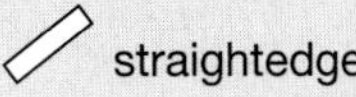 straightedge

Almost everyone has a favorite flavor of jelly bean. What is yours?

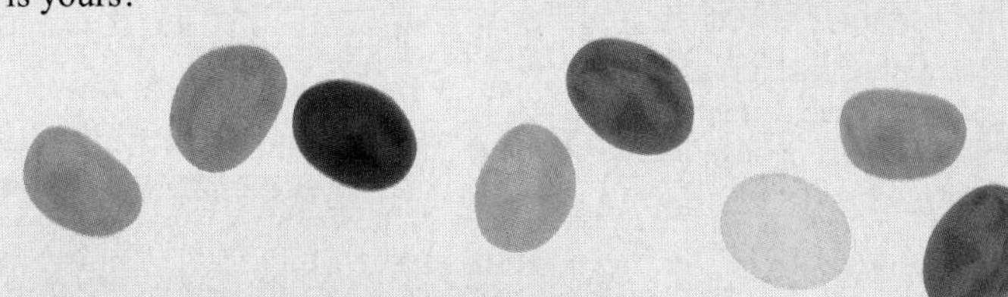

TRY THIS

Work with a partner.

Step 1 Take a survey of the people in your class. Tally responses by flavor in a frequency table. *Refer to Lesson 3-1 to review frequency tables.*

Step 2 Sort the jelly beans to reflect the results of the survey. For example, if there are 3 people whose favorite flavor is cherry (red), you would select 3 red jelly beans, and so on.

Step 3 String the jelly beans with like flavors together.

Step 4 Arrange the jelly beans in a circle. Use a compass to draw a circle the same size.

Step 5 On the circle, mark sections to indicate the separation by flavor.

Step 6 Draw a radius from each mark on the circle to the center.

Step 7 Identify each section by flavor.

1, 3, 5. See students' work.

ON YOUR OWN

2, 4. See margin for sample answers.

1. Write a short paragraph describing the circle graph. Include a description of the sizes of the sections in relation to each other.
2. Is there a relationship between the number of tally marks and the size of a section by flavor? If so, write a sentence to describe that relationship.
3. Use the percent proportion or percent equation to find the percent represented by each flavor. Label each section by flavor and by the percent it represents.
4. Explain how the ratio of each flavor to the whole is represented on the circle graph.
5. ***Reflect Back*** The circle graph represents the same information as the frequency table. Discuss the advantages and disadvantages of each.

Have students write a paragraph describing what would happen to the percents of each flavor if the number of each flavor of jelly bean in the graph was multiplied by 5.

Additional Answers

2. The greater the number of tally marks, the greater the size of a selection.
4. The ratio of each flavor to the whole is the percent of the graph that each flavor makes up.

11-3A HANDS-ON LAB Notes

GET READY

Objective Students make a circle graph.

Optional Resources

Hands-On Lab Masters
- circle graph template, p. 28
- worksheet, p. 65

Manipulative Kit
- compass
- straightedge

Overhead Manipulative Resources
- compass
- straightedge

MANAGEMENT TIPS

Recommended Time
30 minutes

Getting Started Take a survey of the class to determine how many students like pizza; take a second survey to see how many like prunes, and a third survey to see how many like pineapple. Tally the numbers and construct a bar graph comparing the data. Discuss whether another type of graph would work better.

For the **Activity,** point out that each person surveyed can select only one favorite flavor, so the results may be different from the survey above, where each student could be counted more than once.

ASSESS

Have students complete Exercises 1–5. In Exercise 1, encourage students to compare the size of sections in ratio form. In Exercise 2, have them compare tally marks with sections in ratio form.

11-3 Lesson Notes

Instructional Resources

- *Study Guide Masters,* p. 83
- *Practice Masters,* p. 83
- *Enrichment Masters,* p. 83
- Transparencies 11-3, A and B
- *Diversity Masters,* p. 24

CD-ROM Program
- Resource Lesson 11-3
- Extended Activity 11-3

Recommended Pacing	
Standard	Days 5 & 6 of 13
Honors	Day 5 of 12
Block	Day 3 of 7

1 FOCUS

5-Minute Check (Lesson 11-2)

Write an equation for each problem. Then solve. Round answers to the nearest tenth.

1. 20% of what number is 16? $16 \cdot 0.2 = B$; 80
2. Find 34% of 330. $P = 0.34 \cdot 330$; 112.2
3. 8.4 is what percent of 67.2? $8.4 = R \cdot 67.2$; 12.5%
4. 30% of what number is 300? $300 = 0.30 \cdot B$; 1,000
5. What is 45% of $75.80? Round to the nearest cent. $P = 0.45 \cdot 75.80$; $34.11

The 5-Minute Check is also available on **Transparency 11-3A** for this lesson.

Motivating the Lesson

Hands-On Activity Have students conduct a class survey to find out students' favorite movies of the current year. Write the results on the chalkboard. Ask students to sketch a circle graph to display their data.

11-3 Integration: Statistics
Making Circle Graphs

What **you'll learn**

You'll learn to construct and interpret circle graphs.

When **am I ever going to use this?**

Magazines and newspapers often use circle graphs to show results of an opinion survey.

Word Wise

circle graph

Do you believe that there is intelligent life on other planets? The results of a recent poll are shown in the table.

You can draw a **circle graph** to show this information. A circle graph is used to compare parts of a whole.

Follow the steps to make a circle graph of the responses of the men.

The Truth is Out There . . .		
Is there life on other planets?	Men	Women
Yes	54%	33%
No	33%	47%
Don't Know	13%	20%

Source: Fox News/Opinion Dynamics poll

Step 1 Find the number of degrees for each part. Use $P = R \cdot B$.

Yes 54% of $360° = 0.54 \cdot 360° = 194.4°$

No 33% of $360° = 0.33 \cdot 360° = 118.8°$

Don't Know 13% of $360° = 0.13 \cdot 360° = 46.8°$

Step 2 Use a compass to draw a circle. Then draw a radius as shown.

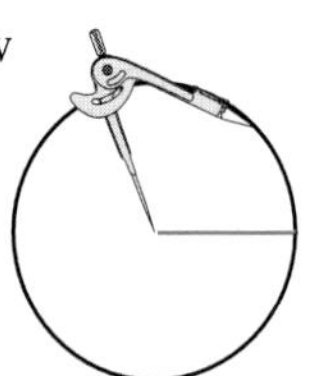

Step 3 You can start with the least number of degrees, in this case, 46.8°. Use your protractor to draw an angle of 46.8°.

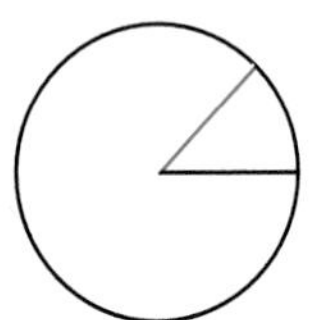

Step 4 Repeat for another section.

You can measure the last section of a circle graph to verify that the angles have the correct measures.

Step 5 In this case, there is only one section left. Label each section of the graph with the category and percent. Give the graph a title.

Life on Other Planets? What Men Think

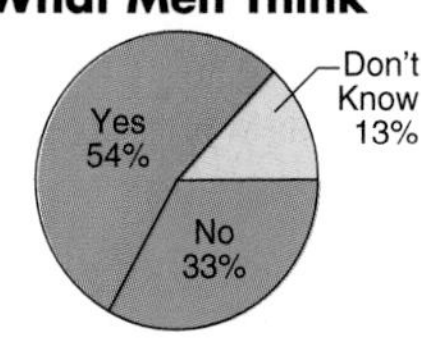

Multiple Learning Styles

Intrapersonal Provide a list of eight occupations (for example, bank manager, carpenter, clothing designer, emergency medical technician, and so on), and have each student rank them by order of preference. Count 8 points for each first choice, 7 for second, and so on. Find the class total for each occupation. Draw a circle graph to show each occupation's total score. Then discuss whether the graph shows the class's preferences.

Oceanography **The table shows the surface area of the four oceans. Make a circle graph to represent the data.**

Ocean Surface Areas	
Ocean	Area (sq mi)
Pacific	64,186,300
Atlantic	33,420,000
Indian	28,350,500
Arctic	5,105,700

- Find the total surface area of the oceans.

Pacific	64,186,300
Atlantic	33,420,000
Indian	28,350,500
Arctic	5,105,700
Total	131,062,500

A ratio is a comparison of two numbers by division.

- Find the ratio that compares each number with the total. Convert the ratio to a decimal. Round to the nearest hundredth.

$$\text{Pacific } \frac{64{,}186{,}300}{131{,}062{,}500} \approx 0.49$$

$$\text{Atlantic } \frac{33{,}420{,}000}{131{,}062{,}500} \approx 0.25$$

$$\text{Indian } \frac{28{,}350{,}500}{131{,}062{,}500} \approx 0.22$$

$$\text{Arctic } \frac{5{,}105{,}700}{131{,}062{,}500} \approx 0.04$$

Study Hint
Technology You can use word processing or spreadsheet software to make circle graphs.

- Find the number of degrees for each section of the graph.

Pacific $0.49 \cdot 360° = 176.4°$

Atlantic $0.25 \cdot 360° = 90°$

Indian $0.22 \cdot 360° = 79.2°$

Arctic $0.04 \cdot 360° = 14.4°$

The sum of the degrees may not always be 360° due to rounding.

- Make the circle graph.

Ocean Surface Areas

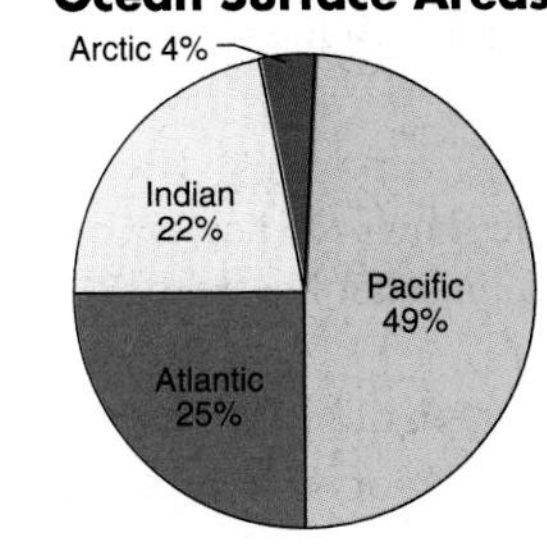

2 TEACH

Transparency 11-3B contains a teaching aid for this lesson.

Modeling Mathematics Have students discuss their ethnic background with their families, and tally the results in a class diversity chart. Together construct a poster using different kinds of beads, as in Exercise 8, to make a circle graph showing the class' ethnicity.

In-Class Example

For the Example
The table shows the results of a survey in which seventh graders named their favorite sport. Make a circle graph to represent the data.

Sport	Number of Votes
Basketball	12
Baseball/Softball	10
Football	6
Hockey	3
Soccer	8
Tennis	2
Track	2
Swimming	5

Favorite Sports

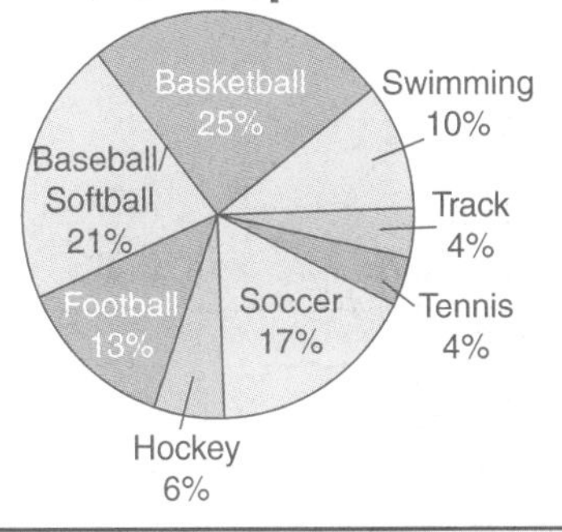

Teaching Tip Point out that a circle graph provides a quick view of how a set of objects is divided into its parts. Ask students what information a circle graph *may not* provide that a bar graph does. **the size of the whole set of objects**

3 PRACTICE/APPLY

Check for Understanding

If students need additional practice or instruction after completing Exercises 1–4, one of these options may be helpful.

- Extra Practice, see p. 599
- Reteaching Activity
- *Study Guide Masters,* p. 83
- *Practice Masters,* p. 83
- Interactive Mathematics Tools Software

Assignment Guide
Core: 5, 7, 10–12 **Enriched:** 6–8, 10–12

Additional Answer

4c. **Vacation Memories**

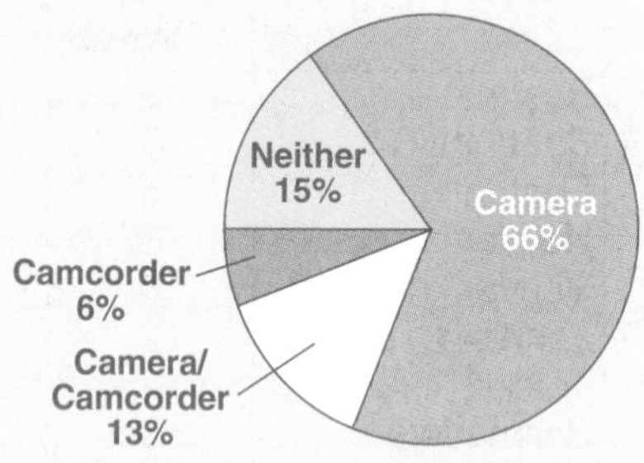

CHECK FOR UNDERSTANDING

Communicating Mathematics

Read and study the lesson to answer each question.

1. ***Tell*** how to make a circle graph when you are given the percents of the whole that each category represents. **Change percents to decimal form. Multiply by 360° to obtain the number of degrees in the sections of the circle graph.**
2. ***Explain*** what the ratios of angle measures to 360 represent in a circle graph. **the percents of the categories**
3. ***You Decide*** The table shows the percent of adults surveyed who visited animal attractions in 1996. Could you make a circle graph of the data? If so, explain the steps. If not, explain why not. **No; the sum of the percents does not equal 100.**

Seeing the Animals	
Attraction	**Percent of Adults**
Zoo	28%
Aquarium	17%
Wild Animal Park	10%

Source: Bruskin/Goldring Research

Guided Practice

4. Refer to the table.
   a. Write a ratio that compares each number with the total. Write as a decimal to the nearest hundredth. **4a. camera, 0.66; camcorder, 0.06; camera/camcorder, 0.13; neither, 0.15**
   b. Find the number of degrees for each section of the graph. Round to the nearest tenth. **4b. camera, 237.6°; camcorder, 21.6° camera/camcorder, 46.8°; neither, 54.0°**
   c. Make a circle graph showing how people record their vacations. **See margin.**

Vacation Memories	
Method	**Number of People**
Camera	667
Camcorder	61
Camera/Camcorder	131
Neither	151

Source: Opinion Research Corp.

EXERCISES

Practice

5–6. See Answer Appendix.

5. Refer to the table.
   a. Write a ratio that compares each number with the total. Write as a decimal to the nearest thousandth.
   b. Find the number of degrees for each section of the graph. Round to the nearest tenth.
   c. Make a circle graph of the park tourists.

Park Tourists	
Park	**Visitors (thousands)**
A	15,509
B	14,100
C	12,900
D	10,700
E	10,700
F	9,500

6. ***Sports*** The table shows the percent of total injuries of high school basketball players.
   a. Make a circle graph of girls' injuries.
   b. Make a circle graph of boys' injuries.
   c. Compare and contrast the graphs.

Injury	Girls	Boys
Ankle/Foot	36%	38%
Hip/Leg/Knee	30%	25%
Arm/Hand	11%	12%
Face/Scalp	9%	12%
All Others	14%	13%

Source: National Athletic Trainers' Association

***Study Guide Masters,* p. 83**

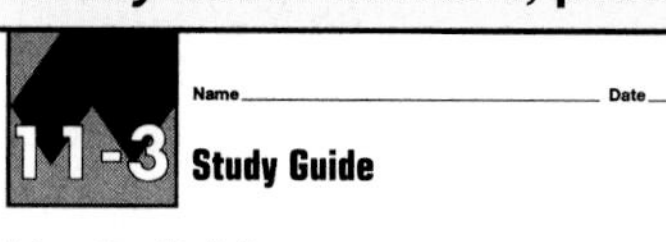

Name__________ Date__________

11-3 Study Guide

Integration: Statistics
Making Circle Graphs

A **circle graph** shows how a whole is divided into parts.

Ocean	Pacific	Atlantic	Indian	Arctic
Area (in millions of mi²)	64.2	33.4	28.4	5.1

To make a circle graph for the data in the table, first find the total area of the oceans: 64.2 + 33.4 + 28.4 + 5.1 = 131.1.

Then find the ratio that compares the area of each of the oceans to the total area. Use a calculator. Round to the nearest hundredth.

Pacific: $\frac{64.2}{131.1} = 0.49$ Indian: $\frac{28.4}{131.1} = 0.22$

Atlantic: $\frac{33.4}{131.1} = 0.25$ Arctic: $\frac{5.1}{131.1} = 0.04$

Ocean Areas

Pacific, Arctic, Indian, Atlantic

To find the number of degrees for each section of the graph, multiply each ratio by 360°. Round to the nearest degree.

Pacific: 0.49 × 360° = 176° Indian: 0.22 × 360° = 79°
Atlantic: 0.25 × 360° = 90° Arctic: 0.04 × 360° = 14°

Use a compass and protractor to construct a circle and angles whose measures are 17°, 90°, 79°, and 14°. Note that the sum of the degrees is not 360° due to rounding.

Make a circle graph to show the data in the chart.

Continent	Area (in millions of mi²)
Europe	3.8
Asia	17.4
North America	9.4
South America	6.9
Africa	11.7
Oceania	3.3
Antarctica	5.4

Europe: 25°
Asia: 108°
N. America: 58°
S. America: 43°
Africa: 72°
Oceania: 22°
Antarctica: 32°

Continent Areas

Asia 30%, Europe 7%, Antarctica 9%, Oceania 6%, Africa 20%, South America 12%, North America 16%

 T83 *Mathematics: Applications and Connections,* Course 2

Reteaching the Lesson

Activity Have students work together in groups to make a circle graph showing the favorite ice cream flavors of 12 classmates. Have them discuss how to calculate the percents and the degree measures of the angles for circle sections.

Error Analysis

Watch for students whose totals are not 100% or 360°.

Prevent by reminding them that they need to adjust how they rounded to get the exact total.

Applications and Problem Solving

7. ***Statistics*** Refer to the beginning of the lesson.
   a. Make a circle graph of the responses of women regarding life on other planets. **a–c. See Answer Appendix.**
   b. Compare this circle graph to the one showing the responses of men.
   c. What advantage is there in showing the data in a circle graph instead of a table?

8. ***Geography*** Students in a New Zealand classroom used a string of beads to make a circle graph showing their ethnicity. A different kind of bead was given to each child depending on his or her ethnicity. Then the string was tied in a circle and divided into segments.

Family Activity

Survey your family members about how many of their meals in a week are fish, chicken, pork, beef, vegetarian, and so on. Make circle graphs for each member's meals and compare.

A New Zealand Classroom

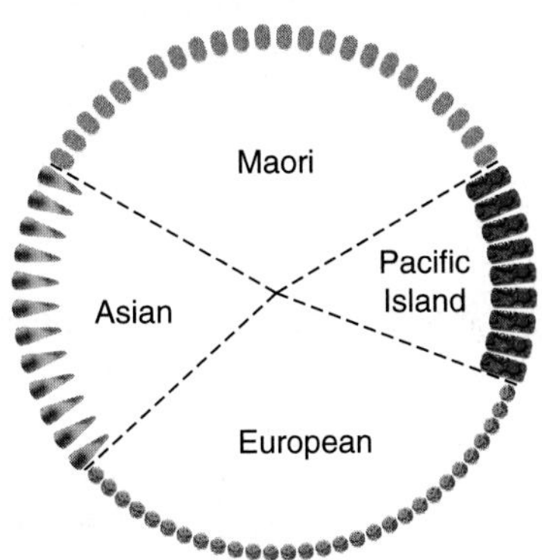

Source: *Teaching Statistics*, Autumn

8a. Maori, 24; Pacific Island, 9; European, 29; Asian, 12

8b. Maori, 32.4%; Pacific Island, 12.2%; European, 39.2%; Asian, 16.2%

   a. Count the beads in each section of the circle graph.
   b. Find the percent of the class that was in each ethnic group. Round to the nearest tenth.

9a–b. See students' work.

9. ***Working on the*** **CHAPTER Project** Refer to Exercise 25 on page 458.
   a. Make a circle graph of your radio programming data.
   b. Compare your circle graph to the circle graphs of other people in your group. Summarize the similarities and differences.

10. ***Critical Thinking*** Line graphs are usually best for data that show change over time. When might it be more appropriate to display data in a circle graph? **See margin.**

Mixed Review

11. Find 16% of 74. *(Lesson 11-2)* **11.84**

12. **Standardized Test Practice** A brochure is 12 inches wide and 8 inches long. If the only photo on the brochure measures 3 inches by 2 inches, which sentence could be used to find x, the amount of space left for information and borders? *(Lesson 1-7)* **D**

   A $x = (12 + 8) - (3 + 2)$
   B $x = 2(12 + 8) - 2(3 + 2)$
   C $x = 12 \times 8 \times 3 \times 2$
   D $x = (12 \times 8) - (3 \times 2)$
   E $x = \frac{12 \times 8}{3 \times 2}$

For **Extra Practice,** see page 599.

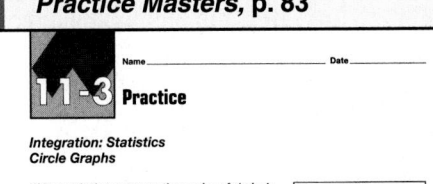

Extending the Lesson

Enrichment Masters, p. 83

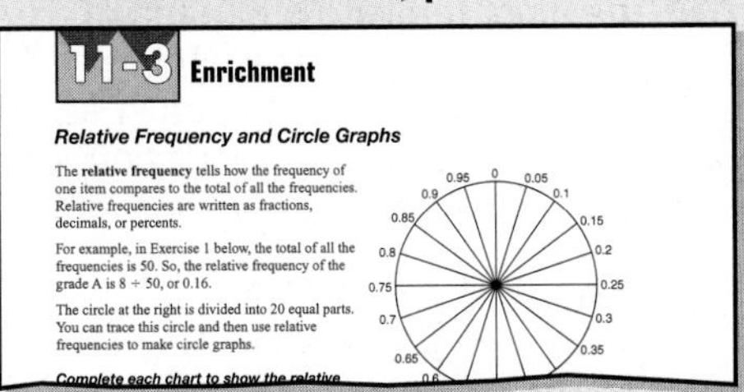
11-3 Enrichment

Relative Frequency and Circle Graphs

The **relative frequency** tells how the frequency of one item compares to the total of all the frequencies. Relative frequencies are written as fractions, decimals, or percents.

For example, in Exercise 1 below, the total of all the frequencies is 50. So, the relative frequency of the grade A is 8 ÷ 50, or 0.16.

The circle at the right is divided into 20 equal parts. You can trace this circle and then use relative frequencies to make circle graphs.

Activity Have students work in groups to write an opinion survey on a topic of interest, such as music, movies, television, books, sports, clothes, current events, or food. When the whole class has answered each group's survey, have each group tally its data and construct a circle graph revealing the results.

Have students write a short summary of their family food surveys, interpreting the results. Ask them how they would change the graph to represent their ideal diet.

Exercise 9 asks students to advance to the next stage of work on the Chapter Project. You may want to have students discuss what accounts for the similarities and differences in their graphs.

4 ASSESS

Closing Activity

Writing Have students list the steps in the process of constructing a circle graph, given a table of data.

Additional Answer

10. **Sample answer: when you want to show how parts are related to the whole, such as a budget**

Practice Masters, p. 83

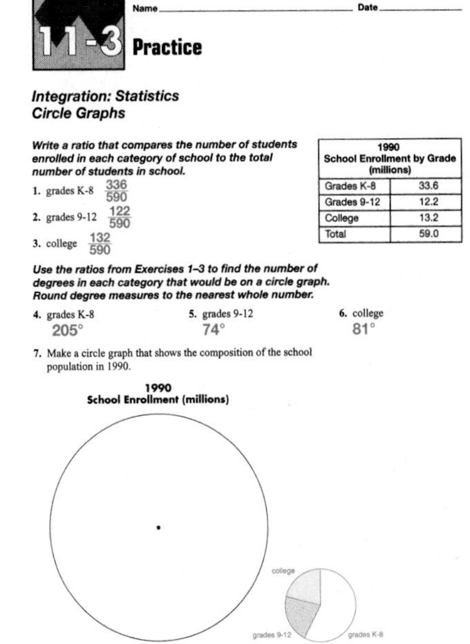
Name ____________ Date ____________

11-3 Practice

Integration: Statistics
Circle Graphs

Write a ratio that compares the number of students enrolled in each category of school to the total number of students in school.

1. grades K-8 $\frac{336}{590}$
2. grades 9-12 $\frac{122}{590}$
3. college $\frac{132}{590}$

1990 School Enrollment by Grade (millions)	
Grades K-8	33.6
Grades 9-12	12.2
College	13.2
Total	59.0

Use the ratios from Exercises 1–3 to find the number of degrees in each category that would be on a circle graph. Round degree measures to the nearest whole number.

4. grades K-8 205°
5. grades 9-12 74°
6. college 81°

7. Make a circle graph that shows the composition of the school population in 1990.

1990 School Enrollment (millions)

© Glencoe/McGraw-Hill T83 *Mathematics: Applications and Connections, Course 2*

11-4 Lesson Notes

Instructional Resources

- *Study Guide Masters,* p. 84
- *Practice Masters,* p. 84
- *Enrichment Masters,* p. 84
- Transparencies 11-4, A and B
- *Assessment and Evaluation Masters,* pp. 294, 295
- *Science and Math Lab Manual,* pp. 45–48

CD-ROM Program
- Resource Lesson 11-4

Recommended Pacing	
Standard	Day 7 of 13
Honors	Day 6 of 12
Block	Day 4 of 7

1 FOCUS

5-Minute Check (Lesson 11-3)

The table shows results of a poll asking 7th graders their favorite 5 music groups. Use the data to make a circle graph.

Music Group	Percent Chosen
Nails	43%
The Muffins	15%
Mole Food	20%
For Profit	8%
Old Kids	14%

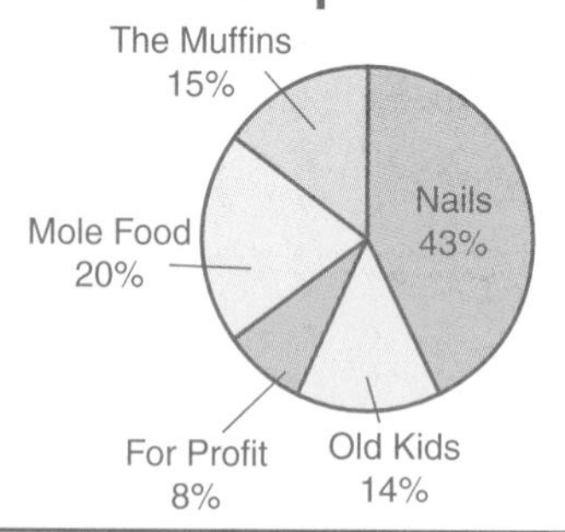

The 5-Minute Check is also available on **Transparency 11-4A** for this lesson.

Motivating the Lesson

Communication Ask students to explain exactly what is meant by "a 40% chance of rain today."
Sample answer: Under similar conditions it usually rains 40% of the time.

11-4 Integration: Statistics
Using Statistics to Predict

What you'll learn
You'll learn to predict actions of a larger group by using a sample.

When am I ever going to use this?
You can use statistics to decide how much of different types of snacks to buy for a party.

Word Wise
population
sample
random

Since 1790, the U.S. government has conducted a census. In a census, every member of a population is contacted by mail or a census taker. The **population** is counted, and other information like annual income, number of people in a household, and ethnic background is gathered.

Surveying every member of a population is very expensive and time consuming. Most of the time pollsters gather information by surveying a **sample**, which is a part of the total population. In order for a sample to be representative, it must be **random**. A random sample will give everyone the same chance of being selected.

1 **Marketing** **One of the reasons that Jay Leno was chosen to promote a snack was to appeal to teenagers. Other celebrities from sports and entertainment were also considered. Would the decision makers have obtained representative results from a survey taken at each location?**

a. 25 eighth graders at a middle school basketball game
b. 500 teens at department stores in all parts of the country

a. This sample is not random because it does not represent all teens. The sample is small, and students at a basketball game may be more likely to suggest a basketball player.

b. This sample is representative and fairly large. Teens of different ages and interests visit malls.

If a random sample of the population is surveyed, then the results can be used to make predictions about the entire population.

2 **Food** **A company surveyed people about the type of crust they preferred on their pizza. Use the results to predict how many of the 1,312 students at Morgan Middle School would choose thin crust.**

Type of Crust	Percent
Thin	48%
Thick	46%
No Preference	6%

Source: *Pizza Today*

You can use the percent proportion to find the number who would prefer thin crust. Find 48% of 1,312 students.

$$\text{rate} \rightarrow \frac{48}{100} = \frac{n}{1{,}312} \begin{array}{l}\leftarrow \text{percentage} \\ \leftarrow \text{base}\end{array}$$

48 [×] 1312 [÷] 100 [=] 629.76

You can predict that about 630 students at Morgan would prefer thin crust pizza.

Multiple Learning Styles

Naturalist Have students measure the length of each of 10 fresh green beans. Then have them count the number of beans in each bean. Ask them to make a prediction for how many beans are in a 6-inch green bean.

CHECK FOR UNDERSTANDING

Communicating Mathematics

Read and study the lesson to answer each question.

1. ***Explain*** how to use the results of a survey to predict the actions of a population. **See margin.**
2. ***Select*** a newspaper article that contains a table or graph. Explain how you think the results were found. **See students' work.**

Guided Practice

3. ***Music*** A company randomly surveyed about 1,800 adults and teens to find the age they began playing musical instruments. They estimate that there are 62 million amateur musicians in the United States.

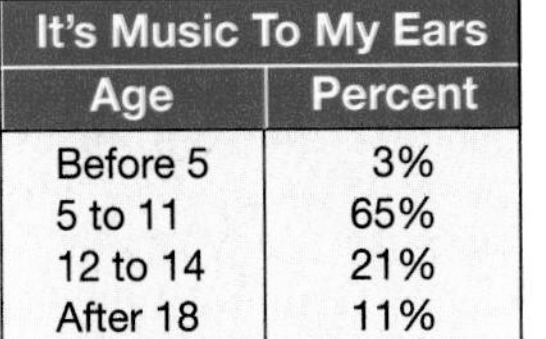

It's Music To My Ears	
Age	**Percent**
Before 5	3%
5 to 11	65%
12 to 14	21%
After 18	11%

Source: National Assoc. of Music Merchants

   a. How many amateur musicians in the United States do you predict learned to play before age 5? **1.86 million**

   b. About how many amateur musicians learned to play between the ages of 12 and 14? **13.02 million**

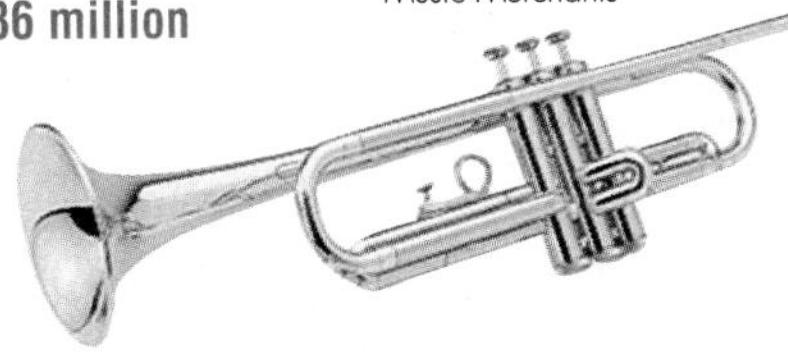

EXERCISES

Practice

4. ***Entertainment*** The table shows the results of a survey of students' favorite TV programs at Trutt Middle School. The school has a total of 840 students.

Program	Number
A	46
B	32
C	28
D	25
E	23
F	21
G	19

   a. What was the sample size?

   b. To the nearest percent, what percent of students preferred Program A? **24%**

   c. How many students in the school would you expect to say that Program A is their favorite? **about 202 students**

   d. Mykia disagreed with the results of the survey and decided to conduct her own. She surveyed all 35 girls in her physical education class. Is Mykia's sample random? Explain.

interNET
CONNECTION
For the latest television programming statistics, visit:
www.glencoe.com/sec/math/mac/mathnet

4a. 194 students
4d. No; the sample does not contain any boys.

5. ***Careers*** Each year, the University of California surveys incoming freshmen on their career intentions.

Career Goal	Percent
Business executive	7.3%
Elementary teacher	5.5%
Engineer	6.4%
Lawyer	3.4%
Physician	5.7%

Source: University of California

   a. Do you think this sample is representative of all college students in the United States? Why or why not? **See margin.**

   b. Of the 3,775 freshmen at the University of California during the 1996-1997 school year, how many would you expect to choose a career as an elementary teacher? **about 208**

Additional Answers

1. To make a prediction based on a sample, write a ratio to express the results of surveying the sample. Then multiply that ratio by the total population.

5a. Sample answer: No; students at the University of California may not be representative of all college students because if their college specializes in a field, they will draw more people interested in that field.

2 TEACH

Transparency 11-4B contains a teaching aid for this lesson.

Reading Mathematics Talk about the meaning of the term *random sample* with students. List examples of random samples and samples that are not random. Ask students to suggest a way to get a random sample of your school or community population.

In-Class Examples

For Example 1

To find out about community support for a new concert hall, a newspaper interviewed 20 members of the Springfield Orchestra and 50 customers at a downtown restaurant. Which one is a more representative sample? **50 restaurant customers**

For Example 2

In a community of 35,000 people, 45 out of 100 randomly selected people prefer vanilla ice cream to chocolate. How many people in the community can be expected to prefer vanilla? **about 15,750 people**

3 PRACTICE/APPLY

Check for Understanding

If students need additional practice or instruction after completing Exercises 1–3, one of these options may be helpful.

- Extra Practice, see p. 599
- Reteaching Activity, see p. 466
- *Study Guide Masters,* p. 84
- *Practice Masters,* p. 84

Assignment Guide

Core: 5–9 odd, 11–13
Enriched: 4, 6, 7–9, 11–13
All: Self Test, 1–10

Exercise 10 asks students to advance to the next stage of work on the Chapter Project. You may want students to share their ideas for a programming schedule.

Additional Answer

7. Sample answer: *Organic Gardening* asked households and NGA asked individuals. They are more likely to find someone in a household who gardens, than to find a particular individual who gardens.

Study Guide Masters, p. 84

Name________________ Date________

Study Guide

Integration: Statistics
Using Statistics to Predict

Data gathered by surveying a random sample of the population may be used to make predictions about the entire population.

Example **200 people from a town of 28,000 people were chosen at random and asked if they thought the town needed more bicycle paths. 78 out of the 200 people responded Yes. 84 responded No. Of those surveyed, 38 were undecided. Predict how many of the 28,000 people in the town think more bicycle paths are needed.**

78 out of 200 is 39%.
39% of 28,000 = $0.39 \times 28{,}000$ or 10,920

You can predict that about 10,920 people think more bicycle paths are needed.

Members of a seventh-grade class were surveyed to find out how much they would be willing to pay to go on a class trip. The results are shown in the chart.

Price Range	\$10 – \$20	\$21 – \$30	\$31 – \$40	\$41 – \$50
Students	4	12	20	14

1. What was the sample size?
   50
2. What percent of the students said they would pay \$31 to \$40?
   40%
3. What percent of the students would go on the trip if it cost \$30?
   92%
4. If there are 360 students in the seventh-grade class, about how many would go on the trip if it cost \$30?
   331 students

Predict each outcome.

5. In a poll of 100 people, 55 said they would vote for Alvarez for city council. If 24,000 people vote in the election, about how many will vote for Alvarez?
   13,200 people
6. A survey showed that 129 out of 300 people in a factory bought lunch in the cafeteria. If the factory employs 2,900 people, about how many buy lunch in the cafeteria?
   1,247 people

 T84 *Mathematics: Applications and Connections, Course 2*

6. ***Entertainment*** A company asked 6,500 teens in 26 countries about their favorite things to do outside of school.

Teens could choose more than one activity.

What Should We Do?	
Activity	**Number**
Watching TV	6,045
Being with friends	6,045
Listening to music	5,915
Listening to radio	5,525
Watching movies at home	5,395
Going to movies	5,200
Going to parties	5,070
Talking on the phone	4,940
Playing sports	4,940

Source: New World Teen Study

   a. What percent of teens said they enjoy going to the movies? **80%**
   b. What percent of teens said they enjoy playing sports? **76%**
   c. If there were 472 students in your school, how many would you expect to say that they enjoy listening to the radio? **about 401**
   d. Survey the students in your math class about their favorite activities. Are the results similar to these? Explain why or why not. **See students' work.**

Applications and Problem Solving

7. ***Gardening*** Recently, *Organic Gardening* magazine and the National Gardening Association (NGA) each conducted surveys on gardening habits. *Organic Gardening* used a mail survey of 40,000 households to ask whether anyone in the household did any gardening at all. They found that gardening has gained popularity in the 1990s. In interviews, the NGA asked individuals whether they had done any gardening in the last 12 months. They found that gardening had declined in the 1990s. Why might the results be different for these surveys? **See margin.**

8. ***Medicine*** Some rural areas of the country have very few doctors. In Mississippi, 0.145% of the population are doctors.
   a. Of the 7,900 people in Benton County, Mississippi, how many would you expect to be doctors? **about 11**
   b. Currently, no doctors reside in Benton County. How does this compare with your estimate? Explain your results.

8b. It is much lower than the estimate. There must be more doctors in other areas of the state.

9. ***Life*** Do you ever wish that life was simpler? In a recent survey, people were asked how complicated they think life will be by the year 2000.

Life is Not That Simple	
How Complicated by Year 2000?	**Percent**
Much more	31%
Little more	31%
Same	20%
Little less	9%
Much less	5%
Don't know	4%

Source: Claris Corp. for ClarisWorks

   a. If there were 1,000 people in the survey, how many said that life would be much more complicated by 2000? **310 people**
   b. Of the 185 million adults in the United States, how many would you expect to say they think life will be a little less complicated by 2000? **16.65 million adults**

Reteaching the Lesson

Activity Have students work in small groups to create a survey to predict the number of seventh graders who are left-handed. Poll the class to use as a representative sample, decide how to use their responses, and then test their prediction.

10. ***Working on the* CHAPTER Project** Refer to the data you collected on radio programming on page 449 and to the circle graph you made in Exercise 9 on page 463. Predict the amount of time the station would spend doing each activity. Use your prediction to make an 8-hour programming schedule for the radio station. **See students' work.**

11. ***Critical Thinking*** A survey of 2,500 teens showed that 45% of girls and 40% of boys are members of the YMCA or YWCA. A marketer has found, based on information obtained from the YMCA and YWCA, that there are 3,959,550 girls and 3,874,000 boys ages 10-14 who are members of a YMCA or YWCA. Estimate how many girls and boys ages 10-14 there are in the United States. **8,799,000 girls and 9,685,000 boys**

For **Extra Practice,** see page 599.

Mixed Review

12. ***Statistics*** Refer to the table in Example 2. Make a circle graph showing pizza crust preference. *(Lesson 11-3)* **See margin.**

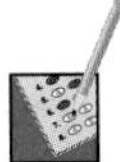

13. **Standardized Test Practice** The length of your calculator is about — *(Lesson 2-8)* **B**

A 16 mm. **B** 16 cm. **C** 16 m. **D** 16 km.

CHAPTER 11

Mid-Chapter Self Test

Estimate. *(Lesson 11-1)* **3. 36(100% + 10%) = 36 + 3.6, or 39.6.**

1. 18% of 41 $\frac{1}{5} \cdot 40 = 8$
2. 32% of 90 $\frac{1}{3} \cdot 90 = 30$
3. 112% of 36

Write an equation for each problem. Then solve. Round answers to the nearest tenth. *(Lesson 11-2)* **5. $P = 0.09 \cdot 72$; 6.5**

4. 24 is what percent of 25? **$24 = R \cdot 25$; 96.0%**
5. 9% of 72 is what number?
6. Find 36% of 15. **$P = 0.36 \cdot 15$; 5.4**
7. 16% of what number is 13.12? **$13.12 = 0.16 \cdot B$; 82.0**

8. The table shows the percent of different kinds of juice sold in the United States. *(Lesson 11-3)* **a. See Answer Appendix.**
   a. Make a circle graph of the data.
   b. If a grocery store is ordering 500 cans of frozen juice concentrate, how many of the cans should be orange juice? **56% of 500 = 280 cans**

Juice	Percent Sold
Orange	56%
Apple	14%
Blends	6%
Grape	5%
Other	19%

Source: Beverage Marketing Corporation

9. ***Statistics*** Members of the Student Council wanted to know if students thought an end-of-school dance was a good idea. They each asked three of their friends to give their opinion, and they tallied the results. Is this a random sample? Explain. *(Lesson 11-4)* **See Answer Appendix.**

10. ***Entertainment*** One hundred people in Houston, ages 13 to 19, are randomly surveyed to find their opinion of their favorite radio station. Sixty-three of them said they liked KLOL-FM. If there are 800,000 people ages 13 to 19 in the listening area, about how many of them would you predict listen to KLOL-FM? *(Lesson 11-4)* **504,000**

4 ASSESS

Closing Activity

Speaking Have students explain how to use samples to make predictions about the actions of a larger population.

Chapter 11, Quiz B (Lessons 11-3 and 11-4) is available in the *Assessment and Evaluation Masters,* p. 295.

Mid-Chapter Test (Lessons 11-1 through 11-4) is available in the *Assessment and Evaluation Masters,* p. 294.

Mid-Chapter Self Test

The Mid-Chapter Self Test reviews the concepts in Lessons 11-1 through 11-4. Lesson references are given so students can review concepts not yet mastered.

Additional Answer

12. **Type of Crust**

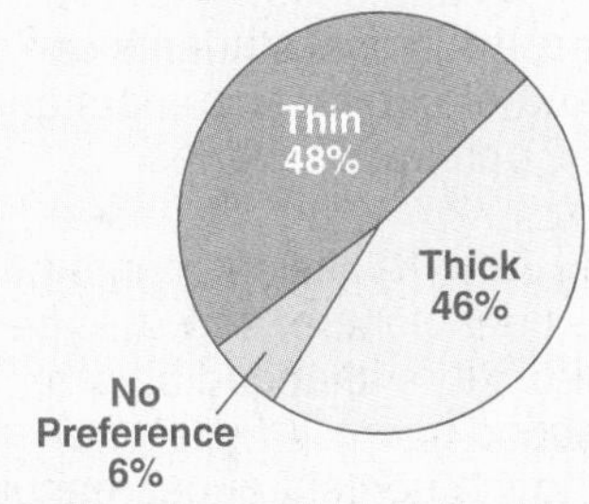

***Practice Masters,* p. 84**

Name ________ Date ________

11-4 Practice

Integration: Statistics
Using Statistics to Predict

Of the TV households surveyed by the Nielson Media Research Company, the top sports shows of 1990-1991 are listed in the table at the right.

Top Sports Shows, 1990-91	
Show	**% of TV households**
1. Super Bowl XXV	41.9
2. NFC Championship	28.5
3. AFC Playoff Bengals vs. Raiders	24.7
4. NFC Playoff Saints vs. Bears	24.2

1. How many households in a town with 40,000 households might you expect to have watched Super Bowl XXV? **16,760**
2. How many households in a town with 80,000 households might you expect to have watched the fourth top show? **19,360**
3. How many households in a town with 100,000 households might you expect to have watched a program *other* than the NFC Championship game? **71,500**

Mrs. Romano surveyed her 7th-grade class about their favorite foods. The results are shown in the table at the right.

Favorite Food	Number of Students
spaghetti	10
pizza	9
hamburgers	4
tacos	4
fried chicken	3

4. What was the sample size? **30**
5. What percent of students liked pizza best? **30%**
6. Mr. Peters' class has 24 students in it but otherwise is about the same as Mrs. Romano's class. How many students would you expect to like spaghetti the best? **8**
7. How many students in Mr. Peters' class would you expect to not like tacos the best? **about 21**
8. For the entire 7th-grade class of 250 students, how many would you expect to like fried chicken the best? **25**

 T84 *Mathematics: Applications and Connections, Course 2*

Extending the Lesson

***Enrichment Masters,* p. 84**

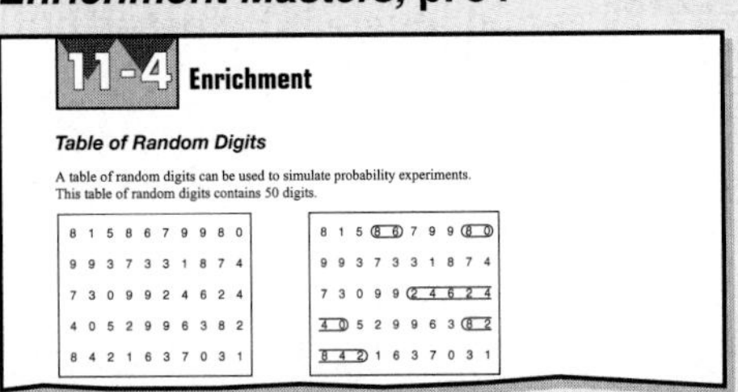

11-4 Enrichment

Table of Random Digits

A table of random digits can be used to simulate probability experiments. This table of random digits contains 50 digits.

```
8 1 5 8 6 7 9 9 8 0
9 9 3 7 3 3 1 8 7 4
7 3 0 9 9 2 4 6 2 4
4 0 5 2 9 9 6 3 8 2
8 4 2 1 6 3 7 0 3 1
```

```
8 1 5 8 6 7 9 9 8 0
9 9 3 7 3 3 1 8 7 4
7 3 0 9 9 2 4 6 2 4
4 0 5 2 9 9 6 3 8 2
8 4 2 1 6 3 7 0 3 1
```

Activity Have students work with a partner to research the performance of a selected market stock in a daily newspaper or on the Internet. Have them record the recent gains and/or losses for a week, and then use that data to predict how it will perform during the following week.

HANDS-ON
11-5A LAB Notes

GET READY

Objective Students use dot paper to show percent of increase and percent of decrease.

Optional Resources
Hands-On Lab Masters
- square dot paper, p. 12
- worksheet, p. 66

Overhead Manipulative Resources
- rectangular dot paper transparency

MANAGEMENT TIPS

Recommended Time
30 minutes

Getting Started Have students use counters to model percent of increase and decrease. One student begins with 10 counters, another adds (or subtracts) 4 counters and finds the percent of change. Additional students can then add or subtract counters and find the percent of change.

For the **Activity,** ask students what the percent of increase would be if the third figure changed back to the second figure. Why is it not equal to the percent of decrease from the second figure to the third? **Because the base upon which the percent is figured is different in each case.**

Additional Answers

3.

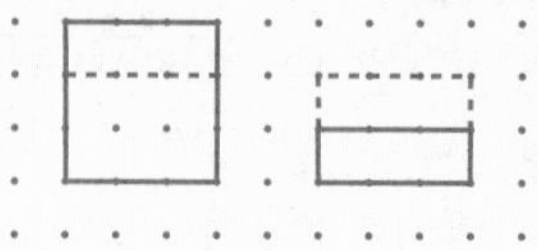

4.

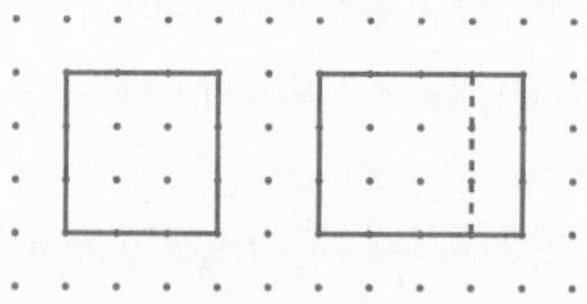

5. **20%; If the rectangle is divided into 5 sections, then 1 of the sections was removed. The decrease is $\frac{1}{5}$, or 20%.**

HANDS-ON LAB

COOPERATIVE LEARNING

11-5A Percent of Change

A Preview of Lesson 11-5

dot paper

You can use dot paper or a geoboard to help you understand the meaning of percent of increase or percent of decrease.

TRY THIS

Work in groups of three.

Step 1 Make a 2 × 2 square like the one shown at the right.

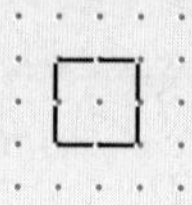

Step 2 Suppose you want to decrease or increase the area of square A by 25%. Think: $25\% = \frac{1}{4}$. Separate the square into 4 equal parts.

Step 3 Remove 25% or $\frac{1}{4}$ from the original figure to show a decrease of 25%.

Step 4 Add 25% or $\frac{1}{4}$ to the original figure to show an increase of 25%.

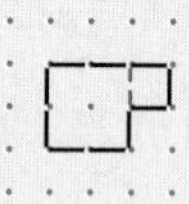

ON YOUR OWN

1. Once you showed a 25% decrease in the figure, what percent remained? **75%**

2a. If there is a 25% increase in area, find the ratio of the new area to the old area. $\frac{5}{4}$

b. If there is a 25% decrease in area, find the ratio of the new area to the old area. $\frac{3}{4}$

c. Write each ratio as a percent. **125%, 75%**

3. Use the figure at the right to draw an increase of 50% and a decrease of 50%. **3–5. See margin.**

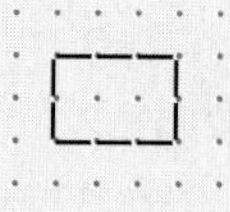

4. Draw a 3 × 3 square. Add $33\frac{1}{3}\%$ to this figure to show an increase of $33\frac{1}{3}\%$.

5. ***Look Ahead*** Refer to the figures at the right. By what percent was the original figure decreased? Explain how you determined the percent.

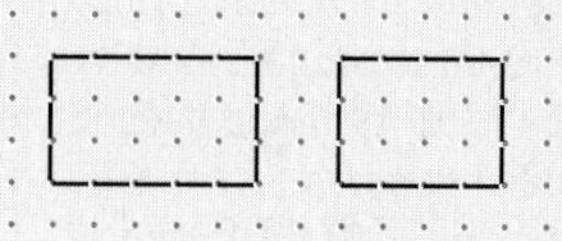

ASSESS

Have students complete Exercises 1–5. Have students formulate other problems about percent of increase and percent of decrease for group members to solve by using dot paper or graph paper.

Math Journal Have students write a paragraph explaining what it means when the price of an item in a store is increased or decreased by 20 percent.

11-5 Percent of Change

What **you'll learn**

You'll learn to find the percent of increase or decrease.

When **am I ever going to use this?**

You'll find percent of change is often used to summarize growth and decline in population.

Courtney Dann of Bellingham, Washington, is the winner of four National Water Ski Championships. Her longest jump is 91 feet, and her goal is to break the girls' jump record of 102 feet. What is the percent of increase from 91 to 102?

You can use the percent proportion to find the percent of increase. Compare the amount of the increase to the original amount.

Step 1 Find the amount of increase. $102 - 91 = 11$

Step 2 Use the percent proportion. $\frac{\text{amount of increase}}{\text{original amount}} = \frac{r}{100}$

$\frac{11}{91} = \frac{r}{100}$

Step 3 Solve for r. $11 \cdot 100 = 91r$ *Find the cross products.*

$\frac{1{,}100}{91} = \frac{91r}{91}$ *Divide each side by 91.*

$12.09 \approx r$ *Use a calculator.*

The percent of increase would be about 12%.

Courtney Dann

MINI-LAB

Work with a partner. 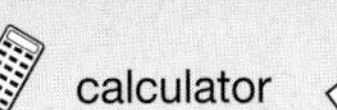 calculator 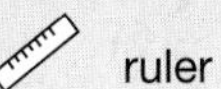 ruler

Try This **1. See students' work.**

1. Draw a segment that you estimate to be 25% longer than $\overline{CD}$. [segment C—D]
2. Measure the length of $\overline{CD}$ to the nearest centimeter. Use this number as the base B. **4 cm**
3. Measure the length of your segment. Use this as the percentage P.

3. See students' work.

Talk About It **7–8. See students' work.**

4. Will 50% of the length of $\overline{CD}$ be greater than, less than, or equal to its length? **less**
5. Will 100% of the length of $\overline{CD}$ be greater than, less than, or equal to its length? **equal**
6. Do you think the length of your segment is greater than, less than, or equal to 100% of the length of $\overline{CD}$? **greater**
7. Write a proportion or equation to find the percent the length of $\overline{CD}$ is of the length of your segment. Solve.
8. The segment you drew is actually what percent longer than $\overline{CD}$?

Multiple Learning Styles

Visual/Spatial Using a word-processing program, have students type a line of text in 10-point, 12-point, 14-point, and 18-point sizes. Have students print and compare what they have typed in each size and calculate the percent of change from one size to the next. Note: 1 point = $\frac{1}{72}$ inch.

11-5 Lesson Notes

Instructional Resources

- *Study Guide Masters,* p. 85
- *Practice Masters,* p. 85
- *Enrichment Masters,* p. 85
- Transparencies 11-5, A and B

CD-ROM Program
- Resource Lesson 11-5
- Interactive Lesson 11-5

Recommended Pacing	
Standard	Days 8 & 9 of 13
Honors	Day 7 of 12
Block	Day 5 of 7

1 FOCUS

5-Minute Check
(Lesson 11-4)

Refer to the table for Exercises 1–3.

Pascal School Survey	
Homework Time (hours per week)	**Number of Students**
Less than 3	6
3 to 5	12
5 to 7	19
7 or more	18

1. What was the sample size? **55**
2. What percent of students spends more than 5 hours on homework each week? **about 67%**
3. If there are 300 students in the school, how many can be expected to spend 7 or more hours on homework each week? **about 98 students**

The 5-Minute Check is also available on **Transparency 11-5A** for this lesson.

Motivating the Lesson

Problem Solving Have students research the different sizes and prices of their favorite candy or snack food. Ask students what percent of the smaller size is the larger size and what percent of the lower price is the higher price.

2 TEACH

Transparency 11-5B contains a teaching aid for this lesson.

Using the Mini-Lab Have students measure and draw segments that are 50%, 75%, and 100% longer than *CD*. Then ask them to find the percent of change from each of the segments to the next. **$16\frac{2}{3}$%; about 14%**

In-Class Examples

For Example 1

Oliver ran 5,000 meters in 21 minutes in the first cross country meet of the season and 19.5 minutes in the last meet. Find the percent of decrease in his time. **about 7%**

For Example 2

Nicola and Marguerite sold their old 6 foot × 6 foot tent and bought a new 8 foot × 5 foot tent. What is the percent of change in the floor area? **about an 11% increase**

You can also find the percent of decrease in a similar way.

1 **Nutrition** **Find the percent of decrease in Calories from Meal A to Meal B.**

	Meal A	Meal B
	cheeseburger buttered ear of corn ice cream root beer float	veggie burger plain ear of corn frozen yogurt root bear float
Total Calories	1,134	683

Source: *Vitality*

Find the amount of decrease.

$1,134 - 683 = 451$

Use the percent proportion.

$$\frac{\text{amount of decrease}}{\text{original amount}} = \frac{r}{100}$$

$$\frac{451}{1,134} = \frac{r}{100}$$

$$451 \cdot 100 = 1,134r \quad \textit{Find the cross products.}$$

$$\frac{45,100}{1,134} = \frac{1,134r}{1,134} \quad \textit{Divide each side by 1,134.}$$

$$39.8 \approx r$$

The percent of decrease in Calories is about 40%.

INTEGRATION

2 **Geometry** **A loop of string measuring 20 centimeters is formed into a rectangle that has a length of 6 centimeters and a width of 4 centimeters. The loop is then changed to a square with each side measuring 5 centimeters. What is the percent of change in area?**

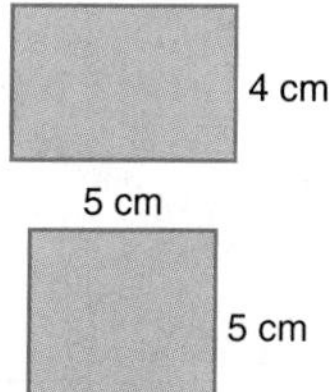

Explore You know the dimensions of both figures. You need to find the area of each figure.

Plan Use the percent proportion to calculate the percent of change from the area of the rectangle to the area of the square.

Solve area of rectangle: $A = \ell \cdot w$

$= 6 \cdot 4$ or 24

area of square: $A = 5 \cdot 5$ or 25

$25 - 24 = 1$ *This is a percent of increase since 25 > 24. Original amount = 24*

$$\frac{1}{24} = \frac{r}{100}$$

$$1 \cdot 100 = 24r$$

$$4.2 = r$$

The percent of increase is about 4%.

Examine Since the difference between the areas is so small, it makes sense that the percent of increase is small.

CHECK FOR UNDERSTANDING

Communicating Mathematics

Read and study the lesson to answer each question. 2–3. See margin.

1. ***Tell*** what amount is used as a base in the percent proportion when finding the percent of change. **original amount**
2. ***Determine*** whether the percent of increase from 30 to 45 equals the percent of decrease from 45 to 30. Explain.

HANDS-ON 

3. If the figure represents 75% of an area, ***draw*** a diagram to represent 100%.

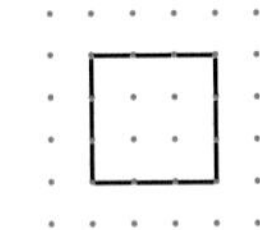

Guided Practice

Find the percent of change. Round to the nearest whole percent.

4. original: \$85 new: \$68 **20%**
5. original: \$456 new: \$500 **10%**
6. original: 1.6 new: 0.95 **41%**
7. ***Entertainment*** The graph shows the percent of movies that received G, PG, and PG-13 ratings in 1984 and in 1996. Find the percent of change to the nearest whole percent from 1984 to 1996 for each rating. Tell whether it is a percent of increase or a percent of decrease.

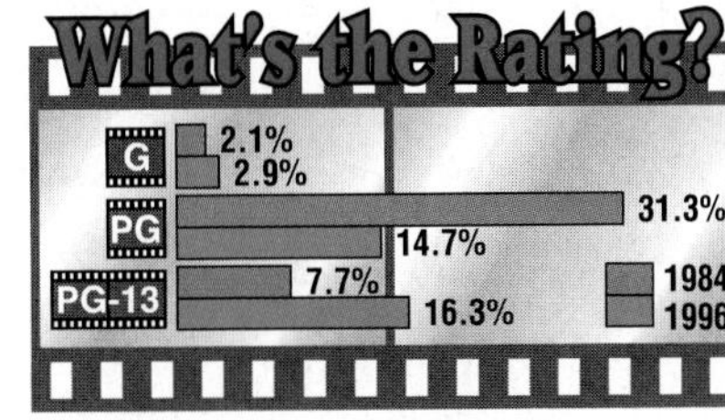

Source: Motion Picture Association of America

a. G **38% increase**
b. PG **53% decrease**
c. PG-13 **112% increase**

EXERCISES

Practice

Find the percent of change. Round to the nearest whole percent.

8. original: \$4 new: \$6 **50%**
9. original: \$60 new: \$38 **37%**
10. original: 20.5 new: 35.5 **73%**
11. original: 35 new: 45 **29%**
12. original: \$126 new: \$150 **19%**
13. original: \$30 new: \$24 **20%**
14. Find the percent of decrease if an item that originally cost \$36 goes on sale for \$18. **50%**
15. Find the percent of change from 87.5 to 112. **28%**
16. ***Write a Problem*** in which the percent of change is 60%.
17. Find the original number if the new number is 16 and the percent of decrease is 68%. **50**

16. Sample answer: a problem using the numbers 10 and 4.

Applications and Problem Solving

18. ***Population*** The Hispanic population is the fastest-growing minority population in the United States. Currently, there are about 29 million Hispanics in the U.S. There are expected to be more than 41 million by 2010. What is the predicted percent of increase? **41%**

3 PRACTICE/APPLY

Check for Understanding

If students need additional practice or instruction after completing Exercises 1–7, one of these options may be helpful.

- Extra Practice, see p. 599
- Reteaching Activity
- *Study Guide Masters,* p. 85
- *Practice Masters,* p. 85

Assignment Guide

Core: 9–19 odd, 20–23
Enriched: 8–16 even, 18–23

Additional Answers

2. No, because the amount of increase equals the amount of decrease, but the original amounts are different. The percent of increase is 50% and the percent of decrease is $33\frac{1}{3}$%.
3. Sample answer:

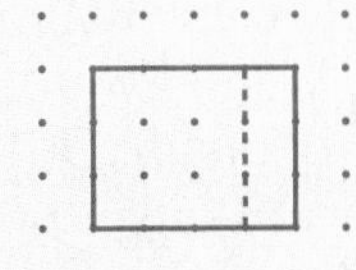

Study Guide Masters, p. 85

Name______ Date______

Study Guide

Percent of Change

To find the percent of change, first find the amount of increase or decrease. Then find the ratio of that amount to the original amount and express the ratio as a percent.

Examples 1 **Last year, 2,376 people attended the rodeo. This year, attendance was 2,954. What was the percent of increase in rodeo attendance?**

$2{,}954 - 2{,}376 = 578$ *Find the amount of the increase.*

$\frac{578}{2{,}376} \approx 0.24$ *Compare the amount of increase to the original amount.*

Rodeo attendance increased by about 24%.

2 **John's grade on the first math exam was 94. His grade on the second math exam was 86. What was the percent of decrease in John's grade?**

$94 - 86 = 8$ *Find the amount of decrease.*

$\frac{8}{96} \approx 0.08$ *Compare the amount of decrease to the original amount.*

John's math grade decreased by about 8%.

Find the percent of change. Round to the nearest whole percent.

1. old: \$12 new: \$15 **25%**
2. old: \$40 new: \$18 **55%**
3. old: 100 new: 67 **33%**
4. old: \$90 new: \$135 **50%**
5. old: \$144 new: \$108 **25%**
6. old: 6.5 new: 8 **23%**
7. old: 280 new: 200 **29%**
8. old: \$86 new: \$70 **19%**
9. old: 69 new: 100 **45%**
10. old: 20.8 new: 12.2 **41%**
11. old: 45 new: 15 **67%**
12. old: \$75 new: \$15 **80%**

 T85 *Mathematics: Applications and Connections, Course 2*

Reteaching the Lesson

Activity Focus on the similarities between percent of increase and percent of decrease. Point out that in both cases one finds the difference between two amounts and then solves a proportion to find what percent of the original amount the difference is.

Error Analysis

Watch for students who calculate percent of change by comparing the amount of change to the amount after change.

Prevent by reinforcing the fact that percent of change is the ratio of the amount of change (P) to the original amount (B).

4 ASSESS

Closing Activity

Modeling Have students work in groups using geoboards or grid paper to demonstrate a series of increases and decreases in the area of a figure.

19. ***Recreation*** The graph shows the millions of tax dollars spent on bike paths and walkways in the United States.

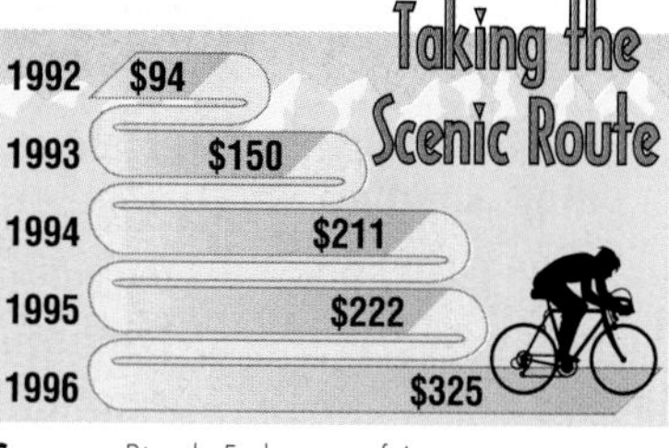

Source: Bicycle Federation of America

a. Between which two consecutive years was the percent of increase the greatest? **1992 and 1993**

b. What was the percent of increase to the nearest whole percent? **60%**

20. ***Critical Thinking*** Find a number such that adding 1 to it represents a percent increase of $33\frac{1}{3}\%$, and subtracting 1 from the new total results in a percent decrease of 25%. How many such numbers do you think there are? Justify your answer. **3; one; see students' work.**

Mixed Review

21. ***Statistics*** Refer to the table in Exercise 6 on page 466. If there were 890 students in your school, how many would you expect to say they enjoy listening to music? *(Lesson 11-4)* **about 810**

22. obtuse, isosceles

22. ***Geometry*** Classify $\triangle KLM$ by its angles and by its sides. *(Lesson 9-4)*

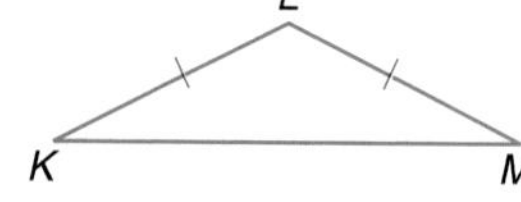

23. **Standardized Test Practice** A piece of wire is 86 inches long. What is the greatest number of 15-inch pieces that can be cut from the wire? *(Lesson 5-7)* **E**

A 2 **B** 4
C 6 **D** 7
E Not Here

For **Extra Practice,** see page 599.

MATH IN THE MEDIA

Smart Shopping

A company recently advertised their new heart-shaped cat treats. Although the size of the container stayed the same, the weight of the treats inside went from 4 ounces to 3 ounces. A company representative explained that they lowered the price of the treats from $1.49 to $1.19 to account for the change in weight. However, she also noted that stores are free to set their own price, and it would be wise for people to shop around.

1. Find the percent of decrease in the size and the percent of decrease in the price of the cat treats. **25%, 20.1%**
2. Do you think the unadvertised change in size of the treats was fair to consumers? Explain. **See students' work.**

Practice Masters, p. 85

11-5 Practice

Name ____________ Date ________

Percent of Change

Find the percent of change. Round to the nearest whole percent.

1. old: $8 new: $12 **50%**
2. old: $45 new: $30 **33%**
3. old: $0.39 new: $0.26 **33%**
4. old: $75 new: $60 **20%**
5. old: $350 new: $400 **14%**
6. old: 0.32 new: 0.48 **50%**
7. old: 35 new: 70 **100%**
8. old: 6.8 new: 8.2 **21%**
9. old: 1.5 new: 2.5 **67%**
10. old: $84 new: $100 **19%**
11. old: $250 new: $100 **60%**
12. old: $87.05 new: $100 **15%**
16. old: $12.50 new: $15 **20%**
17. old: $30 new: $110 **267%**
18. old: 16.5 new: 20 **21%**

 T85 *Mathematics: Applications and Connections, Course 2*

Extending the Lesson

Enrichment Masters, p. 85

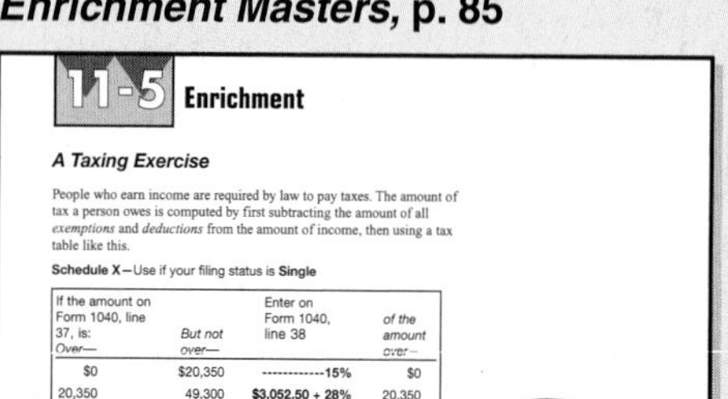

11-5 Enrichment

A Taxing Exercise

People who earn income are required by law to pay taxes. The amount of tax a person owes is computed by first subtracting the amount of all *exemptions* and *deductions* from the amount of income, then using a tax table like this.

Schedule X—Use if your filing status is **Single**

If the amount on Form 1040, line 37, is: *Over—*	*But not over—*	Enter on Form 1040, line 38	*of the amount over—*
$0	$20,350	------------15%	$0
20,350	49,300	$3,052.50 + 28%	20,350

MATH IN THE MEDIA

Ask students what the reduced price of cat treats should be if the percent of decrease in price were to match the percent of decrease in size. **about $1.12**

M E D I A

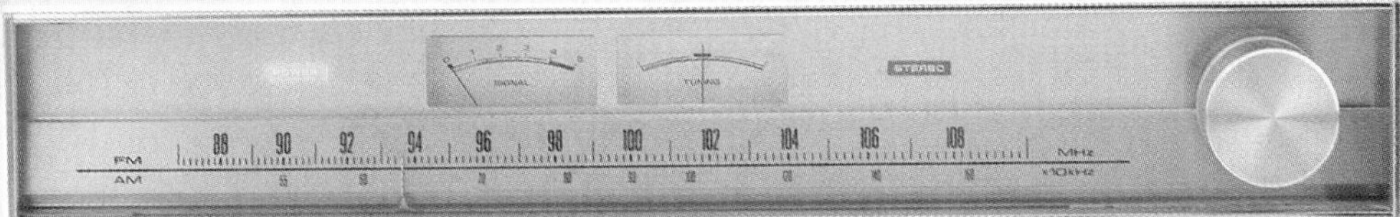

Traci Tong
RADIO PRODUCER/DIRECTOR

Traci Tong is the producer and director of the radio news program *The World* on WGBN in Boston, Massachusetts. Ms. Tong reads, writes, edits, and produces news reports from a large network of international journalists. As in-studio director of the program's daily live broadcast, she ensures that reports are edited to the precise time needed.

To work in radio, a degree in broadcast journalism is usually required. Courses in English, public speaking, foreign languages, mathematics, computers, and electronics are valuable in a field where people work under tight deadlines and accuracy is crucial.

Someday I'd like to direct a radio show where important issues are discussed.

For more information:
Broadcast Education Association
1771 N St., NW
Washington, DC 20036

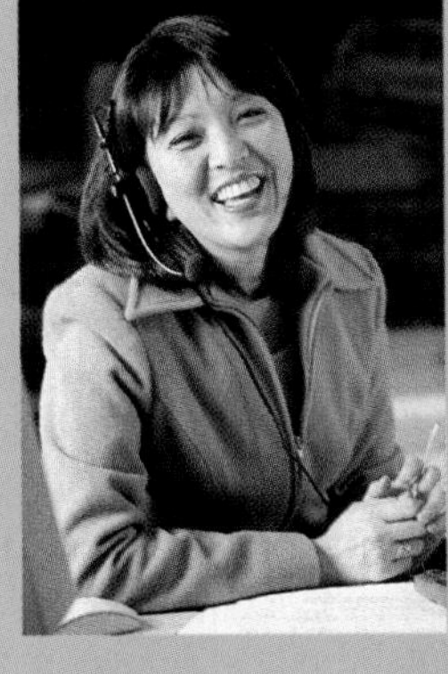

interNET CONNECTION
www.glencoe.com/sec/math/mac/mathnet

Your Turn
Interview a local radio announcer or disc jockey. Make a list of the questions and answers from the interview and write a description of what a job in radio would be like.

More About Traci Tong

- Ms. Tong holds Bachelor's Degrees in Journalism and Communications from the University of Hawaii.
- She has 15 years of experience as a television and radio reporter and producer, and has won many awards during her career.
- In 1995, Ms. Tong helped to create the public radio news program *The World,* heard on more than 110 radio stations nationwide.

Motivating Students

Explain to students that radio stations employ people with many talents to do different jobs. Ask questions to begin a discussion of the skills needed in the radio business.

- Who sells "air time" to advertisers? **marketing director**
- Who budgets income and expenses so employees and bills get paid? **station manager**
- Who operates the audio equipment that transmits radio signals? **engineer**
- Who decides what kind of music or talk is broadcast at each time of day? **program director**

Making the Math Connection

Ask students how they would organize programming time if they ran their own radio station. How many minutes of each hour on the air would be used for music, news, advertising, and discussion? What percent of the total broadcast time would each receive? How would the budget affect programming?

Working on *Your Turn*

Students may want to work in groups to plan their own radio station. Each group should have a station manager, an engineer, a program director, a news director, and a marketing director.

An additional School to Career activity is available on page 24 of the ***School to Career Masters.***

11-6 Lesson Notes

Instructional Resources

- *Study Guide Masters,* p. 86
- *Practice Masters,* p. 86
- *Enrichment Masters,* p. 86
- Transparencies 11-6, A and B
- *Assessment and Evaluation Masters,* p. 296
- *Classroom Games,* pp. 31–32
- *Technology Masters,* p. 47

CD-ROM Program
- Resource Lesson 11-6

Recommended Pacing	
Standard	Day 10 of 13
Honors	Day 8 of 12
Block	Day 6 of 7

1 FOCUS

5-Minute Check
(Lesson 11-5)

Find the percent of change. Round to the nearest whole percent.

1. original: \$75; new: \$85 13%
2. original: 60; new: 45 25%
3. original: 360; new: 200 44%
4. original: 40; new: 86 115%

The 5-Minute Check is also available on **Transparency 11-6A** for this lesson.

Motivating the Lesson

Hands-On Activity Provide students with newspaper ads for clothing sales. Have them use the information in the ads to identify discount prices, and determine total prices, including the sales tax.

11-6 Discount and Sales Tax

What **you'll learn**
You'll learn to solve problems involving sales tax and discount.

When **am I ever going to use this?**
Knowing how to calculate discounts and sales tax will help you determine how much money you're actually spending when you shop.

Recently, tiny video games tucked inside egg-shaped pendants became popular. A toy store in New York City sold nearly 10,000 of the \$17.99 toys in one day.

If the sales tax in New York City is $8\frac{1}{4}$%, what is the total cost of one toy? *Sales tax is the primary way some communities and states raise the money they need to operate.*

One of the following methods can be used to find the total cost.

Method 1 First, find the amount of the sales tax, t.

$8\frac{1}{4}\%$ of \$17.99 $= t$

.0825 [×] 17.99 [=] 1.484175 The sales tax is about \$1.49.

Numbers involving money are usually rounded up.

Then add the sales tax to the price of a toy.

\$17.99 + \$1.49 = \$19.48

The total price of a toy is \$19.48.

Method 2 First, add the percent of tax to 100%.

100% + 8.25% = 108.25%

So, the total price of a toy will be 108.25% of the market price.

Then multiply to find the total cost including tax.

1.0825 [×] 17.99 [=] 19.474175

Again, the total price of a toy is \$19.48.

These methods can also be used to find the sale price of an item.

1 **Money Matters** **A \$53 racquet at Sports Galore is on sale for 20% off the regular price. What is the sale price of the racquet?**

Method 1 First, find the amount of the discount, d.

20% of \$53 $= d$

.2 [×] 53 [=] 10.6 The discount is \$10.60.

Then subtract to find the sale price.

\$53 − \$10.60 = \$42.40 The sale price is \$42.40.

Classroom Vignette

"I challenge students to write real-world problems that involve percents. An example follows. Todd purchased 9 packages of baseball cards. Each package costs \$1.09. The sales tax in his state is 6%. If he handed the cashier a \$20 bill, how much change should he receive?"

Alvin Hampton

Alvin Hampton, Teacher
Stafford Middle School
Stafford, VA

Method 2 First, subtract the percent of discount from 100%.

100% − 20% = 80%

So, the sale price of the racquet will be 80% of the regular price.

Then multiply to find the total cost.

.8 [×] 53 [=] 42.4

Again, the sale price of the racquet is $42.40.

APPLICATION

2 Shopping The advertisement shows the sale price of a new mini portable television. What is the percent of discount?

Find the amount of discount.

$119 − $89 = $30

Use the percent proportion to find what percent $30 is of $119.

$$\frac{\text{amount of decrease}}{\text{original amount}} = \frac{r}{100}$$

$$\frac{30}{119} = \frac{r}{100}$$

$30 \cdot 100 = 119r$ *Find the cross products.*

$3{,}000 = 119r$

$25.21008403 \approx r$ *Divide each side by 119.*

The percent of discount is about 25%.

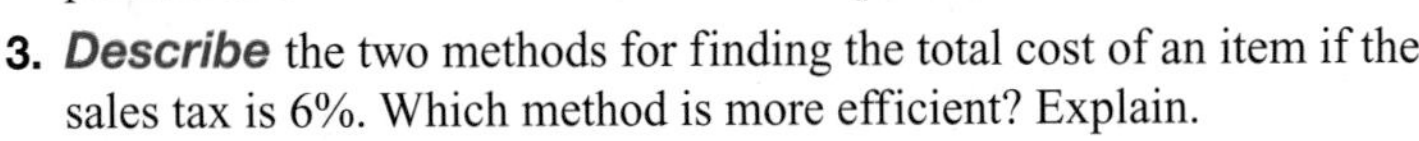

CHECK FOR UNDERSTANDING

Communicating Mathematics

Read and study the lesson to answer each question. **1–3. See margin.**

1. ***Tell*** which watch would be cheaper: a $38 watch that is 15% off, or a $50 watch that is 30% off. Explain.
2. ***Explain*** how you could find the percent of discount of an item that regularly sells for $39, but is marked down to $28. Then find the percent of discount to the nearest whole percent.
3. ***Describe*** the two methods for finding the total cost of an item if the sales tax is 6%. Which method is more efficient? Explain.

Math Journal

Guided Practice

Find the sales tax or discount to the nearest cent.

4. $17.42 book; $5\frac{1}{2}$% tax **$0.96**
5. $145 chair; 33% discount **$47.85**

2 TEACH

Transparency 11-6B contains a teaching aid for this lesson.

Thinking Algebraically After students study both methods in Example 1, have them explain why both methods yield the same result. **Sample answer: 20% off of the whole would yield 80% of the whole. Thus $w - 20\%w = 80\%w$**

In-Class Examples

For Example 1

A pair of tennis shoes that sells for $46 is on sale at Buffy's Sport Store for 40% off. What is the discount price of the shoes? **$27.60**

For Example 2

A sweater that Buffy's normally sells for $30 is on sale for $25.50. What is the percent of discount? **15%**

3 PRACTICE/APPLY

Check for Understanding

If students need additional practice or instruction after completing Exercises 1–9, one of these options may be helpful.

- Extra Practice, see p. 600
- Reteaching Activity
- *Study Guide Masters,* p. 86
- *Practice Masters,* p. 86

Additional Answers

1. **The $38 watch would cost $32.30. It would be cheaper than the $50 watch, which would cost $35.**
2. **Subtract 39 − 28 = 11. Write the ratio $\frac{11}{39}$ and change it to a percent; 28%.**
3. **Method 1: Multiply the price by 0.06, then add the two amounts. Method 2: Multiply the price by 1.06. Method 2 is more efficient since it can be done in one step rather than two.**

Reteaching the Lesson

Activity Focus on the meaning of the terms *discount price, discount,* and *rate of discount.* Guide students to see that the rate of discount is a percent; the discount is the amount of money the price is reduced; and the discount price is the cost after subtracting the discount from the regular price.

Error Analysis

Watch for students who confuse the discount with the discount price.

Prevent by reminding students that the discount price is found by subtracting the discount from the regular price. Show examples.

Assignment Guide

Core: 11–27 odd, 28–32
Enriched: 10–24 even, 26–32

Teaching Tip Even though a sales tax rate is given, the tax tables, or computer programs in cash registers, may yield a slightly different result because of rounding.

Find the total cost or sale price to the nearest cent.

6. \$15.99 T-shirt; 20% off **\$12.79**
7. \$65 video; 7% tax **\$69.55**
8. If the regular price of an item is \$44 and the sale price is \$34, find the percent of discount to the nearest percent. **23%**
9. ***Money Matters*** Jeanelle bought a skirt and a vest on sale. The skirt, originally priced at \$28, was 33% off. The vest, originally priced at \$21, was 15% off. Which item costs less? **vest**

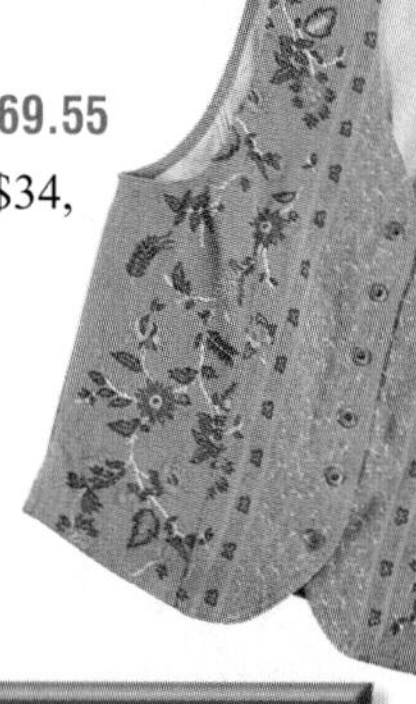

EXERCISES

Practice

Find the sales tax or discount to the nearest cent.

10. \$16.58 gloves; $6\frac{1}{2}$% tax **\$1.08**
11. \$38.50 sweater; 15% off **\$5.78**
12. \$25 watch; 30% discount **\$7.50**
13. \$87 radio; 6% tax **\$5.22**
14. \$36 jeans; $5\frac{1}{2}$% tax **\$1.98**
15. \$72 in-line skates; 25% discount **\$18**

Find the total cost or sale price to the nearest cent. **17. \$132.81**

16. \$3.49 socks; 35% off **\$2.27**
17. \$125.59 speakers; 5.75% tax
18. \$13.99 CD; 10% discount **\$12.59**
19. \$64 shoes; 20% off **\$51.20**
20. \$24 3-D puzzle; $8\frac{1}{2}$% tax **\$26.04**
21. \$31.65 backpack; $6\frac{1}{2}$% tax **\$33.71**

Find the percent of discount to the nearest percent.

22. regular price, \$47 **68%**
sale price, \$15
23. regular price, \$18.99 **30%**
sale price, \$13.29
24. Find the total price to the nearest cent if a \$69 jacket is on sale for 15% off and the sales tax is 7%. **\$62.76**
25. Find the original price of a table if the sale price of \$189 was 45% off the original price. **\$343.64**

Applications and Problem Solving

26a. *L/J Basketball*

26. ***Money Matters*** The table shows the sneakers that a magazine bought on sale for one of their consumer tests.

Shoe	Original Price	Sale Price
Intimidator	\$94	\$76
Instapump	\$120	\$90
L/J Basketball	\$90	\$37

a. Which shoe had the greatest percent of discount?
b. What was the percent of discount? **59%**

27. ***Employment*** Fifteen-year-old Trent Eisenberg owns his own computer company. He offers a 2.5% discount for immediate cash payments. If he collected a \$617.77 cash payment for his first job, how much was his original bill without the discount? **\$633.61**

28. 10.75%; no; multiplication is commutative.

28. ***Critical Thinking*** Find the total percent of change on the final price of an item if the percent of discount is 15% and the sales tax is 5%. Does it matter in which order the discount and the sales tax are applied? Explain.

Study Guide Masters, p. 86

Name__________ Date__________

11-6 Study Guide

Discount and Sales Tax

Sales tax is a percent of the purchase price.

Example 1 **Find the total price of a \$17.75 soccer ball if the sales tax is 6%.**

Method 1	**Method 2**
Find the amount of tax. 6% of \$17.75 = *t* 0.06 × \$17.75 = 1.07 The sales tax is \$1.07.	Add the percent of tax to 100%. 100% + 6% = 106% The total price will be 106% of the price of the soccer ball.
Add to find the total cost. \$17.75 + \$1.07 = \$18.82	Multiply to find the total cost. \$17.75 × 1.06 = \$18.82

The total cost of the soccer ball is \$18.82.

Discount is the amount the sales price is reduced.

Example 2 **Find the price of a \$69.50 tennis racket that is on sale for 20% off.**

\$69.50 × 20% — Find 20% of \$69.50.
\$69.50 × 0.20 = \$13.90 — The discount is \$13.90.
\$69.50 − \$13.90 = \$55.60 — Subtract to find the sale price.

The tennis racket will cost \$55.60 on sale.

Find the sales tax or discount to the nearest cent.

1. \$22.95 jeans, 7% tax **\$1.61**
2. \$39.00 sweater, 25% off **\$9.75**
3. \$35 necklace, 40% off **\$14.00**
4. \$115.48 watch, 6% tax **\$6.93**

Find the total cost or sale price to the nearest cent.

5. \$16.99 book, 5% tax **\$17.84**
6. \$13.99 calendar, 50% off **\$7**
7. \$129.40 rocking horse, 15% off **\$109.99**
8. \$349 television, 6% tax **\$369.94**

 T86 *Mathematics: Applications and Connections, Course 2*

Mixed Review

29. about 10%

29. ***Transportation*** Sports cars make up about 1% of total car sales. In 1996, 68,203 sports cars were sold. In 1997, about 75,000 sports cars were sold. What was the percent of increase from 1996 to 1997? *(Lesson 11-5)*

30. **Standardized Test Practice** Which word, written as shown, does not have a vertical line of symmetry? *(Lesson 9-7)* **C**

A	**B**	**C**	**D**
T O W	W H I M	H A T C H	W H Y

32. The testers probably used mean, since they said an *average* of over 1,100 chips.

31. Express 4.8 as a percent. *(Lesson 8-7)* **480%**

32. ***Advertising*** In 1997, packages of a certain cookie claimed "1,000 chips in every bag!" A magazine took six bags and counted every single chip. Here's what the magazine reported. *(Lesson 3-4)*

> The final tally: an average of over 1,100 chips . . . per package! Of course, that doesn't mean every bag measures up – to find that out, we'd have to buy all of these in the world.

Do you think the testers used the mean, median, or mode to summarize their data? Explain.

For **Extra Practice,** see page 600.

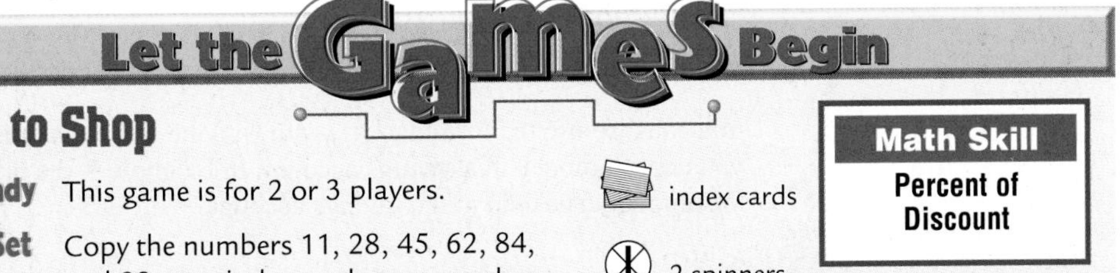

Time to Shop

Math Skill
Percent of Discount

Get Ready This game is for 2 or 3 players.

- index cards
- 2 spinners

Get Set Copy the numbers 11, 28, 45, 62, 84, and 98 onto index cards, one number per card. These numbers are the original price of an item. Shuffle the cards and place them facedown in a pile. Label equal sections of two spinners with the digits 0 through 9. Decide which spinner will stand for digits in the tens place and which spinner will stand for digits in the ones place. The number formed by spinning both spinners is the percent of discount.

Go
- One player selects the top card from the pile.
- The player spins both spinners and records the two-digit number. He or she uses this number as the percent of discount, and the number on the card as the original price, and computes the percent of discount. This is the player's score for this turn.
- Continue in this way, taking turns selecting a card, until no cards remain in the pile. The player with the largest total score wins.

Visit www.glencoe.com/sec/math/mac/mathnet for more games.

4 ASSESS

Closing Activity

Writing Have students explain what information is needed in order to find the total price, including tax, for an item on sale in a store. **regular price, percent of discount or discount, local sales tax**

Chapter 11, Quiz C (Lessons 11-5 and 11-6) is available in the *Assessment and Evaluation Masters,* p. 296.

***Practice Masters,* p. 86**

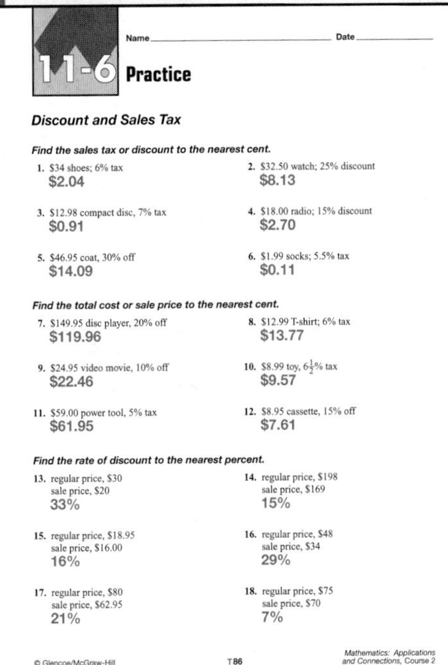

Name______ Date______

11-6 Practice

Discount and Sales Tax

Find the sales tax or discount to the nearest cent.

1. $34 shoes; 6% tax **$2.04**
2. $32.50 watch; 25% discount **$8.13**
3. $12.98 compact disc, 7% tax **$0.91**
4. $18.00 radio; 15% discount **$2.70**
5. $46.95 coat, 30% off **$14.09**
6. $1.99 socks; 5.5% tax **$0.11**

Find the total cost or sale price to the nearest cent.

7. $149.95 disc player, 20% off **$119.96**
8. $12.99 T-shirt; 6% tax **$13.77**
9. $24.95 video movie, 10% off **$22.46**
10. $8.99 toy, $6\frac{1}{2}$% tax **$9.57**
11. $59.00 power tool, 5% tax **$61.95**
12. $8.95 cassette, 15% off **$7.61**

Find the rate of discount to the nearest percent.

13. regular price, $30 sale price, $20 **33%**
14. regular price, $198 sale price, $169 **15%**
15. regular price, $18.95 sale price, $16.00 **16%**
16. regular price, $48 sale price, $34 **29%**
17. regular price, $80 sale price, $62.95 **21%**
18. regular price, $75 sale price, $70 **7%**

 T86 *Mathematics: Applications and Connections, Course 2*

Extending the Lesson

***Enrichment Masters,* p. 86**

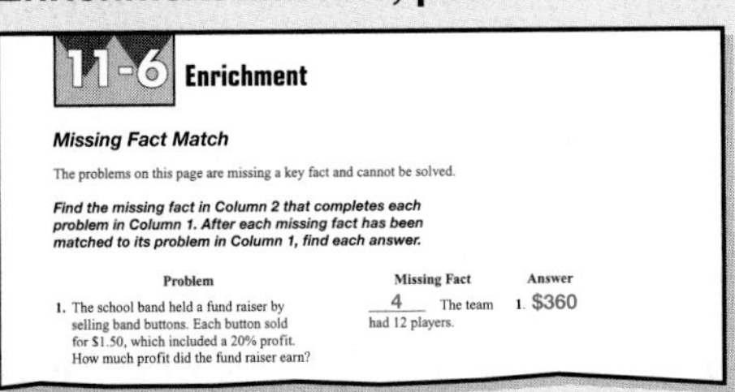

11-6 Enrichment

Missing Fact Match

The problems on this page are missing a key fact and cannot be solved.

Find the missing fact in Column 2 that completes each problem in Column 1. After each missing fact has been matched to its problem in Column 1, find each answer.

Problem	Missing Fact	Answer
1. The school band held a fund raiser by selling band buttons. Each button sold for $1.50, which included a 20% profit. How much profit did the fund raiser earn?	4 The team had 12 players.	1. $360

Ask students to choose a reasonable item they might want to buy for each numbered index card. Remind students to keep a running total of their savings. *Additional resources for this game can be found on page 51 of the **Classroom Games.***

11-7 Lesson Notes

Instructional Resources

- *Study Guide Masters,* p. 87
- *Practice Masters,* p. 87
- *Enrichment Masters,* p. 87
- Transparencies 11-7, A and B
- *Assessment and Evaluation Masters,* p. 296
- *Technology Masters,* p. 48

CD-ROM Program
- Resource Lesson 11-7

Recommended Pacing	
Standard	Day 11 of 13
Honors	Days 9 & 10 of 12
Block	Day 6 of 7

1 FOCUS

5-Minute Check
(Lesson 11-6)

Find the sales tax or discount to the nearest cent.

1. $48 jacket; 5% tax $2.40
2. $70 speaker; 18% off $12.60

Find the total cost or sale price to the nearest cent.

3. $12 scarf; 15% off $10.20
4. $6.79 tape; 8.25% tax $7.35
5. Find the percent of discount to the nearest percent: regular price, $54; sale price, $45.95. 15%

The 5-Minute Check is also available on **Transparency 11-7A** for this lesson.

Motivating the Lesson

Communication Ask students to describe how paying interest is like paying rent. Sample answer: a periodic payment for the use of a good

2 TEACH

Transparency 11-7B contains a teaching aid for this lesson.

Reading Mathematics Have students research various definitions of *interest* and describe the different meanings of the term in their own words.

11-7 Simple Interest

What you'll learn
You'll learn to solve problems involving simple interest.

When am I ever going to use this?
You'll use the simple interest formula to find the interest earned on your savings account.

Word Wise
simple interest
principal
rate
time

Mr. Craig borrowed $3,200 from a bank to help pay for a new all-terrain vehicle. If the bank charges him 9.5% interest, how much interest will he pay in a year?

Simple interest is the amount paid for the use of money. The formula for simple interest is $I = prt$, where I is the interest, p is the **principal**, or the amount of money invested or borrowed, r is the annual interest **rate**, and t is the **time** in years.

$I = prt$

$I = 3{,}200 \cdot 0.095 \cdot 1$ *p = $3,200, r = 9.5% or 0.095, t = 1 year*

$I = 304$

Mr. Craig will pay $304 in interest in a year, in addition to the $3,200 he originally borrowed.

You can also use the formula $I = prt$ to find the simple interest when you deposit money in a savings account. In Example 1, the principal is the amount deposited in the savings account.

1 **Investing** **Cecile has $500 in a savings account that pays 5% simple interest.**

a. **How much interest will she earn in 2 years?**

b. **How much interest will she earn if she withdraws the money after 9 months?**

a. $I = prt$

$I = 500 \cdot 0.05 \cdot 2$ *p = $500, r = 5% or 0.05, t = 2 years*

$I = 50$

Cecile will earn $50 in interest in 2 years.

If t is given in months, write this as a fraction of one year or as a decimal.

b. $I = prt$

$I = 500 \cdot 0.05 \cdot 0.75$ *p = $500, r = 5%, t = 9 months or 0.75 year*

$I = 18.75$

Cecile will earn $18.75 in interest in 9 months.

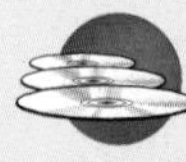

MathPASS CD-ROM

This CD-ROM offers a complete, self-paced mathematics curriculum. Each lesson includes a pretest, tutorial, guided practice, and posttest. MathPASS Lessons 38, 39, and 40 are correlated to this Student Edition lesson.
For Windows & Macintosh

2 **Finance** **Mr. Foose bought a watch for $135. He used his credit card, which charges 21% annual interest from the date of purchase. If he does not make any payments or any additional charges, how much would he owe at the end of the first month? Round to the nearest cent.**

$I = prt$

$I = 135 \cdot 0.21 \cdot \frac{1}{12}$ *$p = \$135, r = 21\%, t = 1$ month or $\frac{1}{12}$ year*

$I = 2.3625$

After 1 month, the interest would be about $2.36. So the total amount owed would be $135 + $2.36 or $137.36.

CHECK FOR UNDERSTANDING

Communicating Mathemations

Read and study the lesson to answer each question.

1. ***Explain*** how to find the interest on $900 at 4.5% for 1 year. **1. Multiply 900 · 0.045 · 1.**
2. ***Tell*** how to determine the value of t in the formula $I = prt$, if time is given in months. **Divide the number of months by 12.**
3. ***Write*** a few sentences comparing and contrasting principal and interest in borrowing money and in saving money. **See Answer Appendix.**

Guided Practice

Find the interest to the nearest cent for each principal, interest rate, and time.

4. $2,250, 7%, 3 years **$472.50**
5. $875, 15%, 4 months **$43.75**

Find the interest to the nearest cent on credit cards for each credit card balance, interest rate, and time.

6. $121, 16%, 2 months **$3.23**
7. $5,096, 17%, 2 years **$1,732.64**
8. ***Home Improvement*** Mr. Alvarez borrows $5,000 for 3 years at 11.5% simple interest to make home repairs and improvements. How much will he have to pay back, including interest? **$6,725**

EXERCISES

Practice

Find the interest to the nearest cent for each principal, interest rate, and time.

9. $340, 12%, 1.5 years **$61.20**
10. $3,186, 10%, 2 years **$637.20**
11. $4,200, $9\frac{1}{4}$%, 3 years **$1,165.50**
12. $98.50, $6\frac{1}{2}$%, 16 months **$8.54**
13. $514, 8.75%, 6 months **$22.49**
14. $175.80, 12%, 1.25 years **$26.37**

In-Class Examples

For Example 1
Mr. Reilly has $800 in a savings account that pays 6% simple interest.

a. How much interest will he earn in 3 years? **$144**
b. How much interest will he earn after six months? **$24**

For Example 2
Carmine charged $52 to his credit card, which charges 18% annual interest. How much would he owe at the end of two months if he didn't make payments or have additional charges? **$53.56**

3 PRACTICE/APPLY

Check for Understanding

If students need additional practice or instruction after completing Exercises 1–8, one of these options may be helpful.

- Extra Practice, see p. 600
- Reteaching Activity
- *Study Guide Masters,* p. 87
- *Practice Masters,* p. 87

Assignment Guide

Core: 9–25 odd, 26–29
Enriched: 10–22 even, 23–29

***Study Guide Masters,* p. 87**

Name__________ Date__________

Study Guide

Simplest Interest

Simple interest (I) is calculated by multiplying the principal (p), times the rate (r), which is given as a percent, times the time (t) given in years: $I = prt$.

Example **Find the interest earned on $1,250 at 6.5% for 9 months.**

$I = prt$

$p = \$1{,}250$, $r = 6.5\%$, or 0.065, and $t = \frac{9}{12}$ year, or 0.75 year.

$I = 1{,}250 \times 0.065 \times 0.75$
$I = 60.94$

The interest earned in 9 months is $60.94.

Find the interest to the nearest cent for each principal, interest rate, and time.

1. $500, 8%, 4 years **$160**
2. $1,600, 18%, 2 years **$576**
3. $480, 15%, 1.5 years **$108**
4. $725, 6%, 1.25 years **$54.38**
5. $2,890, 10%, 6 months **$144.50**
6. $668, 7.5%, 8 years **$400.80**
7. $903, 8.75%, 18 months **$118.52**
8. $4,275, 19%, 3 months **$203.06**
9. $210, 1%, 0.25 years **$0.53**
10. $100, 10%, 10 years **$100**

 T87 *Mathematics: Applications and Connections, Course 2*

Reteaching the Lesson

Activity Encourage students to round interest rates to determine a reasonable range for answers. Then they may use their calculators and apply the interest formula.

Error Analysis

Watch for students who forget to account for the fraction of a year's interest.

Prevent by clarifying the fact that *annual interest* rate includes any part of a year that has passed.

4 ASSESS

Closing Activity

Modeling Have students work in pairs using play money to model the interest earned in 3 months on \$500 at 6% annual interest. **\$7.50** Encourage students to create other problems for each other to solve.

Chapter 11, Quiz D (Lesson 11-7) is available in the *Assessment and Evaluation Masters,* p. 296.

Find the interest to the nearest cent on credit cards for each credit card balance, interest rate, and time.

15. \$839, 21%, 1 year **\$176.19**

16. \$400, 19%, 6 months **\$38**

17. \$1,200, 19%, 9 months **\$171**

18. \$325, 18.5%, 1 year **\$60.13**

19. \$672, $15\frac{1}{2}$%, 2 years **\$208.32**

20. \$1,000, $20\frac{1}{2}$%, 3 months **\$51.25**

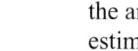

21. ***Write a Problem*** that involves a principal amount of \$2,600, an interest rate of 17%, and a time of 4 years. Then find the interest. **21. See students' work; \$1,768.**

22. If a principal amount of \$600 earned \$75 in 2.5 years, find the interest rate. **5%**

Applications and Problem Solving

23. ***Money Matters*** Nashoba has a balance of \$800 on his credit card from a scuba diving trip that he took in the Cayman Islands. The credit card company charges 18% simple interest. How much interest will he have to pay on the balance in one month? **\$12**

24. ***Finance*** Ms. Rollins deposited \$700 in a savings account that pays 6.75% annual interest. She also deposited \$300 in an account that pays 6% annual interest. If she does not deposit or withdraw any money from her accounts, what will be the total amount in both accounts after 6 months? **\$1,032.63**

25. ***Finance*** Madeline Morgan has invested \$1,500 at 9% annual interest. She has \$3,000 more to invest. At what rate must she invest the \$3,000 to have a total of \$4,950 at the end of the year? **10.5%**

26. ***Critical Thinking*** Maria Constanza deposits \$400 in an account that pays 3.5% annually. At the end of the year, the interest earned is added to the principal. Find the total amount in her account each year for 3 years. **\$414, \$428.49, \$443.49**

Mixed Review

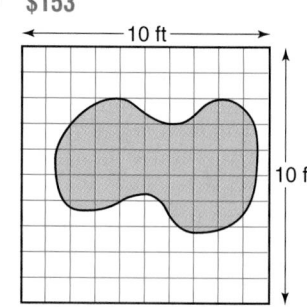

27. ***Money Matters*** Find the price to the nearest cent if a \$180 electric guitar is on sale for 15% off. *(Lesson 11-6)* **\$153**

28. **Standardized Test Practice** Ms. Gonzalez has an irregularly shaped garden in her backyard. To determine the amount of mulch she should buy, she estimates the area of the garden. What is a good estimate of this area based on the sketch of her garden? *(Lesson 10-4)* **A**

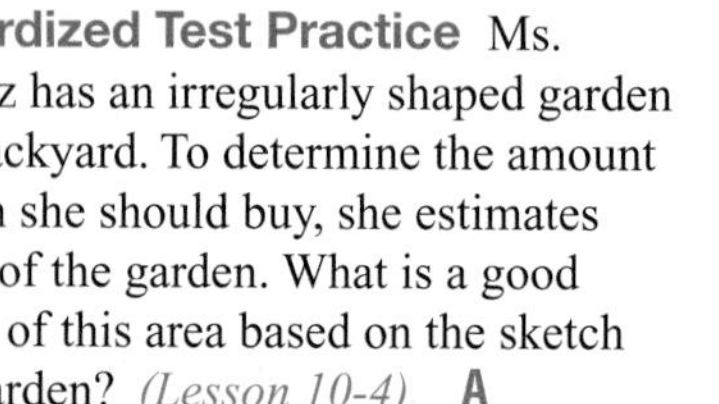

10 ft

10 ft

A 30 ft²

B 10 ft²

C 50 ft²

D 60 ft²

E 40 ft²

For **Extra Practice,** see page 600.

29. Subtract $\frac{1}{9}$ from $\frac{5}{12}$. *(Lesson 7-2)* $\frac{11}{36}$

***Practice Masters,* p. 87**

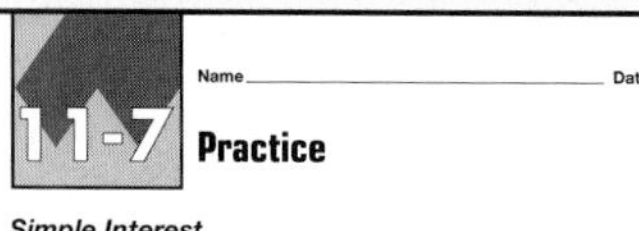

Name________ Date________

11-7 Practice

Simple Interest

Find the interest to the nearest cent for each principal, interest rate, and time.

1. \$300, 5%, 3 years **\$45**
2. \$450.90, 10%, 1.8 years **\$81.16**
3. \$198, 14%, 6 months **\$13.86**
4. \$3,980, $6\frac{1}{2}$%, 4 years **\$1,034.80**
5. \$695, 11%, 1 year **\$76.45**
6. \$189.50, 8%, 2 years **\$30.32**
7. \$2,178, 12%, 5 years **\$1,306.80**
8. \$568, 16%, 8 months **\$60.59**

Find the interest to the nearest cent on credit cards for each credit card balance, interest rate, and time.

9. \$429, 18.5%, 1 year **\$79.37**
10. \$1,400, 16.5%, 8 months **\$154**
11. \$1,000, $22\frac{1}{2}$%, 6 months **\$112.50**
12. \$989, 17%, 2 years **\$336.26**
13. \$3,126, 19%, 9 months **\$445.46**
14. \$549, 21%, 2 years **\$230.58**
15. \$1,050, 16%, 2.5 years **\$420**
16. \$450, 22%, 1 year **\$99**

T87
Mathematics: Applications and Connections, Course 2

Extending the Lesson

***Enrichment Masters,* p. 87**

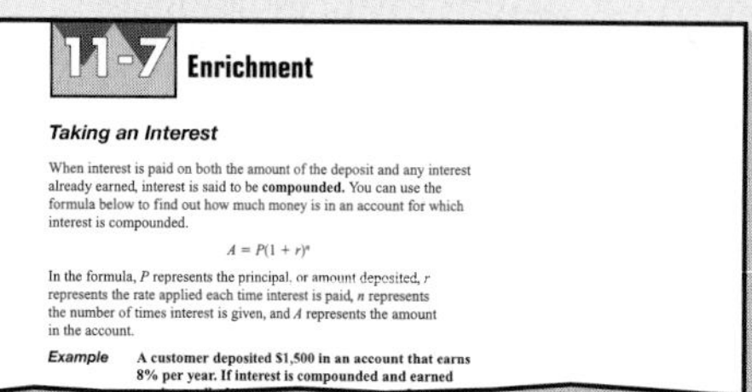

11-7 Enrichment

Taking an Interest

When interest is paid on both the amount of the deposit and any interest already earned, interest is said to be **compounded.** You can use the formula below to find out how much money is in an account for which interest is compounded.

$A = P(1 + r)^n$

In the formula, P represents the principal, or amount deposited, r represents the rate applied each time interest is paid, n represents the number of times interest is given, and A represents the amount in the account.

Example **A customer deposited \$1,500 in an account that earns 8% per year. If interest is compounded and earned**

Activity Have students find the current interest rates paid by local banks for savings accounts and certificates of deposit. Encourage them to compare rates for different kinds of accounts and discuss the reasons banks pay different rates.

SPREADSHEETS

11-7B Simple Interest

A Follow-Up of Lesson 11-7

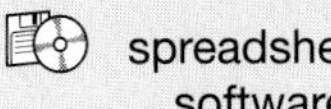 computer

spreadsheet software

Simple interest I is calculated by finding the product of the principal p, the rate r, as a decimal, and the time t in years. The formula used is $I = prt$. The new account balance is then found by adding the interest to the principal, or $A = p + I$.

TRY THIS

Work with a partner.

A spreadsheet can be used to generate a simple interest table for various account balances.

Suppose you are the manager of a local bank. Your bank is starting a "Young Savers" program for children. You want to make a table of the interest that children can earn to show how important saving money is. The current rate on the "Young Savers" account is 5%. Use 2 years as the time period. Substitute the values B2 = 5 and C2 = 2 into the spreadsheet to show how much will be in an account with the different starting balances at the end of 2 years.

	A	B	C	D	E
1	Principal	Rate	Time	Interest	New Balance
2					
3	500	= B2/100	= C2	= A3*B3*C3	= A3+D3
4	1000	= B2/100	= C2	= A4*B4*C4	= A4+D4
5	1500	= B2/100	= C2	= A5*B5*C5	= A5+D5
6	2000	= B2/100	= C2	= A6*B6*C6	= A6+D6
7	2500	= B2/100	= C2	= A7*B7*C7	= A7+D7

ON YOUR OWN

Use the spreadsheet to answer each question.

1. Why is the rate in column B divided by 100? **to change the percent to a decimal**
2. What is the account balance after 2 years if the principal is $1,500 and the simple interest rate is 5%? **$1,650**
3. What is the interest earned in 2 years on an account with a principal of $2,000 and an interest rate of 5%? **$200**
4. Suppose you wanted to add a new row to the spreadsheet that represents a principal of $3,000. List each of the cell entries (A8, B8, C8, D8, and E8) that you would enter. **A8 = 3000; B8 = B2/100; C8 = C2; D8 = A8*B8*C8; E8 = A8 + D8**
5. What entries for cells B2 and C2 would you use to calculate the simple interest on a principal of $1,500 at a rate of 7% for a 9-month period? What is the balance of this account at the end of the 9 months? **B2 = 7, C2 = 0.75; $1,578.75**

Have students write a paragraph explaining how to read a spreadsheet calculating simple interest.

11-7B TECHNOLOGY LAB Notes

GET READY

Objective Students use a spreadsheet to find simple interest.

Technology Resources
- *Lotus 1·2·3*
- *ClarisWorks*
- *Microsoft Excel*

MANAGEMENT TIPS

Recommended Time
20 minutes

Getting Started Point out to students that the number in column B will be a percent of the number in column A.

Using Calculators If spreadsheet software is not available, students can work in pairs to make their own table in spreadsheet form and use calculators to make the computations.

ASSESS

After students answer Exercises 1–5, ask them what pattern they have observed as principal, rate, and time increase.

Vocabulary

This section provides a listing of the new terms, properties, and phrases that were introduced in this chapter. Have students define each term and provide an example or two of it, if appropriate.

Understanding and Using the Vocabulary

These exercises check students' understanding of the terms by using a variety of verbal formats including matching, completion, and true/false.

Glossaries A complete glossary of terms appears on pages 656–663. The glossary also appears in Spanish on pages 664–672. These exercises provide practice for the corresponding objectives.

Additional Answers

11. $\frac{1}{10} \cdot 80 = 8$
12. $\frac{9}{10} \cdot 400 = 360$
13. $30(100\% + 50\%) = 30 + 15$, or 45
14. $\frac{1}{100} \cdot 700 = 7$
15. $\frac{1}{2} \cdot 1{,}000 = 500$
16. $1 \cdot 1 = 1$
17. $32 = R \cdot 50$; 64%
18. $39 = 0.65 \cdot B$; 60
19. $P = 0.62 \cdot 300$; 186
20. $P = 0.57 \cdot 450$; 256.5
21. $108.5 = 0.155 \cdot B$; 700
22. **Favorite Soft Drinks**

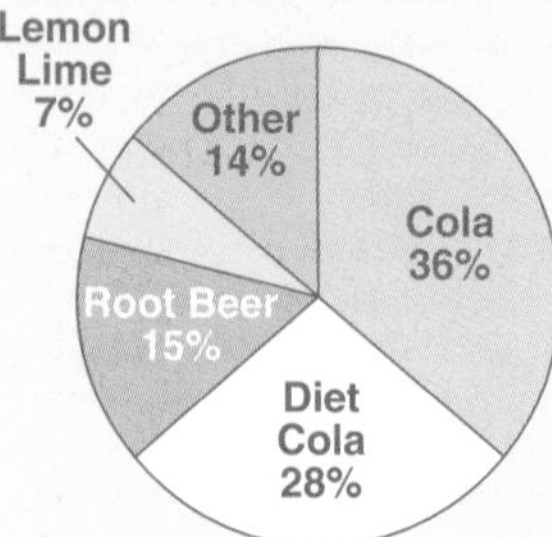

CHAPTER 11

Study Guide and Assessment

Chapter Review For additional lesson-by-lesson review, visit: www.glencoe.com/sec/math/mac/mathnet

Vocabulary

After completing this chapter, you should be able to define each term, concept, or phrase and give an example or two of each.

Statistics and Probability
circle graph (p. 460)
population (p. 464)
random (p. 464)
sample (p. 464)

Number and Operations
principal (p. 478)
rate (p. 478)
simple interest (p. 478)
time (p. 478)

Problem Solving
solve a simpler problem (p. 454)

Understanding and Using the Vocabulary

State whether each sentence is *true* or *false.* If false, replace the underlined word or number to make a true sentence.

1. A percent is a ratio that compares a number to <u>100</u>. **true**
2. A circle graph is used to <u>compare</u> parts of a whole. **true**
3. There are <u>300°</u> in a circle. **false; 360°**
4. When taking a <u>sample</u>, every member of a population is surveyed. **false; census**
5. When finding a percent of increase, compare the amount of the increase to the <u>new</u> amount. **false; original**
6. The formula for simple interest is <u>$I = prt$</u>. **true**
7. In order for a sample to be representative, it must be <u>random</u>. **true**

In Your Own Words

8. ***Explain*** two methods for estimating percents. **Change the percent to a fraction and multiply; find 1% and multiply.**

MindJogger Videoquizzes

MindJogger Videoquizzes provide an alternative review of concepts presented in this chapter. Students work in teams to answer questions, gaining points for correct answers. The questions are presented in three rounds.
Round 1 Concepts–5 questions
Round 2 Skills–4 questions
Round 3 Problem Solving–4 questions

Objectives & Examples

Upon completing this chapter, you should be able to:

- estimate percents by using fractions and decimals *(Lesson 11-1)*

Estimate 52% of 495.

52% is about 50% or $\frac{1}{2}$.

$\frac{1}{2}$ of 500 is 250.

So, 52% of 495 is *about* 250.

11–16. See margin for sample answers.

Review Exercises

Use these exercises to review and prepare for the chapter test.

Write the fraction, decimal, mixed number, or whole number equivalent of each percent that could be used to estimate.

9. 78% **0.8** **10.** 205% **2**

Estimate.

11. 12% of 77 **12.** 88% of 400
13. 149% of 30 **14.** 0.95% of 700
15. 55% of 1,000 **16.** 98% of 1

- solve problems by using the percent equation *(Lesson 11-2)*

What number is 16% of 110?

$P = R \cdot B$

$P = 0.16 \cdot 110$ $R = 0.16, B = 110$

$P = 17.6$ 16% of 110 is 17.6.

Write an equation for each problem. Then solve. Round answers to the nearest tenth. 17–21. See margin.

17. 32 is what percent of 50?
18. 65% of what number is 39?
19. Find 62% of 300.
20. 57% of 450 is what number?
21. 15.5% of what number is 108.5?

- construct and interpret circle graphs *(Lesson 11-3)*

Spring: 40%, 144°
Summer: 26%, 93.6°
Autumn: 22%, 79.2°
Winter: 12%, 43.2°

Favorite Season

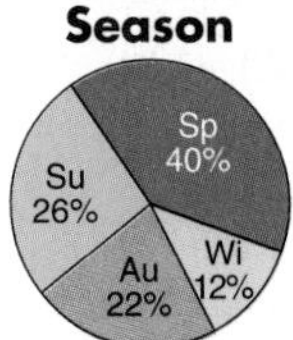

22. Make a circle graph of favorite soft drinks. **See margin.**

Soft Drink	Percent
Cola	36%
Diet Cola	28%
Root Beer	15%
Lemon Lime	7%
Other	14%

- predict actions of a larger group by using a sample *(Lesson 11-4)*

In a random sample of 100 students at McAuliffe Middle School, 10% have after-school jobs. How many of the 600 students have after-school jobs?

10% of 600 $= 0.10 \times 600$
$= 60$ students

23. Of 20,000 registered voters, the voting preferences of 1,000 are listed in the table.

Candidate	Number of Votes
Chung	220
Addair	390
Armas	310
Undecided	80

How many of the 20,000 voters might you expect to vote for Addair? **7,800 voters**

Assessment and Evaluation

Six forms of Chapter 11 Test are available in the *Assessment and Evaluation Masters* as shown in the chart.

1A	Multiple Choice	Honors
1B	Multiple Choice	Average
1C	Multiple Choice	Basic
2A	Free Response	Honors
2B	Free Response	Average
2C	Free Response	Basic

Chapter 11 Test, Form 1B, is shown at the right. Chapter 11 Test, Form 2B, is shown on the next page.

Objectives & Examples

This section reviews the skills and concepts of the chapter and shows completely worked examples.

Review Exercises

These exercises provide practice for the corresponding objectives.

***Assessment and Evaluation Masters,* pp. 283–284**

Name ____________ Date ________

Chapter 11 Test, Form 1B

Estimate.

1. 37% of $293\frac{1}{2}$ — 1. C
   A. 125 B. 75 C. 120 D. 150

2. 0.8% of 192 — 2. B
   A. 12 B. 2 C. 19 D. 8

3. 396% of 24 — 3. C
   A. 75 B. 46 C. 100 D. 115

Write an equation for each problem. Then solve. Round answers to the nearest tenth.

4. Find 16% of 44. — 4. A
   A. $P = 0.16(44)$; 7.0 B. $P = 16(0.4)$; 6.4
   C. $P = 0.2(44)$; 8.8 D. $P = \frac{44}{16}$; 2.8

5. 36% of what number is 27? — 5. B
   A. $0.36(27) = B$; 9.7 B. $B = \frac{27}{0.36}$; 75
   C. $\frac{36}{0.27} = B$; 133.3 D. $B = \frac{27}{36}$; 0.8

The circle graph displays the results of a survey of 365 students on the favorite color of seventh graders at Jones Middle School. Use the circle graph for Questions 6 and 7.

Favorite Color
Blue (32%)
Green (9%)
Black (13%)
Red (37%)

6. Find the percent of students whose favorite color is blue. — 6. A
   A. 32 B. 46 C. 114 D. 132

7. Find the ratio that compares the number of students whose favorite color is black with the total number of students. Round your answer to the nearest hundredth. — 7. B
   A. 0.09 B. 0.13 C. 0.37 D. 0.32

8. Find the percent of change if the original price is $47 and the new price is $21. Round to the nearest whole percent. — 8. B
   A. 45% B. 55% C. 26% D. 50%

 283 *Mathematics: Applications and Connections, Course 2*

Chapter 11 Test, Form 1B (continued)

Of 350,000 registered voters, 800 were surveyed. Their voting preferences are listed in the table. Use the table for Questions 9 and 10.

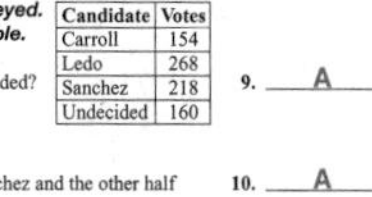

Candidate	Votes
Carroll	154
Ledo	268
Sanchez	218
Undecided	160

9. What percent of the registered voters are undecided? — 9. A
   A. 20% B. 80%
   C. 0.04% D. 25%

10. If one half of the undecided voters vote for Sanchez and the other half vote for Carroll, who can be expected to win? — 10. A
    A. Sanchez B. Ledo C. Carroll D. no winner

11. Find the percent of change from 4 to 9. — 11. B
    A. 44% B. 125% C. 56% D. 80%

12. Find the total price to the nearest cent for a $22 hat that is on sale for 15% off with a sales tax of 8%. — 12. A
    A. $20.20 B. $23.54 C. $18.70 D. $16.94

13. Find the rate of discount to the nearest percent if the regular price is $38 and the sale price is $19.60. — 13. C
    A. 7% B. 3% C. 48% D. 70%

14. Find the interest to the nearest cent for a principal of $250, an interest rate of 11.25%, and a time period of 4 months. — 14. D
    A. $112.50 B. $7.40 C. $88.69 D. $9.37

15. Albert Groe bought a suit for $295. He used his credit card, which charges 19% annual interest from the moment of purchase. If he does not make any payments or any additional charges, how much would he owe at the end of the first month? — 15. D
    A. $301.73 B. $56.05 C. $351.05 D. $299.67

16. Listed in the table is the total circulation of 5-, 10-, and 20-dollar bills in the United States as of March 1996. Estimate how much of the rounded total of $395 billion is in ten-dollar bills. — 16. B

Denomination ($)	% of Total Dollars in Circulation
5	2
10	3
20	20

A. $10,000,000 B. $20,000,000
C. $5,000,000 D. $80,000,000

 284 *Mathematics: Applications and Connections, Course 2*

Study Guide and Assessment

Assessment and Evaluation Masters, pp. 289–290

Name____________ Date____________

Chapter 11 Test, Form 2B

Estimate.

1. $13\frac{2}{3}$% of 22 — 1. 3
2. 0.68% of 41 — 2. 0.4
3. 26% of 47 — 3. 12.5
4. 109% of 30 — 4. 33

Write an equation for each problem. Then solve. Round answers to the nearest tenth.

5. 15 is what percent of 36? — 5. $R = \frac{15}{36}$; 41.7%
6. 45% of what number is 63? — 6. $B = \frac{63}{0.45}$; 140
7. Find 38% of 23. — 7. $P = 0.38 \cdot 23$; 8.7
8. What percent of 56 is 49? — 8. $R = \frac{49}{56}$; 87.5%

Sally's Silly Stuff has the novelty items indicated in the table. Use the table for Questions 9 and 10.

Novelty Item	Number
x-ray glasses	31
spicy gum	25
hand buzzers	40
whoopee cushions	11
other	44

9. Write the ratio of x-ray glasses to the total number of novelty items. Round to the nearest hundredth. — 9. 0.21
10. Make a circle graph of the novelty items. — 10. Spicy Gum (17%); Whoopee Cushions (7%); Other (29%); Hand Buzzers (26%); X-Ray Glasses (21%)

The table shows the survey results of 73 people who chose their favorite shade of blue. Use the table for Questions 11–13. Round to the nearest whole number.

Shade of Blue	Votes
electric	13
sky	21
cobalt	9
navy	14
other	16

11. What percent prefer cobalt blue? — 11. 12%
12. What percent prefer sky blue? — 12. 29%
13. If 900 people were polled, how many would you expect to say electric blue is their favorite shade of blue? — 13. about 160

 289 *Mathematics: Applications and Connections, Course 2*

Chapter 11 Test, Form 2B (continued)

14. Find the percent of change from \$110 to \$85. Round your answer to the nearest whole percent. — 14. 23% decrease
15. Find the percent of change from 15 to 26. Round to the nearest whole percent. — 15. 73% increase
16. Find the percent of change from 16 to 96. Round to the nearest whole percent. — 16. 500% increase
17. Find the percent of decrease if a muffler that originally cost \$59 goes on sale for \$35. Round to the nearest whole percent. — 17. 41%
18. Find the total price to the nearest cent on a \$79 jacket that is 30% off with a sales tax of 7.5%. — 18. \$59.45
19. If the regular price of an item is \$57.50 and the sale price is \$46.00, find the rate of discount to the nearest whole percent. — 19. 20%
20. Find the total price to the nearest cent of an office chair that costs \$165 with a sales tax of 7%. — 20. \$176.55
21. Find the original price of a remote controlled car if the sale price of \$49 is 75% off the original price. — 21. \$196
22. Find the interest to the nearest cent for a principal of \$1,900, an interest rate of 13.25%, and a time of 30 months. — 22. \$629.38
23. A credit card that has a \$500 balance at a 21% interest rate will accumulate how much interest over 6 months? — 23. \$52.50
24. Maxwell borrows \$1,000 to repair his car at 9% interest. If he pays the loan back over $1\frac{1}{2}$ years, how much does he pay back including interest? — 24. \$1,135
25. The table shows the amount of people, in millions, who spoke each language listed in 1995. Of the languages listed, which was spoken by about 25% of the speakers listed? — 25. English

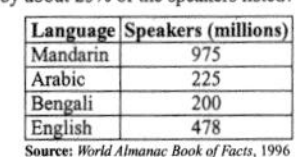

Language	Speakers (millions)
Mandarin	975
Arabic	225
Bengali	200
English	478

Source: *World Almanac Book of Facts*, 1996

 290 *Mathematics: Applications and Connections, Course 2*

Objectives & Examples

find the percent of increase or decrease *(Lesson 11-5)*

original: \$2.75 new: \$3.55

difference: \$3.55 − \$2.75 = \$0.80

$$\frac{0.80}{2.75} = \frac{r}{100}$$

$$80 = 2.75r \quad \textit{Find the cross products.}$$

$$\frac{80}{2.75} = \frac{2.75r}{2.75} \quad \textit{Divide each side by 2.75.}$$

$$29.09 \approx r$$

The percent of increase is about 29%.

Review Exercises

Find the percent of change. Round to the nearest whole percent.

24. original: 44 new: 66 **50%**

25. original: \$22,500 new: \$25,400 **13%**

26. original: \$200 new: \$180 **10%**

27. original: \$25 new: \$33.33 **33%**

28. Find the percent of increase from 106 miles to 122 miles. **15%**

---

solve problems involving sales tax and discount *(Lesson 11-6)*

Find the sales tax on a \$75 pair of shoes if the tax rate is 6%. Let t represent the sales tax.

$$6\% \times \$75 = t$$

$$0.06 \times 75 = t$$

$$\$4.50 = t$$

Find the sales tax or discount to the nearest cent.

29. \$25 shirt; 7% tax **\$1.75**

30. \$210 bicycle; 15% off **\$31.50**

31. \$8,000 car; $5\frac{1}{2}$% tax **\$440**

32. \$40 sweater; 33% discount **\$13.20**

---

solve problems involving simple interest *(Lesson 11-7)*

Find the interest on \$400 at 9% for 3 years.

$I = prt$

$I = 400 \times 0.09 \times 3$ *$p = 400$, $r = 0.09$,*

$I = \$108$ *$t = 3$ years*

Find the interest to the nearest cent for each principal, interest rate, and time.

33. \$5,000, 10% 3 years **\$1,500**

34. \$85, 7.5%, 9 months **\$4.78**

35. \$2,500, 11%, $1\frac{1}{2}$ years **\$412.50**

36. \$775, 19%, 30 months **\$368.13**

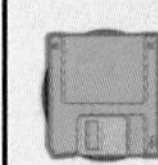

Test and Review Software

You may use this software, a combination of an item generator and item bank, to create your own tests or worksheets. Types of items include free response, multiple choice, short answer, and open ended.

CD-ROM Program

The CD-ROM Program contains an Assessment Game whose questions review the concepts in this chapter.

Applications & Problem Solving

37. ***Solve a Simpler Problem*** Mega Mall had sales of $12.1 million in 1998. Dana's Department Store accounted for 4.9% of the sales. Approximate the sales for Dana's Department Store in 1998. *(Lesson 11-1B)* **Sample answer: $600,000**

38. ***Money Matters*** Ethan has a credit card balance of $1,000. If he pays off the balance over 2 years at an annual simple interest rate of 18%, how much interest will he pay? *(Lesson 11-7)* **$360**

39. ***Money Matters*** Debi bought a CD player for $115. The sales tax rate was 5%. How much sales tax did she pay? *(Lesson 11-3)* **$5.75**

40. ***School*** Brenda's attendance during the 1998-99 school year is summarized in the following circle graph. If she was in class on time a total of 167 days, how many total days were in the school year? *(Lessons 11-2 and 11-3)* **180 days**

School Attendance

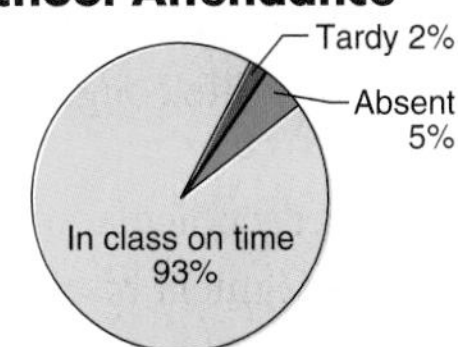

Alternative Assessment

Open Ended See margin.

You made a circle graph to show the results of a survey taken of 100 students in your school about their favorite cafeteria food. It was published in the school newspaper as shown below.

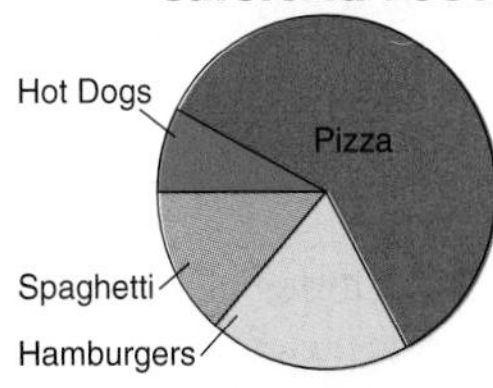

What information is missing from the graph? Explain how you can determine this information. Then add it to the graph.

You now find that one of the sections of the graph is too big. What does that tell you about at least one other section of the graph?

Completing the CHAPTER Project

Use the following checklist to make sure your project is complete.

- ☑ Your data is well-organized and easy to read.
- ☑ The percents used to describe the data are accurate.
- ☑ The circle graph is accurate and neat.
- ☑ The predictions about the radio station programming are logical.
- ☑ You have a report including a summary of your data.

Select one of the words you learned in this chapter and place the word and its definition in your portfolio. Attach a note explaining why you selected it.

A practice test for Chapter 11 is provided on page 617.

Applications & Problem Solving

This section provides additional practice in solving real-world problems that involve the skills of this chapter.

Alternative Assessment

The *Open Ended* section provides students with a performance assessment opportunity to evaluate their work and understanding.

Students should complete the final stages of their project and prepare a class demonstration of their results. A scoring guide for the project is available in the *Investigations and Projects Masters,* p. 59.

Students should add to their portfolios at this time.

***Assessment and Evaluation Masters,* p. 293**

Name__________ Date______

Chapter 11 Performance Assessment

Instructions: Demonstrate your knowledge by giving a clear, concise solution to each problem. Be sure to include all relevant drawings and justify your answers. You may show your solutions in more than one way or investigate beyond the requirements of the problems.

1. Due to health hazards of second-hand smoke, businesses have banned smoking in the work place as seen on the graph.

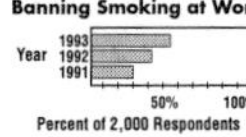

a. If there are 5,000,000 businesses in the U.S. and this sample is from that total amount, is this a good sample size? Why or why not?

b. About how many of the 5 million businesses would you expect to have banned smoking if 56% of the respondents banned smoking in 1993? Show your work.

c. Smoking at work was banned by 43% of the respondents in 1992. Estimate the number of respondents who banned smoking in 1992. Explain your reasoning.

d. Write an equation to find the number of respondents who banned smoking in 1991. Solve. Show your work.

e. Write a ratio that compares each year's percent with the total percent of all 3 added together. Make a circle graph of those ratios.

2. a. Find the rate of discount for a pair of pants that cost $65 and are on sale for $41.99. Explain each step.

b. How would you find the sale price of an item if it originally costs $16.95, is on sale for 22% off, and the sales tax is 6.5%? Explain each step.

c. Find the interest on $1,200 at 8% for 6 months. Explain each step.

d. Find the interest on $900 at 6% for 4 years if the interest is added to the principal at the end of the year. Show your work.

 293 *Mathematics: Applications and Connections, Course 2*

Additional Answer for the Open Ended item

The percents are missing. Find the measure of each angle and divide by 360. Then change the decimal to a percent. See Answer Appendix for revised graph.

Performance Assessment

Additional performance assessment tasks for this chapter are included in the *Assessment and Evaluation Masters* on page 293. A scoring guide is also provided on page 305.

Standardized Test Practice

The Standardized Test Practice may be used to help students prepare for standardized tests. The test items are written in the same style as those in state proficiency tests and standardized tests like CAT, CTBS, ITBS, MAT, SAT, and Terra Nova. The test items cover skills and concepts covered up to this point in the text.

The pages can be used as an overnight assessment. After students have completed the pages, discuss how each problem can be solved, or provide copies of the solutions from the *Solutions Manual.*

***Assessment and Evaluation Masters,* p. 299**

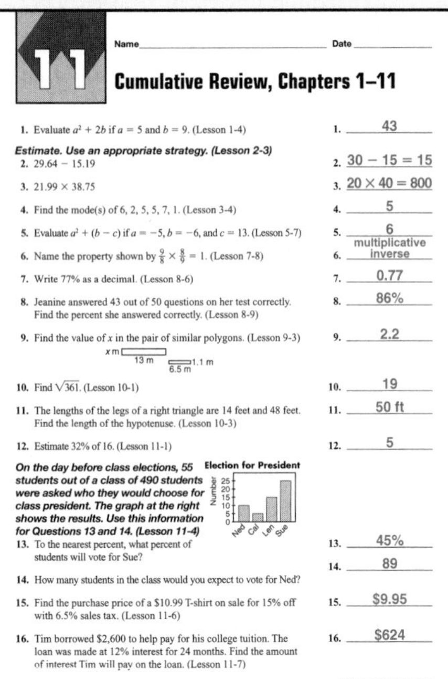

11

Name ______________ Date ______

Cumulative Review, Chapters 1–11

1. Evaluate $a^2 + 2b$ if $a = 5$ and $b = 9$. (Lesson 1-4) — 1. 43

Estimate. Use an appropriate strategy. (Lesson 2-3)

2. 29.64 − 15.19 — 2. $30 - 15 = 15$
3. 21.99 × 38.75 — 3. $20 \times 40 = 800$
4. Find the mode(s) of 6, 2, 5, 5, 7, 1. (Lesson 3-4) — 4. 5
5. Evaluate $a^2 + (b - c)$ if $a = -5$, $b = -6$, and $c = 13$. (Lesson 5-7) — 5. 6
6. Name the property shown by $\frac{9}{8} \times \frac{8}{9} = 1$. (Lesson 7-8) — 6. multiplicative inverse
7. Write 77% as a decimal. (Lesson 8-6) — 7. 0.77
8. Jeanine answered 43 out of 50 questions on her test correctly. Find the percent she answered correctly. (Lesson 8-9) — 8. 86%
9. Find the value of x in the pair of similar polygons. (Lesson 9-3) — 9. 2.2

10. Find $\sqrt{361}$. (Lesson 10-1) — 10. 19
11. The lengths of the legs of a right triangle are 14 feet and 48 feet. Find the length of the hypotenuse. (Lesson 10-3) — 11. 50 ft
12. Estimate 32% of 16. (Lesson 11-1) — 12. 5

On the day before class elections, 55 students out of a class of 490 students were asked who they would choose for class president. The graph at the right shows the results. Use this information for Questions 13 and 14. (Lesson 11-4)

13. To the nearest percent, what percent of students will vote for Sue? — 13. 45%
14. How many students in the class would you expect to vote for Ned? — 14. 89
15. Find the purchase price of a \$10.99 T-shirt on sale for 15% off with 6.5% sales tax. (Lesson 11-6) — 15. \$9.95
16. Tim borrowed \$2,600 to help pay for his college tuition. The loan was made at 12% interest for 24 months. Find the amount of interest Tim will pay on the loan. (Lesson 11-7) — 16. \$624

 299 *Mathematics: Applications and Connections, Course 2*

CHAPTERS 1–11

Standardized Test Practice

Assessing Knowledge & Skills

Section One: Multiple Choice

There are nine multiple-choice questions in this section. Choose the best answer. If a correct answer is *not here,* choose the letter for Not Here.

1.

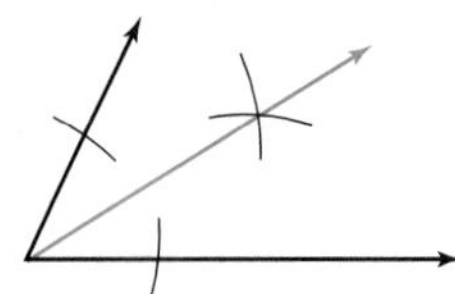

This drawing shows how to — A

A construct an angle bisector.

B construct an angle congruent to a given angle.

C construct perpendicular angles.

D construct a segment bisector.

2. Jesse bought 2.4 meters of blue ribbon and 110 centimeters of white ribbon. How many centimeters longer is the blue ribbon than the white ribbon? J

F 1.3 cm

G 350 cm

H 107.6 cm

J 130 cm

3. Which best represents a pair of similar figures? D

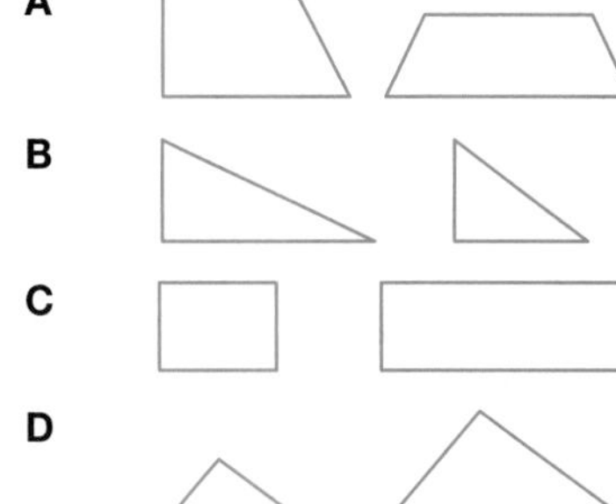

A

B

C

D

Please note that Questions 4–9 have five answer choices.

4. A person's weight on the moon is about $\frac{1}{6}$ of their weight on Earth. About how much would a person weigh on the moon if their weight on Earth is 125 pounds? G

F 12 lb

G 20 lb

H 60 lb

J 200 lb

K 600 lb

5. Which procedure could be used to find b in the triangle? C

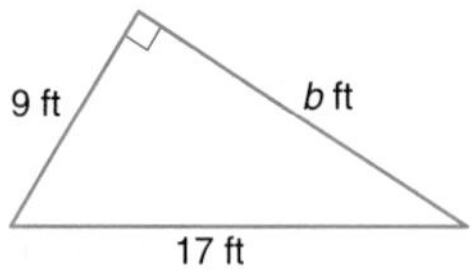

A Add 9 and 17.

B Add 9^2 and 17^2.

C Subtract 9^2 from 17^2.

D Subtract 9 from 17.

E Multiply 9^2 and 17^2.

6. There are 194 Calories in 1 serving of crackers. If a serving consists of 12 crackers, which is the best estimate of the number of Calories in each cracker? G

F 10 Calories

G 20 Calories

H 30 Calories

J 60 Calories

K 100 Calories

◄◄◄ Instructional Resources

Another cumulative review is shown at the left and is available in the *Assessment and Evaluation Masters,* p. 299.

7. A small sample of students were questioned about their favorite ice cream flavors. The chart shows the results.

Ice Cream	Number of Students
chocolate chip	12
vanilla	6
mint chocolate chip	4
chocolate	3
Total	25

If there are 75 students in the class, what is a good prediction of the number of students who would choose chocolate chip as their favorite ice cream? **B**

A 30 **B** 36
C 45 **D** 60
E 25

8. The temperature rose about 2°F each hour for 9 hours. The beginning temperature was −14°F. What was the temperature after 9 hours? **H**

F 32°F **G** −12°F
H 4°F **J** 5°F
K Not Here

9. Tamera had $25.83 in her purse. She spent $6 for lunch. How much money did she have left? **E**

A $20.83 **B** $21.83
C $26.26 **D** $31.83
E Not Here

Test Practice For additional test practice questions, visit:

www.glencoe.com/sec/math/mac/mathnet

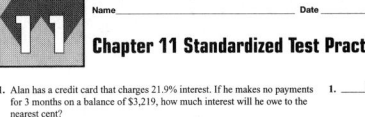

Test-Taking Tip THE PRINCETON REVIEW

As a part of your preparation for a standardized test, review basic formulas such as the Pythagorean Theorem. If you know a few important formulas and their common uses, you will be more prepared.

Section Two: Free Response

This section contains three questions for which you will provide short answers. Write your answers on your paper.

10. The grading scale for a test is shown below.

Wrong Answers	0	1	2	3	4
Score	100	98	95	93	90

Using the pattern in the table, what score would be given for 6 wrong answers? **85**

11. What is the unit price (dollars per ounce) if a 14-ounce can of peaches costs $1.19? **$0.085**

12. Kay spun a spinner 100 times. The results are in the chart.

Color	Number of Spins
Yellow	25
Black	25
Orange	50

If the spinner is divided into four equal sections, how many sections would you expect to be yellow? **1**

Test-Taking Tip

As a study aid, students may find it helpful to make 3 × 5 cards for each formula they will be required to know. An example could also be included on the card.

Assessment and Evaluation Masters, pp. 297–298

Name_______________ Date_______

Chapter 11 Standardized Test Practice

1. Alan has a credit card that charges 21.9% interest. If he makes no payments for 3 months on a balance of $3,219, how much interest will he owe to the nearest cent? 1. __B__
A. $200.03 B. $176.24 C. $704.96 D. $804.75

2. Fran and Zoe went to the grocery store to get four $3\frac{1}{2}$ pound bags of lollipops. How many pounds of lollipops did they get altogether? 2. __A__
A. 14 B. $12\frac{1}{2}$ C. 7 D. 28

3. Georgina really liked crackers. So exactly one week ago she ate 40 crackers. The next day she didn't like them quite so much so she only ate 35. Then 5 days ago she decided she could only handle eating 30 crackers. If she continued on this pattern, how many crackers has Georgina eaten today (Day 7)? 3. __A__
A. 10 B. 5 C. 15 D. 0

4. What is the median number of crackers Georgina ate in Question 3 from one week ago through today? 4. __D__
A. 10 B. 12.5 C. 22.5 D. 25

5. Dave purchased a leather jacket priced at $439. If the sales tax is 7.5%, what was the total amount Dave paid? 5. __B__
A. $329.25 B. $471.93 C. $219.50 D. $464.02

6. Skylar purchased a bottle of syrup for $2.69, a box of pancake mix for $4.89, and a dozen eggs for $1.59. If she started with $15, how much does she have left? 6. __B__
A. $9.17 B. $5.83 C. $7.42 D. $8.52

7. Althea's birthday is in June. And so are the birthdays of 4 of her 25 classmates. How many of the 780 students in Althea's school would you expect to have birthdays in June? 7. __C__
A. 125 B. 142 C. 156 D. 207

8. Rory has 33 pounds of cheese to divide equally among 22 friends. How much cheese will each person get? 8. __C__
A. $\frac{1}{2}$ lb B. 1 lb C. $1\frac{1}{2}$ lb D. 2 lb

9. If Jamie eats 72% of a 3.5 pound bag of tortilla chips, how many pounds has he eaten? 9. __A__
A. 2.52 lb B. 1.6 lb C. 2.71 lb D. 2 lb

 297 *Mathematics: Applications and Connections, Course 2*

Chapter 11 Standardized Test Practice (continued)

10. Which figure is a regular polygon? 10. __D__
A. B. C. D.

11. Sandy builds herself a storage shed with the dimensions indicated. How much area does the shed occupy? 11. __C__

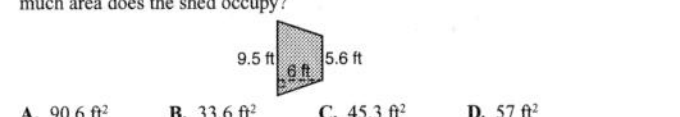

A. 90.6 ft² B. 33.6 ft² C. 45.3 ft² D. 57 ft²

12. Parker wants to give peanut brittle to his friends and family as gifts this year. If he has 18 friends and family, which is a reasonable amount of peanut brittle for him to purchase? 12. __B__
A. 18 ounces B. 18 pounds C. 180 pounds D. 18 tons

13. Janna has 9.236 ounces of water to water 6 plants. Estimate how much water each plant will get. 13. __C__
A. 0.5 oz B. 1 oz C. 1.5 oz D. 2 oz

14. Evaluate $6x + 3 - 4y$ if $x = 2$ and $y = 3$. 14. __A__
A. 3 B. −1 C. 13 D. 5

15. The price of long-sleeved shirts at The Shirt Boutique went from $28.59 to $36.89 last month. Find the percent increase to the nearest whole percent. 15. __C__
A. 22% B. 78% C. 29% D. 129%

16. Which of the following inequalities is equivalent to *six plus seven times a number is less than or equal to minus 5?* 16. __C__
A. $(6 + 7)n \leq -5$ B. $6 - 7n \leq -5$
C. $6 + 7n \leq -5$ D. $7 + 6n \leq -5$

 298 *Mathematics: Applications and Connections, Course 2*

Instructional Resources ▶▶▶

Additional standardized test practice is shown at the right and is available in the *Assessment and Evaluation Masters*, pp. 297–298.

CHAPTER 12

Geometry: Finding Volume and Surface Area

Previewing the Chapter

Overview

This chapter explores surface area and volume of solids, or three-dimensional figures. Students first explore three-dimensional figures by building and drawing the figures. Later, they learn how to calculate the surface areas and volumes of some of these figures, with particular attention paid to prisms and cylinders. Students also solve problems by making models, and apply formulas to solve problems.

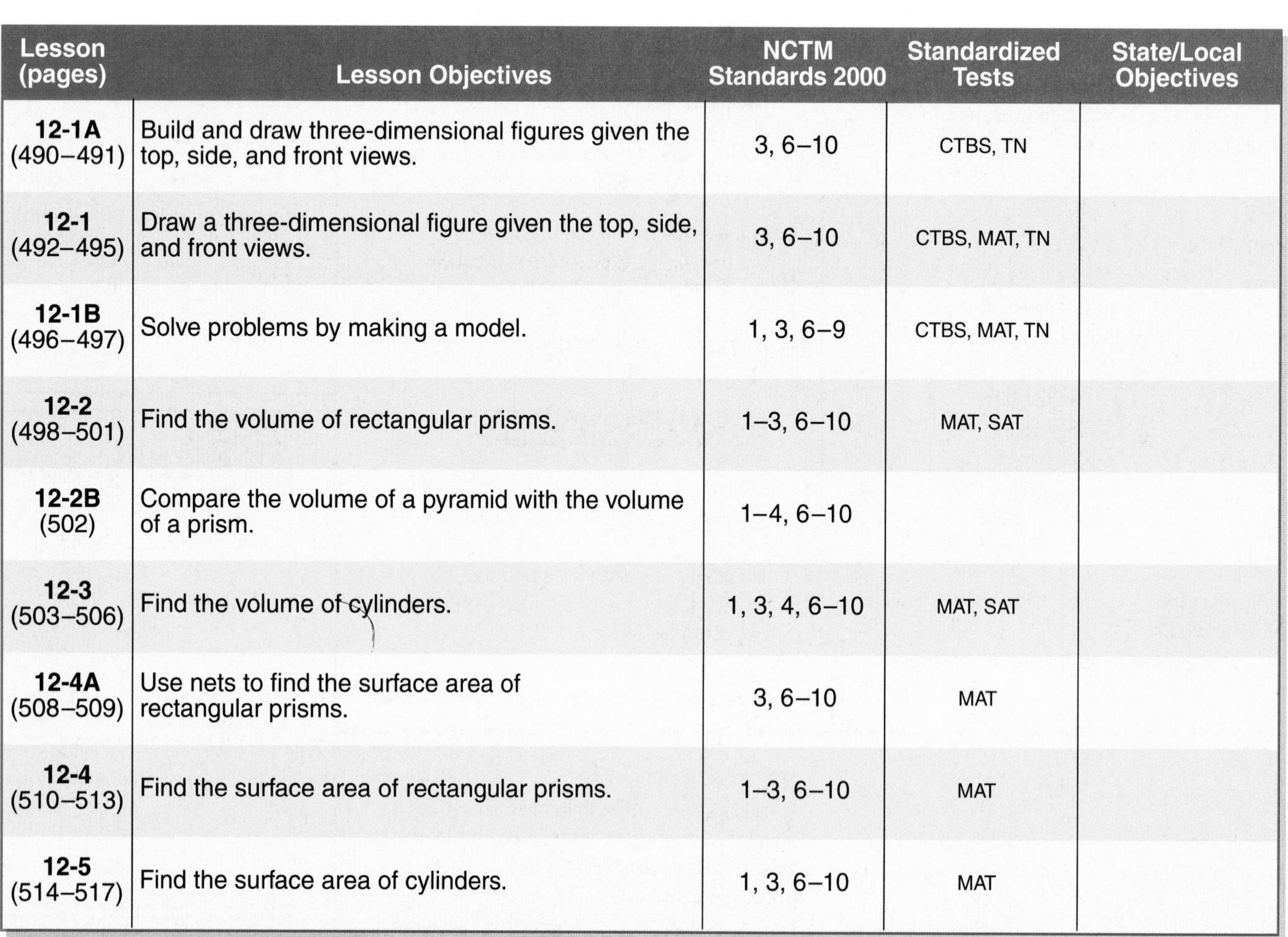

Lesson (pages)	Lesson Objectives	NCTM Standards 2000	Standardized Tests	State/Local Objectives
12-1A (490–491)	Build and draw three-dimensional figures given the top, side, and front views.	3, 6–10	CTBS, TN	
12-1 (492–495)	Draw a three-dimensional figure given the top, side, and front views.	3, 6–10	CTBS, MAT, TN	
12-1B (496–497)	Solve problems by making a model.	1, 3, 6–9	CTBS, MAT, TN	
12-2 (498–501)	Find the volume of rectangular prisms.	1–3, 6–10	MAT, SAT	
12-2B (502)	Compare the volume of a pyramid with the volume of a prism.	1–4, 6–10		
12-3 (503–506)	Find the volume of cylinders.	1, 3, 4, 6–10	MAT, SAT	
12-4A (508–509)	Use nets to find the surface area of rectangular prisms.	3, 6–10	MAT	
12-4 (510–513)	Find the surface area of rectangular prisms.	1–3, 6–10	MAT	
12-5 (514–517)	Find the surface area of cylinders.	1, 3, 6–10	MAT	

CAT = California Achievement Tests, CTBS = Comprehensive Tests of Basic Skills, ITBS = Iowa Tests of Basic Skills, MAT = Metropolitan Achievement Tests, SAT = Stanford Achievement Tests, TN = Terra Nova
For the key to numbering of NCTM Standards 2000, see page T6.

Organizing the Chapter

The **Interactive Lesson Planner** contains all of the blackline masters and transparencies. This CD-ROM also includes an easy-to-use lesson planning calendar.

LESSON PLANNING GUIDE

		Blackline Masters (Page Numbers)										
Lesson	**Extra Practice (Student Edition)**	**Study Guide**	**Practice**	**Enrichment**	**Assessment & Evaluation**	**Classroom Games**	**Diversity**	**Hands-On Lab**	**School to Career**	**Science and Math Lab Manual**	**Technology**	**Transparencies A and B**
12-1A								67				
12-1	p. 600	88	88	88								12-1
12-1B	p. 601											
12-2	p. 601	89	89	89	323				25		50	12-2
12-2B								68				
12-3	p. 601	90	90	90	322, 323		25	83				12-3
12-4A								69				
12-4	p. 602	91	91	91	324							12-4
12-5	p. 602	92	92	92	324	33–34					49	12-5
Study Guide/ Assessment					309–321, 325–327							

Other Chapter Resources

Student Edition

Chapter Project, pp. 489, 501, 513, 521
Math in the Media, p. 495
School to Career, p. 507
Let the Games Begin, p. 513

Technology

 MathPASS CD-ROM

 Interactive Mathematics Tools Software

Teacher's Classroom Resources

Applications

Family Letters and Activities, pp. 49–50
Investigations and Projects Masters, pp. 61–64

Meeting Individual Needs

Investigations for the Special Education Student, pp. 43–44

Teaching Aids

Answer Key Masters
Block Scheduling Booklet
Lesson Planning Guide
Solutions Manual

Professional Publications

Glencoe Mathematics Professional Series

Planning the Chapter

MindJogger Videoquizzes provide a unique format for reviewing concepts presented in the chapter.

Assessment Resources

Student Edition
Mixed Review, pp. 495, 501, 506, 513, 517
Mid-Chapter Self Test, p. 506
Math Journal, pp. 493, 512
Study Guide and Assessment, pp. 518–521
Performance Task, p. 521
Portfolio Suggestion, p. 521
Standardized Test Practice, pp. 522–523
Chapter Test, p. 618

Assessment and Evaluation Masters
Multiple-Choice Tests (Forms 1A, 1B, 1C), pp. 309–314
Free-Response Tests (Forms 2A, 2B, 2C), pp. 315–320
Performance Assessment, p. 321
Mid-Chapter Test, p. 322
Quizzes A–D, pp. 323–324
Standardized Test Practice, pp. 325–326
Cumulative Review, p. 327

Teacher's Wraparound Edition
5-Minute Check, pp. 492, 498, 503, 510, 514
Building Portfolios, p. 488
Math Journal, pp. 491, 502, 509
Closing Activity, pp. 495, 497, 501, 506, 513, 517

Technology
Test and Review Software
MindJogger Videoquizzes
CD-ROM Program

Materials and Manipulatives

Lesson 12-1A
cubes*

Lesson 12-1
isometric dot paper

Lesson 12-1B
straws
gumdrops

Lesson 12-2
grid paper†
scissors*
tape
calculator

Lesson 12-2B
rice
centimeter grid paper

Lesson 12-3
cylinder-shaped objects
centimeter ruler*†

Lesson 12-4A
square dot paper
scissors*
tape

Lesson 12-4
cubes*
index cards
counters*†

Lesson 12-5
calculator
soft drink can
grid paper†
scissors*

*Glencoe Manipulative Kit

†Glencoe Overhead Manipulative Resources

Pacing Chart

See pages T25–T27 for the Course Planning Calendar.

COURSE	DAY 1	DAY 2	DAY 3	DAY 4	DAY 5	DAY 6	DAY 7
Standard	Chapter Project	Lessons 12-1A & 12-1		Lesson 12-1B	Lesson 12-2	Lesson 12-3	Lessons 12-4A & 12-4
Honors	Chapter Project	Lesson 12-1	Lesson 12-1B	Lessons 12-2 & 12-2B		Lesson 12-3	Lesson 12-4
Block	Chapter Project, Lessons 12-1A & 12-1	Lessons 12-1B & 12-2	Lessons 12-3 & 12-4A	Lessons 12-4 & 12-5	Study Guide and Assessment, Chapter Test		

Interactive Mathematics:
Activities and Investigations

is an activity-based program that may be used as an enhancement for chapters in ***Mathematics: Applications and Connections.***

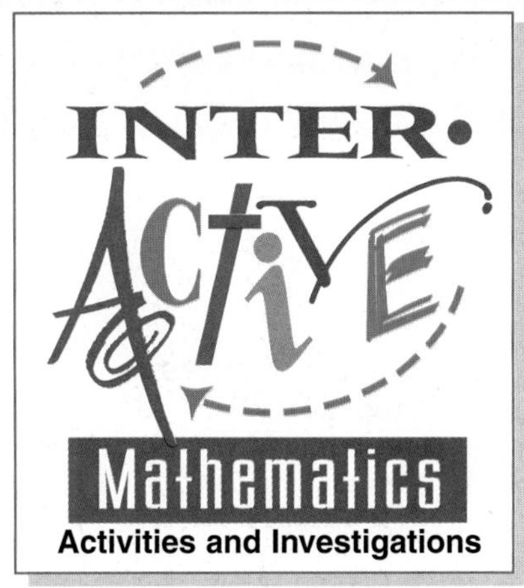

PRE-ASSESSMENT ACTIVITY

May I Take Your Order?

The **surface area** of an object is the number of square units needed to cover the object. The **volume** of an object is the number of cubic units needed to fill the interior space of the object.

Cut out the models on Blackline Masters 14-PA, 14-PB, and 14-PC. Fold and tape them together to form rectangular prisms, cubes, and cylinders.

Using the materials your teacher has provided, arrange the models in order from least to greatest surface area. Then arrange the models from least to greatest volume.

When your group is finished, write down as many conclusions as you can draw from your experiment.

Make a poster that reflects what you have learned. Be prepared to explain your technique for ordering the models.

UNIT 14: Run for Cover 44 May I Take Your Order?

Unit 14, Pre-Assessment Activity *Use with Lesson 12-1B.*

Summary Students work in groups using paper models to make rectangular prisms, cubes, and cylinders. Then they use other materials to fill the models and order them from least to greatest, both in terms of surface area and volume.

Math Connection Students explore the difference between surface area and volume. The surface area is the amount of surface covering a 3-dimensional object. The volume is the amount of space occupied by a 3-dimensional object.

Unit 14, Activity Two, Menu C *Use with Lesson 12-4.*

Summary Students work in groups to design a net that will enclose two 3-dimensional stair shapes. Then they find the surface area and volume of each shape.

Math Connection Students use nets to find the surface area and volume of figures. A net is a paper model that can be cut out and folded to form a 3-dimensional figure.

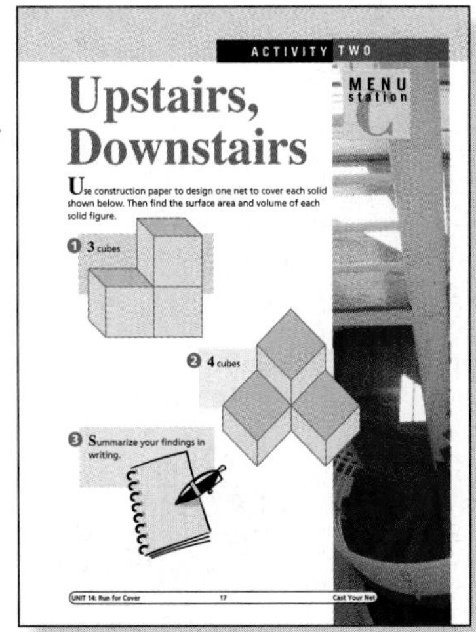
ACTIVITY TWO

MENU station C

Upstairs, Downstairs

Use construction paper to design one net to cover each solid shown below. Then find the surface area and volume of each solid figure.

1. 3 cubes
2. 4 cubes
3. Summarize your findings in writing.

UNIT 14: Run for Cover 17 Cast Your Net

DAY 8	DAY 9	DAY 10	DAY 11	DAY 12	DAY 13	DAY 14	DAY 15
(continue from Day 7)	Lesson 12-5	Study Guide and Assessment	Chapter Test				
Lesson 12-5	Study Guide and Assessment	Chapter Test					

Enhancing the Chapter

APPLICATIONS

Classroom Games, pp. 33–34

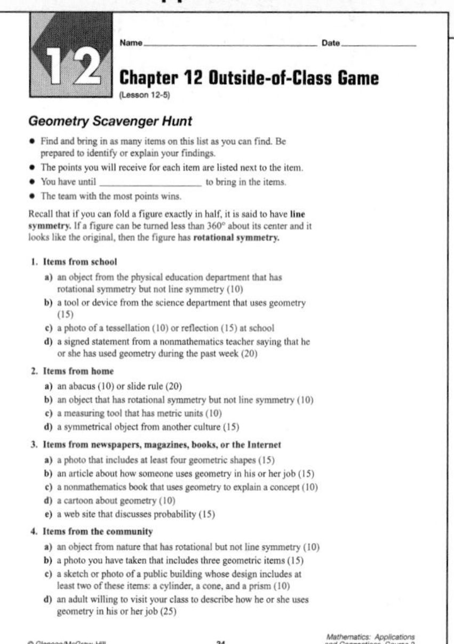

12 Name ______ Date ______

Chapter 12 Outside-of-Class Game
(Lesson 12-5)

Geometry Scavenger Hunt

- Find and bring in as many items on this list as you can find. Be prepared to identify or explain your findings.
- The points you will receive for each item are listed next to the item.
- You have until ______________ to bring in the items.
- The team with the most points wins.

Recall that if you can fold a figure exactly in half, it is said to have **line symmetry.** If a figure can be turned less than 360° about its center and it looks like the original, then the figure has **rotational symmetry.**

1. **Items from school**
   a) an object from the physical education department that has rotational symmetry but not line symmetry (10)
   b) a tool or device from the science department that uses geometry (15)
   c) a photo of a tessellation (10) or reflection (15) at school
   d) a signed statement from a nonmathematics teacher saying that he or she has used geometry during the past week (20)
2. **Items from home**
   a) an abacus (10) or slide rule (20)
   b) an object that has rotational symmetry but not line symmetry (10)
   c) a measuring tool that has metric units (10)
   d) a symmetrical object from another culture (15)
3. **Items from newspapers, magazines, books, or the Internet**
   a) a photo that includes at least four geometric shapes (15)
   b) an article about how someone uses geometry in his or her job (15)
   c) a nonmathematics book that uses geometry to explain a concept (10)
   d) a cartoon about geometry (10)
   e) a web site that discusses probability (15)
4. **Items from the community**
   a) an object from nature that has rotational but not line symmetry (10)
   b) a photo you have taken that includes three geometric items (15)
   c) a sketch or photo of a public building whose design includes at least two of these items: a cylinder, a cone, and a prism (10)
   d) an adult willing to visit your class to describe how he or she uses geometry in his or her job (25)

© Glencoe/McGraw-Hill 34 Mathematics: Applications and Connections, Course 2

Diversity Masters, p. 25

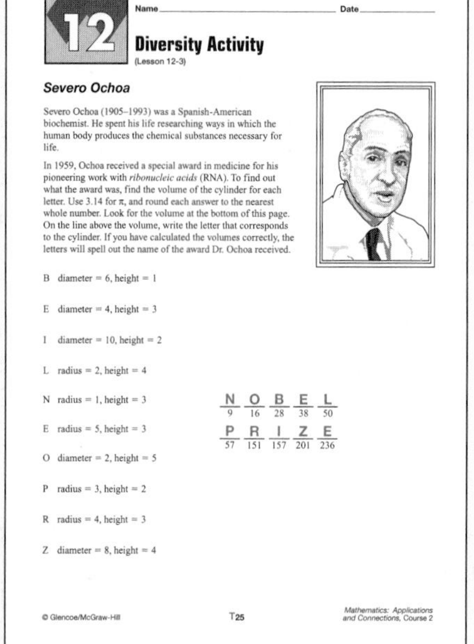

12 Name ______ Date ______

Diversity Activity
(Lesson 12-3)

Severo Ochoa

Severo Ochoa (1905–1993) was a Spanish-American biochemist. He spent his life researching ways in which the human body produces the chemical substances necessary for life.

In 1959, Ochoa received a special award in medicine for his pioneering work with *ribonucleic acids* (RNA). To find out what the award was, find the volume of the cylinder for each letter. Use 3.14 for π, and round each answer to the nearest whole number. Look for the volume at the bottom of this page. On the line above the volume, write the letter that corresponds to the cylinder. If you have calculated the volumes correctly, the letters will spell out the name of the award Dr. Ochoa received.

B diameter = 6, height = 1

E diameter = 4, height = 3

I diameter = 10, height = 2

L radius = 2, height = 4

N radius = 1, height = 3

E radius = 5, height = 3

O diameter = 2, height = 5

P radius = 3, height = 2

R radius = 4, height = 3

Z diameter = 8, height = 4

N	O	B	E	L
9	16	28	38	50

P	R	I	Z	E
57	151	157	201	236

© Glencoe/McGraw-Hill T25 Mathematics: Applications and Connections, Course 2

School to Career Masters, p. 25

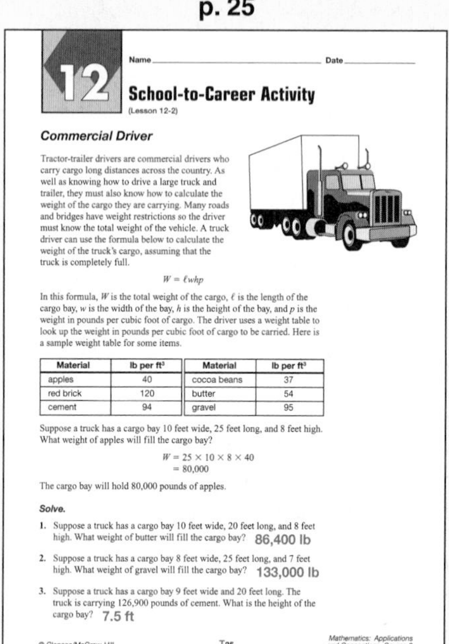

12 Name ______ Date ______

School-to-Career Activity
(Lesson 12-2)

Commercial Driver

Tractor-trailer drivers are commercial drivers who carry cargo long distances across the country. As well as knowing how to drive a large truck and trailer, they must also know how to calculate the weight of the cargo they are carrying. Many roads and bridges have weight restrictions so the driver must know the total weight of the vehicle. A truck driver can use the formula below to calculate the weight of the truck's cargo, assuming that the truck is completely full.

$W = \ell whp$

In this formula, W is the total weight of the cargo, ℓ is the length of the cargo bay, w is the width of the bay, h is the height of the bay, and p is the weight in pounds per cubic foot of cargo. The driver uses a weight table to look up the weight in pounds per cubic foot of cargo to be carried. Here is a sample weight table for some items.

Material	lb per ft³	Material	lb per ft³
apples	40	cocoa beans	37
red brick	120	butter	54
cement	94	gravel	95

Suppose a truck has a cargo bay 10 feet wide, 25 feet long, and 8 feet high. What weight of apples will fill the cargo bay?

$W = 25 \times 10 \times 8 \times 40$
$= 80{,}000$

The cargo bay will hold 80,000 pounds of apples.

Solve.

1. Suppose a truck has a cargo bay 10 feet wide, 20 feet long, and 8 feet high. What weight of butter will fill the cargo bay? **86,400 lb**
2. Suppose a truck has a cargo bay 8 feet wide, 25 feet long, and 7 feet high. What weight of gravel will fill the cargo bay? **133,000 lb**
3. Suppose a truck has a cargo bay 9 feet wide and 20 feet long. The truck is carrying 126,900 pounds of cement. What is the height of the cargo bay? **7.5 ft**

© Glencoe/McGraw-Hill T25 Mathematics: Applications and Connections, Course 2

Family Letters and Activities, pp. 49–50

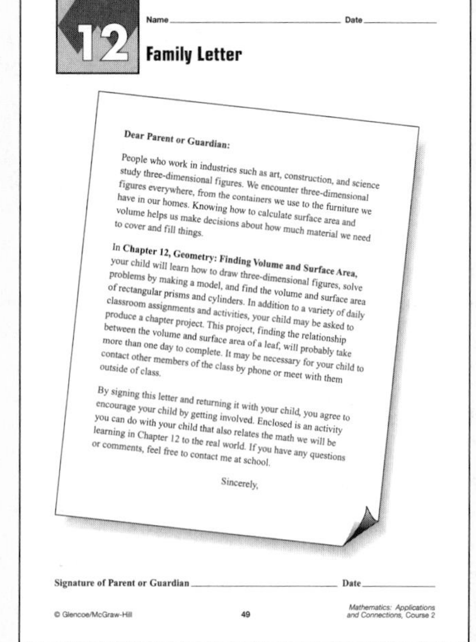

12 Name ______ Date ______

Family Letter

Dear Parent or Guardian:

People who work in industries such as art, construction, and science study three-dimensional figures. We encounter three-dimensional figures everywhere, from the containers we use to the furniture we have in our homes. Knowing how to calculate surface area and volume helps us make decisions about how much material we need to cover and fill things.

In **Chapter 12, Geometry: Finding Volume and Surface Area,** your child will learn how to draw three-dimensional figures, solve problems by making a model, and find the volume and surface area of rectangular prisms and cylinders. In addition to a variety of daily classroom assignments and activities, your child may be asked to produce a chapter project. This project, finding the relationship between the volume and surface area of a leaf, will probably take more than one day to complete. It may be necessary for your child to contact other members of the class by phone or meet with them outside of class.

By signing this letter and returning it with your child, you agree to encourage your child by getting involved. Enclosed is an activity you can do with your child that also relates the math we will be learning in Chapter 12 to the real world. If you have any questions or comments, feel free to contact me at school.

Sincerely,

Signature of Parent or Guardian ______ Date ______

© Glencoe/McGraw-Hill 49 Mathematics: Applications and Connections, Course 2

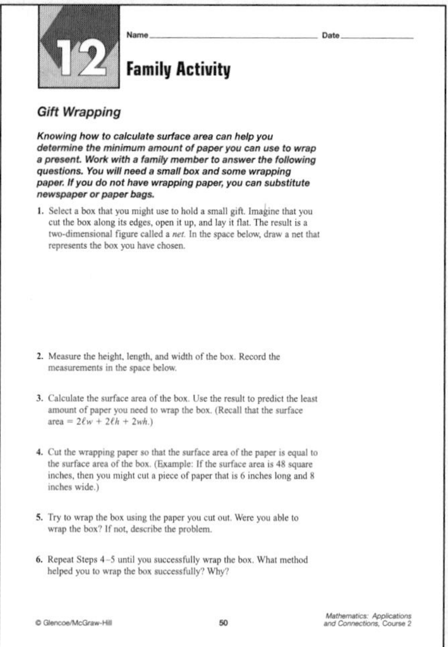

12 Name ______ Date ______

Family Activity

Gift Wrapping

Knowing how to calculate surface area can help you determine the minimum amount of paper you can use to wrap a present. Work with a family member to answer the following questions. You will need a small box and some wrapping paper. If you do not have wrapping paper, you can substitute newspaper or paper bags.

1. Select a box that you might use to hold a small gift. Imagine that you cut the box along its edges, open it up, and lay it flat. The result is a two-dimensional figure called a *net*. In the space below, draw a net that represents the box you have chosen.
2. Measure the height, length, and width of the box. Record the measurements in the space below.
3. Calculate the surface area of the box. Use the result to predict the least amount of paper you need to wrap the box. (Recall that the surface area = $2\ell w + 2\ell h + 2wh$.)
4. Cut the wrapping paper so that the surface area of the paper is equal to the surface area of the box. (Example: If the surface area is 48 square inches, then you might cut a piece of paper that is 6 inches long and 8 inches wide.)
5. Try to wrap the box using the paper you cut out. Were you able to wrap the box? If not, describe the problem.
6. Repeat Steps 4–5 until you successfully wrap the box. What method helped you to wrap the box successfully? Why?

© Glencoe/McGraw-Hill 50 Mathematics: Applications and Connections, Course 2

MANIPULATIVES/MODELING

Hands-On Lab Masters, p. 83

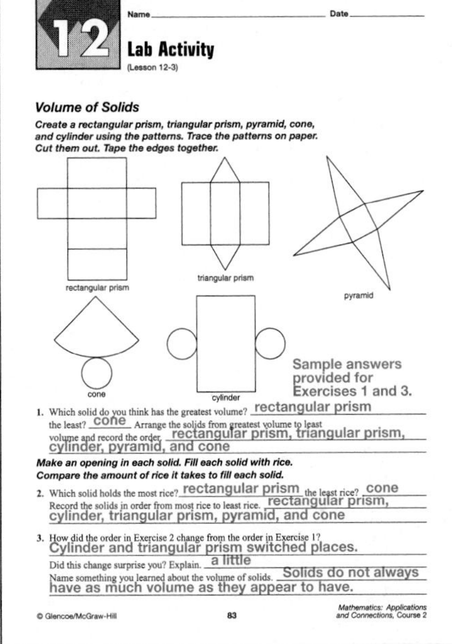

Name ______ Date ______

12 Lab Activity
(Lesson 12-3)

Volume of Solids

Create a rectangular prism, triangular prism, pyramid, cone, and cylinder using the patterns. Trace the patterns on paper. Cut them out. Tape the edges together.

rectangular prism — triangular prism — pyramid — cone — cylinder

Sample answers provided for Exercises 1 and 3.

1. Which solid do you think has the greatest volume? rectangular prism
the least? cone Arrange the solids from greatest volume to least volume and record the order. rectangular prism, triangular prism, cylinder, pyramid, and cone

Make an opening in each solid. Fill each solid with rice. Compare the amount of rice it takes to fill each solid.

2. Which solid holds the most rice? rectangular prism the least rice? cone
Record the solids in order from most rice to least rice. rectangular prism, cylinder, triangular prism, pyramid, and cone

3. How did the order in Exercise 2 change from the order in Exercise 1? Cylinder and triangular prism switched places.
Did this change surprise you? Explain. a little
Name something you learned about the volume of solids. Solids do not always have as much volume as they appear to have.

© Glencoe/McGraw-Hill 83 *Mathematics: Applications and Connections*, Course 2

ASSESSMENT/EVALUATION

Assessment and Evaluation Masters, pp. 322–324

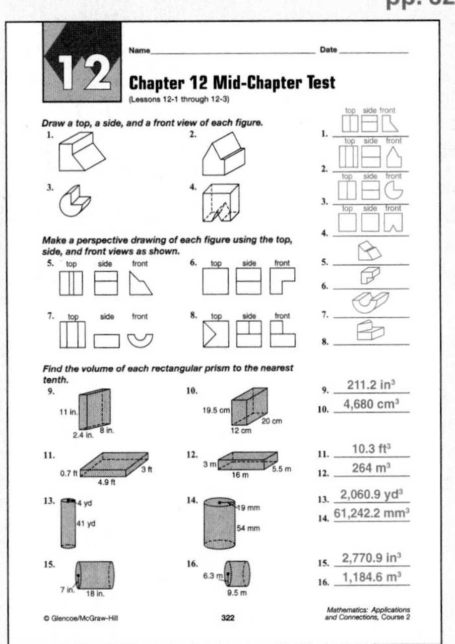

Name ______ Date ______

12 Chapter 12 Mid-Chapter Test
(Lessons 12-1 through 12-3)

Draw a top, a side, and a front view of each figure.

1. 2. 3. 4.

Make a perspective drawing of each figure using the top, side, and front views as shown.

5. top side front 6. top side front 7. top side front 8. top side front

Find the volume of each rectangular prism to the nearest tenth.

9. 11 in., 2.4 in., 8 in. 10. 19.5 cm, 12 cm, 20 cm 11. 0.7 ft, 4.9 ft, 3 ft 12. 3 m, 16 m, 5.5 m 13. 4 yd, 41 yd 14. 19 mm, 54 mm 15. 7 in., 18 in. 16. 6.3 m, 9.5 m

Answers:
1. top side front
2. top side front
3. top side front
4. top side front
5.
6.
7.
8.
9. 211.2 in³
10. 4,680 cm³
11. 10.3 ft³
12. 264 m³
13. 2,060.9 yd³
14. 61,242.2 mm³
15. 2,770.9 in³
16. 1,184.6 m³

© Glencoe/McGraw-Hill 322 *Mathematics: Applications and Connections*, Course 2

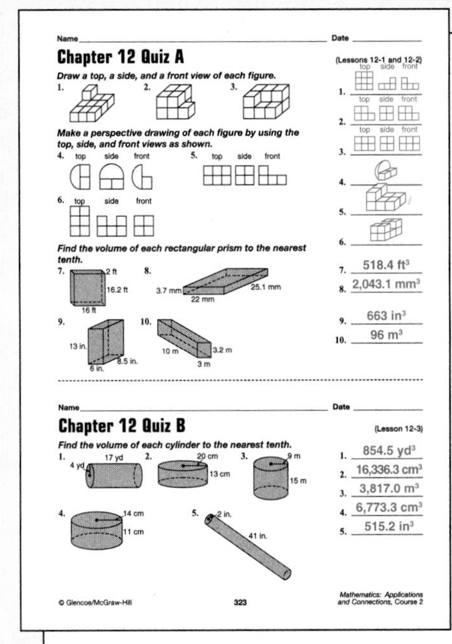

Name ______ Date ______

Chapter 12 Quiz A
(Lessons 12-1 and 12-2)

Draw a top, a side, and a front view of each figure.

1. 2. 3.

Make a perspective drawing of each figure by using the top, side, and front views as shown.

4. top side front 5. top side front 6. top side front

Find the volume of each rectangular prism to the nearest tenth.

7. 2 ft, 16.2 ft, 16 ft 8. 3.7 mm, 22 mm, 25.1 mm 9. 13 in., 6 in., 8.5 in. 10. 10 m, 3 m, 3.2 m

Answers:
1. top side front
2. top side front
3. top side front
4.
5.
6.
7. 518.4 ft³
8. 2,043.1 mm³
9. 663 in³
10. 96 m³

Name ______ Date ______

Chapter 12 Quiz B
(Lesson 12-3)

Find the volume of each cylinder to the nearest tenth.

1. 4 yd, 17 yd 2. 20 cm, 13 cm 3. 9 m, 15 m 4. 14 cm, 11 cm 5. 2 in., 41 in.

Answers:
1. 854.5 yd³
2. 16,336.3 cm³
3. 3,817.0 m³
4. 6,773.3 cm³
5. 515.2 in³

© Glencoe/McGraw-Hill 323 *Mathematics: Applications and Connections*, Course 2

TECHNOLOGY/MULTIMEDIA

Technology Masters, pp. 49–50

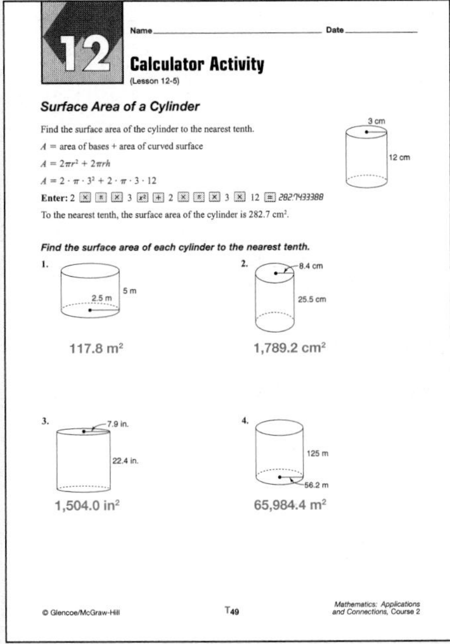

Name ______ Date ______

12 Calculator Activity
(Lesson 12-5)

Surface Area of a Cylinder

Find the surface area of the cylinder to the nearest tenth.

A = area of bases + area of curved surface

$A = 2\pi r^2 + 2\pi rh$

$A = 2 \cdot \pi \cdot 3^2 + 2 \cdot \pi \cdot 3 \cdot 12$

Enter: 2 [×] [π] [×] 3 [x²] [+] 2 [×] [π] [×] 3 [×] 12 [=] 282.7433388

To the nearest tenth, the surface area of the cylinder is 282.7 cm².

3 cm, 12 cm

Find the surface area of each cylinder to the nearest tenth.

1. 2.5 m, 5 m — 117.8 m²
2. 8.4 cm, 25.5 cm — 1,789.2 cm²
3. 7.9 in., 22.4 in. — 1,504.0 in²
4. 125 m, 56.2 m — 65,984.4 m²

© Glencoe/McGraw-Hill T49 *Mathematics: Applications and Connections*, Course 2

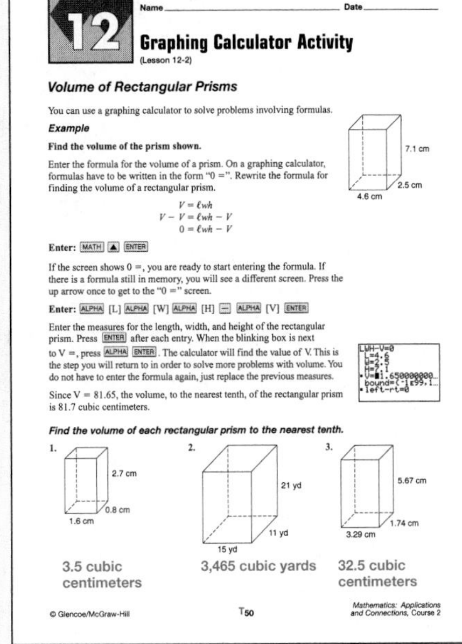

Name ______ Date ______

12 Graphing Calculator Activity
(Lesson 12-2)

Volume of Rectangular Prisms

You can use a graphing calculator to solve problems involving formulas.

Example

Find the volume of the prism shown.

7.1 cm, 2.5 cm, 4.6 cm

Enter the formula for the volume of a prism. On a graphing calculator, formulas have to be written in the form "0 =". Rewrite the formula for finding the volume of a rectangular prism.

$$V = \ell wh$$
$$V - V = \ell wh - V$$
$$0 = \ell wh - V$$

Enter: [MATH] [▲] [ENTER]

If the screen shows 0 =, you are ready to start entering the formula. If there is a formula still in memory, you will see a different screen. Press the up arrow once to get to the "0 =" screen.

Enter: [ALPHA] [L] [ALPHA] [W] [ALPHA] [H] [−] [ALPHA] [V] [ENTER]

Enter the measures for the length, width, and height of the rectangular prism. Press [ENTER] after each entry. When the blinking box is next to V =, press [ALPHA] [ENTER]. The calculator will find the value of V. This is the step you will return to in order to solve more problems with volume. You do not have to enter the formula again, just replace the previous measures.

LWH−V=0
L=4.6
W=2.5
H=7.1
▪V=▮1.650000000…
bound={−1ᴇ99,1…
▪left−rt=0

Since V = 81.65, the volume, to the nearest tenth, of the rectangular prism is 81.7 cubic centimeters.

Find the volume of each rectangular prism to the nearest tenth.

1. 2.7 cm, 0.8 cm, 1.6 cm — 3.5 cubic centimeters
2. 21 yd, 11 yd, 15 yd — 3,465 cubic yards
3. 5.67 cm, 1.74 cm, 3.29 cm — 32.5 cubic centimeters

© Glencoe/McGraw-Hill T50 *Mathematics: Applications and Connections*, Course 2

MEETING INDIVIDUAL NEEDS

Investigations for the Special Education Student, pp. 43–44

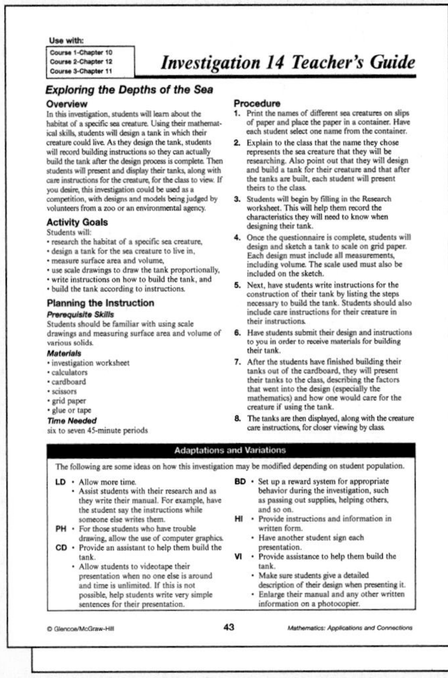

Use with:
Course 1-Chapter 10
Course 2-Chapter 12
Course 3-Chapter 11

Investigation 14 Teacher's Guide

Exploring the Depths of the Sea

Overview

In this investigation, students will learn about the habitat of a specific sea creature. Using their mathematical skills, students will design a tank in which their creature could live. As they design the tank, students will record building instructions so they can actually build the tank after the design process is complete. Then students will present and display their tanks, along with care instructions for the creature, for the class to view. If you desire, this investigation could be used as a competition, with designs and models being judged by volunteers from a zoo or an environmental agency.

Activity Goals

Students will:
- research the habitat of a specific sea creature,
- design a tank for the sea creature to live in,
- measure surface area and volume,
- use scale drawings to draw the tank proportionally,
- write instructions on how to build the tank, and
- build the tank according to instructions.

Planning the Instruction

Prerequisite Skills

Students should be familiar with using scale drawings and measuring surface area and volume of various solids.

Materials
- investigation worksheet
- calculators
- cardboard
- scissors
- grid paper
- glue or tape

Time Needed

six to seven 45-minute periods

Procedure

1. Print the names of different sea creatures on slips of paper and place the paper in a container. Have each student select one name from the container.
2. Explain to the class that the name they chose represents the sea creature that they will be researching. Also point out that they will design and build a tank for their creature and that after the tanks are built, each student will present theirs to the class.
3. Students will begin by filling in the Research worksheet. This will help them record the characteristics they will need to know when designing their tank.
4. Once the questionnaire is complete, students will design and sketch a tank to scale on grid paper. Each design must include all measurements, including volume. The scale used must also be included on the sketch.
5. Next, have students write instructions for the construction of their tank by listing the steps necessary to build the tank. Students should also include care instructions for their creature in their instructions.
6. Have students submit their design and instructions to you in order to receive materials for building their tank.
7. After the students have finished building their tanks out of the cardboard, they will present their tanks to the class, describing the factors that went into the design (especially the mathematics) and how one would care for the creature if using the tank.
8. The tanks are then displayed, along with the creature care instructions, for closer viewing by class.

Adaptations and Variations

The following are some ideas on how this investigation may be modified depending on student population.

LD
- Allow more time.
- Assist students with their research and as they write their manual. For example, have the student say the instructions while someone else writes them.

PH
- For those students who have trouble drawing, allow the use of computer graphics.

CD
- Provide an assistant to help them build the tank.
- Allow students to videotape their presentation when no one else is around and time is unlimited. If this is not possible, help students write very simple sentences for their presentation.

BD
- Set up a reward system for appropriate behavior during the investigation, such as passing out supplies, helping others, and so on.

HI
- Provide instructions and information in written form.
- Have another student sign each presentation.

VI
- Provide assistance to help them build the tank.
- Make sure students give a detailed description of their design when presenting it.
- Enlarge their manual and any other written information on a photocopier.

© Glencoe/McGraw-Hill 43 *Mathematics: Applications and Connections*

CHAPTER 12 NOTES

Theme: Plants

The sweet red fruit of a wild ginger plant, Aframomum, is a favorite treat in Ugandan markets, but it could also be a source of medicine.

Aframomum fruits grow a few inches above the ground on a plant whose eye-catching leaves reach nine feet high. Cornell University biologist John P. Berry has discovered that some species of Aframomum prevent the growth of some disease-causing bacteria.

Question of the Day How do large, spreading leaves help a plant to grow? **They increase exposure to sunlight.**

Assess Prerequisite Skills

Ask students to read through the list of objectives presented in "What you'll learn in Chapter 12." You may wish to ask them what each of the objectives means or if they have experienced or used any of these math concepts before.

Building Portfolios

Encourage students to revise their portfolios as they study this chapter. Encourage students to include a variety of concepts and operations from the chapter.

Math and the Family

In the *Family Letters and Activities* booklet (pp. 49–50), you will find a letter to the parents explaining what students will study in Chapter 12. An activity appropriate for the whole family is also available.

CHAPTER 12

Geometry: Finding Volume and Surface Area

What you'll learn in Chapter 12

- to draw three-dimensional figures when given the top, side, and front views,
- to solve problems by making a model,
- to make a net of the surface area of a solid, and
- to find the volumes and surface areas of rectangular prisms and cylinders.

CD-ROM Program

Activities for Chapter 12

- Chapter 12 Introduction
- Interactive Lessons 12-2, 12-4, 12-5
- Extended Activity 12-1
- Assessment Game
- Resource Lessons 12-1 through 12-5

TURN OVER A NEW LEAF

Leaves come in many different shapes. But one thing that is common to most leaves is that they are flat. Did you ever wonder why? In this project, you will research to find the primary function of a leaf. You will also investigate the relationship between the surface area of a leaf and its volume and summarize your findings in a report.

Getting Started

- Collect a leaf or trace the outline of a picture of a leaf.
- Research leaves and their function.
- Review how to find the area of irregular shapes.

Technology Tips

- Use an **electronic encyclopedia** to do your research.
- Use a **word processor** to write your report.

Research For up-to-date information on botany, visit:

www.glencoe.com/sec/math/mac/mathnet

Working on the Project

You can use what you'll learn in Chapter 12 to help you find the relationship between a leaf's surface area and its volume.

Page	Exercise
501	20
513	17
521	Alternative Assessment

CHAPTER Project NOTES

Objectives Students should
- gain an understanding of the importance of surface area in the structure and function of leaves.
- be able to find the volume and surface area of a leaf and write a ratio of the two.

Project Pointer You may suggest that students begin a *Project Folder* to keep their work as they complete each stage of the Chapter Project. The completed project may also be added to their portfolios.

Have students compare the actual thickness (height) of their leaves as well as the ratios of surface area to volume of leaves of different sizes. Students may want to include a side view of their leaves.

***Investigations and Projects Masters*, p. 64**

Name ______________________ Date ____________

Chapter 12 Project

Turn Over A New Leaf

Page 489, Getting Started

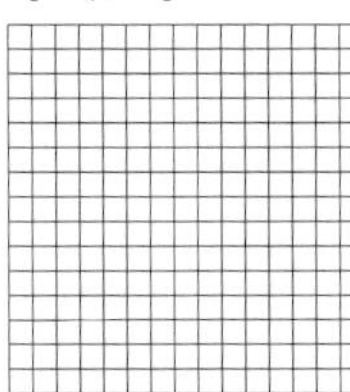

Page 501, Working on the Chapter Project, Exercise 20

a. The estimated area is:

b. The volume is:

Page 513, Working on the Chapter Project, Exercise 17

a. The surface area is:

b. The ratio of the surface area to the volume is:

 64 *Mathematics: Applications and Connections, Course 2*

interNET CONNECTION

Glencoe has made every effort to ensure that the website links for *Mathematics: Applications and Connections* at **www.glencoe.com/sec/math/mac/mathnet** are current and contain appropriate content. However, these website links are not under Glencoe's control.

Instructional Resources 

A recording sheet to help students organize their data for the Chapter Project is shown at the right and is available in the *Investigations and Projects Masters*, p. 64.

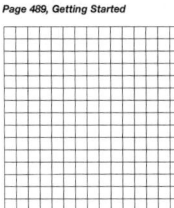

12-1A HANDS-ON LAB Notes

GET READY

Objective Students build and draw three-dimensional figures given the top, side, and front views.

Optional Resources
Hands-On Lab Masters
- worksheet, p. 67

Manipulative Kit
- centimeter cubes

MANAGEMENT TIPS

Recommended Time
45 minutes

Getting Started Provide a shoe box or other rectangular object for students to draw. Have them describe how it appears from the top, side, and front. Then draw perpendicular lines on the box to simulate cubes, and have students determine how many cubes it would take to build the box.

The **Activity** shows how to interpret the top, side, and front views of an object so that students can build the object with cubes. The *top* view means you're standing in front of the figure looking over the top. The *side* view is from the right side.

Teaching Tip Have students build their models so that they sit on index cards. They can rotate the cards so that they can view their models from different perspectives without disturbing their structures.

HANDS-ON LAB

COOPERATIVE LEARNING

12-1A Building Three-Dimensional Figures

cubes

A Preview of Lesson 12-1

If you looked at ordinary table salt under a microscope, you would see that salt crystals are cubes. Cubes are examples of three-dimensional figures. They have length, width, and depth.

In this lab, you will use cubes to build other three-dimensional figures.

TRY THIS

Work with a partner.

The top view, a side view, and the front view of a stack of cubes are given.

top

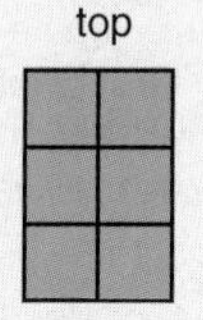

side

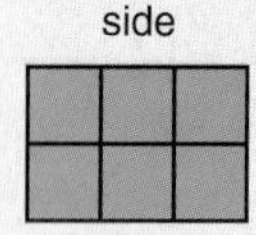

front

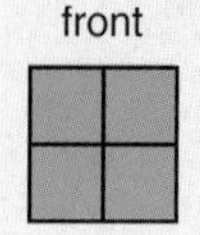

Use cubes to build the three-dimensional figure.

- The top view shows the shape of the base. It is a 3-by-2 rectangle.
- The side view is a 2-by-3 rectangle.
- The front view is a 2-by-2 square.

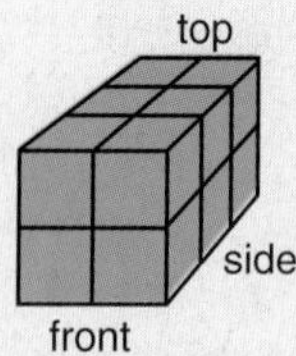

ON YOUR OWN

The top view, a side view, and the front view of three-dimensional figures are shown. Use cubes to build each figure. 1–4. See margin.

1. top

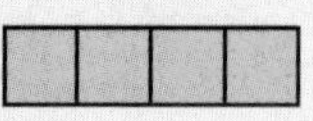

side front

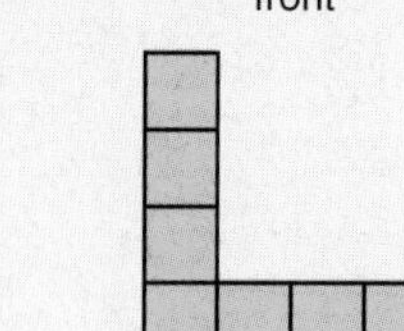

Additional Answers

1.

2.

3.

4.

2. top side front

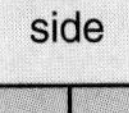
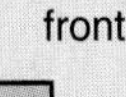
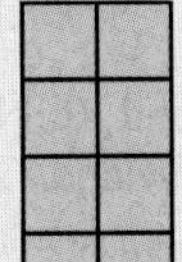
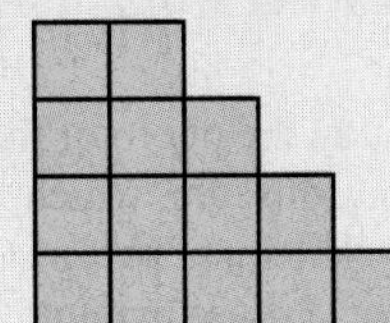

3. top side front

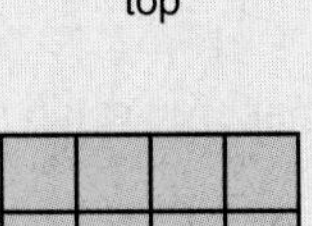
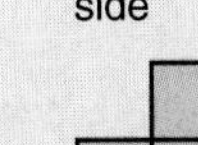
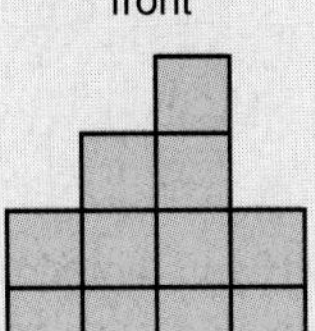

4. top side front

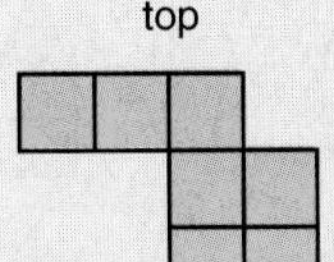
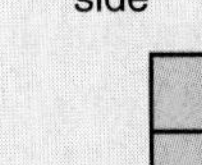
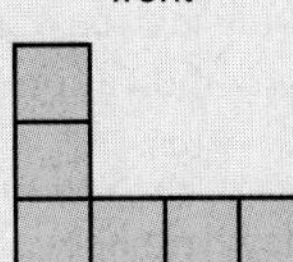

5. Build a model with cubes and draw the top, side, and front views. Give the drawing of the views to your partner and have him or her build the figure with cubes. Repeat with your partner making the drawings and you building the figure. **5–6. See students' work.**
6. Share with other groups how you began building the figures.
7. Could you have built the figures in Exercises 1–4 without one of the views? Explain. **See margin.**
8. Is there only one way to build the figures from the drawings given? If no, build another model. If yes, explain why. **See margin.**
9. Build two different models that would look the same from two views, but not the third view. Draw a top view, side view, and front view of each model. **See margin.**
10. ***Look Ahead*** Describe a real-life situation where it might be necessary for you to draw a top, side, and front view of a three-dimensional figure. **Sample answer: building a dog or bird house**

Have students write a paragraph describing how their idea of the actual shape of a three-dimensional figure changed while drawing or building it.

ASSESS

Have students complete Exercises 5–10. Encourage partners to examine the figure drawn or built by their classmates. For those who are confused by figures that change from bottom to top, suggest that students consider the top view as the base of the figure.

Additional Answers

7. **Exercise 1: Yes; you don't need the side view. Exercises 2–4; No, all views are necessary.**
8. **No; In Exercises 2 and 3, if certain cubes are removed, the front, side, and top views will not change. For example, if the three top cubes are removed from the left front column in Exercise 2, the views will remain the same.**
9. **Sample answer:**

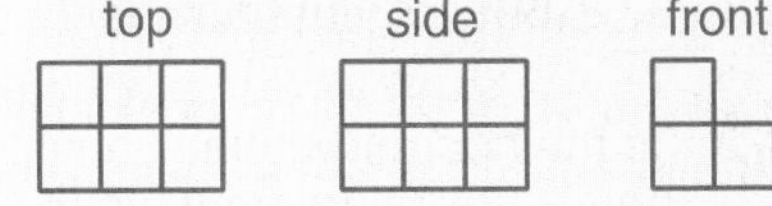

***Hands-On Lab Masters,* p. 67**

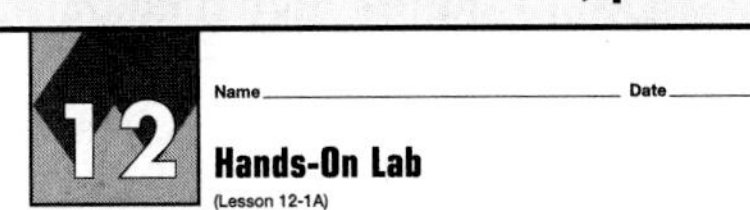

Name______ Date______

Hands-On Lab
(Lesson 12-1A)

Building Three-Dimensional Figures

On Your Own Sample answers are given.

1. 2. 3.

4. 5.

top front side

6. How did you begin building the figures? See students' work.

7. Could you have built the figures in Exercises 1–4 without one of the views? Explain. Exercise 1: Yes, you don't need the side view. Exercises 2–4: No, all views are necessary.

8. Is there only one way to build the figures? Explain. No; in Exercises 2 and 3, if certain cubes are removed, the front, side, and top views will not change. For example, if the three top cubes are removed from the left-hand column in Exercise 2, the views will remain the same.

9. Build two models that would look the same from two views, but not the third view. Sample answer:

10. Look Ahead Describe a real-life situation. Sample answer: building a dog house or a bird house

 67 *Mathematics: Applications and Connections, Course 2*

12-1 Lesson Notes

Instructional Resources

- *Study Guide Masters,* p. 88
- *Practice Masters,* p. 88
- *Enrichment Masters,* p. 88
- Transparencies 12-1, A and B
- *Hands-On Lab Masters,* p. 13

CD-ROM Program
- Resource Lesson 12-1
- Extended Activity 12-1

Recommended Pacing	
Standard	Days 2 & 3 of 11
Honors	Day 2 of 10
Block	Day 1 of 5

1 FOCUS

5-Minute Check *(Chapter 11)*

1. 57 is 60% of what number? 95
2. To the nearest whole percent, what percent of 48 is 38? 79%
3. Find the percent of change. Round to the nearest whole percent. original: $85, new: $66 22%
4. Find the sales tax to the nearest cent. $42 book, 7.25% tax $3.05
5. Find the interest to the nearest cent. $1,200, 6.5%, 6 months $39.00

The 5-Minute Check is also available on **Transparency 12-1A** for this lesson.

2 TEACH

Transparency 12-1B contains a teaching aid for this lesson.

Reading Mathematics Point out to students that any single *view* of a *solid* object is incomplete, and a *perspective* view partially overcomes the limitations of drawing on a two-dimensional surface.

12-1

Drawing Three-Dimensional Figures

What you'll learn

You'll learn to draw a three-dimensional figure given the top, side, and front views.

When am I ever going to use this?

Different perspectives of three-dimensional figures are used in art and architecture.

Word Wise

perspective
solids

Study the photo of the Rock and Roll Hall of Fame and Museum, which is in Cleveland, Ohio. The main part of the building is a large glass pyramid. In the photograph, it has only two dimensions, width and height. Yet when you look at it, you can visualize the building in three dimensions.

Think about drawing a pyramid in two dimensions. You could draw a top view or a side view.

- If you look down from directly above, you would see a square. Drawing a square would not indicate that the figure has three dimensions.

- Looking at the pyramid directly from the side, you can see a triangle. Again this does not give any indication that this is a view of a pyramid.

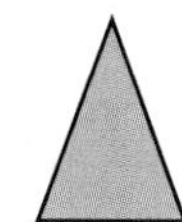

However, if you make a drawing that is somewhere between a top and side view, you are able to see that the figure has three dimensions. This view is called a **perspective** view.

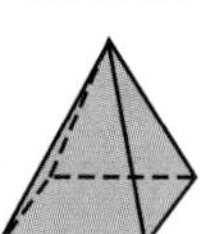

You can use isometric dot paper to draw a perspective view.

Example 1 **Make a perspective drawing of a figure by using the top, side, and front views of the figure below.**

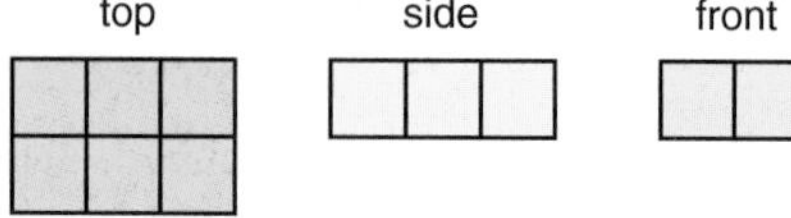

First, sketch a 2-by-3 rectangle for the top. Then, add the front and side views. Finally, add dashed lines to show the hidden edges.

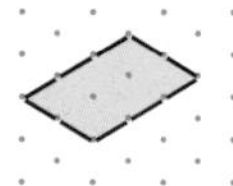

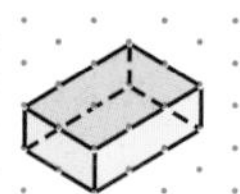

Motivating the Lesson

Hands-On Activity Ask students to make a drawing of the building in which they live. Ask them to draw the shapes they would see if they were to view the building from the top, side, and front.

Cross-Curriculum Cue

Inform the other teachers on your team that your classes are studying surface area and volume. Suggestions for curriculum integration are:
Science: crystals, geology
Art: architecture, sculpture
Social Studies: topographical maps

Artists create the illusion of depth in their drawings by using a technique called one-point perspective.

Example CONNECTION

2 **Art** **The front and side views of an apartment building are shown below. Make a perspective drawing of the building.**

Draw the front of the building like a rectangle. Then, draw lines from the rectangle to a *vanishing point.* Finally, draw the side of the building along the lines to the vanishing point.

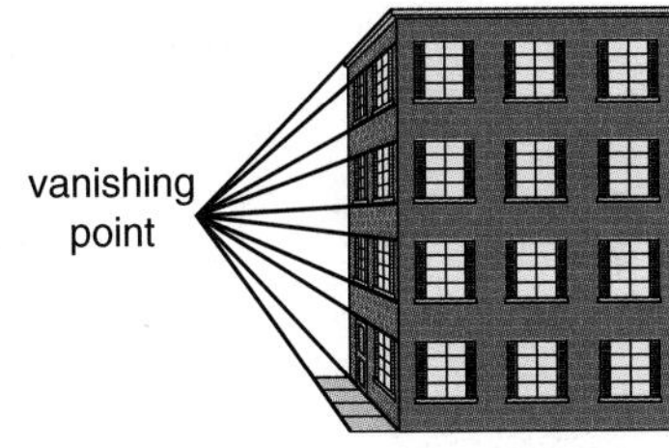

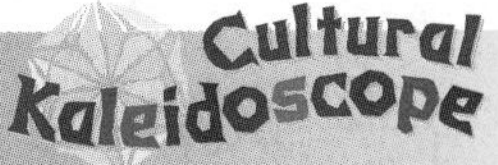

Chinese-born architect I. M. Pei designed the Rock and Roll Hall of Fame, which opened in 1995. He also designed a huge glass pyramid for the entrance of the Louvre Museum in Paris.

In this chapter, you will study three-dimensional figures called **solids**. Some common solids are shown below.

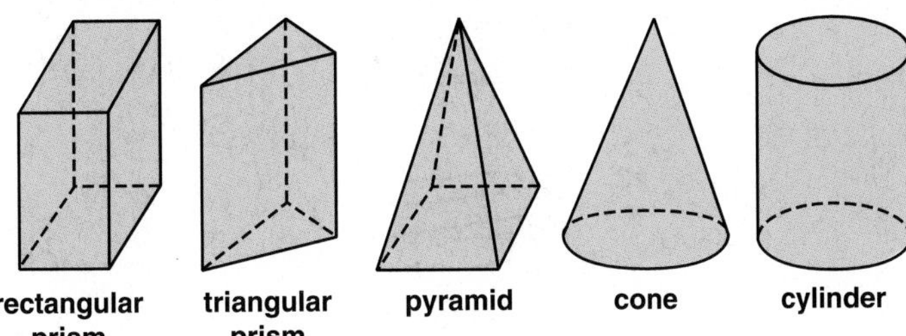

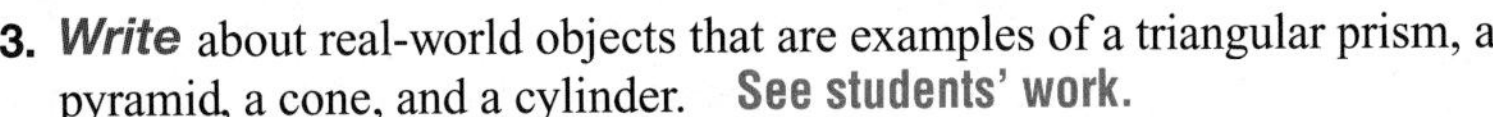

CHECK FOR UNDERSTANDING

Communicating Mathematics

Read and study the lesson to answer each question.

1. ***Draw*** a top view and a side view of a cylinder. **See Answer Appendix.**
2. ***Compare and contrast*** a pyramid with a cone. How are they alike and how are they different? **See margin.**
3. ***Write*** about real-world objects that are examples of a triangular prism, a pyramid, a cone, and a cylinder. **See students' work.**

Math Journal

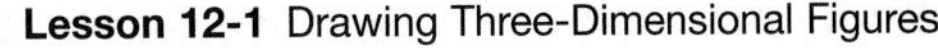

In-Class Examples

For Example 1

Make a perspective drawing of a figure by using the top, side, and front view of the figure.

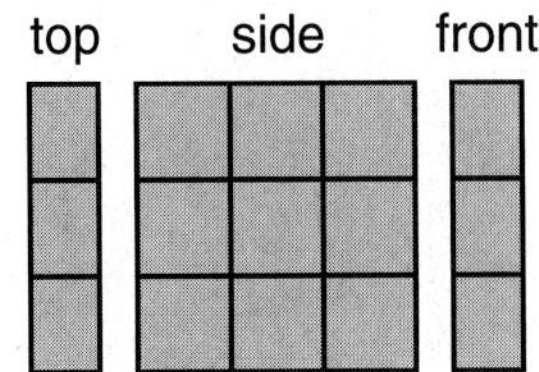

Sample answer:

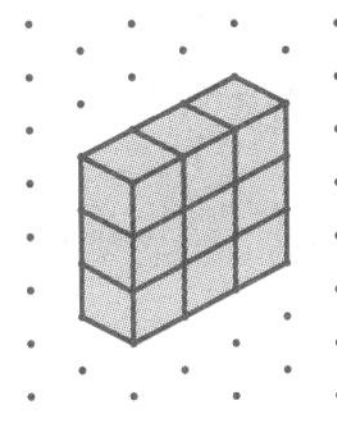

For Example 2

The front and side views of a school are shown below. Make a perspective drawing of the building.

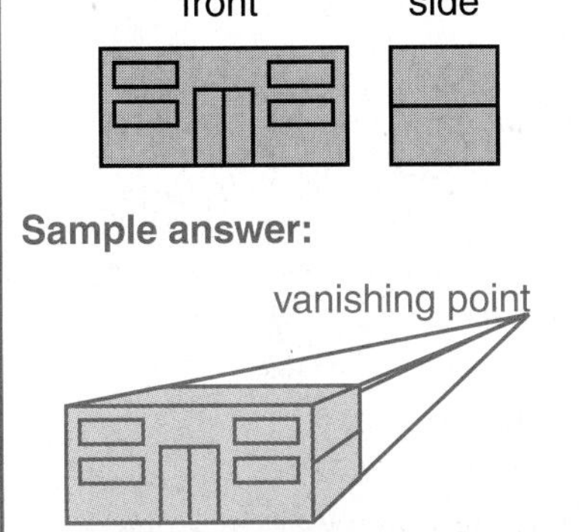

■ Reteaching the Lesson ■

Activity Provide models of each solid figure shown on page 493. Have students manipulate the models in order to see the three views of each. Have them use the models to help them draw the views.

3 PRACTICE/APPLY

Check for Understanding

If students need additional practice or instruction after completing Exercises 1–8, one of these options may be helpful.

- Extra Practice, see p. 600
- Reteaching Activity
- *Study Guide Masters,* p. 88
- *Practice Masters,* p. 88

Additional Answer

2. **Sample answer: Both come to a point at the top. They have different bases.**

Assignment Guide

Core: 9–21 odd, 23–26
Enriched: 10–18 even, 20–26

Additional Answers

6.

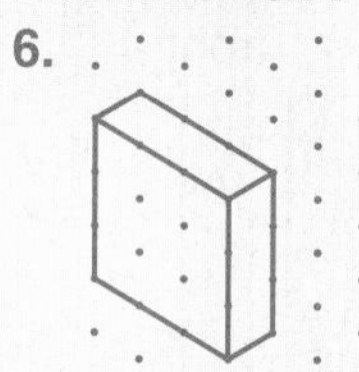

7.

15.

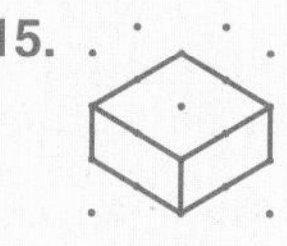

16.

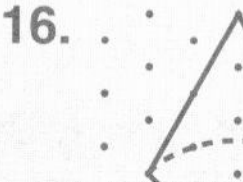

17.

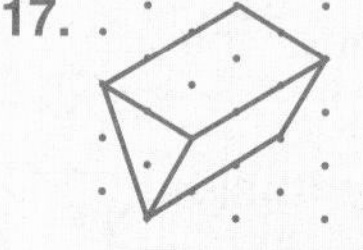

18.

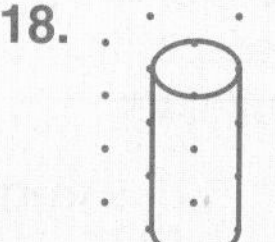

***Study Guide Masters,* p. 88**

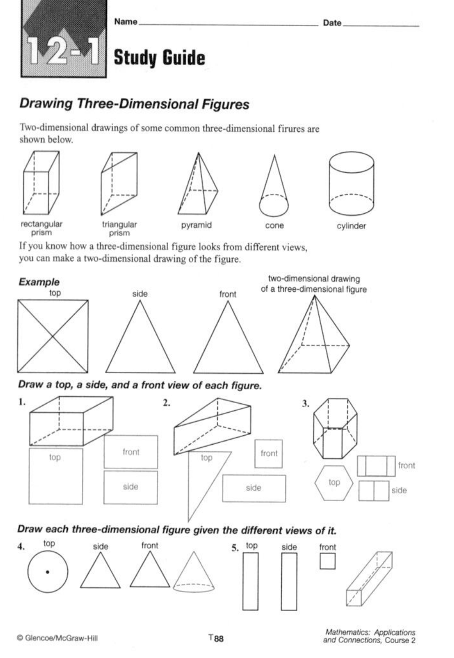

Name __________ Date __________

12-1 **Study Guide**

Drawing Three-Dimensional Figures

Two-dimensional drawings of some common three-dimensional firures are shown below.

If you know how a three-dimensional figure looks from different views, you can make a two-dimensional drawing of the figure.

Example

Draw a top, a side, and a front view of each figure.

Draw each three-dimensional figure given the different views of it.

© Glencoe/McGraw-Hill T88 *Mathematics: Applications and Connections, Course 2*

Guided Practice
4–5. See Answer Appendix.

Draw a top, a side, and a front view of each figure.

4.

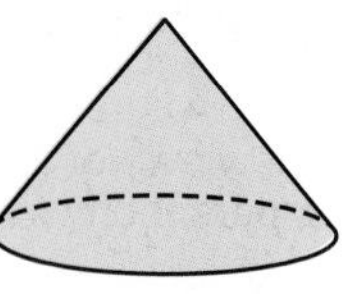

5.

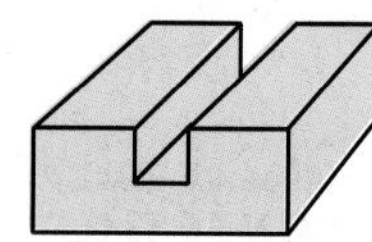

Make a perspective drawing of each figure by using the top, side, and front views as shown. Use isometric dot paper if necessary.

6–7. See margin.

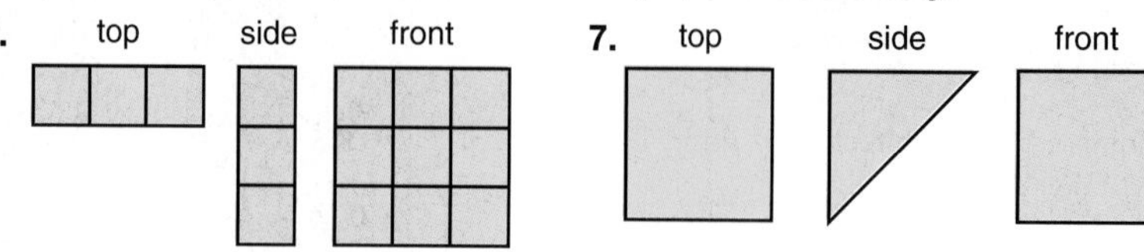

8. ***Industrial Technology*** A cast iron sleeve has a rectangular hole that extends through its entire length. Draw a top, side, and front view of the sleeve. See Answer Appendix.

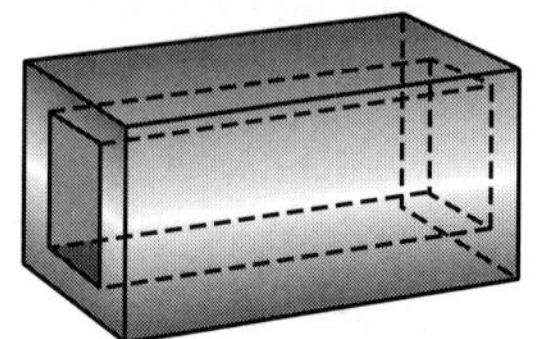

EXERCISES

Practice
9–14. See Answer Appendix.

Draw a top, a side, and a front view of each figure.

9.

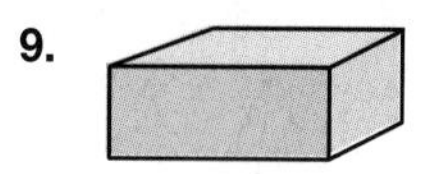

10.

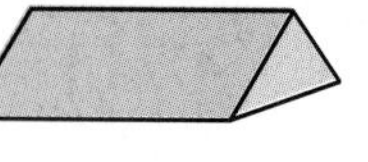

11.

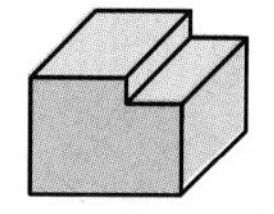

12.

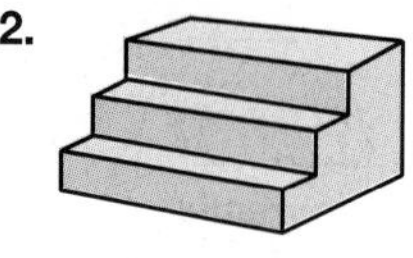

13.

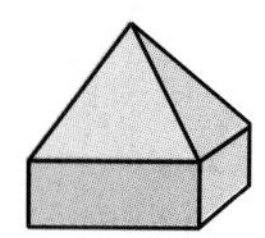

14.

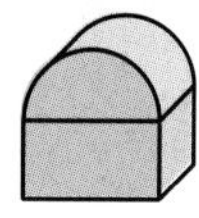

Make a perspective drawing of each figure by using the top, side, and front views as shown. Use isometric dot paper if necessary.

15–18. See margin.

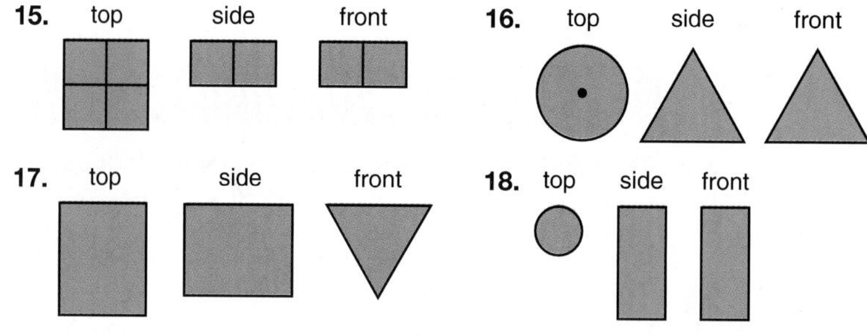

19. Draw a top, a side, and a front view of a piece of furniture. See students' work.

This CD-ROM offers a complete, self-paced mathematics curriculum. Each lesson includes a pretest, tutorial, guided practice, and posttest. MathPASS Lesson 41 is correlated to this Student Edition lesson.
For Windows & Macintosh

Applications and Problem Solving

20. See students' work.

21. See students' work.

20. ***Art*** Make a drawing of your own that shows one-point perspective.

21. ***Architecture*** When a building is being designed, an architect provides a set of elevation drawings. These drawings show how the building appears from each side. Draw a set of elevation drawings for your home or school.

22. ***Toys*** A child's game contains a wood frame with cut-out shapes and some blocks. Name the shape of a block that will fit exactly through both the square and the circle. **cylinder**

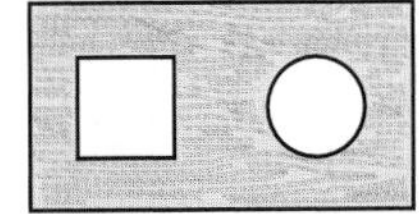

23. ***Critical Thinking*** Draw a three-dimensional figure in which the front and top view has a line of symmetry but the side view does not. **See margin.**

Mixed Review

24. ***Money Matters*** Maria borrowed $3,500 to help pay for her college tuition. The loan was made at 8% interest for 18 months. Find the amount of interest Maria will pay on the loan. *(Lesson 11-7)* **$420**

25. **Standardized Test Practice** Jeremiah walks 7 miles south and 4 miles east. To the nearest tenth of a mile, what is the straight line distance from his starting point? *(Lesson 10-3)* **D**

A 65.0 mi **B** 32.5 mi
C 17.3 mi **D** 8.1 mi

For **Extra Practice,** see page 600.

26. Find the square root of 196. *(Lesson 10-1)* **14**

MATH IN THE MEDIA

SHOE

1. Which view of the Washington Monument is shown in the comic? **top**
2. Find a photograph of the Washington Monument and draw the remaining views. **See students' work.**

4 ASSESS

Closing Activity

Speaking Have students work with a partner. One student draws three different views of a rectangular prism and a cone, while the other draws three different views of a triangular prism and a cylinder. Then have partners exchange drawings and discuss the differences.

Additional Answer

23.

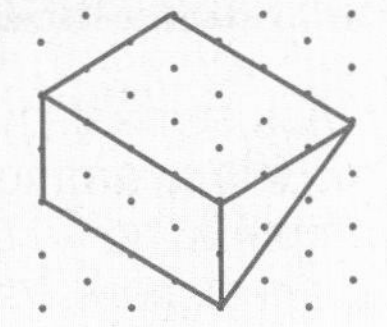

Practice Masters, p. 88

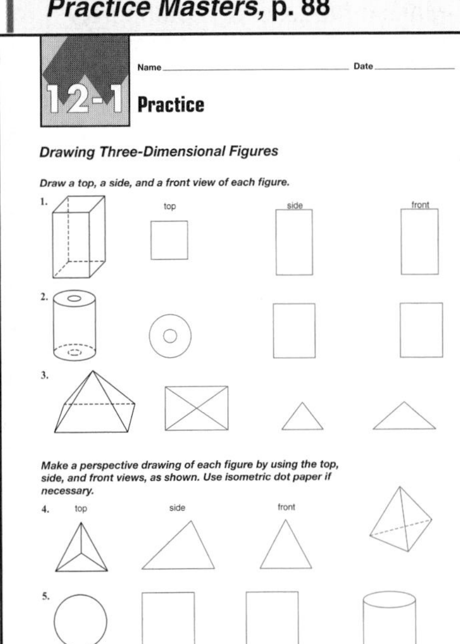

Name ______ Date ______

12-1 **Practice**

Drawing Three-Dimensional Figures

Draw a top, a side, and a front view of each figure.

1. top side front

2.

3.

Make a perspective drawing of each figure by using the top, side, and front views, as shown. Use isometric dot paper if necessary.

4. top side front

5.

© Glencoe/McGraw-Hill T88 *Mathematics: Applications and Connections, Course 2*

Extending the Lesson

Enrichment Masters, p. 88

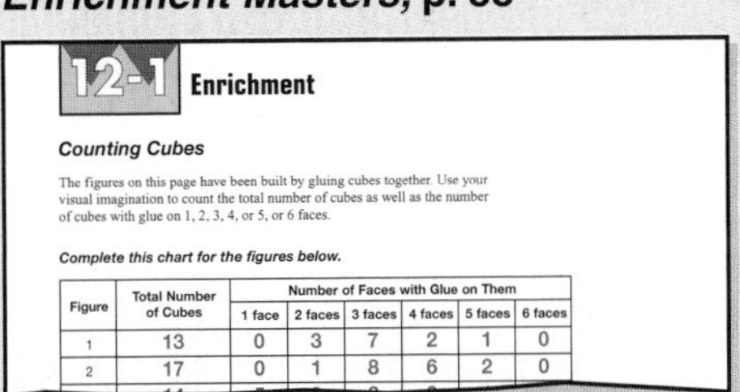

12-1 **Enrichment**

Counting Cubes

The figures on this page have been built by gluing cubes together. Use your visual imagination to count the total number of cubes as well as the number of cubes with glue on 1, 2, 3, 4, or 5, or 6 faces.

Complete this chart for the figures below.

Figure	Total Number of Cubes	Number of Faces with Glue on Them					
		1 face	2 faces	3 faces	4 faces	5 faces	6 faces
1	13	0	3	7	2	1	0
2	17	0	1	8	6	2	0

MATH IN THE MEDIA

Ask students why one view of a three-dimensional figure distorts its actual appearance more than another view.

12-1B THINKING LAB Notes

Objective Students solve problems by making a model.

Recommended Pacing	
Standard	Day 4 of 11
Honors	Day 3 of 10
Block	Day 2 of 5

1 FOCUS

Getting Started Ask students how they would use models to arrange the furniture in a room at home or at school. Have them discuss ways to represent different pieces of furniture with geometric figures.

2 TEACH

Reading Mathematics The names of many geometric figures give clues about their characteristics. For example, a cube is often referred to as a *hexahedron,* which comes from words meaning "six seats." Have students research the origin of the names of each Platonic solid (*tetrahedron, octahedron, dodecahedron, icosahedron*).

In-Class Example

Make a model of an octahedron using straws and gumdrops.

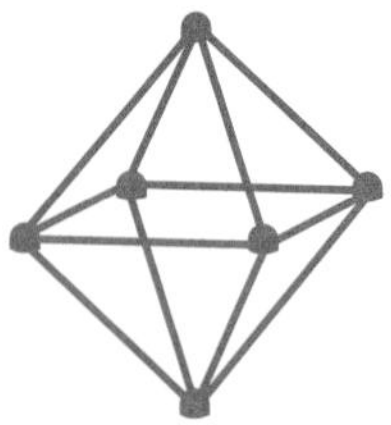

Additional Answer

2. **Sample answer: It allows students to see what the shapes look like in three dimensions.**

THINKING LAB PROBLEM SOLVING

12-1B Make a Model

A Follow-Up of Lesson 12-1

Juan and Jessica are designing decorations for the school dance. They want to cover the ceiling of the gymnasium with large geometric shapes. Their math teacher suggests they find out about *Platonic solids* and use them as the basis of their decorations.

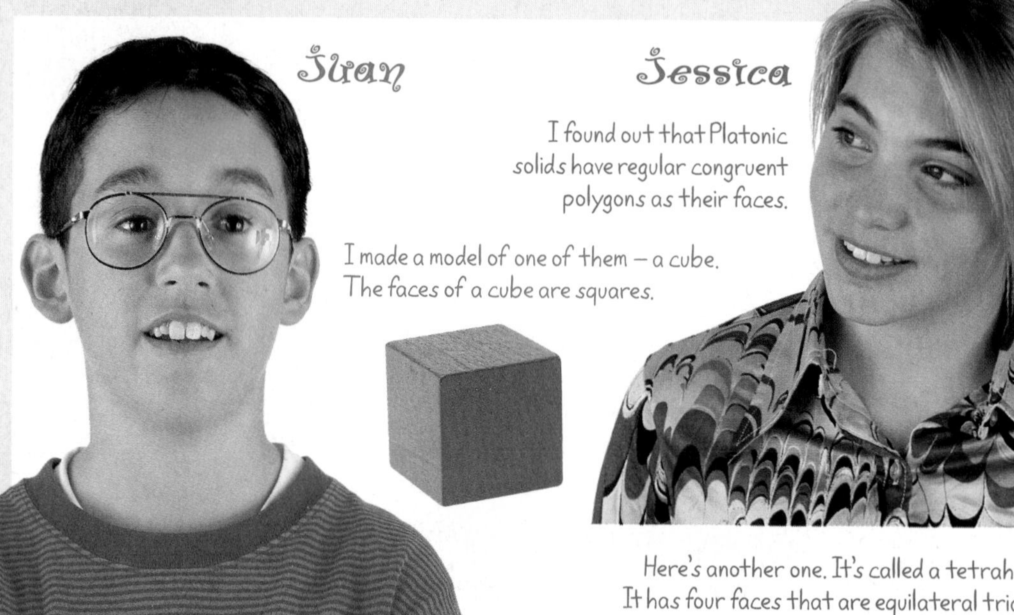

Juan
Jessica
I found out that Platonic solids have regular congruent polygons as their faces.
I made a model of one of them – a cube. The faces of a cube are squares.
Here's another one. It's called a tetrahedron It has four faces that are equilateral triangles
Let's find as many others as we can. We'll make models of them and show the rest of the decoration committee. Then we can figure out what materials we need to make them.

THINK ABOUT IT

Work with a partner.

1. ***Make a model*** of a cube and a tetrahedron using straws for the edges and gumdrops for the vertices. **See students' work.**
2. ***Explain*** when making a model is a better strategy than drawing a picture. **See margin.**
3. ***Apply*** the **make a model** strategy to solve the following problem.

   There are five Platonic solids. One is a cube, and one is a tetrahedron. Find or make a model of the other three. **See Answer Appendix.**

Reteaching the Lesson

Activity Have students work in groups to list real-world applications of making models to solve problems. Ask students how each of the Platonic solids might be used, such as in a model of a stadium, a greenhouse, a school, or a church.

For **Extra Practice,** see page 601.

ON YOUR OWN

4. **See students' work.**

4. ***Write a Problem*** that can be solved by using the make a model strategy.
5. ***Explain*** how sculptors and architects use the make a model strategy. **See margin.**
6. ***Explain*** how Juan and Jessica might use the make a model strategy to plan the decorations for the dance. **See margin.**

MIXED PROBLEM SOLVING

STRATEGIES

Look for a pattern.
Solve a simpler problem.
Act it out.
Guess and check.
Draw a diagram.
Make a chart.
Work backward.

Solve. Use any strategy.

7. **Sample answer: 20 in. × 8 in. × 8 in.**

7. ***Packaging*** A company packages six small books for a children's collection in a decorated 4-inch cube. They are shipped to bookstores in cartons. Twenty cubes fit in a carton with no extra space. What are the dimensions of the carton?
8. ***School*** Fred, Sarah, and Greg take French, Spanish, and German. No person's language class begins with the same letter as their first name. Sarah's best friend takes French. Which language does each person take? **See margin.**
9. Identical boxes are stacked in the corner of a room as shown below. How many boxes are *not* visible? **20 boxes**

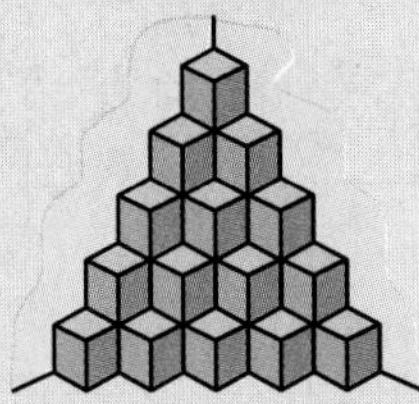

10. During a special on repair work, eight customers lined up outside The Bike Shop with either a bicycle or a tricycle that needed repair. When the owner looked out the window, she counted 21 wheels outside the shop. How many tricycles and bicycles were outside the shop? **See margin.**
11. Jenna spent $1\frac{1}{2}$ hours addressing 50 graduation announcements. At this rate, how long will it take her to address 125 announcements? **3.75 hours**
12. ***Volunteers*** Refer to the graph. If you survey 50 teenage volunteers, predict how many volunteer because the cause is important to them. **42 students**

Teens Help Out

Top reasons they give for volunteering

Feel compassion for needy	84%
Cause important to them	84%
Get new perspective on life	74%
If you help others, others will help you	73%
Is important to people they respect	73%
Looks good on resume	63%

Source: Volunteering and Giving Among Teenagers by Independent Sector

13. **Standardized Test Practice** There are 22 tables for campers in the dining hall at the campground. There are 6 chairs at each of the tables. If 12 chairs in the dining hall are empty, which number sentence could be used to find N, the number of campers seated? **D**

A $N = (22 + 6) - 12$

B $N = (22 \times 6) + 12$

C $N = (22 - 12) \times 6$

D $N = (22 \times 6) - 12$

E $N = (22 + 6) + 12$

3 PRACTICE/APPLY

Check for Understanding

Use the results from Exercise 5 to determine whether students know how to apply building a model to a practical problem, such as presenting an idea for a large sculpture to an art show committee.

Extra Practice If students need additional practice in problem solving, extra practice is available on the following pages.

- Make a Model, see p. 601
- Mixed Problem Solving, see pp. 605–606

Assignment Guide
All: 4–13

4 ASSESS

Closing Activity

Modeling Have students work with a partner to make a model of a new school building. Challenge students to incorporate as many three-dimensional figures as possible into their design.

Additional Answers

5. **Sample answer: They often make small models before starting work on their projects.**
6. **Sample answer: They might make models and then use the models to estimate the amount of material necessary to make the decorations.**
8. **Fred–Spanish, Sarah–German, Greg–French**
10. **5 tricycles and 3 bicycles**

Extending the Lesson

Activity Have groups of students interview people in your community who make models in order to solve work-related problems. Have them report their findings to the class, including pictures of the models, if possible.

12-2 Lesson Notes

Instructional Resources

- *Study Guide Masters,* p. 89
- *Practice Masters,* p. 89
- *Enrichment Masters,* p. 89
- Transparencies 12-2, A and B
- *Assessment and Evaluation Masters,* p. 323
- *School to Career Masters,* p. 25
- *Technology Masters,* p. 50

CD-ROM Program
  - Resource Lesson 12-2
  - Interactive Lesson 12-2

Recommended Pacing	
Standard	Day 5 of 11
Honors	Days 4 & 5 of 10
Block	Day 2 of 5

1 FOCUS

5-Minute Check (Lesson 12-1)

1. Draw a top, a side, and a front view of the figure.

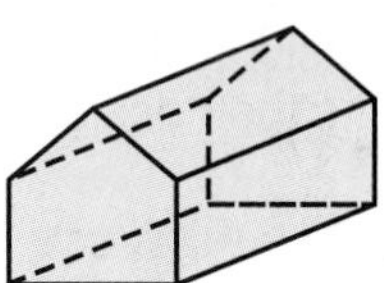

top side front

2. Make a perspective drawing by using the top, side, and front views.

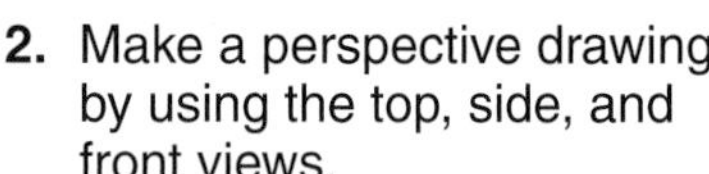

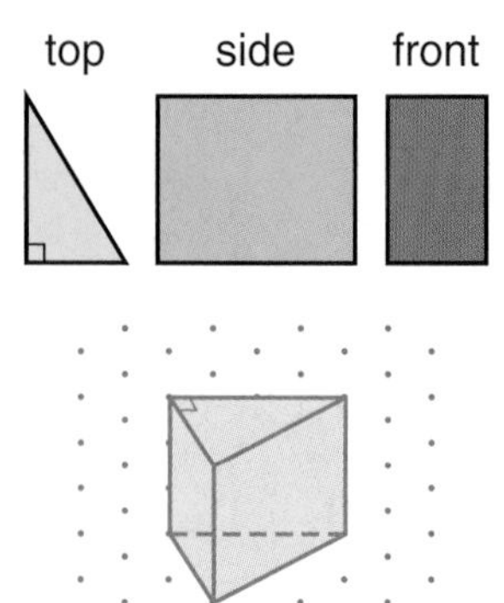

The 5-Minute Check is also available on **Transparency 12-2A** for this lesson.

12-2 Volume of Rectangular Prisms

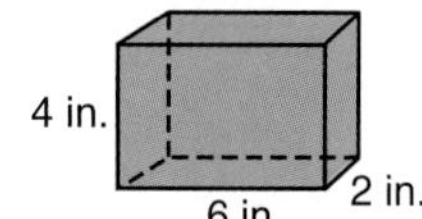

What you'll learn
You'll learn to find the volume of rectangular prisms.

When am I ever going to use this?
You'll use volume to find the density of an object in science.

Word Wise
rectangular prism
volume

During World War I, some bandages were made from wood pulp, cellulose, and small amounts of cotton. After the war, the company that produced the bandages advertised them as disposable handkerchiefs. The sales increased 400% in only two years.

Today, disposable handkerchiefs, or tissues, are sold in boxes that are shaped like **rectangular prisms**. A rectangular prism is a solid figure that has three sets of parallel congruent sides shaped like rectangles. The **volume** of a solid figure is the measure of the space occupied by it. It is measured in cubic units.

The container at the right has a length of 6 inches, a width of 2 inches, and a height of 4 inches. You can make a model using cubes.

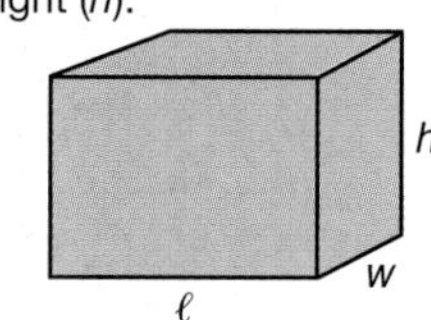

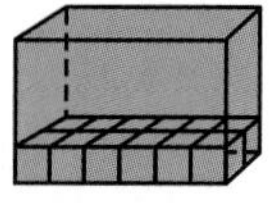

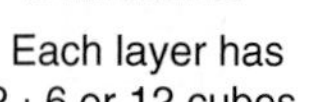

Each layer has $2 \cdot 6$ or 12 cubes.

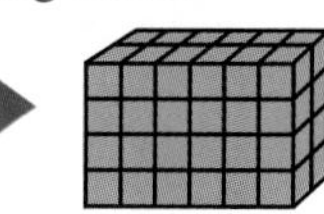

There are 4 layers.

It takes $12 \cdot 4$ or 48 cubes to fill the container. The volume of the container is 48 cubic inches.

Study Hint
Reading Math Prisms have flat surfaces called faces. The faces meet to form the edges of a prism. The edges meet at corners called vertices.

Volume of a Rectangular Prism

Words: The volume (V) of a rectangular prism is found by multiplying the length (ℓ), the width (w), and the height (h).

Symbols: $V = \ell wh$ **Model:**

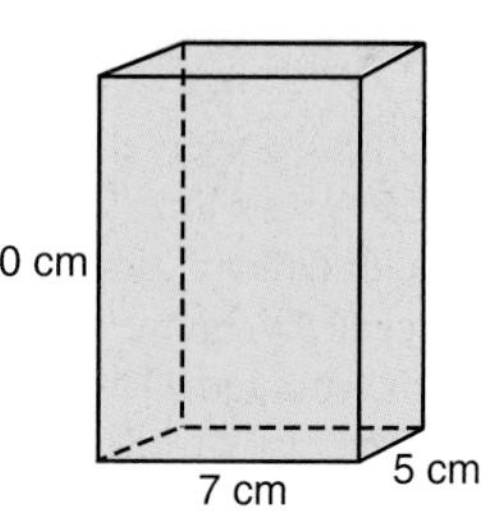

Example 1 **Draw and label a rectangular prism whose length is 7 centimeters, width is 5 centimeters, and height is 10 centimeters. Find its volume.**

$V = \ell wh$

$= 7 \cdot 5 \cdot 10$ *Replace ℓ, with 7, w with 5 and h with 10.*

$= 350$

10 cm, 7 cm, 5 cm

The prism has a volume of 350 cubic centimeters.

Motivating the Lesson

Problem Solving Ask students how they would measure the amount of space within the classroom.

2 **Gardening** Charlita wants to buy enough potting soil to fill a window box that is 42 inches long, 8 inches wide, and 6 inches high. If one bag of potting soil contains 576 cubic inches, how many bags should she buy?

Find the volume of the box and then compare it to the volume of potting soil.

Estimate: $40 \times 10 \times 5 = 2{,}000$

$V = \ell wh$

42 [×] 8 [×] 6 [=] 2016

Charlita needs 2,016 cubic inches of potting soil. One bag contains 576 cubic inches. Therefore, she needs to buy 2,016 ÷ 576 or 4 bags of potting soil.

Study Hint

Reading Math Volume is expressed in cubic units. So, the abbreviations for volume often use the exponent 3.

cubic inch → in^3

cubic centimeter → cm^3

MINI-LAB

Work with a partner. grid paper, scissors, tape

Try This 1–2. See students' work.

1. Cut a piece of grid paper so that it measures 20 × 20 units. Cut off square corner sections from each corner to make an open box that is 14 × 14 × 3.
2. Fold the paper to make a box. Then tape the corners together.
3. Find the volume of the box. Record your answer as an ordered pair (length of base, volume). **588 cubic units; (14, 588)**
4. Continue making boxes by cutting off square corners from 20 × 20 grids and finding their volumes until you have made all possible boxes with whole number lengths. **See students' work.**

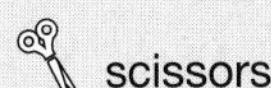

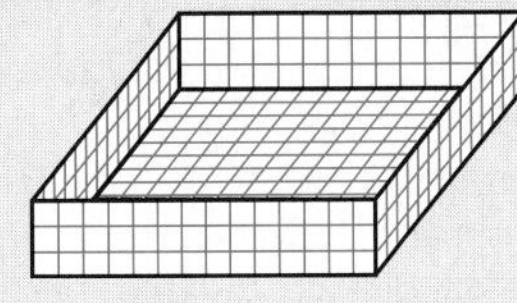

Talk About It

5. Which box has the greatest volume? **14 × 14 × 3**
6. Graph the ordered pairs (length of base, volume) on a coordinate plane. Describe the graph. **See Answer Appendix.**

LOOK BACK You can refer to Lesson 6-6 to review functions and their graphs.

2 TEACH

Transparency 12-2B contains a teaching aid for this lesson.

In-Class Examples

For Example 1

Draw and label a rectangular prism whose length is 6 centimeters, width is 4 centimeters, and height is 10 centimeters. Find its volume. **240 cm^3**

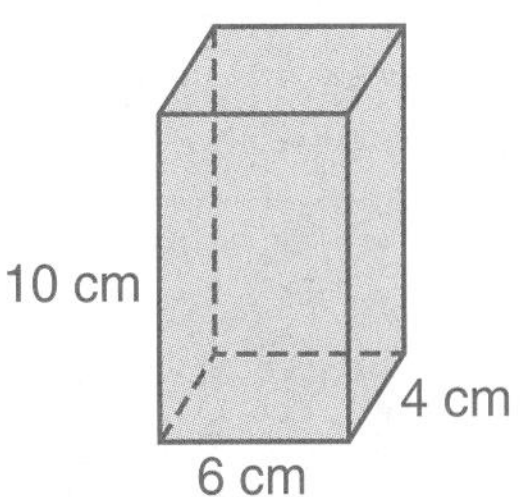

For Example 2

Charlie wants to insulate the ceiling of his cabin. The ceiling measures 8 feet wide by 12 feet long, and Charlie wants insulation 6 inches thick. How many cubic feet of insulation should he buy? **48 cubic feet**

Using the Mini-Lab To save time in class, have each pair perform a different step of the lab. Then compile data from each pair and have the class do Exercises 5 and 6 together.

Multiple Learning Styles

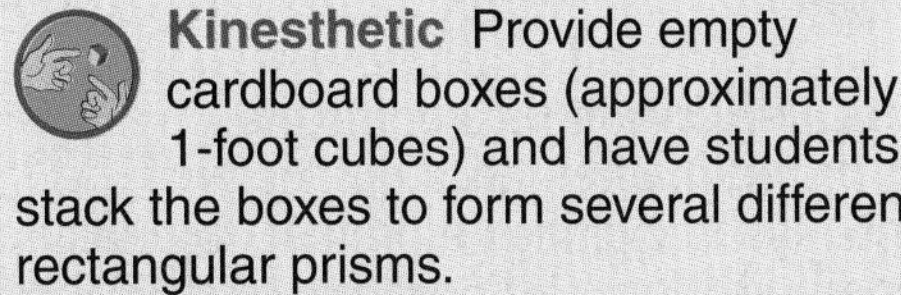

Kinesthetic Provide empty cardboard boxes (approximately 1-foot cubes) and have students stack the boxes to form several different rectangular prisms.

3 PRACTICE/APPLY

Check for Understanding

If students need additional practice or instruction after completing Exercises 1–7, one of these options may be helpful.

- Extra Practice, see p. 601
- Reteaching Activity
- *Study Guide Masters,* p. 89
- *Practice Masters,* p. 89

Assignment Guide

Core: 9–19 odd, 21–24
Enriched: 8–14 even, 16–19, 21–24

Have students measure the outside of the refrigerator and determine the volume of the non-storage parts, such as walls, door, and motor.

***Study Guide Masters,* p. 89**

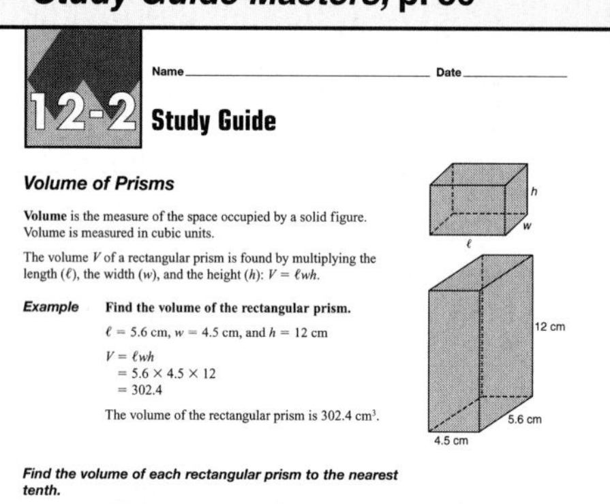

Name__________ Date__________

12-2 Study Guide

Volume of Prisms

Volume is the measure of the space occupied by a solid figure. Volume is measured in cubic units.

The volume V of a rectangular prism is found by multiplying the length (ℓ), the width (w), and the height (h): $V = \ell wh$.

Example **Find the volume of the rectangular prism.**

$\ell = 5.6$ cm, $w = 4.5$ cm, and $h = 12$ cm

$$V = \ell wh = 5.6 \times 4.5 \times 12 = 302.4$$

The volume of the rectangular prism is 302.4 cm³.

Find the volume of each rectangular prism to the nearest tenth.

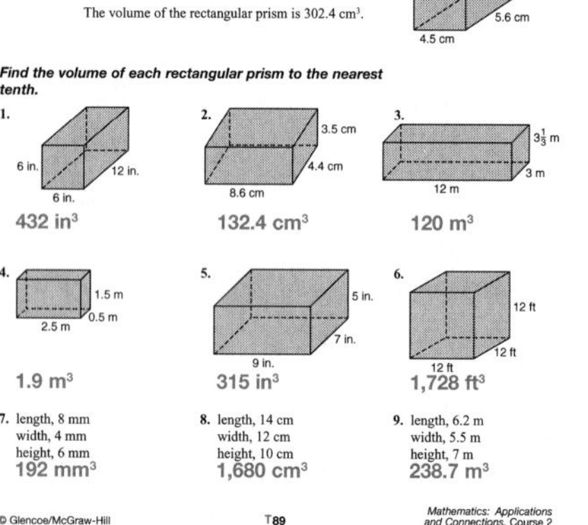

1. 6 in., 12 in., 6 in. — 432 in³
2. 3.5 cm, 4.4 cm, 8.6 cm — 132.4 cm³
3. $3\frac{1}{3}$ m, 3 m, 12 m — 120 m³
4. 1.5 m, 0.5 m, 2.5 m — 1.9 m³
5. 5 in., 7 in., 9 in. — 315 in³
6. 12 ft, 12 ft, 12 ft — 1,728 ft³
7. length, 8 mm; width, 4 mm; height, 6 mm — 192 mm³
8. length, 14 cm; width, 12 cm; height, 10 cm — 1,680 cm³
9. length, 6.2 m; width, 5.5 m; height, 7 m — 238.7 m³

 T89 *Mathematics: Applications and Connections, Course 2*

CHECK FOR UNDERSTANDING

Communicating Mathematics

Read and study the lesson to answer each question.

1. ***Write*** the abbreviation for cubic meters using an exponent. **m³**
2. ***Draw*** and label a rectangular prism whose length is 5 inches, width is 4 inches, and height is 8 inches. **See Answer Appendix.**
3. ***Make models*** of three different prisms that have a volume of 24 cubic units. **See Answer Appendix.**

HANDS-ON MATH

Guided Practice

Find the volume of each rectangular prism to the nearest tenth.

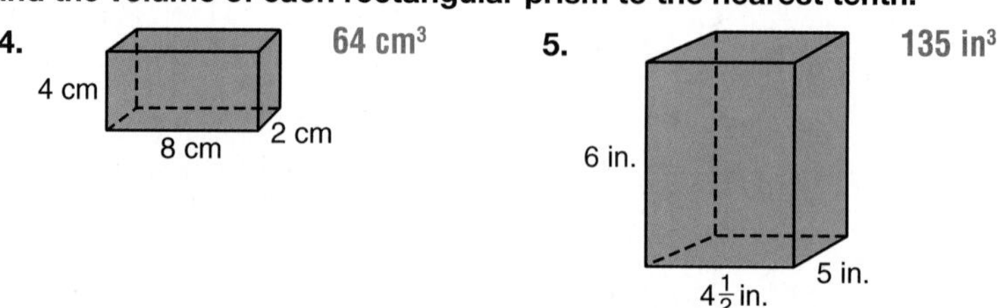

4. **64 cm³**
5. **135 in³**
6. Find the volume of a rectangular prism whose length is 2.2 centimeters, width is 4.4 centimeters, and height is 5.5 centimeters. **53.24 cm³**
7. ***Business*** Donna Mendez's new office is 20 feet long, 15 feet wide, and 12 feet high. On average, it costs 9¢ per year to air condition one cubic foot of space. How much will it cost to air condition her office for one month? **$27**

EXERCISES

Practice

Find the volume of each rectangular prism to the nearest tenth.

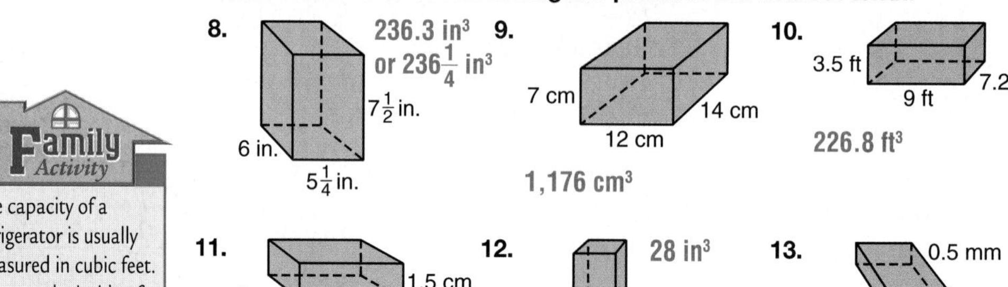

8. **236.3 in³ or $236\frac{1}{4}$ in³**
9. **1,176 cm³**
10. **226.8 ft³**

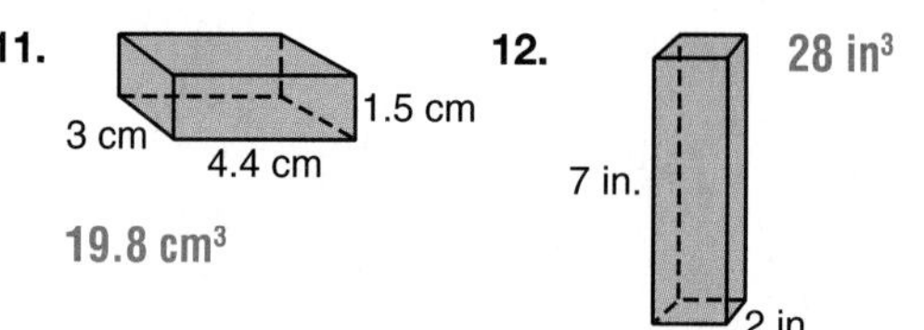

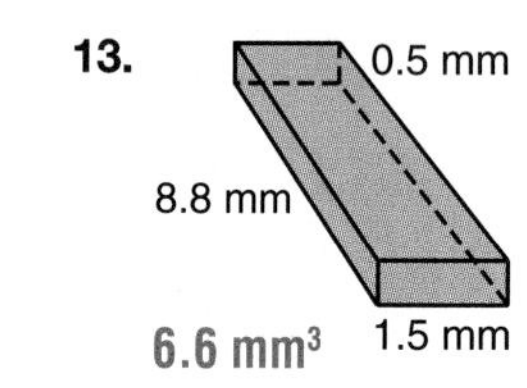

11. **19.8 cm³**
12. **28 in³**
13. **6.6 mm³**
14. Draw and label a rectangular prism whose length is 1 centimeter, width is 8 centimeters, and height is 10 centimeters. Find its volume. **80 cm³**
15. A cube has edges that are 7 inches long. Find its volume. **343 in³**

Family Activity

The capacity of a refrigerator is usually measured in cubic feet. Measure the inside of your refrigerator and see how closely it matches the manufacturer's claims about the capacity.

Reteaching the Lesson

Activity Have students investigate volume by using centimeter cubes to fill boxes, such as jewelry boxes, cereal boxes, and candy boxes. Guide them to recognize shortcuts to counting all cubes in order to find volume.

MathPASS CD-ROM

This CD-ROM offers a complete, self-paced mathematics curriculum. Each lesson includes a pretest, tutorial, guided practice, and posttest. MathPASS Lesson 42 is correlated to this Student Edition lesson.

For Windows & Macintosh

Applications and Problem Solving

16. Use $V = Bh$ to find the volume of the triangular prism. **80 units^3**

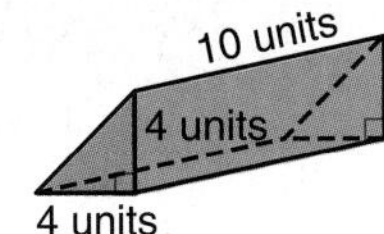

17. ***Measurement*** How many cubic inches are in a cubic foot? **1,728 in^3**
18. ***Swimming*** A competition swimming pool is 25 yards long and has 8 lanes that are each 3 yards wide. The pool is filled to a depth of 6 feet.
    a. Express the measurements of the pool in feet. **75 ft, 72 ft, 6 ft**
    b. Find the number of cubic feet of water in the pool. **32,400 ft^3**
    c. Each cubic foot of volume contains about 7.5 gallons of water. About how many gallons of water are in the pool? **243,000 gallons**
19. ***Landscaping*** A landscape architect is designing the outside of a new restaurant. She wants to cover a 40-foot by 12-foot rectangular area with small stones. If she orders 120 cubic feet of stones to spread over the area, how deep will the stones be? **3 in.**
20. ***Working on the CHAPTER Project*** Use the leaf that you collected from page 489. **a–b. See students' work.**
    a. Trace the outline of the leaf onto centimeter grid paper. Estimate the area of the leaf.
    b. Another formula for the volume of a prism is $V = Bh$, where B is the area of the base and h is the height. Assume the height of your leaf is 0.1 centimeter. Find the volume of the leaf.
21. ***Critical Thinking*** What is the effect on the volume of a cube if the length of each edge is doubled? tripled? Write an equation to show each relationship. **8 times greater; 27 times greater; doubling: $V = 8s^3$; tripling: $V = 27s^3$**

Mixed Review

22. ***Geometry*** Make a perspective drawing of a figure by using the top, side, and front views of the figure. *(Lesson 12-1)* **See margin.**

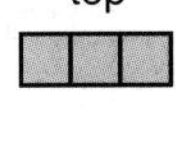
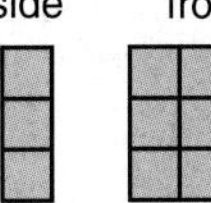

23. ***Money Matters*** At a sale, Barbara finds a \$125 coat marked down to \$87.50. What percent of decrease is this? *(Lesson 11-6)* **30%**

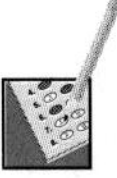

24. **Standardized Test Practice** The manager of a book store conducted a survey of 1,000 adults to find what kinds of books they like to read. The top five choices are shown at the right. How many adults out of 1,000 who were surveyed like to read biographies? *(Lesson 8-8)* **B**

    A 6 **B** 60
    C 600 **D** 6,000

What People Read	
Mystery/Thriller	25%
Romance	11%
History	7%
Biographies	6%
Religious	6%

For **Extra Practice,** see page 601.

Exercise 20 asks students to advance to the next stage of work on the Chapter Project. You may want students to compare their leaves to determine how much they differ in actual height from 0.1 centimeter.

4 ASSESS

Closing Activity

Writing Have students write a problem for classmates that can be solved by finding the volume of a rectangular prism. Students should be sure to include all essential data.

Chapter 12, Quiz A (Lessons 12-1 and 12-2) is available in the *Assessment and Evaluation Masters,* p. 323.

Additional Answer

22.

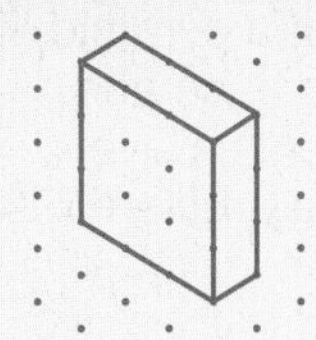

***Practice Masters,* p. 89**

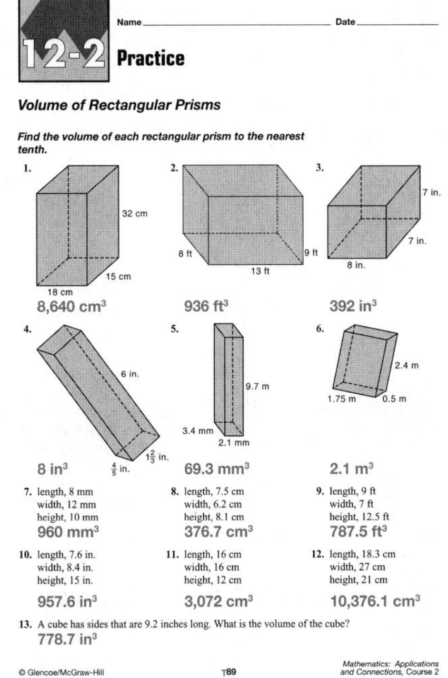

12-2 Practice

Name ______ Date ______

Volume of Rectangular Prisms

Find the volume of each rectangular prism to the nearest tenth.

1. 8,640 cm^3
2. 936 ft^3
3. 392 in^3
4. 8 in^3
5. 69.3 mm^3
6. 2.1 m^3
7. length, 8 mm; width, 12 mm; height, 10 mm — 960 mm^3
8. length, 7.5 cm; width, 6.2 cm; height, 8.1 cm — 376.7 cm^3
9. length, 9 ft; width, 7 ft; height, 12.5 ft — 787.5 ft^3
10. length, 7.6 in.; width, 8.4 in.; height, 15 in. — 957.6 in^3
11. length, 16 cm; width, 16 cm; height, 12 cm — 3,072 cm^3
12. length, 18.3 cm; width, 27 cm; height, 21 cm — 10,376.1 cm^3
13. A cube has sides that are 9.2 inches long. What is the volume of the cube? 778.7 in^3

 T89 *Mathematics: Applications and Connections, Course 2*

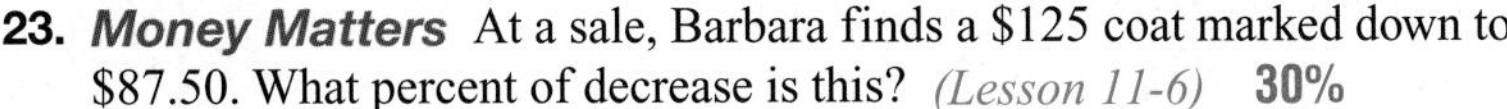

Extending the Lesson

***Enrichment Masters,* p. 89**

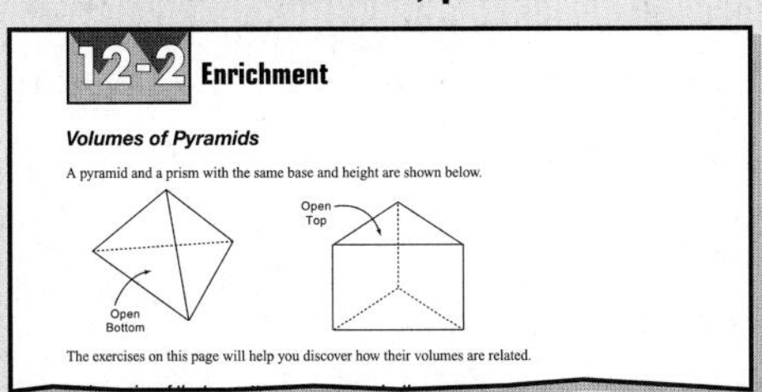

12-2 Enrichment

Volumes of Pyramids

A pyramid and a prism with the same base and height are shown below.

The exercises on this page will help you discover how their volumes are related.

Activity Ask students how they would find the volume of their bodies by using a tub full of water. Hint: find the volume of the bathtub first.

GET READY

Objective Students compare the volume of a pyramid with the volume of a prism.

Optional Resources
Hands-On Lab Masters
- centimeter grid paper, p. 11
- worksheet, p. 68

Overhead Manipulative Resources
- centimeter grid

MANAGEMENT TIPS

Recommended Time
15 minutes

Getting Started Ask students how much more spacious a tent in the shape of a cube would be than a tent in the shape of a pyramid, if both had the same base and height measurements. Have students model the problem with blankets or sheets.

For the **Activity**, you may wish to use a different model to facilitate filling the pyramid with rice. To make the model, draw a circle of diameter 7.3 cm. Draw a radius of the circle. From the point where the radius intersects the circle, draw a segment 6 cm long whose endpoint lies on the circle. Draw another radius to complete the triangle. Repeat this process until there are four adjacent triangles. Cut out the model, fold on the lines, and tape to form a bottomless pyramid.

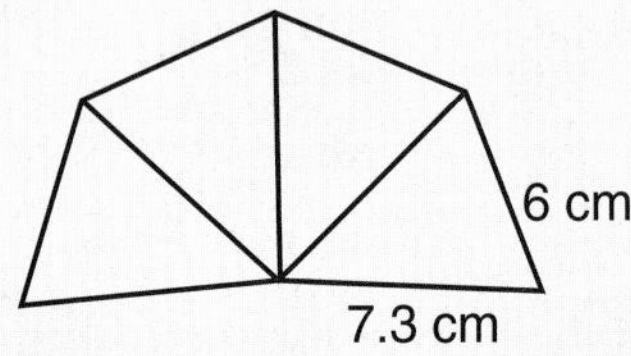

ASSESS

Have students complete Exercises 1–5. Have students explore ways to cut up three pyramids in order to fit them inside the prism so their volumes are equal.

HANDS-ON LAB

COOPERATIVE LEARNING

12-2B Volume of Pyramids

A Follow-Up of Lesson 12-2

rice

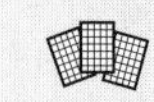

centimeter grid paper

The newly built entrance to the Louvre Museum in Paris is a glass pyramid. A *pyramid* is a solid figure that has all of its faces, except one, intersecting at a point.

In this lab, you'll investigate the relationship between the volume of a prism and the volume of a pyramid with the same base and height.

TRY THIS

Work with a partner.

- Copy the two figures at the right onto centimeter grid paper.
- Cut them out and fold on the dashed lines. They will fold into models of an open prism and a pyramid. Tape the edges together to form the models.
- Estimate the ratio of the volume of the prism to the volume of the pyramid.

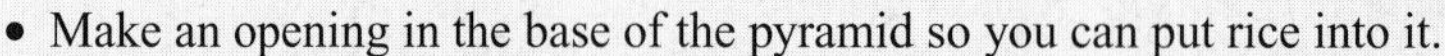

- Make an opening in the base of the pyramid so you can put rice into it.
- Fill the pyramid with rice. Then pour this rice into the prism. Repeat until the prism is full.

ON YOUR OWN

1. How many pyramids of rice did it take to fill the prism?
2. Compare the heights of the prism and the pyramid.
3. Compare the areas of the bases of each solid.
4. Compare the volume of the prism and the pyramid.
5. Write a formula for the volume of a pyramid.

1. Sample answer: about 3
2–3. They are equal.
4. The volume of the prism is three times the volume of the pyramid.
5. $V = \frac{1}{3}\ell wh$

Have students write a paragraph discussing in what ways the dimensions and volume of the pyramidal entrance to the Louvre would be different if it were a cube.

12-3 Volume of Cylinders

What you'll learn
You'll learn to find the volume of cylinders.

When am I ever going to use this?
Many food containers are shaped like cylinders.

Word Wise
cylinder

The stack of quarters is a model of a **cylinder**. A cylinder is a solid figure that has two congruent, parallel circles as its bases.

To find the value of a stack of quarters, you multiply the value of one quarter, 25¢, by the number of quarters in the stack. You can use a similar method to find the volume of a cylinder.

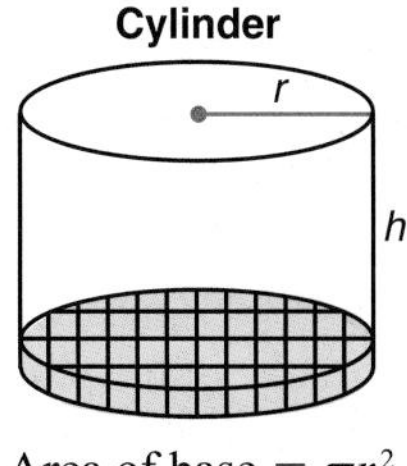

Area of base $= \pi r^2$

The area of the base tells how many unit cubes cover the base. The height tells how many layers there are.

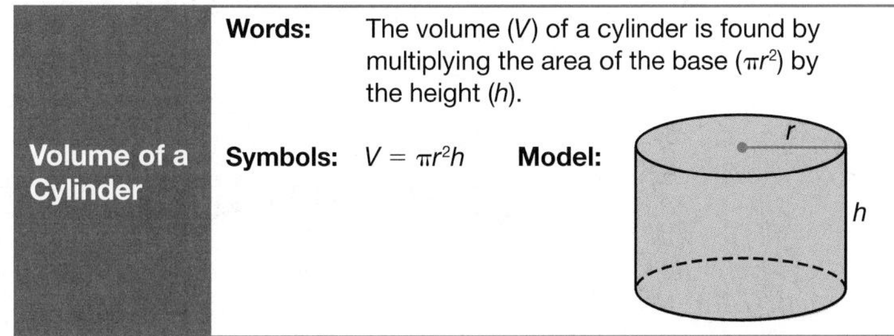

Volume of a Cylinder	
Words:	The volume (V) of a cylinder is found by multiplying the area of the base (πr^2) by the height (h).
Symbols:	$V = \pi r^2 h$
Model:	(cylinder with radius r and height h)

Example

1 **Find the volume of a cylinder with a diameter of 6 inches and a height of 4 inches.**

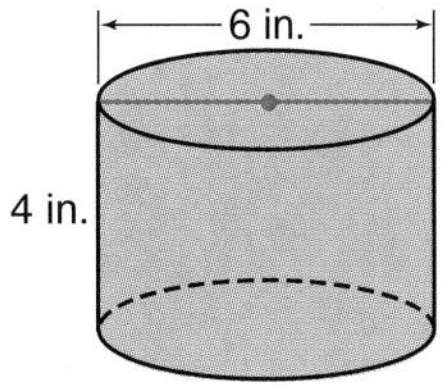

The diameter of the cylinder is 6 inches. Therefore, the radius is 3 inches.

Estimate: $3^2 \times 3 \times 4 = 108$

$V = \pi r^2 h$ *Use 3.14 for π.*

$V \approx 3.14 \cdot 3^2 \cdot 4$ *Replace r with 3 and h with 4.*

$V \approx 113.04$

The cylinder has a volume of about 113 cubic inches.

(Figure: 6 in. diameter, 4 in. height)

Study Hint
Estimation You can estimate the volume of a cylinder by squaring the radius and multiplying the answer by 3 (the approximate value of π) and the height.

Multiple Learning Styles

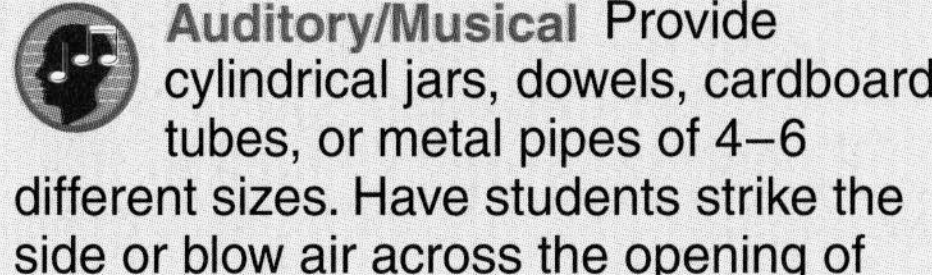

Auditory/Musical Provide cylindrical jars, dowels, cardboard tubes, or metal pipes of 4–6 different sizes. Have students strike the side or blow air across the opening of each, noticing the different pitch produced by larger and smaller cylinders. Ask students whether the length (height) or width (diameter) is more important to the pitch of a cylinder.

12-3 Lesson Notes

Instructional Resources

- *Study Guide Masters,* p. 90
- *Practice Masters,* p. 90
- *Enrichment Masters,* p. 90
- Transparencies 12-3, A and B
- *Assessment and Evaluation Masters,* p. 323
- *Diversity Masters,* p. 25
- *Hands-On Lab Masters,* p. 83

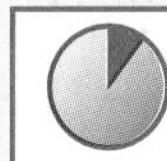

CD-ROM Program
- Resource Lesson 12-3

Recommended Pacing	
Standard	Day 6 of 11
Honors	Day 6 of 10
Block	Day 3 of 5

1 FOCUS

5-Minute Check *(Lesson 12-2)*

Find the volume of each rectangular prism to the nearest tenth.

1. 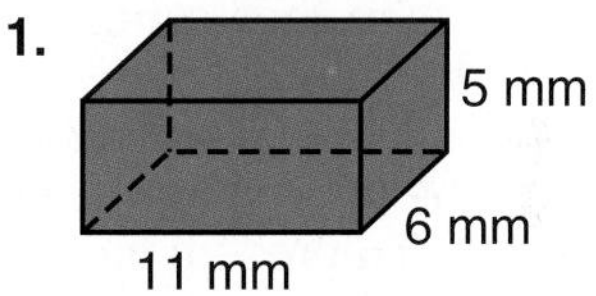

330 mm³

2. 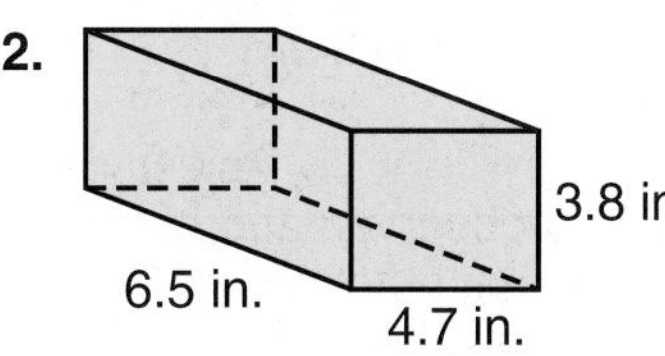

116.1 in³

3. length, $4\frac{1}{3}$ ft
width, $3\frac{3}{4}$ ft
height, 4 ft   65 ft³

The 5-Minute Check is also available on **Transparency 12-3A** for this lesson.

Motivating the Lesson

Problem Solving Have students imagine that they have a bag of sugar and want to pour some of it into a jar. Ask them how they could determine the amount of sugar that would fill the jar without actually pouring it into the jar.

2 TEACH

Transparency 12-3B contains a teaching aid for this lesson.

In-Class Examples

For Example 1

Find the volume of a cylinder with a radius of 5 centimeters and a height of 10 centimeters. **about 785.4 cm³**

For Example 2

Ethan's pencil has a diameter of 0.7 centimeter and a length of 17 centimeters. The graphite center has a diameter of 0.2 centimeter. What is the volume of the wood in the pencil? **about 6.5 cm³**

Thinking Algebraically Some students may think the volume in Example 2 can be found by subtracting the two radii and using that value in the volume formula for a cylinder. Let R represent the radius of the smaller one. Have students use substitution to determine whether $\pi R^2h - \pi r^2h$ is equal to $\pi(R - r)h$. **no**

Using the Mini-Lab Ask students what they observed about the cylinders that determined their rankings. Ask if any students mentally calculated an estimate of the formula $V = \pi r^2h$. Point out any changes in their rankings.

2 **Catering** Mrs. Washington uses a special lemonade pitcher when she caters picnics. It is a cylinder that contains a cylinder on the inside where ice is placed so it does not dilute the lemonade. How many gallons of lemonade can the pitcher hold? (*Hint:* 1 gallon = 231 cubic inches)

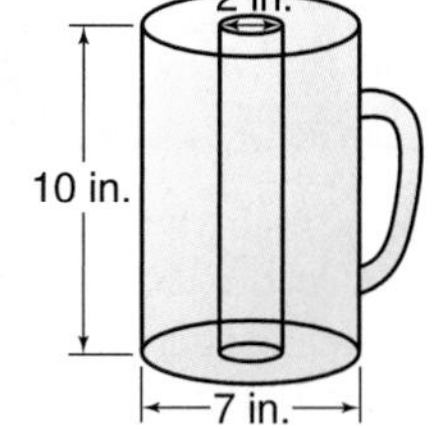

Find the volume of the outside cylinder. Then find the volume of the inside cylinder.

Volume of outside cylinder	Volume of inside cylinder
The radius is 3.5 inches.	*The radius is 1 inch.*
$V = \pi \cdot 3.5^2 \cdot 10$	$V = \pi \cdot 1^2 \cdot 10$
π × 3.5 x^2 × 10	π × 1 x^2 × 10
= 384.8451001	= 31.41592654
The volume is about 385 cubic inches.	The volume is about 31 cubic inches.

To find the volume of the pitcher, subtract the volume of the inside cylinder from the volume of the outside cylinder.

$385 - 31 = 354$

The pitcher has a volume of about 354 cubic inches. Each gallon of lemonade has a volume of 231 cubic inches. So, the volume of the pitcher is $\frac{354}{231}$ or about 1.5 gallons.

HANDS-ON MINI-LAB

Work in a small group. — five cylinder-shaped objects, 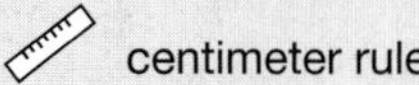 centimeter ruler

Try This **1–3. See students' work.**

1. Based on your observations alone, rank the cylinders in order from least to greatest volume.
2. Estimate the volume of each cylinder. Then rank them in order from least to greatest volume based on your estimates.
3. Measure the height and radius of each cylinder. Calculate the volume of each cylinder and rank them in order from least to greatest volume based on your calculations.

Talk About It **4–5. See students' work.**

4. How close were your estimates to your actual calculations?
5. How precise did you need to be when you measured the cylinders?

Investigations for the Special Education Student

This blackline master booklet helps you plan for the needs of your special education students by providing long-term projects along with teacher notes. Investigation 14, *Exploring the Depths of the Sea,* may be used with this chapter.

CHECK FOR UNDERSTANDING

Communicating Mathematics

1. Sample answer: In both, you multiply the area of the base by the height.
2. See students' work.

Read and study the lesson to answer each question.

1. ***Tell*** how the formula for the volume of a cylinder is similar to the formula for the volume of a prism.
2. ***Write a Problem*** in which you find the volume of a cylinder.
3. ***You Decide*** Refer to the cylinders at the right. Latisha thinks the volumes of the two cylinders are equal. Cleveland thinks they are not equal. Who is correct? If they are not equal, tell which cylinder has the greater volume. **See margin.**

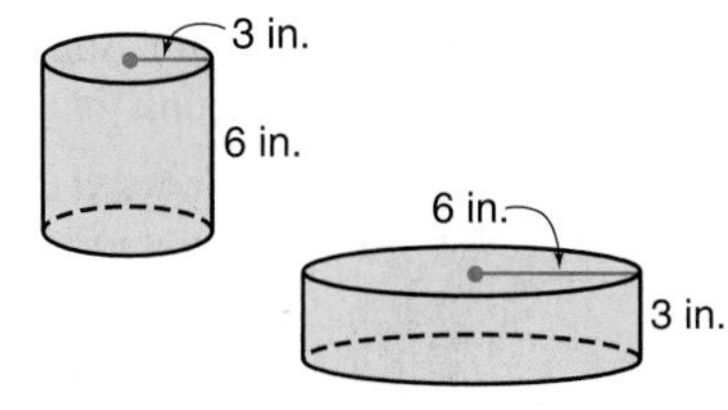

Guided Practice

Answers are calculated using the π key on a calculator and then rounded.

Find the volume of each cylinder to the nearest tenth.

4. 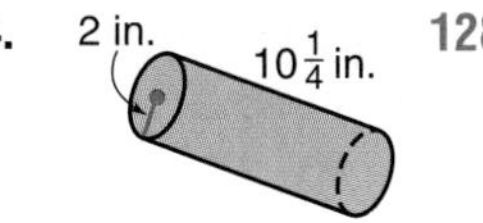

128.8 in³

5. 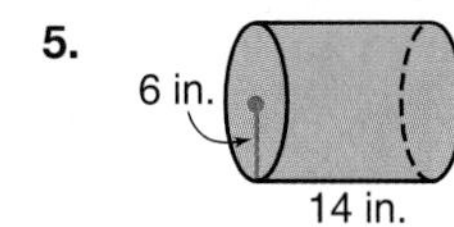

1,583.4 in³

6. ***Food*** A can of potato chips is 8 inches high and has a radius of 1.5 inches. Find the volume of the can. **56.5 in³**

EXERCISES

Practice

Find the volume of each cylinder to the nearest tenth.

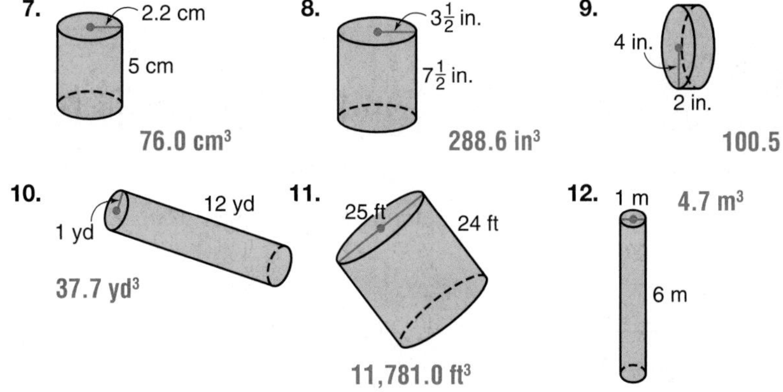

7. **76.0 cm³**
8. **288.6 in³**
9. **100.5 in³**
10. **37.7 yd³**
11. **11,781.0 ft³**
12. **4.7 m³**

13. The diameter of a cylinder is 5 feet, and the height is 8.25 feet. Find the volume of the cylinder. **162.0 ft³**
14. Use the formula πrh^2 for the volume of a right circular cylinder.
    a. What is the ratio of the volume of such a cylinder to the volume of one having twice the height but the same radius? **1 to 4**
    b. What is the volume of such a cylinder to the volume of one having the same height but twice the radius? **1 to 2**

3 PRACTICE/APPLY

Check for Understanding

If students need additional practice or instruction after completing Exercises 1–6, one of these options may be helpful.

- Extra Practice, see p. 601
- Reteaching Activity
- *Study Guide Masters*, p. 90
- *Practice Masters*, p. 90

Assignment Guide

Core: 7–17 odd, 18–21
Enriched: 8–14 even, 15–21
All: Self-Test, 1–5

Additional Answer

3. Cleveland;
radius of 3: $V = 169.6$ in³;
radius of 6: $V = 339.3$ in³

Reteaching the Lesson

Activity Have students use checkers to model the volume of a cylinder. One checker represents the area of the base, just as a layer of cubes represented the area of the base of a prism. Stacking and counting checkers determines the height of the cylinder.

Error Analysis
Watch for students who multiply the height of a cylinder by the circumference rather than the area of the base.
Prevent by guiding students to see that volume is not the measure of the distance around a figure, but of the space the figure occupies.

***Study Guide Masters*, p. 90**

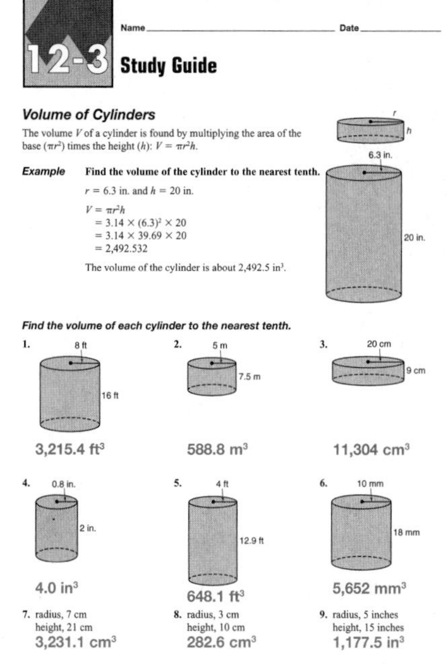

Name________ Date________

12-3 Study Guide

Volume of Cylinders

The volume V of a cylinder is found by multiplying the area of the base (πr^2) times the height (h): $V = \pi r^2 h$.

Example **Find the volume of the cylinder to the nearest tenth.**

$r = 6.3$ in. and $h = 20$ in.

$$V = \pi r^2 h$$
$$= 3.14 \times (6.3)^2 \times 20$$
$$= 3.14 \times 39.69 \times 20$$
$$= 2{,}492.532$$

The volume of the cylinder is about 2,492.5 in³.

Find the volume of each cylinder to the nearest tenth.

1. 8 ft, 16 ft — 3,215.4 ft³
2. 5 m, 7.5 m — 588.8 m³
3. 20 cm, 9 cm — 11,304 cm³
4. 0.8 in., 2 in. — 4.0 in³
5. 4 ft, 12.9 ft — 648.1 ft³
6. 10 mm, 18 mm — 5,652 mm³
7. radius, 7 cm height, 21 cm — 3,231.1 cm³
8. radius, 3 cm height, 10 cm — 282.6 cm³
9. radius, 5 inches height, 15 inches — 1,177.5 in³

 T90 *Mathematics: Applications and Connections, Course 2*

4 ASSESS

Closing Activity

Speaking Have students explain what else they need to know to find the volume of a cylindrical gas tank with a height of 8 feet. **the radius**

Mid-Chapter Self Test

The Mid-Chapter Self Test reviews concepts and skills in Lessons 12-1 through 12-3. Lesson references are given so students can review concepts not yet mastered.

Chapter 12, Quiz B (Lesson 12-3) is available in the *Assessment and Evaluating Masters,* p. 323.

Mid-Chapter Test (Lessons 12-1 through 12-3) is available in the *Assessment and Evaluation Masters,* p. 322.

Additional Answer

18. Sample answer: Make a cone and cylinder with the same base and height. Fill the cone with rich and empty into the cylinder. Find how many cones of rice fill the cylinder. The volume of the cylinder is three times the volume of the cone.

***Practice Masters,* p. 90**

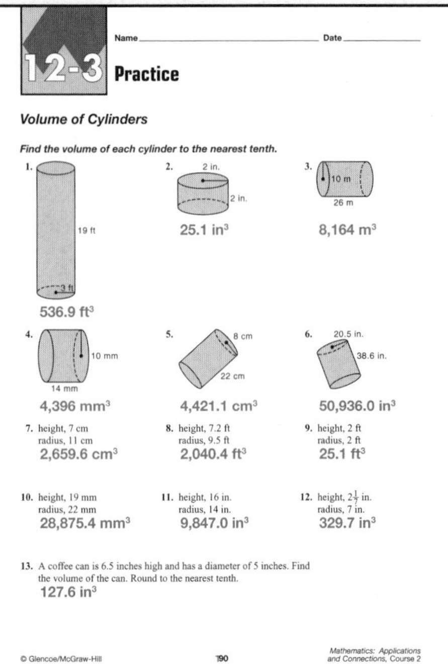

12-3 **Practice**

Name ____________ Date ________

Volume of Cylinders

Find the volume of each cylinder to the nearest tenth.

1. 19 ft, 3 ft — 536.9 ft³
2. 2 in., 2 in. — 25.1 in³
3. 10 m, 26 m — 8,164 m³
4. 10 mm, 14 mm — 4,396 mm³
5. 8 cm, 22 cm — 4,421.1 cm³
6. 20.5 in., 38.6 in. — 50,936.0 in³
7. height, 7 cm radius, 11 cm — 2,659.6 cm³
8. height, 7.2 ft radius, 9.5 ft — 2,040.4 ft³
9. height, 2 ft radius, 2 ft — 25.1 ft³
10. height, 19 mm radius, 22 mm — 28,875.4 mm³
11. height, 16 in. radius, 14 in. — 9,847.0 in³
12. height, $2\frac{1}{7}$ in. radius, 7 in. — 329.7 in³
13. A coffee can is 6.5 inches high and has a diameter of 5 inches. Find the volume of the can. Round to the nearest tenth. 127.6 in³

© Glencoe/McGraw-Hill 90 *Mathematics: Applications and Connections, Course 2*

Applications and Problem Solving

16. rectangular pan

15. ***Energy*** A pipe is 100 feet long and has an inside diameter of 0.5 foot. Find the number of cubic feet of oil that it can hold. **19.6 ft³**
16. ***Baking*** A rectangular cake pan is 13 inches by 9 inches by 2 inches. A round cake pan has a diameter of 8 inches and a height of 2 inches. Which will hold more batter, the rectangular pan or two round pans?
17. ***Measurement*** Firewood is usually sold by a unit of measure known as a cord. A cord is a stack of wood that is 8 feet long, 4 feet wide, and 4 feet high. Suppose a tree has a diameter of 2 feet. Find the height of the tree trunk that would produce about 1 cord of firewood. **about 41 feet**
18. ***Critical Thinking*** Design an activity to find the relationship between the volume of a cylinder and the volume of a cone with the same base and height. Describe the relationship. (*Hint:* See Hands-On Lab 12-2B on page 502.) **See margin.**

Mixed Review

19. 152.88 m³

19. ***Geometry*** Find the volume of a rectangular prism with a length of 6 meters, a width of 4.9 meters, and a height of 5.2 meters. *(Lesson 12-2)*

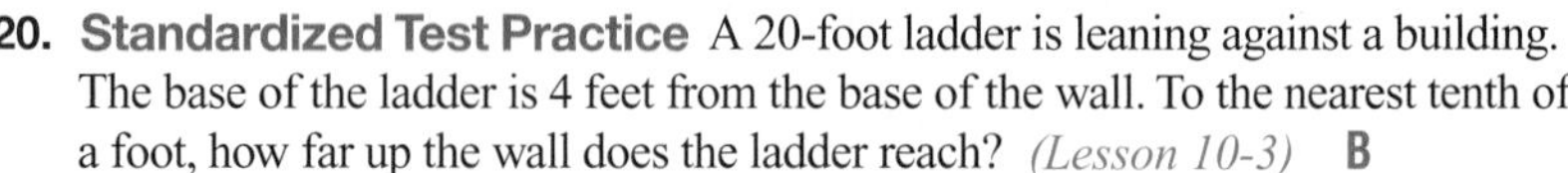

20. **Standardized Test Practice** A 20-foot ladder is leaning against a building. The base of the ladder is 4 feet from the base of the wall. To the nearest tenth of a foot, how far up the wall does the ladder reach? *(Lesson 10-3)* **B**

A 19.2 ft **B** 19.6 ft **C** 29.6 ft **D** 31.4 ft

21. ***Patterns*** Draw the next two figures in the pattern. *(Lesson 1-6)*

 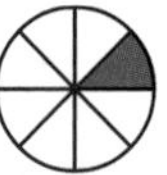   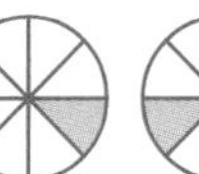

For **Extra Practice,** see page 601.

CHAPTER 12 Mid-Chapter Self Test

1. Draw the top, front, and side views of a cylinder. *(Lesson 12-1)* **See Answer Appendix.**

Find the volume of each rectangular prism or cylinder to the nearest tenth. *(Lessons 12-2 and 12-3)*

2. 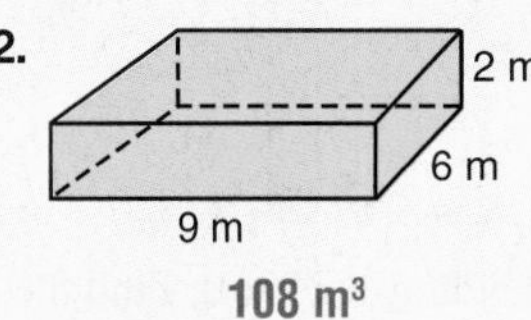

108 m³

3. 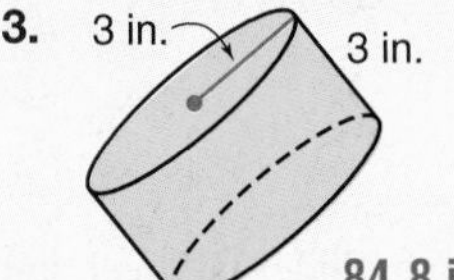

84.8 in³

4. 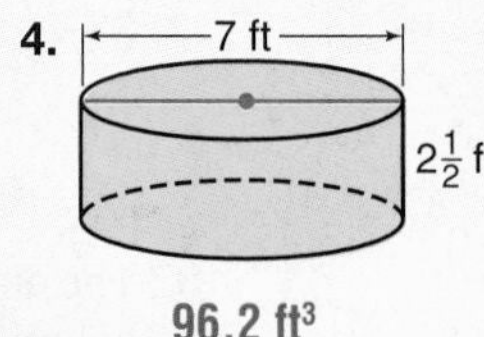

96.2 ft³

5. The members of student council are selling popcorn at home basketball games. They can use a rectangular box that is 5 inches long, 2 inches wide, and 8 inches high, or they can use a cylinder-shaped bag that has a 4-inch diameter and is 6 inches high. Which choice holds more popcorn? *(Lessons 12-2 and 12-3)* **rectangular box**

Extending the Lesson

***Enrichment Masters,* p. 90**

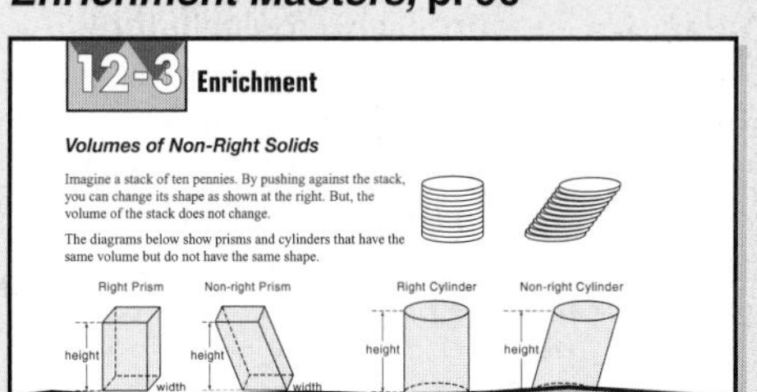

12-3 **Enrichment**

Volumes of Non-Right Solids

Imagine a stack of ten pennies. By pushing against the stack, you can change its shape as shown at the right. But, the volume of the stack does not change.

The diagrams below show prisms and cylinders that have the same volume but do not have the same shape.

Activity Lamar's 4-cylinder car engine has a volume of 141 cubic inches. If each cylinder has a radius of 1.5 inches, what is each cylinder's height? **about 5 inches**

Dr. Eloy Rodriguez

BIOCHEMIST

Dr. Rodriguez, a professor at Cornell University in Ithaca, New York, works in a new field of chemistry called *zoopharmacognosy*. He studies how some animals choose to eat plants with healing substances that cure them of their illnesses. He determines what substances occur in these plants and tries to reproduce them in the laboratory. He hopes that someday these synthetic substances can be used to cure human illnesses.

Someday, I'd like to find a cure for cancer.

Most careers in biochemistry require a minimum of four years of college and a Bachelor's degree. Courses in English, foreign language, mathematics, chemistry, physics, biology, social studies, and humanities will prepare students to work in different communities, countries, and cultures while gathering data for their research.

For more information:
Botanical Society of America
Department of Botany
The Ohio State University
1735 Neil Avenue
Columbus, OH 43210

interNET CONNECTION
www.glencoe.com/sec/math/mac/mathnet

Your Turn

Interview a botanist. Ask what plants they are currently studying and what they hope to learn from their study of such plants. Write a report based on the information gathered in your interview. Request, or find, photos or drawings of the plants being studied. Be sure to include these pictures in your report.

Motivating Students

Budding scientists might be inspired by biomedical research in the forests of Venezuela, Brazil, and Uganda. The leaves of the Aspilia sunflower, for example, have been used for centuries to treat stomach problems. To start the discussion, you may ask students these questions.

- What do mountain gorillas eat? **more than 40 different types of plants, some with medicinal properties and some that are toxic to humans**
- What is the life expectancy of mountain gorillas? **Although they are an endangered species, when they are safe from harm gorillas live 40 to 50 years in good health.**

Making the Math Connection

Precise measurement, data collection, and analysis of plant extracts are tools of the researcher's trade.

Working on *Your Turn*

Encourage students to ask questions about the shape of different plant structures, such as leaves, stems, flowers, and fruit. How do differences in volume and surface area affect a plant's adaptability to extreme weather conditions, such as deserts or rainforests?

More About Dr. Eloy Rodriguez

- Dr. Rodriguez received his Ph. D. in Chemistry from the University of Texas at Austin. He was a professor of phytochemistry (the study of chemicals produced by plants) at the University of California at Irvine. Dr. Rodriguez also studies ethnobotany (how humans use plants).
- Dr. Rodriguez directs the California Alliance for Minority Participation (CAMP), Kids Investigating and Discovering Science (KIDS), and the Minority International Research Training (MIRT) programs.

An additional School to Career activity is available on page 25 of the ***School to Career Masters.***

12-4A HANDS-ON LAB Notes

GET READY

Objective Students use nets to find the surface area of rectangular prisms.

Optional Resources
Hands-On Lab Masters
- square dot paper, p. 12
- worksheet, p. 69

Overhead Manipulative Resources
- rectangular dot paper

Manipulative Kit
- scissors

MANAGEMENT TIPS

Recommended Time
30 minutes

Getting Started Have students work in groups. Provide a box for each group to break down and lay flat. Have students estimate the surface area before viewing the box as a net. Then have them measure the sides and calculate the area.

For the **Activity,** suggest that students imagine the box breaking down and lying flat, and draw the rectangular pieces. Ask students what other arrangements could depict the same box.

Teaching Tip Make sure students understand that there may be more than one correct net for any figure.

Additional Answer

2. Find the sum of the areas of the rectangle.

HANDS-ON LAB COOPERATIVE LEARNING

12-4A Nets and Surface Area

A Preview of Lesson 12-4

- dot paper
- scissors
- tape

Imagine that you cut a cardboard box along its edges, open it up, and lay it flat. The result is a two-dimensional figure called a *net.* Nets can help you see the regions or faces that make up the surface of the figure.

TRY THIS

Work with a partner.

To make a net of the prism shown above, follow these steps.

- Start with the base of the prism. Draw a rectangle that is 5 units long and 4 units wide on dot paper.

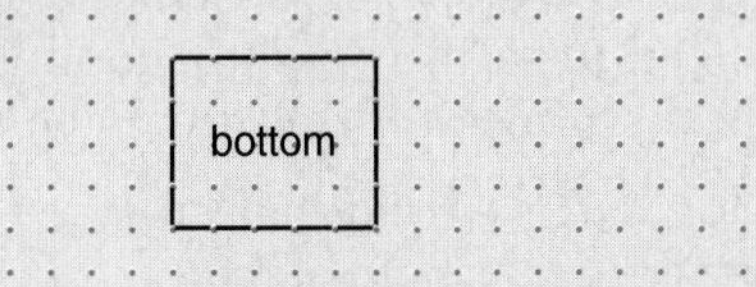

bottom

- Then visualize unfolding the solid along the edges. Draw the rectangles for the front, back, and sides of the prism.

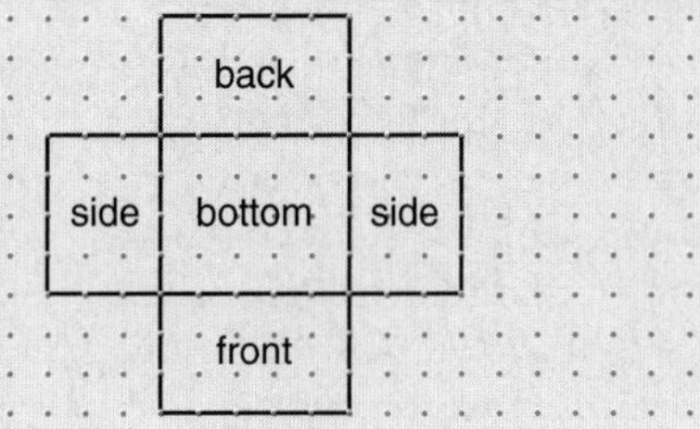

back
side bottom side
front

- Finally, draw the top of the prism. *This is only one of several possible nets that you could draw.*

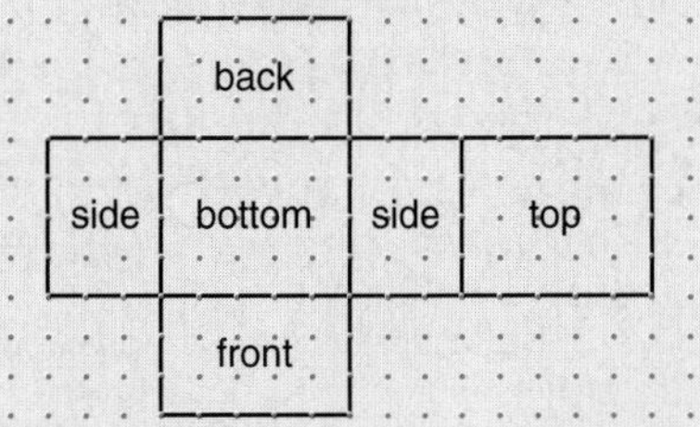

back
side bottom side top
front

ON YOUR OWN

1. The net shown above is made of rectangles. How many rectangles are in the net? **6**
2. Explain how you can find the total area of the rectangles. **See margin.**
3. The *surface area* of a prism is the total area of its net. Find the surface area of the prism. **94 square units**

Draw a net for each figure. Then cut out the net, fold it, and tape it together to form the three-dimensional figure. Find the surface area of each figure. **4–9. See Answer Appendix for drawings.**

4.

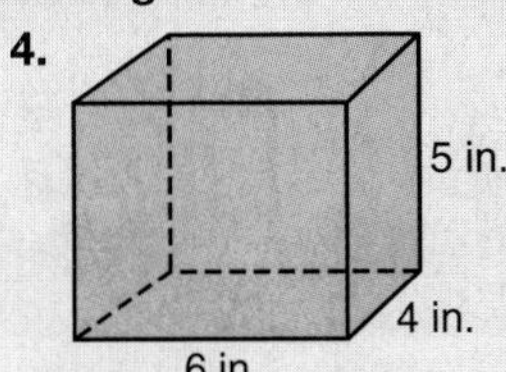

148 in^2

5. **18 cm^2**

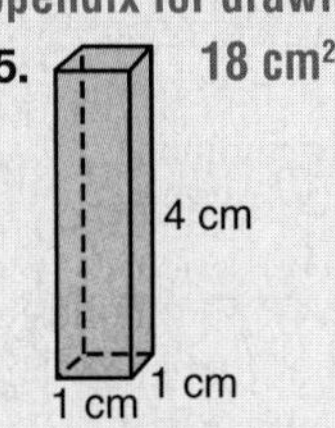

6.

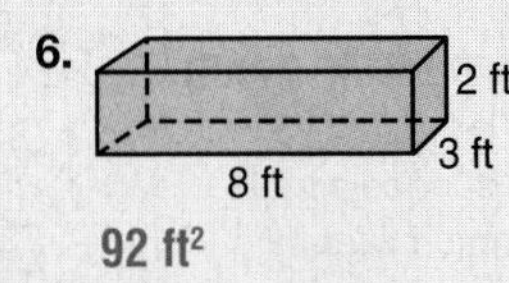

92 ft^2

7.

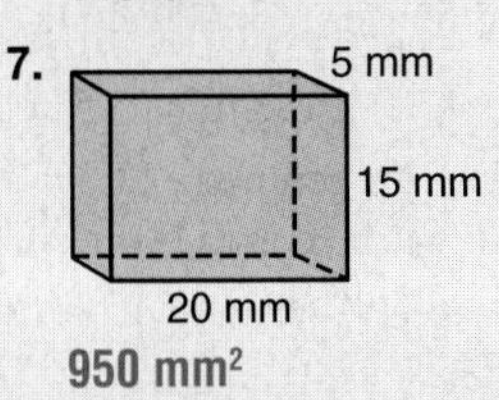

950 mm^2

8.

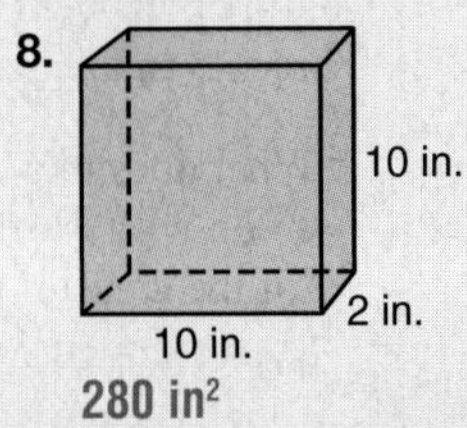

280 in^2

9.

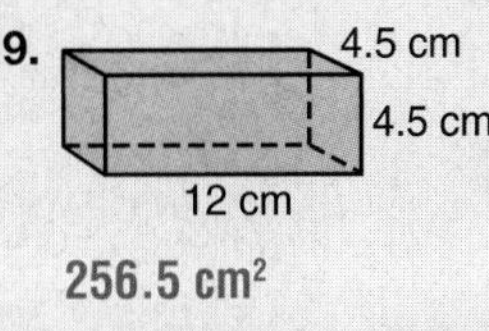

256.5 cm^2

10. A tetrahedron is a three-dimensional figure made of equilateral triangles. Draw a net for a tetrahedron.
10–11. See margin.

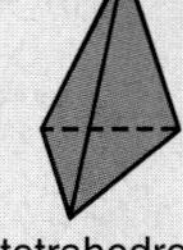

tetrahedron

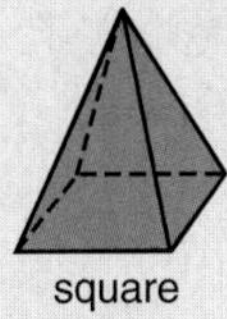

square pyramid

11. Draw a net for a square pyramid.

12. All of the faces of a cube are congruent squares.

a. Copy and complete the table to find the surface area of each cube. Use nets if necessary.

Dimensions of Each Face	Area of Each Face	Surface Area
1 unit by 1 unit	1 sq. unit	6 sq. units
2 units by 2 units	4 sq. units	24 sq. units
3 units by 3 units	9 sq. units	54 sq. units
4 units by 4 units	16 sq. units	96 sq. units
5 units by 5 units	25 sq. units	150 sq. units

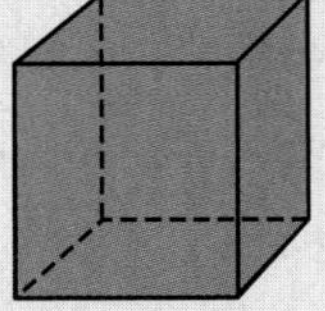

b. What is the effect on the surface area of a cube if its dimensions are doubled? tripled? **4 times greater, 9 times greater**

c. Using the pattern in the table, write an equation to find the surface area of a cube whose length is s units. **600 square units.**

13. ***Look Ahead*** Let ℓ represent the length, w represent the width, and h represent the height of a prism. Write an equation that shows how to find the surface area if you know the length, width, and height of a rectangular prism.
surface area = $\ell w + \ell w + wh + wh + \ell h + \ell h$

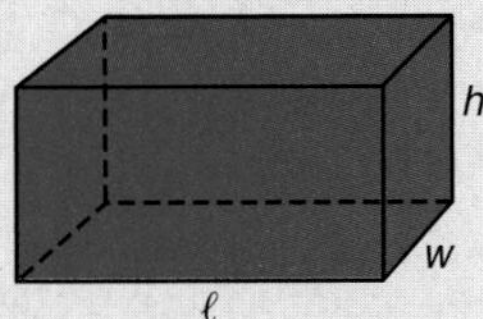

ASSESS

Have students complete Exercises 1–13. Use students' answers to Exercise 2 to evaluate their understanding of nets. Remind students that opposite faces of a rectangular prism have the same area.

Additional Answers

10.

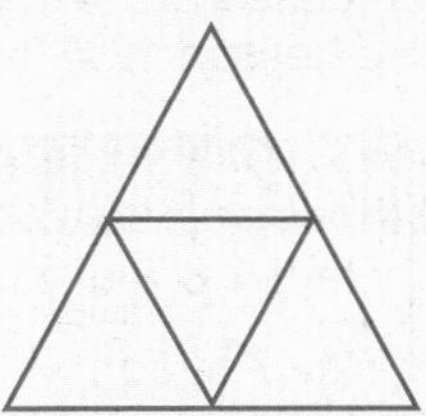

11.

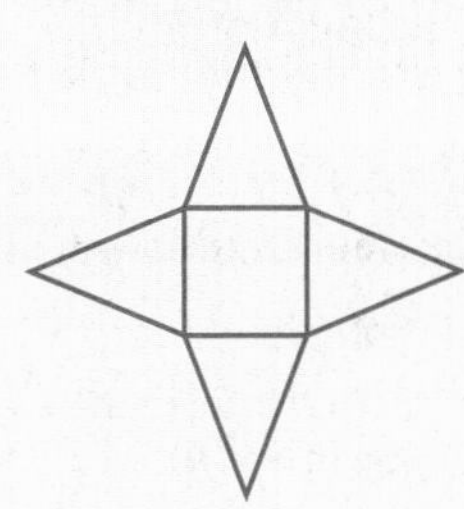

***Hands-On Lab Masters*, p. 69**

Name ____________ Date ________

Hands-On Lab
(Lesson 12-4A)

Nets and Surface Area

On Your Own

1. There are 6 rectangles in the net.
2. Explain how you can find the total area of the rectangles. Sample answer: For each of the rectangles, find the area by multiplying the length by the width. Then find the sum of the areas of all the rectangles.
3. The surface area of the prism is 94 square units.
4. surface area = 148 in^2 5. surface area = 18 cm^2
6. surface area = 92 ft^2 7. surface area = 950 mm^2
8. surface area = 280 in^2 9. surface area = 256.5 cm^2

10.

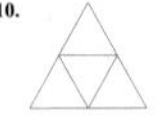

11.

12. a.

Dimensions of Each Face	Area of Each Face	Surface Area
1 unit by 1 unit	1 sq. unit	6 sq. units
2 units by 2 units	4 sq. units	24 sq. units
3 units by 3 units	9 sq. units	54 sq. units
4 units by 4 units	16 sq. units	96 sq. units
5 units by 5 units	25 sq. units	150 sq. units

b. If its dimensions are doubled, the surface area of a cube is 4 times greater. If its dimensions are tripled, the surface area is 9 times greater.
c. For a cube whose length is 10 units, the surface area is 600 square units.

13. **Look Ahead** Write an equation that shows how to find the surface area of a rectangular prism. Sample answer: Surface area of a rectangular prism = $\ell w + \ell w + wh + wh + \ell h + \ell h$

 69 *Mathematics: Applications and Connections, Course 2*

Math Journal Have students write a paragraph comparing and contrasting the nets they drew of rectangular prisms, cubes, pyramids, and tetrahedrons.

12-4 Lesson Notes

Instructional Resources

- *Study Guide Masters,* p. 91
- *Practice Masters,* p. 91
- *Enrichment Masters,* p. 91
- Transparencies 12-4, A and B
- *Assessment and Evaluation Masters,* p. 324

CD-ROM Program
- Resource Lesson 12-4
- Interactive Lesson 12-4

Recommended Pacing	
Standard	Days 7 & 8 of 11
Honors	Day 7 of 10
Block	Day 4 of 5

1 FOCUS

5-Minute Check
(Lesson 12-3)

Find the volume of each cylinder to the nearest tenth.

1. 2 in., 6.5 in. **81.7 in^3**

2. radius, 5m
height, 9.6 m **754.0 m^3**

The 5-Minute Check is also available on **Transparency 12-4A** for this lesson.

Motivating the Lesson

Hands-On Activity Display a closed box and a large sheet of wrapping paper. Ask students how they would figure out the exact amount of paper needed to cover the box.

12-4 Surface Area of Rectangular Prisms

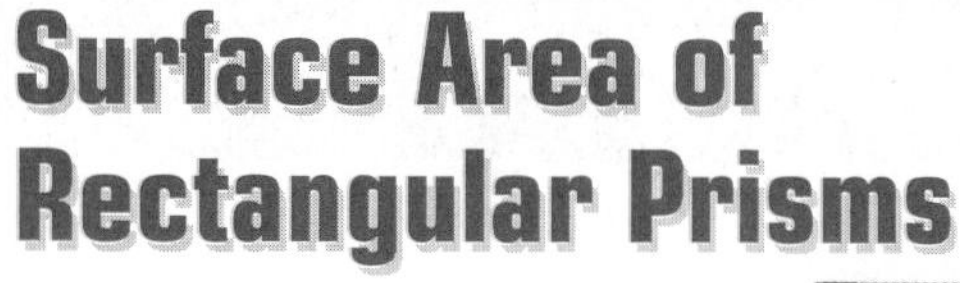

What you'll learn

You'll learn to find the surface area of rectangular prisms.

When am I ever going to use this?

You'll use surface area to find how much wrapping paper you'll need to wrap a present.

Word Wise

surface area

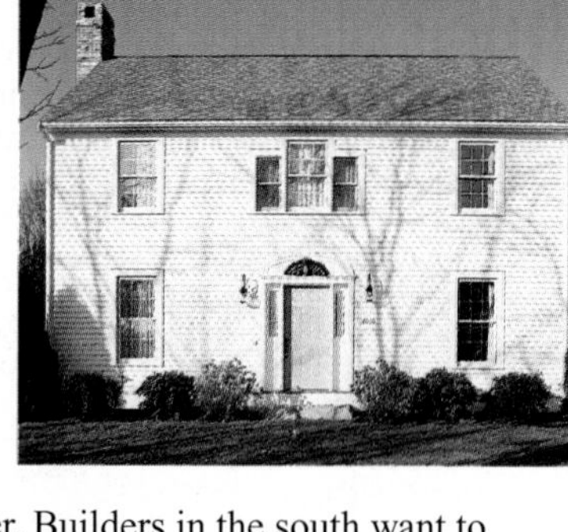

Did you ever wonder why houses in New England are often two-story houses that resemble a cube, but houses in the southern part of the U.S. are often one-story ranch houses? Blame it on the weather.

Builders in the north want to build energy-efficient homes that keep the heat inside in winter. Builders in the south want to build open, well-ventilated houses to let the cool breezes in all year long.

What does this have to do with geometry? It has to do with **surface area.** Surface area is the sum of the areas of all of the outside surfaces of a three-dimensional figure.

HANDS-ON MINI-LAB

Work with a partner.

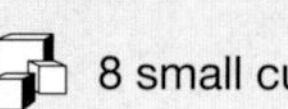

8 small cubes

In this Mini-Lab, you will construct prisms with small cubes. The volume of each small cube is 1 cubic unit, and the area of each face is 1 square unit.

Try This **2–3. See margin.**

1. Arrange the eight cubes into a prism. Count the number of faces that are on the outside of the prism. This number is the surface area of the prism. Don't forget the faces on the bottom. **1. See students' work.**
2. Draw a sketch of your prism and write the surface area beside it.
3. Repeat Steps 1-2 and make other prisms with the eight cubes.

Talk About It

4. Which prism has the least surface area? the greatest? **4. 2 × 2 × 2; 1 × 1 × 8**
5. When you heat a home in the winter, some heat is lost through the walls and roof. What shape house would you want to minimize wall and roof area? **a two-story house**
6. Suppose you want lots of air and light in your house. What shape house would you build to maximize wall and roof area? **a one-story ranch**

Additional Answers for the Mini-Lab

2. Sample answer:

surface area = 34

3. Sample answer:

surface area = 24

Example 1 Find the surface area of the rectangular prism.

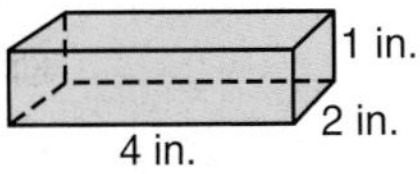

The net shows that there are six faces.

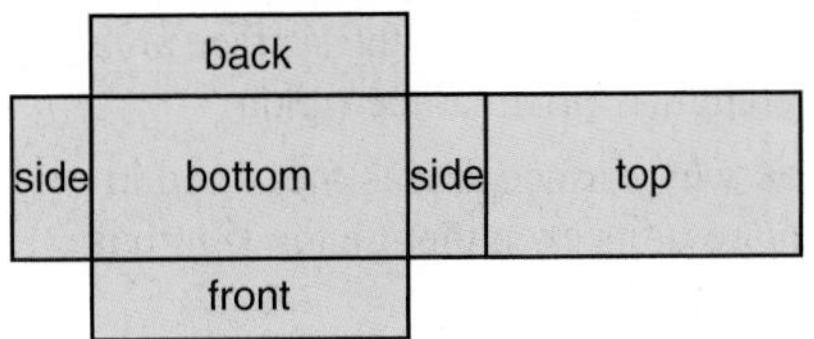

Use the formula $A = \ell w$ to find each area.

Face	Dimensions	Area
front	$\ell = 4, h = 1$	$A = 4 \times 1$ or 4
back	$\ell = 4, h = 1$	$A = 4 \times 1$ or 4
top	$\ell = 4, w = 2$	$A = 4 \times 2$ or 8
bottom	$\ell = 4, w = 2$	$A = 4 \times 2$ or 8
side	$w = 2, h = 1$	$A = 2 \times 1$ or 2
side	$w = 2, h = 1$	$A = 2 \times 1$ or 2
	TOTAL	28

Notice there are three pairs of congruent faces — the front and back, the top and bottom, and the two sides.

The surface area of the prism is 28 square inches.

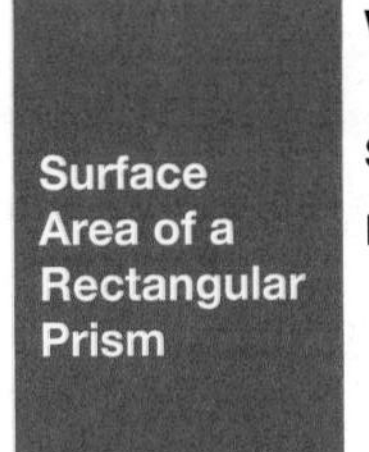

Words: The surface area of a rectangular prism equals the sum of the areas of the faces.

Symbols: surface area $= 2\ell w + 2\ell h + 2wh$

Model:

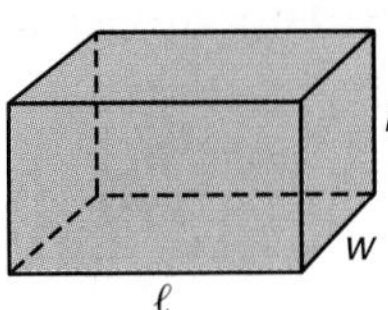

Example 2 **Manufacturing** Find the surface area of a rectangular shipping box that is 15 inches by 10 inches by 12 inches.

12 in.
10 in.
15 in.

Replace ℓ with 15, w with 10, and h with 12.

surface area $= 2\ell w + 2\ell h + 2\,wh$

surface area $= 2 \times 15 \times 10 + 2 \times 15 \times 12 + 2 \times 10 \times 12$

surface area $= 300 + 360 + 240$ *Multiply first. Then add.*

surface area $= 900$

The surface area of the box is 900 square inches.

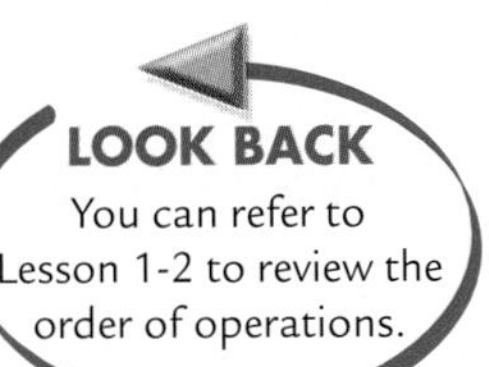

LOOK BACK
You can refer to Lesson 1-2 to review the order of operations.

2 TEACH

Transparency 12-4B contains a teaching aid for this lesson.

Using the Mini-Lab Have students construct as many different prisms as they can, recording the surface area of each. Ask students which constructions would make a better New England house and which would make a better southern house.

In-Class Examples

For Example 1
Find the surface area of the rectangular prism.

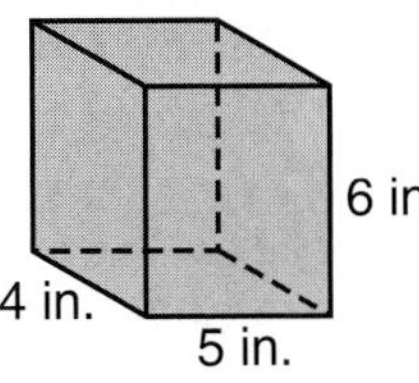

148 in^2

For Example 2
Find the surface area of a rectangular shoe box that is 12 inches by 6 inches by 5 inches.
324 in^2

Teaching Tip In Example 2, caution students to observe the order of operations, but note that factors in a multiplication expression, such as $2\ell w$, $2\ell h$, and $2wh$, can be multiplied in any order.

Reteaching the Lesson

Activity Have students make a net of the closed box (see Motivating the Lesson on page 510) on dot paper. Measure and label the dimensions of each of the six rectangles. Have students find the area of each and the total surface area of the box.

Error Analysis
Watch for students who confuse the surface area of a prism with its volume.
Prevent by reminding students that surface area is a measure in square (not cubic) units of the outside faces of a figure that can be seen.

3 PRACTICE/APPLY

Check for Understanding

If students need additional practice or instruction after completing Exercises 1–7, one of these options may be helpful.

- Extra Practice, see p. 602
- Reteaching Activity, see p. 511
- *Study Guide Masters,* p. 91
- *Practice Masters,* p. 91
- Interactive Mathematics Tools Software

Assignment Guide

Core: 9–15 odd, 18–20
Enriched: 8–14 even, 15, 16, 18–20

Additional Answer

2. Surface area measures the area of the faces, and area is measured in square units.

***Study Guide Masters,* p. 91**

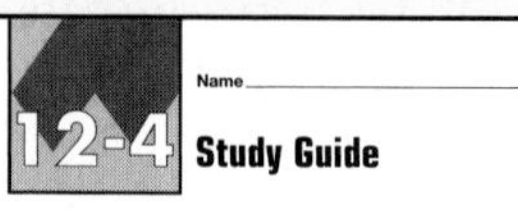

Name ________ Date ________

12-4 Study Guide

Surface Area of Rectangular Prisms

The surface area of a rectangular prism equals the sum of the areas of the faces.

The surface area of a rectangular prism can be found by using the formula $A = 2\ell w + 2\ell h + 2wh$.

Example **Find the surface area of the rectangular prism.**

$\ell = 6.4$ cm, $w = 5.6$ cm, and $h = 4$ cm

$A = 2\ell w + 2\ell h + 2wh$
$= 2(6.4)(5.6) + 2(6.4)(4) + 2(5.6)(4)$
$= 71.68 + 51.2 + 44.8$
$= 167.68$

The surface area of the rectangular prism is 167.68 cm².

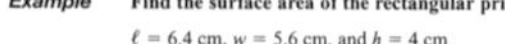

Find the surface area of each rectangular prism to the nearest tenth.

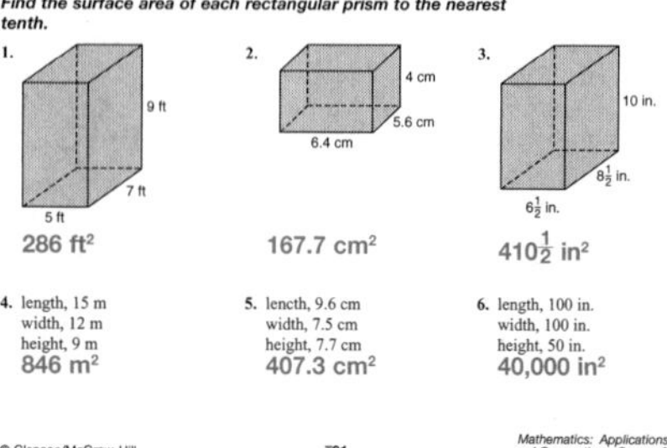

1. 286 ft²
2. 167.7 cm²
3. $410\frac{1}{2}$ in²
4. length, 15 m; width, 12 m; height, 9 m — 846 m²
5. length, 9.6 cm; width, 7.5 cm; height, 7.7 cm — 407.3 cm²
6. length, 100 in.; width, 100 in.; height, 50 in. — 40,000 in²

 T91 *Mathematics: Applications and Connections, Course 2*

CHECK FOR UNDERSTANDING

Communicating Mathematics

Read and study the lesson to answer each question.

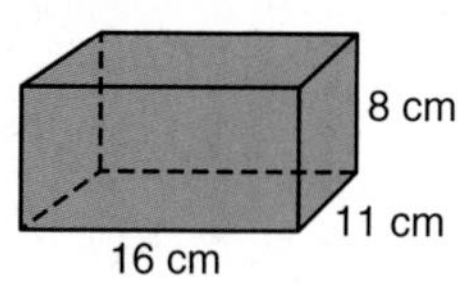

1. ***Explain*** how to find the surface area of the rectangular prism at the right. **1. Find the sum of the areas of the faces.**
2. ***Tell*** why surface area is measured in square units even though the figure is three-dimensional. **See margin.**

3. ***Write a Problem*** about a situation in which you might find the surface area of a rectangular prism. **See students' work.**

Guided Practice

Find the surface area of each rectangular prism to the nearest tenth.

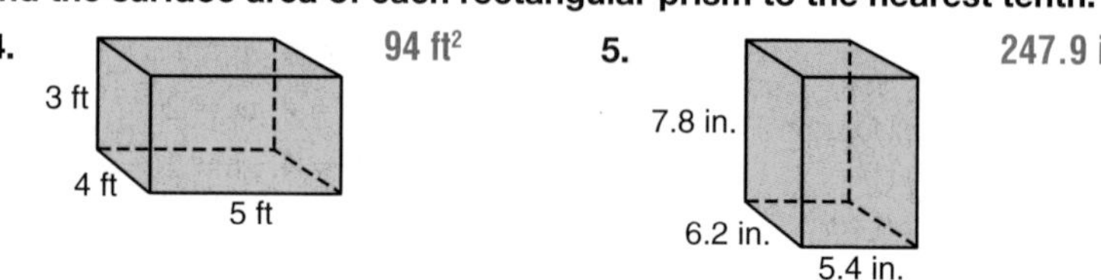

4. **94 ft²**
5. **247.9 in²**
6. Find the surface area of a rectangular prism with a length of 5 centimeters, width of 10 centimeters, and height of 7 centimeters. **310 cm²**
7. ***Packaging*** What is the least amount of wrapping paper that is needed to wrap a gift box that is 2 feet by 1 foot by 3 feet? **22 ft²**

EXERCISES

Practice

Find the surface area of each rectangular prism to the nearest tenth.

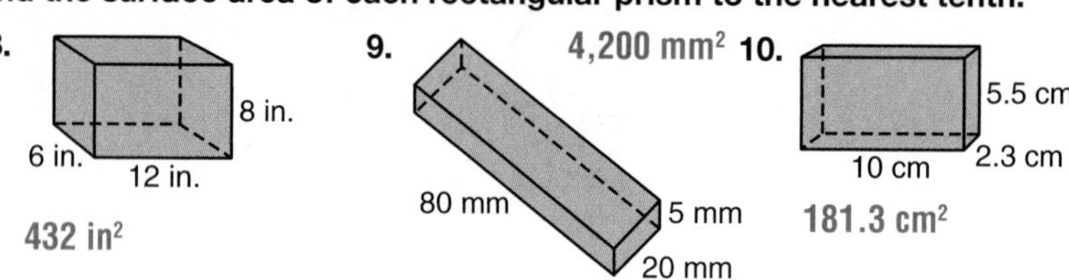

8. **432 in²**
9. **4,200 mm²**
10. **181.3 cm²**

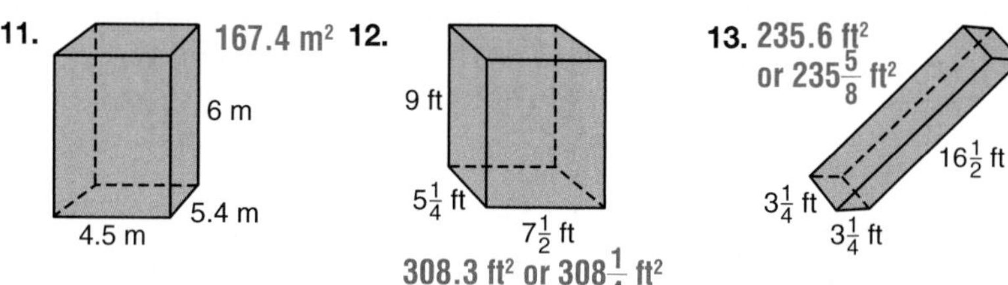

11. **167.4 m²**
12. **308.3 ft² or $308\frac{1}{4}$ ft²**
13. **235.6 ft² or $235\frac{5}{8}$ ft²**
14. Each face of a cube has an area of 8 square inches. What is the surface area of the cube? **48 in²**

Applications and Problem Solving

15. ***Algebra*** Write a formula for the surface area of a cube in which each edge measures x units. **surface area = $6x^2$**

Classroom Vignette

"I love how the Chapter Project unfolds through the chapter in the Working on the Chapter Project sections. My students in life science always have trouble understanding the relationship between surface area and leaf function. By doing this Chapter Project, they learn about it in math class, too!"

Laura J. Young, Ed.D.

Laura J. Young, Ed. D., Teacher
Edwards Middle School
Conyers, GA

16b. 12 cm²
16c. Sample answer: The granulated sugar has a greater surface area than the cubes.

16. ***Physical Science*** When you make fruit-flavored drink mix, you dissolve sugar into water. Granulated sugar dissolves faster than a sugar cube.
   a. Suppose the length of each edge of a sugar cube is 1 centimeter. Find the surface area of the cube. **6 cm²**
   b. Imagine cutting the cube in half horizontally and vertically. Find the total surface area of the eight cubes.
   c. Make a conjecture as to why granulated sugar dissolves faster than a sugar cube.

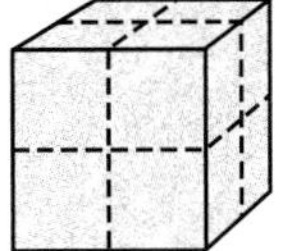

17. ***Working on the CHAPTER Project*** Refer to Exercise 20 on page 501.
   a. What is the surface area of your leaf? **a–b. See students' work.**
   b. Find the ratio of the surface area of your leaf to its volume.
18. ***Critical Thinking*** Draw two prisms such that one has a greater surface area and the other has a greater volume. **See margin.**

Mixed Review

19. ***Geometry*** Find the volume of a cylinder having a radius of 4 centimeters and a height of 6.5 centimeters. *(Lesson 12-3)* **326.7 cm³**
20. **Standardized Test Practice** A football player has made 80% of the field goals he has attempted in his career. If he attempts 5 field goals in a game, how many would he be expected to make? *(Lesson 8-8)* **B**

   A 5 **B** 4 **C** 3 **D** 2

For **Extra Practice,** see page 602.

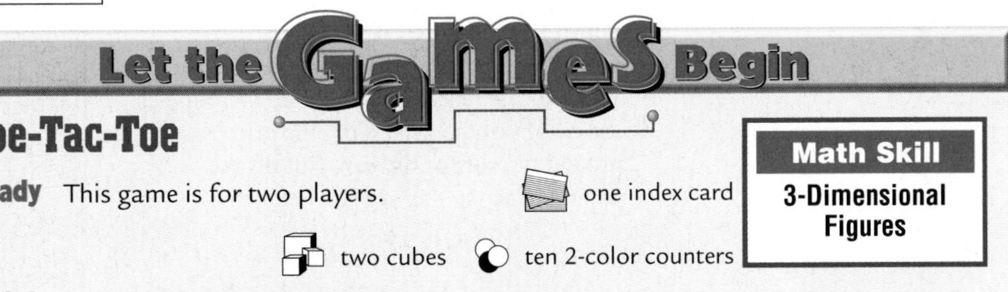

Shape-Tac-Toe

Math Skill
3-Dimensional Figures

Get Ready This game is for two players.

one index card
two cubes
ten 2-color counters

Get Set One player draws a game board on the index card like the one shown. The second player labels the six faces of each cube with these words.

First Cube	Second Cube
prism	circular base
pyramid	triangular base
cylinder	square base
cone	two parallel bases
flat surfaces	one base
curved surface	congruent faces

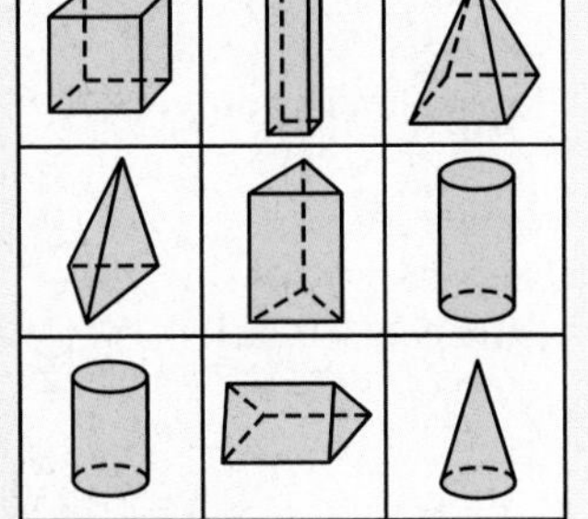

Go
- The first player rolls both cubes and places a counter on any one shape that matches the conditions on the cubes. Players alternate turns.
- The first player to cover three shapes in a row wins.

Visit www.glencoe.com/sec/math/mac/mathnet for more games.

CHAPTER Project

Exercise 17 asks students to advance to the next stage of work on the Chapter Project. You may want students to draw the outline of their leaves on graph paper to make it easier to estimate the area.

4 ASSESS

Closing Activity

Writing Have students use a formula to find the surface area of a dresser shaped like a rectangular prism. Ask them to make up reasonable dimensions to use in their calculations.

Chapter 12, Quiz C (Lesson 12-4) is available in the *Assessment and Evaluation Masters*, p. 324.

Additional Answer

18.

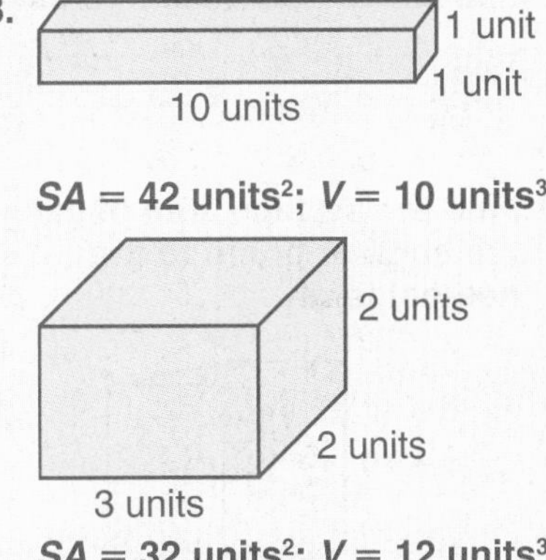

SA = 42 units²; *V* = 10 units³

SA = 32 units²; *V* = 12 units³

***Practice Masters,* p. 91**

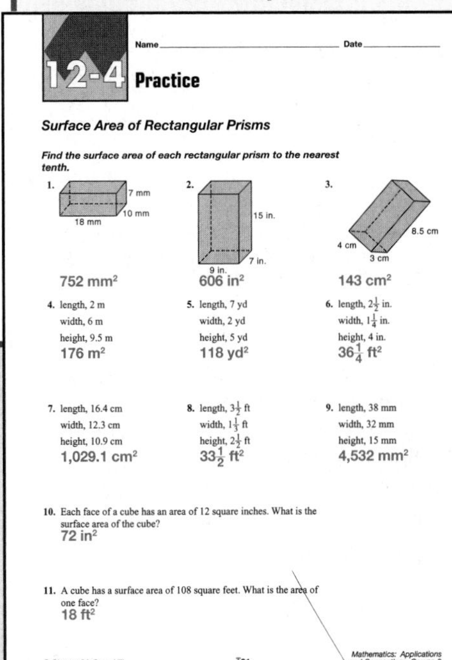

Name ____ Date ____

12-4 Practice

Surface Area of Rectangular Prisms

Find the surface area of each rectangular prism to the nearest tenth.

1. 18 mm, 10 mm, 7 mm — 752 mm²
2. 9 in., 7 in., 15 in. — 606 in²
3. 4 cm, 3 cm, 8.5 cm — 143 cm²
4. length, 2 m; width, 6 m; height, 9.5 m — 176 m²
5. length, 7 yd; width, 2 yd; height, 5 yd — 118 yd²
6. length, $2\frac{1}{2}$ in.; width, $1\frac{1}{4}$ in.; height, 4 in. — $36\frac{1}{4}$ ft²
7. length, 16.4 cm; width, 12.3 cm; height, 10.9 cm — 1,029.1 cm²
8. length, $3\frac{1}{2}$ ft; width, $1\frac{1}{2}$ ft; height, $2\frac{1}{2}$ ft — $33\frac{1}{2}$ ft²
9. length, 38 mm; width, 32 mm; height, 15 mm — 4,532 mm²
10. Each face of a cube has an area of 12 square inches. What is the surface area of the cube? 72 in²
11. A cube has a surface area of 108 square feet. What is the area of one face? 18 ft²

© Glencoe/McGraw-Hill T91 *Mathematics: Applications and Connections, Course 2*

Extending the Lesson

***Enrichment Masters,* p. 91**

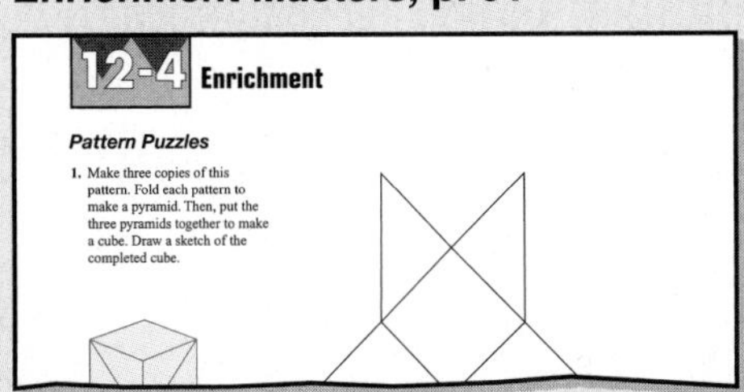

12-4 Enrichment

Pattern Puzzles

1. Make three copies of this pattern. Fold each pattern to make a pyramid. Then, put the three pyramids together to make a cube. Draw a sketch of the completed cube.

When playing the game, the player loses his or her turn if it is impossible to cover a shape. After students have played Shape-Tac-Toe, ask them which faces of the two cubes allow them to cover the most shapes on the game board.

*Additional resources for this game can be found on page 52 of the **Classroom Games.***

12-5 Lesson Notes

Instructional Resources

- *Study Guide Masters,* p. 92
- *Practice Masters,* p. 92
- *Enrichment Masters,* p. 92
- Transparencies 12-5, A and B
- *Assessment and Evaluation Masters,* p. 324
- *Classroom Games,* pp. 33–34
- *Technology Masters,* p. 49

CD-ROM Program
- Resource Lesson 12-5
- Interactive Lesson 12-5

Recommended Pacing	
Standard	Day 9 of 11
Honors	Day 8 of 10
Block	Day 4 of 5

1 FOCUS

5-Minute Check
(Lesson 12-4)

Find the surface area of each rectangular prism to the nearest tenth.

1.
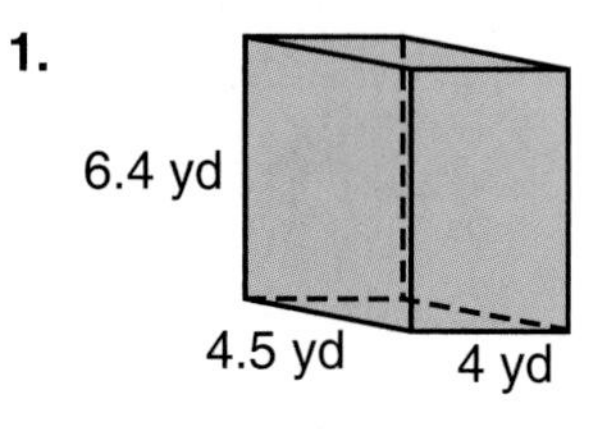

144.8 yd²

2.
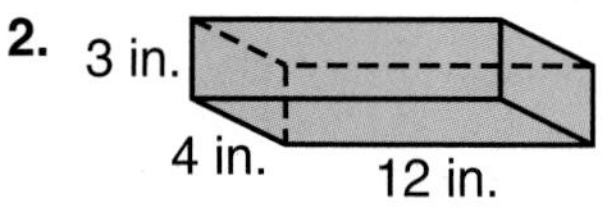

192 in²

The 5-Minute Check is also available on **Transparency 12-5A** for this lesson.

Motivating the Lesson

Communication Ask students to distinguish between a cylinder and a rectangular prism, and between a cylinder and a cone. Ask them what foods are packaged in cylindrical containers, and why so many foods are packaged in cylinders.

12-5 Surface Area of Cylinders

What you'll learn

You'll learn to find the surface area of cylinders.

When am I ever going to use this?

You'll use surface area to find the amount of paint needed to cover a cylindrical container.

Isn't it great to have a cold soft drink on a hot day! Now you can have one without the hassle of carrying a bulky ice chest or finding a refrigerated vending machine. A recently-invented can contains your favorite soft drink and can chill it anytime. Just turn the can over and press the button on the bottom of the can. In about 90 seconds, the temperature inside the can drops by 30°F, and you have a cold soft drink.

Soft drink cans are in the shape of cylinders. You can find the surface area of a cylinder by finding the area of all of the surfaces.

HANDS-ON MINI-LAB

Work with a partner. soft drink can 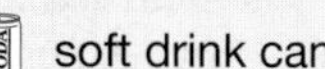 grid paper  scissors

Try This

- Trace the top and bottom of the can on grid paper. Cut out the shapes.
- Cut a long rectangle from grid paper. The width of the rectangle should be the same as the height of the can. Wrap the grid paper around the side of the can. Cut off the excess paper so the edges just meet.

Talk About It

1. Make a net of the cylinder. **See margin.**
2. Describe the shapes in the net. **rectangle, circle**
3. Tell how the length of the rectangle is related to the radii of the circles.
4. Explain how to find the surface area of the cylinder.

3. The length of the rectangle is the circumference of the circle, so the length is $2\pi r$.
4. Add the area of the circles to the area of the rectangle.

The Mini-Lab suggests that you can open a cylinder and lay it flat in the same way you did with a rectangular prism.

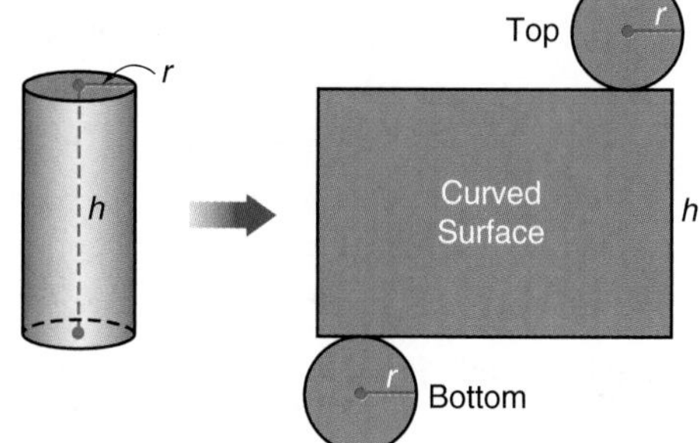

Multiple Learning Styles

Visual/Spatial Have students design a package for a food item, tool, toy, or other product in the shape of a cylinder. Students should determine the appropriate height and radius of the package, as well as how much of its surface area to devote to the name of the product, and illustrations, directions, and other information.

Additional Answer for the Mini-Lab

1.
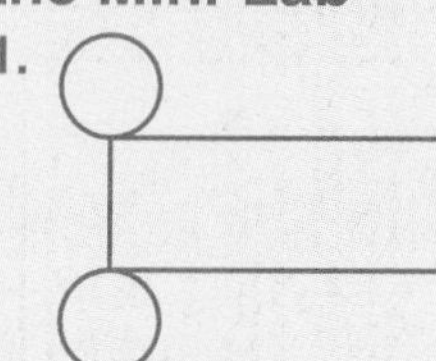

Example 1 Find the surface area of a 12-ounce soft drink can.

- First, find the area of the top and bottom. Use the formula for the area of a circle, $A = \pi r^2$. *The radius of the circle is 3 centimeters.*

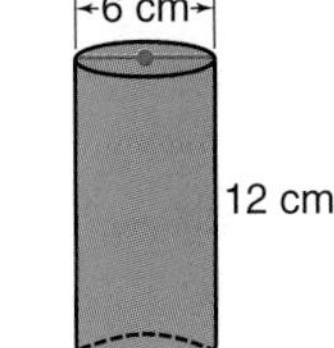

[π] [×] 3 [x^2] [=] 28.27433388

The area of one circle is about 28 square centimeters. So, the area of the top and bottom of the can is about 2×28 or 56 square centimeters.

- Now calculate the area of the curved surface. When unfolded, the curved surface has the shape of a rectangle. The width of the rectangle is the height of the can, and the length is the circumference of the base.

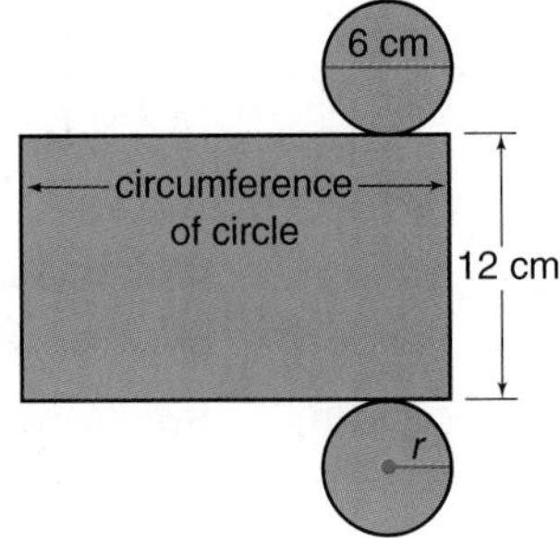

$A = \ell w$

$A = 2\pi r \times w$ *Replace ℓ with $2\pi r$, the formula for circumference.*

$A = 2\pi r \times h$ *Replace w with h.*

$A = 2 \times \pi \times 3 \times 12$ *Replace r with 3 and h with 12.*

2 [×] [π] [×] 3 [×] 12 = 226.1946711

The area of the curved surface is about 226 square centimeters.

- Finally, add the area of the curved surface to the area of the two circles.

$226 + 56 = 282$

The surface area of the soft drink can is about 282 square centimeters.

Surface Area of a Cylinder

Words: The surface area of a cylinder equals the sum of the areas of the circular bases ($2\pi r^2$) and the area of the curved surface ($2\pi rh$).

Symbols: surface area $= 2\pi r^2 + 2\pi rh$

Model: (cylinder with radius r and height h)

2 TEACH

Transparency 12-5B contains a teaching aid for this lesson.

Using the Mini-Lab Once students have demonstrated an understanding of how to use the formula for surface area of a cylinder, ask them how they would find the *height* of a can given the radius or diameter of its base and the total surface area. **Find the area of a base. Subtract double that amount from the surface area; divide what remains by the circumference of the base.**

In-Class Example

For Example 1

Find the surface area of a juice can that is about 15 centimeters high and has a diameter of about 10 centimeters. **about 628 cm²**

MathPASS CD-ROM

This CD-ROM offers a complete, self-paced mathematics curriculum. Each lesson includes a pretest, tutorial, guided practice, and posttest. MathPASS Lesson 43 is correlated to this Student Edition lesson.

For Windows & Macintosh

In-Class Example

For Example 2

August wants to wrap a hat box with a radius of 6 inches and a height of 5 inches. How much paper will he need? **about 414.7 in²**

Teaching Tip Remind students that the order of operations applies in using the formula $A = 2\pi r^2 + 2\pi rh$.

3 PRACTICE/APPLY

Check for Understanding

If students need additional practice or instruction after completing Exercises 1–6, one of these options may be helpful.

- Extra Practice, see p. 602
- Reteaching Activity
- *Study Guide Masters,* p. 92
- *Practice Masters,* p. 92

Assignment Guide

Core: 7–17 odd, 18–21
Enriched: 8–14 even, 16–21

Additional Answer

1. The circumference of the base is the same as the length of the rectangle.

***Study Guide Masters,* p. 92**

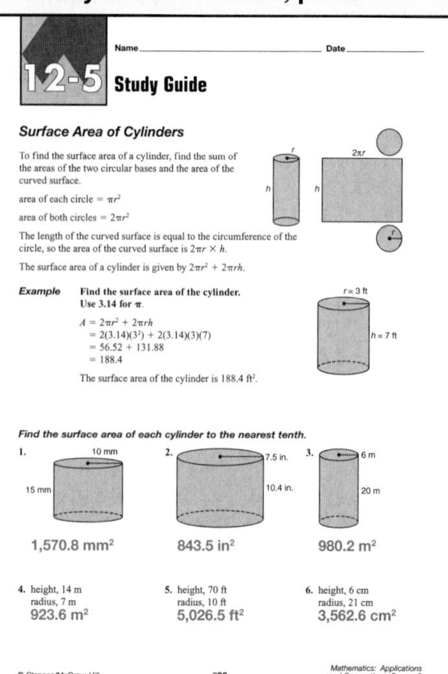

Name________________ Date________

12-5 Study Guide

Surface Area of Cylinders

To find the surface area of a cylinder, find the sum of the areas of the two circular bases and the area of the curved surface.

area of each circle = πr^2

area of both circles = $2\pi r^2$

The length of the curved surface is equal to the circumference of the circle, so the area of the curved surface is $2\pi r \times h$.

The surface area of a cylinder is given by $2\pi r^2 + 2\pi rh$.

Example **Find the surface area of the cylinder. Use 3.14 for π.**

$$A = 2\pi r^2 + 2\pi rh$$
$$= 2(3.14)(3^2) + 2(3.14)(3)(7)$$
$$= 56.52 + 131.88$$
$$= 188.4$$

The surface area of the cylinder is 188.4 ft².

Find the surface area of each cylinder to the nearest tenth.

1. 10 mm, 15 mm — 1,570.8 mm²
2. 7.5 in., 10.4 in. — 843.5 in²
3. 6 m, 20 m — 980.2 m²
4. height, 14 m radius, 7 m 923.6 m²
5. height, 70 ft radius, 10 ft 5,026.5 ft²
6. height, 6 cm radius, 21 cm 3,562.6 cm²

 T92 *Mathematics: Applications and Connections, Course 2*

2 **Agriculture** **A cylindrical gasoline storage tank on Mr. Baker's farm needs to be painted. He has almost one gallon of paint leftover from another painting job. If one gallon of paint covers 350 square feet, does Mr. Baker have enough paint for this job?**

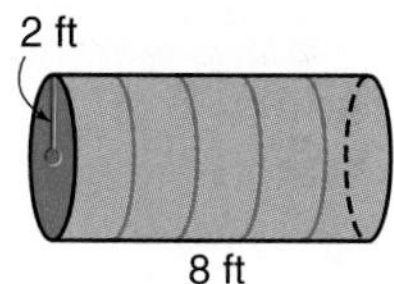

First, find the surface area of the tank.

surface area = $2\pi r^2 + 2\pi rh$

surface area = $(2 \times \pi \times 2^2) + (2 \times \pi \times 2 \times 8)$ *Replace r with 2 and h with 8.*

2 [×] [π] [×] 2 [x²] [+] 2 [×] [π] [×] 2 [×] 8 [=] *125.6637061*

The surface area of the tank is about 126 square feet. Since one gallon of paint will cover 350 square feet and Mr. Baker has almost one gallon of paint, he probably has enough paint.

CHECK FOR UNDERSTANDING

Communicating Mathematics

Read and study the lesson to answer each question.

1. ***Explain*** how you use the circumference of the base of a cylinder to help you find the surface area of the cylinder. **See margin.**
2. ***Choose*** the situation that represents the surface area of a cylinder. **b**
   a. the amount of tomato juice that is inside a can
   b. the amount of sheet metal needed to make the can

HANDS-ON MATH

3. ***Estimate*** the surface area of three different cans of food. Then measure each can, find the surface area, and rank them in order from greatest surface area to least surface area. **See students' work.**

Guided Practice

Answers are calculated using the π key on a calculator and then rounded.

Find the surface area of each cylinder to the nearest tenth.

4. 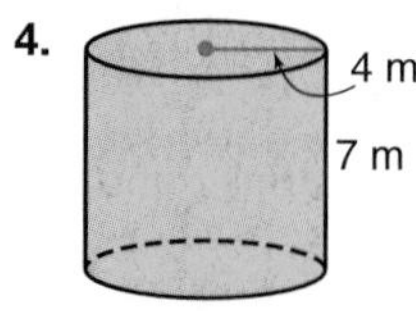

276.5 m²

5. 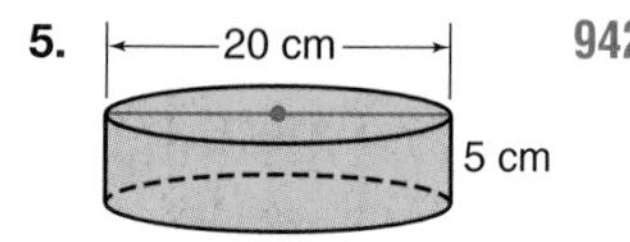

942.5 cm²

6. The radius of a cylinder is 5 feet, and its height is 4 feet. Find the surface area. **282.7 ft²**

EXERCISES

Practice

Find the surface area of each cylinder to the nearest tenth.

7. 8 mm, 4 mm **603.2 mm²**
8. 6 yd, 3 yd **169.6 yd²**
9. 7 in., $2\frac{1}{2}$ in. **149.2 in²**

516 **Chapter 12** Geometry: Finding Volume and Surface Area

Reteaching the Lesson

Activity Have students tear off the paper label that covers a can of soup. Lay the label out flat on a table and measure it. Then measure the circumference of the can to demonstrate that the curved surface of a cylinder is a rectangle whose length is equal to the circumference of the base.

Error Analysis

Watch for students who confuse area with circumference when using the formula to find surface area of a cylinder.

Prevent by pointing out that the circumference of the base is equal to the length of the rectangle obtained by "unrolling" the cylinder.

10. 904.8 m²

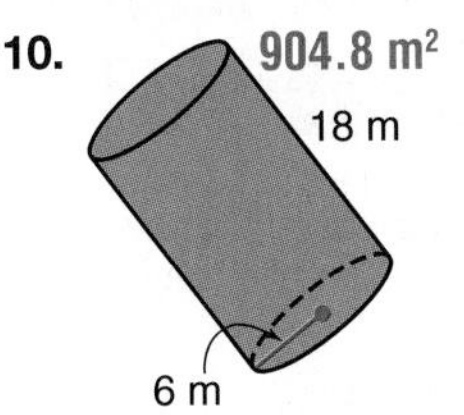

11.

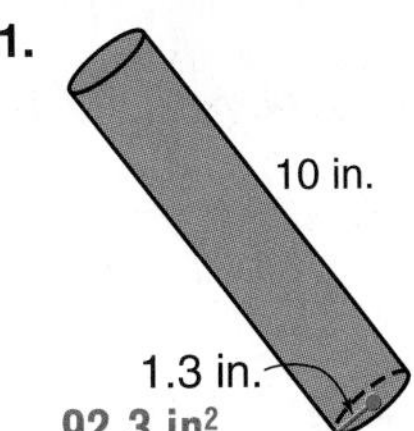

92.3 in²

12. 326.7 in²

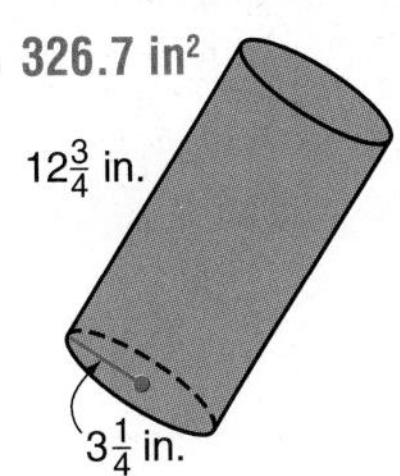

13. Find the surface area of a cylinder whose height is 14 inches and whose base has a diameter of 16 inches. **1,105.8 in²**

14. Find the surface area of a cylinder whose height is 12 inches and whose base has a circumference of 37.88 inches. **678.6 in²**

15. ***Write a Problem*** in which you need to find the surface area of a cylinder. **See students' work.**

Applications and Problem Solving

16. ***Design*** A can of vegetables is 5 inches high, and its base has a radius of 2 inches. How much paper is needed to make the label on the can? **62.8 in²**

17. ***Manufacturing*** The three metal containers below each hold about 1 liter of liquid. Find the surface area of each container.

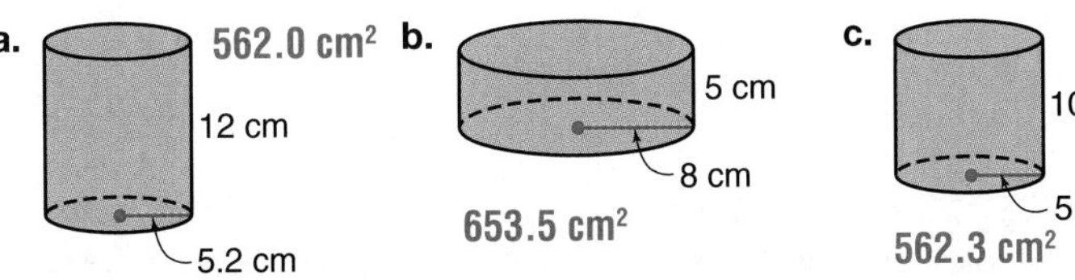

a. **562.0 cm²** b. **653.5 cm²** c. **562.3 cm²**

17d. cylinder from Exercise 17a

d. If you were in charge of manufacturing the containers, which container would you choose so that you would use the least amount of metal?

For **Extra Practice,** see page 602.

18. ***Critical Thinking*** If you double the height of a cylinder, will its surface area also double? Explain your reasoning. **No; the surface area of the side of the cylinder will double, but the area of the bases will not.**

Mixed Review

19. **Standardized Test Practice** The surface area of a cube is 294 mm². What is the length of one side of the cube? *(Lesson 12-4)* **A**

A 7 mm **B** 17 mm **C** 21 mm **D** 27 mm

20. Divide $4\frac{2}{5}$ by $\frac{1}{2}$. *(Lesson 7-9)* $8\frac{4}{5}$

interNET CONNECTION For the latest movie statistics, visit: www.glencoe.com/sec/math/mac/mathnet

21a–b. See Answer Appendix.

21. ***Entertainment*** Refer to the graph. *(Lesson 6-6)*

a. Graph the ordered pairs (year, ticket sales) on a coordinate plane.

b. Write a statement that describes the trend in movie ticket sales.

Movie Magic

Ticket Sales per Film	(million dollars)
1992	$32.5
1993	$32.0
1994	$29.4
1995	$23.5
1996	$24.6

Source: Motion Picture Association of America, 1997

4 ASSESS

Closing Activity

Modeling Have students use $8\frac{1}{2}$" × 11" pieces of paper to make two cylinders—one with a height of $8\frac{1}{2}$ inches and the other with a height of 11 inches. Ask them which cylinder has the greatest volume. **$8\frac{1}{2}$-inch height**

Chapter 12, Quiz D (Lesson 12-5) is available in the *Assessment and Evaluation Masters,* p. 324.

***Practice Masters,* p. 92**

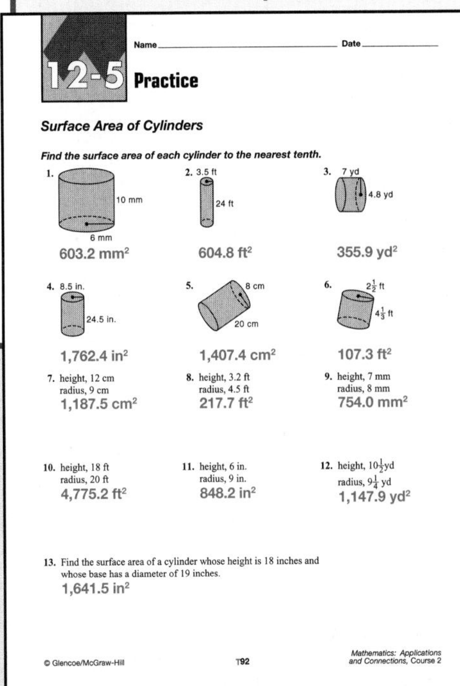

Name______ Date______

12-5 Practice

Surface Area of Cylinders

Find the surface area of each cylinder to the nearest tenth.

1. 10 mm, 6 mm — 603.2 mm²
2. 3.5 ft, 24 ft — 604.8 ft²
3. 7 yd, 4.8 yd — 355.9 yd²
4. 8.5 in., 24.5 in. — 1,762.4 in²
5. 8 cm, 20 cm — 1,407.4 cm²
6. $2\frac{1}{2}$ ft, $4\frac{1}{3}$ ft — 107.3 ft²
7. height, 12 cm radius, 9 cm — 1,187.5 cm²
8. height, 3.2 ft radius, 4.5 ft — 217.7 ft²
9. height, 7 mm radius, 8 mm — 754.0 mm²
10. height, 18 ft radius, 20 ft — 4,775.2 ft²
11. height, 6 in. radius, 9 in. — 848.2 in²
12. height, $10\frac{1}{2}$ yd radius, $9\frac{1}{2}$ yd — 1,147.9 yd²
13. Find the surface area of a cylinder whose height is 18 inches and whose base has a diameter of 19 inches. 1,641.5 in²

© Glencoe/McGraw-Hill T92 *Mathematics: Applications and Connections, Course 2*

Extending the Lesson

***Enrichment Masters,* p. 92**

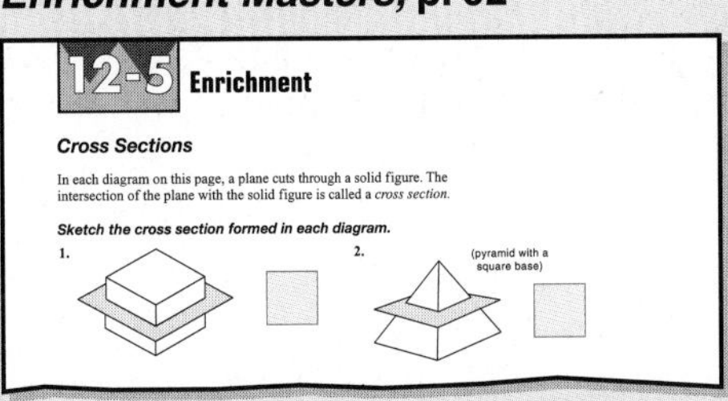

12-5 Enrichment

Cross Sections

In each diagram on this page, a plane cuts through a solid figure. The intersection of the plane with the solid figure is called a *cross section.*

Sketch the cross section formed in each diagram.

1.

2. (pyramid with a square base)

Activity Have students take a walking tour of local architecture and identify cylindrical structures. Have students work with a partner to estimate the surface area of a silo, flag pole, or other cylinder, and then calculate the surface area.

Vocabulary

This section provides a listing of the new terms, properties, and phrases that were introduced in this chapter. Have students define each term and provide an example or two of it, if appropriate.

Understanding and Using the Vocabulary

These exercises check students' understanding of the terms by using a variety of verbal formats including matching, completion, and true/false.

Glossaries A complete glossary of terms appears on pages 656–663. The glossary also appears in Spanish on pages 664–672.

Additional Answers

11. 

12. 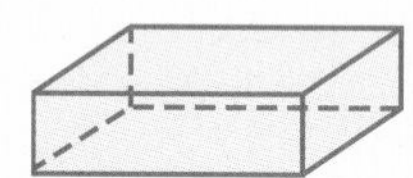

13. 

CHAPTER 12 Study Guide and Assessment

Chapter Review For additional lesson-by-lesson review, visit: www.glencoe.com/sec/math/mac/mathnet

Vocabulary

After completing this chapter, you should be able to define each term, concept or phrase and give an example or two of each.

Geometry
cylinder (p. 503)
net (p. 508)
perspective (p. 492)
Platonic solids (p. 496)
pyramid (p. 502)
rectangular prism (p. 498)
solids (p. 493)
surface area (p. 510)
volume (p. 498)

Problem Solving
make a model (p. 496)

Understanding and Using the Vocabulary

Choose the correct term or number to complete each sentence.

1. When a figure is drawn so you are able to see that it has three dimensions, the view is called a(n) (isometric, perspective) view.
2. A (rectangular prism, rectangle) is a solid figure that has three sets of parallel congruent sides.
3. The (volume, surface area) of a solid figure is the measure of the space occupied by it.
4. Volume is measured in (square, cubic) units.
5. The volume of a rectangular prism is found by (adding, multiplying) the length, the width, and the height.
6. A (cylinder, prism) is a solid figure that has two congruent, parallel circles as its bases.
7. The volume of a cylinder with a radius of 4 inches and a height of 2 inches is about (100.5, 25.1) cubic inches.
8. Surface area is the sum of the (areas, volumes) of all of the outside surfaces of a three-dimensional figure.
9. The surface area of a prism with a length of 6 meters, width of 2 meters, and a height of 1 meter is (20, 40) square meters.

In Your Own Words

10. ***Explain*** how to find the surface area of a cylinder. **Add the areas of the two circular bases and the area of the curved surface.**

MindJogger Videoquizzes

MindJogger Videoquizzes provide an alternative review of concepts presented in this chapter. Students work in teams to answer questions, gaining points for correct answers. The questions are presented in three rounds.

Round 1 Concepts–5 questions
Round 2 Skills–4 questions
Round 3 Problem Solving–4 questions

Objectives & Examples

Upon completing this chapter, you should be able to:

- draw a three-dimensional figure when given the top, side, and front views *(Lesson 12-1)*

Make a perspective drawing by using the top, side, and front views.

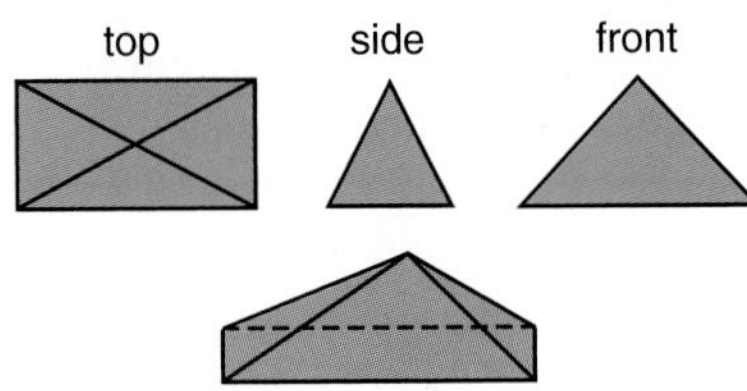

12–13. See margin.

Review Exercises

Use these exercises to review and prepare for the chapter test.

Draw a top, a side, and a front view of the figure.

11. See margin.

Make a perspective drawing of each figure by using the top, side, and front views as shown. Use isometric dot paper if necessary.

top side front

12.

13. 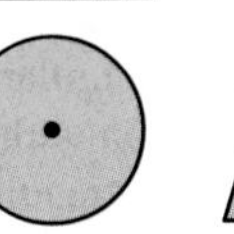  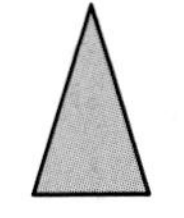

Objectives & Examples

- find the volume of rectangular prisms *(Lesson 12-2)*

Find the volume of a rectangular prism with a length of 5 inches, a width of 3 inches, and a height of 2 inches.

$V = \ell wh$

$V = 5 \times 3 \times 2$

$V = 30$

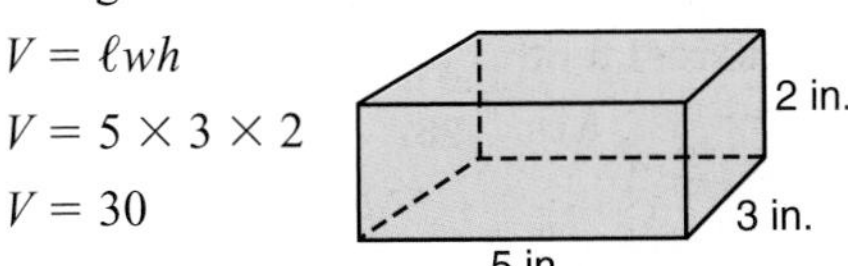

The volume is 30 cubic inches.

Review Exercises

Find the volume of each rectangular prism to the nearest tenth. 15. 168.8 ft³

14. 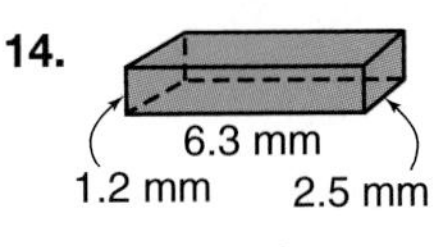

18.9 mm³

15. 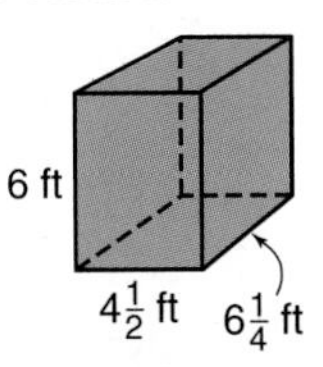

16. 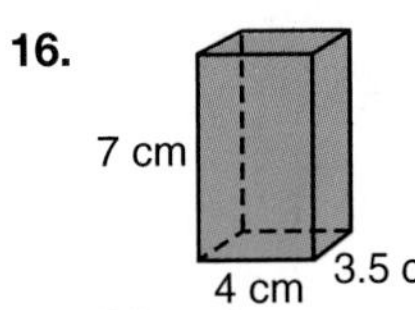

98 cm³

17. 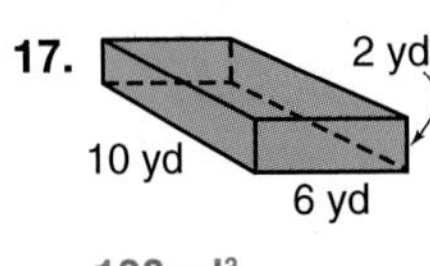

120 yd³

18. Find the volume of a rectangular prism whose length is 9 inches, width is 5 inches, and height is 3 inches. 135 in³

Assessment and Evaluation

Six forms of Chapter 12 Test are available in the *Assessment and Evaluation Masters* as shown in the chart.

1A	Multiple Choice	Honors
1B	Multiple Choice	Average
1C	Multiple Choice	Basic
2A	Free Response	Honors
2B	Free Response	Average
2C	Free Response	Basic

Chapter 12 Test, Form 1B, is shown at the right. Chapter 12 Test, Form 2B, is shown on the next page.

Objectives & Examples

This section reviews the skills and concepts of the chapter and shows completely worked examples.

Review Exercises

These exercises provide practice for the corresponding objectives.

***Assessment and Evaluation Masters*, pp. 311–312**

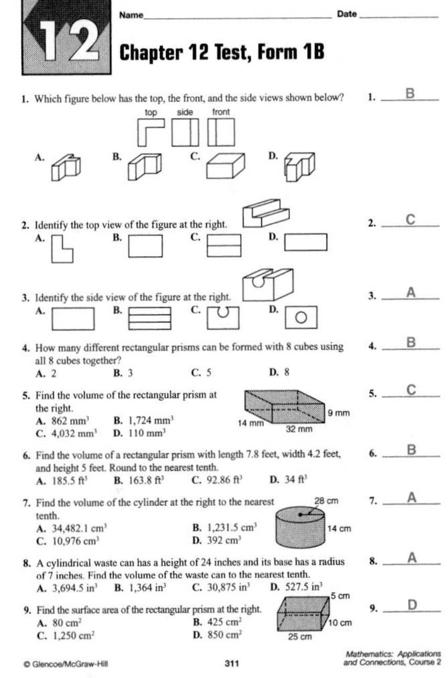

Name________________ Date________

Chapter 12 Test, Form 1B

1. Which figure below has the top, the front, and the side views shown below? 1. B
top side front
A. B. C. D.

2. Identify the top view of the figure at the right. 2. C
A. B. C. D.

3. Identify the side view of the figure at the right. 3. A
A. B. C. D.

4. How many different rectangular prisms can be formed with 8 cubes using all 8 cubes together? 4. B
A. 2 B. 3 C. 5 D. 8

5. Find the volume of the rectangular prism at the right. (14 mm, 32 mm, 9 mm) 5. C
A. 862 mm³ B. 1,724 mm³
C. 4,032 mm³ D. 110 mm³

6. Find the volume of a rectangular prism with length 7.8 feet, width 4.2 feet, and height 5 feet. Round to the nearest tenth. 6. B
A. 185.5 ft³ B. 163.8 ft³ C. 92.86 ft³ D. 34 ft³

7. Find the volume of the cylinder at the right to the nearest tenth. (28 cm, 14 cm) 7. A
A. 34,482.1 cm³ B. 1,231.5 cm³
C. 10,976 cm³ D. 392 cm³

8. A cylindrical waste can has a height of 24 inches and its base has a radius of 7 inches. Find the volume of the waste can to the nearest tenth. 8. A
A. 3,694.5 in³ B. 1,364 in³ C. 30,875 in³ D. 527.5 in³

9. Find the surface area of the rectangular prism at the right. (5 cm, 10 cm, 25 cm) 9. D
A. 80 cm² B. 425 cm²
C. 1,250 cm² D. 850 cm²

© Glencoe/McGraw-Hill 311 *Mathematics: Applications and Connections, Course 2*

Chapter 12 Test, Form 1B (continued)

10. A rectangular prism has a length of 40 inches, a width of 22 inches, and a height of 12 inches. Find the surface area of the prism. 10. A
A. 3,248 in² B. 1,624 in² C. 10,560 in² D. 148 in²

11. Find the surface area of the rectangular prism at the right. 11. B
A. 2,046 cm³ B. 5,112 cm²
C. 176 cm³ D. 24,480 cm²

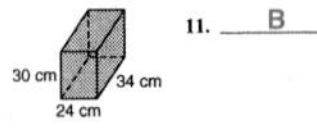

12. Find the surface area of a cylinder with a height of 19 centimeters and a base with a radius of 7 centimeters. Round to the nearest tenth. 12. A
A. 1,143.5 cm² B. 307.7 cm²
C. 2,923.3 cm² D. 614.7 cm²

13. Find the surface area of the cylinder at the right to the nearest tenth. (9 mm, 15 mm) 13. C
A. 508.7 mm² B. 847.8 mm²
C. 1,357.2 mm² D. 423.9 mm²

14. Find the surface area of the cylinder at the right to the nearest tenth. (3 in., 10 in.) 14. D
A. 94.3 in² B. 816.8 in²
C. 90 in² D. 245.0 in²

15. A rectangular trunk has a volume of 26,880 cubic inches. The trunk is 4 feet long by 28 inches wide. How deep is the trunk? 15. A
A. 240 in. B. 20 in. C. 76 in. D. 84 in.

16. A cylindrical storage drum is to be painted on all its outer surfaces. The height of the drum is 4 feet, and the radius of the base is 1.2 feet. Which formula would you use to find the surface area of the drum? 16. C
A. $V = lwh$ B. $V = \pi r^2 h$
C. $A = 2\pi r^2 + 2rh$ D. $A = 2(lh + lw + wh)$

© Glencoe/McGraw-Hill 312 *Mathematics: Applications and Connections, Course 2*

Objectives & Examples

- find the volume of cylinders *(Lesson 12-3)*

Find the volume of a cylinder with a radius of 4 centimeters and a height of 8 centimeters.

$V = \pi r^2 h$

$V \approx 3.14 \times 4^2 \times 8$

$V \approx 401.92$

The volume is about 402 cubic centimeters.

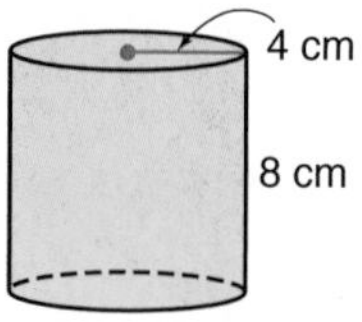

4 cm
8 cm

Review Exercises

Find the volume of each cylinder to the nearest tenth. **20. 9,160.9 mm³**

19. 6 cm, 2.2 cm **91.2 cm³**

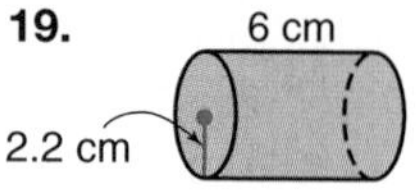

20.

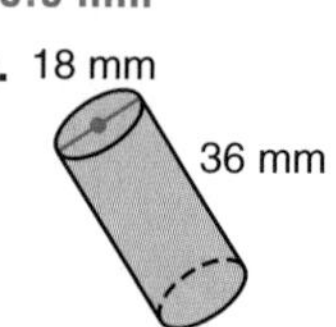

21. The diameter of a cylinder is 3.4 inches, and the height is 5.2 inches. Find the volume of the cylinder. **47.2 in³**

Objectives & Examples

- find the surface area of rectangular prisms *(Lesson 12-4)*

Find the surface area of a rectangular prism with a length of 3 centimeters, a width of 8 centimeters, and a height of 2 centimeters.

surface area $= 2\ell w + 2\ell h + 2wh$

surface area $= 2 \times 3 \times 8 + 2 \times 3 \times 2 + 2 \times 8 \times 2$

surface area $= 48 + 12 + 32$

surface area $= 92$

The surface area is 92 square centimeters.

Review Exercises

Find the surface area of each rectangular prism to the nearest tenth.

22. 4 in., 9 in., 3 in. **150 in²**

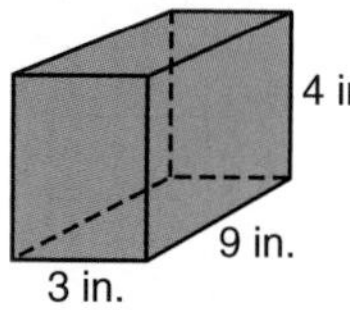

23. 7.1 m, 7.1 m, 7.1 m **302.5 m²**

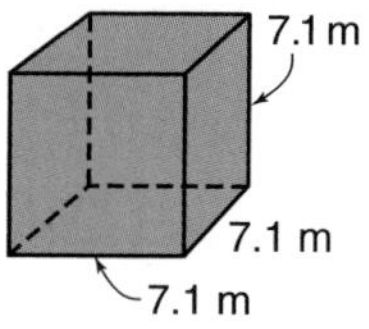

24. Find the surface area of a rectangular prism with a length of 4 meters, width of 3 meters, and height of 4 meters. **80 m²**

Objectives & Examples

- find the surface area of cylinders *(Lesson 12-5)*

Find the surface area of a cylinder whose height is 6 millimeters and whose radius is 2 millimeters.

surface area $= 2\pi r^2 + 2\pi rh$

surface area $= 2 \times \pi \times 2^2 + 2 \times \pi \times 2 \times 6$

surface area ≈ 100.48

The surface area is about 100.5 mm².

Review Exercises

Find the surface area of each cylinder to the nearest tenth.

25. 8 cm, 20 cm **1,407.4 cm²**

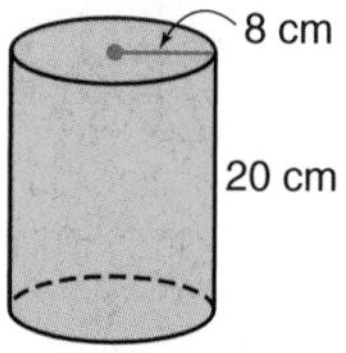

26. 3 m, 9 m **678.6 m²**

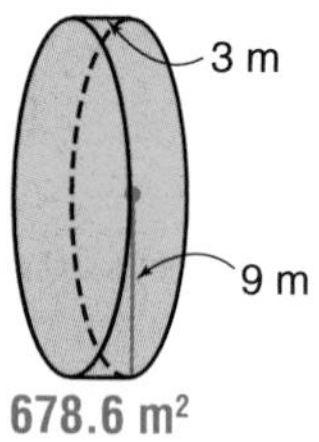

27. Find the surface area of a cylinder whose height is 3.2 inches and whose base has a diameter of 4.6 inches. **79.5 in²**

Assessment and Evaluation Masters, pp. 317–318

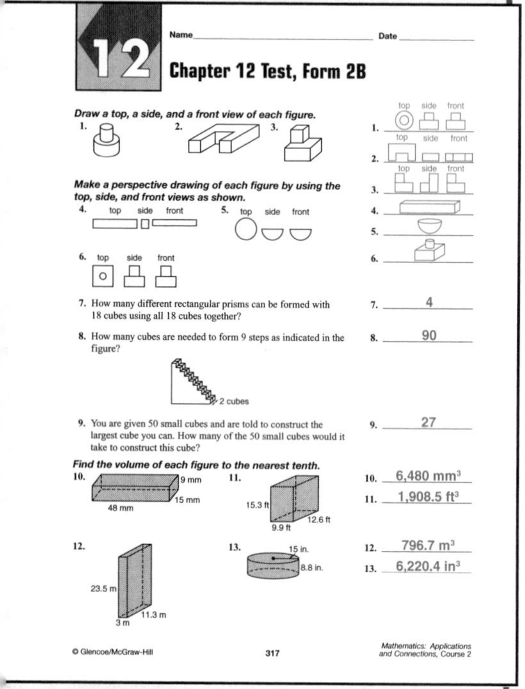

Name______________________ Date__________

Chapter 12 Test, Form 2B

Draw a top, a side, and a front view of each figure.

1. 2. 3.

Make a perspective drawing of each figure by using the top, side, and front views as shown.

4. top side front
5. top side front
6. top side front

7. How many different rectangular prisms can be formed with 18 cubes using all 18 cubes together? — 7. 4

8. How many cubes are needed to form 9 steps as indicated in the figure? — 8. 90

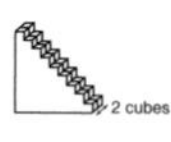

9. You are given 50 small cubes and are told to construct the largest cube you can. How many of the 50 small cubes would it take to construct this cube? — 9. 27

Find the volume of each figure to the nearest tenth.

10. 48 mm, 9 mm, 15 mm — 10. 6,480 mm³

11. 15.3 ft, 9.9 ft, 12.6 ft — 11. 1,908.5 ft³

12.

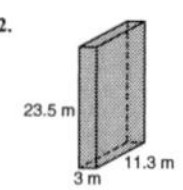

13. 15 in., 8.8 in.

12. 796.7 m³
13. 6,220.4 in³

 317 *Mathematics: Applications and Connections, Course 2*

Chapter 12 Test, Form 2B (continued)

Find the volume of each figure to the nearest tenth.

14. 21.3 cm, 15 cm — 14. 21,379.6 cm³

15. 14 in., 25.8 in. — 15. 15,886.4 in³

Find the surface area of each figures to the nearest tenth.

16. 8 yd, 4 yd, 6.9 yd — 16. 229.6 yd²

17. 46.1 cm, 10 cm, 18 cm — 17. 2,941.6 cm²

18.

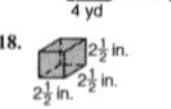

19.

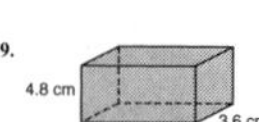

18. 37.5 in²
19. 202.6 cm²

20.

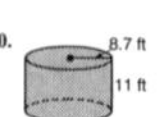

21.

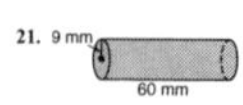

20. 1,076.9 ft²
21. 3,901.9 mm²

22.

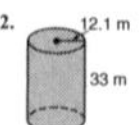

23.

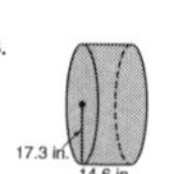

22. 3,428.8 m²
23. 3,467.5 in²

24. A storage shed with a flat roof is 4 yards long by 3 yards wide by $2\frac{1}{2}$ yards tall. A cubic yard is equal to 27 cubic feet. How many cubic feet of storage space does the shed enclose? — 24. 810 ft³

25. A cylindrical carton is filled with sand. The height of the carton is 9 inches and the radius of the base is 2 inches. What is the total volume of the carton? — 25. 113.1 in³

 318 *Mathematics: Applications and Connections, Course 2*

Test and Review Software

You may use this software, a combination of an item generator and item bank, to create your own tests or worksheets. Types of items include free response, multiple choice, short answer, and open ended.

CD-ROM Program

The CD-ROM Program contains an Assessment Game whose questions review the concepts in this chapter.

Applications & Problem Solving

28. ***Make a Model*** A large cube is made up of 27 small cubes. The outside of the cube is painted blue. If the large cube is taken apart, how many small cubes would have none of their sides painted? *(Lesson 12-1B)* **1 cube**

29. ***Manufacturing*** A cereal box has a length of 11 inches, a height of 14 inches, and a depth of 1.5 inches. What is the volume of the box? *(Lesson 12-2)* **231 in^3**

30. ***Pottery*** In his art class, Arturo made a vase in the shape of a cylinder. The diameter is 5 inches, and the height is 10 inches. Find the maximum volume of water the vase can hold. *(Lesson 12-3)* **196.3 in^3**

31. ***Pets*** The Totally-Pets Company wants to make a pet carrier that has a length of 2.5 feet, a height of 1 foot, and a width of 1.25 feet, as shown below. How much plastic is needed to make this carrier? *(Lesson 12-4)* **13.75 ft^2**

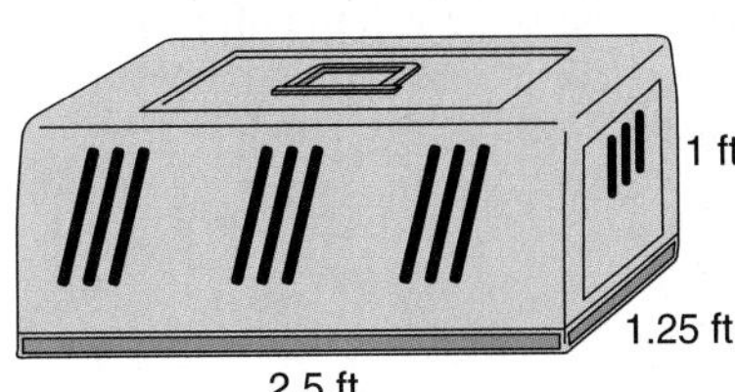

Alternative Assessment

Open Ended

Suppose you are given an empty oatmeal canister that measures 11 inches tall with a 6-inch diameter to use for a class project. You are told to cover the canister with wrapping paper, using the smallest possible amount of paper. How can you determine the amount of paper you will need? **See margin.**

Suppose you found a sheet of wrapping paper at home that is $12\frac{1}{2}$ inches wide by 19 inches long. Is the paper big enough to cover the canister? **See margin.**

Completing the Chapter Project

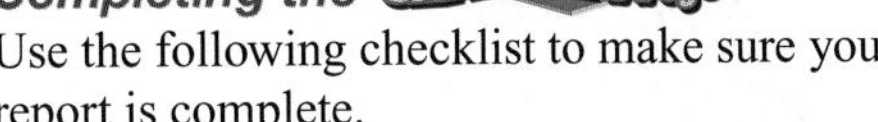

Use the following checklist to make sure your report is complete.

- ☑ You have included a drawing of your leaf.
- ☑ Your report includes a discussion of the main function of a leaf and an explanation why leaves have a large surface area compared to their volume.
- ☑ You have used the terms *ratio, volume,* and *surface area* in your report.

Review the items in your portfolio. Make a table of contents of the items, noting why each item was chosen. Replace any items that are no longer appropriate.

A practice test for Chapter 12 is provided on page 618.

Applications & Problem Solving

This section provides additional practice in solving real-world problems that involve the skills of this chapter.

Alternative Assessment

The ***Open Ended*** section provides students with a performance assessment opportunity to evaluate their work and understanding.

Students should complete the final stages of their project and prepare a class demonstration of their results. A scoring guide for the project is available in the *Investigations and Projects Masters*, p. 63.

Students should add to their portfolios at this time.

***Assessment and Evaluation Masters,* p. 321**

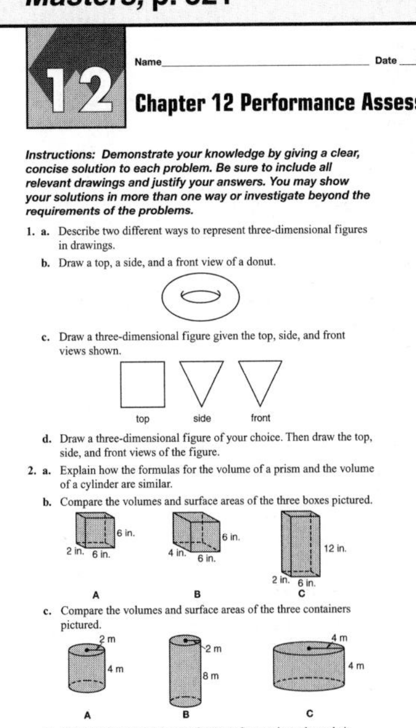

Name__________ Date________

12 Chapter 12 Performance Assessment

Instructions: Demonstrate your knowledge by giving a clear, concise solution to each problem. Be sure to include all relevant drawings and justify your answers. You may show your solutions in more than one way or investigate beyond the requirements of the problems.

1. a. Describe two different ways to represent three-dimensional figures in drawings.

b. Draw a top, a side, and a front view of a donut.

c. Draw a three-dimensional figure given the top, side, and front views shown.

top side front

d. Draw a three-dimensional figure of your choice. Then draw the top, side, and front views of the figure.

2. a. Explain how the formulas for the volume of a prism and the volume of a cylinder are similar.

b. Compare the volumes and surface areas of the three boxes pictured.

A: 6 in., 2 in., 6 in. B: 6 in., 4 in., 6 in. C: 12 in., 2 in., 6 in.

c. Compare the volumes and surface areas of the three containers pictured.

A: 2 m, 4 m B: 2 m, 8 m C: 4 m, 4 m

d. Explain why you think manufacturers frequently package their products in tall boxes, bottles, or cans.

 321 *Mathematics: Applications and Connections*, Course 2

Additional Answer for the Open Ended item

- Find the surface area of the oatmeal canister. It is 263.8 square inches.
- No, because the wrapping paper is 237.5 square inches.

Performance Assessment

Additional performance assessment tasks for this chapter are included in the *Assessment and Evaluation Masters* on page 321. A scoring guide is also provided on page 333.

Standardized Test Practice

The Standardized Test Practice may be used to help students prepare for standardized tests. The test items are written in the same style as those in state proficiency tests and standardized tests like CAT, CTBS, ITBS, MAT, SAT, and Terra Nova. The test items cover skills and concepts covered up to this point in the text.

The pages can be used as an overnight assessment. After students have completed the pages, discuss how each problem can be solved, or provide copies of the solutions from the *Solutions Manual.*

CHAPTERS 1–12

Standardized Test Practice

Assessing Knowledge & Skills

Section One: Multiple Choice

There are nine multiple choice questions in this section. Choose the best answer. If a correct answer is *not here*, choose the letter for Not Here.

1. A CD holder is shaped like a rectangular prism. What is the volume of the box if it measures 6 inches by 6 inches by 12 inches? **D**

A 24 in^3
B 48 in^3
C 72 in^3
D 432 in^3

2. Which figure has exactly four faces? **F**

F

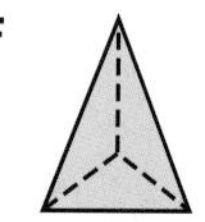

G

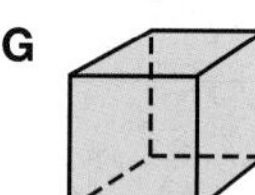

H

J

3. Montega worked 15 hours last week. He earned $5 per hour. Which equation can be used to find his total earnings? **C**

A $x = 15 \div 5$
B $5x = 15$
C $x = 15 \times 5$
D $15x = 5$

4. The top, side, and front views of a three-dimensional figure are given. What is the figure? **F**

top

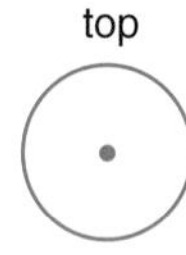

side

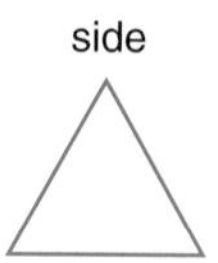

front

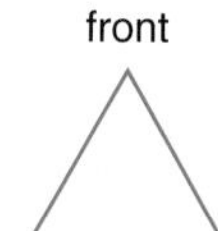

F cone
G cylinder
H rectangular prism
J sphere

Please note that Questions 5–9 have five answer choices.

5. In Fairfield County, about 49% of the registered voters actually vote. If a district in the county has about 600 registered voters, about how many should vote in the next election? **B**

A less than 290
B between 290 and 310
C between 310 and 320
D between 320 and 330
E more than 330

6. Last year, a business owner donated 10% of her profits to a shelter for the homeless. If her business is selling T-shirts and she makes a profit of $9.95 for each shirt, what other information is needed to find how much money she donated? **H**

F the cost of making one T-shirt
G the number of weeks per year
H the total number of T-shirts sold
J the number of shirts in each of her stores
K the selling price of each shirt

◀◀◀ Instructional Resources

Another cumulative review is shown at the left and is available in the *Assessment and Evaluation Masters,* p. 327.

***Assessment and Evaluation Masters,* p. 327**

Name________________ Date________

Cumulative Review, Chapters 1–12

1. Evaluate $(84 - 16) \div 4 + 13 \cdot 2$. (Lesson 1-2) — 1. 43
2. Express $\frac{5}{9}$ as a decimal. (Lesson 2-7) — 2. $0.\overline{5}$
3. Write 187,000 in scientific notation. (Lesson 2-9) — 3. 1.87×10^5
4. Find the median of 55, 49, 54, 49, 50, 48, and 52. (Lesson 3-4) — 4. 50
5. Find the mean of 30, 25, 18, 20, 22, and 19. (Lesson 3-4) — 5. $22\frac{1}{3}$
6. Identify the sequence 3, 9, 27, 81, . . . as *arithmetic, geometric,* or *neither*. Then find the next three terms of the sequence. (Lesson 4-3) — 6. geometric; 243, 729, 2,187
7. Find the GCF and LCM of 18 and 63. (Lessons 4-4 and 4-9) — 7. 9; 126
8. Express the ratio $\frac{98}{126}$ as a fraction in simplest form. (Lesson 8-1) — 8. $\frac{7}{9}$
9. What number is 15% of 87? Round to the nearest tenth. (Lesson 8-8) — 9. 13.1
10. Classify a 70° angle as *acute, obtuse, right,* or *straight*. (Lesson 9-1) — 10. acute
11. Name every term that describes the figure at the right. Then underline the name that best describes the figure. (Lesson 9-4) — 11. quadrilateral, parallelogram, rhombus
12. Draw all lines of symmetry. (Lesson 9-7) — 12. 
13. Find the best whole number estimate for $\sqrt{61}$. (Lesson 10-2) — 13. 8
14. Find the area of a circle with diameter 8.5 cm. (Lesson 10-6) — 14. 56.7 cm^2
15. Estimate 11% of 58.2. (Lesson 11-1) — 15. about 6
16. Find the percent of change if the original price is $52 and the new price is $35. Round to the nearest whole percent. (Lesson 11-5) — 16. 33%

Refer to the figures to find the following. Round answers to the nearest tenth. (Lessons 12-4, 12-2, 12-5, and 12-3)

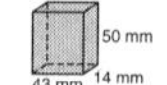

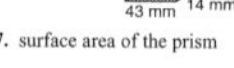

17. surface area of the prism — 17. 6,904 mm^2
18. surface area of the cylinder — 18. 1,526.8 in^2
19. volume of the prism — 19. 30,100 mm^3
20. volume of the cylinder — 20. 4,580.4 in^3

 327 *Mathematics: Applications and Connections, Course 2*

7. Alicia bought a new guitar. She made a 40% down payment and will make 12 monthly payments of \$30 each. What is a reasonable total price for the guitar? **C**

A \$400 **B** \$500
C \$600 **D** \$700
E \$800

8. The seventh grade class collected money each year for the last three years to make a donation to the student council. **F**

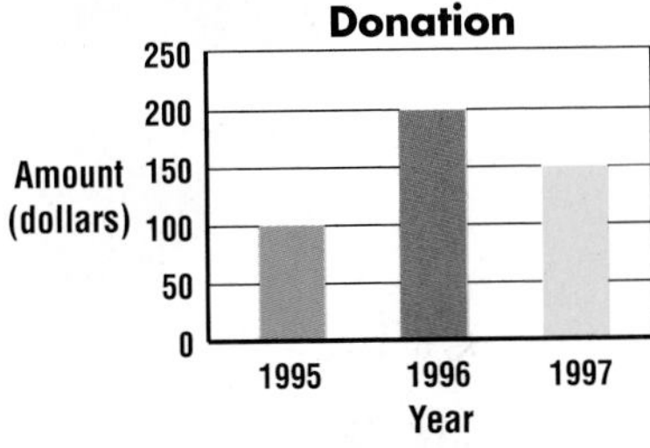

According to the graph, which is the average yearly amount of money collected over the three-year period?

F \$150 **G** \$200
H \$250 **J** \$350
K \$450

9. To the nearest cubic inch, find the volume of the cylinder. **C**

A 7.5 in^3
B 30 in^3
C 35 in^3
D 45 in^3
E Not Here

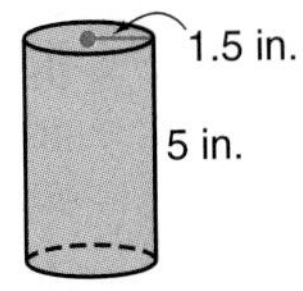

Test Practice For additional test practice questions, visit:

www.glencoe.com/sec/math/mac/mathnet

Test-Taking Tip (THE PRINCETON REVIEW)

Many problems can be solved without much calculating if you estimate carefully. Look to see which answer choices are *not* reasonable for the information given in the problem.

Section Two: Free Response

This section contains six questions for which you will provide short answers. Write your answers on your paper.

10. Colleen wants to buy a pair of shoes that cost \$54.98. She must also pay a sales tax of 6%. To the nearest cent, what is the total cost of the shoes? **\$58.28**

11. What is the reciprocal of $3\frac{3}{4}$? $\frac{4}{15}$

12. Suppose you want to find $12\frac{1}{2}\%$ of a number using a calculator. What decimal can you enter for $12\frac{1}{2}\%$? **0.125**

13. Three out of five students usually buy their lunch from the cafeteria. If there are 500 students in the school on a given day, about how many lunches should be prepared? **300 lunches**

14. What is the prime factorization of 45? $3 \cdot 3 \cdot 5$

15. The figure below shows a rectangular swimming pool. How much water is in the pool when it is filled to a depth of 5 feet? **1,200 ft^3**

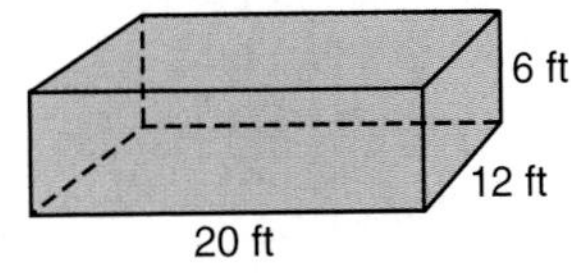

Test-Taking Tip

Remind students that estimation can eliminate one or more possibilities in their answer choices. However, they should check their choice to see if it indeed solves the problem.

Assessment and Evaluation Masters, pp. 325–326

Name__________ Date________

Chapter 12 Standardized Test Practice

1. Choose the top, side, and front views of the figure that are drawn correctly. 1. D

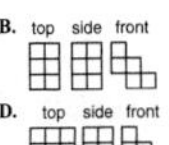

A. top side front B. top side front

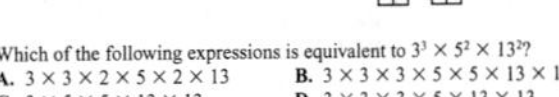

C. top side front D. top side front

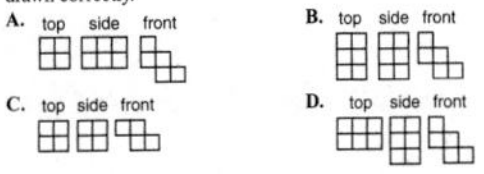

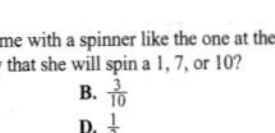

2. Which of the following expressions is equivalent to $3^3 \times 5^2 \times 13^2$? 2. B
A. $3 \times 3 \times 2 \times 5 \times 2 \times 13$ B. $3 \times 3 \times 3 \times 5 \times 5 \times 13 \times 13$
C. $3 \times 5 \times 5 \times 13 \times 13$ D. $3 \times 3 \times 3 \times 5 \times 13 \times 13$

3. Alysen is playing a board game with a spinner like the one at the right. What is the probability that she will spin a 1, 7, or 10? 3. B

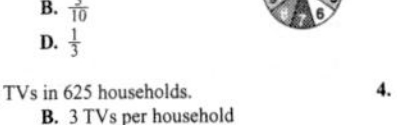

A. $\frac{1}{5}$ B. $\frac{3}{10}$
C. $\frac{2}{5}$ D. $\frac{1}{3}$

4. Determine the unit rate of 1,125 TVs in 625 households. 4. A
A. 1.8 TVs per household B. 3 TVs per household
C. 0.6 TVs per household D. 2.4 TVs per household

5. A cylindrical silo has a radius of 4.2 meters and is 75 meters tall. How much grain can it hold to the nearest tenth? 5. D
A. 74,220.13 m^3 B. 315 m^3 C. 989.60 m^3 D. 4,156.33 m^3

6. Steve Austin is practicing his 50-yard dash the week before track tryouts. The bar graph shows his speed each day. Predict how fast he will run on Saturday. 6. B

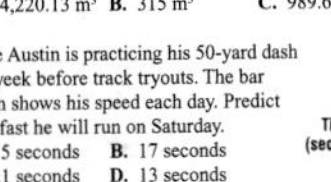
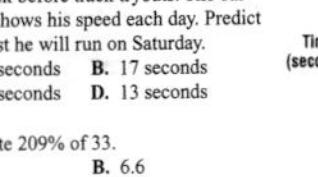

A. 15 seconds B. 17 seconds
C. 21 seconds D. 13 seconds

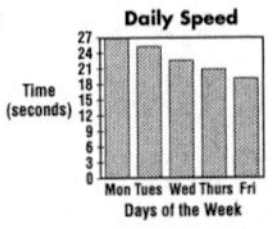

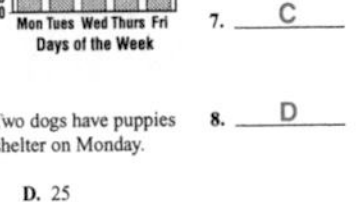

7. Estimate 209% of 33. 7. C
A. 50 B. 6.6
C. 66 D. 70

8. Sally runs a pet shelter and currently has 6 puppies. Two dogs have puppies over the weekend so she has 19 more puppies at the shelter on Monday. How many puppies does she have altogether? 8. D
A. 19 B. 26 C. 13 D. 25

 325 *Mathematics: Applications and Connections*, Course 2

Chapter 12 Standardized Test Practice (continued)

9. Mr. Eric Cartman is making a stop sign for his miniature town model. If he wants the model to be $\frac{1}{72}$ the size of a stop sign, which is 28.3 inches long by 28.3 inches high, how big will it be? 9. A
A. 0.4 in. by 0.4 in. B. 0.9 in. by 0.9 in.
C. 0.01 in. by 0.01 in. D. 0.2 in. by 0.2 in.

10. A matchbox measures 5.3 centimeters long by 3.6 centimeters wide by 1.4 centimeters deep. What is the maximum volume for matches inside? 10. D
A. 8.5 cm^3 B. 83.9 cm^3 C. 10.3 cm^3 D. 26.7 cm^3

11. Mrs. Smith wants a fish pond with an island in the middle like the figure. Estimate the area of the pond. 11. A
A. 20.5 $units^2$ B. 22 $units^2$
C. 18 $units^2$ D. 19.5 $units^2$

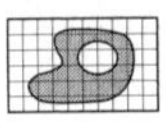

12. Which of the following expressions is equivalent to 1,630,000? 12. B
A. 16.3×10^5 B. 1.63×10^6 C. 1.63×10^4 D. 16.3×10^6

13. Gabrielle purchased a 12.5-pound bag of potatoes and used the bag in 5 different recipes. On average, how much did she use per recipe? 13. C
A. 1.5 lb B. 2 lb C. 2.5 lb D. 3 lb

14. Classify the triangle by its angles and by its sides. 14. B
A. acute, scalene B. acute, equilateral
C. obtuse, scalene D. acute, isosceles

15. Patrick needs to know how many ounces are in 4.5 pints of hot cocoa. Which is the correct amount? 15. B
A. 36 oz B. 72 oz C. 64 oz D. 96 oz

16. Ellenmarie knows that she has 4 hats left and she sold 13 hats. How many did she have to start with? 16. A
A. 17 B. 15 C. 9 D. 10

 326 *Mathematics: Applications and Connections*, Course 2

Instructional Resources ▶▶▶

Additional standardized test practice is shown at the right and is available in the *Assessment and Evaluation Masters*, pp. 325–326.

Interdisciplinary Investigation

GET READY

This optional investigation is designed to be completed by a group of 2 or 3 students over several days or several weeks.

Mathematical Overview

This investigation utilizes the concepts from Chapters 1–12.

- measuring length
- finding the volume and surface area of geometric figures
- making a scale drawing

Time Management	
Gathering Data	40 minutes
Calculations	20 minutes
Creating Graphs	40 minutes
Summarizing Data	15 minutes
Presentation	20 minutes

Instructional Resources

- *Investigations and Projects Masters,* pp. 13–16
- *Manipulative Kit*
    - ruler

***Investigations and Projects Masters,* p. 16**

Name________________ Date________

Interdisciplinary Investigation
(Student Edition, Pages 524–525)

The Perfect Package

Use this table to record your data.

2.

Container	Length	Width	Height	Surface Area	Volume

3.

Container	Length	Width	Height	Volume
prism				
cylinder	Radius =			

4.

Container	Surface Area
prism	
cylinder	

 16 *Mathematics: Applications and Connections, Course 2*

Interdisciplinary Investigation

THE PERFECT PACKAGE

Did you ever buy a product because of the way it was packaged? Manufacturers try to design packages that are economical to produce yet appeal to consumers. Most of the products you buy are packaged. Foods are often in boxes or cans, bars of soap are wrapped in paper, and cologne may be in a bottle that is inside a box. How much material does it take to make a package? How much does a package hold?

What You'll Do

In this investigation, you will find the volume and surface area of some packages from products you use. You will also design your own package.

Materials

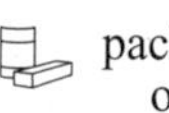 packages from a supermarket or department store

 calculator

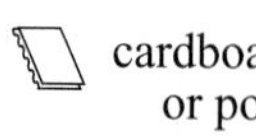 cardboard or poster board

 ruler

Procedure

1. Work individually. Find two packages from products such as an empty vegetable can or a box from a tube of toothpaste. Measure each package and find the volume and surface area.
2. Work with a partner. Make a table to record the measurements, volume, and surface area of the packages.
3. Choose a product for which to design a package. Design two different packages—one should be a prism and the other should be a cylinder. The packages should have about the same volume. Explain how you determined the dimensions of the two containers so that their volumes were about the same.
4. Use cardboard or poster board to make your packages and then find their surface area.
5. Make a display that includes the packages, the surface area and volume, and scale drawings of patterns for the packages.

Technology Tips

- Use a **spreadsheet** to calculate the surface areas and volumes.
- Use a **word processor** to prepare your display.
- Use **geometry software** to help you design a pattern.

Instructional Resources

A recording sheet to help students organize their data for this investigation is shown at the left and is available in the *Investigations and Projects Masters,* p. 16.

Cooperative Learning

This investigation offers an excellent opportunity for using cooperative learning groups. For more information on cooperative learning strategies and group management, see *Cooperative Learning in the Mathematics Classroom.*

Making the Connection

Use the data collected about packages to help in these investigations.

Language Arts

Decide which container would be best for your product, the prism or the cylinder. Prepare a presentation using the facts about volume and surface area to convince your class which package would be best.

Science

Investigate the history of packaging. Research plastic and polystyrene and tell the impact that these materials have on the environment. Which materials are safest for the environment?

Art

Make a logo or design that would help sell your product. Use color and present the logo or design on the container you made.

Go Further

- Investigate the ratio of height to width of packages that are rectangular prisms. Describe what you find.
- Search for unique packages that are not cylinders or rectangular prisms. Find the volumes and surface areas of these containers. Make your own unique packages.

interNET CONNECTION For current information of packaging, visit: **www.glencoe.com/sec/math/mac/mathnet**

You may want to place your work on this investigation in your portfolio.

MANAGEMENT TIPS

Working in Teams Encourage all team members to record their own data in the table and explain their calculations for their partners. Each team member should design one package, combining them in the display.

Making the Connection
You may wish to alert other teachers on your team that your students may need their assistance in this investigation.
Language Arts Have students use critical thinking and writing skills to construct a convincing argument for the package they choose. Encourage them to clearly identify their reasons for deciding it is the best package.
Science Have students consider the advantages and disadvantages of using different materials in their packages, including availability, cost, durability, and disposal.
Art Have students experiment with different sizes and styles of lettering, either freehand or on a computer, and combine words with pictures in order to design an attractive logo.

***Investigations and Projects Masters,* p. 15**

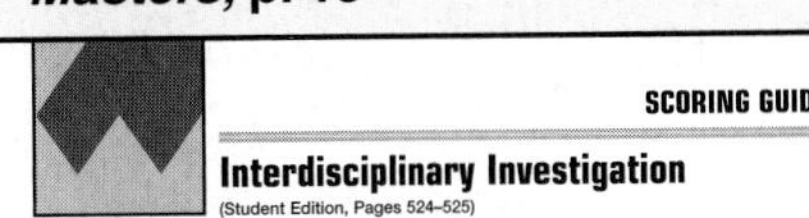

SCORING GUIDE

Interdisciplinary Investigation
(Student Edition, Pages 524–525)

The Perfect Package

Level	Specific Criteria
3 Superior	• Shows a thorough understanding of the concepts of *calculating surface area and volume of rectangular prisms and cylinders.* • Uses appropriate strategies to solve problems. • Computations are correct. • Written explanations are exemplary. • Charts, model, and any statements included are appropriate and sensible. • Goes beyond the requirements of some or all problems.
2 Satisfactory, with minor flaws	• Shows understanding of the concepts of *calculating surface area and volume of rectangular prisms and cylinders.* • Uses appropriate strategies to solve problems. • Computations are mostly correct. • Written explanations are effective. • Charts, model, and any statements included are appropriate and sensible. • Satisfies the requirements of problems.
1 Nearly Satisfactory, with obvious flaws	• Shows understanding of most of the *concepts of calculating surface area and volume of rectangular prisms and cylinders.* • May not use appropriate strategies to solve problems. • Computations are mostly correct. • Written explanations are satisfactory. • Charts, model, and any statements included are appropriate and sensible. • Satisfies the requirements of problems.
0 Unsatisfactory	• Shows little or no understanding of the concepts of *calculating surface area and volume of rectangular prisms and cylinders.* • Does not use appropriate strategies to solve problems. • Computations are incorrect. • Written explanations are not satisfactory. • Charts, model, and any statements included are not appropriate or sensible. • Does not satisfy the requirements of the problems.

 15 *Mathematics: Applications and Connections,* Course 2

ASSESS

Ask students what assumptions they made, if any, about consumer preferences as they created their packaging designs. Have students write a summary of their investigation, drawing conclusions about which packages are appropriate for which products.

Instructional Resources ▶▶▶
Sample solutions for this investigation are provided in the *Investigations and Projects Masters* on p. 14. The scoring guide for assessing student performance shown at the right is also available on p. 15.

CHAPTER 13

Exploring Discrete Math and Probability

Previewing the Chapter

Overview

This chapter examines discrete math and probability. It includes lessons in which students use tree diagrams and the fundamental counting principle to count outcomes. Students also find and use experimental and theoretical probability, use statistics to make predictions, distinguish between dependent and independent events, and find the probability of two events. Finally they explore permutations and combinations.

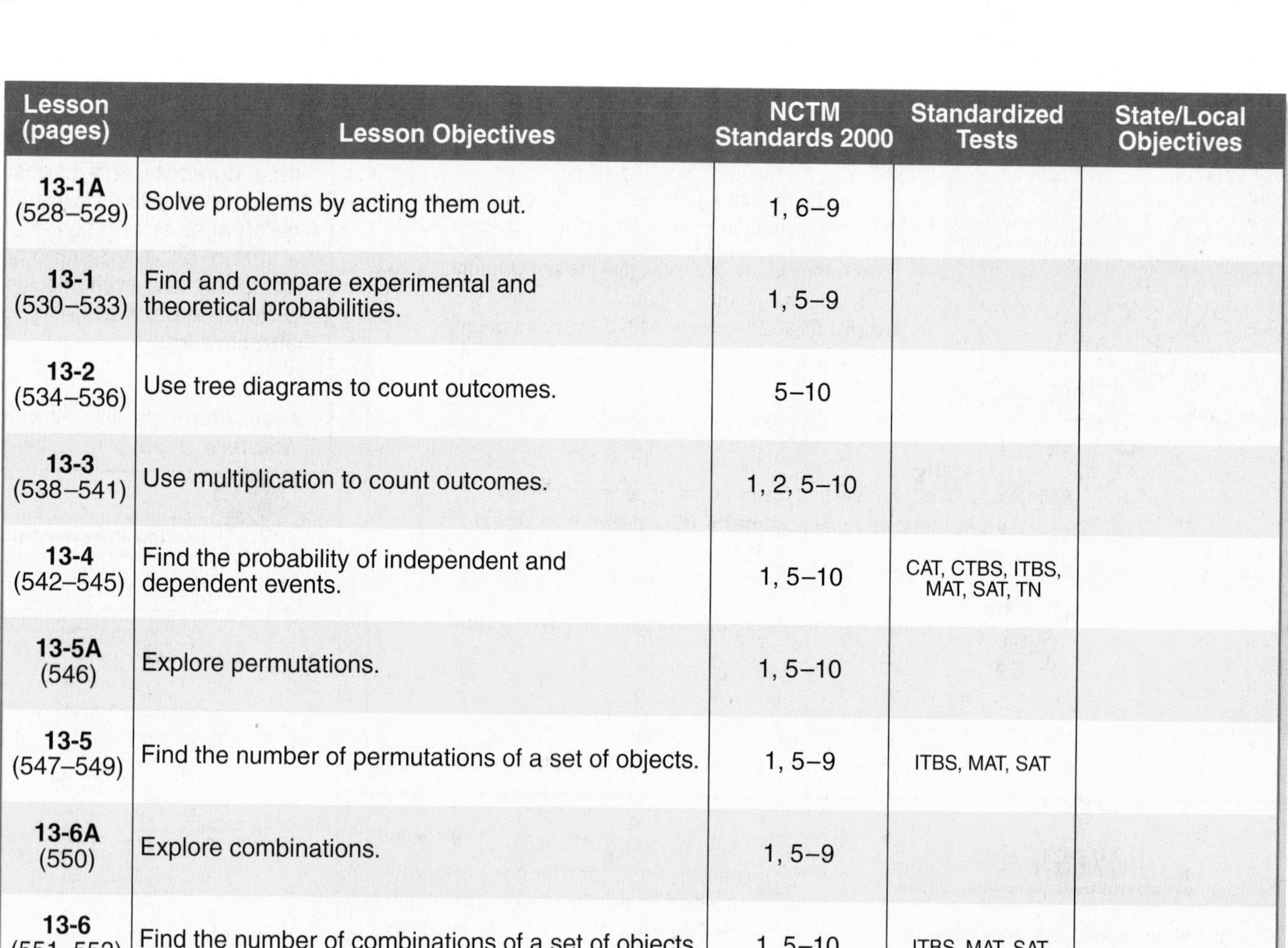

Lesson (pages)	Lesson Objectives	NCTM Standards 2000	Standardized Tests	State/Local Objectives
13-1A (528–529)	Solve problems by acting them out.	1, 6–9		
13-1 (530–533)	Find and compare experimental and theoretical probabilities.	1, 5–9		
13-2 (534–536)	Use tree diagrams to count outcomes.	5–10		
13-3 (538–541)	Use multiplication to count outcomes.	1, 2, 5–10		
13-4 (542–545)	Find the probability of independent and dependent events.	1, 5–10	CAT, CTBS, ITBS, MAT, SAT, TN	
13-5A (546)	Explore permutations.	1, 5–10		
13-5 (547–549)	Find the number of permutations of a set of objects.	1, 5–9	ITBS, MAT, SAT	
13-6A (550)	Explore combinations.	1, 5–9		
13-6 (551–553)	Find the number of combinations of a set of objects.	1, 5–10	ITBS, MAT, SAT	

CAT = California Achievement Tests, CTBS = Comprehensive Tests of Basic Skills, ITBS = Iowa Tests of Basic Skills, MAT = Metropolitan Achievement Tests, SAT = Stanford Achievement Tests, TN = Terra Nova
For the key to numbering of NCTM Standards 2000, see page T6.

Organizing the Chapter

The **Interactive Lesson Planner** contains all of the blackline masters and transparencies. This CD-ROM also includes an easy-to-use lesson planning calendar.

LESSON PLANNING GUIDE

		BLACKLINE MASTERS (PAGE NUMBERS)										
Lesson	**Extra Practice (Student Edition)**	**Study Guide**	**Practice**	**Enrichment**	**Assessment & Evaluation**	**Classroom Games**	**Diversity**	**Hands-On Lab**	**School to Career**	**Science and Math Lab Manual**	**Technology**	**Transparencies A and B**
13-1A	p. 602											
13-1	p. 603	93	93	93								13-1
13-2	p. 603	94	94	94	351				26			13-2
13-3	p. 603	95	95	95	350, 351			84				13-3
13-4	p. 604	96	96	96			26			93–96	51	13-4
13-5A								70				
13-5	p. 604	97	97	97	352						52	13-5
13-6A								71				
13-6	p. 604	98	98	98	352	35–40						13-6
Study Guide/ Assessment					337–349, 353–355							

OTHER CHAPTER RESOURCES

Student Edition

Chapter Project, pp. 527, 533, 545, 557
School to Career, p. 537
Let the Games Begin, pp. 530, 541

Technology

 MathPASS CD-ROM

 Interactive Mathematics Tools Software

Teacher's Classroom Resources

Applications

Family Letters and Activities, pp. 51–52
Investigations and Projects Masters, pp. 65–68

Meeting Individual Needs

Investigations for the Special Education Student, pp. 45–46

Teaching Aids

Answer Key Masters
Block Scheduling Booklet
Lesson Planning Guide
Solutions Manual

Professional Publications

Glencoe Mathematics Professional Series

Planning the Chapter

MindJogger Videoquizzes provide a unique format for reviewing concepts presented in the chapter.

Assessment Resources

Student Edition

Mixed Review, pp. 533, 536, 541, 545, 549, 553
Mid-Chapter Self Test, p. 545
Math Journal, pp. 540, 548
Study Guide and Assessment, pp. 554–557
Performance Task, p. 557
Portfolio Suggestion, p. 557
Standardized Test Practice, pp. 558–559
Chapter Test, p. 619

Assessment and Evaluation Masters

Multiple-Choice Tests (Forms 1A, 1B, 1C), pp. 337–342
Free-Response Tests (Forms 2A, 2B, 2C), pp. 343–348
Performance Assessment, p. 349
Mid-Chapter Test, p. 350
Quizzes A–D, pp. 351–352
Standardized Test Practice, pp. 353–354
Cumulative Review, p. 355

Teacher's Wraparound Edition

5-Minute Check, pp. 530, 534, 538, 542, 547, 551
Building Portfolios, pp. 526, 557
Math Journal, pp. 546, 550
Closing Activity, pp. 529, 533, 536, 541, 545, 549, 553

Technology

Test and Review Software
MindJogger Videoquizzes
CD-ROM Program

Materials and Manipulatives

Lesson 13-1A
spinner*†

Lesson 13-1
number cubes*

Lesson 13-2
counters*†
markers
pennies
number cube*

Lesson 13-3
graph paper†
clothing catalogs
lima beans
bowl
markers

Lesson 13-4
number cube*
paper bag
red beans
white beans

Lesson 13-5
counters*†

Lesson 13-5A
index cards

Lesson 13-6A
index cards

*Glencoe Manipulative Kit

†Glencoe Overhead Manipulative Resources

Pacing Chart

See pages T25–T27 for the Course Planning Calendar.

COURSE	DAY 1	DAY 2	DAY 3	DAY 4	DAY 5	DAY 6	DAY 7
Honors	Chapter Project	Lesson 13-1A	Lesson 13-1	Lesson 13-2	Lesson 13-3	Lesson 13-4	Lesson 13-5

Interactive Mathematics:
Activities and Investigations

is an activity-based program that may be used as an enhancement for chapters in ***Mathematics: Applications and Connections.***

INTER•ACTIVE Mathematics
Activities and Investigations

ACTIVITY FIVE

Paint the Cube Red

Masaki has a cube that is 4 inches long on each side. He paints the cube red and then cuts the cube into smaller cubes that measure 1 inch on each side.

- How many of the smaller cubes does Masaki now have?
- How many of the smaller cubes have exactly three sides painted red?
- How many of the smaller cubes have exactly two sides painted red?
- How many of the smaller cubes have exactly one side painted red?
- How many of the smaller cubes have no sides painted red?
- How could Masaki paint the original cube so that he would have exactly 27 cubes with exactly one side painted red?

UNIT 14: Run for Cover 58 Cool It!

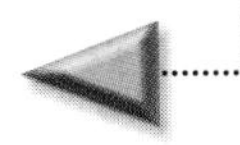

Unit 14, Activity Five
Paint the Cube Red
Use with Lesson 13-1A.

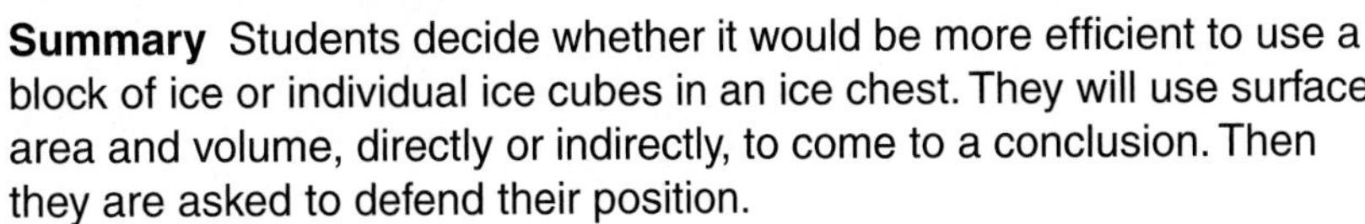

Summary Students decide whether it would be more efficient to use a block of ice or individual ice cubes in an ice chest. They will use surface area and volume, directly or indirectly, to come to a conclusion. Then they are asked to defend their position.

Math Connection Students should begin to formulate a clear understanding of the difference between surface area and volume by *acting out* each situation. Students may discover that the formulas for the surface area and volume of a cube are $SA = 6s^2$ and $V = s^3$, respectively.

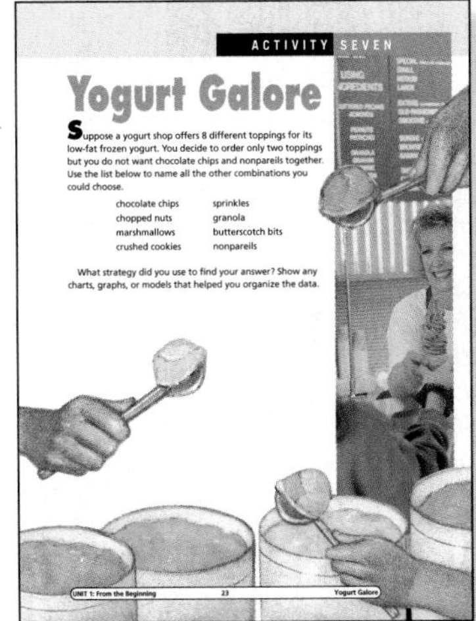

ACTIVITY SEVEN

Yogurt Galore

Suppose a yogurt shop offers 8 different toppings for its low-fat frozen yogurt. You decide to order only two toppings but you do not want chocolate chips and nonpareils together. Use the list below to name all the other combinations you could choose.

chocolate chips	sprinkles
chopped nuts	granola
marshmallows	butterscotch bits
crushed cookies	nonpareils

What strategy did you use to find your answer? Show any charts, graphs, or models that helped you organize the data.

UNIT 1: From the Beginning 23 Yogurt Galore

Unit 1, Activity Seven
Yogurt Galore
Use before Lesson 13-6.

Summary Students make a list of two-topping combinations from a list of 8 toppings. They explain how they arrived at their solutions and are asked to show any charts or graphs they used to solve the problem.

Math Connection Students work in groups to solve logic problems that include combinations. Combinations are arrangements or listings where order is not important. This activity can be used as an introduction to how to accurately list all possible outcomes.

DAY 8	DAY 9	DAY 10	DAY 11	DAY 12	DAY 13	DAY 14	DAY 15
Lesson 13-6	Study Guide and Assessment	Chapter Test					

Enhancing the Chapter

APPLICATIONS

Classroom Games, pp. 35–40

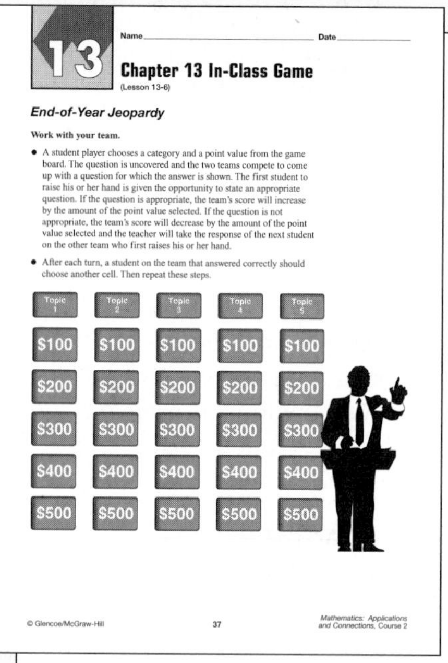

Name ____________ Date ________

13

Chapter 13 In-Class Game

(Lesson 13-6)

End-of-Year Jeopardy

Work with your team.

- A student player chooses a category and a point value from the game board. The question is uncovered and the two teams compete to come up with a question for which the answer is shown. The first student to raise his or her hand is given the opportunity to state an appropriate question. If the question is appropriate, the team's score will increase by the amount of the point value selected. If the question is not appropriate, the team's score will decrease by the amount of the point value selected and the teacher will take the response of the next student on the other team who first raises his or her hand.
- After each turn, a student on the team that answered correctly should choose another cell. Then repeat these steps.

Topic 1	Topic 2	Topic 3	Topic 4	Topic 5
$100	$100	$100	$100	$100
$200	$200	$200	$200	$200
$300	$300	$300	$300	$300
$400	$400	$400	$400	$400
$500	$500	$500	$500	$500

© Glencoe/McGraw-Hill 37 *Mathematics: Applications and Connections, Course 2*

Diversity Masters, p. 26

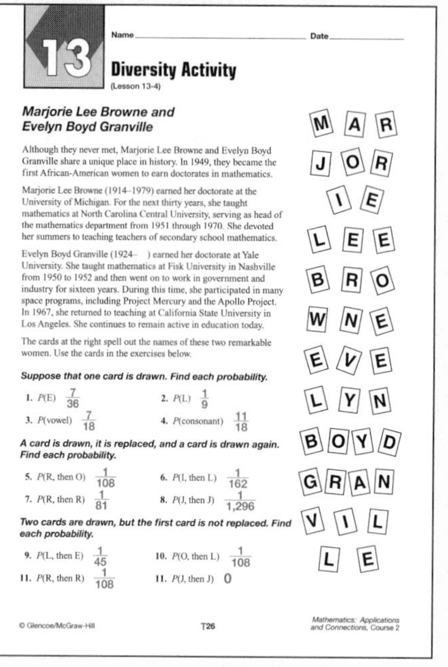

Name ____________ Date ________

13

Diversity Activity

(Lesson 13-4)

Marjorie Lee Browne and Evelyn Boyd Granville

Although they never met, Marjorie Lee Browne and Evelyn Boyd Granville share a unique place in history. In 1949, they became the first African-American women to earn doctorates in mathematics.

Marjorie Lee Browne (1914–1979) earned her doctorate at the University of Michigan. For the next thirty years, she taught mathematics at North Carolina Central University, serving as head of the mathematics department from 1951 through 1970. She devoted her summers to teaching teachers of secondary school mathematics.

Evelyn Boyd Granville (1924–) earned her doctorate at Yale University. She taught mathematics at Fisk University in Nashville from 1950 to 1952 and then went on to work in government and industry for sixteen years. During this time, she participated in many space programs, including Project Mercury and the Apollo Project. In 1967, she returned to teaching at California State University in Los Angeles. She continues to remain active in education today.

The cards at the right spell out the names of these two remarkable women. Use the cards in the exercises below.

M A R / J O R / I E / L E E / B R O / W N E / E V E / L Y N / B O Y D / G R A N / V I L / L E

Suppose that one card is drawn. Find each probability.

1. $P(\text{E})$ $\frac{7}{36}$
2. $P(\text{L})$ $\frac{1}{9}$
3. $P(\text{vowel})$ $\frac{7}{18}$
4. $P(\text{consonant})$ $\frac{11}{18}$

A card is drawn, it is replaced, and a card is drawn again. Find each probability.

5. $P(\text{R, then O})$ $\frac{1}{108}$
6. $P(\text{I, then L})$ $\frac{1}{162}$
7. $P(\text{R, then R})$ $\frac{1}{81}$
8. $P(\text{J, then J})$ $\frac{1}{1{,}296}$

Two cards are drawn, but the first card is not replaced. Find each probability.

9. $P(\text{L, then E})$ $\frac{1}{45}$
10. $P(\text{O, then L})$ $\frac{1}{108}$
11. $P(\text{R, then R})$ $\frac{1}{108}$
11. $P(\text{J, then J})$ 0

© Glencoe/McGraw-Hill T26 *Mathematics: Applications and Connections, Course 2*

School to Career Masters, p. 26

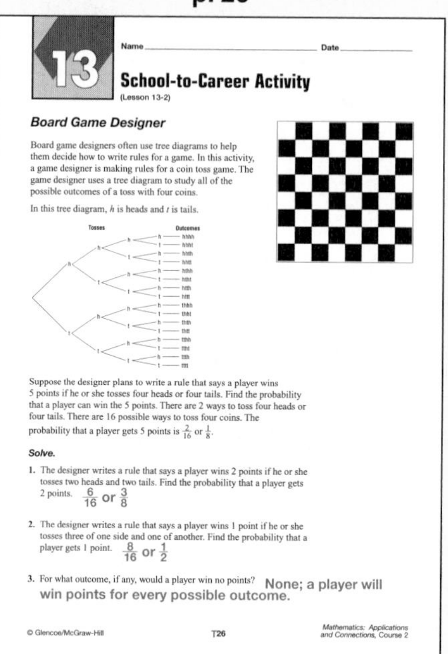

Name ____________ Date ________

13

School-to-Career Activity

(Lesson 13-2)

Board Game Designer

Board game designers often use tree diagrams to help them decide how to write rules for a game. In this activity, a game designer is making rules for a coin toss game. The game designer uses a tree diagram to study all of the possible outcomes of a toss with four coins.

In this tree diagram, h is heads and t is tails.

Suppose the designer plans to write a rule that says a player wins 5 points if he or she tosses four heads or four tails. Find the probability that a player can win the 5 points. There are 2 ways to toss four heads or four tails. There are 16 possible ways to toss four coins. The probability that a player gets 5 points is $\frac{2}{16}$ or $\frac{1}{8}$.

Solve.

1. The designer writes a rule that says a player wins 2 points if he or she tosses two heads and two tails. Find the probability that a player gets 2 points. $\frac{6}{16}$ or $\frac{3}{8}$
2. The designer writes a rule that says a player wins 1 point if he or she tosses three of one side and one of another. Find the probability that a player gets 1 point. $\frac{8}{16}$ or $\frac{1}{2}$
3. For what outcome, if any, would a player win no points? None; a player will win points for every possible outcome.

© Glencoe/McGraw-Hill T26 *Mathematics: Applications and Connections, Course 2*

Family Letters and Activities, pp. 51–52

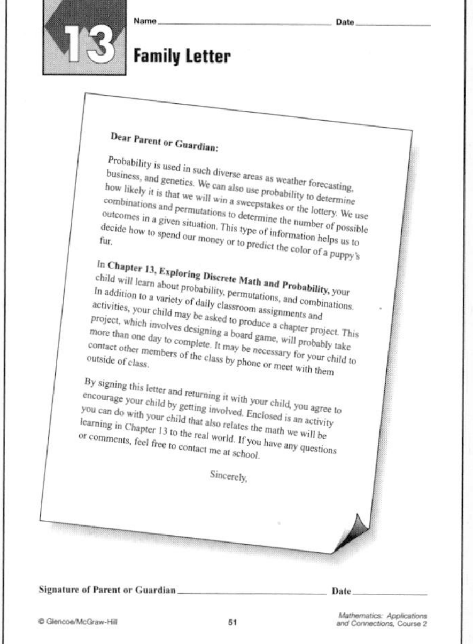

Name ____________ Date ________

13

Family Letter

Dear Parent or Guardian:

Probability is used in such diverse areas as weather forecasting, business, and genetics. We can also use probability to determine how likely it is that we will win a sweepstakes or the lottery. We use combinations and permutations to determine the number of possible outcomes in a given situation. This type of information helps us to decide how to spend our money or to predict the color of a puppy's fur.

In **Chapter 13, Exploring Discrete Math and Probability,** your child will learn about probability, permutations, and combinations. In addition to a variety of daily classroom assignments and activities, your child may be asked to produce a chapter project. This project, which involves designing a board game, will probably take more than one day to complete. It may be necessary for your child to contact other members of the class by phone or meet with them outside of class.

By signing this letter and returning it with your child, you agree to encourage your child by getting involved. Enclosed is an activity you can do with your child that also relates the math we will be learning in Chapter 13 to the real world. If you have any questions or comments, feel free to contact me at school.

Sincerely,

Signature of Parent or Guardian ____________ **Date** ________

© Glencoe/McGraw-Hill 51 *Mathematics: Applications and Connections, Course 2*

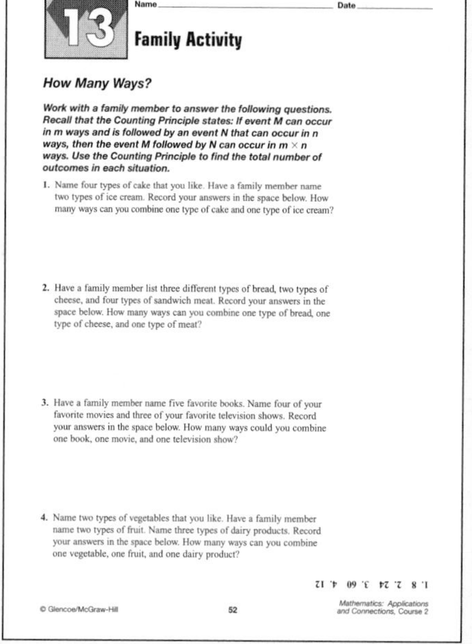

Name ____________ Date ________

13

Family Activity

How Many Ways?

Work with a family member to answer the following questions. Recall that the Counting Principle states: If event M can occur in m ways and is followed by an event N that can occur in n ways, then the event M followed by N can occur in m × n ways. Use the Counting Principle to find the total number of outcomes in each situation.

1. Name four types of cake that you like. Have a family member name two types of ice cream. Record your answers in the space below. How many ways can you combine one type of cake and one type of ice cream?
2. Have a family member list three different types of bread, two types of cheese, and four types of sandwich meat. Record your answers in the space below. How many ways can you combine one type of bread, one type of cheese, and one type of meat?
3. Have a family member name five favorite books. Name four of your favorite movies and three of your favorite television shows. Record your answers in the space below. How many ways could you combine one book, one movie, and one television show?
4. Name two types of vegetables that you like. Have a family member name two types of fruit. Name three types of dairy products. Record your answers in the space below. How many ways can you combine one vegetable, one fruit, and one dairy product?

1. 8 2. 24 3. 60 4. 12

© Glencoe/McGraw-Hill 52 *Mathematics: Applications and Connections, Course 2*

Science and Math Lab Manual, pp. 93–96

Name ____________ Date ________

24

Science and Mathematics Lab

(Course 1, Lesson 13-5; Course 2, Lesson 13-4; Course 3, Lesson 12-6)

The Gender of Children

INTRODUCTION

There is an equal probability that a child will be born female or male. When a family has more than one child, the gender of each child is an independent event that is not influenced by the gender of previously born children.

OBJECTIVES

In this lab, you will:

- explore a series of independent events in a simulation.
- compare the results of your simulation with those of your classmates.

MATERIALS

- coin

DATA AND OBSERVATIONS

Family	Child 1	Child 2	Child 3
A			
B			
C			
D			
E			
F			
G			
H			
I			
J			

© Glencoe/McGraw-Hill 95 *Mathematics: Applications and Connections*

MANIPULATIVES/MODELING

Hands-On Lab Masters, p. 84

13 Name ______ Date ______

Lab Activity
(Lesson 13-1)

Theoretical and Experimental Probability

Toss a coin ten times. Record the results of each toss in the table.

Toss	1	2	3	4	5	6	7	8	9	10
Result	T	T	T	H	T	T	H	T	H	T

Sample answer at left.

1. How many times did the coin land with the tail side up? Sample answer: 7
2. Compute the experimental probability of the coin landing tail side up. Sample answer: $\frac{7}{10}$
3. What is the theoretical probability of the coin landing tail side up? $\frac{1}{2}$
4. Is the experimental probability the same as the theoretical probability? Sample answer: No, in this case the experimental probability is much larger.

Toss a coin 40 more times. Count the number of times the coin lands tail side up.

5. Including your first 10 tosses, how many times did the coin land tail side up? Sample answer: 27
6. How many times did you expect the coin to land tail side up? Sample answer: 25
   Why did you choose this number? Sample answer: I would expect the coin to land tail side up half of the time.
7. What is the experimental probability for 50 tosses? Sample answer: $\frac{27}{50}$
8. What is the theoretical probability for 50 tosses? $\frac{1}{2}$ How does this compare to the theoretical probability for 10 tosses? They are the same.
9. Is the experimental probability for 50 tosses the same as the theoretical probability for 50 tosses? Sample answer: No, but it is closer than for 10 tosses.
10. Write a summary statement. Describe any connections you notice. Mention the number of trials, the experimental probability, and the theoretical probability. Sample answer: The experimental probability was not the same as the theoretical probability. However, the experimental probability of the second experiment was closer to the theoretical probability, suggesting that the more trials you have, the closer the experimental probability will be to the theoretical.

© Glencoe/McGraw-Hill 84 *Mathematics: Applications and Connections, Course 2*

ASSESSMENT/EVALUATION

Assessment and Evaluation Masters, pp. 350–352

13 Name ______ Date ______

Chapter 13 Mid-Chapter Test
(Lessons 13-1 through 13-3)

A cafeteria vending machine contains apples, chicken sandwiches, potato salad, gelatin, lettuce salad, and pudding. Without looking, you select one of the items. Use this information to answer Questions 1–3.

1. What is the theoretical probability that you select a salad? 1. $\frac{1}{3}$
2. If you choose from the vending machine 12 times and choose gelatin 5 times, what is the experimental probability that gelatin will be the food you choose? 2. $\frac{5}{12}$
3. How does the experimental probability in Question 2 compare to the theoretical probability you would choose gelatin? 3. It is greater than the theoretical probability.

Judy is at a pet store that has a cat toy stock of 10 feathers, 3 large scratching posts, 4 small scratching posts, 5 catnip toys, and 6 balls of yarn. Use this information to answer Questions 4–6.

4. If Judy chooses one item at random, what is the probability that Judy buys a feather? 4. $\frac{5}{14}$
5. If Judy picks 13 cat toys at random and 2 of them are catnip toys, what is the experimental probability that she picked a catnip toy? 5. $\frac{2}{13}$
6. How does the experimental probability in Question 5 compare to the theoretical probability that Judy chooses a catnip toy? 6. It is less than the theoretical probability.

For each situation, make a tree diagram and list the outcomes. Then give the total number of outcomes.

7. tossing a quarter and tossing a penny 7. 4
8. choosing to watch TV or read a book and choosing pretzels, an apple, or popcorn for a snack 8. 6
9. choosing a book to read from 5 mysteries and choosing another book to read from 6 biographies. 9. 30
10. rolling a number cube, tossing a penny, and choosing a matchbox car from a truck, race car, police car, and fire engine 10. 48

Use the Counting Principle to find the total number of outcomes in each situation.

11. choosing belt buckles from a collection of 6 bronze, 4 wooden, and 5 silver belt buckles if you choose one of each kind of buckle 11. 120
12. choosing a school sweatshirt that is gray or white and choosing small, medium, large, or extra-large 12. 8
13. choosing toast, muffin, or bagel and choosing coffee, milk, or juice 13. 9
14. choosing an album, CD, and cassette to listen to from a collection of 5 albums, 7 CDs, and 4 cassettes 14. 140
15. tossing a nickel and choosing a crayon from a box of 96 crayons 15. 192
16. choosing erasers from 3 chalkboard, 4 dry-erase, and 5 pencil erasers if you choose one of each kind of eraser 16. 60

© Glencoe/McGraw-Hill 350 *Mathematics: Applications and Connections, Course 2*

Name ______ Date ______

Chapter 13 Quiz A
(Lessons 13-1 and 13-2)

Grant has 6 different shirts to choose from to wear—maroon, blue, brown, gold, green, and purple. Use this information for Questions 1–5.

1. If he selects a shirt at random, what is the probability it will be blue or green? 1. $\frac{1}{3}$
2. If Grant chooses shirts 10 times and chooses the gold one 4 times, what is the experimental probability that the gold shirt is chosen? 2. $\frac{2}{5}$
3. How does the experimental probability in Question 2 compare to the theoretical probability that the gold shirt is chosen? 3. It is greater than the theoretical probability.
4. Use a tree diagram to find how many ways you can arrange four colors—yellow, red, blue, and black—if no color can be used more than once. 4. 24
5. Use a tree diagram to find how many combinations can be made from 2 colors, red and blue, for 4 cars, one color per car. 5. 8

Name ______ Date ______

Chapter 13 Quiz B
(Lesson 13-3)

Use the Counting Principle to find the total number of outcomes in each situation.

1. choosing stuffed animals from 4 bunnies, 3 monkeys, and 3 racoons if you choose one of each kind of animal 1. 36
2. choosing spaghetti, linguine, or rigatoni and choosing white sauce or red sauce 2. 6
3. choosing from 3 summer dresses, 2 purses, a hat, 3 scarves, and 2 belts to dress a mannequin 3. 36
4. Cathy is shopping for shoes. How many ways can she buy a pair of sandals, sneakers, and boots if she can choose from 5 pairs of sandals, 10 pairs of sneakers, and 6 pairs of boots? 4. 300
5. A car comes with 2 or 4 doors, a four- or six-cylinder engine, 3 interior colors, and 6 exterior colors. How many different cars are possible? 5. 72

© Glencoe/McGraw-Hill 351 *Mathematics: Applications and Connections, Course 2*

TECHNOLOGY/MULTIMEDIA

Technology Masters, pp. 51–52

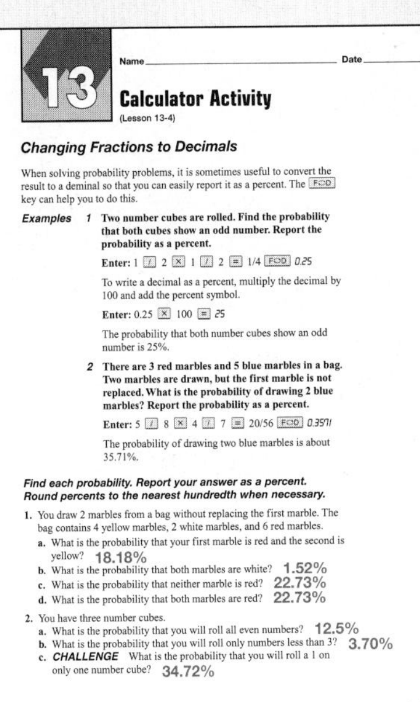

13 Name ______ Date ______

Calculator Activity
(Lesson 13-4)

Changing Fractions to Decimals

When solving probability problems, it is sometimes useful to convert the result to a deminal so that you can easily report it as a percent. The [F◇D] key can help you to do this.

Examples 1 **Two number cubes are rolled. Find the probability that both cubes show an odd number. Report the probability as a percent.**

Enter: 1 [/] 2 [×] 1 [/] 2 [=] 1/4 [F◇D] *0.25*

To write a decimal as a percent, multiply the decimal by 100 and add the percent symbol.

Enter: 0.25 [×] 100 [=] *25*

The probability that both number cubes show an odd number is 25%.

2 **There are 3 red marbles and 5 blue marbles in a bag. Two marbles are drawn, but the first marble is not replaced. What is the probability of drawing 2 blue marbles? Report the probability as a percent.**

Enter: 5 [/] 8 [×] 4 [/] 7 [=] 20/56 [F◇D] *0.3571*

The probability of drawing two blue marbles is about 35.71%.

Find each probability. Report your answer as a percent. Round percents to the nearest hundredth when necessary.

1. You draw 2 marbles from a bag without replacing the first marble. The bag contains 4 yellow marbles, 2 white marbles, and 6 red marbles.
   a. What is the probability that your first marble is red and the second is yellow? 18.18%
   b. What is the probability that both marbles are white? 1.52%
   c. What is the probability that neither marble is red? 22.73%
   d. What is the probability that both marbles are red? 22.73%
2. You have three number cubes.
   a. What is the probability that you will roll all even numbers? 12.5%
   b. What is the probability that you will roll only numbers less than 3? 3.70%
   c. ***CHALLENGE*** What is the probability that you will roll a 1 on only one number cube? 34.72%

© Glencoe/McGraw-Hill T51 *Mathematics: Applications and Connections, Course 2*

13 Name ______ Date ______

Graphing Calculator Activity
(Lesson 13-5)

Permutations

You can use a graphing calculator to help you find the number of permutations.

Examples 1 **Compute 5!.**

Enter: 5 [MATH] [▶] [▶] [▶] 4 [ENTER] *120*

5! = 120

2 **25 people are auditioning for 5 different parts in a play. In how many ways can the 5 parts be assigned?**

To calculate a permutation, find the total number of objects (n) and the number taken at one time (r). In this problem, $n = 25$. Because 5 students are needed, $r = 5$.

Enter: 25 [MATH] [▶] [▶] [▶] 2 5 [ENTER] *6,375,600*

The parts can be assigned in 6,375,600 different ways.

Find the value of each expression.

1. 10! 3,628,800
2. 12 factorial 479,001,600
3. 9! 362,880

Find the value of each permutation for the given values of n and r.

4. $n = 6, r = 2$ 30
5. $n = 10, r = 6$ 151,200
6. $n = 12, r = 4$ 11,880
7. $n = 20, r = 2$ 380
8. $n = 15, r = 7$ 32,432,400
9. $n = 18, r = 3$ 4,896

Solve.

10. Employees of Spies, Inc. are given 3-digit code numbers made up of the digits 1, 3, 5, 7, and 9. How many different 3-digit code numbers can be created? 60
11. How many different 4-letter arrangements are there in the letters A, S, N, D, T, R, and Y? 840
12. Twenty students have entered an art contest. Five students will receive awards. How many different groups of 5 students could be selected to receive the awards? 1,860,480

© Glencoe/McGraw-Hill T52 *Mathematics: Applications and Connections, Course 2*

MEETING INDIVIDUAL NEEDS

Investigations for the Special Education Student, pp. 45–46

Use with:
Course 1-Chapter 14
Course 2-Chapter 13
Course 3-Chapter 13

Investigation 15 Teacher's Guide

The Game Show

Overview

The purpose of this investigation is for students to recognize that problem-solving and mathematical strategies are needed to play even the most enjoyable games. The problem-solving and mathematical value of several games will be evaluated by students during a three-day game review period. At the end of this time, the class will compile the results of their reviews into one master list of the "top ten" mathematics-related games. This list will then be forwarded to the appropriate school personnel along with a letter of recommendation to include such games as part of the mathematics program at the school.

Activity Goals

Students will:
- explore the problem-solving and mathematical strategies used in games,
- review and give feedback for certain games, and
- participate in selecting and recommending games for the school to purchase.

Planning the Instruction

Prerequisite Skills

Students should have a significant amount of practice reading and following directions, and computing with whole numbers. A basic understanding of probability may be helpful.

Materials
- investigation worksheet
- assortment of games for the classroom
- manila envelopes (one per game)

Time Needed

six 45-minute periods

Procedure

1. Given an example of a well-known game such as checkers, have students brainstorm the problem-solving and mathematical strategies that are necessary to play the game. Then, explain to the class that they are about to become game consultants for the school by recommending games that will enhance the problem-solving and mathematical skills of its students.
2. Obtain a variety of games for use in the classroom. Depending on the classroom situation, teachers may bring games from home or have students volunteer to bring them.
3. Students will have three days in class to review as many games as possible. To review a game, students must follow the reviewing procedure on the Game Review worksheet. They will play each game twice, the second time answering the review questions. After reviewing each game, students will place the review sheet for that game in the envelope provided. If time permits, students should review another game using a new Game Review worksheet.
4. At the end of the reviewing periods, the results will be tallied, and, as a class, students and teacher will compile a list of the top ten games.
5. Once the list is established, the class will submit it to the appropriate personnel along with a letter explaining and supporting their research. The letter should also address the need for these games to be part of the mathematics program at the school.
6. An extension of this investigation might require students to create their own game involving the problem-solving and mathematical strategies believed to be the most valuable.

Adaptations and Variations

The following are some ideas on how this investigation may be modified depending on student population.

LD
- Simplify rules for easier comprehension.
- Review several games together with the class.
- Allow students to work with a partner.

PH
- Allow students to type or word process their review.
- Be sure to choose games suitable to their needs.

CD
- Select games suitable to their needs.

BD
- Maintain close proximity during the review process.
- If problems arise, have them play alone until they earn their way back to working with others.

HI
- Select games suitable to their needs.

VI
- Enlarge directions to games.
- Assign an aide to help students with any reading.

© Glencoe/McGraw-Hill 45 *Mathematics: Applications and Connections*

CHAPTER 13 NOTES

Theme: Games

Can a computer beat the best player in the world at checkers? Although computers have been successful in chess competition, some of the earliest research in artificial intelligence involved the game of checkers. Software developed jointly by Americans and Canadians has come in second in the World Checkers Championship.

To compete with a human player, a computer program searches for all of the moves that are possible at each stage of the game. With only four pieces left, there are still seven million possible positions on the board!

Question of the Day How many arrangements can be made from two red checkers placed in a row of four rectangles? 6

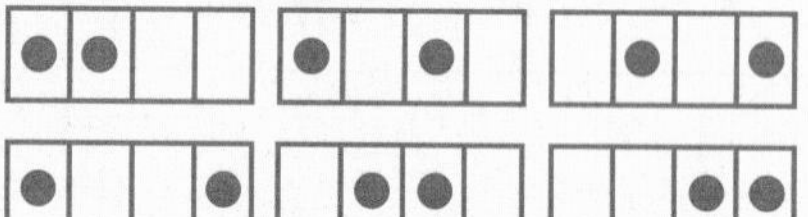

Assess Prerequisite Skills

Ask students to read through the list of objectives presented in "What you'll learn in Chapter 13." You may wish to ask them what each of the objectives means or if they have experienced or used any of these math concepts before.

Building Portfolios

Encourage students to revise their portfolios as they study this chapter. Ask them to evaluate their own progress as they work through the chapter.

Math and the Family

In the *Family Letters and Activities* booklet (pp. 51–52), you will find a letter to the parents explaining what students will study in Chapter 13. An activity appropriate for the whole family is also available.

CHAPTER 13 Exploring Discrete Math and Probability

What you'll learn in Chapter 13

- to find and compare experimental and theoretical probabilities,
- to solve problems by acting them out,
- to count outcomes by using a tree diagram or the Counting Principle,
- to find the probability of independent and dependent events, and
- to find the number of permutations or combinations of a group of objects.

CD-ROM Program

Activities for Chapter 13

- Chapter 13 Introduction
- Interactive Lessons 13-1A, 13-1
- Assessment Game
- Resource Lessons 13-1 through 13-6

CHAPTER Project

ADVANCE TO *GO* AND COLLECT $200

In this project, you will analyze the use of probability in your favorite board game or television game show. You will also design your own game that combines skill and chance.

Getting Started

- Choose a game to analyze.
- Outline a plan for designing your own board game.

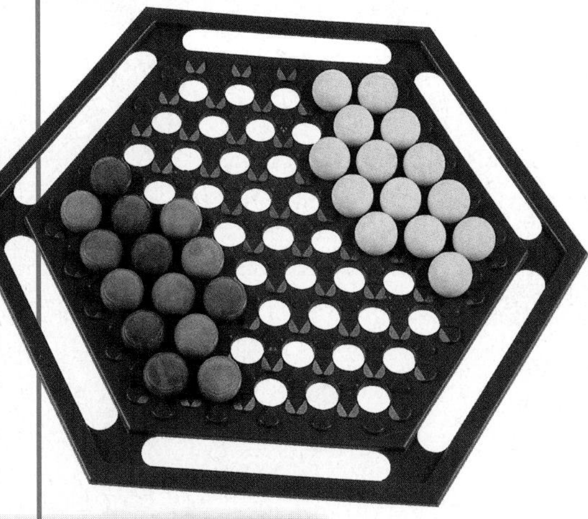

Technology Tips

- Surf the **Internet** for information about games.
- Use a **word processor** to write the rules of your game.

Research For up-to-date information on board games, visit:

www.glencoe.com/sec/math/mac/mathnet

Working on the Project

You can use what you'll learn in Chapter 13 to help you analyze and design your games.

Page	Exercise
533	22
545	18
557	Alternative Assessment

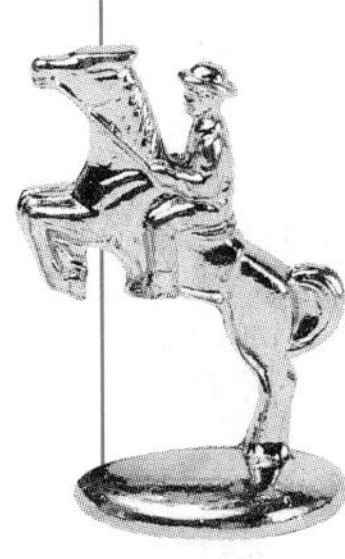

CHAPTER Project NOTES

Objectives Students should

- analyze the use of probability in board games.
- design their own game, combining skill and chance.

Project Pointer You may suggest that students begin a *Project Folder* to keep their work as they complete each stage of the Chapter Project. The completed project may also be added to their portfolios.

Suggest that students brainstorm the possible scenarios for playing their game to anticipate possible questions for the "rules of the game."

***Investigations and Projects Masters*, p. 68**

Name________________ Date________

Chapter 13 Project

Advance to GO and Collect $200

Page 527, Getting Started

Game diagram:

Object of the game:

Number of players:

Rules for play:

Levels of skill:

Use of probability:

 68 *Mathematics: Applications and Connections, Course 2*

interNET CONNECTION

Glencoe has made every effort to ensure that the website links for *Mathematics: Applications and Connections* at **www.glencoe.com/sec/math/mac/mathnet** are current and contain appropriate content. However, these website links are not under Glencoe's control.

Instructional Resources ▶▶▶

A recording sheet to help students organize their data for the Chapter Project is shown at the right and is available in the *Investigations and Projects Masters,* p. 68.

13-1A THINKING LAB Notes

Objective Students solve problems by acting them out.

Recommended Pacing	
Honors	Day 2 of 10

Optional Resources

CD-ROM Program
- Interactive Lesson 13-1A

1 FOCUS

Getting Started Ask students what the probability is that two people playing "Rock, Paper, Scissors" will show the same hand sign. $\frac{1}{3}$ Have them play 20 games, recording how many times they show the same sign, and compare their records to their predictions.

2 TEACH

Teaching Tip Encourage students to act out the scenario one step at a time and to record each trial accurately to be sure they keep track of the data.

In-Class Example

Kevin has 8 pockets in his jacket. He is not sure which pocket holds his keys. What is the probability that he reaches into a pocket and finds the keys? Work in a group to act out this problem using index cards. $\frac{1}{8}$

THINKING LAB **PROBLEM SOLVING**

13-1A Act it Out

A Preview of Lesson 13-1

Do you dread pop quizzes? Most students don't like them. But if you do your homework, you'll be more likely to answer the questions correctly and get a good grade. Dave and Selena just finished taking a pop quiz that had 10 true-false questions. Let's listen in as they talk about it.

Dave: Sometimes I think tossing a coin would be a good way to answer the questions on a true-false test. If the coin showed tails, I'd write T, and if it showed heads, I'd write F.

Selena: That seems risky. Why don't we do an experiment to act it out? We could see if tossing a coin is a good strategy.

Dave: OK–let's experiment with a 10-point quiz. Let's suppose the correct answers are T, F, F, F, T, T, F, T, F, T.

Selena: I'll toss a coin 10 times for each "quiz" and you record the answers. Then we'll circle the ones that are correct for each trial.

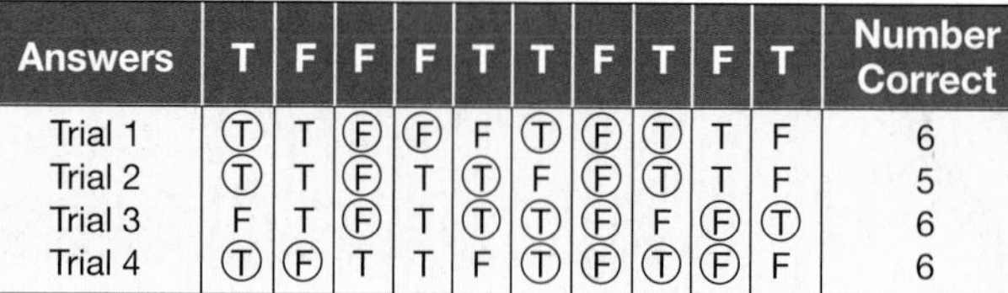

Answers	T	F	F	F	T	T	F	T	F	T	Number Correct
Trial 1	Ⓣ	T	Ⓕ	Ⓕ	F	Ⓣ	Ⓕ	Ⓣ	T	F	6
Trial 2	Ⓣ	T	Ⓕ	T	Ⓣ	F	Ⓕ	Ⓣ	T	F	5
Trial 3	F	T	Ⓕ	T	Ⓣ	Ⓣ	Ⓕ	F	Ⓕ	Ⓣ	6
Trial 4	Ⓣ	Ⓕ	T	T	F	Ⓣ	Ⓕ	Ⓣ	Ⓕ	F	6

THINK ABOUT IT

Work with a partner.

1. ***Compute*** the average score for the four trial quizzes shown above. **5.75**
2. If a passing grade is 70%, ***decide*** whether tossing a coin is a good strategy to use when taking true-false tests. **no**
3. ***Explain*** whether the results of this experiment would be the same if it were repeated. **Sample answer: Results would probably vary.**
4. ***Apply*** the **act it out** strategy to solve this problem. **See students' work.**

   A baseball card manufacturer is holding a contest. Each package of cards contains a puzzle piece. If you collect all 6 different pieces, you win two tickets to a major league game. There is an equally-likely chance of getting a different puzzle piece each time. How many packages of cards would you need to buy to win the contest?

Reteaching the Lesson

Activity Have students use a spinner divided into 6 sections to simulate how many attempts it takes a biologist to capture and tag each dolphin in a school of six. Have them tally the frequency of capturing each dolphin as well as the total attempts.

For **Extra Practice,** see page 602.

ON YOUR OWN

5. ***Make a model*** using a spinner, that will act out a basketball player making free throws, if she usually succeeds in making 75% of her free throws. **See margin.**

6. ***Explain*** an advantage of using the act it out strategy to solve a problem. **See margin.**

7. ***Look Ahead*** Suppose Mavis, Miguel, and Carianne each left one book in the school library. When they returned to their homeroom, their teacher randomly handed out the three books to the students. Act out this situation 20 times. For how many of these times did Carianne receive the same book she was reading in the library? **See students' work.**

MIXED PROBLEM SOLVING

STRATEGIES
- Look for a pattern.
- Solve a simpler problem.
- Act it out.
- Guess and check.
- Draw a diagram.
- Make a chart.
- Work backward.

Solve. Use any strategy.

8. ***Money Matters*** Mikael received a birthday gift of money. He loaned $5 to his friend Tequisha and spent half of the remaining money. The next day he received $10 from his uncle. After spending $9 at the movies, he still had $11 left. How much money did he receive for his birthday? **$25**

9. ***Geometry*** The length of a rectangle is 8 inches longer than its width. What are the length and width of the rectangle if the area is 84 square inches? **14 inches, 6 inches**

10. ***Patterns*** This pattern below is known as Pascal's Triangle. Find the pattern and complete the 6th and 7th rows.

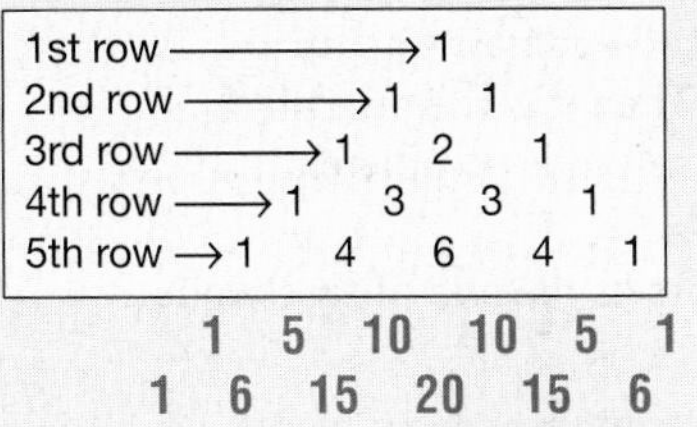

1st row → 1
2nd row → 1 1
3rd row → 1 2 1
4th row → 1 3 3 1
5th row → 1 4 6 4 1

1 5 10 10 5 1
1 6 15 20 15 6 1

11. ***Earth Science*** Mauna Kea, a Hawaiian mountain, is 3.35×10^4 feet tall when its height is measured from the ocean floor. Mt. Everest, the highest mountain above sea level, is about 29,000 feet. Which mountain is taller? **Mauna Kea**

12. ***Life Science*** About 190 million years ago, a giant lizard-like dinosaur called an apatosaurus roamed Earth. It weighed about 30 tons. Today, the largest living land animal is the African elephant. It weighs about 16,500 pounds. How many more tons did the brontosaurus weigh than today's elephant? **21.75 tons**

13. ***Patterns*** Complete the pattern. 100, 98, 94, ?, 80, ?. **88, 70**

14.  **Standardized Test Practice** About 48% of the registered voters actually vote in an election. In a district with 900 registered voters, which is a good estimate of the number who will vote in the next election? **B**
    - **A** less than 300
    - **B** between 300 and 450
    - **C** between 450 and 600
    - **D** between 600 and 750
    - **E** more than 750

Extending the Lesson

Activity A pouch of a golf bag has 3 balls each of three different brands of golf balls. Ask students to tell the least number of golf balls they must take out in order to be sure of getting at least 3 of one brand. **7 golf balls**

3 PRACTICE/APPLY

Check for Understanding

Use the results of Exercise 4 to determine whether students understand how to act out a problem to solve it.

Extra Practice If students need additional practice in problem solving, extra practice is available on the following pages.
- Act It Out, see p. 602
- Mixed Problem Solving, see pp. 605–606

Assignment Guide
All: 5–14

4 ASSESS

Closing Activity

Writing Have students explain how they would use the acting-out strategy to determine the number of handshakes that take place when a committee of 5 meets and everybody shakes everybody else's hand. **Strategies will vary; 10 handshakes**

Additional Answers

5. **Sample answer:**

6. **Sample answer: You can make a prediction about what will actually happen in the problem.**

13-1 Lesson Notes

Instructional Resources

- *Study Guide Masters,* p. 93
- *Practice Masters,* p. 93
- *Enrichment Masters,* p. 93
- Transparencies 13-1, A and B

- CD-ROM Program
  - Resource Lesson 13-1
  - Interactive Lesson 13-1

Recommended Pacing	
Honors	Day 3 of 10

1 FOCUS

5-Minute Check
(Chapter 12)

1. Draw a top, a side, and a front view of the figure.

2. Find the surface area of a rectangular prism that is 4 feet long, 3 feet wide, and 2.75 feet high. **62.5 ft²**
3. What is the volume of a cube with an edge of 4.5 meters? **91.125 m³**

The 5-Minute Check is also available on **Transparency 13-1A** for this lesson.

Motivating the Lesson

Hands-On Activity Have students write their names on index cards and randomly draw names from a hat. Ask students the probability that they will draw their own name. **$\frac{1}{n}$, n = number of students**

The CD-Rom Program contains a simulation tool for rolling number cubes that could be used to save time. Have students determine the experimental probability of rolling a "1" and a "double 1" based on their game.

Additional resources for this game can be found on page 53 of the ***Classroom Games.***

13-1 Theoretical and Experimental Probability

What you'll learn

You'll learn to find and compare experimental and theoretical probabilities.

When am I ever going to use this?

Probability is used in weather forecasting, games, and business.

Word Wise

outcome
sample space
theoretical probability
experimental probability

If you are one of the estimated 480 million people who have played the most popular board game, you know that skill helps you win the game. But there is also an element of chance in the game. Chance makes games more exciting.

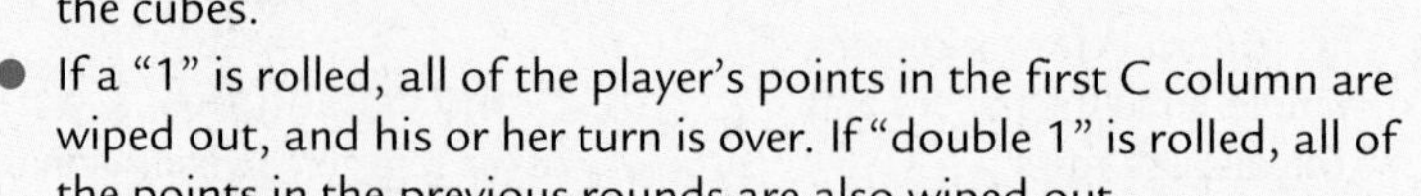

Take a Chance

Math Skill
Probability

Get Ready This game is for two, three, or four players.

 2 number cubes

Get Set Each player makes a score sheet like the one below.

C	H	A	N	C	E

Go Each letter of the word CHANCE represents a different round of the game. The object of the game is to get the greatest number of points during the six rounds.

- The first player rolls the number cubes and records the sum of the numbers in the first C column, unless a "1" is rolled on either of the cubes.
- If a "1" is rolled, all of the player's points in the first C column are wiped out, and his or her turn is over. If "double 1" is rolled, all of the points in the previous rounds are also wiped out.
- If a "1" is *not* rolled, the player chooses to roll again or to stop and keep the points he or she already has. Then it is the next player's turn. After each player has a turn, the first round is complete. Continue in this manner for the next rounds.
- The winner is the player with the most points at the end of six rounds.

Visit www.glencoe.com/sec/math/mac/mathnet for more games.

Cross-Curriculum Cue

Inform the other teachers on your team that your classes are studying statistics and probability. Suggestions for curriculum integration are:
Social Studies: traffic patterns
Science: meteorology; medicines

In the game on page 530, you tried to guess the probability that a "1" would be rolled. There are many possible results, or **outcomes**, when you roll two number cubes. The list of all possible outcomes is called the **sample space**.

1, 1	1, 2	1, 3	1, 4	1, 5	1, 6	*(1, 6) means that the*
2, 1	2, 2	2, 3	2, 4	2, 5	2, 6	*first number cube is*
3, 1	3, 2	3, 3	3, 4	3, 5	3, 6	*a 1 and the second*
4, 1	4, 2	4, 3	4, 4	4, 5	4, 6	*number cube is a 6.*
5, 1	5, 2	5, 3	5, 4	5, 5	5, 6	
6, 1	6, 2	6, 3	6, 4	6, 5	6, 6	

LOOK BACK
Refer to Lesson 4-8 to review how to find the probability of simple events.

There are 36 possible outcomes and 11 ways of rolling at least one "1". The **theoretical probability** of rolling a "1" is $\frac{11}{36}$. Theoretical probability is the ratio of the number of favorable outcomes to the total number of possible outcomes. It tells us that, in the long run, a "1" should occur about 11 times in every 36 rolls.

Example **1** **APPLICATION**

Games **Find the theoretical probability of rolling "double 1" with a pair of number cubes.** *A "double 1" is given by (1, 1).*

$$P(\text{"double 1"}) = \frac{\text{number of ways rolling "double 1"}}{\text{number of possible outcomes}} \text{ or } \frac{1}{36}.$$

The probability of rolling "double 1" is $\frac{1}{36}$ or about 3%.

Study Hint
Reading Math
P("double 1") is read as the probability of rolling "double 1".

You can also conduct an experiment by rolling two number cubes many times and recording the number of times "double 1" occurs. This will give you an **experimental probability**. Experimental probability is based on frequencies obtained in an experiment.

HANDS-ON MINI-LAB

Work with a partner.

 2 number cubes

Try This

- Roll two number cubes 100 times. Record each "double 1".
- Compute the experimental probability of a "double 1" occurring.

Talk About It

1. How does your experimental probability compare to the probabilities of those in other groups? **See students' work.**
2. Compare your experimental probability to the theoretical probability. If the numbers are different, explain why.
3. Combine your results with other groups to find the experimental probability for the entire class. How does it compare to the theoretical probability?

2. Sample answer: For small samples, the numbers may be different.

3. Sample answer: As samples are combined, the experimental probability should approach the theoretical probability.

2 TEACH

Transparency 13-1B contains a teaching aid for this lesson.

In-Class Example

For Example 1
Find the theoretical probability of getting an even number sum when rolling a pair of differently colored number cubes. $\frac{1}{2}$

Using the Mini-Lab Ask students to explain why their experimental probabilities differ from each other. Have them compute the experimental probability of rolling a "double 6," and compare it to the "double 1." Ask them what results they might anticipate if they rolled the number cubes 500 times. Combine the results of five pairs to simulate the larger sample.

Classroom Vignette

"I like to introduce theoretical probability and experimental probability by using 6 cubes (2 yellow, 3 green, 1 blue). Have students put the cubes in a bag and pull a cube out at random. Record the result and replace the cube. Do this 20 times. Ask students to compare their results with the theoretical probabilities."

Debbie Haver
Deborah Haver, Principal
Great Bridge Middle School
Virginia Beach, VA

In-Class Example

For Example 2

Alicia and Lyle rolled their number cubes 40 times and got an even number 23 times. Find the experimental probability of rolling an even number.

$\frac{23}{40}$ or 57.5%

3 PRACTICE/APPLY

Check for Understanding

If students need additional practice or instruction after completing Exercises 1–8, one of these options may be helpful.

- Extra Practice, see p. 603
- Reteaching Activity
- *Study Guide Masters,* p. 93
- *Practice Masters,* p. 93

Assignment Guide

Core: 9–21 odd, 23–26
Enriched: 10–18 even, 19–21, 23–26

Additional Answer

1. **Experimental probability is the result of collecting data; theoretical probability is the ratio of the number of favorable outcomes to the total number of outcomes.**

***Study Guide Masters,* p. 93**

Name ________________ Date ________

Study Guide

Theoretical and Experimental Probability

Theoretical probability is determined by finding the ratio of the number of ways an event can occur to the number of possible outcomes. **Experimental probability** is determined by conducting an experiment.

Example **Julio tossed two coins and tallied the results. He repeated the experiment 20 times. Find the experimental and theoretical probabilities.**

Outcome	Tally	Frequency
2 heads	卌 I	6
1 head, 1 tail	卌 卌 I	11
2 tails	III	3

The experimental probability of tossing 1 head and 1 tail is $\frac{11}{20}$.

The possible outcomes for tossing two coins are: HH, HT, TH, TT. The theoretical probability of tossing 1 head and 1 tail is $\frac{2}{4}$, or $\frac{1}{2}$.

Perform the experiment described above 20 times. Record your results in the chart. Find the experimental probability for each outcome. Answers will vary.

Outcome	Tally	Frequency
2 heads		
1 head, 1 tail		
2 tails		

One card is drawn from a 52-card deck. Find each theoretical probability.

1. P(heart) $\frac{1}{4}$
2. P(king) $\frac{1}{13}$
3. P(king, queen, or jack) $\frac{3}{13}$
4. P(red) $\frac{1}{2}$
5. P(red or black) 1
6. P(number less than 6) $\frac{5}{13}$

 T93 *Mathematics: Applications and Connections, Course 2*

Example 2 The frequency table shows the results of an experiment in which one coin was tossed. Find the experimental probability of tossing heads for this experiment.

Outcome	Tally	Frequency
Heads	卌 卌 II	12
Tails	卌 III	8

$$\frac{\text{number of times heads occur}}{\text{number of possible outcomes}} = \frac{12}{12 + 8} \text{ or } \frac{12}{20}$$

The experimental probability of tossing heads is $\frac{12}{20}$ or 60%.

CHECK FOR UNDERSTANDING

Communicating Mathematics

Read and study the lesson to answer each question.

1. ***Explain*** the difference between theoretical probability and experimental probability. **See margin.**
2. ***Tell*** whether the experimental probability of an event is always the same. Explain your reasoning. **2. No; different experiments may result in different data.**
3. ***Give an example*** of an event with a theoretical probability of $\frac{1}{6}$. **Sample answer: rolling a "1" on a number cube**

Guided Practice

Refer to the sample space on page 531. Find each theoretical probability.

4. a sum of 7 $\frac{1}{6}$
5. 3 on the first cube and 5 on the second $\frac{1}{36}$
6. Find the theoretical probability of choosing a girl's name at random from 20 boy's names and 10 girl's names. $\frac{1}{3}$
7. Ayani spins a spinner like the one at the right 30 times. It lands on red 16 times. What is the experimental probability of spinning red? $\frac{16}{30} = \frac{8}{15}$

8. ***Bowling*** Sonia averages 3 strikes for every 10 frames of bowling. What is the probability she will get a strike in the first frame of her next game? $\frac{3}{10}$ **or 30%**

EXERCISES

Practice

Refer to the sample space on page 531. Find each theoretical probability.

9. the same number on both cubes $\frac{1}{6}$
10. a sum less than 4 $\frac{1}{12}$
11. a sum of 1 **0**
12. a sum less than 15 **1**
13. the first number greater than the second $\frac{15}{36} = \frac{5}{12}$
14. both numbers odd $\frac{1}{4}$

There are 4 red marbles, 5 green marbles, 6 yellow marbles, and 3 blue marbles in a bag. Suppose you select one marble at random. 17. $\frac{1}{2}$

15. Find P(red). $\frac{2}{9}$
16. Find P(green). $\frac{5}{18}$
17. Find P(yellow or blue).

Reteaching the Lesson

Activity Ask students the theoretical probability of opening their books at random to page 123. $\frac{1}{n}$, **n = number of pages in the book** Then ask them to find the experimental probability of opening to a page ending in 3.

Error Analysis

Watch for students who confuse theoretical and experimental probability.
Prevent by guiding them to see that theoretical probability is found by applying a formula and experimental probability by collecting data.

18. Conduct an experiment in which you use small slips of paper. Write "red" on four slips, "green" on five slips, "yellow" on six slips, and "blue" on three slips. Without looking, choose a slip of paper and record the color. Replace the slip and repeat this another nine times. **a. See students' work.**
   a. Find the experimental probability of choosing yellow or blue slip.
   b. How does the experimental probability compare to the theoretical probability you found in Exercise 17? **See students' work.**

Applications and Problem Solving

19. ***Geography*** A state is chosen at random from the United States. Find each probability.
   a. The state borders on the Gulf of Mexico. $\frac{1}{10}$
   b. The state begins with the letter "T". $\frac{1}{25}$

20. $\frac{15}{36} = \frac{5}{12}$

20. ***Games*** Parcheesi is a game that was first played in India. In this game, two dice are rolled. You can put a game piece into play if a total of 5 is shown on the dice or if a 5 is shown on at least one of the dice. What is the probability that a game piece can be put into play in one roll of the dice?

21. ***Advertising*** The results of an Arbitron survey of radio stations in Fayette County, Kentucky, are shown in the chart. Both WVLK-92.9 FM and WWYC-100.1 FM are country music stations. What is the probability that a person chosen at random who is tuned into one of these five stations is tuned into a country station? Express your answer to the nearest whole percent. **44%**

Station	Number of Listeners
WVLK-92.9 FM	115,000
WKQQ-98.1 FM	81,000
WMXL-94.5 FM	76,000
WGKS-96.9 FM	54,100
WWYC-100.1 FM	54,000

Source: Arbitron, December

22. ***Working on the CHAPTER Project*** Make a list of the ways probability is used in the game you have chosen. **See students' work.**

23. ***Critical Thinking*** Twenty red cards are added to a stack of cards with an unknown number of black cards. The stack is then shuffled to thoroughly mix the cards, and the first 20 cards on the stack are turned over. Five of these cards are red. Does this imply that the number of black cards in the stack was 60? Explain. **See margin.**

Mixed Review

24. **Standardized Test Practice** Gilberto is covering a cylindrical can with paper for a school project. The can has a height of 15 inches and a radius of 4 inches. How much paper will he need to cover the can completely? *(Lesson 12-5)* **A**
   A 477.5 in^2 **B** 375.2 in^2 **C** 104.5 in^2 **D** 60.0 in^2

For **Extra Practice,** see page 603.

25. Find 35% of 20 using the percent equation. *(Lesson 11-2)* **7**

26. ***Algebra*** Solve $5t = 125$. *(Lesson 6-2)* **25**

Exercise 22 asks students to advance to the next stage of work on the Chapter Project. You may want students to compare their lists to find additional ideas for designing their own games.

4 ASSESS

Closing Activity

Speaking Have students in small groups explain in their own words the difference between *theoretical* probability and *experimental* probability. Then have each group present its best explanation to the class.

Additional Answer

23. Sample answer: no; however, 60 would be a good estimate of the number of black cards because you would expect that in any large sample, about $\frac{1}{4}$ of the cards would be red.

***Practice Masters,* p. 93**

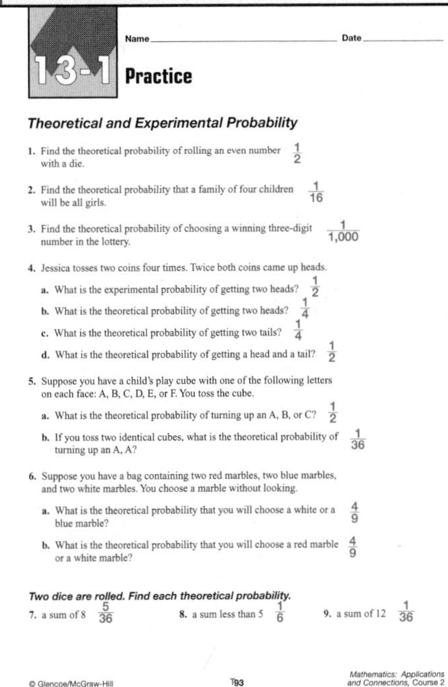
Name ______ Date ______

13-1 Practice

Theoretical and Experimental Probability

1. Find the theoretical probability of rolling an even number with a die. $\frac{1}{2}$
2. Find the theoretical probability that a family of four children will be all girls. $\frac{1}{16}$
3. Find the theoretical probability of choosing a winning three-digit number in the lottery. $\frac{1}{1,000}$
4. Jessica tosses two coins four times. Twice both coins came up heads.
   a. What is the experimental probability of getting two heads? $\frac{1}{2}$
   b. What is the theoretical probability of getting two heads? $\frac{1}{4}$
   c. What is the theoretical probability of getting two tails? $\frac{1}{4}$
   d. What is the theoretical probability of getting a head and a tail? $\frac{1}{2}$
5. Suppose you have a child's play cube with one of the following letters on each face: A, B, C, D, E, or F. You toss the cube.
   a. What is the theoretical probability of turning up an A, B, or C? $\frac{1}{2}$
   b. If you toss two identical cubes, what is the theoretical probability of turning up an A, A? $\frac{1}{36}$
6. Suppose you have a bag containing two red marbles, two blue marbles, and two white marbles. You choose a marble without looking.
   a. What is the theoretical probability that you will choose a white or a blue marble? $\frac{4}{9}$
   b. What is the theoretical probability that you will choose a red marble or a white marble? $\frac{4}{9}$

Two dice are rolled. Find each theoretical probability.

7. a sum of 8 $\frac{5}{36}$ 8. a sum less than 5 $\frac{1}{6}$ 9. a sum of 12 $\frac{1}{36}$

© Glencoe/McGraw-Hill T93 *Mathematics: Applications and Connections, Course 2*

Extending the Lesson

***Enrichment Masters,* p. 93**

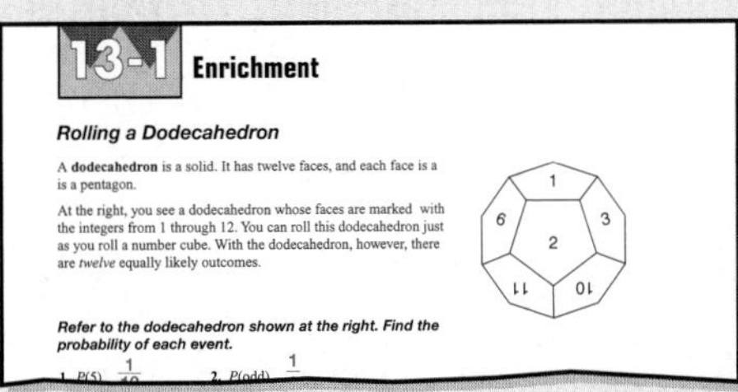
13-1 Enrichment

Rolling a Dodecahedron

A **dodecahedron** is a solid. It has twelve faces, and each face is a is a pentagon.

At the right, you see a dodecahedron whose faces are marked with the integers from 1 through 12. You can roll this dodecahedron just as you roll a number cube. With the dodecahedron, however, there are *twelve* equally likely outcomes.

Refer to the dodecahedron shown at the right. Find the probability of each event.

1. $P(5)$ 2. $P(odd)$

Activity Have students research weather data for their local area and determine the theoretical probability of sunny days (average number of sunny days per year). Then observe the weather for five days to find the experimental probability of sunny days.

13-2 Lesson Notes

Instructional Resources

- *Study Guide Masters,* p. 94
- *Practice Masters,* p. 94
- *Enrichment Masters,* p. 94
- Transparencies 13-2, A and B
- *Assessment and Evaluation Masters,* p. 351
- *School to Career Masters,* p. 26

- CD-ROM Program
  - Resource Lesson 13-2

Recommended Pacing	
Honors	Day 4 of 10

1 FOCUS

5-Minute Check *(Lesson 13-1)*

Two number cubes are rolled. Find each theoretical probability.

1. a sum of 3 $\frac{1}{18}$
2. a sum less than 10 $\frac{5}{6}$
3. a sum greater than 12 **0**
4. Walt's Drive-Through gives a free soft drink to every twentieth customer. From 1:00 P.M. to 2:00 P.M., 9 cars, 6 vans, 4 trucks, and 1 motorcycle stopped at Walt's.
   a. Find P(truck). $\frac{1}{5}$
   b. Find P(car or van). $\frac{3}{4}$

The 5-Minute Check is also available on **Transparency 13-2A** for this lesson.

Motivating the Lesson

Communication Tell students that Dashiell is writing a mystery and his amateur sleuth will be either a dentist, a cook, or a bus driver. He plans to have the crime take place in a park, a bowling alley, or a fish market. Ask students how many detective/crime-scene choices Dashiell has.

2 TEACH

Transparency 13-2B contains a teaching aid for this lesson.

13-2 Tree Diagrams

What you'll learn

You'll learn to use tree diagrams to count outcomes.

When am I ever going to use this?

You can use tree diagrams to analyze games of chance.

Word Wise

tree diagram
fair game

Recently, there were over 5 million families in the United States that had three children under age 18. What is the probability that a family with three children has all boys?

First, find the number of possible outcomes. You can make a list or draw a diagram. The **tree diagram** below shows that each child might be a boy (B) or a girl (G).

First Child	Second Child	Third Child	Outcomes
B	B	B	BBB
		G	BBG
	G	B	BGB
		G	BGG
G	B	B	GBB
		G	GBG
	G	B	GGB
		G	GGG

There are eight possible outcomes, but only one has all boys. So the probability that a family with three children has all boys is $\frac{1}{8}$ or 12.5%.

Inventory **The Sports Store carries one brand of basketball tank-top in four sizes: M, L, XL, and XXL. Each size comes in two colors: gold (G) and black (B). Make a tree diagram that shows all of the possible combinations of size and color.**

Making a tree diagram is a good way to determine a sample space.

Size	Color	Outcomes
M	G	MG
	B	MB
L	G	LG
	B	LB
XL	G	XLG
	B	XLB
XXL	G	XXLG
	B	XXLB

There are eight possible combinations of size and color.

Multiple Learning Styles

Logical After students make several tree diagrams to solve problems, have them make a chart showing the number of possibilities for each event and the final number of outcomes. Ask students to look for a pattern and then tell you how they could predict the number of outcomes without making a tree diagram.

You can use tree diagrams to analyze whether or not games are fair. In a **fair game**, players of equal skill have the same chance of winning.

MINI-LAB

Work with a partner.  3 counters 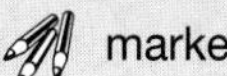 marker

Try This

- Mark one side of a counter A. Mark the other side B.
  Mark one side of another counter A. Mark the other side C.
  Mark one side of the last counter B. Mark the other side C.
- Player 1 tosses the counters. If two counters show the same letter, Player 1 wins. Otherwise, Player 2 wins. Record who wins.
- Repeat the counter toss experiment 19 more times, recording who won each time.

Talk About It

1. Find the experimental probability that Player 1 and Player 2 each won. **See students' work.**
2. Make a tree diagram to show all the possible outcomes for this game. **See margin.**
3. Find the theoretical probability that Player 1 and Player 2 each won. Does this explain the results of your game?
4. Is this game a fair game? Explain your reasoning.

3. $P(\text{Player 1}) = \frac{6}{8}$ or $\frac{3}{4}$; $P(\text{Player 2}) = \frac{2}{8}$ or $\frac{1}{4}$
4. No; Player 2 does not have an equal chance of winning.

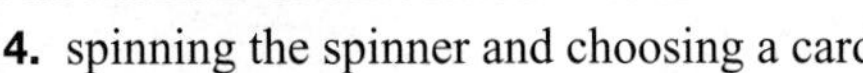

Communicating Mathematics

1–2. See Answer Appendix.

Read and study the lesson to answer each question.

1. ***Tell*** how to use a tree diagram to list outcomes.
2. ***Write a Problem*** that can be solved by using the tree diagram at the right.
3. ***Determine*** whether the following game for two players is fair.
   - Toss three pennies.
   - If exactly two pennies match, Player 1 wins.
   - Otherwise, Player 2 wins.

hot dog — cola, diet cola, root beer
hamburger — cola, diet cola, root beer

HANDS-ON MATH

3. No; $P(\text{Player 1}) = \frac{3}{4}$, $P(\text{Player 2}) = \frac{1}{4}$

Guided Practice

4–5. See Answer Appendix for outcomes.

For each situation, make a tree diagram to show the sample space. Then give the total number of outcomes. 4. 12

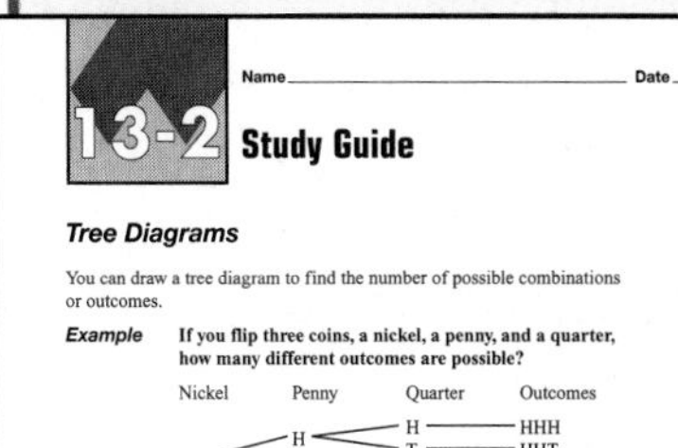

4. spinning the spinner and choosing a card
5. tossing a coin and rolling a number cube 12
6. ***Travel*** Rosa packed a red shirt, a white shirt, blue jeans, and black jeans for a weekend trip. Make a tree diagram to show all of the possible shirt/jeans selections she can make. **See Answer Appendix.**

In-Class Example

For the Example

A restaurant sells pea, lentil, barley, noodle, and tomato soups, as well as rye, wheat, pumpernickel, and sourdough breads. Make a tree diagram to show all of the possible soup/bread choices. 20

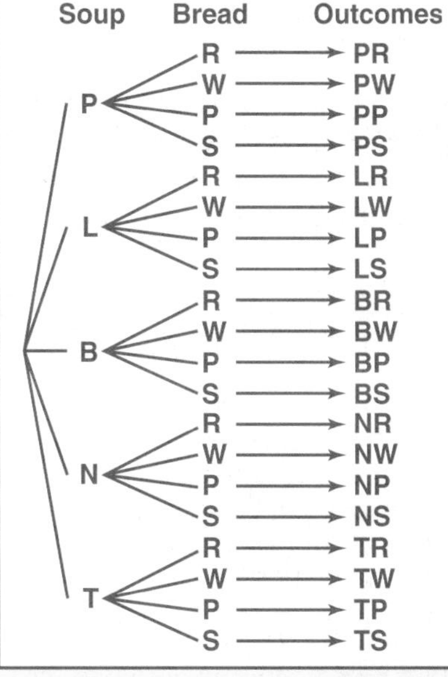

Using the Mini-Lab Ask students to give the probability of having two counters show the same letter and of having three counters show three different letters. $\frac{3}{4}, \frac{1}{4}$

***Study Guide Masters,* p. 94**

Name________ Date________

13-2 Study Guide

Tree Diagrams

You can draw a tree diagram to find the number of possible combinations or outcomes.

Example **If you flip three coins, a nickel, a penny, and a quarter, how many different outcomes are possible?**

Nickel Penny Quarter Outcomes

H — H — H: HHH; T: HHT
H — T — H: HTH; T: HTT
T — H — H: THH; T: THT
T — T — H: TTH; T: TTT

There are 8 possible outcomes.

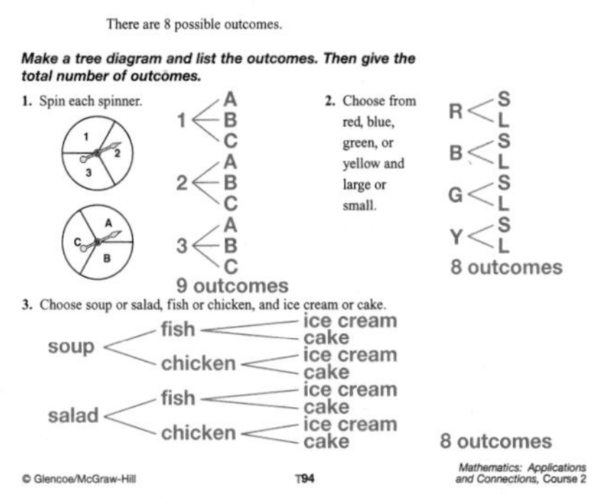

Make a tree diagram and list the outcomes. Then give the total number of outcomes.
1. Spin each spinner.
9 outcomes
2. Choose from red, blue, green, or yellow and large or small.
8 outcomes
3. Choose soup or salad, fish or chicken, and ice cream or cake.
soup
salad
fish
chicken
ice cream
cake
8 outcomes
© Glencoe/McGraw-Hill
T94
Mathematics: Applications and Connections, Course 2

■ Reteaching the Lesson ■

Activity To help students figure out how many possible outcomes there are for a situation, have them use different colored pattern blocks to represent the choices.

Additional Answer for the Mini-Lab

2. See students' diagrams; outcomes are AAB, AAC, ACB, ACC, BAB, BAC, BCB, BCC.

3 PRACTICE/APPLY

Check for Understanding

If students need additional practice or instruction after completing Exercises 1–6, one of these options may be helpful.

- Extra Practice, see p. 603
- Reteaching Activity, see p. 535
- *Study Guide Masters,* p. 94
- *Practice Masters,* p. 94

Assignment Guide

Core: 7–13 odd, 15–18
Enriched: 8–12 even, 13–18

4 ASSESS

Closing Activity

Writing Have students write a paragraph describing the advantages of using a tree diagram over listing outcomes in no particular order.

Chapter 13, Quiz A (Lessons 13-1 and 13-2) is available in the *Assessment and Evaluation Masters,* p. 351.

Additional Answer

15. See students' diagrams; outcomes are J wins first 2 games, JBJ, JBB, BJJ, BJB, B wins first 2 games.

***Practice Masters,* p. 94**

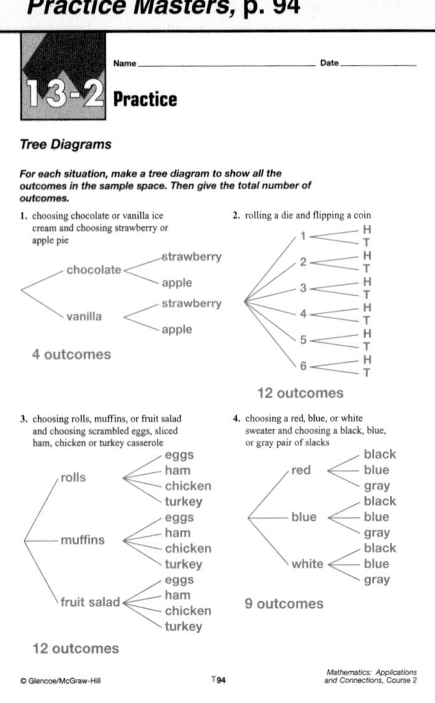

Name ________________ Date ________

13-2 Practice

Tree Diagrams

For each situation, make a tree diagram to show all the outcomes in the sample space. Then give the total number of outcomes.

1. choosing chocolate or vanilla ice cream and choosing strawberry or apple pie

chocolate — strawberry, apple; vanilla — strawberry, apple

4 outcomes

2. rolling a die and flipping a coin

1 — H, T; 2 — H, T; 3 — H, T; 4 — H, T; 5 — H, T; 6 — H, T

12 outcomes

3. choosing rolls, muffins, or fruit salad and choosing scrambled eggs, sliced ham, chicken or turkey casserole

rolls — eggs, ham, chicken, turkey; muffins — eggs, ham, chicken, turkey; fruit salad — eggs, ham, chicken, turkey

12 outcomes

4. choosing a red, blue, or white sweater and choosing a black, blue, or gray pair of slacks

red — black, blue, gray; blue — black, blue, gray; white — black, blue, gray

9 outcomes

© Glencoe/McGraw-Hill T94 Mathematics: Applications and Connections, Course 2

EXERCISES

Practice

For each situation, make a tree diagram to show the sample space. Then give the total number of outcomes. **7–12. See Answer Appendix for outcomes.**

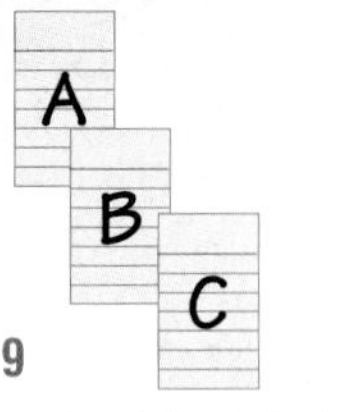

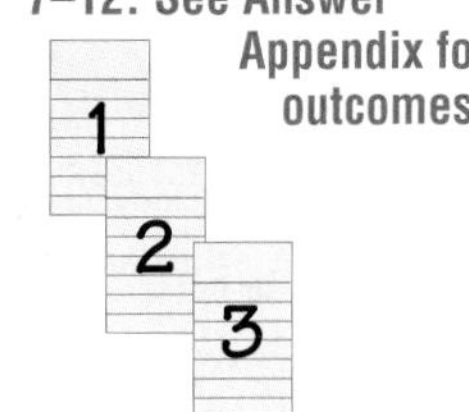

7. tossing a penny and tossing a dime **4**
8. choosing a card with a letter, then choosing a card with a number from the choices shown at the right **9**
9. choosing a wall or portable phone, in either black, beige, red, or white **8**
10. choosing a bicycle having 10 speeds, 18 speeds, or 21 speeds and either red, blue, green, or white in color **12**
11. rolling a number cube, tossing a coin, and choosing a card from among cards marked W, X, Y, and Z **48**
12. choosing cereal, French toast, or pancakes and choosing orange, apple, or grapefruit juice **9**

Applications and Problem Solving

13. ***Geography*** The ZIP codes for Virginia addresses all begin with a 2, which identifies its national area. The second and third digits identify the geographic area. The second digit in Virginia is either a 0, 2, 3, or 4. The third digit can be any digit from 0 to 9. How many geographic areas are possible in Virginia? **40 areas**
14. ***Population*** Refer to the beginning of the lesson. What is the probability that a family with three children has at least two girls? at least two boys? **14.** $\frac{1}{2}, \frac{1}{2}$
15. ***Critical Thinking*** A softball tournament between the Jaguars and the Bandits is won when one team wins two of three games. Construct a tree diagram to show all the possible outcomes for the tournament. **See margin.**

Mixed Review

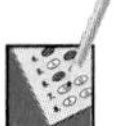

16. **Standardized Test Practice** Poloma has four pennies in her wallet. The dates on the pennies are 1998, 1995, 1989, and 1988. If she picks one penny from her wallet without looking, what is the probability that it will have a date in the 1980s? *(Lesson 13-1)* **B**

A $\frac{1}{4}$ **B** $\frac{1}{2}$ **C** $\frac{2}{3}$ **D** $\frac{3}{4}$

17. ***Geometry*** Draw top, side, and front views of each three-dimensional figure. *(Lesson 12-1)* **a–c. See Answer Appendix.**

a.

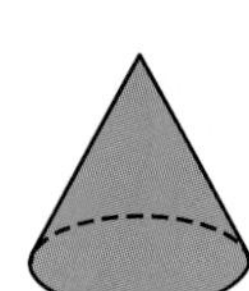

b.

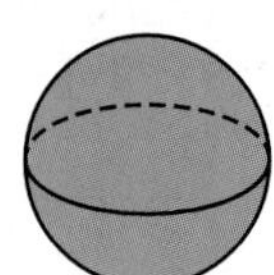

c.

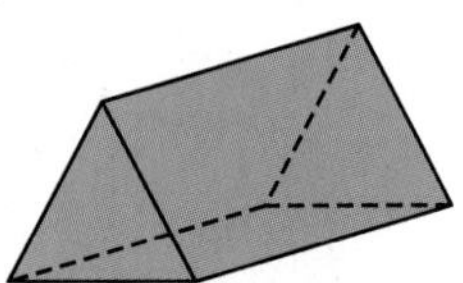

For **Extra Practice,** see page 603.

18. ***Geometry*** What is the diameter of a circle whose radius is 13 feet? *(Lesson 7-7)* **26 feet**

Extending the Lesson

***Enrichment Masters,* p. 94**

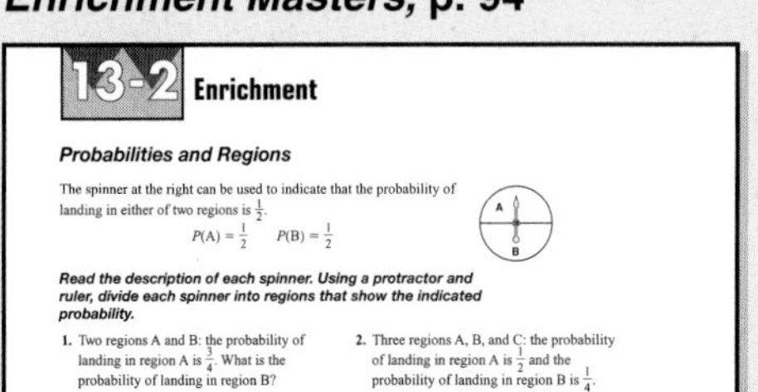

13-2 Enrichment

Probabilities and Regions

The spinner at the right can be used to indicate that the probability of landing in either of two regions is $\frac{1}{2}$.

$P(A) = \frac{1}{2}$ $P(B) = \frac{1}{2}$

Read the description of each spinner. Using a protractor and ruler, divide each spinner into regions that show the indicated probability.

1. Two regions A and B: the probability of landing in region A is $\frac{3}{4}$. What is the probability of landing in region B?

2. Three regions A, B, and C: the probability of landing in region A is $\frac{1}{2}$ and the probability of landing in region B is $\frac{1}{4}$.

Activity Have students make up and describe a fair game that is played with a spinner or number cube. If a spinner is used, students should include a drawing of it. If a cube is used, they should provide the numbers on its faces.

DESIGN

Chris Haney, John Haney, and Scott Abbott
INVENTORS

Canadian entrepreneurs Chris Haney, John Haney, and Scott Abbott dreamed up the idea for a board game in 1979. They started their own company to develop, manufacture, and distribute 1,100 copies of the game. Within fifteen years, 60 million copies of the popular game had been sold.

Independent toy designers are important sources of new game and toy ideas. To become a game and toy inventor or designer, you must be creative and have a good business sense. Other careers in the toy and game industry include toy buyers, who place orders for toys to be sold in stores, and toy assemblers or machine operators, who help manufacture toy products.

For more information:
Toy Manufacturers of America, Inc.
200 Fifth Ave., Suite 740
New York, NY 10010

NET CONNECTION
www.glencoe.com/sec/math/mac/mathnet

Who comes up with ideas for games?

Your Turn

Suppose you have a great new game idea. Make a plan for producing and selling your game.

Motivating Students

As students discovered in the chapter opener on page 527, there are many uses for probability in games. They may be interested in a career in that or a related field. To start the discussion, you may ask students questions about games and game history.

- When and where did the first board game resembling checkers appear? **about 3000 B.C. in the city of Ur, in Iraq**
- Who designed the classic chess pieces still used in tournaments today? **Howard Staunton in the mid-1800's**

Making the Math Connection

Haney and Abbott have 4,800 questions in the Genius IV edition. They have to randomly place these questions on 800 cards with no repeats. They could use permutations to figure out how many ways they could put the questions on the cards.

Working on *Your* Turn

Students may want to play the role of a toy company executive who is considering buying the game. Make sure they investigate alternatives to selling a game to a big company. Not all popular games, like the computer puzzle game Myst, for example, are from big companies.

More About Chris Haney and Scott Abbott

- In 1979, photo editor Chris Haney and sportswriter Scott Abbott invented their board game while playing another word board game. They kept losing the letters!
- It cost $75 each to manufacture the first 1,100 games. Abbott and Haney sold them to retailers for $15 each. Retail sales now exceed $1 billion.
- Chris Haney's older brother John and lawyer Ed Werner were instrumental in getting the game into the marketplace.

An additional School to Career activity is available on page 26 of the ***School to Career Masters.***

13-3 Lesson Notes

Instructional Resources

- *Study Guide Masters,* p. 95
- *Practice Masters,* p. 95
- *Enrichment Masters,* p. 95
- Transparencies 13-3, A and B
- *Assessment and Evaluation Masters,* pp. 350, 351
- *Hands-On Lab Masters,* p. 84
-  CD-ROM Program
  - Resource Lesson 13-3

Recommended Pacing	
Honors	Day 5 of 10

1 FOCUS

5-Minute Check
(Lesson 13-2)

For each situation, make a tree diagram and list the outcomes. Then give the total number of outcomes.
See students' tree diagrams.

1. tossing a quarter and a nickel. **HH, HT, TH, TT; 4**
2. choosing a letter from D, E, and F, and a number from 1 and 2. **D1, D2, E1, E2, F1, F2; 6**
3. choosing a tuna, ham, or egg sandwich and chips, fries, or salad. **TC, TF, TS, HC, HF, HS, EC, EF, ES; 9**

The 5-Minute Check is also available on **Transparency 13-3A** for this lesson.

Motivating the Lesson

Problem Solving In a restaurant, there are 3 kinds of appetizers, 6 main courses, and 4 choices of dessert. Ask students to find the number of possible meals that consist of 1 appetizer, 1 main course, and 1 dessert. **72 meals**

13-3 The Counting Principle

What you'll learn

You'll learn to use multiplication to count outcomes.

When am I ever going to use this?

The Counting Principle can be used to find the number of possible phone numbers in an area code.

Word Wise

Counting Principle

Colonel Mustard, in the kitchen, with the wrench ... . With words like these, players of the popular board game *Clue* accuse a suspect of murder. Players can choose from six suspects, nine rooms, and six weapons. How many different ways are there to make an accusation?

The partial tree diagram helps to show the number of outcomes in the sample space.

6 Suspects	9 Rooms	6 Weapons
Colonel Mustard	kitchen	rope
Professor Plum	study	lead pipe
Mrs. Peacock	library	knife
Miss Scarlet	hall	wrench
Mrs. White	lounge	candlestick
Mr. Green	dining room	revolver
	ballroom	
	conservatory	
	billiard room	

Each suspect has nine possible rooms. So, there are 6×9 or 54 possible suspect/room outcomes. Finally, each of these outcomes has six different weapons to choose from. So, there are 54×6 or 324 possible ways to make an accusation.

In this situation, you used multiplication instead of a tree diagram to find the number of possible outcomes in the sample space.

The Counting Principle	If event M can occur in m ways and is followed by event N that can occur in n ways, then the event M followed by N can occur in $m \times n$ ways.

1 **Retail Sales** **The Jean Scene sells women's jeans in sizes 3, 5, 7, 9, 11, 13, and 15. Each size comes in slim fit, regular fit, and relaxed fit. There are also three possible lengths: petite, regular, and tall. How many different kinds of jeans are there?**

$$\underbrace{7}_{\text{number of sizes}} \times \underbrace{3}_{\text{number of fits}} \times \underbrace{3}_{\text{number of lengths}} = \underbrace{63}_{\text{number of kinds}}$$

There are 63 different kinds of jeans at the Jean Scene.

Multiple Learning Styles

Visual/Spatial Have students outline on graph paper 3 rows of squares running the entire width of the paper. Challenge students to find all the possible combinations of 2 colors in a set of 3 squares by coloring in squares with 2 colored pencils.

2 **Travel** Air Canada offers nonstop flights from several cities in the U.S. to its Canadian hubs. Once in Canada, travelers can fly to destinations across Canada. The figure shows the routes that go through Vancouver, British Columbia. How many different routes are possible from U.S. cities through Vancouver with destinations in Canada?

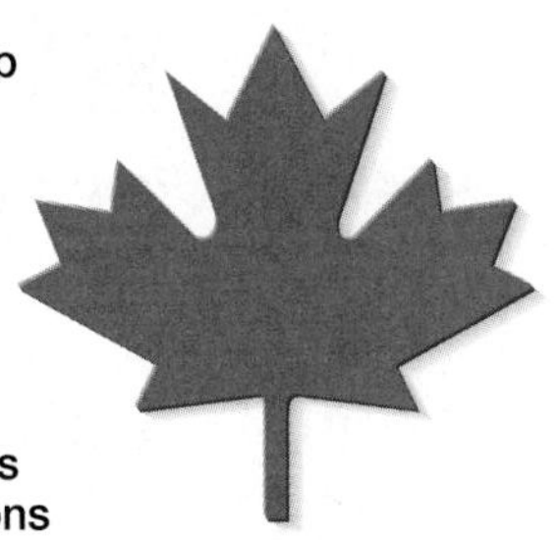

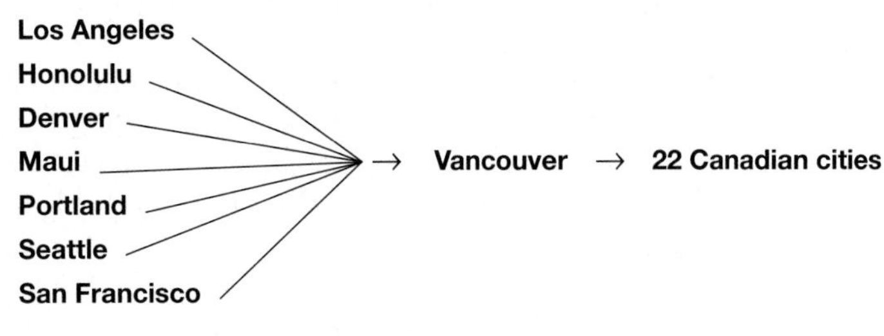

$$\overbrace{7}^{\text{routes from United States}} \times \overbrace{22}^{\text{routes from Vancouver}} = \overbrace{154}^{\text{total routes}}$$

There are 154 different routes.

APPLICATION **3** **Braille** Many people who are visually impaired use a code called Braille to be able to read. Each character in Braille lies in a 3 × 2 cell of raised dots or blank spaces. Some examples are shown at the right. The cell consisting of six blank spaces is not used. How many different cells are possible?

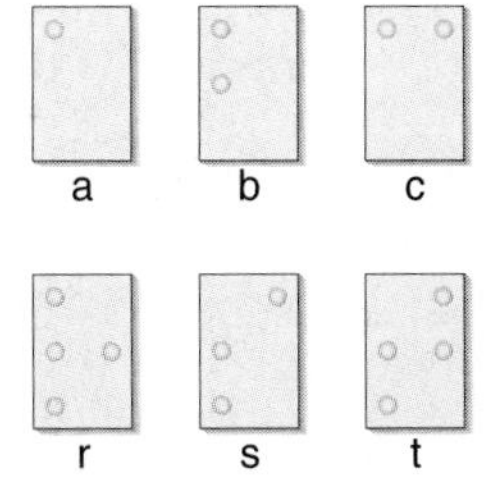

Explore You know that Braille consists of raised dots or blank spaces. There are six positions in each cell. You need to find how many cells are possible.

Plan There are two choices for each of the six positions. You can use the Counting Principle to find the total number of groupings.

Solve $2 \cdot 2 \cdot 2 \cdot 2 \cdot 2 \cdot 2 = 64$

Remember, there is no cell with six blank spaces. Therefore, the total number of cells is $64 - 1$ or 63.

Examine There should be enough cells for 26 letters, 10 digits, and about 10 punctuation marks. So, 63 is a reasonable answer.

2 TEACH

Transparency 13-3B contains a teaching aid for this lesson.

Thinking Algebraically Many students will have discovered the counting principle from their work with tree diagrams. Have students explore any effect on the number of outcomes if the categories are listed in a different order. For example, have many outcomes are there in Clue if weapons are considered first. **The order of the categories is insignificant in the number of outcomes.**

In-Class Examples

For Example 1
The Cheese n' Crackers Shop has 28 kinds of cheese and 20 kinds of crackers. They claim that you could shop there once a week for 10 years and buy a different combination each time. Is their claim true? Explain. **yes; $560 > 520$**

For Example 2
The Marquette bus station has buses arriving from Duluth, Green Bay, Sault Ste. Marie, and Detroit. It has buses departing for Houghton, Ontonogon, Escanaba, Copper Harbor, Baraga, Munising, Manistique, and Gwinn. How many different routes are possible going through Marquette? **32 routes**

For Example 3
In dance notation, movements are described as either light or strong in the weight factor, sustained or quick in the time factor, and direct or flexible in the space factor. How many weight-time-space combinations are possible? **8 combinations**

Investigations for the Special Education Student

This blackline master booklet helps you plan for the needs of your special education students by providing long-term projects along with teacher notes. Investigation 15, *The Game Show,* may be used with this chapter.

3 PRACTICE/APPLY

Check for Understanding

If students need additional practice or instruction after completing Exercises 1–6, one of these options may be helpful.

- Extra Practice, see p. 603
- Reteaching Activity
- *Study Guide Masters,* p. 95
- *Practice Masters,* p. 95

Assignment Guide

Core: 7–13 odd, 15–17
Enriched: 8–12 even, 13–17

Additional Answer

2. See students' diagrams; outcomes are shirt 1 tie1, shirt 1 tie 2, shirt 1 tie 3, shirt 1 tie 4, shirt 2 tie 1, shirt 2 tie 2, shirt 2 tie 3, shirt 2 tie 4, shirt 3 tie 1, shirt 3 tie 2, shirt 3 tie 3, shirt 3 tie 3.

Study Guide Masters, p. 95

Name ________________ Date ________

13-3 Study Guide

The Counting Principle

The Counting Principle uses multiplication to find the number of possible outcomes.

If event M can occur in m ways and is followed by event N that can occur in n ways, then the event M followed by N can occur in $m \times n$ ways.

Example **Pinky's Pizza serves 11 different kinds of pizza with 3 choices of crust and in 4 different sizes. How many different selections are possible?**

Apply the Counting Principle.

number of kinds		*number of crusts*		*number of sizes*		*possible selections*
11	×	3	×	4	=	132

There are 132 possible pizza selections.

Use the Counting Principle to find the total number of outcomes in each situation.

1. The nursery has 14 different colored tulip bulbs. Each color comes in dwarf, average, or giant size. How many different kinds of bulbs are there? 42
2. The type of bicycle Elena wants comes in 12 different colors with 12 different colors of trim. There is also a choice of curved or straight handlebars. How many possible selections are there? 288
3. At a banquet, guests were given a choice of 4 entrees, 3 vegetables, soup or salad, 4 beverages, and 4 desserts. How many different selections were possible? 384
4. Ms. Nitobe is setting the combination lock on her briefcase. If she can choose any digit 0–9 for each of the 6 digits in the combination, how many possible combinations are there? 1,000,000

 T95 *Mathematics: Applications and Connections, Course 2*

CHECK FOR UNDERSTANDING

Communicating Mathematics

Read and study the lesson to answer each question.

1. ***Calculate*** the number of ways of selecting one shirt/tie combination from among 3 different shirts and 4 different ties. 12
2. ***Draw*** a tree diagram to verify the results of Exercise 1. See margin.
3. ***Write*** a problem in which it is easier to use the Counting Principle than a tree diagram. See students' work.

Math Journal

Guided Practice

Use the Counting Principle to find the total number of outcomes in each situation.

4. choosing a car from five different exterior colors, four different interior colors, and automatic or standard transmission 40 outcomes
5. making a sandwich with raisin bread, whole wheat bread, white bread, or a bagel and choosing peanut butter, cream cheese, or jelly 12 outcomes
6. ***Travel*** There are three highways connecting Tomville and Greensburg. There are two roads connecting Greensburg to North Huntingdon. How many ways are there to drive from Tomville to North Huntingdon? 6 ways

EXERCISES

Practice

Use the Counting Principle to find the total number of outcomes in each situation. 8. 16 outcomes

7. spinning the spinners shown at the right 48 outcomes
8. tossing a penny, a nickel, a dime, and a quarter
9. choosing the first two characters for a license plate if it begins with a letter of the alphabet and is followed by a digit 260 outcomes

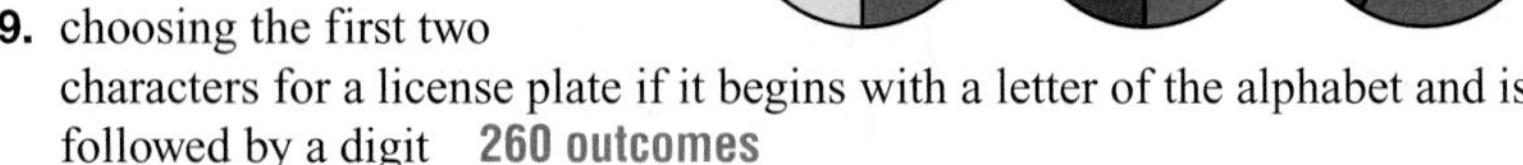

10. choosing a way to drive from Milton to Harper's Township 18 outcomes

11. choosing a dinner with one entrée, one salad, and one dessert 27 outcomes
12. choosing a 4-digit Personal Identification Number (PIN) if the numbers can be repeated 10,000 outcomes

Entrée	Salad	Dessert
ham	potato	ice cream
beef	tossed	pie
turkey	cole slaw	cake

Reteaching the Lesson

Activity Provide a clothing catalog for students to plan outfits, combining pants, shirts, and shoes. Have students choose three of each and calculate how many combinations are possible. 27

Error Analysis

Watch for students who add rather than multiply the number of possible outcomes.

Prevent by having students compare their answers with those they obtain when they use a tree diagram.

Applications and Problem Solving

13. ***Advertising*** The Bowl 'N' Ladle Restaurant advertises that you can have a different lunch every day of the year. It offers 13 different kinds of soups and 24 different kinds of sandwiches. If the restaurant is open every day of the year, is its claim valid? Explain. **See margin.**

14. ***Games*** Refer to the beginning of the lesson. What is the probability that the murder was committed by Miss Scarlet, in the kitchen, with the knife? $\frac{1}{324}$

15. ***Critical Thinking*** How many outcomes are there if you toss
    a. one coin? 2 **b.** two coins? 4 **c.** three coins? 8 **d.** n coins? 2^n

Mixed Review

16. ***School*** Jewel must take a science class, a math class, and an English class next year. She can choose from two science classes, three math classes, and two English classes. Make a tree diagram to show all of the possible schedules she can arrange. *(Lesson 13-2)* **See Answer Appendix.**

17. **Standardized Test Practice** What number should come next in the pattern 3, 7, 15, 31, 63? *(Lesson 4-3)* **D**
    A 73 **B** 84 **C** 106 **D** 127

For **Extra Practice,** see page 603.

Let the Games Begin

Cherokee Butterbean Game

Math Skill
Probability

Get Ready This game is for two, three, or four players. It is a variation of a traditional Cherokee game.

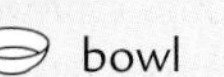 6 dry lima beans 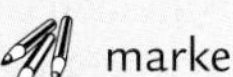 bowl marker

Get Set Color one side of each bean with the marker.

Go The first player places the beans in the bowl, gently tosses the beans into the air, and catches them in the bowl. Points are scored as follows.

- If all of the beans land with the unmarked sides up, score 6 points.
- If all of the beans land with the marked side up, score 4 points.
- If exactly one bean lands with the marked or unmarked side up, score 2 points.
- If three beans are marked and three beans are unmarked, score 1 point.

If a toss scores points, the player takes another turn. If a toss does not score any points, it is the next player's turn.

The winner is the player with the most points after a given number of rounds.

Visit www.glencoe.com/sec/math/mac/mathnet for more games.

4 ASSESS

Closing Activity

Modeling Have students use colored pencils to demonstrate how many combinations of geometric shapes and colors are possible in a problem they create. Example: square, triangle, circle, and pentagon in five colors.

Chapter 13, Quiz B (Lesson 13-3) is available in the *Assessment and Evaluation Masters,* p. 351.

Mid-Chapter Test (Lessons 13-1 through 13-3) is available in the *Assessment and Evaluation Masters,* p. 350.

Additional Answer

13. No; the number of selections is 312, which is less then 365.

***Practice Masters,* p. 95**

Name__________ Date________

Practice

The Counting Principle

Use the Counting Principle to find the total number of outcomes in each situation.

1. choosing a paint color from among 6 color choices, and choosing a wallpaper pattern from among 5 choices
   30
2. flipping a penny, a nickel, and a dime
   8
3. choosing the last three digits in a five-digit zip code if the first digit is 6, the second digit is 1, and no digit is used more than once
   336
4. choosing one of three science courses, one of five mathematics courses, one of two English courses, and one of four social studies courses
   120
5. choosing from one of three appetizers, one of four main dishes, one of six desserts, and one of four soft drinks
   288
6. choosing a book with a mystery, science-fiction, romance, or adventure theme, choosing one of five different authors for each theme, and choosing paperback or hardcover for the type of book
   40
7. choosing a phone number if the first three-digit combination can be one of 8 choices and if the last four digits can be any combination of digits from 1 to 9 without any repeated digits
   24,192

 T95 *Mathematics: Applications and Connections, Course 2*

Extending the Lesson

***Enrichment Masters,* p. 95**

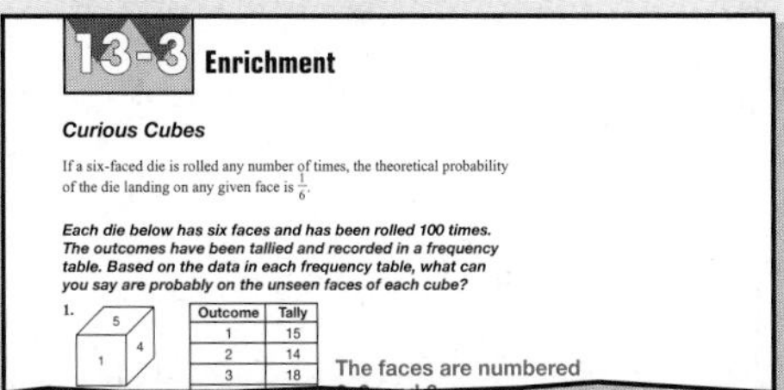

13-3 **Enrichment**

Curious Cubes

If a six-faced die is rolled any number of times, the theoretical probability of the die landing on any given face is $\frac{1}{6}$.

Each die below has six faces and has been rolled 100 times. The outcomes have been tallied and recorded in a frequency table. Based on the data in each frequency table, what can you say are probably on the unseen faces of each cube?

1.

Outcome	Tally
1	15
2	14
3	18

The faces are numbered

Have students determine how many marked/unmarked bean combinations are possible. Then have them find the theoretical probability of each score occurring. After playing several rounds, find the experimental probability.

13-4 Lesson Notes

Instructional Resources

- *Study Guide Masters,* p. 96
- *Practice Masters,* p. 96
- *Enrichment Masters,* p. 96
- Transparencies 13-4, A and B
- *Diversity Masters,* p. 26
- *Science and Math Lab Manual,* pp. 93–96
- *Technology Masters,* p. 51

CD-ROM Program
- Resource Lesson 13-4

Recommended Pacing	
Honors	Day 6 of 10

1 FOCUS

5-Minute Check
(Lesson 13-2)

Use the Counting Principle to find the total number of outcomes in each situation.

1. choosing the first three letters/digits of a license plate if it begins with Y or M, followed by A, B, C, or D, and then a digit from 1 to 5 **40 outcomes**
2. making a lunch of a tuna, avocado, turkey, or chicken sandwich, with coleslaw or salad, and milk, juice, or soda **24 outcomes**
3. choosing a car in one of 6 colors, with or without racing stripes, with a CD-player or a cassette player, with or without air conditioning, and with a standard or automatic transmission **96 outcomes**

The 5-Minute Check is also available on **Transparency 13-4A** for this lesson.

Motivating the Lesson

Hands-On Activity Have students guess the probability of getting both an even number and a "heads" if they were to roll a number cube and toss a coin simultaneously.

13-4 Independent and Dependent Events

What **you'll learn**

You'll learn to find the probability of independent and dependent events.

When **am I ever going to use this?**

You'll use probability of two events when you study genetics in life science.

Word Wise

compound events
independent events
dependent events

Gregor Mendel studied science and math in the 1800s. His observations in his father's orchard made him think it would be possible to predict the kinds of flowers a plant would produce.

In the Mini-Lab, you will conduct an experiment to predict how many white flowers will result from a cross between two parent plants. Each parent has an equal chance of passing on a gene for a red or white flower.

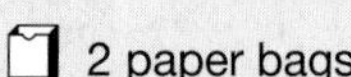

HANDS-ON MINI-LAB

Work with a partner. 2 paper bags; 50 red beans; 50 white beans

Try This

- Place 25 red beans and 25 white beans in bag 1 and 25 red beans and 25 white beans in bag 2.
- Without looking, remove one bean from each bag. The two beans represent the cross between the two flowers. Note the color combination and return the beans to their respective bags.
- Make a frequency table and record the color combination each time you remove two beans. Repeat 99 times.
- Count and record the total number of red/red, red/white, white/red, and white/white combinations.

Talk About It

1. Estimate the probability of each result. **a–d. See students' work.**
   a. red/red **b.** red/white **c.** white/red **d.** white/white
2. Suppose the red color is *dominant* over the white color. That means a red/white and a white/red plant will be red. The only way to have a white flower is with white/white. Estimate the probability of getting a white flower. **See students' work.**

In the experiment, you removed one bean from each bag. This is a **compound event**. Choosing a bean from bag 1 did not affect choosing a bean from bag 2. These events are called **independent events**. You can analyze the experiment with a tree diagram.

Multiple Learning Styles

Kinesthetic Ask for two student volunteers to draw names to choose teams for a game of soccer. Before each choice is made, have students determine the probability that a boy is chosen and the probability that a girl is chosen. Point out how the probability changes after each choice is made.

George Washington Carver (1864–1943) was an African-American scientist who won international recognition for his agricultural research. He made more than 300 products from peanuts, including printer's ink, face powder, and soap.

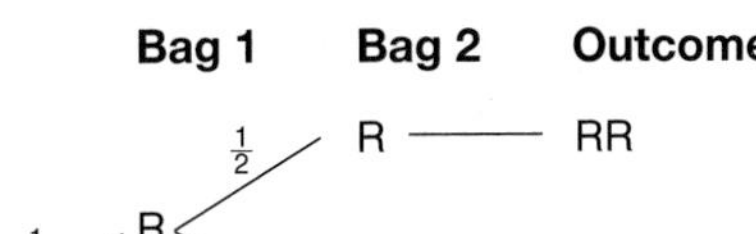

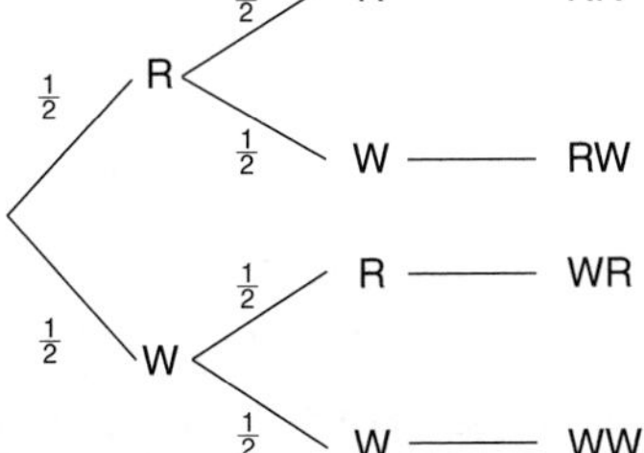

The $\frac{1}{2}$ on the tree diagram indicates the probability of each event.

There are four equally-likely outcomes. So, $P(\text{white/white}) = \frac{1}{4}$.

You can also multiply to find the probability of two independent events.

$$\underbrace{P(\text{white from bag 1})}_{\frac{1}{2}} \times \underbrace{P(\text{white from bag 2})}_{\frac{1}{2}} = \underbrace{P(\text{white/white})}_{\frac{1}{4}}$$

Probability of Independent Events	The probability of two independent events can be found by multiplying the probability of one event by the probability of the second event.

Example **1** **A green number cube and a red number cube are rolled. Find the probability that an odd number is rolled on the green number cube and a multiple of 3 is rolled on the red number cube.**

There are three odd numbers. So, $P(\text{odd}) = \frac{3}{6}$ or $\frac{1}{2}$.

There are two multiples of 3. So, $P(\text{multiple of 3}) = \frac{2}{6}$ or $\frac{1}{3}$.

So, $P(\text{odd and multiple of 3}) = \frac{1}{2} \cdot \frac{1}{3}$ or $\frac{1}{6}$.

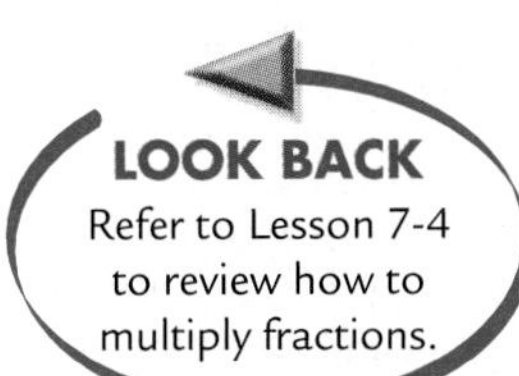

LOOK BACK
Refer to Lesson 7-4 to review how to multiply fractions.

If the result of one event affects the result of a second event, the events are called **dependent events**.

Example **APPLICATION**

2 **Game Shows** **On a popular television game show, contestants can win a car if they draw the five digits of the price of the car before they draw three strikes. Once a digit or strike is drawn, it is not replaced. Find the probability that a contestant draws two strikes in the first two draws.**

$P(\text{strike on first draw}) = \frac{3}{8}$ ← *There are 3 strikes.* ← *There is a total of 8 outcomes—5 digits and 3 strikes.*

The result of the first draw affects the probability of the second draw.

$P(\text{strike on second draw}) = \frac{2}{7}$ ← *There are 2 strikes left.* ← *There are 7 digits or strikes left.*

(continued on the next page)

2 TEACH

Transparency 13-4B contains a teaching aid for this lesson.

Using the Mini-Lab Emphasize that with independent events the probability remains the same for the second time regardless of the results of the first.

In-Class Examples

For Example 1
Three coins are tossed. Find the probability that all three will be tails. $\frac{1}{8}$

For Example 2
Kiyoski has a package of fruit candy containing two pieces each of raspberry, orange, lemon, and cherry flavors. Find the probability that he chooses both lemon pieces first. $\frac{1}{28}$

Teaching Tip In Example 2, point out that the probability of the second draw is influenced by the results of the first draw, which was not the case in Example 1.

3 PRACTICE/APPLY

Check for Understanding

If students need additional practice or instruction after completing Exercises 1–7, one of these options may be helpful.

- Extra Practice, see p. 604
- Reteaching Activity
- *Study Guide Masters,* p. 96
- *Practice Masters,* p. 96

Assignment Guide

Core: 9–17 odd, 19, 20
Enriched: 8–14 even, 15–17, 19, 20
All: Self Test, 1–5

Additional Answer

1. Sample answer: choosing a card from a deck of playing cards, then choosing a second without replacing the first

***Study Guide Masters,* p. 96**

Name__________ Date________

13-4 Study Guide

Independent and Dependent Probability

When the outcome of one event does not influence the outcome of a second event, the two events are **independent.** The probability of two independent events can be found by multiplying the probability of one event by the probability of the second event.

Example 1 **If you draw a card from a deck numbered 1 through 8 and toss a die, what is the probability of getting a 4 and an even number?**

$P(4) = \frac{1}{8}$ $\quad P(\text{even}) = \frac{3}{6}$ or $\frac{1}{2}$

$P(4, \text{even}) = \frac{1}{8} \cdot \frac{1}{2}$ or $\frac{1}{16}$

The probability of a 4 and an even number is $\frac{1}{16}$.

If the outcome of one event affects the outcome of a second event, the events are **dependent.**

Example 2 **There are 6 black pens and 8 blue pens in a jar. If you take a pen without looking and then take another pen without replacing the first, what is the probability that you will get 2 black pens?**

$P(\text{black first}) = \frac{6}{14}$ or $\frac{3}{7}$

$P(\text{black second}) = \frac{5}{13}$ ← *There are 13 pens left; 5 are black.*

$P(\text{black, black}) = \frac{3}{7} \cdot \frac{5}{13}$ or $\frac{15}{91}$

The probability of choosing 2 black pens is $\frac{15}{91}$.

Tell whether each is independent or dependent.

1. selecting a sweater, selecting a shirt independent
2. choosing one card from a deck then choosing a second card without replacing the first dependent
3. A wallet contains two $5 bills, two $10 bills, and three $20 bills. Two bills are selected without the first being replaced. Find $P(\$20, \$20)$. $\frac{1}{7}$
4. Two dice are rolled. Find $P(6, \text{even})$. $\frac{1}{12}$

 T96 *Mathematics: Applications and Connections, Course 2*

To find the probability of 2 strikes in a row, multiply the probability of a first strike and a second strike.

$$P(\text{strike, then strike}) = \frac{3}{8} \cdot \frac{2}{7}$$
$$= \frac{3}{\cancel{8}_4} \cdot \frac{\cancel{2}^1}{7} \text{ or } \frac{3}{28}$$

So, the probability is $\frac{3}{28}$ or about 11%.

CHECK FOR UNDERSTANDING

Communicating Mathematics

Read and study the lesson to answer each question.

1. ***Give an example*** of two events that are dependent. **See margin.**
2. ***Write a Problem*** about the marbles. Then tell whether the events are independent or dependent. **See students' work.**
3. ***You Decide*** Jared thinks that the results of rolling a number cube twice are independent events. Angie thinks they are dependent events. Who is correct? Explain.

3. Jared; the result on one number cube does not affect the result on the other.

Guided Practice

Tell whether the event is *independent* or *dependent*.

4. choosing a card from a hat and then choosing a second card without replacing the first one **dependent**
5. A coin is tossed and a number cube is rolled. Find the probability of getting heads and a multiple of 2. $\frac{1}{4}$
6. A bag contains 10 white, 8 blue, and 6 red marbles. Two marbles are drawn, but the first marble is not replaced. Find *P*(both blue). $\frac{7}{69}$
7. ***Games*** An American game involving five dice is similar to a Puerto Rican dice game called Generala. In both games, players try to roll five of a kind. In Generala, five of a kind in one roll is called a Big General and wins the game automatically. Find the probability of throwing a Big General. $\frac{1}{1,296}$

EXERCISES

Practice

Tell whether each event is *independent* or *dependent*.

8. selecting a name from the Chicago telephone book and a name from the Houston telephone book **independent**
9. tossing a coin twice **independent**
10. choosing a President, Vice President, and Secretary from three members of student council **dependent**
11. A blue number cube and a yellow number cube are rolled. Find the probability that an odd number is rolled on the blue number cube and a multiple of 6 is rolled on the yellow number cube. $\frac{1}{12}$
12. A wallet contains five $5 bills, three $10 bills, and two $20 bills. Two bills are selected without the first selection being replaced. Find *P*($10, then $10). $\frac{1}{15}$

■ Reteaching the Lesson ■

Activity Guide students to see that, for dependent events, the result of the first event affects the probability of the second event because the sample space for the event has been changed. Provide additional examples of the distinction between independent and dependent probability.

MathPASS CD-ROM

This CD-ROM offers a complete, self-paced mathematics curriculum. Each lesson includes a pretest, tutorial, guided practice, and posttest. MathPASS Lesson 44 is correlated to this Student Edition lesson.
For Windows & Macintosh

13. A wallet contains five \$5 bills, three \$10 bills, and two \$20 bills. Three bills are selected without each selection being replaced. Find P(\$5, then \$10, then \$20). $\frac{1}{24}$

14. A blue number cube and a green number cube are rolled. Find the probability that a multiple of 2 is rolled on the blue number cube and a multiple of 3 is rolled on the green number cube. $\frac{1}{6}$

Applications and Problem Solving

15. ***Game Shows*** Refer to Example 2 on page 543. Find the probability that a contestant draws three strikes in the first three draws. $\frac{1}{56}$

16. ***Baseball*** Toshiro hit 9 home runs during his last 100 times at bat during the baseball season. What is the probability that he will hit home runs in his next two times at bat? $\frac{81}{10,000}$ or 0.0081

17. ***Critical Thinking*** Make a tree diagram of all the possible outcomes of three successive spins of the spinner shown. **See students' work.**

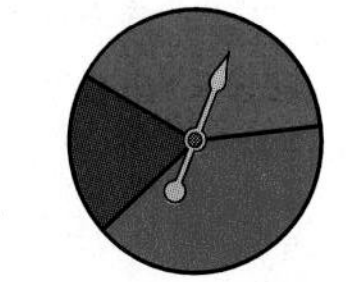

a. How many paths in the tree diagram represent two red spins and one blue? **3**

b. Suppose the spinner is designed so that for each spin there is a 40% probability of spinning red and a 20% chance of spinning blue. What is the probability of spinning two reds and one blue? **0.096**

18. ***Working on the CHAPTER Project*** For the board game that you are designing, describe how you could include a situation that involves the probability of two events. Then explain whether these events are independent or dependent. **See students' work.**

Mixed Review

For **Extra Practice,** see page 604.

19. **Standardized Test Practice** Susanna has 3 sweaters, 5 blouses, and 6 skirts that coordinate. How many different outfits can Susanna make if each outfit consists of a sweater, a blouse, and a skirt? *(Lesson 13-3)* **B**

A 105 **B** 90 **C** 45 **D** 14 **E** Not Here

20. Find $\sqrt{144}$. *(Lesson 10-1)* **12**

CHAPTER 13 Mid-Chapter Self Test

1. Out of 30 rolls of a number cube, Allison rolls a 4 three times. What is the experimental probability of rolling a 4? *(Lesson 13-1)* $\frac{1}{10}$
2. Find the theoretical probability of rolling a 4 on a number cube. *(Lesson 13-1)* $\frac{1}{6}$
3. Dion has a choice of two juices (orange or apple) and three cereals (wheat, rice, or corn) for breakfast. Make a tree diagram to show all the possible outcomes. *(Lesson 13-2)* **See Answer Appendix.**
4. Find the total number of outcomes if you toss a penny and spin the spinner at the right. *(Lesson 13-3)* **6**

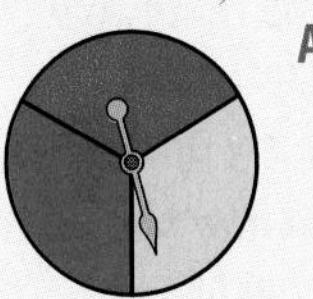

5. ***Traffic Planning*** One traffic light is red 60% of the time. The next traffic light is red 50% of the time. If the lights operate independently of one another, find P(both red). *(Lesson 13-4)* **0.3**

Exercise 18 asks students to advance to the next stage of work on the Chapter Project. You may want to have students work together to brainstorm ideas for each other's games.

4 ASSESS

Closing Activity

Writing Have students write two problems for classmates that involve choosing items from a restaurant menu. One should involve the probability of two independent events and the other of two dependent events.

Mid-Chapter Self Test

The Mid-Chapter Self Test reviews the concepts in Lessons 13-1 through 13-4. Lesson references are given so students can review concepts not yet mastered.

***Practice Masters,* p. 96**

Name________ Date________

13-4 Practice

Independent and Dependent Events

Tell whether each event is independent or dependent. Explain.

1. rolling a die and then rolling a second die
   Independent; the second die doesn't depend on the first.
2. choosing two cards from a deck so that they make a "pair" (the number value is the same)
   Dependent; the first card is not replaced.
3. selecting a compact disc from a storage case and then selecting a second disc without replacing the first
   Dependent; the second disc can't be the same as the first so there are less choices the second time.

Find each probability.

4. Two dice are rolled. Find the probability that an even number is rolled on one die and an odd number is rolled on the second die. $\frac{1}{4}$
5. Two coins are tossed in order. What is the probability of getting a head on the first coin and then getting a tail on the second coin? $\frac{1}{4}$
6. Suppose you have a bag containing two red marbles, two blue marbles, and two white marbles. You choose two marbles without looking.
   a. What is the probability that you will choose a red marble and then a blue marble without replacing the red one? $\frac{2}{15}$
   b. What is the probability that you will choose two red marbles in a row without replacing the first one? $\frac{1}{15}$
7. A coin purse contains 10 pennies, 5 nickels, 3 dimes, and 2 quarters. Two coins are selected without the first one being replaced. Find P(quarter, then nickel). $\frac{1}{38}$
8. A coin purse contains 10 pennies, 5 nickels, 3 dimes, and 2 quarters. Two coins are selected without the first one being replaced. Find P(nickel, then nickel). $\frac{1}{19}$
9. Two dice are rolled. Find the probability that a multiple of three is rolled on one die and an even number is rolled on the second die. $\frac{1}{6}$

 T96 *Mathematics: Applications and Connections, Course 2*

Extending the Lesson

***Enrichment Masters,* p. 96**

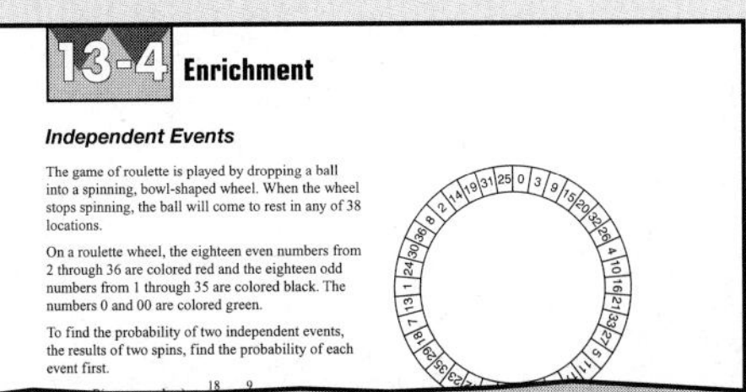

13-4 Enrichment

Independent Events

The game of roulette is played by dropping a ball into a spinning, bowl-shaped wheel. When the wheel stops spinning, the ball will come to rest in any of 38 locations.

On a roulette wheel, the eighteen even numbers from 2 through 36 are colored red and the eighteen odd numbers from 1 through 35 are colored black. The numbers 0 and 00 are colored green.

To find the probability of two independent events, the results of two spins, find the probability of each event first.

Activity Have students list all of the possible outcomes (sample space) to determine the number of times they must roll a number cube if the probability is $\frac{1}{32}$ that every roll produces an even number. Then ask them to create problems like this one for classmates to solve.

13-5A HANDS-ON LAB Notes

GET READY

Objective Students explore permutations.

Optional Resources
Hands-On Lab Masters
• worksheet, p. 70

MANAGEMENT TIPS

Recommended Time
30 minutes

Getting Started Tamaki has four tasks to do every day after school: feed her dog, walk her dog, practice the violin, and start her homework. To vary her routine, how many different ways can she order the four tasks? 24

For the **Activity** remind students that each choice of classes narrows the selections available for the next choice. For example, if math is first, then either science or language arts must be second. Ask students how it would change things if a class were offered more than once a day.

ASSESS

Have students complete Exercises 1–6. Remind students that making a tree diagram can help them to organize their search for all of the possible arrangements.

COOPERATIVE LEARNING

13-5A Exploring Permutations

A Preview of Lesson 13-5

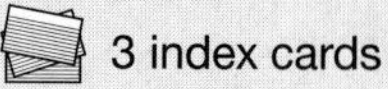

How many different ways are there to arrange your school schedule if you take math, science, and language arts?

TRY THIS

Work with a partner.

1. You can make an organized list.
   • Write math, science, and language arts on the index cards.
   • Choose one of the three subjects as the first class of the day. Choose one of the remaining two subjects for the second class. The third class is the card that remains.

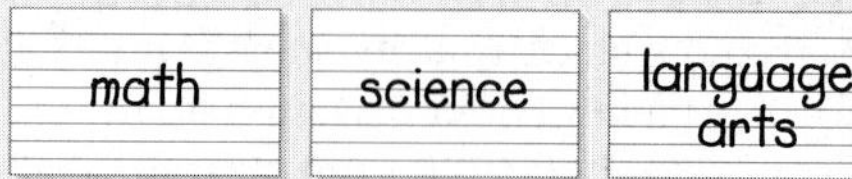

   • Record this arrangement of classes.
   • Change the order of the last two classes. Record this arrangement.

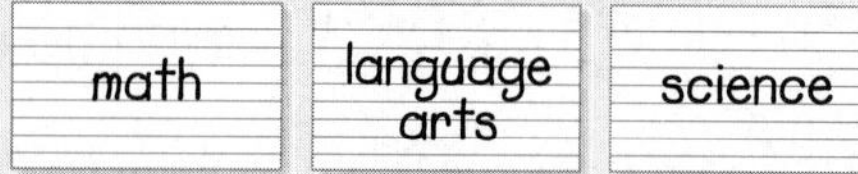

   • Continue rearranging the cards until you have found all of the possible arrangements.

2. You can also make a tree diagram.
   • Copy and complete the tree diagram shown below.

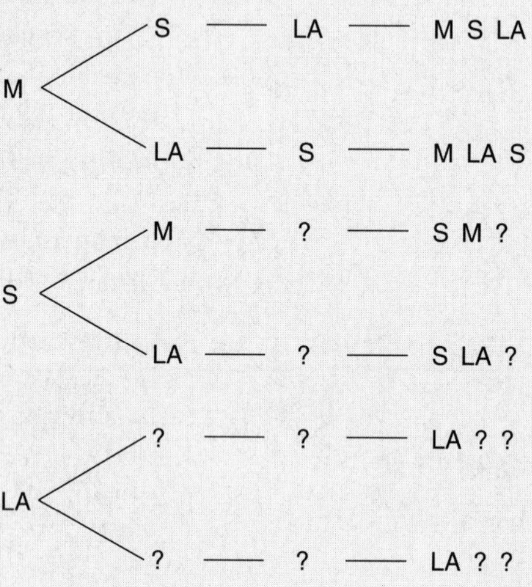

ON YOUR OWN

1. When you first started to make your list or tree diagram, how many choices did you have for your first class? **3**
2. Once your first class was selected, how many choices did you have for the second class? **2**
3. Once the first two were selected, how many choices did you have for the third class? **1**
4. How many different arrangements were possible? **6 arrangements**
5. Explain how you can use the Counting Principle to find the number of arrangements. $3 \times 2 \times 1 = 6$
6. Suppose you also take social studies. How many arrangements are possible? **24 arrangements**

Have students write a paragraph describing the steps by which they find all of the possible arrangements of classes.

13-5 Permutations

What you'll learn

You'll learn to find the number of permutations of a set of objects.

When am I ever going to use this?

You can use permutations to find how many different ways you can arrange a collection of CDs.

Word Wise

permutation
factorial

Have you ever noticed that the characters in Peanuts often discuss mathematics?

PEANUTS

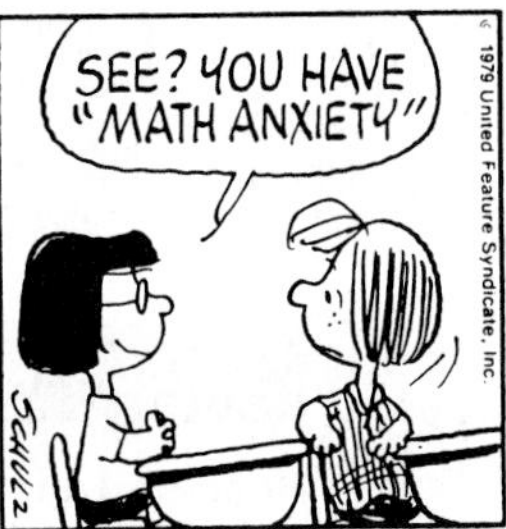

A **permutation** is an arrangement, or listing, of objects in which order is important. Let's help Peppermint Patty overcome her math anxiety and find the number of ways to arrange 9 books on a shelf.

Study Hint
Technology If your calculator has an x! key, you can use it to compute 9!.

Peppermint Patty has 9 different choices for placing the first book on the shelf. Once that book is placed, she then has 8 choices for the second book. This continues until she has 1 choice for the final book.

The following expression shows the number of permutations.

$$9 \cdot 8 \cdot 7 \cdot 6 \cdot 5 \cdot 4 \cdot 3 \cdot 2 \cdot 1 = 362{,}880$$

There are 362,880 ways to arrange 9 books on a shelf.

The expression $9 \cdot 8 \cdot 7 \cdot 6 \cdot 5 \cdot 4 \cdot 3 \cdot 2 \cdot 1$ can be written as 9!, which is read "nine **factorial**." In general, $n!$ is the product of all the counting numbers beginning with n and counting backward to 1.

Example

1 Compute 5!.

$5! = 5 \cdot 4 \cdot 3 \cdot 2 \cdot 1$
$= 120$ Therefore, $5! = 120$.

13-5 Lesson Notes

Instructional Resources

- *Study Guide Masters,* p. 97
- *Practice Masters,* p. 97
- *Enrichment Masters,* p. 97
- Transparencies 13-5, A and B
- *Assessment and Evaluation Masters,* p. 352
- *Technology Masters,* p. 52

CD-ROM Program
- Resource Lesson 13-5

Recommended Pacing	
Honors	Day 7 of 10

1 FOCUS

5-Minute Check
(Lesson 13-4)

Find each probability.

1. If you roll 2 number cubes, a green and a red, what is the probability that a multiple of 2 is rolled on the green one and an odd number on the red one? $\frac{1}{4}$
2. A wallet contains six \$5 bills, four \$10 bills, and two \$20 bills. Two bills are selected without the first being replaced. Find *P*(\$10, then \$5). $\frac{2}{11}$

The 5-Minute Check is also available on **Transparency 13-5A** for this lesson.

Motivating the Lesson

Problem Solving Ursula has 7 pairs of shoes. How many ways can she select her shoes so that she wears a different pair of shoes each day of the week? 5,040

2 TEACH

Transparency13-5B contains a teaching aid for this lesson.

Reading Mathematics Discuss with students what *permutation* means. an exchange or transformation among existing items Challenge students to think of synonyms and different kinds of real-life permutations, such as a baseball team's batting order or a seven-digit phone number.

In-Class Examples

For Example 1

Compute 6!. **720**

For Example 2

How many different flags consisting of 4 vertical stripes can be made from blue, green, red, black, yellow, and white? **360**

Teaching Tip In Example 2, point out that for every first-stripe color chosen, there is one less color from which to choose the second stripe, and so on through third-stripe colors.

3 PRACTICE/APPLY

Check for Understanding

If students need additional practice or instruction after completing Exercises 1–8, one of these options may be helpful.

- Extra Practice, see p. 604
- Reteaching Activity
- *Study Guide Masters,* p. 97
- *Practice Masters,* p. 97

Additional Answers

1. the product of all the counting numbers beginning with *n* and counting backward to 1
2. 246, 264, 426, 462, 624, 642

***Study Guide Masters,* p. 97**

Name________________ Date________

13-5 Study Guide

Permutations

An arrangement or listing in which order is important is called a **permutation.**

Example 1 **There are 6 sailboats in a race. How many arrangements of first, second, and third place are possible?**

There are 6 choices for first place, then 5 choices for second place, then 4 choices for third place.

$6 \times 5 \times 4 = 120$

The number of permutations is 120.

Some arrangements involve all of the members of a group.

Example 2 **There are 6 sailboats in a race. In how many ways can they finish the race?**

There are 6 choices for first, 5 choices for second, and so on.

$6 \times 5 \times 4 \times 3 \times 2 \times 1 = 720$

There are 720 ways in which the sailboats can finish the race.

The expression $6 \times 5 \times 4 \times 3 \times 2 \times 1$ can be written 6!. It is read "six **factorial.**" In general, *n*! is the product of the counting numbers starting at *n* and counting backward to 1.

Find the value of each expression.

1. 1! **1**
2. 4! **24**
3. $P(5, 2)$ **20**
4. $P(7, 3)$ **210**
5. In how many ways can winner, first runner-up and second runner-up be chosen from 8 riders in a horse show? **336 ways**
6. In how many ways can 5 horses in a race cross the finish line? **120 ways**
7. In how many different ways can 4 people stand in line for a movie? **24 ways**
8. In how many ways can the gold, silver, and bronze metals be awarded to 10 swimmers? **720 ways**

 T97 *Mathematics: Applications and Connections, Course 2*

Some arrangements involve only part of a group.

Example 2 CONNECTION

Geography **The flag of Mali has three vertical stripes that are green, yellow, and red. The flag of Italy is very similar. It has three vertical stripes that are green, white, and red. How many different flags can be made from the colors green, white, yellow, and red if each flag has three vertical stripes?**

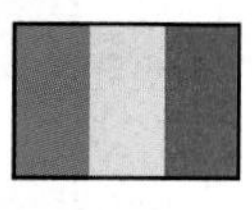

Mali

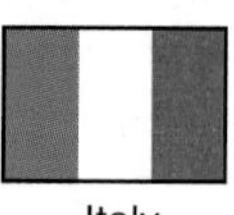

Italy

For the first vertical stripe, there are four possible choices. After that, there are three possible choices. Finally, there are two possible choices for the third stripe.

$$4 \cdot 3 \cdot 2 = 24$$

There are 24 different flags with three vertical stripes that can be made from green, yellow, white, and red. *To check the answer, you could use colored pencils and actually draw each possible flag.*

CHECK FOR UNDERSTANDING

Communicating Mathematics

Math Journal

Read and study the lesson to answer each question.

1. ***Define*** *factorial.* **See margin.**
2. ***List*** all of the permutations of the digits 2, 4, and 6. **See margin.**
3. ***Write a Problem*** in which you need to find the number of permutations of three objects. **See students' work.**

Guided Practice

Find the value of each expression.

4. 3! **6**
5. $5 \cdot 4 \cdot 3$ **60**
6. At a pet show, first, second, and third prizes will be awarded to Cookie, Charlie, and Max. In how many ways can the prizes be awarded? **6 ways**
7. A license plate begins with three letters. If the alphabet contains 26 letters, how many different permutations of these letters can be made if no letter is used more than once? **15,600 ways**
8. ***Music*** The pentatonic scale has five notes, C#, D#, F#, G#, and A#. These are the black keys on a piano. How many different five-note sequences can be written if each note is used only once? **120 melodies**

Reteaching the Lesson

Activity Have students solve Example 2 by drawing flags using all of the arrangements possible and counting the outcomes. Then guide them to use multiplication to obtain the answer and compare the two methods of solution.

Multiple Learning Styles

Auditory/Musical Provide a piano or other keyboard instrument for students to explore permutations using three-, four-, or five-note scales in Exercise 8. Challenge students to create as many different sequences as possible.

EXERCISES

Practice

Find the value of each expression.

9. 4! **24**
10. 6! **720**
11. $6 \cdot 5 \cdot 4$ **120**
12. $9 \cdot 8 \cdot 7 \cdot 6$ **3,024**
13. 2! **2**
14. seven factorial **5,040**
15. In how many ways can the starting five players of a basketball team stand in a row for a team picture? **120 ways**
16. How many different three-letter "words" can be formed from the letters E, N, and D if no letter may be used more than once? (*Hint:* "Words" means any arrangement of letters, not just English words.) **6 words**
17. In how many ways can a president, treasurer, and a secretary be chosen from among 8 candidates? **336 ways**
18. There are five finalists for the science fair, and trophies will be given to the first three finishers. How many ways are there for the three trophy winners to be selected? **60 ways**

Applications and Problem Solving

20. 2,450 ways

21. 7,140 minutes, or about 5 days

19. ***Sports*** A softball team has three power hitters. The coach wants to place them in the 3rd, 4th, and 5th positions in the batting order. How many different ways can these players be placed in those positions? **6 ways**
20. ***Parades*** If there are 50 floats in Pasadena's Rose Parade, how many ways can a first-place and second-place trophy be awarded?

21. ***Critical Thinking*** Suppose Della has forgotten her locker combination. There are three numbers in the combination, and each number is different. The numbers on the locker go from 0 to 35. If she tries one combination every 10 seconds, how long will it take her to test all of the possible combinations?

Mixed Review

22. ***Probability*** John is late for work 15% of the time. Diane is late for work 20% of the time. Find the probability that they will both be late for work on the same day. *(Lesson 13-4)* **3%**

23. **Standardized Test Practice** Amelia performed a probability experiment by spinning a spinner 20 times. The results are shown in the chart.

Color	Red	Green	Blue
Number	5	10	5

If the spinner is divided into four equal sections, how many sections would you expect to be colored blue? *(Lesson 13-1)* **A**

A 1 **B** 2 **C** 3 **D** 4

For **Extra Practice,** see page 604.

24. ***Algebra*** Evaluate $6x - 3(x - y)$ if $x = 8$ and $y = 2$. *(Lesson 1-3)* **30**

Assignment Guide

Core: 9–19 odd, 21–24
Enriched: 10–18 even, 19–24

4 ASSESS

Closing Activity

Modeling Have students create problems for classmates to solve by rearranging counters marked with numerals 0–9 into three-, four-, and five-digit addresses.

Chapter 13, Quiz C (Lessons 13-4 and 13-5) is available in the *Assessment and Evaluation Masters,* p. 352.

Practice Masters, p. 97

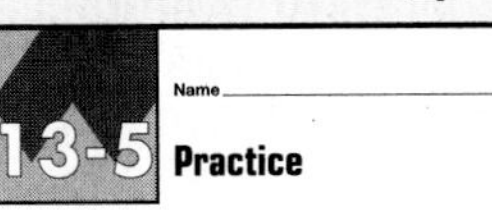

Name ____________ Date ________

13-5 Practice

Permutations

Find the value of each expression.

1. 6! 720
2. 9! 362,880
3. $P(6, 3)$ 120
4. $P(9, 8)$ 362,880
5. $P(10, 1)$ 10
6. $P(8, 8)$ 40,320

Solve.

7. How many different ways can seven people be seated in one row of seven people? 5,040
8. Suppose that eight students out of ten qualify for the cheerleading squad. In how many ways can you choose the squad? 1,814,400
9. In how many ways can a president, vice-president, secretary, and treasurer be chosen from a club with 12 members? 11,880
10. In how many ways can five books be arranged on a shelf? 120
11. In how many ways can a phone number be created if there are ten ways that the first three digits can be arranged and then each of the remaining four digits can be any digit from 0-9 as long as no digit is repeated in the group of four? 50,400
12. How many different four-letter words can be made from the alphabet if the first two letters come from the first half of the alphabet and the second two letters come from the second half of the alphabet? 24,336

 T97 *Mathematics: Applications and Connections, Course 2*

Extending the Lesson

Enrichment Masters, p. 97

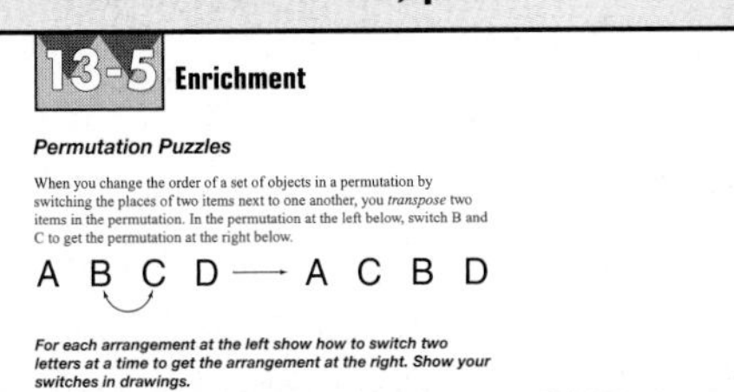

13-5 Enrichment

Permutation Puzzles

When you change the order of a set of objects in a permutation by switching the places of two items next to one another, you *transpose* two items in the permutation. In the permutation at the left below, switch B and C to get the permutation at the right below.

A B C D ⟶ A C B D

For each arrangement at the left show how to switch two letters at a time to get the arrangement at the right. Show your switches in drawings.

Activity Challenge students to simplify $\frac{100!}{99!}$ by first investigating the answers to $\frac{5!}{4!}$, $\frac{4!}{3!}$, and $\frac{3!}{2!}$. **100**

13-6A HANDS-ON LAB Notes

GET READY

Objective Students explore combinations.

Optional Resources
Hands-On Lab Masters
- worksheet, p. 71

MANAGEMENT TIPS

Recommended Time
30 minutes

Getting Started Ask students how many different kinds of one-topping pizzas they could choose from a list of 3 toppings; 3 how many two-topping pizzas from a list of 2 toppings; 1 how many two-topping pizzas from a list of 3 toppings. 3

For the **Activity,** have students compare how they used cards in Hands-On Lab 13-5A and how they are using cards in this Hands-On Lab. Ask why the order of toppings does not matter this time.

ASSESS

Have students complete Exercises 1–5. Ask students to predict the number of combinations of two-topping pizzas possible from a choice of nine toppings and then ten toppings. Have them use the cards to find out. 36 and 45 combinations

HANDS-ON LAB

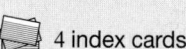

COOPERATIVE LEARNING

13-6A Exploring Combinations

A Preview of Lesson 13-6

4 index cards

The student council at Heritage Middle School is planning to sell pizzas with two different toppings. The choices are shown below.

Pizzas for Sale!
pepperoni
sausage
mushroom
green pepper

How many different combinations are possible?

TRY THIS

Work with a partner.

- Write the names of the four pizza toppings on the index cards.
- To make a pizza, select any pair of cards. Make a list of all the different combinations that are possible. Note that the order of the toppings is not important.

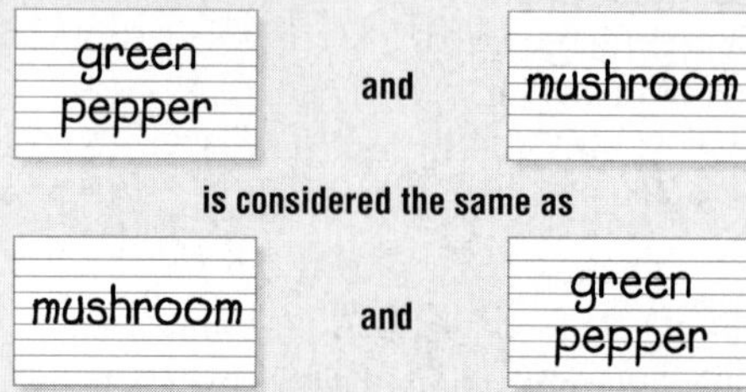

ON YOUR OWN

1. How many different combinations are possible with two toppings? **6 combinations**
2. How many different pizzas could be made with two toppings if the order of the toppings *was* important? **12 pizzas**
3. How many ways are there to arrange two toppings if order is important? **2 ways**
4. How are the answers to Exercises 1, 2, and 3 related? **$12 \div 2 = 6$**
5. Repeat Exercises 1–4 to find how many three-topping pizzas are possible from a list of five toppings. **10, 60, 6, $60 \div 6 = 10$**

Have students describe how a combination differs from a permutation.

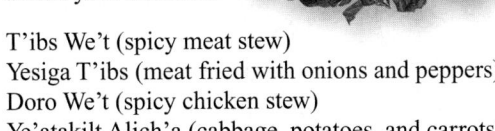

13-6 Combinations

***What* you'll learn**

You'll learn to find the number of combinations of a set of objects.

***When* am I ever going to use this?**

You'll use combinations when you choose a committee of four from a larger group.

Word Wise

combination

Suppose you are invited to an Ethiopian restaurant and the following items on the menu attract your attention.

T'ibs We't (spicy meat stew)
Yesiga T'ibs (meat fried with onions and peppers)
Doro We't (spicy chicken stew)
Ye'atakilt Alich'a (cabbage, potatoes, and carrots)

In how many ways can you choose two different items to sample? *This problem will be solved in Example 1.*

Sometimes, order is *not* important. In this case, choosing T'ibs We't and Yesiga T'ibs is the same as choosing Yesiga T'ibs and T'ibs We't. An arrangement, or listing, of objects in which order is not important is called a **combination**.

Example 1 **Food** **Refer to the beginning of the lesson. In how many ways can two items be chosen from a list of four items?**

Let's call the menu items A, B, C, and D. First, list *all* the arrangements of A, B, C, and D taken two items at a time.

AB	AC	AD	BC	BD	CD
BA	CA	DA	CB	DB	DC

From the list, count only the different arrangements. Arrangements AB and BA are the same in this case.

AB AC AD BC BD CD

So, there are six ways to choose two items from a list of four items.

Permutations and combinations are related. You can find the number of combinations of objects by dividing the number of permutations of the entire set by the number of ways each smaller set can be arranged.

Example 2 **In how many ways can you choose a committee of three people from a group of six people?**

There are $6 \cdot 5 \cdot 4$ permutations of three people chosen from six.
There are 3! or $3 \cdot 2 \cdot 1$ ways to arrange the three people.

$\frac{6 \cdot 5 \cdot 4}{3 \cdot 2 \cdot 1} = \frac{120}{6}$ or 20 There are 20 ways to choose the committee.

Multiple Learning Styles

Interpersonal Have students work in groups of four to determine how many two-player teams they can form for beach volleyball. **6**

Motivating the Lesson

Communication Tell students that the following situation presents a permutation: *In how many ways can 3 books from a set of 5 books be arranged?* Ask them to rewrite it so that it represents a combination. **Sample answer: How many different sets of 3 books can be made from a set of 5 books?**

13-6 Lesson Notes

Instructional Resources

- *Study Guide Masters,* p. 98
- *Practice Masters,* p. 98
- *Enrichment Masters,* p. 98
- Transparencies 13-6, A and B
- *Assessment and Evaluation Masters,* p. 352
- *Classroom Games,* pp. 35–40

CD-ROM Program
- Resource Lesson 13-6

Recommended Pacing	
Honors	Day 8 of 10

1 FOCUS

5-Minute Check *(Lesson 13-5)*

Find the value of each expression.

1. 7! **5,040**
2. $14 \cdot 13 \cdot 12$ **2,184**
3. In how many ways can 6 different books be placed side-by-side on a shelf? **720**
4. In how many different arrangements can 9 students sit in a row of 9 chairs? **362,880**

The 5-Minute Check is also available on **Transparency 13-6A** for this lesson.

2 TEACH

Transparency 13-6B contains a teaching aid for this lesson.

Reading Mathematics Ask students to explain how a certain combination of sandwich toppings could become several permutations. Guide them to see that any combination of items can undergo various permutations, such as by stacking them in a different order.

In-Class Examples

For Example 1
At the Burrito Brothers Grill, Abe can choose 2 toppings from a list that includes cheese, onion, peppers, salsa, tomato, and beans. How many different combinations can he choose? **15**

For Example 2
In how many ways can a baseball coach choose 3 starting pitchers from a group of 5 available pitchers? **10**

For Example 3
In Mr. Wu's kung fu class, each of the 8 students must spar with each of the others. How many matches will there be? **28**

3 PRACTICE/APPLY

Check for Understanding

If students need additional practice or instruction after completing Exercises 1–6, one of these options may be helpful.

- Extra Practice, see p. 604
- Reteaching Activity
- *Study Guide Masters,* p. 98
- *Practice Masters,* p. 98

***Study Guide Masters,* p. 98**

Name________________ Date________

Study Guide

Combinations

Arrangements or listings in which order is not important are called **combinations.**

Example **In how many ways can 3 toppings for a pizza be chosen from a list of 10 toppings?**

There are $10 \cdot 9 \cdot 8$ permutations of three toppings chosen from ten.

There are 3! or $3 \cdot 2 \cdot 1$ ways to arrange the three toppings.

$$\frac{10 \cdot 9 \cdot 8}{3 \cdot 2 \cdot 1} = \frac{720}{6} = 120$$

There are 120 ways that 3 toppings can be chosen.

Solve.

1. In how many ways can 3 representatives be chosen from a group of 11 people? **165 ways**
2. For an English exam, students are asked to write essays on 4 topics from a list of 8 topics. How many different combinations are possible? **70 combinations**
3. In how many ways can a 5-player team be chosen from 16 people? **4,368 ways**
4. In how many different ways can 8 different colors for a crayon box be selected from 24 color choices? **735,471 ways**

 T98 *Mathematics: Applications and Connections, Course 2*

Example 3 INTEGRATION

Problem Solving

A group of six people are meeting each other for the first time. Each person will shake hands with every person exactly once. How many different handshakes are possible?

> **Study Hint**
> Problem Solving Act out this problem with five of your classmates to check your answer.

Explore You know that there are six people. You need to find the number of handshakes.

Plan Find the number of ways that two people can be chosen from a group of six people. In this case, order is not important.

Solve *There are* $6 \cdot 5$ *ways to choose 2 people.* →
There are $2 \cdot 1$ *ways to arrange 2 people.* →

$$\frac{6 \cdot 5}{2 \cdot 1} = \frac{30}{2} = 15$$

There are 15 possible handshakes.

Examine Make a diagram in which each person is represented by points. Draw line segments between two points to represent the handshakes. There are 15 line segments.

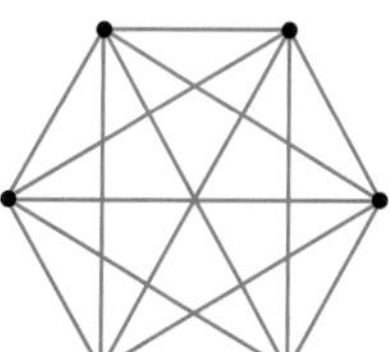

CHECK FOR UNDERSTANDING

Communicating Mathematics

Read and study the lesson to answer each question.

1. ***Explain*** why a combination lock really should be called a permutation lock. **The order of the numbers is important in a lock.**
2. ***Tell*** whether there are more permutations of a set of objects taken three at a time or more combinations of the objects taken three at a time. **permutations**
3. ***You Decide*** Malik thinks that choosing four CDs from a group of 20 to take on a trip is a permutation. Miyoki thinks it is a combination. Who is correct? Explain your reasoning. **Miyoki; order is not important in choosing this group.**

Guided Practice

Tell whether each problem represents a *permutation* or a *combination*. Then solve the problem.

4. In how many ways can four cars line up for a race? **permutation; 24 ways**
5. In how many ways can four swimmers for a team be chosen from six swimmers? **combination; 15 ways**
6. ***Food*** Yogi's Yogurt offers a choice of chocolate syrup, butterscotch syrup, strawberries, pineapple, coconut, and peanuts as toppings for its yogurt. In how many different ways can Brandon choose two different toppings for his yogurt? **15 ways**

Reteaching the Lesson

Activity Use red and green number cubes to demonstrate the difference between permutations and combinations. Guide students to see that every pair of related outcomes, such as 3 red, 1 green, and 1 red, 3 green, represents only one combination but two permutations.

Error Analysis
Watch for students who calculate all the permutations of a number in the numerator, rather than only the permutations of the set of combinations.
Prevent by reminding students that n-factorial (n!) produces more permutations than there are combinations.

EXERCISES

Practice

11. combination; 35 ways

Suppose your family wants to make a decision based on a simple majority. How many different ways can your family make that decision?

Tell whether each problem represents a *permutation* or a *combination*. Then solve the problem. 7. combination; 15 ways

7. Six students remain in a game of musical chairs. If two chairs are removed, how many different groups of four students can remain?
8. In how many ways can three clarinet players be seated in the first, second, and third seats in the orchestra? **permutation; 6 ways**
9. In how many ways can three wooden carvings be displayed from a collection of 10? **combination; 120 ways**
10. Given six different toppings from which to choose, how many different four-topping pizzas are possible? **combination; 15 ways**
11. Any four people on a committee of seven can make a decision for the committee. How many groups of four people are there?
12. In how many ways can five people be seated in a row of five chairs? **permutation; 120 ways**

Applications and Problem Solving

13. ***Lottery*** Each ticket in a lottery has five one-digit numbers, 0 – 9 on it. No two tickets have the same five numbers. The Lottery Commission will announce the combination of five numbers that will win the Grand Prize. You win if your ticket has those five numbers, in any order. What are your chances of winning? $\frac{1}{252}$
14. ***School*** Raul, Debbie, Julio, Terese, Yoki, and Tim have completed their mathematics project. Their teacher will choose three students at random to present the project to the class. Debbie, Terese, and Yoki hope they will be chosen together to present the project. What are their chances of being chosen together? $\frac{1}{20}$
15. ***Geometry*** Eight points are marked on a circle. How many different line segments can be drawn between any two of the points? **28 line segments**
16. ***Critical Thinking*** There are 504 ways in which three students can be selected first, second, and third place in the science fair. How many students are competing? **9 students**

Mixed Review

17. ***Sailing*** When Mr. Rivera purchased his sailboat, it came with six different-colored flags to be used for sending signals. The specific signal depended on the order of the flags. How many different three-flag signals can he send? *(Lesson 13-5)* **120 signals**

18. **Standardized Test Practice** Which figure has exactly 5 faces? *(Lesson 12-1)* **D**

A 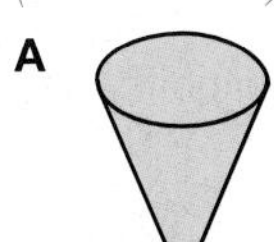 B 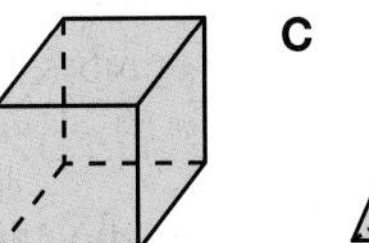 C D 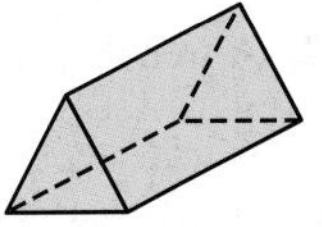

For **Extra Practice**, see page 604.

Assignment Guide

Core: 7–15 odd, 16–18
Enriched: 8–12 even, 13–18

4 ASSESS

Closing Activity

Speaking Have students explain why there are fewer combinations of a set of objects taken two at a time than there are permutations of the objects taken two at a time. **Order doesn't matter; divide the number of permutations by 2! to find the number of combinations.**

Chapter 13, Quiz D (Lesson 13-6) is available in the *Assessment and Evaluation Masters,* p. 352.

Suggest that students begin by finding the least number of family members that is more than half of all family members. That number is $n!$, the denominator, and there are n factors in the numerator.

Practice Masters, p. 98

Name ________ Date ________

13-6 Practice

Combinations

Solve.

1. How many different ways can five out of seven team members be chosen for the basketball team if order is not important?
   21
2. List all combinations of Roshanda, Shelli, Toshi, and Hector, taken three at a time.
   Roshanda, Shelli, Toshi
   Roshanda, Shelli, Hector
   Roshanda, Toshi, Hector
   Shelli, Toshi, Hector
3. At Heavenly Ice Cream, customers may choose three of the following toppings to make an ice cream sundae.

   peanut butter chips, chocolate chips, coconut, chopped nuts, granola, sliced strawberries, fudge sauce, caramel sauce

   If it is equally likely that a customer will choose any combination of three toppings, find the probability that a customer will choose sliced strawberries, caramel sauce, and coconut or peanut butter chips, coconut, and fudge sauce.
   $\frac{1}{28}$
4. In the Illinois State Lottery, balls are numbered from 1 to 54 and put into a machine, which scrambles them. Six balls are then selected in any order. How many different ways can the winning number be chosen?
   25,827,165

 T98 *Mathematics: Applications and Connections, Course 2*

Extending the Lesson

Enrichment Masters, p. 98

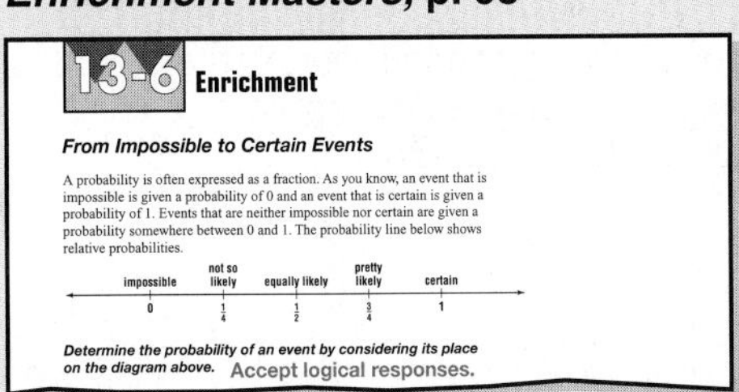

13-6 Enrichment

From Impossible to Certain Events

A probability is often expressed as a fraction. As you know, an event that is impossible is given a probability of 0 and an event that is certain is given a probability of 1. Events that are neither impossible nor certain are given a probability somewhere between 0 and 1. The probability line below shows relative probabilities.

Determine the probability of an event by considering its place on the diagram above. Accept logical responses.

Activity Challenge students to write an equation to express the number of combinations *(C)* of *n* items that can be made from *x* items. *Hint*: numerator = number of permutations; denominator = factorial of the number of things taken at a time. **Sample answer:**

$$C = \frac{x(x-1)(x-2)\ldots(x-(n-1))}{n!}$$

CHAPTER 13 Study Guide and Assessment

interNET CONNECTION Chapter Review For additional lesson-by-lesson review, visit: www.glencoe.com/sec/math/mac/mathnet

Vocabulary

This section provides a listing of the new terms, properties, and phrases that were introduced in this chapter. Have students define each term and provide an example or two of it, if appropriate.

Understanding and Using the Vocabulary

These exercises check students' understanding of the terms by using a variety of verbal formats including matching, completion, and true/false.

Glossaries A complete glossary of terms appears on pages 656–663. The glossary also appears in Spanish on pages 664–672.

Additional Answers

12. 6 outcomes; see students' diagrams; outcomes are red black, red gray, blue black, blue gray, white black, white gray.
13. 12 outcomes; see students' diagrams; outcomes are H1, H2, H3, H4, H5, H6, T1, T2, T3, T4, T5, T6.

Vocabulary

After completing this chapter, you should be able to define each term, concept, or phrase and give an example or two of each.

Statistics and Probability
combination (p. 551)
compound events (p. 542)
Counting Principle (p. 538)
dependent events (p. 543)
experimental probability (p. 531)
factorial (p. 547)
fair game (p. 535)
independent events (p. 542)
outcome (p. 531)
permutation (p. 547)
sample space (p. 531)
theoretical probability (p. 531)
tree diagram (p. 534)

Problem Solving
act it out (p. 528)

Understanding and Using the Vocabulary

Choose the correct term to complete the sentence.

1. The set of all possible outcomes for an experiment is called the (sample space, combination).
2. The Counting Principle counts the number of possible outcomes using the operation of (addition, multiplication).
3. The ratio of the number of times an event occurs to the number of trials done is called the (theoretical, experimental) probability.
4. When the outcome of one event influences the outcome of a second event, the events are called (independent, dependent).
5. A (permutation, combination) is an arrangement of objects in which order is important.
6. In a(n) (fair game, independent event), players of equal skill have the same chance of winning.
7. A tree diagram can be used to find the number of (combinations, outcomes).

In Your Own Words

8. ***Explain*** the difference between a permutation and a combination.

8. Sample answer: A permutation is an arrangement in which order is important. A combination is an arrangement in which order is not important.

MindJogger Videoquizzes

MindJogger Videoquizzes provide an alternative review of concepts presented in this chapter. Students work in teams to answer questions, gaining points for correct answers. The questions are presented in three rounds.

Round 1 Concepts–5 questions
Round 2 Skills–4 questions
Round 3 Problem Solving–4 questions

Objectives & Examples

Upon completing this chapter, you should be able to:

- find and compare experimental and theoretical probabilities *(Lesson 13-1)*

If 1 marble is drawn from a bag containing 8 red and 2 green marbles, the theoretical probability that it is green is $\frac{2}{10}$ or $\frac{1}{5}$.

Review Exercises

Use these exercises to review and prepare for the chapter test.

A bowl contains the names of 25 students. Ten are 10 years old, ten are 11 years old, and five are 12 years old. One name is selected at random. Find each probability.

9. P(10 years old) **$\frac{10}{25}$ or $\frac{2}{5}$**

10. P(12 years old) **$\frac{5}{25}$ or $\frac{1}{5}$**

11. P(at least 11 years old) **$\frac{15}{25}$ or $\frac{3}{5}$**

- use tree diagrams to count outcomes *(Lesson 13-2)*

If a family has two children, there are 4 possible outcomes.

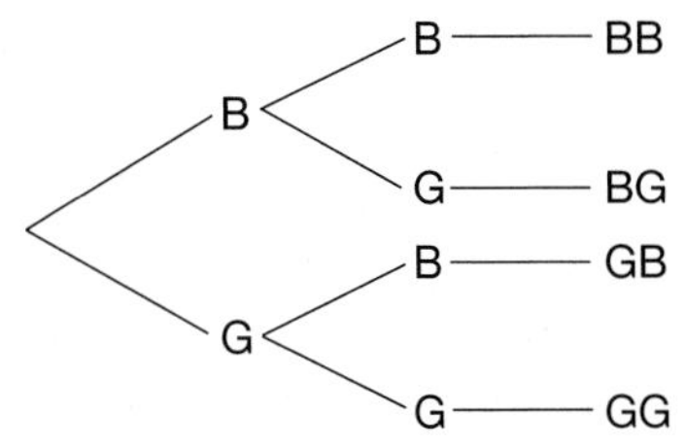

For each situation, make a tree diagram and list the outcomes. Then give the total number of outcomes.

12. choosing a red, blue, or white shirt with either black or gray lettering **6**

13. tossing a coin and choosing a card from six cards numbered from 1 to 6 **12**

12–13. See margin for outcomes.

- use multiplication to count outcomes *(Lesson 13-3)*

There are 2 possible outcomes each time a family has a child. If a family has 2 children, there are 2 × 2 or 4 outcomes.

Use the Counting Principle to find the total number of outcomes in each situation.

14. rolling 2 number cubes **36 outcomes**

15. selecting a car from 3 styles, 3 interior colors, and 3 exterior colors **27 outcomes**

Objectives & Examples

This section reviews the skills and concepts of the chapter and shows completely worked examples.

Review Exercises

These exercises provide practice for the corresponding objectives.

***Assessment and Evaluation Masters*, pp. 339–340**

Name____________________ Date __________

Chapter 13 Test, Form 1B

Tori has four tickets to a football game. She can take three of her friends with her, but five of her friends would like to go. They are Tom, Jill, Joe, Marvin, and Ginger. To decide, Tori writes each of her friends' names on a separate piece of paper and selects one. Use this information to answer Questions 1–4.

1. What is the probability that Tori picks a boy? **1. A**
A. $\frac{3}{5}$ **B.** $\frac{1}{5}$ **C.** $\frac{2}{3}$ **D.** $\frac{2}{5}$

2. What is the probability that Tori picks someone whose name begins with the letter J? **2. B**
A. $\frac{3}{5}$ **B.** $\frac{2}{5}$ **C.** $\frac{1}{2}$ **D.** $\frac{1}{6}$

3. If Tori were to draw a name 15 times and Tom's name is picked five times, what is the experimental probability that Tom's name is picked? **3. C**
A. $\frac{5}{5}$ **B.** $\frac{1}{5}$ **C.** $\frac{1}{3}$ **D.** $\frac{5}{6}$

4. Choose the best comparison between the theoretical and experimental probability that Tom will go to the game. Use the experimental probability from Question 3. **4. B**
A. The theoretical probability is greater than the experimental probability.
B. The theoretical probability is less than the experimental probability.
C. The theoretical probability is equal to the experimental probability.
D. The theoretical probability is not related to the experimental probability.

5. Janet has 4 blouses, 2 pairs of pants, and 3 pairs of socks that can be worn together. Use a tree diagram to find how many outfits she can make. **5. D**
A. 9 **B.** 18 **C.** 20 **D.** 24

6. At Brand-X Ranch you can ride Buckin' Billy, Tennessee Lady, or Lag-Behind Nell. One trail goes through the woods, another goes up a mountain, and a third trail goes by a stream. How many different rides can you take? **6. C**
A. 3 **B.** 6 **C.** 9 **D.** 12

7. Use the Counting Principle to find the number of choices you have in buying a car if you can select from 2 models, 3 colors, and 5 option packages. **7. A**
A. 30 **B.** 16 **C.** 10 **D.** 25

8. If there are 6 baseballs, 10 tennis balls, and 11 golf balls available, how many different combinations of balls could be made? **8. B**
A. 60 **B.** 660 **C.** 66 **D.** 27

© Glencoe/McGraw-Hill 339 *Mathematics: Applications and Connections, Course 2*

Chapter 13 Test, Form 1B (continued)

For Questions 9–10, tell whether each event is independent or dependent. Find each probability.

9. The spinner at the right has an equal chance of landing on each number. Find P(6, then 6). **9. A**
A. independent; $\frac{1}{49}$ **B.** dependent; $\frac{1}{21}$
C. independent; $\frac{2}{7}$ **D.** dependent; $\frac{1}{10}$

10. There are 5 peppermint, 4 licorice, 8 grape, 2 orange, and 9 cherry jelly beans in a bag. Paco picks a jelly bean. Without replacing the first one, he picks a second jelly bean. Find P(grape, then cherry). **10. B**
A. independent; $\frac{8}{9}$ **B.** dependent; $\frac{2}{21}$
C. independent, $\frac{1}{125}$ **D.** dependent; $\frac{12}{145}$

For Questions 11–14, tell whether each problem represents a permutation or a combination. Then solve the problem.

11. Twelve students remain in a game of dodgeball. If 6 students go out in the next minute, how many different groups of six students can remain? **11. A**
A. combination; 924 **B.** permutation; 665,280
C. permutation; 1,140 **D.** combination; 1,638

12. Brandon has 8 different plates with which to set the table. How many different ways can he place the plates? **12. B**
A. combination; 36 **B.** permutation; 40,320
C. permutation; 6,720 **D.** combination; 336

13. In how many ways can Mia choose 10 mugs from a collection of 15? **13. A**
A. combination; 3,003 **B.** combination; 360,360
C. permutation; 105 **D.** combination; 150

14. If Lando will use 7 types of noodles to make 7 different pasta dishes for dinner, how many different ways can he choose the noodles for each dish? **14. C**
A. combination; 823,543 **B.** permutation; 56
C. permutation; 5,040 **D.** combination; 792

15. Ten students are trying out for a school quartet. In how many ways can the members be selected? **15. C**
A. 1,260 **B.** 40 **C.** 210 **D.** 5,040

16. Tim is planning his 8th-grade schedule. He can select 4 of his classes from the following options: algebra, American Sign Language, typing, English, physics, chemistry, and biology. What is the probability that Tim will select biology, algebra, typing, and physics? **16. A**
A. $\frac{1}{35}$ **B.** $\frac{5}{11}$ **C.** $\frac{1}{840}$ **D.** $\frac{1}{22}$

© Glencoe/McGraw-Hill 340 *Mathematics: Applications and Connections, Course 2*

Assessment and Evaluation

Six forms of Chapter 13 Test are available in the *Assessment and Evaluation Masters* as shown in the chart.

1A	Multiple Choice	Honors
1B	Multiple Choice	Average
1C	Multiple Choice	Basic
2A	Free Response	Honors
2B	Free Response	Average
2C	Free Response	Basic

Chapter 13 Test, Form 1B, is shown at the right. Chapter 13 Test, Form 2B, is shown on the next page.

Study Guide and Assessment

Assessment and Evaluation Masters, pp. 345–346

Name________________________ Date________________

Chapter 13 Test, Form 2B

Misu can fit 3 other people into his car but 5 of his friends want to get a ride to the baseball game. His friends are Brittany, Anne, Steve, Monique, and John. To decide, Misu writes each of his friends' names on a separate piece of paper and selects one. Use this information in Questions 1–4.

1. What is the probability that Misu picks a girl? 1. $\frac{3}{5}$
2. What is the probability that Misu picks someone whose name ends with the letter E? 2. $\frac{4}{5}$
3. If Misu chooses a name 15 times and Monique's name is picked 3 times, what is the experimental probability that Monique's name is picked? 3. $\frac{1}{5}$
4. How does the theoretical probability that Monique will get a ride compare to the experimental probability in Question 3? 4. They are equal.
5. Use a tree diagram to find how many different ways you can arrange 4 colored pencils in a 4 pencil holder. 5. 24
6. Barry sells hot dogs with or without mustard. His customers can also choose potato chips, corn chips, or pretzels. How many different kinds of orders might Barry receive? 6. 6
7. Use the Counting Principle to find the total number of toads found by 21 scientists in 3 days if each scientist finds 7 new toads each day. 7. 441
8. Mimi has 4 glowballs, 15 superballs, and 8 moonballs to arrange on a display shelf. How many different ways can she arrange them if she chooses one of each kind? 8. 480
9. Use the Counting Principle to find the total number of trees planted in 5 days by 30 people, who each plant 3 trees per day. 9. 450

Chapter 13 Test, Form 2B (continued)

For Questions 10–12, tell whether each event is independent or dependent. Find each probability.

10. Suzanne's pack of party favors consists of 10 hats, 6 horns, and 9 balloons. Without replacing the first party favor, she takes out a second. Find P(balloon, then hat). 10. dependent; $\frac{3}{20}$
11. Ms. Kaufman has 13 reflectors, 8 license plates, and 3 horns to give to her students who have bikes. Victor chooses something, puts it back, and chooses something else. Find P(license plate, then horn). 11. independent; $\frac{1}{24}$
12. Julian has 4 cucumbers, 12 avocados, and 5 squash in the refrigerator. Without replacing the first vegetable, he takes a second. Find P(squash, then avocado). 12. dependent; $\frac{1}{7}$

Find the value of each expression.

13. 12! 13. 479,001,600
14. $13 \cdot 12 \cdot 11 \cdot 10$ 14. 17,160

For Questions 15–18, tell whether each problem represents a permutation or combination. Then solve the problem.

15. How many different ways can 15 couches be arranged in 5 showrooms if each showroom has 1 couch? 15. combination; 3,003
16. How many different ways can 11 board games be stacked? 16. permutation; 39,916,800
17. Enrique has 9 patterns to choose from to sew a shirt. How many different ways could he sew 6 different shirts? 17. combination; 84
18. Josephine has to choose 5 books from 17 books. How many ways could she choose 5 books? 18. combination; 6,188
19. Adrienne can put 7 candles on her coffee table. Determine the number of ways she can arrange them in a line on the table. 19. 5,040
20. For English class, Aleta must read 5 books from a list of 8. In how many different ways can Aleta complete her assignment if the order in which she reads them is not important? 20. 56

Objectives & Examples

- find the probability of independent and dependent events *(Lesson 13-4)*

Find the probability of spinning a 2 on the first spinner and a 3 on the second spinner.

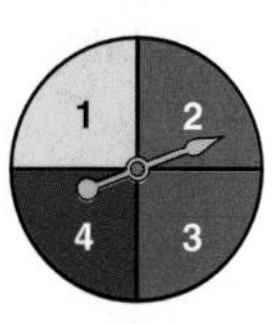

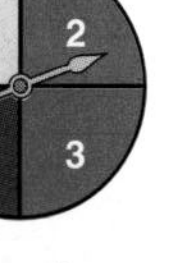

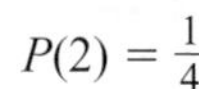

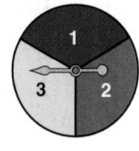

$P(2) = \frac{1}{4}$ $\quad P(3) = \frac{1}{3}$

$P(2, \text{then } 3) = \frac{1}{4} \cdot \frac{1}{3}$ or $\frac{1}{12}$

Review Exercises

A bag contains 4 green, 6 white, and 8 blue counters. Two counters are randomly drawn.

16. Find P(white, white) if the first counter drawn is replaced. $\frac{1}{9}$
17. Find P(white, white) if the first counter drawn is not replaced. $\frac{5}{51}$

A box contains 5 blue, 4 red, and 3 yellow marbles. Two marbles are randomly drawn.

18. Find P(blue, red) if the first marble drawn is not replaced. $\frac{5}{33}$
19. Find P(blue, red) if the first marble drawn is replaced. $\frac{5}{36}$

- find the number of permutations of a set of objects *(Lesson 13-5)*

In how many ways can a president and vice-president be chosen from among 4 candidates?

choices for president

$4 \cdot 3 = 12$

choices for vice-president

Find the value of each expression.

20. 6! **720**
21. 4! **24**
22. In how many ways can five basketball players be placed in three positions? **60**
23. The pole vault competition has 10 people in it. In how many ways can first-, second-, and third-place ribbons be awarded? **720**

- find the number of combinations of a set of objects *(Lesson 13-6)*

In how many ways can you choose two items from a menu with 4 items on it?

$$\frac{4 \cdot 3}{2 \cdot 1} = \frac{12}{2} \text{ or } 6$$

24. Given eight different toppings to choose from, how many three-topping pizzas are possible? **56**
25. Any five people on a committee of nine can make a decision for the committee. How many groups of five people are there? **126**

Test and Review Software

You may use this software, a combination of an item generator and item bank, to create your own tests or worksheets. Types of items include free response, multiple choice, short answer, and open ended.

CD-ROM Program

The CD-ROM Program contains an Assessment Game whose questions review the concepts in this chapter.

Applications & Problem Solving

26. ***Act It Out*** How many times do you need to spin this spinner to spin all six numbers? *(Lesson 13-1A)* **See students' work.**

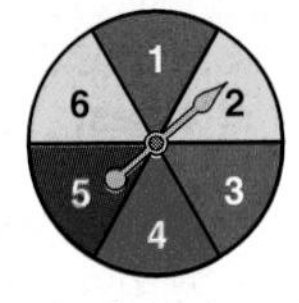

27. ***Shopping*** One catalog offers a jogging suit in two colors, blue and red. It comes in sizes S, M, L, XL, and XXL. How many possible jogging suits can be ordered? *(Lesson 13-3)* **10 jogging suits**

28. ***Raffle*** In how many ways can the grand-prize ticket, second-prize ticket, and third-prize ticket be selected from the 30 raffle tickets sold? *(Lesson 13-5)* **24,360 ways**

29. ***Games*** Andrea has 10 different games that she keeps in her bedroom. She wants to select two of these games to play in the evening. In how many ways can Andrea select the two games? *(Lesson 13-6)* **45 ways**

30. ***Clothes*** A drawer contains two blue socks and four black socks. Without looking, you choose one sock, and then another sock without replacing the first one. What is the probability that you choose two black socks? *(Lesson 13-3)* $\frac{2}{5}$

Alternative Assessment

Open Ended

Mia and her friends are creating a game for her party. They are labeling each side of a six-sided cube with numbers from 1 to 4, using each number at least once. They want to label the faces of the cube so that the probability of rolling a 3 or a 4 is $\frac{1}{2}$ and the probability of not rolling a 1 is $\frac{2}{3}$. How should they label the sides of the cube? **See margin.**

Mia decides to label a second six-sided number cube with numbers from 1 to 4, using each number at least once. She wants to label the faces of this second cube so that the probability of getting a sum of 4 by rolling both cubes is $\frac{1}{6}$. How should she label the sides of the second cube? **See margin.**

A practice test for Chapter 13 is provided on page 619.

Completing the Chapter Project

Use the following checklist to make sure your project is complete.

- ☑ You have listed several examples that describe how probability is used in the board game you have chosen.
- ☑ The design of your own board game includes a complete set of rules for the game, and you have explained the role probability plays in your game.

Select one of the vocabulary words you learned in this chapter and place the word and its definition in your portfolio. Attach a note explaining why you selected it.

Additional Answers for the Open Ended item

- Sample answer: Label two faces with a 1, one with a 2, two with a 3, and one with a 4.
- Sample answer: Label two faces with a 1, one with a 2, one with a 3, and two with a 4.

Performance Assessment

Additional performance assessment tasks for this chapter are included in the *Assessment and Evaluation Masters* on page 349. A scoring guide is also provided on page 361.

Applications & Problem Solving

This section provides additional practice in solving real-world problems that involve the skills of this chapter.

Alternative Assessment

The ***Open Ended*** section provides students with a performance assessment opportunity to evaluate their work and understanding.

Students should complete the final stages of their project and prepare a class demonstration of their results. A scoring guide for the project is available in the *Investigations and Projects Masters,* p. 67.

Students should add to their portfolios at this time.

***Assessment and Evaluation Masters,* p. 349**

Name__________ Date__________

Chapter 13 Performance Assessment

Instructions: Demonstrate your knowledge by giving a clear, concise solution to each problem. Be sure to include all relevant drawings and justify your answers. You may show your solutions in more than one way or investigate beyond the requirements of the problems.

1. Seven Oaks Middle School is having its spring fair.
   a. A game uses spinner A below. If a player spins a 1, he or she wins a prize. Explain how to find the theoretical probability of winning a prize.

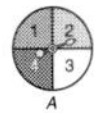

   b. A second game uses spinner B. A player must spin a W to win. Explain how to use experimental probability to find the probability of spinning a W.
2. A bag contains 1 white (W), 3 blue (B_1, B_2, B_3) and 2 red (R_1, R_2) marbles.
   a. Use a tree diagram to list all of the possible outcomes for tossing a coin and then drawing a marble from the bag.
   b. Explain what is meant by *independent events.*
   c. Find the probability of tossing a head and drawing a red marble. Explain your reasoning.
   d. Find the probability of drawing two blue marbles if the first marble is not replaced. Explain each step.
3. Rayna and her husband have 8 nieces, 9 nephews, 6 cousins, 3 aunts, and 5 uncles.
   a. Explain how you could use the Counting Principle to find how many ways Rayna's relatives could stand in line to do the limbo.
   b. How many ways could just the nieces stand in line to limbo? Explain your method.
   c. If everyone wants to play musical chairs but there are only 10 chairs available, how many ways could 10 of the relatives could sit in the chairs when the music stops? Explain your method.

 349 *Mathematics: Applications and Connections,* Course 2

Standardized Test Practice

The Standardized Test Practice may be used to help students prepare for standardized tests. The test items are written in the same style as those in state proficiency tests and standardized tests like CAT, CTBS, ITBS, MAT, SAT, and Terra Nova. The test items cover skills and concepts covered up to this point in the text.

The pages can be used as an overnight assessment. After students have completed the pages, discuss how each problem can be solved, or provide copies of the solutions from the *Solutions Manual.*

***Assessment and Evaluation Masters,* p. 355**

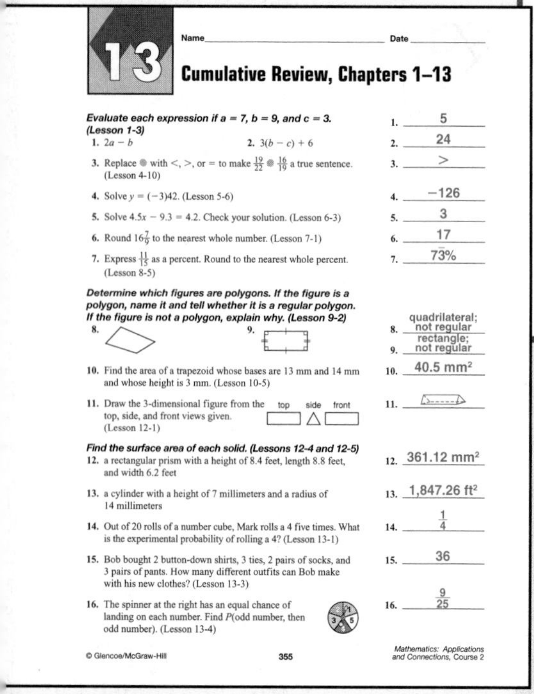

13 Name________________ Date________

Cumulative Review, Chapters 1–13

Evaluate each expression if a = 7, b = 9, and c = 3. (Lesson 1-3)

1. $2a - b$ — **1.** 5
2. $3(b - c) + 6$ — **2.** 24
3. Replace ● with <, >, or = to make $\frac{19}{22}$ ● $\frac{16}{19}$ a true sentence. (Lesson 4-10) — **3.** >
4. Solve $y = (-3)42$. (Lesson 5-6) — **4.** −126
5. Solve $4.5x - 9.3 = 4.2$. Check your solution. (Lesson 6-3) — **5.** 3
6. Round $16\frac{7}{9}$ to the nearest whole number. (Lesson 7-1) — **6.** 17
7. Express $\frac{11}{15}$ as a percent. Round to the nearest whole percent. (Lesson 8-5) — **7.** $7\bar{3}\%$

Determine which figures are polygons. If the figure is a polygon, name it and tell whether it is a regular polygon. If the figure is not a polygon, explain why. (Lesson 9-2)

8. — **8.** quadrilateral; not regular
9. — **9.** rectangle; not regular

10. Find the area of a trapezoid whose bases are 13 mm and 14 mm and whose height is 3 mm. (Lesson 10-5) — **10.** 40.5 mm²
11. Draw the 3-dimensional figure from the top, side, and front views given. (Lesson 12-1) top side front — **11.**

Find the surface area of each solid. (Lessons 12-4 and 12-5)

12. a rectangular prism with a height of 8.4 feet, length 8.8 feet, and width 6.2 feet — **12.** 361.12 mm²
13. a cylinder with a height of 7 millimeters and a radius of 14 millimeters — **13.** 1,847.26 ft²
14. Out of 20 rolls of a number cube, Mark rolls a 4 five times. What is the experimental probability of rolling a 4? (Lesson 13-1) — **14.** $\frac{1}{4}$
15. Bob bought 2 button-down shirts, 3 ties, 2 pairs of socks, and 3 pairs of pants. How many different outfits can Bob make with his new clothes? (Lesson 13-3) — **15.** 36
16. The spinner at the right has an equal chance of landing on each number. Find *P*(odd number, then odd number). (Lesson 13-4) — **16.** $\frac{9}{25}$

 355 *Mathematics: Applications and Connections, Course 2*

CHAPTERS **1–13**

Standardized Test Practice

Assessing Knowledge & Skills

Section One: Multiple Choice

There are nine multiple-choice questions in this section. Choose the best answer. If a correct answer is *not here,* choose the letter for Not Here.

1. There are four flavors of yogurt, six kinds of toppings, and four different kinds of syrup. How many different combinations of yogurt, topping, and syrup can be ordered if you can choose one of each? **D**

A 14
B 24
C 48
D 96

2. A cube has a surface area of 144 square centimeters. How can you find the surface area of one face? **G**

F Divide 144 by 4.
G Divide 144 by 6.
H Divide 144 by 8.
J Divide 144 by 10.

3. What is the theoretical probability of choosing a vowel from the word MATHEMATICS? **B**

A $\frac{4}{7}$ **B** $\frac{4}{11}$
C $\frac{7}{11}$ **D** $\frac{4}{9}$

4. Suppose you need 0.65 liter of water for a science experiment, but the container is measured in milliliters. How much water do you need? **G**

F 6,500 milliliters
G 650 milliliters
H 65 milliliters
J 0.00065 milliliter

Please note that Questions 5–9 have five answer choices.

5. People were asked to choose their favorite type of movie. The graph shows the results of the survey.

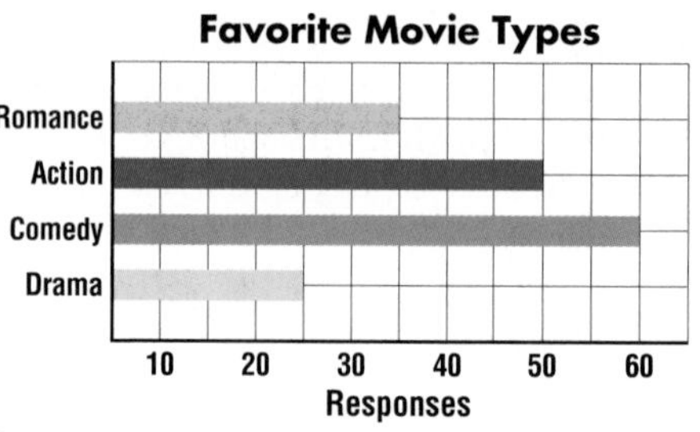

What was the total number of people who were surveyed? **D**

A 60
B 75
C 90
D 170
E 270

6. The Girls Scouts placed a bank in the school office to collect money for a service project. At the end of the week, the bank contained 32 quarters, 27 nickels, and 105 dimes. Which number sentence could be used to find *M*, the total amount of money in the bank? **F**

F $M = (32 \times 0.25) + (27 \times 0.05) + (105 \times 0.10)$
G $M = (32 + 0.25) \times (27 + 0.05) \times (105 + 0.10)$
H $M = (32 \div 0.25) \times (27 \div 0.05) \times (105 \div 0.10)$
J $M = (0.25 + 0.10 + 0.05) \times 86$
K $M = (32 \div 0.25) + (27 \div 0.05) + (105 \div 0.10)$

◀◀◀Instructional Resources

Another cumulative review is shown at the left and is available in the *Assessment and Evaluation Masters,* p. 355.

7. If $592 was made in sales of sweatshirts, what was the total amount of sales to the nearest dollar? **A**

Sales of Items

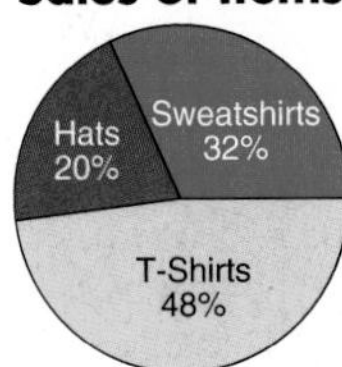

A $1,850 **B** $1,798
C $185 **D** $180
E Not Here

8. Cali bought a sweater priced at $60. If the sales tax is 9%, which is a good estimate for the total purchase price of the jacket, including sales tax? **G**

F $55 **G** $65
H $70 **J** $75
K $80

9. If one chocolate bar contains $\frac{3}{4}$ of a pound of chocolate, how many chocolate bars can be made from $6\frac{1}{2}$ pounds of chocolate? **C**

A $4\frac{7}{8}$ **B** $5\frac{3}{4}$
C $8\frac{2}{3}$ **D** $9\frac{2}{3}$
E Not Here

Test Practice For additional test practice questions, visit:

www.glencoe.com/sec/math/mac/mathnet

Test-Taking Tip (THE PRINCETON REVIEW)

On standardized tests, guessing can improve your score if you make educated guesses. First, find out if there is a penalty for incorrect answers. If there is no penalty, a guess can only increase your score, or at worst, leave your score the same. If there is a penalty for guessing, try to eliminate enough choices to make the probability of a correct guess greater than the probability of an incorrect answer.

Section Two: Free Response

This section contains five questions for which you will provide short answers. Write your answers on your paper.

10. Find 2.36×100. **236**

11. At the school carnival, 10 prizes were written on slips of paper. There were 3 markers, 2 movie passes, 4 pencils, and 1 five-dollar bill. If a slip of paper is selected without looking, what is the probability that it will be a pencil? $\frac{2}{5}$

12. What is the length of the hypotenuse of the triangle? **13 in.**

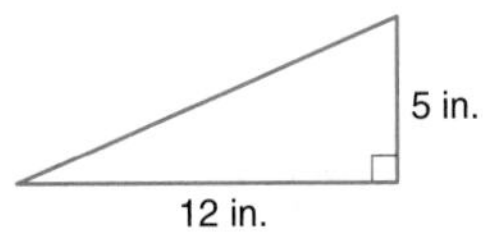

13. A store advertised a backpack for 25% off the regular price. Express 25% as a fraction. $\frac{1}{4}$

14. A deck is shaped like a square with an area of 400 square feet. What is the length of one side of the deck? **20 ft**

Test-Taking Tip

Lead students to see that rounding may increase the probability of guessing correctly. For example, for the equation $49 + 62 + 33 =$
A 288 **B** 144 **C** 441 **D** 882, rounding before adding will eliminate all but the correct answer.

Assessment and Evaluation Masters, pp. 353–354

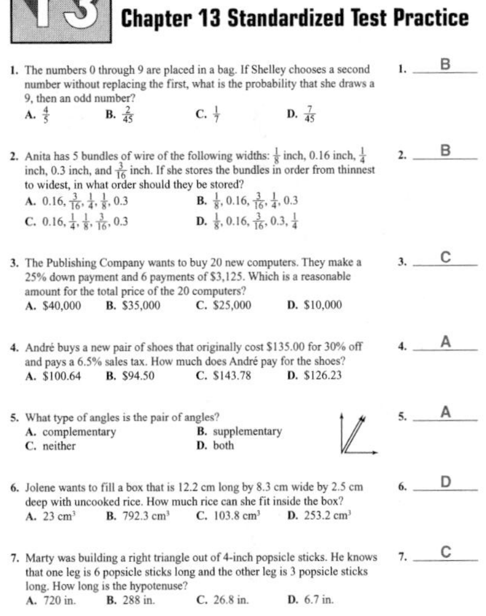

Name________ Date________

13 Chapter 13 Standardized Test Practice

1. The numbers 0 through 9 are placed in a bag. If Shelley chooses a second number without replacing the first, what is the probability that she draws a 9, then an odd number? — 1. B
A. $\frac{4}{5}$ B. $\frac{2}{45}$ C. $\frac{1}{7}$ D. $\frac{7}{45}$

2. Anita has 5 bundles of wire of the following widths: $\frac{1}{8}$ inch, 0.16 inch, $\frac{1}{4}$ inch, 0.3 inch, and $\frac{3}{16}$ inch. If she stores the bundles in order from thinnest to widest, in what order should they be stored? — 2. B
A. 0.16, $\frac{3}{16}$, $\frac{1}{4}$, $\frac{1}{8}$, 0.3 B. $\frac{1}{8}$, 0.16, $\frac{3}{16}$, $\frac{1}{4}$, 0.3
C. 0.16, $\frac{1}{4}$, $\frac{1}{8}$, $\frac{3}{16}$, 0.3 D. $\frac{1}{8}$, 0.16, $\frac{3}{16}$, 0.3, $\frac{1}{4}$

3. The Publishing Company wants to buy 20 new computers. They make a 25% down payment and 6 payments of $3,125. Which is a reasonable amount for the total price of the 20 computers? — 3. C
A. $40,000 B. $35,000 C. $25,000 D. $10,000

4. André buys a new pair of shoes that originally cost $135.00 for 30% off and pays a 6.5% sales tax. How much does André pay for the shoes? — 4. A
A. $100.64 B. $94.50 C. $143.78 D. $126.23

5. What type of angles is the pair of angles? — 5. A
A. complementary B. supplementary
C. neither D. both

6. Jolene wants to fill a box that is 12.2 cm long by 8.3 cm wide by 2.5 cm deep with uncooked rice. How much rice can she fit inside the box? — 6. D
A. 23 cm^3 B. 792.3 cm^3 C. 103.8 cm^3 D. 253.2 cm^3

7. Marty was building a right triangle out of 4-inch popsicle sticks. He knows that one leg is 6 popsicle sticks long and the other leg is 3 popsicle sticks long. How long is the hypotenuse? — 7. C
A. 720 in. B. 288 in. C. 26.8 in. D. 6.7 in.

8. Alex has 4 suits, 8 ties, and 3 pairs of shoes. How many different outfits can he create? — 8. C
A. 28 B. 48 C. 96 D. 15

 353 *Mathematics: Applications and Connections*, Course 2

13 Chapter 13 Standardized Test Practice (continued)

9. Meg needs to discover what percent of her grocery bill, $73, is the sales tax, $5.48. Which equation should she use to find it? — 9. B
A. $73 = (5.48)x$ B. $5.48 = 73x$
C. $x = 73(5.48)$ D. $x = 5.48(73)$

10. Winfield has 17 cats to feed. If he has $10\frac{1}{5}$ cups of cat food and each cat has its own food bowl, how much food does each cat receive? — 10. A
A. $\frac{3}{5}$ cup B. 1 cup C. $3\frac{2}{5}$ cup D. $\frac{1}{6}$ cup

11. Which of the following inequalities is equivalent to *nine minus four times a number is less than negative five*? — 11. D
A. $9 + 4n < -5$ B. $4 - 9n < -5$
C. $9 - 4n < 5$ D. $9 - 4n < -5$

12. Tionna has a display that holds 8 horse figurines. If she has 17 horse figurines, how many combinations of 8 can she create? — 12. D
A. 40,320 B. 136 C. 2,312 D. 24,310

13. Jacques has 4 bottles of lemonade. If he gets 14 more from Ellen, how many bottles does he have altogether? — 13. B
A. 16 B. 18 C. 20 D. 10

14. Which of the following expressions is equivalent to $3^2 \times 7^4 \times 13$? — 14. B
A. $3 \times 2 \times 7 \times 4 \times 13$ B. $3 \times 3 \times 7 \times 7 \times 7 \times 7 \times 13$
C. $3 \times 7 \times 7 \times 7 \times 13$ D. $3 \times 7 \times 13$

15. How many different ways can 7 shells be rearranged on a shelf? — 15. C
A. 42 B. 840 C. 5,040 D. 40,320

16. Complete the translation of the pattern unit. — 16. A

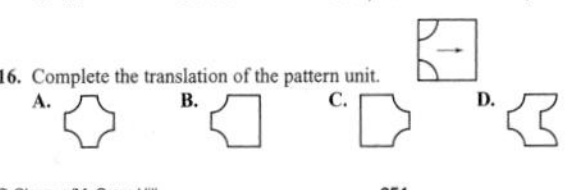

 354 *Mathematics: Applications and Connections*, Course 2

Instructional Resources ▶▶▶

Additional standardized test practice is shown at the right and is available in the *Assessment and Evaluation Masters*, pp. 353–354.

Student Handbook Table of Contents

Extra Practice
- Basic Skills 562–567
- Lesson by Lesson 568–604
- Mixed Problem Solving 605–606

Chapter Tests 607–619

Getting Acquainted with the Graphing Calculator 620–621

Getting Acquainted with Spreadsheets 622–623

Selected Answers 624–653

Photo Credits 654–655

Glossary 656–663

Spanish Glossary 664–672

Index 673–682

Symbols, Formulas, and Measurement Conversions .... inside back cover

Basic Skills

Adding and Subtracting Decimals

1. $0.132 - 0.021 = $ **0.111**

2. $3.78 + 0.21 = $ **3.99**

3. $12.3 - 0.847 = $ **11.453**

4. $5.86 - 1.51 = $ **4.35**

5. $128.01 - 39.117 = $ **88.893**

6. $14.7 + 351.82 = $ **366.52**

7. $42.3 + .81 = $ **43.11**

8. $13.2 + 12.8 = $ **26.0**

9. $342.9 - 0.18 = $ **342.72**

10. $282.45 - 111.3 = $ **171.15**

11. $100 - 0.48 = $ **99.52**

12. $12.888 - 4.996 = $ **7.892**

13. $42.07 - 38.78 = $ **3.29**

14. $80.05 - 79.06 = $ **0.99**

15. $104.98 - 0.12 = $ **104.86**

16. $304.999 + 1.1 = $ **306.099**

17. $82.23 + 0.88 = $ **83.11**

18. $898.667 - 0.56 = $ **898.107**

19. $13 - 0.324 = $ **12.676**

20. $0.42 + 0.68 = $ **1.1**

21. $9.1 - 5.625$ **3.475**

22. $0.48 + 2.901$ **3.381**

23. $5.8 + 3.92$ **9.72**

24. $38.63 + 38.63$ **77.26**

25. $8 - 2.54$ **5.46**

26. $16.354 - 0.2$ **16.154**

27. $0.125 + 0.78$ **0.905**

28. $8.2 - 6.9$ **1.3**

29. $1.245 + 3.842$ **5.087**

30. $3.2 + 1.23$ **4.43**

31. $0.889 - 0.3$ **0.589**

32. $22.22 + 1.475$ **23.695**

33. $10 - 0.25$ **9.75**

34. $33.16 - 0.08$ **33.08**

35. $1.254 + 0.5$ **1.754**

36. $44.698 - 14.903$ **29.795**

37. $10 - 0.005$ **9.995**

38. $722.86 + 0.024$ **722.884**

39. $100.211 + 8.004$ **108.215**

40. $86.124 + 32.822$ **118.946**

41. $6.9 + 1.1$ **8**

42. $75 - 0.24$ **74.76**

43. $822.003 + 0.22$ **822.223**

44. $84.98 + 0.129$ **85.109**

45. $3.2 - 1.3$ **1.9**

46. $35.009 + 3.6$ **38.609**

47. $800.972 + 0.4$ **801.372**

48. $125.011 - 2.344$ **122.667**

49. $0.8 + 1.2$ **2**

50. $0.1 + 0.2$ **0.3**

Basic Skills

Multiplying Decimals

1. $\begin{array}{r} 5.08 \\ \times 0.19 \\ \hline \end{array}$ **0.9652**

2. $\begin{array}{r} 15.8 \\ \times \quad 11 \\ \hline \end{array}$ **173.8**

3. $\begin{array}{r} 1.6 \\ \times 1.6 \\ \hline \end{array}$ **2.56**

4. $\begin{array}{r} 3.5 \\ \times 1.5 \\ \hline \end{array}$ **5.25**

5. $\begin{array}{r} 88 \\ \times 2.5 \\ \hline \end{array}$ **220**

6. $\begin{array}{r} 99 \\ \times 1.1 \\ \hline \end{array}$ **108.9**

7. $\begin{array}{r} 0.042 \\ \times \quad 6 \\ \hline \end{array}$ **0.252**

8. $\begin{array}{r} 16.8 \\ \times \ 2.2 \\ \hline \end{array}$ **36.96**

9. $\begin{array}{r} 33 \\ \times 1.2 \\ \hline \end{array}$ **39.6**

10. $\begin{array}{r} 1.25 \\ \times 1.33 \\ \hline \end{array}$ **1.6625**

11. $\begin{array}{r} 1.23 \\ \times \ 8.8 \\ \hline \end{array}$ **10.824**

12. $\begin{array}{r} 18.9 \\ \times \ 0.8 \\ \hline \end{array}$ **15.12**

13. $\begin{array}{r} 100 \\ \times \ .04 \\ \hline \end{array}$ **4**

14. $\begin{array}{r} 4.32 \\ \times 1.23 \\ \hline \end{array}$ **5.3136**

15. $\begin{array}{r} 3.6 \\ \times 1.2 \\ \hline \end{array}$ **4.32**

16. $\begin{array}{r} 8.2 \\ \times 3.9 \\ \hline \end{array}$ **31.98**

17. $\begin{array}{r} 0.6 \\ \times \quad 2 \\ \hline \end{array}$ **1.2**

18. $\begin{array}{r} 3.2 \\ \times 0.8 \\ \hline \end{array}$ **2.56**

19. $\begin{array}{r} 43.2 \\ \times 0.13 \\ \hline \end{array}$ **5.616**

20. $\begin{array}{r} 68 \\ \times 1.9 \\ \hline \end{array}$ **129.2**

21. 2×0.3 **0.6**

22. 0.4×3.8 **1.52**

23. 9×0.5 **4.5**

24. 0.3×1.2 **0.36**

25. 1.88×1.11 **2.0868**

26. $33 \times .03$ **0.99**

27. 0.003×482 **1.446**

28. 5×0.9 **4.5**

29. 0.4×16 **6.4**

30. 1.23×3 **3.69**

31. 0.8×1 **0.8**

32. 36×0.46 **16.56**

33. 0.5×1.6 **0.8**

34. 200×0.004 **0.8**

35. 0.7×18 **12.6**

36. 18×0.04 **0.72**

37. 12.2×12.4 **151.28**

38. 4.3×2.8 **12.04**

39. 800×0.8 **640**

40. 125×1.29 **161.25**

41. 8×0.3 **2.4**

42. 4×0.4 **1.6**

43. 0.3×2.3 **0.69**

44. 0.23×0.2 **0.046**

45. 380×0.125 **47.5**

46. 0.004×2 **0.008**

47. 38.3×29.1 **1114.53**

48. 0.44×0.5 **0.22**

49. 34.2×80.1 **2739.42**

50. 42×0.17 **7.14**

Basic Skills

Dividing Decimals

1. $0.3\overline{)9.81}$ 32.7
2. $12\overline{)0.12}$ 0.01
3. $3.2\overline{)5.76}$ 1.8
4. $0.22\overline{)0.0132}$ 0.06
5. $0.04\overline{)0.008}$ 0.2
6. $3.18\overline{)0.636}$ 0.2
7. $0.2\overline{)8.24}$ 41.2
8. $82.3\overline{)823}$ 10
9. $49.92\overline{)803.712}$ 16.1
10. $100\overline{)0.01}$ 0.0001
11. $13.8\overline{)131.1}$ 9.5
12. $10.81\overline{)363.216}$ 33.6
13. $74.9\overline{)5.992}$ 0.08
14. $0.5\overline{)85}$ 170
15. $1.9\overline{)38.57}$ 20.3
16. $100\overline{)8.235}$ 0.08235
17. $64.80\overline{)25920}$ 400
18. $19.2\overline{)4.416}$ 0.23
19. $8.43\overline{)0.02529}$ 0.003
20. $12.02\overline{)24.04}$ 2
21. $812 \div 0.4$ **2030**
22. $0.34 \div 0.2$ **1.7**
23. $1680.042 \div 44.2$ **38.01**
24. $90.175 \div 2.5$ **36.07**
25. $39.95 \div 799$ **0.05**
26. $88.8 \div 444$ **0.2**
27. $613.8 \div 66$ **9.3**
28. $2445.3 \div 33$ **74.1**
29. $500 \div 0.10$ **5000**
30. $44.82 \div 45$ **0.996**
31. $0.01197 \div 3.99$ **0.003**
32. $2.232 \div 0.036$ **62**
33. $14.4 \div 0.12$ **120**
34. $4.6848 \div 0.366$ **12.8**
35. $2.475 \div 0.03$ **82.5**
36. $45 \div 0.09$ **500**
37. $180 \div 0.36$ **500**
38. $97.812 \div 1.1$ **88.92**
39. $23 \div 0.023$ **1,000**
40. $20.24 \div 2.3$ **8.8**
41. $0.004 \div 0.0002$ **20**
42. $10.557 \div 0.23$ **45.9**
43. $485.76 \div 8.8$ **55.2**
44. $493.19 \div 33.1$ **14.9**

EXTRA PRACTICE

Basic Skills

Adding and Subtracting Fractions

1. $\frac{17}{5} - \frac{2}{5}$ **3**

2. $\frac{1}{10} + \frac{1}{6}$ $\mathbf{\frac{4}{15}}$

3. $\frac{1}{32} + \frac{2}{3}$ $\mathbf{\frac{67}{96}}$

4. $\frac{4}{5} - \frac{1}{3}$ $\mathbf{\frac{7}{15}}$

5. $\frac{3}{7} + \frac{1}{4}$ $\mathbf{\frac{19}{28}}$

6. $\frac{2}{25} + \frac{10}{30}$ $\mathbf{\frac{31}{75}}$

7. $\frac{17}{20} - \frac{3}{10}$ $\mathbf{\frac{11}{20}}$

8. $\frac{10}{11} + \frac{1}{2}$ $\mathbf{1\frac{9}{22}}$

9. $\frac{9}{11} - \frac{2}{11}$ $\mathbf{\frac{7}{11}}$

10. $\frac{3}{4} - \frac{1}{2}$ $\mathbf{\frac{1}{4}}$

11. $\frac{10}{11} - \frac{1}{2}$ $\mathbf{\frac{9}{22}}$

12. $\frac{1}{2} - \frac{1}{3}$ $\mathbf{\frac{1}{6}}$

13. $\frac{6}{7} - \frac{2}{3}$ $\mathbf{\frac{4}{21}}$

14. $\frac{4}{5} - \frac{1}{5}$ $\mathbf{\frac{3}{5}}$

15. $\frac{14}{45} - \frac{3}{10}$ $\mathbf{\frac{1}{90}}$

16. $\frac{3}{8} - \frac{2}{8}$ $\mathbf{\frac{1}{8}}$

17. $\frac{7}{100} + \frac{3}{100}$ $\mathbf{\frac{1}{10}}$

18. $\frac{3}{10} - \frac{1}{5}$ $\mathbf{\frac{1}{10}}$

19. $\frac{8}{14} + \frac{2}{5}$ $\mathbf{\frac{34}{35}}$

20. $\frac{3}{10} + \frac{5}{16}$ $\mathbf{\frac{49}{80}}$

21. $\frac{7}{22} - \frac{1}{11}$ $\mathbf{\frac{5}{22}}$

22. $\frac{3}{4} - \frac{1}{4}$ $\mathbf{\frac{1}{2}}$

23. $\frac{18}{50} - \frac{1}{25}$ $\mathbf{\frac{8}{25}}$

24. $\frac{6}{13} + \frac{4}{13}$ $\mathbf{\frac{10}{13}}$

25. $\frac{6}{7} - \frac{1}{7}$ $\mathbf{\frac{5}{7}}$

26. $\frac{5}{46} + \frac{4}{23}$ $\mathbf{\frac{13}{46}}$

27. $\frac{1}{12} + \frac{1}{6}$ $\mathbf{\frac{1}{4}}$

28. $\frac{1}{99} + \frac{3}{99}$ $\mathbf{\frac{4}{99}}$

29. $\frac{5}{90} - \frac{1}{30}$ $\mathbf{\frac{1}{45}}$

30. $\frac{8}{15} + \frac{4}{15}$ $\mathbf{\frac{4}{5}}$

31. $\frac{4}{5} - \frac{1}{25}$ $\mathbf{\frac{19}{25}}$

32. $\frac{1}{6} + \frac{2}{6}$ $\mathbf{\frac{1}{2}}$

33. $\frac{11}{12} - \frac{1}{2}$ $\mathbf{\frac{5}{12}}$

34. $\frac{1}{3} + \frac{2}{3}$ **1**

35. $\frac{1}{6} + \frac{2}{3}$ $\mathbf{\frac{5}{6}}$

36. $\frac{1}{3} + \frac{4}{9}$ $\mathbf{\frac{7}{9}}$

37. $\frac{3}{4} + \frac{1}{12}$ $\mathbf{\frac{5}{6}}$

38. $\frac{1}{20} - \frac{1}{100}$ $\mathbf{\frac{1}{25}}$

39. $\frac{1}{8} + \frac{2}{3}$ $\mathbf{\frac{19}{24}}$

40. $\frac{99}{100} - \frac{24}{25}$ $\mathbf{\frac{3}{100}}$

Basic Skills

Multiplying Fractions

1. $\frac{1}{3} \times \frac{1}{6}$ $\frac{1}{18}$
2. $\frac{3}{4} \times \frac{2}{3}$ $\frac{1}{2}$
3. $\frac{10}{5} \times \frac{5}{6}$ $1\frac{2}{3}$
4. $\frac{1}{2} \times \frac{4}{5}$ $\frac{2}{5}$
5. $120 \times \frac{3}{10}$ 36
6. $144 \times \frac{3}{12}$ 36
7. $\frac{6}{11} \times \frac{121}{3}$ 22
8. $\frac{4}{5} \times \frac{20}{2}$ 8
9. $\frac{1}{4} \times 30$ $7\frac{1}{2}$
10. $\frac{1}{3} \times \frac{1}{2}$ $\frac{1}{6}$
11. $\frac{3}{8} \times \frac{10}{21}$ $\frac{5}{28}$
12. $\frac{18}{3} \times \frac{2}{9}$ $1\frac{1}{3}$
13. $\frac{15}{7} \times \frac{3}{2}$ $3\frac{3}{14}$
14. $\frac{4}{100} \times \frac{5}{6}$ $\frac{1}{30}$
15. $\frac{11}{17} \times \frac{1}{2}$ $\frac{11}{34}$
16. $\frac{12}{13} \times \frac{39}{6}$ 6
17. $\frac{6}{7} \times \frac{42}{3}$ 12
18. $\frac{3}{19} \times \frac{19}{27}$ $\frac{1}{9}$
19. $\frac{3}{40} \times \frac{4}{9}$ $\frac{1}{30}$
20. $36 \times \frac{1}{6}$ 6
21. $\frac{18}{25} \times \frac{10}{90}$ $\frac{2}{25}$
22. $\frac{1}{3} \times \frac{3}{4}$ $\frac{1}{4}$
23. $\frac{1}{8} \times 64$ 8
24. $\frac{3}{2} \times \frac{4}{9}$ $\frac{2}{3}$
25. $\frac{48}{50} \times \frac{3}{2}$ $1\frac{11}{25}$
26. $\frac{102}{121} \times \frac{11}{51}$ $\frac{2}{11}$
27. $\frac{1}{2} \times \frac{4}{7}$ $\frac{2}{7}$
28. $\frac{80}{90} \times \frac{9}{10}$ $\frac{4}{5}$
29. $\frac{1}{5} \times 25$ 5
30. $\frac{8}{9} \times \frac{81}{4}$ 18
31. $\frac{64}{2} \times \frac{2}{18}$ $3\frac{5}{9}$
32. $5 \times \frac{3}{4}$ $3\frac{3}{4}$
33. $\frac{36}{38} \times \frac{76}{12}$ 6
34. $\frac{32}{37} \times \frac{1}{8}$ $\frac{4}{37}$
35. $\frac{40}{55} \times \frac{5}{10}$ $\frac{4}{11}$
36. $9 \times \frac{1}{3}$ 3
37. $\frac{72}{80} \times \frac{3}{4}$ $\frac{27}{40}$
38. $\frac{18}{32} \times \frac{22}{46}$ $\frac{99}{368}$
39. $\frac{3}{8} \times 24$ 9
40. $\frac{82}{85} \times \frac{15}{16}$ $\frac{123}{136}$

EXTRA PRACTICE

Basic Skills

Dividing Fractions

1. $\frac{15}{7} \div \frac{3}{2}$ $1\frac{3}{7}$

2. $5 \div \frac{3}{4}$ $6\frac{2}{3}$

3. $\frac{42}{3} \div \frac{7}{6}$ 12

4. $\frac{3}{19} \div \frac{27}{19}$ $\frac{1}{9}$

5. $\frac{6}{11} \div \frac{3}{121}$ 22

6. $\frac{4}{5} \div \frac{2}{20}$ 8

7. $\frac{3}{40} \div \frac{9}{4}$ $\frac{1}{30}$

8. $9 \div \frac{1}{3}$ 27

9. $\frac{2}{9} \div \frac{3}{18}$ $1\frac{1}{3}$

10. $\frac{1}{6} \div \frac{1}{36}$ 6

11. $\frac{1}{3} \div \frac{3}{4}$ $\frac{4}{9}$

12. $\frac{80}{9} \div \frac{10}{9}$ 8

13. $\frac{10}{90} \div \frac{25}{18}$ $\frac{2}{25}$

14. $\frac{15}{7} \div \frac{2}{3}$ $3\frac{3}{14}$

15. $\frac{48}{50} \div \frac{2}{3}$ $1\frac{11}{25}$

16. $\frac{1}{8} \div 64$ $\frac{1}{512}$

17. $\frac{12}{13} \div \frac{6}{39}$ 6

18. $\frac{4}{100} \div \frac{6}{5}$ $\frac{1}{30}$

19. $\frac{1}{2} \div \frac{5}{4}$ $\frac{2}{5}$

20. $\frac{4}{9} \div \frac{2}{3}$ $\frac{2}{3}$

21. $\frac{64}{4} \div \frac{18}{4}$ $3\frac{5}{9}$

22. $\frac{11}{17} \div 2$ $\frac{11}{34}$

23. $\frac{3}{12} \div \frac{1}{144}$ 36

24. $\frac{1}{4} \div \frac{1}{30}$ $7\frac{1}{2}$

25. $5 \div \frac{4}{3}$ $3\frac{3}{4}$

26. $\frac{3}{10} \div \frac{1}{120}$ 36

27. $\frac{10}{5} \div \frac{6}{5}$ $1\frac{2}{3}$

28. $\frac{1}{3} \div \frac{1}{6}$ 2

29. $\frac{3}{4} \div \frac{2}{3}$ $1\frac{1}{8}$

30. $24 \div \frac{3}{8}$ 64

31. $\frac{1}{2} \div \frac{5}{4}$ $\frac{2}{5}$

32. $\frac{1}{5} \div 25$ $\frac{1}{125}$

33. $\frac{36}{38} \div \frac{12}{76}$ 6

34. $\frac{8}{9} \div \frac{4}{81}$ 18

35. $\frac{110}{121} \div \frac{50}{11}$ $\frac{1}{5}$

36. $\frac{1}{3} \div 2$ $\frac{1}{6}$

37. $\frac{1}{3} \div \frac{1}{9}$ 3

38. $24 \div \frac{2}{3}$ 36

39. $\frac{1}{25} \div 5$ $\frac{1}{125}$

40. $\frac{3}{8} \div \frac{21}{10}$ $\frac{5}{28}$

Extra Practice

Lesson 1-1 *(Pages 4–7)*

Use the four-step plan to solve each problem.

1. The Gonzales family rode their bicycles for 10 miles to the campground. The ride back was along a different route for 13 miles. How many miles did they ride in all? **23 miles**
2. A farmer planted 405 acres of land with 71,685 corn plants. How many plants were planted per acre? **177 plants**
3. A group of 251 people is eating dinner at a school fundraiser. If each person pays \$4.00 for their meal, how much money is raised? **\$1004.00**
4. When Marcy calls home from college, she talks ten minutes per call for 3 calls per week. How many minutes does she call in a 15-week semester? **450 minutes**

Lesson 1-2 *(Pages 8–10)*

Evaluate each expression.

1. $14 - 5 + 7$ **16**
2. $12 + 10 - 5 - 6$ **11**
3. $50 - 6 + 12 + 4$ **60**
4. $12 - 2 \cdot 3$ **6**
5. $16 + 4 \times 5$ **36**
6. $5 + 3 \times 4 - 7$ **10**
7. $2 \times 3 + 9 \times 2$ **24**
8. $6 \cdot 8 + 4 \div 2$ **50**
9. $7 \times 6 - 14$ **28**
10. $8 + 12 \times 4 \div 8$ **14**
11. $13 - 6 \times 2 + 1$ **2**
12. $80 \div 10 \times 8$ **64**
13. $1 + 2 + 3 + 4$ **10**
14. $1 \cdot 2 \cdot 3 \cdot 4$ **24**
15. $6 + 6 \times 6$ **42**
16. $14 - 2 \times 7 + 0$ **0**
17. $156 - 6 \times 0$ **156**
18. $30 - 14 \cdot 2 + 8$ **10**

Lesson 1-3 *(Pages 12–15)*

Evaluate each expression if $a = 3$, $b = 4$, and $c = 12$.

1. $a + b$ **7**
2. $c - a$ **9**
3. $a + b + c$ **19**
4. $b - a$ **1**
5. $c - a \times b$ **0**
6. $a + 2 \times b$ **11**
7. $b + c \div 2$ **10**
8. ab **12**
9. $a + 3b$ **15**
10. $a + c \div 6$ **5**
11. $25 + c \div b$ **28**
12. abc **144**
13. $2(a + b) \div 7$ **2**
14. $2c \div b$ **6**
15. $144 - abc$ **0**
16. $2ab$ **24**
17. $c \div a + 10$ **14**
18. $9b \div 3$ **12**
19. $2b - a$ **5**
20. ac **36**

Lesson 1-4 *(Pages 17–20)*

Write each power as a product of the same factor.

1. 13^4 **13 · 13 · 13 · 13**
2. 9^6 **9 · 9 · 9 · 9 · 9 · 9**
3. $2^3 \cdot 3^2$ **2 · 2 · 2 · 3 · 3**
4. x^5 **x · x · x · x · x**
5. 169^3 **169 · 169 · 169**
6. $13{,}410^2$ **13,410 · 13,410**

Write each product using exponents.

7. $2 \cdot 2 \cdot 2 \cdot 2 \cdot 2$ **2^5**
8. $6 \cdot 6 \cdot 6 \cdot 7 \cdot 7$ **$6^3 \cdot 7^2$**
9. $9 \cdot 9 \cdot 9 \cdot 9 \cdot 9 \cdot 9 \cdot 10$ **$9^6 \cdot 10$**
10. $k \cdot k \cdot k \cdot \ell \cdot \ell \cdot \ell$ **$k^3 \cdot \ell^3$**
11. $14 \cdot 14 \cdot 6$ **$14^2 \cdot 6$**
12. $3 \cdot 3 \cdot 3 \cdot 3 \cdot y \cdot y$ **$3^4 \cdot y^2$**

Evaluate each expression.

13. 5^6 **15,625**
14. 17^3 **4,913**
15. 2^{12} **4,096**
16. $3^5 \cdot 2^3$ **1,944**
17. $6^4 \cdot 3$ **3,888**
18. $2^2 \cdot 3^2 \cdot 4^2$ **576**
19. 176^2 **30,976**
20. $6 \cdot 4^3$ **384**
21. five squared **25**
22. 2 to the fifth power **32**
23. 4 cubed **64**

Lesson 1-5 *(Pages 21–23)*

Solve each equation.

1. $b + 7 = 12$ **5**
2. $a + 3 = 15$ **12**
3. $s + 10 = 23$ **13**
4. $9 + n = 13$ **4**
5. $20 = 24 - n$ **4**
6. $4x = 36$ **9**
7. $2y = 10$ **5**
8. $15 = 5h$ **3**
9. $j \div 3 = 2$ **6**
10. $14 = w - 4$ **18**
11. $24 \div k = 6$ **4**
12. $b - 3 = 12$ **15**
13. $c \div 10 = 8$ **80**
14. $y \div 2 = 8$ **16**
15. $6 = t \div 5$ **30**
16. $42 = 6n$ **7**
17. $14 + m = 24$ **10**
18. $g - 3 = 10$ **13**
19. $7 + a = 10$ **3**
20. $3y = 39$ **13**
21. $\frac{f}{2} = 12$ **24**
22. $16 = 4v$ **4**
23. $81 = 80 + a$ **1**
24. $9 = \frac{72}{x}$ **8**

Lesson 1-6 *(Pages 24–27)*

Draw the next two figures that continue each pattern.

1. 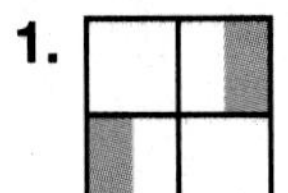 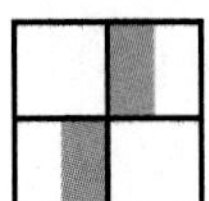 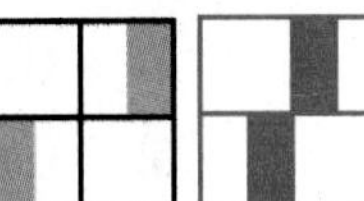 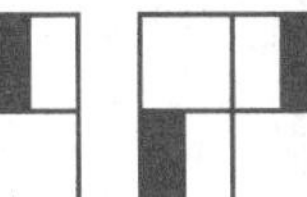 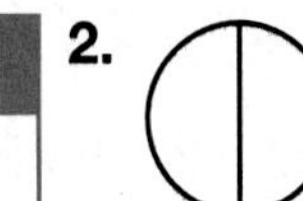

2. 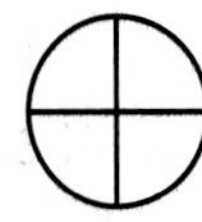   

3. 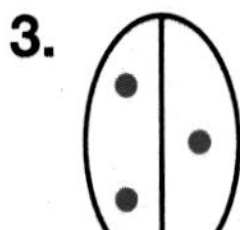 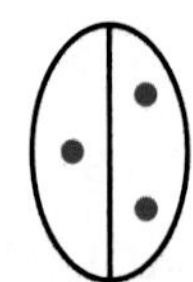 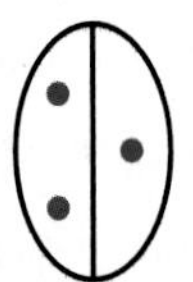 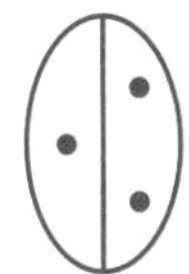 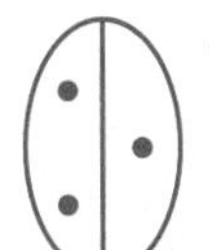

4. 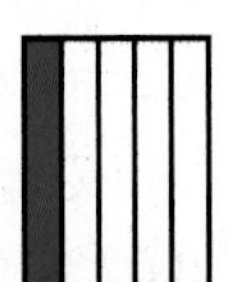 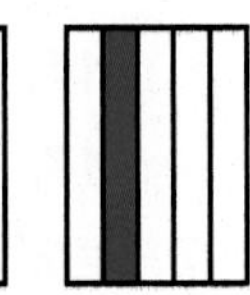 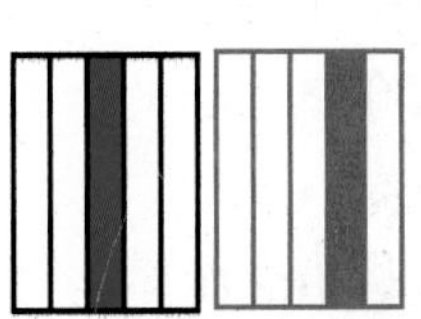 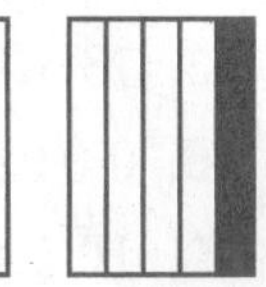

EXTRA PRACTICE

Lesson 1-7 *(Pages 30–33)*

Find the area of each rectangle or parallelogram.

1. 7 cm; 2 cm — 14 cm²

2. 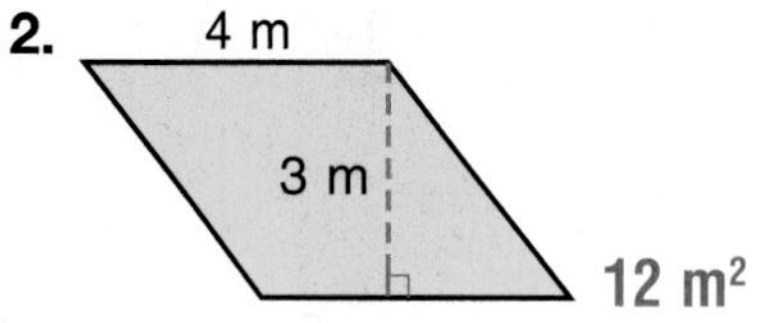

12 m²

3. 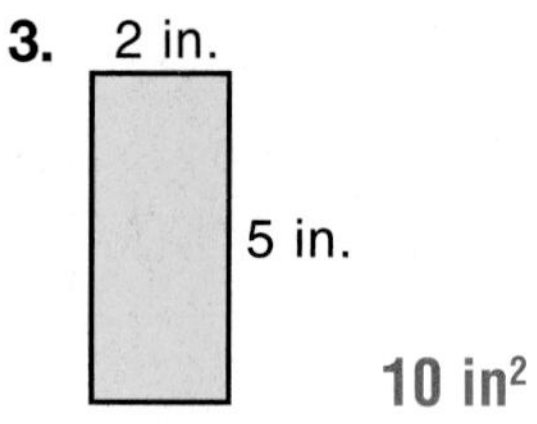

10 in²

4. 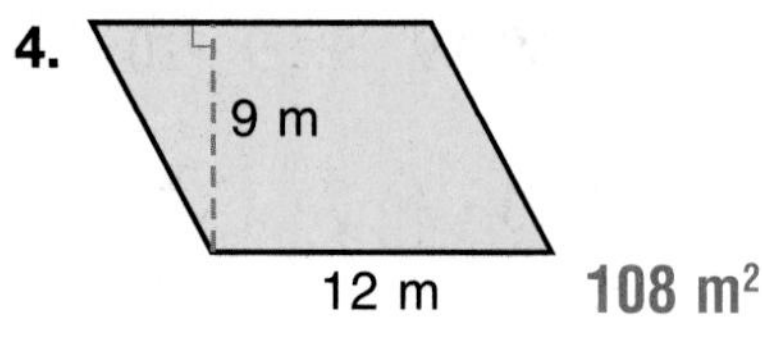

108 m²

5. 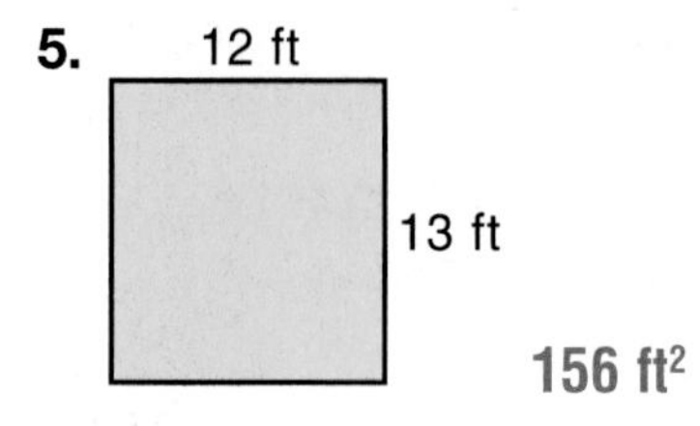

156 ft²

6. 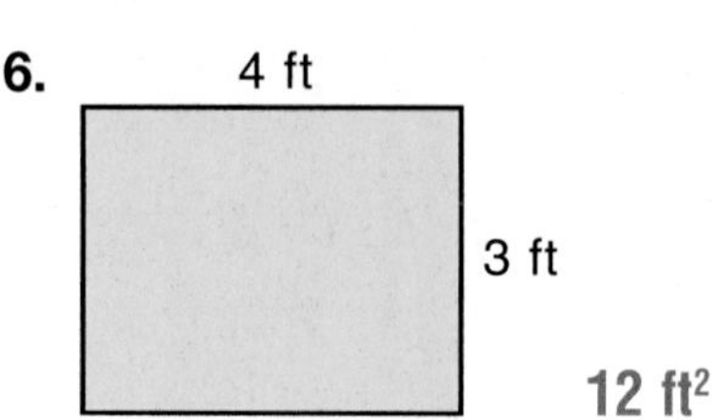

12 ft²

7. rectangle: ℓ, 19 m; w, 6 m **114 m²**

8. parallelogram: b, 15 m; h, 12 m **180 m²**

9. rectangle: ℓ, 8 m; w, 5 m **40 m²**

Lesson 1-7B *(Pages 34–35)*

Solve.

1. A trip from Cleveland to Columbus is 120 miles. If 5 gallons of gasoline are used, how many miles per gallon is this? **24 mpg**

2. A national debate tournament had 2,673 students registered. The tournament director had to assign 336 students per hotel. To how many different hotels did the director have to assign the students? **8 hotels**

3. During a political campaign, each of 125 persons donated $100. How much money was donated? **$12,500**

4. Marnie is planting a garden that is 18 feet long and 12 feet wide. How many feet of fencing will be needed to enclose the entire garden? **60 feet**

5. If a bag of fertilizer feeds 75 square feet of garden, how many bags will Marnie need for the garden in Problem 4? **3 bags**

Lesson 2-1 *(Pages 44–46)*

Replace each ● with <, >, or = to make a true sentence.

1. 0.36 ● 0.63 <
2. 1.74 ● 1.7 >
3. 4.03 ● 4.003 >
4. 0.06 ● 0.066 <
5. 10.5 ● 10.05 >
6. 3.0 ● 3 =
7. 5.632 ● 5.623 >
8. 0.423 ● 0.5 <
9. 2.020 ● 2.202 <
10. 0.93 ● 0.9 >
11. 0.205 ● 0.025 >
12. 0.46 ● 0.49 <
13. 13.100 ● 13.1 =
14. 6.25 ● 6.20 >
15. 9.99 ● 9.099 >
16. 0.030 ● 0.03 =
17. 0.062 ● 0.62 <
18. 1.14 ● 1.09 >
19. 10.1 ● 100.0 <
20. 0.02 ● 0.002 >
21. 2.101 ● 2.11 <

Lesson 2-2 *(Pages 47–49)*

Round each number to the place indicated.

1. 5.64; tenth **5.6**
2. 0.2625; hundredth **0.26**
3. 0.45695; thousandth **0.457**
4. 6.249; tenth **6.2**
5. 0.00263; thousandth **0.003**
6. 758.997; hundredth **759.00**

Round each number to the underlined place-value position.

7. $32.65\underline{8}2$ **32.658**
8. $\underline{0}.025$ **0**
9. $1.00\underline{4}9$ **1.005**
10. $9.\underline{2}5$ **9.3**
11. $67.4\underline{9}2$ **67.49**
12. $25.\underline{1}9$ **25.2**
13. $26.\underline{9}6$ **27.0**
14. $4.0\underline{0}65$ **4.01**
15. $26.96\underline{6}6$ **26.967**
16. $1.\underline{2}499999$ **1.2**
17. $2.0\underline{1}2$ **2.01**
18. $1\underline{6}.569$ **17**

Lesson 2-3 *(Pages 50–53)*

Estimate by rounding. **Sample answers given.**

1. $0.245 + 0.256$ — $0.2 + 0.2 = 0.4$
2. $2.45698 - 1.26589$ — $2 - 1 = 1$
3. $0.5962 + 1.2598$ — $1 + 1 = 2$
4. $17.985 - 9.001$ — $18 - 9 = 9$
5. 8.5×9.1 — $9 \times 9 = 81$
6. 12.9568×6.1563 — $13 \times 6 = 78$
7. 9.652×6.2 — $10 \times 6 = 60$
8. 25.49862×4.2136 — $25 \times 4 = 100$
9. $3\overline{)11.75}$ — $12 \div 3 = 4$
10. $4.1\overline{)16.123}$ — $16 \div 4 = 4$
11. $2.7\overline{)29.5}$ — $30 \div 3 = 10$
12. $8.14\overline{)81.27}$ — $80 \div 8 = 10$

Estimate by clustering.

13. $1.12 + 0.9865 + 1.023 + 0.89 + 0.99 + 1.03569$ **6(1) = 6**
14. $82.1 + 79.3 + 81.5 + 79 + 80 + 81.256$ **6(80) = 480**

Lesson 2-3B *(Pages 54–55)*

Solve.

1. Mr. Ludwig eats food that has 3,115 calories in an average day. When he multiplied the number of calories he eats per day by the number of days in a week, the calculator showed 218,050. Is this answer reasonable? Explain. **No; 3,000 × 7 = 21,000.**
2. You need to buy 3 cans of tomato soup at 79¢ each, a box of crackers at $1.89, and a gallon of orange juice at $2.39. Should you take $10.00 with you to the store or will $5 be enough? **$10**
3. When Nia received her work schedule for the week, she multiplied the 28 hours she was scheduled to work by her wage of $5.15 per hour. Her calculator showed that her pay for the week should be $112.75. Is this answer reasonable? **No; 30 × 5 = 150.**
4. A newspaper article reported that a running back ran for 182 yards in 17 carries during the football game. Jamison determined that this was about 10 yards per carry. Is his answer reasonable? **Yes; 200 ÷ 20 = 10.**
5. There were three recycling centers set up for the Wyandot Junior High aluminum can drive. One center collected 867 pounds of cans, the second collected 1,236 pounds of cans, and the third collected 1,827 pounds of cans. The Junior High reported that they had collected 4,000 pounds of cans. Is this answer reasonable? **Yes; 1,000 + 1,000 + 2,000 = 4,000.**

Lesson 2-4 *(Pages 56–59)*

Multiply.

1. 9.6×10.5 **100.8**
2. 3.2×0.1 **0.32**
3. 10.5×9.6 **100.8**
4. 5.42×0.21 **1.1382**
5. 7.42×0.2 **1.484**
6. 0.001×0.02 **0.00002**
7. 0.6×542 **325.2**
8. 6.7×5.8 **38.86**
9. 3.24×6.7 **21.708**
10. 9.8×4.62 **45.276**
11. 7.32×9.7 **71.004**
12. 0.008×0.007 **0.000056**
13. 0.0001×56 **0.0056**
14. 4.5×0.2 **0.9**
15. 9.6×2.3 **22.08**
16. 5.63×8.1 **45.603**
17. 10.35×9.1 **94.185**
18. 28.2×3.9 **109.98**
19. 102.13×1.221 **124.70073**
20. 2.02×1.25 **2.525**
21. 8.37×89.6 **749.952**

Lesson 2-5 *(Pages 61–63)*

Multiply mentally.

1. 1.2×10 **12**
2. 0.23×100 **23**
3. $1.235 \times 1{,}000$ **1,235**
4. 1.2×10^3 **1,200**
5. 3.97×0.1 **0.397**
6. 3.56×10^2 **356**
7. 123.92×0.01 **1.2392**
8. 95.23×10^1 **952.3**
9. 76.425×0.1 **7.6425**
10. $1.0056 \times 10{,}000$ **10,056**
11. 4.7×10^0 **4.7**
12. 9.6×10^0 **9.6**

Solve each equation.

13. $1.47 \times 10^3 = x$ **1,470**
14. $y = 0.82 \times 1{,}000$ **820**
15. $m = 2.8 \times 0.1$ **0.28**
16. $h = 15.23 \times 10^4$ **152,300**
17. $53.7 \times 0.01 = y$ **0.537**
18. $0.9 \times 10^0 = w$ **0.9**

Lesson 2-6 *(Pages 66–69)*

Without finding or changing each quotient, change each problem so that the divisor is a whole number.

1. $3.6 \div 0.6$ **36 ÷ 6**
2. $0.36 \div 0.4$ **3.6 ÷ 4**
3. $82 \div 0.4$ **820 ÷ 4**
4. $4.876 \div 0.72$ **487.6 ÷ 72**
5. $0.009 \div 0.03$ **0.9 ÷ 3**
6. $21.8 \div 0.005$ **21800 ÷ 5**

Divide.

7. $7.2 \div 0.4$ **18**
8. $0.76 \div 0.5$ **1.52**
9. $8.4 \div 0.8$ **10.5**
10. $0.23\overline{)2.76}$ **12**
11. $3.2\overline{)8.32}$ **2.6**
12. $0.003\overline{)0.018}$ **6**
13. $51 \div 0.8$ **63.75**
14. $1.826 \div 8.3$ **0.22**
15. $702 \div 6.5$ **108**
16. Round the quotient of 6.51 and 0.8 to the nearest tenth. **8.1**
17. What is \$31.76 divided by 0.7, rounded to the nearest cent? **\$45.37**

Lesson 2-7 *(Pages 70–73)*

Write each repeating decimal using bar notation.

1. 0.3333333.... $0.\overline{3}$
2. 0.121212.... $0.\overline{12}$
3. 4.3151515.... $4.3\overline{15}$
4. 7.023023023.... $7.\overline{023}$
5. 0.544444.... $0.5\overline{4}$
6. 18.75484848.... $18.75\overline{48}$

Express each fraction or mixed number as a decimal. If the decimal is a repeating decimal, use bar notation.

7. $\frac{16}{20}$ 0.8
8. $\frac{25}{100}$ 0.25
9. $1\frac{7}{8}$ 1.875
10. $\frac{1}{6}$ $0.1\overline{6}$
11. $\frac{11}{40}$ 0.275
12. $5\frac{13}{50}$ 5.26
13. $\frac{55}{300}$ $0.18\overline{3}$
14. $\frac{18}{12}$ 1.5

Lesson 2-8 *(Pages 74–76)*

Complete.

1. 400 mm = ____ cm 40
2. 4 km = ____ m 4,000
3. 660 cm = ____ m 6.6
4. 0.3 km = ____ m 300
5. 30 mm = ____ cm 3
6. 84.5 m = ____ km 0.0845
7. ____ m = 54 cm 0.54
8. 18 km = ____ cm 1,800,000
9. ____ mm = 45 cm 450
10. 4 kg = ____ g 4,000
11. 632 mg = ____ g 0.632
12. 4,497 g = ____ kg 4.497
13. ____ mg = 21 g 21,000
14. 61.2 mg = ____ g 0.0612
15. 61 g = ____ mg 61,000
16. ____ mg = 0.51 kg 510,000
17. 0.63 kg = ____ g 630
18. ____ kg = 563 g 0.563

Lesson 2-9 *(Pages 77–79)*

Write each number in scientific notation.

1. 720 7.2×10^2
2. 7,560 7.56×10^3
3. 892 8.92×10^2
4. 1,400 1.4×10^3
5. 91,200 9.12×10^4
6. 51,000 5.1×10^4
7. 145,000 1.45×10^5
8. 90,100 9.01×10^4
9. 123,000,000,000 1.23×10^{11}
10. 4,500 4.5×10^3
11. 20,000 2.0×10^4
12. 1,700,000 1.7×10^6
13. 961 9.61×10^2
14. 10,000,000 1.0×10^7
15. 820,000,000 8.2×10^8
16. 52,000 5.2×10^4
17. 680,000 6.8×10^5

EXTRA PRACTICE

Lesson 3-1 *(Pages 88–91)*

Choose an appropriate scale and interval for each set of data. Make a frequency table.

1.

Length of Time Walking (min.)			
15	30	15	45
45	30	30	60
30	60	15	30
45	45	60	15

2.

Number of Raisins Eaten in Preschool			
40	49	45	49
42	41	45	41
45	41	41	40
41	43	40	41

1–2. See Answer Appendix.

Lesson 3-2A *(Pages 92–93)*

Use the circle graph to solve each problem.

1. What part of the budget is spent on printing? $\frac{1}{2}$
2. How much more money is spent on photography than design? $279.55
3. If the total budget is increased by $200 next year, about how much could be spent on printing? $1,100

Annual Newspaper Budget

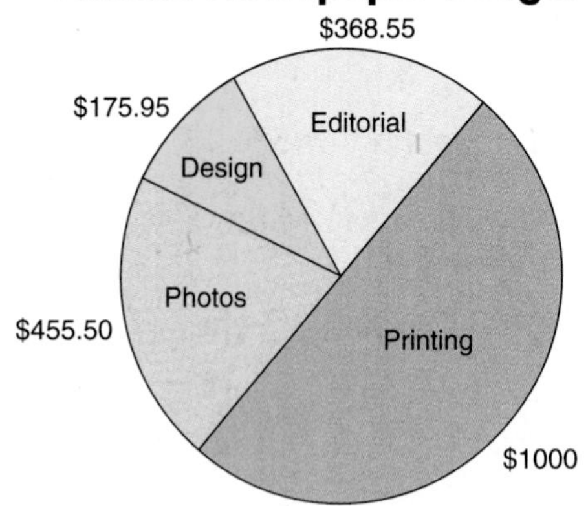

Lesson 3-2 *(Pages 94–97)*

1. Darlene's quiz scores in science have been steadily going up since her parents hired a tutor for her. Based on the graph below, predict what Darlene's score will be on the next quiz. 7

Quiz Scores

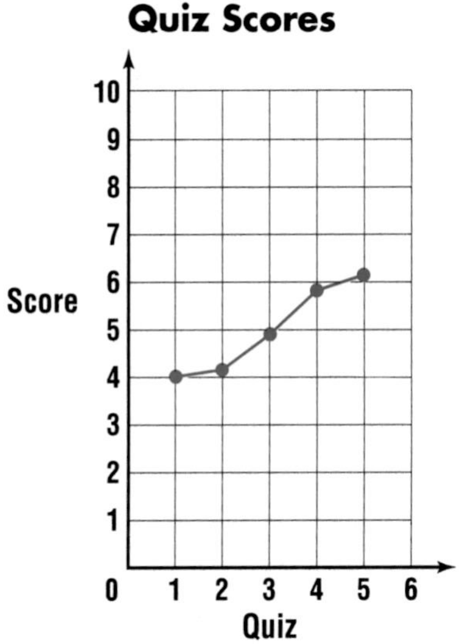

2. A balloon maker asked 100 kids what their favorite color of balloon is. The graph below shows their responses. What color of balloon should he make the most of? blue

Favorite Color of Balloon

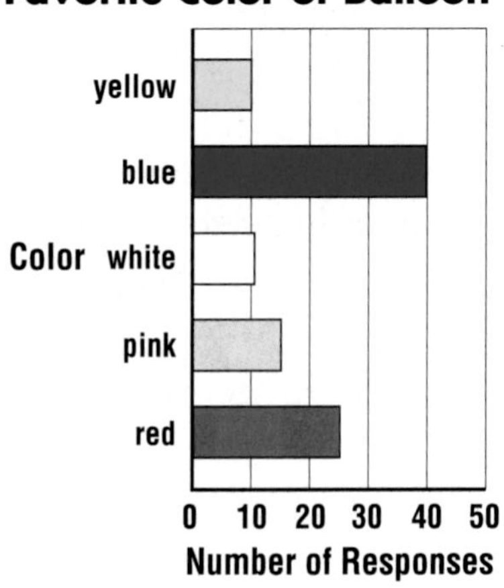

Lesson 3-3 *(Pages 98–101)*

Make a line plot for each set of data.

1. 25, 26, 27, 25, 28, 27, 21, 26, 28, 25

2. 110, 210, 156, 174, 125, 196, 165, 185

3. 600, 650, 700, 600, 625, 675, 450, 650

4. 0.5, 0.6, 0.1, 0.4, 0.8, 0.6, 0.7, 0.5

5. 3, 4, 5, 2, 6, 1, 2, 4, 3, 6, 9, 1, 2, 3, 4

1.
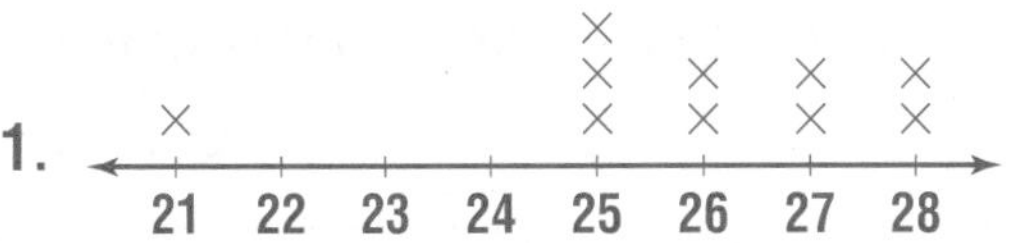

2.
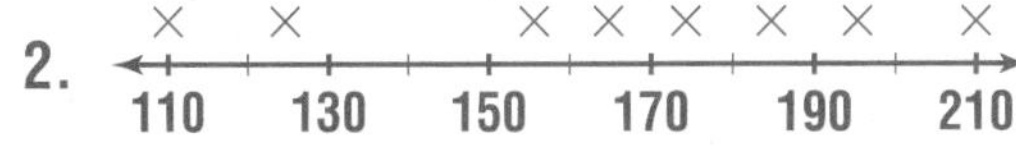

3.

4. 0.1 0.2 0.3 0.4 0.5 0.6 0.7 0.8

5. 1 2 3 4 5 6 7 8 9

Lesson 3-4 *(Pages 102–105)*

Find the mean, mode(s), and median for each set of data. Round answers to the nearest tenth.

1. 1, 5, 9, 1, 2, 5, 8, 2 **4.1; 1, 2, and 5; 3.5**

2. 2, 5, 8, 9, 7, 6, 3, 5 **5.6, 5, 5.5**

3. 1, 2, 1, 2, 2, 1, 2 **1.6, 2, 2**

4. 12, 13, 15, 12, 12, 11 **12.5, 12, 12**

5. 256, 265, 247, 256 **256, 256, 256**

6. 957, 562, 462, 847, 721 **709.8, no mode, 721**

7. 46, 54, 66, 54, 46, 66 **55.3; 46, 54 and 66; 54**

8. 81, 82, 83, 84, 85, 86, 87 **84, no mode, 84**

Lesson 3-5 *(Pages 108–111)*

Write the stems that would be used in a stem-and-leaf plot for each set of data. Then make the stem-and-leaf plot. **1–4. See Answer Appendix.**

1. 23, 15, 39, 68, 57, 42, 51, 52, 41, 18, 29

2. 5, 14, 39, 28, 14, 6, 7, 18, 13, 28, 9, 14

3. 189, 182, 196, 184, 197, 183, 196, 194, 184

4. 71, 82, 84, 95, 76, 92, 83, 74, 81, 75, 96

Lesson 3-6 *(Pages 114–117)*

Use the box-and-whisker plot to answer each question.

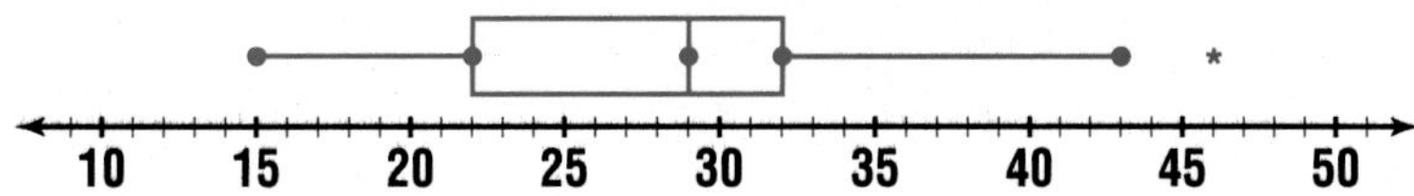

1. What is the median? 29
2. What is the upper quartile? 32
3. What is the lower quartile? 22
4. What is the upper extreme? 43
5. What is the lower extreme? 15
6. What is the interquartile range? 10
7. Name any outliers. 46
8. What fraction of the data fall between 22 and 29? $\frac{1}{4}$

Lesson 3-7 *(Pages 119–121)*

Which graph could be misleading? How are the graphs misleading?

1. Both graphs show pounds of grapes sold to Westview School in one week.
   Graph B is misleading. The change in the vertical scale is misleading.

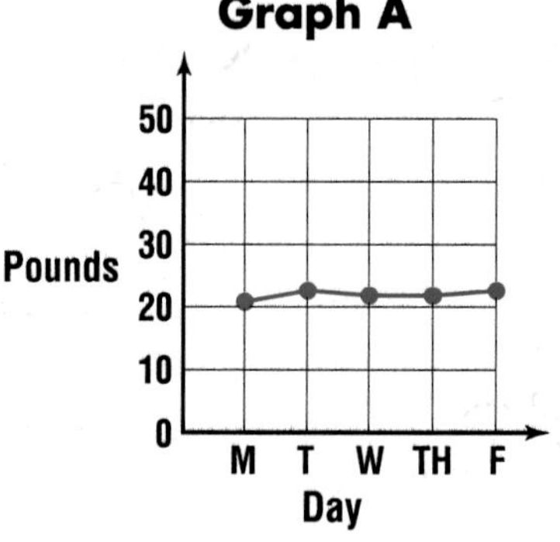

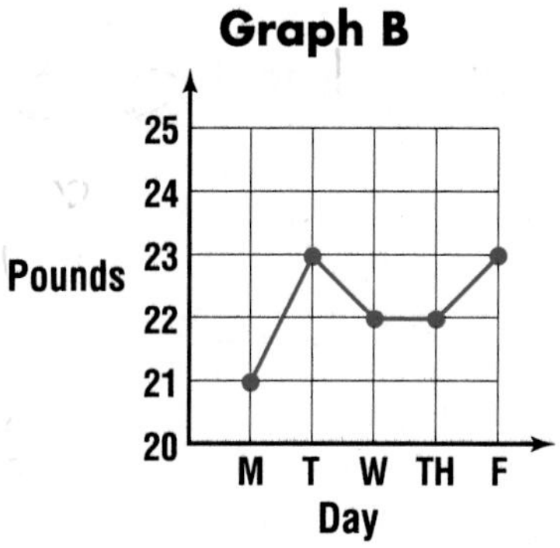

Graph B

Pounds

25 24 23 22 21 20

M T W TH F

Day

2. Both graphs show commissions made by Mai-Lin for a four-week pay period.
   Graph C is misleading. The change in vertical scale makes it seem as if more money is made than really is.

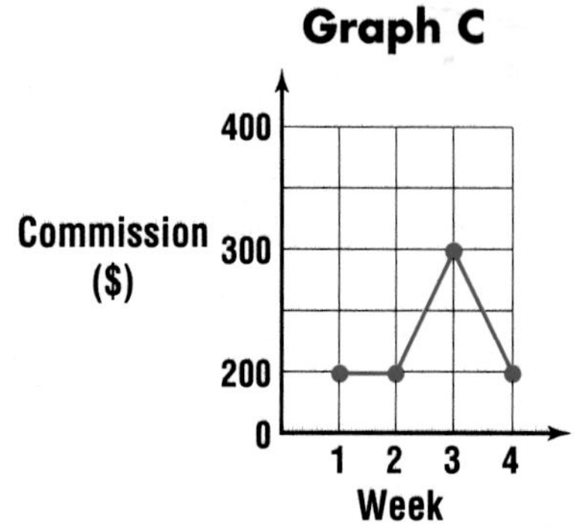

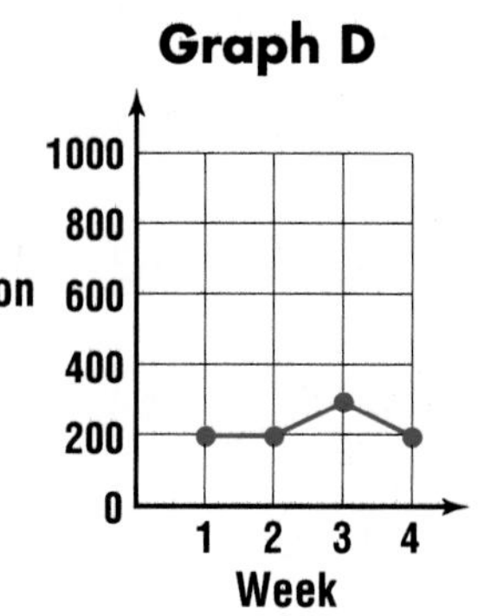

Lesson 4-1 *(Pages 133–136)*

Determine whether the first number is divisible by the second number.

1. 279;3 yes
2. 1,240; 6 no
3. 3,250; 5 yes
4. 835;4 no
5. 5,550; 10 yes
6. 315; 9 yes
7. 777; 6 no
8. 4,214; 3 no
9. 3,012; 2 yes
10. 244; 4 yes
11. 984; 6 yes
12. 1,000; 5 yes

Determine whether each number is divisible by 2, 3, 4, 5, 6, 9, or 10.

13. 453 3
14. 2,225 5
15. 504 2, 3, 4, 6, 9
16. 4,300 2, 4, 5, 10
17. 672 2, 3, 4, 6
18. 8,240 2, 4, 5, 10
19. 111 3
20. 6,232 2, 4
21. 999 3, 9
22. 5,200 2, 4, 5, 10
23. 3,217 none
24. 804 2, 3, 4, 6

Lesson 4-2 *(Pages 138–141)*

Determine whether each number is *composite* or *prime*.

1. 32 composite **2.** 417 composite **3.** 5,212 composite **4.** 2,111 prime

5. 71 prime **6.** 1,005 composite **7.** 239 prime **8.** 3,215 composite

Use a factor tree to find the prime factorization of each number.

9. 81 3^4 **10.** 525 $3 \times 5^2 \times 7$ **11.** 245 5×7^2 **12.** 1,120 $2^5 \times 5 \times 7$

13. 750 $2 \times 3 \times 5^3$ **14.** 2,400 $2^5 \times 3 \times 5^2$ **15.** 914 2×457 **16.** 975 $3 \times 5^2 \times 13$

Use your calculator to find the prime factors of each number. Then write the prime factorization of each number.

17. 423 $3^2 \times 47$ **18.** 972 $2^2 \times 3^5$ **19.** 144 $2^4 \times 3^2$ **20.** 72 $2^3 \times 3^2$

Lesson 4-3 *(Pages 142–145)*

Describe the pattern in each sequence. Identify the sequence as *arithmetic*, *geometric*, or *neither*. Then find the next three terms.

1. 5, 9, 13, 17, ... arithmetic; 21, 25, 29

2. 3, 6, 12, 24, ... geometric; 48, 96, 192

3. 10, 15, 25, 40, ... neither; 60, 85, 115

4. 4.5, 5.4, 6.3, 7.2, ... arithmetic; 8.1, 9.0, 9.9

5. 90, 91, 94, 99, ... neither; 106, 115, 126

6. 0.3, 0.4, 0.5, ... arithmetic; 0.6, 0.7, 0.8

7. 8, 24, 72, 216, ... geometric; 648; 1,944; 5,832

8. 16, 17, 19, 22, ... neither; 26, 31, 37

1–8. See Answer Appendix for patterns.

Create a sequence using each rule. Provide four terms for the sequence beginning with the given number. State whether the sequence is *arithmetic*, *geometric*, or *neither*. 9–13. See Answer Appendix.

9. Add 9 to each term; 1.

10. Multiply each term by 4; 3.

11. Multiply each term by 0.2; 6.

12. Add 16 to each term; 14.

13. Add 1 to the first term, 11 to the second term, 111 to the third term, and so on; 40.

Lesson 4-4A *(Pages 148–149)*

Solve.

1. Jo sees that every third Fibonacci number is even. (F3 = 2, F6 = 8, F9 = 34). Find F30. 832,040

2. Are there any perfect squares (for example: $4 \times 4 = 16$) or perfect cubes (for example: $4 \times 4 \times 4 = 64$) in the first 12 terms of the Fibonacci sequence? If so, name them. Yes; 1, 144; 1, 8

3. Make a list to find the number of 4-person teams that can be formed from a 5-member group. Use the letters A, B, C, D, E to represent the people. 5 different teams are possible.

4. Study the pattern below. List the next three numbers in the pattern. 10, 15, 21

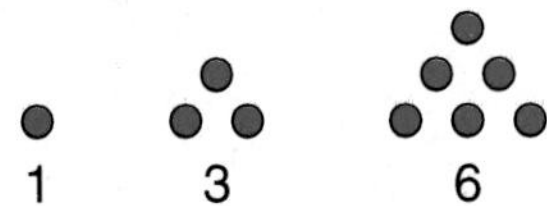

EXTRA PRACTICE

Lesson 4-4 *(Pages 150–153)*

Find the GCF of each set of numbers.

1. 12, 16 4
2. 63, 81 9
3. 225, 500 25
4. 37, 100 1
5. 240, 32 16
6. 640, 412 4
7. 36, 81 9
8. 350, 140 70
9. 72, 170 2
10. 255, 51 51
11. 48, 72 24
12. 86, 200 2
13. 24, 56, 120 8
14. 48, 60, 84 12
15. 32, 80, 96 16
16. 49, 14, 70 7
17. 6, 8, 12 2
18. 33, 55, 77 11
19. 27, 15, 300 3
20. 45, 150, 225 15

Lesson 4-5 *(Pages 154–157)*

Express each fraction or ratio in simplest form.

1. $\frac{14}{28}$ $\frac{1}{2}$
2. 15:25 3:5
3. $\frac{100}{300}$ $\frac{1}{3}$
4. 14:35 2:5
5. 9:51 3:17
6. $\frac{54}{56}$ $\frac{27}{28}$
7. 75:90 5:6
8. $\frac{24}{40}$ $\frac{3}{5}$
9. 180:270 2:3
10. $\frac{312}{390}$ $\frac{4}{5}$
11. 240:448 15:28
12. $\frac{71}{82}$ $\frac{71}{82}$
13. $\frac{333}{900}$ $\frac{37}{100}$
14. 85:255 1:3
15. $\frac{84}{128}$ $\frac{21}{32}$
16. 64:96 2:3

Lesson 4-6 *(Pages 158–160)*

Write a percent to represent the shaded area.

1.
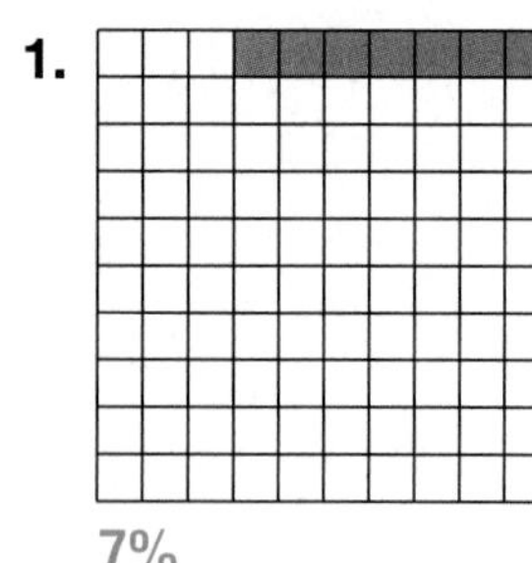
7%

2.
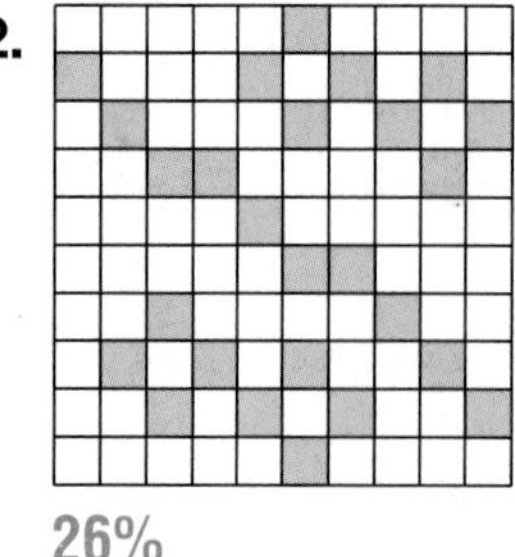
26%

3.
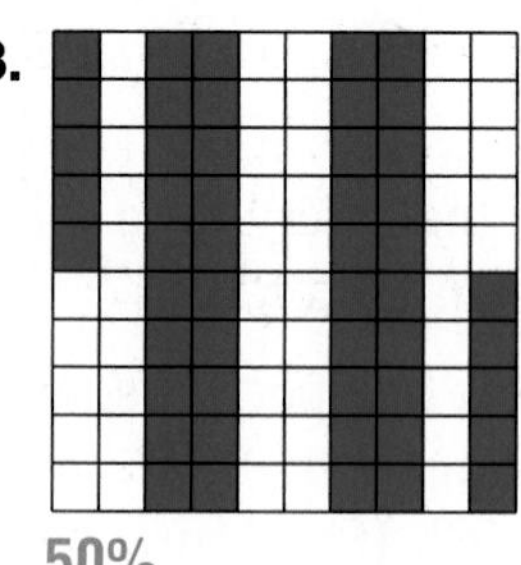
50%

Express each ratio as a percent.

4. 39 out of 100 39%
5. $\frac{23}{100}$ 23%
6. 17:100 17%
7. \$72 per \$100 72%
8. 4 to 100 4%
9. 98 in 100 98%

Lesson 4-7 *(Pages 161–164)*

Express each fraction as a percent.

1. $\frac{1}{2}$ **50%**
2. $\frac{6}{6}$ **100%**
3. $\frac{8}{10}$ **80%**
4. $\frac{3}{5}$ **60%**
5. $\frac{1}{4}$ **25%**
6. $\frac{21}{25}$ **84%**
7. $\frac{16}{100}$ **16%**
8. $\frac{13}{20}$ **65%**
9. $\frac{3}{10}$ **30%**
10. $\frac{17}{20}$ **85%**
11. $\frac{9}{10}$ **90%**
12. $\frac{9}{50}$ **18%**

Express each percent or decimal as a fraction in simplest form.

13. 28% $\frac{7}{25}$
14. 0.10 $\frac{1}{10}$
15. 18% $\frac{9}{50}$
16. 0.02 $\frac{1}{50}$
17. 0.09 $\frac{9}{100}$
18. 36% $\frac{9}{25}$
19. 49% $\frac{49}{100}$
20. 3% $\frac{3}{100}$
21. 0.25 $\frac{1}{4}$
22. 0.98 $\frac{49}{50}$
23. 0.88 $\frac{22}{25}$
24. 50% $\frac{1}{2}$

Lesson 4-8 *(Pages 165–168)*

The spinner shown is equally likely to stop on each of its regions numbered 1 to 8. Find the probability that the spinner will stop on each of the following.

1. an even number $\frac{1}{2}$
2. a prime number $\frac{1}{2}$
3. a factor of 12 $\frac{5}{8}$
4. a composite number $\frac{3}{8}$
5. a number less than 5 $\frac{1}{2}$
6. a factor of 36 $\frac{5}{8}$

A package of balloons contains 5 green, 3 yellow, 4 red, and 8 pink balloons. If you reach in the package and choose one balloon at random, what is the probability that you will select each of the following? Express each ratio as a fraction in simplest form and as a percent.

7. a red balloon $\frac{1}{5}$, **20%**
8. a green balloon $\frac{1}{4}$, **25%**
9. a pink balloon $\frac{2}{5}$, **40%**
10. a yellow balloon $\frac{3}{20}$, **15%**
11. a red or yellow balloon $\frac{7}{20}$, **35%**

Lesson 4-9 *(Pages 169–171)*

Find the LCM of each set of numbers.

1. 4, 9 **36**
2. 6, 16 **48**
3. 3, 8, 14 **168**
4. 24, 36 **72**
5. 48, 84 **336**
6. 12, 18, 28 **252**
7. 8, 9 **72**
8. 49, 56 **392**
9. 42, 66 **462**
10. 15, 39 **195**
11. 32, 80, 96 **480**
12. 56, 64 **448**
13. 24, 42 **168**
14. 250, 80 **2,000**
15. 26, 169 **338**
16. 5, 18, 45 **90**
17. 11, 22, 33 **66**
18. 56, 14, 70 **280**
19. 16, 24 **48**
20. 13, 14 **182**

Lesson 4-10 (Pages 172–175)

Find the LCD for each pair of fractions.

1. $\frac{3}{8}, \frac{2}{3}$ 24
2. $\frac{5}{9}, \frac{7}{12}$ 36
3. $\frac{4}{9}, \frac{8}{15}$ 45
4. $\frac{11}{24}, \frac{17}{42}$ 168
5. $\frac{12}{36}, \frac{15}{42}$ 252
6. $\frac{25}{27}, \frac{43}{81}$ 81
7. $\frac{32}{64}, \frac{15}{48}$ 192
8. $\frac{2}{6}, \frac{14}{15}$ 30

Replace each ● with <, >, or = to make a true sentence.

9. $\frac{7}{9}$ ● $\frac{3}{5}$ $>$
10. $\frac{14}{25}$ ● $\frac{3}{4}$ $<$
11. $\frac{8}{24}$ ● $\frac{20}{60}$ $=$
12. $\frac{5}{12}$ ● $\frac{4}{9}$ $<$
13. $\frac{18}{24}$ ● $\frac{10}{18}$ $>$
14. $\frac{4}{6}$ ● $\frac{5}{9}$ $>$
15. $\frac{11}{49}$ ● $\frac{12}{42}$ $<$
16. $\frac{5}{14}$ ● $\frac{2}{6}$ $>$

Lesson 5-1 (Pages 184–186)

Write an integer for each situation.

1. a gain of 14 points +14
2. a $25 withdrawal −25
3. six degrees below zero −6
4. a loss of 3 pounds −3
5. a loss of 20 yards −20
6. a profit of $16 +16

Write the integer represented by the point for each letter. Then find its opposite and its absolute value.

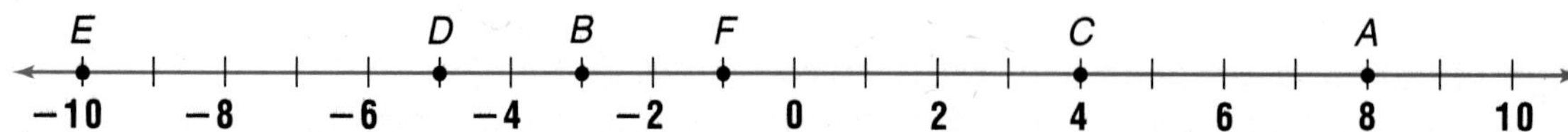

7. *A* 8, −8, 8
8. *B* −3, 3, 3
9. *C* 4, −4, 4
10. *D* −5, 5, 5
11. *E* −10, 10, 10
12. *F* −1, 1, 1

Lesson 5-2 (Pages 188–190)

Replace each ● with < or > to make a true sentence.

1. 7 ● −7 $>$
2. −8 ● 4 $<$
3. −4 ● −9 $>$
4. −3 ● 0 $<$
5. 8 ● 10 $<$
6. −5 ● −4 $<$
7. 6 ● −7 $>$
8. −12 ● −13 $>$

Order the integers from least to greatest.

9. −2, −8, 4, 10, −6, −12
   −12, −8, −6, −2, 4, 10
10. 19, −19, −21, 32, −14, 18
   −21, −19, −14, 18, 19, 32
11. 18, 23, 95, −95, −18, −23, 2
   −95, −23, −18, 2, 18, 23, 95
12. 46, −48, −47, −52, −18, 12
   −52, −48, −47, −18, 12, 46

EXTRA PRACTICE

Lesson 5-3 *(Pages 191–194)*

Name the *x*-coordinate and the *y*-coordinate for each point labeled at the right. Then tell in which quadrant each point lies.

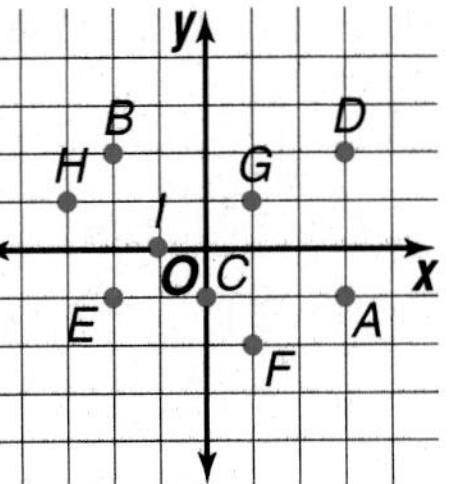

1. A (3, −1), IV **2.** B (−2, 2), II **3.** C (0, −1), *x*-axis

4. D (3, 2), I **5.** E (−2, −1), III **6.** F (1, −2), IV

7. G (1, 1), I **8.** H (−3, 1), II **9.** I (−1, 0), *y*-axis

On graph paper, draw a coordinate plane. Then graph and label each point.

10. $N(-4, 3)$ **11.** $K(2, 5)$ **12.** $W(-6, -2)$ **13.** $X(5, 0)$

14. $Y(4, -4)$ **15.** $M(0, -3)$ **16.** $Z(-2, 0.5)$ **17.** $S(-1, -3)$

10–17. See Answer Appendix.

Lesson 5-4 *(Pages 197–200)*

Solve each equation.

1. $a = -4 + 8$ 4 **2.** $14 + 16 = b$ 30 **3.** $-7 + (-7) = h$ −14

4. $g = -9 + (-6)$ −15 **5.** $-18 + 11 = d$ −7 **6.** $k = -36 + 40$ 4

7. $42 + (-18) = f$ 24 **8.** $-42 + 29 = r$ −13 **9.** $m = 18 + (-32)$ −14

Evaluate each expression if *a* = 6, *b* = −2, and *c* = −6.

10. $-96 + a$ −90 **11.** $b + (-5)$ −7 **12.** $c + (-32)$ −38

13. $a + 98$ 104 **14.** $-120 + b$ −122 **15.** $-120 + c$ −126

16. $5 + b$ 3 **17.** $a + b$ 4 **18.** $c + a$ 0

Lesson 5-5 *(Pages 202–205)*

Solve each equation.

1. $3 - 7 = y$ −4 **2.** $-5 - 4 = w$ −9 **3.** $a = -6 - 2$ −8

4. $r = 8 - 13$ −5 **5.** $6 - (-4) = b$ 10 **6.** $12 - 9 = x$ 3

7. $-2 - 23 = c$ −25 **8.** $z = 63 - 78$ −15 **9.** $a = 0 - (-14)$ 14

Evaluate each expression if *k* = −3, *p* = 6, and *n* = 1.

10. $55 - k$ 58 **11.** $p - 7$ −1 **12.** $n - 15$ −14

13. $n - 12$ −11 **14.** $-51 - p$ −57 **15.** $k - 21$ −24

16. $n - k$ 4 **17.** $-99 - k$ −96 **18.** $p - k$ 9

Lesson 5-6 *(Pages 207–209)*

Solve each equation.

1. $5(-2) = d$ **−10**
2. $a = 6(-4)$ **−24**
3. $4(21) = y$ **84**
4. $-11(-5) = c$ **55**
5. $x = -6(5)$ **−30**
6. $a = -50(0)$ **0**
7. $-5(-5) = z$ **25**
8. $-4(8) = q$ **−32**
9. $b = 3(-13)$ **−39**

Evaluate each expression if $a = -5$, $b = 2$, $c = -3$, and $d = 4$.

10. $-2d$ **−8**
11. $6a$ **−30**
12. $3ab$ **−30**
13. $-12d$ **−48**
14. $-4b^2$ **−16**
15. $-5cd$ **60**
16. a^2 **25**
17. $13ab$ **−130**
18. $-6ac$ **−90**

Lesson 5-7A *(Pages 210–211)*

Solve.

1. Kit received an e-mail message from a Simon in England. After 10 minutes, she forwarded the message to 3 of her friends. After 10 more minutes, each of those friends forwarded the message to 3 more people. If the message was forwarded like this every 10 minutes, how many people received Simon's e-mail message after 40 minutes? **121 people**
2. A display of laundry detergent boxes at Mike's Market is stacked in the shape of a pyramid. There are 2 boxes in the first row, 4 in the second row, 6 in the next row, and so on. The display contains 10 rows of boxes. How many boxes are in the display? **110 boxes**
3. State the pattern and find the next three terms in the sequence 8, 12, 18, 27, … . **multiply by 1.5; 40.5, 60.75, 91.125**
4. Sheri has decided to start an exercise program. She plans to begin by running 4 laps and then doubling her number of laps. Write a sequence showing the number of laps she runs each day for one week. If each lap is $\frac{1}{4}$ mile, is her plan reasonable? Why or why not? **4 laps, 8 laps, 16 laps, 32 laps, 64 laps, 128 laps, 256 laps; No; on the last day she would have to run 64 miles.**

Lesson 5-7 *(Pages 212–214)*

Solve each equation.

1. $a = 4 \div (-2)$ **−2**
2. $16 \div (-8) = x$ **−2**
3. $-14 \div (-2) = c$ **7**
4. $d = 32 \div 8$ **4**
5. $g = 18 \div (-3)$ **−6**
6. $h = -18 \div 3$ **−6**
7. $8 \div (-8) = y$ **−1**
8. $t = 0 \div (-1)$ **0**
9. $-25 \div 5 = k$ **−5**
10. $c = -14 \div (-7)$ **2**
11. $-32 \div 8 = m$ **−4**
12. $n = -56 \div (-8)$ **7**
13. $-81 \div 9 = y$ **−9**
14. $81 \div (-9) = w$ **−9**
15. $x = 81 \div 9$ **9**
16. $q = -81 \div (-9)$ **9**
17. $18 \div (-2) = a$ **−9**
18. $-55 \div 11 = c$ **−5**
19. $25 \div (-5) = r$ **−5**
20. $x = -21 \div 3$ **−7**
21. $-42 \div (-7) = y$ **6**
22. $y = -121 \div (-11)$ **11**

Lesson 5-8 *(Pages 215–217)*

Graph each figure and its transformation. Write the ordered pairs for the vertices of the new figure. 1–5. See Answer Appendix for graphs.

1. $\triangle ABC$ with vertices $A(-4, 3)$, $B(2, -1)$, and $C(0, 5)$ translated 3 units left and 4 units down. $A'(-7, -1)$, $B'(-1, -5)$, $C'(-3, 1)$
2. $\triangle DEF$ with vertices $D(5, 2)$, $E(-1, -1)$, and $F(3, 4)$ reflected over the x-axis. $D'(5, -2)$, $E'(-1, 1)$, $F'(3, -4)$
3. $\triangle GHI$ with vertices $G(0, 7)$, $H(5, 0)$, and $I(-2, -4)$ translated 2 units right and 3 units up. $G'(2, 10)$, $H'(7, 3)$, $I'(0, -1)$
4. $\triangle JKL$ with vertices $J(-4, -4)$, $K(4, -4)$, and $L(0, 0)$ reflected over the y-axis. $J'(4, -4)$, $K'(-4, -4)$, $L'(0, 0)$
5. Rectangle $PQRS$ with vertices $P(3, 5)$, $Q(-4, 5)$, $R(-4, -1)$, and $S(3, -1)$ translated 1 unit down and 4 units left. $P'(-1, 4)$, $Q'(-8, 4)$, $R'(-8, -2)$, $S'(-1, -2)$

Lesson 6-1 *(Pages 228–231)*

Solve each equation. Check your solution.

1. $r - 3 = 14$ 17
2. $t + 3 = 21$ 18
3. $s + 10 = 23$ 13
4. $7 + a = -10$ −17
5. $14 + m = 24$ 10
6. $-9 + n = 13$ 22
7. $s - 2 = -6$ −4
8. $x - 1.3 = 12$ 13.3
9. $y + 3.4 = 18$ 14.6
10. $0.013 + h = 4.0$ 3.987
11. $6 + f = 71$ 65
12. $7.2 + g = 9.1$ 1.9
13. $z - 12.1 = 14$ 26.1
14. $w - 0.1 = 0.32$ 0.42
15. $v - 18 = 13.7$ 31.7
16. $s + 1.3 = 18$ 16.7
17. $t + 3.43 = 7.4$ 3.97
18. $x + 7.4 = 23.5$ 16.1
19. $p + 3.1 = 18$ 14.9
20. $q - 2.17 = 21$ 23.17
21. $w - 3.7 = 4.63$ 8.33
22. $m - 4.8 = 7.4$ 12.2

Lesson 6-1B *(Pages 232–233)*

Solve.

1. I'm thinking of a number. If I multiply it by 7 and add 23, the result is 107. What is the number? 12
2. Sam is planning a luncheon. He goes to the grocery store and buys a ham for $24.98 and a vegetable tray for $17.49. There is no tax on food. He gives the cashier one bill and receives less than $10 in change. What was the denomination of the bill Sam gave the cashier? $50
3. Maya is two years older than her sister Jana. Jana is 5 years older than her brother Trevor, who is 9 years younger than his brother Trent. If Trent is 17 years old, how old is Maya? 15 years old
4. A can of evaporated milk weighs 15 ounces. Mrs. Martinez uses half of the milk to make pumpkin pudding. The can and the milk that is left weigh 9 ounces. How much does the can weigh? 3 ounces
5. A parking garage in New York City charges $3 for the first two hours and then $0.75 for each additional hour. Walter parks his car in the garage at 9:00 A.M. and when he returns must pay a $5.25 parking fee. What time did Walter return? 2:00 P.M.

Lesson 6-2 *(Pages 234-237)*

Solve each equation. Check your solution.

1. $2m = 18$ **9**
2. $-42 = 6n$ **−7**
3. $72 = 8k$ **9**
4. $-20r = 20$ **−1**
5. $420 = 5s$ **84**
6. $325 = 25t$ **13**
7. $-14 = -2p$ **7**
8. $18q = 36$ **2**
9. $40 = 10a$ **4**
10. $100 = 20b$ **5**
11. $416 = 4c$ **104**
12. $45 = 9d$ **5**
13. $0.5m = 3.5$ **7**
14. $1.8 = 0.6x$ **3**
15. $0.4y = 2$ **5**
16. $1.86 = 6.2z$ **0.3**
17. $-8x = 24$ **−3**
18. $8.34 = 2r$ **4.17**

Lesson 6-3 *(Pages 239-241)*

Solve each equation. Check your solution.

1. $3x + 6 = 6$ **0**
2. $2r - 7 = -1$ **3**
3. $-10 + 2d = 8$ **9**
4. $2b + 4 = -8$ **−6**
5. $5w - 12 = 3$ **3**
6. $5t - 4 = 6$ **2**
7. $2q - 6 = 4$ **5**
8. $2g - 3 = -9$ **−3**
9. $15 = 6y + 3$ **2**
10. $3s - 4 = 8$ **4**
11. $18 - 7f = 4$ **2**
12. $13 + 3p = 7$ **−2**
13. $7.5r + 2 = -28$ **−4**
14. $4.2 + 7z = 2.8$ **−0.2**
15. $-9m - 9 = 9$ **−2**
16. $32 + 0.2c = 1$ **−155**
17. $5t - 14 = -14$ **0**
18. $-0.25x + 0.5 = 4$ **−14**
19. $5w - 4 = 8$ **2.4**
20. $4d - 3 = 9$ **3**
21. $2g - 16 = -9$ **3.5**
22. $4k + 13 = 20$ **1.75**
23. $7 = 5 - 2x$ **−1**
24. $8z + 15 = -1$ **−2**
25. $92 - 16b = 12$ **5**
26. $14e + 14 = 28$ **1**
27. $1.1j + 2 = 7.5$ **5**
28. $4r + 3 = 25$ **5.5**

Lesson 6-4 *(Pages 242–245)*

Write each phrase as an algebraic expression.

1. six less than p **$p - 6$**
2. twenty more than c **$20 + c$**
3. the quotient of a and b **$\frac{a}{b}$**
4. Ann's age plus 6 **$a + 6$**
5. x increased by twelve **$x + 12$**
6. \$1,000 divided by z **$\frac{\$1,000}{z}$**
7. 3 divided into y **$\frac{y}{3}$**
8. the product of 7 and m **$7m$**
9. the difference of f and 9 **$f - 9$**
10. twenty-six less q **$26 - q$**
11. 19 decreased by z **$19 - z$**
12. two less than x **$x - 2$**

Write each sentence as an algebraic equation. **13. $3n - 4 = 17$**

13. Three times a number less four is 17.
14. The sum of a number and 6 is 5. **$n + 6 = 5$**
15. Twenty more than twice a number is -30.
16. The quotient of a number and -2 is -42.
17. Four plus three times a number is 18.
18. Five times a number minus 15 is 92.

15. $20 + 2n = -30$ 16. $n \div (-2) = -42$ 17. $4 + 3n = 18$ 18. $5n - 15 = 92$

EXTRA PRACTICE

Lesson 6-5 *(Pages 246–248)*

Solve each inequality. Graph the solution on a number line.

1. $x + 2 > -3$ $x > -5$
2. $x + 2.9 \leq 9.1$ $x \leq 6.2$
3. $8t \geq 24$ $t \geq 3$
4. $v - 3 < -3$ $v < 0$
5. $6y \geq -12$ $y \geq -2$
6. $a + 3 \leq -2$ $a \leq -5$
7. $k - 5 < -2$ $k < 3$
8. $q - 3 \leq 14$ $q \leq 17$
9. $c - 4 \leq -2$ $c \leq 2$
10. $n + 2 > -5$ $n > -7$
11. $j + 1.2 > 4.8$ $j > 3.6$
12. $4x < 40$ $x < 10$
13. $2y \leq 10$ $y \leq 5$
14. $g + 8 < 10$ $g < 2$
15. $2 + b > 4$ $b > 2$
16. $3m \geq 9$ $m \geq 3$
17. $2y \leq 6$ $y \leq 3$
18. $w - 6 \geq 4$ $w \geq 10$

1–18. See Answer Appendix for graphs.

Lesson 6-6 *(Pages 249–252)*

Graph the ordered pairs in each table on a coordinate plane. Then write a sentence describing each relationship as a function. 1–2. See Answer Appendix.

1. In the nitrogen family of elements, the atomic number and the atomic mass are given.

Element Name	Atomic Number	Atomic Mass
Nitrogen	7	14
Phosphorus	15	31
Arsenic	33	75
Antimony	51	122
Bismuth	82	209

2. The mass for different numbers of pennies is given.

Number of pennies	1	2	3	4	6
Mass of pennies (g)	5.1	6.2	9.3	12.4	13.6

Lesson 6-7 *(Pages 254–257)*

Copy and complete each table. Then graph the ordered pairs. 1–4. See Answer Appendix for graphs.

1.

x	2x	y
2	2(2)	4
1	2(1)	2
0	2(0)	0
−1	2(−1)	−2

2.

x	3x + 1	y
1	3(1) + 1	4
0	3(0) + 1	1
−1	3(−1) + 1	−2
−2	3(−2) + 1	−5

3.

x	−2x − 3	y
0	−2(0) − 3	−3
1	−2(1) − 3	−5
2	−2(2) − 3	−7
3	−2(3) − 3	−9

4.

x	−0.5x − 1	y
2	−0.5(2) − 1	−2
4	−0.5(4) − 1	−3
6	−0.5(6) − 1	−4
8	−0.5(8) − 1	−5

Graph each equation. 5–20. See Answer Appendix.

5. $y = 3x$
6. $y = 2x + 3$
7. $y = -x$
8. $y = 4x + 2$
9. $y = 0.5x + 2$
10. $y = -x + 3$
11. $y = 0.25x + 6$
12. $y = -3x + 6$
13. $y = 2x + 7$
14. $y = -5x + 1$
15. $y = 13 + x$
16. $y = 5 - 0.5x$
17. $y = x - 6$
18. $y = 5x + 1.5$
19. $y = 16 - 4x$
20. $y = 4x + 5$

Lesson 7-1 *(Pages 268–271)*

Round each fraction to 0, $\frac{1}{2}$, or 1.

1. $\frac{3}{8}$ $\frac{1}{2}$
2. $\frac{1}{9}$ 0
3. $\frac{6}{7}$ 1
4. $\frac{7}{12}$ $\frac{1}{2}$
5. $\frac{1}{6}$ 0
6. $\frac{10}{12}$ 1

Round to the nearest whole number.

7. $5\frac{7}{8}$ 6
8. $3\frac{7}{12}$ 4
9. $7\frac{1}{10}$ 7
10. $2\frac{5}{12}$ 2
11. $2\frac{4}{9}$ 2
12. $8\frac{3}{4}$ 9

Estimate. Sample answers given.

13. $\frac{3}{7}+\frac{6}{8}$ $\frac{1}{2}+1=1\frac{1}{2}$
14. $\frac{3}{9}+\frac{7}{8}$ $\frac{1}{2}+1=1\frac{1}{2}$
15. $\frac{1}{8}+\frac{8}{9}$ $0+1=1$
16. $3\frac{1}{8}+7\frac{6}{7}$ $3+8=11$
17. $4\frac{2}{3}+6\frac{7}{8}$ $5+7=12$
18. $3\frac{2}{3}\times 2\frac{1}{3}$ $4\times 2=8$
19. $\frac{4}{5}\times 3$ $1\times 3=3$
20. $9\frac{7}{8}-6\frac{2}{3}$ $10-7=3$
21. $\frac{3}{7}-\frac{1}{15}$ $\frac{1}{2}-0=\frac{1}{2}$

Lesson 7-2 *(Pages 272–275)*

Add or subtract. Write each sum or difference in simplest form.

1. $\frac{5}{11}+\frac{9}{11}$ $1\frac{3}{11}$
2. $\frac{5}{8}-\frac{1}{8}$ $\frac{1}{2}$
3. $\frac{7}{10}+\frac{7}{10}$ $1\frac{2}{5}$
4. $\frac{9}{12}-\frac{5}{12}$ $\frac{1}{3}$
5. $\frac{2}{9}+\frac{1}{3}$ $\frac{5}{9}$
6. $\frac{1}{2}+\frac{3}{4}$ $1\frac{1}{4}$
7. $\frac{1}{4}-\frac{3}{12}$ 0
8. $\frac{3}{7}+\frac{6}{14}$ $\frac{6}{7}$
9. $\frac{1}{4}+\frac{3}{5}$ $\frac{17}{20}$
10. $\frac{4}{9}+\frac{1}{2}$ $\frac{17}{18}$
11. $\frac{5}{7}-\frac{4}{6}$ $\frac{1}{21}$
12. $\frac{3}{4}-\frac{1}{6}$ $\frac{7}{12}$
13. $\frac{3}{5}+\frac{3}{4}$ $1\frac{7}{20}$
14. $\frac{2}{3}-\frac{1}{8}$ $\frac{13}{24}$
15. $\frac{9}{10}+\frac{1}{3}$ $1\frac{7}{30}$
16. $\frac{8}{15}+\frac{2}{9}$ $\frac{34}{45}$
17. $\frac{6}{7}+\frac{6}{9}$ $1\frac{11}{21}$
18. $\frac{3}{7}+\frac{3}{4}$ $1\frac{5}{28}$
19. $\frac{5}{7}+\frac{5}{9}$ $1\frac{17}{63}$
20. $\frac{7}{8}+\frac{5}{6}$ $1\frac{17}{24}$
21. $\frac{5}{8}+\frac{3}{4}$ $1\frac{3}{8}$

Lesson 7-3 *(Pages 276–279)*

Add or subtract. Write each sum or difference in simplest form.

1. $2\frac{1}{3}+1\frac{1}{3}$ $3\frac{2}{3}$
2. $5\frac{2}{7}-2\frac{3}{7}$ $2\frac{6}{7}$
3. $6\frac{3}{8}+7\frac{1}{8}$ $13\frac{1}{2}$
4. $2\frac{3}{4}-1\frac{1}{4}$ $1\frac{1}{2}$
5. $5\frac{1}{2}-3\frac{1}{4}$ $2\frac{1}{4}$
6. $2\frac{2}{3}+4\frac{1}{9}$ $6\frac{7}{9}$
7. $7\frac{4}{5}+9\frac{3}{10}$ $17\frac{1}{10}$
8. $3\frac{3}{4}+5\frac{5}{8}$ $9\frac{3}{8}$
9. $10\frac{2}{3}+5\frac{6}{7}$ $16\frac{11}{21}$
10. $17\frac{2}{9}-12\frac{1}{3}$ $4\frac{8}{9}$
11. $6\frac{5}{12}+12\frac{5}{12}$ $18\frac{5}{6}$
12. $7\frac{1}{4}+15\frac{5}{6}$ $23\frac{1}{12}$
13. $6\frac{1}{8}+4\frac{2}{3}$ $10\frac{19}{24}$
14. $7-6\frac{4}{9}$ $\frac{5}{9}$
15. $8\frac{1}{12}+12\frac{6}{11}$ $20\frac{83}{132}$
16. $7\frac{2}{3}+8\frac{1}{4}$ $15\frac{11}{12}$
17. $12\frac{3}{11}+14\frac{3}{13}$ $26\frac{72}{143}$
18. $21\frac{1}{3}+15\frac{3}{8}$ $36\frac{17}{24}$
19. $19\frac{1}{7}+6\frac{1}{4}$ $25\frac{11}{28}$
20. $9\frac{2}{5}-8\frac{1}{3}$ $1\frac{1}{15}$
21. $18\frac{1}{4}-3\frac{3}{8}$ $14\frac{7}{8}$

Lesson 7-3B (Pages 280–281)

Solve.

1. A fishbowl holds $2\frac{1}{2}$ gallons of water. If there is $\frac{2}{3}$ gallon of water in the bowl, how many more gallons are needed to fill the bowl? **D**
   A $2\frac{5}{6}$ gal **B** $\frac{1}{3}$ gal
   C $3\frac{1}{6}$ gal **D** $1\frac{5}{6}$ gal

2. Ryla bought apples, 2 for $0.79; oranges, 3 for $2.49; and grapes, 1 pound for $1.29. Choose the best estimate for the amount of change she will get from $10. **C**
   A $0.40 **B** $4.60
   C $5.40 **D** $6.20

3. A taxi charges $1.25 for the first 0.5 mile and $0.50 for each additional 0.25 mile. Choose the best estimate for the cost of a 10-mile taxi ride. **B**
   A $18.25 **B** $20.25
   C $22.25 **D** $24.25

4. Jeremiah runs 15.5 miles every week. He ran 3 miles on Monday, 4.25 miles on Tuesday, and 5 miles on Thursday. How many more miles does he have to run this week? **A**
   A 3.25 **B** 4.25
   C 2.75 **D** 3.75

Lesson 7-4 (Pages 284–287)

Multiply. Write each product in simplest form.

1. $\frac{2}{3} \times \frac{3}{5}$ **$\frac{2}{5}$** **2.** $\frac{1}{6} \times \frac{2}{5}$ **$\frac{1}{15}$** **3.** $\frac{4}{9} \times \frac{3}{7}$ **$\frac{4}{21}$** **4.** $\frac{5}{12} \times \frac{6}{11}$ **$\frac{5}{22}$**

5. $\frac{3}{8} \times \frac{8}{9}$ **$\frac{1}{3}$** **6.** $\frac{3}{5} \times \frac{1}{12}$ **$\frac{1}{20}$** **7.** $\frac{2}{5} \times \frac{5}{8}$ **$\frac{1}{4}$** **8.** $\frac{7}{15} \times \frac{3}{21}$ **$\frac{1}{15}$**

9. $\frac{5}{6} \times \frac{15}{16}$ **$\frac{25}{32}$** **10.** $\frac{6}{14} \times \frac{12}{18}$ **$\frac{2}{7}$** **11.** $\frac{2}{3} \times \frac{3}{13}$ **$\frac{2}{13}$** **12.** $\frac{4}{9} \times \frac{1}{6}$ **$\frac{2}{27}$**

13. $3 \times \frac{1}{9}$ **$\frac{1}{3}$** **14.** $5 \times \frac{6}{7}$ **$4\frac{2}{7}$** **15.** $\frac{3}{5} \times 15$ **9** **16.** $3\frac{1}{2} \times 4\frac{1}{3}$ **$15\frac{1}{6}$**

17. $3\frac{5}{8} \times 4\frac{1}{2}$ **$16\frac{5}{16}$** **18.** $\frac{4}{5} \times 2\frac{3}{4}$ **$2\frac{1}{5}$** **19.** $6\frac{1}{8} \times 5\frac{1}{7}$ **$31\frac{1}{2}$** **20.** $2\frac{2}{3} \times 2\frac{1}{4}$ **6**

Lesson 7-5 (Pages 289–291)

Complete.

1. 4,000 lb = ____ T **2 T** **2.** 5 T = ____ lb **10,000** **3.** 2 lb = ____ oz **32**

4. 12,000 lb = ____ T **6 T** **5.** $\frac{1}{4}$ lb = ____ oz **4** **6.** 6 lb 2 oz = ____ oz **98**

7. 3 gal = ____ pt **24** **8.** 24 fl oz = ____ c **3** **9.** 8 pt = ____ c **16**

10. 10 pt = ____ qt **5** **11.** $2\frac{1}{4}$c = ____ fl oz **18** **12.** 12 pt = ____ c **24**

13. 4 gal = ____ qt **16** **14.** 4 qt = ____ fl oz **128** **15.** 4 pt = ____ c **8**

16. 9 lb = ____ oz **144** **17.** 15 qt = ____ gal **$3\frac{3}{4}$** **18.** 6 lb = ____ oz **96**

19. 2 gal = ____ fl oz **256** **20.** 3 T = ____ lb **6,000** **21.** 18 qt = ____ pt **36**

Lesson 7-6 *(Pages 292–295)*

Find the perimeter of each figure.

1.

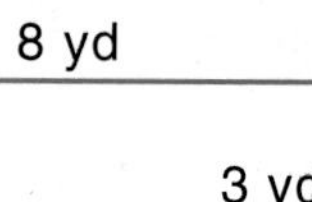

22 yd

2.

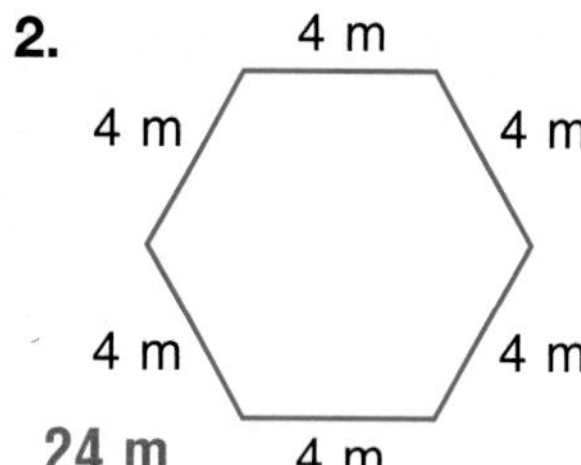

24 m

3.

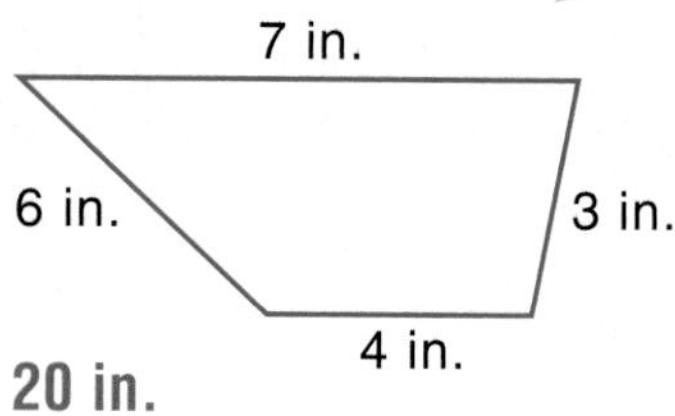

20 in.

4. rectangle: $\ell = 7\frac{1}{2}$ inches, $w = 4\frac{3}{4}$ inches **$24\frac{1}{2}$ in.**

5. rectangle: $\ell = 8\frac{1}{3}$ feet, $w = 2\frac{1}{6}$ feet **21 ft**

Lesson 7-7 *(Pages 297–300)*

Find the circumference of each circle to the nearest tenth. Use $\frac{22}{7}$ or 3.14 for π.

1.

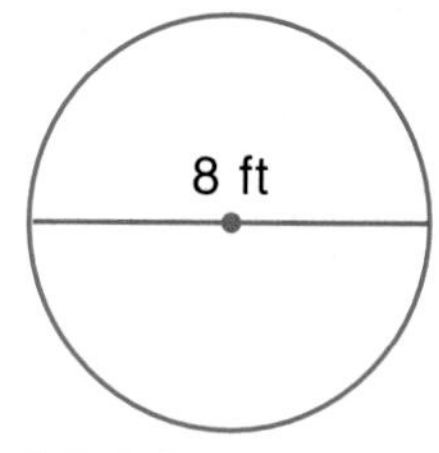

25.1 ft

2.

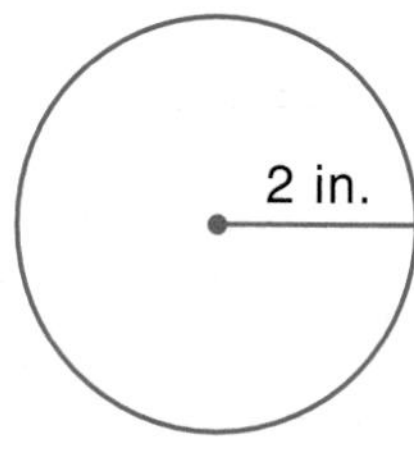

12.6 in.

3.

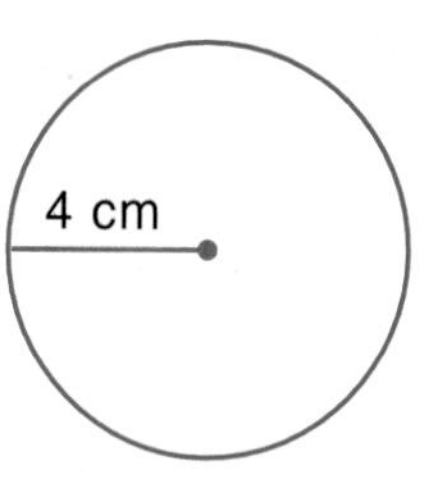

25.1 cm

4.

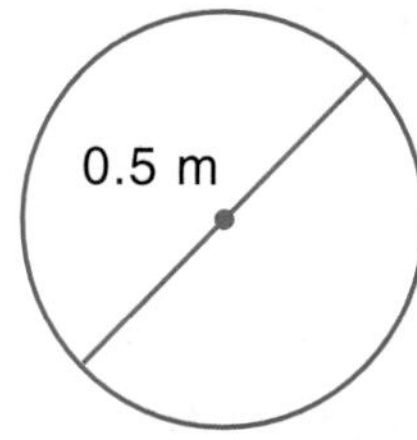

1.6 m

5. $r = 1.5$ in. **9.4 in.** **6.** $d = \frac{2}{3}$ cm **2.1 cm** **7.** $r = 4$ yd **25.1 yd**

8. $d = 1$ m **3.1 m** **9.** $r = 6$ cm **37.7 cm** **10.** $r = 1$ m **6.3 m**

11. $d = 1.5$ in. **4.7 in.** **12.** $d = 2$ yd **6.3 yd** **13.** $r = 0.5$ cm **3.1 cm**

Answers are calculated using $\frac{22}{7}$ or 3.14 and then rounded.

Lesson 7-8 *(Pages 301–304)*

Name the property shown by each statement.

1. $\frac{4}{5} \times \frac{2}{3} = \frac{2}{3} \times \frac{4}{5}$ **commutative (×)**

2. $\frac{3}{10} \times 3\frac{1}{3} = 1$ **multiplicative inverse**

3. $\frac{24}{27} \times 1 = \frac{24}{27}$ **identity (×)**

4. $\left(\frac{1}{2} + \frac{3}{4}\right) + \frac{5}{6} = \frac{1}{2} + \left(\frac{3}{4} + \frac{5}{6}\right)$ **associative (+)**

5. $\frac{2}{3} \times \left(\frac{1}{2} + \frac{5}{6}\right) = \frac{2}{3} \times \frac{1}{2} + \frac{2}{3} \times \frac{5}{6}$ **distributive**

6. $\frac{2}{3} \times \frac{3}{2} = 1$ **multiplicative inverse**

Solve each equation. Write the solution in simplest form.

7. $\frac{a}{13} = 2$ **26** **8.** $3 \times 1\frac{2}{5} = p$ **$4\frac{1}{5}$** **9.** $\frac{8}{9}x = 24$ **27** **10.** $\frac{3}{8}r = 36$ **96**

11. $\frac{3}{4}t = \frac{1}{2}$ **$\frac{2}{3}$** **12.** $16 = \frac{h}{4}$ **64** **13.** $\frac{1}{5} \times 10 = b$ **2** **14.** $\frac{k}{2.1} = 0.7$ **1.47**

Lesson 7-9 *(Pages 305–307)*

Divide. Write each quotient in simplest form.

1. $\frac{2}{3} \div \frac{3}{2}$ **$\frac{4}{9}$**
2. $\frac{3}{5} \div \frac{2}{5}$ **$1\frac{1}{2}$**
3. $\frac{7}{10} \div \frac{3}{8}$ **$1\frac{13}{15}$**
4. $\frac{5}{9} \div \frac{2}{5}$ **$1\frac{7}{18}$**
5. $4 \div \frac{2}{3}$ **6**
6. $8 \div \frac{4}{5}$ **10**
7. $9 \div \frac{5}{9}$ **$16\frac{1}{5}$**
8. $\frac{2}{7} \div 2$ **$\frac{1}{7}$**
9. $\frac{1}{14} \div 7$ **$\frac{1}{98}$**
10. $\frac{2}{13} \div \frac{5}{26}$ **$\frac{4}{5}$**
11. $\frac{4}{7} \div \frac{6}{7}$ **$\frac{2}{3}$**
12. $\frac{7}{8} \div \frac{1}{3}$ **$2\frac{5}{8}$**
13. $15 \div \frac{3}{5}$ **25**
14. $\frac{9}{14} \div \frac{3}{4}$ **$\frac{6}{7}$**
15. $\frac{8}{9} \div \frac{5}{6}$ **$1\frac{1}{15}$**
16. $\frac{4}{9} \div 36$ **$\frac{1}{81}$**
17. $\frac{3}{5} \div \frac{2}{3}$ **$\frac{9}{10}$**
18. $\frac{8}{9} \div \frac{4}{5}$ **$1\frac{1}{9}$**
19. $\frac{3}{4} \div \frac{15}{16}$ **$\frac{4}{5}$**
20. $6 \div \frac{1}{5}$ **30**
21. $\frac{5}{8} \div 2$ **$\frac{5}{16}$**

Lesson 8-1 *(Pages 317–320)*

Express each ratio as a fraction in simplest form.

1. 45 to 15 **$\frac{3}{1}$**
2. 64:128 **$\frac{1}{2}$**
3. 12 weeks out of 15 **$\frac{4}{5}$**
4. 14 to 49 **$\frac{2}{7}$**
5. 125:25 **$\frac{5}{1}$**
6. 18 to 81 **$\frac{2}{9}$**
7. 33 minutes:60 minutes **$\frac{11}{20}$**
8. 16:40 **$\frac{2}{5}$**
9. 120 to 180 **$\frac{2}{3}$**
10. 32:64 **$\frac{1}{2}$**
11. 10 ft to 8 yd **$\frac{5}{12}$**
12. 90 to 100 **$\frac{9}{10}$**

Tell whether the ratios are equivalent. Show your answer by simplifying.

13. 14 to 77 and 8 to 44 **yes**
14. $\frac{48}{16}$ and $\frac{1}{3}$ **no**
15. 65:13 and 500:100 **yes**
16. 72 to 90 and 20 to 16 **no**
17. 250:100 and 5:2 **yes**
18. $\frac{32}{2}$ and $\frac{3}{48}$ **no**
19. 8 hours to 5 days and 24 hours to 15 days **yes**

Lesson 8-2 *(Pages 321–324)*

Express each rate as a unit rate.

1. \$240 for 4 days **\$60/day**
2. 250 people in 5 buses **50 people/bus**
3. 500 miles in 10 hours **50 miles/hour**
4. 18 cups for 24 pounds **$\frac{3}{4}$ cup/pound**
5. 32 people in 8 cars **4 people/car**
6. 3 dozen for \$4.50 **$\frac{2}{3}$ dozen/dollar**
7. 245 tickets in 5 days **49 tickets/day**
8. 12 classes in 4 semesters **3 classes/semester**
9. 60 people in 4 rows **15 people/row**
10. 48 ounces in 3 pounds **16 ounces/pound**
11. 20 people in 4 groups **5 people/group**
12. 1.5 pounds for \$3.00 **0.5 pound/dollar**
13. 45 miles in 60 minutes **0.75 mile/minute**
14. \$5.50 for 10 disks **\$0.55/disk**
15. 360 miles for 12 gallons **30 miles/gallon**
16. \$8.50 for 5 yards **\$1.70/yard**
17. 24 cups for \$1.20 **20 cups/dollar**
18. 160 words in 4 minutes **40 words/minute**
19. \$60 for 5 books **\$12/book**
20. \$24 for 6 hours **\$4/hour**

Lesson 8-3 *(Pages 325–328)*

Solve each proportion.

1. $\frac{4}{9} = \frac{x}{3}$ $1\frac{1}{3}$
2. $\frac{12}{m} = \frac{15}{10}$ 8
3. $\frac{36}{90} = \frac{16}{t}$ 40
4. $\frac{g}{32} = \frac{8}{64}$ 4
5. $\frac{5}{14} = \frac{10}{a}$ 28
6. $\frac{k}{18} = \frac{5}{3}$ 30
7. $\frac{120}{150} = \frac{p}{20}$ 16
8. $\frac{15}{w} = \frac{60}{4}$ 1
9. $\frac{81}{90} = \frac{y}{20}$ 18
10. $\frac{14}{s} = \frac{8}{4}$ 7
11. $\frac{h}{3} = \frac{36}{9}$ 12
12. $\frac{44}{8} = \frac{150}{t}$ $27\frac{3}{11}$
13. $\frac{42}{8} = \frac{36}{d}$ $6\frac{6}{7}$
14. $\frac{125}{v} = \frac{35}{5}$ $17\frac{6}{7}$
15. $\frac{u}{72} = \frac{2}{4}$ 36
16. $\frac{45}{80} = \frac{j}{3}$ $1\frac{11}{16}$
17. $\frac{3}{7} = \frac{21}{d}$ 49
18. $\frac{3}{10} = \frac{z}{36}$ $10\frac{4}{5}$

Lesson 8-4A *(Pages 330–331)*

Solve.

1. Thirty-two basketball teams are participating in a single-elimination tournament; that means that if a team loses one game it is eliminated. How many games will the winning team have played? **5 games**
2. After a student council meeting, each of the seven members shook hands with each other. How many handshakes were there in all? **21 handshakes**
3. A shuttle bus at Cedar Point Amusement Park holds 28 passengers. It starts out empty and picks up 1 passenger at the first stop, 2 passengers at the second stop, 3 at the third stop and so on. After how many stops will the bus be full? **7 stops**
4. Madrina mails a recipe to five of her friends. Each of the five friends mails the recipe to five of their friends and so on. How many recipes are in the fourth mailing? **625 recipes**
5. Rene is arranging chairs in a meeting room. Each row has 1 more chair than the last so that no chair is directly behind another. If there are 6 chairs in the first row, how many will be in the fifth row? **10 chairs**

Lesson 8-4 *(Pages 332–335)*

On a map, the scale is 1 inch:50 miles. For each map distance, find the actual distance. 4. $118\frac{3}{4}$ mi 8. 400 mi

1. 5 inches **250 mi**
2. 12 inches **600 mi**
3. $3\frac{1}{2}$ inches **175 mi**
4. $2\frac{3}{8}$ inches
5. $\frac{4}{5}$ inch **40 mi**
6. $6\frac{3}{4}$ inches **337.5 mi**
7. $2\frac{5}{6}$ inches **$141\frac{2}{3}$ mi**
8. 8 inches

On a scale drawing, the scale is $\frac{1}{2}$ inch:2 feet. Find the dimensions of each room in the scale drawing.

9. 14 feet by 18 feet **$3\frac{1}{2}$ inches by $4\frac{1}{2}$ inches**
10. 32 feet by 6 feet **8 inches by $1\frac{1}{2}$ inches**
11. 3 feet by 5 feet **$\frac{3}{4}$ inch by $1\frac{1}{4}$ inches**
12. 20 feet by 30 feet **5 inches by $7\frac{1}{2}$ inches**
13. 8 feet by 15 feet **2 inches by $3\frac{3}{4}$ inches**
14. 25 feet by 80 feet **$6\frac{1}{4}$ inches by 20 inches**

Lesson 8-5 *(Pages 336–338)*

Express each fraction as a percent.

1. $\frac{14}{25}$ 56% **2.** $\frac{28}{50}$ 56% **3.** $\frac{14}{20}$ 70% **4.** $\frac{9}{12}$ 75%

5. $\frac{4}{6}$ $66\frac{2}{3}\%$ **6.** $\frac{3}{8}$ 37.5% **7.** $\frac{7}{10}$ 70% **8.** $\frac{17}{17}$ 100%

9. $\frac{9}{16}$ 56.25% **10.** $\frac{80}{125}$ 64% **11.** $\frac{8}{9}$ $88\frac{8}{9}\%$ **12.** $\frac{3}{16}$ 18.75%

Express each percent as a fraction in simplest form.

13. 32% $\frac{8}{25}$ **14.** 18.5% $\frac{37}{200}$ **15.** 89% $\frac{89}{100}$ **16.** 72% $\frac{18}{25}$

17. $52\frac{1}{4}\%$ $\frac{209}{400}$ **18.** $33\frac{1}{3}\%$ $\frac{1}{3}$ **19.** 11% $\frac{11}{100}$ **20.** 1% $\frac{1}{100}$

21. 28% $\frac{7}{25}$ **22.** 55% $\frac{11}{20}$ **23.** $26\frac{1}{4}\%$ $\frac{21}{80}$ **24.** $3\frac{1}{3}\%$ $\frac{1}{30}$

Lesson 8-6 *(Pages 339–341)*

Express each decimal as a percent.

1. 0.03 3% **2.** 0.16 16% **3.** 0.1 10% **4.** 0.5 50%

5. 0.08 8% **6.** 0.98 98% **7.** 0.666 66.6% **8.** 0.31 31%

9. 0.76 76% **10.** 0.725 72.5% **11.** 0.07 7% **12.** 0.8 80%

Express each percent as a decimal.

13. 42% 0.42 **14.** 100% 1.00 **15.** 8% 0.08 **16.** 20% 0.2

17. 35% 0.35 **18.** 3% 0.03 **19.** 62% 0.62 **20.** 1% 0.01

21. 50% 0.5 **22.** 7.5% 0.075 **23.** $2\frac{1}{2}\%$ 0.025 **24.** 87.5% 0.875

Lesson 8-7 *(Pages 342–345)*

Express each percent as a decimal. 4. 0.00000075

1. 125% 1.25 **2.** 0.045% 0.00045 **3.** 895% 8.95 **4.** 0.000075%

5. 200% 2.0 **6.** 0.001% 0.00001 **7.** 0.01345% 0.0001345 **8.** 555% 5.55

Express each number as a percent.

9. $4\frac{1}{4}$ 425% **10.** $7\frac{9}{10}$ 790% **11.** 3.245 324.5% **12.** 0.003 0.3%

13. 25 2,500% **14.** 16.74 1,674% **15.** $2\frac{3}{5}$ 260% **16.** 900 90,000%

Replace each ● with <, >, or = to make a true sentence.

17. 3.25 ● 325% = **18.** 2,000% ● 2 > **19.** 45 ● 4.5% > **20.** 245% ● 2.45 =

21. $24 \times \frac{1}{4}$ ● $24 \times 25\%$ = **22.** $16 \times 1\frac{1}{3}$ ● $133\frac{1}{3}\% \times 16$ =

EXTRA PRACTICE

Lesson 8-8 *(Pages 346–348)*

Find each number. Round to the nearest tenth if necessary.

1. 5% of 40 is what number? 2
2. What number is 10% of 120? 12
3. Find 12% of 150. 18
4. Find 12.5% of 40. 5
5. What number is 75% of 200? 150
6. Find 13% of 25.3. 3.3
7. 250% of 44 is what number? 110
8. What number is 0.5% of 13.7? 0.1
9. Find 600% of 7. 42
10. Find 1.5% of $25. $0.38
11. Find 81% of 134. 108.5
12. What number is 43% of 110? 47.3
13. What number is 61% of 524? 319.6
14. Find 100% of 3.5. 3.5
15. 20% of 58.5 is what number? 11.7
16. Find 45% of 125.5 56.5
17. What number is 23% of 500? 115
18. Find 80% of 8. 6.4
19. 90% of 72 is what number? 64.8
20. What number is 32% of 54? 17.3

EXTRA PRACTICE

Lesson 8-9 *(Pages 349–351)*

Find each number. Round to the nearest tenth if necessary.

1. What number is 25% of 280? 70
2. 38 is what percent of 50? 76%
3. 54 is 25% of what number? 216
4. 24.5% of what number is 15? 61.2
5. What number is 80% of 500? 400
6. 12% of 120 is what number? 14.4
7. Find 68% of 50. 34
8. What percent of 240 is 32? 13.3%
9. 99 is what percent of 150? 66%
10. Find 75% of 1. 0.8
11. What number is $33\frac{1}{3}$% of 66? 22
12. 50% of 350 is what number? 175
13. What percent of 450 is 50? 11.1%
14. What number is $37\frac{1}{2}$% of 32? 12
15. 95% of 40 is what number? 38
16. Find 30% of 26. 7.8
17. 9 is what percent of 30? 30%
18. 52% of what number is 109.2? 210
19. What number is 65% of 200? 130
20. What number is 15.5% of 45? 7.0

Lesson 9-1 *(Pages 362–365)*

Classify each angle as *acute*, *obtuse*, *right*, or *straight*.

1. obtuse

2. 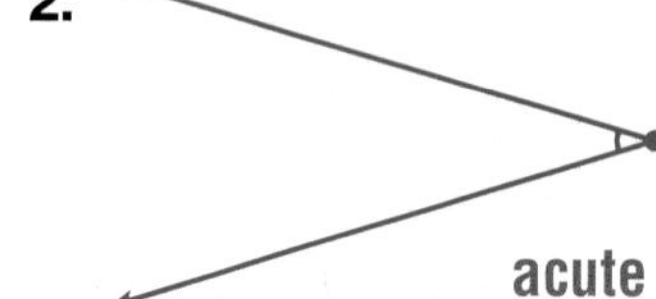
acute

3. 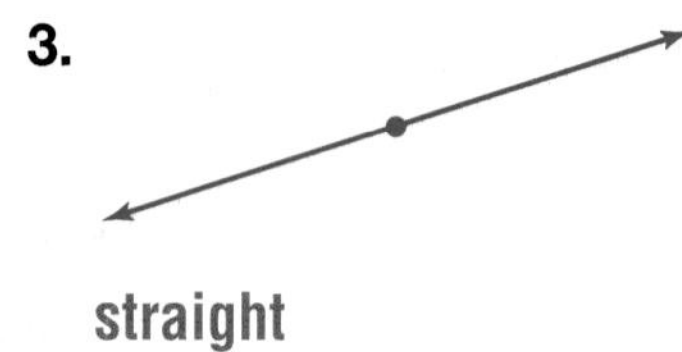
straight

4. 65° angle acute
5. 24° angle acute
6. 110° angle obtuse
7. 112° angle obtuse
8. 90° angle right
9. 97° angle obtuse

Lesson 9-2 *(Pages 370–373)*

Determine which figures are polygons. If the figure is a polygon, name it and tell whether it is a regular polygon. If the figure is *not* a polygon, explain why.

1. 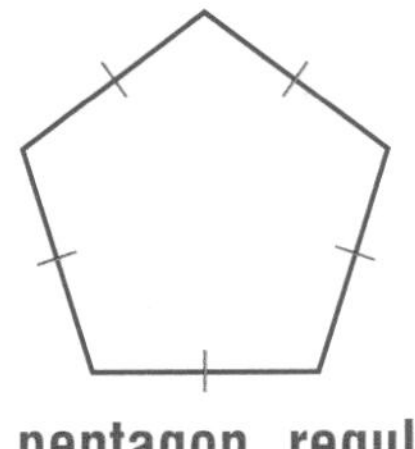

pentagon, regular

2. 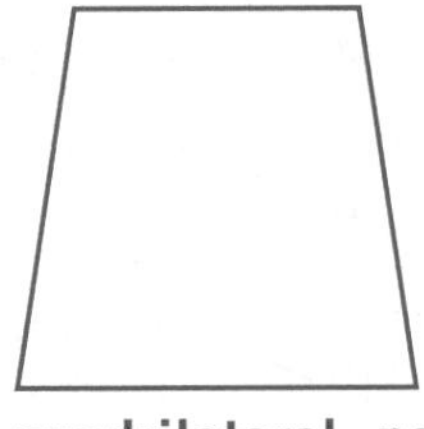

quadrilateral, not regular

3. 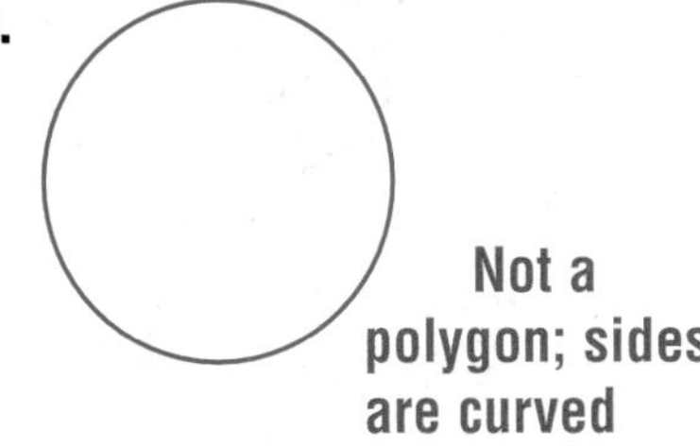

Not a polygon; sides are curved

4. 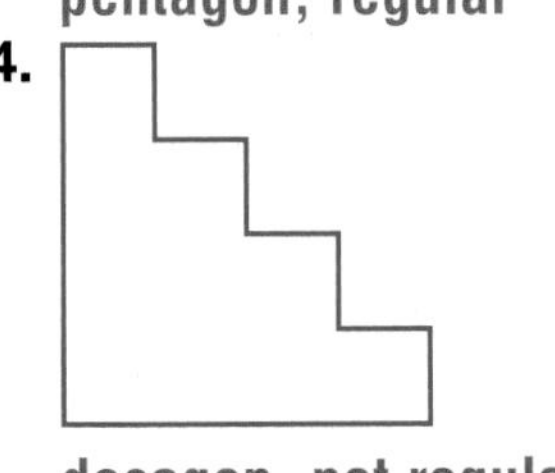

decagon, not regular

5. 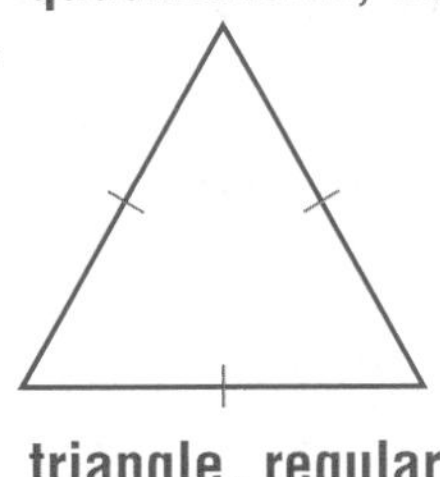

triangle, regular

6. 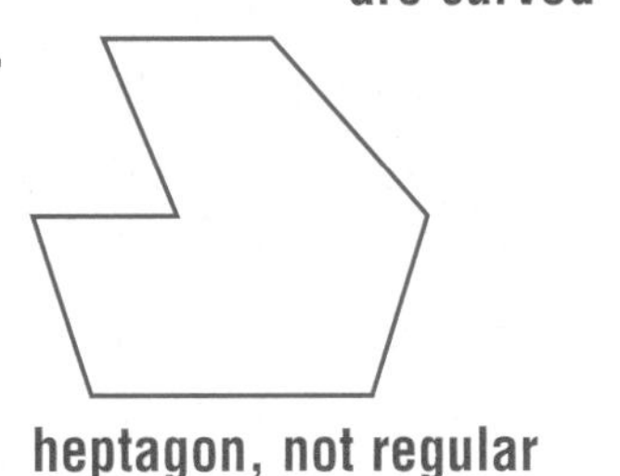

heptagon, not regular

Lesson 9-3 *(Pages 376–379)*

Find the value of *x* in each pair of similar polygons.

1. 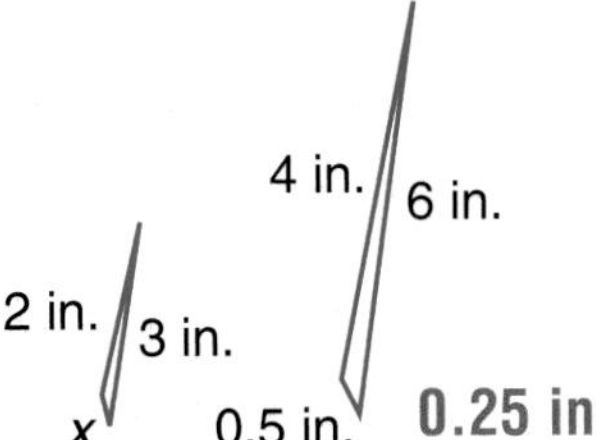

0.25 in.

2. 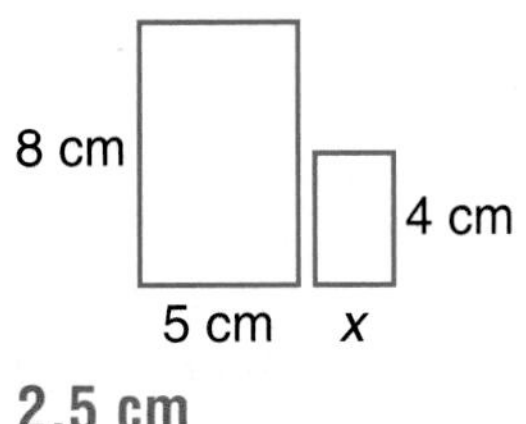

2.5 cm

3. 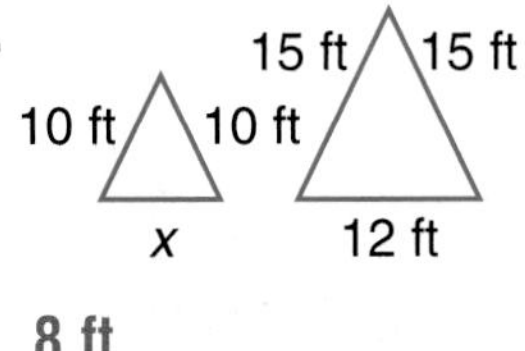

8 ft

Lesson 9-4 *(Pages 382–385)*

Classify each triangle by its angles and its sides.

1. 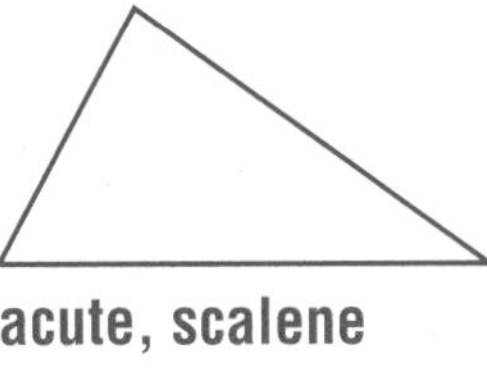

acute, scalene

2. 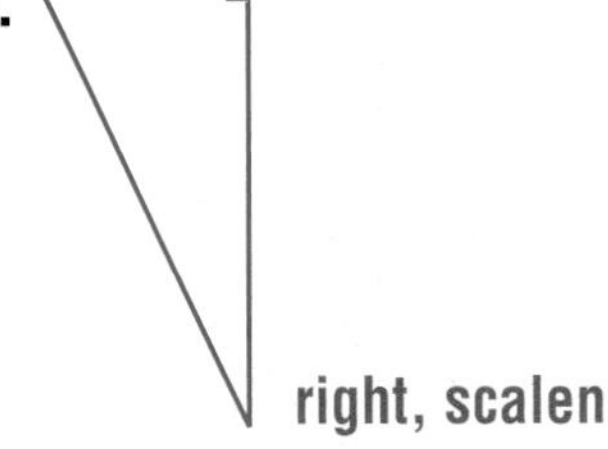

right, scalene

3. 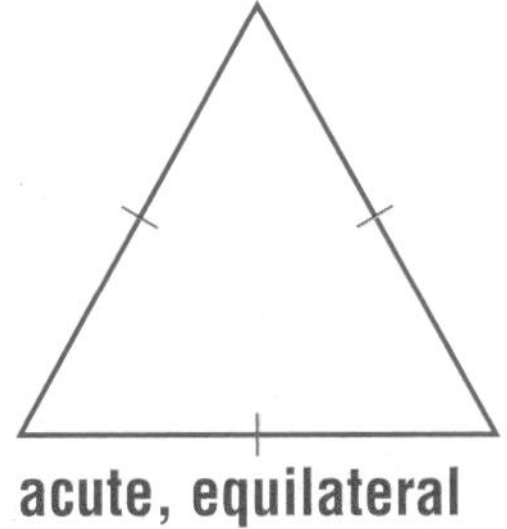

acute, equilateral

Name every quadrilateral that describes each figure. Then underline the name that best describes the figure.

4. 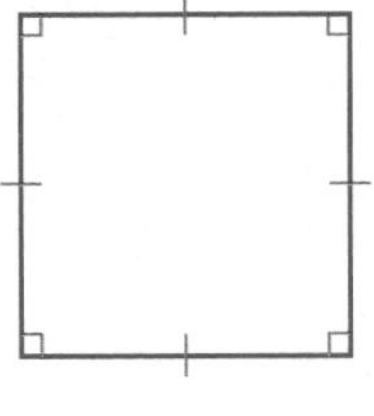

quadrilateral
parallelogram
rectangle
rhombus
<u>square</u>

5. 

quadrilateral
<u>parallelogram</u>

6. 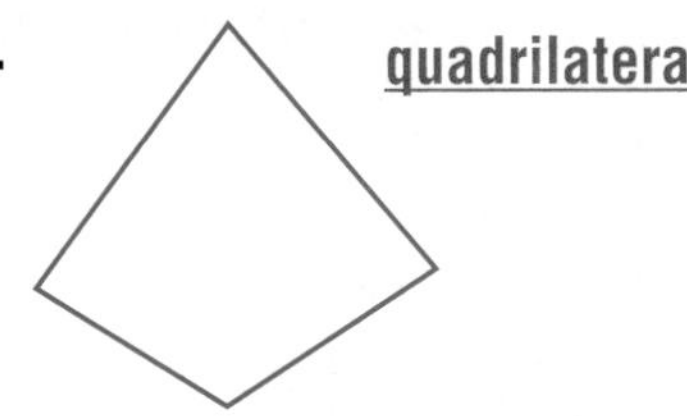

<u>quadrilateral</u>

Lesson 9-4B *(Pages 386–387)*

Solve.

1. Pam, Bob, and Chi each have a collection. One collects stamps, one coins, and the other pins. The coin collector showed Bob and Pam his collection last Saturday. Pam does not collect pins. Who collects stamps? **Pam**
2. Ana, Iris, and Oki each have a pet. The pets are a fish, a cat, and a bird. Ana is allergic to cats. Oki's pet has 2 legs. Whose pet is a fish? **Ana**
3. Regular polygons Q, R, and S are a hexagon, a square, and an octagon but not necessarily in that order. Polygon Q and S have the same number of letters in their names. Each angle of polygon S measures less than 135°. Classify the polygons. ***Q*, octagon; *R*, square; *S*, hexagon**
4. A number is divisible by three if the sum of its digits is divisible by three. Is 92,742 divisible by 3? **Yes**
5. A banker, a cook, and a farmer are named Benjamin, Carl, and Fernando. No one's job starts with the same letter as his name. Benjamin bought eggs from the farmer. Who is the banker? **Fernando**

EXTRA PRACTICE

Lesson 9-5 *(Pages 388–391)*

Determine whether each polygon can be used by itself to make a tessellation. Verify your results by finding the number of angles at a vertex. The sum of the measures of the angles of each polygon is given.

1. triangle; 180° **yes; 6**
2. square; 360° **yes; 4**
3. dodecagon; 1800° **no**

4. Regular hexagons and triangles tessellate. Determine how many of each polygon you need at each vertex. Draw a sketch of the tessellation.
1 hexagon, 4 triangles

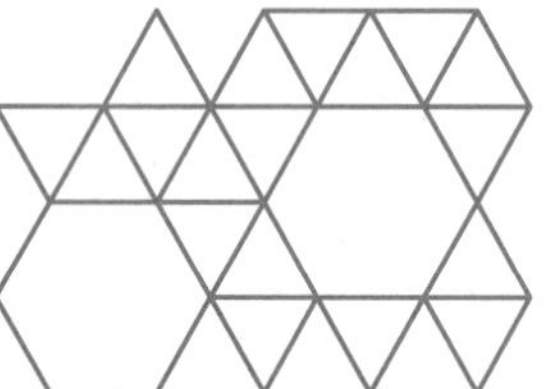

1. 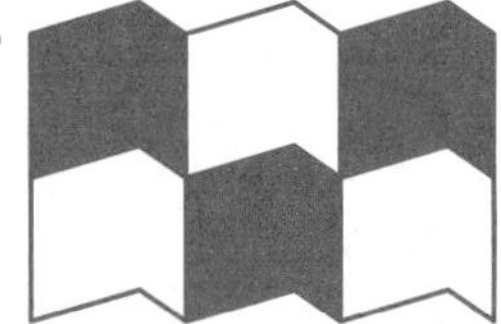

2. 

3. 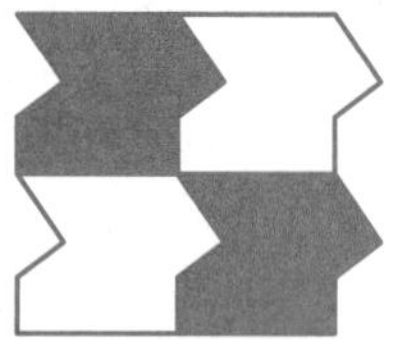

Lesson 9-6 *(Pages 392–394)*

Complete the pattern unit for each translation. Then draw the tessellation.

1. 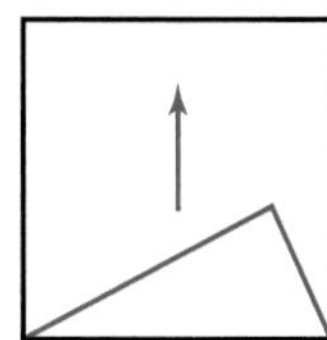

2. 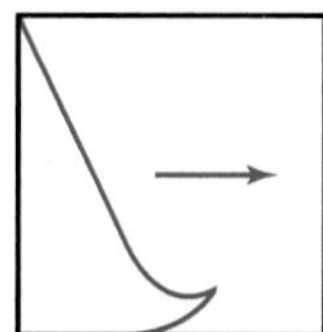

3. 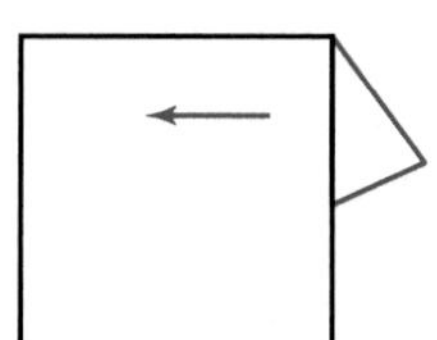

Lesson 9-7 *(Pages 395–397)*

Copy each figure. Draw all lines of symmetry.

1. 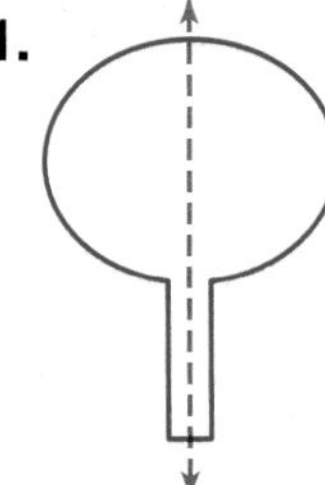

2. 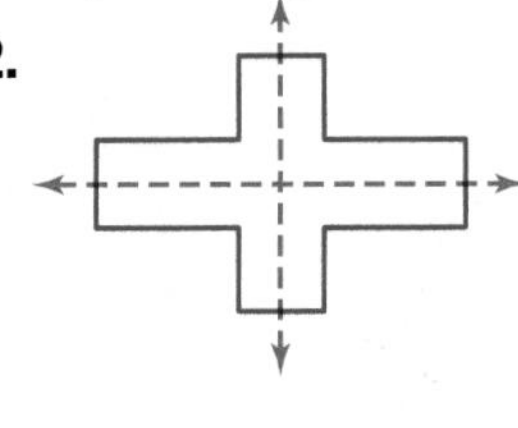

3. 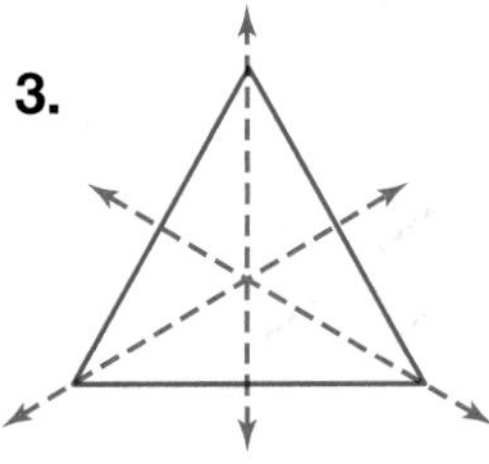

Lesson 10-1A *(Pages 408–409)*

Solve.

1. Josie arranged square tables, each seating 4 people, into one long rectangular table so that her 12 dinner guests could eat together. How many tables did she use? **5**
2. Mariko is thinking of two whole numbers. When she adds them together, the sum is 123. When she subtracts the lesser number from the greater number, their difference is 69. What are the numbers? **27, 96**
3. Seth is the oldest of four children. Each of his sisters is 3 years older than the next oldest sibling. The combined age of Seth and his three sisters is 46. None of the children is over the age of 20. How old is Seth? **16 years old**
4. The length of a rectangle is 6 inches longer than its width. What are the length and width if the area of the rectangle is 216 square inches? **length: 18 in., width: 12 in.**
5. Three consecutive integers have a sum of 33 and a product of 1,320. What are the integers? **10, 11, 12**

Lesson 10-1 *(Pages 410–414)*

Find the square of each number.

1. 6 **36**	**2.** 12 **144**	**3.** 7 **49**
4. 15 **225**	**5.** 20 **400**	**6.** 14 **196**
7. 24 **576**	**8.** 1 **1**	**9.** 11 **121**
10. 40 **1,600**	**11.** 25 **625**	**12.** 9 **81**

Find each square root.

13. $\sqrt{49}$ **7**	**14.** $\sqrt{64}$ **8**	**15.** $\sqrt{169}$ **13**
16. $\sqrt{324}$ **18**	**17.** $\sqrt{900}$ **30**	**18.** $\sqrt{225}$ **15**
19. $\sqrt{2,500}$ **50**	**20.** $\sqrt{81}$ **9**	**21.** $\sqrt{289}$ **17**
22. $\sqrt{576}$ **24**	**23.** $\sqrt{8,100}$ **90**	**24.** $\sqrt{676}$ **26**

EXTRA PRACTICE

Lesson 10-2 *(Pages 415–417)*

Estimate each square root to the nearest whole number.

1. $\sqrt{15}$ 4
2. $\sqrt{35}$ 6
3. $\sqrt{112}$ 11
4. $\sqrt{75}$ 9
5. $\sqrt{27}$ 5
6. $\sqrt{249}$ 16
7. $\sqrt{88}$ 9
8. $\sqrt{1{,}500}$ 39
9. $\sqrt{612}$ 25
10. $\sqrt{340}$ 18
11. $\sqrt{495}$ 22
12. $\sqrt{264}$ 16
13. $\sqrt{350}$ 19
14. $\sqrt{834}$ 29
15. $\sqrt{3{,}700}$ 61
16. $\sqrt{298}$ 17
17. $\sqrt{101}$ 10
18. $\sqrt{800}$ 28
19. $\sqrt{58}$ 8
20. $\sqrt{750}$ 27
21. $\sqrt{1{,}200}$ 35
22. $\sqrt{1{,}000}$ 32
23. $\sqrt{5{,}900}$ 77
24. $\sqrt{999}$ 32
25. $\sqrt{374}$ 19
26. $\sqrt{512}$ 23
27. $\sqrt{3{,}750}$ 61
28. $\sqrt{255}$ 16
29. $\sqrt{83}$ 9
30. $\sqrt{845}$ 29
31. $\sqrt{200}$ 14
32. $\sqrt{500}$ 22
33. $\sqrt{10{,}001}$ 100

Lesson 10-3 *(Pages 419–422)*

Use the Pythagorean Theorem to find the length of each hypotenuse given the lengths of the legs. Round to the nearest tenth. 2. 27.7 cm 4. 13.6 mm

1. 4 ft, 6 ft 7.2 ft
2. 12 cm, 25 cm
3. 15 yd, 24 yd 28.3 yd
4. 8 mm, 11 mm

Find the missing measure for each right triangle. Round to the nearest tenth. 5. 11.3 cm

5. *a*: 14 cm; *c*: 18 cm
6. *b*: 15 ft; *c*: 24 ft 18.7 ft
7. *a*: 5 yd; *b*: 8 yd 9.4 yd

Given the lengths of the sides of a triangle, determine whether each triangle is a right triangle. Write *yes* or *no*.

8. 6 mm, 8 mm, 10 mm yes
9. 12 ft, 15 ft, 20 ft no
10. 300 m, 400 m, 500 m yes

Lesson 10-4 *(Pages 423–426)*

Estimate the area of each figure. 1–6. Sample answers given.

1. 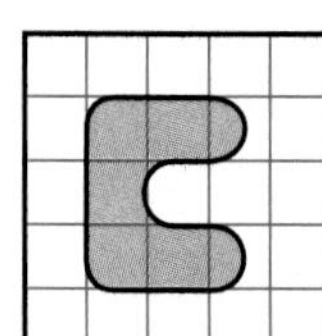 6 square units
2. 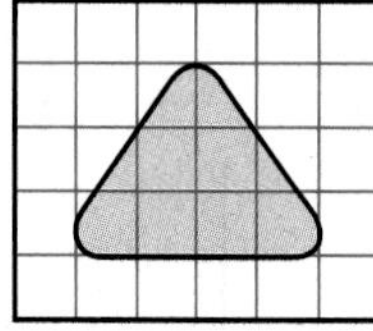 7 square units
3. 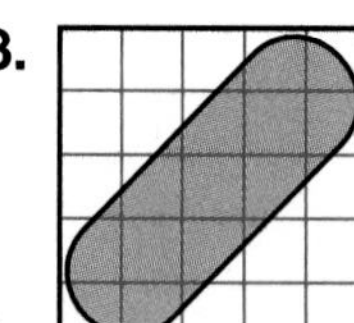 11 square units
4. 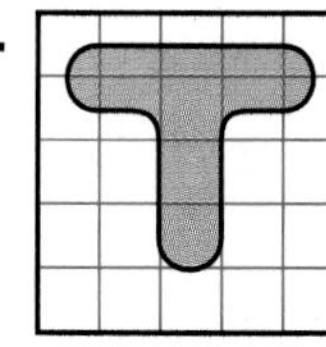 7 square units
5. 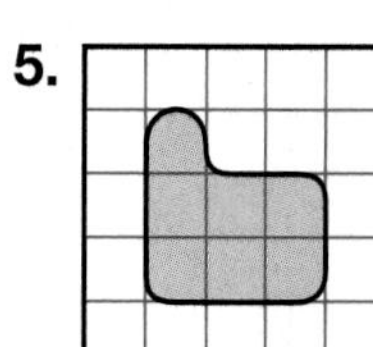 7 square units
6. 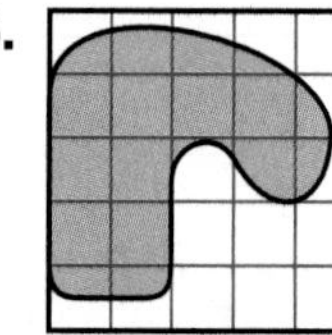 12.5 square units

Lesson 10-5 *(Pages 428–431)*

Find the area of each triangle to the nearest tenth.

1. 4 ft, 10 ft **20 ft²**

2. base: 5 in.
height: 9 in.
22.5 in²

3.

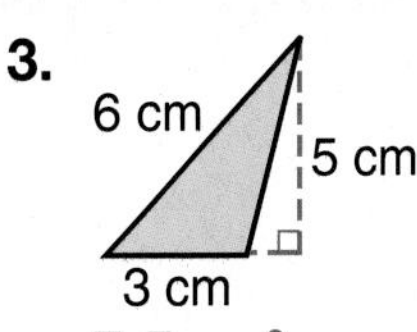

7.5 cm²

4. base: 12 cm
height: 8 cm
48 cm²

Find the area of each trapezoid to the nearest tenth.

5. 8 cm, 5 cm, 3 cm, 4 cm, 15 cm
34.5 cm²

6. bases: 3 cm, 8 cm
height: 12 cm
66 cm²

7.

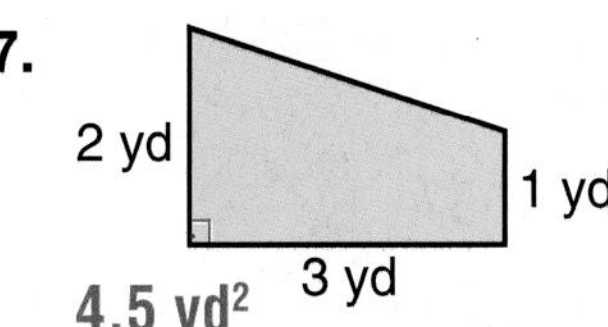

4.5 yd²

8. bases: 10 ft, 15 ft
height: 12 ft
150 ft²

9. 12 in., 6 in., 15 in.
81 in²

10. bases: 5 m, 9 m
height: 10 m
70 m²

Lesson 10-6 *(Pages 432–435)*

Answers were calculated using the π key on a calculator and then rounded.

Find the area of each circle to the nearest tenth.

1. radius, 8 in.
201.1 in²

2.

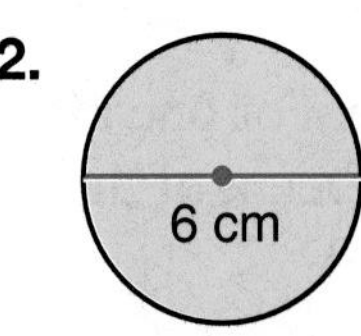

28.3 cm²

3. diameter, 5 ft
19.6 ft²

4.

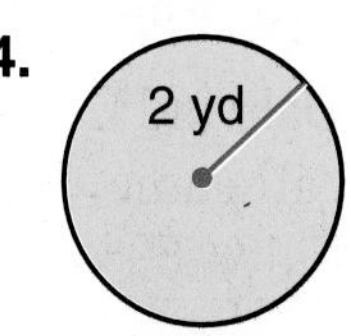

12.6 yd²

5. radius, 24 cm
1,809.6 cm²

6.

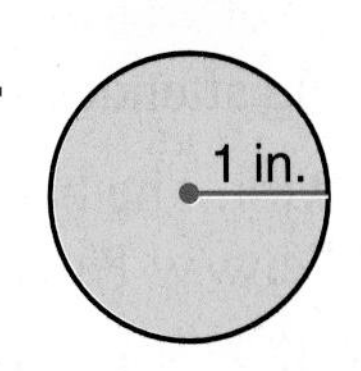

3.1 in²

7. diameter, 2.3 m
4.2 m²

8.

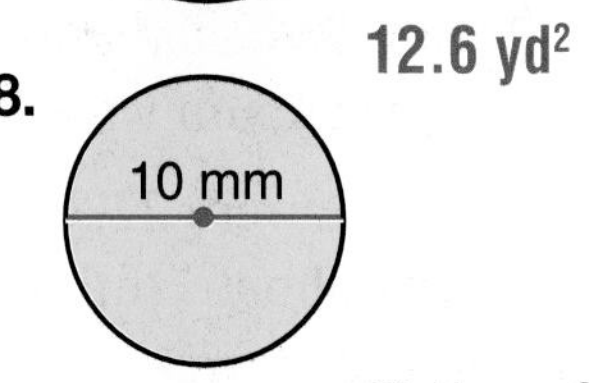

78.5 mm²

Find the length of the radius of each circle given the following areas. Round to the nearest tenth.

9. 15 cm² **2.2 cm** **10.** 24 ft² **2.8 ft** **11.** 125 in² **6.3 in.** **12.** 36 yd² **3.4 yd**

13. 100 m² **5.6 m** **14.** 200 mm² **8.0 mm** **15.** 72 ft² **4.8 ft** **16.** 142 in² **6.7 in.**

Lesson 10-7 *(Pages 438–441)*

Find the probability that a randomly-dropped counter will fall in the shaded region.

1. **$\frac{1}{5}$**

2.

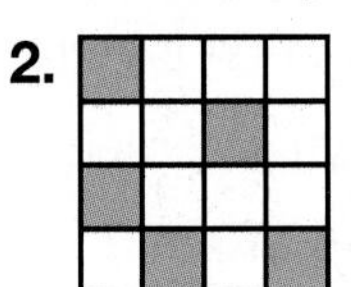

$\frac{5}{16}$

3.

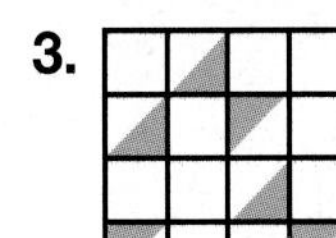

$\frac{3}{16}$

4.

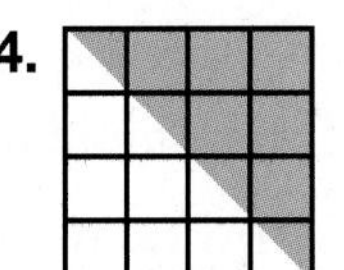

$\frac{1}{2}$

5. **$\frac{1}{4}$**

6.

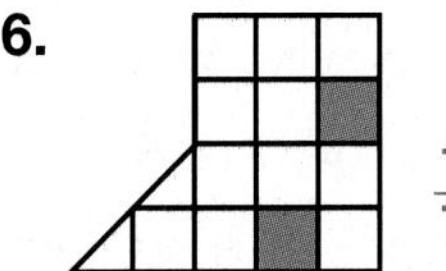

$\frac{1}{7}$

7.

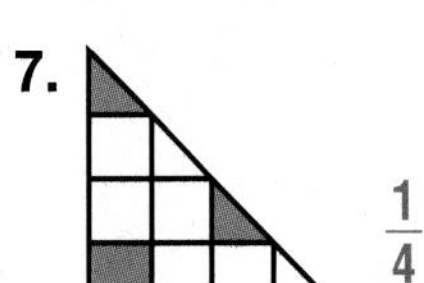

$\frac{1}{4}$

8.

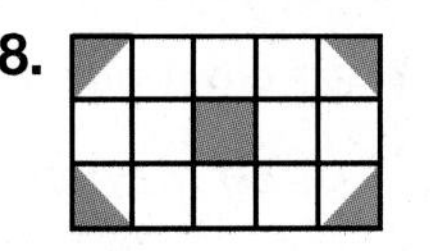

$\frac{1}{5}$

Lesson 11-1 *(Pages 450–453)*

Write the fraction, decimal, mixed number, or whole number equivalent of each percent that could be used to estimate.

1. 28% $\frac{1}{4}$
2. 99% 1
3. 450% $4\frac{1}{2}$
4. 0.09% 0.001
5. $\frac{3}{4}$% 0.01
6. 65.5% $\frac{2}{3}$
7. $15\frac{3}{5}$% $\frac{1}{8}$
8. 39.45% $\frac{2}{5}$
9. $8\frac{1}{2}$% 0.1
10. 48.2% $\frac{1}{2}$
11. 0.009% 0
12. 287% 3

16. 200(100% + 100% + 100%) = 600 20. 10(100% + 100% + 100% + 100%) = 40

Estimate.

13. 50% of 37 $\frac{1}{2} \cdot 40 = 20$
14. 18% of 90 $\frac{1}{5} \cdot 100 = 20$
15. 60.5% of 60 $\frac{3}{5} \cdot 60 = 36$
16. 300% of 245
17. 0.7% of 200 $\frac{1}{100} \cdot 200 = 2$
18. 1% of 48 $\frac{1}{100} \cdot 50 = 0.5$
19. 7% of 24 $\frac{1}{10} \cdot 24 = 2.4$
20. 400% of 13
21. $5\frac{1}{2}$% of 100 $\frac{3}{50} \cdot 100 = 6$
22. 40.01% of 16 $\frac{2}{5} \cdot 15 = 6$
23. 70% of 300 $\frac{7}{10} \cdot 300 = 210$
24. 35% of 35 $\frac{7}{20} \cdot 40 = 14$

Lesson 11-1B *(Pages 454–455)*

Solve. 1–4. Sample answers given.

1. The Oakland Coliseum has a capacity of 48,621 people. For one afternoon baseball game, 38,824 tickets were sold. About what percent of the stadium was full? 80%
2. Olympic stadium in Montreal has a capacity of 59,511. For a baseball game the stadium was about 75% full. About how many people attended the game? 45,000
3. There were 22,306 fans at a baseball game in Fenway Park. The ballpark was about $\frac{2}{3}$ full. What is the approximate capacity of Fenway Park? 33,000
4. Of the people Joaquin surveyed, 60% had eaten a meal in a restaurant in the past two weeks. If Joaquin surveyed 150 people, how many had eaten a meal in a restaurant in the past two weeks? 90

Lesson 11-2 *(Pages 456–458)* 1–16. For equations, see Answer Appendix.

Write an equation for each problem. Then solve. Round answers to the nearest tenth.

1. 12% of what number is 50? 416.7
2. Find 45% of 50. 22.5
3. 38 is what percent of 62? 61.3%
4. $28\frac{1}{2}$% of 64 is what number? 18.2
5. 5% of what number is 12? 240
6. 80 is what percent of 90? 88.9%
7. $66\frac{2}{3}$% of what number is 40? 60
8. Find 46.5% of 75. 34.9
9. 90 is what percent of 95? 94.7%
10. Find 22% of 22. 4.8
11. 16% of what number is 2? 12.5
12. 75 is what percent of 300? 25%
13. 75% of 80 is what number? 60
14. Find 60% of 45. 27
15. What number is 55.5% of 70? 38.9
16. 80.5% of what number is 80.5? 100

Lesson 11-3 *(Pages 460–463)*

Use the information in the following charts to make a circle graph.

1.

Car Sales	
Style	**Percent**
Sedan	45
Station Wagon	22
Pickup Truck	9
Sports Car	13
Compact Car	11

2.

Favorite Flavor of Ice Cream	
Flavor	**Percent**
Vanilla	28
Chocolate	35
Strawberry	19
Mint Chip	12
Coffee	6

1–2. See Answer Appendix.

Lesson 11-4 *(Pages 464–467)*

The table shows the results of a survey of students' favorite cookie flavors at Bush Middle School. The school has 328 students.

Cookie	Number
Chocolate chip	49
Peanut butter	12
Oatmeal	10
Sugar	8
Raisin	3

1. What was the sample size? **82 students**
2. To the nearest percent, what percent of students preferred peanut butter cookies? **15%**
3. How many students in the school would you expect to say that sugar cookies are their favorite? **32 students**

Lesson 11-5 *(Pages 469–472)*

Find the percent of change. Round to the nearest whole percent.

1. original: $75
   new: $50 **33%**
2. original: 450
   new: 675 **50%**
3. original: 3.25
   new: 2.95 **9%**
4. original: $5.75
   new: $6.25 **9%**
5. original: 180
   new: 160 **11%**
6. original: 32.5
   new: 44 **35%**
7. original: 1.5
   new: 1.0 **33%**
8. original: 450
   new: 400 **11%**
9. original: $1,500
   new: $1,200 **20%**
10. original: 750
    new: 600 **20%**
11. original: $65
    new: $75 **15%**
12. original: 380
    new: 320 **16%**
13. original: 0.75
    new: 1.0 **33%**
14. original: $3.95
    new: $4.25 **8%**
15. original: 350
    new: 420 **20%**
16. original: 500
    new: 100 **80%**

Lesson 11-6 (Pages 474–477)

Find the sales tax or discount to the nearest cent. 2. $2.85 3. $2.15

1. $45 sweater; 6% tax $2.70
2. $18.99 CD; 15% off
3. $39 shoes; $5\frac{1}{2}$% tax
4. $199 ring; 10% off $19.90
5. $29 shirt; 7% tax $2.03
6. $55 plant; 20% off $11

Find the total cost or sale price to the nearest cent. 8. $157.50 10. $154.06

7. $19 purse; 25% off $14.25
8. $150 clock; 5% tax
9. $2 notebook; 15% off $1.70
10. $145 coat; $6\frac{1}{4}$% tax
11. $89 radio; 30% off $62.30
12. $300 table; $\frac{1}{3}$ off $200

Find the rate of discount to the nearest percent.

13. regular price, $45
    sale price, $40 11%
14. regular price, $250
    sale price, $200 20%
15. regular price, $89
    sale price, $70 21%

Lesson 11-7 (Pages 478–480)

Find the interest to the nearest cent for each principal, interest rate, and time.

1. $2,000, 8%, 5 years
2. $500, 10%, 8 months
3. $750, 5%, 1 year
4. $175.50, $6\frac{1}{2}$%, 18 months
5. $236.20, 9%, 16 months
6. $89, $7\frac{1}{2}$%, 6 months
7. $800, 5.75%, 3 years
8. $5,500, 7.2%, 4 years
9. $245, 6%, 13 months

1. $800 2. $33.33 3. $37.50 4. $17.11 5. $28.34 6. $3.34 7. $138 8. $1,584 9. $15.93

Find the interest to the nearest cent on credit cards for each credit card balance, interest rate, and time.

10. $750, 18%, 2 years
11. $1,500, 19%, 16 months
12. $300, 9%, 1 year
13. $4,750, $19\frac{1}{2}$%, 30 months
14. $2,345, 17%, 9 months
15. $689, 12%, 2 years
16. $390, 18.75%, 15 months
17. $1,250, 22%, 8 months
18. $3,240, 18%, 14 months

10. $270 11. $380 12. $27 13. $2,315.63 14. $298.99 15. $165.36 16. $91.41 17. $183.33 18. $680.40

Lesson 12-1 (Pages 492–495)

Draw a top, a side, and a front view of each figure. 1–6. See Answer Appendix.

1. 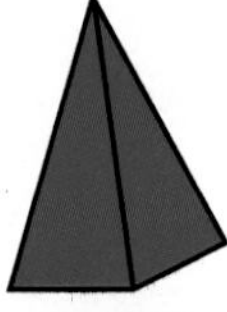
2. 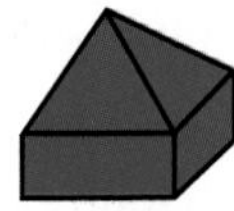
3. 
4. 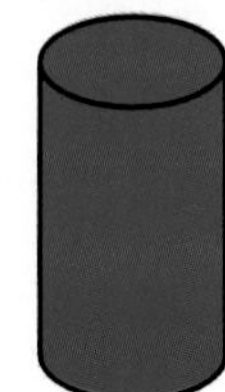
5. 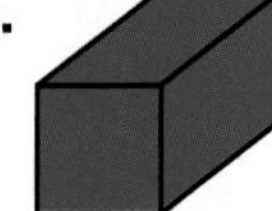
6. 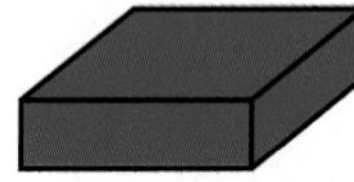

EXTRA PRACTICE

Lesson 12-1B *(Pages 496–497)*

Solve.

1. Mark wants to make a pyramid-shaped display of basketballs for his sports shop. Each basketball comes in a 10-inch cubic box. Mark starts with a base six boxes wide and six boxes long. He decreases each dimension by one box for each layer, how many basketballs will he need for his display? **91 basketballs**
2. How many different rectangular prisms can be formed with 12 cubes? **4**
3. How many 9-inch by 6-inch by 2-inch paperback books can be shipped in a carton 18-inches by 12-inches by 12-inches? **24**
4. Wes, Yoki, Gabe, and Beth each live in a different colored house. The houses are white, green, blue, and yellow. No person's house color starts with the same letter as his or her name. Gabe and Yoki stop at the white house each morning to pick up their friend. Who lives in the white house? **Beth**

Lesson 12-2 *(Pages 498–501)*

Find the volume of each rectangular prism to the nearest tenth. **4. 134.4 mm^3**

1. length, 1.5 in.; width, 3 in.; height, 6 in. **27 in^3**
2. length, 4.5 cm; width, 6.75 cm; height, 2 cm **60.8 cm^3**
3. length, 3 ft; width, 10 ft; height, 2 ft **60 ft^3**
4. length, 16 mm; width, 0.7 mm; height, 12 mm
5. length, 18 cm; width, 23 cm; height, 15 cm **6,210 cm^3**
6. length, $3\frac{1}{2}$ ft; width, 10 ft; height, 6 ft **210 ft^3**
7. length, 25 mm; width, 32 mm; height, 10 mm **8,000 mm^3**
8. length, 12 in.; width, $5\frac{1}{2}$ in.; height, $3\frac{3}{8}$ in. **222.8 in^3**

9. 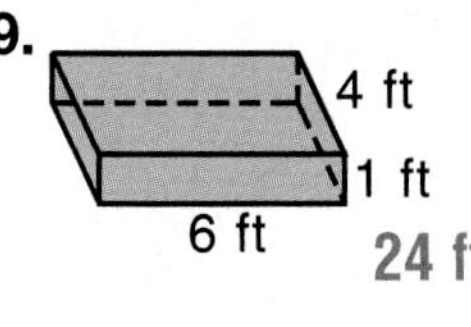

24 ft^3

10. 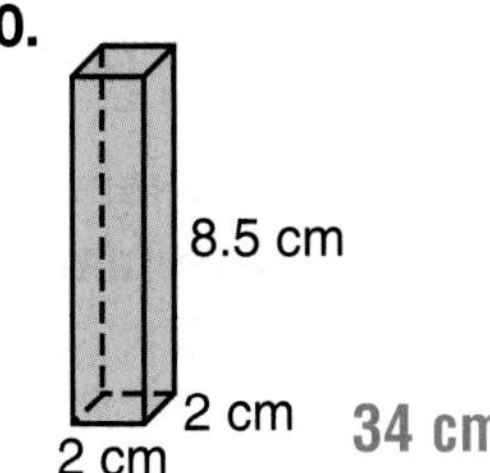

34 cm^3

11. 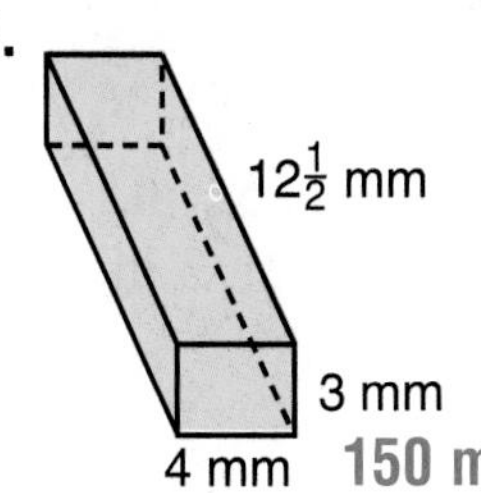

150 mm^3

12. 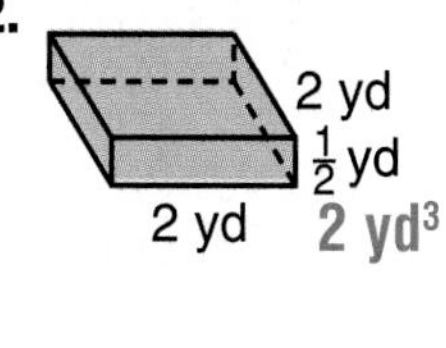

2 yd^3

Lesson 12-3 *(Pages 503–506)*

Find the volume of each cylinder to the nearest tenth. **Answers are calculated using the π key on a calculator and then rounded.**

1. radius, 6 in.; height, 3 in. **339.3 in^3**
2. radius, 8.5 cm; height, 3 cm **680.9 cm^3**
3. diameter, 16 yd; height, 4.5 yd **904.8 yd^3**
4. diameter, 3.5 mm; height, 2.5 mm **24.1 mm^3**
5. radius, 8 ft; height, 10 ft **2,010.6 ft^3**
6. diameter, 12 m; height, 4.75 m **537.2 m^3**
7. radius, 6 cm; height, 12 cm **1,357.2 cm^3**
8. diameter, $\frac{5}{8}$ in.; height, 4 in. **1.2 in^3**

9. 2 cm; 4 cm **50.3 cm^3**
10. 3 yd; 6.5 yd **45.9 yd^3**
11. 16 mm; 7.5 mm **2,827.4 mm^3**
12. 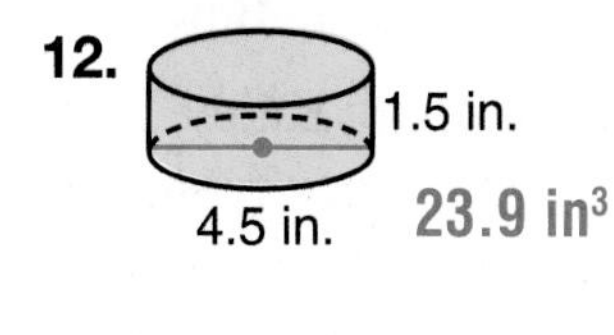

23.9 in^3

Lesson 12-4 (Pages 510–513)

Find the surface area of each rectangular prism to the nearest tenth.

1. length, 8 ft
   width, 6.5 ft
   height, 7 ft **307 ft²**
2. length, $4\frac{1}{2}$ cm
   width, 10 cm
   height, $8\frac{3}{4}$ cm
   343.8 cm²
3. length, 9.4 yd
   width, 2 yd
   height, 5.2 yd
   156.2 yd²
4. length, 20 mm
   width, 15 mm
   height, 25 mm
   2,350 mm²

5. 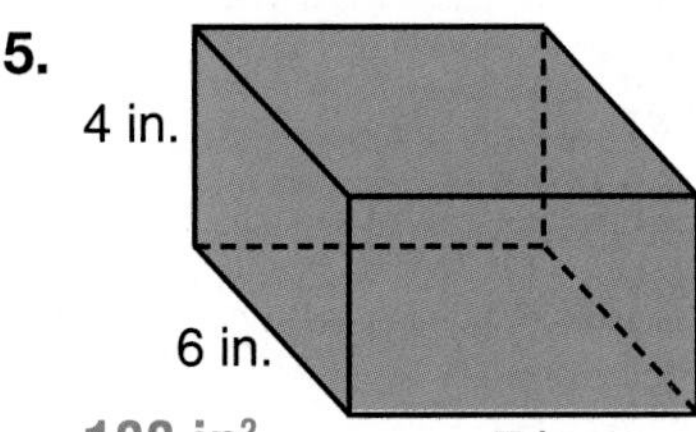

188 in²

6. 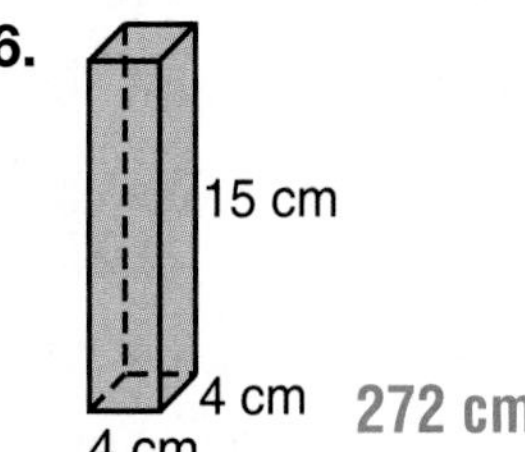

272 cm²

7. 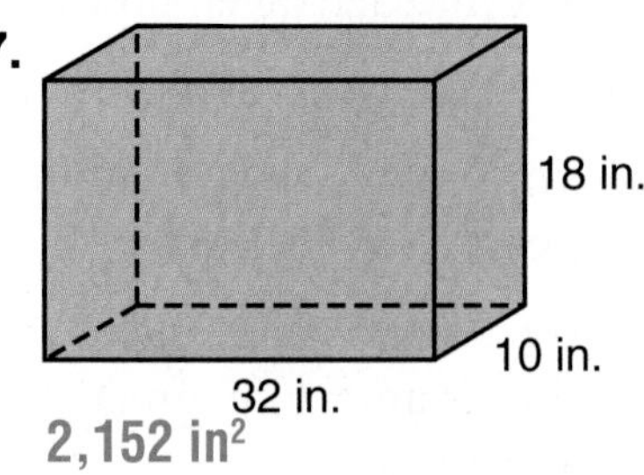

2,152 in²

Lesson 12-5 (Pages 514–517)

Find the surface area of each cylinder to the nearest tenth.

1. 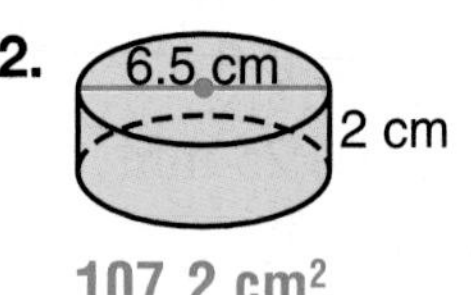

188.5 in²

2.
107.2 cm²

3. 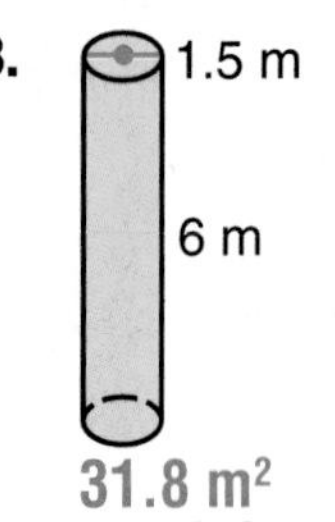

31.8 m²

4. 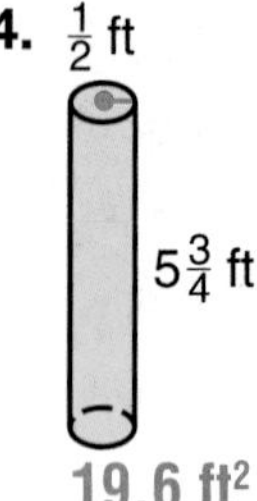

19.6 ft²

Answers are calculated using the π key on a calculator and then rounded.

5. height, 6 cm
   radius, 3.5 cm
   208.9 cm²
6. height, $5\frac{1}{2}$ in.
   diameter, 3 in.
   66.0 in²
7. height, 16.5 mm
   diameter, 18 mm
   1,442.0 mm²
8. height, 22 yd
   radius, 10.5 yd
   2,144.1 yd²

Lesson 13-1A (Pages 528–529)

Apply the act it out strategy to solve each problem. **1–3. See students' work.**

1. A fast food restaurant is giving away sports pins with each children's meal. There are 4 different pins: baseball, football, basketball, and soccer. If the pins are given out randomly, how many times would you need to purchase a children's meal to be sure you get one of each of the pins?
2. How many times do you need to toss a die to get all 6 numbers?
3. Suppose Kaley, Marla, and Sophie each left one book in the school library. When they returned to their literature class, their teacher randomly handed out the three books to the students. Act out this situation 25 times. For how many of these times did Sophie receive the same book she was reading in the library?

Lesson 13-1 *(Pages 530–533)*

Refer to the sample space below. Find each theoretical probability.

1, 1	1, 2	1, 3	1, 4	1, 5	1, 6
2, 1	2, 2	2, 3	2, 4	2, 5	2, 6
3, 1	3, 2	3, 3	3, 4	3, 5	3, 6
4, 1	4, 2	4, 3	4, 4	4, 5	4, 6
5, 1	5, 2	5, 3	5, 4	5, 5	5, 6
6, 1	6, 2	6, 3	6, 4	6, 5	6, 6

1. a sum of 4 $\frac{1}{12}$

2. a sum less than 3 $\frac{1}{36}$

3. the first number equals the second $\frac{1}{6}$

4. a sum of 6 $\frac{5}{36}$

5. both numbers are even $\frac{1}{4}$

6. both numbers are prime $\frac{1}{4}$

Lesson 13-2 *(Pages 534–536)* 1–5. See Answer Appendix for outcomes.

Make a tree diagram and list the outcomes. Then give the total number of outcomes.

1. rolling 2 number cubes 36 outcomes

2. choosing an ice cream cone from waffle, plain, or sugar and a flavor of ice cream from chocolate, vanilla, or strawberry 9 outcomes

3. making a sandwich from white, wheat, or rye bread, cheddar or swiss cheese and ham, turkey, or roast beef 18 outcomes

4. flipping a penny twice 4 outcomes

5. choosing one math class from algebra and geometry and one foreign language class from French, Spanish, or Latin 6 outcomes

Lesson 13-3 *(Pages 538–541)*

Use the Counting Principle to find the total number of outcomes in each situation.

1. choosing a local phone number if the exchange is 234 and each of the four remaining digits is different 5,040 outcomes

2. choosing a way to drive from Millville to Westwood if there are 4 roads that lead from Millville to Miamisburg, 2 roads that connect Miamisburg to Hathaway, and 4 highways that connect Hathaway to Westwood 32 outcomes

3. tossing a quarter, rolling a number cube, and tossing a dime 24 outcomes

4. spinning the spinners shown below 96 outcomes

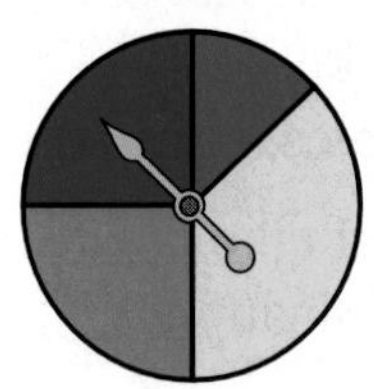 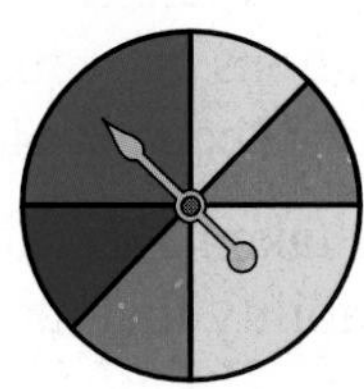 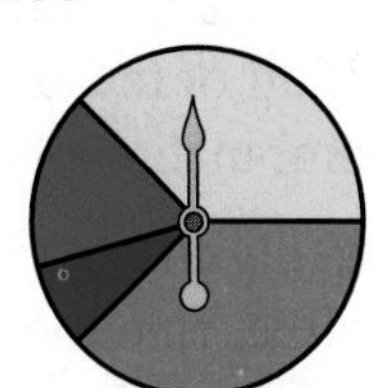

EXTRA PRACTICE

Lesson 13-4 *(Pages 542–545)*

Find each probability.

1. Two evenly-balanced nickels are flipped. Find the probability that one head and one tail result. $\frac{1}{2}$
2. A wallet contains four \$5 bills, two \$10 bills, and eight \$1 bills. Two bills are selected without the first selection being replaced. Find *P*(\$5, then \$5). $\frac{6}{91}$
3. Two chips are selected from a box containing 6 blue chips, 4 red chips, and 3 green chips. The first chip selected is not replaced before the second is drawn. Find *P*(red, then green). $\frac{1}{13}$
4. A blue die and a red die are rolled. Find the probability that an odd number is rolled on the blue die and a multiple of 3 is rolled on the red die. $\frac{1}{6}$

Lesson 13-5 *(Pages 547–549)*

Find the value of each expression.

1. 3! 6
2. 0! 1
3. 6! 720
4. *P*(5, 3) 60
5. *P*(6, 6) 720
6. *P*(10, 2) 90
7. *P*(5, 0) 1
8. *P*(3, 2) 6

Solve.

9. How many different five-digit zip codes can be formed if no digit can be repeated? 30,240 zip codes
10. Eight runners are competing in a 100-meter sprint. In how many ways can the gold, silver, and bronze medals be awarded? 336 ways
11. In a lottery for which 30 tickets were sold (all to different people), in how many ways can the grand prize, second prize, and third prizes be awarded? 24,360 ways

3. Andrew, Jonathan; Andrew, Megan; Andrew, Rebecca; Andrew, Jeffrey; Jonathan, Megan; Jonathan, Rebecca; Jonathan, Jeffrey; Megan, Rebecca; Megan, Jeffrey;

Lesson 13-6 *(Pages 551–553)*

Tell whether each situation represents a *permutation* or *combination*.

1. Six people remaining in a game of musical chairs. combination
2. First, second, and third place awards of three students who are finalists in a writing competition. permutation

Solve.

3. List all of the possible combinations of Andrew, Jonathan, Megan, Rebecca, and Jeffrey taken 2 at a time. If all of the combinations are equally likely, find the probability that the combination chosen will consist of 2 males. $\frac{3}{10}$
4. List all the combinations of the digits 1, 3, 5, 7, 9 taken 3 at a time. If all of the combinations are equally alike, find the probability that the combination chosen will contain a 1. 135, 137, 139, 157, 159, 179, 357, 359, 579, 379; $\frac{6}{10}$ or $\frac{3}{5}$

EXTRA PRACTICE

Mixed Problem Solving

Solve using any strategy.

1. ***Money Matters*** Cara needs to buy five different colored pens for a writing project. She has \$12.00. Does she have enough money if each pen costs \$1.98? **yes**

2. ***Patterns*** Study the pattern below.

$$1 = 1$$
$$1 + 3 = 4$$
$$1 + 3 + 5 = 9$$

List the next 3 lines in the pattern. What is the pattern of the sums?
$1 + 3 + 5 + 7 = 16$; $1 + 3 + 5 + 7 + 9 = 25$; $1 + 3 + 5 + 7 + 9 + 11 = 36$; They are perfect squares.

3. ***Money Matters*** The You-Rent-It Auto Company charges \$30 a day or \$165 a week to rent a compact car. Choose the best estimate of how much money the weekly rate saves the customer who rents a car for 7 days. **c.**
   a. \$25
   b. \$35
   c. \$45
   d. \$55

4. Coach Williams wants to schedule a round-robin tournament for his chess club where every student plays every other student. If there are seven club members, how many games should the coach schedule? **21 games**

5. ***Geometry*** A fence is put around a square dog run whose area is 400 feet. Enough is left over to fence a square garden whose area is 25 square feet. What is the minimum amount of fencing used? **100 ft**

6. ***School*** Dan, Nan, and Fran have lockers next to each other. Nan rides the bus with the person whose locker is at the right. Dan's locker is not next to Nan's locker. Who has the locker at the left? **Nan**

7. ***Money Matters*** Andrea has \$2.80 worth of quarters and dimes in her pocket. If the number of quarters equals the number of dimes, how many quarters does she have? **8 quarters**

8. Logan used blocks to build a "fort." The blocks were cubes and were stacked five high. The top, side, and front views were all squares. How many blocks did Logan need to build the fort? **80 cubes**

Mixed Problem Solving

Solve using any strategy.

1. ***Patterns*** The NCAA basketball tournament starts with 64 teams. After the first round, there are 32 teams left; after the second round there are 16 teams left, and so on. Complete the pattern until there is only one team left. How many rounds does it take to determine a winner? **6 rounds**

2. ***Nutrition*** The average American eats 28 pounds of cheese a year, and the population of the U.S. was 248,709,873 in 1990. The product manager at Franklin Dairy reported that about 2 billion pounds of cheese were sold in 1990. Is this reasonable? **no**

3. An elevator starts with four passengers and stops at three floors. How many possible ways can the passengers get off the elevator? **34**

4. ***Geometry*** How many diagonals does a 20-sided polygon have? **170 diagonals**

5. ***Statistics*** Use the bar graph to predict which age group will be increasing in numbers over the next century. **65 and over**

Percent Distribution of the Population by Age

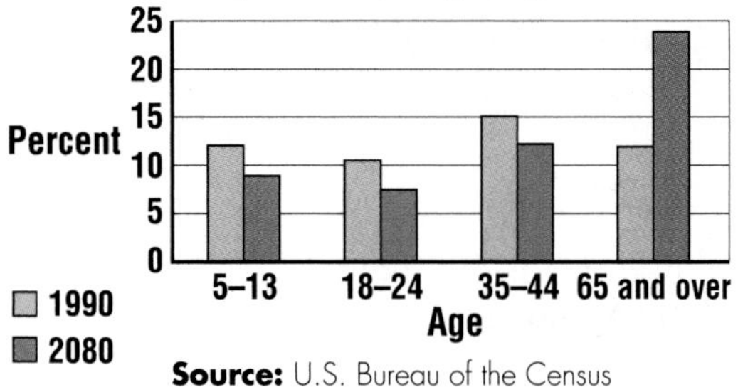

Source: U.S. Bureau of the Census

6. ***School*** Ms. Bosco's class started a six-day problem-solving contest. Each day, only students who correctly solved the previous day's problem are allowed to participate. There are 32 students in the class. If only half of the students get a problem correct on any day, how many students can participate on the fourth day? **4 students**

7. ***Money Matters*** The sale price of a sweater was $19 after an additional $5 was taken off the sweater that was already marked 50% off. What was the original price of the sweater? **$48**

8. ***Sports*** American football is played on a rectangular field that is 160 feet by 120 yards including the end zones. What is a reasonable estimate of the area of the playing field in square feet? **58,000 square feet**

CHAPTER 1 Test

1. ***Transportation*** The Lewis Middle School Band is planning a bus trip to a band competition. There are 138 members in the band, and each bus will hold 32 people. How many buses are needed for the trip? **5 buses**

2. Name the operation to be done first in the expression $26 + 12 \div 3$. **division**

Evaluate each expression.

3. $10 \cdot 2 + 3$ **23**
4. $7 - 5 + 3$ **5**
5. $(3 + 6) \div (2 + 1)$ **3**
6. $7 + 12 \div 4 - 2$ **8**
7. 5^2 **25**
8. $4 \cdot 2 + 3^3$ **35**

9. ***Entertainment*** An adult movie ticket costs $7.25, and a child's ticket costs $5.50. If two adults and three children go to the movie, find the total cost. **$31**

Evaluate each expression if $j = 4$, $k = 7$, and $m = 12$.

10. $\frac{m}{j}$ **3**
11. $3k - m$ **9**
12. $4j - m + 2k$ **18**
13. j^3 **64**
14. $k^2 - 2j$ **41**
15. $2(j + k)$ **22**

16. Write b^5 as a product of the same factor. $b \cdot b \cdot b \cdot b \cdot b$
17. Write $11 \cdot 11 \cdot 11 \cdot 11 \cdot 11 \cdot 11 \cdot 11$ using exponents. 11^7

Solve each equation.

18. $6a = 72$ **12**
19. $\frac{x}{8} = 100$ **800**
20. $p + 13 = 25$ **12**
21. $35 - m = 19$ **16**

22. Draw the next two figures that continue the pattern.

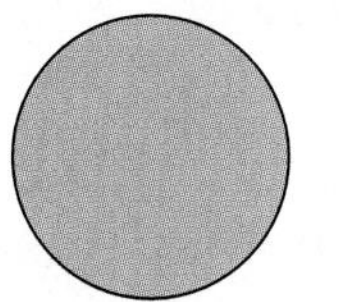
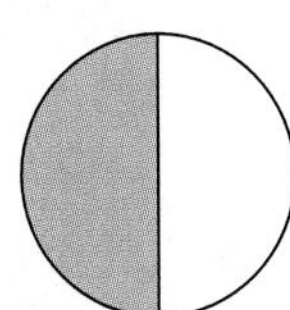
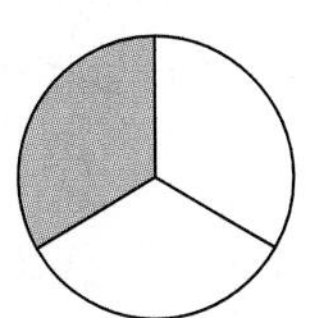
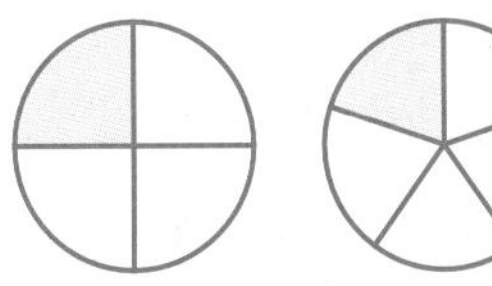

Find the area of each rectangle or parallelogram.

23. rectangle: ℓ, 12 in.; w, 7 in. **84 in^2**
24. parallelogram: b, 50 cm; h, 20 cm **1,000 cm^2**

25. ***Animals*** Heather left both her dog and cat at a kennel for 3 nights. The kennel charges $8 per night for the dog and $5 per night for the cat. Compute Heather's total bill. **$39**

CHAPTER 2

Test

Order each set of decimals from least to greatest.

1. 12.6, 4.3, 8.7, 4, 12.06 4, 4.3, 8.7, 12.06, 12.6

2. 0.07, 0.7, 0.71, 1.07, 1.71 0.07, 0.7, 0.71, 1.07, 1.71

Round each number to the underlined place-value position.

3. 13.2<u>7</u>5 13.28 **4.** 0.<u>0</u>76 0.1 **5.** 1<u>2</u>,436 12,000 **6.** <u>0</u>.995 1

7. ***Sports*** The average attendance at football games last season was 2,176.34. Round this number to the nearest whole number. 2,176

Estimate. 8. $30 + 10 = 40$ 9. $200 - 100 = 100$

8. $27.34 + 12.95$

9. $236.95 - 107.07$

10. 23.6×2.95 $20 \times 3 = 60$

11. $11.1\overline{)142.6}$ $140 \div 10 = 14$

12. 91.6×7.999 $90 \times 8 = 720$

13. ***Money Matters*** During a two-week period, Hiroko worked 89.7 hours. Her hourly wage is $6.85. Estimate the amount she earned during that period. $90 \times \$7 = \$630$

Multiply or divide. 15. 0.022 16. 6,700 17. 470 18. 300,300

14. 0.3×8 2.4

15. 5.5×0.004

16. $6.7 \times 1,000$

17. 0.0047×10^5

18. $3.003 \times 100,000$

19. $0.4\overline{)4.8}$ 12

20. $0.24\overline{)0.0072}$ 0.03

21. $0.016\overline{)64}$ 4,000

22. ***Pets*** Phillip's cat Felix weighed 0.95 pound at birth. On his first birthday, Felix weighed 9.2 times his birth weight. What was Felix's weight on his first birthday? 8.74 pounds

Express each fraction or mixed number as a decimal. If the decimal is a repeating decimal, use bar notation.

23. $\frac{5}{8}$ 0.625

24. $\frac{1}{9}$ $0.\overline{1}$

25. $5\frac{1}{20}$ 5.05

Express each number in scientific notation.

26. 23,000 2.3×10^4

27. 632 6.32×10^2

28. 518,000,000 5.18×10^8

Complete.

29. 1.62 L = __?__ mL 1,620

30. 243 g = __?__ kg 0.243

31. 0.09 km = __?__ mm 90,000

32. ***Food*** To mix a punch, Andrea starts with 4 liters of ginger ale and adds 2,650 milliliters of cranberry juice.

a. How many liters are in the punch bowl when the punch is complete? 6.65 liters

b. How many 200-mL servings of punch can be served? about 33 servings

33. ***Money Matters*** Booker bought a 3-pound bag of apples for $2.89, a 2-pound bag of carrots for $1.79, and 4 avocados for $0.99 each. Should he expect to pay about $5 or $10 at the checkout? $10

Test

The French test grades were 95, 76, 82, 90, 71, 76, 79, 82, 95, 85, 93, 71, and 63.

1. Find the range. 32

2. Choose an appropriate scale and an interval for a frequency table. 2. Sample answer: 61-100, 10

3. Make a frequency table of the data. See Answer Appendix.

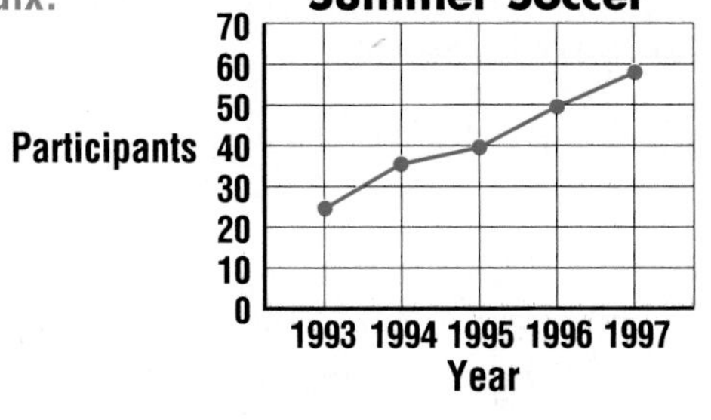

4. ***Sports*** The number of girls participating in the summer soccer league has increased during the last five years. Predict the number of girls participating in the year 2000. Sample answer: 90 girls

5. ***Employment*** The line graph shows the percent of women holding jobs outside the home from 1975 to 1995. In which year were the greatest number of women working outside the home? 1995

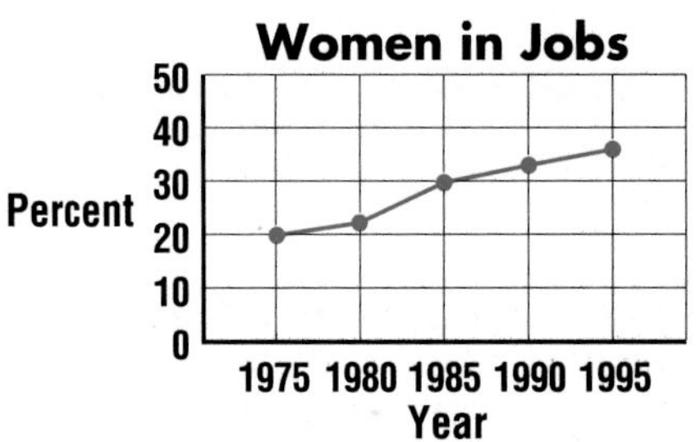

6. Use the graph to predict the percent of women who will hold jobs outside the home in the year 2000. Sample answer: 45%

7. Name the outliers on the line plot. 10, 28

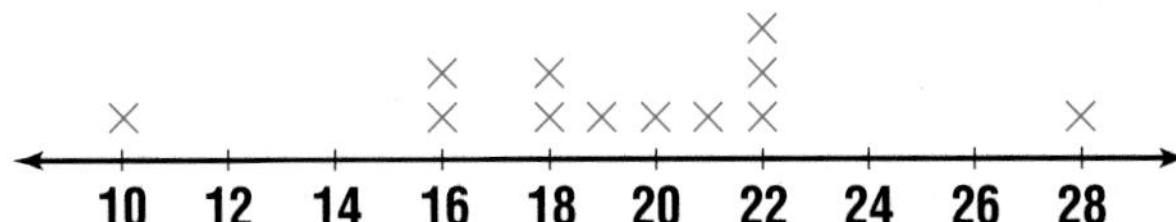

8. ***Families*** The Hanna family has five children whose ages are 20, 20, 19, 17, and 26. Make a line plot of the ages. See Answer Appendix.

Find the mean, mode(s), and median for each set of data.

9. 4, 6, 11, 7, 4, 11, 4 6.7, 4, 6

10. 12.4, 17.9, 16.5, 10.2 14.25, none, 14.45

Make a stem-and-leaf plot for each set of data. 11–12. See Answer Appendix.

11. 37, 59, 26, 42, 57, 53, 31, 58.

12. 46¢, 59¢, 42¢, 69¢, 55¢, 48¢, 66¢, 43¢

13. Refer to the box-and-whisker plot. b. 21, 16

a. What is the median? 19

b. What is the upper quartile and lower quartile?

c. What is the interquartile range? 5

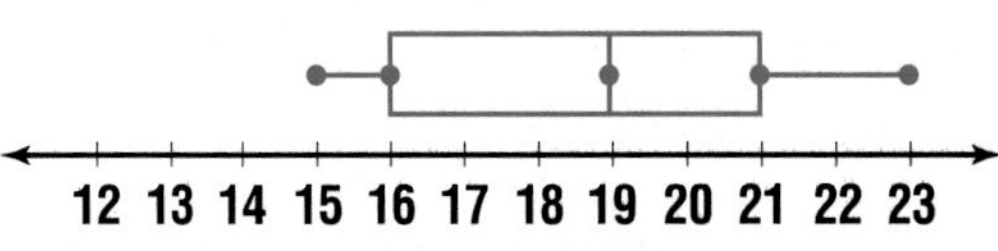

The prices of 15 pairs of shoes at a local shoe store are $34, $28, $32, $28, $25, $69, $25, $75, $30, $29, $32, $28, $27, $30, and $26.

14. Find the mean, mode(s), and median. Round to the nearest cent. $34.53, $28, $29

15. Which average might the manager prefer to quote to a cost-conscious customer? mode

CHAPTER 4 Test

1. Determine whether 639 is divisible by 2, 3, 4, 5, 6, 9, or 10. **3, 9**

2. Write the prime factorization of 250. 2×5^3

Identify each sequence as *arithmetic*, *geometric*, or *neither*. Then find the next three terms.

3. 9, 15, 21, 27, 33, . . . **arithmetic; 39, 45, 51**

4. 2, 6, 18, 54, 162, . . . **geometric; 486, 1,458, 4,374**

5. ***Savings*** In January, Elena deposited $50 in her savings account. She plans to increase the amount she deposits by $5 each month. How much will Elena deposit in April? **$65**

Find the GCF of each set of numbers.

6. 36, 54 **18**

7. 52, 100 **4**

Express each fraction or ratio in simplest form.

8. $\frac{33}{55}$ $\frac{3}{5}$

9. 24:64 **3:8**

Express each fraction or ratio as a percent.

10. $\frac{28}{70}$ **40%**

11. 34:100 **34%**

Express each percent or decimal as a fraction in simplest form.

12. 0.32 $\frac{8}{25}$

13. 73% $\frac{73}{100}$

The spinner at the right is equally likely to stop on each of the regions. Find the probability that the spinner will stop on each of the following.

14. a prime number $\frac{1}{2}$

15. a factor of 24 $\frac{3}{4}$

Find the LCM of each set of numbers.

16. 8, 28 **56**

17. 14, 21, 27 **378**

18. ***Life Science*** One type of cicada emerges from hibernation every 17 years. Another type emerges every 13 years. If both types came out of hibernation one year, in how many years would this happen again? **221 years**

Replace each ● with <, >, or = to make a true sentence.

19. $\frac{5}{8}$ ● $\frac{12}{20}$ $>$

20. $\frac{12}{15}$ ● $\frac{9}{12}$ $>$

CHAPTER 5

Test

Write the integer represented by each letter. Then find its opposite and its absolute value.

1. A −2, 2, 2 **2.** B 1, −1, 1 **3.** C 4, −4, 4

Replace each ● with < or > to make a true sentence.

4. $-9 \bullet 6$ <

5. $0 \bullet -3$ >

6. ***Earth Science*** On the same day, the thermometer registered 5° below 0 in Cleveland, 2° above 0 in Columbus, and 2° below 0 in Cincinnati. Which city was the coldest? **Cleveland**

On graph paper, draw a coordinate plane. Then graph and label each point.

7. $P(6, -3)$

8. $B(0, -4)$

9. $T(-5, 1)$

7–9. See Answer Appendix.

Solve each equation.

10. $g = 5 + (-3)$ 2

11. $-9 + (-3) = m$ −12

12. $r = -4 + 4$ 0

13. $k = 11 - 15$ −4

14. $-7 - (-2) = s$ −5

15. $b = -3 - 4$ −7

16. $c = -5(-3)$ 15

17. $h = 12(-2)$ −24

18. $(-7)^2 = p$ 49

19. $q = 90 \div (-3)$ −30

20. $(-25) \div 5 = t$ −5

21. $m = (-72) \div (-9)$ 8

Evaluate each expression if $a = 8$, $b = -3$, $c = 2$, and $d = -8$.

22. $-10 + a$ −2

23. $b + d$ −11

24. $d - c$ −10

25. $23 - b$ 26

26. $-9a$ −72

27. d^2 64

28. $5ac$ 80

29. $a \div c$ 4

30. ***Games*** Byron is playing a popular board game and has \$250 left. He lands on Boardwalk and needs \$200 more than he has to pay rent. How much is the rent on Boardwalk? **\$450**

31. ***Allowance*** Ming is supposed to receive an allowance of \$25 each month. However, for each day he forgets to take out the garbage, his allowance decreases by \$2. Ming forgets to take the garbage out three times during October. Find the amount of his allowance for October. **\$19**

Graph each triangle and its transformation. Write the ordered pairs for the vertices of the new triangle. **32–33. See Answer Appendix for graphs.**

32. $\triangle ABC$ with vertices $A(-4, 2)$, $B(3, 4)$, and $C(-1, 6)$ translated 2 units right and 4 units down **A′(−2, −2), B′(5, 0), C′(1, 2)**

33. $\triangle KLM$ with vertices $K(2, 2)$, $L(4, -1)$, and $M(0, 0)$ reflected over the y-axis **K′(−2, 2), L′(−4, −1), M′(0, 0)**

CHAPTER TEST

CHAPTER 6

Test

Solve each equation. Check your solution.

1. $12 + t = 32$ 20
2. $m + 7 = 2$ −5
3. $2.9 = w + 1.7$ 1.2
4. $12e = -120$ −10
5. $14.7 = 3.5d$ 4.2
6. $s - 5.9 = 12.1$ 18
7. $6x + 4 = 10$ 1
8. $-2b - 5 = 25$ −15
9. $2.6 = 0.2n - 4$ 33
10. $-14s + 5 = 33$ −2
11. $3f - 15 = 6$ 7
12. $0.42 = 0.17 + 0.5j$ 0.5

13. ***Physical Science*** During a chemical reaction, 3 milliliters of the original chemical evaporates, leaving 2.6 milliliters in the test tube. Write and solve an equation to find a, the amount of the chemical in the test tube before the reaction occurs. $a - 3 = 2.6$, $a = 5.6$

14. ***Money Matters*** Ann prices a sweater in two stores. It is \$29 in one store and \$34 in the other. Write and solve an equation to find p, the price difference between the two stores. $34 - p = 29$, $p = 5$

Write each phrase as an algebraic expression.

15. 26 less than x $x - 26$
16. t increased by 23 $t + 23$

Write each sentence as an algebraic equation.

17. The product of 7 and a number is 35. $7n = 35$
18. A number increased by 125 is 315. $n + 125 = 315$
19. Twice a number less 5 is 19. $2n - 5 = 19$

20–23. See Answer Appendix for graphs.

Solve each inequality. Graph the solution on a number line.

20. $y + 5 < 13$ $y < 8$
21. $3n \leq 21$ $n \leq 7$
22. $4c - 3 > 17$ $c > 5$

23. Graph the ordered pairs in the table on a coordinate plane. Then write a sentence describing the relationship as a function. As the number of months increase, the enrollment also increases.

Month	1	2	3	4
Enrollment at Small Tots Day Care	40	42	42	44

Graph each equation. 24–25. See Answer Appendix for graphs.

24. $y = -2x - 1$
25. $y = 3x + 1$

CHAPTER 7

Test

Estimate.

1. $1\frac{1}{3} + \frac{6}{7}$ **1 + 1 = 2**

2. $10\frac{4}{5} - 4\frac{1}{8}$ **11 − 4 = 7**

3. $5\frac{1}{8} \div \frac{5}{6}$ **5 ÷ 1 = 5**

Add, subtract, or multiply. Write each sum, difference, or product in simplest form.

4. $\frac{1}{10} + \frac{2}{5}$ $\frac{1}{2}$

5. $\frac{5}{6} - \frac{2}{9}$ $\frac{11}{18}$

6. $\frac{4}{9} \times \frac{3}{8}$ $\frac{1}{6}$

(12) **7.** $2\frac{1}{4} \times 6$ $13\frac{1}{2}$

(13) **8.** $2\frac{1}{7} - \frac{3}{7}$ $1\frac{5}{7}$

9. $\frac{3}{5} + \frac{5}{9}$ $1\frac{7}{45}$

10. $5\frac{1}{3} + 4\frac{3}{4}$ $10\frac{1}{12}$

11. $\frac{6}{7} \times \frac{5}{8}$ $\frac{15}{28}$

12. $15\frac{4}{9} - 5\frac{5}{12}$ $10\frac{1}{36}$

Complete.

13. 4 lb = __?__ oz **64**

14. 20 qt = __?__ gal **5**

15. How many fluid ounces are in 3 cups? **24**

16. Find the perimeter of a rectangle with a length of $6\frac{1}{2}$ yards and a width of $3\frac{1}{4}$ yards. $19\frac{1}{2}$ **yd**

Find the circumference of each circle to the nearest tenth.

17. $d = 2.8$ cm **8.8 in.**

18. $r = \frac{1}{3}$ yd **2.1 yd**

Solve each equation.

19. $w = 5 \times 2\frac{2}{5}$ **12**

20. $\frac{3}{4}b = \frac{1}{3}$ $\frac{4}{9}$

Divide. Write each quotient in simplest form.

21. $\frac{3}{5} \div \frac{9}{10}$ $\frac{2}{3}$

(14) **22.** $2\frac{5}{12} \div \frac{5}{6}$ $2\frac{9}{10}$

(15) **23.** $3\frac{1}{3} \div 1\frac{1}{6}$ $2\frac{6}{7}$

24. ***Money Matters*** Willie found a jacket he likes that costs \$60. If he waits until the store has its annual $\frac{1}{3}$-off sale, how much can he save? **\$20**

25. ***Cooking*** A recipe calls for 2 cups of milk. Miriam wants to double this recipe. How many *quarts* of milk will she need? **1 qt**

CHAPTER TEST

CHAPTER 8

Test

Express each ratio as a fraction in simplest form.

1. $\frac{20}{24}$ $\frac{5}{6}$

2. 35:15 $\frac{7}{3}$

3. 42 out of 60 days $\frac{7}{10}$

4. Tell whether 21:35 and 15:30 are equivalent. no

Express each rate as a unit rate.

5. 24 cards for $4.80 $0.20 per card

6. 330 miles on 15 gallons of gas 22 mpg

7. ***Population Density*** In 1994, Washington, D.C. had a population of 567,094 people and an area of 67 square miles. To the nearest whole number, how many people per square mile were there in Washington, D.C. in 1994? 8,464 people per square mile

Solve each proportion.

8. $\frac{2}{3} = \frac{x}{42}$ 28

9. $\frac{9}{m} = \frac{12}{36}$ 27

10. ***Physical Fitness*** Alyssa swims 3 laps in 12 minutes. At this same rate, how many laps will she swim in 10 minutes? $2\frac{1}{2}$ laps

Find the distance between each pair of cities, given the map distance and scale.

11. Indianapolis, Indiana and Columbus, Ohio; $3\frac{3}{4}$ inches; 1 inch:49 miles $183\frac{3}{4}$ miles

12. Pensacola and Tallahassee, Florida; $3\frac{1}{2}$ inches; $\frac{1}{2}$ inch:50 km 350 km

Express each fraction as a percent.

13. $\frac{3}{8}$ 37.5%

14. $\frac{51}{200}$ 25.5%

15. $2\frac{1}{2}$ 250%

Express each decimal as a percent.

16. 0.65 65%

17. 0.079 7.9%

18. 0.0091 0.91%

Express each percent as a fraction in simplest form and as a decimal.

19. 47% $\frac{47}{100}$; 0.47

20. 80% $\frac{4}{5}$; 0.8

21. 450% $4\frac{1}{2}$; 4.5

Find each number. Round to the nearest tenth if necessary.

22. What number is 35% of 650? 227.5

23. Find 69% of 2,398. 1,654.6

24. 82 is what percent of 415? 19.8%

25. 458 is 105% of what number? 436.2

CHAPTER 9

Test

Classify each angle as *acute*, *obtuse*, *right*, or *straight*.

1.  acute

2. 135° obtuse

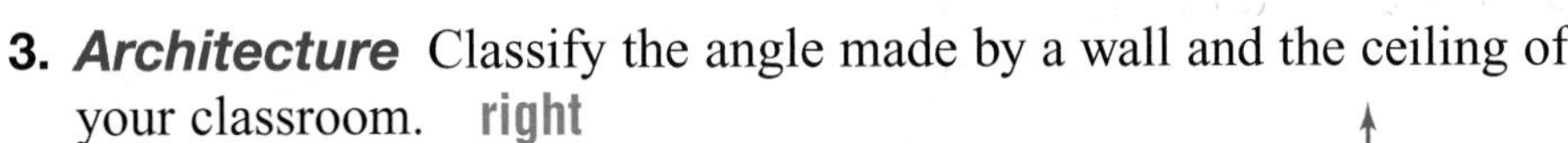

3. ***Architecture*** Classify the angle made by a wall and the ceiling of your classroom. right

4. Classify the angles at the right as complementary, supplementary, or neither. complementary

Determine which figures are polygons. If the figure is a polygon, name it and tell whether it is a regular polygon. If the figure is *not* a polygon, explain why.

5. 

6.

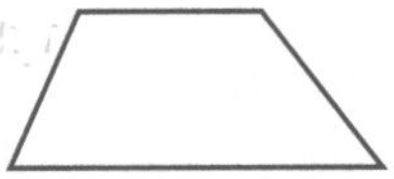

7. 

8. 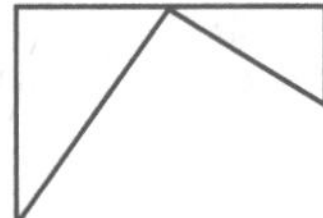

5–8. See Answer Appendix.

Tell whether each pair of polygons is similar. Justify your answer.

9. 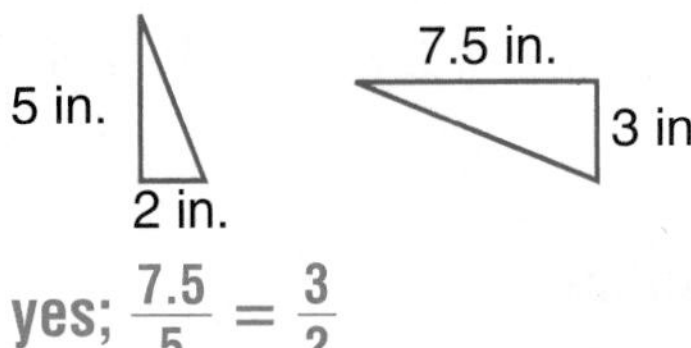

yes; $\frac{7.5}{5} = \frac{3}{2}$

10. 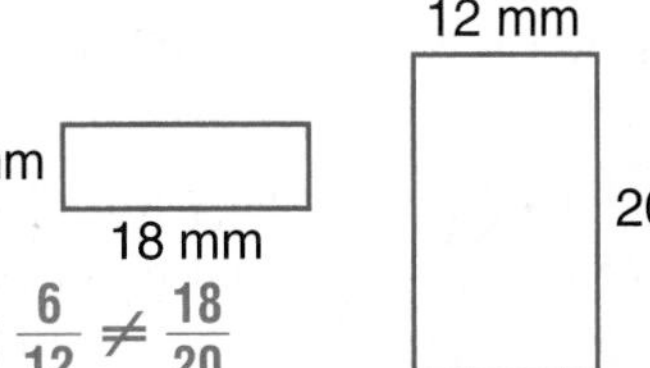

no; $\frac{6}{12} \neq \frac{18}{20}$

11. ***Geography*** Dan wants to draw a map on the chalkboard that is similar to a map in his book. The outline of the map is a rectangle that is 6 inches wide and 8 inches long. If he draws the longer side 36 inches long, how wide should he draw the map? 27 inches

Classify each triangle by its angles and by its sides.

12. 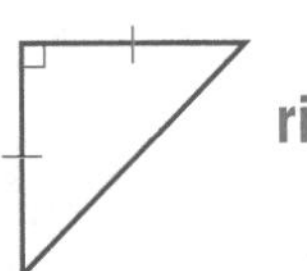
right, isosceles

13. 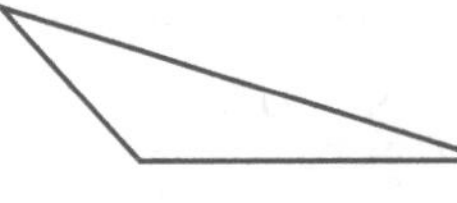
obtuse, scalene

Name every quadrilateral that describes the figure. Then underline the name that best describes it. 14–16. See Answer Appendix.

14. 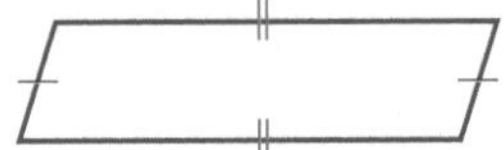

15. 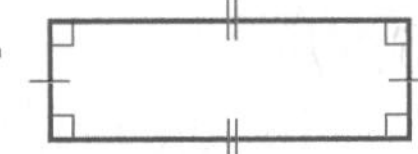

16. 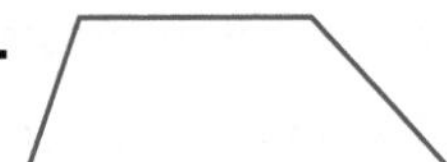

17. Determine if a regular heptagon, whose angle measures total 900°, can be used by itself to make a tessellation. no

Complete the pattern unit for each translation. Then draw the tessellation.

18. 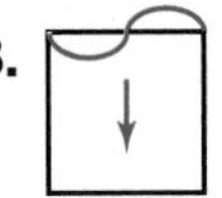

19.

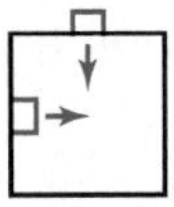

18–19. See Answer Appendix.

20. Draw a figure that has no lines of symmetry. See Answer Appendix.

CHAPTER TEST

CHAPTER 10

Test

1. Amanda is thinking of two numbers. When she adds them together, the sum is 107. When she subtracts the lesser number from the greater number, their difference is 17. What are the numbers? **45 and 62**

Find the square of each number.

2. 8 **64**
3. 34 **1,156**

Find each square root.

4. $\sqrt{81}$ **9**
5. $\sqrt{400}$ **20**

6. ***Physical Fitness*** Every morning, Elisa jogs around a square region that has an area of 9 square miles. How far does Elisa jog each morning? **12 mi**

Estimate each square root to the nearest whole number.

7. $\sqrt{24}$ **5**
8. $\sqrt{120}$ **11**

Find the missing measure for each right triangle. Round to the nearest tenth.

9. a: 5 m; b: 4 m **6.4 m**
10. b: 12 in.; c: 14 in. **7.2 in.**
11. a: 5 yd; c: 10 yd **8.7 yd**

12. ***Traveling*** Jerome gets lost while driving to a new vacation spot. After looking at a map, he sees that he is 16 miles too far east and 8 miles too far north. What is the straight-line distance to Jerome's destination? Round to the nearest tenth. **17.9 mi**

Estimate the area of each figure.

13. 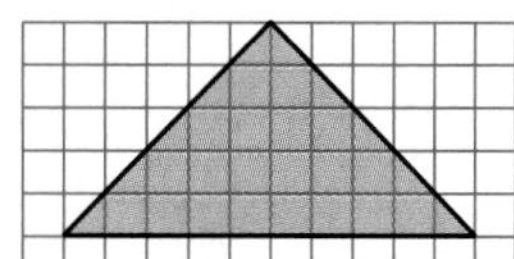 **about 25 units²**

14. 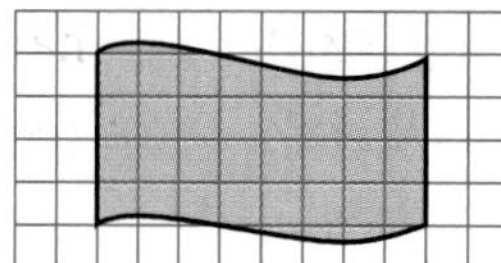 **about 32 units²**

Find the area of each figure.

15. triangle: base: 15 ft, height: 4 ft **30 ft²**
16. trapezoid: bases: 5 km, 10 km, height: 6 km **45 km²**

Find the area of each circle to the nearest tenth.

17. radius: 14 cm **615.8 cm²**
18. diameter: 25 in. **490.9 in²**

Answers are calculated using the π key on a calculator and then rounded.

19. ***Recreation*** A circular playground at a park covers an area of 1,000 square feet. Find the length of the diameter of the playground to the nearest tenth. **35.7 ft**

20. ***Games*** To win a carnival game, you must throw a dart at a board and hit one of the several cards on the board. The board is 7 feet by 4 feet. If the cards cover 3 square feet, what is the probability that a randomly-thrown dart will hit a card? $\frac{3}{28}$

CHAPTER TEST

Test

Estimate. 2. $80(100\% + 50\%) = 80 + 40$ or 120

1. 18% of 246 $0.2 \cdot 250 = 50$
2. 145% of 81

Write an equation for each problem. Then solve. Round answers to the nearest tenth. 4. $75 = R \cdot 50$; 150%

3. Find 15% of 60. $P = 0.15 \cdot 60$; 9
4. 75 is what percent of 50?
5. 50% of what number is 335.8? $335.8 = 0.5 \cdot B$; 671.6
6. What percent of 48 is 9? $9 = R \cdot 48$; 18.8%
7. The table shows the result of a survey of students' favorite types of fiction at Haskell Middle School. Find the number of degrees for each section if you make a circle graph of the data.
   a. Mystery 86.4° **b.** Science Fiction 28.8°

Type of Fiction	Number of Students
Mystery	24
Science Fiction	8
Sports	30
Romance	38

8. Refer to the table above. If Haskell Middle School has a total of 500 students, how many would you expect to choose each of the following types of fiction as their favorite?
   a. Sports 150 students **b.** Romance 190 students

Find the percent of change. Round to the nearest whole percent.

9. original: \$60 25%
   new: \$75
10. original: 145 49%
    new: 216
11. Find the percent of decrease if an item that originally cost \$54 goes on sale for \$48. 11%
12. One pocket calendar can display 42 characters on its screen. A newer model of the pocket calendar can display 64 characters. Find the percent of increase in displayed characters. 52%

Find the sales tax or discount to the nearest cent.

13. \$19.99 book, 20% off \$4.00
14. \$2,200 computer, $6\frac{1}{2}$% sales tax \$143
15. \$35.49 jeans, 33% discount \$11.71
16. \$85 boots, 5.75% tax \$4.89

Find the interest to the nearest cent for each principal, interest rate, and time.

17. \$1,250, 11%, 3 years \$412.50
18. \$2,000, 11.75%, 18 months \$352.50
19. ***Education*** The University of North Carolina presently charges \$1,091 per year for tuition for residents of North Carolina. If tuition increases 7% for the coming academic year, what will the tuition be next year? \$1,167.37
20. ***Money Matters*** Jorge borrows \$4,500 to buy a new motorcycle. His loan is for 4 years at an annual interest rate of 10%. Find the total amount Jorge will pay for his motorcycle. \$6,300

CHAPTER TEST

CHAPTER 12 Test

Draw a top, a side, and a front view of each figure. 1–4. See Answer Appendix.

1. 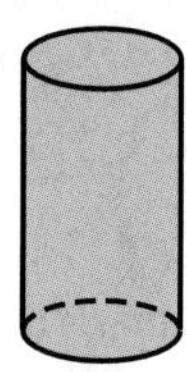

2. 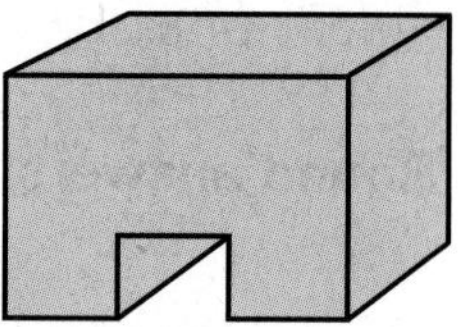

3. 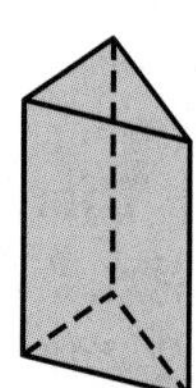

4. 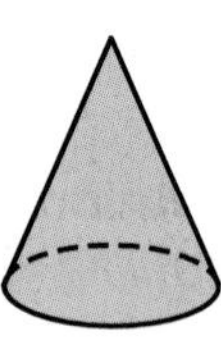

7, 8, 11, 12, 15, 16, 19. Answers are calculated using the π key on a calculator and then rounded.

Find the volume of each rectangular prism or cylinder to the nearest tenth.

5. 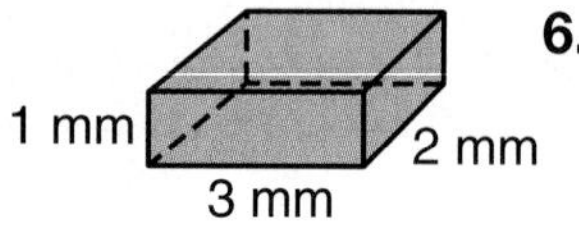
1 mm
2 mm
3 mm

6 mm³

6. 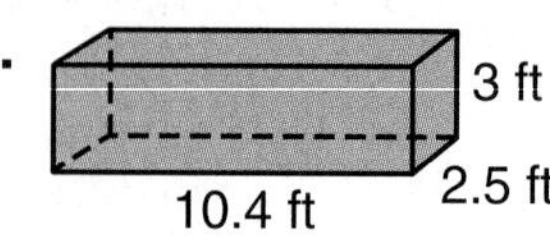

78 ft³

7. 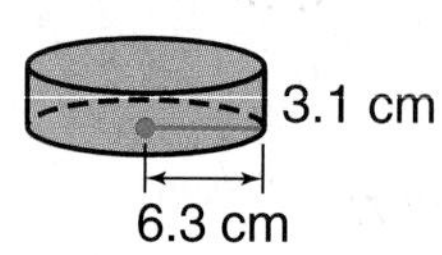

386.5 cm³

8. 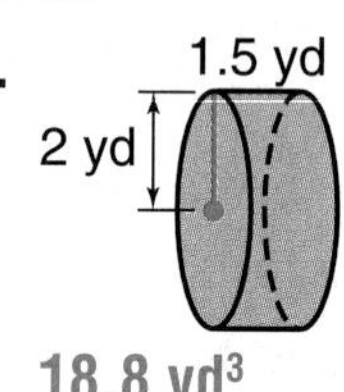

18.8 yd³

9. A rectangular prism has a length of 1 inch, a width of 6 inches, and a height of 9 inches. Find the volume of the prism. 54 in³

10. Find the volume of a cube with sides 4 centimeters long. 64 cm³

11. Find the volume of a cylinder with a height of 5 feet and a diameter of 12 feet. 565.5 ft³

12. ***Drinking Straws*** The standard-size drinking straw has a radius of $\frac{1}{8}$ inch and a height of $7\frac{3}{4}$ inches. What is the maximum volume of liquid that can be contained in the straw at any given time? 0.4 in³

Find the surface area of each rectangular prism or cylinder to the nearest tenth.

13. 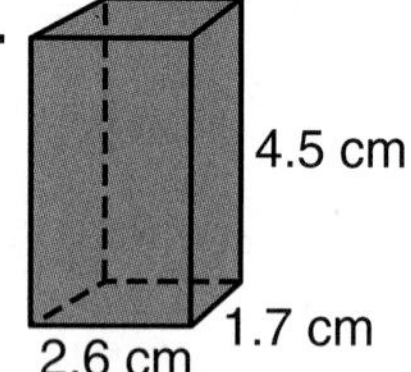

47.5 cm²

14. 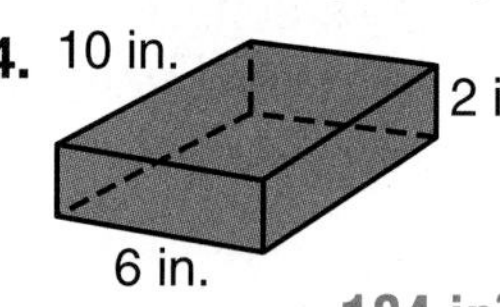

184 in²

15. 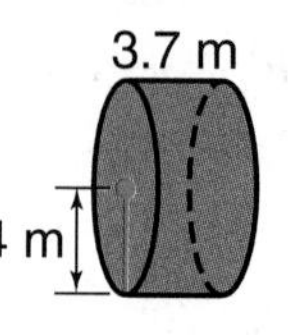

193.5 m²

16. 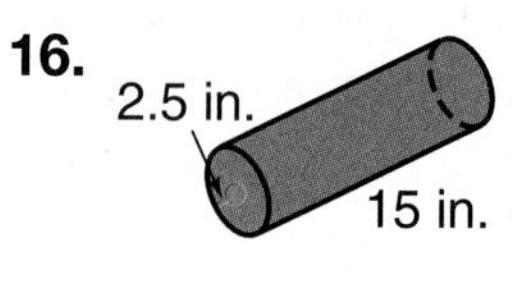

274.9 in²

17. Find the surface area of a rectangular prism with a length of 3.6 centimeters, a width of 2.1 centimeters, and a height of 8 centimeters. 106.3 cm²

18. ***Packaging*** What is the least amount of paper needed to wrap a box that is 12 inches by 20 inches by 2 inches? 608 in²

19. Find the surface area of a cylinder whose height is $\frac{1}{3}$ yard and whose base has a diameter of 14 yards. 322.5 yd²

20. ***Woodworking*** Sheri built a jewelry box as a class project. It is 14 inches long, 12 inches wide, and 8 inches high. She would like to paint the outside of the box. What is the surface area of the box? 752 in²

Test

1. Gary is making a sandwich. He has two kinds of bread and four kinds of meat. If he only uses one kind of bread and one kind of meat, how many different sandwiches can Gary make? **8 sandwiches**

2. A coin is tossed three times. Make a tree diagram to show all the possible outcomes. **See Answer Appendix.**

Use the Counting Principle to find the total number of outcomes in each situation.

3. choosing a three-digit security code

4. rolling 4 number cubes **1,296 outcomes**

5. choosing a pair of slacks from three pairs, a shirt from five shirts, and a pair of shoes from two pairs **30 outcomes**

3. 1,000 outcomes

The spinner at the right has an equal chance of landing on each number. Find each probability.

6. P(odd number) $\frac{1}{2}$

7. P(1 or 7) $\frac{1}{4}$

8. P(number greater than 2) $\frac{3}{4}$

The entry forms for a contest are in a container. There are forms for 100 students of which 30 are sixth graders, 35 are seventh graders, and 35 are eighth graders. One entry form is selected. Find each probability. **10.** $\frac{65}{100}$ **or** $\frac{13}{20}$

9. P(a sixth grader) $\frac{30}{100}$ **or** $\frac{3}{10}$

10. P(not an eighth grader)

11. P(at least a seventh grader) $\frac{70}{100}$ **or** $\frac{7}{10}$

Tell whether the events are independent or dependent.

12. rolling a pair of number cubes and getting a 5 on the first cube and a sum of 10 for both cubes **dependent**

13. having black hair and owning a black car **independent**

14. The two fire engines in a small town operate independently. The probability that each engine is available when needed is 0.95. Find the probability that both engines are available at one time. **0.9025**

Find the value of each expression.

15. 5! **120**

16. 7! **5,040**

17. In how many ways can a president, vice president, and secretary be chosen from among eight candidates? **336 ways**

18. A menu has 15 different items. In how many ways can you choose three items from the menu? **455 ways**

19. ***Sports*** Eight runners are participating in a 200-meter race. In how many ways can the gold, silver, and bronze medals be awarded? **336 ways**

20. ***School Government*** From a student council consisting of nine students, three are selected to represent the student body at a school board meeting. In how many ways can these students be selected? **84 ways**

Getting Acquainted with the Graphing Calculator

When some students first see a graphing calculator, they think, "Oh, no! Do we ***have*** to use one?", while others may think, "All right! We get to use these neat calculators!" There are as many thoughts and feelings about graphing calculators as there are students, but one thing is for sure: a graphing calculator *can* help you learn mathematics. Keep reading for answers to some frequently asked questions.

What is it?

So what is a graphing calculator? Very simply, it is a calculator that draws graphs. This means that it will do all of the things that a "regular" calculator will do, *plus* it will draw graphs of equations.

What does it do?

A graphing calculator can do more than just calculate and draw graphs. For example, you can program it and work with data to make statistical graphs and computations. If you need to generate random numbers, you can do that on the graphing calculator. If you need to find the absolute value of a number, you can do that too. It's really a very powerful tool, so powerful that it is often called a pocket computer.

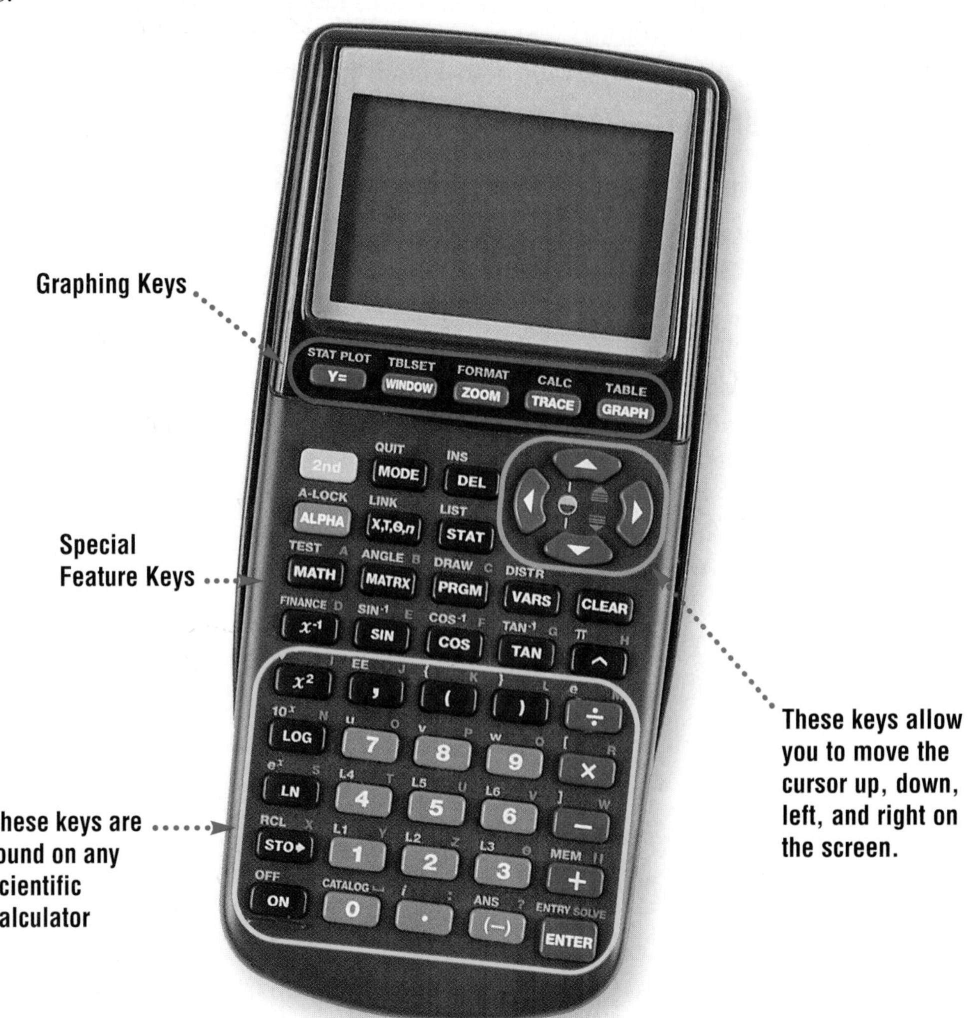
Graphing Keys
Special Feature Keys
These keys are found on any scientific calculator
These keys allow you to move the cursor up, down, left, and right on the screen.

Basic Keystrokes

- The yellow commands written above the calculator keys are accessed with the 2nd key, which is also yellow. Similarly, the green characters above the keys are accessed with the ALPHA key, which is also green. In this text, commands that are accessed by the 2nd and ALPHA keys are shown in brackets. For example, 2nd [QUIT] means to press the 2nd key followed by the key below the yellow QUIT command.
- 2nd [ENTRY] copies the previous calculation so you can edit and use it again.
- 2nd [QUIT] will return you to the home (or text) screen.
- Negative numbers are entered using the (–) key, not the minus sign, – .
- 2nd [OFF] turns the calculator off.

Order of Operations

As with any scientific calculator, the graphing calculator observes the order of operations.

Example	Keystrokes	Display
4 + 13	4 + 13 ENTER	4 + 13 17
5^3	5 ^ 3 ENTER	5 ^ 3 125
4 (9 + 18)	4 (9 + 18) ENTER	4(9 + 18) 108
$\sqrt{24}$	2nd [√‾] 24 ENTER	√‾(24 4.8989 79486

Programming

Programming features allow you to write and execute a series of commands for tasks that may be too complex or cumbersome to perform otherwise. Each program is given a name. Commands begin with a colon (:), which the calculator enters automatically, followed by an expression or an instruction.

When you press PRGM , you see three menus: EXEC, EDIT, and NEW. EXEC allows you to execute a stored program, EDIT allows you to edit or change a program, and NEW allows you to create a program.

- To begin entering a new program, press PRGM ▶ ▶ ENTER .
- You do not need to type each letter using the ALPHA key. Any command that contains lowercase letters should be entered by choosing it from a menu. Check your user's guide to find any commands that are unfamiliar.
- After a program is entered, press 2nd [QUIT] to exit the program mode and return to the home screen.
- To execute a program, press PRGM . Then use the down arrow key to locate the program name and press ENTER twice, or press the number or letter next to the program name followed by ENTER .
- If you wish to edit a program, press PRGM ▶ and choose the program from the menu.
- To immediately re-execute a program after it is run, press ENTER when Done appears on the screen.
- To stop a program during execution, press ON or 2nd [QUIT].

While a graphing calculator cannot do everything, it can make some things easier and help your understanding of math. To prepare for whatever lies ahead, you should try to learn as much as you can. Who knows? Maybe one day you will be designing the next satellite or building the next skyscraper with the help of a graphing calculator!

Getting Acquainted with Spreadsheets

What do you think of when people talk about computers? Maybe you think of computer games or using a word processor to write a school paper. But a computer is a powerful tool that can be used for many things.

One of the most common computer applications is a spreadsheet program. Here are answers to some of the questions you may have if you're new to using spreadsheets.

What is it?

You have probably seen tables of numbers in newspapers and magazines. Similar to those tables, a spreadsheet is a table that you can use to organize information. But a spreadsheet is more than just a table. You can also use a spreadsheet to perform calculations or make graphs.

Why use a spreadsheet?

The advantage a spreadsheet has over a simple calculator is that when a number is changed, the entire spreadsheet is recalculated and the new results are displayed. So with a spreadsheet, you can see patterns in data and investigate what happens if one or more of the numbers is changed.

How do I use a spreadsheet?

A spreadsheet is organized into boxes called *cells*. The cells are named by a letter, that identifies the column, and a number, that identifies the row. In the spreadsheet below, cell C4 is highlighted.

	A	B	C
1	Width	Length	Area
2	3	4	12
3	2	10	20
4	5	12	60
5	8	14	112

To enter information in a spreadsheet, simply move the cursor to the cell you want to access and click the mouse. Then type in the information and press Enter.

How do I enter formulas?

If you want to use the spreadsheet as a calculator, begin by choosing the cell where you want the result to appear.

- For a simple calculation, type = followed by the formula. For example, in the spreadsheet above, the formula in cell C2 is entered as "=A2*B2." *Notice that * is the symbol for multiplication in a spreadsheet.*
- Sometimes you will want similar formulas in more than one cell. First type the formula in one cell. Then select the cell and click the copy button. Finally select the cells where you want to copy the formula and click the paste button.

- Often it is useful to find the sum or average of a row or column of numbers. The spreadsheet allows you to choose from several functions like this instead of entering the formula manually. To enter a function, click the cell where you want the result to appear. Then click on the = button above the cells. A list of formulas will appear to the left. Click the down arrow button and choose your function. The spreadsheet will enter a range, which you may alter. For example, to find the average of row 2 of the spreadsheet below, the function chooses to find the average of cells B2, C2, and D2.

	A	B	C	D	E
1	Student	Test 1	Test 2	Test 3	Average
2	Kathy	88	85	91	88
3	Ben	86	89	92	89
4	Carmen	92	86	92	90
5	Anthony	80	88	87	85

The formula for cell E2 is =(B2+C2+D2)/3.

Spreadsheet software is one of the most common tools used in business today. You should try to learn as much as you can to prepare for your future. Who knows? Maybe you'll use what you're learning today as a company president tomorrow!

Selected Answers

CHAPTER 1 Problem Solving, Algebra, and Geometry

Pages 6–7 Lesson 1-1

1. You need to determine how all the facts are related and what strategy to use to solve the problem. **5.** 58 tables **7.** Sample answer: They both have 4 congruent sides; one has right angles and the other does not. **9.** Sample answer: Assuming it takes 1 second to say a number, it would take about 11.5 days. **11.** Sample answer: bicycling and in-line skating would burn 708 + 600 or 1,308 calories

Pages 9–10 Lesson 1-2

1. addition **3.** Tia; you should divide first. **5.** subtraction **7.** 16 **9.** 13 **11.** multiplication **13.** subtraction **15.** subtraction **17.** 23 **19.** 28 **21.** 8 **23.** 6 **25.** 20 **27.** 14 **29.** 83 **31.** $2(14 - 9) - (17 - 14) = 7$ **33.** $64 \div (8 + 24) - 1 = 1$ **35a.** $2 \cdot 5 + 1 \cdot 4 + 3 \cdot 3$ **35b.** \$23 **37.** Sample answer: For 150 pounds, sleep for 8 hours, in-line skate for 2 hours, and swim for 1 hour; $8 \times 90 + 2 \times 600 + 1 \times 497 = 2{,}417$ **39.** A

Page 11 Lesson 1-3A

1. 7 **3.** 9 **5.** Sample answer: The cup represents the variable or unknown quantity.

Pages 14–15 Lesson 1-3

1. Sample answer: Numbers have a constant value, while variables represent many different values. **3a.** Sample answer: The perimeter is two more than the number of triangles. **3b.** $n + 2$ **5.** 10 **7.** 20 **9.** 4 **11.** 9 **13.** 12 **15.** 17 **17.** 11 **19.** 16 **21.** 36 **23.** 2 **25.** 3 **27.** 16 **29.** 1,000

31a.

Number of hours	1	2	3	4	5
Amount earned	3	6	9	12	15

31b. $3n$ **31c.** \$24 **33.** \$246 **35.** C

Page 15 Mid-Chapter Self Test

1. about 498 **3.** 35 **5.** about 4 quarts

Page 16 Lesson 1-3B

1. 48 **3.** 72 **5.** 6 **7.** Sample answer: Store the value of $4 + 8 \times 2$ in a and the value of $15 - 4 + 2$ in b. Then find ab.

Pages 18–20 Lesson 1-4

1. $6 \cdot 6 = 36$ **3.** Sample answer: Using exponents is more convenient and saves space. **5.** $z \cdot z \cdot z$ **7.** x^6 **9.** 16 **11.** 35 **13.** $2 \cdot 2 \cdot 2 \cdot 2$ **15.** $4 \cdot 4 \cdot 4 \cdot 4 \cdot 4$ **17.** $m \cdot m \cdot m \cdot m$ **19.** 12^2 **21.** 15^4 **23.** n^2 **25.** 49 **27.** 21 **29.** 23 **31.** 90 **33.** 54 **35.** 90 **37.** 16 **39.** false **41a.** $1^3, 2^3, 3^3, 4^3, 5^3$ **41b.** Sample answer: A number, n, taken to the third power is the same as the volume of a cube whose edge is n units long. **43.** Sample answer: $3^3 = 27$, $3^2 = 9$, $3^1 = 3$, $3^0 = 1$; Each power is three times greater than the next. **45.** 110 **47.** false

Pages 22–23 Lesson 1-5

1. Sample answer: Find the value of the variable that makes a true sentence. **3.** Latisha; $343 \div 7 = 49$ **5.** 41 **7.** 80 **9.** 18 **11.** 8 **13.** 4 **15.** 7 **17.** 18 **19.** 56 **21.** 86 **23.** 72 **25.** 10 **27.** 6 **29.** 63 **31.** 55 **33.** 143 **35.** 173 **37.** 7.5 hours **39.** 84 centimeters **41.** They are equal. **43.** 32 **45.** 9

Pages 26–27 Lesson 1-6

1. Small parts of the fern look like the entire fern.

3.

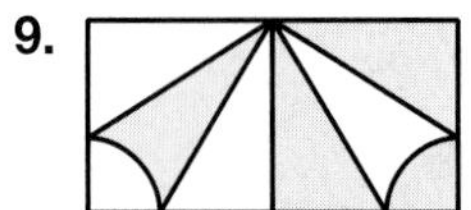

7.

9.

13. 75

Pages 28–29 Lesson 1-7A

1. 15 square units **3.** 16 square units **5.** 10 square units **7.** 36 square units **9.** 135 square units **11.** They have the same area. **13.** 8 square units **15.** The base and height of the parallelogram are the same as the length and width of the rectangle. **17.** 32 square units **19.** 60 square units

Pages 32–33 Lesson 1-7

1.

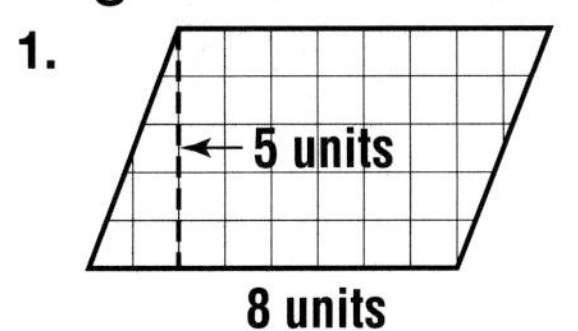

3. Since the length and width are each doubled, the area increases by 2×2 or 4 times. **5.** 40 cm^2 **7.** 30 ft^2 **9.** 14 m^2 **11.** 80 ft^2 **13.** 72 ft^2 **15.** 216 cm^2 **17.** 375 ft^2 **19.** 132 yd^2 **21.** 7 yd **23.** 1,960 ft^2; from 1,200 to 1,999 ft^2 **25.** Sample answer:

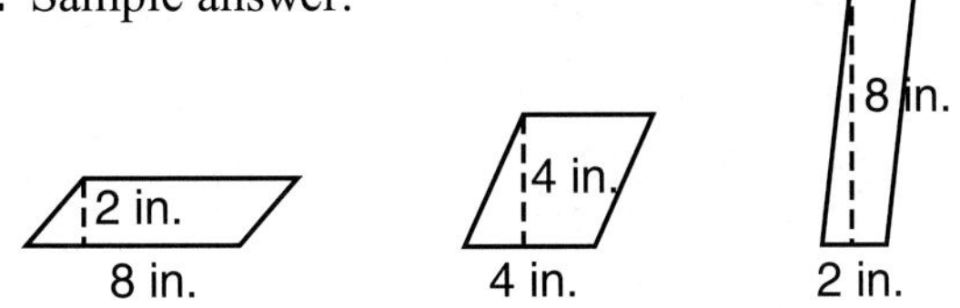

27. A

Pages 34–35 Lesson 1-7B

1. Sample answer: You can use the exact answer as a basis when you estimate other quantities. **3.** Sample answer: If no advantage is obtained by having an exact answer then estimation is an acceptable method. **5.** Sample answer: You can compare your answer against your estimate to determine whether your answer is reasonable. **7.** Sample answer: An estimate is close to 1,999 square feet, which is the dividing point for two categories. **9a.** yes **9b.** 126 ft^2 **11.** about $\$16 \times 12$ or \$192 **13.** yes; $3{,}000 + 3{,}000 + 4{,}000 + 3{,}000 = 13{,}000$

Pages 36–39 Study Guide and Assessment

1. true **3.** false, squared **5.** true **7.** true **9.** false, 15 square inches **11.** true **13.** 420 miles **15.** 5,932 books **17.** 82 **19.** 89 **21.** 10 **23.** 3 **25.** 40 **27.** 78 **29.** 729 **31.** 225 **33.** 64 **35.** 9 **37.** 47 **39.** 64 **41.** [two-square domino: 5 dots | 2 dots] **43.** 45 square yards **45.** 168 square meters **47.** 12 square feet **49.** no **51.** 63°F

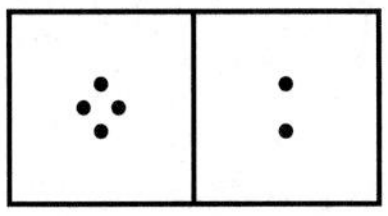

Pages 40–41 Standardized Test Practice

1. C **3.** C **5.** C **7.** D **9.** B **11.** Sample answer: $240 \div 8 = 30$; about 30 hours **13.** 604,800 seconds **15.** 20 days

CHAPTER 2
Applying Decimals

Pages 45–46 Lesson 2-1

1. Sample answer: $0.30 < 0.50$ **3.** Sample answer: You can add a zero to the right of a decimal without changing the value. So, $0.4 = 0.40$. **5.** $<$ **7.** $<$ **9.** chocolate jimmies **11.** $>$ **13.** $=$ **15.** $<$ **17.** $<$ **19.** $<$ **21.** $>$ **23.** 0.087 **25.** 6.55, 6.505, 6.5, 6.05 **27a.** visiting friends, reading **27b.** teenagers: 17.7, 4.4, 1.3, 1.2, 1.1, 0.9; unmarried adults: 14.2, 7.8, 1.9, 0.7, 0.7, 0.5

27c.

Leisure Time

Legend: Teenagers; Unmarried Adults

Hours Per Week (0–20)

	Teenagers	Unmarried Adults
organizations	1.2	0.5
visiting friends	4.4	7.8
hobbies	1.1	0.7
listening to music	0.9	0.7
television	17.7	14.2
reading	1.3	1.9

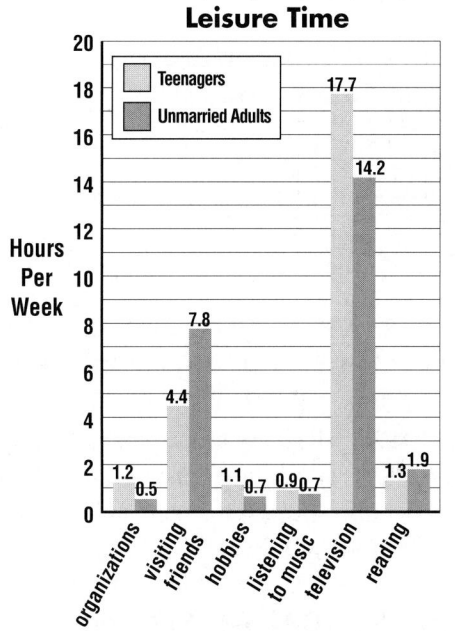

29. 0.999, 4.63, 20.8, 175 **31.** B **33.** 26

Pages 48–49 Lesson 2-2

1. 14.4 **3.** Tomas; 12.0 is expressed in tenths. **5.** 0.25 **7.** 0.79 **9.** 1.57 **11.** 0.22 **13.** 10 **15.** 16.4 **17.** 9.128 **19.** 0.45 **21.** 1.70 **23.** 15.5 **25.** 0.8 **27.** 60

29. [number line from 5.0 to 6.0 with arrow at 5.67]

5.0 6.0

5.67

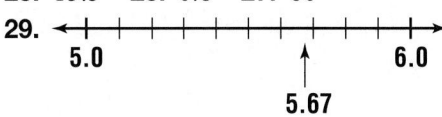

31a. 11.9 lb **31b.** 5.9 lb **33.** 8, 8.75, 9.15, 9.5 **35.** 29

Pages 51–53 Lesson 2-3

1. Sample answer: to help you catch errors in entering the numbers **5.** $30 - 20 = 10$ **7.** $42 \div 7 = 6$ **9.** $3(20) = 60$

11. about 1 million **13.** $30 - 20 = 10$
15. $63 \div 9 = 7$ **17.** $30 - 8 = 22$
19. $40 \div 20 = 2$ **21.** $72 \div 8 = 9$
23. $30 \times 80 = 2{,}400$ **25.** $36 \div 12 = 3$
27. $7 \times 5 = 35$ **29.** $4(40) = 160$
31. $4(200) = 800$ **33.** $5(50) = 250$ **35.** about 350 million **37.** about 70 million **39.** Sample answer: Using 15 miles per gallon, he will use 100 ÷ 15 or about 6 gallons of gasoline. At $1.25 per gallon, he will pay about $7.50. **41.** $<$
43. $500 + 5n$

Pages 54–55 Lesson 2-3B

5. Sample answer: Estimate before you calculate.
9. 10 cars **11.** about 300 times **13.** $9 **15.** C

Pages 58–59 Lesson 2-4

3.

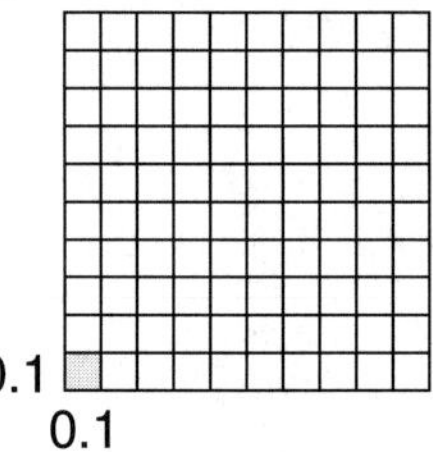

5. 0.077

7. 0.1845 **9.** 0.35 km **11.** 1.14 **13.** 19.728
15. 0.009 **17.** 0.27 **19.** 0.0736 **21.** 0.000805
23. 4.05 **25.** 0.152 **27.** 0.1053 **29.** 6,423 pesetas **31a.** VCR, 33.6; video game, 27.0; cable, 23.1; computer, 16.1; cellular phone, 12.3; on-line service, 6.0 **33.** Always; the rectangle will always be a portion of the full model. **35.** 1.0 **37.** C

Page 59 Mid-Chapter Self Test

1. 0.28 **3.** 350 **5.** 0.0025 km

Pages 62–63 Lesson 2-5

1. Move the decimal point 2 places to the right; $x = 237.8$ **5.** 4,600 **7.** 20,310 **9.** 0.045 **11.** 5
13. 2,780 **15.** 5,490 **17.** 9.25 **19.** 0.16
21. 560 **23.** 1,123,000 **25.** 0.8 **27.** 930
29. 2.53 **31a.** 0.72 million **31b.** 7.92 million
33. 1.2 **35.** 0.01

Pages 64–65 Lesson 2-6A

1. $0.14 \div 0.2 = 0.7$ **3.** $0.16 \div 0.4 = 0.4$
5. 0.6

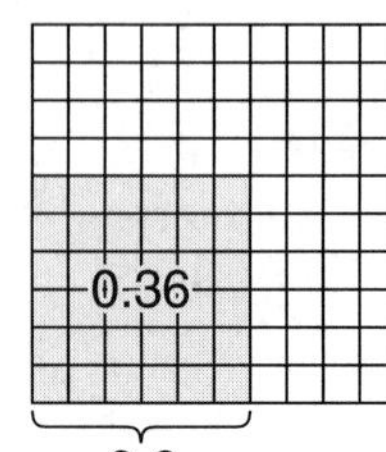

7. 1

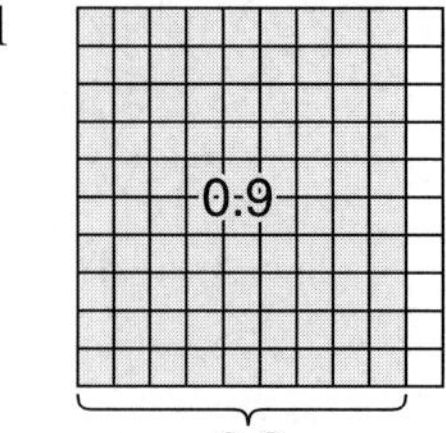

9. 0.6

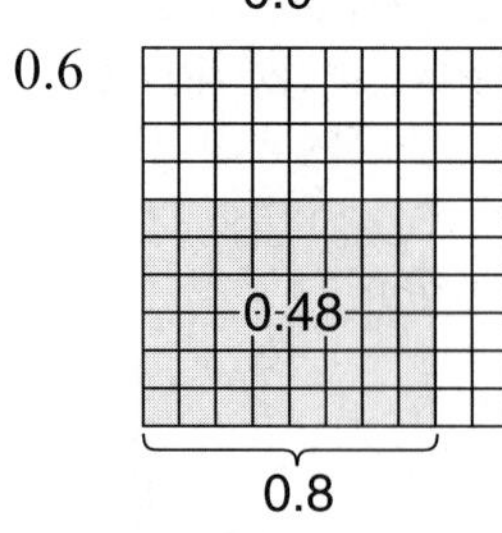

11. $0.45 \div 0.3 = 1.5$
13. 4

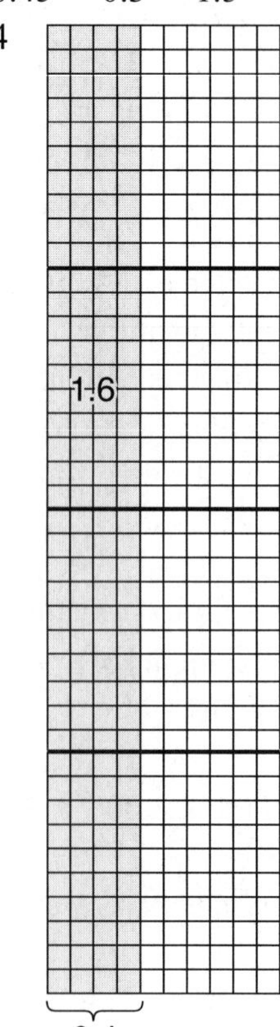

15. 0.7

Pages 68–69 Lesson 2-6

1. Sample answer: Yes; dividing both the dividend and divisor of 35 ÷ 0.5 by 10 results in 3.5 ÷ 0.05.
3. $3.6 \div 4$ **5.** $5{,}040 \div 56$ **7.** 1.5 **9.** 0.12
11. 62.61 times **13.** $2{,}940 \div 84$ **15.** $8.2 \div 4$
17. $26 \div 13$ **19.** $14.88 \div 31$ **21.** 3.5 **23.** 0.35
25. 0.3 **27.** 0.48 **29.** 4.6 **31.** 0.088 **33.** 140
35. 0.65 **37.** $1.54 **39a.** $0.26, $0.24
39b. the large box **39c.** Sample answer: You only want small servings. **39d.** Two regular boxes cost $4.58, which is less than $4.99. **41.** 9.2 meters per second **43.** 283 **45.** $20 \times 6 = 120$ **47.** 10

Pages 71–73 Lesson 2-7

1. Divide the numerator by the denominator.
3. Kim; $0.\overline{5} = 0.55555555...$ **5.** $6.\overline{34}$ **7.** 0.8
9. $0.\overline{7}$ **11.** $0.\overline{4}$ **13.** $1.\overline{12}$ **15.** $13.\overline{245}$ **17.** $0.8\overline{3}$
19. $3.01\overline{523}$ **21.** 0.55 **23.** $0.8\overline{3}$ **25.** 0.032
27. 3.875 **29.** = **31.** = **33.** > **35.** 0.27
37a. 3.141, 3.143; yes **37b.** 3.160, Archimedes'
39. Sample answer: 0.7, $0.\overline{71}$ **41.** 0.108 **43.** 81

Page 76 Lesson 2-8

1. You should divide because you are changing from a smaller unit to a larger unit. **3.** 75,000 **5.** 0.923 **7.** 8.2 **9.** 1,240 g **11.** 67,100 **13.** 23.4 **15.** 0.132 **17.** 46,000 **19.** 0.567 **21.** 8,100 **23.** 0.047 **25.** 90 mL **27a.** Mercury – 0.38 cm; Venus – 0.95cm; Mars – 0.53 cm; Jupiter – 11.19 cm; Saturn – 9.46 cm; Uranus – 4.01 cm; Neptune 3.88 cm; Pluto – 0.18 cm **27b.** Mercury – 0.387 cm; Venus – 0.723 cm; Mars – 1.524 cm; Jupiter – 5.203 cm; Saturn – 9.529 cm; Uranus – 19.191 cm; Neptune – 30.061 cm; Pluto – 39.529 cm **29.** $0.\overline{59}$ **31.** 0.1145

Pages 78–79 Lesson 2-9

1. It is more convenient. **3.** Alma; 24.59 is not less than 10. **5.** 8.3×10^3 **7.** 5.2×10^4 **9.** 1.264×10^8 **11.** 7.5×10^3 **13.** 4.07×10^4 **15.** 6×10^2 **17.** 2.3×10^4 **19.** 3.2×10^7 **21.** 5.7×10^5 **23.** 8.08×10^3 **25.** 2.71×10^7 **27.** 5.58×10^5 **29.** = **31.** < **33.** >
35. 3.4×10^6, 3,400,000 **37.** 3.0×10^6; Chicago is one of the largest cities in the U.S., and a population of 3,000,000 is reasonable.
39. 5.95×10^{10} cans **41.** 1,010 g **43.** C **45.** 13

Pages 80–83 Study Guide and Assessment

1. less **3.** sum **5.** gram **7.** $0.5 \times 0.3 = 0.15$ **9.** $0.2\overline{3}$ **11.** Sample answer: One centimeter is one-hundredth of a meter. **13.** 0.06, 0.159, 1.4, 1.59, 15.91 **15.** 15.0, 15.99, 16, 16.03, 16.3 **17.** 13.27 **19.** 0.1 **21.** 57.20 **23.** $40 \times 3 = 120$ **25.** $12 \times 3 = 36$ **27.** $150 \div 5 = 30$ **29.** 0.26 **31.** 22.725 **33.** 13,700 **35.** 0.0637 **37.** 10 **39.** 0.004 **41.** 2.7 **43.** 0.4 **45.** 0.375 **47.** $0.\overline{5}$ **49.** 0.027 **51.** 0.0033 **53.** 160 **55.** 0.043 **57.** 6×10^3 **59.** 29.13, 29.97, 30.22, 30.53, 31.01 **61.** 200 geysers

Pages 84–85 Standardized Test Practice

1. D **3.** D **5.** B **7.** C **9.** D **11.** D
13. $905 **15.** 9.2 cm **17.** 65 miles per hour

CHAPTER 3 Statistics: Analyzing Data

Pages 89–91 Lesson 3-1

1. Range: find the difference between the greatest number and the least number. Scale: include all numbers of the data set, plus numbers that are higher or lower than the set, to get an appropriate scale. Interval: choose the number of categories that you want and divide the scale by that number.
3. Tatanka is correct. A frequency table includes all the numbers in a set of data.
5. 19; Sample answer: 0-19, 5

<table>
<tr><th>Interval</th><th>Tally</th><th>Frequency</th></tr>
<tr><td>0-4</td><td>|||</td><td>3</td></tr>
<tr><td>5-9</td><td>|||</td><td>3</td></tr>
<tr><td>10-14</td><td>|</td><td>1</td></tr>
<tr><td>15-19</td><td>||</td><td>2</td></tr>
</table>

7a. 62
7b. Sample answer: 1-70, 10

<table>
<tr><th>Reign</th><th>Tally</th><th>Frequency</th></tr>
<tr><td>1-10</td><td>||||</td><td>4</td></tr>
<tr><td>11-20</td><td>||</td><td>2</td></tr>
<tr><td>21-30</td><td>|</td><td>1</td></tr>
<tr><td>31-40</td><td>|</td><td>1</td></tr>
<tr><td>41-50</td><td>|</td><td>1</td></tr>
<tr><td>51-60</td><td>|</td><td>1</td></tr>
<tr><td>61-70</td><td>|</td><td>1</td></tr>
</table>

9–13. Sample scales and intervals are given.
9. 100; 20-120, 20 **11.** 19; 0-20, 2 **13.** 7.5; 14-22, 1 **15–17.** Sample answers are given.

15.

<table>
<tr><th>Number of Books</th><th>Tally</th><th>Frequency</th></tr>
<tr><td>0</td><td>|||</td><td>3</td></tr>
<tr><td>1</td><td>𝍸 |</td><td>6</td></tr>
<tr><td>2</td><td>𝍸 |||</td><td>8</td></tr>
<tr><td>3</td><td>|||</td><td>3</td></tr>
<tr><td>4</td><td>|</td><td>1</td></tr>
<tr><td>5</td><td>||</td><td>2</td></tr>
<tr><td>6</td><td>|</td><td>1</td></tr>
</table>

0–6, 1

17.

Rainfall (in.)	Tally	Frequency
7	|||	3
8	|||	3
9	||	2
10	||||	4

7–10, 1

19. 0 5 10 15 20 25 30 35 40 45 50

21a.

Year	Tally	Frequency
1900-1919	|||	3
1920-1939	||||	4
1940-1959	~~||||~~	5
1960-1979	~~||||~~ |	6
1980-1999	||||	4

21b. 1960-1979 **25.** C

Pages 92–93 Lesson 3-2A

1. Sample answer: The table gives information about each kind of bike. The graph shows the relationship between rating and price. **3.** 2 games **5.** Using a graph can help you analyze whether a solution is correct. **7.** 1.5 in. **9.** 11 **11a.** about 3 in. **11b.** Sample answer: May

Pages 96–97 Lesson 3-2

1. Graphs often show trends over time. **5.** Sample answer: 3.5 million people

7a.

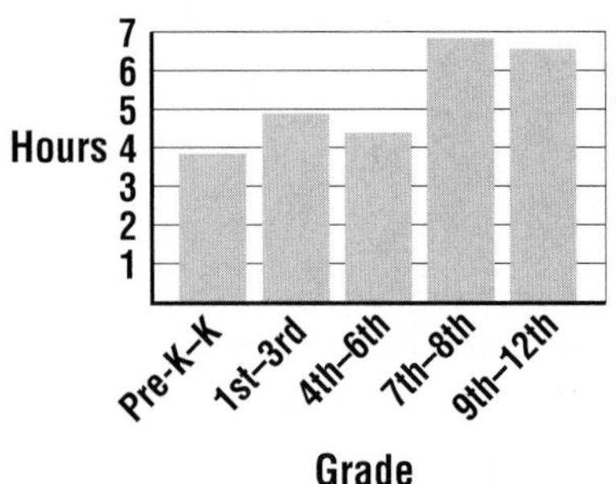

7b. Students in grades 7-8 and 9-12 spend the most time using computers, so the new computer software should be designed for students in these grades.
9. Sample answer: Wally World probably will not catch up to Valley World in attendance, since Valley World's attendance appears to be increasing faster than Wally World's. **11.** 29; sample answer: 18-48, 2 **13.** C

Pages 100–101 Lesson 3-3

1. Sample answer: It's easier to see trends over time.

3.

5a.

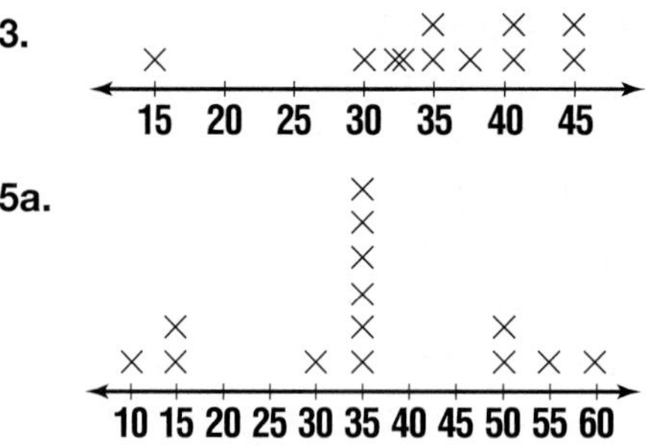

5b. 35; Many of the items contain 35 mg of caffeine.

7.

9.

11.

13.

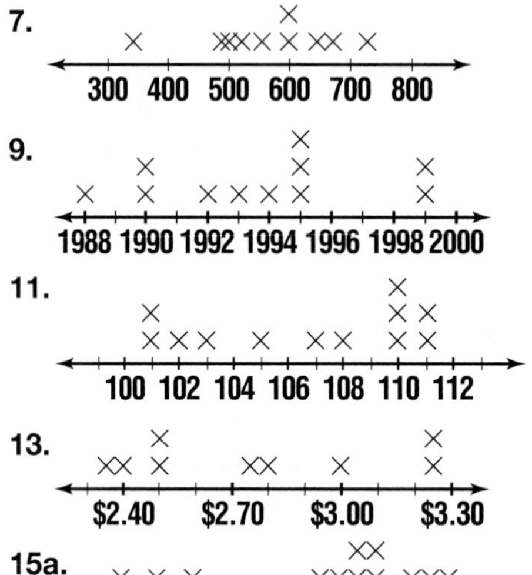

15a. 2 3 4 5 6 7 8 9 10 11

15b. A majority of the players lose between 7.5 and 9 pounds during the game. **17a.** They both can show the number of times data occur. **17b.** A line plot shows points of data. A bar graph can show intervals of data. **19.** B

Pages 104–105 Lesson 3-4

1a. List the data in ascending order. Choose the middle number. **1b.** List the data in ascending order. Find the mean of the two middle numbers.
3. Erica; the data do not all have to be the same for the mean, median, and mode to be equal. For example, in the set 7, 8, 8, 9, the mean, median, and mode all equal 8. **5.** 8.95, none, 9.05 **7.** The mode, because it appears most often. **9.** 93, 90 and 94, 93 **11.** $65\frac{1}{2}$, 65, 65 **13.** 1,780; 1,755 and 1,805; 1,780 **15.** 90.95, 95, 95 **17.** Sample answer: Mean; this represents the average size of all families. **19.** mean: $331.0 million; median: $310.9 million

21. 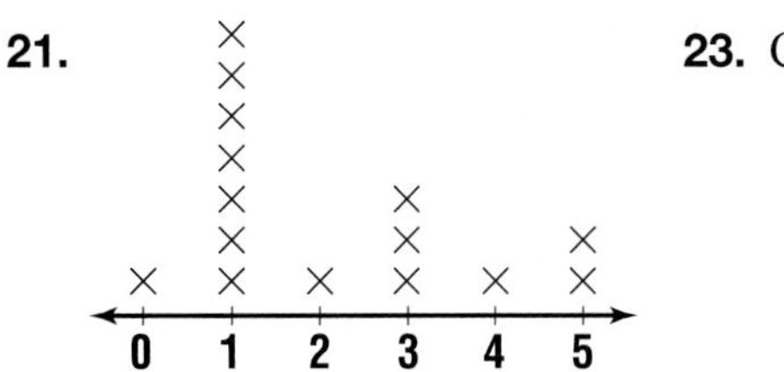

23. C

Page 105 Mid-Chapter Self Test

1. 13; Sample answer: 10-24, 2 **3.** Sample answer: 25 million bales **5.** 46.9, 45, 46

Page 106 Lesson 3-4B

1. Sample answer: You would probably not get exactly the same results, but the average student would probably be similar. **3a.** Sample answer: The median; it averages the data. **3b.** Sample answer: Line plots; they show the distribution graphically.

Pages 109–111 Lesson 3-5

1. Both a stem-and-leaf plot and a bar graph show the frequency of data occurring. However, a stem-and-leaf plot shows individual data values and a bar graph shows only a bar for each interval with the length representing the number of data in the interval.

5. stems: 1, 2, 3

Stem	Leaf
1	3 3 5
2	4 8
3	0 1 2 2 5 6 8 8 8 *1|3 = 13*

7a. 0, 1, 2, 3, 4, 5, 6, 7, 8, 9, 10

7b.

Stem	Leaf
0	1 3 4 5 6 7 7
1	0 0 0 2 2 2 2 5 5 8
2	0 0 0 0 5
3	
4	0
5	
6	
7	
8	
9	
10	0 *1|2 = 12 years*

7c. 1 year, 100 years **7d.** 10-19 years

9. stems: 0, 1, 2, 3

Stem	Leaf
0	1 2 7 8 9
1	1 2 4 8 8 9
2	1 2
3	1 *0|7 = 7*

11. stems: 1, 2, 3, 4, 5, 6, 7, 8, 9

Stem	Leaf
1	5 8
2	6 7
3	6 7 9
4	4 9
5	6 8
6	1 8
7	5
8	
9	0 *1|8 = 18*

13a.

Top Ranked	Stem	Lower Ranked
8 7	1	3 5 7 8
9 9 8 5 5 5 0	2	0 2 2 6
0 0 0	3	0 0 1 8
8|1 = $18		*1|3 = $13*

Sample answer: There are more lower ranked jeans available at lower prices. But there are several types of jeans of top quality available at lower prices.

13b.

Male	Stem	Female
7 5 3	1	7 8 8
9 5 5 2 2 0	2	0 5 6 8 9
0 0 0	3	0 0 1 8
5|1 = $15		*1|7 = $17*

Sample answer: It appears that jeans for females are somewhat more expensive than jeans for males.

15a.

Stem	Leaf
0	NENNEEE
1	ENNNNEEN
2	ENN
3	
4	
5	E

15b. You gain information about how the pasta consumption of European Union countries compares to pasta consumption of nonmember countries. You lose information about the exact amounts of pasta eaten. **15c.** This plot is similar to a line plot written horizontally. However, a line plot shows exact data values; this plot shows intervals of 10.
17. 16

Page 113 Lesson 3-6A

1. 221 **3.** 3 or 4

Pages 116–117 Lesson 3-6

1. Sample answer: You can see the range of each quartile, and you know that one-fourth of the data fall in each quartile. **3.** Sample answer: All of the data do not need to be displayed; it doesn't show all the frequency. **5a.** 54.5 **5b.** 58 **5c.** 51 **5d.** 69 **5e.** 42 **5f.** 7 **5g.** 40.5, 68.5

5h.

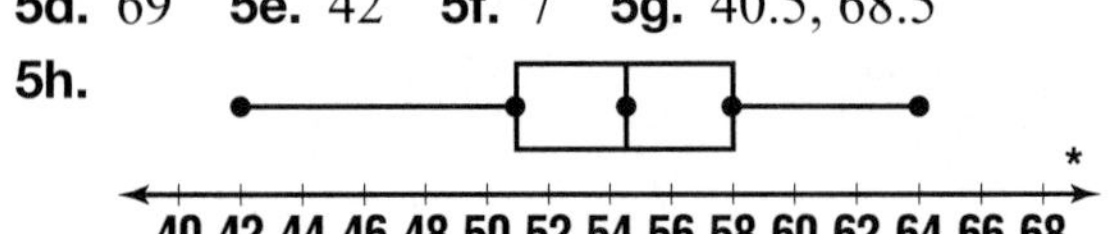

7.

9.

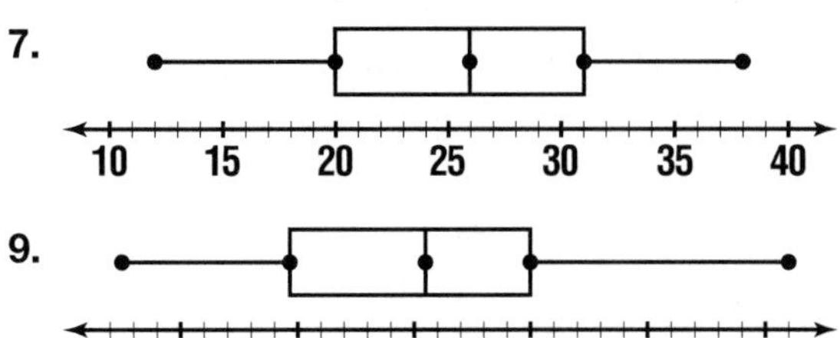

11.

Stem	Leaf
1	0 1 2 8
2	0 1 2
3	4 5 8
4	
5	6 *1|8 = 18*

Page 118 Lesson 3-6B

1. Sample answer: The mean best describes this set of data because the data are centered and evenly distributed. **3a.** Answers will vary depending on class's data. Prediction should reflect this data. **3b.** Sample answer: The mean is very close to the prediction. **3c.** Sample answer: The teacher grabbed more kernels than most of the students. Just data from her alone would not be sufficient data to predict for the rest of the adults.

Pages 120–121 Lesson 3-7

1. Sample answer: Outlier may distort the data; data may be inaccurate; data may be incomplete. **5a.** Graph B **5b.** Graph B could be misleading because of the change in the vertical scale. **7.** Either; accept answers students can justify. **9.** Sample answer:

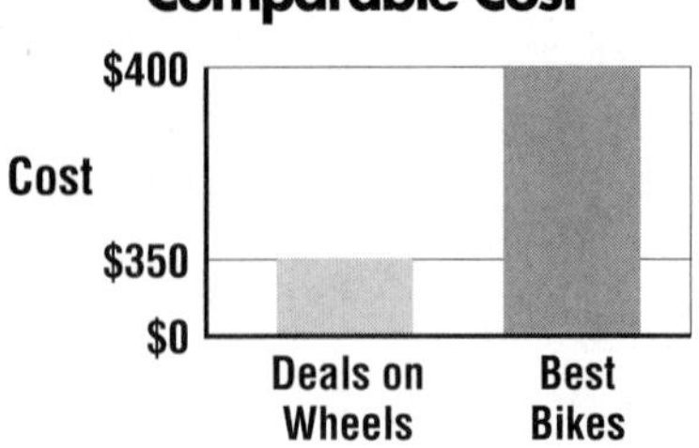

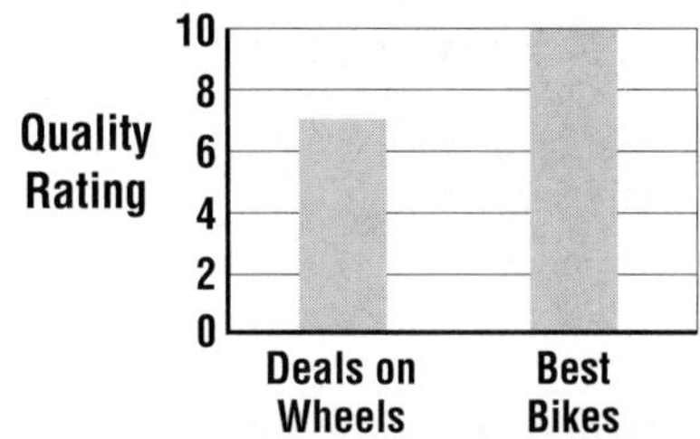

11. No, for example, the median of the set 9, 10, 11, 12, 100 is the same as the median of the set 9, 10, 11, 12, 13. **13.** E

Pages 122–125 Study Guide and Assessment

1. e **3.** g **5.** b **7.** k **9.** d **11.** Find the least and greatest numbers. Draw a vertical line and determine the stems. Write these numbers from least to greatest to the left of the line. Write the leaves, which are the last digits, from least to greatest to the right of the line, next to the corresponding stems. Include an explanation. **13.** 475; Sample answer: 50 – 600; 50 **15.** Sample answer: 2 – 6; 1

Number of People	Tally	Frequency
2	||	2
3	𝍸	5
4	𝍸 𝍸	10
5	𝍸	5
6	||	2

17.

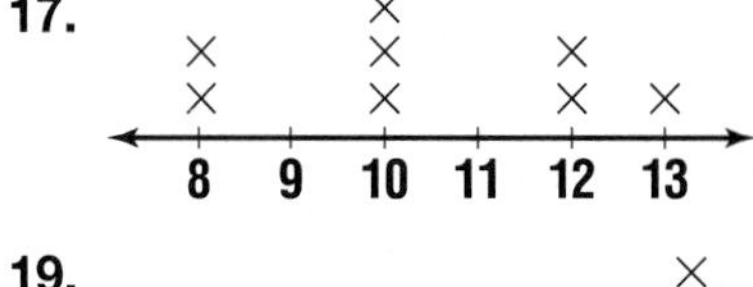

19.

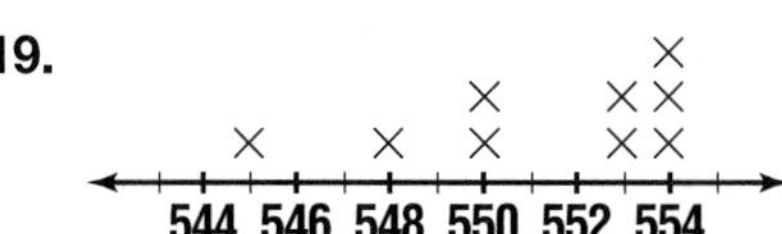

21. 4, 3, 3 **23.** 84.3, none, 86 **25.** 5, 6, 7, 8, 9

Stem	Leaf
5	3
6	0 1
7	5 7 8 8
8	3 5 7 7 9
9	0 1 2 9 *5|3 = 53*

27.

Seattle	Stem	Olympia
6	4	5 8
2 3 4	5	1 3 6
9 8 2 2 1 0	6	0 2 5 6 8
8 7 2 0	7	2 3 7 9
5 0	8	0 4

6|4 = 46°F *4|5 = 45°F*

29a. 81.6, none, 89 **29b.** The mean; six of the scores were well above 81.6. **31.** \$5.02, \$4.90, \$4.95

Pages 126–127 Standardized Test Practice

1. C **3.** C **5.** A **7.** B **9.** 0 **11.** mode

CHAPTER 4 Using Number Patterns, Fractions, and Percents

Page 132 Lesson 4-1A

1. Numbers on back are factors of the numbers on the front. **3.** 2, 3, 5, 7, 11, 13, 17, 19, 23, 29 **5.** 24 and 30 **7.** 1, 4, 9, 16, 25, 36, 49; perfect square numbers because there is an odd number of factors.

Pages 134–136 Lesson 4-1

1. Sample answer: 15 is not divisible by 4, because a rectangle cannot be formed with 4 as the length of one side. **3.** Rectangles should have dimensions 1×18, 2×9, 3×6; 7 is not a factor of 18. **5.** no **7.** 2, 4 **9.** 2, 3, 4, 6, 9 **11.** no **13.** yes **15.** no **17.** yes **19.** no **21.** 2, 3, 5, 6, 9, 10 **23.** none **25.** 2, 4, 5, 10 **27.** 2 **29.** yes **31.** 3, 4, 6, 12, 15, 20, 30, 60 **33.** 252 **35.** \$42,100 is considerably higher than all the other salaries. **37.** 6.35×10^5

Page 137 Lesson 4-1B

1. 96, 108, 36 **3.** In column A, beginning with A2, enter the numbers to be tested. In E1, enter the number 228. In E2, enter A2/E1; in E3, enter A3/E1, and so on. **5.** Place the numbers 2, 3, 4, 5, 6, 7, 8, 9, and 10 in row 1. Place the numbers 1 through 100 in column A.

Pages 140–141 Lesson 4-2

1. The sum of the digits is divisible by 3, so 3 is a factor of 387. **3.** Sample answer: You can use divisibility rules to find factors of a number. If the number has a factor other than 1 and itself, then it is not prime. **5.** prime **7.** $2^2 \times 3 \times 11$ **9.** $2^5 \times 3^2$ **11.** 3×5^3 **13.** composite **15.** composite **17.** composite **19.** prime **21.** composite **23.** $2^5 \times 3$ **25.** $2^4 \times 3^2$ **27.** $2 \times 3^2 \times 5 \times 11$ **29.** $2^2 \times 5^2 \times 17$ **31.** 2^6 **33.** $2 \times 3^3 \times 5$ **35.** $2^4 \times 5 \times 11$ **37.** $5^2 \times 59$ **39.** 3^2 **41a.** Sample answer: $2 \times 2 \times 6$, $1 \times 3 \times 8$, $1 \times 4 \times 6$, or $1 \times 1 \times 24$ **41b.** Sample answer: $2 \times 3 \times 6$, $2 \times 2 \times 9$, $3 \times 3 \times 4$, $1 \times 6 \times 6$, $1 \times 2 \times 18$, or $1 \times 4 \times 9$ **41c.** 5 ways **41d.** $1 \times 1 \times 17$ **41e.** Sample answer: 32; $2 \times 4 \times 4$; it takes the least amount of space. **43a.** 4, 9, 16, 25, . . . **43b.** a square number **43c.** 21, 28; $15 + 21 = 36$ or 6^2, $21 + 28 = 49$ or 7^2 **45.** A **47.** 48 mph

Pages 144–145 Lesson 4-3

1. 1, 3, 7, 13, 21, 31 (+2, +4, +6, +8, +10)

3. Add 5; arithmetic; 28, 33, 38. **5.** Multiply by 0.5; geometric; 0.25, 0.125, 0.0625. **7.** 35, 105, 315, 945; geometric **9.** \$125, \$62.50, \$31.25 **11.** Multiply by 3; geometric; 324, 972, 2,916. **13.** Add 2 more than was added to the previous term; neither; 220, 230, 242. **15.** Multiply by 3; geometric; 405, 1,215, 3,645. **17.** Each term has one more digit, and the digits are 1 greater than in the previous term; neither; 55,555, 666,666, 7,777,777. **19.** The terms are $1^3, 2^3, 3^3, 4^3, \ldots$; neither; 125, 216, 343. **21.** 7, 35, 175, 875; geometric **23.** 5, 5.4, 5.8, 6.2; arithmetic **25.** 70, 7, 0.7, 0.07; geometric **27.** 3, 3, 6, 18; neither **29.** 54, 486 **31.** 1, 3, 6, 10, 15, 21, 28, 36; add 2 to the first term, add 3 to the second term, add 4 to the third term, and so on. **33a.** 39 **33b.** 8,748 **35.** Sample answer: scale = 0-40; interval = 5; range = 33

0 5 10 15 20 25 30 35 40

37. 10

Pages 146–147 Lesson 4-3B

1. geometric **3.** 14 folds is 32.768 in., 15 folds is 65.536 in., and 16 folds is 131.072 in. **5.** The terms in the sequences would increase faster.

Pages 148–149 Lesson 4-4A

1. 89, 144, 233 **3.** 13 pairs; the pattern is the

Fibonacci sequence. **7.** Yes; 250,000 stades is approximately 25,000 miles. This is close to the actual measure of 24,901 miles. **9.** 186 miles **11.** about 25 Skybabies

Pages 152–153 Lesson 4-4

1. Identify the common prime factors, 2 and 7, and find their product; 14. **3.** 4 **5.** 2 **7.** 15 **9.** 5 **11.** $5a$ **13.** 28 **15.** 2 **17.** 2 **19.** 3 **21.** 18 **23.** 10 **25.** 10 **27.** 24 **29.** 12 **31.** 1 **33.** 13 **35.** Sample answer: 26, 52 and 52, 78 **37.** 4, 9 **41.** C **43.** 18

Page 153 Mid-Chapter Self Test

1. 2, 5, 10 **3.** 3, 5, 9 **5.** $2 \times 3 \times 5 \times 11$ **7.** Add 5; arithmetic; 29, 34, 39. **9.** Multiply by 2; geometric; 384, 768, 1,536.

Pages 155–157 Lesson 4-5

1. You cannot cancel out the units digits in the numerator and the denominator. Divide 16 and 36 by the GCF 4 to get $\frac{4}{9}$, not $\frac{1}{3}$. **3.** $\frac{5}{6}$ **5.** $\frac{2}{5}$ **7.** Sample answer: $\frac{4}{18}, \frac{6}{27}$ **9.** $\frac{7}{9}$ **11.** $\frac{61}{102}$ **13.** 1:2 **15.** 16:35 **17.** 11:50 **19.** 2:5 **21.** $\frac{2}{3}$ **23.** $\frac{4}{5}$ **25.** Sample answer: $\frac{6}{8}, \frac{9}{12}$ **27.** Sample answer: $\frac{10}{18}, \frac{15}{27}$ **29.** 8:13 **31.** 13:4 **33a.** $\frac{8}{17}$ **33b.** $\frac{6}{85}$ **33c.** $\frac{2}{17}$ **35.** Multiply the numerator and the denominator of a fraction by 13. (Both numbers must be greater than 7.) Sample answer: $\frac{8 \times 13}{9 \times 13} = \frac{104}{117}$ **37.** $-17°, -3°$ **39.** 18,700

Pages 159–160 Lesson 4-6

1. Sample answer: a ratio that compares a number to 100 **3.**

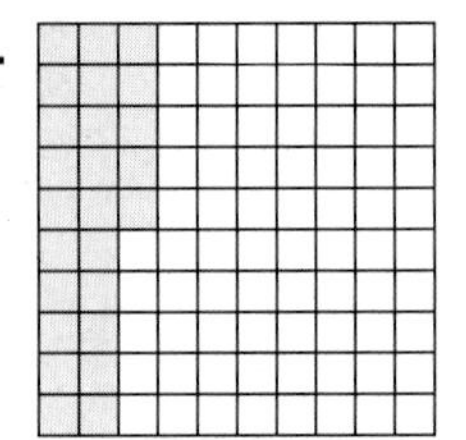

5. 60% **7.** 34% **9.** 77% **11.** 23% **13.** 18% **15.** 50% **17.** 57% **19.** 38.4% **21.** 1% **23.** 15% **25.** 36% **27.** 61% **29.** 40% **31.** 2 groups of 18, 3 groups of 12, 4 groups of 9, 6 groups of 6, 9 groups of 4, 12 groups of 3, or 18 groups of 2 **33.** D

Pages 162–164 Lesson 4-7

1. 36%, $\frac{9}{25}$ **3.** Juliana; $0.250 = \frac{1}{4}$ and $0.025 = \frac{1}{40}$ **5.** 65% **7.** 90% **9.** $\frac{11}{50}$ **11.** $\frac{4}{5}$ **13.** 74% **15.** 10% **17.** 91% **19.** 30% **21.** 75% **23.** 55% **25.** $\frac{1}{4}$ **27.** $\frac{4}{5}$ **29.** $\frac{9}{10}$ **31.** $\frac{8}{25}$ **33.** $\frac{1}{10}$ **35.** $\frac{1}{50}$ **37.** 20% **39.** 75% **41a.** $\frac{3}{10}$ **41b.** 0.3

43.

Company	Decimal	Percent
A	0.02	2
B	0.10	10
C	0.23	23
D	0.42	42
E	0.10	10
F	0.03	3
G	0.05	5
H	0.02	2
I	0.08	8
Other	0.00	0

45. 47%

47.

Stem	Leaf
0	2 5 9
1	0 2 3 6 7
2	3 5 5
3	1 $2\|3 = 23$

49. 48 miles

Pages 167–168 Lesson 4-8

1. $\frac{2}{5}$ or 40% **3.**

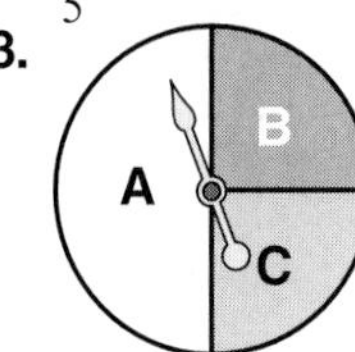

5. $\frac{3}{10}$ **7.** $\frac{3}{14} \approx 21.4\%$ **9.** $\frac{1}{20}$ **11.** $\frac{3}{20}$ **13.** $\frac{2}{5}$ **15.** $\frac{4}{25} = 16\%$ **17.** $\frac{6}{25} = 24\%$ **19.** $\frac{12}{25} = 48\%$ **21.** $\frac{1}{5}$ **23.** $\frac{1}{14}$ **25.** $\frac{1}{6} \approx 16.7\%$ **27.** No; the chance of rolling a 5 $\left(\frac{4}{36}\right)$, 6 $\left(\frac{5}{36}\right)$, 7 $\left(\frac{6}{36}\right)$, or 8 $\left(\frac{5}{36}\right)$ gives Marvin $\frac{20}{36}$ chance of winning a point. The probability of Naomi winning is only $\frac{16}{36}$. **29.** A

Pages 170–171 Lesson 4-9

1. A common multiple should have all the prime

factors of each number; $2^3 \times 3^2 = 72$ **3.** Sample answer: List several multiples of each number. To do the problem mentally, you could find the multiples of 9 and see which ones were multiples of both 3 and 5; 45. **5.** 45 **7.** 24 **9.** 225 **11.** 60 **13.** 30 **15.** 900 **17.** 24 **19.** 60 **21.** 784 **23.** 102 **25.** 3,750 **27.** 336 **29.** 20 **31.** 12 weeks **33.** Sample answer: {2, 3, 5} **35.** 18 **37.** $2.10

Pages 174–175 Lesson 4-10

3. $\frac{5}{7}$ and $\frac{4}{9}$; you can see from the graph that $\frac{5}{7}$ of the circle is a greater part than $\frac{4}{9}$ of the circle. So, $\frac{5}{7} > \frac{4}{9}$. **5.** 65 **7.** 24 **9.** < **11.** > **13.** 45 **15.** 16 **17.** 8 **19.** 36 **21.** 24 **23.** 68 **25.** < **27.** < **29.** > **31.** = **33.** < **35.** > **36.** < **37.** 126 **39.** students in math **41.** 5-6 hours **43.** 42 **45.**

65 70 75 80 85 90 95

47. B

Pages 176–179 Study Guide and Assessment

1. false, $2^3 \times 3$ **3.** true **5.** false, $\frac{2}{3}$ **7.** yes **9.** no **11.** 5 **13.** $2^3 \times 5^3$ **15.** $2 \times 5^2 \times 19$ **17.** $2^5 \times 3$ **19.** $2^4 \times 5^2 \times 7$ **21.** Add 5; arithmetic; 41, 46, 51. **23.** Add 3 more than was added to the previous term; neither; 63, 84, 108. **25.** 9 **27.** 84 **29.** 8 **31.** $\frac{4}{5}$ **33.** 2:3 **35.** $\frac{7}{11}$ **37.** 56% **39.** 49% **41.** 56% **43.** 40% **45.** $\frac{3}{20}$ **47.** $\frac{29}{50}$ **49.** $\frac{1}{2} = 50\%$ **51.** $\frac{1}{4} = 25\%$ **53.** 30 **55.** 80 **57.** 3,969 **59.** 12 **61.** < **63.** 2 **65.** 97.3%

Pages 180–181 Standardized Test Practice

1. B **3.** A **5.** B **7.** B **9.** E **11.** arithmetic; 62, 74, 86 **13.** 0.3 **15.** $\frac{2}{5}$

CHAPTER 5
Algebra: Using Integers

Pages 185–186 Lesson 5-1

1. It has a decimal part. **3.** Keisha; −3 and 7 are not the same distance from 0. **5.** +5 **7.** −76 **9.** 7, −7, 7 **11.** +9 **13.** −120 **15.** +1600 **17.** −4 **19.** 0 **21.** +15 **23.** −1, 1, 1 **25.** 0, 0, 0 **27.** 7, −7, 7 **29.** 0 **31.** 3,212; −8,685 **33a.** 7 **33b.** −7 **33c.** odd number of times, the result is negative; even number of times, the result is positive **35.** > **37.** 3, 3, 3

Pages 189–190 Lesson 5-2

1.

−6 −5 −4 −3 −2 −1

3. > **5.** > **7.** 15 **9.** > **11.** > **13.** > **15.** > **17.** −59, −43, −3, 0, 5, 11 **19.** 7 **21.** −35,800; −20,000; −13,000; −4,000; −1,000 **23a.** Mt. Elbert **23b.** Granite Peak, Wheeler Peak, Mt. Hood

25a.

City	Latitude (nearest degree)	Low Temp. (°F)
Honolulu, HI	21	56
San Diego, CA	33	43
Atlanta, GA	34	13
Nashville, TN	36	9
Denver, CO	40	−7
New York, NY	41	6
Minneapolis, MN	45	−11
Bismarck, ND	47	−28
Seattle, WA	48	22
Fairbanks, AK	65	−48

25b. Generally, as the latitude increases, the low temperature decreases. **27.** A **29.** 0.003 g

Pages 193–194 Lesson 5-3

1. quadrant II **5.** (1, 0), x-axis

7-9.

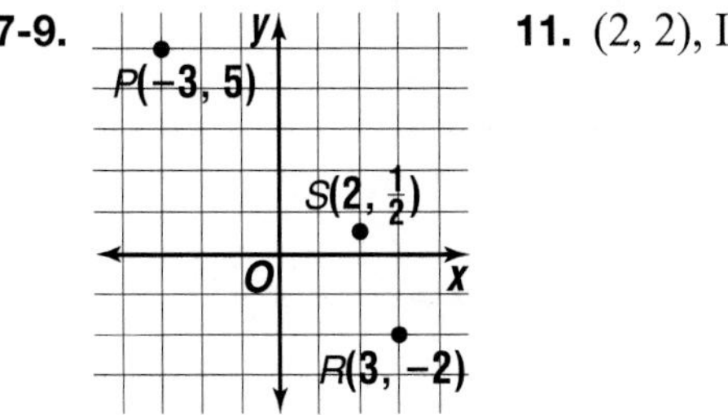

11. (2, 2), I

13. (5, −2), IV **15.** (0, −4), y-axis **17.** (−1, 4), II **19.** (−2, −2), III

21–27.

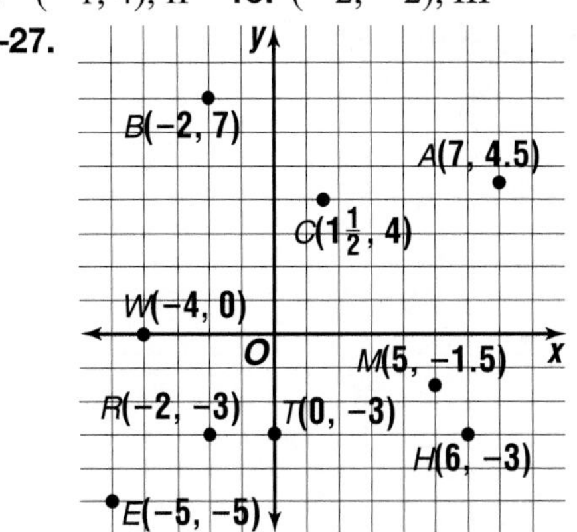

29. quadrant IV **31a.** (3, 3) **31b.** (−3, −1) **31c.** (−2, −2) **31d.** (−2, 3) **33a.** Honolulu (21, 56), San Diego (33, 43), Atlanta (34, 13), Nashville (36, 9), Denver (40, −7), New York (41, 6), Minneapolis (45, −11), Bismarck (47, −28), Seattle (48, 22), Fairbanks (65, −48)

33b.

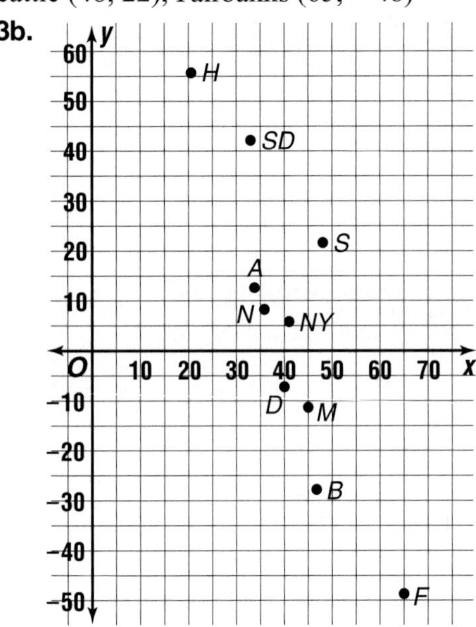

35. −5, −1, 3, 5 **37.** \$0.05

Page 195 Lesson 5-3B

1.

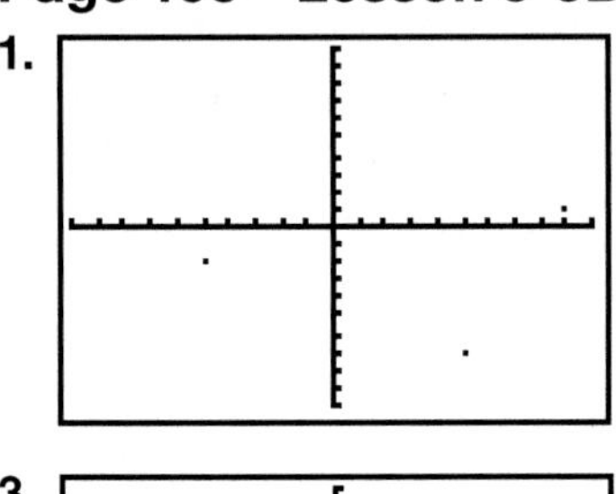

3.

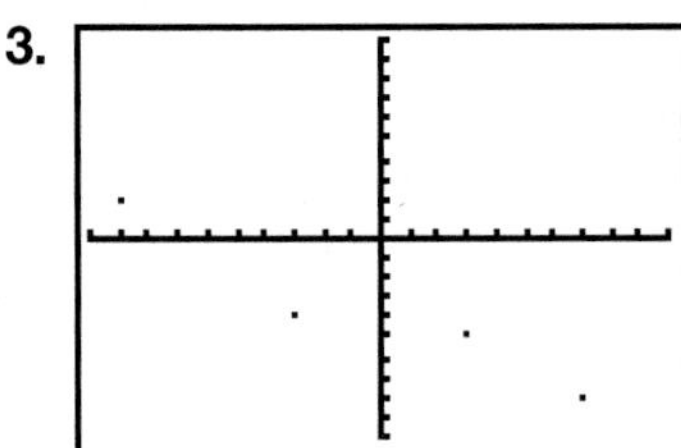

Page 196 Lesson 5-4A

1. −7 + 2 = −5

3. −4 + 1 = −3

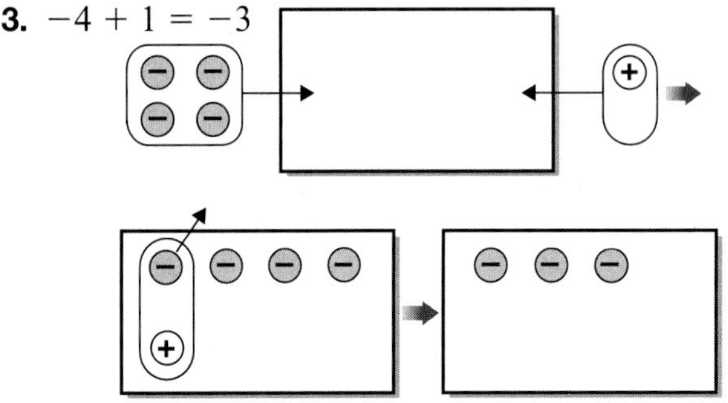

5. negative

Pages 199–200 Lesson 5-4

1. Not always; there may be 1 or 2 positive integers, but they have a smaller absolute value than the negative integer(s).

3. Sample answer:

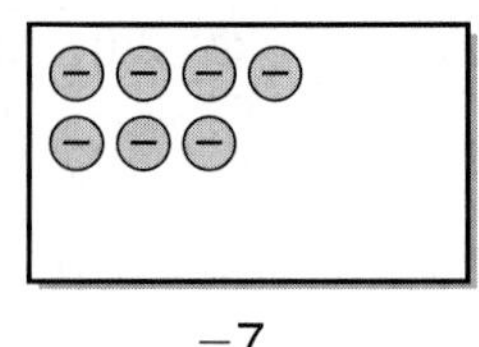

−7

5. zero **7.** −9 **9.** 7 **11.** −4 **13.** −56°F **15.** negative **17.** positive **19.** negative **21.** zero **23.** 4 **25.** 6 **27.** 13 **29.** 1 **31.** −19 **33.** −17 **35.** 2 **37.** 11 **39.** 0 **41.** −86 **43.** 9 yards gained **45.** Marsha did not owe Yori any money, because she did not initially borrow any money. **47.** 21, 21

49.

Stem	Leaf
0	3 7 9 9
1	0 3 4 5
2	4
3	1

2|4 = 24

Page 201 Lesson 5-5A

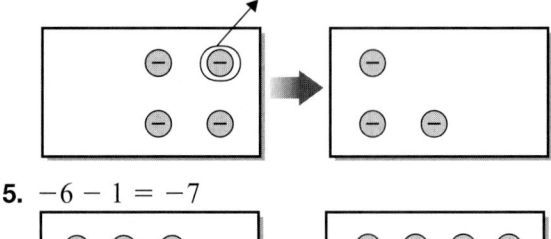

1. −7 − (−3) = −4

3. −4 − (−1) = −3

5. −6 − 1 = −7

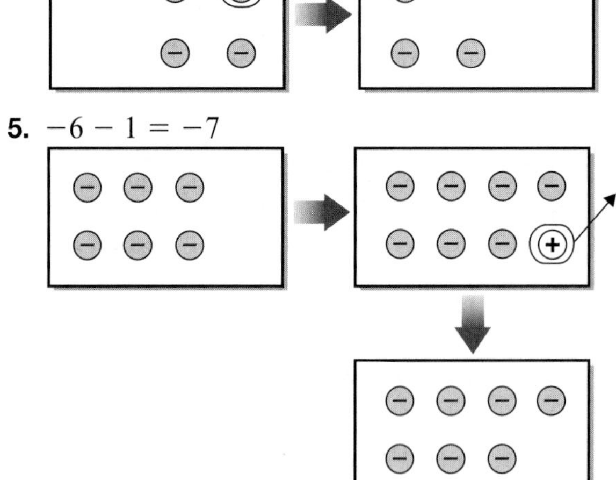

Pages 203–205 Lesson 5-5

1. $a + b$ **3.** Ellen; 15 − 24 = −9, but 24 − (15) = 9. **5.** −13 **7.** −6 **9.** 23 **11.** 4 **13a.** 506 years **13b.** 1,300 years **15.** 35 **17.** 10 **19.** −1 **21.** −53 **23.** −32 **25.** 40 **27.** 38 **29.** 32 **31.** −19 **33.** −8 **35.** −3

37. 4 **39.** -7 **41.** -2 **43.** 221°

45a. Honolulu (21, 38), San Diego (33, 47), Atlanta (34, 89), Nashville (36, 90), Denver (40, 106), New York (41, 96), Minneapolis (45, 112), Bismarck (47, 126), Seattle (48, 74), Fairbanks (65, 136)

45b.

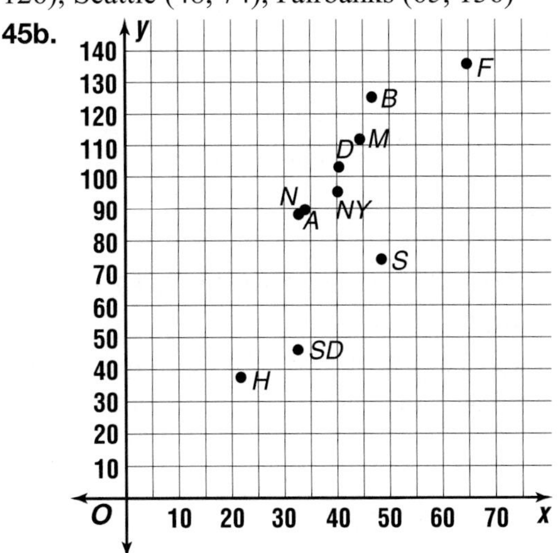

47. A **49.** 3, 5, 9 **51.** 0.375

Page 205 Mid-Chapter Self Test

1. $+7$ **3.** $>$ **5.** $>$ **7.** $(-1, -4)$, III **9.** -9

Page 206 Lesson 5-6A

1. $2 \times 3 = 6$

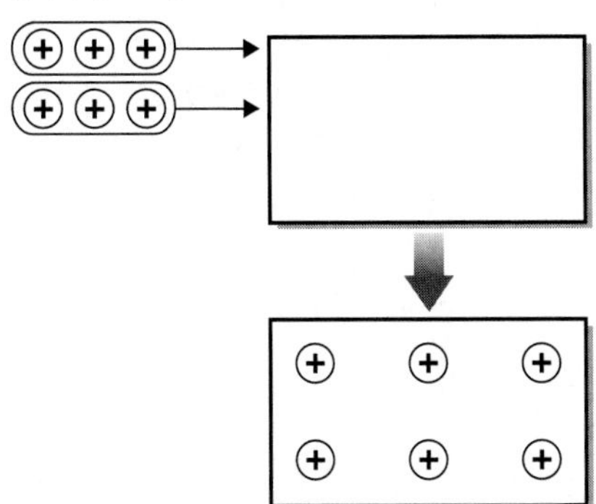

3. $-2 \times (-3) = 6$

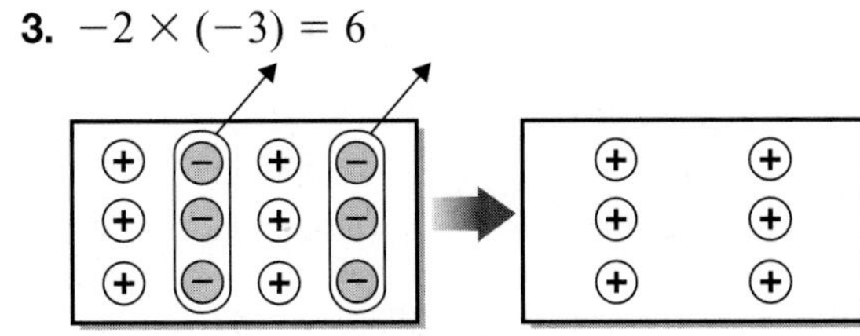

5.  $4 \times 0 = 0$

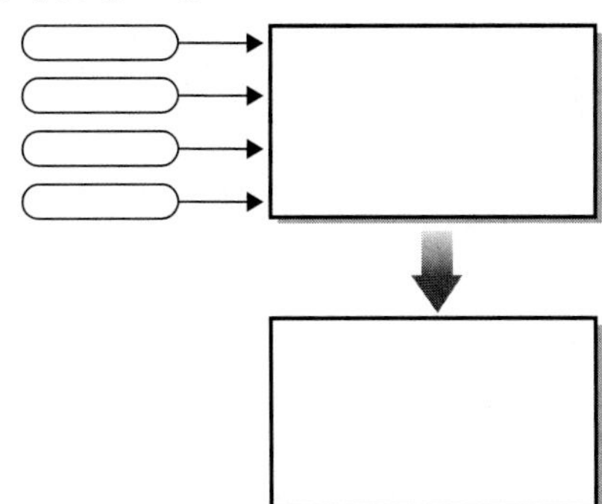

7. -27

Pages 208–209 Lesson 5-6

1. One is positive and one is negative.

3. $-3 \times (-4) = 12$

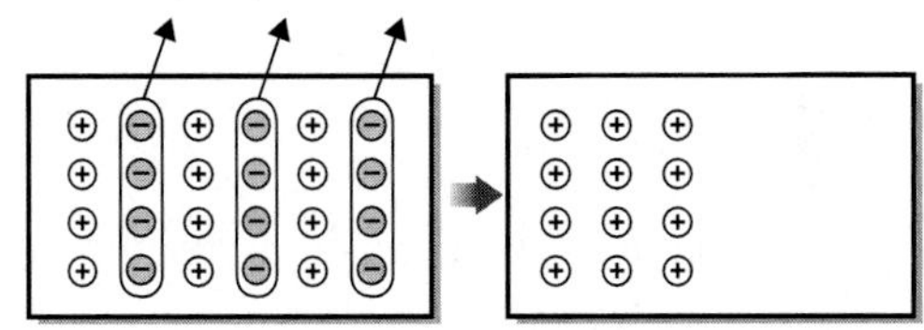

5. 35 **7.** -108 **9.** 36 **11.** 24 **13.** -78 **15.** 9 **17.** -56 **19.** -20 **21.** 16 **23.** -63 **25.** -100 **27.** -126 **29.** -24 **31.** -225 **33.** -78 **35.** -100 **37a.** $-2(14) = x$

37b. -28 or 28 cubic meters removed **39.** One of the integers is negative or all three integers are negative. If all three integers are positive, or if two of the integers are negative, the product is positive. If all three integers are negative, or if one of the integers is negative, the product is negative.

41. $-8, -4, -3, 0, 1, 4, 6$ **43.** 0.75

Pages 210–211 Lesson 5-7A

1. Multiply by 3; 486; 1,458; 4,374. **3.** 70 boxes **7.** 5, 10, 20, 40, 80, 160, 320; no, because 320 min. $= 5\frac{1}{3}$ hr, so she will be exercising more than 5 hours each day by the 7th day. **9.** 24 pegs **11.** 120 feet

Pages 213–214 Lesson 5-7

1. $-12 \div 4 = -3$; $-12 \div (-3) = 4$ **3.** 4 **5.** -6 **7.** -3 **9.** -32 **11.** -2 **13.** -5 **15.** 14 **17.** 12 **19.** -9 **21.** 3 **23.** -7 **25.** 220 **27.** -20 **29.** 9 **31.** 81 **33.** 1 **35.** -27 **37.** $y = 24 \div 6$ **39.** $-30, -15, -10, -6, -5, -3, -2, -1, 1, 2, 3, 5, 6, 10, 15, 30$

41. $>$ **43a.** 115.2 **43b.** 225.6

Pages 216–217 Lesson 5-8

1.

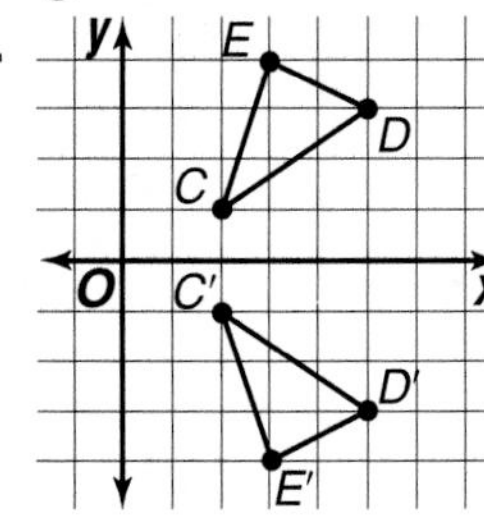

3. Sample answer: The diamonds are both translations and reflections of each other.

5. $A'(-1, 2), B'(-1, -4), C'(-5, -1)$

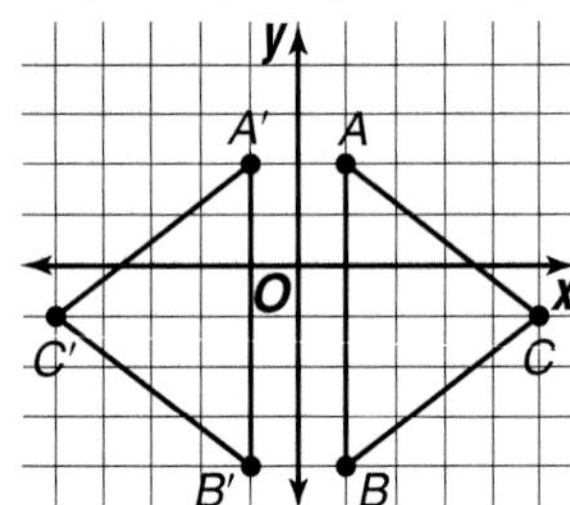

7. on the lid: reflections; on the side: translations and reflections **9.** translation

11. $X'(1, -3), Y'(5, -1), Z'(5, -8)$

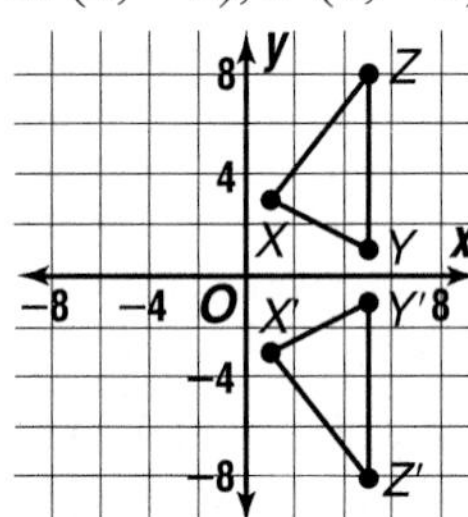

13. $W'(7, 4), X'(6, 9), Y'(3, 7)$

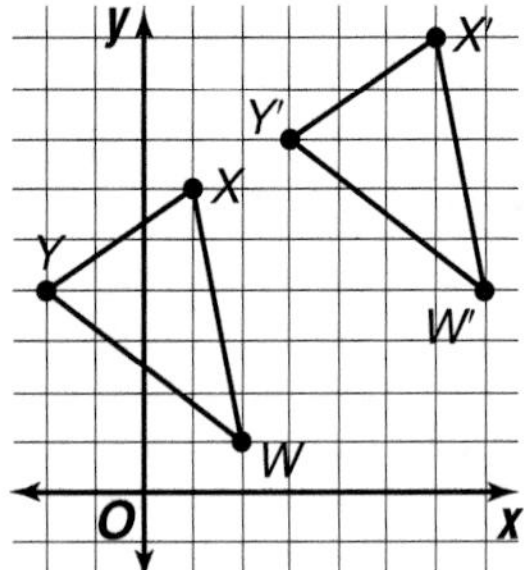

15. $J'(7, 1), K'(2, 5), L'(5, 7)$

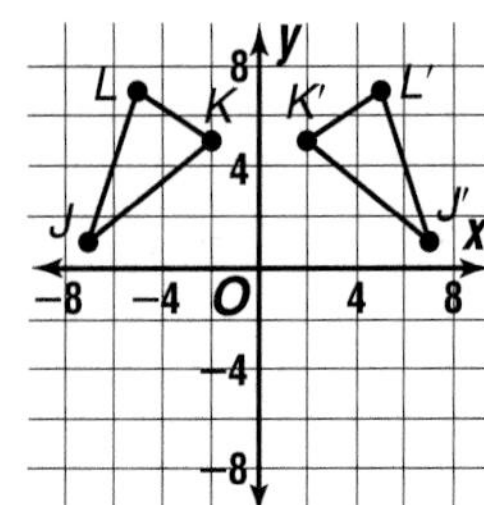

17a. translation **17b.** $(-2, -4)$

19.

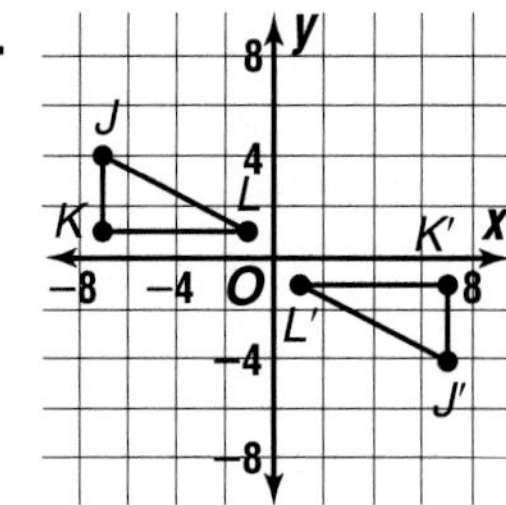

$\triangle JKL$ was reflected over the y-axis and then over the x-axis. This is a double reflection.

21. $2 \times 3^2 \times 5 \times 7$

Pages 218–221 Study Guide and Assessment

1. negative **3.** 7 **5.** origin **7.** quadrants **9.** y-coordinate **11.** zero **13.** A reflection is a transformation where a figure is flipped. A translation is a transformation where a figure is slid.

15. $+14$ **17.** -5 **19.** $-1, 1, 1$ **21.** $4, -4, 4$

23. $>$ **25.** $>$ **27.** $-13, -11, 0, 5, 8, 10$

29. $(1, 3)$, I **31.** $(-2, -3)$, III

33-37.

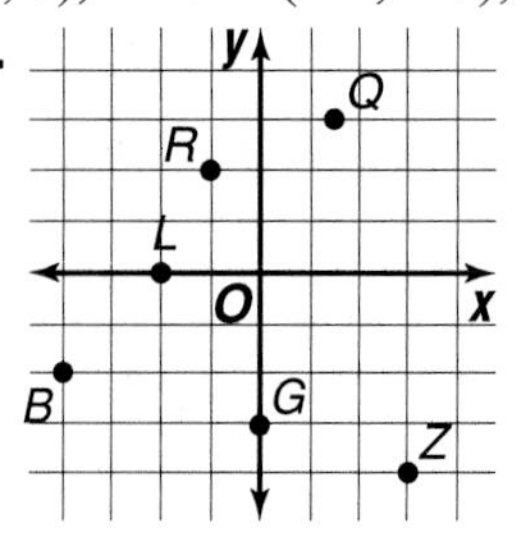

39. -6

41. -13 **43.** 0 **45.** 24 **47.** 8 **49.** 2

51. 9 **53.** -25 **55.** 24 **57.** -5 **59.** 6

61. -2 **63.** $A'(7, 2), B'(1, 1), C'(2, 10)$

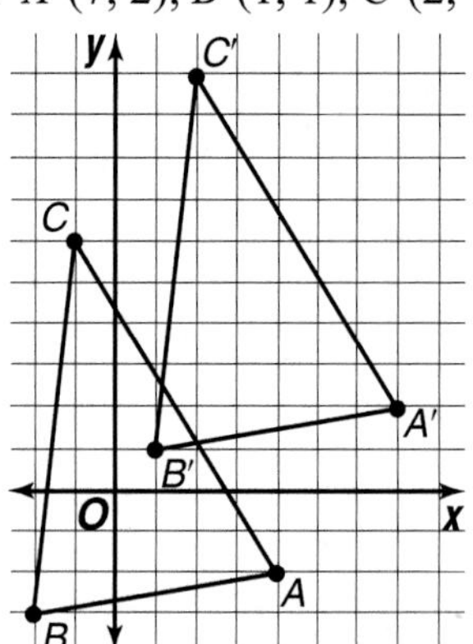

65. -18 **67.** 4 yards lost **69.** $x = \$327 \div 3$

Pages 222–223 Standardized Test Practice

1. D **3.** C **5.** C **7.** A **9.** D **11.** 7 **13.** 86

15. $\frac{13}{20}$

CHAPTER 6
Algebra: Exploring Equations and Functions

Pages 226–227 Lesson 6-1A

1. 5 **3.** 5

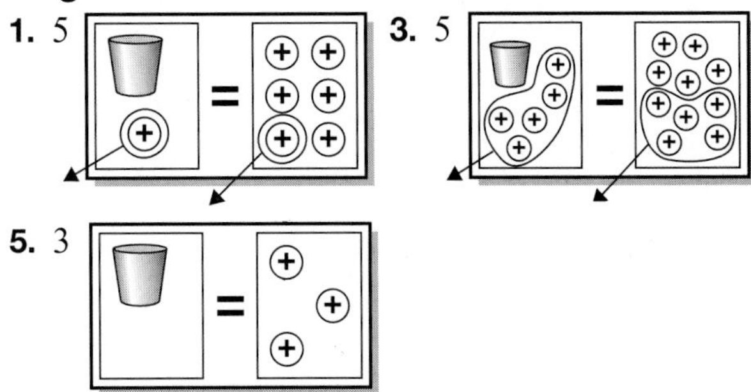

5. 3

7. Sample answer: The forces on each arm of the seesaw are equal; each side of an equation has the same value.

9. −5 **11.** −3 **13.** −2

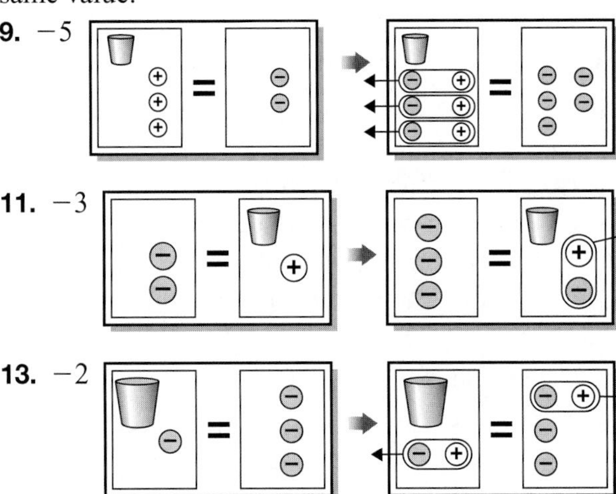

15. Sample answer: A zero pair has a value of 0. So, adding or subtracting a zero pair is like adding or subtracting zero.

Pages 230–231 Lesson 6-1

1.

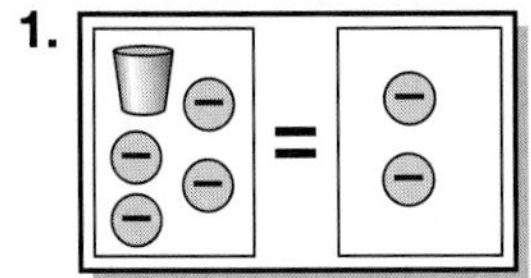

3.
$$x - 6 = 3$$
$$x - 6 + 6 = 3 + 6$$
$$x = 9$$

5. 3 **7.** 2 **9.** −8 **11.** 555 feet **13.** 21 **15.** −8 **17.** 25 **19.** 8 **21.** −12 **23.** −43 **25.** 1.7 **27.** 8.5 **29.** 11 **31.** −4 **33.** $a + 50 + 75 = 180$; 55° **35.** Sample answer: $x - 5 = -7, x + 4 = 2$ **37.** 16 **39.** The one very high salary increases the mean.

Pages 232–233 Lesson 6-1B

1. 1952 **3.** Sample answer: There are too many guesses you might make; it would take less time to work backward. **5.** Sample answer: Since 13 was added to x to get 25, subtract 13 from 25. The solution is 12. **7.** Sample answer: Subtract 120 from 364. **9.** 2 letters and 10 postcards **11.** 1894 **13.** 55 **15.** B

Pages 236–237 Lesson 6-2

1. $3x = -15$; −5

3. 6

5. −6 **7.** 12 **9.** 6 **11.** 7 **13.** −17 **15.** 2 **17.** −49 **19.** 5 **21.** 15 **23.** 4.7 **25.** 5.4 **27.** 18 **29.** −5 **31.** 50 inches **33.** 100 seconds **35.** 7.6 **37.** 1

Page 238 Lesson 6-3A

1. 2 **3.** 2 **5.** 0

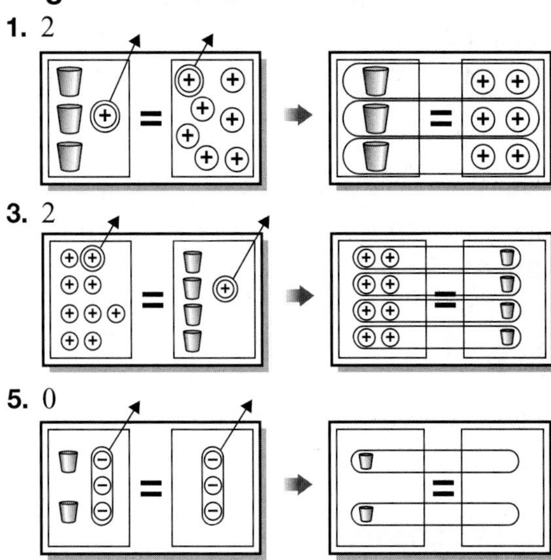

7. It is made up of two operations and takes two steps to solve.

Pages 240–241 Lesson 6-3

1. −2

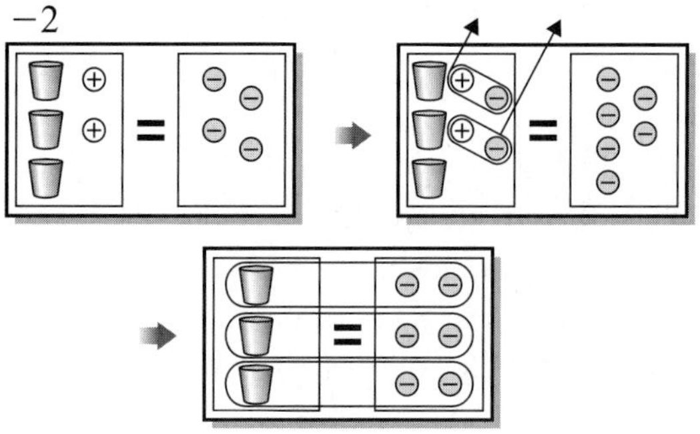

3. Hector; the first step is to create zero pairs. **5.** −4 **7.** −4 **9.** 2.1 **11.** 2 **13.** −3 **15.** 3 **17.** 2.4 **19.** −5 **21.** 1 **23.** −4 **25.** 0 **27.** 4 **29.** 3 **31.** 5 balloons

33. 3

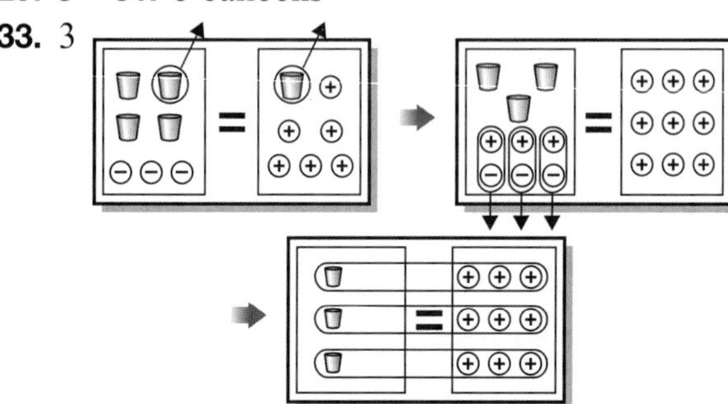

35. D **37.** 9.8×10^3

Pages 244–245 Lesson 6-4

1. c **3.** Sample answers: the age of a person 3 years older; the person's age in 3 years **5.** $p - 8$ **7.** $-9 + n$ **9.** $20n = 120$ **11.** $m + 10.1 = 33.0$; $m = 22.9$ **13.** $x \cdot 2$ or $2x$ **15.** $9 + x$ **17.** $a \div 3$ or $\frac{a}{3}$ **19.** $2a$ **21.** $s + 10$ **23.** $\frac{n^2}{10}$ **25.** $8n = -64$ **27.** $7n - 5 = 37$ **29.** $s + 15 = 220$ **31.** $8 + 2a = 60$ **33.** $p + 0.2 = 1.9$; $p = 1.7$ **35.** $1.5m + 10 = 19$; $m = 6$ **37.** −13 **39.** 18 **41.** 243

Page 245 Mid-Chapter Self Test

1. 30 **3.** 5.2 **5.** 12 **7.** 1 **9.** −4

Page 248 Lesson 6-5

1. $x \leq -1$

3.

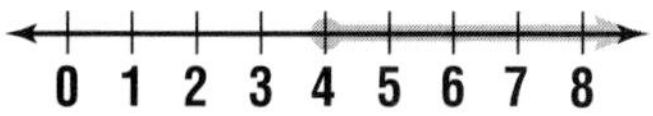

5. $a \geq -2$,

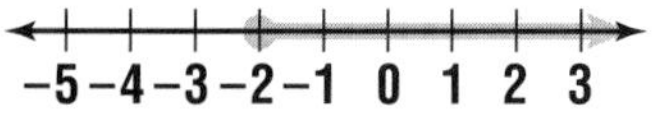

7. $x \leq -6$,

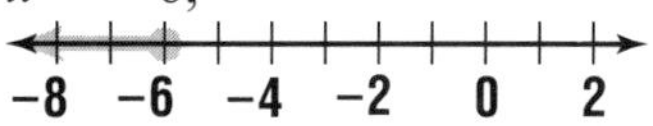

9. $x > -7$,

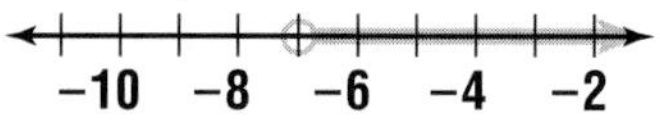

11. $d \geq 4$,

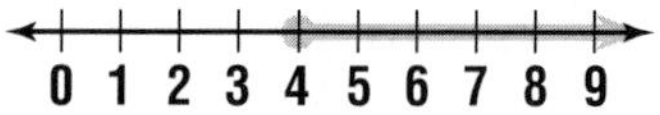

13. $p > -2$,

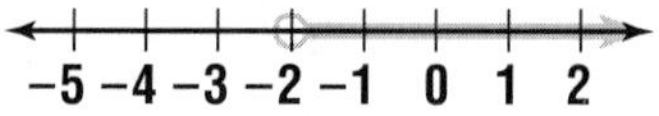

15. $r < 8$,

17. $y < 3.2$,

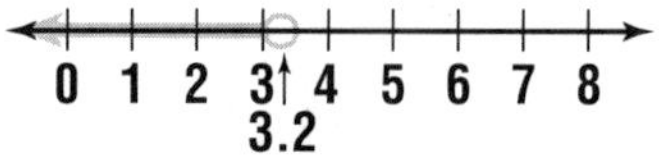

19. $a > 7$,

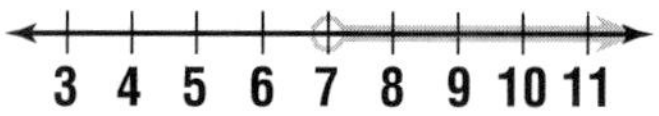

21. $5n > 60$, $n > 12$ **23.** $a \geq 18$ **25.** $0.06 < s < 2$ **27.** 11

Pages 251–252 Lesson 6-6

1. a relationship between two quantities

3. Sample answer: It would take longer for each student, so the graph would be above the original graph.

5. The population increases each year.

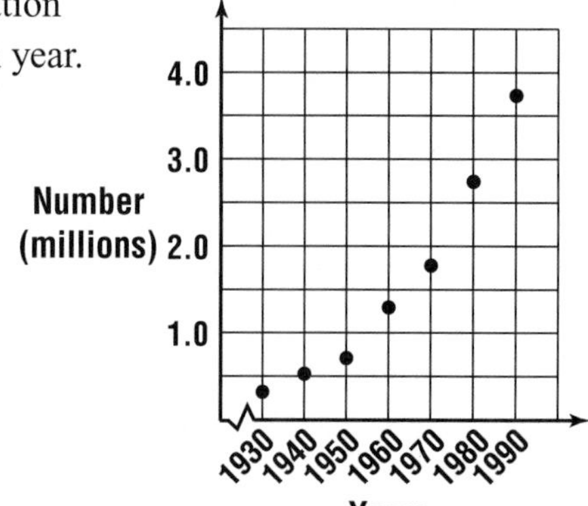

7a.

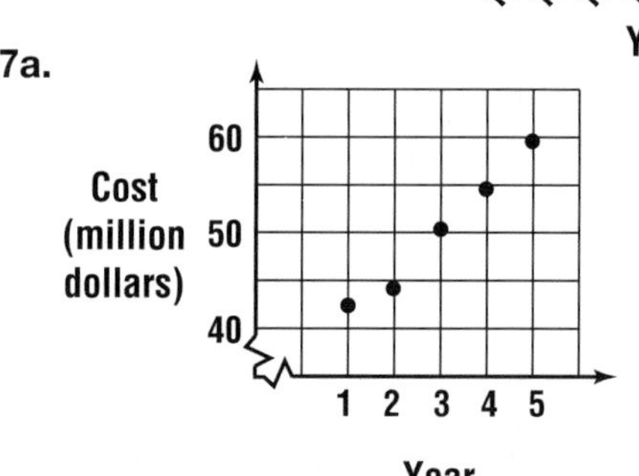

7b. Production costs have increased each year.

9. As you grow older, you are more likely to snore and less likely to talk in your sleep. **11.** Between 12 and 14; the line connecting the points is steeper for these years. **13.** 55

Page 253 Lesson 6-7A

3. Extend the line.

Pages 256–257 Lesson 6-7

1. d **3.** Grace; $2(1) - 1 \neq -1$

5.

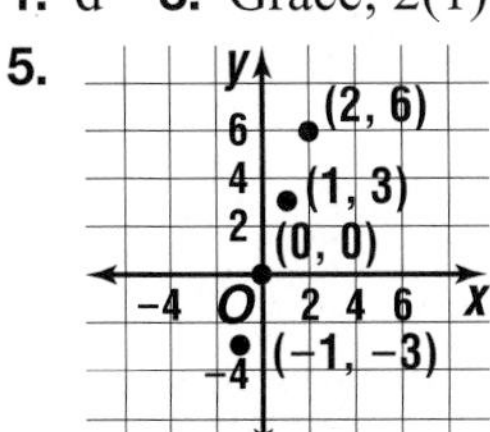

7.

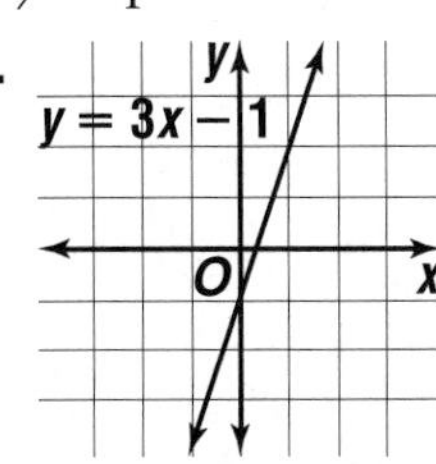

9.

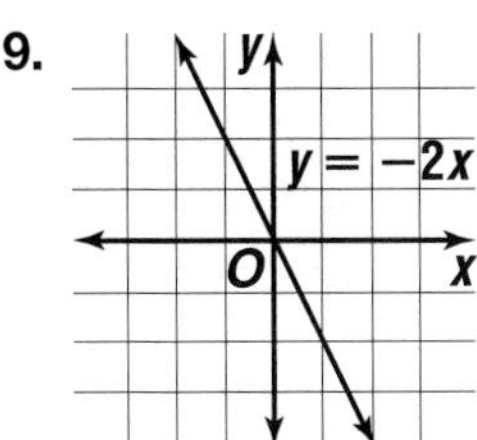

11a.

Hours	Earnings
3	18
5	30
7	42
9	54

11b. $y = 6x$

11c.

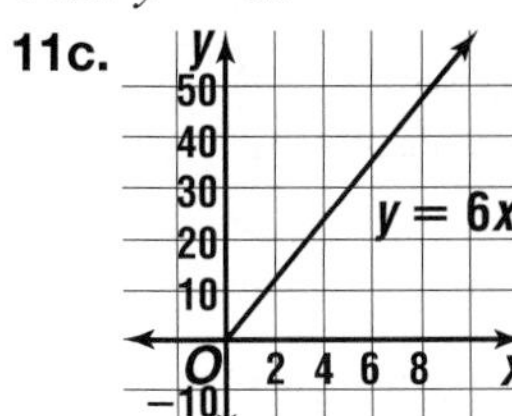

13.

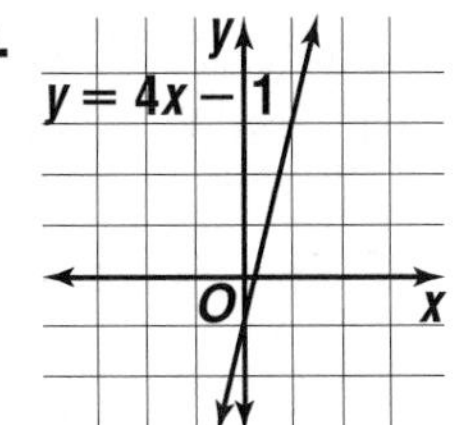

15.

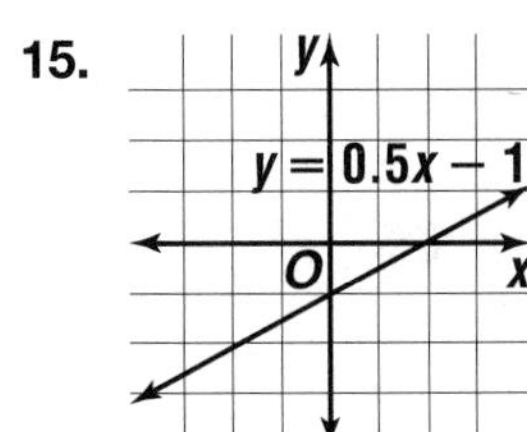

17.

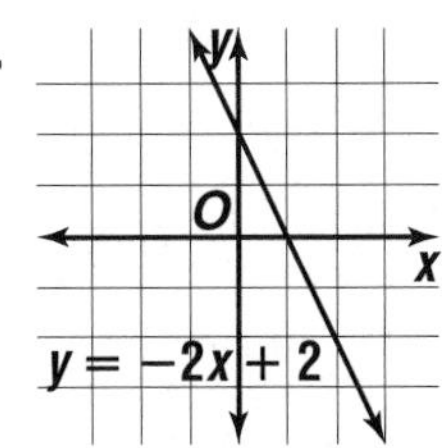

19.

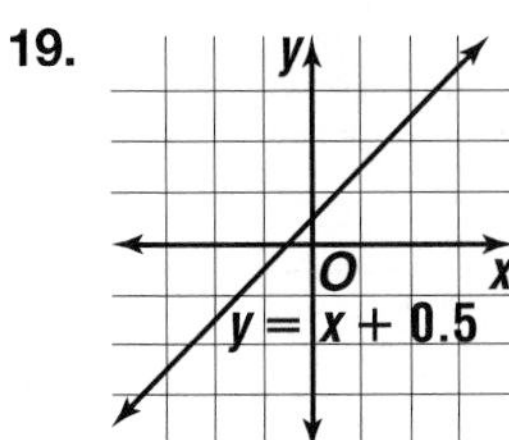

21.

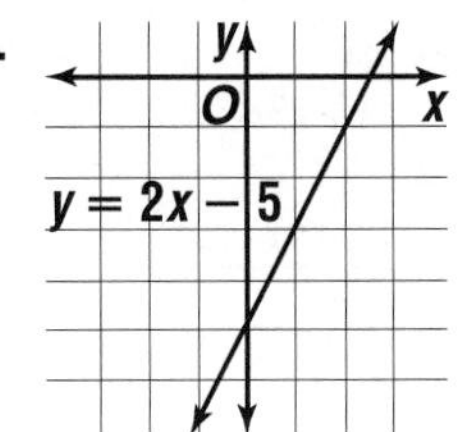

23.

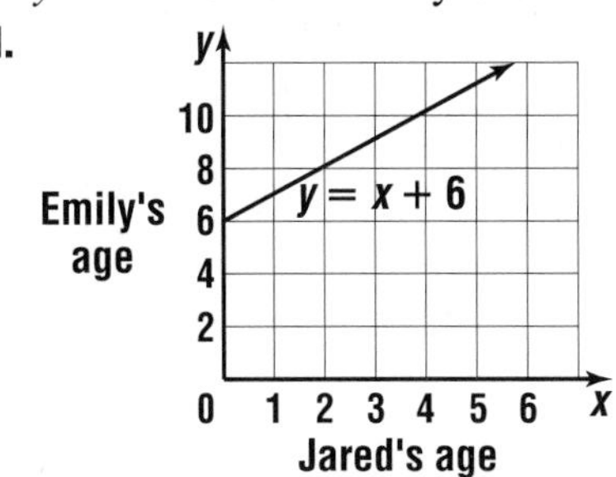

25. $y = 2x$ **27.** $x + y = 10$ **29a.** Sample answer: Emily is 6 years older than Jared. **29b.** $y = x + 6$ **29c.** 16 years

29d.

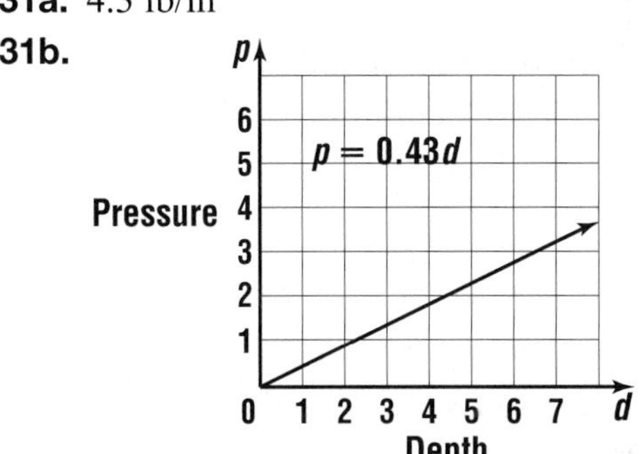

31a. 4.3 lb/in^2

31b.

31c. about 12 or 13 lb/in^2 **33.** No; the number of members of the band can only be represented with whole numbers. **35.** 12 **37.** B

Pages 258–261 Study Guide and Assessment

1. false, variable **3.** true **5.** true **7.** false, 7 **9.** false, −6 **11.** If you add the same number to each side of an equation, the two sides will still be equal. **13.** −38 **15.** 63 **17.** 1.5 **19.** 4 **21.** 9 **23.** −3 **25.** −1 **27.** −2 **29.** −10 **31.** −4 **33.** $s - 13$ **35.** $14n = 56$

37. $g \leq 2$

39. $m \geq -3$

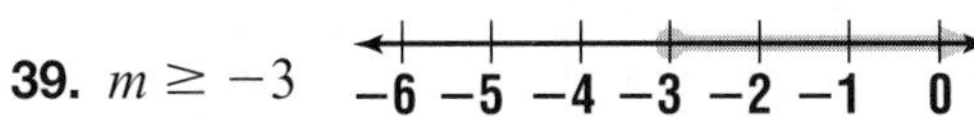

41. As the length of a side of a square increases, the area also increases.

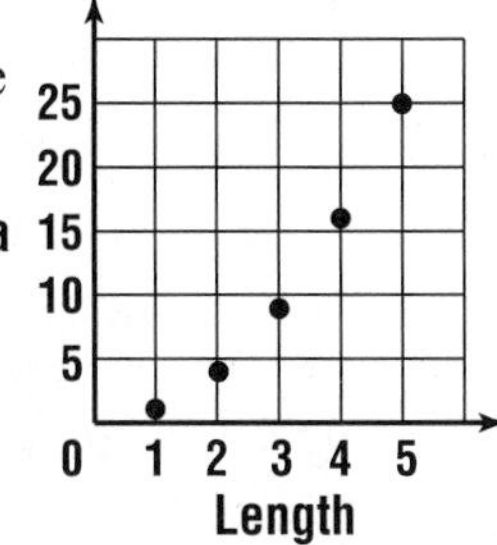

43. $y = 2x$ **45.** $y = 3x + 2$

47. Jeff: 27, Fina: 9, Mario: 12, Danielle: 16
49a. $y = 12.50x$ **49b.** \$500

Pages 262–263 Standardized Test Practice

1. D **3.** B **5.** A **7.** C **9.** B **11.** E **13.** 3
15. $E = 6(20)$ **17.** -1

CHAPTER 7 Applying Fractions

Pages 270–271 Lesson 7-1

1a. $\frac{6}{11}, \frac{1}{2}$ **1b.** $\frac{6}{7}, 1$ **3.** 0 **5.** $\frac{1}{2}$ **7.** 9
9. $\frac{1}{2} + 1 = 1\frac{1}{2}$ **11.** $1 \times 11 = 11$ **13.** $5 \times 3 = 15$ **15.** Sample answer: $1 \times 24 = 24$ cups **17.** $\frac{1}{2}$
19. 1 **21.** 0 **23.** 1 **25.** 3 **27.** 4 **29.** 6
31. 7 **33–49.** Sample answers are given.
33. $\frac{1}{2} - 0 = \frac{1}{2}$ **35.** $1 \div 1 = 1$ **37.** $5 - 3 = 2$
39. $\frac{1}{2} \times 18 = 9$ **41.** $12 - 2 = 10$
43. $22 \div 2 = 11$ **45.** $\frac{1}{2} \times \frac{1}{2} = \frac{1}{4}$ **47.** $2 + 1 + 6 = 9$ **49.** $1 \times 250 = 250$ pounds **53.** Sample answer: (1, 4), (2, 7), (3, 10), (4, 13) **55.** 23
57. $<$

Pages 274–275 Lesson 7-2

1. The units of measure must be the same.
3.

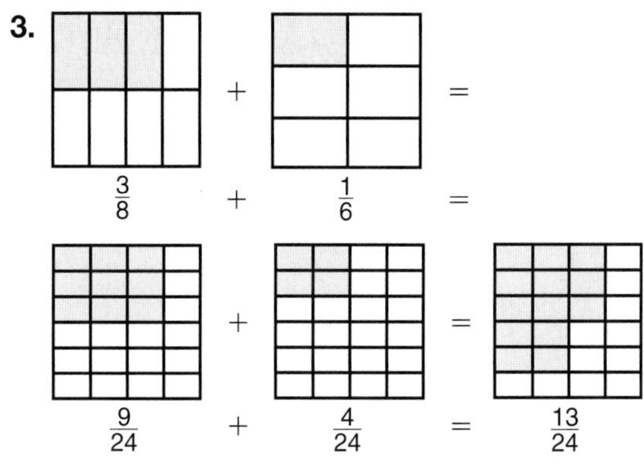

5. $\frac{2}{3}$ **7.** $\frac{1}{4}$ **9.** $1\frac{7}{18}$ **11.** $\frac{3}{8}$ tank **13.** $\frac{11}{15}$
15. $1\frac{8}{35}$ **17.** $\frac{1}{6}$ **19.** $\frac{19}{30}$ **21.** $\frac{26}{45}$ **23.** $1\frac{1}{6}$
25. $1\frac{16}{45}$ **27.** $\frac{7}{24}$ **29.** $1\frac{11}{18}$ **31.** $\frac{21}{44}$ **33.** $\frac{3}{5}$

35. No; commutative property does not hold for subtraction. **37.** 2 **39.** A

Pages 277–279 Lesson 7-3

1. $(3\frac{1}{4})$ → $(2\frac{5}{4})$

3. Renaming of mixed numbers is used when the fraction in the first mixed number is less than the fraction in the second. Renaming of whole numbers is used when the digit in the first number is less than the digit in the same place value in the second number. **5.** 7 **7.** $8\frac{1}{3}$ **9.** $1\frac{3}{4}$ **11.** $212\frac{4}{5}$ carats
13. 3 **15.** 8 **17.** 11 **19.** 13 **21.** $4\frac{2}{3}$ **23.** $4\frac{1}{2}$
25. $29\frac{23}{40}$ **27.** $3\frac{7}{9}$ **29.** $11\frac{13}{24}$ **31.** $2\frac{1}{6}$ **33.** $2\frac{11}{20}$
35. $3\frac{1}{18}$ **37.** No, the ammonia and vinegar make $2\frac{5}{6}$ cups. A $\frac{1}{2}$-quart pan holds only 2 cups.
39. 20 ft **41.** Sample answers: $(-1, 10)$, (0, 7), (1, 4), (2, 1) **43a.** $\frac{1}{25}$ **43b.** $\frac{13}{100}$ **43c.** $\frac{7}{50}$

Pages 280–281 Lesson 7-3B

1. Sample answer: Use estimation, work backward, draw a diagram. **3.** D **7.** $4\frac{1}{6}$ c **9.** no; $2\frac{5}{6} + 3\frac{1}{2} > 6$ **11.** Sample answer: about 98,000 thousand

Page 283 Lesson 7-4A

1. $\frac{1}{2} \times \frac{1}{3} = \frac{1}{6}$

3. $3 \times \frac{1}{2} = \frac{3}{2}$ or $1\frac{1}{2}$

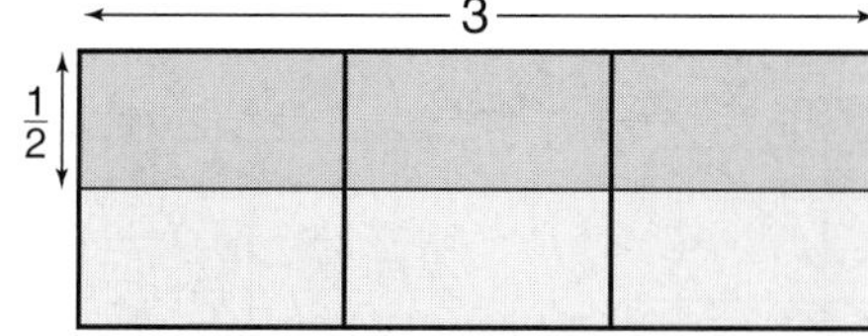

5. $1\frac{1}{3} \times \frac{1}{4} = \frac{4}{12}$ or $\frac{1}{3}$

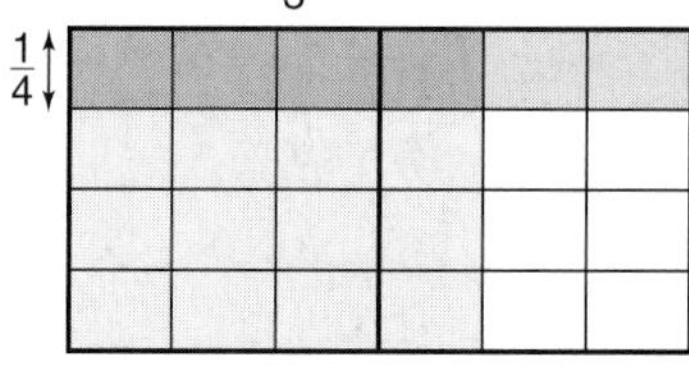

7. $\frac{20}{6}$ or $3\frac{1}{3}$

Pages 285–287 Lesson 7-4

1. Rename each mixed number as an improper fraction. Multiply the numerators and the denominators. Simplify.
3. $\frac{4}{5} \times \frac{1}{4} = \frac{4}{20}$ or $\frac{1}{5}$

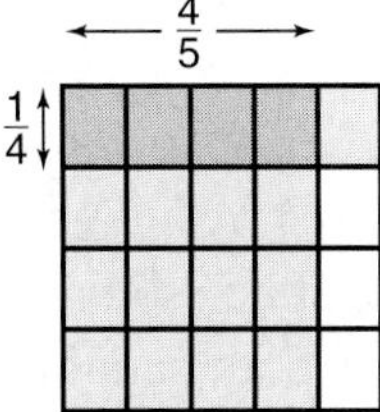

5. $\frac{2}{7}$ **7.** $\frac{1}{4}$ **9.** $4\frac{4}{15}$ **11.** $6\frac{13}{20}$ ft **13.** $\frac{3}{32}$ **15.** $1\frac{3}{5}$ **17.** $\frac{1}{2}$ **19.** $\frac{3}{10}$ **21.** $\frac{2}{7}$ **23.** $1\frac{9}{16}$ **25.** 33 **27.** 6 **29.** $42\frac{1}{6}$ **31.** $7\frac{1}{3}$ **33.** $\frac{1}{4}$ **35.** $1{,}500\frac{3}{4}$ mi **37.** $\frac{2}{3}, \frac{2}{5}$ **39.** $r > -8$ **41.** 52, 47, 36, 27, 13, 0, −2, −3, −6, −14

Page 287 Mid-Chapter Self Test

1. $\frac{1}{2} + 1 = 1\frac{1}{2}$ **3.** $\frac{1}{2} \times 14 = 7$ **5.** $1\frac{7}{36}$ **7.** $6\frac{1}{3}$ **9.** $32\frac{2}{15}$

Page 288 Lesson 7-4B

1. 72 sq units; 64 sq units **3.** You can multiply the area of each stage by $\frac{8}{9}$ to get the area of the next stage. **5a.** $\frac{3}{4}$ sq units **5b.** $\frac{9}{16}$ sq units **5c.** $\frac{27}{64}$ sq units

Pages 290–291 Lesson 7-5

1. Division; pints are larger than cups. **3.** 80 **5.** 9 **7.** 24 **9.** 3.5 lb **11.** 10,000 **13.** 6 **15.** 4 **17.** 48 **19.** 5 **21.** 40 **23.** 9 **25.** $\frac{1}{4}$ **27.** 2 **29.** $\frac{3}{8}$ gal **31.** 52 fl oz **33.** $7\frac{3}{4}$ T **35.** No, the recipe makes 9 cups of punch and the pitcher holds only 2 quarts, or 8 cups. **37.** D **39.** 80

Pages 293–295 Lesson 7-6

3. Sample answer: wallpaper border around bedroom **5.** 56 cm **7.** 10.4 yd **9.** 300 ft **11.** 18.8 ft **13.** 50 mi **15.** 110 m **17.** $21\frac{3}{4}$ in. **19.** 24 m **21.** 52.2 cm **23.** $2\frac{3}{16}$ ft **25.** $2\frac{3}{4}$ in. **27.** $3\frac{1}{2}$ in. **29.** 132 ft **31.** Sample answer: 4 in., 4 in., 4 in., $3\frac{5}{6}$ in. **33.** 99.9 **35.** A

Pages 299–300 Lesson 7-7

3. 29.8 km **5.** 9.4 yd **7.** 32.3 cm **9.** 31.4 ft **11.** 38.3 m **13.** 3.1 mi **15.** 44 m **17.** 38.9 cm **19.** $2\frac{18}{35}$ or 2.5 yd **21.** 55 ft **23a.** 201.0 in. **23b.** 5.3 times **25.** 4.7 ft **27.** 2π **29.** A **31.** $\frac{49}{100}, \frac{7}{20}, \frac{4}{25}$

Pages 303–304 Lesson 7-8

1. No; $4 \cdot 20 \neq 5$. **3a.** $80 + 20 + 276 = 100 + 276 = 376$; commutative **3b.** $-26 + 26 + 54 = 0 + 54 = 54$; commutative, additive inverse, identity (+) **3c.** $\left(-\frac{5}{9}\right)(1) = -\frac{5}{9}$; identity (×) **3d.** $(-7)(3)(-15)(0) = 0$; additive inverse, multiplicative prop. of zero **5.** Identity (+) **7.** $\frac{5}{22}$ **9.** 32 **11.** 11 **13.** commutative (+) **15.** identity (×) **17.** multiplication (=) **19.** $\frac{3}{2}$ or $1\frac{1}{2}$ **21.** $\frac{1}{12}$ **23** 36 **25.** 24 **27.** 112 **29.** $24\frac{1}{2}$ **31.** $\frac{4}{5}$ **33.** Yes; there is enough turkey for 16 people. **35.** 420 **37.** D **39.** 20; Sample answer: 20-50; 5

Pages 306–307 Lesson 7-9

1. Rename $1\frac{1}{9}$ as $\frac{10}{9}$, and multiply by the inverse of $\frac{8}{9}$. **3.** Omar; each person will get $2\frac{1}{4} \div 4 = \frac{9}{16}$ or 0.5625 lb. **5.** 12 **7.** $5\frac{1}{3}$ **9.** $\frac{4}{15}$ **11.** $\frac{7}{16}$ **13.** $2\frac{2}{5}$ **15.** $1\frac{1}{4}$ **17.** 2 **19.** $\frac{3}{8}$ **21.** $\frac{4}{15}$ **23.** $1\frac{2}{3}$ **25.** $1\frac{3}{4}$ **27.** $3\frac{3}{8}$ **29.** $\frac{5}{14}$ **31.** $\frac{16}{21}$ **33.** 20 packages **37.** $\frac{8}{29}$ **39.** 18% **41.** C

Pages 308–311 Study Guide and Assessment

1. e **3.** c **5.** j **7.** d **9.** g **11–17.** Sample answers are given. **11.** $1 + 1 = 2$ **13.** $12 \div 1 = 12$ **15.** $1 - 0 = 1$ **17.** $2 \times 16 = 32$ **19.** $1\frac{1}{35}$ **21.** $\frac{3}{5}$ **23.** $13\frac{5}{9}$ **25.** $3\frac{1}{24}$ **27.** $\frac{1}{3}$ **29.** $34\frac{4}{7}$ **31.** 8 **33.** 4 **35.** 6 **37.** 16.6 m **39.** 9.4 yd **41.** 44 in. **43.** 4 ft **45.** $18\frac{3}{4}$ **47.** 6 **49.** 6 **51.** $7\frac{6}{7}$ **53.** $5\frac{11}{12}$ cups **55.** yes

Pages 312–313 Standardized Test Practice

1. A **3.** B **5.** B **7.** C **9.** C **11.** D **13.** $\frac{5}{8}$ **15.** $Q(-6, 3)$, II; $R(-3\frac{1}{2}, -4)$, III; $S(2, 0)$, x-axis

CHAPTER 8 Using Proportional Reasoning

Page 316 Lesson 8-1A

1. Sample answer: Make equivalent fractions. $\frac{2}{3} = \frac{4}{6} = \frac{6}{9} = \frac{10}{15}$

3.

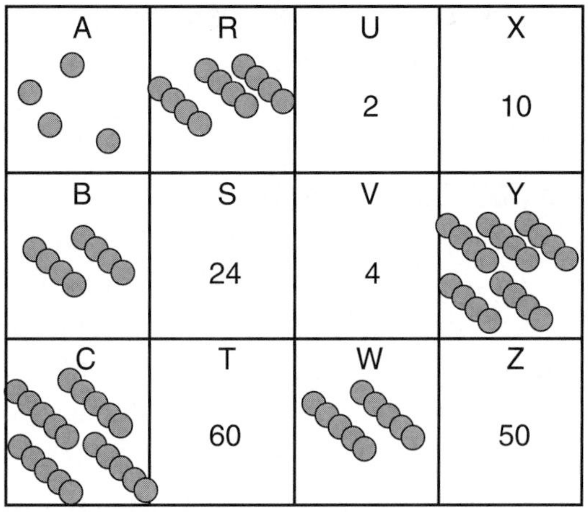

A	R	U	X
		2	10
B	S	V	Y
	24	4	
C	T	W	Z
	60		50

Pages 318–320 Lesson 8-1

1. $\frac{15}{20}$, 15:20, 15 to 20 **3.** Sample answer: Write both ratios as fractions in simplest form. If the fractions are equal, then the ratios are equivalent. **5.** $\frac{8}{21}$ **7.** $\frac{1}{21}$ **9.** Yes; $\frac{12}{16} = \frac{3}{4}$ and $\frac{21}{28} = \frac{3}{4}$ **11.** Yes; $\frac{15}{6} = \frac{5}{2}$ and $\frac{90}{36} = \frac{5}{2}$ **13.** $\frac{7}{15}$ **15.** $\frac{7}{2}$ **17.** $\frac{5}{1}$ **19.** $\frac{35}{36}$ **21.** $\frac{31}{44}$ **23.** $\frac{32}{9}$ **25.** $\frac{7}{40}$ **27.** $\frac{9}{26}$ **29.** No; 150:15 = 10:1 **31.** No; $\frac{65}{5} = \frac{13}{1}$ **33.** No; 14:42 = 1:3 and 58:1,218 = 1:21 **35.** Yes; 3 days:4 hours = 18:1 and 9 days to 12 hours = 18:1 **37.** $\frac{36}{73}$ **39.** $\frac{1}{300}$ **41a.** $\frac{1}{25}$ **41b.** Yes; the ratios of successive terms decrease by 1. **43.** 45; they are all 1:25. **45.** 3 **47.** 2, 3, 6

Pages 323–324 Lesson 8-2

1a. No; the denominator is not 1. **1b.** Yes; the denominator is 1. **1c.** Yes; the denominator is 1. **3.** April is correct. The \$3.99 bag has a unit price of about 24.94¢ and the \$2.99 bag has a unit price of about 24.92¢. **5.** 60 miles per hour **7.** 15 people per van **9.** 6.1875¢ per ounce **11.** 40 miles per hour **13.** \$70 per day **15.** 3 pounds per week **17.** 5 meters per second **19.** about 29.08¢ per ounce **21.** \$1.24 per pound **23.** 3 people per car **25.** 9.5 feet per second **27.** 90 rotations per minute **29.** 24.5¢ per ounce **31.** 2,160,000 toys per year **33a.** adult human **33b.** adult human **35.** about 4.9 hours **37.** $a \geq 25$ **39.** D

Pages 327–328 Lesson 8-3

1. Compare the cross products. If they are equal, the ratios are equivalent. **3.** 6 **5.** 6 **7a.** 6 bicycles **7b.** 7 feet **9.** 22.5 **11.** 2 **13.** 75 **15.** 2.5 **17.** 42 **19.** $\frac{1}{3}$ **21.** 210 words **23a.** tuna: $918\frac{3}{4}$ oz; pita breads: 300; dill: $37\frac{1}{2}$ t; yogurt: 50 c; celery: $18\frac{3}{4}$ c; mustard: 225 t; lettuce: 600 leaves; tomatoes: 150 **25.** Sample answers: 1 and 36; 2 and 18; 4 and 9 **27.** $17\frac{1}{2}$

Page 329 Lesson 8-3B

1. Sample answer: Yes; it uses all of the samples to find a more accurate estimate. **3.** The sample needs to be a random handful of the total number of beans.

Pages 330–331 Lesson 8-4A

1. 27 people **3.** 121 people **7.** 12 right, 2 wrong, 1 unanswered **9.** 36 handshakes **11a.** $\frac{5}{8}$ feet **11b.** $28\frac{3}{4}$ feet or 345 inches

Pages 334–335 Lesson 8-4

1. the scale **5.** 9,650 km **7.** 50 inches **9.** $134\frac{1}{5}$ miles **11.** $647\frac{1}{2}$ miles **13.** 4,125 km **15.** 32 inches **17.** 0.6 cm **19.** 20 cm **21.** 18.48 cm **23.** 1 inch:16 miles **25.**

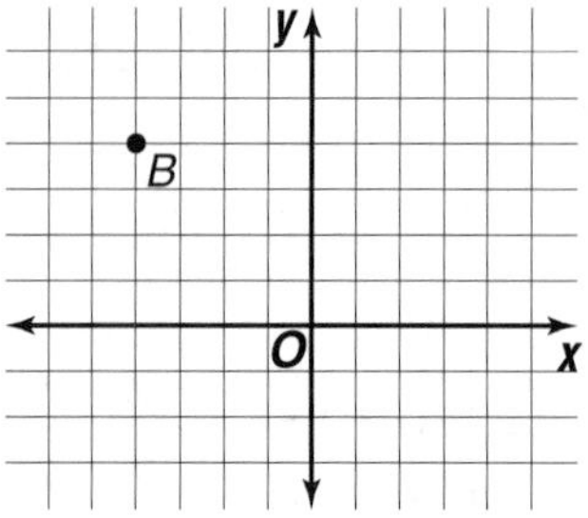

y B O x

Page 335 Mid-Chapter Self Test

1. $\frac{1}{9}$ **3.** $\frac{8}{1}$ **5.** \$1.19 per disk **7.** 12 **9.** 2.5

Pages 337–338 Lesson 8-5

1. Set up a proportion with a fraction with a denominator of 100.

$\frac{3}{16} = \frac{n}{100}$

Use cross products to solve.

$300 = 16n$

$18.75 = n$

So, $\frac{3}{16} = 18.75\%$.

3. 30% **5.** 31.25% **7.** $\frac{18}{25}$ **9.** $\frac{3}{4}$ **11.** 43.75%
13. 11.5% **15.** about 41.7% **17.** about 36.4%
19. about 3.3% **21.** $\frac{2}{5}$ **23.** $\frac{69}{200}$ **25.** $\frac{5}{8}$
27. $\frac{901}{2{,}000}$ **29.** 1 **31.** 32% **33.** about 8.3%
35. A **37.** −3

Pages 340–341 Lesson 8-6

1. b **3.** Sample answer: A number can be expressed as a fraction, a decimal, or a percent.
5. 6% **7.** 0.65 **9.** 0.185 **11.** 17% **13.** 85%
15. 9.9% **17.** 1% **19.** 0.9% **21.** 0.45
23. 0.16 **25.** 0.081 **27.** 0.1425 **29.** 0.9475
31. 84.8% **33.** 4%, 33% **35a.** 3.5 **35b.** 0.175
35c. 0.60 **37.** $t \div 8$ or $\frac{t}{8}$ **39.** 26-30 and 31-35

Pages 344–345 Lesson 8-7

1. 150% is greater than 100%.

3a.

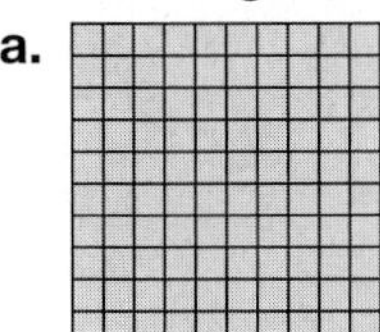

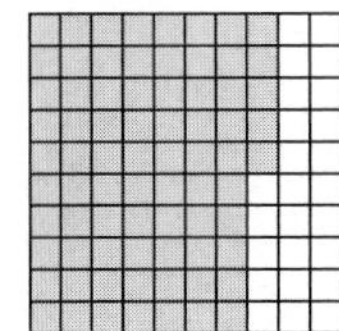

3b.

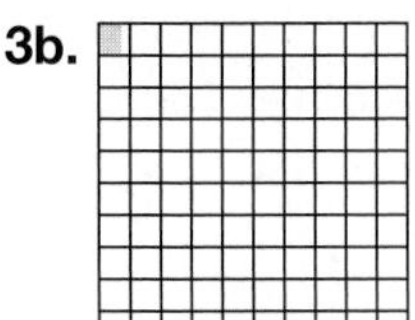

5. 0.0055 **7.** 0.002 **9.** 1,550% **11.** about 0.29% **13.** Yes; This means that they can expect a price higher than the minimum guaranteed. **15.** 5
17. 1.15 **19.** 1.005 **21.** 0.00068 **23.** 0.000025
25. 0.00032 **27.** 900% **29.** 775% **31.** 3,400%
33. 0.9% **35.** 0.4% **37.** 0.01% **39.** 180%
41. No; You would be shorter than when you were born. **43.** No; The greatest possible percent of the attendance from one group would be 100%.
45. No; The population in 1990 would not be less than the population in 1790. **47.** 26.69
49. about 0.22% **51.** 73,592,376 **53.** yes; 13 to 39 = $\frac{1}{3}$ and 26 to 78 = $\frac{1}{3}$
55. $X'(2, -4)$, $Y'(1, 1)$, $Z'(3, -5)$

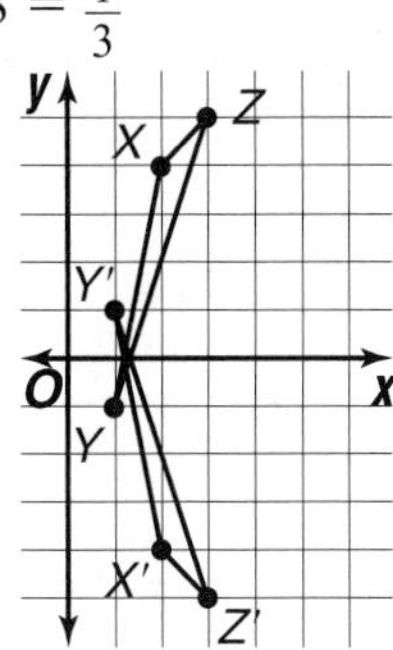

57.

Stem	Leaf
6	2 6
7	
8	1 3 5
9	0 2 5

6|2 = 62

Pages 347–348 Lesson 8-8

1. Sample answer: Each square represents 3. Sixty squares are shaded. So, 60% of 300 is 60 × 3 or 180. **3.** 200.0 **5.** 308 **7.** \$9.10 **9.** 24
11. 9 **13.** 69 **15.** 124.8 **17.** 4 **19.** 10
21. \$11.22 **23.** \$0.52 billion or \$520 million
25. 0.006 **27.** 32 servings

Pages 350–351 Lesson 8-9

1. P is the percentage, B is the base, and r is the number per hundred. **3.** Meredith; 30 is being compared to 20, so 20 is the base. **5.** 7.5%
7. 50% **9.** 125 **11.** 50% **13.** 29.1 **15.** 26.6
17. 174.3 **19.** 16.7% **21.** 150% **23.** 14.7
25. 10% **27.** 60 **29.** 50 grams **33.** 18.7
35. B

Pages 352–355 Study Guide and Assessment

1. e **3.** a **5.** c **7.** d **9.** b **11.** $\frac{5}{2}$ **13.** $\frac{1}{6}$
15. $\frac{30}{11}$ **17.** no **19.** 4 cups per person
21. \$4.75 per pound **23.** \$9.50 per hour **25.** 75
27. 1,750 **29.** 2.5 **31.** 10 inches **33.** 62.5%
35. $\frac{27}{200}$ **37.** $\frac{87}{200}$ **39.** 32.5% **41.** 0.1575
43. 0.0025 **45.** 5.63 **47.** 475% **49.** 0.95%
51. 16.2 **53.** $50.\overline{4}$ **55.** 0.3 **57.** 6,000 **59.** 39 students **61.** $0.00\overline{3}$

Pages 356–357 Standardized Test Practice

1. C **3.** B **5.** D **7.** D **9.** A **11.** Associative property of equality **13.** −40° **15.** 2,000 mL

CHAPTER 9 Geometry: Investigating Patterns

Pages 360–361 Lesson 9-1A

1. 27° **3.** 74° **5.** You can conveniently read the measure of an acute or obtuse angle from one scale or the other. **7.** 34°: ∠1, ∠4, ∠5, ∠8; 146°:∠2, ∠3, ∠6, ∠7 **9.** 45°:∠3, ∠6, ∠7; 135°:∠1, ∠4, ∠5, ∠8

Pages 364–365 Lesson 9-1

3. Vertical angles are congruent. **5.** acute **7.** straight **9.** 75° **11.** straight **13.** acute **15.** acute **17.** obtuse **19.** supplementary **21.** complementary **23.** 155° **25a.** $\angle EDG$ **25b.** $\angle ABC$ in 100,000 years or $\angle DGF$ and $\angle EDG$ today **27.** A **29.** $3\frac{5}{12}$

Pages 366–367 Lesson 9-1B

1.

3.

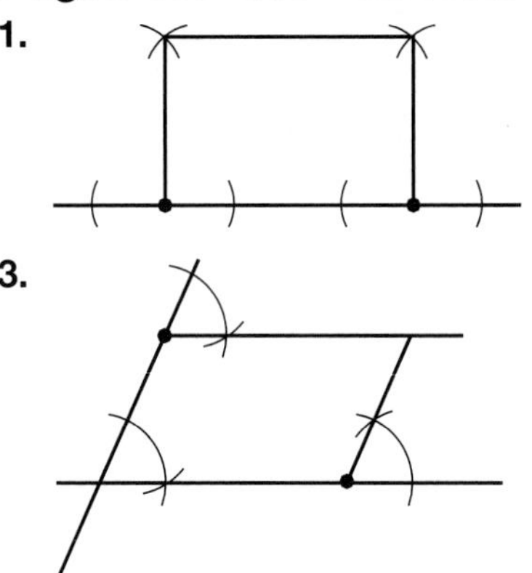

Page 369 Lesson 9-2A

1. straight **3.** 180° **5.** Sample answer: 360°; Since the sum of the measures of each triangle is 180°, there should be 2 × 180° or 360°. **7a.** 540° **7b.** 720° **7c.** 1,080° **7d.** 1,440°

Pages 372–373 Lesson 9-2

1. No; angles are not congruent. **5.** Not a polygon; sides are not line segments. **7.** quadrilateral, regular **9.** Not a polygon; figure is not closed. **11.** Not a polygon; figure is not closed.

13.

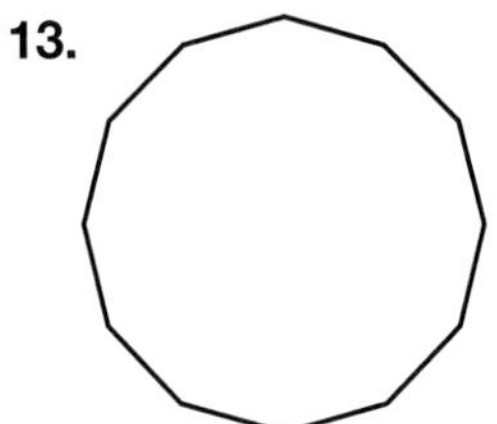

15. bleach, dry

17a. e, f **17b.** a, b or b, c **17c.** a, c **17d.** c, d **17e.** a, d **17f.** e or f **17g.** g **19.** about 4.5 billion pounds

Pages 374–375 Lesson 9-2B

1. The angles are 90° and the sides are congruent. **3.** Sample answer: Follow the same steps as inscribing a square, but fold the circle in half one more time. **5.** Sample answer: Follow the same steps to inscribe a hexagon in a circle, but connect every other intersection point with a line segment.

Pages 378–379 Lesson 9-3

1. $\frac{4}{2.4} = \frac{10}{n}$ **3.** Nikki; $\frac{2}{3} \neq \frac{3}{4}$ **5.** Yes; $\frac{2}{6} = \frac{1}{3}$ and $\frac{3}{9} = \frac{1}{3}$ **7.** 5 cm **9.** Yes; $\frac{2}{6} = \frac{1}{3}$ **11.** 8 m **13.** 10 km **15.** 125 feet **19.** D

Page 379 Mid-Chapter Self Test

1. obtuse **3.** No; figure is not closed. **5.** 5.25 cm

Page 380 Lesson 9-3B

1. enlarged; doubled **3.** one with smaller squares

Page 381 Lesson 9-4A

1. no **3.** Triangles are rigid shapes and do not shift.

Pages 384–385 Lesson 9-4

1.

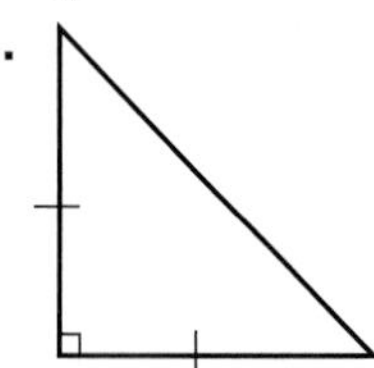

3. Sample answer: Both a rhombus and a square are parallelograms; they are different because a square has 4 right angles and a rhombus may not. **5.** acute, equilateral **7.** quadrilateral **9.** acute, isosceles **11.** obtuse, scalene **13.** quadrilateral, parallelogram, rhombus

15.

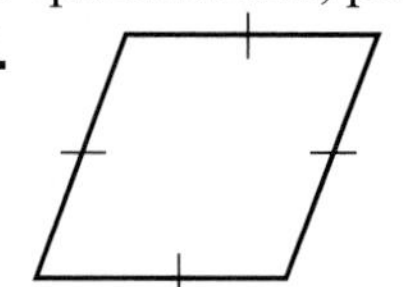

17. right

19a. 60° **19b.** 65° **19c.** $a = 55°, b = 65°, c = 60°, d = 30°$ **21a.** always **21b.** sometimes **21c.** always **21d.** sometimes **21e.** never **23.** 2 × 12 = 24

Pages 386–387 Lesson 9-4B

1. Sample answer: Vince is making a rule from a pattern; Carlos has a rule. **3.** Carlos **5a.** The diagonals are congruent. **5b.** inductive

9.

11. 101.7; All of the data are greater than 10.17.

13. C

Pages 390–391 Lesson 9-5

1. The angle measure is a factor of 360°.

3a. 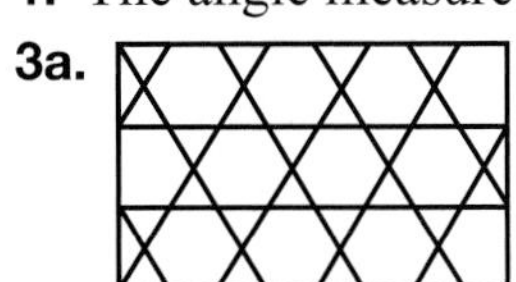

3b. $120° + 60° + 120° + 60° = 360°$ 7. no; 140°

11. 1 square, 2 octagons; 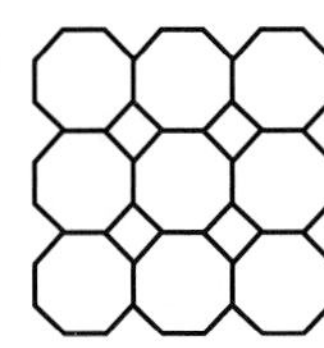

13. Sample answer: There are no gaps.

15. Yes; the sum of the measures of angles of any triangle is 180°, which is a factor of 360°.

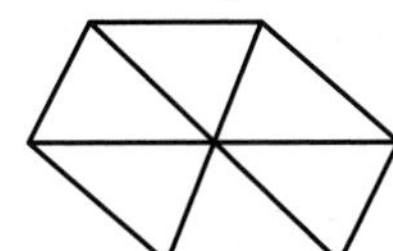

17.

height (thousand feet)	temperature (°F)
1	61.5
2	58.0
3	54.5

Page 394 Lesson 9-6

1. A translation is the result of sliding a figure from one place to another without turning it. 3. Talutah; the patterns on the top and bottom will not tessellate.

5.

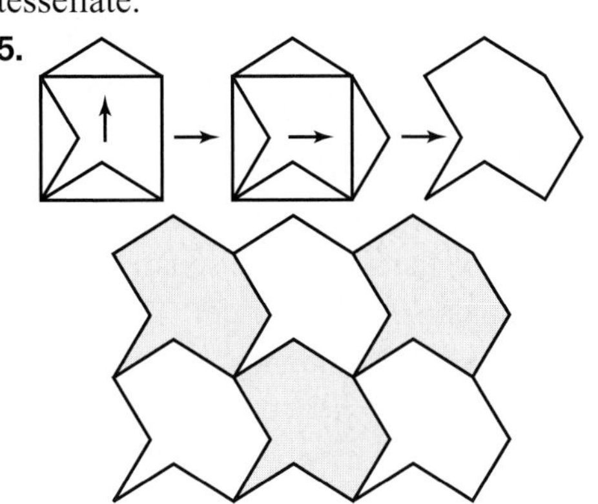

7.

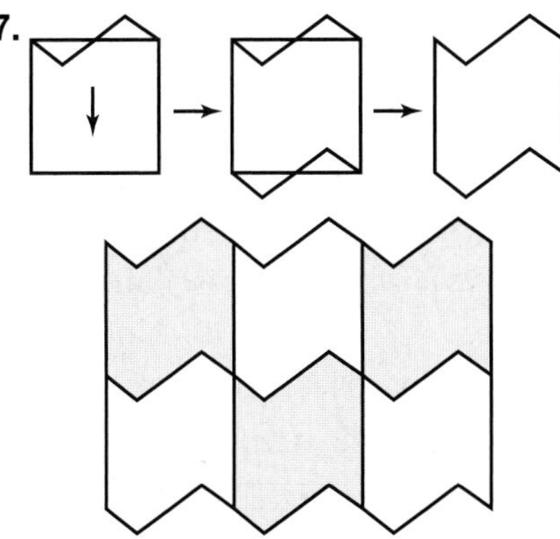

11. Sample answer: birds, fish 13. No; There is no opposite side to translate the change. 15. A

Pages 396–397 Lesson 9-7

1. A line of symmetry divides a figure so that one side is the reflection of the other side.

3. 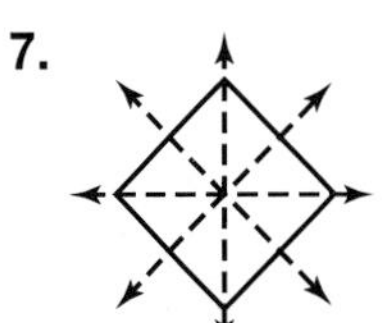 5. no lines of symmetry

7.

9.

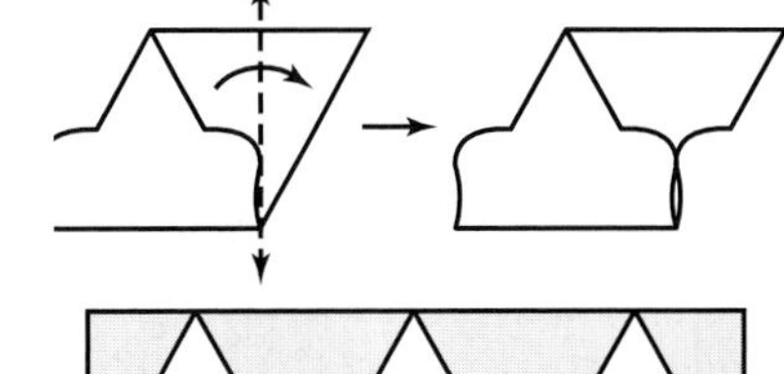

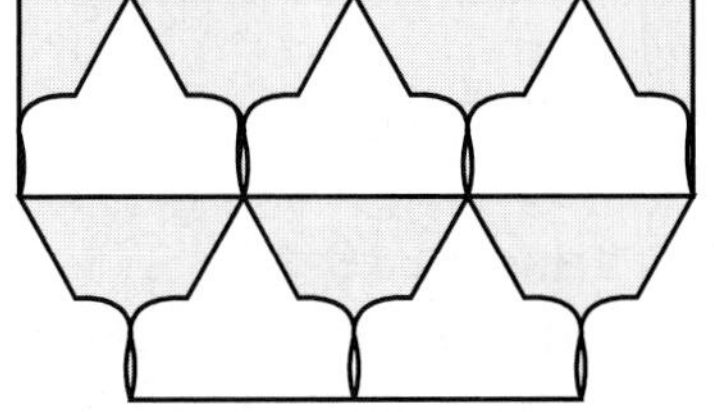

13.

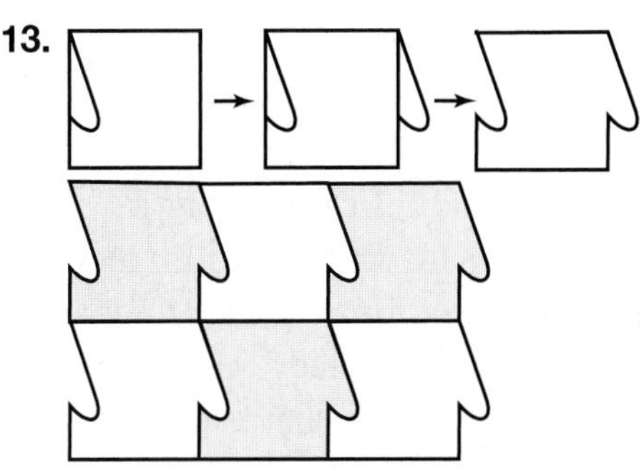

Pages 398–401 Study Guide and Assessment

1. vertex **3.** 180° **5.** regular **7.** equilateral **9.** line symmetry **11.** A translation is a slide of the same pattern over and over. Translating an image that can cover an entire surface is a tessellation. **13.** right **15.** obtuse **17.** acute **19.** Not a polygon; more than 2 sides meet at a vertex. **21.** heptagon, not regular **23.** yes; $\frac{3}{2} = \frac{3}{2}$ **25.** 6 ft **27.** obtuse, isosceles **29.** trapezoid **31.** no, 135°
33.

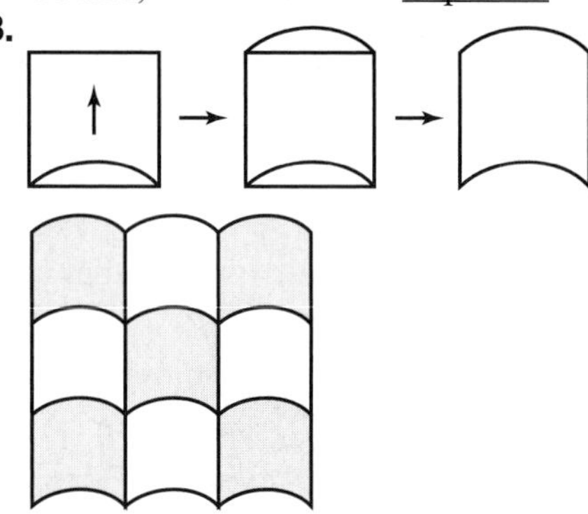

35.

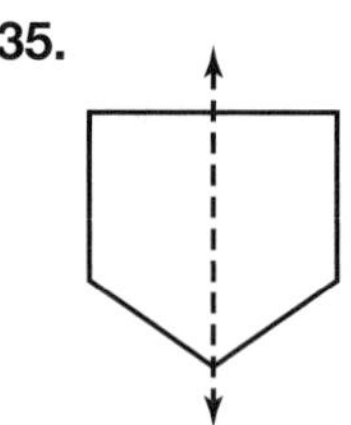

37. isosceles right **39.** 1 hexagon, 4 triangles; 2 hexagons, 2 triangles

Pages 402–403 Standardized Test Practice

1. A **3.** C **5.** C **7.** B **9.** C **11.** 18, 35 **13.** 11

CHAPTER 10 Geometry: Exploring Area

Pages 408–409 Lesson 10-1A

1. Sample answer: Charo picked 6 1-point shots and 10 2-point shots because it is easy to see that 6 + 10 = 16. The guess results in 26 points which is less than 30. She should decrease the number of 1-point shots and increase the number of 2-point shots. **3.** 2 5-card packages and 2 3-card packages **5.** Sample answer: The car wash to raise money for band uniforms charged $4 for a car and $6 for a van or truck. During the first hour, they washed 16 vehicles and earned $78. How many cars did they wash? [answer: 9 cars] **7.** 3, 4 and 5 **9.** 24 ways **11.** 441 units^2

Pages 411–413 Lesson 10-1

1. The area of the square is 16 units and each side is 4 units long.
3a. 2 units, 2 units; $A = 4$ units^2
3b. $A = 81$ units^2

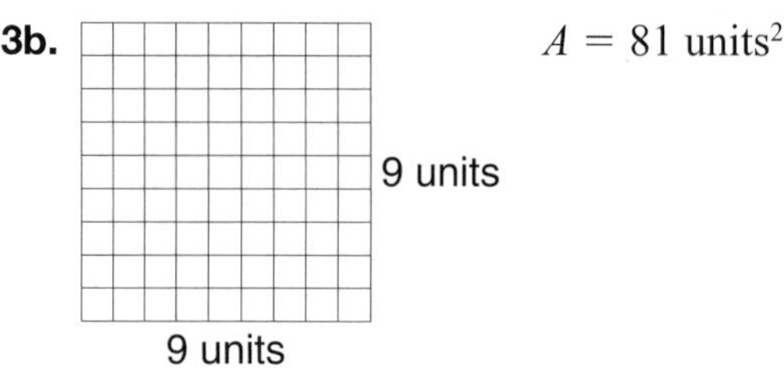

5. 225 **7.** 12 **9.** 18 **11.** 1 **13.** 1,024 **15.** 1,600 **17.** 729 **19.** 11 **21.** 17 **23.** 33 **25.** 24 **27.** 1,444 **29.** 22 in. **31.** 576 ft^2 **33a.** a square house that is 40 ft by 40 ft **33b.** a square house that is 35 ft by 35 ft **35a.** 50 ft by 50 ft **35b.** 3 bags **37.** C **39.** −5

Pages 416–417 Lesson 10-2

1. 34 is between 25 and 36. Since 34 is closer to 36 than 25, $\sqrt{34}$ is closer to 6 than 5.
3. 4

5. 7 **7.** 3.9 **9.** 15.2 **11.** 3 **13.** 8 **15.** 12 **17.** 11 **19.** 4.5 **21.** 8.5 **23.** 11.2 **25.** 25.4 **27.** $\sqrt{34}$ **29a.** about 23.4 ft **29b.** about 15.5 ft **31.** about 15.8 ft **33.** $\frac{7}{20}$ **35.** 2

Page 418 Lesson 10-3A

1. The sum of the area of the two smaller squares equals the area of the largest square. **3.** The sum of the squares of the lengths of the two perpendicular sides of a right triangle equals the square of the length of the side opposite the right angle.

Pages 420–422 Lesson 10-3

1. $4^2 + 3^2 = 5^2$ **3.** Ricardo; the length of the hypotenuse is 8 m, so the sum of the squares of the other two sides equals 8^2. **5.** 23.7 cm **7.** $6^2 + 3^2 = x^2$; 6.7 m **9.** yes **11.** 15.8 mm **13.** 17.6 m **15.** 7 m **17.** $12^2 + 5^2 = x^2$; 13 cm **19.** $7^2 + x^2 = 18^2$; 16.6 m **21.** $13^2 + x^2 = 18^2$; 12.4 in.

23. no **25.** yes **27.** yes **29.** about 11.5 m **31.** about 8.7 ft **33.** A **35.** $2^2 \cdot 3^2$

Pages 424–426 Lesson 10-4

1. Some figures are irregular with curved lines and corners that are not square. **5.** about 46 units^2 **7.** about 51 units^2 **9.** about 44 units^2 **11.** about 53 units^2 **15.** Yes; if the figure is divided into shapes that include a 8-by-7 rectangle and a 5-by-13 rectangle, the area will be 121 in^2. However the figure is at least 2 squares less than this area, so the area of the irregular shape will be less than 120 in^2.

17a. Sample answer: 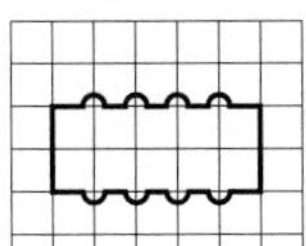 **17b.** Sample answer: 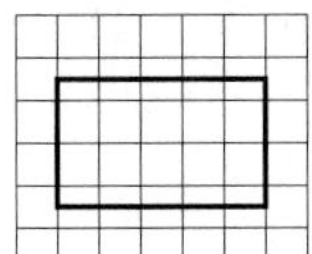

17c. Sample answer: **19.** C

Page 426 Mid-Chapter Self Test

1. 324 **3.** 16 **5.** 5 **7.** 26 in. **9.** about 394.0 ft

Page 427 Lesson 10-5A

1. 2 triangles **5.** The area of a triangle is half the base times the height.

Pages 430–431 Lesson 10-5

1. The area of a triangle is $\frac{1}{2}$ the area of the parallelogram with the same base and height, because the two of these triangles can be formed by drawing a diagonal of the parallelogram.

3.

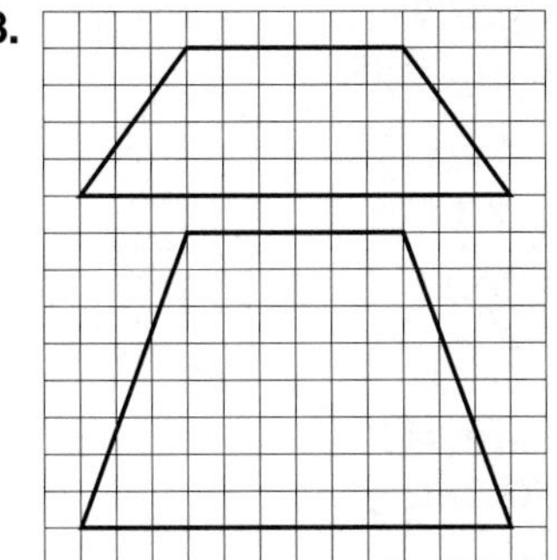

3a. 36 units^2; 72 units^2 **3b.** 1:2 **3c.** 1:2 **5.** 57 cm^2 **7.** 7.5 m^2 **9.** 96 yd^2 **11.** 30 ft^2 **13.** 36 in^2 **15.** 56 cm^2 **17.** 162 m^2 **19.** 220 cm^2 **21.** 30 in^2 **23.** 195 ft^2 **25.** $A = 2h$ **27.** hexagon

Pages 434–435 Lesson 10-6

1. Square the radius and multiply by π. **3.** Briana; if the diameter is 20 cm, the radius is 10 cm. Since $\pi \times 10^2 \approx 314$, the area is about 314 square cm. **5.** 78.5 m^2 **7.** 254.5 in^2 **9.** 3.0 m **11a.** about 15,836.8 ft^2 **11b.** about 363,168.1 ft^2 **11c.** The area of the Superdome is about 23 times the area of the Pantheon. **13.** 1,385.4 cm^2 **15.** 615.8 in^2 **17.** 18.1 cm^2 **19.** 907.9 m^2 **21.** 380.1 in^2 **23.** 132.7 yd^2 **25.** 4.7 in. **27.** 7.3 cm

29a.

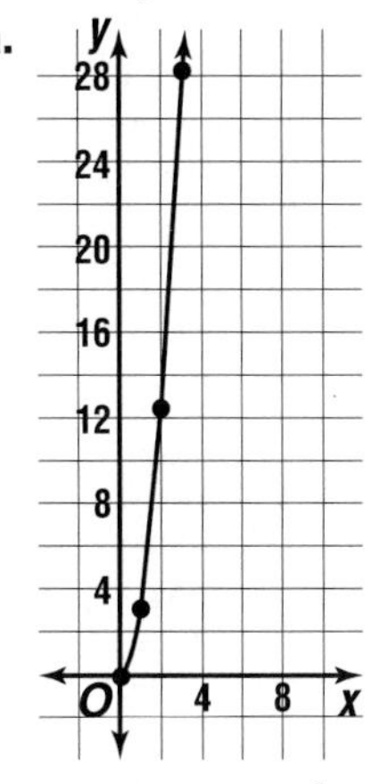

29b. 1:2; 1:4; No, $\frac{1}{2} \neq \frac{1}{4}$. **29c.** The area is quadrupled; no. **31.** 14-inch pizza **33.** 154 cm^2

35.

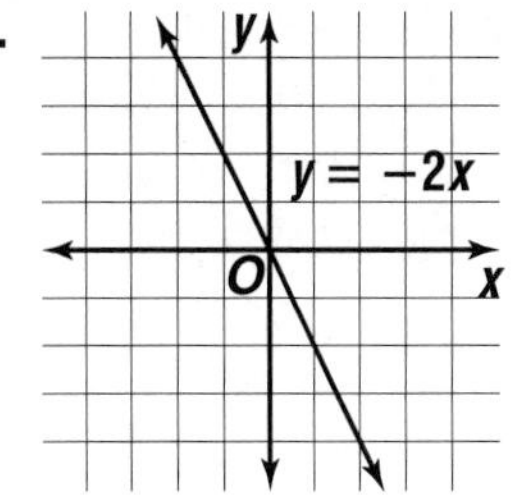

Page 437 Lesson 10-7A

1. About 20 in^2; they are about the same. **5.** $\frac{2}{7}$

Page 439–441 Lesson 10-7

1. 29 out of 30 random landings should be dry. The sky diver has a good chance of a dry landing.

3a. Sample answer:

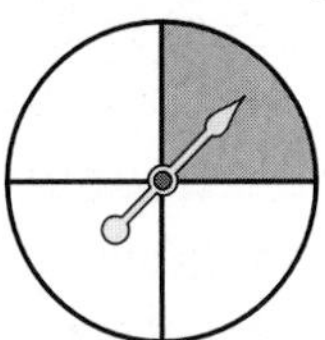

3b. Sample answer:

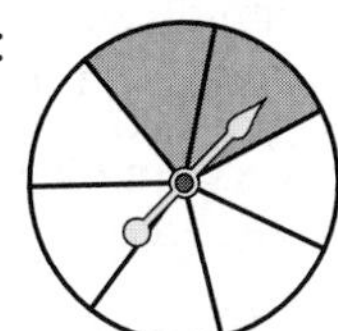

SELECTED ANSWERS

3c. Sample answer:

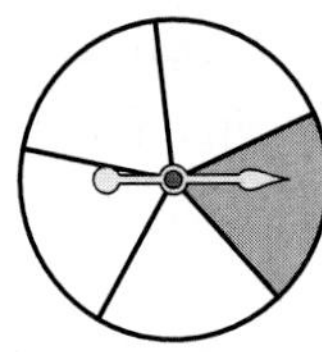

3d. The spinner in part b; since $\frac{1}{4} = \frac{35}{140}$, $\frac{2}{7} = \frac{40}{140}$, and $20\% = \frac{20}{100} = \frac{1}{5} = \frac{28}{140}$; $\frac{2}{7} > \frac{1}{4} > 20\%$. **5.** $\frac{6}{55}$ or about 0.109 **7.** $\frac{9}{40}$ or 0.225 **9.** $\frac{2}{7}$ or about 0.286 **11.** $\frac{6}{35}$ or about 0.171
13. Sample answer: $\frac{1}{6}$ or about 0.167

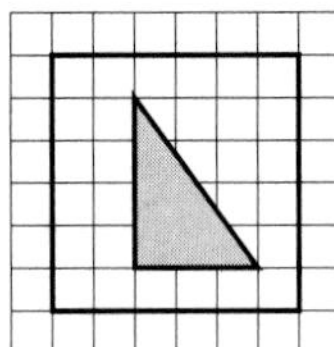

15. $\frac{1}{8}$ or 0.125 **17.** $\frac{2{,}842}{2{,}847}$ or about 0.998
19. $\frac{4}{25}$ or 0.16 **21.** D

Pages 442–445 Study Guide and Assessment

1. 64 **3.** parallel **5.** circle **7.** 81 **9.** radical **11.** right angle **13.** $6^2 = 36$, $7^2 = 49$, and 45 is between 36 and 45. Since 45 is closer to 49 than 36, $\sqrt{45}$ is about 7. **15.** 484 **17.** 2,500 **19.** 0 **21.** 16 **23.** 6 **25.** 7 **27.** 20 **29.** 6.6 yd **31.** 13.3 m **33.** 21 units^2 **35.** 75 yd^2 **37.** 36 ft^2 **39.** 153.9 mm^2 **41.** 1,963.5 in^2 **43.** $\frac{1}{4}$ **45.** 36.1 ft **47.** $\frac{1}{5}$

Pages 446–447 Standardized Test Practice

1. B **3.** C **5.** C **7.** C **9.** B **11.** C **13.** $n + 5$ **15.** 120 ft^2

CHAPTER 11 Applying Percents

Pages 452–453 Lesson 11-1

1. Sample answer: You can estimate the percent of the shaded portion of the area model. **3.** 40% **5.** 0.4 **7.** $\frac{1}{4}$ **9.** Sample answer: 56(100% + 20%) = 56 + 12, or \$68 **11.** $\frac{1}{100} \cdot 2{,}000 = 20$ lb **13-33.** Sample answers are given. **13.** 20%, 26% **15.** 0.9 **17.** 0.1 **19.** 0.01 **21.** 0.2 **23.** 3.5 **25.** $\frac{1}{4} \cdot 400 = 100$ **27.** $\frac{3}{4} \cdot 120 = 90$ **29.** $0.3 \cdot 50 = 15$ **31.** 50(100% + 50%) = 50 + 25, or 75 **33.** $\frac{1}{5} \cdot 20 = \$4$ **35.** $\frac{7}{10} \cdot 800 = 560$ **37.** $\frac{2}{5} \cdot 120 = 48$ lb **39.** $\frac{16}{40} = \frac{2}{5}$ **41.** 8% **43.** $\frac{1}{16}, \frac{1}{2}, \frac{2}{3}, \frac{5}{6}, \frac{7}{8}$

Pages 454–455 Lesson 11-1B

3. $\frac{1}{20} \cdot 740 = \$37$ billion **7.** $2{,}500 \cdot \frac{1}{5} =$ 500 women **9.** about \$4 **11.** C

Pages 457–458 Lesson 11-2

1. Sample answer: The percent equation uses the decimal form of rate; the percent proportion uses rate as a number out of 100. **3.** Sample answer: If the rate and the base are known, it is easier to use the percent equation. **5.** $27 = 0.30 \cdot B$; 90.0 **7.** $P = 0.08 \cdot 38$; 3.0 **9.** $P = 0.16 \cdot 32$; 5.1 **11.** $75 = 0.78 \cdot B$; 96.2 **13.** $45 = R \cdot 36$; 125% **15.** $17 = 0.4 \cdot B$; 42.5 **17.** $P = 0.26 \cdot 48$; 12.5 **19.** $30 = R \cdot 500$; 6% **21.** \$3.97 **23.** 26.9% **27.** $0.2 \cdot 40 = 8$ **29.** 40 ft/min

Pages 462–463 Lesson 11-3

1. Change percents to decimal form. Multiply by 360° to obtain the number of degrees in the sections of the circle graph. **3.** No; the sum of the percents does not equal 100. **5a.** Park A, 0.211; Park B, 0.192; Park C, 0.176; Park D, 0.146; Park E, 0.146; Park F, 0.129 **5b.** Park A, 76.0°; Park B, 69.1°; Park C, 63.4°; Park D, 52.6°; Park E, 52.6°; Park F, 46.4°
5c. **Park Tourists**

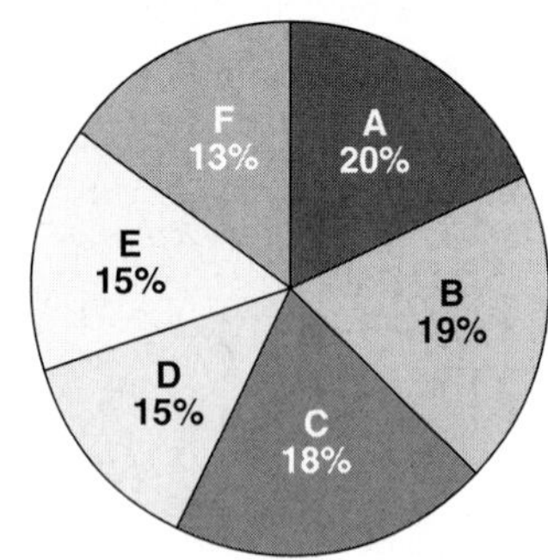

7a. **Life on Other Planets? What Women Think**

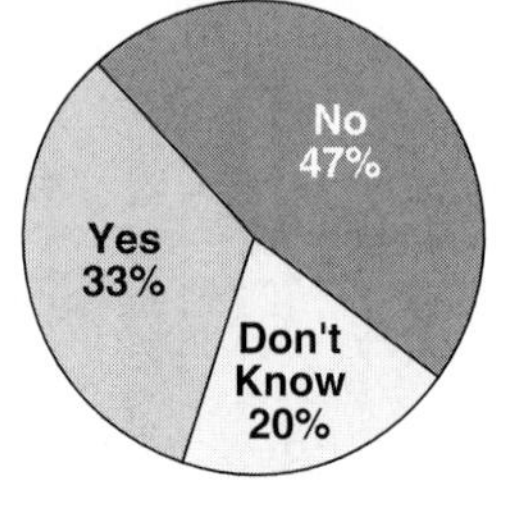

7b. Sample answer: A greater percentage of men believe in life on other planets. **7c.** Sample answer: A graph provides a visual representation that allows you to easily compare data. **11.** 11.84

Pages 465–467 Lesson 11-4

1. To make a prediction based on a sample, write a ratio to express the results of surveying the sample. Then multiply that ratio by the total population. **3a.** 1.86 million **3b.** 13.02 million **5a.** Sample answer: No; Students at the University of California may not be representative of all college students because if their college specializes in a field, they will draw more people interested in that field. **5b.** about 208 **7.** Sample answer: *Organic Gardening* asked households and NGA asked individuals. They are more likely to find someone in a household who gardens, than to find a particular individual who gardens. **9a.** 310 people **9b.** 16.65 million adults **11.** 8,799,000 girls and 9,685,000 boys **13.** B

Page 467 Mid-Chapter Self Test

1. $\frac{1}{5} \cdot 40 = 8$ **3.** $36(100\% + 10\%) = 36 + 3.6$ or 39.6 **5.** $P = 0.09 \cdot 72$; 6.5 **7.** $13.12 = 0.16 \cdot B$; 82.0 **9.** No, this sample is not random, because the students may have all been from the same social group. Their opinion cannot be used to predict what the student body as a whole might believe.

Page 468 Lesson 11-5A

1. 75%

3.

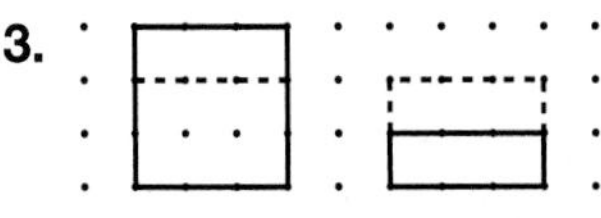

5. 20%; if the rectangle is divided into 5 sections, then 1 of the sections was removed. The decrease is $\frac{1}{5}$, or 20%.

Pages 471–472 Lesson 11-5

1. original amount

3. Sample answer:

5. 10% **7a.** 38% increase **7b.** 53% decrease **7c.** 112% increase **9.** 37% **11.** 29% **13.** 20% **15.** 28% **17.** 50 **19a.** 1992 and 1993 **19b.** 60% **21.** about 810 **23.** E

Pages 475–477 Lesson 11-6

1. The $38 watch would cost $32.30. It would be cheaper than the $50 watch, which would cost $35. **3.** Method 1: Multiply the price by 0.06, then add the two amounts. Method 2: Multiply the price by 1.06. Method 2 is more efficient, since it can be done in one step rather than two. **5.** $47.85 **7.** $69.55 **9.** vest **11.** $5.78 **13.** $5.22 **15.** $18 **17.** $132.81 **19.** $51.20 **21.** $33.71 **23.** 30% **25.** $343.64 **27.** $633.61 **29.** about 10% **31.** 480%

Pages 479–480 Lesson 11-7

1. Multiply $900 \cdot 0.045 \cdot 1$. **3.** Sample Answer: When you borrow money, the principal is the amount that you borrow, and the interest is the additional amount you pay. When you save money, the principal is the amount you loan to the bank and the interest is what they pay you. **5.** $43.75 **7.** $1,732.64 **9.** $61.20 **11.** $1,165.50 **13.** $22.49 **15.** $176.19 **17.** $171 **19.** $208.32 **21.** $1,768 **23.** $12 **25.** 10.5% **27.** $153 **29.** $\frac{11}{36}$

Page 481 Lesson 11-7B

1. to change the percent to a decimal **3.** $200 **5.** B2 = 7, C2 = 0.75; $1,578.75

Pages 482–485 Study Guide and Assessment Answers

1. true **3.** false; 360° **5.** false; original **7.** true **9.** 0.8 **11–15.** Samples answers are given. **11.** $\frac{1}{10} \cdot 80 = 8$ **13.** $30(100\% + 50\%) = 30 + 15$ or 45 **15.** $\frac{1}{2} \cdot 1{,}000 = 500$ **17.** $32 = R \cdot 50$; 64% **19.** $P = 0.62 \cdot 300$; 186 **21.** $108.5 = 0.155 \cdot B$; 700 **23.** 7,800 voters **25.** 13% **27.** 33% **29.** $1.75 **31.** $440 **33.** $1,500 **35.** $412.50 **37.** Sample answer: $600,000 **39.** $5.75

Pages 486–487 Standardized Test Practice

1. A **3.** D **5.** C **7.** B **9.** E **11.** $0.085

CHAPTER 12
Geometry: Finding Volume and Surface Area

Pages 490–491 Lesson 12-1A

1. 

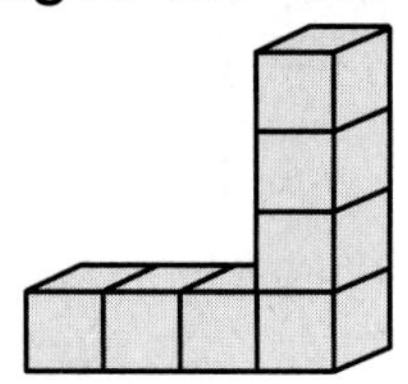

3. Sample answer:

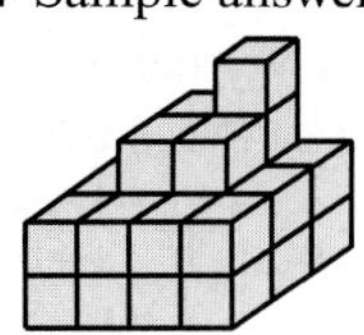

7. Exercise 1: Yes; you don't need the side view. Exercises 2-4: No, all views are necessary.

9. Sample answer:

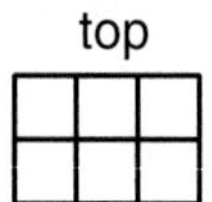

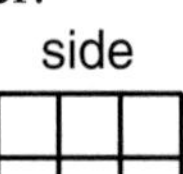

Pages 493–495 Lesson 12-1

1. 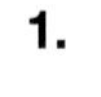

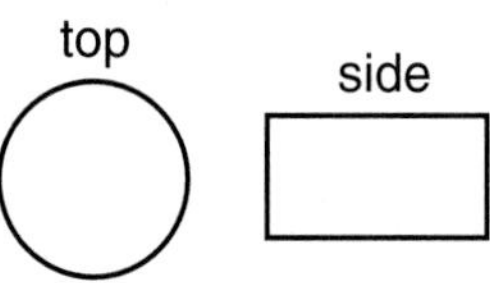

5. 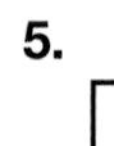

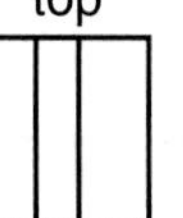

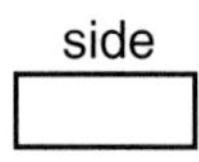

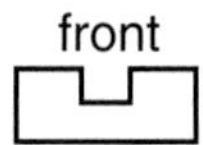

7. 

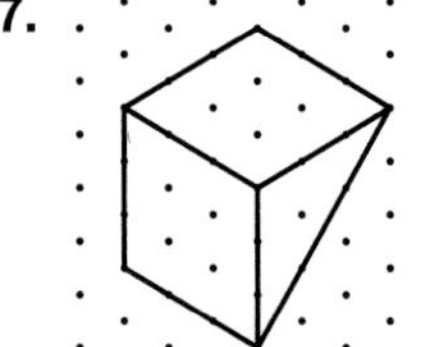

9. 

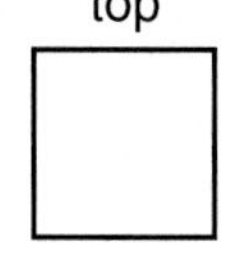

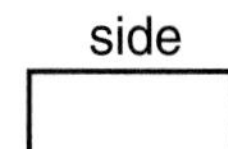

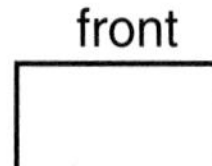

11. 

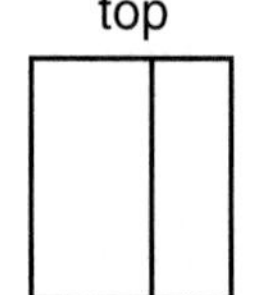

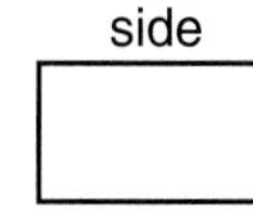

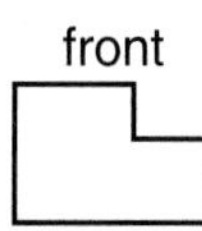

13.

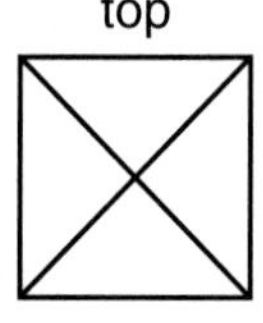

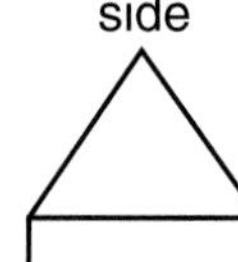

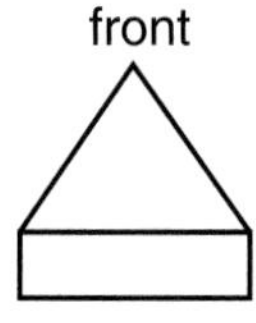

15.

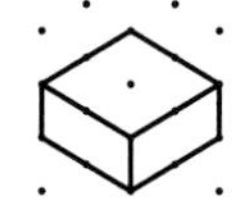

17.

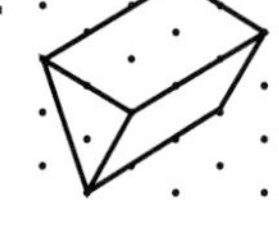

23. Sample answer

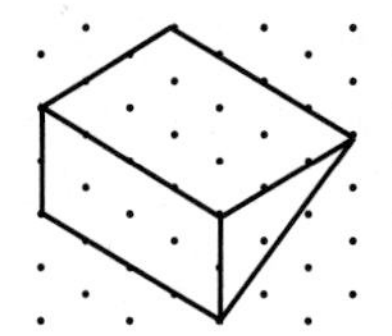

25. D

Pages 496–497 Lesson 12-1B

3.

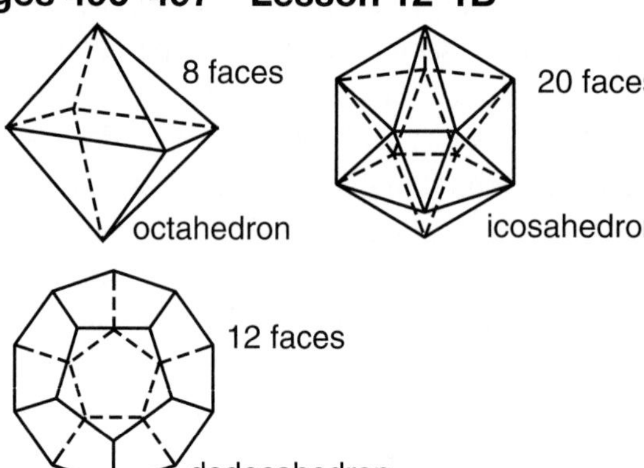

5. Sample answer: They often make small models before starting work on their projects. **7.** Sample answer: 20 in. × 8 in. × 8 in. **9.** 20 boxes **11.** 3.75 hours **13.** D

Pages 500–501 Lesson 12-2

1. m^3

3. Sample answer:

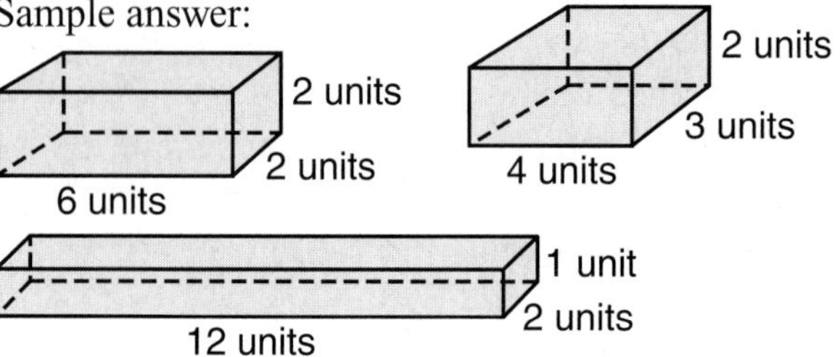

5. 135 in^3 **7.** $27 **9.** 1,176 cm^3 **11.** 19.8 cm^3 **13.** 6.6 mm^3 **15.** 343 in^3 **17.** 1,728 in^3 **19.** 3 in. **21.** 8 times greater; 27 times greater **23.** 30%

Page 502 Lesson 12-2B

1. Sample answer: about 3 **3.** They are equal.
5. $V = \frac{1}{3}\ell wh$

Pages 505–506 Lesson 12-3

1. Sample answer: In both, you multiply the area of the base by the height. **3.** Cleveland; radius of 3: $V = 169.6$ in^3; radius of 6: $V = 339.3$ in^3
5. 1,583.4 in^3 **7.** 76.0 cm^3 **9.** 100.5 in^3 **11.** 11,781.0 ft^3 **13.** 162.0 ft^3 **15.** 19.6 ft^3 **17.** about 41 feet **19.** 152.88 m^3

21. 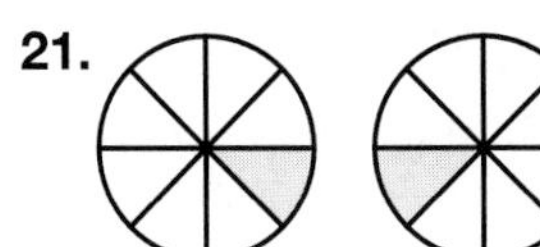

Page 506 Mid-Chapter Self Test

1. 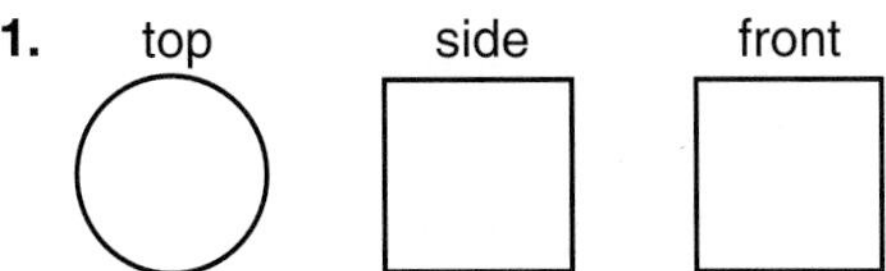

3. 84.8 in^3 **5.** rectangular box

Pages 508–509 Lesson 12-4A

1. 6 **3.** 94 square units

5. 18 cm^2

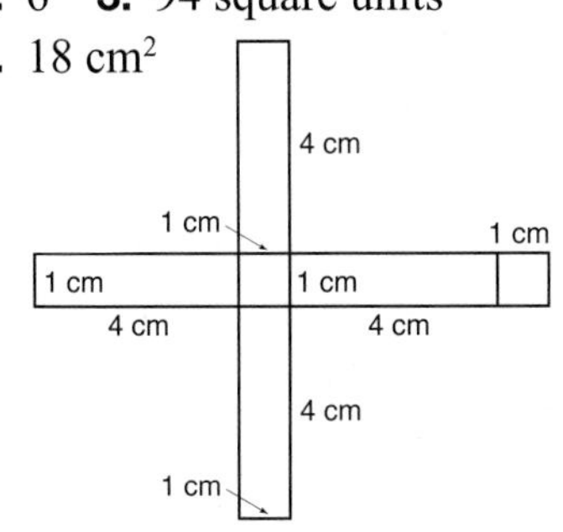

7. 950 mm^2

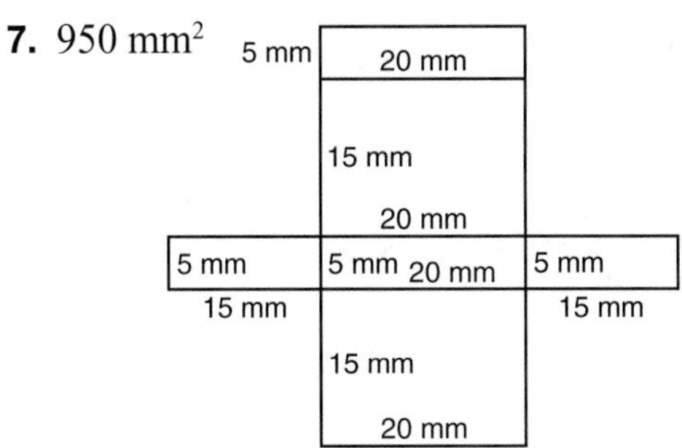

9. 256.5 cm^2

4.5 cm
4.5 cm
12 cm
4.5 cm
4.5 cm
12 cm
4.5 cm
4.5 cm
12 cm
4.5 cm 12 cm

11.

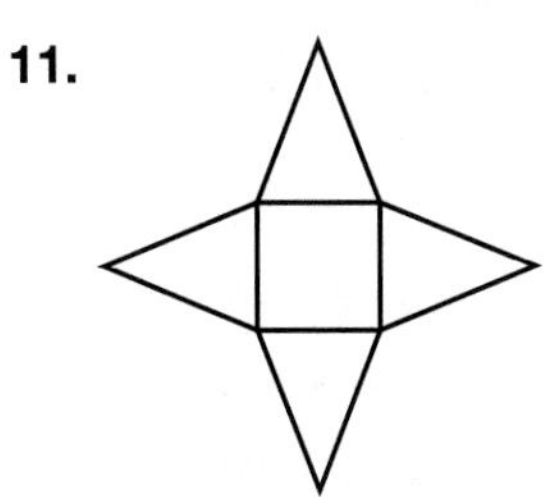

13. surface area = $\ell w + \ell w + wh + wh + \ell h + \ell h$

Pages 512–513 Lesson 12-4

1. Find the sum of the areas of the faces.
5. 247.9 in^2 **7.** 22 ft^2 **9.** 4,200 mm^2

11. 167.4 m^2 **13.** 235.6 ft^2 or $235\frac{5}{8}$ ft^2
15. surface area = $6x^2$ **19.** 326.7 cm^3

Pages 516–517 Lesson 12-5

1. The circumference of the base is the same as the length of the rectangle. **5.** 942.5 cm^2
7. 603.2 mm^2 **9.** 149.2 in^2 **11.** 92.3 in^2
13. 1,105.8 in^2 **17a.** 562.0 cm^2 **17b.** 653.5 cm^2
17c. 562.3 cm^2 **17d.** cylinder from Exercise 17a
19. A

21a.

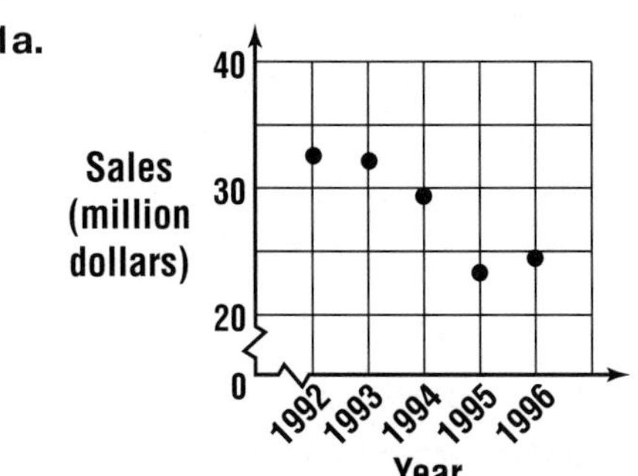

21b. Tickets sales per film have decreased.

Pages 518–521 Study Guide and Assessment

1. perspective **3.** volume **5.** multiplying
7. 100.5 **9.** 40

11. 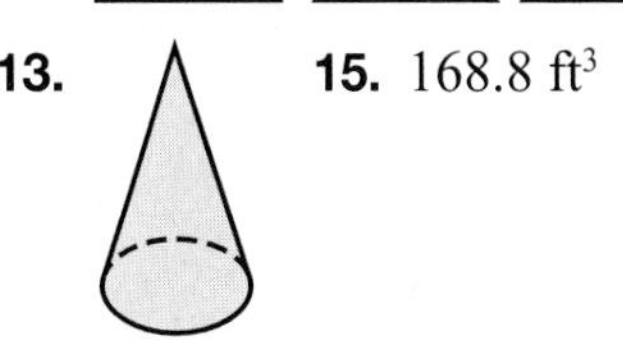

13.

15. 168.8 ft^3

17. 120 yd^3 **19.** 91.2 cm^3 **21.** 47.2 in^3
23. 302.5 m^2 **25.** 1,407.4 cm^2 **27.** 79.5 in^2
29. 231 in^3 **31.** 13.75 ft^2

Pages 522–523 Standardized Test Practice

1. D **3.** C **5.** B **7.** C **9.** C **11.** $\frac{4}{15}$
13. 300 lunches **15.** 1,200 ft^3

CHAPTER 13 Exploring Discrete Math and Probability

Pages 528–529 Lesson 13-1A

1. 5.75 **3.** Sample answer: Results would

probably vary.

5. Sample answer:

9. 14 inches, 6 inches **11.** Mauna Kea **13.** 88, 70

Pages 532–533 Lesson 13-1

1. Experimental probability is the result of collecting data; theoretical probability is the ratio of the number of favorable outcomes to the total number of outcomes. **3.** Sample answer: rolling a "1" on a number cube **5.** $\frac{1}{36}$ **7.** $\frac{16}{30} = \frac{8}{15}$ **9.** $\frac{1}{6}$ **11.** 0 **13.** $\frac{15}{36} = \frac{5}{12}$ **15.** $\frac{2}{9}$ **17.** $\frac{1}{2}$ **19a.** $\frac{1}{10}$ **19b.** $\frac{1}{25}$ **21.** 44% **23.** Sample answer: no, however, 60 would be a good estimate of the number of black cards because you would expect that in any large enough sample, about $\frac{1}{4}$ of the cards would be red. **25.** 7

Pages 535–536 Lesson 13-2

1. Start by listing the choices for the first event. From each choice, draw branches for the choices for the next event. Continue until you have listed all the choices for the final event. **3.** No; P(Player 1) = $\frac{3}{4}$, P(Player 2) = $\frac{1}{4}$ **5.** 12 outcomes **7.** 4 outcomes **9.** 8 outcomes **11.** 48 outcomes **13.** 40 areas

15.

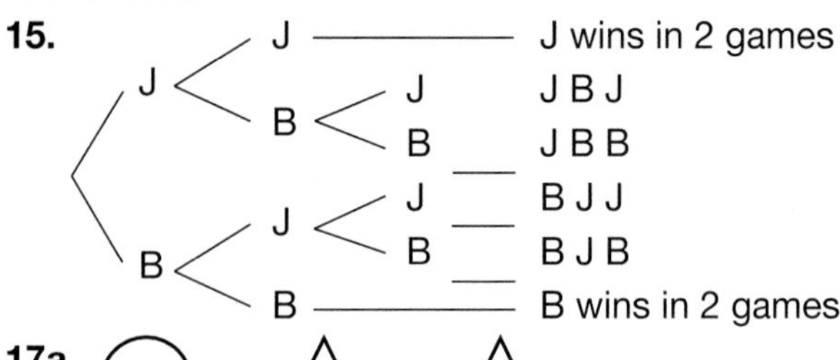

17a.

17b.

17c.

Pages 540–541 Lesson 13-3

1. 12 **5.** 12 outcomes **7.** 48 outcomes **9.** 260 outcomes **11.** 27 outcomes **13.** No; the number of selections is 312, which is less than 365. **15a.** 2 **15b.** 4 **15c.** 8 **15d.** 2^n **17.** D

Pages 544–545 Lesson 13-4

1. Sample answer: choosing a card from a deck of playing cards then choosing a second without replacing the first **3.** Jared; the result on one number cube does not affect the result on the other. **5.** $\frac{1}{4}$ **7.** $\frac{1}{1,296}$ **9.** independent **11.** $\frac{1}{12}$ **13.** $\frac{1}{24}$ **15.** $\frac{1}{56}$ **17b.** 3 **17c** 0.096 **19.** B

Page 545 Mid-Chapter Self Test

1. $\frac{1}{10}$

3.

orange
- wheat — orange, wheat
- corn — orange, corn
- rice — orange, rice

apple
- wheat — apple, wheat
- corn — apple, corn
- rice — apple, rice

5. 0.3

Page 546 Lesson 13-5A

1. 3 **3.** 1 **5.** $3 \times 2 \times 1 = 6$

Pages 548–549 Lesson 13-5

1. the product of all the counting numbers beginning with n and counting backward to 1 **5.** 60 **7.** 15,600 ways **9.** 24 **11.** 120 **13.** 2 **15.** 120 ways **17.** 336 ways **19.** 6 ways **21.** 7,140 minutes, or about 5 days **23.** A

Page 550 Lesson 13-6A

1. 6 combinations **3.** 2 ways **5.** 10, 60, 6, $60 \div 6 = 10$

Pages 552–553 Lesson 13-6

1. The order of the numbers is important in a lock. **3.** Miyoki; order is not important in choosing this group. **5.** combination; 15 ways **7.** combination; 15 ways **9.** combination; 120 ways **11.** combination; 35 ways **13.** $\frac{1}{252}$ **15.** 28 line segments **17.** 120 signals

Pages 554–557 Study Guide and Assessment

1. sample space **3.** experimental **5.** permutation **7.** outcomes **9.** $\frac{10}{25}$ or $\frac{2}{5}$ **11.** $\frac{15}{25}$ or $\frac{3}{5}$ **13.** 12 outcomes **15.** 27 outcomes **17.** $\frac{5}{51}$ **19.** $\frac{5}{36}$ **21.** 24 **23.** 720 **25.** 126 **27.** 10 jogging suits **29.** 45 ways

Pages 558–559 Standardized Test Practice

1. D **3.** B **5.** D **7.** A **9.** C **11.** $\frac{2}{5}$ **13.** $\frac{1}{4}$

Photo Credits

Cover: (bkgd)Index Stock, (inset)Index Stock, (hologram) Glencoe photo; **iv v viii** Mark Burnett; **ix** David Epperson/Tony Stone Images; **x** William J. Weber; **xi** Jeff Smith/FOTOSMITH; **xii** Chip Henderson/Tony Stone Images; **xiii** Uniphoto; **xiv** (l)Bob Martin/Sports Illustrated, (c)Bill Eppridge/Sports Illustrated, (r)Allsport USA/Mike Powell; **xv** Timothy Fuller; **xvi** Marmel Studio/FPG; **xvii** Runk/Schoenberger/Grant Heilman Photography; **xviii** Sean Ellis/Tony Stone Images; **xix** Jeff Hunter/The Image Bank; **xx** SuperStock; **xxi** Dominic Oldershaw; **2** (t)Uniphoto, (b)Lori Adamski Peek/Tony Stone Images; **2-3** David Epperson/Tony Stone Images; **8** Jeff Smith/FOTOSMITH; **11** Timothy Fuller; **12** UPI/Corbis-Bettmann; **14** Richard Kaylin/Tony Stone Images; **15** Joseph Sohm/Tony Stone Images; **16** Jeff Smith/FOTOSMITH; **17** Dallas & John Heaton/Uniphoto; **19** Jeff Smith/FOTOSMITH; **22** John Raffo/Science Source/Photo Researchers; **24** Art Matrix/Visuals Unlimited; **25** Andrea Soracco/Sweet & Rose; **26** E.R. Degginger; **27** (t)*Studies of Designs on the Pulpit of the Ravello Cathedral* by M.C. Escher. © 1997 Cordon Art - Baarn - Holland. All rights reserved. (b)THE FAR SIDE © FARWORKS, INC. Used by permission of Universal Press Syndicate. All rights reserved; **30** Jim Steinberg/Photo Researchers; **31** Dominic Oldershaw; **34** (l)Jeff Smith/FOTOSMITH, (r)Timothy Fuller; **42** (t)Lynette Cook/Science Photo Library/Photo Researchers, (b)NASA; **42-43** NASA/Tom Stack & Assoc.; **43** NASA; **47** Shooting Star; **48** Aaron Haupt; **49** K.S. Studio; **50** Archive Photos; **51** (t)Allsport USA/Mike Powell, (b)Timothy Fuller; **52** Francois Gohier/Photo Researchers; **53** (t)K.S. Studio, (b)Mark Lohman/FPG; **54** Jeff Smith/FOTOSMITH; **58** Frans Lanting/Photo Researchers; **60** (tr,bl)NASA, (br)Timothy Fuller, (bkgd)Nigel Press/Tony Stone Images; **61** Glencoe photo; **66** Stock Market/Photri; **67** (l)Elaine Shay, (r) Mary Lou Uttermohlen; **68 69** K.S. Studio; **70** (t)Joe Sohm/Chromosohm/Stock Market, (b)Yoram Kahana/Shooting Star, (c)Ron Davis/Shooting Star; **71** (l)K.S. Studio, (r)Allsport USA/Jed Jacobson; **72** (t)Richard Parker/Photo Researchers, (b)Zefa Germany/Stock Market; **74** Julius Fekete/FPG; **75** E. Gray/Science Photo Library/Photo Researchers; **77** Archive Photos; **78** (t)NASA/Stock Market, (b)Science VU/Visuals Unlimited; **79** William J. Weber; **86** (l)LucasFilm/The Kobal Collection, (r)Everett Collection; **86-87** Disney/Everett Collection; **87** Everett Collection; **88** Timothy Fuller; **90** Petrified Colle/The Image Bank; **91** Paul Hurd/Tony Stone Images; **92** Jeff Smith/FOTOSMITH; **94** Alan Carey; **95** Tom McHugh/Photo Researchers; **97** Timothy Fuller; **98** Museum of the City of New York/Archive Photos; **99** Thomas Veneklasen; **101** Bob Mullenix; **103** Timothy Fuller; **107** (t)Timothy Fuller, (b)Dominic Oldershaw; **109** First Image; **110** Bildarchiv Okapia/Photo Researchers; **111** Dominic Oldershaw; **113** Larry Ulrich/Tony Stone Images; **114** Elliot Smith/International Stock; **115** Donald C. Johnson/Stock Market; **116** Gary W. Carter/Visuals Unlimited; **118** K.S. Studio; **119** Timothy Fuller; **120** Thomas Veneklasen; **128-129** Jeff Smith/FOTOSMITH; **130** Andrew Sacks/Tony Stone Images; **130-131** Peter Poulides/Tony Stone Images; **133** Thomas Veneklasen; **135** (t)Terje Rakke/The Image Bank, (b)Bruce Smith, Rodel Sports Equipment; **138** (t)Amanita Pictures, (b)Dominic Oldershaw; **140** (l)Chip Henderson/Tony Stone Images, (r)Jeff Smith/FOTOSMITH; **142** (t)James P. Rowan/Tony Stone Images, (b)Alvin E. Staffan/Photo Researchers; **144** Jerry Wachter/Photo Researchers; **145** Kevin Schafer/Peter Arnold, Inc.; **146 147** Dominic Oldershaw; **148** Jeff Smith/FOTOSMITH; **150 151** Thomas Veneklasen; **153** Robert & Linda Mitchell; **154** Chris Butler/Science Photo Library/Photo Researchers; **155** Jeff Hunter/The Image Bank; **156** Ron Kimball; **157** Wayne R. Bilenduke/Tony Stone Images; **159** (t)Franklin Over, (b)Richard Thom/Visuals Unlimited; **161** Uniphoto; **163** GK & Vikki Hart/The Image Bank; **164** Disney/The Kobal Collection; **165** Jeff Smith/FOTOSMITH; **169** (l)Western Reserve Historical Society, (r)John Livzey/Tony Stone Images; **171** Aaron Haupt; **172** Paul Kenward/Tony Stone Images; **173** (t)Jeff Smith/FOTOSMITH, (b)Aaron Haupt; **179** Tom Till/International Stock; **180** First Image; **182** (t)Bob Ashe/Stock Imagery; (b)Uniphoto; **182** Uniphoto; **183** David Olsen/Tony Stone Images; **184** (t)Brian Parker/Tom Stack & Assoc., (b)Mark Burnett; **186** Ron Kimball; 187 (tl)Donna Coveney/MIT, (tr)European Space Agency, Science Photo Library/Photo Researchers, (b)Jeff Smith/FOTOSMITH, (bkgd)Wm. L. Wantland/Tom Stack & Assoc.; **189** Brian Peterson; **191** Les Goldberg Public Relations; **195** Jeff Smith/FOTOSMITH; **197** Hulton Getty/Tony Stone Images; **200** Rich Kane/SportsChrome; **202 203** NASA/JPL; **204** Greg Johnston/International Stock; **207** Michael Burr/NFL Photos; **209** Steve Kaufman; **210** (l)Dominic Oldershaw, (r)Jeff Smith/FOTOSMITH; **212** Lionel F. Stevenson/Photo Researchers; **213** Marc Epstein/Visuals Unlimited; **216** The Denver Art Museum; **224-225** Dan Feicht; **228** Rob Tringali Jr./SportsChrome; **230** Nick Gunderson/Tony Stone Images; **231** Tim Courlas; **232** Timothy Fuller; **235** Aaron Haupt; **236** Thomas Kitchin/Tom Stack & Assoc.; **239** (t)Everett Collection, (b)Jim Stamates/Tony Stone Images; **242** (t)PEANUTS reprinted by permission of United Feature Syndicate, Inc., (b)Jeff Smith/FOTOSMITH; **244** Jeff Smith/FOTOSMITH; **246** (tr)Bob Martin/Sports Illustrated, (bl)Bill Eppridge/Sports Illustrated, (br)Allsport USA/Mike Powell; **248** Jeffrey Sylvester/FPG; **249** Allsport USA/J. Patronite; **251** SuperStock; **254** Aaron Haupt; **257** Geri Murphy; **264-265** Mark Steinmetz; **265** Morton & White; **266** SuperStock; **266-267** Thomas Veneklasen; **268** Mark Burnett; **269** Dominic Oldershaw; **270** Timothy Fuller; **271** Manfred Gottschalk/Tom Stack & Assoc.; **272** Charles Gupton/Tony Stone Images; **273** David Madison; **275** Timothy Fuller; **276 277** Bill Cleaver, Wild Bill's Originals; **278** "Crown copyright is reproduced with the permission of the Controller of Her Majesty's Stationery Office"; **279** Norbert Wu; **280** Timothy Fuller; **284** ABC/Everett Collection; **286** Hulton Getty/Tony Stone Images; **289** Suzanne Murphy/Tony Stone Images; **290** Dominic Oldershaw; **292** Uniphoto; **294** AP/Wide World Photos; **296** (t)Joe Fisher, (b)Jeff Smith/FOTOSMITH, (bkgd)John Kieffer/Peter Arnold, Inc.; **297** courtesy Purdue University; **299** Crown Studios; **301** David W. Hamilton/The Image Bank; **303** Tom & Pat Leeson/Photo Researchers; **304** Gerard Lacz/Peter Arnold, Inc.; **305** E.R. Degginger; **306 307** Timothy Fuller; **314** (c)David Woodfall/Tony Stone Images, (tr)Glencoe photo, (bl)Ray Pfortner/Peter Arnold, Inc.; **314-315** Marmel Studio/FPG; **315** Ken Frick; **317** (t)Dominic Oldershaw, (b)Aaron Haupt; **318** (l)Aaron Ferster/Photo Researchers, (r)Thomas Kitchin/Tom Stack & Assoc.; **319** Timothy Fuller; **320** Richard T. Nowitz; **321** Mark E. Gibson; **323** Phyllis Picardi/International Stock; **324** By permission of Johnny Hart and Creators Syndicate, Inc.; **325** Dominic Oldershaw; **326** Dominic Oldershaw; **327** Sam Kittner/National Geographic Image Collection; **329** Stephen Krasemann/Tony Stone Images; **330** (t)USDA Extension Service, (others)Thomas Veneklasen; **332** North Wind Pictures; **333** Tomo Narashima/Warner & Assoc.; **334** Reuters/Vanderlei Almeida/Archive Photos; **335** courtesy Valerie Thomas; **336** Randy Morse/Zephyr Images; **338** NASA; **339** E.R. Degginger; **340** Brian Parker/Tom Stack & Assoc.; **342** Gavriel Jecan/Tony Stone Images; **343** Dominic Oldershaw; **344** UPI/Corbis-Bettmann; **345** Stephen Dalton/Photo Researchers; **346** Thomas Veneklasen; **348** Bill Nation/Sygma; **349** John Mitchell/Photo Researchers; **351** Thomas Veneklasen; **355** Bruno Dittrich/Tony Stone Images; **358** (t)Thomas Veneklasen, (c)Erich Lessing/Art Resource, NY, (b)Jeff Smith/FOTOSMITH; **358-359** Thomas

Veneklasen; **359** Matt Bradley/Tom Stack & Assoc.; **362** Mark E. Gibson; **368** (t)Michael Hirst, (bc)Dan Lecca, (br)Timothy Fuller, (bkgd)Thomas Veneklasen; **370** (b)Jeff Smith/FOTOSMITH; **376** WorldSat International, Science Source/Photo Researchers; **379** Rich Iwasaki/Tony Stone Images; **383** Peter Pearson/Tony Stone Images; **384** Tony Stone Images; **385** Scott Berner/Visuals Unlimited; **386** Timothy Fuller; **388** Thomas Veneklasen; **390** Mark E. Gibson; **392** *Symmetry Drawing E72* by M.C. Escher. ©1997 Cordon Art - Baarn - Holland. All rights reserved; **395** Steve Dunwell/The Image Bank; **397** (l)Fred Bavendam/Peter Arnold, Inc., (r)Secret Sea Visions/Peter Arnold, Inc.; **404-405** Scott Camazine/Photo Researchers; **405** L. West/Photo Researchers; **406** (t)Sean Ellis/Tony Stone Images, (b)Benelux Press B.V./Photo Researchers; **406-407** Earth Imaging/Tony Stone Images; **407** Mary Evans Picture Library/Photo Researchers; **408** Jeff Smith/FOTOSMITH; **409** Allsport USA/Al Bello; **410** Dan Ham/Tony Stone Images; **411 412** David Madison; **413** Larry Lefever/Grant Heilman Photography; **416** Brian Seed/Tony Stone Images; **417** David Madison; **419** (t)William Katz/Photo Researchers, (b)Hulton Getty/Tony Stone Images; **421** Timothy Fuller; **422** Jim Steinberg/Photo Researchers; **423** A.L. Parnes/Photo Researchers; **427** Timothy Fuller; **432** AP/Wide World Photos; **436** Dominic Oldershaw; **438** AP/Wide World Photos; **439** Dominic Oldershaw; **441** Jeff Smith/FOTOSMITH; **448** (l)Hulton Getty Images/Tony Stone Images, (r)Jay Thomas/International Stock; **448-449** Timothy Fuller; **450** James A. Sugar/National Geographic Image Collection; **451** Timothy Fuller; **453** The Stock Shop/Medichrome/Vincent Perez; **454** Timothy Fuller; **456** Guido A. Rossi/The Image Bank; **457** Michael Zito/SportsChrome; **459** Timothy Fuller; **461** Phil Degginger/Color-Pic; **464** courtesy U.S. Census Bureau; **465** Timothy Fuller; **466** D. Cavagnaro/Visuals Unlimited; **469** Phil Schofield/National Geographic Image Collection; **470** Dominic Oldershaw; **472** Dominic Oldershaw; **473** (t)Timothy Fuller, (bl)Tracy Aiguier, (br)Timothy Fuller; **474** Dominic Oldershaw; **475** Timothy Fuller; **476** (t)Dominic Oldershaw, (b)Franklin Over; **478** Dominic Oldershaw; **480** Jeff Hunter/The Image Bank; **488** (t)Art Wolfe/Tony Stone Images, (c)S.J. Krasemann/Peter Arnold, Inc., (b)Walter H. Hodge/Peter Arnold, Inc.; **488-489** Jeff Smith/FOTOSMITH; **489** (t)Catherine Ursillo/Photo Researchers, (b)E.R. Degginger; **490** E.R. Degginger; **491** Dominic Oldershaw; **492** (l)Mandolin Brothers/Photo Researchers, (r)G. Randall/FPG; **495** (t)Jose L. Pelaez/Stock Market, (b)Tribune Media Services, Inc. All Rights Reserved. Reprinted with permission; **496** Dominic Oldershaw; **498** Jeff Smith/FOTOSMITH; **499** SuperStock; **502** John Lawrence/Tony Stone Images; **503** Jeff Smith/FOTOSMITH; **504** Dominic Oldershaw; **507** (t,b)Dominic Oldershaw, (c)Charles Harrington, (bkgd)Frans Lanting/Tony Stone Images; **510** (l)Alon Reininger/Leo de Wys, Inc., (r)Peter Bennett/The Viesti Collection; **524-525** Dominic Oldershaw; **526** (l)Dominic Oldershaw; (r)CBS/Monty Brinton; **526-527** Dominic Oldershaw; 527 (t)Aaron Haupt, (b)Dominic Oldershaw; **528 530** Dominic Oldershaw; **535** Dominic Oldershaw; **537** (bl)Rex Features, (others) Timothy Fuller; **538 540** Timothy Fuller; **542** (t)Archive Photos, (b)Nigel Cattlin/Holt Studios International/Photo Researchers; **544** Dominic Oldershaw; **547** PEANUTS reprinted by permission of United Feature Syndicate, Inc.; **548** E.R. Degginger; **549** AP/Wide World Photos; **551 552** Dominic Oldershaw; **553** Uniphoto; **561** (t)NASA, (cl)The Denver Art Museum, (c)Jeff Smith/FOTOSMITH, (cr)Jeff Hunter/The Image Bank, (bl)Mark Steinmetz/Amanita Pictures, (br)Ron Kimball.

Glossary

A

absolute value (185) The number of units a number is from zero on the number line.

acute (362) An angle with a measure greater than 0° and less than 90°.

addition property of equality (229) If you add the same number to each side of an equation, the two sides remain equal. For any numbers a, b, and c, if $a = b$, then $a + c = b + c$.

additive inverse (197) An integer and its opposite. The sum of an integer and its additive inverse is zero.

algebra (12) A mathematical language that uses variables along with numbers. The variables stand for numbers that are unknown. $10n - 3 = 17$ is an example of an algebra problem.

algebraic expression (12) A combination of variables, numbers, and at least one operation.

angle (362) Two rays with a common endpoint form an angle. The rays and vertex are used to name an angle.

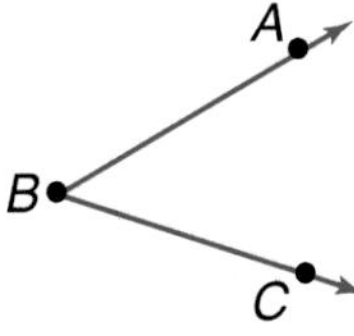

angle ABC or $\angle ABC$

area (30) The number of square units needed to cover a surface enclosed by a geometric figure.

arithmetic average (102) The mean of a set of data.

arithmetic sequence (142) A sequence in which the difference between any two consecutive terms is the same.

associative property of addition (301) For any numbers a, b, and c, $(a + b) + c = a + (b + c)$.

associative property of multiplication (301) For any numbers a, b, and c, $(ab)c = a(bc)$.

B

back-to-back stem-and-leaf plot (109) Used to compare two sets of data. The leaves for one set of data are on one side of the stem and the leaves for the other set of data are on the other side.

bar graph (94) A graphic form using bars to make comparisons of statistics.

bar notation (70) In repeating decimals the line or bar placed over the digits that repeat. For example, $2.\overline{63}$ indicates the digits 63 repeat.

base (17) In a power, the number used as a factor. In 5^3, the base is 5. That is, $5^3 = 5 \times 5 \times 5$.

base (349) In a percent proportion, the number to which the percentage is compared.

base (31) Any side of a parallelogram.

box-and-whisker plot (114) A diagram that summarizes data using the median, the upper and lower quartiles, and the extreme values. A box is drawn around the quartile value and whiskers extend from each quartile to the extreme data points.

C

capture-recapture technique (329) A method used to estimate animal populations. The following proportion is used to estimate the entire population by first capturing a part of the population, tagging the sample, releasing the sample, and then recapturing another sample.

$$\frac{\textit{original number captured}}{\textit{total population (P)}} = \frac{\textit{tagged in sample}}{\textit{recaptured}}$$

cell (137) The basic unit of a spreadsheet. A cell can contain data, labels, or formulas.

center (297) The given point from which all points on a circle or a sphere are the same distance.

circle (297) The set of all points in a plane that are the same distance from a given point called the center.

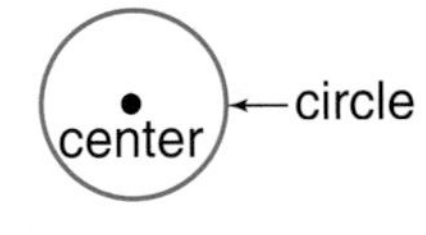

circle graph (460) A type of statistical graph used to compare parts of a whole.

circumference (297) The distance around a circle.

cluster (98) Data that are grouped closely together.

clustering (51) A method used to estimate decimal sums and differences by rounding a group of closely related numbers to the same whole number.

coefficient (234) The numerical part of an expression.

combination (551) An arrangement or listing of objects in which order is not important.

common denominator (172) A common multiple of the denominators of two or more fractions. 24 is a common denominator for $\frac{1}{3}$, $\frac{5}{8}$, and $\frac{3}{4}$ because 24 is the LCM of 3, 8, and 4.

commutative property of addition (301) For any numbers a and b, $a + b = b + a$.

commutative property of multiplication (301) For any numbers a and b, $ab = ba$.

complementary (362) Two angles are complementary if the sum of their measures is 90°.

composite number (138) Any whole number greater than 1 that has more than two factors.

compound event (542) A compound event consists of two or more simple events.

congruent (371) Line segments that have the same length, or angles that have the same measure, or figures that have the same size and shape.

coordinate system (191) A plane in which a horizontal number line and a vertical number line intersect at their zero points.

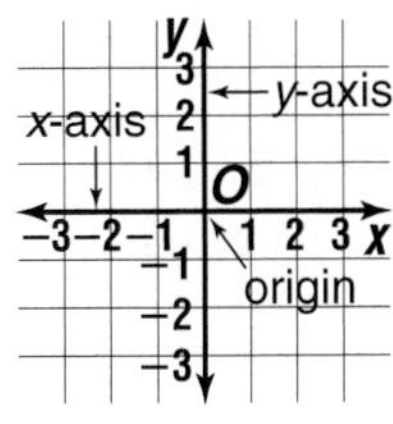

Counting Principle (538) A method for finding the number of ways that two or more events can occur by multiplying the number of ways that each event can occur.

cross products (325) The products of the terms on the diagonals when two ratios are compared. If the cross products are equal, then the ratios form a proportion. In the proportion $\frac{3}{6} = \frac{4}{8}$, the cross products are 3×8 and 6×4.

cubed (17) The product in which a number is a factor three times. Two cubed is 8 because $2 \times 2 \times 2 = 8$.

cup (290) A customary unit of capacity equal to 8 fluid ounces.

cylinder (503) A three-dimensional figure with two parallel congruent circular bases.

D

decagon (370) A polygon having ten sides.

defining a variable (243) Choosing a variable and a quantity for the variable to represent in an equation.

degree (362) The most common unit of measure for angles.

dependent events (543) Two or more events in which the outcome of one event does affect the outcome of the other event(s).

diameter (297) The distance across a circle through its center.

distributive property (302) For any numbers a, b, and c, $a(b + c) = ab + ac$ and $(b + c)a = ba + ca$.

divisible (133) A number is divisible by another if, upon division, the remainder is zero.

division property of equality (234) For any numbers a, b, and c, with $c \neq 0$, if $a = b$, then $\frac{a}{c} = \frac{b}{c}$.

E

equation (21) A mathematical sentence that contains the equal sign, =.

equilateral (382) All sides of a figure are congruent.

equivalent ratios (318) Two ratios that have the same value.

evaluate (12) To find the value of an expression by replacing variables with numerals.

event (165) A specific outcome or type of outcome.

experimental probability (531) An estimated probability based on the relative frequency of positive outcomes occurring during an experiment.

exponent (17) In a power, the number of times the base is used as a factor. In 5^3, the exponent is 3. That is, $5^3 = 5 \times 5 \times 5$.

F

factor (17, 133) A number that divides into a whole number with a remainder of zero.

factorial (547) The expression $n!$ is the product of all counting numbers beginning with n and counting backward to 1.

factor tree (138) A diagram showing the prime factorization of a number. The factors branch out from the previous factors until all the factors are prime numbers.

fair game (535) A game in which players have an equal chance of winning.

fractal (24) An geometric figure that is made when a rule is applied to smaller and smaller parts. The parts of a fractal are similar to the whole figure.

frequency table (88) A table for organizing a set of data that shows the number of times each item or number appears.

function (249) A relation in which each element of the input is paired with exactly one element of the output according to a specified rule.

G

gallon (290) A customary unit of capacity equal to 4 quarts.

geometric sequence (142) A sequence of numbers in which you can find the next term by multiplying the previous term by the same number.

gram (75) A unit of mass in the metric system.

greatest common factor (GCF) (150) The greatest of the common factors of two or more numbers. The GCF of 18 and 24 is 6.

H

height (31) The shortest distance from the base of a parallelogram to its opposite side.

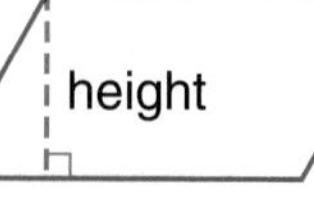

heptagon (370) A polygon having seven sides.

hexagon (370) A polygon having six sides.

hypotenuse (419) The side opposite the right angle in a right triangle.

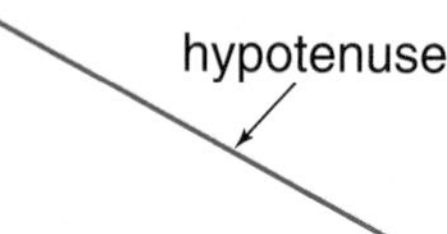

I

identity property of addition (301) For any number a, $a + 0 = a$.

identity property of multiplication (301) For any number a, $a \times 1 = a$.

independent events (542) Two or more events in which the outcome of one event does *not* affect the outcome of the other event(s).

indirect measurement (377) Finding a measurement by using similar triangles and writing a proportion.

inequality (246) A mathematical sentence that contains $<$, $>$, $\neq$, $\leq$, or $\geq$.

inner measure (423) The number of whole squares within a figure.

integer (184) The whole numbers and their opposites.

$$\ldots, -3, -2, -1, 0, 1, 2, 3, \ldots$$

interquartile range (112, 115) The range of the middle half of a set of numbers.

Interquartile range = $UQ - LQ$.

interval (88) The difference between successive values on a scale.

irregular figure (423) A figure that does not have straight sides and square corners.

isosceles (382) An isosceles triangle has two congruent sides.

leaf (108) The second greatest place value of data in a stem-and-leaf plot.

least common denominator (LCD) (172) The least common multiple of the denominators of two or more fractions.

least common multiple (LCM) (169) The least of the common multiples of two or more numbers. The LCM of 2 and 3 is 6.

leg (419) Either of the two sides that form the right angle of a right triangle.

linear equation (255) An equation for which the graph is a straight line.

line graph (94) A type of statistical graph using lines to show how values change over a period of time.

line of symmetry (395) A line that divides a figure into two halves that are reflections of each other.

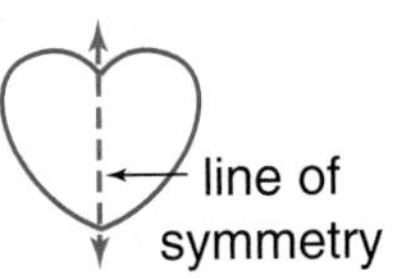

line plot (98) A graph that uses an × above a number on a number line each time that number occurs in a set of data.

line symmetry (395) Figures that match exactly when folded in half have line symmetry.

liter (75) The basic unit of capacity in the metric system. A liter is a little more than a quart.

lower extreme (114) The least number of a set of data.

lower quartile (114) The median of the lower half of a set of numbers indicated by LQ.

mean (102) The sum of the numbers in a set of data divided by the number of pieces of data.

median (102) The middle number in a set of data when the data are arranged in numerical order. If the data has an even number, the median is the mean of the two middle numbers.

meter (74) The basic unit of length in the metric system.

metric system (74) A base-ten system of measurement using the basic units: meter for length, gram for mass, and liter for capacity.

mode (102) The number(s) or item(s) that appear most often in a set of data.

modeling (22) Writing an equation that represents a real-world problem.

multiple (169) The product of the number and any whole number.

multiplication property of equality (302) If each side of an equation is multiplied by the same number, then the two sides remain equal. If $a = b$, then $ac = bc$.

multiplicative inverse (301) A number times its multiplicative inverse is equal to 1. The multiplicative inverse of $\frac{2}{3}$ is $\frac{3}{2}$.

negative integer (184) Integer that is less than zero.

nonagon (370) A polygon having nine sides.

obtuse (362) Any angle that measures greater than 90° but less than 180°.

octagon (370) A polygon having eight sides.

opposite (184) Two integers are opposite if they are represented on the number line by points that are the same distance from zero, but on opposite sides of zero. The sum of opposites is zero.

order of operations (18) The rules to follow when more than one operation is used.
1. Do all operations within grouping symbols first.
2. Do all powers before other operations.
3. Multiply and divide in order from left to right.
4. Add and subtract in order from left to right.

ordered pair (191) A pair of numbers used to locate a point in the coordinate system. The ordered pair is written in this form: (x-coordinate, y-coordinate).

origin (191) The point of intersection of the x-axis and y-axis in a coordinate system.

ounce (289) A customary unit of weight. 16 ounces equals 1 pound.

outcome (531) One possible result of a probability event. For example, 4 is an outcome when a number cube is rolled.

outer measure (423) The number of squares within and containing part of the figure.

outlier (115) Data that is more than 1.5 times the interquartile range from the quartiles.

P

parallelogram (31) A quadrilateral with two pairs of parallel sides.

pentagon (370) A polygon having five sides.

percent (158) A ratio that compares a number to 100.

percentage (349) In a percent proportion, a number that is compared to another number called the base.

percent proportion (349) $\frac{P}{B} = \frac{r}{100}$ where P represents the percentage, B represents the base, and r represents the number per hundred.

perfect square (411) A number whose square root is a whole number. 25 is a perfect square because $\sqrt{25} = 5$.

perimeter (292) The distance around a geometric figure.

permutation (547) An arrangement or listing in which order is important.

perspective (492) A perspective view of a three-dimensional figure is an angled view that shows the three dimensions of the figure.

pint (290) A customary unit of capacity equal to two cups.

polygon (370) A simple closed figure in a plane formed by three or more line segments.

population (5, 464) The entire group of items or individuals from which the samples under consideration are taken.

population density (322) The population per square mile.

positive integer (184) Integer that is greater than zero.

pound (289) A customary unit of weight equal to 16 ounces.

power (17) A number that can be written using an exponent. The power 7^3 is read *seven to the third power*, or *seven cubed.*

prime factorization (138) Expressing a composite number as the product of prime numbers. For example, the prime factorization of 63 is $3 \times 3 \times 7$.

prime number (138) A whole number greater than 1 that has exactly two factors, 1 and itself.

principal (478) The amount of an investment or a debt.

probability (165) The chance that some event will happen. It is the ratio of the number of ways a certain event can occur to the number of possible outcomes.

property of proportions (325) If $\frac{a}{b} = \frac{c}{d}$, then $ad = bc$. If $ad = bc$, then $\frac{a}{b} = \frac{c}{d}$.

proportion (325) An equation that shows that two ratios are equivalent, $\frac{a}{b} = \frac{c}{d}$, $b \neq 0$, $d \neq 0$.

Pythagorean Theorem (419) In a right triangle, the square of the length of the hypotenuse is equal to the sum of the squares of the lengths of the legs. $c^2 = a^2 + b^2$

quadrant (191) One of the four regions into which two perpendicular number lines separate the plane.

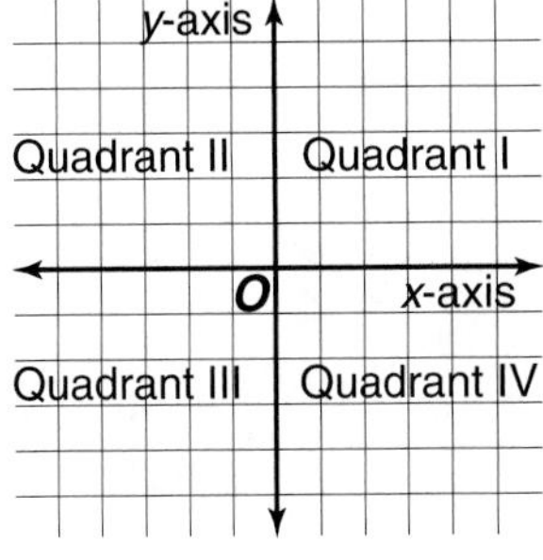

quadrilateral (370) A polygon having four sides.

quart (290) A customary unit of capacity equal to two pints.

quartile (112) One of four equal parts of data from a large set of numbers.

radical sign (411) The symbol used to indicate a nonnegative square root is $\sqrt{\ }$.

radius (297) The distance from the center of a circle to any point on the circle.

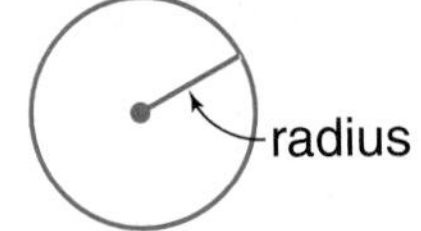

random (165) Outcomes occur at random if each outcome is equally likely to occur.

random (464) A sample is called random if the members of the sample are selected purely on the basis of chance.

range (88) The difference between the greatest number and the least number in a set of data.

rate (321) A ratio of two measurements having different units.

rate (349) In a percent proportion, the ratio of a number to 100.

rate (478) The percent charged or paid for the use of money.

ratio (154, 317) A comparison of two numbers by division. The ratio of 2 to 3 can be stated as 2 out of 3, 2 to 3, 2:3, or $\frac{2}{3}$.

reciprocal (301) The multiplicative inverse of a number.

rectangle (30) A quadrilateral with four equal angles.

rectangular prism (498) A prism with rectangular bases.

reflection (215, 395) A type of transformation where a figure is flipped over a line of symmetry.

regular polygon (371) A polygon having all sides congruent and all angles congruent.

repeating decimal (70) A decimal whose digits repeat in groups of one or more. Examples are 0.181818... and 0.8333... .

rhombus (383) A parallelogram with four congruent sides.

right (362) An angle that measures 90°.

S

sample (5, 329, 464) A randomly-selected group that is used to represent a whole population.

sample space (531) The set of all possible outcomes.

scale (88) The set of all possible values of a given measurement, including the least and greatest numbers in the set, separated by the intervals used.

scale (332) On a map, intervals used representing the ratio of distance on the map to the actual distance.

scale drawing (332) A drawing that is similar but either larger or smaller than the actual object.

scalene (382) A triangle with no congruent sides.

scatter plot (92, 95) In a scatter plot, two sets of related data are plotted as ordered pairs on the same graph.

scientific notation (77) A way of expressing a number as the product of a number that is at least 1 but less than 10 and a power of 10. For example, $687{,}000 = 6.87 \times 10^5$.

sequence (142) A list of numbers in a certain order, such as, 0, 1, 2, 3, or 2, 4, 6, 8.

similar (376) Figures that have the same shape but not necessarily the same size.

simple interest (478) The amount paid for the use of money. The formula for simple interest is $I = prt$.

simplest form (154) A fraction is in simplest form when the GCF of the numerator and the denominator is 1.

solids (493) Three-dimensional figures. Prisms, pyramids, cones, and cylinders are examples of solids.

solution (21) A value for the variable that makes an equation true. The solution for $12 = x + 7$ is 5.

solve (21) To replace a variable with a number that makes an equation true.

spreadsheet (137) A tool used for organizing and analyzing data.

square (410) The product of a number and itself. 36 is the square of 6×6.

squared (17) A number multiplied by itself. 7^2 is read *7 squared.*

square root (411) One of the two equal factors of a number. If $a^2 = b$, then a is the square root of b. The square root of 144 is 12 since $12^2 = 144$.

stem (108) The greatest place value common to all the data values is used for the stem of a stem-and-leaf plot.

stem-and-leaf plot (108) A system used to condense a set of data where the greatest place value of the data forms the stem and the next greatest place value forms the leaves.

straight (362) An angle is straight if it measures exactly 180°.

subtraction property of equality (228) If you subtract the same number from each side of an equation, the two sides remain equal. For any numbers a, b, and c, if $a = b$, then $a - c = b - c$.

supplementary (362) Two angles are supplementary if the sum of their measures is 180°.

surface area (510) The sum of the areas of all the surfaces (faces) of a three-dimensional figure.

term (239) A number, a variable, or a product of numbers and variables.

term (142) Each number within a sequence is called a term.

terminating decimal (70) A quotient in which the division ends with a remainder of zero. 0.25 and 0.125 are terminating decimals.

tessellation (388) A repetitive pattern of polygons that fit together with no holes or gaps.

theoretical probability (531) The ratio of the number of ways an event can occur to the number of possible outcomes.

time (478) When used to calculate interest, time is given in years.

ton (289) A customary unit of weight equal to 2,000 pounds.

transformation (215) Movements of geometric figures.

translation (215, 392) One type of transformation where a figure is slid horizontally, vertically, or both.

trapezoid (383, 429) A quadrilateral with exactly one pair of parallel sides.

tree diagram (534) A diagram used to show the total number of possible outcomes in a probability experiment.

triangle (370, 428) A polygon that has three angles.

unit rate (321) A rate with denominator of 1.

upper extreme (114) The greatest number of a set of data.

upper quartile (114) The median of the upper half of a set of numbers.

variable (12) A symbol, usually a letter, used to represent a number in mathematical expressions or sentences. In $3 + a = 6$, a is a variable.

vertex (362) A vertex of an angle is the common endpoint of the rays forming the angle.

volume (498) The number of cubic units needed to fill the space occupied by a solid.

***x*-axis** (191) The horizontal number line which helps to form the coordinate system.

***x*-coordinate** (191) The first number of an ordered pair.

***y*-axis** (191) The vertical number line which helps to form the coordinate system.

***y*-coordinate** (191) The second number of an ordered pair.

zero pair (196, 227) The result of pairing one positive counter with one negative counter.

Spanish Glossary

A

absolute value / valor absoluto (185) Número de unidades en la recta numérica que un número dista de cero.

acute / agudo (362) Ángulo que mide más de 0° y menos de 90°.

addition property of equality / propiedad de adición de la igualdad (229) Si sumas el mismo número a ambos lados de una ecuación, los lados permanecen iguales. Para números a, b y c cualesquiera, si $a = b$, entonces $a + c = b + c$.

additive inverse / inverso aditivo (197) Opuesto de un entero. La suma de un entero y su inverso aditivo es cero.

algebra / álgebra (12) Lenguaje matemático que usa letras y números. Las letras representan números desconocidos. $10n - 3 = 17$ es un ejemplo de un problema de álgebra.

algebraic expression / expresión algebraica (12) Combinación de variables, números y al menos una operación.

angle / ángulo (362) Dos rayos con un extremo común forman un ángulo. Los rayos y el vértice se usan para nombrar o identificar el ángulo.

ángulo ABC o $\angle ABC$

area / área (30) Número de unidades cuadradas que se requieren para cubrir la superficie encerrada por una figura geométrica.

arithmetic average / promedio aritmético (102) La media de un conjunto de datos.

arithmetic sequence / sucesión aritmética (142) Sucesión en que la diferencia entre dos términos consecutivos es constante.

associative property of addition / propiedad asociativa de la adición (301) Para números a, b y c cualesquiera, $(a + b) + c = a + (b + c)$.

associative property of multiplication / propiedad asociativa de la multiplicación (301) Para números a, b y c cualesquiera, $(ab)c = a(bc)$.

B

back-to-back stem-and-leaf plot /diagrama de tallo y hojas consecutivo (109) El que se usa para comparar dos conjuntos de datos. Las hojas de uno de los conjuntos de datos se escriben a un lado del tallo y las del segundo conjunto de datos al otro lado del tallo.

bar graph / gráfica de barras (94) Tipo de gráfica que usa barras para comparar estadísticas.

bar notation / notación de barra (70) En los decimales periódicos, la línea o barra que se escribe encima de los dígitos que se repiten. En $2.\overline{63}$, por ejemplo, la barra encima de 63 indica que el bloque de dos dígitos, 63, se repite indefinidamente.

base / base (17) Número que se usa como factor en una potencia. En 5^3, la base es 5, es decir, $5^3 = 5 \times 5 \times 5$.

base / base (349) Número con que se compara el porcentaje en una proporción porcentual.

base / base (31) Cualquier lado de un paralelogramo.

box-and-whisker plot / diagrama de caja y patillas (114) Diagrama que resume información usando la mediana, los cuartiles superior e inferior y los valores extremos. Se dibuja una caja alrededor de los cuartiles y se trazan patillas que los unan a los valores extremos respectivos.

C

capture-recapture technique / técnica de captura-recaptura (329) Método que se usa para estimar poblaciones de animales. El procedimiento a seguir es capturar una muestra, marcarla y devolverla a su hábitat. Más tarde, se captura otra muestra. La siguiente proporción se usa para estimar el tamaño de la población.

$$\frac{\textit{número capturado inicialmente}}{\textit{población total (p)}} = \frac{\textit{número marcado en la muestra}}{\textit{recapturados}}$$

cell / celda (137) Unidad básica de una hoja de cálculos. Las celdas pueden contener datos, rótulos o fórmulas.

center / centro (297) Punto en el plano, del cual equidistan todos los puntos de un círculo o de una esfera.

circle / círculo (297) Conjunto de todos los puntos en un plano que equidistan de un punto dado llamado centro.

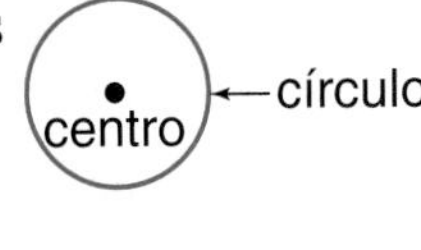

circle graph / gráfica circular (460) Tipo de gráfica estadística que se usa para comparar las partes de un todo.

circumference / circunferencia (297) La distancia alrededor de un círculo.

cluster / agrupamiento (98) Datos estrechamente agrupados.

clustering / agrupar (51) Método que se usa para estimar sumas y restas de decimales, redondeando al mismo número entero un grupo de números estrechamente relacionados.

coefficient / coeficiente (234) Parte numérica de un término.

combination / combinación (551) Arreglo o lista de objetos en que el orden no es importante.

common denominator / denominador común (172) Múltiplo común de los denominadores de dos o más fracciones. 24 es un denominador común de $\frac{1}{3}$, $\frac{5}{8}$ y $\frac{3}{4}$, porque 24 el mcm de 3, 8 y 4.

commutative property of addition / propiedad conmutativa de la adición (301) Para números a y b cualesquiera, $a + b = b + a$.

commutative property of multiplication / propiedad conmutativa de la multiplicación (301) Para números a y b cualesquiera, $ab = ba$.

complementary / complementarios (362) Dos ángulos son complementarios si la suma de sus medidas es 90°.

composite number / número compuesto (138) Cualquier número entero mayor que 1 que posee más de dos factores.

compound event / evento compuesto (542) Un evento compuesto consiste en dos o más eventos simples.

congruent / congruentes (371) Segmentos de recta que tienen la misma longitud; ángulos que tienen la misma medida; figuras que tienen la misma forma y tamaño.

coordinate system / sistema de coordenadas (191) Plano en el cual se han trazado dos rectas numéricas, una horizontal y una vertical, que se intersecan en sus puntos cero.

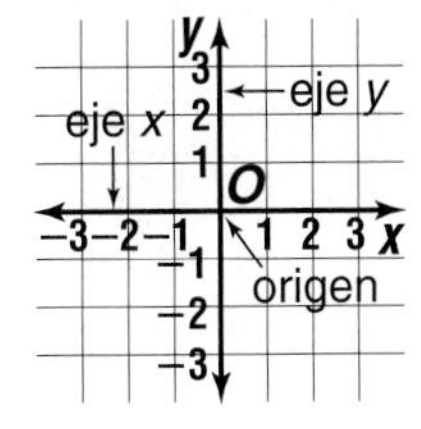

Counting Principle / Principio de Conteo (538) Método para calcular el número de maneras en que dos o más eventos pueden ocurrir, lo cual se logra multiplicando entre sí el número de maneras en que puede ocurrir cada evento individualmente.

cross products / productos cruzados (325) Los productos que resultan de la comparación de los términos de las diagonales de dos razones. Las razones forman una proporción si y sólo si los productos son iguales. En la proporción $\frac{3}{6} = \frac{4}{8}$, los productos cruzados son 3×8 y 6×4.

cubed / al cubo (17) Producto de un número por sí mismo tres veces. Dos al cubo es 8 ya que $2 \times 2 \times 2 = 8$.

SPANISH GLOSSARY

cup / taza (290) Unidad de capacidad del sistema inglés de medidas que equivale a 8 onzas líquidas.

cylinder / cilindro (503) Figura tridimensional que tiene dos bases circulares congruentes y paralelas.

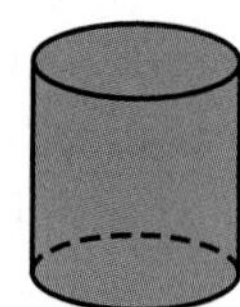

D

decagon / decágono (370) Polígono de diez lados.

defining a variable / definir una variable (243) El elegir una variable y una cantidad que esté representada por la variable en una ecuación.

degree / grado (362) La unidad de medida angular más común.

dependent events / eventos dependientes (543) Dos o más eventos en que el resultado de uno de ellos afecta el resultado de otros eventos.

diameter / diámetro (297) La longitud de cualquier segmento de recta cuyos extremos yacen en un círculo y que pasa por su centro.

distributive property / propiedad distributiva (302) Para números a, b y c cualesquiera, $a(b + c) = ab + ac$ y $(b + c)a = ba + ca$.

divisible / divisible (133) Un número es divisible entre otro si, después de dividirlos, el residuo es cero.

division property of equality / propiedad de división de la igualdad (234) Para números a, b y c cualesquiera, con $c \neq 0$, si $a = b$, entonces $\frac{a}{c} = \frac{b}{c}$.

equation / ecuación (21) Enunciado matemático que contiene el signo de igualdad, =.

equilateral / equilátero (382) Figura en el plano que tiene todos sus lados congruentes entre sí.

equivalent ratios / razones equivalentes (318) Dos razones que tienen el mismo valor.

evaluate / evaluar (12) Calcular el valor de una expresión sustituyendo las variables con números.

event / evento (165) Resultado específico o tipo de resultado de un experimento probabilístico.

experimental probability / probabilidad experimental (531) Probabilidad de un evento que se calcula o estima basándose en la frecuencia relativa de los resultados favorables al evento en cuestión, que ocurren durante un experimento probabilístico.

exponent / exponente (17) Número de veces que la base de una potencia se usa como factor. En 5^3, el exponente es 3, o sea, $5^3 = 5 \times 5 \times 5$.

factor / factor (17, 133) Número entero que divide otro número entero con un residuo de 0.

factorial / factorial (547) La expresión $n!$ es el producto de los n primeros números de contar, contando al revés.

factor tree / árbol de factores (138) Diagrama que sirve para encontrar la factorización prima de un número. Los factores se ramifican de los factores anteriores hasta que todos los factores son primos.

fair game / juego justo (535) Juego en que los jugadores tienen la misma oportunidad de ganar.

fractal / fractal (24) Figura geométrica que se construye aplicando una regla a partes más y más pequeñas de la figura. Las partes de un fractal son semejantes a la figura entera.

frequency table / tabla de frecuencia (88) Tabla que se usa para organizar un conjunto de datos y que muestra cuántas veces aparece cada dato.

function / función (249) Relación en que cada elemento de entrada es apareado con un único elemento de salida, según una regla específica.

gallon / galón (290) Unidad de capacidad del sistema inglés de medidas que equivale a 4 cuartos de galón.

geometric sequence / sucesión geométrica (142) Sucesión de números en la cual se puede calcular cualquier término, a partir del segundo, multiplicando el término anterior por el mismo número.

gram / gramo (75) Unidad de masa del sistema métrico.

greatest common factor (GCF) / máximo común divisor (MCD) (150) El mayor factor común de dos o más números. El MCD de 18 y 24 es 6.

height / altura (31) La distancia más corta desde la base de un paralelogramo hasta su lado opuesto.

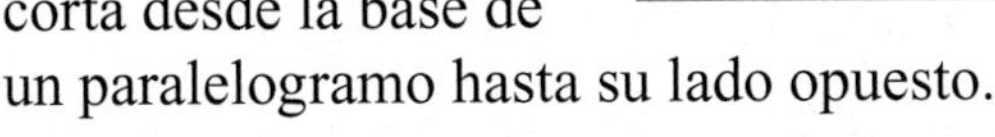

heptagon / heptágono (370) Polígono de siete lados.

hexagon / hexágono (370) Polígono de seis lados.

hypotenuse / hipotenusa (419) El lado de un triángulo rectángulo opuesto a su ángulo recto.

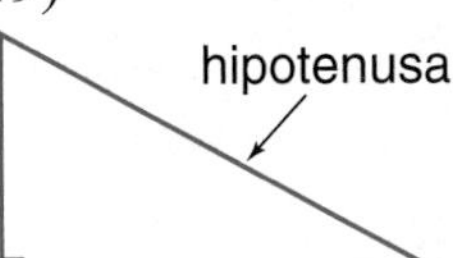

identity property of addition / propiedad de identidad de la adición (301) Para cualquier número a, $a + 0 = a$.

identity property of multiplication / propiedad de identidad de la multiplicación (301) Para cualquier número a, $a \times 1 = a$.

independent events / eventos independientes (542) Dos o más eventos en que el resultado de uno de ellos *no* afecta el resultado de los otros eventos.

indirect measurement / medida indirecta (377) Cálculo de una medida a partir de triángulos semejantes y proporciones.

inequality / desigualdad (246) Enunciado matemático que contiene $<$, $>$, $\neq$, $\leq$ o $\geq$.

inner measure / medida interior (423) El número de cuadrados enteros que contiene una figura.

integer / entero (184) Los números enteros no negativos y sus opuestos. $\ldots, -3, -2, -1, 0, 1, 2, 3, \ldots$

interquartile range / amplitud intercuartílica (112, 115) El rango de la mitad central de un conjunto de datos o números.

Amplitud intercuartílica $= CS - CI$

interval / intervalo (88) Diferencia entre valores sucesivos en una escala.

irregular figure / figura irregular (423) Figura que carece de lados rectos y esquinas cuadradas.

isosceles / isósceles (382) Triángulo que tiene dos lados congruentes.

leaf / hoja (108) El segundo valor de posición mayor en un diagrama de tallo y hojas.

least common denominator (LCD) / mínimo común denominador (mcd) (172) El menor múltiplo común de los denominadores de dos o más fracciones.

least common multiple (LCM) / mínimo común múltiplo (mcm) (169) El menor múltiplo común de dos o más números. El mcm de 2 y 3 es 6.

leg / cateto (419) Cualquiera de los lados que forman el ángulo recto de un triángulo rectángulo.

linear equation / ecuación lineal (255) Ecuación cuya gráfica es una recta.

line graph / gráfica lineal (94) Tipo de gráfica estadística que usa segmentos de recta para mostrar cómo cambian los valores durante un período de tiempo.

line of symmetry / eje de simetría (395) Recta que divide una figura en dos mitades que son reflexiones una de la otra.

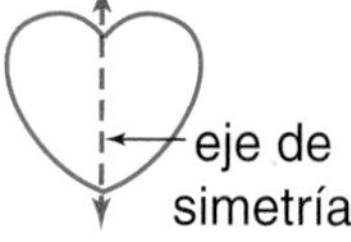

line plot / esquema lineal (98) Gráfica que usa una recta numérica y un × sobre un número en la recta numérica cada vez que el número aparece en un conjunto de datos.

line symmetry / simetría lineal (395) Exhiben simetría lineal las figuras que coinciden exactamente cuando se doblan.

liter / litro (75) Unidad fundamental de capacidad del sistema métrico. Un litro es un poco más de un cuarto de galón.

lower extreme / extremo inferior (114) El número menor de un conjunto de datos.

lower quartile / cuartil inferior (114) La mediana de la mitad inferior de un conjunto de datos o números, la cual se denota por *CI*.

M

mean / media (102) La suma de los números de un conjunto de datos dividida entre el número total de datos.

median / mediana (102) El número central de un conjunto de datos, una vez que los datos han sido ordenados numéricamente. Si hay un número par de datos, la mediana es el promedio de los dos datos centrales.

meter / metro (74) Unidad fundamental de longitud del sistema métrico.

metric system / sistema métrico (74) Sistema de medidas de base diez que usa las siguientes unidades fundamentales: metro para longitud, gramo para masa y litro para capacidad.

mode / modal (102) Número(s) de un conjunto de datos que aparece(n) más frecuentemente.

modeling / hacer un modelo (22) La escritura de una ecuación que represente un problema de la vida real.

multiple / múltiplo (169) El múltiplo de un número entero es el producto del número por cualquier otro número entero.

multiplication property of equality / propiedad de multiplicación de la igualdad (302) Si cada lado de una ecuación se multiplica por el mismo número, entonces los dos lados permanecen iguales. Si $a = b$, entonces, $ac = bc$.

multiplicative inverse / inverso multiplicativo (301) El producto de un número por su inverso multiplicativo es igual a 1. El inverso multiplicativo de $\frac{2}{3}$ es $\frac{3}{2}$ y viceversa.

N

negative integer / entero negativo (184) Entero que es menor que cero.

nonagon / eneágono (370) Polígono de nueve lados.

O

obtuse / obtuso (362) Cualquier ángulo que mide más de 90° pero menos de 180°.

octagon / octágono (370) Polígono de ocho lados.

opposite / opuestos (184) Dos enteros son opuestos si, en la recta numérica, están representados por puntos que equidistan de cero, pero en direcciones opuestas. La suma de opuestos es cero.

order of operations / orden de las operaciones (18) Reglas a seguir cuando hay más de una operación involucrada.

1. Primero ejecuta todas las operaciones dentro de los símbolos de agrupamiento.
2. Ejecuta todos las potencias antes que cualquier otra opercíon.
3. Multiplica y divide, ordenadamente, de izquierda a derecha.
4. Suma y resta, ordenadamente, de izquierda a derecha.

ordered pair / par ordenado (191) Par de números que se usa para ubicar un punto en un plano de coordenadas. Se escribe de la siguiente forma: (coordenada x, coordenada y).

origin / origen (191) Punto de intersección axial en un plano de coordenadas.

ounce / onza (289) Unidad de peso del sistema inglés de medidas. 16 onzas equivalen a una libra.

outcome / resultado (531) Uno de los resultados posibles de un experimento probabilístico. Por ejemplo, 4 es un resultado posible cuando se lanza un dado.

outer measure / medida exterior (423) Número de cuadrados dentro de una figura y que contienen parte de la figura.

outlier / valor atípico (115) Dato o datos que dista(n) de los cuartiles respectivos más de 1.5 veces la amplitud intercuartílica.

P

parallelogram / paralelogramo (31) Cuadrilátero con dos pares de lados paralelos.

pentagon / pentágono (370) Polígono de cinco lados.

percent / tanto por ciento (158) Razón que compara un número con 100.

percent proportion / proporción porcentual (349) La proporción $\frac{P}{B} = \frac{r}{100}$ en que P representa el porcentaje, B representa la base y r representa el número por cada 100.

percentage / porcentaje (349) Número de una proporción porcentual que se compara con otro número llamado base.

perfect square / cuadrado perfecto (411) Número cuya raíz cuadrada es un número entero. 25 es un cuadrado perfecto porque $\sqrt{25} = 5$.

perimeter / perímetro (292) La medida del contorno de una figura geométrica cerrada.

permutation / permutación (547) Arreglo o lista en que el orden es importante.

perspective / perspectiva (492) Una vista de perspectiva de una figura tridimensional es una vista de esquina que muestra las tres dimensiones de la figura.

pint / pinta (290) Unidad de capacidad del sistema inglés de medidas que equivale a dos tazas.

polygon / polígono (370) Figura simple cerrada en un plano, formada por tres o más segmentos de recta.

population / población (5, 464) El grupo total de individuos del cual se toman las muestras bajo estudio.

population density / densidad demográfica (322) Población por milla cuadrada.

positive integer / entero positivo (184) Entero que es mayor que cero.

pound / libra (289) Unidad de peso del sistema inglés de medidas que equivale a 16 onzas.

power / potencia (17) Número que se puede escribir usando un exponente. La potencia 7^3 se lee *siete a la tercera potencia* o *siete al cubo.*

prime factorization / factorización prima (138) Escritura de un número compuesto como el producto de números primos. La factorización prima de 63, por ejemplo, es $3 \times 3 \times 7$.

prime number / número primo (138) Número entero mayor que 1 que sólo tiene dos factores, 1 y sí mismo.

principal / capital (478) Cantidad de dinero invertido o adeudado.

probability / probabilidad (165) La posibilidad de que suceda un evento. Es la razón del número de maneras en que puede ocurrir un evento al número total de resultados posibles.

property of proportions / propiedad de las proporciones (325) Si $\frac{a}{b} = \frac{c}{d}$, entonces $ad = bc$. Si $ad = bc$, entonces $\frac{a}{b} = \frac{c}{d}$.

proportion / proporción (325) Ecuación que demuestra la igualdad de dos razones, $\frac{a}{b} = \frac{c}{d}$, $b \neq 0, d \neq 0$.

Pythagorean Theorem / Teorema de Pitágoras (419) En un triángulo rectángulo, el cuadrado de la longitud de la hipotenusa es igual a la suma de los cuadrados de las longitudes de los catetos. $c^2 = a^2 + b^2$

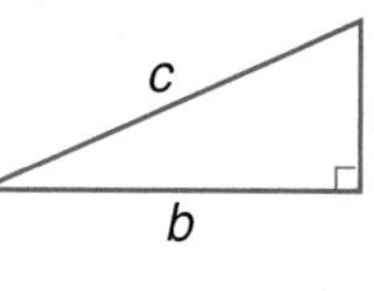

quadrant / cuadrante (191) Una de las cuatro regiones en que dos rectas perpendiculares dividen un plano.

quadrilateral / cuadrilátero (370) Polígono de cuatro lados.

quart / cuarto de galón (290) Unidad de capacidad del sistema inglés de medidas que equivale a dos pintas.

quartile / cuartil (112) Una de las cuatro partes iguales en que están divididos los datos de un conjunto grande de números.

radical sign / signo radical (411) El símbolo con que se indica la raíz cuadrada no negativa es $\sqrt{}$.

radius / radio (297) Distancia desde el centro del un círculo hasta cualquier punto del mismo.

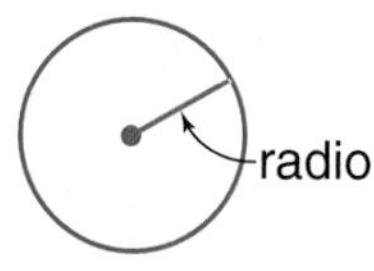

random / al azar (165) Los resultados ocurren al azar si cada resultado tiene la misma posibilidad de ocurrir.

random / aleatoria (464) Una muestra recibe el nombre de aleatoria si sus miembros han sido seleccionados basándose puramente en el azar.

range / rango (88) La diferencia entre los valores máximo y mínimo de un conjunto de datos.

rate / tasa (321) Razón de dos medidas que tienen distintas unidades de medida.

rate / tasa (349) Razón de un número a 100 en una proporción porcentual.

rate / tasa (478) El tanto por ciento que se cobra o se paga por el uso del dinero.

ratio / razón (154, 317) Comparación de dos números mediante división. La razón de 2 a 3 puede escribirse como 2 de cada 3, 2 a 3, 2:3 ó $\frac{2}{3}$.

reciprocal / recíproco (301) Inverso multiplicativo de un número.

rectangle / rectángulo (30) Cuadrilátero cuyos cuatro ángulos son congruentes entre sí.

rectangular prism / prisma rectangular (498) Prisma con bases rectangulares.

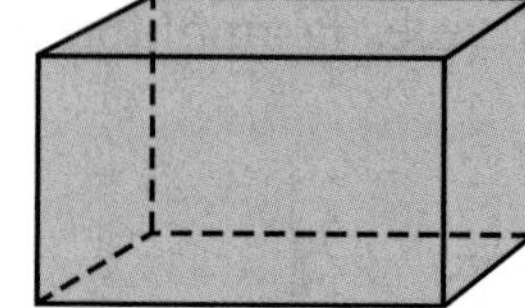

reflection / reflexión (215, 395) Transformación en que a una figura se le da vuelta de campana por encima de un eje de simetría.

regular polygon / polígono regular (371) Polígono cuyos lados, así como sus ángulos, son todos congruentes.

repeating decimal / decimal periódico (70) Decimal en el cual los dígitos, en algún momento, comienzan a repetirse en bloques de uno o más números. Por ejemplo, 0.181818... y 0.8333....

rhombus / rombo (383) Paralelogramo cuyos lados son todos congruentes.

right / recto (362) Ángulo que mide 90°.

S

sample / muestra (5, 329, 464) Grupo escogido al azar o aleatoriamente que se usa para representar la población entera.

sample space / espacio muestral (531) Conjunto de todos los resultados posibles de un experimento probabilístico.

scale / escala (88) Conjunto de todos los valores posibles de una medida dada, el cual incluye los valores máximo y mínimo del conjunto, separados mediante los intervalos que se han usado.

scale / escala (332) Intervalos que se usan en un mapa para representar la razón de las distancias en el mapa a las distancias verdaderas.

scale drawing / dibujo a escala (332) Dibujo que es semejante, pero más grande o más pequeño que el objeto real.

scalene / escaleno (382) Triángulo sin ningún par de lados congruentes.

scatter plot / diagrama de dispersión (92, 95) Diagrama en que dos conjuntos de datos relacionados aparecen graficados como pares ordenados en la misma gráfica.

scientific notation / notación científica (77) Escritura de un número como el producto de un número que es al menos igual a 1, pero menor que 10, multiplicado por una potencia de diez. Por ejemplo, $687{,}000 = 6.87 \times 10^5$.

sequence / sucesión (142) Lista de números en cierto orden, como, por ejemplo, 0, 1, 2, 3 ó 2, 4, 6, 8.

similar / semejantes (376) Figuras que tienen la misma forma, pero no necesariamente el mismo tamaño.

simple interest / interés simple (478) Cantidad que se paga por el uso del dinero. La fórmula para calcular el interés simple es $I = prt$.

simplest form / forma reducida (154) Una fracción está escrita en forma reducida si el MCD de su numerador y denominador es 1.

solids / sólidos (493) Figuras tridimensionales. Los prismas, las pirámides, los conos y los cilindros son algunos ejemplos de sólidos.

solution / solución (21) Valor de la variable de una ecuación que hace verdadera la ecuación. La solución de $12 = x + 7$ es 5.

solve / resolver (21) Proceso de encontrar el número o números que satisfagan una ecuación.

spreadsheet / hoja de cálculos (137) Herramienta que se usa para organizar y analizar datos.

square / cuadrado (410) Número multiplicado por sí mismo; 36 es el cuadrado de 6 porque $6^2 = 6 \times 6 = 36$.

squared / al cuadrado (17) Número multiplicado por sí mismo. 7^2 se lee *7 al cuadrado*.

square root / raíz cuadrada (411) Uno de dos factores iguales de un número. Si $a^2 = b$, entonces a es una raíz cuadrada de b. La raíz cuadrada no negativa de 144 es 12 porque 12 es un número no negativo y $12^2 = 144$.

stem / tallo (108) El mayor valor de posición común a todos los datos es el que se usa como tallo en un diagrama de tallo y hojas.

stem-and-leaf plot / diagrama de tallo y hojas (108) Sistema que se usa para condensar un conjunto de datos y en el cual el mayor valor de posición de los datos forma el tallo y el segundo mayor valor de posición de los datos forma las hojas.

straight / llano (362) Ángulo que mide 180°.

subtraction property of equality / propiedad de sustracción de la igualdad (228) Si sustraes el mismo número de ambos lados de una ecuación, los lados permanecen iguales. Para números a, b y c cualesquiera, si $a = b$, entonces $a - c = b - c$.

supplementary / suplementarios (362) Dos ángulos son suplementarios si la suma de sus medidas es 180°.

surface area / área de superficie (510) Suma de las áreas de todas las superficies de una figura tridimensional.

term / término (239) Número, variable o producto de números y variables.

term / término (142) Nombre que recibe cada número de una sucesión.

terminating decimal / decimal terminal (70) Cociente en que la división termina, es decir, tiene un residuo de cero. 0.25 y 0.125 son ejemplos de decimales terminales.

tessellation / teselado (388) Un patrón repetitivo de polígonos que encajan perfectamente, sin dejar huecos o espacios.

theoretical probability / probabilidad teórica (531) Razón del número de maneras en que puede ocurrir un evento al número total de resultados posibles.

time / tiempo (478) Cuando se usa para calcular interés, el tiempo se da en años.

ton / tonelada (289) Unidad de peso del sistema inglés de medidas que equivale a 2,000 libras.

transformation / transformación (215) Movimientos de figuras geométricas.

translation /traslación (215, 392) Tipo de transformación en que una figura se desliza horizontalmente, verticalmente o de ambas maneras.

trapezoid / trapecio (383, 429) Cuadrilátero con un único par de lados paralelos.

tree diagram / diagrama de árbol (534) Diagrama que se usa para encontrar y mostrar el número total de resultados posibles de un experimento probabilístico.

triangle / triángulo (370, 428) Polígono que posee tres ángulos.

unit rate / tasa unitaria (321) Tasa cuyo denominador es 1.

upper extreme / extremo superior (114) El número máximo de un conjunto de datos o números.

upper quartile / cuartil superior (114) La mediana de la mitad superior de un conjunto de números o datos.

variable / variable (12) Un símbolo, por lo general, una letra, que se usa para representar números en expresiones o enunciados matemáticos. En $3 + a = 6$, a es una variable.

vertex / vértice (362) El vértice de un ángulo es el extremo común de los rayos que lo forman.

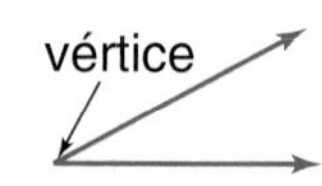

volume / volumen (498) Número de unidades cúbicas que se requieren para llenar el espacio que ocupa un sólido.

x*-axis / eje *x (191) La recta numérica horizontal que ayuda a formar el sistema de coordenadas.

x*-coordinate / coordenada *x (191) Primer número de un par ordenado.

y*-axis / eje *y (191) La recta numérica vertical que ayuda a formar el sistema de coordenadas.

y*-coordinate / coordenada *y (191) Segundo número de un par ordenado.

zero pair / par nulo (196, 227) Resultado de aparear una ficha positiva con una negativa.

Index

Absolute value, 185

Act it Out, 528–529

Acute angles, 362

Addition
- equations, 226–231
- estimating, 50–53, 268
- of decimals, 50–53
- of fractions, 268–275
- of integers, 196–200
- of mixed numbers, 276–279
- in order of operations, 8
- property of equality, 229
- of whole numbers, 21–23

Addition property of equality, 229

Additive inverse, 197

Algebra
- evaluating expressions, 11–15, 18–20, 23, 49, 58, 63, 69, 73, 139–140, 145, 203, 208, 213, 245, 252, 278, 286, 307, 549
- functions, 249–257
- solving equations, 21–23, 27, 33, 49, 53, 63, 76, 226–231, 234–237, 238–242, 245, 248, 255, 271, 279, 295, 302, 304, 320, 326, 351, 364–365, 371, 373, 385, 389, 413, 435, 453, 458, 533
- variables, 11–15
- writing equations, 231, 242–245, 453, 501, 512
- writing expressions, 53, 242–245, 248, 271, 341, 369
- *See also* Applications, Connections, and Integration Index on pages xxii–1

Alternate exterior angles, 361

Alternate interior angles, 361, 373

Alternative Assessment, 39, 83, 125, 179, 221, 261, 311, 355, 401, 445, 485, 521, 557

Angles
- acute, 362
- adjacent, 361
- alternate exterior, 361
- alternate interior, 361, 373
- classifying by measure, 362
- complementary, 363
- congruent, 371
- corresponding, 361, 373
- measure of, 360–365
- naming, 362
- obtuse, 362
- of polygons, 369
- right, 362
- sides, 362
- straight, 362
- supplementary, 363–364
- symbol, 363
- using protractor to measure, 360
- vertex, 362

Applications, 2e, 42e, 86e, 130e, 182e, 224e, 266e, 314e, 358e, 406e, 448e, 488e, 526e

Applications *See* Applications, Connections, and Integration Index on pages xxii–1

Annexing zeros, 44

Annulus, 439

Area, 28, 30–33
- of circles, 433
- models, 410, 427, 429, 432, 436–437
- of parallelograms, 28–29, 31, 427
- and probability, 436
- of rectangles, 28–33, 56
- of trapezoids, 429–430
- of triangles, 427–428

Arithmetic average, 102

Arithmetic sequence, 142

Assessment Resources, 2c, 2f, 37, 38, 42c, 42f, 81, 82, 86c, 86f, 123, 124, 130c, 130f, 177, 178, 182c, 182f, 219, 220, 224c, 224f, 259, 260, 266c, 266f, 309, 310, 314c, 314f, 353, 354, 358c, 358f, 399, 400, 406c, 406f, 443, 444, 448c, 448f, 483, 484, 488c, 488f, 519, 520, 526c, 526f, 555, 556

Associative property, 301

Auditory/Musical Learning Style, *see Multiple Learning Styles*

Average, 102, 107, 119
- arithmetic, 102

B

Back-to-back stem-and-leaf plot, 109

Bar graphs, 94–95
- interpreting, 48, 49, 53, 59, 63, 94–95, 101, 119, 136, 453, 455, 471, 497, 517
- making, 96, 118
- misleading, 119
- scale, 94
- using to make predictions, 94–95

Bar notation, 70

Base, 17, 349, 410
- of parallelograms, 28, 29, 31

Bilateral symmetry, 395

Box-and-whisker plot, 114–117
- extreme values, 114
- interquartile range, 115
- lower extreme, 114
- lower quartile, 114–116
- making, 114–117
- median, 114–116
- outliers, 115–116
- upper extreme, 114
- upper quartile, 114–116
- using a number line to draw, 114
- whiskers, 114–116

C

Calculator, 18, 19, 66, 128, 134, 135, 139, 146, 175, 264, 344, 346, 404, 407, 417, 438, 449, 469, 524
- fraction, 273, 276
- graphing, 16, 102, 114, 115, 195, 225

Calculators, *see Technology*

Capacity, 75, 290
- changing units, 74–76, 290–291
- cup, 290
- customary, 290
- fluid ounce, 290
- gallon, 290
- kiloliter, 75
- liter, 75
- metric, 75
- milliliter, 75
- pint, 290
- quart, 290

Capture-recapture technique, 329

CD-ROM Program, *see Technology*

Careers
- astronaut, 60
- banker, 296
- biochemist, 507
- fashion designer, 368
- inventor, 537
- mathematician, 187
- meteorologist, 187
- radio producer/director, 473

Center of a circle, 297

Centimeter, 74

INDEX

Chance, 530
Chapter Projects
Advance to Go and Collect $200, 527
America's Scream Machines, 225
Don't Turn that Dial!, 449
Fun Ways to be Fit, 3
Geometric Art, 359
How Big is Our Solar System?, 43
It's a Small World, 407
Latitude vs. Temperature, 183
Lights! Camera! Action!, 87
Turn Over a New Leaf, 489
Ups and Downs, 267
Waste Not, Want Not, 315
What Color was that Car?, 131
See also Working on the Chapter Project

Chapter Resources, *see Organizing the Chapter*

Charts, 17, 35, 44, 46, 50, 52, 53, 73, 74, 89, 91, 99, 101, 110, 121, 148, 156, 164, 188, 189, 249, 410, 435, 454, 549

Choose the Method of Computation, 34–35

Circle, 297
annulus, 439
area, 433
center, 297
circumference, 297–298
diameter, 297
radius, 297

Circle graphs
interpreting, 347, 348, 373
making, 449, 459–463

Circumference, 297–298

Classroom Games, 2e, 42e, 86e, 130e, 182e, 224e, 266e, 314e, 358e, 406e, 448e, 488e, 526e

Classroom Vignettes, 30, 67, 74, 110, 114, 119, 133, 138, 150, 193, 197, 204, 212, 228, 239, 294, 298, 332, 346, 370, 383, 423, 432, 474, 512, 530

Closing Activity
Modeling, 10, 46, 69, 97, 111, 145, 153, 160, 168, 194, 200, 214, 252, 275, 287, 291, 295, 320, 338, 379, 397, 417, 435, 441, 472, 480, 497, 517, 541, 549
Speaking, 7, 27, 33, 49, 53, 55, 59, 93, 101, 117, 141, 157, 175, 186, 190, 217, 237, 257, 271, 300, 341, 345, 351, 365, 385, 391, 426, 431, 453, 455, 467, 495, 506, 533, 553
Writing, 15, 20, 23, 35, 63, 73, 76, 79, 91, 105, 121, 136, 149, 164, 171, 204, 209, 211, 231, 233, 241, 244, 248, 279, 281, 304, 307, 324, 328, 331, 335, 348, 373, 387, 394, 409, 413, 422, 458, 463, 477, 501, 513, 529, 536, 545

Cluster of data, 98

Clustering, 51

Coefficient, 234

Combinations, 550–553
related to permutations, 551

Comics, 27, 324, 495

Common denominator, 172

Communication, *see Motivating the Lesson*

Commutative property, 301

Comparing
decimals, 44–46
fractions, 172–175
integers, 188–190

Complementary angles, 363

Composite numbers, 138

Compound events, 542

Computers, 3, 43, 87, 131, 137, 183, 267, 315, 359, 407, 449, 481, 489, 524, 527
Internet, 3, 20, 23, 43, 60, 73, 87, 107, 117, 129, 131, 136, 174, 175, 183, 187, 190, 192, 198, 225, 237, 252, 265, 267, 285, 291, 296, 315, 328, 351, 359, 368, 391, 394, 405, 407, 414, 434, 449, 462, 473, 477, 507, 513, 517, 525, 527, 530, 536, 537, 541
software, 128, 131, 359, 404, 461, 489, 524
to construct graphs, 87, 128, 183, 225, 315, 449
spreadsheet, 3, 43, 87, 128, 137, 183, 225, 264, 315, 404, 461, 481, 524, 622–623
See also Applications, Connections, and Integration Index on pages xxii–1

Cones, 493

Congruent, 371
angles, 371
figures, 371
line segments, 371

Connections *See* Applications, Connections, and Integration Index on pages xxii–1

Constructions
parallel lines, 367
parallelogram, 367
perpendicular lines, 366

Cooperative Learning, 128, 129, 264, 265, 404, 405, 524, 525

Cooperative Learning, 28, 29, 64, 65, 106, 112, 113, 118, 132, 146, 196, 201, 206, 226, 238, 253, 288, 316, 329, 360, 366, 369, 374, 380, 381, 418, 427, 436, 437, 459, 468, 490, 491, 502, 508, 546, 550

Coordinate system, 191
graphing points on, 192, 195
ordered pair, 191–192
origin, 191
quadrants, 191–192
x-axis, 191–192
x-coordinate, 191
y-axis, 191–192
y-coordinate, 191

Corresponding angles, 361, 373

Counting Principle, 538–541

Critical Thinking, 7, 10, 15, 20, 23, 27, 33, 91, 97, 101, 105, 111, 117, 121, 136, 141, 145, 153, 157, 160, 164, 168, 171, 175, 186, 190, 194, 200, 205, 209, 214, 217, 231, 237, 241, 245, 248, 252, 257, 271, 275, 279, 287, 291, 295, 300, 304, 307, 320, 324, 328, 335, 338, 341, 345, 348, 351, 363, 365, 373, 379, 385, 391, 394, 397, 413, 417, 422, 426, 431, 435, 441, 453, 463, 467, 472, 477, 480, 495, 501, 506, 513, 517, 533, 536, 541, 545, 549, 553

Cross-Curriculum Cue, 17, 44, 94, 154, 184, 243, 268, 317, 362, 412, 450, 492, 531

Cross products, 325–326

Cubed, 17

Cubic units, 498, 499

Cultural Kaleidoscope, 24, 98, 155, 169, 197, 235, 305, 322, 428, 493, 542

Cup, 290

Customary measurement, 289–291
capacity, 290
changing units, 289–291
cup, 290
fluid ounce, 290
foot, 294, 335
gallon, 290
inch, 293, 332
length, 292–294
mile, 292, 332
ounce, 289

pint, 290
pound, 289
quart, 290
ton, 289
weight, 289
yard, 294

Cylinders, 493, 503
surface area of, 514–517
volume of, 503–506

Data, 88
cluster of, 98
range, 88

Data Analysis *See* Applications, Connections, and Integration Index on pages xxii–1.

Decagon, 370

Decimal points, 44
aligning, 44, 48

Decimals
adding, 50–53
bar notation, 70
comparing, 44–46
dividing, 66–69
estimating with, 50–53
as fractions, 162
fractions as, 70–73
mixed numbers as, 71
modeling, 44, 56, 57, 58, 64–65
multiplying, 56–59
ordering, 44–46
as percents, 339
percents as, 339–340
place value, 44
repeating, 70–72
rounding, 47–49
rounding quotients, 66–69
subtracting, 48
terminating, 70

Decision Making, 9, 22, 89, 104, 162, 174, 185, 203, 240, 256, 303, 306, 323, 350, 378, 394, 421, 434, 462, 505, 544, 552

Deductive reasoning, 386–387

Degrees, 360

Dependent events, 542–545

Diagonal, 143

Diameter, 297

Did you know?, 6, 30, 94, 139, 142, 202, 212, 228, 254, 285, 333, 388, 423, 527, 539

Dilations, 380

Discount, 474–477

Discrete Mathematics
combinations, 550–553
Counting Principle, 538–541
factorial, 547
permutations, 546–549, 551
tree diagrams, 534–536, 538–539, 546

Distributive property, 302

Diversity, 2e, 42e, 86e, 130e, 182e, 224e, 266e, 314e, 358e, 406e, 448e, 488e, 526e

Divisibility patterns, 133–136
testing for, 137

Divisible, 133

Division
of decimals, 64–69
divisibility, 137
equations, 302
estimating, 50–53, 269
of fractions, 269, 305–307
in order of operations, 8
of integers, 212–214
of mixed numbers, 305–307
modeling, 64–65
property of equality, 234
of whole numbers, 21–23

Division property of equality, 234

Dodecagon, 373

Draw a diagram, 330–331

Eliminate possibilities, 280–281

Endpoint, 362

Enhancing the Chapter, 2e, 2f, 42e, 42f, 86e, 86f, 130e, 130f, 182e, 182f, 224e, 224f, 266e, 266f, 314e, 314f, 358e, 358f, 406e, 406f, 448e, 448f, 488e, 488f, 526e, 526f

Equality
properties of, 228–229, 234, 302

Equations
addition, 228
division, 302
linear, 255
modeling, 22, 226–227
multiplication, 234–237
solution of, 21
solving, 21–23, 228–231, 234–237, 238–241
solving using models, 226–227
subtraction, 229
two-step, 238–241
using mental math to check, 229
writing, 230, 236, 243–244

Equilateral triangle, 382

Equivalent ratios, 318

Error Analysis, *see Reteaching the Lesson*

Escher, 392, 396

Estimation
area of irregular figures, 423–426
with decimals, 50–53
differences of fractions, 269
with percents, 450–453
products of fractions, 269
quotients of fractions, 269
of square roots, 415–417
study hints, 5, 336, 420, 503
sums of fractions, 269
using clustering, 50
using rounding, 50, 450

Evaluate expressions, 12–16
using a graphing calculator, 16

Evaluation, *see Assessment Resources*

Events, 165
compound, 542–545
dependent, 542–545
equally-likely, 543
independent, 542–545

Experimental probability, 530–533

Exponent, 17, 410

Expressions
algebraic, 11–15
evaluating, 11–15
exponents in, 18
modeling, 11, 12
writing, 12, 14, 242–244

Extending the Lesson Activity, 7, 10, 15, 23, 33, 35, 46, 49, 53, 55, 59, 63, 69, 76, 79, 91, 93, 97, 101, 105, 111, 117, 121, 141, 145, 149, 153, 157, 160, 164, 168, 171, 186, 190, 194, 200, 205, 209, 211, 214, 217, 231, 233, 241, 245, 248, 252, 257, 271, 275, 279, 281, 287, 291, 295, 300, 304, 307, 320, 331, 335, 338, 341, 345, 348, 351, 365, 373, 379, 385, 387, 394, 397, 409, 413, 417, 422, 426, 431, 435, 441, 453, 455, 458, 463, 467, 480, 497, 501, 506, 517, 529, 533, 536, 545, 549, 553

Factorial, 547

Factors, 17, 133
exploring, 132

greatest common, 150–153

Factor tree, 138

Fair game, 535

Family Activities, 33, 111, 168, 217, 245, 324, 372, 425, 500, 553

Family Letters and Activities, 2e, 42e, 86e, 130e, 182e, 224e, 266e, 314e, 358e, 406e, 448e, 488e, 526e
Math in the Family, 2, 42, 86, 130, 182, 224, 266, 314, 358, 406, 448, 488, 526
Family Activity, 33, 68, 111, 216, 245, 271, 324, 372, 425, 463, 500, 553

Fibonacci sequence, 148

5-Minute Checks, 4, 8, 12, 17, 21, 24, 30, 44, 47, 50, 56, 61, 66, 70, 74, 77, 88, 94, 98, 102, 108, 114, 119, 133, 138, 142, 150, 154, 158, 161, 165, 169, 172, 184, 188, 191, 197, 202, 207, 212, 215, 228, 234, 239, 242, 246, 249, 254, 268, 272, 276, 284, 289, 292, 297, 301, 305, 317, 321, 325, 332, 336, 339, 342, 346, 349, 362, 370, 376, 382, 388, 392, 395, 410, 415, 419, 423, 428, 432, 438, 450, 456, 460, 464, 469, 474, 478, 492, 498, 503, 510, 514, 530, 534, 538, 542, 547, 551

Formulas
for area of circles, 433
for area of parallelograms, 31
for area of trapezoids, 429
for area of triangles, 428
for circumference of circles, 298
for perimeter of rectangles, 292
for simple interest, 478
for surface area of cylinders, 515
for surface area of rectangular prisms, 511
for volume of cylinders, 503
for volume of pyramids, 502
for volume of rectangular prisms, 498

Four-step plan, 4–7, 102, 170, 199, 215, 230, 269, 277, 322, 326, 389, 419–420, 433, 457, 539, 552

Fractals, 24–27
patterns, 288

Fractions
adding, 272–275
common denominator, 172
comparing, 172–175
as decimals, 70
denominator, 172
dividing, 305–307
equivalent, 318
estimating, 268–269
estimating differences of, 269
estimating products of, 269
estimating quotients of, 269
estimating sums of, 269
least common denominator, 172–175
modeling, 268, 269, 270, 272, 282, 284, 305
multiplying, 282–287
ordering, 172–175
as percents, 161, 336
ratios as, 317
reciprocals, 301
renaming, 273, 276, 285
rounding, 269
simplifying, 154–157
subtracting, 272–275

Frequency tables, 88–91
interval, 88–89
scale, 88–89
tally in, 88–89

Functions,
graphing, 249–253
representing as ordered pairs, 249–257
writing equations for, 254–257
writing expressions for, 253

Gallon, 290

Games
fair, 535
See also Let the Games Begin!

Geometric mean, 328

Geometric sequence, 142

Geometry
acute angles, 362
angles, 360–365, 369
annulus, 439
area, 28–33
bilateral symmetry, 395
complementary angles, 363
congruent, 371
constructions, 366–367
decagon, 370
degrees, 360
diagonal, 143
dilations, 380
dodecagon, 373
endpoint, 362
equilateral triangle, 382
Escher, 392, 396
estimating area of irregular figures, 423–426
heptagon, 370
hexagon, 370
hypotenuse, 419
indirect measurement, 377
inner measure, 423
inscribed, 374–375
inscribed polygons, 374–375
intersect, 366
intersecting lines, 366
irregular figures, 423
isosceles triangle, 382
Koch curve, 26
leg, 419
line of symmetry, 395
lines, 366
line segments, 371
line symmetry, 395
nonagon, 370
obtuse angles, 362
octagon, 370
outer measure, 423
parallel lines, 367
parallelograms, 28–29, 31–33, 383, 427, 432
pentagon, 370
perimeter, 292–295
perpendicular lines, 366
polygons, 369–373
protractor, 360
Pythagorean Theorem, 418–422
quadrilaterals, 370, 381–385
rays, 362
rectangles, 28–30, 32–33, 383
reflections, 395–397
regular, 371
regular polygons, 371
rhombus, 383
right angle, 362
right triangle, 382
scalene triangle, 382
sides, 370
Sierpinski's triangle, 25
similar, 376
similar polygons, 376–379
squares, 27, 383
straight angle, 362
supplementary angles, 363–364
symmetry, 395
tessellations, 388–394
transformations, 380
translations, 392–394
transversal, 361
trapezoids, 383, 429–430
triangles, 25, 381–385, 370, 427–428
vertex, 370
See also Applications, Connections, and Integration Index on pages xxii–1

Gram, 75

Graphing
functions, 249–252
integers on number line, 184–185, 188

integers on the coordinate system, 192
ordered pairs, 191–192

Graphing calculator, 16, 102, 114, 115, 195, 225, 620–621

Graphs, 175, 300, 341
bar, 94–95
circle, 459–463
coordinate, 191–192
interpreting, 55, 92, 93, 95, 97, 102–104, 116, 117, 120, 163, 245, 249–253, 279, 349, 350, 415, 472
line, 94
making, 46, 92, 93, 95, 96, 98–101, 108–111, 114–118, 121, 247–257, 459, 517
misleading, 119–121
number line, 184–185, 246

Greater than, 44

Greatest common factor, 150–153
of algebraic expressions, 151

Guess and check, 408–409

Hands-On Activity, *see Motivating the Lesson*

Hands-On Labs, 26, 32, 134, 159, 167
Adding Integers, 196
Angles of a Polygon, 369
Area, 28–29
Are You Average?, 106
Building Three-Dimensional Figures, 490–491
Dilations, 380
Division with Decimal Models, 64–65
Equal Ratios, 316
Exploring Combinations, 550
Exploring Factors, 132
Exploring Permutations, 546
Exploring Sequences, 146
Finding the Area of a Triangle, 427
Fractal Patterns, 288
A Function of Time, 253
How Much Is a Handful?, 118
Inscribed Polygons, 374
Investigating Triangles and Quadrilaterals, 381
Jelly Bean Statistics, 459
Measuring Angles, 360
Multiplying Fractions and Mixed Numbers, 282
Multiplying Integers, 206
Nets and Surface Area, 508
Percent of Change, 468
Perpendicular and Parallel Lines, 366
Probability and Area Models, 436–437
The Pythagorean Theorem, 418
Quartiles, 112–113
Solving Equations Using Models, 226
Solving Two-Step Equations, 238
Subtracting Integers, 201
Variables and Expressions, 11
Volume of Pyramids, 502
Wildlife Sampling, 329

Hands-On Math, 14, 96, 199, 208, 248, 251, 274, 285, 334, 344, 364, 390, 412, 416, 424, 430, 434, 452, 471, 500, 516, 532, 535

Hands-On Mini-Labs, 13, 24, 32, 56, 95, 133, 158, 166, 234, 246, 250, 272, 297, 333, 342, 363, 376, 388, 410, 415, 423, 432, 450, 469, 499, 504, 510, 514, 531, 535, 542

Height
of parallelograms, 28, 31

Heptagon, 370

Hexagon, 370

Hypotenuse, 419

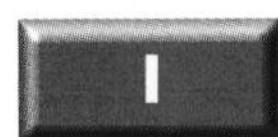

Identity, 301
additive, 301
multiplicative, 301

Independent events, 542–545

Indirect measurement, 377

Inductive reasoning, 386–387

Inequalities, 246
graphing on number line, 246
greater than, 44
less than, 44
solving, 247
writing, 247

Inner measure, 423

Inscribed polygons, 374–375

Integers,
absolute value of, 185
adding, 196–200
comparing, 188–190
dividing, 212–214
graphing, 184–185, 188, 192
modeling addition of, 196–199
modeling division of, 212
modeling multiplication of, 206–208
modeling subtraction of, 201–203
multiplying, 206–209
negative, 184
on number line, 184–185, 188
opposite of, 184
ordering, 188–190
positive, 184
subtracting, 201–205

Integration *See* Applications, Connections, and Integration Index on pages xxii–1

Interactive Mathematics: Activities and Investigations, 2d, 42d, 86d, 130d, 182d, 224d, 266d, 314d, 358d, 406d, 448d, 488d, 526d

Interdisciplinary Investigation
"A" is for Apple, 264–265
If the Shoe Fits, 128–129
The Perfect Package, 524–525
Pi for Polygons, 404–405

Internet Connections, 3, 20, 23, 43, 60, 73, 87, 107, 117, 129, 131, 136, 174, 175, 183, 187, 190, 192, 198, 225, 237, 257, 265, 267, 285, 291, 296, 315, 328, 351, 359, 368, 391, 394, 405, 407, 414, 434, 449, 462, 473, 477, 489, 507, 513, 517, 525, 527, 530, 536, 537, 541

Interquartile range, 112–113, 115

Interpersonal Learning Style, *see Multiple Learning Styles*

Intersect, 366

Intervals, 88
in frequency tables, 88
on line plots, 98

Intrapersonal Learning Style, *see Multiple Learning Styles*

Inverse
additive, 197
multiplicative, 301

Investigations *See* Interdisciplinary Investigations

Investigations for the Special Education Student, 24, 50, 98, 198, 235, 269, 319, 421, 456, 504, 539

Irregular figures, 423
estimating area of, 423–426
inner measure, 423
outer measure, 423

Isosceles triangle, 382

Kilogram, 75

Kiloliter, 75

Kilometer, 74

Kinesthetic Learning Style, *see Multiple Learning Styles*

Koch curve, 26

Labs *See* Hands-On Labs, Problem Solving Labs, Technology Labs, and Thinking Labs

Leaf, 108

Least common denominator, 172

Least common multiple, 169–171
- finding mentally, 170

Leg
- of right triangle, 419

Length
- in customary system, 292–294
- in metric system, 75
- of rectangles, 30

Less than, 44

Lesson Objectives, 2a, 42a, 86a, 130a, 182a, 224a, 266a, 314a, 358a, 406a, 448a, 488a, 526a

Lesson Planning Guide, *see Organizing the Chapter*

Let the Games Begin!
- Alge-bridge, 20
- Can You Guess?, 107
- Cherokee Butterbean Game, 541
- The Factor Fair, 136
- Fractions and Ladders, 175
- Left from the Start, 328
- Match-Up, 73
- Math-O, 237
- Shape-Tac-Toe, 513
- Take a Chance, 530
- Tic Tac Root, 414
- Tic-Tac Squares, 391
- Tic-Tac-Toe, 192
- Time to Shop, 477
- Totally Mental, 285
- War of Integers, 198
- "X" Marks the Spot, 252

Linear equation, 255

Line graphs, 94
- interpreting, 6, 94, 96, 120, 121, 205
- interval, 94
- making, 94
- making predictions from, 94
- misleading, 120
- scale, 94

Line of symmetry, 395

Line plot, 98
- cluster of data, 98
- interval, 98
- making, 98–101
- scale, 98

Lines
- constructing parallel, 367
- constructing perpendicular, 366
- parallel, 366–367
- perpendicular, 366–367

Line segments
- congruent, 371

Line symmetry, 395

Liter, 75

Logical Learning Style, *see Multiple Learning Styles*

Look for a pattern, 210–211

Lower extreme, 114

Lower quartile, 113–116

Make a list, 148–149

Make a Model, 496–497

Making the Connection
- Math Connections, 60, 187, 296, 368, 473, 507, 537
- Interdisciplinary Connections, 129, 265, 405, 525

Manipulatives, 2c, 2f, 42c, 42f, 86c, 86f, 130c, 130f, 182c, 182f, 224c, 224f, 266c, 266f, 314c, 314f, 358c, 358f, 406c, 406f, 448c, 448f, 488c, 488f, 526c, 526f

Mass,
- changing units of, 75–76
- gram, 75
- kilogram, 75
- milligram, 75

Math Journal, 11, 16, 29, 65, 106, 113, 118, 132, 137, 147, 195, 196, 201, 206, 227, 238, 253, 282, 288, 316, 329, 361, 367, 369, 375, 380, 381, 418, 427, 437, 459, 468, 481, 491, 502, 509, 546, 550

Mathematical Techniques
- estimation, 5, 50–53, 269, 336, 415–417, 420, 423–426, 450–453, 503
- mental math, 61, 63, 170, 229, 347
- number sense, 19, 153, 171, 175
- *See also* Problem Solving

Mathematical Tools
- paper/pencil, 6, 45, 51, 58, 92, 116, 140, 144, 159, 174, 199, 203, 213, 216, 230, 236, 244, 248, 270, 277, 290, 293, 303, 338, 347, 378, 384, 394, 420, 457, 479, 493, 500
- real objects, 167
  - algebra tiles, 133
  - base-ten blocks, 133
  - compass, 366, 374, 404, 432, 436, 437, 459, 460–463
  - counters, 11, 196, 201, 206, 207, 208, 226, 234, 238, 316, 328, 391, 436, 437, 513, 535
  - cubes, 490, 510, 513
  - dot paper, 24, 288, 363, 376, 391, 468, 508
  - equation mats, 226, 234, 238
  - grid paper, 28, 29, 64, 65, 158, 192, 253, 272, 333, 342, 380, 410, 415, 418, 423, 427, 429, 434, 436, 437, 450, 499, 502, 514
  - integer mat, 11, 196, 201, 206
  - number cubes, 531, 543
  - pattern blocks, 388
  - protractor, 360, 363, 369, 374, 376, 381, 404
  - ruler, 95, 106, 166, 297, 333, 404, 418, 436, 469, 504, 524
  - straightedge, 366, 374, 380, 432, 459
- technology. *See* Calculators, Computers, Technology Labs, Technology Mini-Labs, and Technology Tips
- *See also* Problem Solving

Math in the Media, 27, 324, 472, 495

Math Journal, 6, 18, 109, 116, 140, 170, 193, 216, 230, 236, 244, 277, 293, 318, 340, 372, 440, 457, 475, 479, 493, 512, 540, 548

Mean, 102–105
- arithmetic average, 102

Measurement
- capacity, 75, 290
- centimeters, 74
- cup, 290
- customary system, 289–291
- foot, 294, 335
- gallon, 290
- gram, 75
- inch, 293, 332
- indirect, 377
- kilogram, 75
- kilometers, 74
- length, 74
- liter, 75
- mass, 75
- meters, 74

INDEX

metric system, 74–76
mile, 292, 332
milligram, 75
milliliter, 75
millimeters, 74
ounce, 289
pint, 290
pound, 289
quart, 290
temperature, 103
ton, 289
weight, 289–291
yard, 294

Measures of central tendency
average, 102
mean, 102–105
median, 102–105
mode, 102–105
range, 88

Median, 102–105
box-and-whisker plot, 114–116
finding from line plot, 102

Meeting Individual Needs, 2f, 42f, 86f, 130f, 182f, 224f, 266f, 314f, 358f, 406f, 448f, 488f, 526f,

Mental math, 61, 63, 170
study hints, 229, 347

Meter, 74

Metric system,
capacity, 75
centimeter, 74
changing units, 74–75
gram, 75
kilogram, 75
kiloliter, 75
kilometer, 74
liter, 75
mass, 75
meter, 74
milligram, 75
milliliter, 75
millimeter, 74

Mid-Chapter Self Test, 15, 59, 105, 153, 205, 245, 287, 335, 379, 426, 467, 506, 545

Milligram, 75

Milliliter, 75

Millimeter, 74

MindJogger Videoquizzes, *see Technology*

Misleading statistics, 119–121

Mixed numbers,
adding, 276–279
as decimals, 71
dividing, 305–307
modeling, 277, 283
multiplying, 282–287
as percents, 343
subtracting, 276–279

Mode, 102–105
finding from line plot, 102

Modeling, 22

Modeling Mathematics, 2c, 2f, 42c, 42f, 86c, 86f, 130c, 130f, 182c, 182f, 224c, 224f, 266c, 266f, 314c, 314f, 347, 358c, 358f, 383, 406c, 406f, 448c, 448f, 461, 488c, 488f, 526c, 526f, *see Closing Activity*

Motivating the Lesson
Communication, 24, 30, 44, 66, 98, 108, 133, 138, 154, 191, 202, 215, 239, 249, 276, 305, 317, 342, 346, 370, 382, 419, 432, 456, 464, 478, 514, 534, 551
Hands-On Activity, 4, 12, 50, 56, 74, 77, 94, 115, 142, 165, 172, 197, 207, 212, 228, 254, 272, 289, 292, 325, 332, 410, 428, 438, 460, 474, 492, 510, 530, 542
Problem Solving, 8, 17, 21, 47, 61, 70, 88, 102, 150, 158, 161, 169, 184, 188, 234, 242, 268, 284, 297, 301, 321, 336, 339, 349, 377, 395, 415, 423, 450, 469, 498, 504, 538, 547

Motivating Students, 60, 187, 296, 368, 473, 507, 537

Multimedia, *see Technology*

Multiple Learning Styles
Auditory/Musical, 188, 242, 503, 548
Interpersonal, 12, 47, 88, 202, 234, 551
Intrapersonal, 61, 460
Kinesthetic, 77, 165, 229, 292, 321, 388, 419, 499, 542
Logical, 4, 56, 161, 272, 339, 363, 415, 534
Naturalist, 325, 395, 464
Verbal/Linguistic, 21, 108, 191
Visual/Spatial, 99, 284, 336, 428, 469, 514, 538

Multiples, 169
common, 169
least common, 169–171

Multiplication
equations, 234–237
estimating, 50–53, 269
of decimals, 56–59
of fractions, 282–287
of integers, 206–209
of mixed numbers, 282–287
in order of operations, 8
property of equality, 302
of whole numbers, 21–23

Multiplication property of equality, 302

Multiplicative inverse, 301
using to divide fractions, 305

Naturalist Learning Style, *see Multiple Learning Styles*

Negative integers, 184

Nets, 508–509

Nonagon, 370

Nonexamples, 25, 70–71, 78, 119–121, 139–140, 143, 185, 203, 256, 350, 363, 370–372, 378–379, 389–390, 394, 413, 415, 420–422, 435, 442, 542–544, 552–553, 558

Number line
graphing inequalities on, 246
integers on, 184–185
pi on, 47
showing probability on, 166
using to add integers, 197
using to compare decimals, 44, 45
using to draw a box-and-whisker plot, 114
using to order integers, 188

Numbers
composite, 138
prime, 138
rational, 266–307

Obtuse angles, 362

Octagon, 370

Opposite, 184

Ordered pair, 191–192

Ordering
decimals, 44–46
fractions, 172–175
integers, 88–190

Order of operations, 8–10, 18
grouping symbols in, 8
powers in, 18

Organizing the Chapter, 2b, 42b, 86b, 130b, 182b, 224b, 266b, 314b, 358b, 406b, 448b, 488b, 526b

INDEX

Origin, 191

Ounce, 289

Outcomes, 531, 538
equally-likely, 543
possible, 534

Outer measure, 423

Outlier, 115–116

Pacing Chart, 2c, 2d, 42c, 42d, 86c, 86d, 130c, 130d, 182c, 182d, 224c, 224d, 266c, 266d, 314c, 314d, 358c, 358d, 406c, 406d, 448c, 448d, 488c, 488d, 526c, 526d

Parallel lines, 367
constructing 367

Parallelograms, 28–29, 31–33, 383
area of, 28–29, 31, 427
base, 28, 29, 31
diagonal of, 427
height, 28, 31
using to find area of circle, 432
using to find area of triangle, 427

Parents. *See* Family Activities

Patterns, 8–11, 15, 39, 62

Pentagon, 370

Percentage, 349

Percent proportion, 349

Percents, 158–160
base, 349, 456
of change, 468–472
and circle graphs, 459–463
as decimals, 339–340
decimals as, 339
of decrease, 470
discount, 474–477
equation, 456–458
estimating with, 337, 450–453
expressed as fractions, 161
expressed as ratios, 161
as fractions, 161, 336–337
greater than 100%, 342–345
of increase, 469
less than 1%, 342–345
mixed numbers as, 343
modeling, 158–162, 342, 346, 450, 451
of a number, 346–348
proportion, 349–351, 456, 469
rate, 349, 456
as ratios, 161
sales tax, 474–477
symbol, 158
tips, 161, 348
using proportions with, 336, 346

Perfect square, 411

Performance Assessment, 39, 83, 125, 179, 221, 261, 311, 355, 401, 445, 485, 521, 557

Perimeter, 292–295
of a rectangle, 292

Permutations, 546–549
related to combinations, 551

Perpendicular lines, 366
constructing, 366

Perspective
one-point, 493
vanishing point, 493
view, 492

Pi, 47, 297
approximations for, 297
on number line, 47

Pint, 290

Place value
chart, 44
in measurement, 74
position, 44, 47, 50
position in decimals, 44
using to compare decimals, 44

Planning the Chapter, 2c, 2d, 42c, 42d, 86c, 86d, 130c, 130d, 182c, 182d, 224c, 224d, 266c, 266d, 314c, 314d, 358c, 358d, 406c, 406d, 448c, 448d, 488c, 488d, 526c, 526d

Points
on a coordinate plane, 191
graphing on a coordinate plane, 192, 195
transformations of, 215–217
vanishing, 493

Polygons, 370
angles of, 369
bilateral symmetry, 395
congruent, 371
decagon, 370
dilations, 380
dodecagon, 373
endpoint, 362
Escher, 392, 396
estimating area of irregular figures, 423–426
heptagon, 370
hexagon, 370
hypotenuse, 419
inscribed, 374–375
irregular figures, 423
leg, 419
nonagon, 370
octagon, 370
parallelograms, 383, 427, 432
pentagon, 370
Pythagorean Theorem, 418–422
quadrilateral, 370
rectangle, 383
reflection, 395–397
regular, 371
rhombus, 383
right triangle, 382
scalene triangle, 382
sides, 370
similar, 376
square, 383
symmetry, 395
tessellations with, 388–389
transformations, 380
translations, 392–394
trapezoids, 383, 429–430
triangles, 370, 427–428
vertex of, 370

Population, 5
density, 322

Portfolio, 2, 39, 42, 83, 86, 125, 130, 179, 182, 221, 224, 261, 266, 311, 314, 355, 358, 401, 406, 445, 448, 485, 488, 521, 526, 557

Portfolio, 39, 83, 125, 129, 179, 221, 261, 311, 355, 401, 405, 445, 485, 521, 525, 557

Positive integers, 184

Pound, 289

Powers, 17–20
base, 17
cubed, 17
exponents, 17
squared, 17
of ten, 61–63

Powers of ten, 61–63
in scientific notation, 77–79

Predictions
making from bar graphs, 94–95
making from line graphs, 94

Previewing the Chapter, 2a, 42a, 86a, 130a, 182a, 224a, 266a, 314a, 358a, 406a, 448a, 488a, 526a

Prime factorization, 138–141, 150

Prime numbers, 138

Principal
in simple interest, 478

Prism
rectangular, 493, 498
triangular, 493, 501

Probability, 165–168, 436
and area, 436–441
compound events, 542
counting principle, 538–539
of dependent events, 542–545
equally-likely outcomes, 542
event, 165

experimental, 436, 530–533, 542
expressed as a fraction, 165–166
expressed as a percent, 165–166
fair game, 535
of independent events, 542–545
outcomes, 165, 531
random, 165
as a ratio, 438
sample space, 531
using a list, 531, 546, 550
using a tree diagram, 534–535
simple events, 165–168
theoretical, 530–533
tree diagrams, 534–536, 538–539

Problem Solving, *see Motivating the Lesson*

Problem solving
four-step plan, 4–7, 102, 170, 199, 215, 230, 269, 277, 322, 326, 389, 419–420, 433, 457, 539, 552
labs, 34–35, 54–55, 92–93, 148–149, 210–211, 232–233, 280–281, 330–331, 386–387, 408–409, 454–455, 496–497, 528–529
mathematical techniques, 34–35, 54–55, 92–93, 148–149, 210–211, 232–233, 280–281, 330–331, 386–387, 408–409, 454–455, 496–497, 528–529
mathematical tools, 34–35, 54–55, 92–93, 148–149, 210–211, 232–233, 280–281, 330–331, 386–387, 408–409, 454–455, 496–497, 528–529

Problem-Solving Strategies
Act it Out, 528–529
Choose the Method of Computation, 34–35
Draw a Diagram, 330–331
Eliminate Possibilities, 280–281
Guess and Check, 408–409
Look for a Pattern, 210–211
Make a List, 148–149
Make a Model, 496–497
Reasonable Answers, 54–55
Solve a Simpler Problem, 454–455
Use a Graph, 92–93
Use Logical Reasoning, 386–387
Work Backward, 232–233

Problem Solving Study Hints, 32, 326, 396, 552

Projects. *See* Chapter Projects and Interdisciplinary Investigations

Properties
associative, 301
calculations, 303
commutative, 301
distributive, 302
of equality
addition, 228
division, 234
multiplication, 302
subtraction, 229
evaluate expressions, 302–304
identity, 301
of proportions, 325

Property of proportions, 325

Proportional Reasoning
area, 332–335
conversions, 332–335
examples, 332–335, 376–377
geometry, 376–377
measurement, 332–335
number, 317–324
percent, 346–351
perimeter, 376–377
predictions, 325–328
probability, 438
proportion, 325–328
ratio, 154–157, 316–320
recipes, 327
sequences, 143
student-teacher ratio, 323
surface area, 508–517
volume, 498–506

Proportions, 314–351
cross products, 325–326
on spreadsheets, 329
scale drawings, 332–335
solving, 325–328

Protractor, 360

Pyramids, 492, 493
drawing, 492
volume of, 502

Pythagorean Theorem, 418–422
model for, 418

Quadrant, 191–192

Quadrilateral, 370
parallelogram, 383
rectangle, 383
rhombus, 383
square, 383
trapezoid, 383

Quart, 290

Quartile, 112–113

Radical sign, 411

Radius, 297

Random
outcome, 165
sample, 464

Range, 88

Rate, 321–324, 349
population density, 322
in simple interest, 478
unit, 321

Rational numbers, 266–307

Ratios, 154–157, 316–320
as decimals, 317
equivalent, 318
expressed as fractions, 154
expressed as percents, 158–160
as fractions, 317
geometry, 376–379
measurement, 332–335
models, 316
percents expressed as, 161
probability, 438
simplifying, 317–318

Rays, 362
endpoint, 362

Reading Mathematics, 5, 18, 48, 71, 88, 103, 115, 170, 188, 215, 239, 243, 289, 302, 318, 336, 371, 392, 439, 465, 478, 492, 496, 547, 551

Reading Math Study Hints, 12, 13, 31, 154, 165, 184, 215, 243, 298, 317, 325, 350, 362, 363, 370, 376, 383, 393, 411, 456, 498, 499, 531

Reasonable answers, 54–55

Reciprocal, 301
using to divide fractions, 305

Rectangle, 28–30, 32–33, 338
area of, 28–30
length, 30
perimeter of, 292
width, 30

Rectangular prism, 493, 498
surface area of, 510–513
volume of, 498–501

Reflection, 215–217, 395–397
Escher, 396
line of symmetry, 395
mirror image, 395

Regular polygon, 371

Repeating decimal, 70–73

Reteaching the Lesson
Activity, 6, 9, 14, 19, 22, 26, 32, 34, 45, 48, 52, 54, 58, 62, 68, 71, 75, 78, 89, 92, 96, 100, 104, 109, 115, 120, 135, 140, 144, 148, 151, 156, 159, 162,

166, 170, 174, 185, 189, 192, 199, 203, 208, 210, 213, 216, 230, 232, 236, 240, 244, 247, 251, 256, 270, 274, 277, 280, 286, 290, 293, 299, 303, 306, 318, 322, 327, 330, 334, 337, 340, 344, 347, 350, 364, 371, 378, 384, 386, 390, 393, 396, 408, 411, 416, 420, 425, 429, 434, 439, 452, 454, 457, 462, 466, 471, 475, 479, 493, 496, 500, 505, 511, 516, 528, 532, 535, 540, 544, 548, 552
Error Analysis, 6, 14, 32, 45, 52, 58, 62, 71, 78, 96, 100, 109, 115, 140, 144, 151, 156, 170, 189, 199, 208, 230, 236, 256, 274, 293, 299, 306, 318, 322, 327, 334, 344, 364, 378, 384, 390, 420, 429, 434, 457, 462, 471, 475, 479, 505, 511, 516, 532, 540, 552

Rhombus, 383

Right angle, 362

Right triangle, 382
3-4-5, 418
hypotenuse, 419
legs, 419
Pythagorean Theorem, 418–422

Rounding
decimals, 47–49
fractions, 269

S

Sales tax, 474–477

Sample, 5, 464
random, 464
space, 531–536

Sample space, 531

Scale drawings, 332–335
making, 333
scales, 332
using proportions, 332–333

Scalene triangle, 382

Scales, 332
for bar graph, 94
on blueprints, 333
for frequency table, 88
for line graph, 94
for line plot, 98
on maps, 332
on protractor, 360

Scatter plot, 92

School to Career, 2e, 42e, 86e,130e, 182e, 224e, 266e, 314e, 358e, 406e, 448e, 488e, 526e

School to Career
Aerospace, 60
Biochemistry, 507
Design, 537
Fashion, 368
Finance, 296
Media, 473
Meteorology, 187

Science and Math Lab Manual, 42e, 86e, 130e, 182e, 224e, 314e, 358e, 448e, 526e

Scientific calculator *See* calculator

Scientific notation, 77–79

Sequences, 142–145
arithmetic, 142
exploring, 146–147
Fibonacci, 148
geometric, 143
terms of, 142

Sides
of polygons, 370

Sierpinski's triangle, 25, 288

Sieve of Eratosthenes, 153

Similar, 376
polygons, 376–379
symbol for, 376

Similar figures
corresponding parts, 376
indirect measurement, 377
using proportions, 377

Simple interest, 478–480
formula, 478
principal, 478
rate, 478
time, 478
using a spreadsheet to find, 481

Simplest form, 154

Simplifying
fractions, 154–157
ratios, 154–157

Solar system, 43

Solids, 493
Platonic, 496

Solution
of an equation, 21

Solve a simpler problem. 454–455

Solving equations, 21–23
using a calculator, 235
using mental math, 21–22
using models, 226–227, 234–235, 238–239
using symbols, 228–229, 235, 239

Solving proportions, 325

Spatial Reasoning, 490–497

Speaking, *see Closing Activity*

Spreadsheets, *see Technology*

Spreadsheets, 3, 43, 87, 128, 131, 137, 183, 225, 264, 315, 404, 461, 481, 524, 622–623

Square root, 411
estimating, 415–417
modeling, 415
using calculators to find, 416

Squared, 17

Squares, 383, 410–413
perfect, 411
root, 411

Standardized Test Practice, 40–41, 84–85, 126–127, 180–181, 222–223, 262–263, 312–313, 356–357, 402–403, 446–447, 486–487, 522–523, 558–559

Statistics,
average, 102, 106
bar graph, 94–95
box-and-whisker plot, 114–116
cluster, 98–99
frequency table, 88–89
interquartile range, 112–116
interval, 88–89
line graph, 94–95
line plot, 98–99
making predictions, 94–95, 464–467
mean, 102–103, 106
median, 102–103, 106
misleading, 119–121
mode, 102–103, 106
outlier, 115–116
population, 5, 464
quartile, 112–116
range, 88–89
sample, 5, 464
scale, 88–89
scatter plot, 92, 95
stem-and-leaf plot, 108–109
back-to-back, 109
See also Applications, Connections, and Integration Index on pages xxii–1

Stem, 108

Stem-and-leaf plot, 108–111
back-to-back, 109
intervals, 108–109
key, 108
leaves, 108
making, 108–111
stems, 108

Straight angle, 362

Study Guide and Assessment, 36–39, 80–83, 122–125, 176–179, 218–221, 258, 261, 308–311, 352–355, 398–401, 442–445, 482–485, 518–521, 554–557

Study Hints
Estimation, 5, 289, 336, 377, 420, 503
Mental Math, 229, 347
Problem Solving, 32, 326, 396, 552
Reading Math, 12, 13, 31, 154, 165, 184, 215, 243, 298, 317, 325, 350, 362, 363, 370, 376, 383, 393, 411, 456, 498, 499, 531
Technology, 8, 18, 102, 114, 115, 170, 184, 273, 276, 298, 346, 411, 438, 461, 547

Subtraction
equations, 226–231
estimating, 50–53, 269
of decimals, 48
of fractions, 269, 272–275
of integers, 201–205
of mixed numbers, 276–279
in order of operations, 8
property of equality, 229
of whole numbers, 21–23

Subtraction property of equality, 229

Supplementary angles, 363–364

Surface area, 508–509
of cylinders, 514–517
and nets, 508–509
of rectangular prisms, 510–513

Symmetry
bilateral, 395
line, 395
line of, 395

Tables, 3, 6, 8, 13, 43, 45, 51, 67, 69, 87–90, 92, 94–96, 98–101, 108, 110–115, 117, 119, 135, 147, 157, 183, 188, 189, 210, 214, 215, 216, 225, 251, 253–257, 267, 271, 279, 319, 320, 322, 324, 329, 334, 337, 387, 388, 404, 408, 458, 460–462, 464–466, 470, 476, 481, 501, 509, 528, 533, 545
frequency, 88–91, 118, 532, 542

Tally, 88

Techniques. *See* Mathematical Techniques

Technology
Calculators and Spreadsheets, 2f, 16, 42f, 44, 78, 86f, 130f, 137, 173, 182f, 195, 224f, 266f, 269, 314f, 339, 358f, 406f, 448f, 457, 481, 488f, 526f
CD-ROM Program, 2, 38, 42, 82, 86, 124, 130, 178, 182, 220, 224, 260, 266, 310, 314, 354, 358, 400, 406, 444, 448, 484, 488, 520, 526, 556
MindJogger Videoquizzes, 36, 80, 122, 176, 218, 258, 308, 352, 398, 442, 482, 518, 554
Test and Review Software, 38, 82, 124, 178, 220, 260, 310, 354, 400, 444, 484, 520, 556

Technology Labs
Divisibility, 137
Evaluating Expression, 16
Graphing Points, 195
Simple Interest, 481

Technology Mini-Labs, 66

Technology tips, 3, 43, 87, 128, 131, 183, 225, 267, 315, 359, 404, 449, 489, 524, 527

Technology Study Hints, 8, 18, 102, 114, 115, 170, 184, 273, 276, 298, 346, 411, 438, 461, 547

Temperatures, 103

Terminating decimal, 70

Terms
of expressions, 239
of sequence, 142

Tessellations, 388–394

Test and Review Software, *see Technology*

Test Practice, 7, 10, 15, 20, 23, 27, 33, 35, 46, 49, 53, 55, 59, 63, 69, 73, 76, 79, 91, 93, 97, 101, 105, 111, 117, 121, 136, 141, 145, 149, 153, 157, 160, 164, 168, 171, 175, 186, 190, 194, 200, 205, 209, 211, 214, 217, 231, 233, 237, 241, 245, 248, 252, 257, 271, 275, 279, 281, 287, 291, 295, 300, 304, 307, 320, 324, 328, 331, 335, 338, 341, 345, 348, 351, 365, 373, 379, 385, 387, 391, 394, 397, 409, 413, 417, 422, 426, 431, 435, 441, 453, 455, 458, 463, 467, 472, 477, 480, 495, 497, 501, 506, 513, 517, 529, 533, 536, 541, 545, 549, 553

Test-Taking Tips, 41, 85, 127, 181, 223, 263, 313, 357, 403, 447, 487, 523, 559

Theoretical probability, 530–533

Thinking Algebraically, 62, 75, 99, 155, 203, 229, 255, 285, 293, 322, 349, 420, 475, 504, 539

Thinking Labs
Act it Out, 528–529
Choose the Method of Computation, 34–35
Draw a Diagram, 330–331
Eliminate Possibilities, 280–281
Guess and Check, 408–409
Look for a Pattern, 210–211
Make a List, 148–149
Make a Model, 496–497
Reasonable Answers, 54–55
Solve a Simpler Problem, 454–455
Use a Graph, 92–93
Use Logical Reasoning, 386–387
Work Backward, 232–233

Three-dimensional figures
building, 490–491
cone, 493
cylinder, 493, 503–506
drawing, 492–495
edges, 498
faces, 498
modeling, 496–497
nets, 508–509
one-point perspective, 493
perspective view of, 492
Platonic solids, 496
pyramids, 493, 502
rectangular prisms, 493, 498–501, 510–513
solids, 493
surface area of, 508–517
triangular prisms, 493
vanishing point, 493
vertex, 498
volume of, 498–506

Time
in simple interest, 478

Tips, 161, 348

Ton, 289

Tools. *See* Mathematical Tools

Transformations, 215
dilations, 380
graphing, 215–217
reflection, 215–217
translation, 215–217

Translation, 215–217, 392
Escher, 392
slide, 392
tessellations, 392–394

Transversal, 361

Trapezoid, 383, 429
area of, 429–430
formula for area of, 429

INDEX

Tree diagram, 534–536, 538–539, 546
possible outcomes, 534

Triangle, 370, 428
acute, 382
area of, 427–428
equilateral, 382
formula for area of, 428
investigating, 381
isosceles, 382
obtuse, 382
right, 382
scalene, 382
similar, 376–379
symbol, 383

Triangular numbers, 141

Triangular prism, 493, 501

Truncate, 70

Two-dimensional figures
congruent, 371
decagon, 370
hexagon, 370
octagon, 370
parallelogram, 28–29, 31–33, 427, 432
pentagon, 370
polygons, 369–373
quadrilateral, 370, 381–385
rectangle, 28–30, 32–33, 383
regular polygon, 371
similar, 376–379
square, 27, 383
triangle, 25, 370, 381–385, 427–428

Unit rate, 321

Upper extreme, 114

Upper quartile, 113–116

Use a graph, 92–93

Use logical reasoning, 386–387
deductive reasoning, 386–387
inductive reasoning, 386–387

Vanishing point, 493

Variable, 11–15
defining, 243
in equations, 21–23, 243
in expressions, 12

Verbal/Linguistic Learning Style, *see Mulitple Learning Styles*

Vertex
of angles, 362
of polygons, 370

Vertical angles, 361, 373

Visual/Spatial Learning Style, *see Multiple Learning Styles*

Volume, 498
of cylinders, 503–506
of pyramids, 502
of rectangular prisms, 498–501
of triangular prisms, 501

Weight, 289–291
changing units of, 289–291
ounce, 289
pound, 289
ton, 289

Whole numbers
adding, 21–23
dividing, 21–23
factors of, 132
multiplying, 21–23
in order of operations, 8–10
subtracting, 21–23

Width
of rectangles, 30

Work backward, 232–233

Working on the Chapter Project
Advance to Go and Collect $200, 533, 545, 557
America's Scream Machines, 236, 252, 257, 261
Don't Turn that Dial!, 458, 463, 467, 485
Fun Ways to be Fit, 3, 10, 23, 39
Geometric Art, 391, 394, 397, 401
How Big is Our Solar System?, 46, 59, 76, 83
It's a Small World, 426, 431, 441, 445
Latitude vs. Temperature, 190, 194, 205, 221
Lights! Camera! Action!, 91, 105, 121, 125
Turn Over a New Leaf, 501, 513, 521
Ups and Downs, 271, 287, 307, 311
Waste Not, Want Not, 320, 345, 355
What Color was that Car?, 157, 164, 168, 179

Write a problem, 23, 104, 209, 211, 233, 257, 281, 291, 327, 351, 379, 409, 455, 472, 480, 497, 505, 512, 517, 535, 540, 544, 548

Writing, *see Closing Activity*

***x*-axis,** 191–192

***x*-coordinate,** 191

***y*-axis,** 191–192

***y* coordinate,** 191

Zero pair, 197, 227

Zero, 169
as additive inverse, 197

Answer Appendix

CHAPTER 1
Problem Solving, Algebra, and Geometry

Pages 8–10, Lesson 1-2

37. Sample answer: For 150 pounds, sleep for 8 hours, in-line skate for 2 hours, and swim for 1 hour; $8 \times 90 + 2 \times 600 + 1 \times 497 = 2{,}417$.

38. Sample answer: Enter 2 [+] 4 [×] 5 [=]. If the calculator displays 22, it follows the order of operations. If it displays 30, it does not.

CHAPTER 2
Applying Decimals

Pages 45–46, Lesson 2-1

2. $0.2 > 0.18$

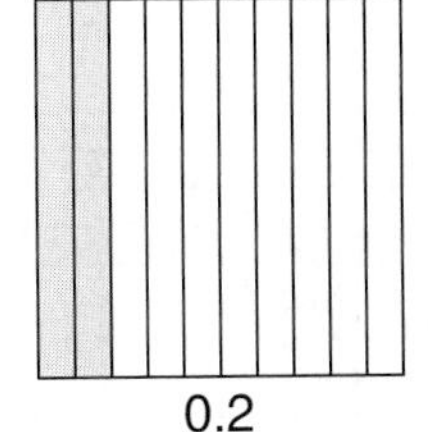
0.2

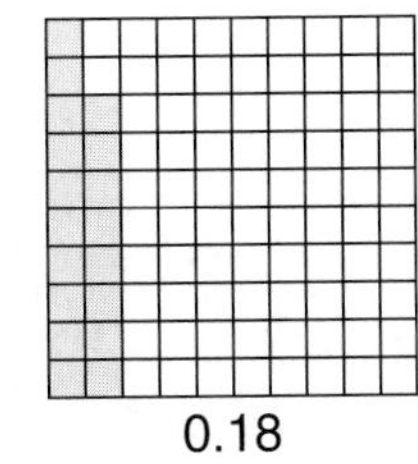
0.18

27c.

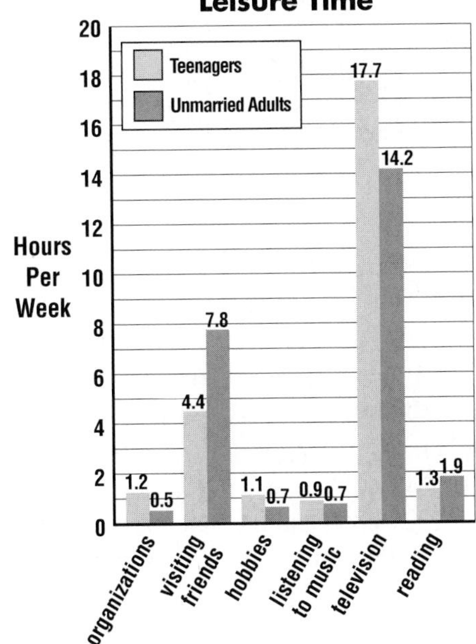

28a.

Planet	Diameter
Jupiter	11.19
Saturn	9.46
Uranus	4.01
Neptune	3.88
Earth	1.00
Venus	0.95
Mars	0.53
Mercury	0.38
Pluto	0.18

28b.

Planet	Distance
Pluto	39.529
Neptune	30.061
Uranus	19.191
Saturn	9.529
Jupiter	5.203
Mars	1.524
Earth	1.000
Venus	0.723
Mercury	0.387

Page 56, Lesson 2-4, Mini-Lab

1a.

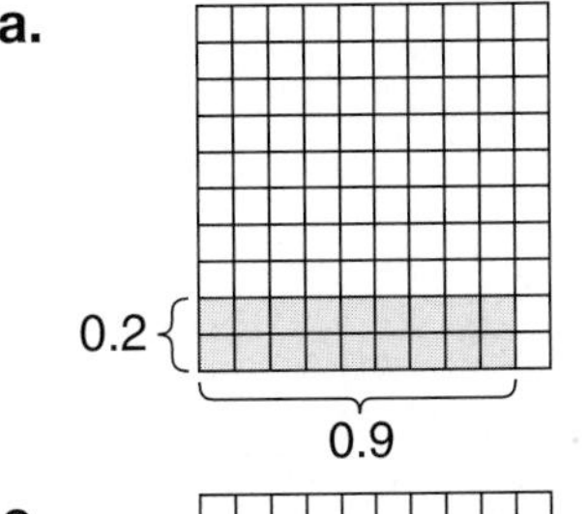

1b.

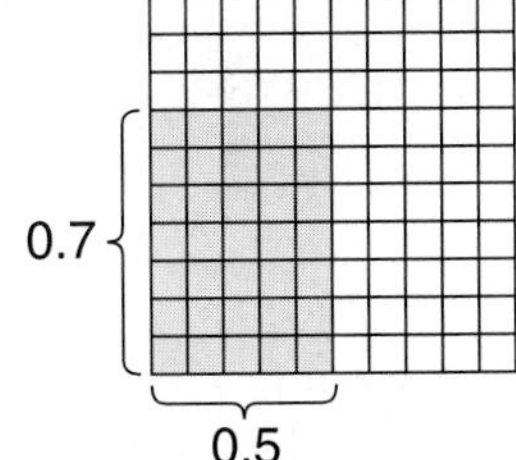

1c.

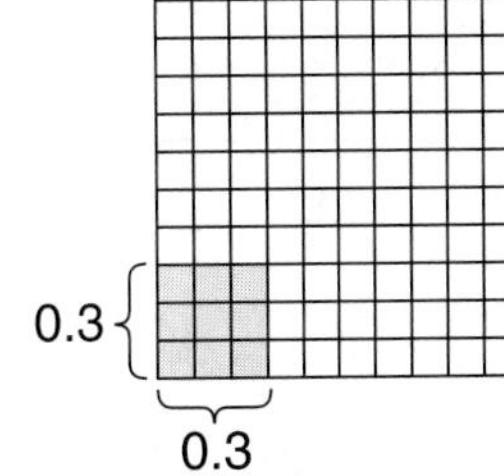

1d.

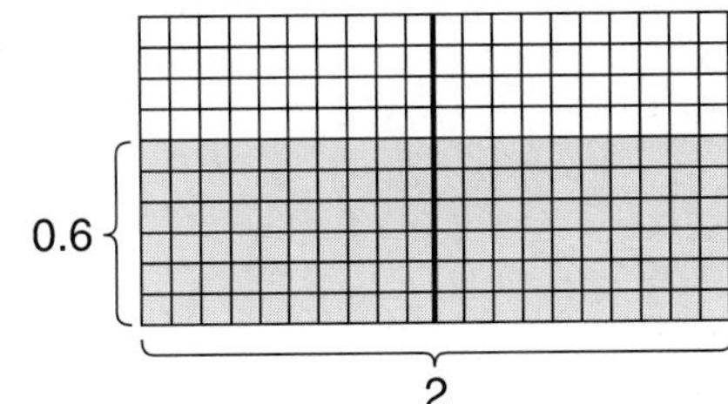

ANSWER APPENDIX

Pages 58–59, Lesson 2-4

3. 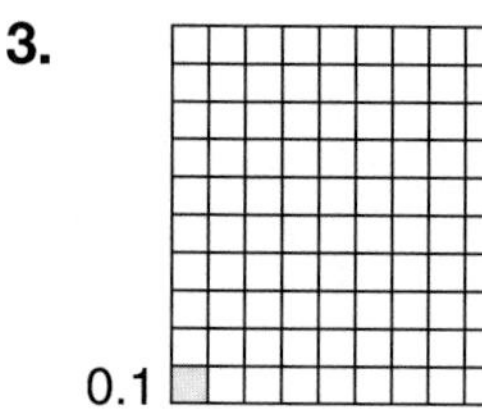

Pages 62–63, Lesson 2-5

1. Move the decimal point 2 places to the right; $x = 237.8$
2. Move the decimal point in the cost of one item one place to the right.

Pages 64–65, Lesson 2-6A

4. 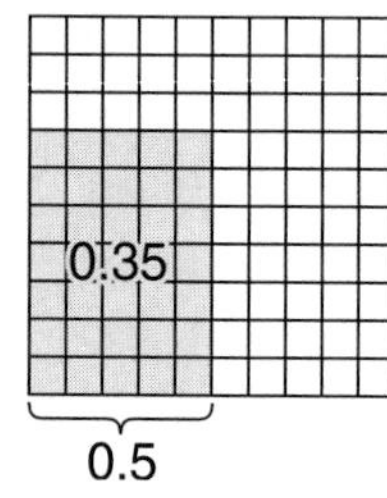

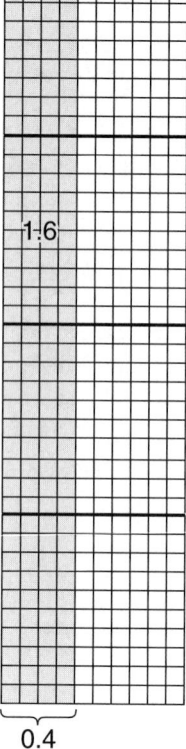

5. 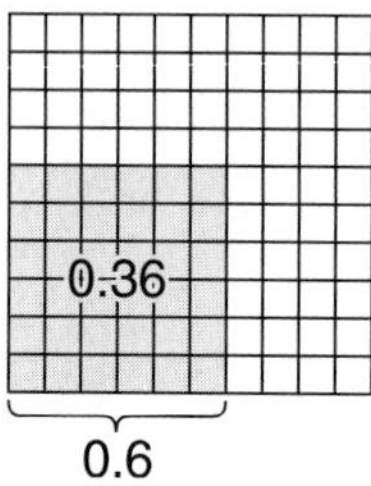

6. 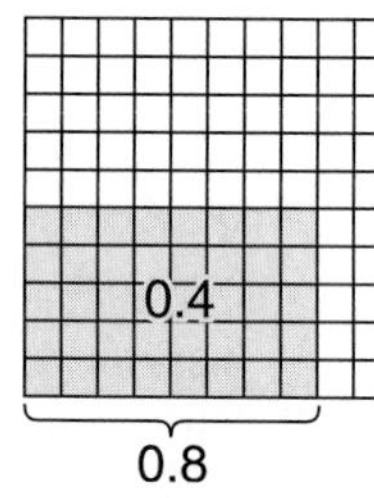

7. 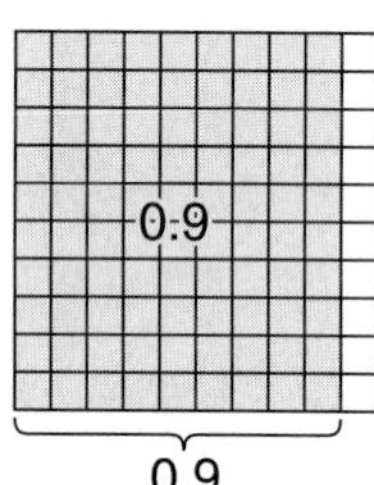

8. 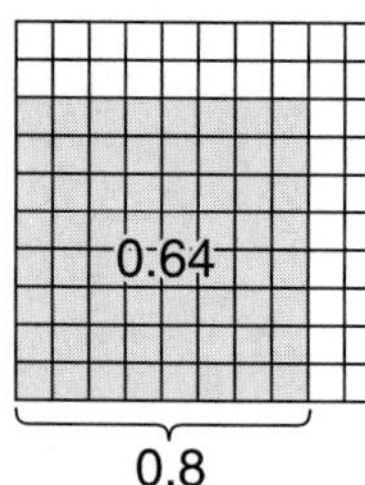

9. 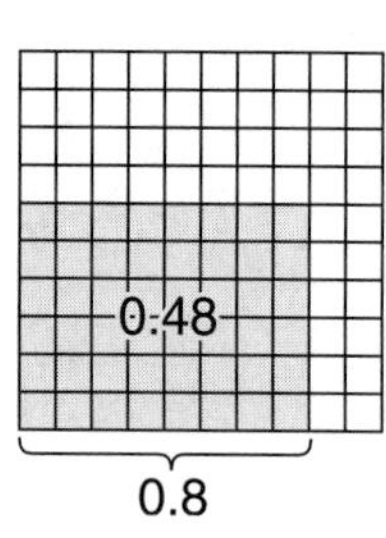

12. 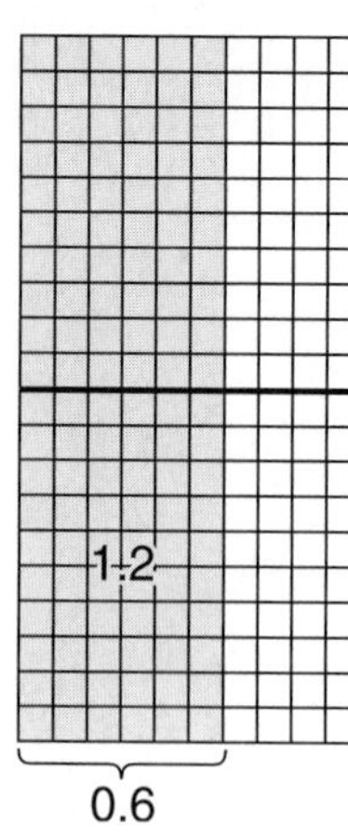

13. 

14. 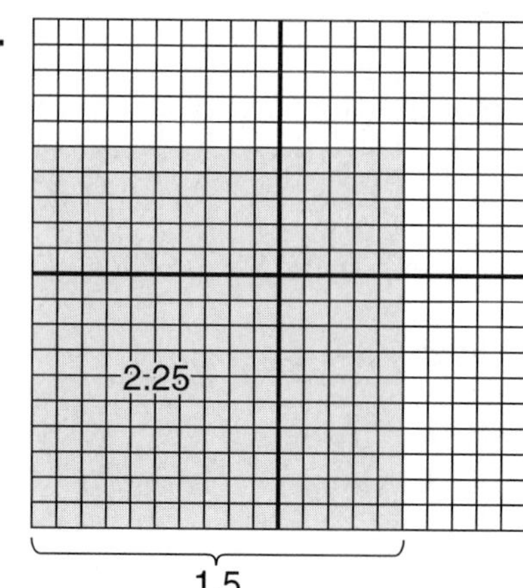

Page 76, Lesson 2-8

27a. Mercury – 0.38 cm; Venus – 0.95 cm; Mars – 0.53 cm; Jupiter – 11.19 cm; Saturn – 9.46 cm; Uranus – 4.01 cm; Neptune 3.88 cm; Pluto – 0.18 cm

27b. Mercury – 0.387 cm; Venus – 0.723 cm; Mars – 1.524 cm; Jupiter – 5.203 cm; Saturn – 9.529 cm; Uranus – 19.191 cm; Neptune – 30.061 cm; Pluto – 39.529 cm

Page 83, Performance Task

- Find the unit price for each type of package. The unit price of 2-L bottle is \$0.65 and the unit price of the six packs is \$1.17. The 2-L bottle is more economical.
- You can buy 30 2-L bottles, or 60 liters of soda, for \$39.

CHAPTER 3
Statistics: Analyzing Data

Pages 89–91, Lesson 3-1

1. Range: find the difference between the greatest number and the least number.

   Scale: include all numbers of the data set, plus numbers that are higher or lower than the set, to get an appropriate scale.

   Interval: choose the number of categories that you want and divide the scale by that number.

2. Sample answer: The greatest number of cameras costs from $7 to $10.

Cost ($)	Tally	Frequency
3–6	III	3
7–10	卌卌II	12
11–14	II	2
15–18	IIII	4

5.

Interval	Tally	Frequency
0–4	III	3
5–9	III	3
10–14	I	1
15–19	II	2

6.

Value	Tally	Frequency
2.0–3.9	II	2
4.0–5.9	IIII	4
6.0–7.9	I	1

Pages 96–97, Lesson 3-2

7a. **Computers in School**

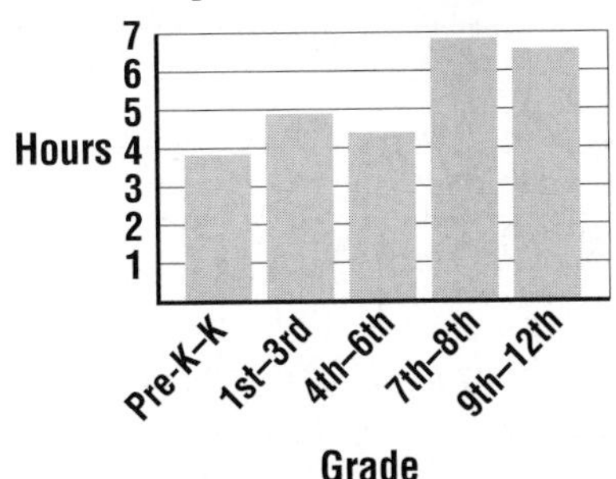

10a. See students' work.

High School Graduates

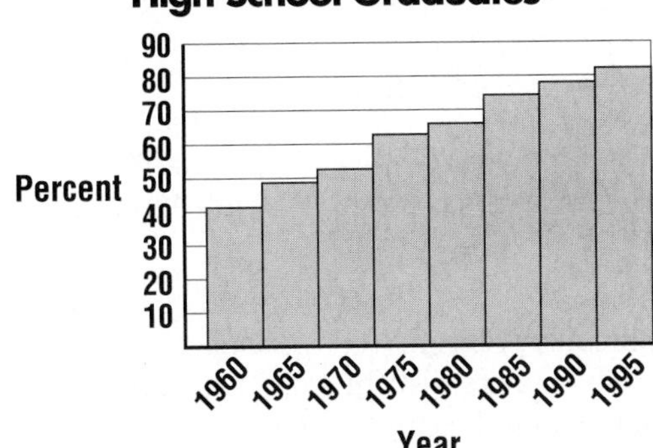

Pages 100–101, Lesson 3-3

6.

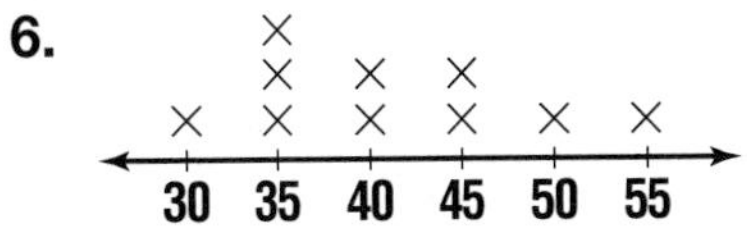

7. 300 400 500 600 700 800

8. 4 8 12 16 20 24 28 32 36

9. 1988 1990 1992 1994 1996 1998 2000

10. 3.0 3.2 3.4 3.6 3.8 4.0

11. 100 102 104 106 108 110 112

12. cluster: 88 to 91

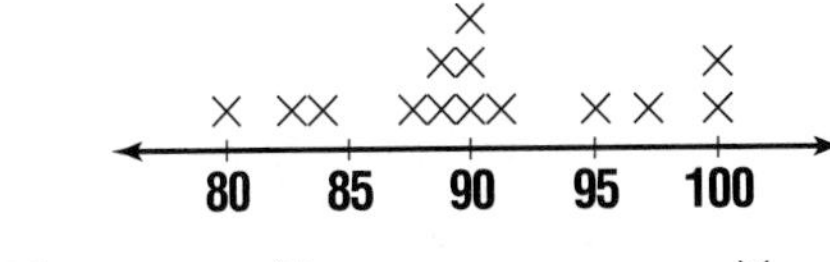

13. $2.40 $2.70 $3.00 $3.30

14b. 0 1,000 2,000 3,000 6,000

Pages 104–105, Lesson 3-4

17. Sample answer: Mean; this represents the average size of all families. See students' work.

21.

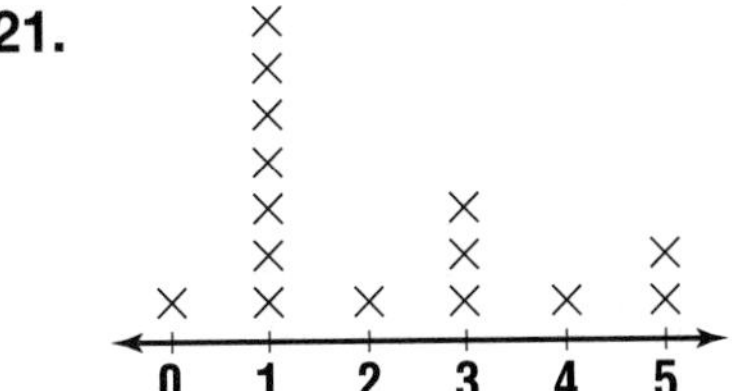

Page 105, Mid-Chapter Self Test

4.

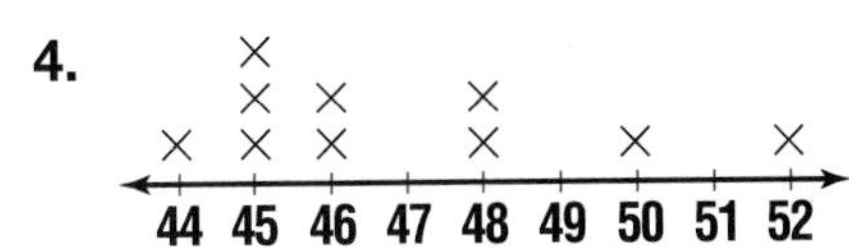

ANSWER APPENDIX

Pages 108–111, Lesson 3-5

5. stems: 1, 2, 3

Stem	Leaf
1	3 3 5
2	4 8
3	0 1 2 2 5 6 8 8 8

1|3 = 13

6. stems: 5, 6, 7, 8, 9

Stem	Leaf
5	5 6
6	0 0 2 3 6 7 9
7	0
8	0 0
9	0 1 3 3 5 6

5|6 = 56

8. stems: 1, 2, 3, 4

Stem	Leaf
1	6 9
2	1 3 5 5 9
3	1 3 4 5 9
4	1 7 9

1|6 = 16

9. stems: 0, 1, 2, 3

Stem	Leaf
0	1 2 7 8 9
1	1 2 4 8 8 9
2	1 2
3	1

0|7 = 7

10. stems: 40, 41, 42, 43, 44, 45, 46, 47, 48, 49

Stem	Leaf
40	3
41	1
42	
43	9
44	3 4
45	9
46	9
47	2
48	1
49	1 2 8

41|1 = 411

11. stems: 1, 2, 3, 4, 5, 6, 7, 8, 9

Stem	Leaf
1	5 8
2	6 7
3	6 7 9
4	4 9
5	6 8
6	1 8
7	5
8	
9	0

1|8 = 18

12.

Stem	Leaf
8	0 0 1 2 2 5 7 7 8
9	0 2 3 3 9 9
10	0

8|0 = 8.0

13a.

Top Ranked	Stem	Lower Ranked
8 7	1	3 5 7 8
9 9 8 5 5 5 0	2	0 2 2 6
0 0 0	3	0 0 1 8

8|1 = $18　　*1|3 = $13*

Sample answer: There are more lower ranked jeans available at lower prices. But there are several types of jeans of top quality available at lower prices.

13b.

Male	Stem	Female
7 5 3	1	7 8 8
9 5 5 2 2 0	2	0 5 6 8 9
0 0 0	3	0 0 1 8

5|1 = $15　　*1|7 = $17*

Sample answer: It appears that jeans for females are somewhat more expensive than jeans for males.

15a.

Stem	Leaf
0	N E N N E E E
1	E N N N N E E N
2	E N N
3	
4	
5	E

15b. You gain information about how the pasta consumption of European Union countries compares to pasta consumption of nonmember countries. You lose information about the exact amounts of pasta eaten.

15c. This plot is similar to a line plot written horizontally. However, a line plot shows exact data values; this plot shows intervals of 10.

Pages 116–117, Lesson 3-6

7.

9.

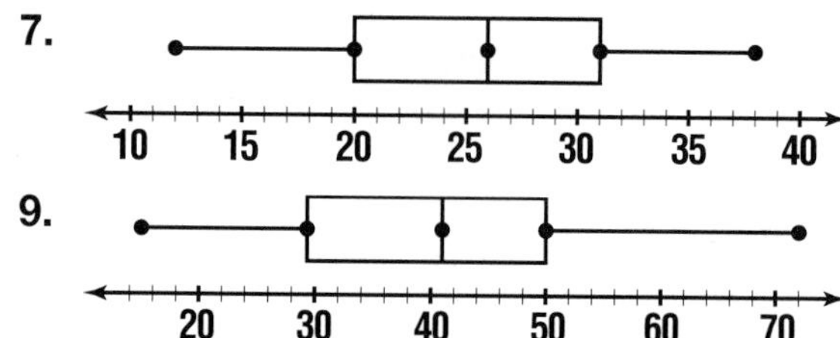

11.

Stem	Leaf
1	0 1 2 8
2	0 1 2
3	4 5 8
4	
5	6

1|8 = 18

Page 118, Lesson 3-6B

1. Sample answer: The mean best describes this set of data because the data are centered and evenly distributed.

2. Sample answer: A line plot would be the best graphical representation of the data. It would show how the data are distributed visually. Also, the median would be easy to find.

3a. Answers will vary depending on class's data. Prediction should reflect this data.

3b. Sample answer: The mean is very close to the prediction.

3c. Sample answer: The teacher grabbed more kernels than most of the students. Just data from her alone would not be sufficient data to predict for the rest of the adults.

Pages 120–121, Lesson 3-7

1. Sample answer: Outlier may distort the data; data may be inaccurate; data may be incomplete.

2. Graph B, since the decrease in viewers is more apparent.

6. Sample answer: Belinda could use the mode of the test scores, which is 96. However, this number could be misleading since all the other test scores were lower than 96.

9. Sample answer:

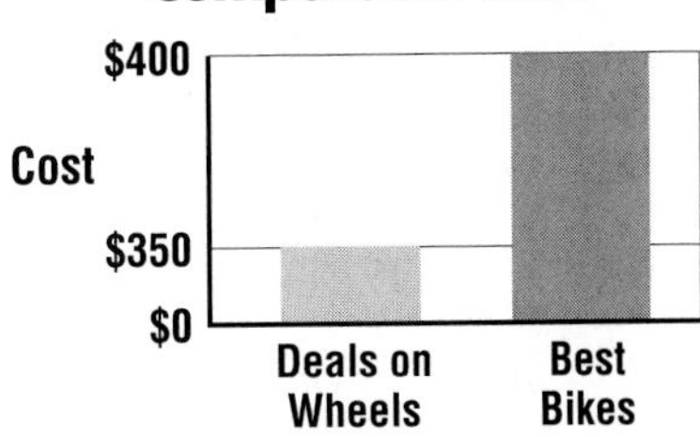

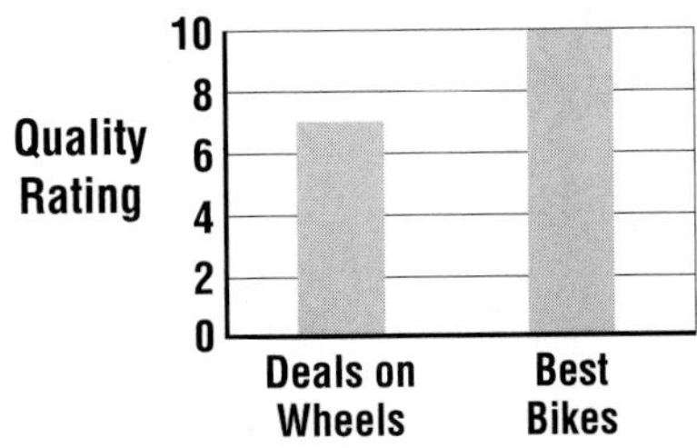

Pages 122–125, Chapter 3 Study Guide and Assessment

17. **18.** **19.** **20.**

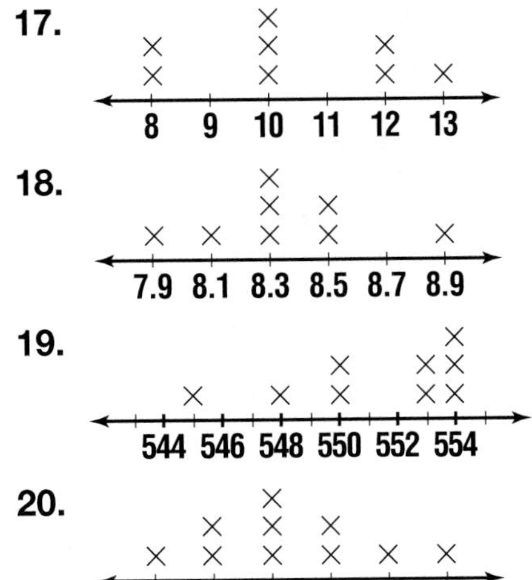

25. stems: 5, 6, 7, 8, 9

Stem	Leaf
5	3
6	0 1
7	5 7 8 8
8	3 5 7 7 9
9	0 1 2 9

5|3 = 53

26. stems: 2, 3, 4, 5

Stem	Leaf
2	1 3 6 9
3	1 2 7 8
4	6
5	4

2|1 = 21¢

27.

Seattle	Stem	Olympia
6	4	5 8
4 3 2	5	1 3 6
9 8 2 2 1 0	6	0 2 5 6 8
8 7 2 0	7	2 3 7 9
5 0	8	0 4

6|4 = 46°F *4|5 = 45°F*

28d.

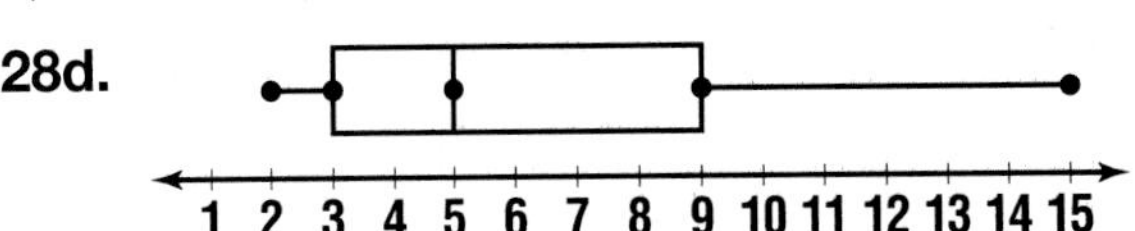

Page 125, Performance Task

Sample answers: make a frequency table, construct a line plot or a stem-and-leaf plot.

CHAPTER 4
Using Number Patterns, Fractions, and Percents

Pages 134–136, Lesson 4-1

2.

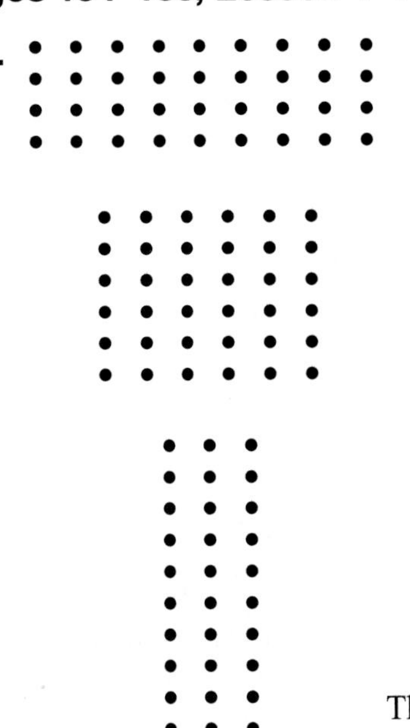

These arrays can be turned 90° to obtain 3 other possible arrays.

Pages 142–145, Lesson 4-3

1. 1, 3, 7, 13, 21, 31
+2 +4 +6 +8 +10

2. Sample answer: first number: 2; rule: 3 more than the previous number

Pages 155–157, Lesson 4-5

34a-b.

U.S. Car Production		
Company	**Number of Cars**	**Fraction**
A	100,000	$\frac{1}{60} = \frac{1}{60}$
B	600,000	$\frac{6}{60} = \frac{1}{10}$
C	1,400,000	$\frac{14}{60} = \frac{7}{30}$
D	2,500,000	$\frac{25}{60} = \frac{5}{12}$
E	600,000	$\frac{6}{60} = \frac{1}{10}$
F	200,000	$\frac{2}{60} = \frac{1}{30}$
G	300,000	$\frac{3}{60} = \frac{1}{20}$
H	100,000	$\frac{1}{60} = \frac{1}{60}$
I	500,000	$\frac{5}{60} = \frac{1}{12}$
Other	0	$\frac{0}{60} = 0$
Total	6,000,000	

Pages 161–164, Lesson 4-7

43.

U.S. Car Production			
Company	**Fraction**	**Decimal**	**Percent**
A	$\frac{1}{60}$	0.02	2
B	$\frac{1}{10}$	0.10	10
C	$\frac{7}{30}$	0.23	23
D	$\frac{5}{12}$	0.42	42
E	$\frac{1}{10}$	0.10	10
F	$\frac{1}{30}$	0.03	3
G	$\frac{1}{20}$	0.05	5
H	$\frac{1}{60}$	0.02	2
I	$\frac{1}{12}$	0.08	8
Other	0	0.00	0

Pages 167–168, Lesson 4-8

27. No; the chance of rolling a 5 $\left(\frac{4}{36}\right)$, 6 $\left(\frac{5}{36}\right)$, 7 $\left(\frac{6}{36}\right)$, or 8 $\left(\frac{5}{36}\right)$ gives Marvin $\frac{20}{36}$ chances of winning a point. The probability of Naomi winning is only $\frac{16}{36}$.

Pages 170–171, Lesson 4-9

1. A common multiple should have all the prime factors of each number; $2^3 \times 3^2 = 72$.

2. when the smaller number is a factor of the larger number

3. Sample answer: List several multiples of each number. To do the problem mentally, you could find the multiples of 9 and see which ones were multiples of both 3 and 5; 45.

Page 179, Performance Task

Number of Bagels	Cost ($)
1	0.45
2	0.85
3	1.25
4	1.65
5	2.05
6	2.45
7	2.85
8	3.25
9	3.65
10	4.05
11	4.45
12	4.85

CHAPTER 5
Algebra: Using Integers

Pages 189–190, Lesson 5-2

1. 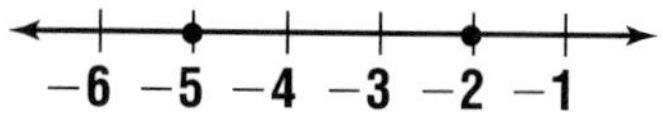

2. The number farthest to the right on a number line is the greater number.

25a.

City	Latitude (nearest degree)	Low Temp. (°F)
Honolulu, HI	21	56
San Diego, CA	33	43
Atlanta, GA	34	13
Nashville, TN	36	9
Denver, CO	40	−7
New York, NY	41	6
Minneapolis, MN	45	−11
Bismarck, ND	47	−28
Seattle, WA	48	22
Fairbanks, AK	65	−48

Pages 193–194, Lesson 5-3

20-28.

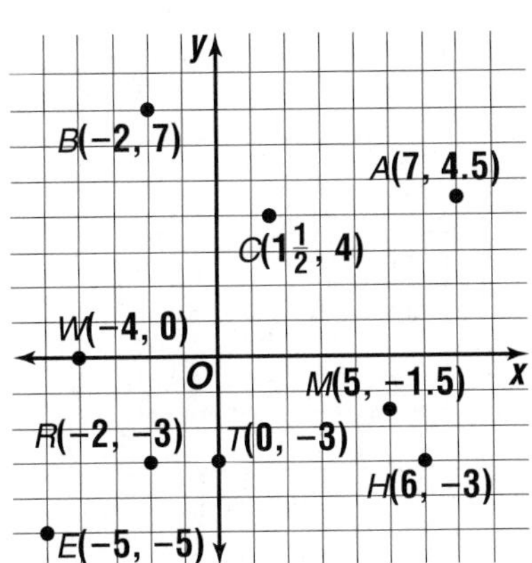

Page 195, Lesson 5-3B

1.

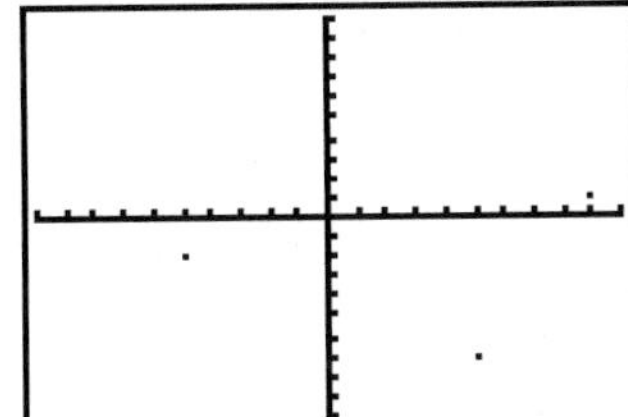

2.

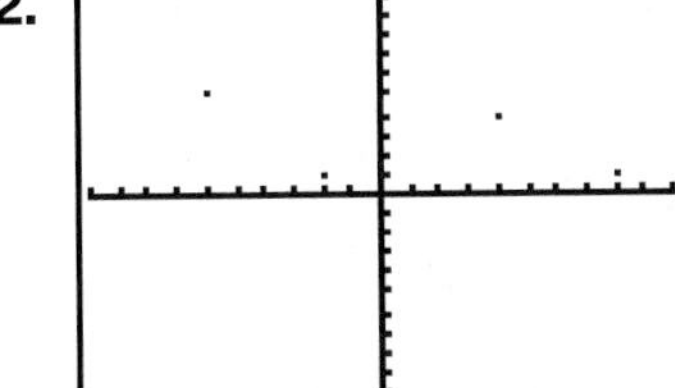

3.

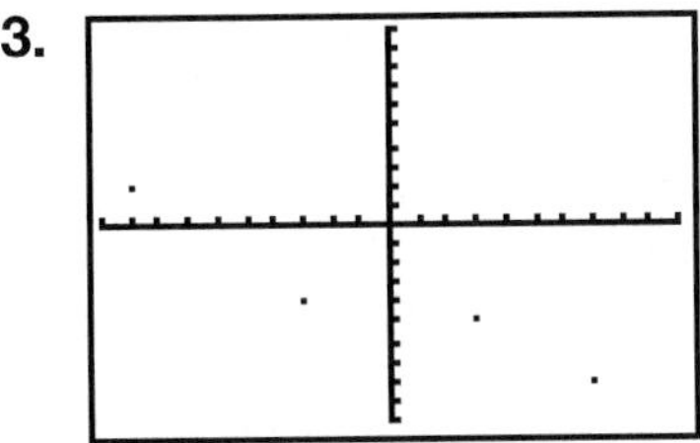

Page 196, Lesson 5-4A

2.

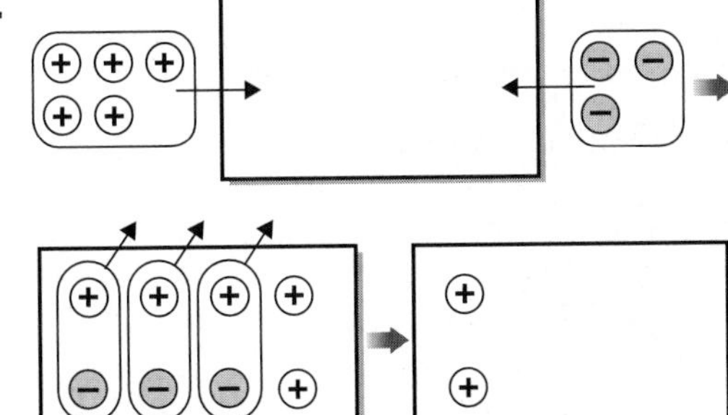

3.

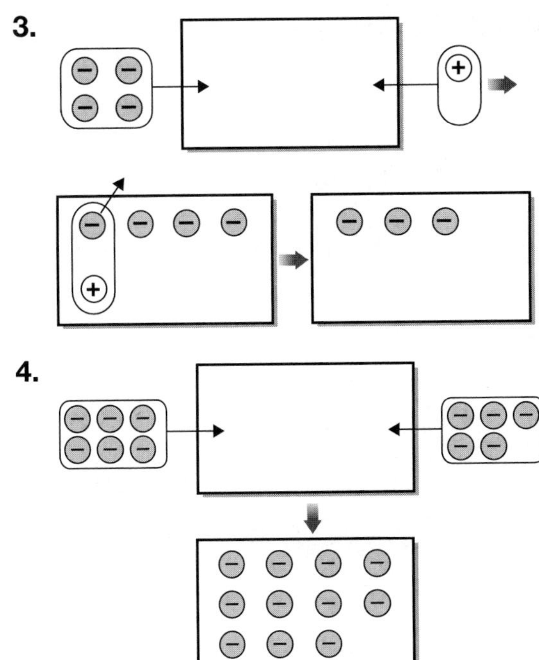

4.

Page 201, Lesson 5-5A

2.

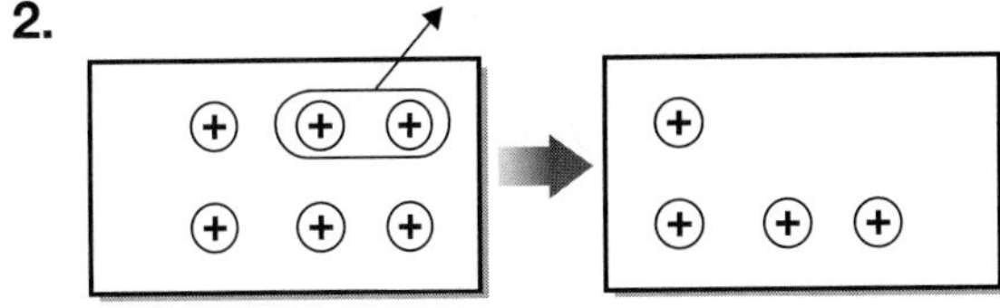

3.

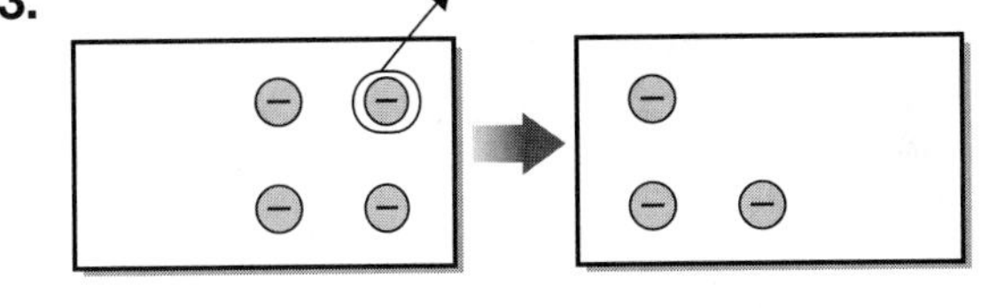

4.

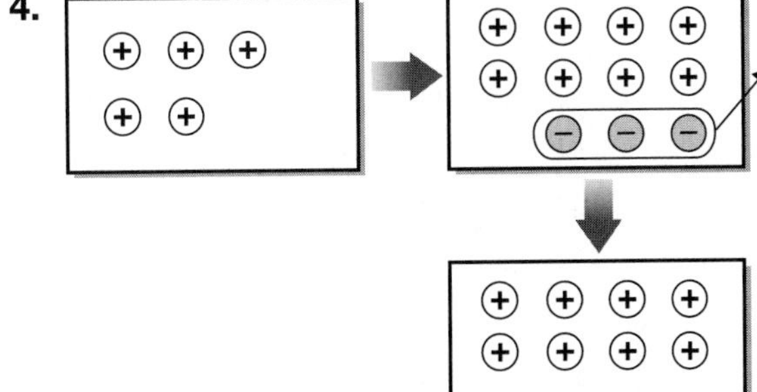

5.

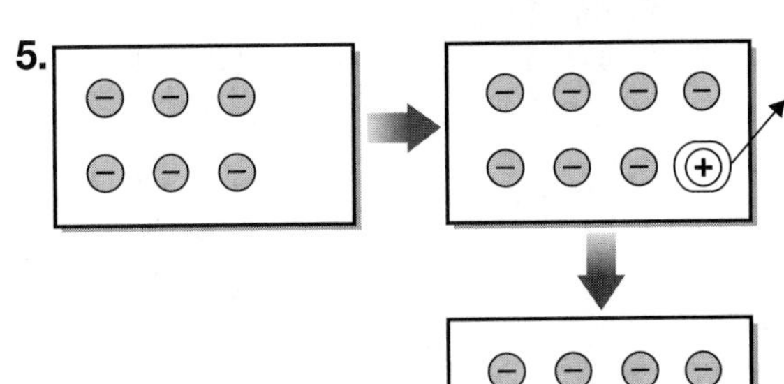

Pages 202–205, Lesson 5-5

45b.

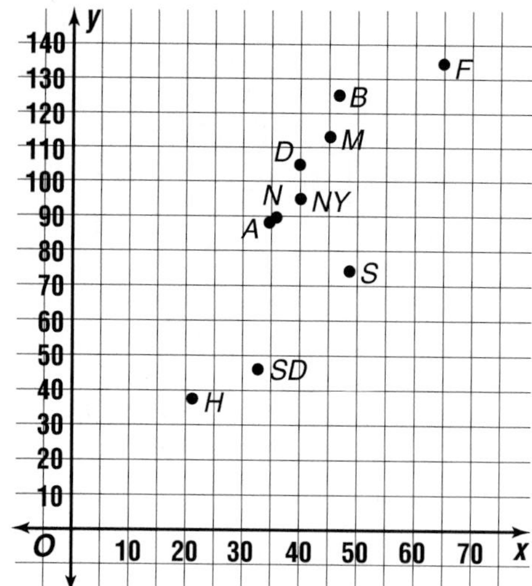

Page 206, Lesson 5-6A

1.

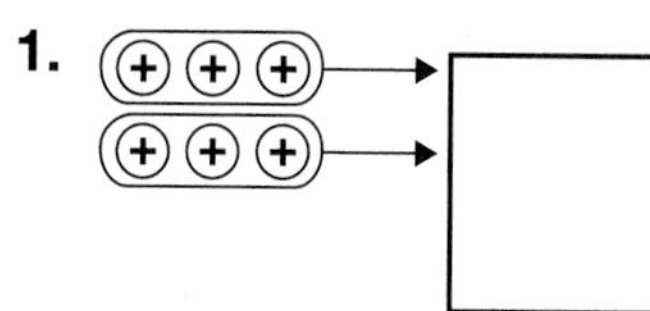

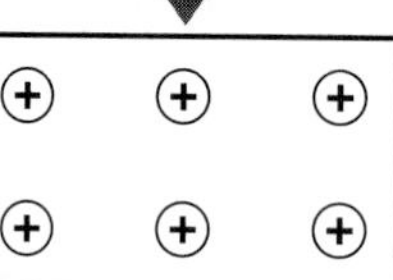

2.

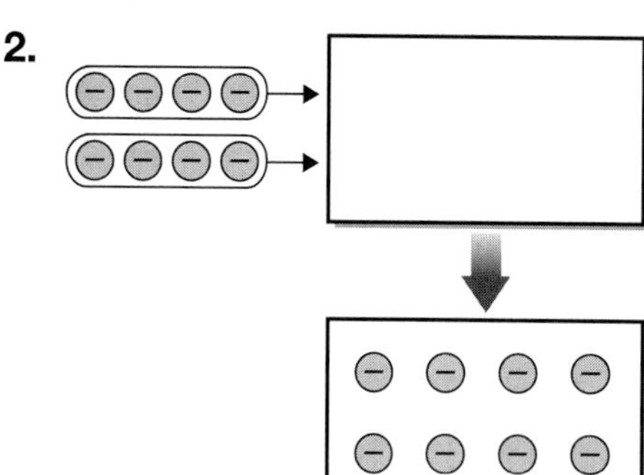

3.

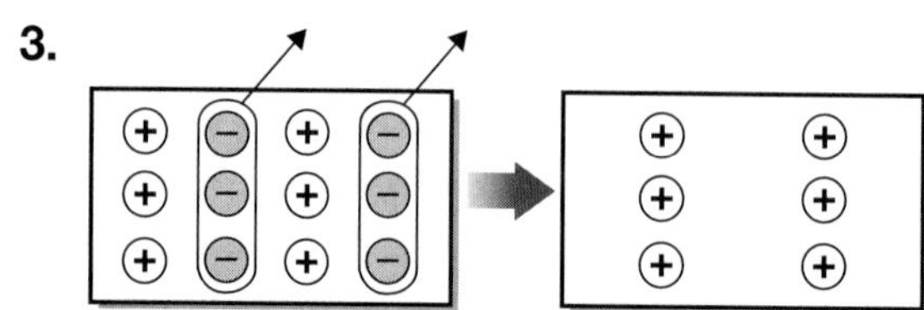

4.

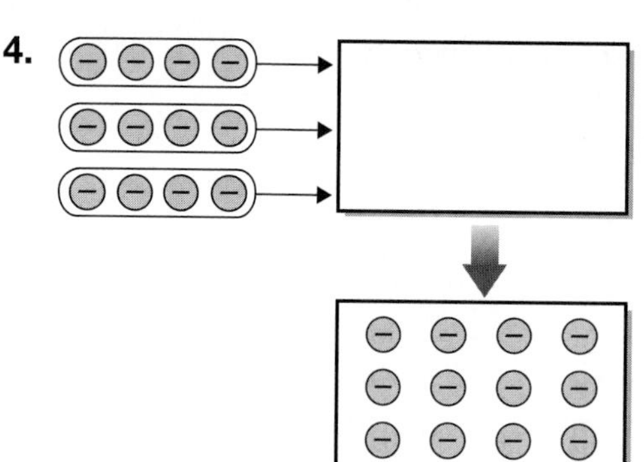

5.

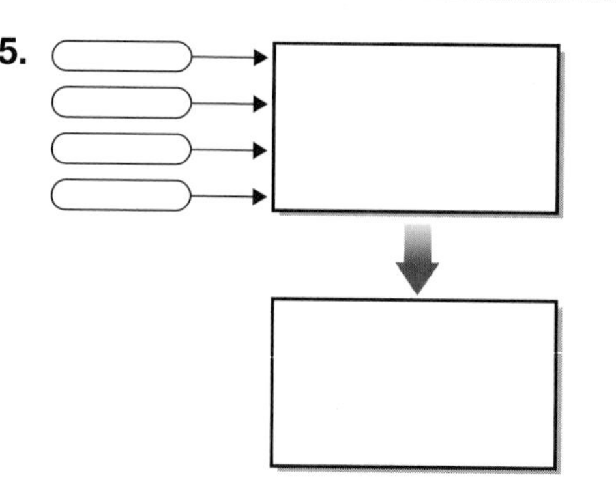

6.

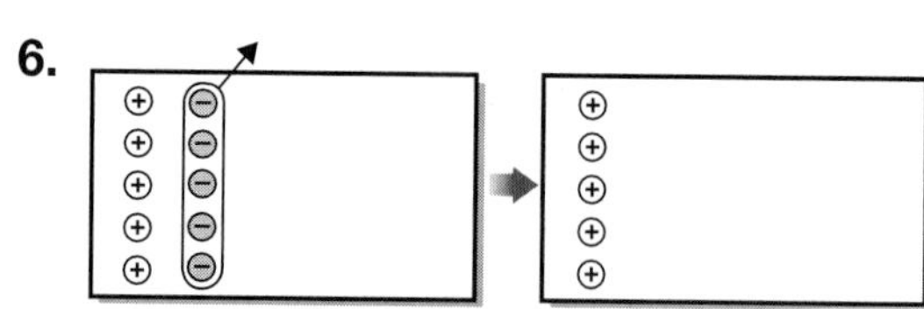

Pages 208–209, Lesson 5-6

1. One is positive and one is negative.

2. $7 \cdot 2 = 14$
$7 \cdot 1 = 7$
$7 \cdot 0 = 0$
$7 \cdot (-1) = -7$
$7 \cdot (-2) = -14$
$7 \cdot (-3) = -21$

3. $-3 \times (-4) = 12$

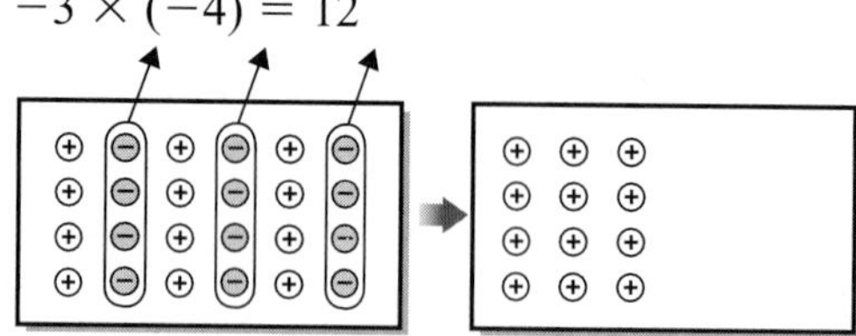

Pages 215–217, Lesson 5-8

1.

3. Sample answer: The diamonds are both translations and reflections of each other.

5.

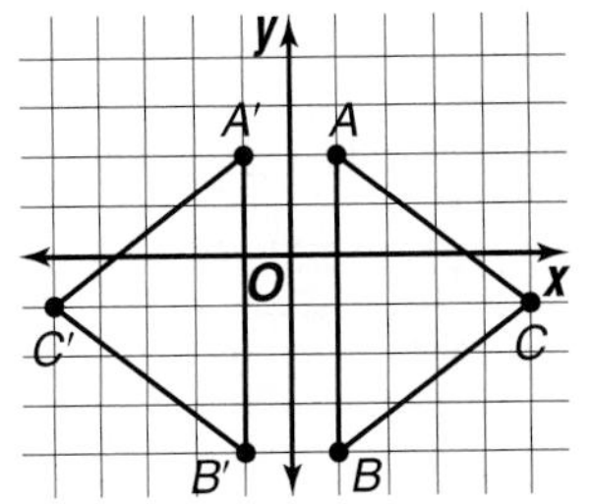

6.

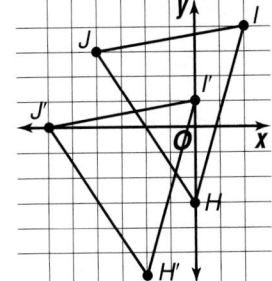

11.

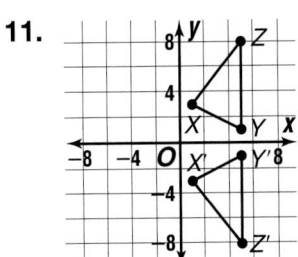

12.

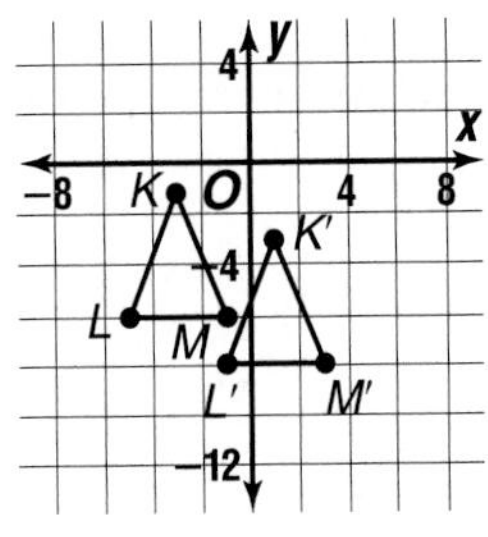

13.

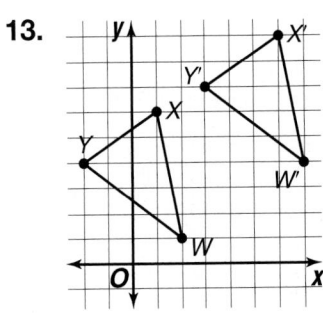

14.

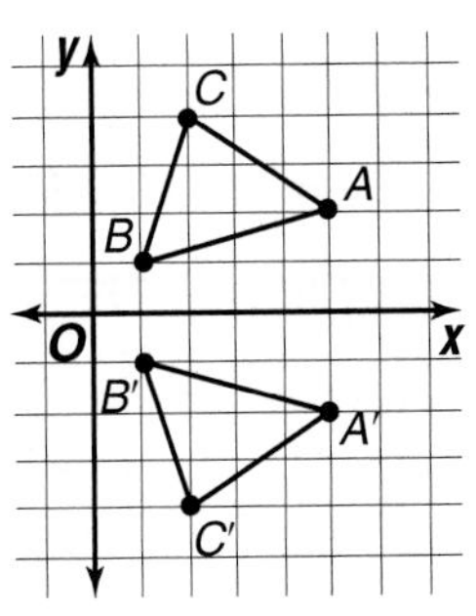

15.

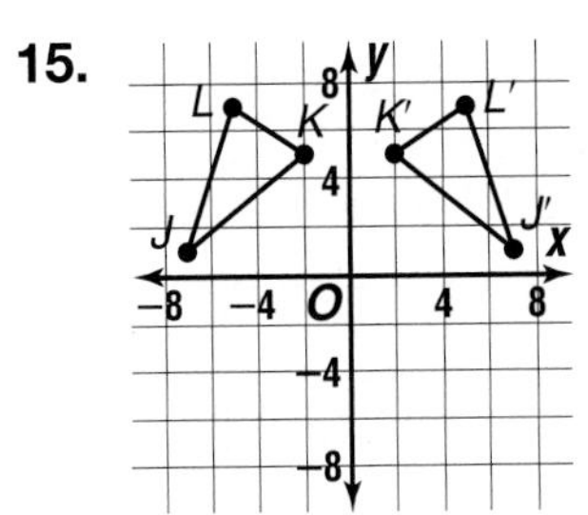

16.

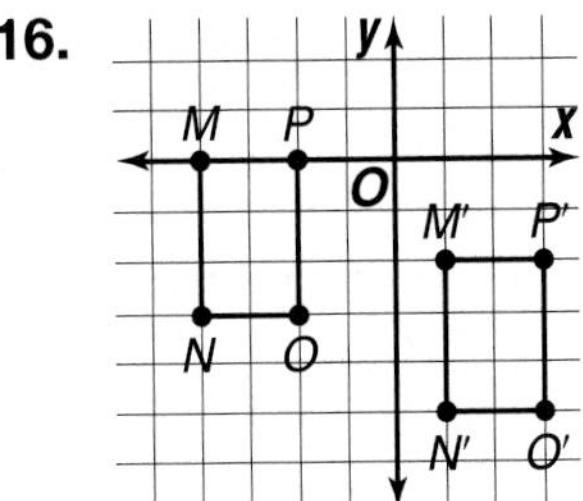

19.

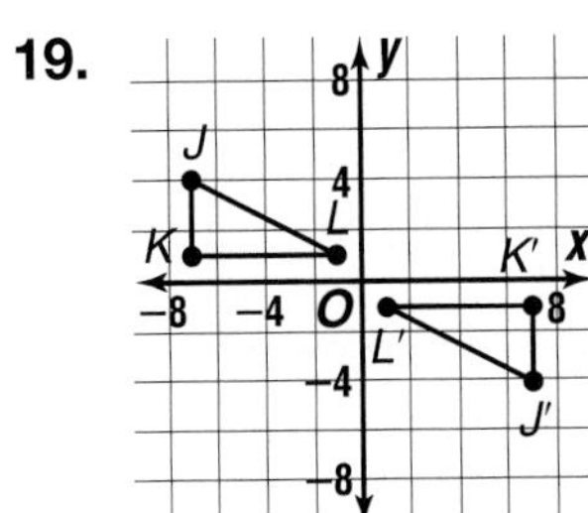

$\triangle JKL$ was reflected over the y-axis and then over the x-axis. This is a double reflection.

Pages 218–221, Chapter 5 Study Guide and Assessment

63. $A'(7, 2)$, $B'(1, 1)$, $C'(2, 10)$

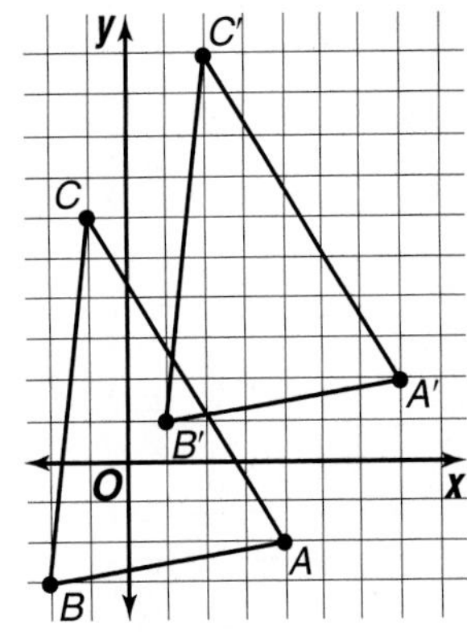

64. $R'(-1, -3)$, $S'(2, -6)$, $T'(6, -1)$

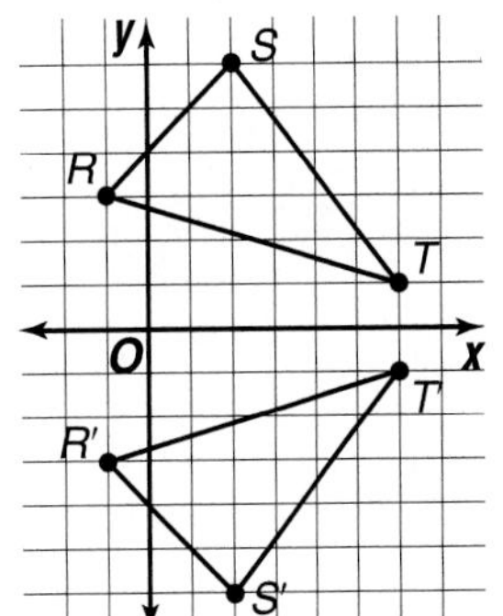

CHAPTER 6 Algebra: Exploring Equations and Functions

Pages 226–227, Lesson 6-1A

1.

2.

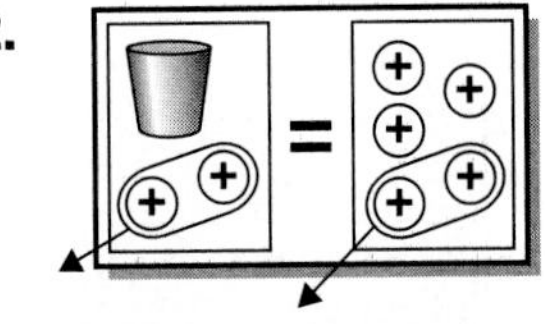

3.

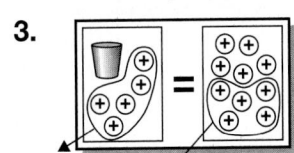

4.

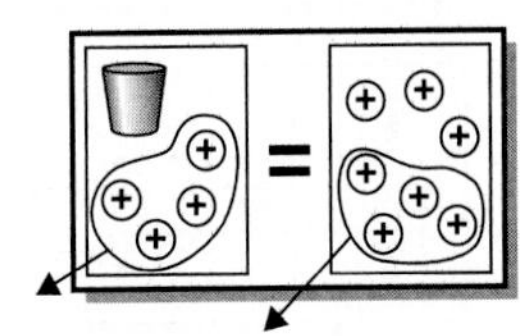

5.

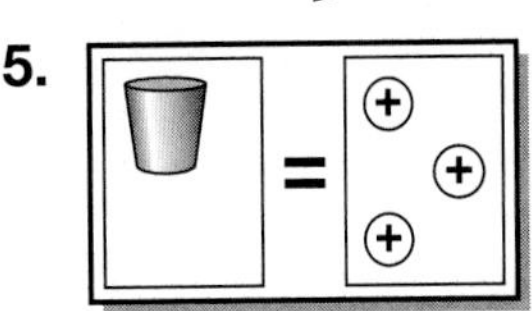

6.

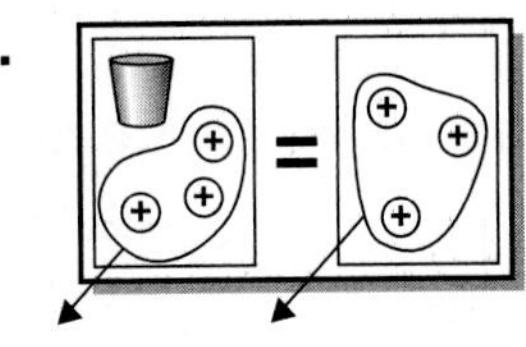

9.

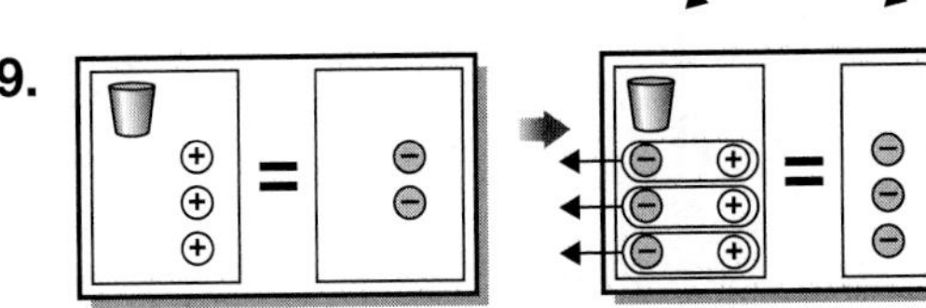

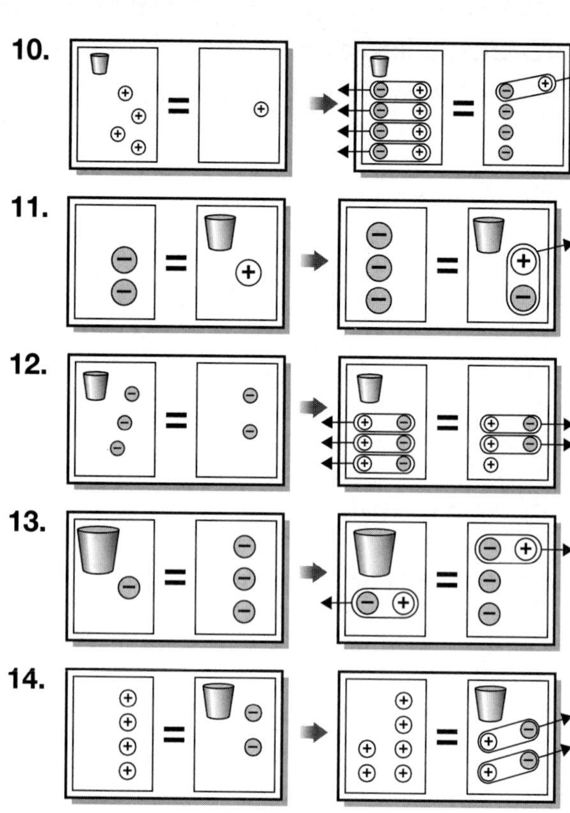

Pages 230–231, Lesson 6-1

3. $x - 6 = 3$

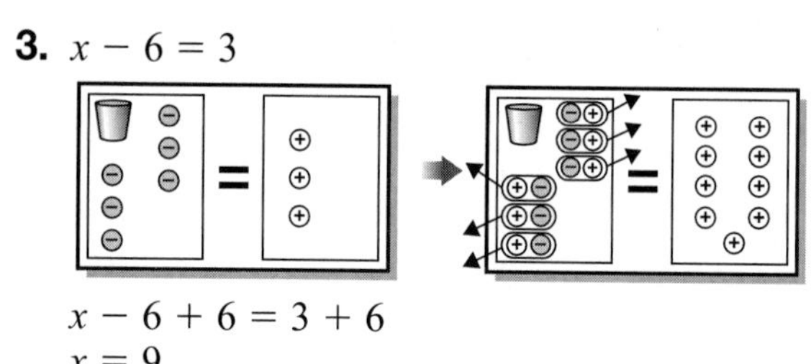

$x - 6 + 6 = 3 + 6$
$x = 9$

Page 234, Lesson 6-2, Mini-Lab

1a. 1b. 1c.

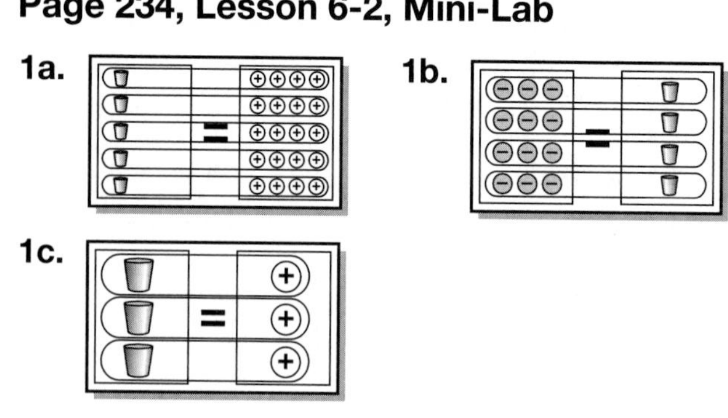

Page 236–237, Lesson 6-2

3.

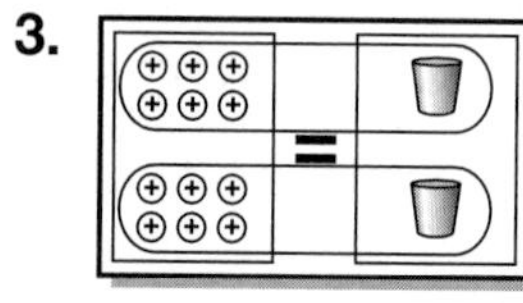

Page 238, Lesson 6-3A

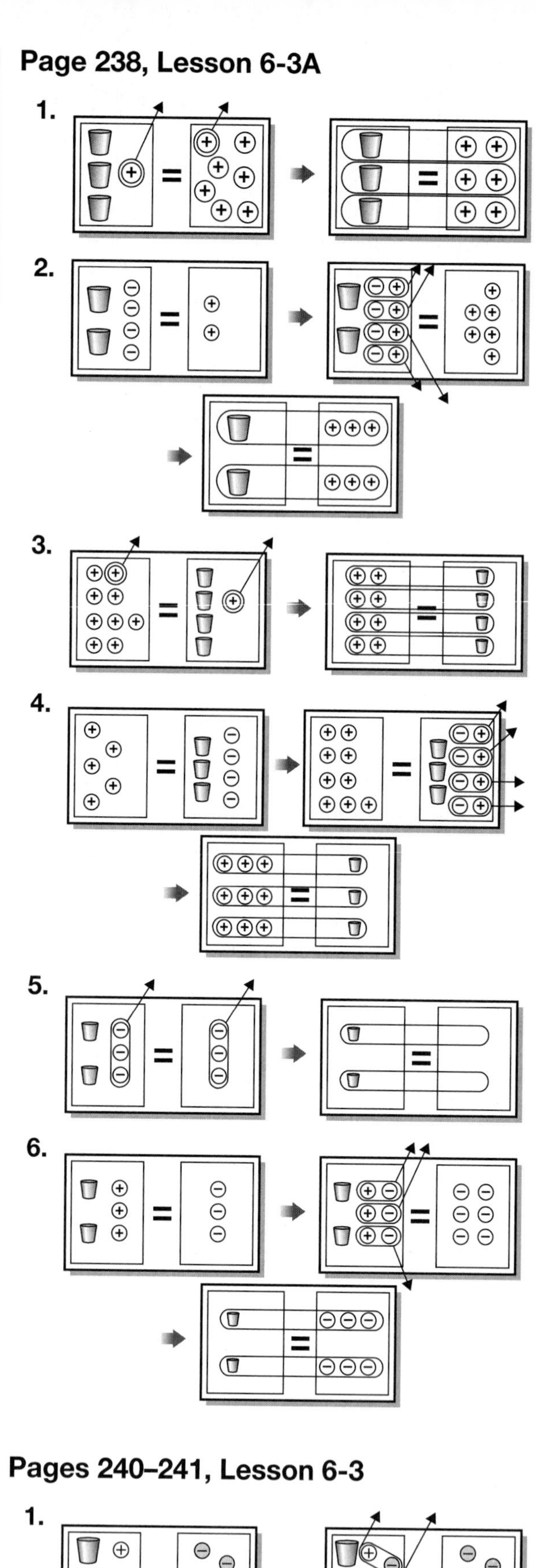

Pages 240–241, Lesson 6-3

1.

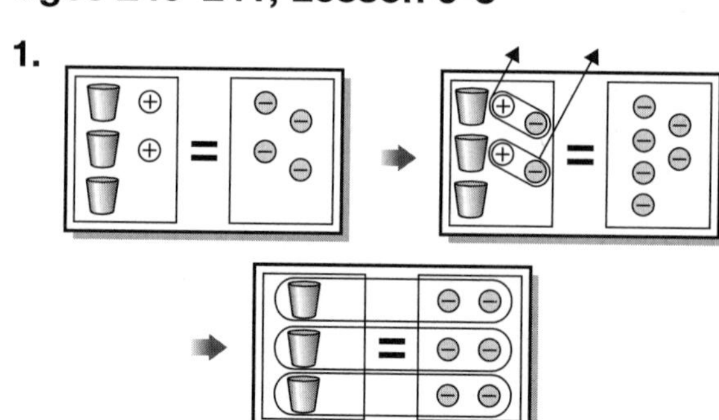

33.

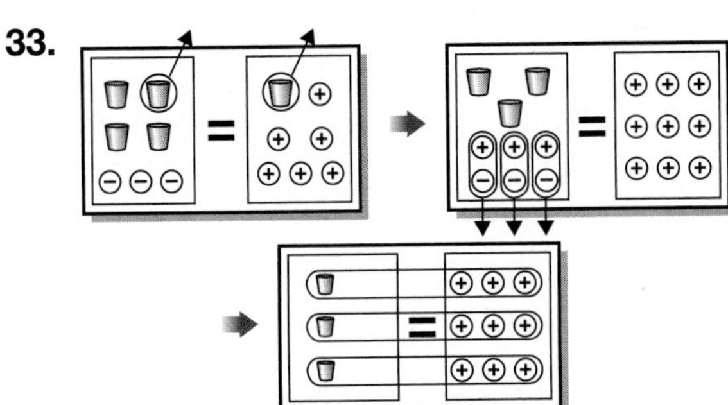

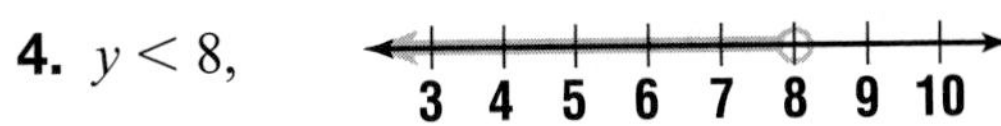

Page 248, Lesson 6-5

4. $y < 8$, 3 4 5 6 7 8 9 10

5. $a \geq -2$, −5 −4 −3 −2 −1 0 1 2 3

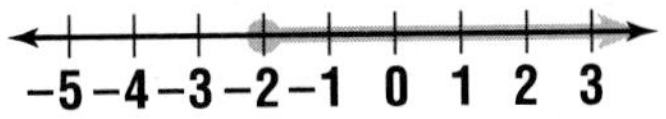

6. $t > 4$, 0 1 2 3 4 5 6 7 8 9 10

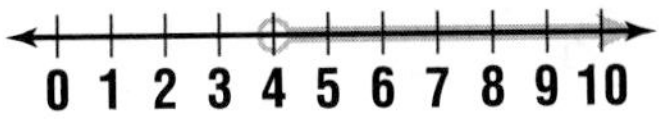

7. $x \leq -6$, −8 −7 −6 −5 −4 −3 −2 −1 0 1 2

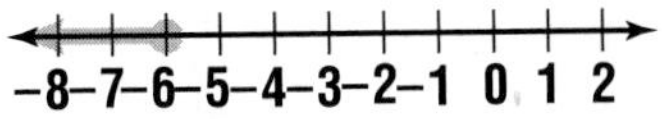

9. $x > -7$, 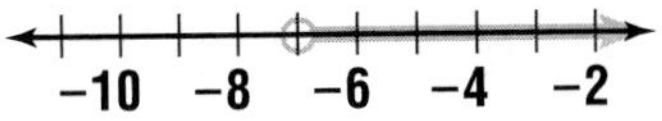 −10 −8 −6 −4 −2

10. $g > 7$, 3 4 5 6 7 8 9 10 11

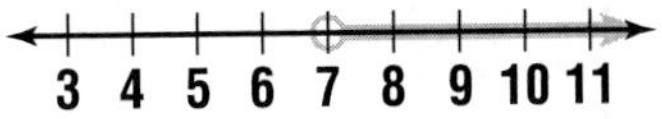

11. $d \geq 4$, 0 1 2 3 4 5 6 7 8 9

12. $t < 1$, −3 −2 −1 0 1 2 3 4

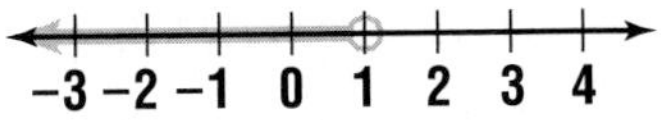

13. $p > -2$, −5 −4 −3 −2 −1 0 1 2

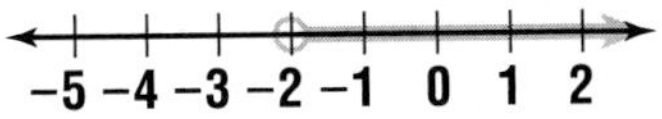

14. $y \leq 7.5$, 4 5 6 7 8 9; 7.5

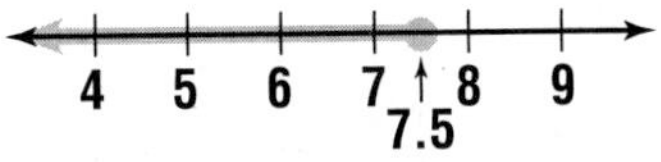

15. $r < 8$, −2 −1 0 1 2 3 4 5 6 7 8

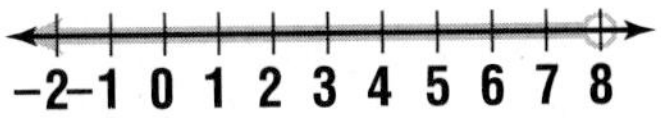

16. $b \leq -1$, −4 −3 −2 −1 0 1 2 3 4

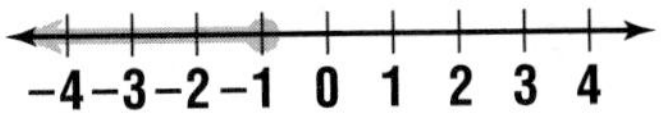

17. $y < 3.2$, 0 1 2 3 4 5 6 7 8; 3.2

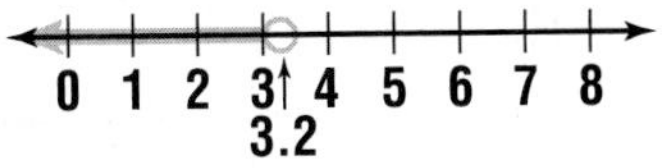

18. $x < 5$, −2 −1 0 1 2 3 4 5 6 7

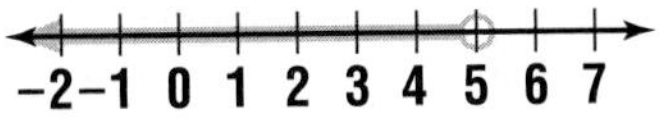

19. $a > 7$, 3 4 5 6 7 8 9 10 11

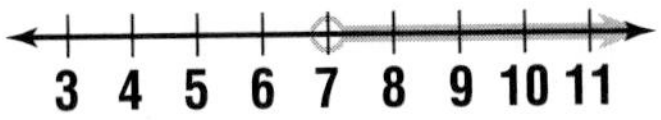

20. $d \geq 2$, −1 0 1 2 3 4 5 6

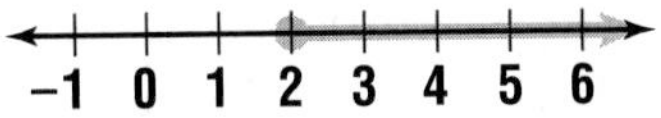

Pages 249–252, Lesson 6-6

4. The beats per minute decrease as age increases.

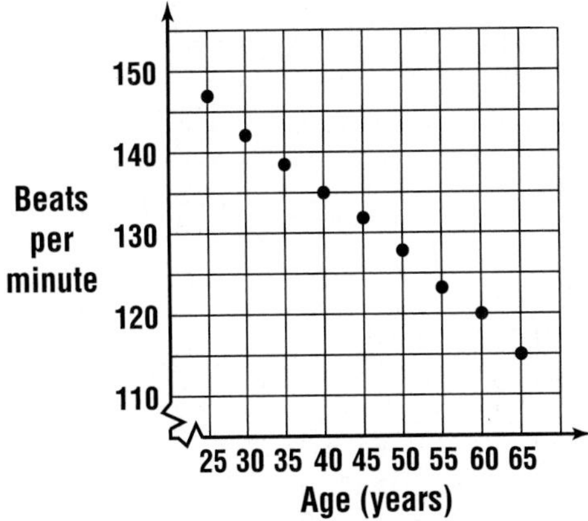

5. The population increases each year.

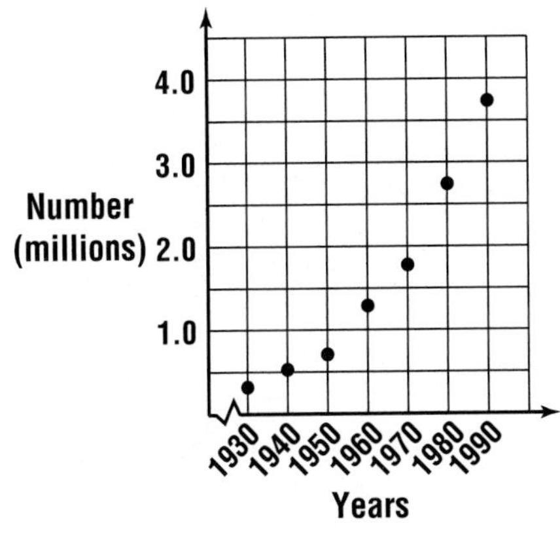

6a.

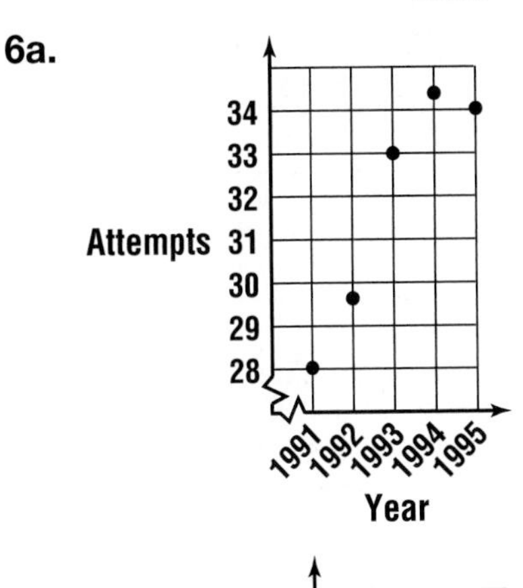

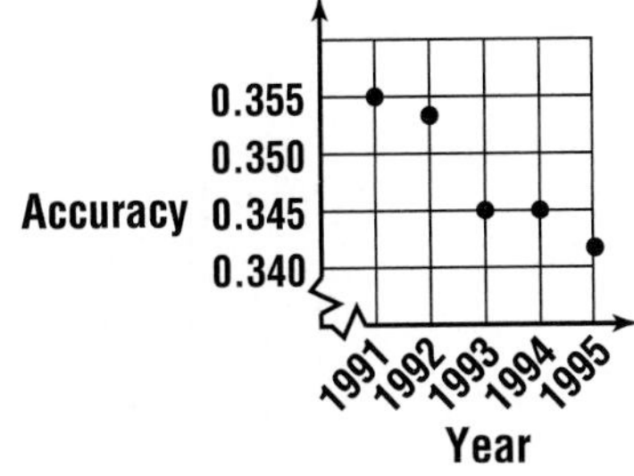

6c. Increasing attempts tends to reduce accuracy.

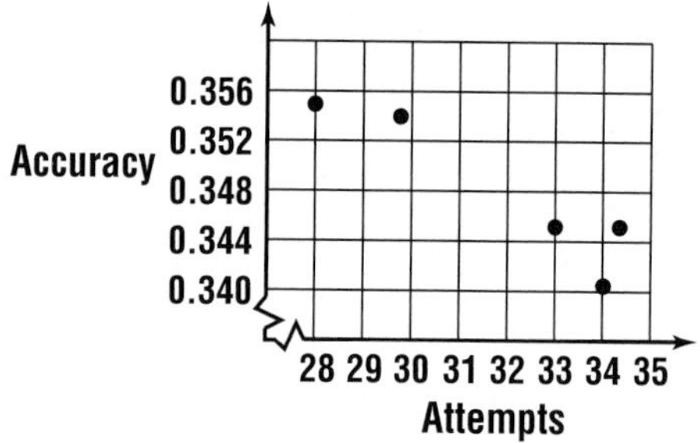

7a.

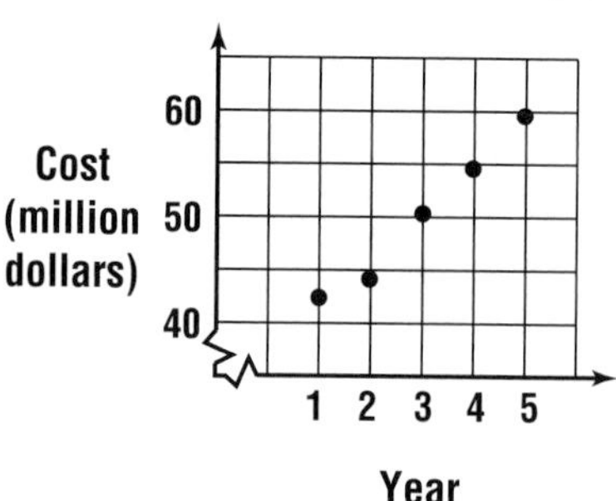

Pages 254–257, Lesson 6-7

4.

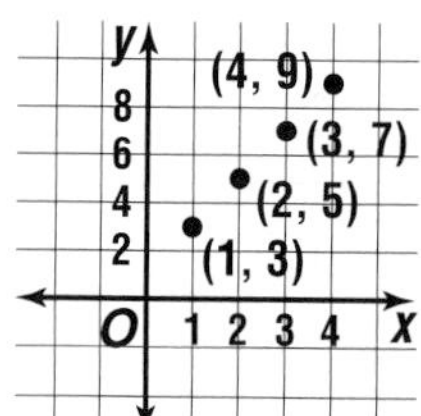

5.

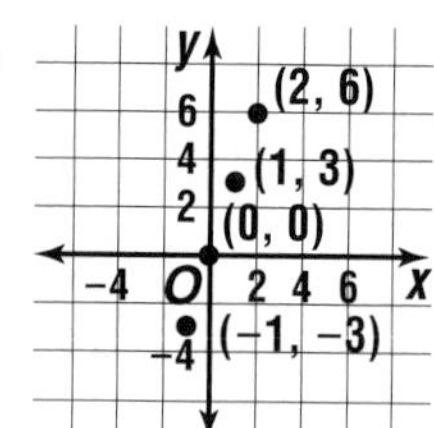

6.

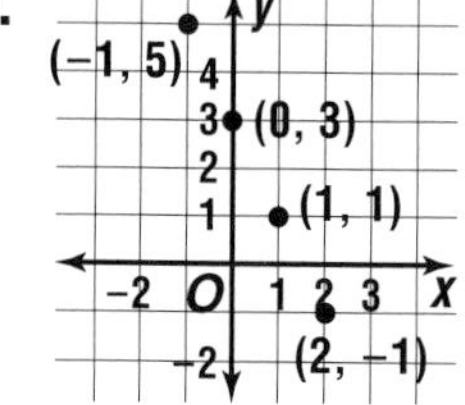

7.

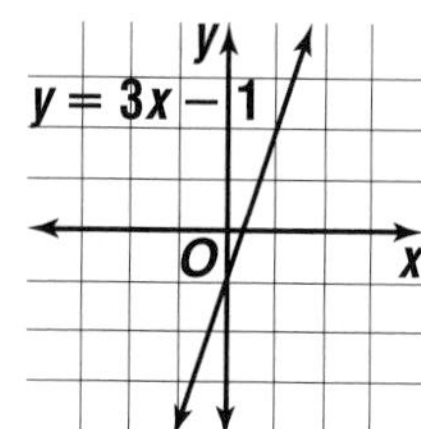

8.

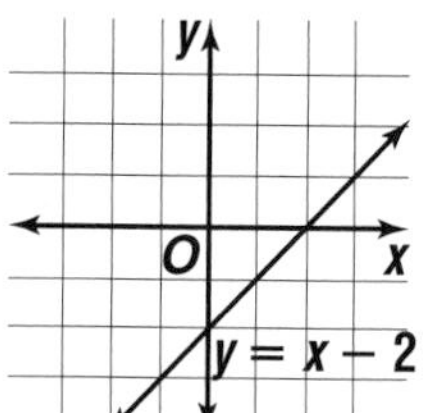

9.

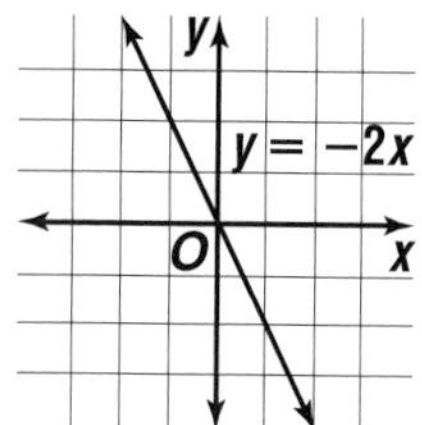

10.

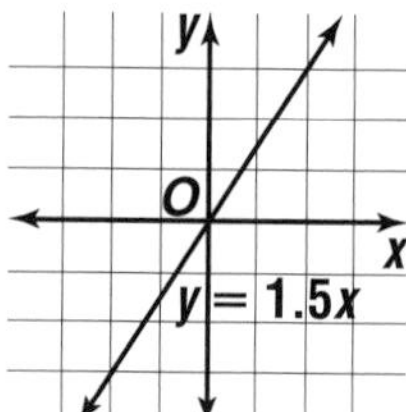

12.

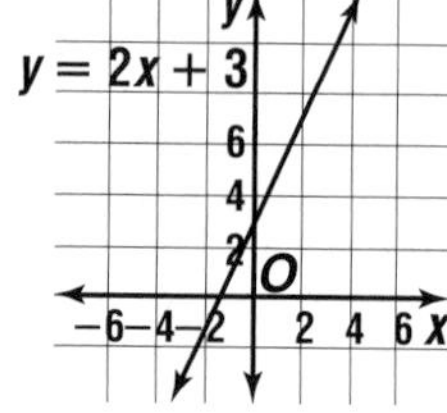

13.

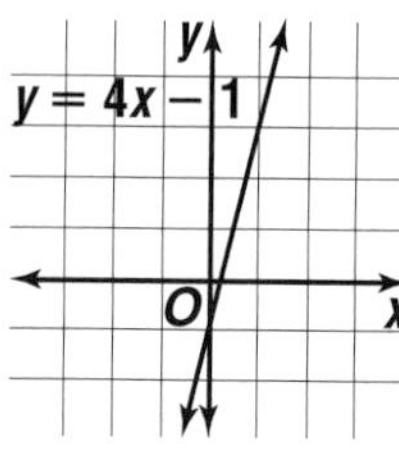

14.

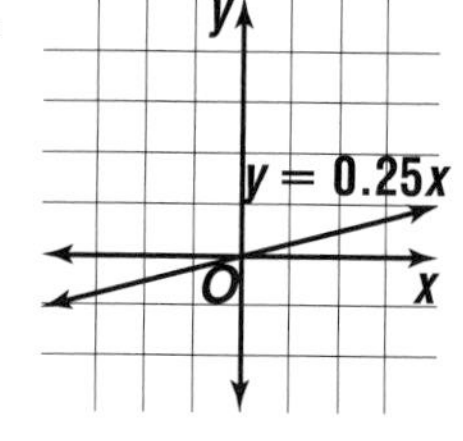

15.

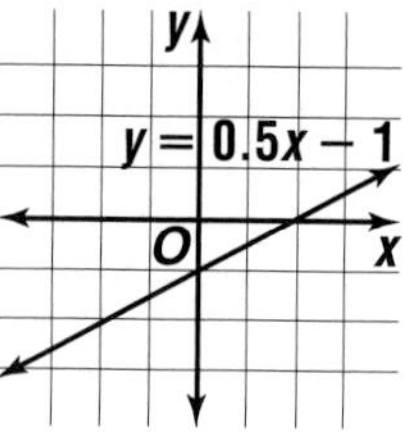

16.

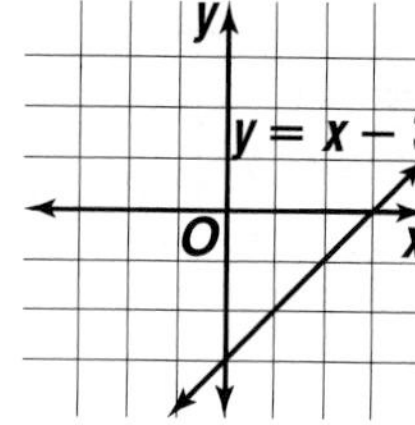

17.

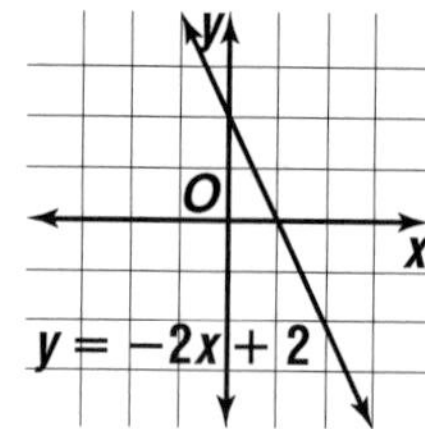

18.

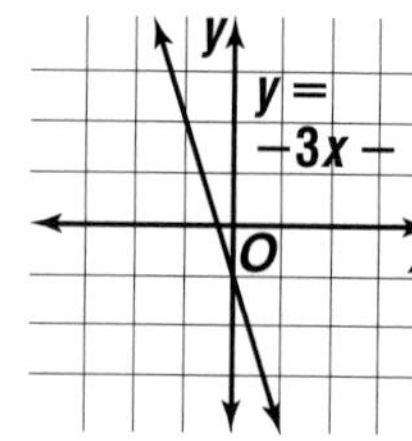

19.

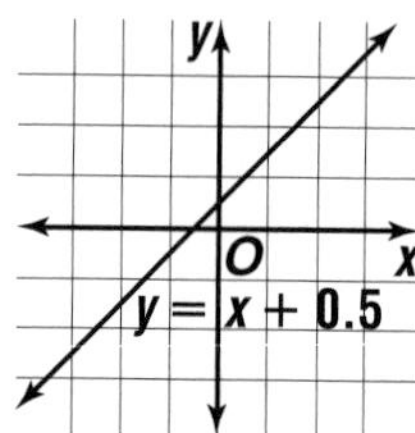

20.

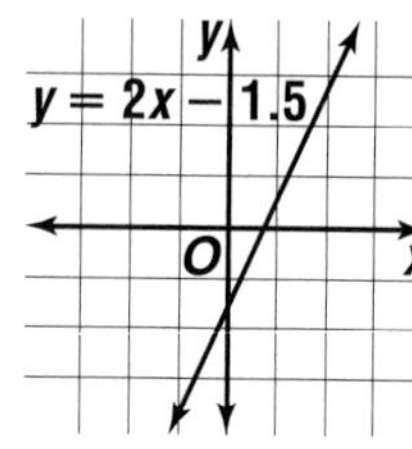

21.

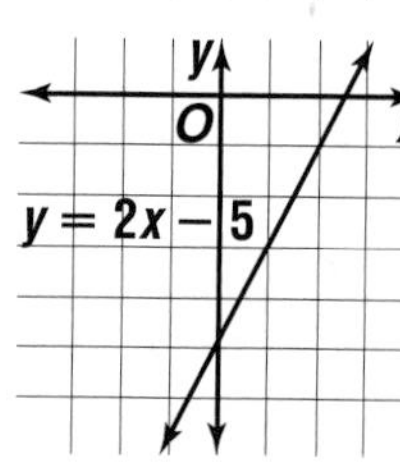

22.

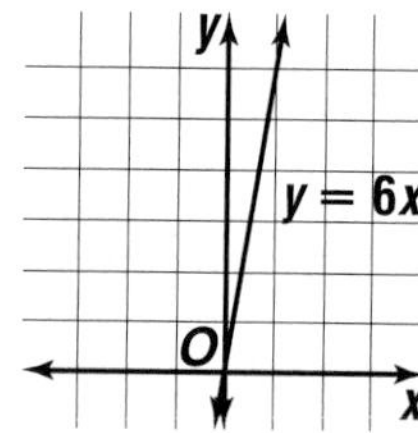

23.

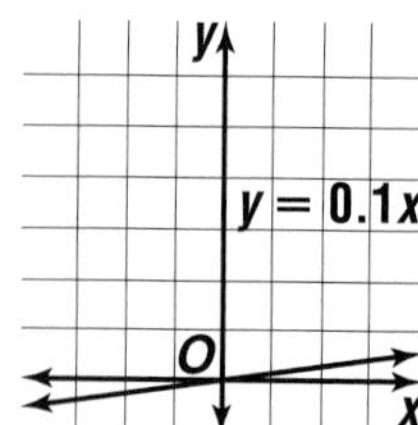

28.

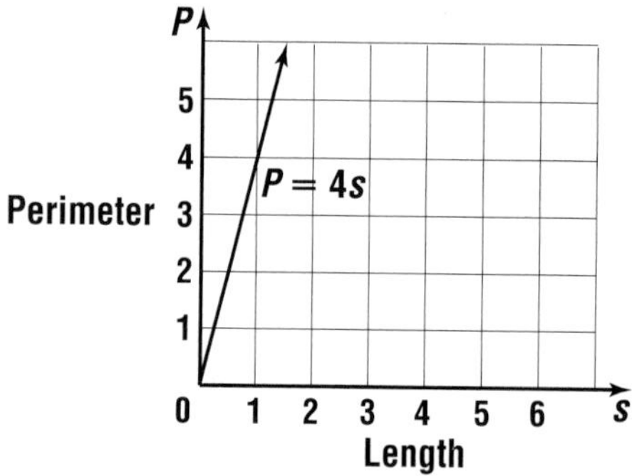

29d.

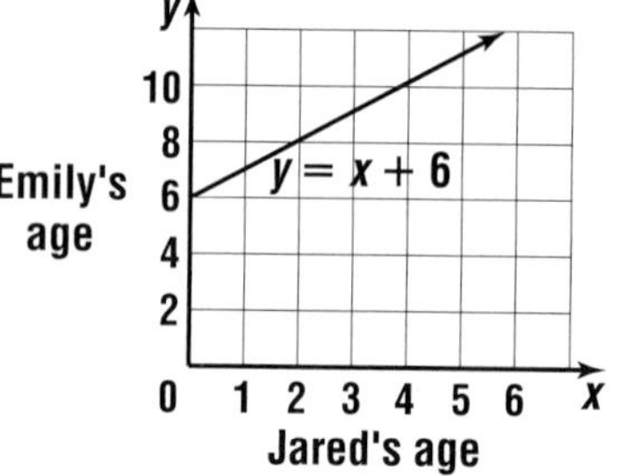

31b.

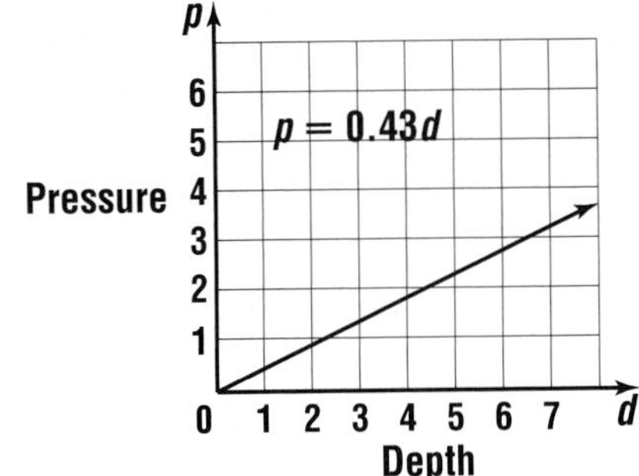

Pages 258–261, Chapter 6 Study Guide and Assessment

37. 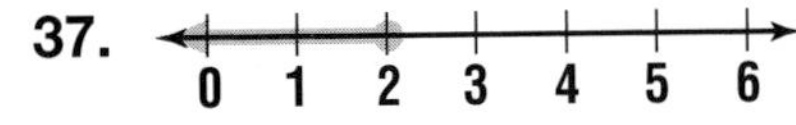

38. 4 5 6 7 8 9 10

39. −6 −5 −4 −3 −2 −1 0

40. 2 3 4 5 6 7 8

41.

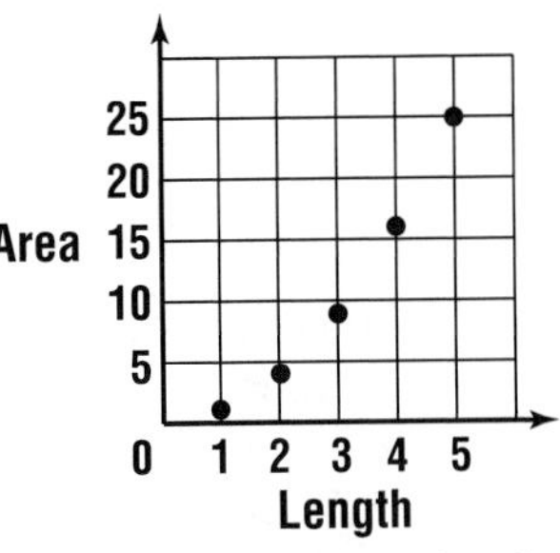

As the length of a side of a square increases, the area also increases.

42.

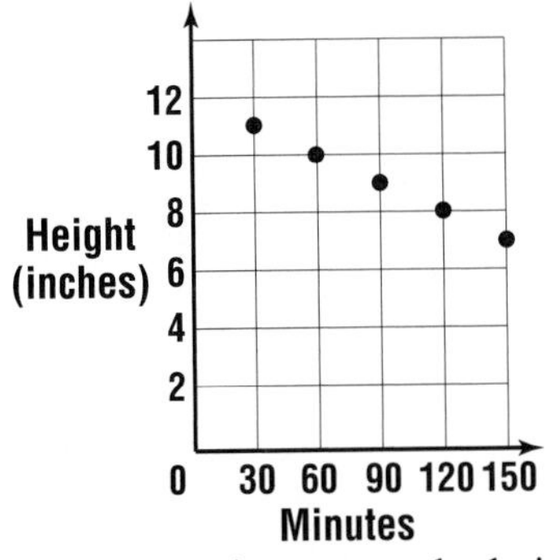

As the time increases, the height decreases.

43. 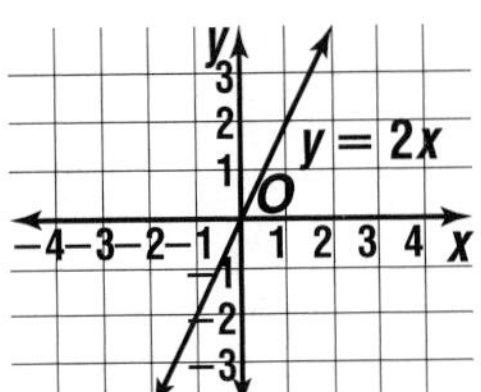

44. 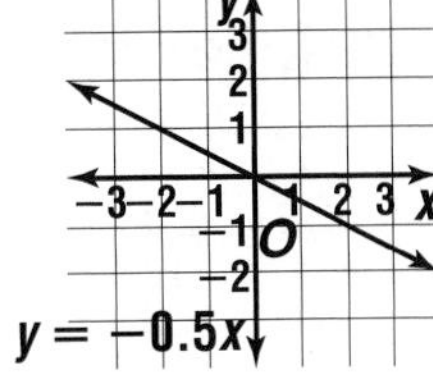

45. 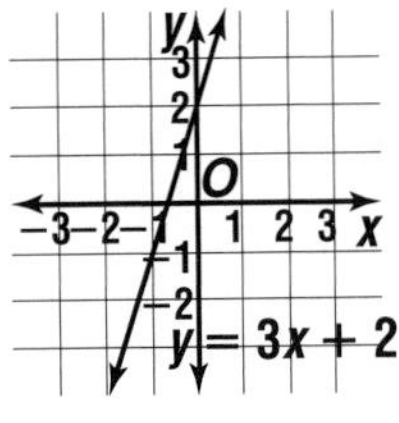

46. 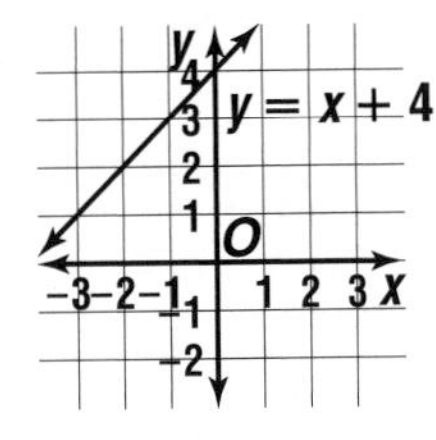

50.

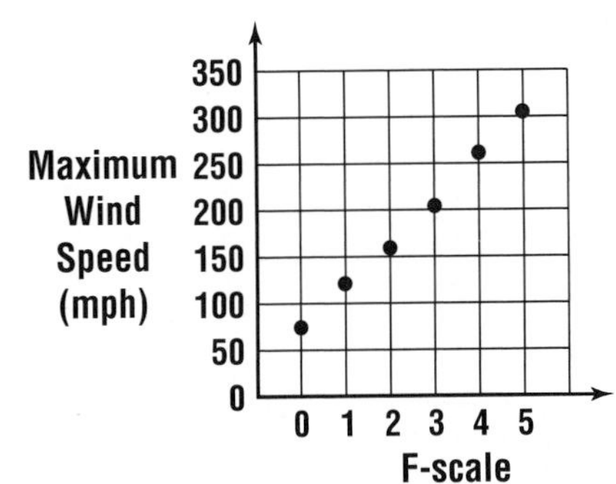

As the maximum wind speed increases, the F-scale also increases.

CHAPTER 7 Applying Fractions

Page 272, Lesson 7-2, Mini-Lab

1. 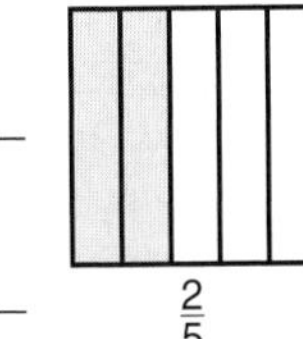 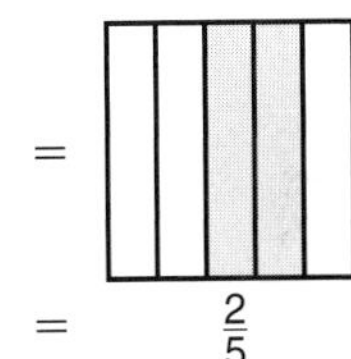

$\frac{4}{5} - \frac{2}{5} = \frac{2}{5}$

2. 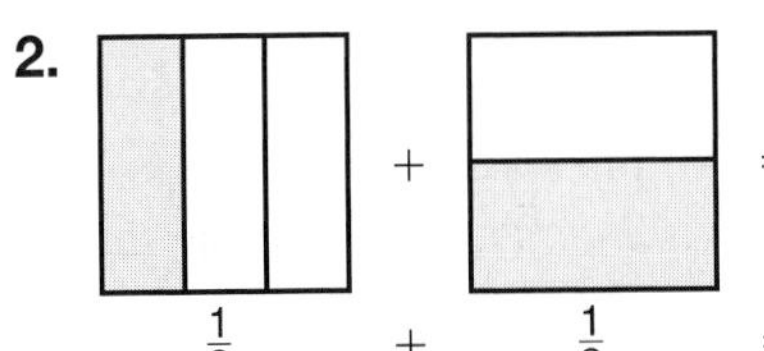

$\frac{1}{3} + \frac{1}{2} =$

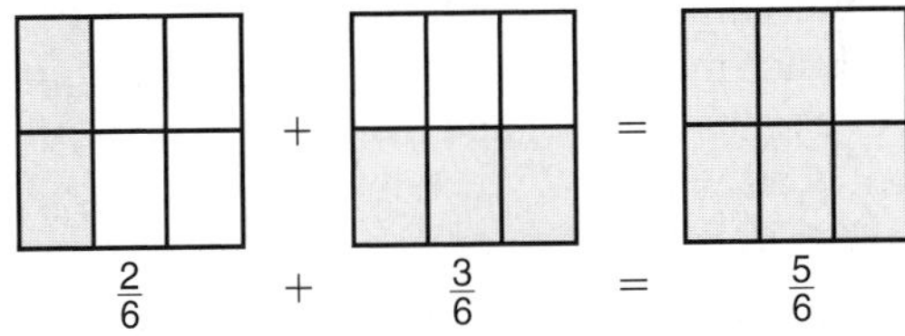

$\frac{2}{6} + \frac{3}{6} = \frac{5}{6}$

3. 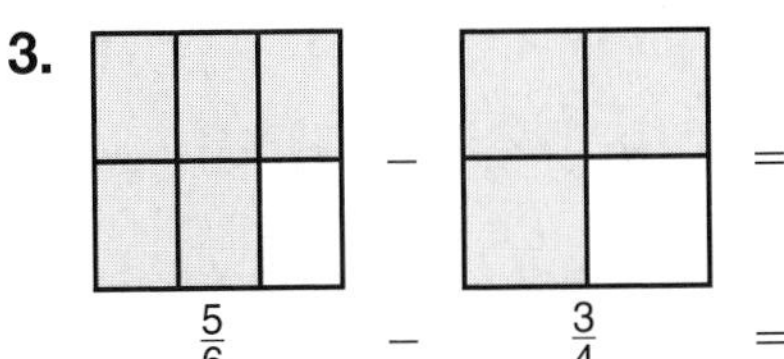

$\frac{5}{6} - \frac{3}{4} =$

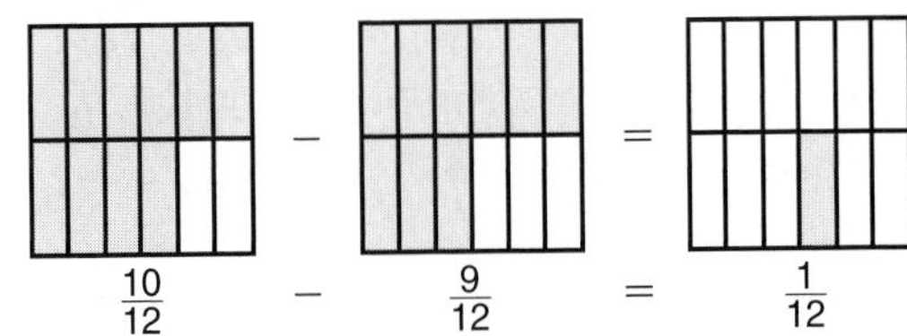

$\frac{10}{12} - \frac{9}{12} = \frac{1}{12}$

ANSWER APPENDIX

Pages 274–275, Lesson 7-2

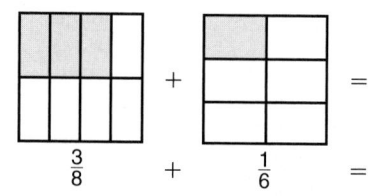

3.

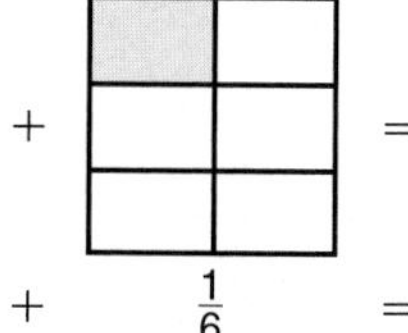

$\frac{3}{8} + \frac{1}{6} =$

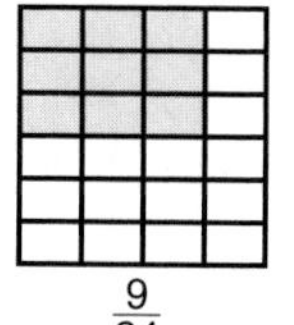

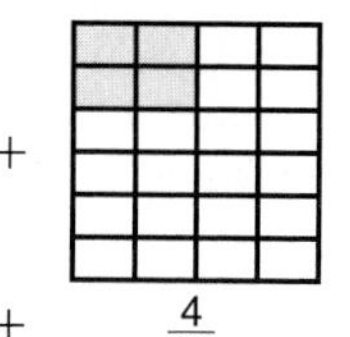

$\frac{9}{24} + \frac{4}{24} = \frac{13}{24}$

Pages 306–307, Lesson 7-9

2.

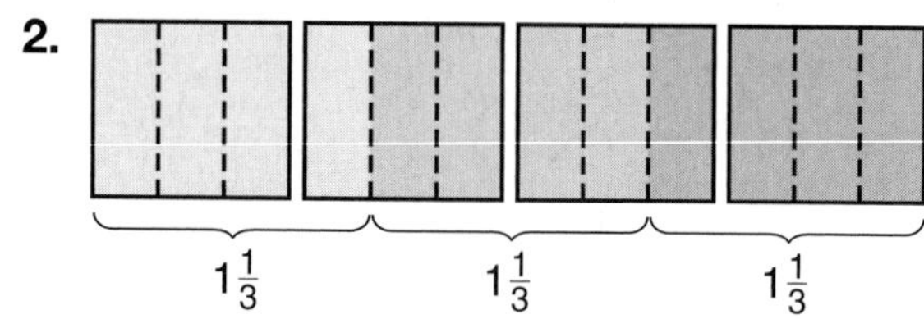

Page 311, Perfomance Task

- Since 66 inches equals $5\frac{1}{2}$ feet and the deck is 4 feet wide, the total radius of the area to be fenced is $9\frac{1}{2}$ feet. The diameter is $2 \times 9\frac{1}{2} = 19$ feet, so the circumference is $19 \times 3.14 \approx 59.66$ feet. You need 60 feet of fencing.
- \$15; the circumference of the pool is $11 \times 3.14 \approx$ 35 feet. Since the difference between the circumference of the deck plus the pool and the circumference of just the pool is $60 - 35 = 25$ feet, the cost of one foot of fencing is \$375 ÷ 25 feet or \$15.

CHAPTER 8 Using Proportional Reasoning

Pages 336–338, Lesson 8-5

1. Set up a proportion with a fraction with a denominator of 100.

$\frac{3}{16} = \frac{n}{100}$ Use cross products to solve.

$300 = 16n$

$18.75 = n$

So, $\frac{3}{16} = 18.75\%$.

Pages 342–345, Lesson 8-7

3a.

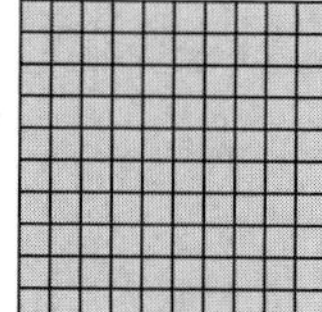

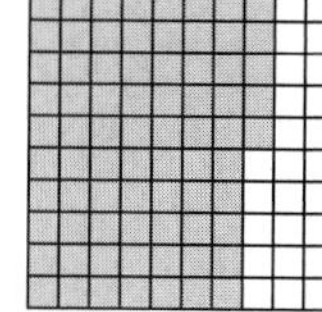

3b.

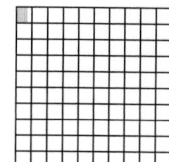

41. No; You would be shorter than when you were born.

42. Yes; The enrollment could grow from one year to the next.

43. No; The greatest possible percent of the attendance from one group would be 100%.

44. No; She could not give away more than 100% of the collection.

45. No; The population in 1990 would not be less than the population in 1790.

46. Yes; A small part of the population could move out.

55.

$X'(2, -4)$
$Y'(1, 1)$
$Z'(3, -5)$

57.

Stem	Leaf
6	2 6
7	
8	1 3 5
9	0 2 5

$6|2 = 62$

Pages 346–348, Lesson 8-8

24. The result is less than the original number; you are subtracting 10% of a greater number.

CHAPTER 9 Geometry: Investigating Patterns

Pages 390–391, Lesson 9-5

10. 2 squares, 3 triangles;

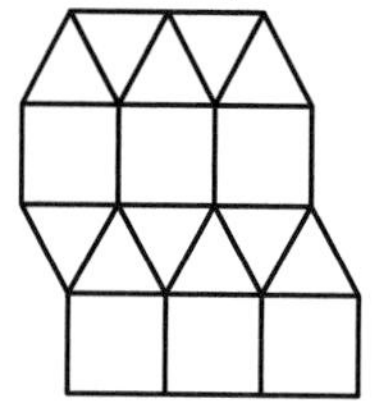

11. 1 square, 2 octagons;

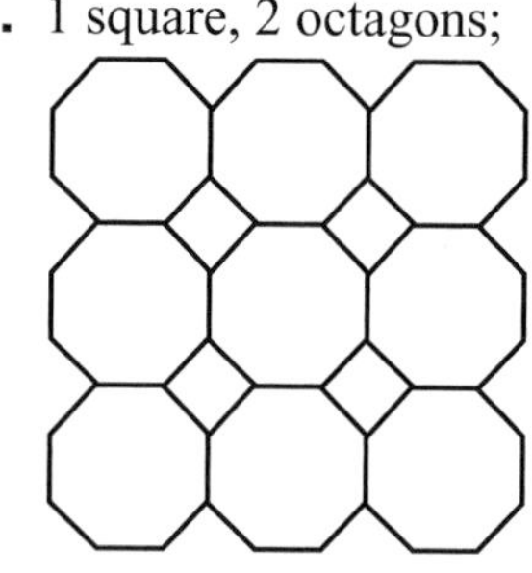

Page 394, Lesson 9-6

4.

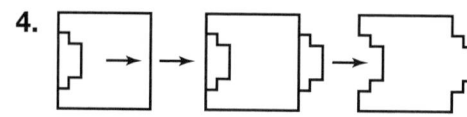

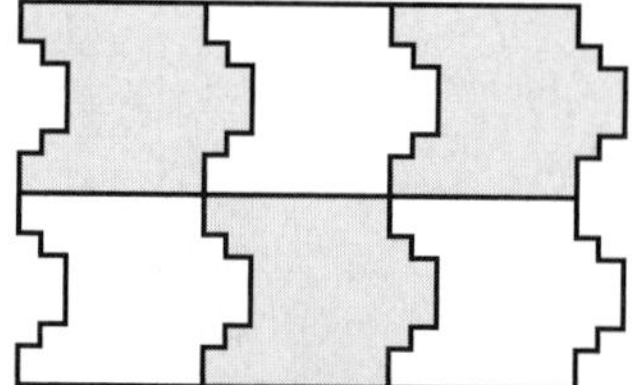

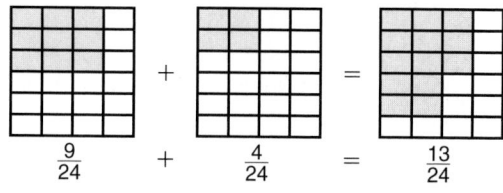

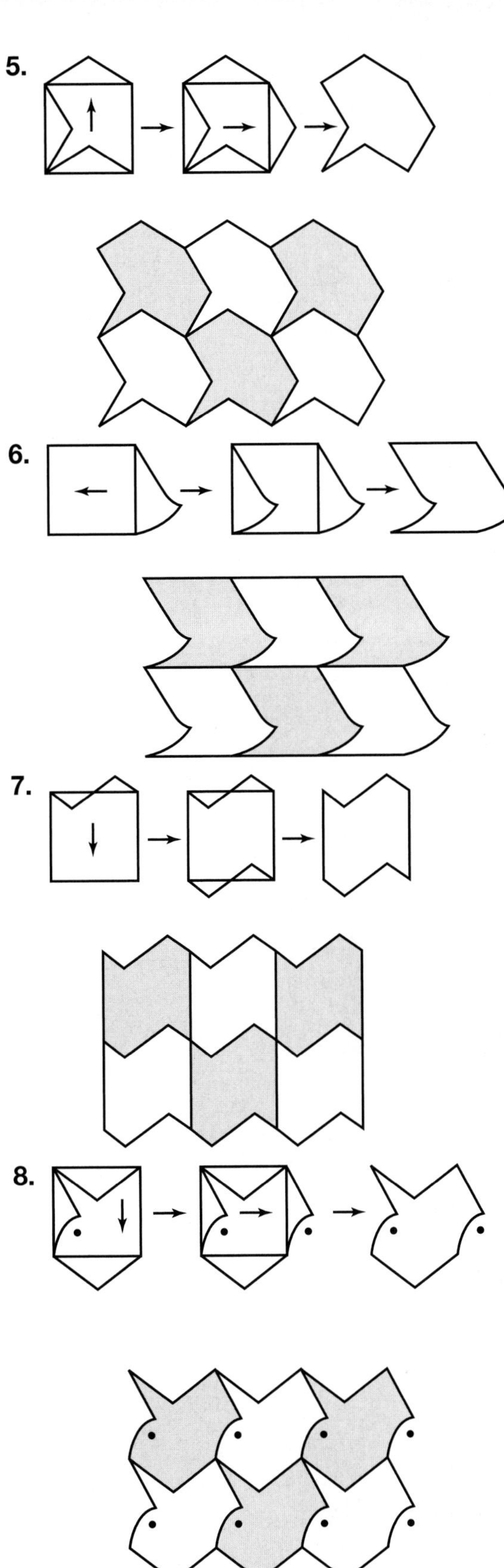

Pages 396–397, Lesson 9-7

1. A line of symmetry divides a figure so that one side is the reflection of the other side.
2. In a translation, the figure stays the same but moves to a different position. In a reflection, the figure is "flipped" over a line of symmetry.

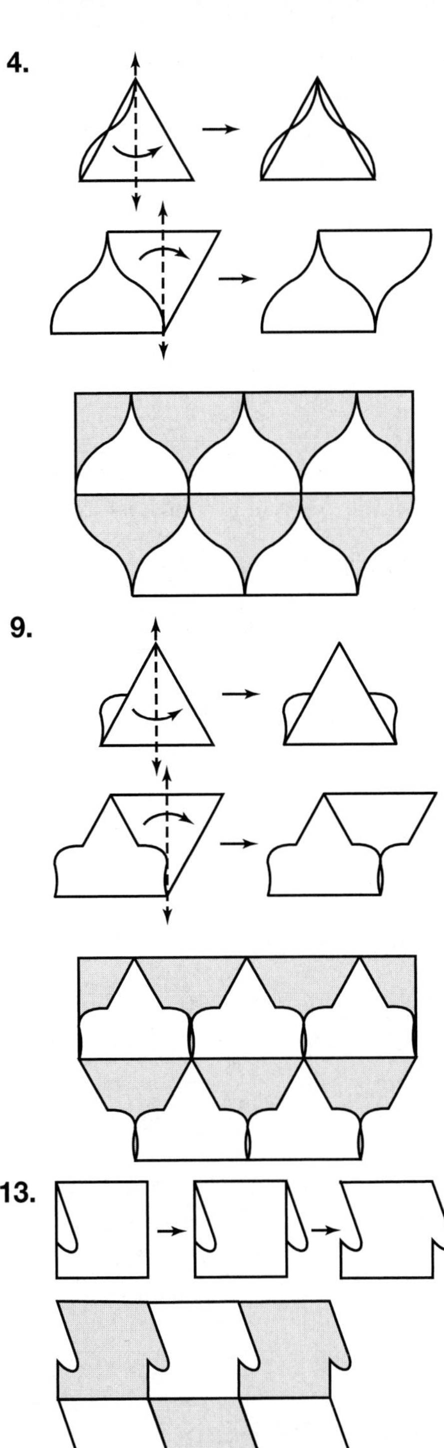

Pages 398–401, Chapter 9 Study Guide and Assessment

33.

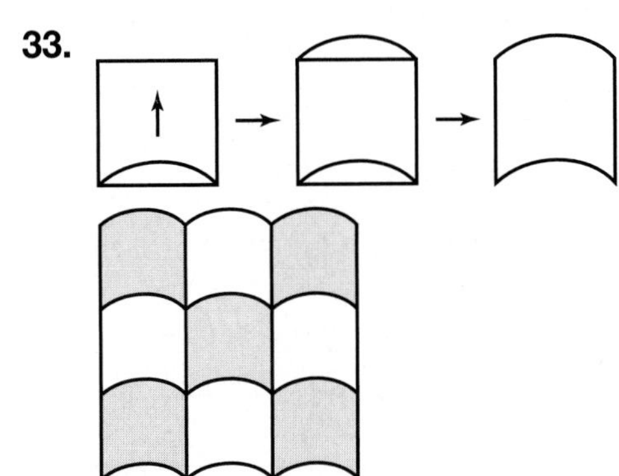

34.

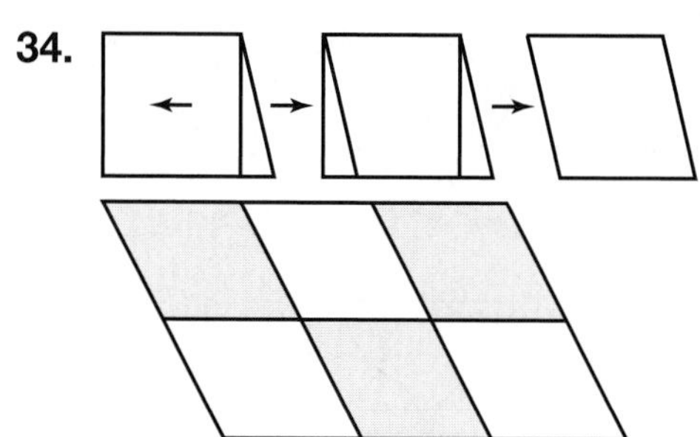

38. 7 9

39. 1 hexagon, 4 triangles; 2 hexagons, 2 triangles

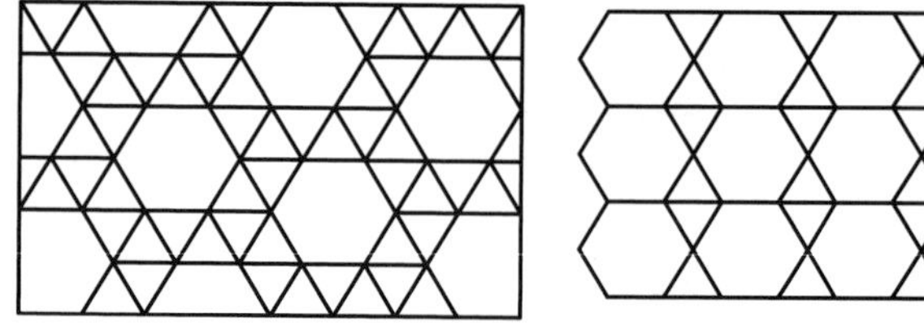

CHAPTER 10
Geometry: Exploring Area

Pages 408–409, Lesson 10-1A

2. Sample answer:

Guess	Shots Made	Check	Comments
1st	7 1-pt shots 9 2-pt shots	$7 + 9 = 16$ $7 \times 1 + 9 \times 2 = 25$	Need more 2-point shots.
2nd	5 1-pt shots 11 2-pt shots	$5 + 11 = 16$ $5 \times 1 + 11 \times 2 = 27$	Still need more 2-point shots.
3rd	3 1-pt shots 13 2-pt shots	$3 + 13 = 16$ $3 \times 1 + 13 \times 2 = 29$	The number of points is close to 30.
4th	2 1-pt shots 14 2-pt shots	$2 + 14 = 16$ $2 \times 1 + 14 \times 2 = 30$	It checks!

Page 410, Lesson 10-1, Mini-Lab

1.

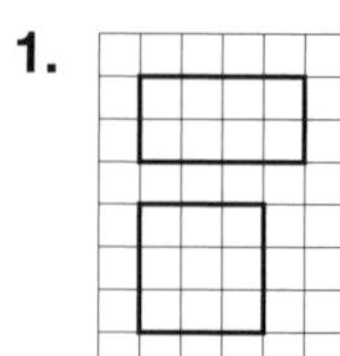

2.

Drawing	Perimeter	Area
	12 units	5 units^2
	12 units	8 units^2
	12 units	9 units^2

3.

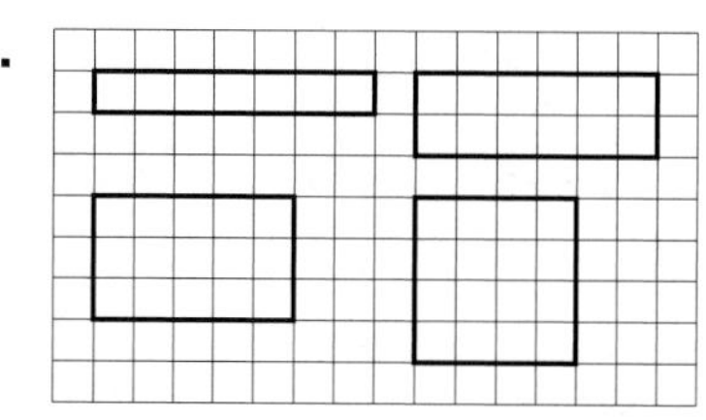

Drawing	Perimeter	Area
	16 units	7 units^2
	16 units	12 units^2
	16 units	15 units^2
	16 units	16 units^2

Pages 424–426, Lesson 10-4

17a. Sample answer:

17b. Sample answer:

17c. Sample answer:

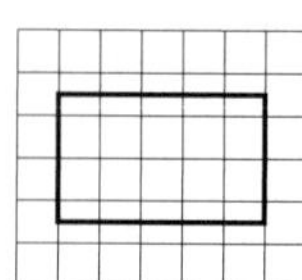

Pages 434–435, Lesson 10-6

29a.

Page 445, Performance Task

Sample answer:

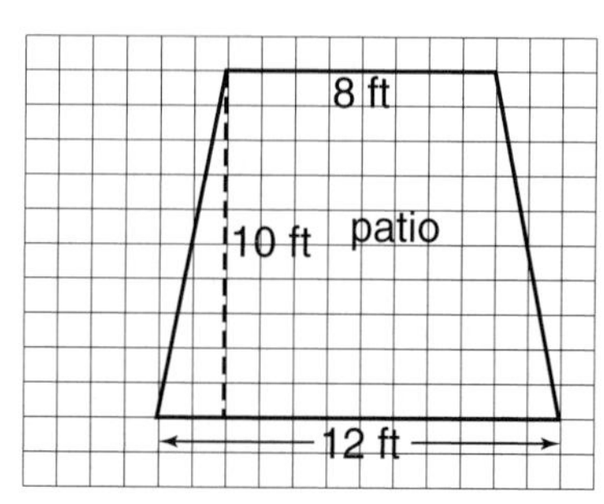

$A = \frac{1}{2}h(a + b)$
$A = \frac{1}{2}(10)(12 + 8)$
$A = 100$

The area of the patio is 100 ft^2.

Sample answer:

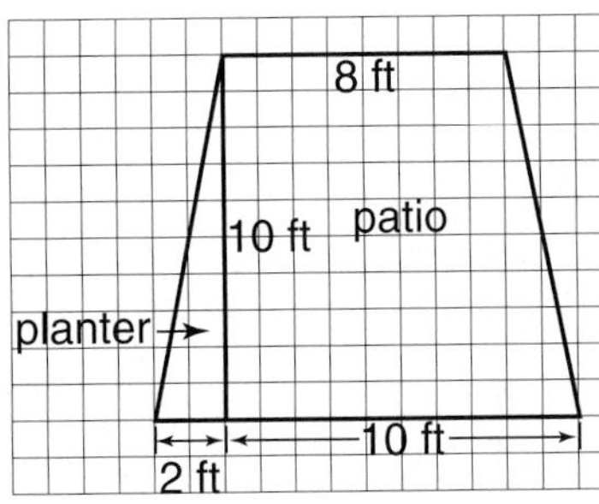

$A = \frac{1}{2}bh$
$A = \frac{1}{2}(10)(2)$
$A = 10$

The area of the planter is 10 ft^2.

$A = \frac{1}{2}h(a + b)$
$A = \frac{1}{2}(10)(10 + 8)$
$A = 90$

The area of the patio is 90 ft^2.

CHAPTER 11 Applying Percents

Pages 457–458, Lesson 11-2

1. Sample answer: The percent equation uses the decimal form of rate; the percent proportion uses rate as a number out of 100.

2. Sample answer: The rate describes how many out of 100.

26. Sample answer: If the rate is less than 100%, then $P < B$; if the rate equals 100%, then $P = B$; if the rate is greater than 100%, then $P > B$.

Pages 462–463, Lesson 11-3

5a. Park A, 0.211; Park B, 0.192; Park C, 0.176; Park D, 0.146; Park E, 0.146; Park F, 0.129

5b. Park A, 76.0°; Park B, 69.1°; Park C, 63.4°; Park D, 52.6°; Park E, 52.6°; Park F, 46.4°

5c. **Park Tourists**

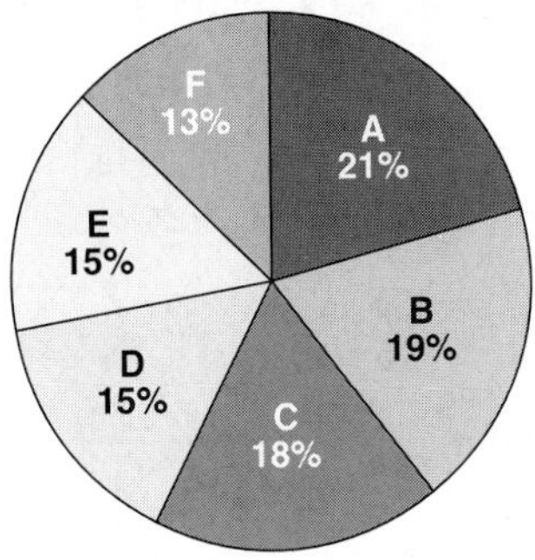

The sum of the percents is greater than 100% due to rounding.

6a. **Girls' Injuries**

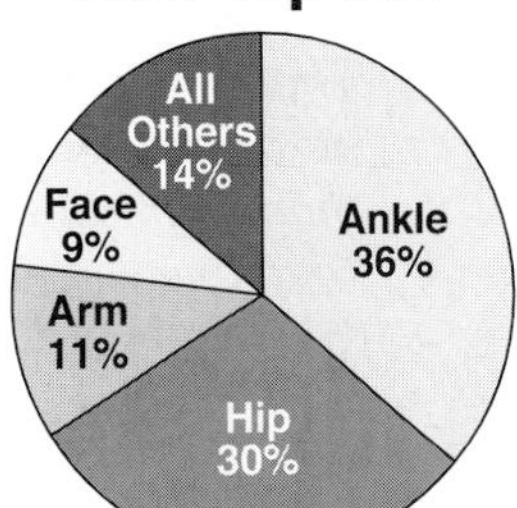

6b. **Boys' Injuries**

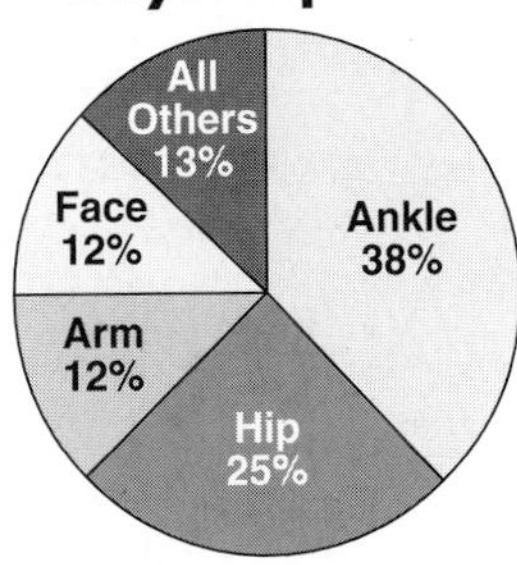

6c. Sample answer: The graphs show that girls have a greater percent of injuries on their hip/leg/knee. Boys tend to injure their ankles/feet and faces more than girls do.

7a. **Life on Other Planets? What Women Think**

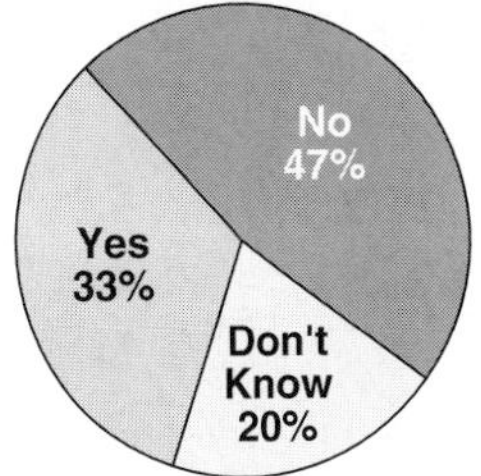

7b. Sample answer: A greater percentage of men believe in life on other planets.

7c. Sample answer: A graph provides a visual representation that allows you to easily compare data.

Page 467, Chapter 11 Mid-Chapter Self Test

8a. **Juice Sold**

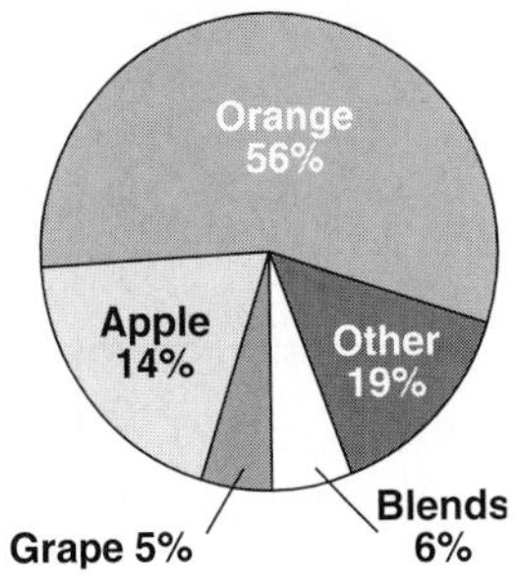

9. No, this sample is not random, because the students may have all been from the same social group. Their opinion cannot be used to predict what the student body as a whole might believe.

Pages 479–480, Lesson 11-7

3. Sample Answer: When you borrow money, the principal is the amount that you borrow, and the interest is the additional amount you pay. When you save money, the principal is the amount you loan to the bank and the interest is what they pay you.

Page 485, Performance Task

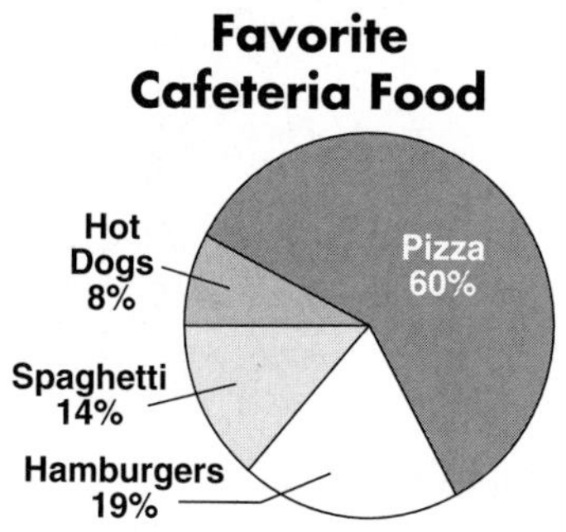

Favorite Cafeteria Food

Pizza 60%
Hot Dogs 8%
Spaghetti 14%
Hamburgers 19%

The sum of the percents is greater than 100% due to rounding.

At least one of them is too small.

CHAPTER 12
Geometry: Finding Volume and Surface Area

Pages 493–495, Lesson 12-1

1.

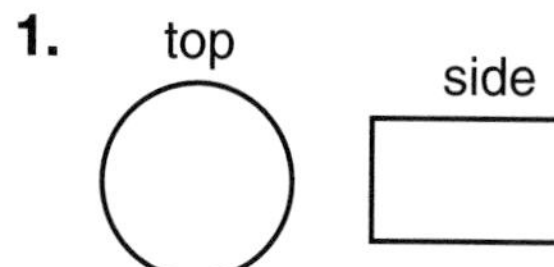

4.

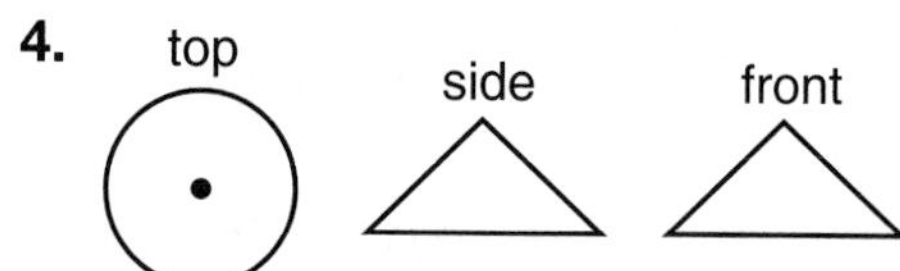

5.

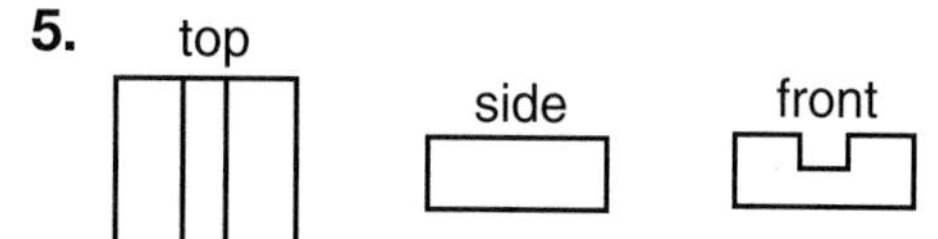

8.

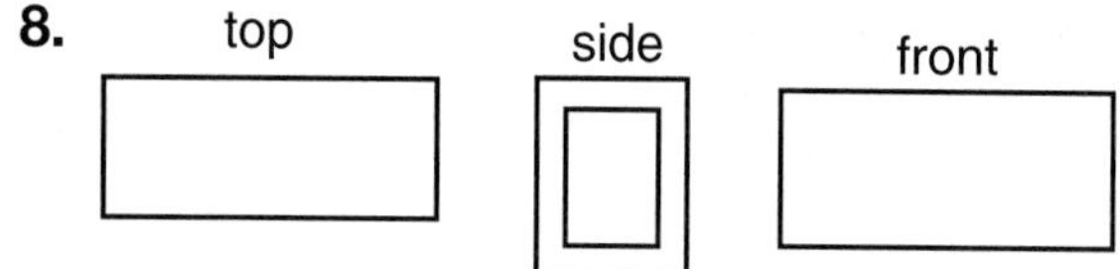

9.

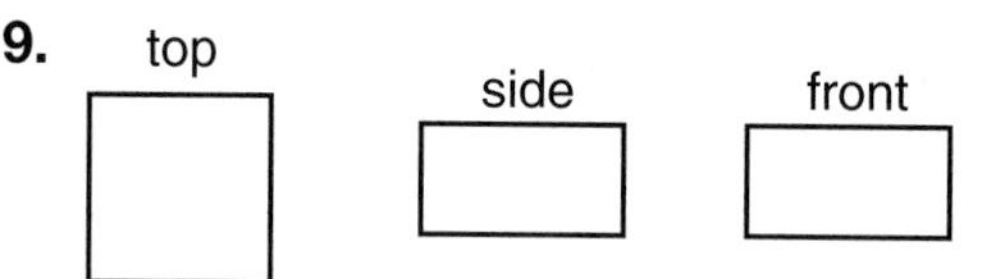

10.

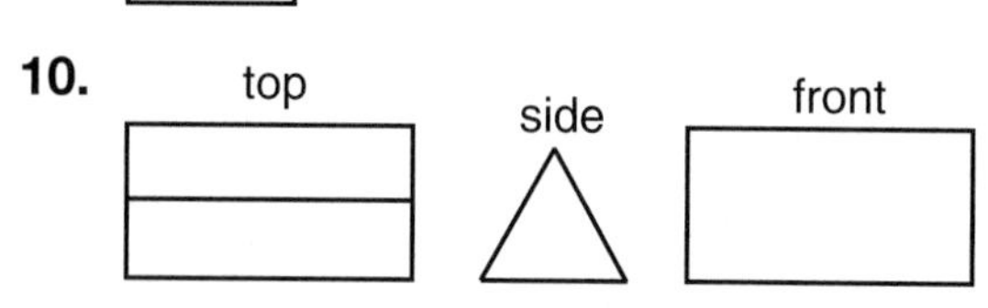

11.

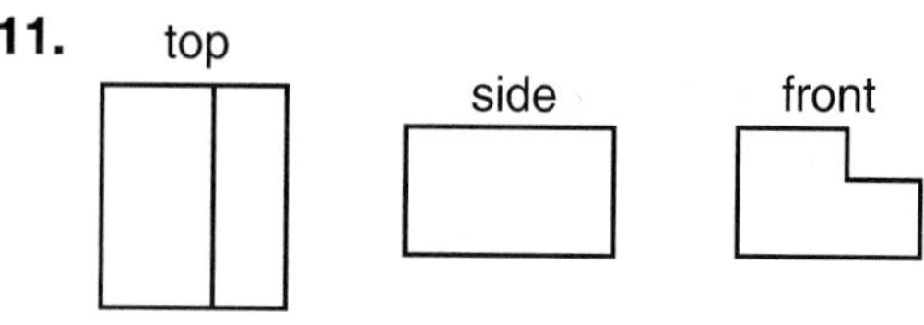

12.
13.
14.

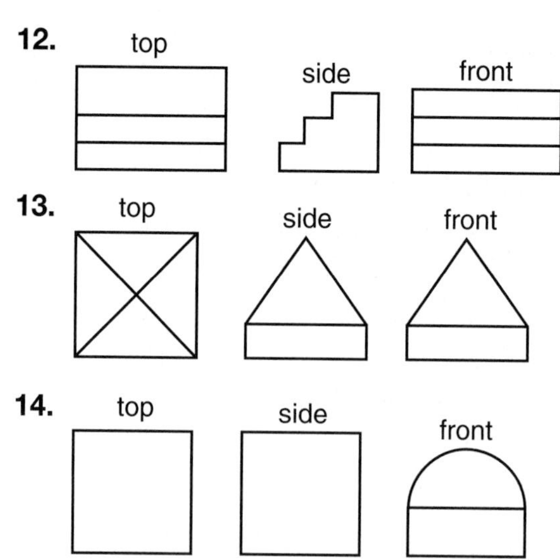

Pages 496–497, Lesson 12-1B

3.

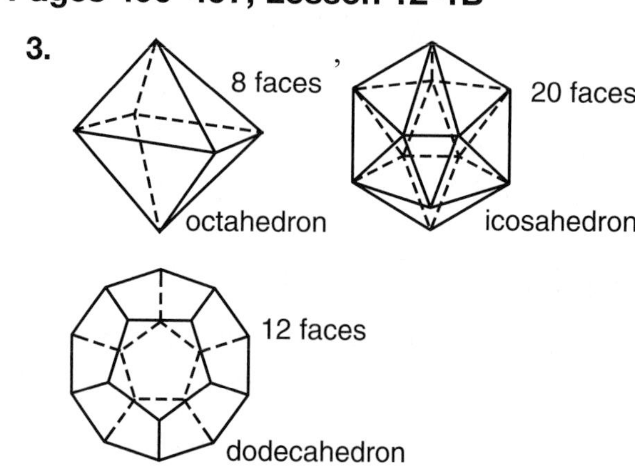

Page 499, Lesson 12-2, Mini-Lab

6.

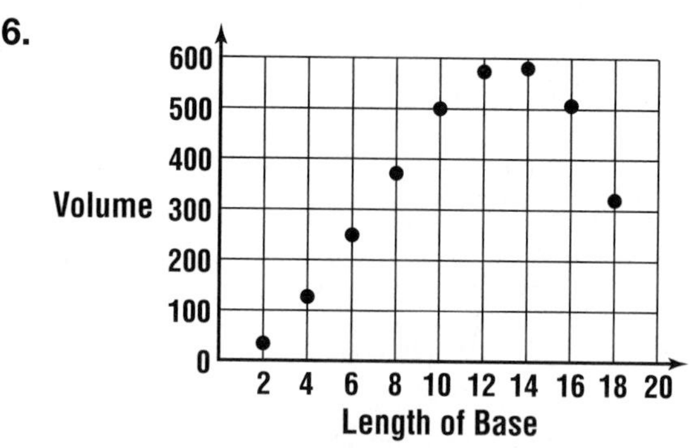

Pages 500–501, Lesson 12-2

2.

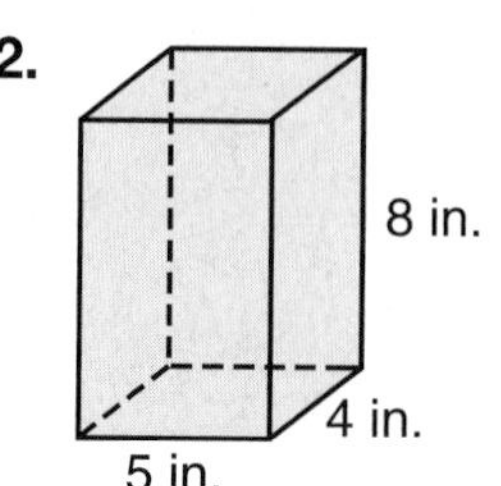

3. Sample answer:

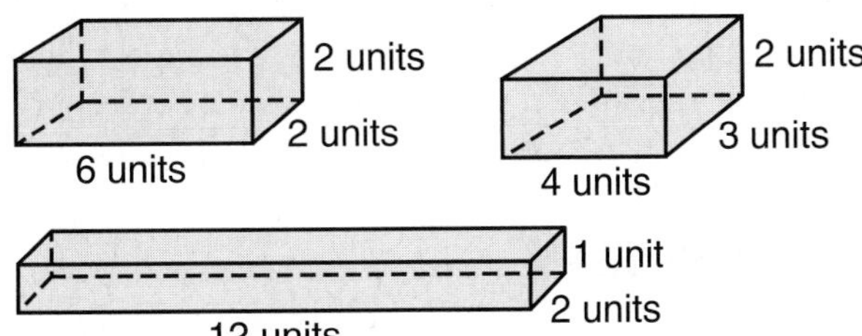

Page 506, Mid-Chapter Self Test

1.

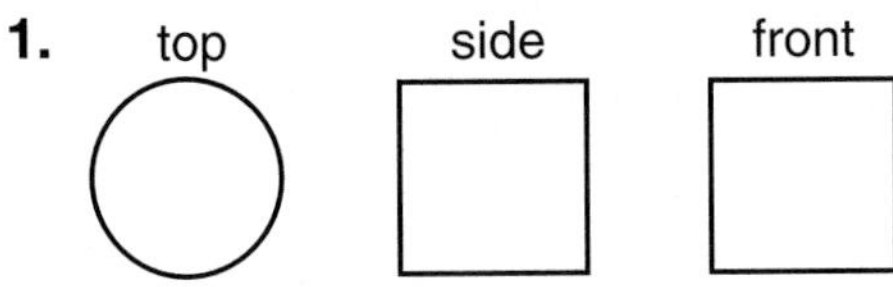

Pages 508–509, Lesson 12-4A

4.

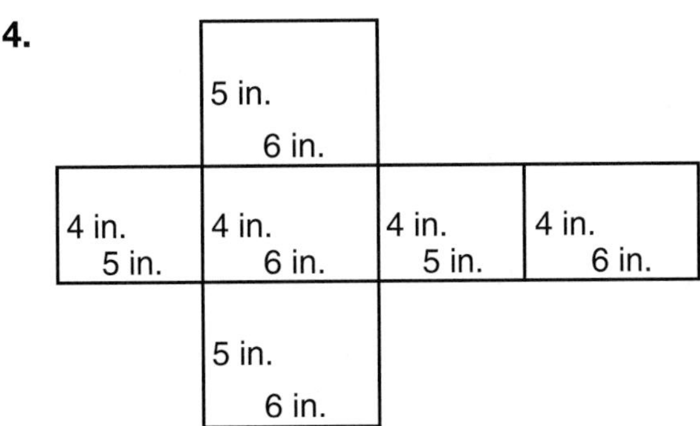

5.

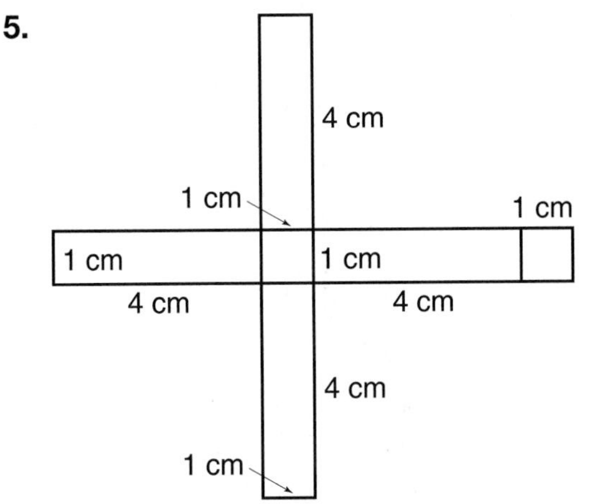

6.

2 ft 8 ft
3 ft 3 ft 8 ft 3 ft 3 ft 8 ft
2 ft 2 ft 8 ft 2 ft

7.

5 mm 20 mm
15 mm
20 mm
5 mm 5 mm 20 mm 5 mm
15 mm 15 mm
15 mm
20 mm

8.

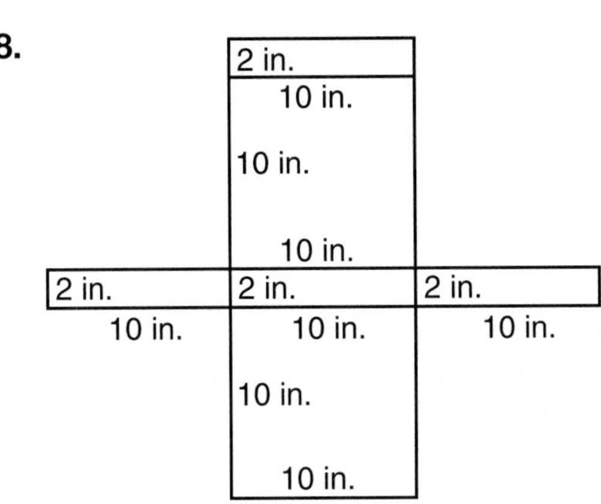

9.

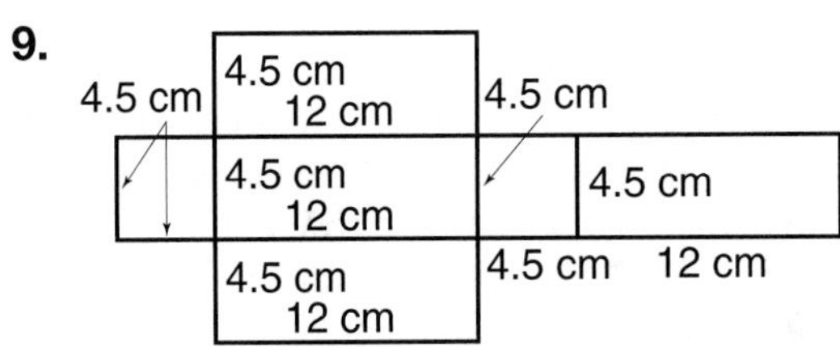

Pages 516–517, Lesson 12-5

21a.

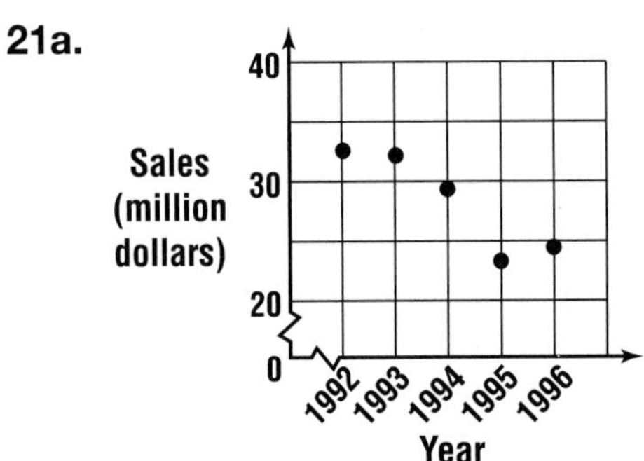

21b. Tickets sales per film have decreased.

CHAPTER 13 Exploring Discrete Math and Probability

Pages 535–536, Lesson 13-2

1. Start by listing the choices for the first event. From each choice, draw branches for the choices for the next event. Continue until you have listed all the choices for the final event.

2. Sample answer: You can choose a hot dog or hamburger for a picnic lunch and a cola, diet cola, or root beer for a drink. How many different sandwich/drink selections can you make?

4. 12 outcomes; see students' diagrams; outcomes are red, 1; red, 2; red, 3; blue, 1; blue, 2; blue, 3; yellow, 1; yellow, 2; yellow, 3; green, 1; green, 2; green, 3.

5. 12 outcomes; see students' diagrams; outcomes are H1, H2, H3, H4, H5, H6, T1, T2, T3, T4, T5, T6.

6. See students' diagrams; outcomes are red shirt, black jeans; red shirt, blue jeans; white shirt, black jeans; white shirt, blue jeans.

7. 4 outcomes; see students' diagrams; outcomes are HH, HT, TH, TT.

8. 9 outcomes; see students' diagrams; outcomes are A1, A2, A3, B1, B2, B3, C1, C2, C3.

9. 8 outcomes; see students' diagrams; outcomes are wall, black; wall, beige; wall, red; wall, white; portable, black; portable, beige; portable, red; portable, white.

10. 12 outcomes; see students' diagrams; outcomes are 10, red; 10, blue; 10, green; 10, white; 18, red; 18, blue; 18, green; 18, white; 21, red; 21, blue; 21, green; 21, white.

11. 48 outcomes; see students' diagrams; outcomes are 1HW, 1HX, 1HY, 1HZ, 1TW, 1TX, 1TY, 1TZ, 2HW, 2HX, 2HY, 2HZ, 2TW, 2TX, 2TY, 2TZ, 3HW, 3HX, 3HY, 3HZ, 3TW, 3TX, 3TY, 3TZ, 4HW, 4HX, 4HY, 4HZ, 4TW, 4TX, 4TY, 4TZ, 5HW, 5HX, 5HY, 5HZ, 5TW, 5TX, 5TY, 5TZ, 6HW, 6HX, 6HY, 6HZ, 6TW, 6TX, 6TY, 6TZ.

12. 9 outcomes; see students' diagrams; outcomes are cereal, orange; cereal, apple; cereal, grapefruit; French toast, orange; French toast, apple; French toast, grapefruit; pancakes, orange; pancakes, apple; pancakes, grapefruit.

17a.  

17b.  

17c. 

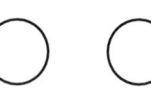

Pages 540–541, Lesson 13-3

16. See students' diagrams; outcomes are S1, M1, E1; S1, M1, E2; S1, M2, E1; S1, M2, E2; S1, M3, E1; S1, M3, E2; S2, M1, E1; S2, M1, E2; S2, M2, E1; S2, M2, E2; S2, M3, E1; S2, M3, E2.

Page 545, Mid-Chapter Self Test

3. See students' diagrams; outcomes are orange, wheat; orange, corn; orange, rice; apple, wheat; apple, corn; apple, rice.

Page 574, Extra Practice, Lesson 3-1

1.

Time	Tally	Frequency
15	IIII	4
30	~~IIII~~	5
45	IIII	4
60	III	3

0–60; 15

2.

Number	Tally	Frequency
40	III	3
41	~~IIII~~ I	6
42	I	1
43	I	1
45	III	3
49	II	2

40–50; 1

Page 575, Extra Practice, Lesson 3-5

1. stems: 1, 2, 3, 4, 5, 6

Stem	Leaf
1	5 8
2	3 9
3	9
4	1 2
5	1 2 7
6	8

1|5 = 15

2. stems: 0, 1, 2, 3

Stem	Leaf
0	5 6 7 9
1	3 4 4 4 8
2	8 8
3	9

0|5 = 5

3. stems: 18, 19

Stem	Leaf
18	2 3 4 4 9
19	4 6 6 7

18|9 = 189

4. stems: 7, 8, 9

Stem	Leaf
7	1 4 5 6
8	1 2 3 4
9	2 5 6

7|1 = 71

Page 577, Extra Practice, Lesson 4-3

1. Add 4.
2. Multiply by 2.
3. Add 5 more than was added to the previous term.
4. Add 0.9.
5. Add 2 more than was added to the previous term.
6. Add 0.1.

7. Multiply by 3.
8. Add 1 more than was added to the previous term.
9. 1, 10, 19, 28; arithmetic
10. 3, 12, 48, 192; geometric
11. 6, 1.2, 0.24, 0.048; geometric
12. 14, 30, 46, 62; arithmetic
13. 40, 41, 52, 163; neither

Page 581, Extra Practice, Lesson 5-3

10–17.

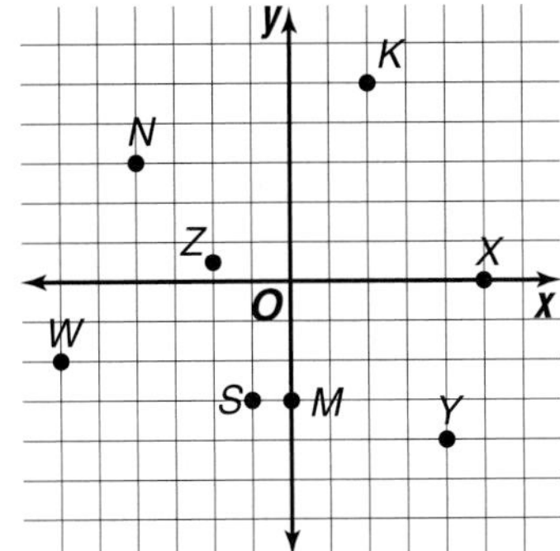

Page 583, Extra Practice, Lesson 5-8

1.

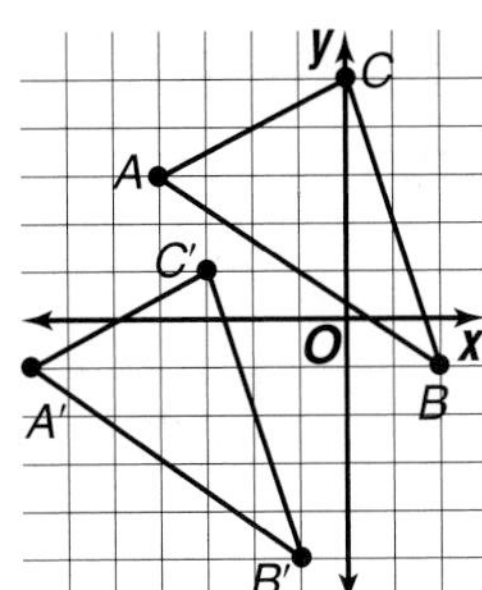

2.

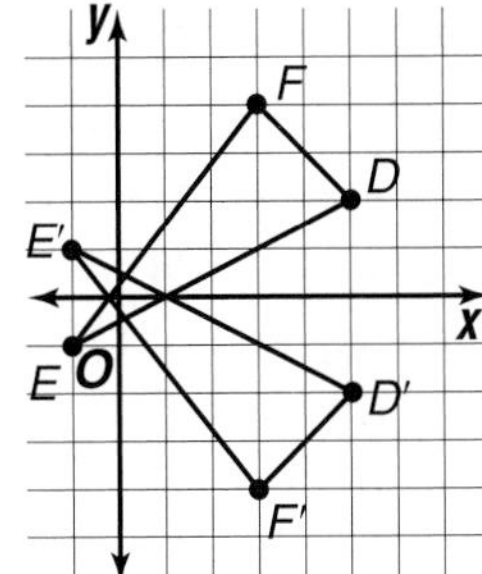

3.

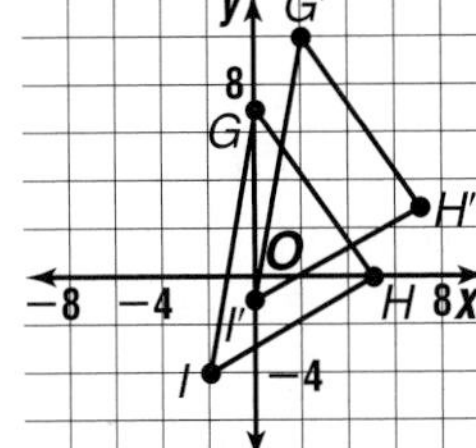

4.

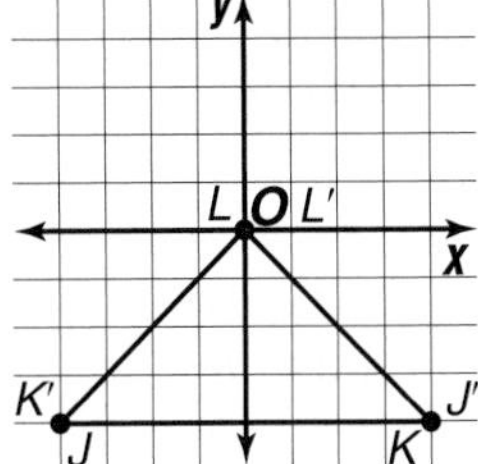

5.

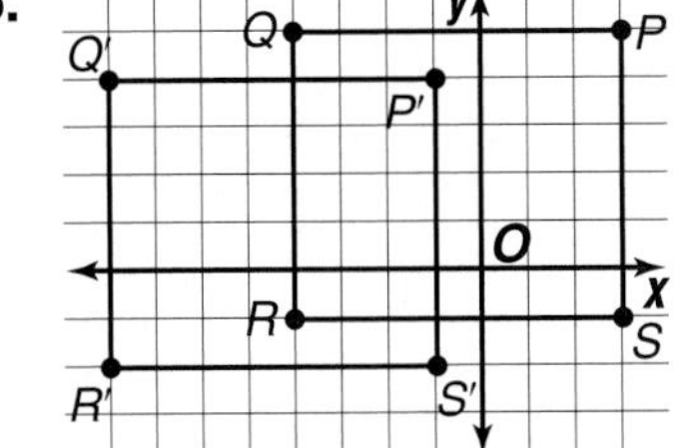

Page 585, Extra Practice, Lesson 6-5

1.

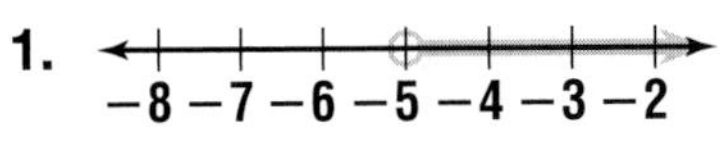

2. 2 3 4 5 6 7 8 9

3. 0 1 2 3 4 5 6

4. −3 −2 −1 0 1 2 3

5. −5 −4 −3 −2 −1 0 1

6. −8 −7 −6 −5 −4 −3 −2

7. 0 1 2 3 4 5 6

8. 14 15 16 17 18 19 20

9. −1 0 1 2 3 4 5

10. −10 −9 −8 −7 −6 −5 −4

11. 0 1 2 3 4 5 6

12. 7 8 9 10 11 12 13

13. 2 3 4 5 6 7 8

14. −1 0 1 2 3 4 5

15. −1 0 1 2 3 4 5

16. 0 1 2 3 4 5 6

17. 0 1 2 3 4 5 6

18. 7 8 9 10 11 12 13

Page 585, Extra Practice, Lesson 6-6

1.

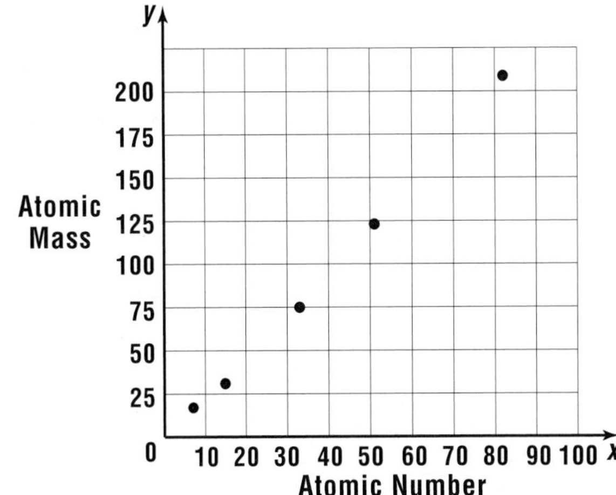

As atomic number increases, mass increases.

2.

Mass of Pennies: 5, 10, 15, 20

Number of Pennies: 1, 2, 3, 4, 5, 6

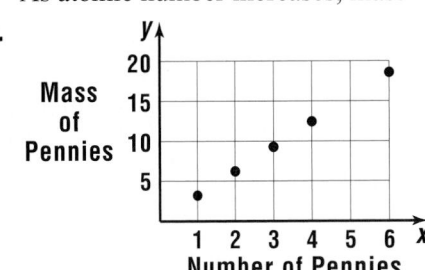

As number of pennies increases, mass increases.

Page 585, Extra Practice, Lesson 6-7

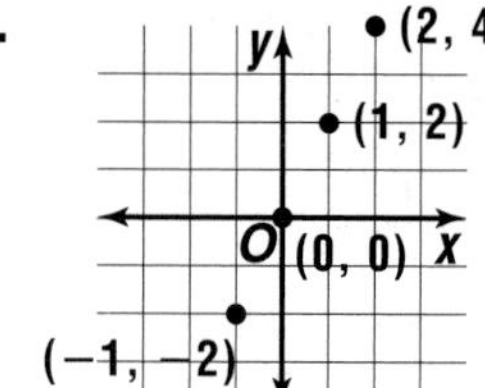

2. 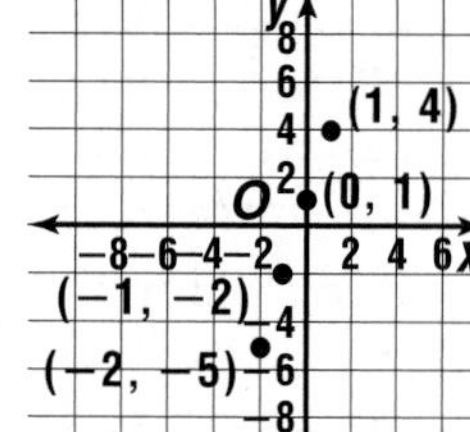

3. 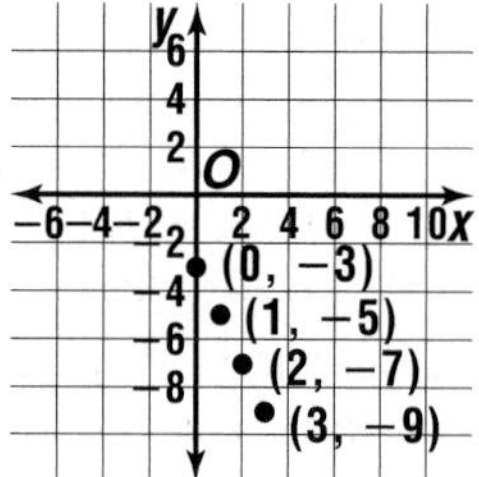

4. 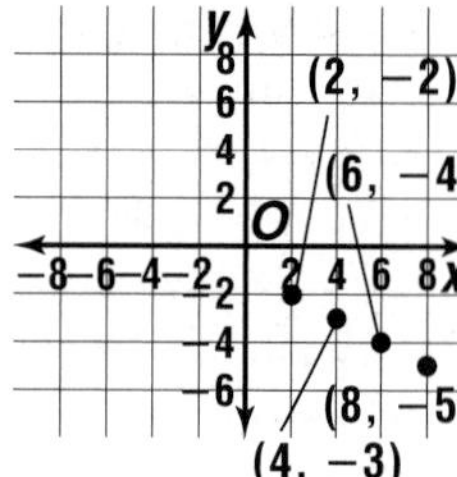

5. 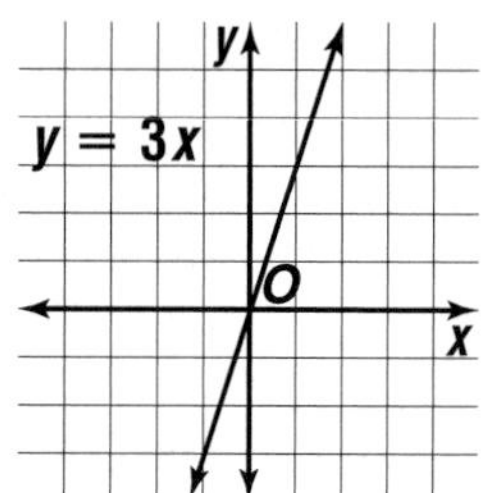

6. 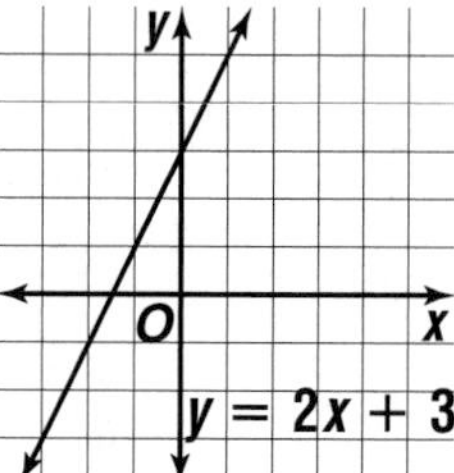

7. 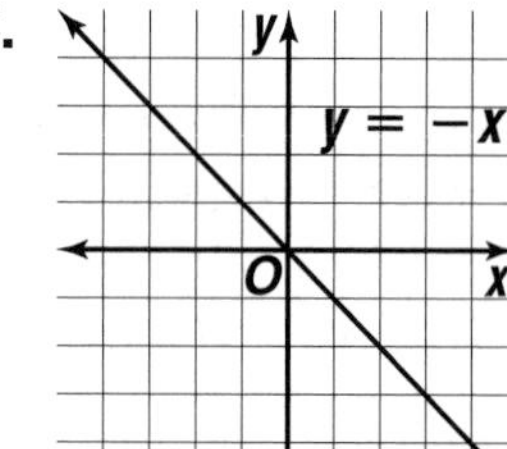

8. 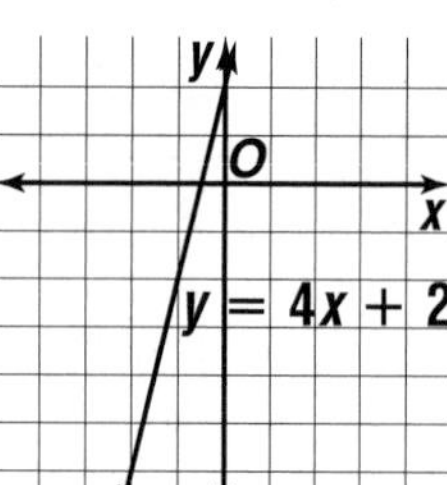

9. 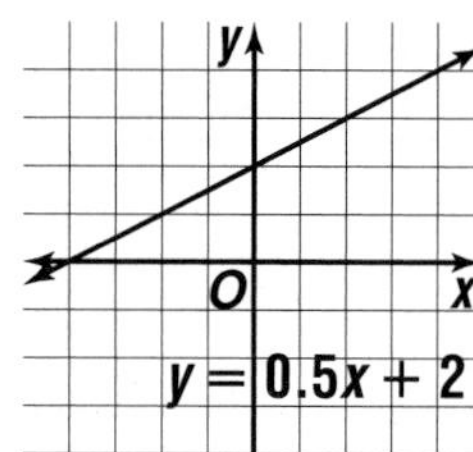

10. 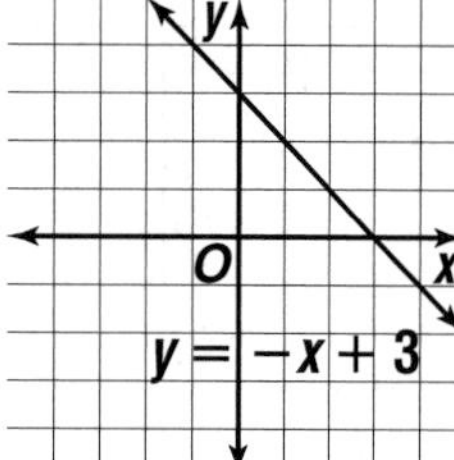

11. 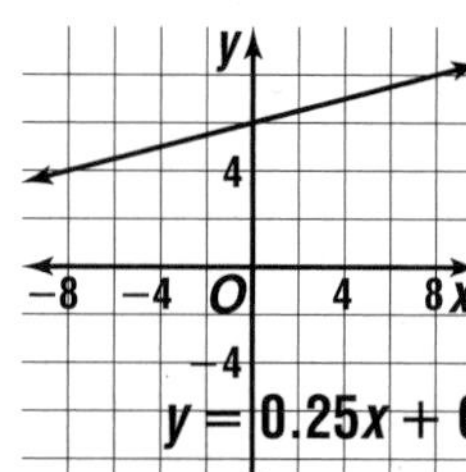

12. 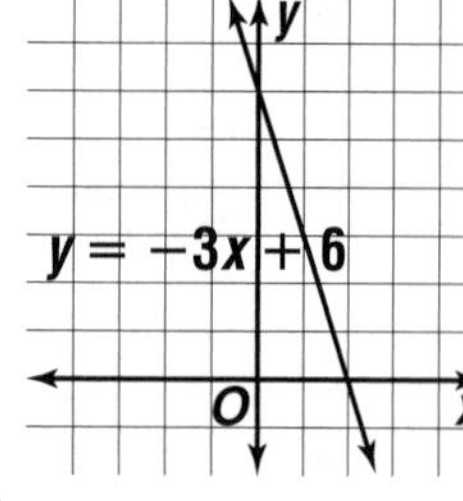

13. 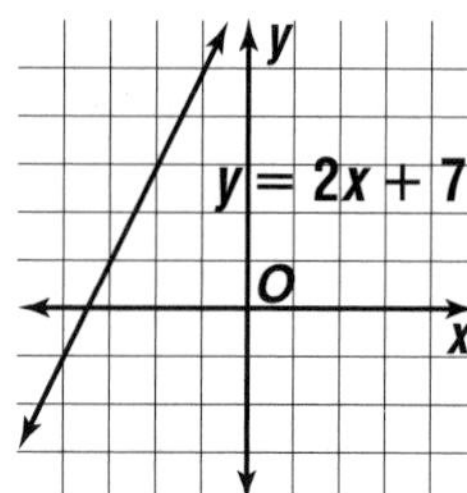

14. 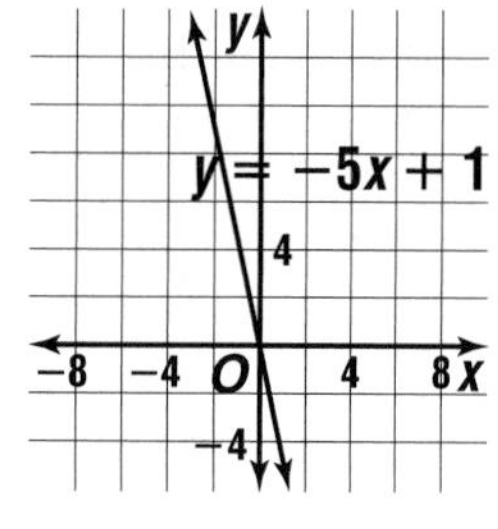

15. 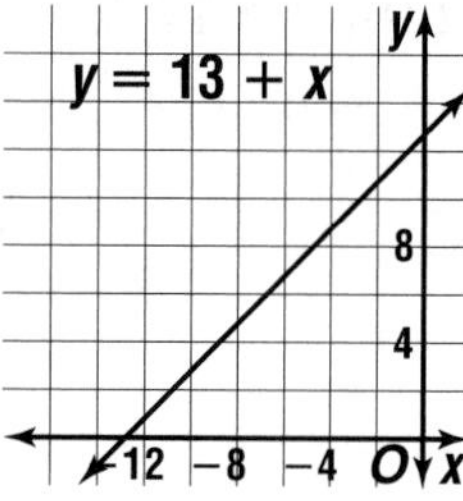

16. 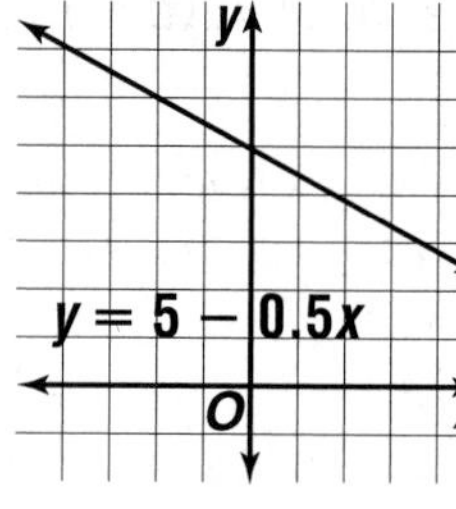

17. 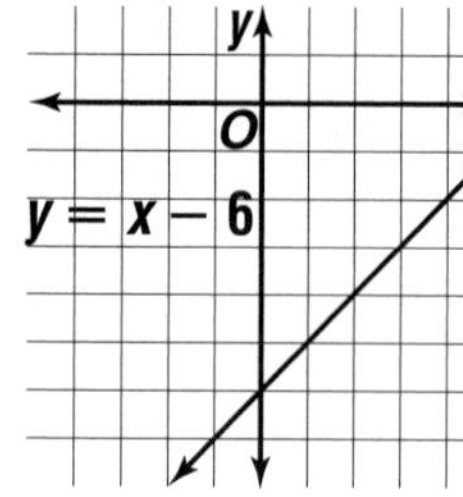

18. 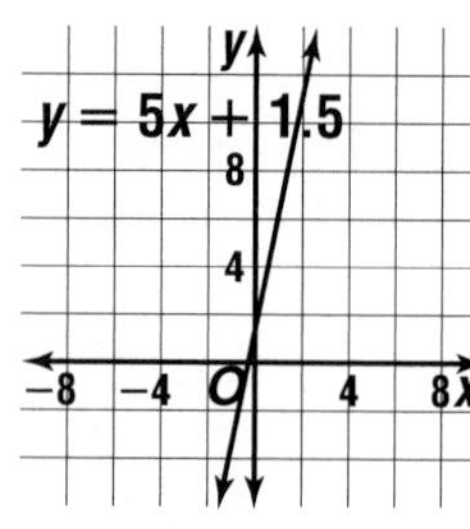

19. 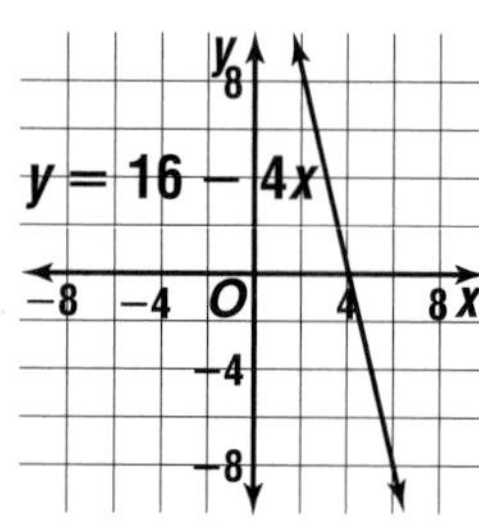

20. 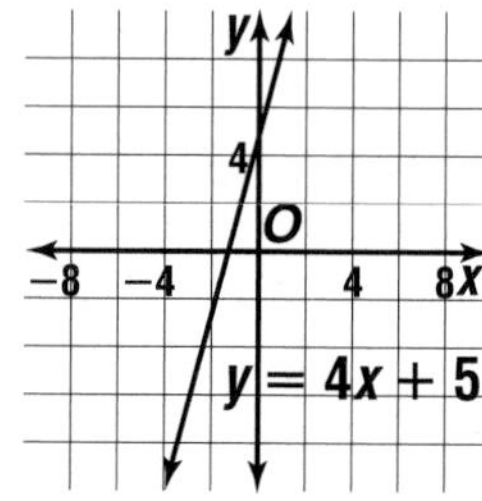

Page 598, Extra Practice, Lesson 11-2

1. $50 = 0.12 \cdot B$
$50 + 0.12 \approx 416.7$
$416.7 \approx B$

2. $P = 0.45 \cdot 50$
$P = 22.5$

3. $38 = R \cdot 62$
$38 \div 62 \approx 0.613$
$61.3 \approx R$
61.3%

4. $P = 0.285 \cdot 64$
$P = 18.24$ or 18.2

5. $12 = 0.05 \cdot B$
$12 \div 0.05 = 240$
$240 = B$

6. $80 = R \cdot 90$
$80 \div 90 \approx 0.889$
$88.9 \approx R$
88.9%

7. $40 = 0.667 \cdot B$
$40 \div 0.667 \approx 60.0$
$60 \approx B$

8. $P = 0.465 \cdot 75$
$P = 34.875 \approx 34.9$

9. $90 = R \cdot 95$
$90 \div 95 \approx 0.947$
$0.947 \approx R$
94.7%

10. $P = 0.22 \cdot 22$
$P = 4.84 \approx 4.8$

11. $2 = 0.16 \cdot B$
$2 \div 0.16 = 12.5$
$12.5 = B$

12. $75 = R \cdot 300$
$75 \div 300 = 0.25$
$0.25 = R$
25%

13. $P = 0.75 \cdot 80$
$P = 60$

14. $P = 0.60 \cdot 45$
$P = 27$

15. $P = 0.555 \cdot 70$
$P = 38.85 \approx 38.9$

16. $80.5 = 0.805 \cdot B$
$80.5 \div 0.805 = 100$
$100 = B$

Page 599, Extra Practice, Lesson 11-3

1. Sedan: 0.45 × 360° = 162°
   Station Wagon: 0.22 × 360° = 79°
   Pickup Truck: 0.09 × 360° = 32°
   Sports Car: 0.13 × 360° = 47°
   Compact Car: 0.11 × 360° = 40°

Car Sales by Body Style

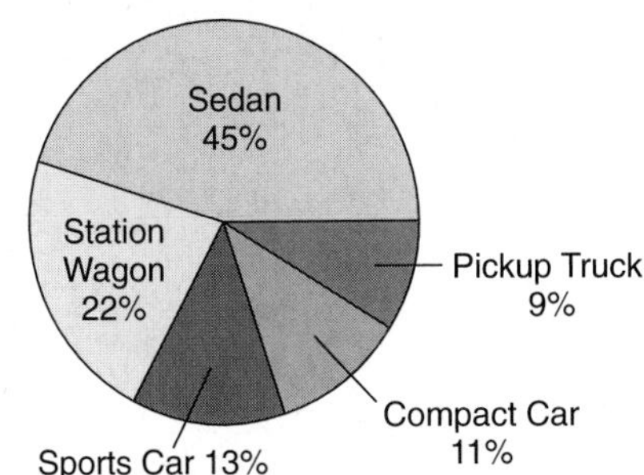

2. Vanilla: 0.28 × 360° = 101°
   Chocolate: 0.35 × 360° = 126°
   Strawberry: 0.19 × 360° = 68°
   Mint Chip: 0.12 × 360° = 43°
   Coffee: 0.06 × 360° = 22°

Favorite Flavor of Ice Cream

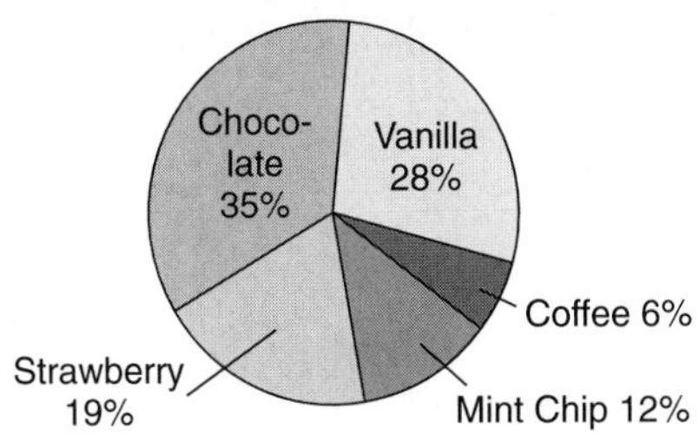

Page 600, Extra Practice, Lesson 12-1

1. top side front 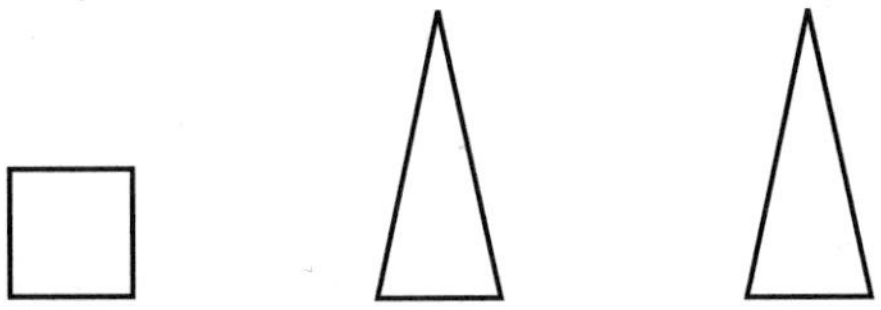
2. top side front 
3. top side front 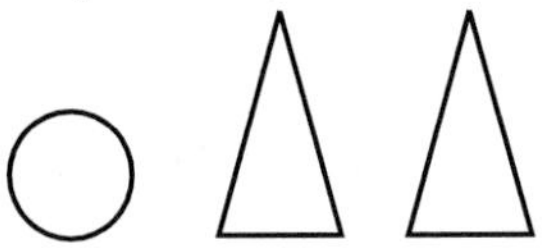
4. top side front
5. top side front 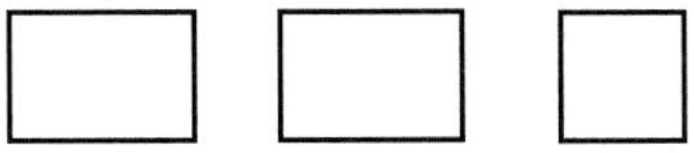
6. top side front

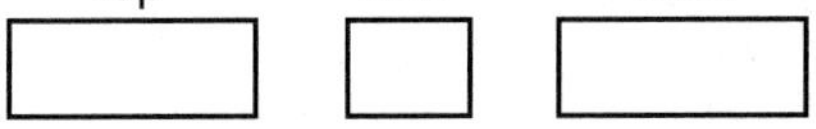

Page 603, Extra Practice, Lesson 13-2

1. See students' diagrams; outcomes are 1, 1; 1, 2; 1, 3; 1, 4; 1, 5; 1, 6; 2, 1; 2, 2; 2, 3; 2, 4; 2, 5; 2, 6; 3, 1; 3, 2; 3, 3; 3, 4; 3, 5; 3, 6; 4, 1; 4, 2; 4, 3; 4, 4; 4, 5; 4, 6; 5, 1; 5, 2; 5, 3; 5, 4; 5, 5; 5, 6; 6, 1; 6, 2; 6, 3; 6, 4; 6, 5; 6, 6.
2. See students' diagrams; outcomes are waffle, chocolate; waffle, vanilla; waffle, strawberry; plain, chocolate; plain, vanilla; plain, strawberry; sugar, chocolate; sugar, vanilla; sugar, strawberry.
3. See students' diagrams; outcomes are white, cheddar, ham; white, cheddar, turkey; white, cheddar; roast beef; white, swiss, ham; white, swiss, turkey; white, swiss, roast beef; wheat, cheddar, ham; wheat, cheddar, turkey; wheat, cheddar, roast beef; wheat, swiss, ham; wheat, swiss, turkey; wheat, swiss, roast beef; rye, chedder, ham; rye, cheddar, turkey; rye, cheddar, roast beef; rye, swiss, ham; rye, swiss, turkey; rye, swiss, roast beef.
4. See students' diagrams; outcomes are HH; HT; TH; TT.
5. See students' diagrams; outcomes are algebra, French; algebra, Spanish; algebra, Latin; geometry, French; geometry, Spanish; geometry, Latin.

Page 609, Chapter 3 Test

3.

Grade	Tally	Frequency
61–70	I	1
71–80	~~IIII~~	5
81–90	IIII	4
91–100	III	3

8. Line plot: × at 17; × at 19; ××× at 20; × at 26 (axis 16 18 20 22 24 26)

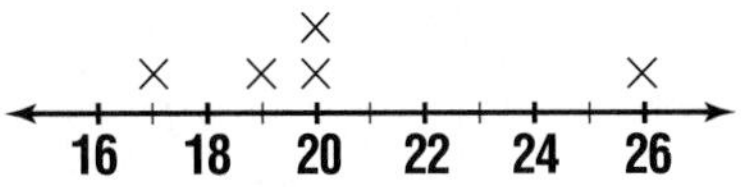

11.

Stem	Leaf
2	6
3	1 7
4	2
5	3 7 8 9

2|6 = 26

12.

Stem	Leaf
4	2 3 6 8
5	5 9
6	6 9

4|2 = 42¢

ANSWER APPENDIX

Page 611, Chapter 5 Test

7–9.

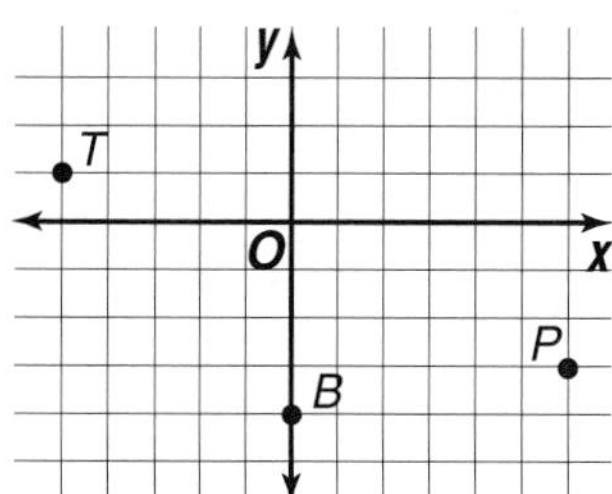

32.

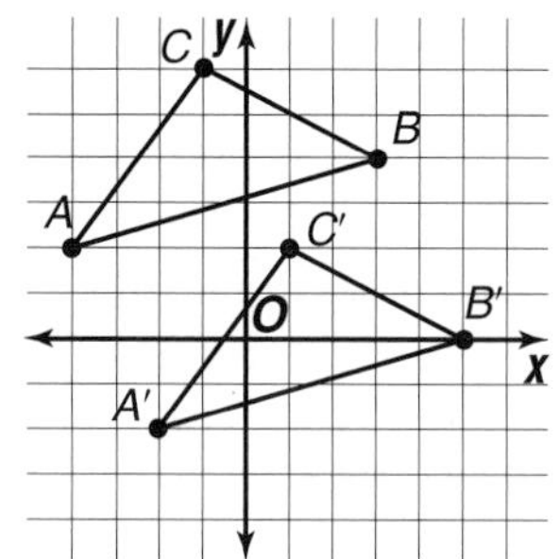

33.

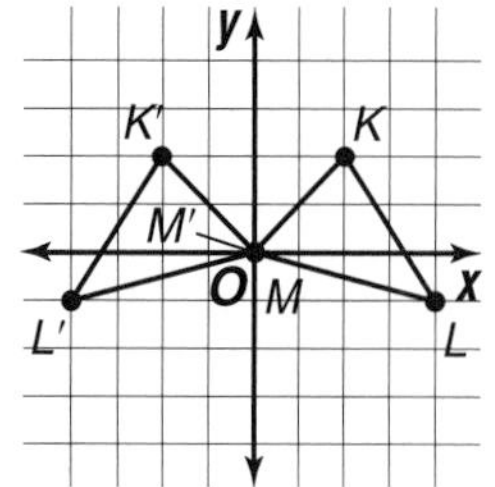

Page 612, Chapter 6 Test

20.

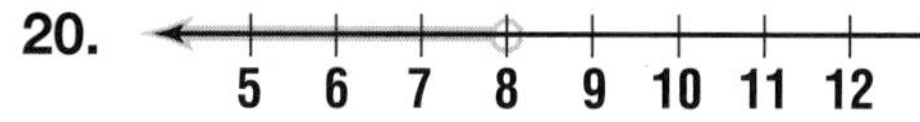

21. 5 6 7 8 9 10 11 12

22. 2 3 4 5 6 7 8 9

23.

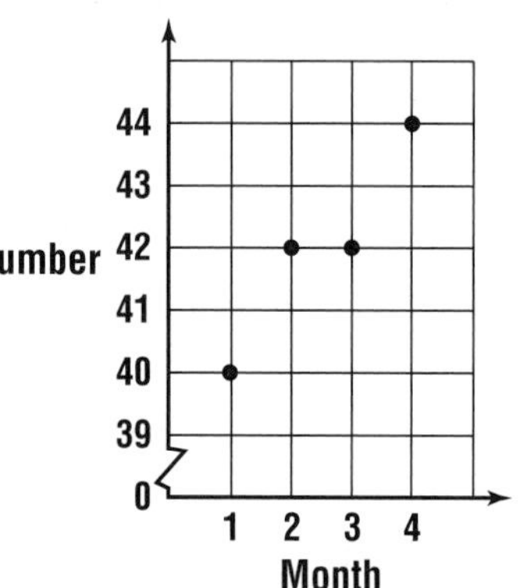

24.

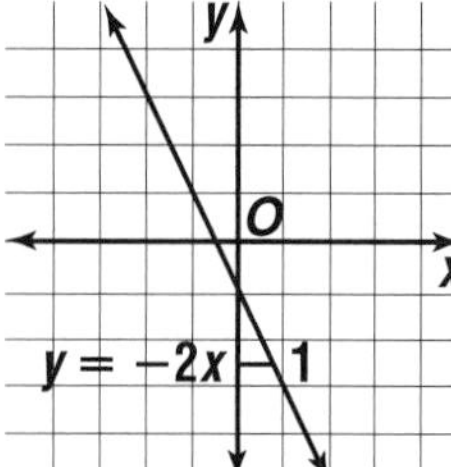

25.

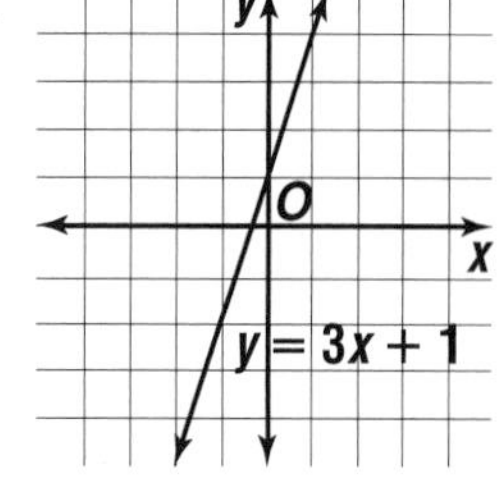

Page 615, Chapter 9 Test

5. hexagon, not regular

6. quadrilateral, not regular

7. hexagon, regular

8. not a polygon, not simple

14. quadrilateral, <u>parallelogram</u>

15. quadrilateral, parallelogram, <u>rectangle</u>

16. quadrilateral, <u>trapezoid</u>

18.

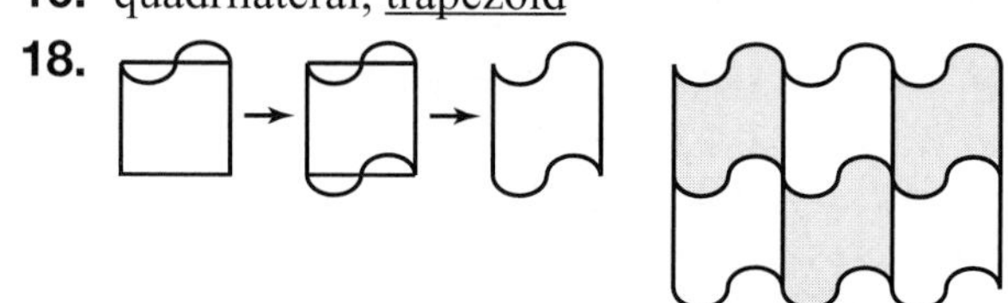

19.

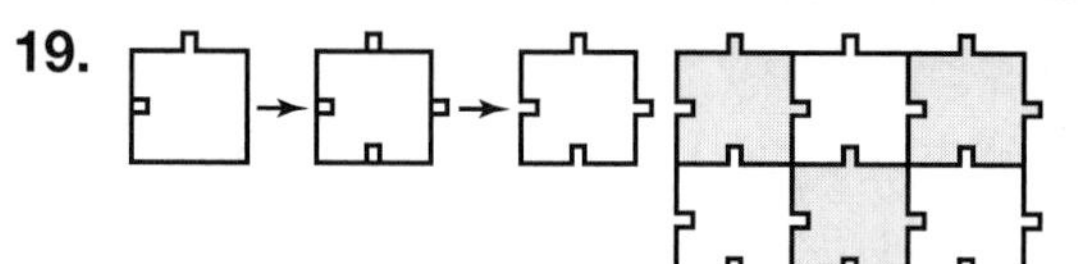

20.

Page 618, Chapter 12 Test

1.

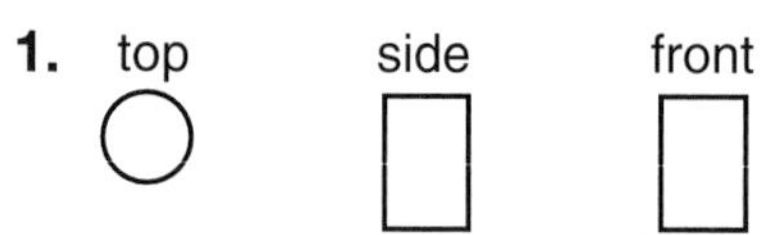

2. top side front

3.

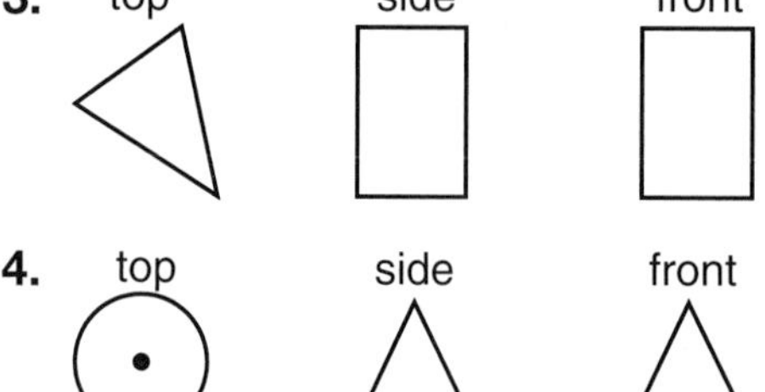

4. top side front

Page 619, Chapter 13 Test

2. See students' diagrams; outcomes are HHH; HHT; HTH; HTT; THH; THT; TTH; TTT.

SYMBOLS

Number and Operations

$+$	plus or positive
$-$	minus or negative
$a \cdot b$ $a \times b$ ab or $a(b)$	a times b
$\div$	divided by
$\pm$	positive or negative
$=$	is equal to
$\neq$	is not equal to
$<$	is less than
$>$	is greater than
$\leq$	is less than or equal to
$\geq$	is greater than or equal to
$\approx$	is approximately equal to
%	percent
$a{:}b$	the ratio of a to b, or $\frac{a}{b}$

Algebra and Functions

a'	a prime
a^n	a to the nth power
a^{-n}	$\frac{1}{a^n}$ (one over a to the nth power)
$\lvert x \rvert$	absolute value of x
$\sqrt{x}$	principal (positive) square root of x
$f(n)$	function, f of n

Geometry and Measurement

$\cong$	is congruent to
$\sim$	is similar to
$\circ$	degree(s)
$\overleftrightarrow{AB}$	line AB
$\overline{AB}$	segment AB
$\overrightarrow{AB}$	ray AB
∟	right angle
$\perp$	is perpendicular to
$\parallel$	is parallel to
AB	length of $\overline{AB}$, distance between A and B
$\triangle ABC$	triangle ABC
$\angle ABC$	angle ABC
$\angle B$	angle B
$m\angle ABC$	measure of angle ABC
$\odot C$	circle C
$\overset{\frown}{AB}$	arc AB
π	pi $\left(\text{approximately } 3.14159 \text{ or } \frac{22}{7}\right)$
(a, b)	ordered pair with x-coordinate a and y-coordinate b
$\sin A$	sine of angle A
$\cos A$	cosine of angle A
$\tan A$	tangent of angle A

Probability and Statistics

$P(A)$	the probability of event A
$n!$	n factorial
$P(n, r)$	permutation of n things taken r at a time
$C(n, r)$	combination of n things taken r at a time